Contents

Preface   1

UNIT 1 LEVELS OF ORGANIZATION

CHAPTER 1
An Introduction to the Human Body   7
Introduction   7
1.1 Overview of Anatomy and Physiology   8
1.2 Structural Organization of the Human Body   9
1.3 Functions of Human Life   14
1.4 Requirements for Human Life   16
1.5 Homeostasis   20
1.6 Anatomical Terminology   23
1.7 Medical Imaging   28
Key Terms   32
Chapter Review   33
Interactive Link Questions   34
Review Questions   35
Critical Thinking Questions   36

CHAPTER 2
The Chemical Level of Organization   39
Introduction   39
2.1 Elements and Atoms: The Building Blocks of Matter   40
2.2 Chemical Bonds   47
2.3 Chemical Reactions   51
2.4 Inorganic Compounds Essential to Human Functioning   54
2.5 Organic Compounds Essential to Human Functioning   61
Key Terms   75
Chapter Review   76
Interactive Link Questions   78
Review Questions   78
Critical Thinking Questions   80

CHAPTER 3
The Cellular Level of Organization   81
Introduction   81
3.1 The Cell Membrane   82
3.2 The Cytoplasm and Cellular Organelles   91
3.3 The Nucleus and DNA Replication   98
3.4 Protein Synthesis   103
3.5 Cell Growth and Division   107
3.6 Cellular Differentiation   112
Key Terms   116

Chapter Review   118
Interactive Link Questions   120
Review Questions   120
Critical Thinking Questions   122

CHAPTER 4
The Tissue Level of Organization   125

Introduction   125
4.1 Types of Tissues   126
4.2 Epithelial Tissue   130
4.3 Connective Tissue Supports and Protects   140
4.4 Muscle Tissue and Motion   147
4.5 Nervous Tissue Mediates Perception and Response   149
4.6 Tissue Injury and Aging   151
Key Terms   155
Chapter Review   157
Interactive Link Questions   159
Review Questions   159
Critical Thinking Questions   160

UNIT 2 SUPPORT AND MOVEMENT

CHAPTER 5
The Integumentary System   163

Introduction   163
5.1 Layers of the Skin   163
5.2 Accessory Structures of the Skin   172
5.3 Functions of the Integumentary System   177
5.4 Diseases, Disorders, and Injuries of the Integumentary System   180
Key Terms   186
Chapter Review   187
Interactive Link Questions   188
Review Questions   188
Critical Thinking Questions   190

CHAPTER 6
Bone Tissue and the Skeletal System   191

Introduction   191
6.1 The Functions of the Skeletal System   191
6.2 Bone Classification   194
6.3 Bone Structure   196
6.4 Bone Formation and Development   206
6.5 Fractures: Bone Repair   212
6.6 Exercise, Nutrition, Hormones, and Bone Tissue   215
6.7 Calcium Homeostasis: Interactions of the Skeletal System and Other Organ Systems   219
Key Terms   221
Chapter Review   222
Review Questions   223
Critical Thinking Questions   226

Anatomy and Physiology 2e

SENIOR CONTRIBUTING AUTHORS

J. Gordon Betts, Tyler Junior College
Peter Desaix, University of North Carolina at Chapel Hill
Eddie Johnson, Central Oregon Community College
Jody E. Johnson, Arapahoe Community College
Oksana Korol, Aims Community College
Dean Kruse, Portland Community College
Brandon Poe, Springfield Technical Community College
James A. Wise, Hampton University
Mark Womble, Youngstown State University
Kelly A. Young, California State University, Long Beach

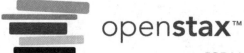

ISBN: 978-1-711494-06-7

OpenStax
Rice University
6100 Main Street MS-375
Houston, Texas 77005

To learn more about OpenStax, visit https://openstax.org.
Individual print copies and bulk orders can be purchased through our website.

©**2022 Rice University.** Textbook content produced by OpenStax is licensed under a Creative Commons Attribution 4.0 International License (CC BY 4.0). Under this license, any user of this textbook or the textbook contents herein must provide proper attribution as follows:

- If you redistribute this textbook in a digital format (including but not limited to PDF and HTML), then you must retain on every page the following attribution:
  "Access for free at openstax.org."
- If you redistribute this textbook in a print format, then you must include on every physical page the following attribution:
  "Access for free at openstax.org."
- If you redistribute part of this textbook, then you must retain in every digital format page view (including but not limited to PDF and HTML) and on every physical printed page the following attribution:
  "Access for free at openstax.org."
- If you use this textbook as a bibliographic reference, please include
  https://openstax.org/details/books/anatomy-and-physiology-2e in your citation.

For questions regarding this licensing, please contact support@openstax.org.

Trademarks

The OpenStax name, OpenStax logo, OpenStax book covers, OpenStax CNX name, OpenStax CNX logo, OpenStax Tutor name, Openstax Tutor logo, Connexions name, Connexions logo, Rice University name, and Rice University logo are not subject to the license and may not be reproduced without the prior and express written consent of Rice University. XANEDU and the XanEdu Logo are trademarks of Xanedu Publishing, Inc. The XANEDU mark is registered in the United States, Canada, and the European Union. These trademarks may not be used without the prior and express written consent of XanEdu Publishing, Inc.

HARDCOVER BOOK ISBN-13	**978-1-711494-06-7**
B&W PAPERBACK BOOK ISBN-13	**978-1-711494-05-0**
DIGITAL VERSION ISBN-13	**978-1-951693-42-8**
ORIGINAL PUBLICATION YEAR	**2022**

1 2 3 4 5 6 7 8 9 10 CJP 22

Printed by

XanEdu

17177 Laurel Park Dr., Suite 233
Livonia, MI 48152
800-562-2147
www.xanedu.com

OpenStax

OpenStax provides free, peer-reviewed, openly licensed textbooks for introductory college and Advanced Placement® courses and low-cost, personalized courseware that helps students learn. A nonprofit ed tech initiative based at Rice University, we're committed to helping students access the tools they need to complete their courses and meet their educational goals.

Rice University

OpenStax, OpenStax CNX, and OpenStax Tutor are initiatives of Rice University. As a leading research university with a distinctive commitment to undergraduate education, Rice University aspires to path-breaking research, unsurpassed teaching, and contributions to the betterment of our world. It seeks to fulfill this mission by cultivating a diverse community of learning and discovery that produces leaders across the spectrum of human endeavor.

Philanthropic Support

OpenStax is grateful for the generous philanthropic partners who advance our mission to improve educational access and learning for everyone. To see the impact of our supporter community and our most updated list of partners, please visit openstax.org/impact.

Arnold Ventures

Chan Zuckerberg Initiative

Chegg, Inc.

Arthur and Carlyse Ciocca Charitable Foundation

Digital Promise

Ann and John Doerr

Bill & Melinda Gates Foundation

Girard Foundation

Google Inc.

The William and Flora Hewlett Foundation

The Hewlett-Packard Company

Intel Inc.

Rusty and John Jaggers

The Calvin K. Kazanjian Economics Foundation

Charles Koch Foundation

Leon Lowenstein Foundation, Inc.

The Maxfield Foundation

Burt and Deedee McMurtry

Michelson 20MM Foundation

National Science Foundation

The Open Society Foundations

Jumee Yhu and David E. Park III

Brian D. Patterson USA-International Foundation

The Bill and Stephanie Sick Fund

Steven L. Smith & Diana T. Go

Stand Together

Robin and Sandy Stuart Foundation

The Stuart Family Foundation

Tammy and Guillermo Treviño

Valhalla Charitable Foundation

White Star Education Foundation

Schmidt Futures

William Marsh Rice University

CHAPTER 7
Axial Skeleton 227
Introduction 227
7.1 Divisions of the Skeletal System 228
7.2 The Skull 229
7.3 The Vertebral Column 248
7.4 The Thoracic Cage 259
7.5 Embryonic Development of the Axial Skeleton 260
Key Terms 263
Chapter Review 267
Interactive Link Questions 270
Review Questions 270
Critical Thinking Questions 271

CHAPTER 8
The Appendicular Skeleton 273
Introduction 273
8.1 The Pectoral Girdle 273
8.2 Bones of the Upper Limb 277
8.3 The Pelvic Girdle and Pelvis 285
8.4 Bones of the Lower Limb 289
8.5 Development of the Appendicular Skeleton 297
Key Terms 301
Chapter Review 306
Interactive Link Questions 309
Review Questions 309
Critical Thinking Questions 311

CHAPTER 9
Joints 313
Introduction 313
9.1 Classification of Joints 314
9.2 Fibrous Joints 316
9.3 Cartilaginous Joints 319
9.4 Synovial Joints 320
9.5 Types of Body Movements 327
9.6 Anatomy of Selected Synovial Joints 332
9.7 Development of Joints 344
Key Terms 346
Chapter Review 349
Interactive Link Questions 352
Review Questions 354
Critical Thinking Questions 356

CHAPTER 10
Muscle Tissue 357
Introduction 357
10.1 Overview of Muscle Tissues 357
10.2 Skeletal Muscle 359

10.3 Muscle Fiber Contraction and Relaxation   364
10.4 Nervous System Control of Muscle Tension   372
10.5 Types of Muscle Fibers   377
10.6 Exercise and Muscle Performance   378
10.7 Cardiac Muscle Tissue   381
10.8 Smooth Muscle   383
10.9 Development and Regeneration of Muscle Tissue   386
Key Terms   388
Chapter Review   389
Interactive Link Questions   391
Review Questions   392
Critical Thinking Questions   394

CHAPTER 11
The Muscular System   395

Introduction   395
11.1 Interactions of Skeletal Muscles, Their Fascicle Arrangement, and Their Lever Systems   395
11.2 Naming Skeletal Muscles   400
11.3 Axial Muscles of the Head, Neck, and Back   403
11.4 Axial Muscles of the Abdominal Wall, and Thorax   414
11.5 Muscles of the Pectoral Girdle and Upper Limbs   421
11.6 Appendicular Muscles of the Pelvic Girdle and Lower Limbs   432
Key Terms   441
Chapter Review   445
Review Questions   447
Critical Thinking Questions   449

UNIT 3 REGULATION, INTEGRATION, AND CONTROL

CHAPTER 12
The Nervous System and Nervous Tissue   451

Introduction   451
12.1 Basic Structure and Function of the Nervous System   452
12.2 Nervous Tissue   458
12.3 The Function of Nervous Tissue   465
12.4 The Action Potential   468
12.5 Communication Between Neurons   476
Key Terms   483
Chapter Review   486
Interactive Link Questions   488
Review Questions   489
Critical Thinking Questions   490

CHAPTER 13
Anatomy of the Nervous System   493

Introduction   493
13.1 The Embryologic Perspective   494
13.2 The Central Nervous System   499

13.3 Circulation and the Central Nervous System   511
13.4 The Peripheral Nervous System   518
Key Terms   528
Chapter Review   532
Interactive Link Questions   534
Review Questions   535
Critical Thinking Questions   537

CHAPTER 14
The Somatic Nervous System   539

Introduction   539
14.1 Sensory Perception   540
14.2 Central Processing   559
14.3 Motor Responses   571
Key Terms   579
Chapter Review   583
Interactive Link Questions   585
Review Questions   586
Critical Thinking Questions   587

CHAPTER 15
The Autonomic Nervous System   589

Introduction   589
15.1 Divisions of the Autonomic Nervous System   590
15.2 Autonomic Reflexes and Homeostasis   599
15.3 Central Control   607
15.4 Drugs that Affect the Autonomic System   610
Key Terms   616
Chapter Review   618
Interactive Link Questions   620
Review Questions   621
Critical Thinking Questions   622

CHAPTER 16
The Neurological Exam   625

Introduction   625
16.1 Overview of the Neurological Exam   626
16.2 The Mental Status Exam   629
16.3 The Cranial Nerve Exam   635
16.4 The Sensory and Motor Exams   644
16.5 The Coordination and Gait Exams   649
Key Terms   653
Chapter Review   655
Interactive Link Questions   657
Review Questions   658
Critical Thinking Questions   660

CHAPTER 17
The Endocrine System   661

Introduction   661

17.1 An Overview of the Endocrine System   661

17.2 Hormones   664

17.3 The Pituitary Gland and Hypothalamus   673

17.4 The Thyroid Gland   680

17.5 The Parathyroid Glands   685

17.6 The Adrenal Glands   688

17.7 The Pineal Gland   691

17.8 Gonadal and Placental Hormones   692

17.9 The Endocrine Pancreas   693

17.10 Organs with Secondary Endocrine Functions   697

17.11 Development and Aging of the Endocrine System   700

Key Terms   702

Chapter Review   704

Interactive Link Questions   706

Review Questions   707

Critical Thinking Questions   709

UNIT 4 FLUIDS AND TRANSPORT

CHAPTER 18
The Cardiovascular System: Blood   711

Introduction   711

18.1 An Overview of Blood   711

18.2 Production of the Formed Elements   716

18.3 Erythrocytes   719

18.4 Leukocytes and Platelets   727

18.5 Hemostasis   733

18.6 Blood Typing   739

Key Terms   744

Chapter Review   746

Interactive Link Questions   748

Review Questions   748

Critical Thinking Questions   750

CHAPTER 19
The Cardiovascular System: The Heart   751

Introduction   751

19.1 Heart Anatomy   752

19.2 Cardiac Muscle and Electrical Activity   772

19.3 Cardiac Cycle   784

19.4 Cardiac Physiology   788

19.5 Development of the Heart   799

Key Terms   801

Chapter Review   805

Interactive Link Questions   806

Review Questions   806

Critical Thinking Questions   808

CHAPTER 20
The Cardiovascular System: Blood Vessels and Circulation

809

Introduction   809
20.1 Structure and Function of Blood Vessels   810
20.2 Blood Flow, Blood Pressure, and Resistance   821
20.3 Capillary Exchange   830
20.4 Homeostatic Regulation of the Vascular System   832
20.5 Circulatory Pathways   842
20.6 Development of Blood Vessels and Fetal Circulation   878
Key Terms   881
Chapter Review   887
Interactive Link Questions   889
Review Questions   889
Critical Thinking Questions   891

CHAPTER 21
The Lymphatic and Immune System   893

Introduction   893
21.1 Anatomy of the Lymphatic and Immune Systems   894
21.2 Barrier Defenses and the Innate Immune Response   905
21.3 The Adaptive Immune Response: T lymphocytes and Their Functional Types   912
21.4 The Adaptive Immune Response: B-lymphocytes and Antibodies   920
21.5 The Immune Response against Pathogens   926
21.6 Diseases Associated with Depressed or Overactive Immune Responses   930
21.7 Transplantation and Cancer Immunology   934
Key Terms   940
Chapter Review   942
Interactive Link Questions   943
Review Questions   944
Critical Thinking Questions   946

UNIT 5 ENERGY, MAINTENANCE, AND ENVIRONMENTAL EXCHANGE

CHAPTER 22
The Respiratory System   947

Introduction   947
22.1 Organs and Structures of the Respiratory System   948
22.2 The Lungs   959
22.3 The Process of Breathing   961
22.4 Gas Exchange   970
22.5 Transport of Gases   975
22.6 Modifications in Respiratory Functions   981
22.7 Embryonic Development of the Respiratory System   983
Key Terms   986

Chapter Review 988

Interactive Link Questions 991

Review Questions 992

Critical Thinking Questions 994

CHAPTER 23
The Digestive System 995
Introduction 995

23.1 Overview of the Digestive System 995

23.2 Digestive System Processes and Regulation 1001

23.3 The Mouth, Pharynx, and Esophagus 1005

23.4 The Stomach 1016

23.5 The Small and Large Intestines 1022

23.6 Accessory Organs in Digestion: The Liver, Pancreas, and Gallbladder 1032

23.7 Chemical Digestion and Absorption: A Closer Look 1037

Key Terms 1048

Chapter Review 1051

Interactive Link Questions 1052

Review Questions 1053

Critical Thinking Questions 1055

CHAPTER 24
Metabolism and Nutrition 1057
Introduction 1057

24.1 Overview of Metabolic Reactions 1058

24.2 Carbohydrate Metabolism 1063

24.3 Lipid Metabolism 1075

24.4 Protein Metabolism 1081

24.5 Metabolic States of the Body 1087

24.6 Energy and Heat Balance 1091

24.7 Nutrition and Diet 1093

Key Terms 1101

Chapter Review 1102

Review Questions 1104

Critical Thinking Questions 1106

CHAPTER 25
The Urinary System 1109
Introduction 1109

25.1 Physical Characteristics of Urine 1110

25.2 Gross Anatomy of Urine Transport 1113

25.3 Gross Anatomy of the Kidney 1117

25.4 Microscopic Anatomy of the Kidney 1121

25.5 Physiology of Urine Formation 1125

25.6 Tubular Reabsorption 1128

25.7 Regulation of Renal Blood Flow 1137

25.8 Endocrine Regulation of Kidney Function 1139

25.9 Regulation of Fluid Volume and Composition 1141

25.10 The Urinary System and Homeostasis 1143

Key Terms   1147
Chapter Review   1149
Review Questions   1151
Critical Thinking Questions   1153

CHAPTER 26
Fluid, Electrolyte, and Acid-Base Balance   1155
Introduction   1155
26.1 Body Fluids and Fluid Compartments   1155
26.2 Water Balance   1163
26.3 Electrolyte Balance   1166
26.4 Acid-Base Balance   1171
26.5 Disorders of Acid-Base Balance   1176
Key Terms   1180
Chapter Review   1180
Interactive Link Questions   1181
Review Questions   1181
Critical Thinking Questions   1183

UNIT 6 HUMAN DEVELOPMENT AND THE CONTINUITY OF LIFE

CHAPTER 27
The Reproductive System   1185
Introduction   1185
27.1 Anatomy and Physiology of the Testicular Reproductive System   1186
27.2 Anatomy and Physiology of the Ovarian Reproductive System   1196
27.3 Development of the Male and Female Reproductive Systems   1212
Key Terms   1216
Chapter Review   1218
Interactive Link Questions   1219
Review Questions   1219
Critical Thinking Questions   1220

CHAPTER 28
Development and Inheritance   1223
Introduction   1223
28.1 Fertilization   1223
28.2 Embryonic Development   1228
28.3 Fetal Development   1239
28.4 Changes During Pregnancy, Labor, and Birth   1243
28.5 Adjustments of the Infant at Birth and Postnatal Stages   1250
28.6 Lactation   1252
28.7 Patterns of Inheritance   1256
Key Terms   1266
Chapter Review   1268
Interactive Link Questions   1270
Review Questions   1270
Critical Thinking Questions   1272

References   1275

Index   1279

PREFACE

About OpenStax

OpenStax is part of Rice University, which is a 501(c)(3) nonprofit charitable corporation. As an educational initiative, it's our mission to transform learning so that education works for every student. Through our partnerships with philanthropic foundations and our alliance with other educational resource companies, we're breaking down the most common barriers to learning. Because we believe that everyone should and can have access to knowledge.

About OpenStax Resources

Customization

Anatomy and Physiology 2e is licensed under a Creative Commons Attribution 4.0 International (CC BY) license, which means that you can distribute, remix, and build upon the content, as long as you provide attribution to OpenStax and its content contributors.

Because our books are openly licensed, you are free to use the entire book or select the sections that are most relevant to the needs of your course. Feel free to remix the content by assigning your students certain chapters and sections in your syllabus, in the order that you prefer. You can even provide a direct link in your syllabus to the sections in the web view of your book.

Instructors also have the option of creating a customized version of their OpenStax book. The custom version can be made available to students in low-cost print or digital form through their campus bookstore. Visit your book page on OpenStax.org for more information.

Errata

All OpenStax textbooks undergo a rigorous review process. However, like any professional-grade textbook, errors sometimes occur. Since our books are web based, we can make updates periodically when deemed pedagogically necessary. If you have a correction to suggest, submit it through the link on your book page on OpenStax.org. Subject matter experts review all errata suggestions. OpenStax is committed to remaining transparent about all updates, so you will also find a list of past errata changes on your book page on OpenStax.org.

Format

You can access this textbook for free in web view or PDF through OpenStax.org, and for a low-cost in print.

About Anatomy and Physiology 2e

Coverage and Scope

The units of Anatomy and Physiology 2e adhere to the scope and sequence followed by most two-semester courses. The development choices for this textbook were guided by hundreds of faculty who are deeply involved in teaching this course, as well as instructional designers, academic success experts, and educational researchers who have supported A&P educators and students. These choices led to innovations in art, terminology, career orientation, practical applications, and multimedia-based learning, all with a goal of increasing relevance to students. We strove to make the discipline engaging and relevant to students, so that they can draw from it a working knowledge that will enrich their future studies and support them in their careers.

Unit 1: Levels of Organization
Chapters 1–4 provide students with a basic understanding of human anatomy and physiology, including its language, the levels of organization, and the basics of chemistry and cell biology. These chapters provide a foundation for the further study of the body. They also focus particularly on how the body's regions, important chemicals, and cells maintain homeostasis.
Chapter 1 An Introduction to the Human Body
Chapter 2 The Chemical Level of Organization
Chapter 3 The Cellular Level of Organization
Chapter 4 The Tissue Level of Organization

Unit 2: Support and Movement
In Chapters 5–11, students explore the skin, the largest organ of the body, and examine the body's skeletal and muscular systems, following a traditional sequence of topics. This unit is the first to walk students through specific systems of the body, and as it does so, it maintains a focus on homeostasis as well as those diseases and conditions that can disrupt it.
Chapter 5 The Integumentary System
Chapter 6 Bone and Skeletal Tissue
Chapter 7 The Axial Skeleton
Chapter 8 The Appendicular Skeleton
Chapter 9 Joints
Chapter 10 Muscle Tissue
Chapter 11 The Muscular System

Unit 3: Regulation, Integration, and Control
Chapters 12–17 help students answer questions about

nervous and endocrine system control and regulation. In a break with the traditional sequence of topics, the special senses are integrated into the chapter on the somatic nervous system. The chapter on the neurological examination offers students a unique approach to understanding nervous system function using five simple but powerful diagnostic tests.

Chapter 12 Introduction to the Nervous System
Chapter 13 The Anatomy of the Nervous System
Chapter 14 The Somatic Nervous System
Chapter 15 The Autonomic Nervous System
Chapter 16 The Neurological Exam
Chapter 17 The Endocrine System

Unit 4: Fluids and Transport

In Chapters 18–21, students examine the principal means of transport for materials needed to support the human body, regulate its internal environment, and provide protection.

Chapter 18 Blood
Chapter 19 The Cardiovascular System: The Heart
Chapter 20 The Cardiovascular System: Blood Vessels and Circulation
Chapter 21 The Lymphatic System and Immunity

Unit 5: Energy, Maintenance, and Environmental Exchange

In Chapters 22–26, students discover the interaction between body systems and the outside environment for the exchange of materials, the capture of energy, the release of waste, and the overall maintenance of the internal systems that regulate the exchange. The explanations and illustrations are particularly focused on how structure relates to function.

Chapter 22 The Respiratory System
Chapter 23 The Digestive System
Chapter 24 Nutrition and Metabolism
Chapter 25 The Urinary System
Chapter 26 Fluid, Electrolyte, and Acid–Base Balance

Unit 6: Human Development and the Continuity of Life

The closing chapters examine the male and female reproductive systems, describe the process of human development and the different stages of pregnancy, and end with a review of the mechanisms of inheritance.

Chapter 27 The Reproductive System
Chapter 28 Development and Genetic Inheritance

Changes to the Second Edition

The **Anatomy and Physiology 2e** revision focuses on inclusive and equitable instruction, scientific accuracy, and enhanced instructor and student support. The improvements have been informed by extensive feedback from adopting faculty, curricular innovators, and equity experts.

The revision includes the following core changes:

- In explanations of endocrine function, reproduction, development, inheritance, and related topics, the second edition is clearer and more accurate in differentiations related to sex, and eliminates incorrect equivalencies and generalizations regarding sex and gender. OpenStax thanks Sam Long and River Suh, founders of Gender-Inclusive Biology, for their extensive guidance and support
- Many of the illustrations have been improved to be more representative of diverse populations. We have also added photos of many conditions, symptoms, and disorders that present differently depending on skin tone. (Note that many of the illustration changes were made prior to the second edition revision.)
- In discussions and illustrations of genetics and inheritance, the text is clearer in its terminology and explanations related to parenting and parental roles.
- Several research references, data, and terminology have been improved to improve representation and currency.

These improvements are designed to create welcoming and inclusive learning experiences and promote scientifically accurate practices that students will encounter in their studies and careers. The additions and changes were made in a manner designed to enrich and support all users while maintaining the general approach of the text. Because OpenStax and our authors are aware of the difficulties posed by reorganization and renumbering, the extensive text and illustration changes have been implemented within the existing structure and organization of the book. A detailed transition guide will be available within the book's Instructor Resources at OpenStax.org.

Pedagogical Foundation and Features

Anatomy and Physiology 2e is designed to promote scientific literacy. Throughout the text, you will find features that engage the students by taking selected topics a step further.

- **Homeostatic Imbalances** discusses the effects and results of imbalances in the body.
- **Disorders** showcases a disorder that is relevant to the body system at hand. This feature may focus on a specific disorder or a set of related disorders.
- **Diseases** showcases a disease that is relevant to the body system at hand.

- **Aging** explores the effect aging has on a body's system and specific disorders that manifest over time.
- **Career Connections** presents information on the various careers often pursued by allied health students, such as medical technician, medical examiner, and neurophysiologist. Students are introduced to the educational requirements for and day-to-day responsibilities in these careers.
- **Everyday Connections** tie anatomical and physiological concepts to emerging issues and discuss these in terms of everyday life. Topics include "Anabolic Steroids" and "The Effect of Second-Hand Tobacco Smoke."
- **Interactive Links** direct students to online exercises, simulations, animations, and videos to add a fuller context to core content and help improve understanding of the material. Many features include links to the University of Michigan's interactive WebScopes, which allow students to zoom in on micrographs in the collection. These resources were vetted by reviewers and other subject matter experts to ensure that they are effective and accurate. We strongly urge students to explore these links, whether viewing a video or inputting data into a simulation, to gain the fullest experience and to learn how to search for information independently.

Dynamic, Learner-Centered Art

Our unique approach to visuals is designed to emphasize only the components most important in any given illustration. The art style is particularly aimed at focusing student learning through a powerful blend of traditional depictions and instructional innovations.

Much of the art in this book consists of black line illustrations. The strongest line is used to highlight the most important structures, and shading is used to show dimension and shape. Color is used sparingly to highlight and clarify the primary anatomical or functional point of the illustration. This technique is intended to draw students' attention to the critical learning point in the illustration, without distraction from excessive gradients, shadows, and highlights. Full color is used when the structure or process requires it (for example, muscle diagrams and cardiovascular system illustrations).

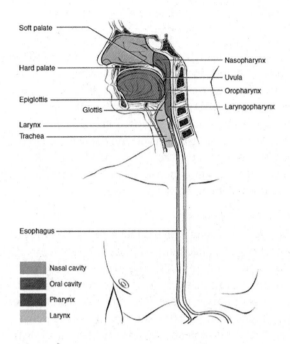

By highlighting the most important portions of the illustration, the artwork helps students focus on the most important points without overwhelming them.

Micrographs

Micrograph magnifications have been calculated based on the objective provided with the image. If a micrograph was recorded at 40×, and the image was magnified an additional 2×, we calculated the final magnification of the micrograph to be 80×.

Please note that, when viewing the textbook electronically, the micrograph magnification provided in the text does not take into account the size and magnification of the screen on your electronic device. There may be some variation.

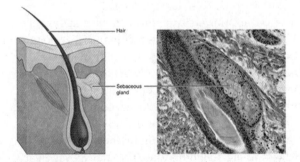

These glands secrete oils that lubricate and protect the skin. LM × 400. (Micrograph provided by the Regents of University of Michigan Medical School © 2012)

Additional Resources

Student and Instructor Resources

We've compiled additional resources for both students and instructors, including Getting Started Guides, an instructor solution guide, a curated video guide, and several types of PowerPoint slides and image resources. Instructor resources require a verified instructor account, which you can apply for when you log in or create your account on OpenStax.org. Student resources include guided lecture notes, a student solutions manual, and a pronunciation guide.

Community Hubs

OpenStax partners with the Institute for the Study of Knowledge Management in Education (ISKME) to offer Community Hubs on OER Commons—a platform for instructors to share community-created resources that support OpenStax books, free of charge. Through our Community Hubs, instructors can upload their own materials or download resources to use in their own courses, including additional ancillaries, teaching material, multimedia, and relevant course content. We encourage instructors to join the hubs for the subjects most relevant to your teaching and research as an opportunity both to enrich your courses and to engage with other faculty. To reach the Community Hubs, visit www.oercommons.org/hubs/openstax.

Technology Partners

As allies in making high-quality learning materials accessible, our technology partners offer optional low-cost tools that are integrated with OpenStax books. To access the technology options for your text, visit your book page on OpenStax.org.

About the Authors

Senior Contributing Authors

J. Gordon Betts, Tyler Junior College
Peter Desaix, University of North Carolina at Chapel Hill
Eddie Johnson, Central Oregon Community College
Jody E. Johnson, Arapahoe Community College
Oksana Korol, Aims Community College
Dean Kruse, Portland Community College
Brandon Poe, Springfield Technical Community College
James A. Wise, Hampton University
Mark Womble, Youngstown State University
Kelly A. Young, California State University, Long Beach

Advisor

Robin J. Heyden

Contributing Authors

Kim Aaronson, Aquarius Institute; Triton College
Lopamudra Agarwal, Augusta Technical College

Gary Allen, Dalhousie University
Robert Allison, McLennan Community College
Heather Armbruster, Southern Union State Community College
Timothy Ballard, University of North Carolina Wilmington
Matthew Barlow, Eastern New Mexico University
William Blaker, Furman University
Julie Bowers, East Tennessee State University
Emily Bradshaw, Florida Southern College
Nishi Bryska, University of North Carolina, Charlotte
Susan Caley Opsal, Illinois Valley Community College
Boyd Campbell, Southwest College of Naturopathic Medicine and Health Sciences
Ann Caplea, Walsh University
Marnie Chapman, University of Alaska, Sitka
Barbara Christie-Pope, Cornell College
Kenneth Crane, Texarkana College
Maurice Culver, Florida State College at Jacksonville
Heather Cushman, Tacoma Community College
Noelle Cutter, Molloy College
Lynnette Danzl-Tauer, Rock Valley College
Jane Davis, Aurora University
AnnMarie DelliPizzi, Dominican College
Susan Dentel, Washtenaw Community College
Pamela Dobbins, Shelton State Community College
Patty Dolan, Pacific Lutheran University
Sondra Dubowsky, McLennan Community College
Peter Dukehart, Three Rivers Community College
Ellen DuPré, Central College
Elizabeth DuPriest, Warner Pacific College
Pam Elf, University of Minnesota
Sharon Ellerton, Queensborough Community College
Carla Endres, Utah State University - College of Eastern Utah: San Juan Campus
Myriam Feldman, Lake Washington Institute of Technology; Cascadia Community College
Greg Fitch, Avila University
Lynn Gargan, Tarant County College
Michael Giangrande, Oakland Community College
Chaya Gopalan, St. Louis College of Pharmacy
Victor Greco, Chattahoochee Technical College
Susanna Heinze, Skagit Valley College
Ann Henninger, Wartburg College
Dale Horeth, Tidewater Community College
Michael Hortsch, University of Michigan
Rosemary Hubbard, Marymount University
Mark Hubley, Prince George's Community College
Branko Jablanovic, College of Lake County
Norman Johnson, University of Massachusetts Amherst
Mark Jonasson, North Arkansas College
Jeff Keyte, College of Saint Mary
William Kleinelp, Middlesex County College

Leigh Kleinert, Grand Rapids Community College
Brenda Leady, University of Toledo
John Lepri, University of North Carolina, Greensboro
Sarah Leupen, University of Maryland, Baltimore County
Lihua Liang, Johns Hopkins University
Robert Mallet, University of North Texas Health Science Center
Bruce Maring, Daytona State College
Elisabeth Martin, College of Lake County
Natalie Maxwell, Carl Albert State College, Sallisaw
Julie May, William Carey University
Debra McLaughlin, University of Maryland University College
Nicholas Mitchell, St. Bonaventure University
Shobhana Natarajan, Brookhaven College
Phillip Nicotera, St. Petersburg College
Mary Jane Niles, University of San Francisco
Ikemefuna Nwosu, Parkland College; Lake Land College
Betsy Ott, Tyler Junior College
Ivan Paul, John Wood Community College
Aaron Payette, College of Southern Nevada
Scott Payne, Kentucky Wesleyan College
Cameron Perkins, South Georgia College
David Pfeiffer, University of Alaska, Anchorage
Thomas Pilat, Illinois Central College
Eileen Preston, Tarrant County College
Mike Pyle, Olivet Nazarene University
Robert Rawding, Gannon University
Jason Schreer, State University of New York at Potsdam
Laird Sheldahl, Mt. Hood Community College
Brian Shmaefsky, Lone Star College System

Douglas Sizemore, Bevill State Community College
Susan Spencer, Mount Hood Community College
Cynthia Standley, University of Arizona
Robert Sullivan, Marist College
Eric Sun, Middle Georgia State College
Tom Swenson, Ithaca College
Kathleen Tallman, Azusa Pacific University
Rohinton Tarapore, University of Pennsylvania
Elizabeth Tattersall, Western Nevada College
Mark Thomas, University of Northern Colorado
Janis Thompson, Lorain County Community College
Rita Thrasher, Pensacola State College
David Van Wylen, St. Olaf College
Lynn Wandrey, Mott Community College
Margaret Weck, St. Louis College of Pharmacy
Kathleen Weiss, George Fox University
Neil Westergaard, Williston State College
David Wortham, West Georgia Technical College
Umesh Yadav, University of Texas Medical Branch
Tony Yates, Oklahoma Baptist University
Justin York, Glendale Community College
Cheri Zao, North Idaho College
Elena Zoubina, Bridgewater State University; Massasoit Community College
Shobhana Natarajan, Alcon Laboratories, Inc.

Special Thanks

OpenStax wishes to thank the Regents of University of Michigan Medical School for the use of their extensive micrograph collection. Many of the UM micrographs that appear in *Anatomy and Physiology 2e* are interactive WebScopes, which students can explore by zooming in and out.

CHAPTER 1
An Introduction to the Human Body

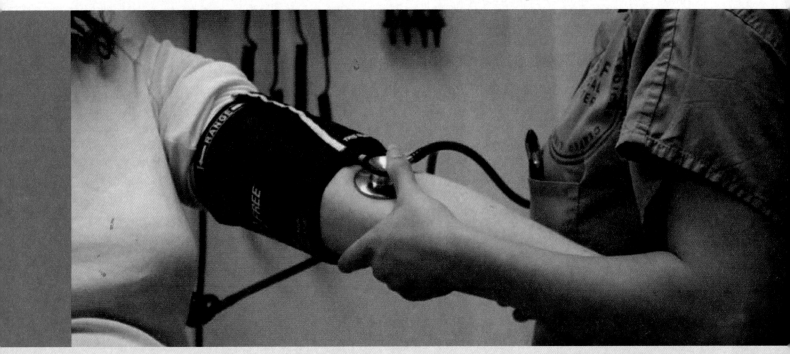

Figure 1.1 **Blood Pressure** A proficiency in anatomy and physiology is fundamental to any career in the health professions. (credit: Bryan Mason/flickr)

CHAPTER OBJECTIVES
After studying this chapter, you will be able to:

- Distinguish between anatomy and physiology, and identify several branches of each
- Describe the structure of the body, from simplest to most complex, in terms of the six levels of organization
- Identify the functional characteristics of human life
- Identify the four requirements for human survival
- Define homeostasis and explain its importance to normal human functioning
- Use appropriate anatomical terminology to identify key body structures, body regions, and directions in the body
- Compare and contrast at least four medical imaging techniques in terms of their function and use in medicine

INTRODUCTION Though you may approach a course in anatomy and physiology strictly as a requirement for your field of study, the knowledge you gain in this course will serve you well in many aspects of your life. An understanding of anatomy and physiology is not only fundamental to any career in the health professions, but it can also benefit your own health. Familiarity with the human body can help you make healthful choices and prompt you to take appropriate action when signs of illness arise. Your knowledge in this field will help you understand news about nutrition, medications, medical devices, and procedures and help you understand genetic or infectious diseases. At some point, everyone will have a problem with some aspect of their body and your knowledge can help you to be a better parent, spouse, partner, friend, colleague, or caregiver.

This chapter begins with an overview of anatomy and physiology and a preview of the body regions and functions. It then covers the characteristics of life and how the body works to maintain stable conditions. It introduces a set of standard terms for body structures and for planes and positions in the body that will serve as a foundation for more comprehensive information covered later in the text. It ends with examples of medical imaging used to see inside the living body.

1.1 Overview of Anatomy and Physiology

LEARNING OBJECTIVES

By the end of this section, you will be able to:

- Compare and contrast anatomy and physiology, including their specializations and methods of study
- Discuss the fundamental relationship between anatomy and physiology

Human **anatomy** is the scientific study of the body's structures. Some of these structures are very small and can only be observed and analyzed with the assistance of a microscope. Other larger structures can readily be seen, manipulated, measured, and weighed. The word "anatomy" comes from a Greek root that means "to cut apart." Human anatomy was first studied by observing the exterior of the body and observing the wounds of soldiers and other injuries. Later, physicians were allowed to dissect bodies of the dead to augment their knowledge. When a body is dissected, its structures are cut apart in order to observe their physical attributes and their relationships to one another. Dissection is still used in medical schools, anatomy courses, and in pathology labs. In order to observe structures in living people, however, a number of imaging techniques have been developed. These techniques allow clinicians to visualize structures inside the living body such as a cancerous tumor or a fractured bone.

Like most scientific disciplines, anatomy has areas of specialization. **Gross anatomy** is the study of the larger structures of the body, those visible without the aid of magnification (Figure 1.2 **a**). Macro- means "large," thus, gross anatomy is also referred to as macroscopic anatomy. In contrast, micro- means "small," and **microscopic anatomy** is the study of structures that can be observed only with the use of a microscope or other magnification devices (Figure 1.2 **b**). Microscopic anatomy includes cytology, the study of cells and histology, the study of tissues. As the technology of microscopes has advanced, anatomists have been able to observe smaller and smaller structures of the body, from slices of large structures like the heart, to the three-dimensional structures of large molecules in the body.

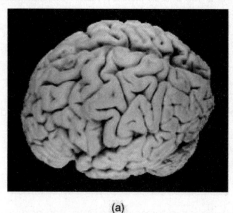 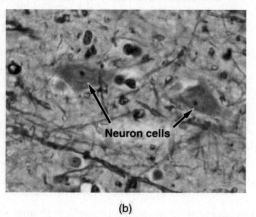

Neuron cells

(a)   (b)

FIGURE 1.2 Gross and Microscopic Anatomy   (a) Gross anatomy considers large structures such as the brain. (b) Microscopic anatomy can deal with the same structures, though at a different scale. This is a micrograph of nerve cells from the brain. LM × 1600. (credit a: "WriterHound"/Wikimedia Commons; credit b: Micrograph provided by the Regents of University of Michigan Medical School © 2012)

Anatomists take two general approaches to the study of the body's structures: regional and systemic. **Regional anatomy** is the study of the interrelationships of all of the structures in a specific body region, such as the abdomen. Studying regional anatomy helps us appreciate the interrelationships of body structures, such as how muscles, nerves, blood vessels, and other structures work together to serve a particular body region. In contrast, **systemic anatomy** is the study of the structures that make up a discrete body system—that is, a group of structures that work together to perform a unique body function. For example, a systemic anatomical study of the muscular system would consider all of the skeletal muscles of the body.

Whereas anatomy is about structure, physiology is about function. Human **physiology** is the scientific study of the chemistry and physics of the structures of the body and the ways in which they work together to support the functions of life. Much of the study of physiology centers on the body's tendency toward homeostasis. **Homeostasis** is the state of steady internal conditions maintained by living things. The study of physiology certainly includes observation, both with the naked eye and with microscopes, as well as manipulations and measurements. However, current advances in physiology usually depend on carefully designed laboratory experiments that reveal the functions of the many structures and chemical compounds that make up the human body.

Like anatomists, physiologists typically specialize in a particular branch of physiology. For example, neurophysiology is the study of the brain, spinal cord, and nerves and how these work together to perform functions as complex and diverse as vision, movement, and thinking. Physiologists may work from the organ level (exploring, for example, what different parts of the brain do) to the molecular level (such as exploring how an electrochemical signal travels along nerves).

Form is closely related to function in all living things. For example, the thin flap of your eyelid can snap down to clear away dust particles and almost instantaneously slide back up to allow you to see again. At the microscopic level, the arrangement and function of the nerves and muscles that serve the eyelid allow for its quick action and retreat. At a smaller level of analysis, the function of these nerves and muscles likewise relies on the interactions of specific molecules and ions. Even the three-dimensional structure of certain molecules is essential to their function.

Your study of anatomy and physiology will make more sense if you continually relate the form of the structures you are studying to their function. In fact, it can be somewhat frustrating to attempt to study anatomy without an understanding of the physiology that a body structure supports. Imagine, for example, trying to appreciate the unique arrangement of the bones of the human hand if you had no conception of the function of the hand. Fortunately, your understanding of how the human hand manipulates tools—from pens to cell phones—helps you appreciate the unique alignment of the thumb in opposition to the four fingers, making your hand a structure that allows you to pinch and grasp objects and type text messages.

1.2 Structural Organization of the Human Body

LEARNING OBJECTIVES

By the end of this section, you will be able to:

- Describe the structure of the human body in terms of six levels of organization
- List the eleven organ systems of the human body and identify at least one organ and one major function of each

Before you begin to study the different structures and functions of the human body, it is helpful to consider its basic architecture; that is, how its smallest parts are assembled into larger structures. It is convenient to consider the structures of the body in terms of fundamental levels of organization that increase in complexity: subatomic particles, atoms, molecules, organelles, cells, tissues, organs, organ systems, organisms and biosphere (Figure 1.3).

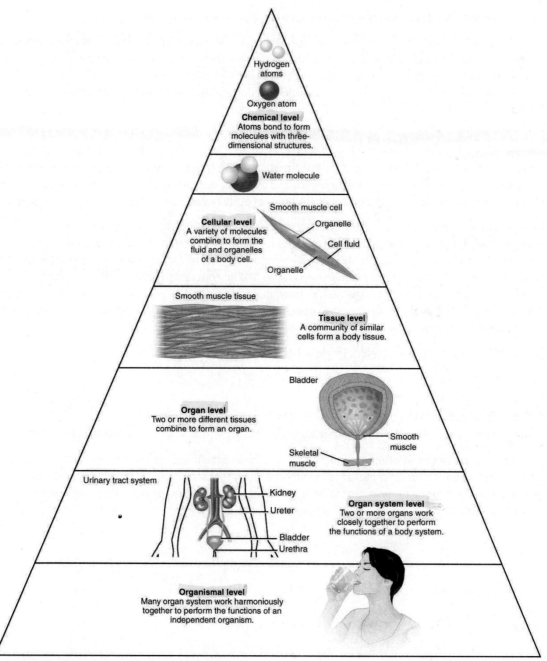

FIGURE 1.3   Levels of Structural Organization of the Human Body   The organization of the body often is discussed in terms of six distinct levels of increasing complexity, from the smallest chemical building blocks to a unique human organism.

The Levels of Organization

To study the chemical level of organization, scientists consider the simplest building blocks of matter: subatomic particles, atoms and molecules. All matter in the universe is composed of one or more unique pure substances called elements, familiar examples of which are hydrogen, oxygen, carbon, nitrogen, calcium, and iron. The smallest unit of any of these pure substances (elements) is an atom. Atoms are made up of subatomic particles such as the proton, electron and neutron. Two or more atoms combine to form a molecule, such as the water molecules, proteins, and sugars found in living things. Molecules are the chemical building blocks of all body structures.

A **cell** is the smallest independently functioning unit of a living organism. Even bacteria, which are extremely small, independently-living organisms, have a cellular structure. Each bacterium is a single cell. All living structures of human anatomy contain cells, and almost all functions of human physiology are performed in cells or are initiated by cells.

A human cell typically consists of flexible membranes that enclose cytoplasm, a water-based cellular fluid together with a variety of tiny functioning units called **organelles**. In humans, as in all organisms, cells perform all functions of life. A **tissue** is a group of many similar cells (though sometimes composed of a few related types) that work together to perform a specific function. An **organ** is an anatomically distinct structure of the body composed of two or more tissue types. Each organ performs one or more specific physiological functions. An **organ system** is a group of organs that work together to perform major functions or meet physiological needs of the body.

This book covers eleven distinct organ systems in the human body (Figure 1.4 and Figure 1.5). Assigning organs to organ systems can be imprecise since organs that "belong" to one system can also have functions integral to another system. In fact, most organs contribute to more than one system.

In this book and throughout your studies of biological sciences, you will often read descriptions related to similarities and differences among biological structures, processes, and health related to a person's biological sex. People often use the words "female" and "male" to describe two different concepts: our sense of gender identity, and our biological sex as determined by our chromosomes, hormones, organs, and other physical characteristics. For some people, gender identity is different from biological sex or their sex assigned at birth. Throughout this book, "female" and "male" refer to sex only, and the typical anatomy and physiology of XX and XY individuals is discussed.

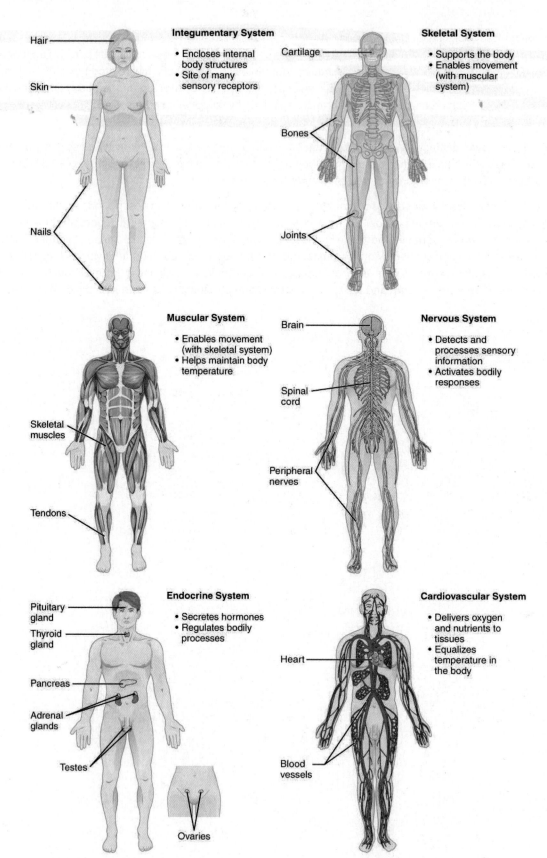

FIGURE 1.4   Organ Systems of the Human Body   Organs that work together are grouped into organ systems.

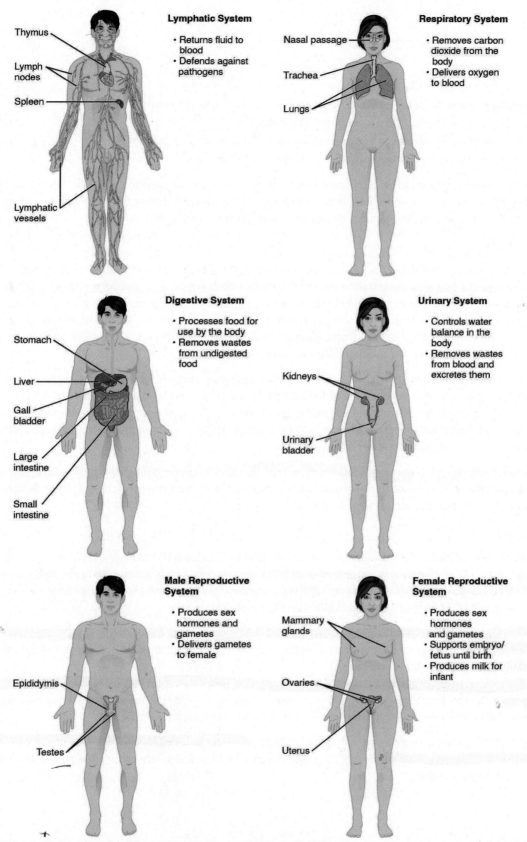

FIGURE 1.5   Organ Systems of the Human Body (continued)   Organs that work together are grouped into organ systems.

The organism level is the highest level of organization. An **organism** is a living being that has a cellular structure and that can independently perform all physiologic functions necessary for life. In multicellular organisms, including humans, all cells, tissues, organs, and organ systems of the body work together to maintain the life and health of the organism.

1.3 Functions of Human Life

LEARNING OBJECTIVES

By the end of this section, you will be able to:

- Explain the importance of organization to the function of the human organism
- Distinguish between metabolism, anabolism, and catabolism
- Provide at least two examples of human responsiveness and human movement
- Compare and contrast growth, differentiation, and reproduction

The different organ systems each have different functions and therefore unique roles to perform in physiology. These many functions can be summarized in terms of a few that we might consider definitive of human life: organization, metabolism, responsiveness, movement, development, and reproduction.

Organization

A human body consists of trillions of cells organized in a way that maintains distinct internal compartments. These compartments keep body cells separated from external environmental threats and keep the cells moist and nourished. They also separate internal body fluids from the countless microorganisms that grow on body surfaces, including the lining of certain passageways that connect to the outer surface of the body. The intestinal tract, for example, is home to more bacterial cells than the total of all human cells in the body, yet these bacteria are outside the body and cannot be allowed to circulate freely inside the body.

Cells, for example, have a cell membrane (also referred to as the plasma membrane) that keeps the intracellular environment—the fluids and organelles—separate from the extracellular environment. Blood vessels keep blood inside a closed circulatory system, and nerves and muscles are wrapped in connective tissue sheaths that separate them from surrounding structures. In the chest and abdomen, a variety of internal membranes keep major organs such as the lungs, heart, and kidneys separate from others.

The body's largest organ system is the integumentary system, which includes the skin and its associated structures, such as hair and nails. The surface tissue of skin is a barrier that protects internal structures and fluids from potentially harmful microorganisms and other toxins.

Metabolism

The first law of thermodynamics holds that energy can neither be created nor destroyed—it can only change form. Your basic function as an organism is to consume (ingest) energy and molecules in the foods you eat, convert some of it into fuel for movement, sustain your body functions, and build and maintain your body structures. There are two types of reactions that accomplish this: **anabolism** and **catabolism**.

- **Anabolism** is the process whereby smaller, simpler molecules are combined into larger, more complex substances. Your body can assemble, by utilizing energy, the complex chemicals it needs by combining small molecules derived from the foods you eat
- **Catabolism** is the process by which larger more complex substances are broken down into smaller simpler molecules. Catabolism releases energy. The complex molecules found in foods are broken down so the body can use their parts to assemble the structures and substances needed for life.

Taken together, these two processes are called metabolism. **Metabolism** is the sum of all anabolic and catabolic reactions that take place in the body (Figure 1.6). Both anabolism and catabolism occur simultaneously and continuously to keep you alive.

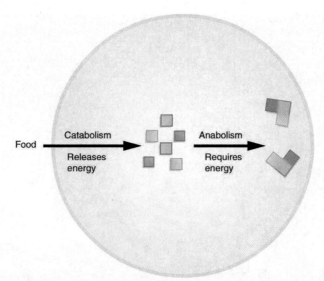

FIGURE 1.6 **Metabolism**   Anabolic reactions are building reactions, and they consume energy. Catabolic reactions break materials down and release energy. Metabolism includes both anabolic and catabolic reactions.

Every cell in your body makes use of a chemical compound, **adenosine triphosphate (ATP)**, to store and release energy. The cell stores energy in the synthesis (anabolism) of ATP, then moves the ATP molecules to the location where energy is needed to fuel cellular activities. Then the ATP is broken down (catabolism) and a controlled amount of energy is released, which is used by the cell to perform a particular job.

🔗 INTERACTIVE LINK

View this animation (http://openstax.org/l/metabolic) to learn more about metabolic processes. Which organs of the body likely carry out anabolic processes? What about catabolic processes?

Responsiveness

Responsiveness is the ability of an organism to adjust to changes in its internal and external environments. An example of responsiveness to external stimuli could include moving toward sources of food and water and away from perceived dangers. Changes in an organism's internal environment, such as increased body temperature, can cause the responses of sweating and the dilation of blood vessels in the skin in order to decrease body temperature, as shown by the runners in Figure 1.7.

Movement

Human movement includes not only actions at the joints of the body, but also the motion of individual organs and even individual cells. As you read these words, red and white blood cells are moving throughout your body, muscle cells are contracting and relaxing to maintain your posture and to focus your vision, and glands are secreting chemicals to regulate body functions. Your body is coordinating the action of entire muscle groups to enable you to move air into and out of your lungs, to push blood throughout your body, and to propel the food you have eaten through your digestive tract. Consciously, of course, you contract your skeletal muscles to move the bones of your skeleton to get from one place to another (as the runners are doing in Figure 1.7), and to carry out all of the activities of your daily life.

FIGURE 1.7   Marathon Runners   Runners demonstrate two characteristics of living humans—responsiveness and movement. Anatomic structures and physiological processes allow runners to coordinate the action of muscle groups and sweat in response to rising internal body temperature. (credit: Phil Roeder/flickr)

Development, growth and reproduction

Development is all of the changes the body goes through in life. Development includes the process of **differentiation**, in which unspecialized cells become specialized in structure and function to perform certain tasks in the body. Development also includes the processes of growth and repair, both of which involve cell differentiation.

Growth is the increase in body size. Humans, like all multicellular organisms, grow by increasing the number of existing cells, increasing the amount of non-cellular material around cells (such as mineral deposits in bone), and, within very narrow limits, increasing the size of existing cells.

Reproduction is the formation of a new organism from parent organisms. In humans, reproduction is carried out by the male and female reproductive systems. Because death will come to all complex organisms, without reproduction, the line of organisms would end.

1.4 Requirements for Human Life

LEARNING OBJECTIVES

By the end of this section, you will be able to:
- Discuss the role of oxygen and nutrients in maintaining human survival
- Explain why extreme heat and extreme cold threaten human survival
- Explain how the pressure exerted by gases and fluids influences human survival

Humans have been acclimating to life on Earth for at least the past 200,000 years. Earth and its atmosphere have provided us with air to breathe, water to drink, and food to eat, but these are not the only requirements for survival. Although you may rarely think about it, you also cannot live outside of a certain range of temperature and pressure that the surface of our planet and its atmosphere provides. The next sections explore these four requirements of life.

Oxygen

Atmospheric air is only about 20 percent oxygen, but that oxygen is a key component of the chemical reactions that keep the body alive, including the reactions that produce ATP. Brain cells are especially sensitive to lack of oxygen because of their requirement for a high-and-steady production of ATP. Brain damage is likely within five minutes without oxygen, and death is likely within ten minutes.

Nutrients

A **nutrient** is a substance in foods and beverages that is essential to human survival. The three basic classes of nutrients are water, the energy-yielding and body-building nutrients, and the micronutrients (vitamins and minerals).

The most critical nutrient is water. Depending on the environmental temperature and our state of health, we may be able to survive for only a few days without water. The body's functional chemicals are dissolved and transported in water, and the chemical reactions of life take place in water. Moreover, water is the largest component of cells, blood, and the fluid between cells, and water makes up about 70 percent of an adult's body mass. Water also helps regulate our internal temperature and cushions, protects, and lubricates joints and many other body structures.

The energy-yielding nutrients are primarily carbohydrates and lipids, while proteins mainly supply the amino acids that are the building blocks of the body itself. You ingest these in plant and animal foods and beverages, and the digestive system breaks them down into molecules small enough to be absorbed. The breakdown products of carbohydrates and lipids can then be used in the metabolic processes that convert them to ATP. Although you might feel as if you are starving after missing a single meal, you can survive without consuming the energy-yielding nutrients for at least several weeks.

Water and the energy-yielding nutrients are also referred to as macronutrients because the body needs them in large amounts. In contrast, micronutrients are vitamins and minerals. These elements and compounds participate in many essential chemical reactions and processes, such as nerve impulses, and some, such as calcium, also contribute to the body's structure. Your body can store some of the micronutrients in its tissues, and draw on those reserves if you fail to consume them in your diet for a few days or weeks. Some others micronutrients, such as vitamin C and most of the B vitamins, are water-soluble and cannot be stored, so you need to consume them every day or two.

Narrow Range of Temperature

You have probably seen news stories about athletes who died of heat stroke, or hikers who died of exposure to cold. Such deaths occur because the chemical reactions upon which the body depends can only take place within a narrow range of body temperature, from just below to just above 37°C (98.6°F). When body temperature rises well above or drops well below normal, certain proteins (enzymes) that facilitate chemical reactions lose their normal structure and their ability to function and the chemical reactions of metabolism cannot proceed.

That said, the body can respond effectively to short-term exposure to heat (Figure 1.8) or cold. One of the body's responses to heat is, of course, sweating. As sweat evaporates from skin, it removes some thermal energy from the body, cooling it. Adequate water (from the extracellular fluid in the body) is necessary to produce sweat, so adequate fluid intake is essential to balance that loss during the sweat response. Not surprisingly, the sweat response is much less effective in a humid environment because the air is already saturated with water. Thus, the sweat on the skin's surface is not able to evaporate, and internal body temperature can get dangerously high.

FIGURE 1.8   Extreme Heat   Humans acclimate to some degree to repeated exposure to high temperatures. (credit: McKay Savage/flickr)

The body can also respond effectively to short-term exposure to cold. One response to cold is shivering, which is random muscle movement that generates heat. Another response is increased breakdown of stored energy to generate heat. When that energy reserve is depleted, however, and the core temperature begins to drop significantly, red blood cells will lose their ability to give up oxygen, denying the brain of this critical component of ATP production. This lack of oxygen can cause confusion, lethargy, and eventually loss of consciousness and death. The body responds to cold by reducing blood circulation to the extremities, the hands and feet, in order to prevent blood from cooling there and so that the body's core can stay warm. Even when core body temperature remains stable, however, tissues exposed to severe cold, especially the fingers and toes, can develop frostbite when blood flow to the extremities has been much reduced. This form of tissue damage can be permanent and lead to gangrene, requiring amputation of the affected region.

Everyday Connection

Controlled Hypothermia

As you have learned, the body continuously engages in coordinated physiological processes to maintain a stable temperature. In some cases, however, overriding this system can be useful, or even life-saving. Hypothermia is the clinical term for an abnormally low body temperature (hypo- = "below" or "under"). Controlled hypothermia is clinically induced hypothermia performed in order to reduce the metabolic rate of an organ or of a person's entire body.

Controlled hypothermia often is used, for example, during open-heart surgery because it decreases the metabolic needs of the brain, heart, and other organs, reducing the risk of damage to them. When controlled hypothermia is used clinically, the patient is given medication to prevent shivering. The body is then cooled to 25–32°C (79–89°F). The heart is stopped and an external heart-lung pump maintains circulation to the patient's body. The heart is cooled further and is maintained at a temperature below 15°C (60°F) for the duration of the surgery. This very cold temperature helps the heart muscle to tolerate its lack of blood supply during the surgery.

Some emergency department physicians use controlled hypothermia to reduce damage to the heart in patients who have suffered a cardiac arrest. In the emergency department, the physician induces coma and lowers the patient's body temperature to approximately 91 degrees. This condition, which is maintained for 24 hours, slows the patient's metabolic rate. Because the patient's organs require less blood to function, the heart's workload is reduced.

Narrow Range of Atmospheric Pressure

Pressure is a force exerted by a substance that is in contact with another substance. Atmospheric pressure is pressure exerted by the mixture of gases (primarily nitrogen and oxygen) in the Earth's atmosphere. Although you may not perceive it, atmospheric pressure is constantly pressing down on your body. This pressure keeps gases within your body, such as the gaseous nitrogen in body fluids, dissolved. If you were suddenly ejected from a space ship above Earth's atmosphere, you would go from a situation of normal pressure to one of very low pressure. The pressure of the nitrogen gas in your blood would be much higher than the pressure of nitrogen in the space surrounding your body. As a result, the nitrogen gas in your blood would expand, forming bubbles that could block blood vessels and even cause cells to break apart.

Atmospheric pressure does more than just keep blood gases dissolved. Your ability to breathe—that is, to take in oxygen and release carbon dioxide—also depends upon a precise atmospheric pressure. Altitude sickness occurs in part because the atmosphere at high altitudes exerts less pressure, reducing the exchange of these gases, and causing shortness of breath, confusion, headache, lethargy, and nausea. Mountain climbers carry oxygen to reduce the effects of both low oxygen levels and low barometric pressure at higher altitudes (Figure 1.9).

FIGURE 1.9   Harsh Conditions   Climbers on Mount Everest must accommodate extreme cold, low oxygen levels, and low barometric pressure in an environment hostile to human life. (credit: Melanie Ko/flickr)

 HOMEOSTATIC IMBALANCES

Decompression Sickness

Decompression sickness (DCS) is a condition in which gases dissolved in the blood or in other body tissues are no longer dissolved following a reduction in pressure on the body. This condition affects underwater divers who surface from a deep dive too quickly, and it can affect pilots flying at high altitudes in planes with unpressurized cabins. Divers often call this condition "the bends," a reference to joint pain that is a symptom of DCS.

In all cases, DCS is brought about by a reduction in barometric pressure. At high altitude, barometric pressure is much less than on Earth's surface because pressure is produced by the weight of the column of air above the body pressing down on the body. The very great pressures on divers in deep water are likewise from the weight of a column of water pressing down on the body. For divers, DCS occurs at normal barometric pressure (at sea level), but it is brought on by the relatively rapid decrease of pressure as divers rise from the high pressure conditions of deep water to the now low, by comparison, pressure at sea level. Not surprisingly, diving in deep mountain lakes, where barometric pressure at the surface of the lake is less than that at sea level is more likely to result in DCS than diving in water at sea level.

In DCS, gases dissolved in the blood (primarily nitrogen) come rapidly out of solution, forming bubbles in the blood and in other body tissues. This occurs because when pressure of a gas over a liquid is decreased, the amount of gas that can remain dissolved in the liquid also is decreased. It is air pressure that keeps your normal blood gases dissolved in the blood. When pressure is reduced, less gas remains dissolved. You have seen this in effect when you open a carbonated drink. Removing the seal of the bottle reduces the pressure of the gas over the liquid. This in turn causes bubbles as dissolved gases (in this case, carbon dioxide) come out of solution in the liquid.

The most common symptoms of DCS are pain in the joints, with headache and disturbances of vision occurring in 10 percent to 15 percent of cases. Left untreated, very severe DCS can result in death. Immediate treatment is with pure oxygen. The affected person is then moved into a hyperbaric chamber. A hyperbaric chamber is a reinforced, closed chamber that is pressurized to greater than atmospheric pressure. It treats DCS by repressurizing the body so that pressure can then be removed much more gradually. Because the hyperbaric chamber introduces oxygen to the body at high pressure, it increases the concentration of oxygen in the blood. This has the effect of replacing some of the nitrogen in the blood with oxygen, which is easier to tolerate out of solution.

The dynamic pressure of body fluids is also important to human survival. For example, blood pressure, which is the pressure exerted by blood as it flows within blood vessels, must be great enough to enable blood to reach all body tissues, and yet low enough to ensure that the delicate blood vessels can withstand the friction and force of the pulsating flow of pressurized blood.

1.5 Homeostasis

LEARNING OBJECTIVES

By the end of this section, you will be able to:

- Discuss the role of homeostasis in healthy functioning
- Contrast negative and positive feedback, giving one physiologic example of each mechanism

Maintaining homeostasis requires that the body continuously monitor its internal conditions. From body temperature to blood pressure to levels of certain nutrients, each physiological condition has a particular set point. A **set point** is the physiological value around which the normal range fluctuates. A **normal range** is the restricted set of values that is optimally healthful and stable. For example, the set point for normal human body temperature is approximately 37°C (98.6°F) Physiological parameters, such as body temperature and blood pressure, tend to fluctuate within a normal range a few degrees above and below that point. Control centers in the brain and other parts of the body monitor and react to deviations from homeostasis using negative feedback. **Negative feedback** is a mechanism that reverses a deviation from the set point. Therefore, negative feedback maintains body parameters within their normal range. The maintenance of homeostasis by negative feedback goes on throughout the body at all times, and an understanding of negative feedback is thus fundamental to an understanding of human physiology.

Negative Feedback

A negative feedback system has three basic components (Figure 1.10**a**). A **sensor**, also referred to a receptor, is a component of a feedback system that monitors a physiological value. This value is reported to the control center. The **control center** is the component in a feedback system that compares the value to the normal range. If the value deviates too much from the set point, then the control center activates an effector. An **effector** is the component in a feedback system that causes a change to reverse the situation and return the value to the normal range.

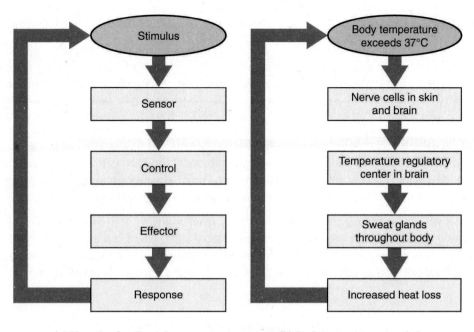

(a) Negative feedback loop

(b) Body temperature regulation

FIGURE 1.10 Negative Feedback System In a negative feedback system, a stimulus—a deviation from a set point—is resisted through a physiological process that returns the body to homeostasis. (a) A negative feedback system has five basic parts. (b) Body temperature is regulated by negative feedback.

In order to set the system in motion, a stimulus must drive a physiological parameter beyond its normal range (that is, beyond homeostasis). This stimulus is "heard" by a specific sensor. For example, in the control of blood glucose, specific endocrine cells in the pancreas detect excess glucose (the stimulus) in the bloodstream. These pancreatic beta cells respond to the increased level of blood glucose by releasing the hormone insulin into the bloodstream. The insulin signals skeletal muscle fibers, fat cells (adipocytes), and liver cells to take up the excess glucose, removing it from the bloodstream. As glucose concentration in the bloodstream drops, the decrease in concentration—the actual negative feedback—is detected by pancreatic alpha cells, and insulin release stops. This prevents blood sugar levels from continuing to drop below the normal range.

Humans have a similar temperature regulation feedback system that works by promoting either heat loss or heat gain (Figure 1.10**b**). When the brain's temperature regulation center receives data from the sensors indicating that the body's temperature exceeds its normal range, it stimulates a cluster of brain cells referred to as the "heat-loss center." This stimulation has three major effects:

- Blood vessels in the skin begin to dilate allowing more blood from the body core to flow to the surface of the skin allowing the heat to radiate into the environment.
- As blood flow to the skin increases, sweat glands are activated to increase their output. As the sweat evaporates from the skin surface into the surrounding air, it takes heat with it.
- The depth of respiration increases, and a person may breathe through an open mouth instead of through the nasal passageways. This further increases heat loss from the lungs.

In contrast, activation of the brain's heat-gain center by exposure to cold reduces blood flow to the skin, and blood returning from the limbs is diverted into a network of deep veins. This arrangement traps heat closer to the body core and restricts heat loss. If heat loss is severe, the brain triggers an increase in random signals to skeletal muscles, causing them to contract and producing shivering. The muscle contractions of shivering release heat while using up ATP. The brain triggers the thyroid gland in the endocrine system to release thyroid hormone, which increases metabolic activity and heat production in cells throughout the body. The brain also signals the adrenal glands to release epinephrine (adrenaline), a hormone that causes the breakdown of glycogen into glucose, which can be used as an energy source. The breakdown of glycogen into glucose also results in increased metabolism and heat production.

⊘ INTERACTIVE LINK

Water concentration in the body is critical for proper functioning. A person's body retains very tight control on water levels without conscious control by the person. Watch this video (http://openstax.org/l/H2Ocon) to learn more about water concentration in the body. Which organ has primary control over the amount of water in the body?

Positive Feedback

Positive feedback intensifies a change in the body's physiological condition rather than reversing it. A deviation from the normal range results in more change, and the system moves farther away from the normal range. Positive feedback in the body is normal only when there is a definite end point. Childbirth and the body's response to blood loss are two examples of positive feedback loops that are normal but are activated only when needed.

Childbirth at full term is an example of a situation in which the maintenance of the existing body state is not desired. Enormous changes in a person's body are required to expel the baby at the end of pregnancy. And the events of childbirth, once begun, must progress rapidly to a conclusion or the life of a person giving bith and the baby are at risk. The extreme muscular work of labor and delivery are the result of a positive feedback system (Figure 1.11).

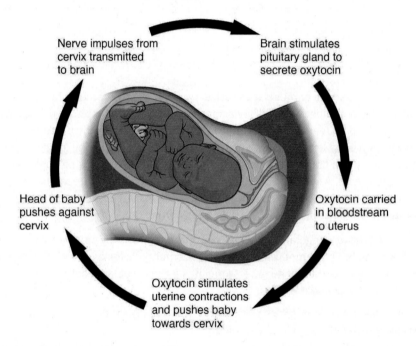

FIGURE 1.11 Positive Feedback Loop   Normal childbirth is driven by a positive feedback loop. A positive feedback loop results in a change in the body's status, rather than a return to homeostasis.

The first contractions of labor (the stimulus) push the baby toward the cervix (the lowest part of the uterus). The cervix contains stretch-sensitive nerve cells that monitor the degree of stretching (the sensors). These nerve cells send messages to the brain, which in turn causes the pituitary gland at the base of the brain to release the hormone oxytocin into the bloodstream. Oxytocin causes stronger contractions of the smooth muscles in of the uterus (the effectors), pushing the baby further down the birth canal. This causes even greater stretching of the cervix. The cycle of stretching, oxytocin release, and increasingly more forceful contractions stops only when the baby is born. At this point, the stretching of the cervix halts, stopping the release of oxytocin.

A second example of positive feedback centers on reversing extreme damage to the body. Following a penetrating wound, the most immediate threat is excessive blood loss. Less blood circulating means reduced blood pressure and reduced perfusion (penetration of blood) to the brain and other vital organs. If perfusion is severely reduced, vital organs will shut down and the person will die. The body responds to this potential catastrophe by releasing substances in the injured blood vessel wall that begin the process of blood clotting. As each step of clotting occurs, it stimulates the release of more clotting substances. This accelerates the processes of clotting and sealing off the damaged area. Clotting is contained in a local area based on the tightly controlled availability of clotting proteins. This is an adaptive, life-saving cascade of events.

1.6 Anatomical Terminology

LEARNING OBJECTIVES

By the end of this section, you will be able to:

- Demonstrate the anatomical position
- Describe the human body using directional and regional terms
- Identify three planes most commonly used in the study of anatomy
- Distinguish between the posterior (dorsal) and the anterior (ventral) body cavities, identifying their subdivisions and representative organs found in each
- Describe serous membrane and explain its function

Anatomists and health care providers use terminology that can be bewildering to the uninitiated. However, the purpose of this language is not to confuse, but rather to increase precision and reduce medical errors. For example, is a scar "above the wrist" located on the forearm two or three inches away from the hand? Or is it at the base of the hand? Is it on the palm-side or back-side? By using precise anatomical terminology, we eliminate ambiguity. Anatomical terms derive from ancient Greek and Latin words. Because these languages are no longer used in everyday conversation, the meaning of their words does not change.

Anatomical terms are made up of roots, prefixes, and suffixes. The root of a term often refers to an organ, tissue, or condition, whereas the prefix or suffix often describes the root. For example, in the disorder hypertension, the prefix "hyper-" means "high" or "over," and the root word "tension" refers to pressure, so the word "hypertension" refers to abnormally high blood pressure.

Anatomical Position

To further increase precision, anatomists standardize the way in which they view the body. Just as maps are normally oriented with north at the top, the standard body "map," or **anatomical position**, is that of the body standing upright, with the feet at shoulder width and parallel, toes forward. The upper limbs are held out to each side, and the palms of the hands face forward as illustrated in Figure 1.12. Using this standard position reduces confusion. It does not matter how the body being described is oriented, the terms are used as if it is in anatomical position. For example, a scar in the "anterior (front) carpal (wrist) region" would be present on the palm side of the wrist. The term "anterior" would be used even if the hand were palm down on a table.

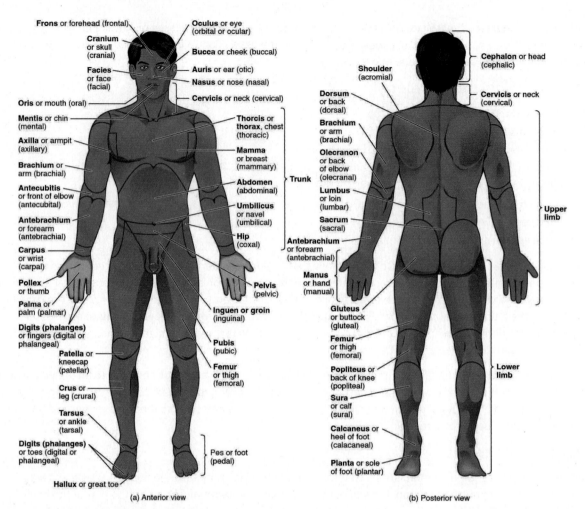

FIGURE 1.12   Regions of the Human Body   The human body is shown in anatomical position in an (a) anterior view and a (b) posterior view. The regions of the body are labeled in boldface.

A body that is lying down is described as either prone or supine. **Prone** describes a face-down orientation, and **supine** describes a face up orientation. These terms are sometimes used in describing the position of the body during specific physical examinations or surgical procedures.

Regional Terms

The human body's numerous regions have specific terms to help increase precision (see Figure 1.12). Notice that the term "brachium" or "arm" is reserved for the "upper arm" and "antebrachium" or "forearm" is used rather than "lower arm." Similarly, "femur" or "thigh" is correct, and "leg" or "crus" is reserved for the portion of the lower limb between the knee and the ankle. You will be able to describe the body's regions using the terms from the figure.

Directional Terms

Certain directional anatomical terms appear throughout this and any other anatomy textbook (Figure 1.13). These terms are essential for describing the relative locations of different body structures. For instance, an anatomist might describe one band of tissue as "inferior to" another or a physician might describe a tumor as "superficial to" a deeper body structure. Commit these terms to memory to avoid confusion when you are studying or describing the locations of particular body parts.

- **Anterior** (or **ventral**) Describes the front or direction toward the front of the body. The toes are anterior to the foot.
- **Posterior** (or **dorsal**) Describes the back or direction toward the back of the body. The popliteus is posterior to the patella.
- **Superior** (or **cranial**) describes a position above or higher than another part of the body proper. The orbits are superior to the oris.

- **Inferior** (or **caudal**) describes a position below or lower than another part of the body proper; near or toward the tail (in humans, the coccyx, or lowest part of the spinal column). The pelvis is inferior to the abdomen.
- **Lateral** describes the side or direction toward the side of the body. The thumb (pollex) is lateral to the digits.
- **Medial** describes the middle or direction toward the middle of the body. The hallux is the medial toe.
- **Proximal** describes a position in a limb that is nearer to the point of attachment or the trunk of the body. The brachium is proximal to the antebrachium.
- **Distal** describes a position in a limb that is farther from the point of attachment or the trunk of the body. The crus is distal to the femur.
- **Superficial** describes a position closer to the surface of the body. The skin is superficial to the bones.
- **Deep** describes a position farther from the surface of the body. The brain is deep to the skull.

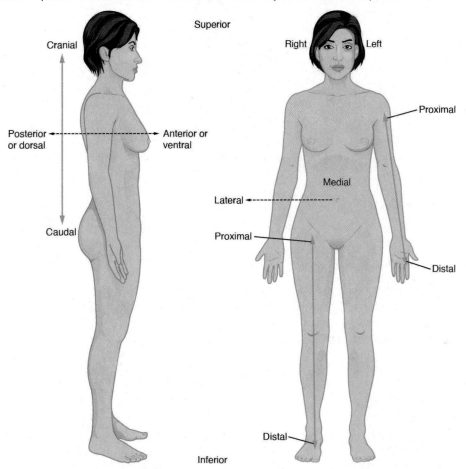

FIGURE 1.13   Directional Terms Applied to the Human Body   Paired directional terms are shown as applied to the human body.

Body Planes

A **section** is a two-dimensional surface of a three-dimensional structure that has been cut. Modern medical imaging devices enable clinicians to obtain "virtual sections" of living bodies. We call these scans. Body sections and scans can be correctly interpreted, however, only if the viewer understands the plane along which the section was made. A **plane** is an imaginary two-dimensional surface that passes through the body. There are three planes commonly referred to in anatomy and medicine, as illustrated in <u>Figure 1.14</u>.

- The **sagittal plane** is the plane that divides the body or an organ vertically into right and left sides. If this vertical plane runs directly down the middle of the body, it is called the midsagittal or median plane. If it divides the body into unequal right and left sides, it is called a parasagittal plane or less commonly a longitudinal section.
- The **frontal plane** is the plane that divides the body or an organ into an anterior (front) portion and a posterior (rear) portion. The frontal plane is often referred to as a coronal plane. ("Corona" is Latin for "crown.")
- The **transverse plane** is the plane that divides the body or organ horizontally into upper and lower portions.

Transverse planes produce images referred to as cross sections.

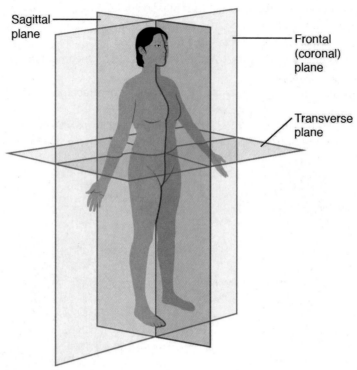

FIGURE 1.14   Planes of the Body   The three planes most commonly used in anatomical and medical imaging are the sagittal, frontal (or coronal), and transverse plane.

Body Cavities and Serous Membranes

The body maintains its internal organization by means of membranes, sheaths, and other structures that separate compartments. The **dorsal (posterior) cavity** and the **ventral (anterior) cavity** are the largest body compartments (Figure 1.15). These cavities contain and protect delicate internal organs, and the ventral cavity allows for significant changes in the size and shape of the organs as they perform their functions. The lungs, heart, stomach, and intestines, for example, can expand and contract without distorting other tissues or disrupting the activity of nearby organs.

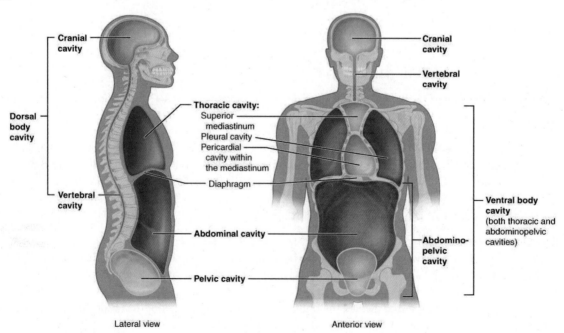

FIGURE 1.15   Dorsal and Ventral Body Cavities   The ventral cavity includes the thoracic and abdominopelvic cavities and their subdivisions. The dorsal cavity includes the cranial and spinal cavities.

Access for free at openstax.org

Subdivisions of the Posterior (Dorsal) and Anterior (Ventral) Cavities

The posterior (dorsal) and anterior (ventral) cavities are each subdivided into smaller cavities. In the posterior (dorsal) cavity, the **cranial cavity** houses the brain, and the **spinal cavity** (or vertebral cavity) encloses the spinal cord. Just as the brain and spinal cord make up a continuous, uninterrupted structure, the cranial and spinal cavities that house them are also continuous. The brain and spinal cord are protected by the bones of the skull and vertebral column and by cerebrospinal fluid, a colorless fluid produced by the brain, which cushions the brain and spinal cord within the posterior (dorsal) cavity.

The anterior (ventral) cavity has two main subdivisions: the thoracic cavity and the abdominopelvic cavity (see Figure 1.15). The **thoracic cavity** is the more superior subdivision of the anterior cavity, and it is enclosed by the rib cage. The thoracic cavity contains the lungs and the heart, which is located in the mediastinum. The diaphragm forms the floor of the thoracic cavity and separates it from the more inferior abdominopelvic cavity. The **abdominopelvic cavity** is the largest cavity in the body. Although no membrane physically divides the abdominopelvic cavity, it can be useful to distinguish between the abdominal cavity, the division that houses the digestive organs, and the pelvic cavity, the division that houses the organs of reproduction.

Abdominal Regions and Quadrants

To promote clear communication, for instance about the location of a patient's abdominal pain or a suspicious mass, health care providers typically divide up the cavity into either nine regions or four quadrants (Figure 1.16).

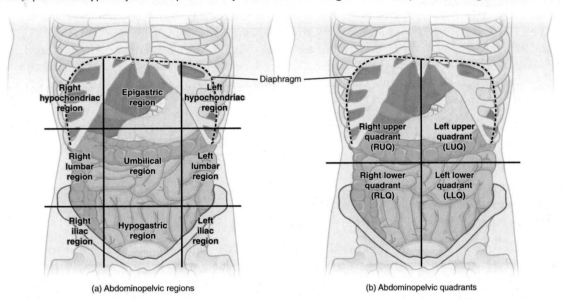

(a) Abdominopelvic regions   (b) Abdominopelvic quadrants

FIGURE 1.16   Regions and Quadrants of the Peritoneal Cavity   There are (a) nine abdominal regions and (b) four abdominal quadrants in the peritoneal cavity.

The more detailed regional approach subdivides the cavity with one horizontal line immediately inferior to the ribs and one immediately superior to the pelvis, and two vertical lines drawn as if dropped from the midpoint of each clavicle (collarbone). There are nine resulting regions. The simpler quadrants approach, which is more commonly used in medicine, subdivides the cavity with one horizontal and one vertical line that intersect at the patient's umbilicus (navel).

Membranes of the Anterior (Ventral) Body Cavity

A **serous membrane** (also referred to a serosa) is one of the thin membranes that cover the walls and organs in the thoracic and abdominopelvic cavities. The parietal layers of the membranes line the walls of the body cavity (pariet- refers to a cavity wall). The visceral layer of the membrane covers the organs (the viscera). Between the parietal and visceral layers is a very thin, fluid-filled serous space, or cavity (Figure 1.17).

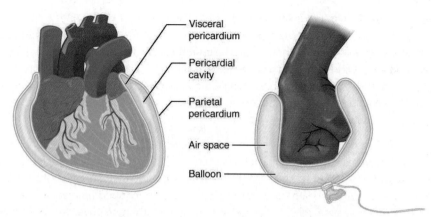

FIGURE 1.17   Serous Membrane   Serous membrane lines the pericardial cavity and reflects back to cover the heart—much the same way that an underinflated balloon would form two layers surrounding a fist.

There are three serous cavities and their associated membranes. The **pleura** is the serous membrane that encloses the pleural cavity; the pleural cavity surrounds the lungs. The **pericardium** is the serous membrane that encloses the pericardial cavity; the pericardial cavity surrounds the heart. The **peritoneum** is the serous membrane that encloses the peritoneal cavity; the peritoneal cavity surrounds several organs in the abdominopelvic cavity. The serous membranes form fluid-filled sacs, or cavities, that are meant to cushion and reduce friction on internal organs when they move, such as when the lungs inflate or the heart beats. Both the parietal and visceral serosa secrete the thin, slippery serous fluid located within the serous cavities. The pleural cavity reduces friction between the lungs and the body wall. Likewise, the pericardial cavity reduces friction between the heart and the wall of the pericardium. The peritoneal cavity reduces friction between the abdominal and pelvic organs and the body wall. Therefore, serous membranes provide additional protection to the viscera they enclose by reducing friction that could lead to inflammation of the organs.

1.7 Medical Imaging

LEARNING OBJECTIVES

By the end of this section, you will be able to:

- Discuss the uses and drawbacks of X-ray imaging
- Identify four modern medical imaging techniques and how they are used

For thousands of years, fear of the dead and legal sanctions limited the ability of anatomists and physicians to study the internal structures of the human body. An inability to control bleeding, infection, and pain made surgeries infrequent, and those that were performed—such as wound suturing, amputations, tooth and tumor removals, skull drilling, and cesarean births—did not greatly advance knowledge about internal anatomy. Theories about the function of the body and about disease were therefore largely based on external observations and imagination. During the fourteenth and fifteenth centuries, however, the detailed anatomical drawings of Italian artist and anatomist Leonardo da Vinci and Flemish anatomist Andreas Vesalius were published, and interest in human anatomy began to increase. Medical schools began to teach anatomy using human dissection; although some resorted to grave robbing to obtain corpses. Laws were eventually passed that enabled students to dissect the corpses of criminals and those who donated their bodies for research. Still, it was not until the late nineteenth century that medical researchers discovered non-surgical methods to look inside the living body.

X-Rays

German physicist Wilhelm Röntgen (1845–1923) was experimenting with electrical current when he discovered that a mysterious and invisible "ray" would pass through his flesh but leave an outline of his bones on a screen coated with a metal compound. In 1895, Röntgen made the first durable record of the internal parts of a living human: an "X-ray" image (as it came to be called) of his wife's hand. Scientists around the world quickly began their own experiments with X-rays, and by 1900, X-rays were widely used to detect a variety of injuries and diseases. In 1901, Röntgen was awarded the first Nobel Prize for physics for his work in this field.

The **X-ray** is a form of high energy electromagnetic radiation with a short wavelength capable of penetrating solids and ionizing gases. As they are used in medicine, X-rays are emitted from an X-ray machine and directed toward a specially treated metallic plate placed behind the patient's body. The beam of radiation results in darkening of the X-ray plate. X-rays are slightly impeded by soft tissues, which show up as gray on the X-ray plate, whereas hard tissues, such as bone, largely block the rays, producing a light-toned "shadow." Thus, X-rays are best used to visualize hard body structures such as teeth and bones (Figure 1.18). Like many forms of high energy radiation, however, X-rays are capable of damaging cells and initiating changes that can lead to cancer. This danger of excessive exposure to X-rays was not fully appreciated for many years after their widespread use.

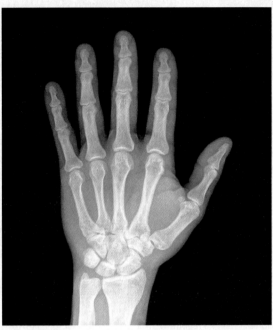

FIGURE 1.18   X-Ray of a Hand   High energy electromagnetic radiation allows the internal structures of the body, such as bones, to be seen in X-rays like these. (credit: Trace Meek/flickr)

Refinements and enhancements of X-ray techniques have continued throughout the twentieth and twenty-first centuries. Although often supplanted by more sophisticated imaging techniques, the X-ray remains a "workhorse" in medical imaging, especially for viewing fractures and for dentistry. The disadvantage of irradiation to the patient and the operator is now attenuated by proper shielding and by limiting exposure.

Modern Medical Imaging

X-rays can depict a two-dimensional image of a body region, and only from a single angle. In contrast, more recent medical imaging technologies produce data that is integrated and analyzed by computers to produce three-dimensional images or images that reveal aspects of body functioning.

Computed Tomography

Tomography refers to imaging by sections. **Computed tomography (CT)** is a noninvasive imaging technique that uses computers to analyze several cross-sectional X-rays in order to reveal minute details about structures in the body (Figure 1.19**a**). The technique was invented in the 1970s and is based on the principle that, as X-rays pass through the body, they are absorbed or reflected at different levels. In the technique, a patient lies on a motorized platform while a computerized axial tomography (CAT) scanner rotates 360 degrees around the patient, taking X-ray images. A computer combines these images into a two-dimensional view of the scanned area, or "slice."

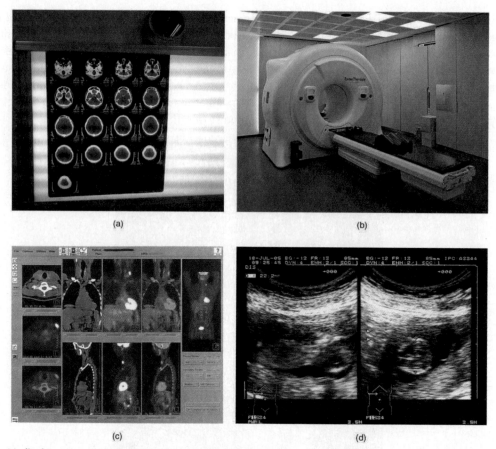

(a)   (b)

(c)   (d)

FIGURE 1.19 Medical Imaging Techniques   (a) The results of a CT scan of the head are shown as successive transverse sections. (b) An MRI machine generates a magnetic field around a patient. (c) PET scans use radiopharmaceuticals to create images of active blood flow and physiologic activity of the organ or organs being targeted. (d) Ultrasound technology is used to monitor pregnancies because it is the least invasive of imaging techniques and uses no electromagnetic radiation. (credit a: Akira Ohgaki/flickr; credit b: "Digital Cate"/flickr; credit c: "Raziel"/Wikimedia Commons; credit d: "Isis"/Wikimedia Commons)

Since 1970, the development of more powerful computers and more sophisticated software has made CT scanning routine for many types of diagnostic evaluations. It is especially useful for soft tissue scanning, such as of the brain and the thoracic and abdominal viscera. Its level of detail is so precise that it can allow physicians to measure the size of a mass down to a millimeter. The main disadvantage of CT scanning is that it exposes patients to a dose of radiation many times higher than that of X-rays. In fact, children who undergo CT scans are at increased risk of developing cancer, as are adults who have multiple CT scans.

⊘ INTERACTIVE LINK

A CT or CAT scan relies on a circling scanner that revolves around the patient's body. Watch this video (http://openstax.org/l/CATscan) to learn more about CT and CAT scans. What type of radiation does a CT scanner use?

Magnetic Resonance Imaging

Magnetic resonance imaging (MRI) is a noninvasive medical imaging technique based on a phenomenon of nuclear physics discovered in the 1930s, in which matter exposed to magnetic fields and radio waves was found to emit radio signals. In 1970, a physician and researcher named Raymond Damadian noticed that malignant (cancerous) tissue gave off different signals than normal body tissue. He applied for a patent for the first MRI scanning device, which was in use clinically by the early 1980s. The early MRI scanners were crude, but advances in digital computing and electronics led to their advancement over any other technique for precise imaging, especially to discover tumors. MRI also has the major advantage of not exposing patients to radiation.

Drawbacks of MRI scans include their much higher cost, and patient discomfort with the procedure. The MRI scanner subjects the patient to such powerful electromagnets that the scan room must be shielded. The patient must be enclosed in a metal tube-like device for the duration of the scan (see Figure 1.19**b**), sometimes as long as thirty minutes, which can be uncomfortable and impractical for ill patients. The device is also so noisy that, even with earplugs, patients can become anxious or even fearful. These problems have been overcome somewhat with the development of "open" MRI scanning, which does not require the patient to be entirely enclosed in the metal tube. Patients with iron-containing metallic implants (internal sutures, some prosthetic devices, and so on) cannot undergo MRI scanning because it can dislodge these implants.

Functional MRIs (fMRIs), which detect the concentration of blood flow in certain parts of the body, are increasingly being used to study the activity in parts of the brain during various body activities. This has helped scientists learn more about the locations of different brain functions and more about brain abnormalities and diseases.

⊘ INTERACTIVE LINK

A patient undergoing an MRI is surrounded by a tube-shaped scanner. Watch this video (http://openstax.org/l/MRI) to learn more about MRIs. What is the function of magnets in an MRI?

Positron Emission Tomography

Positron emission tomography (PET) is a medical imaging technique involving the use of so-called radiopharmaceuticals, substances that emit radiation that is short-lived and therefore relatively safe to administer to the body. Although the first PET scanner was introduced in 1961, it took 15 more years before radiopharmaceuticals were combined with the technique and revolutionized its potential. The main advantage is that PET (see Figure 1.19**c**) can illustrate physiologic activity—including nutrient metabolism and blood flow—of the organ or organs being targeted, whereas CT and MRI scans can only show static images. PET is widely used to diagnose a multitude of conditions, such as heart disease, the spread of cancer, certain forms of infection, brain abnormalities, bone disease, and thyroid disease.

⊘ INTERACTIVE LINK

PET relies on radioactive substances administered several minutes before the scan. Watch this video (http://openstax.org/l/PET) to learn more about PET. How is PET used in chemotherapy?

Ultrasonography

Ultrasonography is an imaging technique that uses the transmission of high-frequency sound waves into the body to generate an echo signal that is converted by a computer into a real-time image of anatomy and physiology (see Figure 1.19**d**). Ultrasonography is the least invasive of all imaging techniques, and it is therefore used more freely in sensitive situations such as pregnancy. The technology was first developed in the 1940s and 1950s. Ultrasonography is used to study heart function, blood flow in the neck or extremities, certain conditions such as gallbladder disease, and fetal growth and development. The main disadvantages of ultrasonography are that the image quality is heavily operator-dependent and that it is unable to penetrate bone and gas.

Key Terms

abdominopelvic cavity   division of the anterior (ventral) cavity that houses the abdominal and pelvic viscera

anabolism   assembly of more complex molecules from simpler molecules

anatomical position   standard reference position used for describing locations and directions on the human body

anatomy   science that studies the form and composition of the body's structures

anterior   describes the front or direction toward the front of the body; also referred to as ventral

anterior cavity   larger body cavity located anterior to the posterior (dorsal) body cavity; includes the serous membrane-lined pleural cavities for the lungs, pericardial cavity for the heart, and peritoneal cavity for the abdominal and pelvic organs; also referred to as ventral cavity

catabolism   breaking down of more complex molecules into simpler molecules

caudal   describes a position below or lower than another part of the body proper; near or toward the tail (in humans, the coccyx, or lowest part of the spinal column); also referred to as inferior

cell   smallest independently functioning unit of all organisms; in animals, a cell contains cytoplasm, composed of fluid and organelles

computed tomography (CT)   medical imaging technique in which a computer-enhanced cross-sectional X-ray image is obtained

control center   compares values to their normal range; deviations cause the activation of an effector

cranial   describes a position above or higher than another part of the body proper; also referred to as superior

cranial cavity   division of the posterior (dorsal) cavity that houses the brain

deep   describes a position farther from the surface of the body

development   changes an organism goes through during its life

differentiation   process by which unspecialized cells become specialized in structure and function

distal   describes a position farther from the point of attachment or the trunk of the body

dorsal   describes the back or direction toward the back of the body; also referred to as posterior

dorsal cavity   posterior body cavity that houses the brain and spinal cord; also referred to the posterior body cavity

effector   organ that can cause a change in a value

frontal plane   two-dimensional, vertical plane that divides the body or organ into anterior and posterior portions

gross anatomy   study of the larger structures of the body, typically with the unaided eye; also referred to macroscopic anatomy

growth   process of increasing in size

homeostasis   steady state of body systems that living organisms maintain

inferior   describes a position below or lower than another part of the body proper; near or toward the tail (in humans, the coccyx, or lowest part of the spinal column); also referred to as caudal

lateral   describes the side or direction toward the side of the body

magnetic resonance imaging (MRI)   medical imaging technique in which a device generates a magnetic field to obtain detailed sectional images of the internal structures of the body

medial   describes the middle or direction toward the middle of the body

metabolism   sum of all of the body's chemical reactions

microscopic anatomy   study of very small structures of the body using magnification

negative feedback   homeostatic mechanism that tends to stabilize an upset in the body's physiological condition by preventing an excessive response to a stimulus, typically as the stimulus is removed

normal range   range of values around the set point that do not cause a reaction by the control center

nutrient   chemical obtained from foods and beverages that is critical to human survival

organ   functionally distinct structure composed of two or more types of tissues

organ system   group of organs that work together to carry out a particular function

organism   living being that has a cellular structure and that can independently perform all physiologic functions necessary for life

pericardium   sac that encloses the heart

peritoneum   serous membrane that lines the abdominopelvic cavity and covers the organs found there

physiology   science that studies the chemistry, biochemistry, and physics of the body's functions

plane   imaginary two-dimensional surface that passes through the body

pleura   serous membrane that lines the pleural cavity and covers the lungs

positive feedback   mechanism that intensifies a change in the body's physiological condition in response to a stimulus

positron emission tomography (PET) medical imaging technique in which radiopharmaceuticals are traced to reveal metabolic and physiological functions in tissues

posterior describes the back or direction toward the back of the body; also referred to as dorsal

posterior cavity posterior body cavity that houses the brain and spinal cord; also referred to as dorsal cavity

pressure force exerted by a substance in contact with another substance

prone face down

proximal describes a position nearer to the point of attachment or the trunk of the body

regional anatomy study of the structures that contribute to specific body regions

renewal process by which worn-out cells are replaced

reproduction process by which new organisms are generated

responsiveness ability of an organisms or a system to adjust to changes in conditions

sagittal plane two-dimensional, vertical plane that divides the body or organ into right and left sides

section in anatomy, a single flat surface of a three-dimensional structure that has been cut through

sensor (also, receptor) reports a monitored physiological value to the control center

serosa membrane that covers organs and reduces friction; also referred to as serous membrane

serous membrane membrane that covers organs and reduces friction; also referred to as serosa

set point ideal value for a physiological parameter; the level or small range within which a physiological parameter such as blood pressure is stable and

optimally healthful, that is, within its parameters of homeostasis

spinal cavity division of the dorsal cavity that houses the spinal cord; also referred to as vertebral cavity

superficial describes a position nearer to the surface of the body

superior describes a position above or higher than another part of the body proper; also referred to as cranial

supine face up

systemic anatomy study of the structures that contribute to specific body systems

thoracic cavity division of the anterior (ventral) cavity that houses the heart, lungs, esophagus, and trachea

tissue group of similar or closely related cells that act together to perform a specific function

transverse plane two-dimensional, horizontal plane that divides the body or organ into superior and inferior portions

ultrasonography application of ultrasonic waves to visualize subcutaneous body structures such as tendons and organs

ventral describes the front or direction toward the front of the body; also referred to as anterior

ventral cavity larger body cavity located anterior to the posterior (dorsal) body cavity; includes the serous membrane-lined pleural cavities for the lungs, pericardial cavity for the heart, and peritoneal cavity for the abdominal and pelvic organs; also referred to as anterior body cavity

X-ray form of high energy electromagnetic radiation with a short wavelength capable of penetrating solids and ionizing gases; used in medicine as a diagnostic aid to visualize body structures such as bones

Chapter Review

1.1 Overview of Anatomy and Physiology

Human anatomy is the scientific study of the body's structures. In the past, anatomy has primarily been studied via observing injuries, and later by the dissection of anatomical structures of cadavers, but in the past century, computer-assisted imaging techniques have allowed clinicians to look inside the living body. Human physiology is the scientific study of the chemistry and physics of the structures of the body. Physiology explains how the structures of the body work together to maintain life. It is difficult to study structure (anatomy) without knowledge of function (physiology). The two disciplines are typically studied together because form and function are closely related in all living things.

1.2 Structural Organization of the Human Body

Life processes of the human body are maintained at several levels of structural organization. These include the chemical, cellular, tissue, organ, organ system, and the organism level. Higher levels of organization are built from lower levels. Therefore, molecules combine to form cells, cells combine to form tissues, tissues combine to form organs, organs combine to form organ systems, and organ systems combine to form organisms.

1.3 Functions of Human Life

Most processes that occur in the human body are not

consciously controlled. They occur continuously to build, maintain, and sustain life. These processes include: organization, in terms of the maintenance of essential body boundaries; metabolism, including energy transfer via anabolic and catabolic reactions; responsiveness; movement; and growth, differentiation, reproduction, and renewal.

1.4 Requirements for Human Life

Humans cannot survive for more than a few minutes without oxygen, for more than several days without water, and for more than several weeks without carbohydrates, lipids, proteins, vitamins, and minerals. Although the body can respond to high temperatures by sweating and to low temperatures by shivering and increased fuel consumption, long-term exposure to extreme heat and cold is not compatible with survival. The body requires a precise atmospheric pressure to maintain its gases in solution and to facilitate respiration—the intake of oxygen and the release of carbon dioxide. Humans also require blood pressure high enough to ensure that blood reaches all body tissues but low enough to avoid damage to blood vessels.

1.5 Homeostasis

Homeostasis is the activity of cells throughout the body to maintain the physiological state within a narrow range that is compatible with life. Homeostasis is regulated by negative feedback loops and, much less frequently, by positive feedback loops. Both have the same components of a stimulus, sensor, control center, and effector; however, negative feedback loops work to prevent an excessive response to the stimulus, whereas positive feedback loops intensify the

response until an end point is reached.

1.6 Anatomical Terminology

Ancient Greek and Latin words are used to build anatomical terms. A standard reference position for mapping the body's structures is the normal anatomical position. Regions of the body are identified using terms such as "occipital" that are more precise than common words and phrases such as "the back of the head." Directional terms such as anterior and posterior are essential for accurately describing the relative locations of body structures. Images of the body's interior commonly align along one of three planes: the sagittal, frontal, or transverse. The body's organs are organized in one of two main cavities—dorsal (also referred to posterior) and ventral (also referred to anterior)—which are further sub-divided according to the structures present in each area. The serous membranes have two layers—parietal and visceral—surrounding a fluid filled space. Serous membranes cover the lungs (pleural serosa), heart (pericardial serosa), and some abdominopelvic organs (peritoneal serosa).

1.7 Medical Imaging

Detailed anatomical drawings of the human body first became available in the fifteenth and sixteenth centuries; however, it was not until the end of the nineteenth century, and the discovery of X-rays, that anatomists and physicians discovered non-surgical methods to look inside a living body. Since then, many other techniques, including CT scans, MRI scans, PET scans, and ultrasonography, have been developed, providing more accurate and detailed views of the form and function of the human body.

Interactive Link Questions

1. View this animation (http://openstax.org/l/metabolic) to learn more about metabolic processes. What kind of catabolism occurs in the heart?
2. Water concentration in the body is critical for proper functioning. A person's body retains very tight control on water levels without conscious control by the person. Watch this video (http://openstax.org/l/H2Ocon) to learn more about water concentration in the body. Which organ has primary control over the amount of water in the body?

3. A CT or CAT scan relies on a circling scanner that revolves around the patient's body. Watch this video (http://openstax.org/l/CATscan) to learn more about CT and CAT scans. What type of radiation does a CT scanner use?
4. A patient undergoing an MRI is surrounded by a tube-shaped scanner. Watch this video (http://openstax.org/l/MRI) to learn more about MRIs. What is the function of magnets in an MRI?
5. PET relies on radioactive substances administered several minutes before the scan. Watch this video (http://openstax.org/l/PET) to learn more about PET. How is PET used in chemotherapy?

Review Questions

6. Which of the following specialties might focus on studying all of the structures of the ankle and foot?
   a. microscopic anatomy
   b. muscle anatomy
   c. regional anatomy
   d. systemic anatomy

7. A scientist wants to study how the body uses foods and fluids during a marathon run. This scientist is most likely a(n) _____.
   a. exercise physiologist
   b. microscopic anatomist
   c. regional physiologist
   d. systemic anatomist

8. The smallest independently functioning biological unit of an organism is a(n) _____.
   a. cell
   b. molecule
   c. organ
   d. tissue

9. A collection of similar tissues that performs a specific function is an _____.
   a. organ
   b. organelle
   c. organism
   d. organ system

10. The body system responsible for structural support and movement is the _____.
    a. cardiovascular system
    b. endocrine system
    c. muscular system
    d. skeletal system

11. Metabolism can be defined as the _____.
    a. adjustment by an organism to external or internal changes
    b. process whereby all unspecialized cells become specialized to perform distinct functions
    c. process whereby new cells are formed to replace worn-out cells
    d. sum of all chemical reactions in an organism

12. Adenosine triphosphate (ATP) is an important molecule because it _____.
    a. is the result of catabolism
    b. release energy in uncontrolled bursts
    c. stores energy for use by body cells
    d. All of the above

13. Cancer cells can be characterized as "generic" cells that perform no specialized body function. Thus cancer cells lack _____.
    a. differentiation
    b. reproduction
    c. responsiveness
    d. both reproduction and responsiveness

14. Humans have the most urgent need for a continuous supply of _____.
    a. food
    b. nitrogen
    c. oxygen
    d. water

15. Which of the following statements about nutrients is true?
    a. All classes of nutrients are essential to human survival.
    b. Because the body cannot store any micronutrients, they need to be consumed nearly every day.
    c. Carbohydrates, lipids, and proteins are micronutrients.
    d. Macronutrients are vitamins and minerals.

16. C.J. is stuck in their car during a bitterly cold blizzard. Their body responds to the cold by _____.
    a. increasing the blood to the hands and feet
    b. becoming lethargic to conserve heat
    c. breaking down stored energy
    d. significantly increasing blood oxygen levels

17. After you eat lunch, nerve cells in your stomach respond to the distension (the stimulus) resulting from the food. They relay this information to _____.
    a. a control center
    b. a set point
    c. effectors
    d. sensors

18. Stimulation of the heat-loss center causes _____.
    a. blood vessels in the skin to constrict
    b. breathing to become slow and shallow
    c. sweat glands to increase their output
    d. All of the above

19. Which of the following is an example of a normal physiologic process that uses a positive feedback loop?
  a. blood pressure regulation
  b. childbirth
  c. regulation of fluid balance
  d. temperature regulation

20. What is the position of the body when it is in the "normal anatomical position?"
  a. The person is prone with upper limbs, including palms, touching sides and lower limbs touching at sides.
  b. The person is standing facing the observer, with upper limbs extended out at a ninety-degree angle from the torso and lower limbs in a wide stance with feet pointing laterally
  c. The person is supine with upper limbs, including palms, touching sides and lower limbs touching at sides.
  d. None of the above

21. To make a banana split, you halve a banana into two long, thin, right and left sides along the

  _____.
  a. coronal plane
  b. longitudinal plane
  c. midsagittal plane
  d. transverse plane

22. The lumbar region is _____.
  a. inferior to the gluteal region
  b. inferior to the umbilical region
  c. superior to the cervical region
  d. superior to the popliteal region

23. The heart is within the _____.
  a. cranial cavity
  b. mediastinum
  c. posterior (dorsal) cavity
  d. All of the above

24. In 1901, Wilhelm Röntgen was the first person to win the Nobel Prize for physics. For what discovery did he win?
  a. nuclear physics
  b. radiopharmaceuticals
  c. the link between radiation and cancer
  d. X-rays

25. Which of the following imaging techniques would be best to use to study the uptake of nutrients by rapidly multiplying cancer cells?
  a. CT
  b. MRI
  c. PET
  d. ultrasonography

26. Which of the following imaging studies can be used most safely during pregnancy?
  a. CT scans
  b. PET scans
  c. ultrasounds
  d. X-rays

27. What are two major disadvantages of MRI scans?
  a. release of radiation and poor quality images
  b. high cost and the need for shielding from the magnetic signals
  c. can only view metabolically active tissues and inadequate availability of equipment
  d. release of radiation and the need for a patient to be confined to metal tube for up to 30 minutes

Critical Thinking Questions

28. Name at least three reasons to study anatomy and physiology.

29. For whom would an appreciation of the structural characteristics of the human heart come more easily: an alien who lands on Earth, abducts a human, and dissects his heart, or an anatomy and physiology student performing a dissection of the heart on her very first day of class? Why?

30. Name the six levels of organization of the human body.

31. The and the testes are a part of which body system? Can these organs be members of more than one organ system? Why or why not?

32. Explain why the smell of smoke when you are sitting at a campfire does not trigger alarm, but the smell of smoke in your residence hall does.

33. Identify three different ways that growth can occur in the human body.

34. When you open a bottle of sparkling water, the carbon dioxide gas in the bottle form bubbles. If the bottle is left open, the water will eventually "go flat." Explain these phenomena in terms of atmospheric pressure.

35. On his midsummer trek through the desert, Josh ran out of water. Why is this particularly dangerous?

36. Identify the four components of a negative feedback loop and explain what would happen if secretion of a body chemical controlled by a negative feedback system became too great.

37. What regulatory processes would your body use if you were trapped by a blizzard in an unheated, uninsulated cabin in the woods?

38. In which direction would an MRI scanner move to produce sequential images of the body in the frontal plane, and in which direction would an MRI scanner move to produce sequential images of the body in the sagittal plane?

39. If a bullet were to penetrate a lung, which three anterior thoracic body cavities would it enter, and which layer of the serous membrane would it encounter first?

40. Which medical imaging technique is most dangerous to use repeatedly, and why?

41. Explain why ultrasound imaging is the technique of choice for studying fetal growth and development.

Access for free at openstax.org

CHAPTER 2
The Chemical Level of Organization

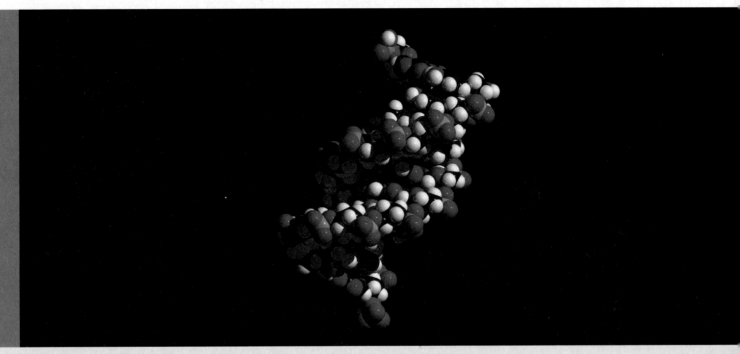

Figure 2.1 **Human DNA** Human DNA is described as a double helix that resembles a molecular spiral staircase. In humans the DNA is organized into 46 chromosomes.

CHAPTER OBJECTIVES

After studying this chapter, you will be able to:

- Describe the fundamental composition of matter
- Identify the three subatomic particles
- Identify the four most abundant elements in the body
- Explain the relationship between an atom's number of electrons and its relative stability
- Distinguish between ionic bonds, covalent bonds, and hydrogen bonds
- Explain how energy is invested, stored, and released via chemical reactions, particularly those reactions that are critical to life
- Explain the importance of the inorganic compounds that contribute to life, such as water, salts, acids, and bases
- Compare and contrast the four important classes of organic (carbon-based) compounds—proteins, carbohydrates, lipids and nucleic acids—according to their composition and functional importance to human life

INTRODUCTION The smallest, most fundamental material components of the human body are basic chemical elements. In fact, chemicals called nucleotide bases are the foundation of the genetic code with the instructions on how to build and maintain the human body from conception through old age. There are about three billion of these base pairs in human DNA.

Human chemistry includes organic molecules (carbon-based) and biochemicals (those produced by the body). Human chemistry also includes elements. In fact, life cannot exist without many of the elements that are part of the earth. All of the elements that contribute to chemical reactions, to the transformation of energy, and to electrical activity and muscle contraction—elements that include phosphorus, carbon, sodium, and calcium, to name a few—originated in stars.

These elements, in turn, can form both the inorganic and organic chemical compounds important to life, including, for example, water, glucose, and proteins. This chapter begins by examining elements and how the structures of atoms, the basic units of matter, determine the characteristics of elements by the number of protons, neutrons, and electrons in the atoms. The chapter then builds the framework of life from there.

2.1 Elements and Atoms: The Building Blocks of Matter

LEARNING OBJECTIVES

By the end of this section, you will be able to:

- Discuss the relationships between matter, mass, elements, compounds, atoms, and subatomic particles
- Distinguish between atomic number and mass number
- Identify the key distinction between isotopes of the same element
- Explain how electrons occupy electron shells and their contribution to an atom's relative stability

The substance of the universe—from a grain of sand to a star—is called **matter**. Scientists define matter as anything that occupies space and has mass. An object's mass and its weight are related concepts, but not quite the same. An object's mass is the amount of matter contained in the object, and the object's mass is the same whether that object is on Earth or in the zero-gravity environment of outer space. An object's weight, on the other hand, is its mass as affected by the pull of gravity. Where gravity strongly pulls on an object's mass its weight is greater than it is where gravity is less strong. An object of a certain mass weighs less on the moon, for example, than it does on Earth because the gravity of the moon is less than that of Earth. In other words, weight is variable, and is influenced by gravity. A piece of cheese that weighs a pound on Earth weighs only a few ounces on the moon.

Elements and Compounds

All matter in the natural world is composed of one or more of the 92 fundamental substances called elements. An **element** is a pure substance that is distinguished from all other matter by the fact that it cannot be created or broken down by ordinary chemical means. While your body can assemble many of the chemical compounds needed for life from their constituent elements, it cannot make elements. They must come from the environment. A familiar example of an element that you must take in is calcium (Ca). Calcium is essential to the human body; it is absorbed and used for a number of processes, including strengthening bones. When you consume dairy products your digestive system breaks down the food into components small enough to cross into the bloodstream. Among these is calcium, which, because it is an element, cannot be broken down further. The elemental calcium in cheese, therefore, is the same as the calcium that forms your bones. Some other elements you might be familiar with are oxygen, sodium, and iron. The elements in the human body are shown in Figure 2.2, beginning with the most abundant: oxygen (O), carbon (C), hydrogen (H), and nitrogen (N). Each element's name can be replaced by a one- or two-letter symbol; you will become familiar with some of these during this course. All the elements in your body are derived from the foods you eat and the air you breathe.

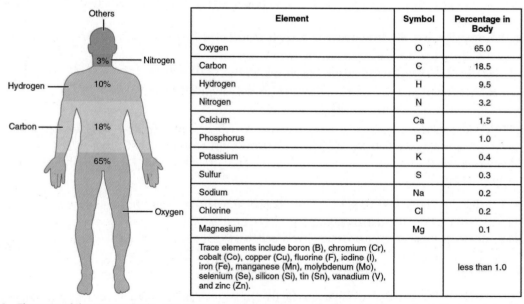

Element	Symbol	Percentage in Body
Oxygen	O	65.0
Carbon	C	18.5
Hydrogen	H	9.5
Nitrogen	N	3.2
Calcium	Ca	1.5
Phosphorus	P	1.0
Potassium	K	0.4
Sulfur	S	0.3
Sodium	Na	0.2
Chlorine	Cl	0.2
Magnesium	Mg	0.1
Trace elements include boron (B), chromium (Cr), cobalt (Co), copper (Cu), fluorine (F), iodine (I), iron (Fe), manganese (Mn), molybdenum (Mo), selenium (Se), silicon (Si), tin (Sn), vanadium (V), and zinc (Zn).		less than 1.0

FIGURE 2.2 Elements of the Human Body   The main elements that compose the human body are shown from most abundant to least abundant.

Access for free at openstax.org

In nature, elements rarely occur alone. Instead, they combine to form compounds. A **compound** is a substance composed of two or more elements joined by chemical bonds. For example, the compound glucose is an important body fuel. It is always composed of the same three elements: carbon, hydrogen, and oxygen. Moreover, the elements that make up any given compound always occur in the same relative amounts. In glucose, there are always six carbon and six oxygen units for every twelve hydrogen units. But what, exactly, are these "units" of elements?

Atoms and Subatomic Particles

An **atom** is the smallest quantity of an element that retains the unique properties of that element. In other words, an atom of hydrogen is a unit of hydrogen—the smallest amount of hydrogen that can exist. As you might guess, atoms are almost unfathomably small. The period at the end of this sentence is millions of atoms wide.

Atomic Structure and Energy

Atoms are made up of even smaller subatomic particles, three types of which are important: the **proton, neutron, and electron**. The number of positively-charged protons and non-charged ("neutral") neutrons, gives mass to the atom, and the number of protons determines the element. The number of negatively-charged electrons that "spin" around the nucleus at close to the speed of light equals the number of protons. An electron has about 1/2000th the mass of a proton or neutron.

Figure 2.3 shows two models that can help you imagine the structure of an atom—in this case, helium (He). In the planetary model, helium's two electrons are shown circling the nucleus in a fixed orbit depicted as a ring. Although this model is helpful in visualizing atomic structure, in reality, electrons do not travel in fixed orbits, but whiz around the nucleus erratically in a so-called electron cloud.

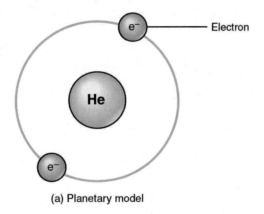

(a) Planetary model

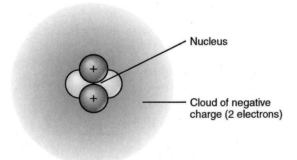

(b) Electron cloud model

FIGURE 2.3   Two Models of Atomic Structure   (a) In the planetary model, the electrons of helium are shown in fixed orbits, depicted as rings, at a precise distance from the nucleus, somewhat like planets orbiting the sun. (b) In the electron cloud model, the electrons of helium are shown in the variety of locations they would have at different distances from the nucleus over time.

An atom's protons and electrons carry electrical charges. Protons, with their positive charge, are designated p^+. Electrons, which have a negative charge, are designated e^-. An atom's neutrons have no charge: they are electrically neutral. Just as a magnet sticks to a steel refrigerator because their opposite charges attract, the positively charged protons attract the negatively charged electrons. This mutual attraction gives the atom some structural stability. The attraction by the positively charged nucleus helps keep electrons from straying far. The number of protons and electrons within a neutral atom are equal, thus, the atom's overall charge is balanced.

Atomic Number and Mass Number

An atom of carbon is unique to carbon, but a proton of carbon is not. One proton is the same as another, whether it is found in an atom of carbon, sodium (Na), or iron (Fe). The same is true for neutrons and electrons. So, what gives an element its distinctive properties—what makes carbon so different from sodium or iron? The answer is the unique quantity of protons each contains. Carbon by definition is an element whose atoms contain six protons. No other element has exactly six protons in its atoms. Moreover, *all* atoms of carbon, whether found in your liver or in a lump of coal, contain six protons. Thus, the **atomic number**, which is the number of protons in the nucleus of the atom, identifies the element. Because an atom usually has the same number of electrons as protons, the atomic number identifies the usual number of electrons as well.

In their most common form, many elements also contain the same number of neutrons as protons. The most common form of carbon, for example, has six neutrons as well as six protons, for a total of 12 subatomic particles in its nucleus. An element's **mass number** is the sum of the number of protons and neutrons in its nucleus. So the most common form of carbon's mass number is 12. (Electrons have so little mass that they do not appreciably contribute to the mass of an atom.) Carbon is a relatively light element. Uranium (U), in contrast, has a mass number of 238 and is referred to as a heavy metal. Its atomic number is 92 (it has 92 protons) but it contains 146 neutrons; it has the most mass of all the naturally occurring elements.

The **periodic table of the elements**, shown in Figure 2.4, is a chart identifying the 92 elements found in nature, as well as several larger, unstable elements discovered experimentally. The elements are arranged in order of their atomic number, with hydrogen and helium at the top of the table, and the more massive elements below. The periodic table is a useful device because for each element, it identifies the chemical symbol, the atomic number, and the mass number, while organizing elements according to their propensity to react with other elements. The number of protons and electrons in an element are equal. The number of protons and neutrons may be equal for some elements, but are not equal for all.

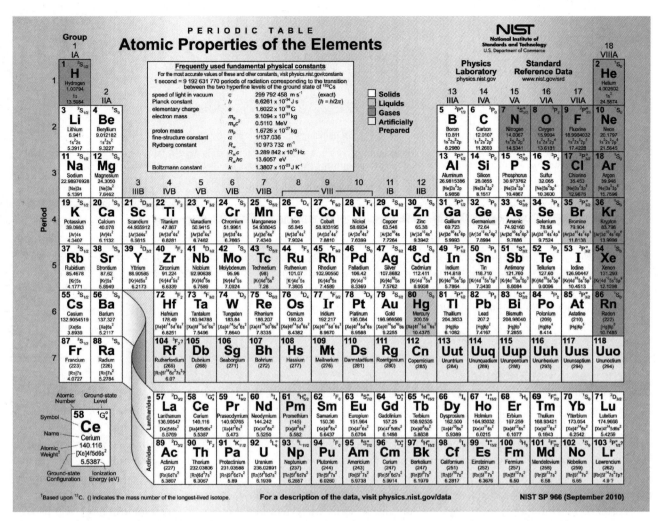

FIGURE 2.4   The Periodic Table of the Elements   (credit: R.A. Dragoset, A. Musgrove, C.W. Clark, W.C. Martin)

🔗 INTERACTIVE LINK

Visit this website (http://openstax.org/l/ptable) to view the periodic table. In the periodic table of the elements, elements in a single column have the same number of electrons that can participate in a chemical reaction. These electrons are known as "valence electrons." For example, the elements in the first column all have a single valence electron, an electron that can be "donated" in a chemical reaction with another atom. What is the meaning of a mass number shown in parentheses?

Isotopes

Although each element has a unique number of protons, it can exist as different isotopes. An **isotope** is one of the different forms of an element, distinguished from one another by different numbers of neutrons. The standard isotope of carbon is ^{12}C, commonly called carbon twelve. ^{12}C has six protons and six neutrons, for a mass number of twelve. All of the isotopes of carbon have the same number of protons; therefore, ^{13}C has seven neutrons, and ^{14}C has eight neutrons. The different isotopes of an element can also be indicated with the mass number hyphenated (for example, C-12 instead of ^{12}C). Hydrogen has three common isotopes, shown in Figure 2.5.

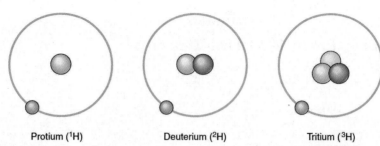

Protium (^{1}H)   Deuterium (^{2}H)   Tritium (^{3}H)

FIGURE 2.5   Isotopes of Hydrogen   Protium, designated ^{1}H, has one proton and no neutrons. It is by far the most abundant isotope of hydrogen in nature. Deuterium, designated ^{2}H, has one proton and one neutron. Tritium, designated ^{3}H, has two neutrons.

An isotope that contains more than the usual number of neutrons is referred to as a heavy isotope. An example is ^{14}C. Heavy isotopes tend to be unstable, and unstable isotopes are radioactive. A **radioactive isotope** is an isotope whose nucleus readily decays, giving off subatomic particles and electromagnetic energy. Different radioactive isotopes (also called radioisotopes) differ in their half-life, the time it takes for half of any size sample of an isotope to decay. For example, the half-life of tritium—a radioisotope of hydrogen—is about 12 years, indicating it takes 12 years for half of the tritium nuclei in a sample to decay. Excessive exposure to radioactive isotopes can damage human cells and even cause cancer and birth defects, but when exposure is controlled, some radioactive isotopes can be useful in medicine. For more information, see the Career Connections.

 CAREER CONNECTION

Interventional Radiologist

The controlled use of radioisotopes has advanced medical diagnosis and treatment of disease. Interventional radiologists are physicians who treat disease by using minimally invasive techniques involving radiation. Many conditions that could once only be treated with a lengthy and traumatic operation can now be treated non-surgically, reducing the cost, pain, length of hospital stay, and recovery time for patients. For example, in the past, the only options for a patient with one or more tumors in the liver were surgery and chemotherapy (the administration of drugs to treat cancer). Some liver tumors, however, are difficult to access surgically, and others could require the surgeon to remove too much of the liver. Moreover, chemotherapy is highly toxic to the liver, and certain tumors do not respond well to it anyway. In some such cases, an interventional radiologist can treat the tumors by disrupting their blood supply, which they need if they are to continue to grow. In this procedure, called radioembolization, the radiologist accesses the liver with a fine needle, threaded through one of the patient's blood vessels. The radiologist then inserts tiny radioactive "seeds" into the blood vessels that supply the tumors. In the days and weeks following the procedure, the radiation emitted from the seeds destroys the vessels and directly kills the tumor cells in the vicinity of the treatment.

Radioisotopes emit subatomic particles that can be detected and tracked by imaging technologies. One of the most advanced uses of radioisotopes in medicine is the positron emission tomography (PET) scanner, which detects the activity in the body of a very small injection of radioactive glucose, the simple sugar that cells use for energy. The PET camera reveals to the medical team which of the patient's tissues are taking up the most glucose. Thus, the most metabolically active tissues show up as bright "hot spots" on the images (Figure 2.6). PET can reveal some cancerous masses because cancer cells consume glucose at a high rate to fuel their rapid reproduction.

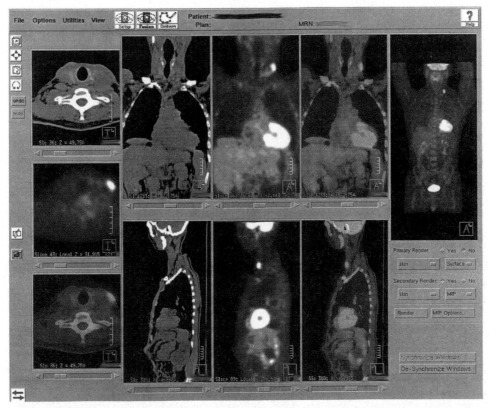

FIGURE 2.6   PET Scan   PET highlights areas in the body where there is relatively high glucose use, which is characteristic of cancerous tissue. This PET scan shows sites of the spread of a large primary tumor to other sites.

The Behavior of Electrons

In the human body, atoms do not exist as independent entities. Rather, they are constantly reacting with other atoms to form and to break down more complex substances. To fully understand anatomy and physiology you must grasp how atoms participate in such reactions. The key is understanding the behavior of electrons.

Although electrons do not follow rigid orbits a set distance away from the atom's nucleus, they do tend to stay within certain regions of space called electron shells. An **electron shell** is a layer of electrons that encircle the nucleus at a distinct energy level.

The atoms of the elements found in the human body have from one to five electron shells, and all electron shells hold eight electrons except the first shell, which can only hold two. This configuration of electron shells is the same for all atoms. The precise number of shells depends on the number of electrons in the atom. Hydrogen and helium have just one and two electrons, respectively. If you take a look at the periodic table of the elements, you will notice that hydrogen and helium are placed alone on either sides of the top row; they are the only elements that have just one electron shell (Figure 2.7). A second shell is necessary to hold the electrons in all elements larger than hydrogen and helium.

Lithium (Li), whose atomic number is 3, has three electrons. Two of these fill the first electron shell, and the third spills over into a second shell. The second electron shell can accommodate as many as eight electrons. Carbon, with its six electrons, entirely fills its first shell, and half-fills its second. With ten electrons, neon (Ne) entirely fills its two electron shells. Again, a look at the periodic table reveals that all of the elements in the second row, from lithium to neon, have just two electron shells. Atoms with more than ten electrons require more than two shells. These elements occupy the third and subsequent rows of the periodic table.

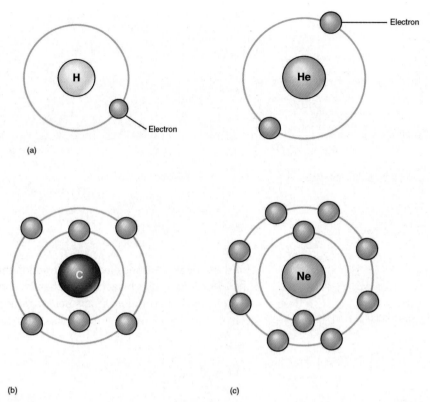

FIGURE 2.7 Electron Shells   Electrons orbit the atomic nucleus at distinct levels of energy called electron shells. (a) With one electron, hydrogen only half-fills its electron shell. Helium also has a single shell, but its two electrons completely fill it. (b) The electrons of carbon completely fill its first electron shell, but only half-fills its second. (c) Neon, an element that does not occur in the body, has 10 electrons, filling both of its electron shells.

The factor that most strongly governs the tendency of an atom to participate in chemical reactions is the number of electrons in its valence shell. A **valence shell** is an atom's outermost electron shell. If the valence shell is full, the atom is stable; meaning its electrons are unlikely to be pulled away from the nucleus by the electrical charge of other atoms. If the valence shell is not full, the atom is reactive; meaning it will tend to react with other atoms in ways that make the valence shell full. Consider hydrogen, with its one electron only half-filling its valence shell. This single electron is likely to be drawn into relationships with the atoms of other elements, so that hydrogen's single valence shell can be stabilized.

All atoms (except hydrogen and helium with their single electron shells) are most stable when there are exactly eight electrons in their valence shell. This principle is referred to as the octet rule, and it states that an atom will give up, gain, or share electrons with another atom so that it ends up with eight electrons in its own valence shell. For example, oxygen, with six electrons in its valence shell, is likely react with other atoms in a way that results in the addition of two electrons to oxygen's valence shell, bringing the number to eight. When two hydrogen atoms each share their single electron with oxygen, covalent bonds are formed, resulting in a molecule of water, H_2O.

In nature, atoms of one element tend to join with atoms of other elements in characteristic ways. For example, carbon commonly fills its valence shell by linking up with four atoms of hydrogen. In so doing, the two elements form the simplest of organic molecules, methane, which also is one of the most abundant and stable carbon-containing compounds on Earth. As stated above, another example is water; oxygen needs two electrons to fill its valence shell. It commonly interacts with two atoms of hydrogen, forming H_2O. Incidentally, the name "hydrogen" reflects its contribution to water (hydro- = "water"; -gen = "maker"). Thus, hydrogen is the "water maker."

Access for free at openstax.org

2.2 Chemical Bonds

LEARNING OBJECTIVES

By the end of this section, you will be able to:

- Explain the relationship between molecules and compounds
- Distinguish between ions, cations, and anions
- Identify the key difference between ionic and covalent bonds
- Distinguish between nonpolar and polar covalent bonds
- Explain how water molecules link via hydrogen bonds

Atoms separated by a great distance cannot link; rather, they must come close enough for the electrons in their valence shells to interact. But do atoms ever actually touch one another? Most physicists would say no, because the negatively charged electrons in their valence shells repel one another. No force within the human body—or anywhere in the natural world—is strong enough to overcome this electrical repulsion. So when you read about atoms linking together or colliding, bear in mind that the atoms are not merging in a physical sense.

Instead, atoms link by forming a chemical bond. A **bond** is a weak or strong electrical attraction that holds atoms in the same vicinity. The new grouping is typically more stable—less likely to react again—than its component atoms were when they were separate. A more or less stable grouping of two or more atoms held together by chemical bonds is called a **molecule**. The bonded atoms may be of the same element, as in the case of H_2, which is called molecular hydrogen or hydrogen gas. When a molecule is made up of two or more atoms of different elements, it is called a chemical **compound**. Thus, a unit of water, or H_2O, is a compound, as is a single molecule of the gas methane, or CH_4.

Three types of chemical bonds are important in human physiology, because they hold together substances that are used by the body for critical aspects of homeostasis, signaling, and energy production, to name just a few important processes. These are ionic bonds, covalent bonds, and hydrogen bonds.

Ions and Ionic Bonds

Recall that an atom typically has the same number of positively charged protons and negatively charged electrons. As long as this situation remains, the atom is electrically neutral. But when an atom participates in a chemical reaction that results in the donation or acceptance of one or more electrons, the atom will then become positively or negatively charged. This happens frequently for most atoms in order to have a full valence shell, as described previously. This can happen either by gaining electrons to fill a shell that is more than half-full, or by giving away electrons to empty a shell that is less than half-full, thereby leaving the next smaller electron shell as the new, full, valence shell. An atom that has an electrical charge—whether positive or negative—is an **ion**.

🔗 INTERACTIVE LINK

Visit this website (http://openstax.org/l/electenergy) to learn about electrical energy and the attraction/repulsion of charges. What happens to the charged electroscope when a conductor is moved between its plastic sheets, and why?

Potassium (K), for instance, is an important element in all body cells. Its atomic number is 19. It has just one electron in its valence shell. This characteristic makes potassium highly likely to participate in chemical reactions in which it donates one electron. (It is easier for potassium to donate one electron than to gain seven electrons.) The loss will cause the positive charge of potassium's protons to be more influential than the negative charge of potassium's electrons. In other words, the resulting potassium ion will be slightly positive. A potassium ion is written K^+, indicating that it has lost a single electron. A positively charged ion is known as a **cation**.

Now consider fluorine (F), a component of bones and teeth. Its atomic number is nine, and it has seven electrons in its valence shell. Thus, it is highly likely to bond with other atoms in such a way that fluorine accepts one electron (it is easier for fluorine to gain one electron than to donate seven electrons). When it does, its electrons will outnumber its protons by one, and it will have an overall negative charge. The ionized form of fluorine is called fluoride, and is written as F^-. A negatively charged ion is known as an **anion**.

Atoms that have more than one electron to donate or accept will end up with stronger positive or negative charges. A cation that has donated two electrons has a net charge of +2. Using magnesium (Mg) as an example, this can be written Mg^{++} or Mg^{2+}. An anion that has accepted two electrons has a net charge of −2. The ionic form of selenium (Se), for example, is typically written Se^{2-}.

The opposite charges of cations and anions exert a moderately strong mutual attraction that keeps the atoms in close proximity forming an ionic bond. An **ionic bond** is an ongoing, close association between ions of opposite charge. The table salt you sprinkle on your food owes its existence to ionic bonding. As shown in Figure 2.8, sodium commonly donates an electron to chlorine, becoming the cation Na^+. When chlorine accepts the electron, it becomes the chloride anion, Cl^-. With their opposing charges, these two ions strongly attract each other.

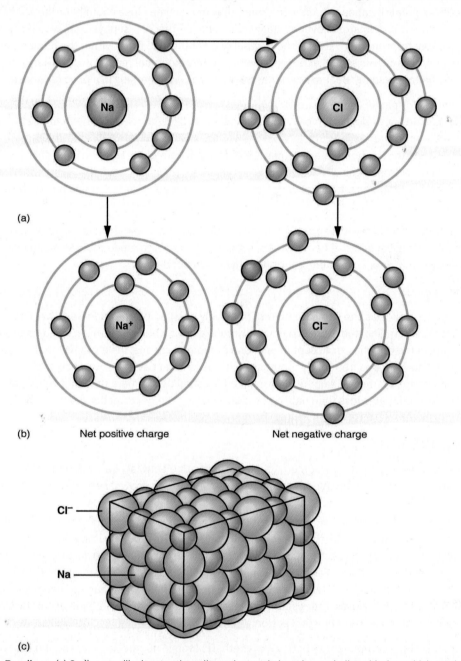

FIGURE 2.8   Ionic Bonding   (a) Sodium readily donates the solitary electron in its valence shell to chlorine, which needs only one electron to have a full valence shell. (b) The opposite electrical charges of the resulting sodium cation and chloride anion result in the formation of a bond of attraction called an ionic bond. (c) The attraction of many sodium and chloride ions results in the formation of large groupings called crystals.

Water is an essential component of life because it is able to break the ionic bonds in salts to free the ions. In fact, in biological fluids, most individual atoms exist as ions. These dissolved ions produce electrical charges within the body. The behavior of these ions produces the tracings of heart and brain function observed as waves on an electrocardiogram (EKG or ECG) or an electroencephalogram (EEG). The electrical activity that derives from the interactions of the charged ions is why they are also called electrolytes.

Covalent Bonds

Unlike ionic bonds formed by the attraction between a cation's positive charge and an anion's negative charge, molecules formed by a **covalent bond** share electrons in a mutually stabilizing relationship. Like next-door neighbors whose kids hang out first at one home and then at the other, the atoms do not lose or gain electrons permanently. Instead, the electrons move back and forth between the elements. Because of the close sharing of pairs of electrons (one electron from each of two atoms), covalent bonds are stronger than ionic bonds.

Nonpolar Covalent Bonds

Figure 2.9 shows several common types of covalent bonds. Notice that the two covalently bonded atoms typically share just one or two electron pairs, though larger sharings are possible. The important concept to take from this is that in covalent bonds, electrons in the two atoms' overlapping atomic orbitals are shared to fill the valence shells of both atoms, ultimately stabilizing both of the atoms involved. In a single covalent bond, a single electron pair is shared between two atoms, while in a double covalent bond, two pairs of electrons are shared between two atoms. There even are triple covalent bonds, where three electron pairs are shared between two atoms.

(a) A single covalent bond: hydrogen gas (H—H). Two atoms of hydrogen each share their solitary electron in a single covalent bond.

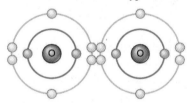

(b) A double covalent bond: oxygen gas (O=O). An atom of oxygen has six electrons in its valence shell; thus, two more would make it stable. Two atoms of oxygen achieve stability by sharing two pairs of electrons in a double covalent bond.

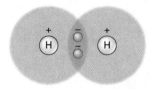

Molecule of oxygen gas (O_2)

(c) Two double covalent bonds: carbon dioxide (O=C=O). An atom of carbon has four electrons in its valence shell; thus, four more would make it stable. An atom of carbon and two atoms of oxygen achieve stability by sharing two electron pairs each, in two double covalent bonds.

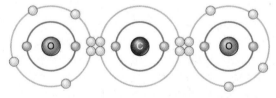

FIGURE 2.9   Covalent Bonding

You can see that the covalent bonds shown in Figure 2.9 are balanced. The sharing of the negative electrons is relatively equal, as is the electrical pull of the positive protons in the nucleus of the atoms involved. This is why covalently bonded molecules that are electrically balanced in this way are described as nonpolar; that is, no region of the molecule is either more positive or more negative than any other.

Polar Covalent Bonds

Groups of legislators with completely opposite views on a particular issue are often described as "polarized" by news writers. In chemistry, a **polar molecule** is a molecule that contains regions that have opposite electrical charges. Polar molecules occur when atoms share electrons unequally, in polar covalent bonds.

The most familiar example of a polar molecule is water (Figure 2.10). The molecule has three parts: one atom of oxygen, the nucleus of which contains eight protons, and two hydrogen atoms, whose nuclei each contain only one proton. Because every proton exerts an identical positive charge, a nucleus that contains eight protons exerts a charge eight times greater than a nucleus that contains one proton. This means that the negatively charged electrons present in the water molecule are more strongly attracted to the oxygen nucleus than to the hydrogen nuclei. Each hydrogen atom's single negative electron therefore migrates toward the oxygen atom, making the oxygen end of their bond slightly more negative than the hydrogen end of their bond.

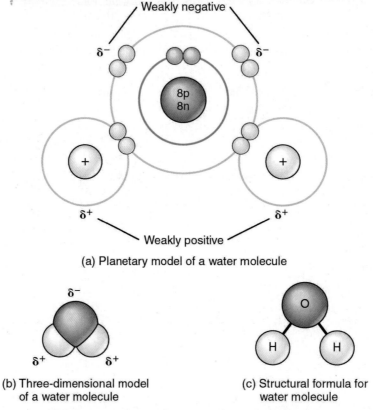

(a) Planetary model of a water molecule

(b) Three-dimensional model
of a water molecule

(c) Structural formula for
water molecule

FIGURE 2.10   **Polar Covalent Bonds in a Water Molecule**

What is true for the bonds is true for the water molecule as a whole; that is, the oxygen region has a slightly negative charge and the regions of the hydrogen atoms have a slightly positive charge. These charges are often referred to as "partial charges" because the strength of the charge is less than one full electron, as would occur in an ionic bond. As shown in Figure 2.10, regions of weak polarity are indicated with the Greek letter delta (δ) and a plus (+) or minus (−) sign.

Even though a single water molecule is unimaginably tiny, it has mass, and the opposing electrical charges on the molecule pull that mass in such a way that it creates a shape somewhat like a triangular tent (see Figure 2.10**b**). This dipole, with the positive charges at one end formed by the hydrogen atoms at the "bottom" of the tent and the negative charge at the opposite end (the oxygen atom at the "top" of the tent) makes the charged regions highly likely to interact with charged regions of other polar molecules. For human physiology, the resulting bond is one of the most important formed by water—the hydrogen bond.

Hydrogen Bonds

A **hydrogen bond** is formed when a weakly positive hydrogen atom already bonded to one electronegative atom (for example, the oxygen in the water molecule) is attracted to another electronegative atom from another molecule. In other words, hydrogen bonds always include hydrogen that is already part of a polar molecule.

The most common example of hydrogen bonding in the natural world occurs between molecules of water. It happens before your eyes whenever two raindrops merge into a larger bead, or a creek spills into a river. Hydrogen bonding occurs because the weakly negative oxygen atom in one water molecule is attracted to the weakly positive hydrogen atoms of two other water molecules (Figure 2.11).

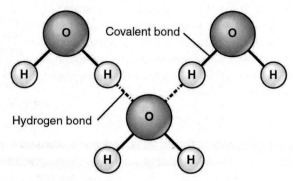

FIGURE 2.11   Hydrogen Bonds between Water Molecules   Notice that the bonds occur between the weakly positive charge on the hydrogen atoms and the weakly negative charge on the oxygen atoms. Hydrogen bonds are relatively weak, and therefore are indicated with a dotted (rather than a solid) line.

Water molecules also strongly attract other types of charged molecules as well as ions. This explains why "table salt," for example, actually is a molecule called a "salt" in chemistry, which consists of equal numbers of positively-charged sodium (Na^+) and negatively-charged chloride (Cl^-), dissolves so readily in water, in this case forming dipole-ion bonds between the water and the electrically-charged ions (electrolytes). Water molecules also repel molecules with nonpolar covalent bonds, like fats, lipids, and oils. You can demonstrate this with a simple kitchen experiment: pour a teaspoon of vegetable oil, a compound formed by nonpolar covalent bonds, into a glass of water. Instead of instantly dissolving in the water, the oil forms a distinct bead because the polar water molecules repel the nonpolar oil.

2.3 Chemical Reactions

LEARNING OBJECTIVES

By the end of this section, you will be able to:

- Distinguish between kinetic and potential energy, and between exergonic and endergonic chemical reactions
- Identify four forms of energy important in human functioning
- Describe the three basic types of chemical reactions
- Identify several factors influencing the rate of chemical reactions

One characteristic of a living organism is metabolism, which is the sum total of all of the chemical reactions that go on to maintain that organism's health and life. The bonding processes you have learned thus far are anabolic chemical reactions; that is, they form larger molecules from smaller molecules or atoms. But recall that metabolism can proceed in another direction: in catabolic chemical reactions, bonds between components of larger molecules break, releasing smaller molecules or atoms. Both types of reaction involve exchanges not only of matter, but of energy.

The Role of Energy in Chemical Reactions

Chemical reactions require a sufficient amount of energy to cause the matter to collide with enough precision and force that old chemical bonds can be broken and new ones formed. In general, **kinetic energy** is the form of energy powering any type of matter in motion. Imagine you are building a brick wall. The energy it takes to lift and place one brick atop another is kinetic energy—the energy matter possesses because of its motion. Once the wall is in place, it stores potential energy. **Potential energy** is the energy of position, or the energy matter possesses because of the positioning or structure of its components. If the brick wall collapses, the stored potential energy is released as kinetic energy as the bricks fall.

In the human body, potential energy is stored in the bonds between atoms and molecules. **Chemical energy** is the form of potential energy in which energy is stored in chemical bonds. When those bonds are formed, chemical energy is invested, and when they break, chemical energy is released. Notice that chemical energy, like all energy, is neither created nor destroyed; rather, it is converted from one form to another. When you eat an energy bar before heading out the door for a hike, the honey, nuts, and other foods the bar contains are broken down and rearranged by your body into molecules that your muscle cells convert to kinetic energy.

Chemical reactions that release more energy than they absorb are characterized as exergonic. The catabolism of the foods in your energy bar is an example. Some of the chemical energy stored in the bar is absorbed into molecules your body uses for fuel, but some of it is released—for example, as heat. In contrast, chemical reactions that absorb more energy than they release are endergonic. These reactions require energy input, and the resulting molecule stores not only the chemical energy in the original components, but also the energy that fueled the reaction. Because energy is neither created nor destroyed, where does the energy needed for endergonic reactions come from? In many cases, it comes from exergonic reactions.

Forms of Energy Important in Human Functioning

You have already learned that chemical energy is absorbed, stored, and released by chemical bonds. In addition to chemical energy, mechanical, radiant, and electrical energy are important in human functioning.

- Mechanical energy, which is stored in physical systems such as machines, engines, or the human body, directly powers the movement of matter. When you lift a brick into place on a wall, your muscles provide the mechanical energy that moves the brick.
- Radiant energy is energy emitted and transmitted as waves rather than matter. These waves vary in length from long radio waves and microwaves to short gamma waves emitted from decaying atomic nuclei. The full spectrum of radiant energy is referred to as the electromagnetic spectrum. The body uses the ultraviolet energy of sunlight to convert a compound in skin cells to vitamin D, which is essential to human functioning. The human eye evolved to see the wavelengths that comprise the colors of the rainbow, from red to violet, so that range in the spectrum is called "visible light."
- Electrical energy, supplied by electrolytes in cells and body fluids, contributes to the voltage changes that help transmit impulses in nerve and muscle cells.

Characteristics of Chemical Reactions

All chemical reactions begin with a **reactant**, the general term for the one or more substances that enter into the reaction. Sodium and chloride ions, for example, are the reactants in the production of table salt. The one or more substances produced by a chemical reaction are called the **product**.

In chemical reactions, the components of the reactants—the elements involved and the number of atoms of each—are all present in the product(s). Similarly, there is nothing present in the products that are not present in the reactants. This is because chemical reactions are governed by the law of conservation of mass, which states that matter cannot be created or destroyed in a chemical reaction.

Just as you can express mathematical calculations in equations such as $2 + 7 = 9$, you can use chemical equations to show how reactants become products. As in math, chemical equations proceed from left to right, but instead of an equal sign, they employ an arrow or arrows indicating the direction in which the chemical reaction proceeds. For example, the chemical reaction in which one atom of nitrogen and three atoms of hydrogen produce ammonia would be written as $N + 3H \rightarrow NH_3$. Correspondingly, the breakdown of ammonia into its components would be written as $NH_3 \rightarrow N + 3H$.

Notice that, in the first example, a nitrogen (N) atom and three hydrogen (H) atoms bond to form a compound. This anabolic reaction requires energy, which is then stored within the compound's bonds. Such reactions are referred to as synthesis reactions. A **synthesis reaction** is a chemical reaction that results in the synthesis (joining) of components that were formerly separate (Figure 2.12**a**). Again, nitrogen and hydrogen are reactants in a synthesis reaction that yields ammonia as the product. The general equation for a synthesis reaction is $A + B \rightarrow AB$.

a) In a synthesis reaction, two components bond to make a larger molecule. Energy is required and is stored in the bond:

$$NOTE + BOOK \longrightarrow NOTEBOOK$$

b) In a decomposition reaction, bonds between components of a larger molecule are broken, resulting in smaller products:

$$BOOKWORM \longrightarrow BOOK + WORM$$

c) In an exchange reaction, bonds are both formed and broken such that the components of the reactants are rearranged:

$$NOTEBOOK + WORM \longrightarrow NOTE + BOOKWORM$$

FIGURE 2.12   The Three Fundamental Chemical Reactions   The atoms and molecules involved in the three fundamental chemical reactions can be imagined as words.

In the second example, ammonia is catabolized into its smaller components, and the potential energy that had been stored in its bonds is released. Such reactions are referred to as decomposition reactions. A **decomposition reaction** is a chemical reaction that breaks down or "de-composes" something larger into its constituent parts (see Figure 2.12**b**). The general equation for a decomposition reaction is: $AB \rightarrow A + B$.

An **exchange reaction** is a chemical reaction in which both synthesis and decomposition occur, chemical bonds are both formed and broken, and chemical energy is absorbed, stored, and released (see Figure 2.12**c**). The simplest form of an exchange reaction might be: $A + BC \rightarrow AB + C$. Notice that, to produce these products, B and C had to break apart in a decomposition reaction, whereas A and B had to bond in a synthesis reaction. A more complex exchange reaction might be: $AB + CD \rightarrow AC + BD$. Another example might be: $AB + CD \rightarrow AD + BC$.

In theory, any chemical reaction can proceed in either direction under the right conditions. Reactants may synthesize into a product that is later decomposed. Reversibility is also a quality of exchange reactions. For instance, $A + BC \rightarrow AB + C$ could then reverse to $AB + C \rightarrow A + BC$. This reversibility of a chemical reaction is indicated with a double arrow: $A + BC \rightleftarrows AB + C$. Still, in the human body, many chemical reactions do proceed in a predictable direction, either one way or the other. You can think of this more predictable path as the path of least resistance because, typically, the alternate direction requires more energy.

Factors Influencing the Rate of Chemical Reactions

If you pour vinegar into baking soda, the reaction is instantaneous; the concoction will bubble and fizz. But many chemical reactions take time. A variety of factors influence the rate of chemical reactions. This section, however, will consider only the most important in human functioning.

Properties of the Reactants

If chemical reactions are to occur quickly, the atoms in the reactants have to have easy access to one another. Thus, the greater the surface area of the reactants, the more readily they will interact. When you pop a cube of cheese into your mouth, you chew it before you swallow it. Among other things, chewing increases the surface area of the food so that digestive chemicals can more easily get at it. As a general rule, gases tend to react faster than liquids or solids, again because it takes energy to separate particles of a substance, and gases by definition already have space between their particles. Similarly, the larger the molecule, the greater the number of total bonds, so reactions involving smaller molecules, with fewer total bonds, would be expected to proceed faster.

In addition, recall that some elements are more reactive than others. Reactions that involve highly reactive elements like hydrogen proceed more quickly than reactions that involve less reactive elements. Reactions involving stable elements like helium are not likely to happen at all.

Temperature

Nearly all chemical reactions occur at a faster rate at higher temperatures. Recall that kinetic energy is the energy of matter in motion. The kinetic energy of subatomic particles increases in response to increases in thermal energy. The higher the temperature, the faster the particles move, and the more likely they are to come in contact and react.

Concentration and Pressure

If just a few people are dancing at a club, they are unlikely to step on each other's toes. But as more and more people get up to dance—especially if the music is fast—collisions are likely to occur. It is the same with chemical reactions: the more particles present within a given space, the more likely those particles are to bump into one another. This means that chemists can speed up chemical reactions not only by increasing the **concentration** of particles—the number of particles in the space—but also by decreasing the volume of the space, which would correspondingly increase the pressure. If there were 100 dancers in that club, and the manager abruptly moved the party to a room half the size, the concentration of the dancers would double in the new space, and the likelihood of collisions would increase accordingly.

Enzymes and Other Catalysts

For two chemicals in nature to react with each other they first have to come into contact, and this occurs through random collisions. Because heat helps increase the kinetic energy of atoms, ions, and molecules, it promotes their collision. But in the body, extremely high heat—such as a very high fever—can damage body cells and be life-threatening. On the other hand, normal body temperature is not high enough to promote the chemical reactions that sustain life. That is where catalysts come in.

In chemistry, a **catalyst** is a substance that increases the rate of a chemical reaction without itself undergoing any change. You can think of a catalyst as a chemical change agent. They help increase the rate and force at which atoms, ions, and molecules collide, thereby increasing the probability that their valence shell electrons will interact.

The most important catalysts in the human body are enzymes. An **enzyme** is a catalyst composed of protein or ribonucleic acid (RNA), both of which will be discussed later in this chapter. Like all catalysts, enzymes work by lowering the level of energy that needs to be invested in a chemical reaction. A chemical reaction's **activation energy** is the "threshold" level of energy needed to break the bonds in the reactants. Once those bonds are broken, new arrangements can form. Without an enzyme to act as a catalyst, a much larger investment of energy is needed to ignite a chemical reaction (Figure 2.13).

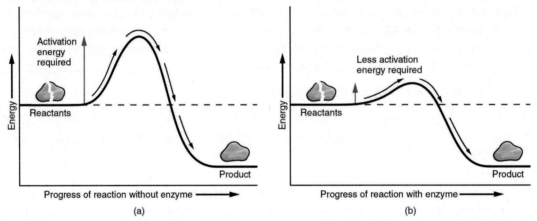

FIGURE 2.13   Enzymes   Enzymes decrease the activation energy required for a given chemical reaction to occur. (a) Without an enzyme, the energy input needed for a reaction to begin is high. (b) With the help of an enzyme, less energy is needed for a reaction to begin.

Enzymes are critical to the body's healthy functioning. They assist, for example, with the breakdown of food and its conversion to energy. In fact, most of the chemical reactions in the body are facilitated by enzymes.

2.4 Inorganic Compounds Essential to Human Functioning

LEARNING OBJECTIVES

By the end of this section, you will be able to:

- Compare and contrast inorganic and organic compounds
- Identify the properties of water that make it essential to life
- Explain the role of salts in body functioning
- Distinguish between acids and bases, and explain their role in pH
- Discuss the role of buffers in helping the body maintain pH homeostasis

The concepts you have learned so far in this chapter govern all forms of matter, and would work as a foundation for geology as well as biology. This section of the chapter narrows the focus to the chemistry of human life; that is, the compounds important for the body's structure and function. In general, these compounds are either inorganic or organic.

- An **inorganic compound** is a substance that does not contain both carbon and hydrogen. A great many inorganic compounds do contain hydrogen atoms, such as water (H_2O) and the hydrochloric acid (HCl) produced by your stomach. In contrast, only a handful of inorganic compounds contain carbon atoms. Carbon dioxide (CO_2) is one of the few examples.
- An **organic compound**, then, is a substance that contains both carbon and hydrogen. Organic compounds are synthesized via covalent bonds within living organisms, including the human body. Recall that carbon and hydrogen are the second and third most abundant elements in your body. You will soon discover how these two elements combine in the foods you eat, in the compounds that make up your body structure, and in the chemicals that fuel your functioning.

The following section examines the three groups of inorganic compounds essential to life: water, salts, acids, and bases. Organic compounds are covered later in the chapter.

Water

As much as 70 percent of an adult's body weight is water. This water is contained both within the cells and between the cells that make up tissues and organs. Its several roles make water indispensable to human functioning.

Water as a Lubricant and Cushion

Water is a major component of many of the body's lubricating fluids. Just as oil lubricates the hinge on a door, water in synovial fluid lubricates the actions of body joints, and water in pleural fluid helps the lungs expand and recoil with breathing. Watery fluids help keep food flowing through the digestive tract, and ensure that the movement of adjacent abdominal organs is friction free.

Water also protects cells and organs from physical trauma, cushioning the brain within the skull, for example, and protecting the delicate nerve tissue of the eyes. Water cushions a developing fetus in the mother's womb as well.

Water as a Heat Sink

A heat sink is a substance or object that absorbs and dissipates heat but does not experience a corresponding increase in temperature. In the body, water absorbs the heat generated by chemical reactions without greatly increasing in temperature. Moreover, when the environmental temperature soars, the water stored in the body helps keep the body cool. This cooling effect happens as warm blood from the body's core flows to the blood vessels just under the skin and is transferred to the environment. At the same time, sweat glands release warm water in sweat. As the water evaporates into the air, it carries away heat, and then the cooler blood from the periphery circulates back to the body core.

Water as a Component of Liquid Mixtures

A mixture is a combination of two or more substances, each of which maintains its own chemical identity. In other words, the constituent substances are not chemically bonded into a new, larger chemical compound. The concept is easy to imagine if you think of powdery substances such as flour and sugar; when you stir them together in a bowl, they obviously do not bond to form a new compound. The room air you breathe is a gaseous mixture, containing three discrete elements—nitrogen, oxygen, and argon—and one compound, carbon dioxide. There are three types of liquid mixtures, all of which contain water as a key component. These are solutions, colloids, and suspensions.

For cells in the body to survive, they must be kept moist in a water-based liquid called a solution. In chemistry, a liquid **solution** consists of a solvent that dissolves a substance called a solute. An important characteristic of solutions is that they are homogeneous; that is, the solute molecules are distributed evenly throughout the solution. If you were to stir a teaspoon of sugar into a glass of water, the sugar would dissolve into sugar molecules separated by water molecules. The ratio of sugar to water in the left side of the glass would be the same as the ratio of sugar to water in the right side of the glass. If you were to add more sugar, the ratio of sugar to water would change, but the distribution—provided you had stirred well—would still be even.

Water is considered the "universal solvent" and it is believed that life cannot exist without water because of this.

Water is certainly the most abundant solvent in the body; essentially all of the body's chemical reactions occur among compounds dissolved in water. Because water molecules are polar, with regions of positive and negative electrical charge, water readily dissolves ionic compounds and polar covalent compounds. Such compounds are referred to as hydrophilic, or "water-loving." As mentioned above, sugar dissolves well in water. This is because sugar molecules contain regions of hydrogen-oxygen polar bonds, making it hydrophilic. Nonpolar molecules, which do not readily dissolve in water, are called hydrophobic, or "water-fearing."

Concentrations of Solutes

Various mixtures of solutes and water are described in chemistry. The concentration of a given solute is the number of particles of that solute in a given space (oxygen makes up about 21 percent of atmospheric air). In the bloodstream of humans, glucose concentration is usually measured in milligram (mg) per deciliter (dL), and in a healthy adult averages about 100 mg/dL. Another method of measuring the concentration of a solute is by its molarity—which is moles (M) of the molecules per liter (L). The mole of an element is its atomic weight, while a mole of a compound is the sum of the atomic weights of its components, called the molecular weight. An often-used example is calculating a mole of glucose, with the chemical formula $C_6H_{12}O_6$. Using the periodic table, the atomic weight of carbon (C) is 12.011 grams (g), and there are six carbons in glucose, for a total atomic weight of 72.066 g. Doing the same calculations for hydrogen (H) and oxygen (O), the molecular weight equals 180.156g (the "gram molecular weight" of glucose). When water is added to make one liter of solution, you have one mole (1M) of glucose. This is particularly useful in chemistry because of the relationship of moles to "Avogadro's number." A mole of any solution has the same number of particles in it: 6.02×10^{23}. Many substances in the bloodstream and other tissue of the body are measured in thousandths of a mole, or millimoles (mM).

A **colloid** is a mixture that is somewhat like a heavy solution. The solute particles consist of tiny clumps of molecules large enough to make the liquid mixture opaque (because the particles are large enough to scatter light). Familiar examples of colloids are milk and cream. In the thyroid glands, the thyroid hormone is stored as a thick protein mixture also called a colloid.

A **suspension** is a liquid mixture in which a heavier substance is suspended temporarily in a liquid, but over time, settles out. This separation of particles from a suspension is called sedimentation. An example of sedimentation occurs in the blood test that establishes sedimentation rate, or sed rate. The test measures how quickly red blood cells in a test tube settle out of the watery portion of blood (known as plasma) over a set period of time. Rapid sedimentation of blood cells does not normally happen in the healthy body, but aspects of certain diseases can cause blood cells to clump together, and these heavy clumps of blood cells settle to the bottom of the test tube more quickly than do normal blood cells.

The Role of Water in Chemical Reactions

Two types of chemical reactions involve the creation or the consumption of water: dehydration synthesis and hydrolysis.

- In dehydration synthesis, one reactant gives up an atom of hydrogen and another reactant gives up a hydroxyl group (OH) in the synthesis of a new product. In the formation of their covalent bond, a molecule of water is released as a byproduct (Figure 2.14). This is also sometimes referred to as a condensation reaction.
- In hydrolysis, a molecule of water disrupts a compound, breaking its bonds. The water is itself split into H and OH. One portion of the severed compound then bonds with the hydrogen atom, and the other portion bonds with the hydroxyl group.

These reactions are reversible, and play an important role in the chemistry of organic compounds (which will be discussed shortly).

(a) Dehydration synthesis

Monomers are joined by removal of OH from one monomer and removal of H from the other at the site of bond formation.

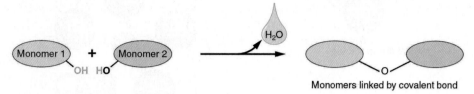

Monomers linked by covalent bond

(b) Hydrolysis

Monomers are released by the addition of a water molecule, adding OH to one monomer and H to the other.

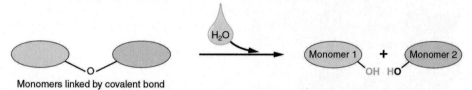

Monomers linked by covalent bond

FIGURE 2.14   Dehydration Synthesis and Hydrolysis   Monomers, the basic units for building larger molecules, form polymers (two or more chemically-bonded monomers). (a) In dehydration synthesis, two monomers are covalently bonded in a reaction in which one gives up a hydroxyl group and the other a hydrogen atom. A molecule of water is released as a byproduct during dehydration reactions. (b) In hydrolysis, the covalent bond between two monomers is split by the addition of a hydrogen atom to one and a hydroxyl group to the other, which requires the contribution of one molecule of water.

Salts

Recall that salts are formed when ions form ionic bonds. In these reactions, one atom gives up one or more electrons, and thus becomes positively charged, whereas the other accepts one or more electrons and becomes negatively charged. You can now define a salt as a substance that, when dissolved in water, dissociates into ions other than H^+ or OH^-. This fact is important in distinguishing salts from acids and bases, discussed next.

A typical salt, NaCl, dissociates completely in water (Figure 2.15). The positive and negative regions on the water molecule (the hydrogen and oxygen ends respectively) attract the negative chloride and positive sodium ions, pulling them away from each other. Again, whereas nonpolar and polar covalently bonded compounds break apart into molecules in solution, salts dissociate into ions. These ions are electrolytes; they are capable of conducting an electrical current in solution. This property is critical to the function of ions in transmitting nerve impulses and prompting muscle contraction.

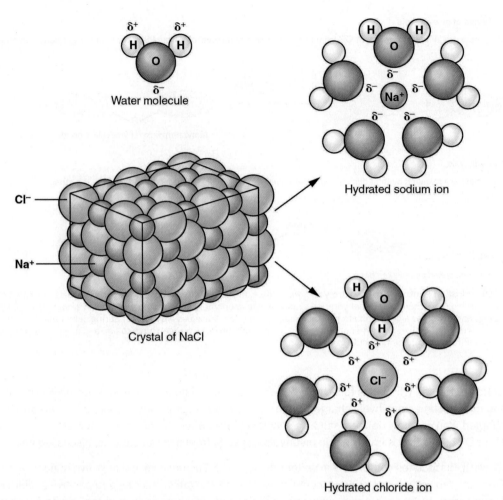

FIGURE 2.15   Dissociation of Sodium Chloride in Water   Notice that the crystals of sodium chloride dissociate not into molecules of NaCl, but into Na⁺ cations and Cl⁻ anions, each completely surrounded by water molecules.

Many other salts are important in the body. For example, bile salts produced by the liver help break apart dietary fats, and calcium phosphate salts form the mineral portion of teeth and bones.

Acids and Bases

Acids and bases, like salts, dissociate in water into electrolytes. Acids and bases can very much change the properties of the solutions in which they are dissolved.

Acids

An **acid** is a substance that releases hydrogen ions (H^+) in solution (Figure 2.16**a**). Because an atom of hydrogen has just one proton and one electron, a positively charged hydrogen ion is simply a proton. This solitary proton is highly likely to participate in chemical reactions. Strong acids are compounds that release all of their H^+ in solution; that is, they ionize completely. Hydrochloric acid (HCl), which is released from cells in the lining of the stomach, is a strong acid because it releases all of its H^+ in the stomach's watery environment. This strong acid aids in digestion and kills ingested microbes. Weak acids do not ionize completely; that is, some of their hydrogen ions remain bonded within a compound in solution. An example of a weak acid is vinegar, or acetic acid; it is called acetate after it gives up a proton.

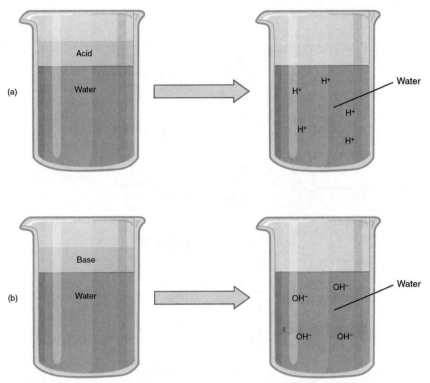

FIGURE 2.16 Acids and Bases   (a) In aqueous solution, an acid dissociates into hydrogen ions (H⁺) and anions. Nearly every molecule of a strong acid dissociates, producing a high concentration of H⁺. (b) In aqueous solution, a base dissociates into hydroxyl ions (OH⁻) and cations. Nearly every molecule of a strong base dissociates, producing a high concentration of OH⁻.

Bases

A **base** is a substance that releases hydroxyl ions (OH⁻) in solution, or one that accepts H⁺ already present in solution (see Figure 2.16**b**). The hydroxyl ions (also known as hydroxide ions) or other basic substances combine with H⁺ present to form a water molecule, thereby removing H⁺ and reducing the solution's acidity. Strong bases release most or all of their hydroxyl ions; weak bases release only some hydroxyl ions or absorb only a few H⁺. Food mixed with hydrochloric acid from the stomach would burn the small intestine, the next portion of the digestive tract after the stomach, if it were not for the release of bicarbonate (HCO_3^-), a weak base that attracts H⁺. Bicarbonate accepts some of the H⁺ protons, thereby reducing the acidity of the solution.

The Concept of pH

The relative acidity or alkalinity of a solution can be indicated by its pH. A solution's **pH** is the negative, base-10 logarithm of the hydrogen ion (H⁺) concentration of the solution. As an example, a pH 4 solution has an H⁺ concentration that is ten times greater than that of a pH 5 solution. That is, a solution with a pH of 4 is ten times more acidic than a solution with a pH of 5. The concept of pH will begin to make more sense when you study the pH scale, like that shown in Figure 2.17. The scale consists of a series of increments ranging from 0 to 14. A solution with a pH of 7 is considered neutral—neither acidic nor basic. Pure water has a pH of 7. The lower the number below 7, the more acidic the solution, or the greater the concentration of H⁺. The concentration of hydrogen ions at each pH value is 10 times different than the next pH. For instance, a pH value of 4 corresponds to a proton concentration of 10^{-4} M, or 0.0001M, while a pH value of 5 corresponds to a proton concentration of 10^{-5} M, or 0.00001M. The higher the number above 7, the more basic (alkaline) the solution, or the lower the concentration of H⁺. Human urine, for example, is ten times more acidic than pure water, and HCl is 10,000,000 times more acidic than water.

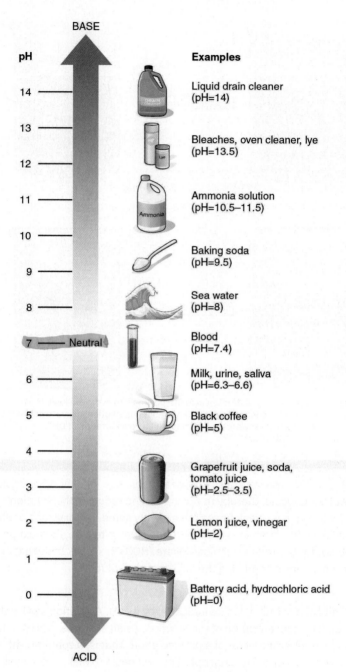

FIGURE 2.17   The pH Scale

Buffers

The pH of human blood normally ranges from 7.35 to 7.45, although it is typically identified as pH 7.4. At this slightly basic pH, blood can reduce the acidity resulting from the carbon dioxide (CO_2) constantly being released into the bloodstream by the trillions of cells in the body. Homeostatic mechanisms (along with exhaling CO_2 while breathing) normally keep the pH of blood within this narrow range. This is critical, because fluctuations—either too acidic or too alkaline—can lead to life-threatening disorders.

All cells of the body depend on homeostatic regulation of acid–base balance at a pH of approximately 7.4. The body therefore has several mechanisms for this regulation, involving breathing, the excretion of chemicals in urine, and the internal release of chemicals collectively called buffers into body fluids. A **buffer** is a solution of a weak acid and its conjugate base. A buffer can neutralize small amounts of acids or bases in body fluids. For example, if there is even a slight decrease below 7.35 in the pH of a bodily fluid, the buffer in the fluid—in this case, acting as a weak base—will bind the excess hydrogen ions. In contrast, if pH rises above 7.45, the buffer will act as a weak acid and contribute hydrogen ions.

Access for free at openstax.org

HOMEOSTATIC IMBALANCES

Acids and Bases

Excessive acidity of the blood and other body fluids is known as acidosis. Common causes of acidosis are situations and disorders that reduce the effectiveness of breathing, especially the person's ability to exhale fully, which causes a buildup of CO_2 (and H^+) in the bloodstream. Acidosis can also be caused by metabolic problems that reduce the level or function of buffers that act as bases, or that promote the production of acids. For instance, with severe diarrhea, too much bicarbonate can be lost from the body, allowing acids to build up in body fluids. In people with poorly managed diabetes (ineffective regulation of blood sugar), acids called ketones are produced as a form of body fuel. These can build up in the blood, causing a serious condition called diabetic ketoacidosis. Kidney failure, liver failure, heart failure, cancer, and other disorders also can prompt metabolic acidosis.

In contrast, alkalosis is a condition in which the blood and other body fluids are too alkaline (basic). As with acidosis, respiratory disorders are a major cause; however, in respiratory alkalosis, carbon dioxide levels fall too low. Lung disease, aspirin overdose, shock, and ordinary anxiety can cause respiratory alkalosis, which reduces the normal concentration of H^+.

Metabolic alkalosis often results from prolonged, severe vomiting, which causes a loss of hydrogen and chloride ions (as components of HCl). Medications also can prompt alkalosis. These include diuretics that cause the body to lose potassium ions, as well as antacids when taken in excessive amounts, for instance by someone with persistent heartburn or an ulcer.

2.5 Organic Compounds Essential to Human Functioning

LEARNING OBJECTIVES

By the end of this section, you will be able to:

- Identify four types of organic molecules essential to human functioning
- Explain the chemistry behind carbon's affinity for covalently bonding in organic compounds
- Provide examples of three types of carbohydrates, and identify the primary functions of carbohydrates in the body
- Discuss four types of lipids important in human functioning
- Describe the structure of proteins, and discuss their importance to human functioning
- Identify the building blocks of nucleic acids, and the roles of DNA, RNA, and ATP in human functioning

Organic compounds typically consist of groups of carbon atoms covalently bonded to hydrogen, usually oxygen, and often other elements as well. They are found throughout the world, in soils and seas, commercial products, and every cell of the human body. The four types most important to human structure and function are carbohydrates, lipids, proteins, and nucleic acids. Before exploring these compounds, you need to first understand the chemistry of carbon.

The Chemistry of Carbon

What makes organic compounds ubiquitous is the chemistry of their carbon core. Recall that carbon atoms have four electrons in their valence shell, and that the octet rule dictates that atoms tend to react in such a way as to complete their valence shell with eight electrons. Carbon atoms do not complete their valence shells by donating or accepting four electrons. Instead, they readily share electrons via covalent bonds.

Commonly, carbon atoms share with other carbon atoms, often forming a long carbon chain referred to as a carbon skeleton. When they do share, however, they do not share all their electrons exclusively with each other. Rather, carbon atoms tend to share electrons with a variety of other elements, one of which is always hydrogen. Carbon and hydrogen groupings are called hydrocarbons. If you study the figures of organic compounds in the remainder of this chapter, you will see several with chains of hydrocarbons in one region of the compound.

Many combinations are possible to fill carbon's four "vacancies." Carbon may share electrons with oxygen or nitrogen or other atoms in a particular region of an organic compound. Moreover, the atoms to which carbon atoms bond may also be part of a functional group. A **functional group** is a group of atoms linked by strong covalent bonds and tending to function in chemical reactions as a single unit. You can think of functional groups as tightly knit "cliques" whose members are unlikely to be parted. Five functional groups are important in human physiology; these are the hydroxyl, carboxyl, amino, methyl and phosphate groups (Table 2.1).

Functional Groups Important in Human Physiology

Functional group	Structural formula	Importance
Hydroxyl	—O—H	Hydroxyl groups are polar. They are components of all four types of organic compounds discussed in this chapter. They are involved in dehydration synthesis and hydrolysis reactions.
Carboxyl	$R-C{\overset{\displaystyle O}{\underset{\textstyle O-H}{}}}$	Carboxyl groups are found within fatty acids, amino acids, and many other acids.
Amino	$-N-H_2$	Amino groups are found within amino acids, the building blocks of proteins.
Methyl	$-C-H_3$	Methyl groups are found within amino acids.
Phosphate	$-P-O_4{}^{2-}$	Phosphate groups are found within phospholipids and nucleotides.

TABLE 2.1

Carbon's affinity for covalent bonding means that many distinct and relatively stable organic molecules nevertheless readily form larger, more complex molecules. Any large molecule is referred to as **macromolecule** (macro- = "large"), and the organic compounds in this section all fit this description. However, some macromolecules are made up of several "copies" of single units called monomer (mono- = "one"; -mer = "part"). Like beads in a long necklace, these monomers link by covalent bonds to form long polymers (poly- = "many"). There are many examples of monomers and polymers among the organic compounds.

Monomers form polymers by engaging in dehydration synthesis (see Figure 2.14). As was noted earlier, this reaction results in the release of a molecule of water. Each monomer contributes: One gives up a hydrogen atom and the other gives up a hydroxyl group. Polymers are split into monomers by hydrolysis (-lysis = "rupture"). The bonds between their monomers are broken, via the donation of a molecule of water, which contributes a hydrogen atom to one monomer and a hydroxyl group to the other.

Carbohydrates

The term carbohydrate means "hydrated carbon." Recall that the root hydro- indicates water. A **carbohydrate** is a molecule composed of carbon, hydrogen, and oxygen; in most carbohydrates, hydrogen and oxygen are found in the same two-to-one relative proportions they have in water. In fact, the chemical formula for a "generic" molecule of carbohydrate is $(CH_2O)_n$.

Carbohydrates are referred to as saccharides, a word meaning "sugars." Three forms are important in the body. Monosaccharides are the monomers of carbohydrates. Disaccharides (di- = "two") are made up of two monomers. **Polysaccharides** are the polymers, and can consist of hundreds to thousands of monomers.

Monosaccharides

A **monosaccharide** is a monomer of carbohydrates. Five monosaccharides are important in the body. Three of these are the hexose sugars, so called because they each contain six atoms of carbon. These are glucose, fructose, and galactose, shown in Figure 2.18**a**. The remaining monosaccharides are the two pentose sugars, each of which contains five atoms of carbon. They are ribose and deoxyribose, shown in Figure 2.18**b**.

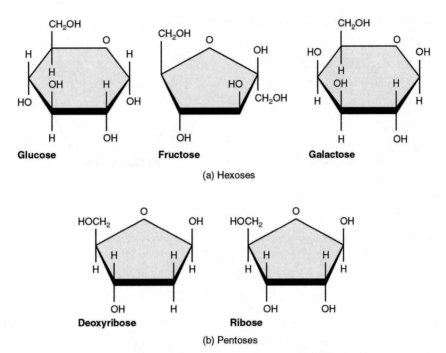

(a) Hexoses

(b) Pentoses

FIGURE 2.18   Five Important Monosaccharides

Disaccharides

A **disaccharide** is a pair of monosaccharides. Disaccharides are formed via dehydration synthesis, and the bond linking them is referred to as a glycosidic bond (glyco- = "sugar"). Three disaccharides (shown in Figure 2.19) are important to humans. These are sucrose, commonly referred to as table sugar; lactose, or milk sugar; and maltose, or malt sugar. As you can tell from their common names, you consume these in your diet; however, your body cannot use them directly. Instead, in the digestive tract, they are split into their component monosaccharides via hydrolysis.

(a) The monosaccharides glucose and fructose bond to form sucrose

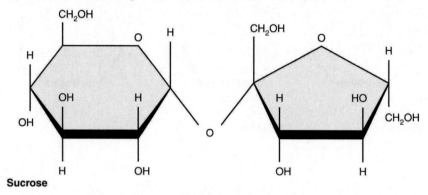

Sucrose

(b) The monosaccharides galactose and glucose bond to form lactose.

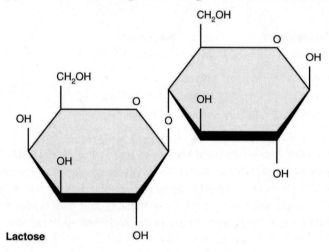

Lactose

(c) Two glucose monosaccharides bond to form maltose.

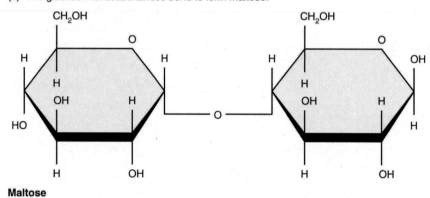

Maltose

FIGURE 2.19 **Three Important Disaccharides** All three important disaccharides form by dehydration synthesis.

🔗 INTERACTIVE LINK

Watch this video (http://openstax.org/l/disaccharide) to observe the formation of a disaccharide. What happens when water encounters a glycosidic bond?

***

Polysaccharides

Polysaccharides can contain a few to a thousand or more monosaccharides. Three are important to the body (Figure 2.20):

- Starches are polymers of glucose. They occur in long chains called amylose or branched chains called amylopectin, both of which are stored in plant-based foods and are relatively easy to digest.

Access for free at openstax.org

- Glycogen is also a polymer of glucose, but it is stored in the tissues of animals, especially in the muscles and liver. It is not considered a dietary carbohydrate because very little glycogen remains in animal tissues after slaughter; however, the human body stores excess glucose as glycogen, again, in the muscles and liver.
- Cellulose, a polysaccharide that is the primary component of the cell wall of green plants, is the component of plant food referred to as "fiber". In humans, cellulose/fiber is not digestible; however, dietary fiber has many health benefits. It helps you feel full so you eat less, it promotes a healthy digestive tract, and a diet high in fiber is thought to reduce the risk of heart disease and possibly some forms of cancer.

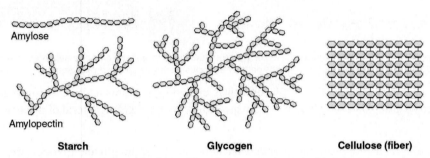

Amylose

Amylopectin

Starch   **Glycogen**   **Cellulose (fiber)**

FIGURE 2.20   **Three Important Polysaccharides**   Three important polysaccharides are starches, glycogen, and fiber.

Functions of Carbohydrates

The body obtains carbohydrates from plant-based foods. Grains, fruits, and legumes and other vegetables provide most of the carbohydrate in the human diet, although lactose is found in dairy products.

Although most body cells can break down other organic compounds for fuel, all body cells can use glucose. Moreover, nerve cells (neurons) in the brain, spinal cord, and through the peripheral nervous system, as well as red blood cells, can use only glucose for fuel. In the breakdown of glucose for energy, molecules of adenosine triphosphate, better known as ATP, are produced. **Adenosine triphosphate (ATP)** is composed of a ribose sugar, an adenine base, and three phosphate groups. ATP releases free energy when its phosphate bonds are broken, and thus supplies ready energy to the cell. More ATP is produced in the presence of oxygen (O_2) than in pathways that do not use oxygen. The overall reaction for the conversion of the energy in glucose to energy stored in ATP can be written:

$$C_6H_{12}O_6 + 6\,O_2 \;\rightarrow\; 6\,CO_2 + 6\,H_2O + ATP$$

In addition to being a critical fuel source, carbohydrates are present in very small amounts in cells' structure. For instance, some carbohydrate molecules bind with proteins to produce glycoproteins, and others combine with lipids to produce glycolipids, both of which are found in the membrane that encloses the contents of body cells.

Lipids

A **lipid** is one of a highly diverse group of compounds made up mostly of hydrocarbons. The few oxygen atoms they contain are often at the periphery of the molecule. Their nonpolar hydrocarbons make all lipids hydrophobic. In water, lipids do not form a true solution, but they may form an emulsion, which is the term for a mixture of solutions that do not mix well.

Triglycerides

A **triglyceride** is one of the most common dietary lipid groups, and the type found most abundantly in body tissues. This compound, which is commonly referred to as a fat, is formed from the synthesis of two types of molecules (Figure 2.21):

- A glycerol backbone at the core of triglycerides, consists of three carbon atoms.
- Three fatty acids, long chains of hydrocarbons with a carboxyl group and a methyl group at opposite ends, extend from each of the carbons of the glycerol.

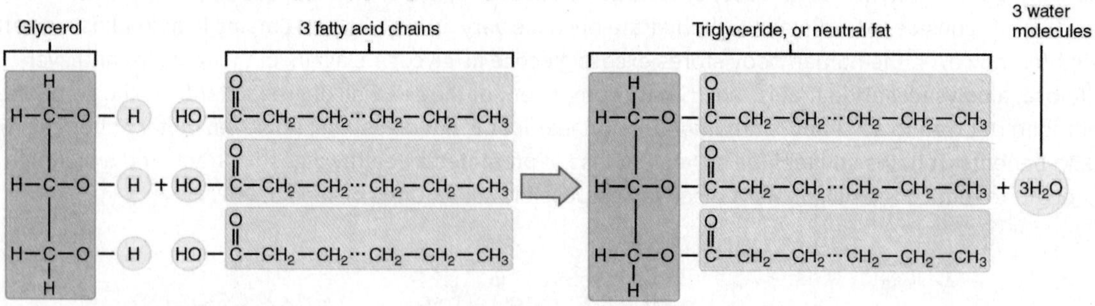

Three fatty acid chains are bound to glycerol by dehydration synthesis.

FIGURE 2.21 **Triglycerides**   Triglycerides are composed of glycerol attached to three fatty acids via dehydration synthesis. Notice that glycerol gives up a hydrogen atom, and the carboxyl groups on the fatty acids each give up a hydroxyl group.

Triglycerides form via dehydration synthesis. Glycerol gives up hydrogen atoms from its hydroxyl groups at each bond, and the carboxyl group on each fatty acid chain gives up a hydroxyl group. A total of three water molecules are thereby released.

Fatty acid chains that have no double carbon bonds anywhere along their length and therefore contain the maximum number of hydrogen atoms are called saturated fatty acids. These straight, rigid chains pack tightly together and are solid or semi-solid at room temperature (Figure 2.22**a**). Butter and lard are examples, as is the fat found on a steak or in your own body. In contrast, fatty acids with one double carbon bond are kinked at that bond (Figure 2.22**b**). These monounsaturated fatty acids are therefore unable to pack together tightly, and are liquid at room temperature. Polyunsaturated fatty acids contain two or more double carbon bonds, and are also liquid at room temperature. Plant oils such as olive oil typically contain both mono- and polyunsaturated fatty acids.

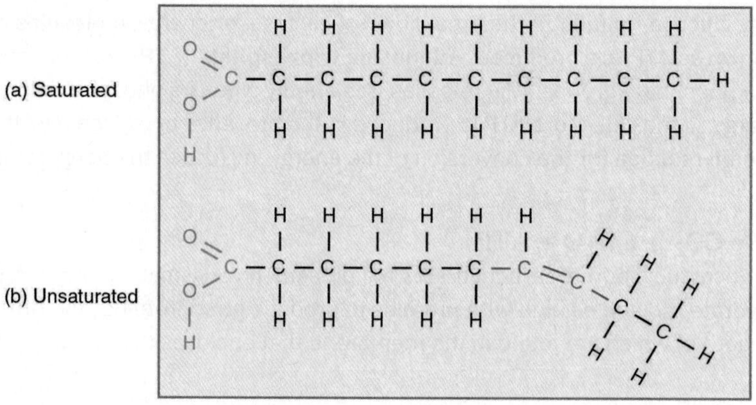

FIGURE 2.22 **Fatty Acid Shapes**   The level of saturation of a fatty acid affects its shape. (a) Saturated fatty acid chains are straight. (b) Unsaturated fatty acid chains are kinked.

Whereas a diet high in saturated fatty acids increases the risk of heart disease, a diet high in unsaturated fatty acids is thought to reduce the risk. This is especially true for the omega-3 unsaturated fatty acids found in cold-water fish such as salmon. These fatty acids have their first double carbon bond at the third hydrocarbon from the methyl group (referred to as the omega end of the molecule).

Finally, *trans* fatty acids found in some processed foods, including some stick and tub margarines, are thought to be even more harmful to the heart and blood vessels than saturated fatty acids. *Trans* fats are created from unsaturated fatty acids (such as corn oil) when chemically treated to produce partially hydrogenated fats.

As a group, triglycerides are a major fuel source for the body. When you are resting or asleep, a majority of the energy used to keep you alive is derived from triglycerides stored in your fat (adipose) tissues. Triglycerides also fuel long, slow physical activity such as gardening or hiking, and contribute a modest percentage of energy for vigorous physical activity. Dietary fat also assists the absorption and transport of the nonpolar fat-soluble vitamins A, D, E, and K. Additionally, stored body fat protects and cushions the body's bones and internal organs, and acts as insulation to retain body heat.

Fatty acids are also components of glycolipids, which are sugar-fat compounds found in the cell membrane. Lipoproteins are compounds in which the hydrophobic triglycerides are packaged in protein envelopes for transport in body fluids.

Phospholipids

As its name suggests, a **phospholipid** is a bond between the glycerol component of a lipid and a phosphorous molecule. In fact, phospholipids are similar in structure to triglycerides. However, instead of having three fatty acids, a phospholipid is generated from a diglyceride, a glycerol with just two fatty acid chains (Figure 2.23). The third binding site on the glycerol is taken up by the phosphate group, which in turn is attached to a polar "head" region of the molecule. Recall that triglycerides are nonpolar and hydrophobic. This still holds for the fatty acid portion of a phospholipid compound. However, the head of a phospholipid contains charges on the phosphate groups, as well as on the nitrogen atom. These charges make the phospholipid head hydrophilic. Therefore, phospholipids are said to have hydrophobic tails, containing the neutral fatty acids, and hydrophilic heads, containing the charged phosphate groups and nitrogen atom.

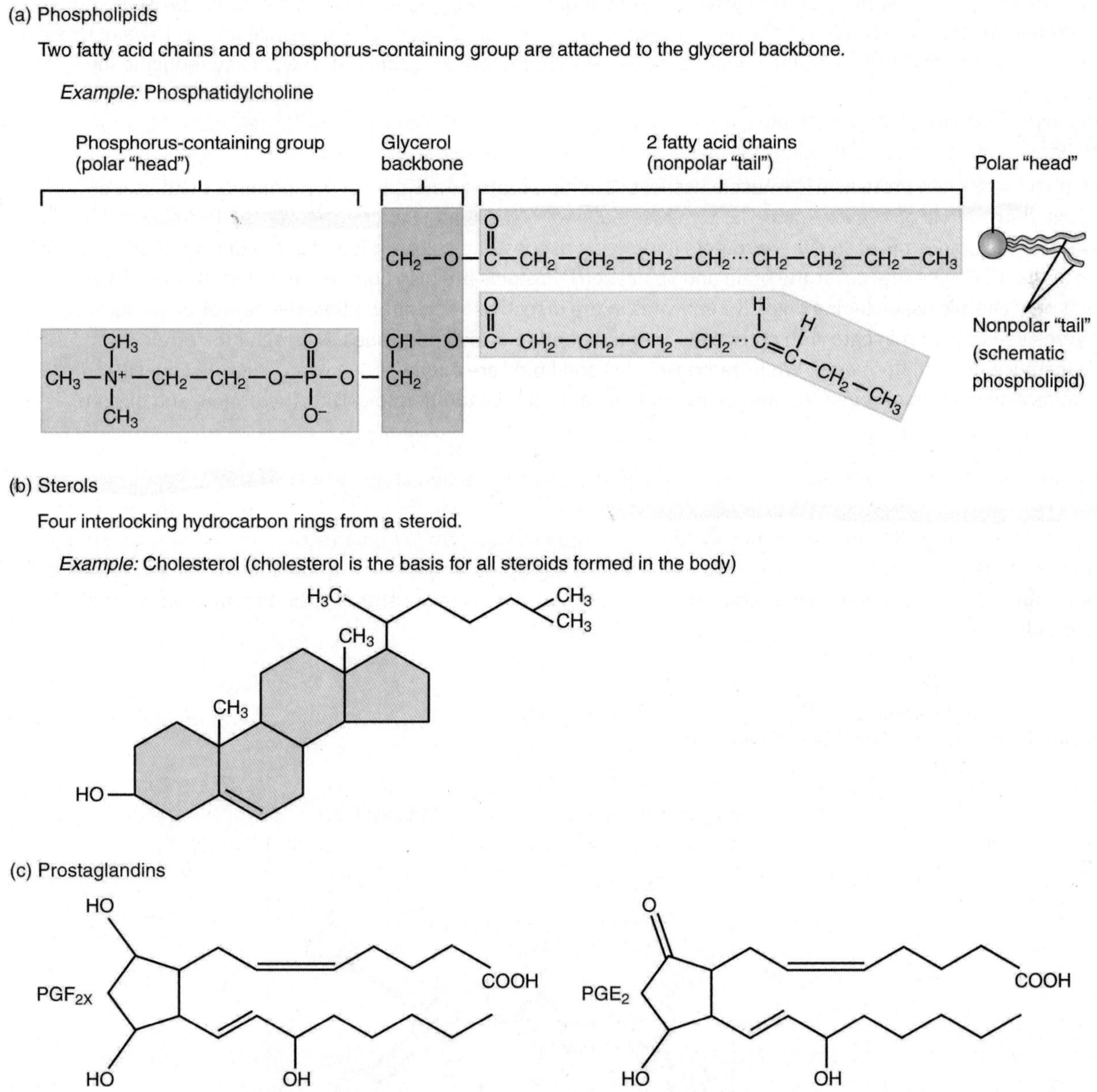

(a) Phospholipids

Two fatty acid chains and a phosphorus-containing group are attached to the glycerol backbone.

Example: Phosphatidylcholine

(b) Sterols

Four interlocking hydrocarbon rings from a steroid.

Example: Cholesterol (cholesterol is the basis for all steroids formed in the body)

(c) Prostaglandins

FIGURE 2.23 Other Important Lipids   (a) Phospholipids are composed of two fatty acids, glycerol, and a phosphate group. (b) Sterols are ring-shaped lipids. Shown here is cholesterol. (c) Prostaglandins are derived from unsaturated fatty acids. Prostaglandin E2 (PGE2) includes hydroxyl and carboxyl groups.

Steroids

A **steroid** compound (referred to as a sterol) has as its foundation a set of four hydrocarbon rings bonded to a variety of other atoms and molecules (see Figure 2.23b). Although both plants and animals synthesize sterols, the type that makes the most important contribution to human structure and function is cholesterol, which is synthesized by the liver in humans and animals and is also present in most animal-based foods. Like other lipids, cholesterol's hydrocarbons make it hydrophobic; however, it has a polar hydroxyl head that is hydrophilic. Cholesterol is an important component of bile acids, compounds that help emulsify dietary fats. In fact, the word root chole- refers to bile. Cholesterol is also a building block of many hormones, signaling molecules that the body releases to regulate processes at distant sites. Finally, like phospholipids, cholesterol molecules are found in the cell membrane, where their hydrophobic and hydrophilic regions help regulate the flow of substances into and out of the cell.

Prostaglandins

Like a hormone, a **prostaglandin** is one of a group of signaling molecules, but prostaglandins are derived from unsaturated fatty acids (see Figure 2.23c). One reason that the omega-3 fatty acids found in fish are beneficial is that they stimulate the production of certain prostaglandins that help regulate aspects of blood pressure and inflammation, and thereby reduce the risk for heart disease. Prostaglandins also sensitize nerves to pain. One class of pain-relieving medications called nonsteroidal anti-inflammatory drugs (NSAIDs) works by reducing the effects of prostaglandins.

Proteins

You might associate proteins with muscle tissue, but in fact, proteins are critical components of all tissues and organs. A **protein** is an organic molecule composed of amino acids linked by peptide bonds. Proteins include the keratin in the epidermis of skin that protects underlying tissues, the collagen found in the dermis of skin, in bones, and in the meninges that cover the brain and spinal cord. Proteins are also components of many of the body's functional chemicals, including digestive enzymes in the digestive tract, antibodies, the neurotransmitters that neurons use to communicate with other cells, and the peptide-based hormones that regulate certain body functions (for instance, growth hormone). While carbohydrates and lipids are composed of hydrocarbons and oxygen, all proteins also contain nitrogen (N), and many contain sulfur (S), in addition to carbon, hydrogen, and oxygen.

Microstructure of Proteins

Proteins are polymers made up of nitrogen-containing monomers called amino acids. An **amino acid** is a molecule composed of an amino group and a carboxyl group, together with a variable side chain. Just 20 different amino acids contribute to nearly all of the thousands of different proteins important in human structure and function. Body proteins contain a unique combination of a few dozen to a few hundred of these 20 amino acid monomers. All 20 of these amino acids share a similar structure (Figure 2.24). All consist of a central carbon atom to which the following are bonded:

- a hydrogen atom
- an alkaline (basic) amino group NH_2 (see Table 2.1)
- an acidic carboxyl group COOH (see Table 2.1)
- a variable group

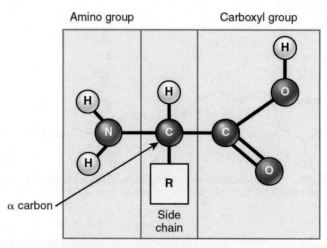

FIGURE 2.24   Structure of an Amino Acid

Notice that all amino acids contain both an acid (the carboxyl group) and a base (the amino group) (amine = "nitrogen-containing"). For this reason, they make excellent buffers, helping the body regulate acid–base balance. What distinguishes the 20 amino acids from one another is their variable group, which is referred to as a side chain or an R-group. This group can vary in size and can be polar or nonpolar, giving each amino acid its unique characteristics. For example, the side chains of two amino acids—cysteine and methionine—contain sulfur. Sulfur does not readily participate in hydrogen bonds, whereas all other amino acids do. This variation influences the way that proteins containing cysteine and methionine are assembled.

Amino acids join via dehydration synthesis to form protein polymers (Figure 2.25). The unique bond holding amino acids together is called a peptide bond. A **peptide bond** is a covalent bond between two amino acids that forms by dehydration synthesis. A peptide, in fact, is a very short chain of amino acids. Strands containing fewer than about 100 amino acids are generally referred to as polypeptides rather than proteins.

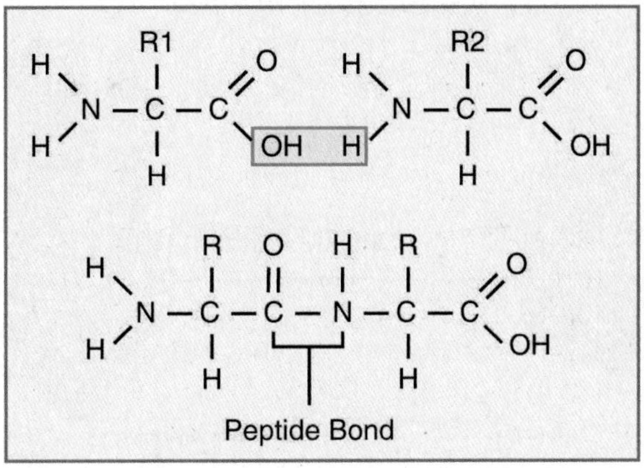

FIGURE 2.25 Peptide Bond   Different amino acids join together to form peptides, polypeptides, or proteins via dehydration synthesis. The bonds between the amino acids are peptide bonds R1 and R2 may be the same or different side chains.

The body is able to synthesize most of the amino acids from components of other molecules; however, nine cannot be synthesized and have to be consumed in the diet. These are known as the essential amino acids.

Free amino acids available for protein construction are said to reside in the amino acid pool within cells. Structures within cells use these amino acids when assembling proteins. If a particular essential amino acid is not available in sufficient quantities in the amino acid pool, however, synthesis of proteins containing it can slow or even cease.

Shape of Proteins

Just as a fork cannot be used to eat soup and a spoon cannot be used to spear meat, a protein's shape is essential to its function. A protein's shape is determined, most fundamentally, by the sequence of amino acids of which it is made (Figure 2.26**a**). The sequence is called the primary structure of the protein.

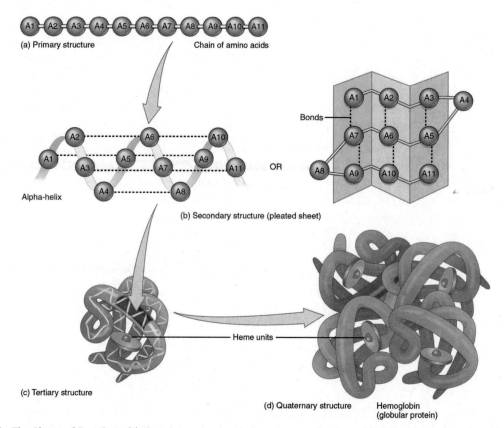

(a) Primary structure   Chain of amino acids

Alpha-helix

OR

Bonds

(b) Secondary structure (pleated sheet)

Heme units

(c) Tertiary structure

(d) Quaternary structure   Hemoglobin (globular protein)

FIGURE 2.26   The Shape of Proteins   (a) The primary structure is the sequence of amino acids that make up the polypeptide chain. (b) The secondary structure, which can take the form of an alpha-helix or a beta-pleated sheet, is maintained by hydrogen bonds between amino acids in different regions of the original polypeptide strand. (c) The tertiary structure occurs as a result of further folding and bonding of the secondary structure. (d) The quaternary structure occurs as a result of interactions between two or more tertiary subunits. The example shown here is hemoglobin, a protein in red blood cells which transports oxygen to body tissues.

Although some polypeptides exist as linear chains, most are twisted or folded into more complex secondary structures that form when bonding occurs between amino acids with different properties at different regions of the polypeptide. The most common secondary structure is a spiral called an alpha-helix. If you were to take a length of string and simply twist it into a spiral, it would not hold the shape. Similarly, a strand of amino acids could not maintain a stable spiral shape without the help of hydrogen bonds, which create bridges between different regions of the same strand (see Figure 2.26**b**). Less commonly, a polypeptide chain can form a beta-pleated sheet, in which hydrogen bonds form bridges between different regions of a single polypeptide that has folded back upon itself, or between two or more adjacent polypeptide chains.

The secondary structure of proteins further folds into a compact three-dimensional shape, referred to as the protein's tertiary structure (see Figure 2.26**c**). In this configuration, amino acids that had been very distant in the primary chain can be brought quite close via hydrogen bonds or, in proteins containing cysteine, via disulfide bonds. A **disulfide bond** is a covalent bond between sulfur atoms in a polypeptide. Often, two or more separate polypeptides bond to form an even larger protein with a quaternary structure (see Figure 2.26**d**). The polypeptide subunits forming a quaternary structure can be identical or different. For instance, hemoglobin, the protein found in red blood cells is composed of four tertiary polypeptides, two of which are called alpha chains and two of which are called beta chains.

When they are exposed to extreme heat, acids, bases, and certain other substances, proteins will denature. **Denaturation** is a change in the structure of a molecule through physical or chemical means. Denatured proteins lose their functional shape and are no longer able to carry out their jobs. An everyday example of protein denaturation is the curdling of milk when acidic lemon juice is added.

The contribution of the shape of a protein to its function can hardly be exaggerated. For example, the long, slender shape of protein strands that make up muscle tissue is essential to their ability to contract (shorten) and relax (lengthen). As another example, bones contain long threads of a protein called collagen that acts as scaffolding upon which bone minerals are deposited. These elongated proteins, called fibrous proteins, are strong and durable and typically hydrophobic.

In contrast, globular proteins are globes or spheres that tend to be highly reactive and are hydrophilic. The hemoglobin proteins packed into red blood cells are an example (see Figure 2.26d); however, globular proteins are abundant throughout the body, playing critical roles in most body functions. Enzymes, introduced earlier as protein catalysts, are examples of this. The next section takes a closer look at the action of enzymes.

Proteins Function as Enzymes

If you were trying to type a paper, and every time you hit a key on your laptop there was a delay of six or seven minutes before you got a response, you would probably get a new laptop. In a similar way, without enzymes to catalyze chemical reactions, the human body would be nonfunctional. It functions only because enzymes function.

Enzymatic reactions—chemical reactions catalyzed by enzymes—begin when substrates bind to the enzyme. A **substrate** is a reactant in an enzymatic reaction. This occurs on regions of the enzyme known as active sites (Figure 2.27). Any given enzyme catalyzes just one type of chemical reaction. This characteristic, called specificity, is due to the fact that a substrate with a particular shape and electrical charge can bind only to an active site corresponding to that substrate.

Due to this jigsaw puzzle-like match between an enzyme and its substrates, enzymes are known for their specificity. In fact, as an enzyme binds to its substrate(s), the enzyme structure changes slightly to find the best fit between the transition state (a structural intermediate between the substrate and product) and the active site, just as a rubber glove molds to a hand inserted into it. This active-site modification in the presence of substrate, along with the simultaneous formation of the transition state, is called induced fit. Overall, there is a specifically matched enzyme for each substrate and, thus, for each chemical reaction; however, there is some flexibility as well. Some enzymes have the ability to act on several different structurally related substrates.

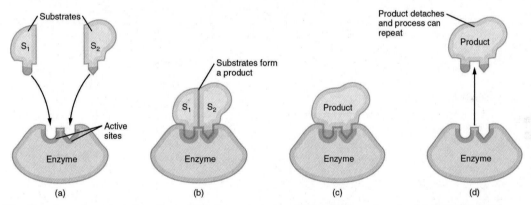

FIGURE 2.27 Steps in an Enzymatic Reaction   According to the induced-fit model, the active site of the enzyme undergoes conformational changes upon binding with the substrate.(a) Substrates approach active sites on enzyme. (b) Substrates bind to active sites, producing an enzyme–substrate complex. (c) Changes internal to the enzyme–substrate complex facilitate interaction of the substrates. (d) Products are released and the enzyme returns to its original form, ready to facilitate another enzymatic reaction.

Binding of a substrate produces an enzyme–substrate complex. It is likely that enzymes speed up chemical reactions in part because the enzyme–substrate complex undergoes a set of temporary and reversible changes that cause the substrates to be oriented toward each other in an optimal position to facilitate their interaction. This promotes increased reaction speed. The enzyme then releases the product(s), and resumes its original shape. The enzyme is then free to engage in the process again, and will do so as long as substrate remains.

Other Functions of Proteins

Advertisements for protein bars, powders, and shakes all say that protein is important in building, repairing, and maintaining muscle tissue, but the truth is that proteins contribute to all body tissues, from the skin to the brain cells. Also, certain proteins act as hormones, chemical messengers that help regulate body functions, For example, growth hormone is important for skeletal growth, among other roles.

As was noted earlier, the basic and acidic components enable proteins to function as buffers in maintaining acid–base balance, but they also help regulate fluid–electrolyte balance. Proteins attract fluid, and a healthy concentration of proteins in the blood, the cells, and the spaces between cells helps ensure a balance of fluids in these various "compartments." Moreover, proteins in the cell membrane help to transport electrolytes in and out of the cell, keeping these ions in a healthy balance. Like lipids, proteins can bind with carbohydrates. They can thereby produce glycoproteins or proteoglycans, both of which have many functions in the body.

The body can use proteins for energy when carbohydrate and fat intake is inadequate, and stores of glycogen and adipose tissue become depleted. However, since there is no storage site for protein except functional tissues, using protein for energy causes tissue breakdown, and results in body wasting.

Nucleotides

The fourth type of organic compound important to human structure and function are the nucleotides (Figure 2.28). A **nucleotide** is one of a class of organic compounds composed of three subunits:

- one or more phosphate groups
- a pentose sugar: either deoxyribose or ribose
- a nitrogen-containing base: adenine, cytosine, guanine, thymine, or uracil

Nucleotides can be assembled into nucleic acids (DNA or RNA) or the energy compound adenosine triphosphate.

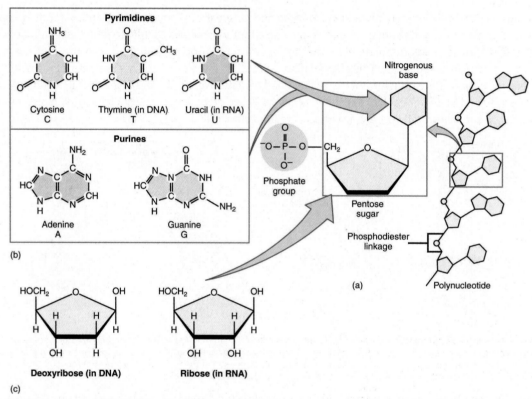

FIGURE 2.28 Nucleotides (a) The building blocks of all nucleotides are one or more phosphate groups, a pentose sugar, and a nitrogen-containing base. (b) The nitrogen-containing bases of nucleotides. (c) The two pentose sugars of DNA and RNA.

Nucleic Acids

The nucleic acids differ in their type of pentose sugar. **Deoxyribonucleic acid (DNA)** is nucleotide that stores genetic information. DNA contains deoxyribose (so-called because it has one less atom of oxygen than ribose) plus one phosphate group and one nitrogen-containing base. The "choices" of base for DNA are adenine, cytosine, guanine, and thymine. **Ribonucleic acid (RNA)** is a ribose-containing nucleotide that helps manifest the genetic code as protein. RNA contains ribose, one phosphate group, and one nitrogen-containing base, but the "choices" of base for RNA are adenine, cytosine, guanine, and uracil.

The nitrogen-containing bases adenine and guanine are classified as purines. A **purine** is a nitrogen-containing molecule with a double ring structure, which accommodates several nitrogen atoms. The bases cytosine, thymine (found in DNA only) and uracil (found in RNA only) are pyramidines. A **pyramidine** is a nitrogen-containing base with

Access for free at openstax.org

a single ring structure

Bonds formed by dehydration synthesis between the pentose sugar of one nucleic acid monomer and the phosphate group of another form a "backbone," from which the components' nitrogen-containing bases protrude. In DNA, two such backbones attach at their protruding bases via hydrogen bonds. These twist to form a shape known as a double helix (Figure 2.29). The sequence of nitrogen-containing bases within a strand of DNA form the genes that act as a molecular code instructing cells in the assembly of amino acids into proteins. Humans have almost 22,000 genes in their DNA, locked up in the 46 chromosomes inside the nucleus of each cell (except red blood cells which lose their nuclei during development). These genes carry the genetic code to build one's body, and are unique for each individual except identical twins.

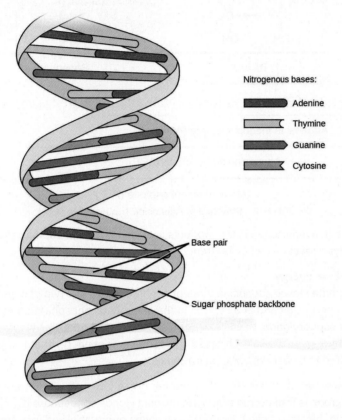

Nitrogenous bases:

Adenine

Thymine

Guanine

Cytosine

Base pair

Sugar phosphate backbone

FIGURE 2.29   **DNA**   In the DNA double helix, two strands attach via hydrogen bonds between the bases of the component nucleotides.

In contrast, RNA consists of a single strand of sugar-phosphate backbone studded with bases. Messenger RNA (mRNA) is created during protein synthesis to carry the genetic instructions from the DNA to the cell's protein manufacturing plants in the cytoplasm, the ribosomes.

Adenosine Triphosphate

The nucleotide adenosine triphosphate (ATP), is composed of a ribose sugar, an adenine base, and three phosphate groups (Figure 2.30). ATP is classified as a high energy compound because the two covalent bonds linking its three phosphates store a significant amount of potential energy. In the body, the energy released from these high energy bonds helps fuel the body's activities, from muscle contraction to the transport of substances in and out of cells to anabolic chemical reactions.

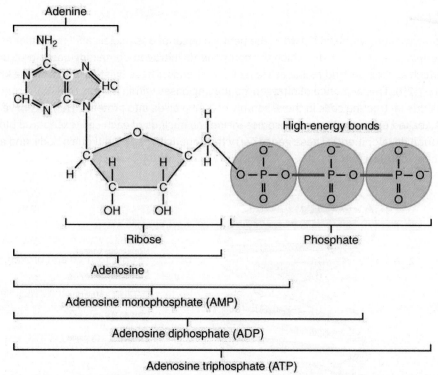

FIGURE 2.30   Structure of Adenosine Triphosphate (ATP)

When a phosphate group is cleaved from ATP, the products are adenosine diphosphate (ADP) and inorganic phosphate (P_i). This hydrolysis reaction can be written:

$$ATP + H_2O \rightarrow ADP + P_i + energy$$

Removal of a second phosphate leaves adenosine monophosphate (AMP) and two phosphate groups. Again, these reactions also liberate the energy that had been stored in the phosphate-phosphate bonds. They are reversible, too, as when ADP undergoes phosphorylation. **Phosphorylation** is the addition of a phosphate group to an organic compound, in this case, resulting in ATP. In such cases, the same level of energy that had been released during hydrolysis must be reinvested to power dehydration synthesis.

Cells can also transfer a phosphate group from ATP to another organic compound. For example, when glucose first enters a cell, a phosphate group is transferred from ATP, forming glucose phosphate ($C_6H_{12}O_6$—P) and ADP. Once glucose is phosphorylated in this way, it can be stored as glycogen or metabolized for immediate energy.

Key Terms

acid   compound that releases hydrogen ions (H^+) in solution

activation energy   amount of energy greater than the energy contained in the reactants, which must be overcome for a reaction to proceed

adenosine triphosphate (ATP)   nucleotide containing ribose and an adenine base that is essential in energy transfer

amino acid   building block of proteins; characterized by an amino and carboxyl functional groups and a variable side-chain

anion   atom with a negative charge

atom   smallest unit of an element that retains the unique properties of that element

atomic number   number of protons in the nucleus of an atom

base   compound that accepts hydrogen ions (H^+) in solution

bond   electrical force linking atoms

buffer   solution containing a weak acid or a weak base that opposes wide fluctuations in the pH of body fluids

carbohydrate   class of organic compounds built from sugars, molecules containing carbon, hydrogen, and oxygen in a 1-2-1 ratio

catalyst   substance that increases the rate of a chemical reaction without itself being changed in the process

cation   atom with a positive charge

chemical energy   form of energy that is absorbed as chemical bonds form, stored as they are maintained, and released as they are broken

colloid   liquid mixture in which the solute particles consist of clumps of molecules large enough to scatter light

compound   substance composed of two or more different elements joined by chemical bonds

concentration   number of particles within a given space

covalent bond   chemical bond in which two atoms share electrons, thereby completing their valence shells

decomposition reaction   type of catabolic reaction in which one or more bonds within a larger molecule are broken, resulting in the release of smaller molecules or atoms

denaturation   change in the structure of a molecule through physical or chemical means

deoxyribonucleic acid (DNA)   deoxyribose-containing nucleotide that stores genetic information

disaccharide   pair of carbohydrate monomers bonded by dehydration synthesis via a glycosidic bond

disulfide bond   covalent bond formed within a polypeptide between sulfide groups of sulfur-containing amino acids, for example, cysteine

electron   subatomic particle having a negative charge and nearly no mass; found orbiting the atom's nucleus

electron shell   area of space a given distance from an atom's nucleus in which electrons are grouped

element   substance that cannot be created or broken down by ordinary chemical means

enzyme   protein or RNA that catalyzes chemical reactions

exchange reaction   type of chemical reaction in which bonds are both formed and broken, resulting in the transfer of components

functional group   group of atoms linked by strong covalent bonds that tends to behave as a distinct unit in chemical reactions with other atoms

hydrogen bond   dipole-dipole bond in which a hydrogen atom covalently bonded to an electronegative atom is weakly attracted to a second electronegative atom

inorganic compound   substance that does not contain both carbon and hydrogen

ion   atom with an overall positive or negative charge

ionic bond   attraction between an anion and a cation

isotope   one of the variations of an element in which the number of neutrons differ from each other

kinetic energy   energy that matter possesses because of its motion

lipid   class of nonpolar organic compounds built from hydrocarbons and distinguished by the fact that they are not soluble in water

macromolecule   large molecule formed by covalent bonding

mass number   sum of the number of protons and neutrons in the nucleus of an atom

matter   physical substance; that which occupies space and has mass

molecule   two or more atoms covalently bonded together

monosaccharide   monomer of carbohydrate; also known as a simple sugar

neutron   heavy subatomic particle having no electrical charge and found in the atom's nucleus

nucleotide   class of organic compounds composed of one or more phosphate groups, a pentose sugar, and a base

organic compound   substance that contains both carbon and hydrogen

peptide bond   covalent bond formed by dehydration synthesis between two amino acids

periodic table of the elements   arrangement of the elements in a table according to their atomic number; elements having similar properties because of their electron arrangements compose columns in the table, while elements having the same number of valence shells compose rows in the table

pH   negative logarithm of the hydrogen ion (H^+) concentration of a solution

phospholipid   a lipid compound in which a phosphate group is combined with a diglyceride

phosphorylation   addition of one or more phosphate groups to an organic compound

polar molecule   molecule with regions that have opposite charges resulting from uneven numbers of electrons in the nuclei of the atoms participating in the covalent bond

polysaccharide   compound consisting of more than two carbohydrate monomers bonded by dehydration synthesis via glycosidic bonds

potential energy   stored energy matter possesses because of the positioning or structure of its components

product   one or more substances produced by a chemical reaction

prostaglandin   lipid compound derived from fatty acid chains and important in regulating several body processes

protein   class of organic compounds that are composed of many amino acids linked together by peptide bonds

proton   heavy subatomic particle having a positive charge and found in the atom's nucleus

purine   nitrogen-containing base with a double ring structure; adenine and guanine

pyrimidine   nitrogen-containing base with a single ring structure; cytosine, thiamine, and uracil

radioactive isotope   unstable, heavy isotope that gives off subatomic particles, or electromagnetic energy, as it decays; also called radioisotopes

reactant   one or more substances that enter into the reaction

ribonucleic acid (RNA)   ribose-containing nucleotide that helps manifest the genetic code as protein

solution   homogeneous liquid mixture in which a solute is dissolved into molecules within a solvent

steroid   (also, sterol) lipid compound composed of four hydrocarbon rings bonded to a variety of other atoms and molecules

substrate   reactant in an enzymatic reaction

suspension   liquid mixture in which particles distributed in the liquid settle out over time

synthesis reaction   type of anabolic reaction in which two or more atoms or molecules bond, resulting in the formation of a larger molecule

triglyceride   lipid compound composed of a glycerol molecule bonded with three fatty acid chains

valence shell   outermost electron shell of an atom

Chapter Review

2.1 Elements and Atoms: The Building Blocks of Matter

The human body is composed of elements, the most abundant of which are oxygen (O), carbon (C), hydrogen (H) and nitrogen (N). You obtain these elements from the foods you eat and the air you breathe. The smallest unit of an element that retains all of the properties of that element is an atom. But, atoms themselves contain many subatomic particles, the three most important of which are protons, neutrons, and electrons. These particles do not vary in quality from one element to another; rather, what gives an element its distinctive identification is the quantity of its protons, called its atomic number. Protons and neutrons contribute nearly all of an atom's mass; the number of protons and neutrons is an element's mass number. Heavier and lighter versions of the same element can occur in nature because these versions have different numbers of neutrons. Different versions of an element are called isotopes.

The tendency of an atom to be stable or to react readily with other atoms is largely due to the behavior of the electrons within the atom's outermost electron shell, called its valence shell. Helium, as well as larger atoms with eight electrons in their valence shell, is unlikely to participate in chemical reactions because they are stable. All other atoms tend to accept, donate, or share electrons in a process that brings the electrons in their valence shell to eight (or in the case of hydrogen, to two).

2.2 Chemical Bonds

Each moment of life, atoms of oxygen, carbon, hydrogen, and the other elements of the human body are making and breaking chemical bonds. Ions are charged atoms that form when an atom donates or accepts one or more negatively charged electrons. Cations (ions with a positive charge) are attracted to anions (ions with a negative charge). This attraction is called an ionic bond. In covalent bonds, the participating atoms do not lose or gain electrons, but rather share them. Molecules with nonpolar covalent bonds are electrically balanced, and have a linear three-dimensional shape. Molecules with polar covalent bonds have "poles"—regions of weakly positive and negative charge—and have a triangular three-dimensional shape. An atom of oxygen and two atoms of hydrogen form water molecules by means of polar covalent bonds. Hydrogen bonds link hydrogen atoms already participating in polar covalent bonds to anions or electronegative regions of other polar molecules. Hydrogen bonds link water molecules, resulting in the properties of water that are important to living things.

2.3 Chemical Reactions

Chemical reactions, in which chemical bonds are broken and formed, require an initial investment of energy. Kinetic energy, the energy of matter in motion, fuels the collisions of atoms, ions, and molecules that are necessary if their old bonds are to break and new ones to form. All molecules store potential energy, which is released when their bonds are broken.

Four forms of energy essential to human functioning are: chemical energy, which is stored and released as chemical bonds are formed and broken; mechanical energy, which directly powers physical activity; radiant energy, emitted as waves such as in sunlight; and electrical energy, the power of moving electrons.

Chemical reactions begin with reactants and end with products. Synthesis reactions bond reactants together, a process that requires energy, whereas decomposition reactions break the bonds within a reactant and thereby release energy. In exchange reactions, bonds are both broken and formed, and energy is exchanged.

The rate at which chemical reactions occur is influenced by several properties of the reactants: temperature, concentration and pressure, and the presence or absence of a catalyst. An enzyme is a catalytic protein that speeds up chemical reactions in the human body.

2.4 Inorganic Compounds Essential to Human Functioning

Inorganic compounds essential to human functioning include water, salts, acids, and bases. These compounds are inorganic; that is, they do not contain both hydrogen and carbon. Water is a lubricant and cushion, a heat sink, a component of liquid mixtures, a byproduct of dehydration synthesis reactions, and a reactant in hydrolysis reactions. Salts are compounds that, when dissolved in water, dissociate into ions other than H^+ or OH^-. In contrast, acids release H^+ in solution, making it more acidic. Bases accept H^+, thereby making the solution more alkaline (caustic).

The pH of any solution is its relative concentration of H^+. A solution with pH 7 is neutral. Solutions with pH below 7 are acids, and solutions with pH above 7 are bases. A change in a single digit on the pH scale (e.g., from 7 to 8) represents a ten-fold increase or decrease in the concentration of H^+. In a healthy adult, the pH of blood ranges from 7.35 to 7.45. Homeostatic control mechanisms important for keeping blood in a healthy pH range include chemicals called buffers, weak acids and weak bases released when the pH of blood or other body fluids fluctuates in either direction outside of this normal range.

2.5 Organic Compounds Essential to Human Functioning

Organic compounds essential to human functioning include carbohydrates, lipids, proteins, and nucleotides. These compounds are said to be organic because they contain both carbon and hydrogen. Carbon atoms in organic compounds readily share electrons with hydrogen and other atoms, usually oxygen, and sometimes nitrogen. Carbon atoms also may bond with one or more functional groups such as carboxyls, hydroxyls, aminos, or phosphates. Monomers are single units of organic compounds. They bond by dehydration synthesis to form polymers, which can in turn be broken by hydrolysis.

Carbohydrate compounds provide essential body fuel. Their structural forms include monosaccharides such as glucose, disaccharides such as lactose, and polysaccharides, including starches (polymers of glucose), glycogen (the storage form of glucose), and fiber. All body cells can use glucose for fuel. It is converted via an oxidation-reduction reaction to ATP.

Lipids are hydrophobic compounds that provide body fuel and are important components of many biological compounds. Triglycerides are the most abundant lipid in the body, and are composed of a glycerol backbone attached to three fatty acid chains. Phospholipids are compounds composed of a diglyceride with a phosphate group attached at the molecule's head. The result is a molecule with polar and nonpolar regions. Steroids are lipids formed of four hydrocarbon rings. The most important is cholesterol. Prostaglandins are signaling molecules derived from unsaturated fatty acids.

Proteins are critical components of all body tissues. They are made up of monomers called amino acids, which contain nitrogen, joined by peptide bonds. Protein shape is critical to its function. Most body proteins are globular. An example is enzymes, which catalyze chemical reactions.

Nucleotides are compounds with three building blocks: one or more phosphate groups, a pentose sugar, and a nitrogen-containing base. DNA and RNA are nucleic acids that function in protein synthesis. ATP is the body's fundamental molecule of energy transfer. Removal or addition of phosphates releases or invests energy.

Interactive Link Questions

1. Visit this website (http://openstax.org/l/ptable) to view the periodic table. In the periodic table of the elements, elements in a single column have the same number of electrons that can participate in a chemical reaction. These electrons are known as "valence electrons." For example, the elements in the first column all have a single valence electron—an electron that can be "donated" in a chemical reaction with another atom. What is the meaning of a mass number shown in parentheses?

2. Visit this website (http://openstax.org/l/electenergy) to learn about electrical energy and the attraction/repulsion of charges. What happens to the charged electroscope when a conductor is moved between its plastic sheets, and why?

3. Watch this video (http://openstax.org/l/disaccharide) to observe the formation of a disaccharide. What happens when water encounters a glycosidic bond?

Review Questions

4. Together, just four elements make up more than 95 percent of the body's mass. These include _____.
   a. calcium, magnesium, iron, and carbon
   b. oxygen, calcium, iron, and nitrogen
   c. sodium, chlorine, carbon, and hydrogen
   d. oxygen, carbon, hydrogen, and nitrogen

5. The smallest unit of an element that still retains the distinctive behavior of that element is an _____.
   a. electron
   b. atom
   c. elemental particle
   d. isotope

6. The characteristic that gives an element its distinctive properties is its number of _____.
   a. protons
   b. neutrons
   c. electrons
   d. atoms

7. On the periodic table of the elements, mercury (Hg) has an atomic number of 80 and a mass number of 200.59. It has seven stable isotopes. The most abundant of these probably have _____.
   a. about 80 neutrons each
   b. fewer than 80 neutrons each
   c. more than 80 neutrons each
   d. more electrons than neutrons

8. Nitrogen has an atomic number of seven. How many electron shells does it likely have?
   a. one
   b. two
   c. three
   d. four

9. Which of the following is a molecule, but not a compound?
   a. H_2O
   b. ^2H
   c. H_2
   d. H^+

10. A molecule of ammonia contains one atom of nitrogen and three atoms of hydrogen. These are linked with _____.
    a. ionic bonds
    b. nonpolar covalent bonds
    c. polar covalent bonds
    d. hydrogen bonds

11. When an atom donates an electron to another atom, it becomes
    a. an ion
    b. an anion
    c. nonpolar
    d. all of the above

12. A substance formed of crystals of equal numbers of cations and anions held together by ionic bonds is called a(n) _____.
    a. noble gas
    b. salt
    c. electrolyte
    d. dipole

13. Which of the following statements about chemical bonds is true?
    a. Covalent bonds are stronger than ionic bonds.
    b. Hydrogen bonds occur between two atoms of hydrogen.
    c. Bonding readily occurs between nonpolar and polar molecules.
    d. A molecule of water is unlikely to bond with an ion.

14. The energy stored in a foot of snow on a steep roof is _____.
    a. potential energy
    b. kinetic energy
    c. radiant energy
    d. activation energy

15. The bonding of calcium, phosphorus, and other elements produces mineral crystals that are found in bone. This is an example of a(n) _____ reaction.
    a. catabolic
    b. synthesis
    c. decomposition
    d. exchange

16. $AB \rightarrow A + B$ is a general notation for a(n) _____ reaction.
    a. anabolic
    b. endergonic
    c. decomposition
    d. exchange

17. _____ reactions release energy.
    a. Catabolic
    b. Exergonic
    c. Decomposition
    d. Catabolic, exergonic, and decomposition

18. Which of the following combinations of atoms is *most likely* to result in a chemical reaction?
    a. hydrogen and hydrogen
    b. hydrogen and helium
    c. helium and helium
    d. neon and helium

19. Chewing a bite of bread mixes it with saliva and facilitates its chemical breakdown. This is *most likely* due to the fact that _____.
    a. the inside of the mouth maintains a very high temperature
    b. chewing stores potential energy
    c. chewing facilitates synthesis reactions
    d. saliva contains enzymes

20. CH_4 is methane. This compound is _____.
    a. inorganic
    b. organic
    c. reactive
    d. a crystal

21. Which of the following is most likely to be found evenly distributed in water in a homogeneous solution?
    a. sodium ions and chloride ions
    b. NaCl molecules
    c. salt crystals
    d. red blood cells

22. Jenny mixes up a batch of pancake batter, then stirs in some chocolate chips. As she is waiting for the first few pancakes to cook, she notices the chocolate chips sinking to the bottom of the clear glass mixing bowl. The chocolate-chip batter is an example of a _____.
    a. solvent
    b. solute
    c. solution
    d. suspension

23. A substance dissociates into K^+ and Cl^- in solution. The substance is a(n) _____.
    a. acid
    b. base
    c. salt
    d. buffer

24. Ty is three years old and as a result of a "stomach bug" has been vomiting for about 24 hours. His blood pH is 7.48. What does this mean?
    a. Ty's blood is slightly acidic.
    b. Ty's blood is slightly alkaline.
    c. Ty's blood is highly acidic.
    d. Ty's blood is within the normal range

25. $C_6H_{12}O_6$ is the chemical formula for a _____.
    a. polymer of carbohydrate
    b. pentose monosaccharide
    c. hexose monosaccharide
    d. all of the above

26. What organic compound do brain cells primarily rely on for fuel?
    a. glucose
    b. glycogen
    c. galactose
    d. glycerol

27. Which of the following is a functional group that is part of a building block of proteins?
    a. phosphate
    b. adenine
    c. amino
    d. ribose

28. A pentose sugar is a part of the monomer used to build which type of macromolecule?
    a. polysaccharides
    b. nucleic acids
    c. phosphorylated glucose
    d. glycogen

29. A phospholipid _____.
    a. has both polar and nonpolar regions
    b. is made up of a triglyceride bonded to a phosphate group
    c. is a building block of ATP
    d. can donate both cations and anions in solution

30. In DNA, nucleotide bonding forms a compound with a characteristic shape known as a(n) _____.
    a. beta chain
    b. pleated sheet
    c. alpha helix
    d. double helix

31. Uracil _____.
    a. contains nitrogen
    b. is a pyrimidine
    c. is found in RNA
    d. all of the above

32. The ability of an enzyme's active sites to bind only substrates of compatible shape and charge is known as _____.
    a. selectivity
    b. specificity
    c. subjectivity
    d. specialty

Critical Thinking Questions

33. The most abundant elements in the foods and beverages you consume are oxygen, carbon, hydrogen, and nitrogen. Why might having these elements in consumables be useful?

34. Oxygen, whose atomic number is eight, has three stable isotopes: ^{16}O, ^{17}O, and ^{18}O. Explain what this means in terms of the number of protons and neutrons.

35. Magnesium is an important element in the human body, especially in bones. Magnesium's atomic number is 12. Is it stable or reactive? Why? If it were to react with another atom, would it be more likely to accept or to donate one or more electrons?

36. Explain why CH_4 is one of the most common molecules found in nature. Are the bonds between the atoms ionic or covalent?

37. In a hurry one day, you merely rinse your lunch dishes with water. As you are drying your salad bowl, you notice that it still has an oily film. Why was the water alone not effective in cleaning the bowl?

38. Could two atoms of oxygen engage in ionic bonding? Why or why not?

39. $AB + CD \rightarrow AD + BE$ Is this a legitimate example of an exchange reaction? Why or why not?

40. When you do a load of laundry, why do you not just drop a bar of soap into the washing machine? In other words, why is laundry detergent sold as a liquid or powder?

41. The pH of lemon juice is 2, and the pH of orange juice is 4. Which of these is more acidic, and by how much? What does this mean?

42. During a party, Eli loses a bet and is forced to drink a bottle of lemon juice. Not long thereafter, he begins complaining of having difficulty breathing, and his friends take him to the local emergency room. There, he is given an intravenous solution of bicarbonate. Why?

43. If the disaccharide maltose is formed from two glucose monosaccharides, which are hexose sugars, how many atoms of carbon, hydrogen, and oxygen does maltose contain and why?

44. Once dietary fats are digested and absorbed, why can they not be released directly into the bloodstream?

CHAPTER 3
The Cellular Level of Organization

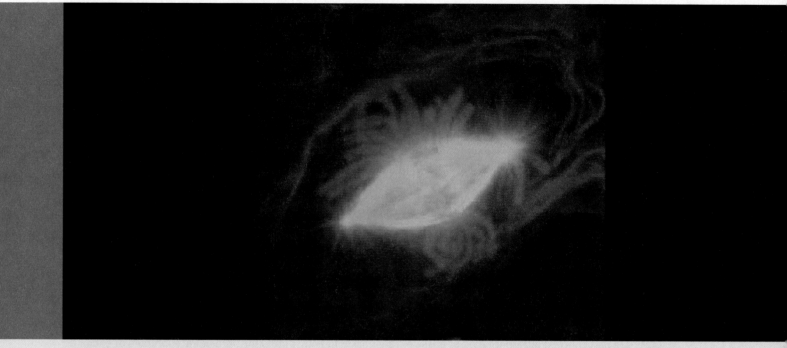

Figure 3.1 **Fluorescence-stained Cell Undergoing Mitosis** A lung cell from a newt, commonly studied for its similarity to human lung cells, is stained with fluorescent dyes. The green stain reveals mitotic spindles, red is the cell membrane and part of the cytoplasm, and the structures that appear light blue are chromosomes. This cell is in anaphase of mitosis. (credit: "Mortadelo2005"/Wikimedia Commons)

CHAPTER OBJECTIVES

After studying this chapter, you will be able to:

- Describe the structure and function of the cell membrane, including its regulation of materials into and out of the cell
- Describe the functions of the various cytoplasmic organelles
- Explain the structure and contents of the nucleus, as well as the process of DNA replication
- Explain the process by which a cell builds proteins using the DNA code
- List the stages of the cell cycle in order, including the steps of cell division in somatic cells
- Discuss how a cell differentiates and becomes more specialized
- List the morphological and physiological characteristics of some representative cell types in the human body

INTRODUCTION You developed from a single fertilized egg cell into the complex organism containing trillions of cells that you see when you look in a mirror. During this developmental process, early, undifferentiated cells differentiate and become specialized in their structure and function. These different cell types form specialized tissues that work in concert to perform all of the functions necessary for the living organism. Cellular and developmental biologists study how the continued division of a single cell leads to such complexity and differentiation.

Consider the difference between a structural cell in the skin and a nerve cell. A structural skin cell may be shaped like a flat plate (squamous) and live only for a short time before it is shed and replaced. Packed tightly into rows and sheets, the squamous skin cells provide a protective barrier for the cells and tissues that lie beneath. A nerve cell, on the other hand, may be shaped something like a star, sending out long processes up to a meter in length and may live for the entire lifetime of the organism. With their long winding appendages, nerve cells can communicate with one another and with other types of body cells and send rapid signals that inform the organism about its environment and allow it to interact with that environment. These differences illustrate one very important theme that is consistent at all organizational levels of biology: the form of a structure is optimally suited to perform particular functions assigned to that structure. Keep this theme in mind as you tour the inside of a cell and are introduced to the various types of cells in the body.

A primary responsibility of each cell is to contribute to homeostasis. Homeostasis is a term used in biology that refers to a dynamic state of balance within parameters that are compatible with life. For example, living cells require a water-based environment to survive in, and there are various physical (anatomical) and physiological mechanisms that keep all of the trillions of living cells in the human body moist. This is one aspect of homeostasis. When a particular parameter, such as blood pressure or blood oxygen content, moves far enough *out* of homeostasis (generally becoming too high or too low), illness or disease—and sometimes death—inevitably results.

The concept of a cell started with microscopic observations of dead cork tissue by scientist Robert Hooke in 1665. Without realizing their function or importance, Hook coined the term "cell" based on the resemblance of the small subdivisions in the cork to the rooms that monks inhabited, called cells. About ten years later, Antonie van Leeuwenhoek became the first person to observe living and moving cells under a microscope. In the century that followed, the theory that cells represented the basic unit of life would develop. These tiny fluid-filled sacs house components responsible for the thousands of biochemical reactions necessary for an organism to grow and survive. In this chapter, you will learn about the major components and functions of a prototypical, generalized cell and discover some of the different types of cells in the human body.

3.1 The Cell Membrane

LEARNING OBJECTIVES

By the end of this section, you will be able to:

- Describe the molecular components that make up the cell membrane
- Explain the major features and properties of the cell membrane
- Differentiate between materials that can and cannot diffuse through the lipid bilayer
- Compare and contrast different types of passive transport with active transport, providing examples of each

Despite differences in structure and function, all living cells in multicellular organisms have a surrounding cell membrane. As the outer layer of your skin separates your body from its environment, the cell membrane (also known as the plasma membrane) separates the inner contents of a cell from its exterior environment. This cell membrane provides a protective barrier around the cell and regulates which materials can pass in or out.

Structure and Composition of the Cell Membrane

The **cell membrane** is an extremely pliable structure composed primarily of back-to-back phospholipids (a "bilayer"). Cholesterol is also present, which contributes to the fluidity of the membrane, and there are various proteins embedded within the membrane that have a variety of functions.

A single phospholipid molecule has a phosphate group on one end, called the "head," and two side-by-side chains of fatty acids that make up the lipid tails (Figure 3.2). The phosphate group is negatively charged, making the head polar and hydrophilic—or "water loving." A **hydrophilic** molecule (or region of a molecule) is one that is attracted to water. The phosphate heads are thus attracted to the water molecules of both the extracellular and intracellular environments. The lipid tails, on the other hand, are uncharged, or nonpolar, and are hydrophobic—or "water fearing." A **hydrophobic** molecule (or region of a molecule) repels and is repelled by water. Some lipid tails consist of saturated fatty acids and some contain unsaturated fatty acids. This combination adds to the fluidity of the tails that are constantly in motion. Phospholipids are thus amphipathic molecules. An **amphipathic** molecule is one that contains both a hydrophilic and a hydrophobic region. In fact, soap works to remove oil and grease stains because it has amphipathic properties. The hydrophilic portion can dissolve in water while the hydrophobic portion can trap grease in micelles that then can be washed away.

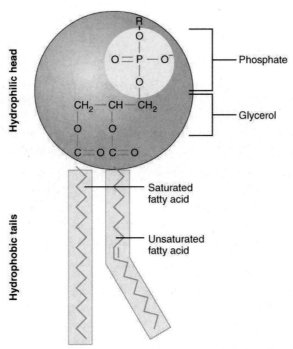

FIGURE 3.2 Phospholipid Structure   A phospholipid molecule consists of a polar phosphate "head," which is hydrophilic and a non-polar lipid "tail," which is hydrophobic. Unsaturated fatty acids result in kinks in the hydrophobic tails.

The cell membrane consists of two adjacent layers of phospholipids. The lipid tails of one layer face the lipid tails of the other layer, meeting at the interface of the two layers. The phospholipid heads face outward, one layer exposed to the interior of the cell and one layer exposed to the exterior (Figure 3.3). Because the phosphate groups are polar and hydrophilic, they are attracted to water in the intracellular fluid. **Intracellular fluid (ICF)** is the fluid interior of the cell. The phosphate groups are also attracted to the extracellular fluid. **Extracellular fluid (ECF)** is the fluid environment outside the enclosure of the cell membrane. **Interstitial fluid (IF)** is the term given to extracellular fluid not contained within blood vessels. Because the lipid tails are hydrophobic, they meet in the inner region of the membrane, excluding watery intracellular and extracellular fluid from this space. The cell membrane has many proteins, as well as other lipids (such as cholesterol), that are associated with the phospholipid bilayer. An important feature of the membrane is that it remains fluid; the lipids and proteins in the cell membrane are not rigidly locked in place.

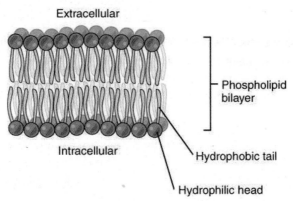

FIGURE 3.3 Phospholipid Bilayer   The phospholipid bilayer consists of two adjacent sheets of phospholipids, arranged tail to tail. The hydrophobic tails associate with one another, forming the interior of the membrane. The polar heads contact the fluid inside and outside of the cell.

Membrane Proteins

The lipid bilayer forms the basis of the cell membrane, but it is peppered throughout with various proteins. Two different types of proteins that are commonly associated with the cell membrane are the integral proteins and peripheral protein (Figure 3.4). As its name suggests, an **integral protein** is a protein that is embedded in the membrane. A **channel protein** is an example of an integral protein that selectively allows particular materials, such as certain ions, to pass into or out of the cell.

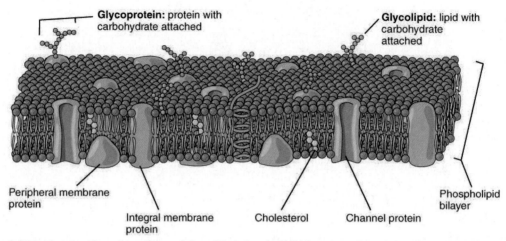

FIGURE 3.4 Cell Membrane The cell membrane of the cell is a phospholipid bilayer containing many different molecular components, including proteins and cholesterol, some with carbohydrate groups attached.

Another important group of integral proteins are cell recognition proteins, which serve to mark a cell's identity so that it can be recognized by other cells. A **receptor** is a type of recognition protein that can selectively bind a specific molecule outside the cell, and this binding induces a chemical reaction within the cell. A **ligand** is the specific molecule that binds to and activates a receptor. Some integral proteins serve dual roles as both a receptor and an ion channel. One example of a receptor-ligand interaction is the receptors on nerve cells that bind neurotransmitters, such as dopamine. When a dopamine molecule binds to a dopamine receptor protein, a channel within the transmembrane protein opens to allow certain ions to flow into the cell.

Some integral membrane proteins are glycoproteins. A **glycoprotein** is a protein that has carbohydrate molecules attached, which extend into the extracellular matrix. The attached carbohydrate tags on glycoproteins aid in cell recognition. The carbohydrates that extend from membrane proteins and even from some membrane lipids collectively form the glycocalyx. The **glycocalyx** is a fuzzy-appearing coating around the cell formed from glycoproteins and other carbohydrates attached to the cell membrane. The glycocalyx can have various roles. For example, it may have molecules that allow the cell to bind to another cell, it may contain receptors for hormones, or it might have enzymes to break down nutrients. The glycocalyces found in a person's body are products of that person's genetic makeup. They give each of the individual's trillions of cells the "identity" of belonging in the person's body. This identity is the primary way that a person's immune defense cells "know" not to attack the person's own body cells, but it also is the reason organs donated by another person might be rejected.

Peripheral proteins are typically found on the inner or outer surface of the lipid bilayer but can also be attached to the internal or external surface of an integral protein. These proteins typically perform a specific function for the cell. Some peripheral proteins on the surface of intestinal cells, for example, act as digestive enzymes to break down nutrients to sizes that can pass through the cells and into the bloodstream.

Transport across the Cell Membrane

One of the great wonders of the cell membrane is its ability to regulate the concentration of substances inside the cell. These substances include ions such as Ca^{++}, Na^+, K^+, and Cl^-; nutrients including sugars, fatty acids, and amino acids; and waste products, particularly carbon dioxide (CO_2), which must leave the cell.

The membrane's lipid bilayer structure provides the first level of control. The phospholipids are tightly packed together, and the membrane has a hydrophobic interior. This structure causes the membrane to be selectively permeable. A membrane that has **selective permeability** allows only substances meeting certain criteria to pass through it unaided. In the case of the cell membrane, only relatively small, nonpolar materials can move through the lipid bilayer (remember, the lipid tails of the membrane are nonpolar). Some examples of these are other lipids, oxygen and carbon dioxide gases, and alcohol. However, water-soluble materials—like glucose, amino acids, and electrolytes—need some assistance to cross the membrane because they are repelled by the hydrophobic tails of the phospholipid bilayer. All substances that move through the membrane do so by one of two general methods, which are categorized based on whether or not energy is required. **Passive transport** is the movement of substances across the membrane without the expenditure of cellular energy. In contrast, **active transport** is the movement of substances across the membrane using energy from adenosine triphosphate (ATP).

Passive Transport

In order to understand *how* substances move passively across a cell membrane, it is necessary to understand concentration gradients and diffusion. A **concentration gradient** is the difference in concentration of a substance across a space. Molecules (or ions) will spread/diffuse from where they are more concentrated to where they are less concentrated until they are equally distributed in that space. (When molecules move in this way, they are said to move *down* their concentration gradient.) **Diffusion** is the movement of particles from an area of higher concentration to an area of lower concentration. A couple of common examples will help to illustrate this concept. Imagine being inside a closed bathroom. If a bottle of perfume were sprayed, the scent molecules would naturally diffuse from the spot where they left the bottle to all corners of the bathroom, and this diffusion would go on until no more concentration gradient remains. Another example is a spoonful of sugar placed in a cup of tea. Eventually the sugar will diffuse throughout the tea until no concentration gradient remains. In both cases, if the room is warmer or the tea hotter, diffusion occurs even faster as the molecules are bumping into each other and spreading out faster than at cooler temperatures. Having an internal body temperature around 98.6° F thus also aids in diffusion of particles within the body.

⊚ INTERACTIVE LINK

Visit this link (http://openstax.org/l/diffusion) to see diffusion and how it is propelled by the kinetic energy of molecules in solution. How does temperature affect diffusion rate, and why?

Whenever a substance exists in greater concentration on one side of a semipermeable membrane, such as the cell membranes, any substance that can move down its concentration gradient across the membrane will do so. Consider substances that can easily diffuse through the lipid bilayer of the cell membrane, such as the gases oxygen (O_2) and CO_2. O_2 generally diffuses into cells because it is more concentrated outside of them, and CO_2 typically diffuses out of cells because it is more concentrated inside of them. Neither of these examples requires any energy on the part of the cell, and therefore they use passive transport to move across the membrane.

Before moving on, you need to review the gases that can diffuse across a cell membrane. Because cells rapidly use up oxygen during metabolism, there is typically a lower concentration of O_2 inside the cell than outside. As a result, oxygen will diffuse from the interstitial fluid directly through the lipid bilayer of the membrane and into the cytoplasm within the cell. On the other hand, because cells produce CO_2 as a byproduct of metabolism, CO_2 concentrations rise within the cytoplasm; therefore, CO_2 will move from the cell through the lipid bilayer and into the interstitial fluid, where its concentration is lower. This mechanism of molecules moving across a cell membrane from the side where they are more concentrated to the side where they are less concentrated is a form of passive transport called simple diffusion (Figure 3.5).

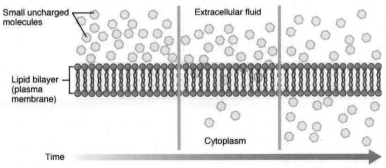

FIGURE 3.5   Simple Diffusion across the Cell (Plasma) Membrane   The structure of the lipid bilayer allows small, uncharged substances such as oxygen and carbon dioxide, and hydrophobic molecules such as lipids, to pass through the cell membrane, down their concentration gradient, by simple diffusion.

Large polar or ionic molecules, which are hydrophilic, cannot easily cross the phospholipid bilayer. Very small polar molecules, such as water, can cross via simple diffusion due to their small size. Charged atoms or molecules of any size cannot cross the cell membrane via simple diffusion as the charges are repelled by the hydrophobic tails in the interior of the phospholipid bilayer. Solutes dissolved in water on either side of the cell membrane will tend to diffuse down their concentration gradients, but because most substances cannot pass freely through the lipid bilayer of the cell membrane, their movement is restricted to protein channels and specialized transport mechanisms in the membrane. **Facilitated diffusion** is the diffusion process used for those substances that cannot cross the lipid bilayer due to their size, charge, and/or polarity (Figure 3.6). A common example of facilitated diffusion is the movement of glucose into the cell, where it is used to make ATP. Although glucose can be more concentrated outside of a cell, it cannot cross the lipid bilayer via simple diffusion because it is both large and polar. To resolve this, a specialized carrier protein called the glucose transporter will transfer glucose molecules into the cell to facilitate its inward diffusion.

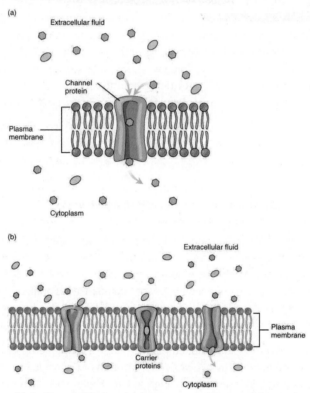

FIGURE 3.6   Facilitated Diffusion   (a) Facilitated diffusion of substances crossing the cell (plasma) membrane takes place with the help of proteins such as channel proteins and carrier proteins. Channel proteins are less selective than carrier proteins, and usually mildly discriminate between their cargo based on size and charge. (b) Carrier proteins are more selective, often only allowing one particular type of molecule to cross.

As an example, even though sodium ions (Na^+) are highly concentrated outside of cells, these electrolytes are charged and cannot pass through the nonpolar lipid bilayer of the membrane. Their diffusion is facilitated by membrane proteins that form sodium channels (or "pores"), so that Na^+ ions can move down their concentration gradient from outside the cells to inside the cells. There are many other solutes that must undergo facilitated diffusion to move into a cell, such as amino acids, or to move out of a cell, such as wastes. Because facilitated diffusion is a passive process, it does not require energy expenditure by the cell.

Water also can move freely across the cell membrane of all cells, either through protein channels or by slipping between the lipid tails of the membrane itself. **Osmosis** is the diffusion of water through a semipermeable membrane (Figure 3.7).

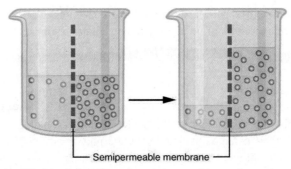

FIGURE 3.7   Osmosis   Osmosis is the diffusion of water through a semipermeable membrane down its concentration gradient. If a membrane is permeable to water, though not to a solute, water will equalize its own concentration by diffusing to the side of lower water concentration (and thus the side of higher solute concentration). In the beaker on the left, the solution on the right side of the membrane is hypertonic.

The movement of water molecules is not itself regulated by some cells, so it is important that these cells are exposed to an environment in which the concentration of solutes outside of the cells (in the extracellular fluid) is equal to the concentration of solutes inside the cells (in the cytoplasm). Two solutions that have the same concentration of solutes are said to be **isotonic** (equal tension). When cells and their extracellular environments are isotonic, the concentration of water molecules is the same outside and inside the cells, and the cells maintain their normal shape (and function).

Osmosis occurs when there is an imbalance of solutes outside of a cell versus inside the cell. A solution that has a higher concentration of solutes than another solution is said to be **hypertonic,** and water molecules tend to diffuse into a hypertonic solution (Figure 3.8). Cells in a hypertonic solution will shrivel as water leaves the cell via osmosis. In contrast, a solution that has a lower concentration of solutes than another solution is said to be **hypotonic**, and water molecules tend to diffuse out of a hypotonic solution. Cells in a hypotonic solution will take on too much water and swell, with the risk of eventually bursting. A critical aspect of homeostasis in living things is to create an internal environment in which all of the body's cells are in an isotonic solution. Various organ systems, particularly the kidneys, work to maintain this homeostasis.

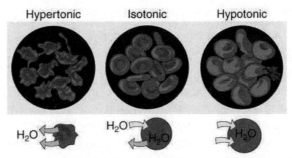

FIGURE 3.8   Concentration of Solutions   A hypertonic solution has a solute concentration higher than another solution. An isotonic solution has a solute concentration equal to another solution. A hypotonic solution has a solute concentration lower than another solution.

Another mechanism besides diffusion to passively transport materials between compartments is filtration. Unlike diffusion of a substance from where it is more concentrated to less concentrated, filtration uses a hydrostatic pressure gradient that pushes the fluid—and the solutes within it—from a higher pressure area to a lower pressure area. Filtration is an extremely important process in the body. For example, the circulatory system uses filtration to move plasma and substances across the endothelial lining of capillaries and into surrounding tissues, supplying cells with the nutrients. Filtration pressure in the kidneys provides the mechanism to remove wastes from the bloodstream.

Active Transport

For all of the transport methods described above, the cell expends no energy. Membrane proteins that aid in the passive transport of substances do so without the use of ATP. During active transport, ATP is required to move a substance across a membrane, often with the help of protein carriers, and usually *against* its concentration gradient.

One of the most common types of active transport involves proteins that serve as pumps. The word "pump" probably conjures up thoughts of using energy to pump up the tire of a bicycle or a basketball. Similarly, energy from

ATP is required for these membrane proteins to transport substances—molecules or ions—across the membrane, usually against their concentration gradients (from an area of low concentration to an area of high concentration).

The **sodium-potassium pump**, which is also called Na^+/K^+ ATPase, transports sodium out of a cell while moving potassium into the cell. The Na^+/K^+ pump is an important ion pump found in the membranes of many types of cells. These pumps are particularly abundant in nerve cells, which are constantly pumping out sodium ions and pulling in potassium ions to maintain an electrical gradient across their cell membranes. An **electrical gradient** is a difference in electrical charge across a space. In the case of nerve cells, for example, the electrical gradient exists between the inside and outside of the cell, with the inside being negatively-charged (at around -70 mV) relative to the outside. The negative electrical gradient is maintained because each Na^+/K^+ pump moves three Na^+ ions out of the cell and two K^+ ions into the cell for each ATP molecule that is used (Figure 3.9). This process is so important for nerve cells that it accounts for the majority of their ATP usage.

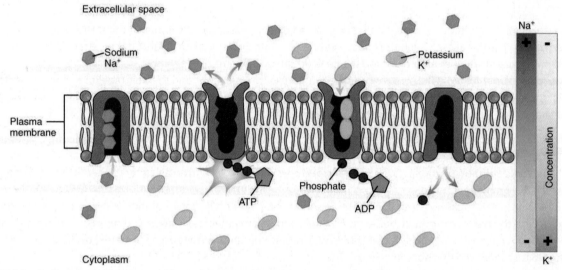

FIGURE 3.9   Sodium-Potassium Pump   The sodium-potassium pump is found in many cell (plasma) membranes. Powered by ATP, the pump moves sodium and potassium ions in opposite directions, each against its concentration gradient. In a single cycle of the pump, three sodium ions are extruded from and two potassium ions are imported into the cell.

Active transport pumps can also work together with other active or passive transport systems to move substances across the membrane. For example, the sodium-potassium pump maintains a high concentration of sodium ions outside of the cell. Therefore, if the cell needs sodium ions, all it has to do is open a passive sodium channel, as the concentration gradient of the sodium ions will drive them to diffuse into the cell. In this way, the action of an active transport pump (the sodium-potassium pump) powers the passive transport of sodium ions by creating a concentration gradient. When active transport powers the transport of another substance in this way, it is called secondary active transport.

Symporters are secondary active transporters that move two substances in the same direction. For example, the sodium-glucose symporter uses sodium ions to "pull" glucose molecules into the cell. Because cells store glucose for energy, glucose is typically at a higher concentration inside of the cell than outside. However, due to the action of the sodium-potassium pump, sodium ions will easily diffuse into the cell when the symporter is opened. The flood of sodium ions through the symporter provides the energy that allows glucose to move through the symporter and into the cell, against its concentration gradient.

Conversely, antiporters are secondary active transport systems that transport substances in opposite directions. For example, the sodium-hydrogen ion antiporter uses the energy from the inward flood of sodium ions to move hydrogen ions (H+) out of the cell. The sodium-hydrogen antiporter is used to maintain the pH of the cell's interior.

Other forms of active transport do not involve membrane carriers. **Endocytosis** (bringing "into the cell") is the process of a cell ingesting material by enveloping it in a portion of its cell membrane, and then pinching off that portion of membrane (Figure 3.10). Once pinched off, the portion of membrane and its contents becomes an independent, intracellular vesicle. A **vesicle** is a membranous sac—a spherical and hollow organelle bounded by a lipid bilayer membrane. Endocytosis often brings materials into the cell that must be broken down or digested.

Phagocytosis ("cell eating") is the endocytosis of large particles. Many immune cells engage in phagocytosis of invading pathogens. Like little Pac-men, their job is to patrol body tissues for unwanted matter, such as invading bacterial cells, phagocytize them, and digest them. In contrast to phagocytosis, **pinocytosis** ("cell drinking") brings fluid containing dissolved substances into a cell through membrane vesicles.

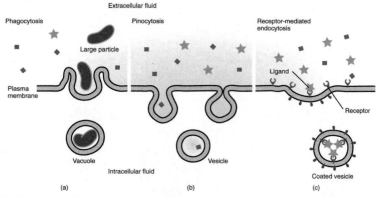

FIGURE 3.10   Three Forms of Endocytosis   Endocytosis is a form of active transport in which a cell envelopes extracellular materials using its cell membrane. (a) In phagocytosis, which is relatively nonselective, the cell takes in a large particle. (b) In pinocytosis, the cell takes in small particles in fluid. (c) In contrast, receptor-mediated endocytosis is quite selective. When external receptors bind a specific ligand, the cell responds by endocytosing the ligand.

Phagocytosis and pinocytosis take in large portions of extracellular material, and they are typically not highly selective in the substances they bring in. Cells regulate the endocytosis of specific substances via receptor-mediated endocytosis. **Receptor-mediated endocytosis** is endocytosis by a portion of the cell membrane that contains many receptors that are specific for a certain substance. Once the surface receptors have bound sufficient amounts of the specific substance (the receptor's ligand), the cell will endocytose the part of the cell membrane containing the receptor-ligand complexes. Iron, a required component of hemoglobin, is endocytosed by red blood cells in this way. Iron is bound to a protein called transferrin in the blood. Specific transferrin receptors on red blood cell surfaces bind the iron-transferrin molecules, and the cell endocytoses the receptor-ligand complexes.

In contrast with endocytosis, **exocytosis** (taking "out of the cell") is the process of a cell exporting material using vesicular transport (Figure 3.11). Many cells manufacture substances that must be secreted, like a factory manufacturing a product for export. These substances are typically packaged into membrane-bound vesicles within the cell. When the vesicle membrane fuses with the cell membrane, the vesicle releases it contents into the interstitial fluid. The vesicle membrane then becomes part of the cell membrane. Cells of the stomach and pancreas produce and secrete digestive enzymes through exocytosis (Figure 3.12). Endocrine cells produce and secrete hormones that are sent throughout the body, and certain immune cells produce and secrete large amounts of histamine, a chemical important for immune responses.

Exocytosis

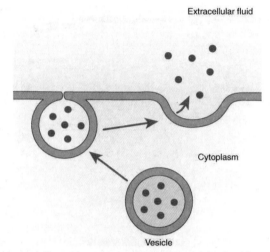

FIGURE 3.11 **Exocytosis** Exocytosis is much like endocytosis in reverse. Material destined for export is packaged into a vesicle inside the cell. The membrane of the vesicle fuses with the cell membrane, and the contents are released into the extracellular space.

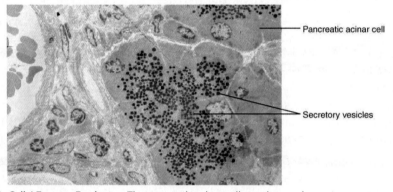

FIGURE 3.12 **Pancreatic Cells' Enzyme Products** The pancreatic acinar cells produce and secrete many enzymes that digest food. The tiny black granules in this electron micrograph are secretory vesicles filled with enzymes that will be exported from the cells via exocytosis. LM × 2900. (Micrograph provided by the Regents of University of Michigan Medical School © 2012)

🔗 INTERACTIVE LINK

View the University of Michigan WebScope (http://openstax.org/l/pcells) to explore the tissue sample in greater detail.

Diseases of the...

Cell: Cystic Fibrosis   Cystic fibrosis (CF) affects approximately 30,000 people in the United States, with about 1,000 new cases reported each year. The genetic disease is most well known for its damage to the lungs, causing breathing difficulties and chronic lung infections, but it also affects the liver, pancreas, and intestines. Only about 50 years ago, the prognosis for children born with CF was very grim—a life expectancy rarely over 10 years. Today, with advances in medical treatment, many CF patients live into their 30s.

The symptoms of CF result from a malfunctioning membrane ion channel called the cystic fibrosis transmembrane conductance regulator, or CFTR. In healthy people, the CFTR protein is an integral membrane protein that transports Cl^- ions out of the cell. In a person who has CF, the gene for the CFTR is mutated, thus, the cell manufactures a defective channel protein that typically is not incorporated into the membrane, but is instead degraded by the cell.

The CFTR requires ATP in order to function, making its Cl^- transport a form of active transport. This characteristic puzzled researchers for a long time because the Cl^- ions are actually flowing *down* their concentration gradient when transported out of cells. Active transport generally pumps ions *against* their concentration gradient, but the CFTR presents an exception to this rule.

In normal lung tissue, the movement of Cl^- out of the cell maintains a Cl^--rich, negatively charged environment immediately outside of the cell. This is particularly important in the epithelial lining of the respiratory system. Respiratory epithelial cells secrete mucus, which serves to trap dust, bacteria, and other debris. A cilium (plural = cilia) is one of the hair-like appendages found on certain cells. Cilia on the epithelial cells move the mucus and its trapped particles up the airways away from the lungs and toward the outside. In order to be effectively moved upward, the mucus cannot be too viscous; rather it must have a thin, watery consistency. The transport of Cl^- and the maintenance of an electronegative environment outside of the cell attract positive ions such as Na^+ to the extracellular space. The accumulation of both Cl^- and Na^+ ions in the extracellular space creates solute-rich mucus, which has a low concentration of water molecules. As a result, through osmosis, water moves from cells and extracellular matrix into the mucus, "thinning" it out. This is how, in a normal respiratory system, the mucus is kept sufficiently watered-down to be propelled out of the respiratory system.

If the CFTR channel is absent, Cl^- ions are not transported out of the cell in adequate numbers, thus preventing them from drawing positive ions. The absence of ions in the secreted mucus results in the lack of a normal water concentration gradient. Thus, there is no osmotic pressure pulling water into the mucus. The resulting mucus is thick and sticky, and the ciliated epithelia cannot effectively remove it from the respiratory system. Passageways in the lungs become blocked with mucus, along with the debris it carries. Bacterial infections occur more easily because bacterial cells are not effectively carried away from the lungs.

3.2 The Cytoplasm and Cellular Organelles

LEARNING OBJECTIVES

By the end of this section, you will be able to:

- Describe the structure and function of the cellular organelles associated with the endomembrane system, including the endoplasmic reticulum, Golgi apparatus, and lysosomes
- Describe the structure and function of mitochondria and peroxisomes
- Explain the three components of the cytoskeleton, including their composition and functions

Now that you have learned that the cell membrane surrounds all cells, you can dive inside of a prototypical human cell to learn about its internal components and their functions. All living cells in multicellular organisms contain an internal cytoplasmic compartment, and a nucleus within the cytoplasm. **Cytosol**, the jelly-like substance within the cell, provides the fluid medium necessary for biochemical reactions. Eukaryotic cells, including all animal cells, also contain various cellular organelles. An **organelle** ("little organ") is one of several different types of membrane-enclosed bodies in the cell, each performing a unique function. Just as the various bodily organs work together in harmony to perform all of a human's functions, the many different cellular organelles work together to keep the cell healthy and performing all of its important functions. The organelles and cytosol, taken together, compose the cell's **cytoplasm**. The **nucleus** is a cell's central organelle, which contains the cell's DNA (Figure 3.13).

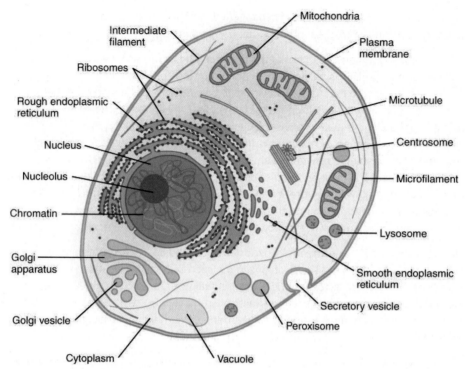

FIGURE 3.13   Prototypical Human Cell   While this image is not indicative of any one particular human cell, it is a prototypical example of a cell containing the primary organelles and internal structures.

Organelles of the Endomembrane System

A set of three major organelles together form a system within the cell called the endomembrane system. These organelles work together to perform various cellular jobs, including the task of producing, packaging, and exporting certain cellular products. The organelles of the endomembrane system include the endoplasmic reticulum, Golgi apparatus, and vesicles.

Endoplasmic Reticulum

The **endoplasmic reticulum (ER)** is a system of channels that is continuous with the nuclear membrane (or "envelope") covering the nucleus and composed of the same lipid bilayer material. The ER can be thought of as a series of winding thoroughfares similar to the waterway canals in Venice. The ER provides passages throughout much of the cell that function in transporting, synthesizing, and storing materials. The winding structure of the ER results in a large membranous surface area that supports its many functions (Figure 3.14).

Access for free at openstax.org

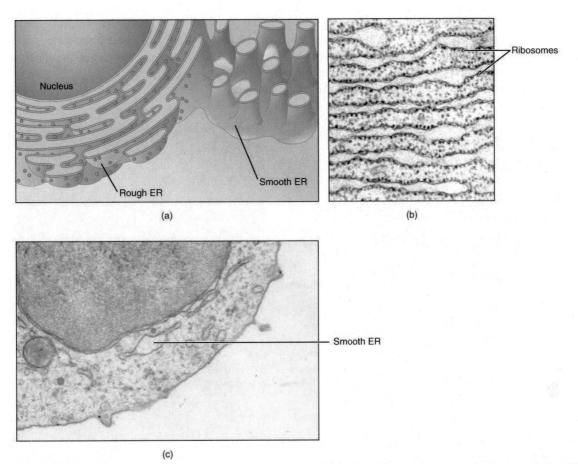

FIGURE 3.14 Endoplasmic Reticulum (ER)   (a) The ER is a winding network of thin membranous sacs found in close association with the cell nucleus. The smooth and rough endoplasmic reticula are very different in appearance and function (source: mouse tissue). (b) Rough ER is studded with numerous ribosomes, which are sites of protein synthesis (source: mouse tissue). EM × 110,000. (c) Smooth ER synthesizes phospholipids, steroid hormones, regulates the concentration of cellular Ca^{++}, metabolizes some carbohydrates, and breaks down certain toxins (source: mouse tissue). EM × 110,510. (Micrographs provided by the Regents of University of Michigan Medical School © 2012)

Endoplasmic reticulum can exist in two forms: rough ER and smooth ER. These two types of ER perform some very different functions and can be found in very different amounts depending on the type of cell. Rough ER (RER) is so-called because its membrane is dotted with embedded granules—organelles called ribosomes, giving the RER a bumpy appearance. A **ribosome** is an organelle that serves as the site of protein synthesis. It is composed of two ribosomal RNA subunits that wrap around mRNA to start the process of translation, followed by protein synthesis. Smooth ER (SER) lacks these ribosomes.

One of the main functions of the smooth ER is in the synthesis of lipids. The smooth ER synthesizes phospholipids, the main component of biological membranes, as well as steroid hormones. For this reason, cells that produce large quantities of such hormones, such as those of the female ovaries and male testes, contain large amounts of smooth ER. In addition to lipid synthesis, the smooth ER also sequesters (i.e., stores) and regulates the concentration of cellular Ca^{++}, a function extremely important in cells of the nervous system where Ca^{++} is the trigger for neurotransmitter release. The smooth ER additionally metabolizes some carbohydrates and performs a detoxification role, breaking down certain toxins.

In contrast with the smooth ER, the primary job of the rough ER is the synthesis and modification of proteins destined for the cell membrane or for export from the cell. For this protein synthesis, many ribosomes attach to the ER (giving it the studded appearance of rough ER). Typically, a protein is synthesized within the ribosome and released inside the channel of the rough ER, where sugars can be added to it (by a process called glycosylation) before it is transported within a vesicle to the next stage in the packaging and shipping process: the Golgi apparatus.

The Golgi Apparatus

The **Golgi apparatus** is responsible for sorting, modifying, and shipping off the products that come from the rough

ER, much like a post-office. The Golgi apparatus looks like stacked flattened discs, almost like stacks of oddly shaped pancakes. Like the ER, these discs are membranous. The Golgi apparatus has two distinct sides, each with a different role. One side of the apparatus receives products in vesicles. These products are sorted through the apparatus, and then they are released from the opposite side after being repackaged into new vesicles. If the product is to be exported from the cell, the vesicle migrates to the cell surface and fuses to the cell membrane, and the cargo is secreted (Figure 3.15).

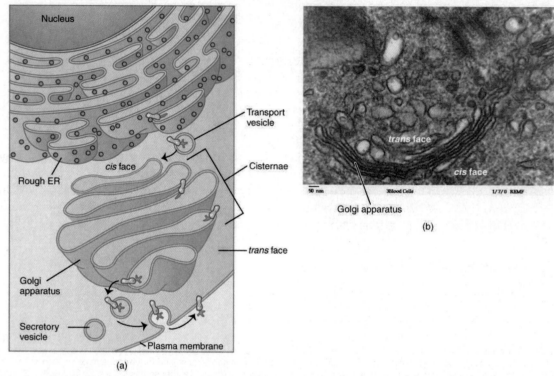

FIGURE 3.15   Golgi Apparatus   (a) The Golgi apparatus manipulates products from the rough ER, and also produces new organelles called lysosomes. Proteins and other products of the ER are sent to the Golgi apparatus, which organizes, modifies, packages, and tags them. Some of these products are transported to other areas of the cell and some are exported from the cell through exocytosis. Enzymatic proteins are packaged as new lysosomes (or packaged and sent for fusion with existing lysosomes). (b) An electron micrograph of the Golgi apparatus.

Lysosomes

Some of the protein products packaged by the Golgi include digestive enzymes that are meant to remain inside the cell for use in breaking down certain materials. The enzyme-containing vesicles released by the Golgi may form new lysosomes, or fuse with existing, lysosomes. A **lysosome** is an organelle that contains enzymes that break down and digest unneeded cellular components, such as a damaged organelle. (A lysosome is similar to a wrecking crew that takes down old and unsound buildings in a neighborhood.) **Autophagy** ("self-eating") is the process of a cell digesting its own structures. Lysosomes are also important for breaking down foreign material. For example, when certain immune defense cells (white blood cells) phagocytize bacteria, the bacterial cell is transported into a lysosome and digested by the enzymes inside. As one might imagine, such phagocytic defense cells contain large numbers of lysosomes.

Under certain circumstances, lysosomes perform a more grand and dire function. In the case of damaged or unhealthy cells, lysosomes can be triggered to open up and release their digestive enzymes into the cytoplasm of the cell, killing the cell. This "self-destruct" mechanism is called **autolysis**, and makes the process of cell death controlled (a mechanism called "apoptosis").

⊘ INTERACTIVE LINK

Watch this video (http://openstax.org/l/endomembrane1) to learn about the endomembrane system, which includes the rough and smooth ER and the Golgi body as well as lysosomes and vesicles. What is the primary role of the endomembrane system?

Organelles for Energy Production and Detoxification

In addition to the jobs performed by the endomembrane system, the cell has many other important functions. Just as you must consume nutrients to provide yourself with energy, so must each of your cells take in nutrients, some of which convert to chemical energy that can be used to power biochemical reactions. Another important function of the cell is detoxification. Humans take in all sorts of toxins from the environment and also produce harmful chemicals as byproducts of cellular processes. Cells called hepatocytes in the liver detoxify many of these toxins.

Mitochondria

A **mitochondrion** (plural = mitochondria) is a membranous, bean-shaped organelle that is the "energy transformer" of the cell. Mitochondria consist of an outer lipid bilayer membrane as well as an additional inner lipid bilayer membrane (Figure 3.16). The inner membrane is highly folded into winding structures with a great deal of surface area, called cristae. It is along this inner membrane that a series of proteins, enzymes, and other molecules perform the biochemical reactions of cellular respiration. These reactions convert energy stored in nutrient molecules (such as glucose) into adenosine triphosphate (ATP), which provides usable cellular energy to the cell. Cells use ATP constantly, and so the mitochondria are constantly at work. Oxygen molecules are required during cellular respiration, which is why you must constantly breathe it in. One of the organ systems in the body that uses huge amounts of ATP is the muscular system because ATP is required to sustain muscle contraction. As a result, muscle cells are packed full of mitochondria. Nerve cells also need large quantities of ATP to run their sodium-potassium pumps. Therefore, an individual neuron will be loaded with over a thousand mitochondria. On the other hand, a bone cell, which is not nearly as metabolically-active, might only have a couple hundred mitochondria.

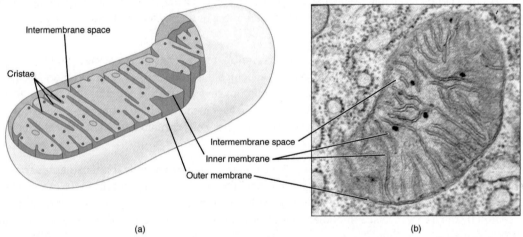

(a)   (b)

FIGURE 3.16   Mitochondrion   The mitochondria are the energy-conversion factories of the cell. (a) A mitochondrion is composed of two separate lipid bilayer membranes. Along the inner membrane are various molecules that work together to produce ATP, the cell's major energy currency. (b) An electron micrograph of mitochondria. EM × 236,000. (Micrograph provided by the Regents of University of Michigan Medical School © 2012)

Peroxisomes

Like lysosomes, a **peroxisome** is a membrane-bound cellular organelle that contains mostly enzymes (Figure 3.17). Peroxisomes perform a couple of different functions, including lipid metabolism and chemical detoxification. In contrast to the digestive enzymes found in lysosomes, the enzymes within peroxisomes serve to transfer hydrogen atoms from various molecules to oxygen, producing hydrogen peroxide (H_2O_2). In this way, peroxisomes neutralize poisons such as alcohol. In order to appreciate the importance of peroxisomes, it is necessary to understand the concept of reactive oxygen species.

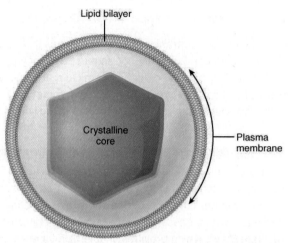

FIGURE 3.17 Peroxisome Peroxisomes are membrane-bound organelles that contain an abundance of enzymes for detoxifying harmful substances and lipid metabolism.

Reactive oxygen species (ROS) such as peroxides and free radicals are the highly reactive products of many normal cellular processes, including the mitochondrial reactions that produce ATP and oxygen metabolism. Examples of ROS include the hydroxyl radical OH, H_2O_2, and superoxide (O_2^-). Some ROS are important for certain cellular functions, such as cell signaling processes and immune responses against foreign substances. Free radicals are reactive because they contain free unpaired electrons; they can easily oxidize other molecules throughout the cell, causing cellular damage and even cell death. Free radicals are thought to play a role in many destructive processes in the body, from cancer to coronary artery disease.

Peroxisomes, on the other hand, oversee reactions that neutralize free radicals. Peroxisomes produce large amounts of the toxic H_2O_2 in the process, but peroxisomes contain enzymes that convert H_2O_2 into water and oxygen. These byproducts are safely released into the cytoplasm. Like miniature sewage treatment plants, peroxisomes neutralize harmful toxins so that they do not wreak havoc in the cells. The liver is the organ primarily responsible for detoxifying the blood before it travels throughout the body, and liver cells contain an exceptionally high number of peroxisomes.

Defense mechanisms such as detoxification within the peroxisome and certain cellular antioxidants serve to neutralize many of these molecules. Some vitamins and other substances, found primarily in fruits and vegetables, have antioxidant properties. Antioxidants work by being oxidized themselves, halting the destructive reaction cascades initiated by the free radicals. Sometimes though, ROS accumulate beyond the capacity of such defenses.

Oxidative stress is the term used to describe damage to cellular components caused by ROS. Due to their characteristic unpaired electrons, ROS can set off chain reactions where they remove electrons from other molecules, which then become oxidized and reactive, and do the same to other molecules, causing a chain reaction. ROS can cause permanent damage to cellular lipids, proteins, carbohydrates, and nucleic acids. Damaged DNA can lead to genetic mutations and even cancer. A **mutation** is a change in the nucleotide sequence in a gene within a cell's DNA, potentially altering the protein coded by that gene. Other diseases believed to be triggered or exacerbated by ROS include Alzheimer's disease, cardiovascular diseases, diabetes, Parkinson's disease, arthritis, Huntington's disease, and schizophrenia, among many others. It is noteworthy that these diseases are largely age-related. Many scientists believe that oxidative stress is a major contributor to the aging process.

Aging and the...

Cell: The Free Radical Theory
The free radical theory on aging was originally proposed in the 1950s, and still remains under debate. Generally speaking, the free radical theory of aging suggests that accumulated cellular damage from oxidative stress contributes to the physiological and anatomical effects of aging. There are two significantly different versions of this theory: one states that the aging process itself is a result of oxidative damage, and the other states that oxidative damage causes age-related disease and disorders. The latter version of the theory is more widely

accepted than the former. However, many lines of evidence suggest that oxidative damage does contribute to the aging process. Research has shown that reducing oxidative damage can result in a longer lifespan in certain organisms such as yeast, worms, and fruit flies. Conversely, increasing oxidative damage can shorten the lifespan of mice and worms. Interestingly, a manipulation called calorie-restriction (moderately restricting the caloric intake) has been shown to increase life span in some laboratory animals. It is believed that this increase is at least in part due to a reduction of oxidative stress. However, a long-term study of primates with calorie-restriction showed no increase in their lifespan. A great deal of additional research will be required to better understand the link between reactive oxygen species and aging.

The Cytoskeleton

Much like the bony skeleton structurally supports the human body, the cytoskeleton helps the cells to maintain their structural integrity. The **cytoskeleton** is a group of fibrous proteins that provide structural support for cells, but this is only one of the functions of the cytoskeleton. Cytoskeletal components are also critical for cell motility, cell reproduction, and transportation of substances within the cell.

The cytoskeleton forms a complex thread-like network throughout the cell consisting of three different kinds of protein-based filaments: microfilaments, intermediate filaments, and microtubules (Figure 3.18). The thickest of the three is the **microtubule**, a structural filament composed of subunits of a protein called tubulin. Microtubules maintain cell shape and structure, help resist compression of the cell, and play a role in positioning the organelles within the cell. Microtubules also make up two types of cellular appendages important for motion: cilia and flagella. **Cilia** are found on many cells of the body, including the epithelial cells that line the airways of the respiratory system. Cilia move rhythmically; they beat constantly, moving waste materials such as dust, mucus, and bacteria upward through the airways, away from the lungs and toward the mouth. Beating cilia on cells in the female fallopian tubes move egg cells from the ovary towards the uterus. A **flagellum** (plural = flagella) is an appendage larger than a cilium and specialized for cell locomotion. The only flagellated cell in humans is the sperm cell that must propel itself towards female egg cells.

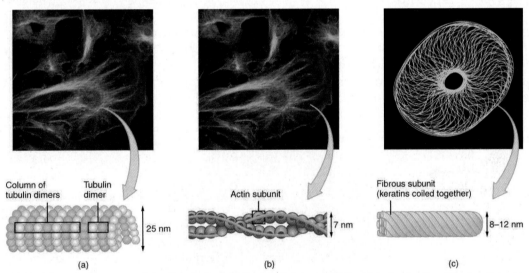

FIGURE 3.18   The Three Components of the Cytoskeleton   The cytoskeleton consists of (a) microtubules, (b) microfilaments, and (c) intermediate filaments. The cytoskeleton plays an important role in maintaining cell shape and structure, promoting cellular movement, and aiding cell division.

A very important function of microtubules is to set the paths (somewhat like railroad tracks) along which the genetic material can be pulled (a process requiring ATP) during cell division, so that each new daughter cell receives the appropriate set of chromosomes. Two short, identical microtubule structures called centrioles are found near the nucleus of cells. A **centriole** can serve as the cellular origin point for microtubules extending outward as cilia or flagella or can assist with the separation of DNA during cell division. Microtubules grow out from the centrioles by adding more tubulin subunits, like adding additional links to a chain.

In contrast with microtubules, the **microfilament** is a thinner type of cytoskeletal filament (see Figure 3.18**b**). Actin, a protein that forms chains, is the primary component of these microfilaments. Actin fibers, twisted chains of actin filaments, constitute a large component of muscle tissue and, along with the protein myosin, are responsible for muscle contraction. Like microtubules, actin filaments are long chains of single subunits (called actin subunits). In muscle cells, these long actin strands, called thin filaments, are "pulled" by thick filaments of the myosin protein to contract the cell.

Actin also has an important role during cell division. When a cell is about to split in half during cell division, actin filaments work with myosin to create a cleavage furrow that eventually splits the cell down the middle, forming two new cells from the original cell.

The final cytoskeletal filament is the intermediate filament. As its name would suggest, an **intermediate filament** is a filament intermediate in thickness between the microtubules and microfilaments (see Figure 3.18**c**). Intermediate filaments are made up of long fibrous subunits of a protein called keratin that are wound together like the threads that compose a rope. Intermediate filaments, in concert with the microtubules, are important for maintaining cell shape and structure. Unlike the microtubules, which resist compression, intermediate filaments resist tension—the forces that pull apart cells. There are many cases in which cells are prone to tension, such as when epithelial cells of the skin are compressed, tugging them in different directions. Intermediate filaments help anchor organelles together within a cell and also link cells to other cells by forming special cell-to-cell junctions.

3.3 The Nucleus and DNA Replication

LEARNING OBJECTIVES

By the end of this section, you will be able to:

- Describe the structure and features of the nuclear membrane
- List the contents of the nucleus
- Explain the organization of the DNA molecule within the nucleus
- Describe the process of DNA replication

The nucleus is the largest and most prominent of a cell's organelles (Figure 3.19). The nucleus is generally considered the control center of the cell because it stores all of the genetic instructions for manufacturing proteins. Interestingly, some cells in the body, such as muscle cells, contain more than one nucleus (Figure 3.20), which is known as multinucleated. Other cells, such as mammalian red blood cells (RBCs), do not contain nuclei at all. RBCs eject their nuclei as they mature, making space for the large numbers of hemoglobin molecules that carry oxygen throughout the body (Figure 3.21). Without nuclei, the life span of RBCs is short, and so the body must produce new ones constantly.

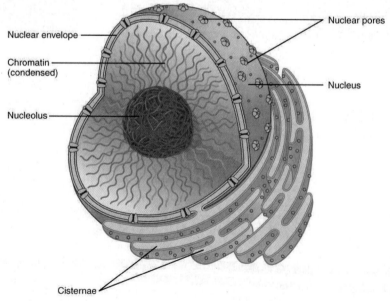

FIGURE 3.19   The Nucleus   The nucleus is the control center of the cell. The nucleus of living cells contains the genetic material that determines the entire structure and function of that cell.

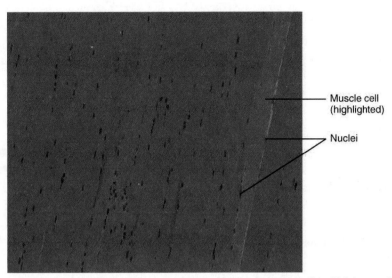

Muscle cell
(highlighted)

Nuclei

FIGURE 3.20   Multinucleate Muscle Cell   Unlike cardiac muscle cells and smooth muscle cells, which have a single nucleus, a skeletal muscle cell contains many nuclei, and is referred to as "multinucleated." These muscle cells are long and fibrous (often referred to as muscle fibers). During development, many smaller cells fuse to form a mature muscle fiber. The nuclei of the fused cells are conserved in the mature cell, thus imparting a multinucleate characteristic to mature muscle cells. LM × 104.3. (Micrograph provided by the Regents of University of Michigan Medical School © 2012)

🔗 INTERACTIVE LINK

View the University of Michigan WebScope (http://openstax.org/l/mnucleate) to explore the tissue sample in greater detail.

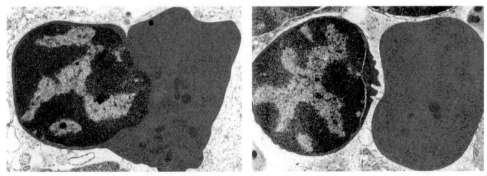

FIGURE 3.21   Red Blood Cell Extruding Its Nucleus   Mature red blood cells lack a nucleus. As they mature, erythroblasts extrude their nucleus, making room for more hemoglobin. The two panels here show an erythroblast before and after ejecting its nucleus, respectively. (credit: modification of micrograph provided by the Regents of University of Michigan Medical School © 2012)

🔗 INTERACTIVE LINK

View the University of Michigan WebScope (http://openstax.org/l/RBC) to explore the tissue sample in greater detail.

Inside the nucleus lies the blueprint that dictates everything a cell will do and all of the products it will make. This information is stored within DNA. The nucleus sends "commands" to the cell via molecular messengers that translate the information from DNA. Each cell in your body (with the exception of germ cells) contains the complete set of your DNA. When a cell divides, the DNA must be duplicated so that the each new cell receives a full complement of DNA. The following section will explore the structure of the nucleus and its contents, as well as the process of DNA replication.

Organization of the Nucleus and Its DNA

Like most other cellular organelles, the nucleus is surrounded by a membrane called the **nuclear envelope**. This membranous covering consists of two adjacent lipid bilayers with a thin fluid space in between them. Spanning these two bilayers are nuclear pores. A **nuclear pore** is a tiny passageway for the passage of proteins, RNA, and solutes between the nucleus and the cytoplasm. Proteins called pore complexes lining the nuclear pores regulate the passage of materials into and out of the nucleus.

Inside the nuclear envelope is a gel-like nucleoplasm with solutes that include the building blocks of nucleic acids. There also can be a dark-staining mass often visible under a simple light microscope, called a **nucleolus** (plural = nucleoli). The nucleolus is a region of the nucleus that is responsible for manufacturing the RNA necessary for construction of ribosomes. Once synthesized, newly made ribosomal subunits exit the cell's nucleus through the nuclear pores.

The genetic instructions that are used to build and maintain an organism are arranged in an orderly manner in strands of DNA. Within the nucleus are threads of **chromatin** composed of DNA and associated proteins (Figure 3.22). Along the chromatin threads, the DNA is wrapped around a set of **histone** proteins. A **nucleosome** is a single, wrapped DNA-histone complex. Multiple nucleosomes along the entire molecule of DNA appear like a beaded necklace, in which the string is the DNA and the beads are the associated histones. When a cell is in the process of division, the chromatin condenses into chromosomes, so that the DNA can be safely transported to the "daughter cells." The **chromosome** is composed of DNA and proteins; it is the condensed form of chromatin. It is estimated that humans have almost 22,000 genes distributed on 46 chromosomes.

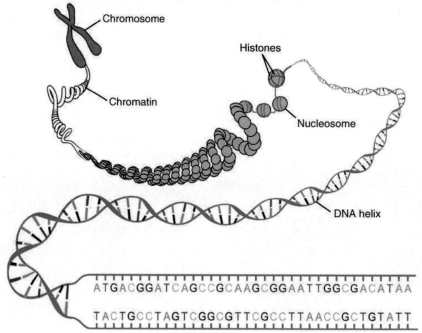

ATGACGGATCAGCCGCAAGCGGAATTGGCGACATAA
TACTGCCTAGTCGGCGTTCGCCTTAACCGCTGTATT

FIGURE 3.22 DNA Macrostructure   Strands of DNA are wrapped around supporting histones. These proteins are increasingly bundled and condensed into chromatin, which is packed tightly into chromosomes when the cell is ready to divide.

DNA Replication

In order for an organism to grow, develop, and maintain its health, cells must reproduce themselves by dividing to produce two new daughter cells, each with the full complement of DNA as found in the original cell. Billions of new cells are produced in an adult human every day. Only very few cell types in the body do not divide, including nerve cells, skeletal muscle fibers, and cardiac muscle cells. The division time of different cell types varies. Epithelial cells of the skin and gastrointestinal lining, for instance, divide very frequently to replace those that are constantly being rubbed off of the surface by friction.

A DNA molecule is made of two strands that "complement" each other in the sense that the molecules that compose the strands fit together and bind to each other, creating a double-stranded molecule that looks much like a long, twisted ladder. This double helix can be constructed easily because the two strands are antiparallel, meaning the two strands run in opposite directions. Each side rail of the DNA ladder is composed of alternating sugar and phosphate groups (Figure 3.23). The two sides of the ladder are not identical, but are complementary. These two backbones are bonded to each other across pairs of protruding bases, each bonded pair forming one "rung," or cross member. The four DNA bases are adenine (A), thymine (T), cytosine (C), and guanine (G). Because of their shape and charge, the two bases that compose a pair always bond together. Adenine always binds with thymine, and

Access for free at openstax.org

cytosine always binds with guanine. The particular sequence of bases along the DNA molecule determines the genetic code. Therefore, if the two complementary strands of DNA were pulled apart, you could infer the order of the bases in one strand from the bases in the other, complementary strand. For example, if one strand has a region with the sequence AGTGCCT, then the sequence of the complementary strand would be TCACGGA.

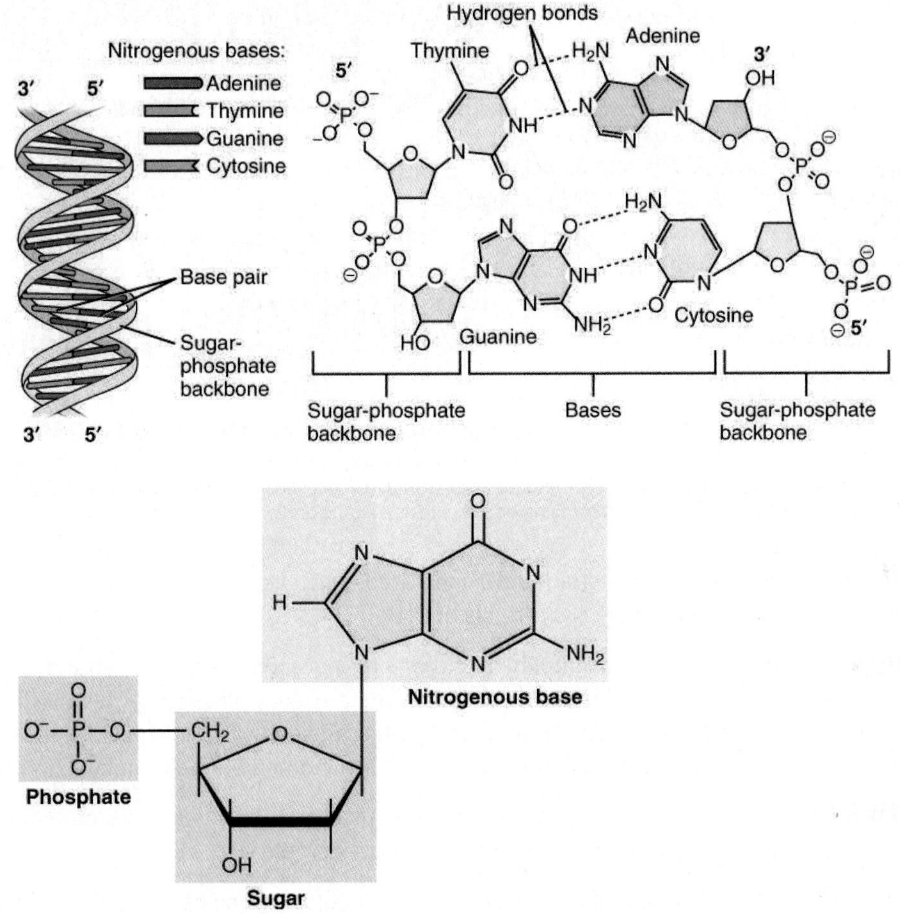

FIGURE 3.23   **Molecular Structure of DNA**   The DNA double helix is composed of two complementary strands. The strands are bonded together via their nitrogenous base pairs using hydrogen bonds.

DNA replication is the copying of DNA that occurs before cell division can take place. After a great deal of debate and experimentation, the general method of DNA replication was deduced in 1958 by two scientists in California, Matthew Meselson and Franklin Stahl. This method is illustrated in <u>Figure 3.24</u> and described below.

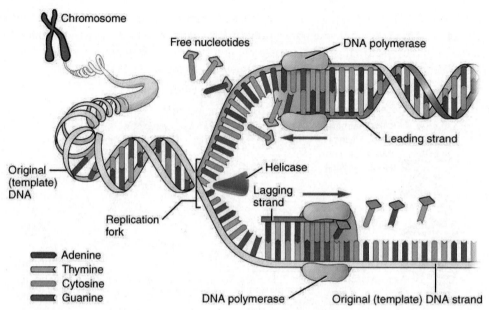

FIGURE 3.24 **DNA Replication** DNA replication faithfully duplicates the entire genome of the cell. During DNA replication, a number of different enzymes work together to pull apart the two strands so each strand can be used as a template to synthesize new complementary strands. The two new daughter DNA molecules each contain one pre-existing strand and one newly synthesized strand. Thus, DNA replication is said to be "semiconservative."

Stage 1: Initiation. The two complementary strands are separated, much like unzipping a zipper. Special enzymes, including **helicase**, untwist and separate the two strands of DNA.

Stage 2: Elongation. Each strand becomes a template along which a new complementary strand is built. **DNA polymerase** brings in the correct bases to complement the template strand, synthesizing a new strand base by base. A DNA polymerase is an enzyme that adds free nucleotides to the end of a chain of DNA, making a new double strand. This growing strand continues to be built until it has fully complemented the template strand.

Stage 3: Termination. Once the two original strands are bound to their own, finished, complementary strands, DNA replication is stopped and the two new identical DNA molecules are complete.

Each new DNA molecule contains one strand from the original molecule and one newly synthesized strand. The term for this mode of replication is "semiconservative," because half of the original DNA molecule is conserved in each new DNA molecule. This process continues until the cell's entire **genome**, the entire complement of an organism's DNA, is replicated. As you might imagine, it is very important that DNA replication take place precisely so that new cells in the body contain the exact same genetic material as their parent cells. Mistakes made during DNA replication, such as the accidental addition of an inappropriate nucleotide, have the potential to render a gene dysfunctional or useless. Fortunately, there are mechanisms in place to minimize such mistakes. A DNA proofreading process enlists the help of special enzymes that scan the newly synthesized molecule for mistakes and corrects them. Once the process of DNA replication is complete, the cell is ready to divide. You will explore the process of cell division later in the chapter.

⊛ INTERACTIVE LINK

Watch this video (http://openstax.org/l/DNArep) to learn about DNA replication. DNA replication proceeds simultaneously at several sites on the same molecule. What separates the base pair at the start of DNA replication?

3.4 Protein Synthesis

LEARNING OBJECTIVES

By the end of this section, you will be able to:

- Explain how the genetic code stored within DNA determines the protein that will form
- Describe the process of transcription
- Describe the process of translation
- Discuss the function of ribosomes

It was mentioned earlier that DNA provides a "blueprint" for the cell structure and physiology. This refers to the fact that DNA contains the information necessary for the cell to build one very important type of molecule: the protein. Most structural components of the cell are made up, at least in part, by proteins and virtually all the functions that a cell carries out are completed with the help of proteins. One of the most important classes of proteins is enzymes, which help speed up necessary biochemical reactions that take place inside the cell. Some of these critical biochemical reactions include building larger molecules from smaller components (such as occurs during DNA replication or synthesis of microtubules) and breaking down larger molecules into smaller components (such as when harvesting chemical energy from nutrient molecules). Whatever the cellular process may be, it is almost sure to involve proteins. Just as the cell's genome describes its full complement of DNA, a cell's **proteome** is its full complement of proteins. Protein synthesis begins with genes. A **gene** is a functional segment of DNA that provides the genetic information necessary to build a protein. Each particular gene provides the code necessary to construct a particular protein. **Gene expression**, which transforms the information coded in a gene to a final gene product, ultimately dictates the structure and function of a cell by determining which proteins are made.

The interpretation of genes works in the following way. Recall that proteins are polymers, or chains, of many amino acid building blocks. The sequence of bases in a gene (that is, its sequence of A, T, C, G nucleotides) translates to an amino acid sequence. A **triplet** is a section of three DNA bases in a row that codes for a specific amino acid. Similar to the way in which the three-letter code *d-o-g* signals the image of a dog, the three-letter DNA base code signals the use of a particular amino acid. For example, the DNA triplet CAC (cytosine, adenine, and cytosine) specifies the amino acid valine. Therefore, a gene, which is composed of multiple triplets in a unique sequence, provides the code to build an entire protein, with multiple amino acids in the proper sequence (Figure 3.25). The mechanism by which cells turn the DNA code into a protein product is a two-step process, with an RNA molecule as the intermediate.

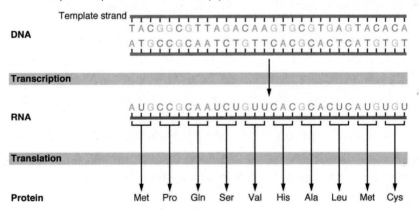

FIGURE 3.25   The Genetic Code   DNA holds all of the genetic information necessary to build a cell's proteins. The nucleotide sequence of a gene is ultimately translated into an amino acid sequence of the gene's corresponding protein.

From DNA to RNA: Transcription

DNA is housed within the nucleus, and protein synthesis takes place in the cytoplasm, thus there must be some sort of intermediate messenger that leaves the nucleus and manages protein synthesis. This intermediate messenger is **messenger RNA (mRNA)**, a single-stranded nucleic acid that carries a copy of the genetic code for a single gene out of the nucleus and into the cytoplasm where it is used to produce proteins.

There are several different types of RNA, each having different functions in the cell. The structure of RNA is similar to DNA with a few small exceptions. For one thing, unlike DNA, most types of RNA, including mRNA, are single-stranded and contain no complementary strand. Second, the ribose sugar in RNA contains an additional oxygen atom compared with DNA. Finally, instead of the base thymine, RNA contains the base uracil. This means that adenine will always pair up with uracil during the protein synthesis process.

Gene expression begins with the process called **transcription,** which is the synthesis of a strand of mRNA that is complementary to the gene of interest. This process is called transcription because the mRNA is like a transcript, or copy, of the gene's DNA code. Transcription begins in a fashion somewhat like DNA replication, in that a region of DNA unwinds and the two strands separate, however, only that small portion of the DNA will be split apart. The triplets within the gene on this section of the DNA molecule are used as the template to transcribe the complementary strand of RNA (Figure 3.26). A **codon** is a three-base sequence of mRNA, so-called because they directly encode amino acids. Like DNA replication, there are three stages to transcription: initiation, elongation, and termination.

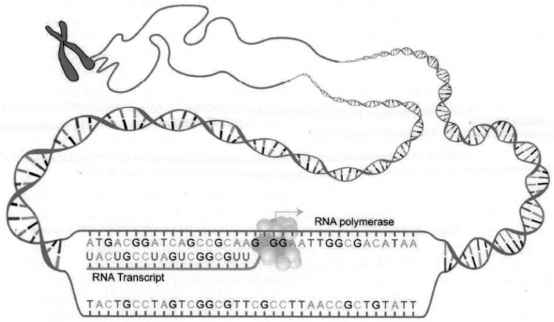

FIGURE 3.26   Transcription: from DNA to mRNA   In the first of the two stages of making protein from DNA, a gene on the DNA molecule is transcribed into a complementary mRNA molecule.

Stage 1: Initiation. A region at the beginning of the gene called a **promoter**—a particular sequence of nucleotides—triggers the start of transcription.

Stage 2: Elongation. Transcription starts when RNA polymerase unwinds the DNA segment. One strand, referred to as the coding strand, becomes the template with the genes to be coded. The polymerase then aligns the correct nucleic acid (A, C, G, or U) with its complementary base on the coding strand of DNA. **RNA polymerase** is an enzyme that adds new nucleotides to a growing strand of RNA. This process builds a strand of mRNA.

Stage 3: Termination. At the end of the gene, a sequence of nucleotides called the terminator sequence causes the new RNA to fold up on itself. This fold causes the RNA to separate from the gene and from RNA polymerase, ending transcription.

Before the mRNA molecule leaves the nucleus and proceeds to protein synthesis, it is modified in a number of ways. For this reason, it is often called a pre-mRNA at this stage. For example, your DNA, and thus complementary mRNA, contains long regions called non-coding regions that do not code for amino acids. Their function is still a mystery, but the process called **splicing** removes these non-coding regions from the pre-mRNA transcript (Figure 3.27). A **spliceosome**—a structure composed of various proteins and other molecules—attaches to the mRNA and "splices" or cuts out the non-coding regions. The removed segment of the transcript is called an **intron**. The remaining exons are pasted together. An **exon** is a segment of RNA that remains after splicing. Interestingly, some introns that are removed from mRNA are not always non-coding. When different coding regions of mRNA are spliced out, different variations of the protein will eventually result, with differences in structure and function. This process results in a much larger variety of possible proteins and protein functions. When the mRNA transcript is ready, it travels out of the nucleus and into the cytoplasm.

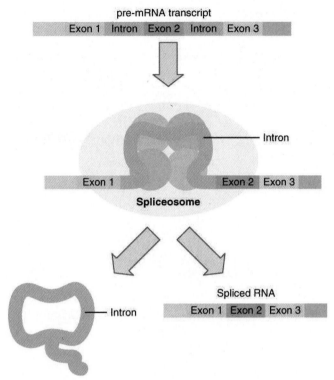

FIGURE 3.27   Splicing DNA   In the nucleus, a structure called a spliceosome cuts out introns (noncoding regions) within a pre-mRNA transcript and reconnects the exons.

From RNA to Protein: Translation

Like translating a book from one language into another, the codons on a strand of mRNA must be translated into the amino acid alphabet of proteins. **Translation** is the process of synthesizing a chain of amino acids called a **polypeptide**. Translation requires two major aids: first, a "translator," the molecule that will conduct the translation, and second, a substrate on which the mRNA strand is translated into a new protein, like the translator's "desk." Both of these requirements are fulfilled by other types of RNA. The substrate on which translation takes place is the ribosome.

Remember that many of a cell's ribosomes are found associated with the rough ER, and carry out the synthesis of proteins destined for the Golgi apparatus. **Ribosomal RNA (rRNA)** is a type of RNA that, together with proteins, composes the structure of the ribosome. Ribosomes exist in the cytoplasm as two distinct components, a small and a large subunit. When an mRNA molecule is ready to be translated, the two subunits come together and attach to the mRNA. The ribosome provides a substrate for translation, bringing together and aligning the mRNA molecule with the molecular "translators" that must decipher its code.

The other major requirement for protein synthesis is the translator molecules that physically "read" the mRNA codons. **Transfer RNA (tRNA)** is a type of RNA that ferries the appropriate corresponding amino acids to the ribosome, and attaches each new amino acid to the last, building the polypeptide chain one-by-one. Thus tRNA transfers specific amino acids from the cytoplasm to a growing polypeptide. The tRNA molecules must be able to recognize the codons on mRNA and match them with the correct amino acid. The tRNA is modified for this function. On one end of its structure is a binding site for a specific amino acid. On the other end is a base sequence that matches the codon specifying its particular amino acid. This sequence of three bases on the tRNA molecule is called an **anticodon**. For example, a tRNA responsible for shuttling the amino acid glycine contains a binding site for glycine on one end. On the other end it contains an anticodon that complements the glycine codon (GGA is a codon for glycine, and so the tRNAs anticodon would read CCU). Equipped with its particular cargo and matching anticodon, a tRNA molecule can read its recognized mRNA codon and bring the corresponding amino acid to the growing chain (Figure 3.28).

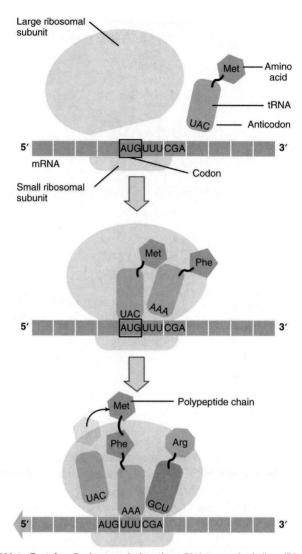

FIGURE 3.28 Translation from RNA to Protein   During translation, the mRNA transcript is "read" by a functional complex consisting of the ribosome and tRNA molecules. tRNAs bring the appropriate amino acids in sequence to the growing polypeptide chain by matching their anti-codons with codons on the mRNA strand.

Much like the processes of DNA replication and transcription, translation consists of three main stages: initiation, elongation, and termination. Initiation takes place with the binding of a ribosome to an mRNA transcript. The elongation stage involves the recognition of a tRNA anticodon with the next mRNA codon in the sequence. Once the anticodon and codon sequences are bound (remember, they are complementary base pairs), the tRNA presents its amino acid cargo and the growing polypeptide strand is attached to this next amino acid. This attachment takes place with the assistance of various enzymes and requires energy. The tRNA molecule then releases the mRNA strand, the mRNA strand shifts one codon over in the ribosome, and the next appropriate tRNA arrives with its matching anticodon. This process continues until the final codon on the mRNA is reached which provides a "stop" message that signals termination of translation and triggers the release of the complete, newly synthesized protein. Thus, a gene within the DNA molecule is transcribed into mRNA, which is then translated into a protein product (Figure 3.29).

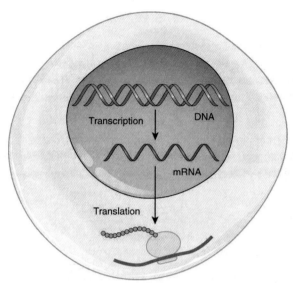

FIGURE 3.29 From DNA to Protein: Transcription through Translation   Transcription within the cell nucleus produces an mRNA molecule, which is modified and then sent into the cytoplasm for translation. The transcript is decoded into a protein with the help of a ribosome and tRNA molecules.

Commonly, an mRNA transcription will be translated simultaneously by several adjacent ribosomes. This increases the efficiency of protein synthesis. A single ribosome might translate an mRNA molecule in approximately one minute; so multiple ribosomes aboard a single transcript could produce multiple times the number of the same protein in the same minute. A **polyribosome** is a string of ribosomes translating a single mRNA strand.

⊚ INTERACTIVE LINK

Watch this video (http://openstax.org/l/ribosome) to learn about ribosomes. The ribosome binds to the mRNA molecule to start translation of its code into a protein. What happens to the small and large ribosomal subunits at the end of translation?

3.5 Cell Growth and Division

LEARNING OBJECTIVES

By the end of this section, you will be able to:

- Describe the stages of the cell cycle
- Discuss how the cell cycle is regulated
- Describe the implications of losing control over the cell cycle
- Describe the stages of mitosis and cytokinesis, in order

So far in this chapter, you have read numerous times of the importance and prevalence of cell division. While there are a few cells in the body that do not undergo cell division (such as gametes, red blood cells, most neurons, and some muscle cells), most somatic cells divide regularly. A **somatic cell** is a general term for a body cell, and all human cells, except for the cells that produce eggs and sperm (which are referred to as germ cells), are somatic cells. Somatic cells contain *two* copies of each of their chromosomes (one copy received from each parent). A **homologous** pair of chromosomes is the two copies of a single chromosome found in each somatic cell. The human is a **diploid** organism, having 23 homologous pairs of chromosomes in each of the somatic cells. The condition of having pairs of chromosomes is known as diploidy.

Cells in the body replace themselves over the lifetime of a person. For example, the cells lining the gastrointestinal tract must be frequently replaced when constantly "worn off" by the movement of food through the gut. But what triggers a cell to divide, and how does it prepare for and complete cell division? The **cell cycle** is the sequence of events in the life of the cell from the moment it is created at the end of a previous cycle of cell division until it then divides itself, generating two new cells.

The Cell Cycle

One "turn" or cycle of the cell cycle consists of two general phases: interphase, followed by mitosis and cytokinesis. **Interphase** is the period of the cell cycle during which the cell is not dividing. The majority of cells are in interphase most of the time. **Mitosis** is the division of genetic material, during which the cell nucleus breaks down and two new, fully functional, nuclei are formed. **Cytokinesis** divides the cytoplasm into two distinctive cells.

Interphase

A cell grows and carries out all normal metabolic functions and processes in a period called G_1 (Figure 3.30). **G_1 phase** (gap 1 phase) is the first gap, or growth phase in the cell cycle. For cells that will divide again, G_1 is followed by replication of the DNA, during the S phase. The **S phase** (synthesis phase) is period during which a cell replicates its DNA.

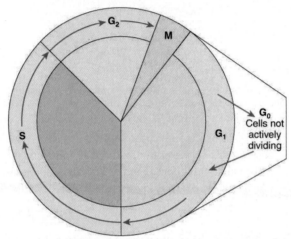

FIGURE 3.30   Cell Cycle   The two major phases of the cell cycle include mitosis (designated M), when the cell divides, and interphase, when the cell grows and performs all of its normal functions. Interphase is further subdivided into G_1, S, and G_2 phases.

After the synthesis phase, the cell proceeds through the G_2 phase. The **G_2 phase** is a second gap phase, during which the cell continues to grow and makes the necessary preparations for mitosis. Between G_1, S, and G_2 phases, cells will vary the most in their duration of the G1 phase. It is here that a cell might spend a couple of hours, or many days. The S phase typically lasts between 8-10 hours and the G_2 phase approximately 5 hours. In contrast to these phases, the **G_0 phase** is a resting phase of the cell cycle. Cells that have temporarily stopped dividing and are resting (a common condition) and cells that have permanently ceased dividing (like nerve cells) are said to be in G_0.

The Structure of Chromosomes

Billions of cells in the human body divide every day. During the synthesis phase (S, for DNA synthesis) of interphase, the amount of DNA within the cell precisely doubles. Therefore, after DNA replication but before cell division, each cell actually contains *two* copies of each chromosome. Each copy of the chromosome is referred to as a **sister chromatid** and is physically bound to the other copy.(Note that the term "sister chromatid" is used regardless of the sex of the person.) The **centromere** is the structure that attaches one sister chromatid to another. Because a human cell has 46 chromosomes, during this phase, there are 92 chromatids (46 × 2) in the cell. Make sure not to confuse the concept of a pair of chromatids (one chromosome and its exact copy attached during mitosis) and a homologous pair of chromosomes (two paired chromosomes which were inherited separately, one from each parent) (Figure 3.31).

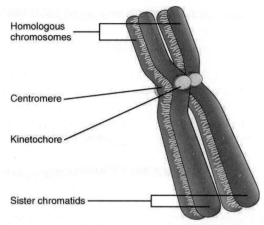

Homologous
chromosomes

Centromere

Kinetochore

Sister chromatids

FIGURE 3.31   A Homologous Pair of Chromosomes with their Attached Sister Chromatids   The red and blue colors correspond to a homologous pair of chromosomes. Each member of the pair was separately inherited from one parent. Each chromosome in the homologous pair is also bound to an identical sister chromatid, which is produced by DNA replication, and results in the familiar "X" shape.

Mitosis and Cytokinesis

The **mitotic phase** of the cell typically takes between 1 and 2 hours. During this phase, a cell undergoes two major processes. First, it completes mitosis, during which the contents of the nucleus are equitably pulled apart and distributed between its two halves. Cytokinesis then occurs, dividing the cytoplasm and cell body into two new cells. Mitosis is divided into four major stages that take place after interphase (Figure 3.32) and in the following order: prophase, metaphase, anaphase, and telophase. The process is then followed by cytokinesis.

Prophase	Prometaphase	Metaphase	Anaphase	Telophase	Cytokinesis
• Chromosomes condense and become visible • Spindle fibers emerge from the centrosomes • Nuclear envelope breaks down • Centrosomes move toward opposite poles	• Chromosomes continue to condense • Kinetochores appear at the centromeres • Mitotic spindle microtubules attach to kinetochores	• Chromosomes are lined up at the metaphase plate • Each sister chromatid is attached to a spindle fiber originating from opposite poles	• Centromeres split in two • Sister chromatids (now called chromosomes) are pulled toward opposite poles • Certain spindle fibers begin to elongate the cell	• Chromosomes arrive at opposite poles and begin to decondense • Nuclear envelope material surrounds each set of chromosomes • The mitotic spindle breaks down • Spindle fibers continue to push poles apart	• Animal cells: a cleavage furrow separates the daughter cells • Plant cells: a cell plate, the precursor to a new cell wall, separates the daughter cells
5 µm	5 µm	5 µm	5 µm	5 µm	5 µm

MITOSIS

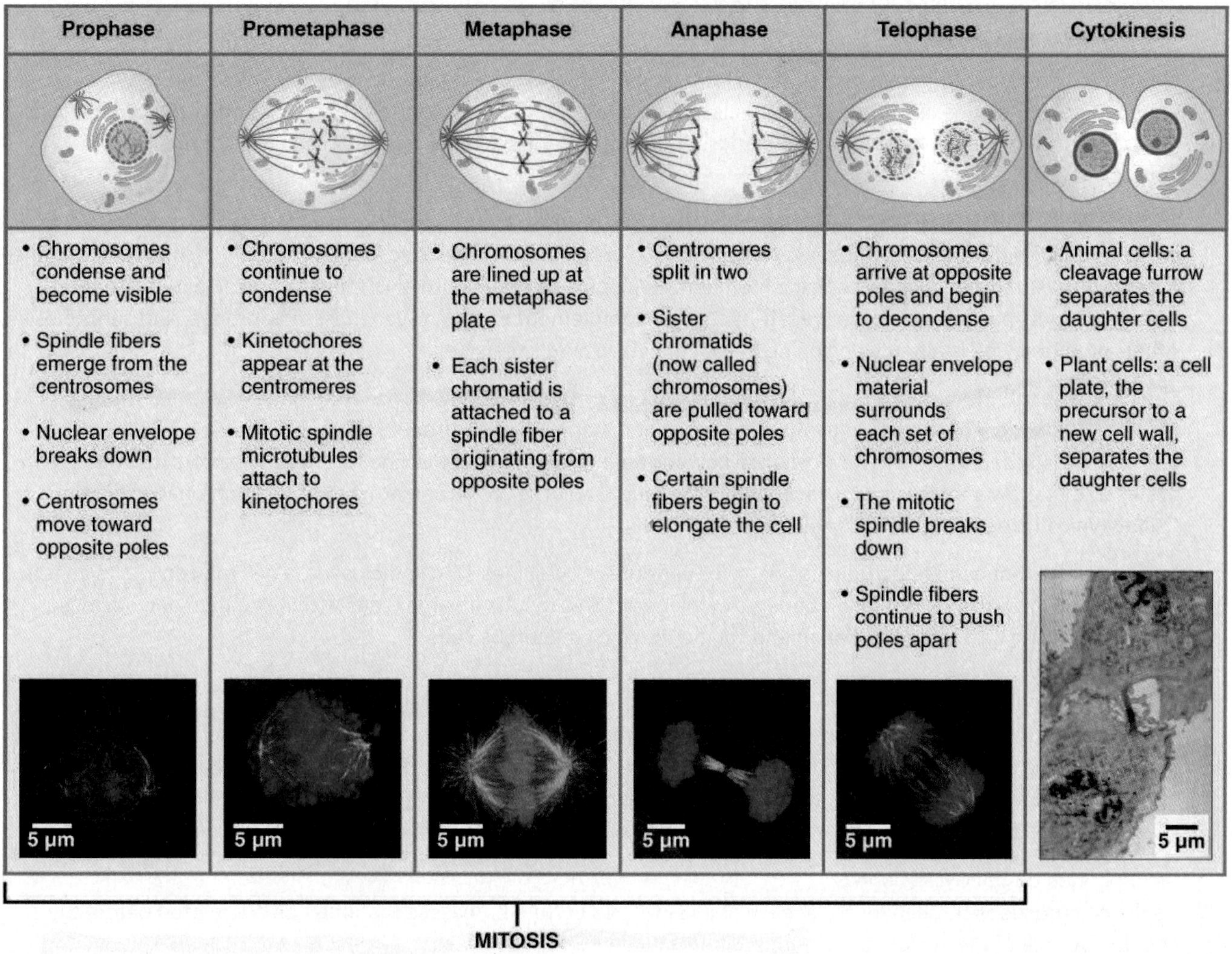

FIGURE 3.32   Cell Division: Mitosis Followed by Cytokinesis   The stages of cell division oversee the separation of identical genetic material into two new nuclei, followed by the division of the cytoplasm.

Prophase is the first phase of mitosis, during which the loosely packed chromatin coils and condenses into visible chromosomes. During prophase, each chromosome becomes visible with its identical partner attached, forming the familiar X-shape of sister chromatids. The nucleolus disappears early during this phase, and the nuclear envelope also disintegrates.

A major occurrence during prophase concerns a very important structure that contains the origin site for microtubule growth. Recall the cellular structures called centrioles that serve as origin points from which microtubules extend. These tiny structures also play a very important role during mitosis. A **centrosome** is a pair of centrioles together. The cell contains two centrosomes side-by-side, which begin to move apart during prophase. As the centrosomes migrate to two different sides of the cell, microtubules begin to extend from each like long fingers from two hands extending toward each other. The **mitotic spindle** is the structure composed of the centrosomes and their emerging microtubules.

Near the end of prophase there is an invasion of the nuclear area by microtubules from the mitotic spindle. The nuclear membrane has disintegrated, and the microtubules attach themselves to the centromeres that adjoin pairs of sister chromatids. The **kinetochore** is a protein structure on the centromere that is the point of attachment between the mitotic spindle and the sister chromatids. This stage is referred to as late prophase or "prometaphase" to indicate the transition between prophase and metaphase.

Metaphase is the second stage of mitosis. During this stage, the sister chromatids, with their attached microtubules, line up along a linear plane in the middle of the cell. A metaphase plate forms between the centrosomes that are now located at either end of the cell. The **metaphase plate** is the name for the plane through the center of the spindle on which the sister chromatids are positioned. The microtubules are now poised to pull apart the sister chromatids and bring one from each pair to each side of the cell.

Anaphase is the third stage of mitosis. Anaphase takes place over a few minutes, when the pairs of sister chromatids are separated from one another, forming individual chromosomes once again. These chromosomes are pulled to opposite ends of the cell by their kinetochores, as the microtubules shorten. Each end of the cell receives one partner from each pair of sister chromatids, ensuring that the two new daughter cells will contain identical genetic material.

Telophase is the final stage of mitosis. Telophase is characterized by the formation of two new daughter nuclei at either end of the dividing cell. These newly formed nuclei surround the genetic material, which uncoils such that the chromosomes return to loosely packed chromatin. Nucleoli also reappear within the new nuclei, and the mitotic spindle breaks apart, each new cell receiving its own complement of DNA, organelles, membranes, and centrioles. At this point, the cell is already beginning to split in half as cytokinesis begins.

The **cleavage furrow** is a contractile band made up of microfilaments that forms around the midline of the cell during cytokinesis. (Recall that microfilaments consist of actin.) This contractile band squeezes the two cells apart until they finally separate. Two new cells are now formed. One of these cells (the "stem cell") enters its own cell cycle; able to grow and divide again at some future time. The other cell transforms into the functional cell of the tissue, typically replacing an "old" cell there.

Imagine a cell that completed mitosis but never underwent cytokinesis. In some cases, a cell may divide its genetic material and grow in size, but fail to undergo cytokinesis. This results in larger cells with more than one nucleus. Usually this is an unwanted aberration and can be a sign of cancerous cells.

Cell Cycle Control

A very elaborate and precise system of regulation controls direct the way cells proceed from one phase to the next in the cell cycle and begin mitosis. The control system involves molecules within the cell as well as external triggers. These internal and external control triggers provide "stop" and "advance" signals for the cell. Precise regulation of the cell cycle is critical for maintaining the health of an organism, and loss of cell cycle control can lead to cancer.

Mechanisms of Cell Cycle Control

As the cell proceeds through its cycle, each phase involves certain processes that must be completed before the cell should advance to the next phase. A **checkpoint** is a point in the cell cycle at which the cycle can be signaled to move forward or stopped. At each of these checkpoints, different varieties of molecules provide the stop or go signals, depending on certain conditions within the cell. A **cyclin** is one of the primary classes of cell cycle control molecules (Figure 3.33). A **cyclin-dependent kinase (CDK)** is one of a group of molecules that work together with cyclins to determine progression past cell checkpoints. By interacting with many additional molecules, these triggers push the cell cycle forward unless prevented from doing so by "stop" signals, if for some reason the cell is not ready. At the G_1 checkpoint, the cell must be ready for DNA synthesis to occur. At the G_2 checkpoint the cell must be fully prepared for mitosis. Even during mitosis, a crucial stop and go checkpoint in metaphase ensures that the cell is fully prepared to complete cell division. The metaphase checkpoint ensures that all sister chromatids are properly attached to their respective microtubules and lined up at the metaphase plate before the signal is given to separate them during anaphase.

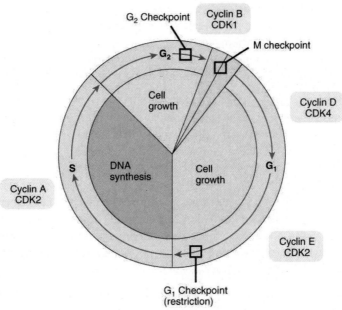

FIGURE 3.33   Control of the Cell Cycle   Cells proceed through the cell cycle under the control of a variety of molecules, such as cyclins and cyclin-dependent kinases. These control molecules determine whether or not the cell is prepared to move into the following stage.

The Cell Cycle Out of Control: Implications

Most people understand that cancer or tumors are caused by abnormal cells that multiply continuously. If the abnormal cells continue to divide unstopped, they can damage the tissues around them, spread to other parts of the body, and eventually result in death. In healthy cells, the tight regulation mechanisms of the cell cycle prevent this from happening, while failures of cell cycle control can cause unwanted and excessive cell division. Failures of control may be caused by inherited genetic abnormalities that compromise the function of certain "stop" and "go" signals. Environmental insult that damages DNA can also cause dysfunction in those signals. Often, a combination of both genetic predisposition and environmental factors lead to cancer.

The process of a cell escaping its normal control system and becoming cancerous may actually happen throughout the body quite frequently. Fortunately, certain cells of the immune system are capable of recognizing cells that have become cancerous and destroying them. However, in certain cases the cancerous cells remain undetected and continue to proliferate. If the resulting tumor does not pose a threat to surrounding tissues, it is said to be benign and can usually be easily removed. If capable of damage, the tumor is considered malignant and the patient is diagnosed with cancer.

 HOMEOSTATIC IMBALANCES

Cancer Arises from Homeostatic Imbalances

Cancer is an extremely complex condition, capable of arising from a wide variety of genetic and environmental causes. Typically, mutations or aberrations in a cell's DNA that compromise normal cell cycle control systems lead to cancerous tumors. Cell cycle control is an example of a homeostatic mechanism that maintains proper cell function and health. While progressing through the phases of the cell cycle, a large variety of intracellular molecules provide stop and go signals to regulate movement forward to the next phase. These signals are maintained in an intricate balance so that the cell only proceeds to the next phase when it is ready. This homeostatic control of the cell cycle can be thought of like a car's cruise control. Cruise control will continually apply just the right amount of acceleration to maintain a desired speed, unless the driver hits the brakes, in which case the car will slow down. Similarly, the cell includes molecular messengers, such as cyclins, that push the cell forward in its cycle.

In addition to cyclins, a class of proteins that are encoded by genes called proto-oncogenes provide important signals that regulate the cell cycle and move it forward. Examples of proto-oncogene products include cell-surface receptors for growth factors, or cell-signaling molecules, two classes of molecules that can promote DNA replication and cell division. In contrast, a second class of genes known as tumor suppressor genes sends stop signals during a cell cycle. For example, certain protein products of tumor suppressor genes signal potential problems with the DNA and thus stop the cell from dividing, while other proteins signal the cell to die if it is damaged beyond repair. Some tumor suppressor proteins also signal a sufficient surrounding cellular density, which indicates that the cell need not presently divide. The latter function is uniquely important in preventing tumor growth: normal cells exhibit a phenomenon called "contact inhibition;" thus, extensive cellular contact with neighboring cells causes a signal that stops further cell division.

These two contrasting classes of genes, proto-oncogenes and tumor suppressor genes, are like the accelerator and brake pedal of the cell's own "cruise control system," respectively. Under normal conditions, these stop and go signals are maintained in a homeostatic balance. Generally speaking, there are two ways that the cell's cruise control can lose control: a malfunctioning (overactive) accelerator, or a malfunctioning (underactive) brake. When compromised through a mutation, or otherwise altered, proto-oncogenes can be converted to oncogenes, which produce oncoproteins that push a cell forward in its cycle and stimulate cell division even when it is undesirable to do so. For example, a cell that should be programmed to self-destruct (a process called apoptosis) due to extensive DNA damage might instead be triggered to proliferate by an oncoprotein. On the other hand, a dysfunctional tumor suppressor gene may fail to provide the cell with a necessary stop signal, also resulting in unwanted cell division and proliferation.

A delicate homeostatic balance between the many proto-oncogenes and tumor suppressor genes delicately controls the cell cycle and ensures that only healthy cells replicate. Therefore, a disruption of this homeostatic balance can cause aberrant cell division and cancerous growths.

⊘ INTERACTIVE LINK

Visit this link (http://openstax.org/l/mitosis) to learn about mitosis. Mitosis results in two identical diploid cells. What structures forms during prophase?

3.6 Cellular Differentiation

LEARNING OBJECTIVES

By the end of this section, you will be able to:

- Discuss how the generalized cells of a developing embryo or the stem cells of an adult organism become differentiated into specialized cells
- Distinguish between the categories of stem cells

How does a complex organism such as a human develop from a single cell—a fertilized egg—into the vast array of cell types such as nerve cells, muscle cells, and epithelial cells that characterize the adult? Throughout development and adulthood, the process of cellular differentiation leads cells to assume their final morphology and physiology. Differentiation is the process by which unspecialized cells become specialized to carry out distinct functions.

Stem Cells

A **stem cell** is an unspecialized cell that can divide without limit as needed and can, under specific conditions, differentiate into specialized cells. Stem cells are divided into several categories according to their potential to differentiate.

The first embryonic cells that arise from the division of the zygote are the ultimate stem cells; these stems cells are described as **totipotent** because they have the potential to differentiate into any of the cells needed to enable an organism to grow and develop.

The embryonic cells that develop from totipotent stem cells and are precursors to the fundamental tissue layers of the embryo are classified as pluripotent. A **pluripotent** stem cell is one that has the potential to differentiate into any type of human tissue but cannot support the full development of an organism. These cells then become slightly more specialized, and are referred to as multipotent cells.

A **multipotent** stem cell has the potential to differentiate into different types of cells within a given cell lineage or small number of lineages, such as a red blood cell or white blood cell.

Finally, multipotent cells can become further specialized oligopotent cells. An **oligopotent** stem cell is limited to becoming one of a few different cell types. In contrast, a **unipotent** cell is fully specialized and can only reproduce to generate more of its own specific cell type.

Stem cells are unique in that they can also continually divide and regenerate new stem cells instead of further specializing. There are different stem cells present at different stages of a human's life. They include the embryonic stem cells of the embryo, fetal stem cells of the fetus, and adult stem cells in the adult. One type of adult stem cell is the epithelial stem cell, which gives rise to the keratinocytes in the multiple layers of epithelial cells in the epidermis of skin. Adult bone marrow has three distinct types of stem cells: hematopoietic stem cells, which give rise to red blood cells, white blood cells, and platelets (Figure 3.34); endothelial stem cells, which give rise to the endothelial cell types that line blood and lymph vessels; and mesenchymal stem cells, which give rise to the different types of muscle cells.

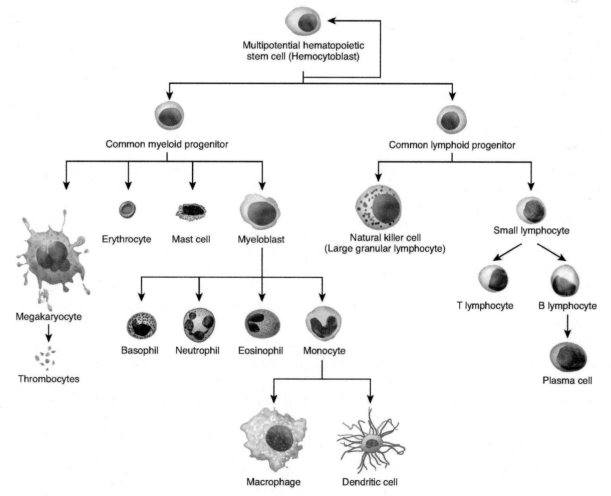

FIGURE 3.34 Hematopoiesis The process of hematopoiesis involves the differentiation of multipotent cells into blood and immune cells. The multipotent hematopoietic stem cells give rise to many different cell types, including the cells of the immune system and red

blood cells.

Differentiation

When a cell differentiates (becomes more specialized), it may undertake major changes in its size, shape, metabolic activity, and overall function. Because all cells in the body, beginning with the fertilized egg, contain the same DNA, how do the different cell types come to be so different? The answer is analogous to a movie script. The different actors in a movie all read from the same script, however, they are each only reading their own part of the script. Similarly, all cells contain the same full complement of DNA, but each type of cell only "reads" the portions of DNA that are relevant to its own function. In biology, this is referred to as the unique genetic expression of each cell.

In order for a cell to differentiate into its specialized form and function, it need only manipulate those genes (and thus those proteins) that will be expressed, and not those that will remain silent. The primary mechanism by which genes are turned "on" or "off" is through transcription factors. A **transcription factor** is one of a class of proteins that bind to specific genes on the DNA molecule and either promote or inhibit their transcription (Figure 3.35).

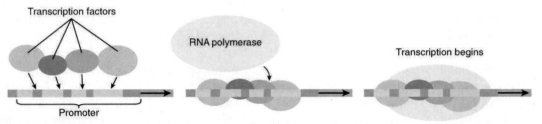

FIGURE 3.35   Transcription Factors Regulate Gene Expression   While each body cell contains the organism's entire genome, different cells regulate gene expression with the use of various transcription factors. Transcription factors are proteins that affect the binding of RNA polymerase to a particular gene on the DNA molecule.

Everyday Connection

Stem Cell Research

Stem cell research aims to find ways to use stem cells to regenerate and repair cellular damage. Over time, most adult cells undergo the wear and tear of aging and lose their ability to divide and repair themselves. Stem cells do not display a particular morphology or function. Adult stem cells, which exist as a small subset of cells in most tissues, keep dividing and can differentiate into a number of specialized cells generally formed by that tissue. These cells enable the body to renew and repair body tissues.

The mechanisms that induce a non-differentiated cell to become a specialized cell are poorly understood. In a laboratory setting, it is possible to induce stem cells to differentiate into specialized cells by changing the physical and chemical conditions of growth. Several sources of stem cells are used experimentally and are classified according to their origin and potential for differentiation. Human embryonic stem cells (hESCs) are extracted from embryos and are pluripotent. The adult stem cells that are present in many organs and differentiated tissues, such as bone marrow and skin, are multipotent, being limited in differentiation to the types of cells found in those tissues. The stem cells isolated from umbilical cord blood are also multipotent, as are cells from deciduous teeth (baby teeth). Researchers have recently developed induced pluripotent stem cells (iPSCs) from mouse and human adult stem cells. These cells are genetically reprogrammed multipotent adult cells that function like embryonic stem cells; they are capable of generating cells characteristic of all three germ layers.

Because of their capacity to divide and differentiate into specialized cells, stem cells offer a potential treatment for diseases such as diabetes and heart disease (Figure 3.36). Cell-based therapy refers to treatment in which stem cells induced to differentiate in a growth dish are injected into a patient to repair damaged or destroyed cells or tissues. Many obstacles must be overcome for the application of cell-based therapy. Although embryonic stem cells have a nearly unlimited range of differentiation potential, they are seen as foreign by the patient's immune system and may trigger rejection. Also, the destruction of embryos to isolate embryonic stem cells raises considerable ethical and legal questions.

Access for free at openstax.org

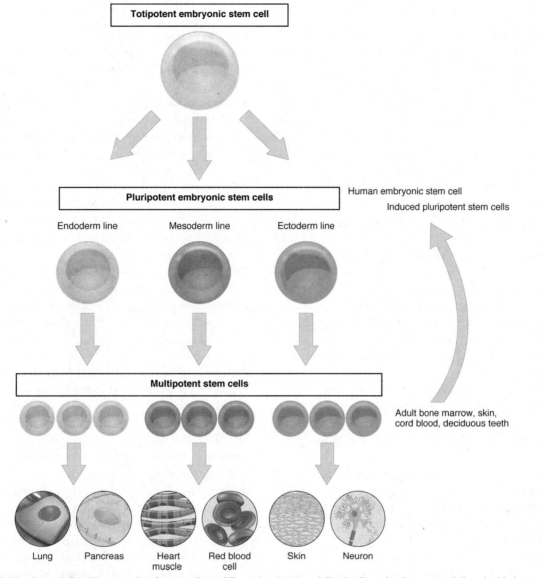

FIGURE 3.36 Stem Cells The capacity of stem cells to differentiate into specialized cells make them potentially valuable in therapeutic applications designed to replace damaged cells of different body tissues.

In contrast, adult stem cells isolated from a patient are not seen as foreign by the body, but they have a limited range of differentiation. Some individuals bank the cord blood or deciduous teeth of their child, storing away those sources of stem cells for future use, should their child need it. Induced pluripotent stem cells are considered a promising advance in the field because using them avoids the legal, ethical, and immunological pitfalls of embryonic stem cells.

Key Terms

active transport   form of transport across the cell membrane that requires input of cellular energy

amphipathic   describes a molecule that exhibits a difference in polarity between its two ends, resulting in a difference in water solubility

anaphase   third stage of mitosis (and meiosis), during which sister chromatids separate into two new nuclear regions of a dividing cell

anticodon   consecutive sequence of three nucleotides on a tRNA molecule that is complementary to a specific codon on an mRNA molecule

autolysis   breakdown of cells by their own enzymatic action

autophagy   lysosomal breakdown of a cell's own components

cell cycle   life cycle of a single cell, from its birth until its division into two new daughter cells

cell membrane   membrane surrounding all animal cells, composed of a lipid bilayer interspersed with various molecules; also known as plasma membrane

centriole   small, self-replicating organelle that provides the origin for microtubule growth and moves DNA during cell division

centromere   region of attachment for two sister chromatids

centrosome   cellular structure that organizes microtubules during cell division

channel protein   membrane-spanning protein that has an inner pore which allows the passage of one or more substances

checkpoint   progress point in the cell cycle during which certain conditions must be met in order for the cell to proceed to a subsequence phase

chromatin   substance consisting of DNA and associated proteins

chromosome   condensed version of chromatin

cilia   small appendage on certain cells formed by microtubules and modified for movement of materials across the cellular surface

cleavage furrow   contractile ring that forms around a cell during cytokinesis that pinches the cell into two halves

codon   consecutive sequence of three nucleotides on an mRNA molecule that corresponds to a specific amino acid

concentration gradient   difference in the concentration of a substance between two regions

cyclin   one of a group of proteins that function in the progression of the cell cycle

cyclin-dependent kinase (CDK)   one of a group of enzymes associated with cyclins that help them perform their functions

cytokinesis   final stage in cell division, where the cytoplasm divides to form two separate daughter cells

cytoplasm   internal material between the cell membrane and nucleus of a cell, mainly consisting of a water-based fluid called cytosol, within which are all the other organelles and cellular solute and suspended materials

cytoskeleton   "skeleton" of a cell; formed by rod-like proteins that support the cell's shape and provide, among other functions, locomotive abilities

cytosol   clear, semi-fluid medium of the cytoplasm, made up mostly of water

diffusion   movement of a substance from an area of higher concentration to one of lower concentration

diploid   condition marked by the presence of a double complement of genetic material (two sets of chromosomes, one set inherited from each of two parents)

DNA polymerase   enzyme that functions in adding new nucleotides to a growing strand of DNA during DNA replication

DNA replication   process of duplicating a molecule of DNA

electrical gradient   difference in the electrical charge (potential) between two regions

endocytosis   import of material into the cell by formation of a membrane-bound vesicle

endoplasmic reticulum (ER)   cellular organelle that consists of interconnected membrane-bound tubules, which may or may not be associated with ribosomes (rough type or smooth type, respectively)

exocytosis   export of a substance out of a cell by formation of a membrane-bound vesicle

exon   one of the coding regions of an mRNA molecule that remain after splicing

extracellular fluid (ECF)   fluid exterior to cells; includes the interstitial fluid, blood plasma, and fluid found in other reservoirs in the body

facilitated diffusion   diffusion of a substance with the aid of a membrane protein

flagellum   appendage on certain cells formed by microtubules and modified for movement

G_0 phase   phase of the cell cycle, usually entered from the G_1 phase; characterized by long or permanent periods where the cell does not move forward into the DNA synthesis phase

G_1 phase   first phase of the cell cycle, after a new cell is born

G_2 phase   third phase of the cell cycle, after the DNA synthesis phase

gene   functional length of DNA that provides the genetic information necessary to build a protein

gene expression   active interpretation of the information coded in a gene to produce a functional gene product

genome   entire complement of an organism's DNA; found within virtually every cell

glycocalyx   coating of sugar molecules that surrounds the cell membrane

glycoprotein   protein that has one or more carbohydrates attached

Golgi apparatus   cellular organelle formed by a series of flattened, membrane-bound sacs that functions in protein modification, tagging, packaging, and transport

helicase   enzyme that functions to separate the two DNA strands of a double helix during DNA replication

histone   family of proteins that associate with DNA in the nucleus to form chromatin

homologous   describes two copies of the same chromosome (not identical), one inherited from each parent

hydrophilic   describes a substance or structure attracted to water

hydrophobic   describes a substance or structure repelled by water

hypertonic   describes a solution concentration that is higher than a reference concentration

hypotonic   describes a solution concentration that is lower than a reference concentration

integral protein   membrane-associated protein that spans the entire width of the lipid bilayer

intermediate filament   type of cytoskeletal filament made of keratin, characterized by an intermediate thickness, and playing a role in resisting cellular tension

interphase   entire life cycle of a cell, excluding mitosis

interstitial fluid (IF)   fluid in the small spaces between cells not contained within blood vessels

intracellular fluid (ICF)   fluid in the cytosol of cells

intron   non-coding regions of a pre-mRNA transcript that may be removed during splicing

isotonic   describes a solution concentration that is the same as a reference concentration

kinetochore   region of a centromere where microtubules attach to a pair of sister chromatids

ligand   molecule that binds with specificity to a specific receptor molecule

lysosome   membrane-bound cellular organelle originating from the Golgi apparatus and containing digestive enzymes

messenger RNA (mRNA)   nucleotide molecule that serves as an intermediate in the genetic code between DNA and protein

metaphase   second stage of mitosis (and meiosis), characterized by the linear alignment of sister chromatids in the center of the cell

metaphase plate   linear alignment of sister chromatids in the center of the cell, which takes place during metaphase

microfilament   the thinnest of the cytoskeletal filaments; composed of actin subunits that function in muscle contraction and cellular structural support

microtubule   the thickest of the cytoskeletal filaments, composed of tubulin subunits that function in cellular movement and structural support

mitochondrion   one of the cellular organelles bound by a double lipid bilayer that function primarily in the production of cellular energy (ATP)

mitosis   division of genetic material, during which the cell nucleus breaks down and two new, fully functional, nuclei are formed

mitotic phase   phase of the cell cycle in which a cell undergoes mitosis

mitotic spindle   network of microtubules, originating from centrioles, that arranges and pulls apart chromosomes during mitosis

multipotent   describes the condition of being able to differentiate into different types of cells within a given cell lineage or small number of lineages, such as a red blood cell or white blood cell

mutation   change in the nucleotide sequence in a gene within a cell's DNA

nuclear envelope   membrane that surrounds the nucleus; consisting of a double lipid-bilayer

nuclear pore   one of the small, protein-lined openings found scattered throughout the nuclear envelope

nucleolus   small region of the nucleus that functions in ribosome synthesis

nucleosome   unit of chromatin consisting of a DNA strand wrapped around histone proteins

nucleus   cell's central organelle; contains the cell's DNA

oligopotent   describes the condition of being more specialized than multipotency; the condition of being able to differentiate into one of a few possible cell types

organelle   any of several different types of membrane-enclosed specialized structures in the cell that perform specific functions for the cell

osmosis   diffusion of water molecules down their concentration gradient across a selectively permeable membrane

passive transport   form of transport across the cell

membrane that does not require input of cellular energy

peripheral protein   membrane-associated protein that does not span the width of the lipid bilayer, but is attached peripherally to integral proteins, membrane lipids, or other components of the membrane

peroxisome   membrane-bound organelle that contains enzymes primarily responsible for detoxifying harmful substances

phagocytosis   endocytosis of large particles

pinocytosis   endocytosis of fluid

pluripotent   describes the condition of being able to differentiate into a large variety of cell types

polypeptide   chain of amino acids linked by peptide bonds

polyribosome   simultaneous translation of a single mRNA transcript by multiple ribosomes

promoter   region of DNA that signals transcription to begin at that site within the gene

prophase   first stage of mitosis (and meiosis), characterized by breakdown of the nuclear envelope and condensing of the chromatin to form chromosomes

proteome   full complement of proteins produced by a cell (determined by the cell's specific gene expression)

reactive oxygen species (ROS)   a group of extremely reactive peroxides and oxygen-containing radicals that may contribute to cellular damage

receptor   protein molecule that contains a binding site for another specific molecule (called a ligand)

receptor-mediated endocytosis   endocytosis of ligands attached to membrane-bound receptors

ribosomal RNA (rRNA)   RNA that makes up the subunits of a ribosome

ribosome   cellular organelle that functions in protein synthesis

RNA polymerase   enzyme that unwinds DNA and then adds new nucleotides to a growing strand of RNA for the transcription phase of protein synthesis

S phase   stage of the cell cycle during which DNA replication occurs

selective permeability   feature of any barrier that allows certain substances to cross but excludes others

sister chromatid   one of a pair of identical chromosomes, formed during DNA replication

sodium-potassium pump   (also, Na^+/K^+ ATP-ase) membrane-embedded protein pump that uses ATP to move Na^+ out of a cell and K^+ into the cell

somatic cell   all cells of the body excluding gamete cells

spliceosome   complex of enzymes that serves to splice out the introns of a pre-mRNA transcript

splicing   the process of modifying a pre-mRNA transcript by removing certain, typically non-coding, regions

stem cell   cell that is oligo-, multi-, or pleuripotent that has the ability to produce additional stem cells rather than becoming further specialized

telophase   final stage of mitosis (and meiosis), preceding cytokinesis, characterized by the formation of two new daughter nuclei

totipotent   embryonic cells that have the ability to differentiate into any type of cell and organ in the body

transcription   process of producing an mRNA molecule that is complementary to a particular gene of DNA

transcription factor   one of the proteins that regulate the transcription of genes

transfer RNA (tRNA)   molecules of RNA that serve to bring amino acids to a growing polypeptide strand and properly place them into the sequence

translation   process of producing a protein from the nucleotide sequence code of an mRNA transcript

triplet   consecutive sequence of three nucleotides on a DNA molecule that, when transcribed into an mRNA codon, corresponds to a particular amino acid

unipotent   describes the condition of being committed to a single specialized cell type

vesicle   membrane-bound structure that contains materials within or outside of the cell

Chapter Review

3.1 The Cell Membrane

The cell membrane provides a barrier around the cell, separating its internal components from the extracellular environment. It is composed of a phospholipid bilayer, with hydrophobic internal lipid "tails" and hydrophilic external phosphate "heads." Various membrane proteins are scattered throughout the bilayer, both inserted within it and attached to it peripherally. The cell membrane is selectively permeable, allowing only a limited number of materials to diffuse through its lipid bilayer. All materials that cross the membrane do so using passive (non energy-requiring) or active (energy-requiring) transport processes. During passive transport, materials move by simple diffusion or by facilitated diffusion through the membrane, down their concentration gradient. Water passes through the membrane in a diffusion process called osmosis. During active transport, energy is expended to assist material movement across the membrane in a direction against their concentration gradient. Active transport may take place with the help of protein pumps or through the use of vesicles.

3.2 The Cytoplasm and Cellular Organelles

The internal environmental of a living cell is made up of a fluid, jelly-like substance called cytosol, which consists mainly of water, but also contains various dissolved nutrients and other molecules. The cell contains an array of cellular organelles, each one performing a unique function and helping to maintain the health and activity of the cell. The cytosol and organelles together compose the cell's cytoplasm. Most organelles are surrounded by a lipid membrane similar to the cell membrane of the cell. The endoplasmic reticulum (ER), Golgi apparatus, and lysosomes share a functional connectivity and are collectively referred to as the endomembrane system. There are two types of ER: smooth and rough. While the smooth ER performs many functions, including lipid synthesis and ion storage, the rough ER is mainly responsible for protein synthesis using its associated ribosomes. The rough ER sends newly made proteins to the Golgi apparatus where they are modified and packaged for delivery to various locations within or outside of the cell. Some of these protein products are enzymes destined to break down unwanted material and are packaged as lysosomes for use inside the cell.

Cells also contain mitochondria and peroxisomes, which are the organelles responsible for producing the cell's energy supply and detoxifying certain chemicals, respectively. Biochemical reactions within mitochondria transform energy-carrying molecules into the usable form of cellular energy known as ATP. Peroxisomes contain enzymes that transform harmful substances such as free radicals into oxygen and water. Cells also contain a miniaturized "skeleton" of protein filaments that extend throughout its interior. Three different kinds of filaments compose this cytoskeleton (in order of increasing thickness): microfilaments, intermediate filaments, and microtubules. Each cytoskeletal component performs unique functions as well as provides a supportive framework for the cell.

3.3 The Nucleus and DNA Replication

The nucleus is the command center of the cell, containing the genetic instructions for all of the materials a cell will make (and thus all of its functions it can perform). The nucleus is encased within a membrane of two interconnected lipid bilayers, side-by-side. This nuclear envelope is studded with protein-lined pores that allow materials to be trafficked into and out of the nucleus. The nucleus contains one or more nucleoli, which serve as sites for ribosome synthesis. The nucleus houses the genetic material of the cell: DNA. DNA is normally found as a loosely contained structure called chromatin within the nucleus, where it is wound up and associated with a variety of histone proteins. When a cell is about to divide, the chromatin coils tightly and condenses to form chromosomes.

There is a pool of cells constantly dividing within your body. The result is billions of new cells being created each day. Before any cell is ready to divide, it must replicate its DNA so that each new daughter cell will receive an exact copy of the organism's genome. A variety of enzymes are enlisted during DNA replication. These enzymes unwind the DNA molecule, separate the two strands, and assist with the building of complementary strands along each parent strand. The original DNA strands serve as templates from which the nucleotide sequence of the new strands are determined and synthesized. When replication is completed, two identical DNA molecules exist. Each one contains one original strand and one newly synthesized complementary strand.

3.4 Protein Synthesis

DNA stores the information necessary for instructing the cell to perform all of its functions. Cells use the genetic code stored within DNA to build proteins, which ultimately determine the structure and function of the cell. This genetic code lies in the particular sequence of nucleotides that make up each gene along the DNA molecule. To "read" this code, the cell must perform two sequential steps. In the first step, transcription, the DNA code is converted into an RNA code. A molecule of messenger RNA that is complementary to a specific gene is synthesized in a process similar to DNA replication. The molecule of mRNA provides the code to synthesize a protein. In the process of translation, the mRNA attaches to a ribosome. Next, tRNA molecules shuttle the appropriate amino acids to the ribosome, one-by-one, coded by sequential triplet codons on the mRNA, until the protein is fully synthesized. When completed, the mRNA detaches from the ribosome, and the protein is released. Typically, multiple ribosomes attach to a single mRNA molecule at once such that multiple proteins can be manufactured from the mRNA concurrently.

3.5 Cell Growth and Division

The life of cell consists of stages that make up the cell cycle. After a cell is born, it passes through an interphase before it is ready to replicate itself and produce daughter cells. This interphase includes two gap phases (G_1 and G_2), as well as an S phase, during which its DNA is replicated in preparation for cell division. The cell cycle is under precise regulation by chemical messengers both inside and outside the cell that provide "stop" and "go" signals for movement from one phase to the next. Failures of these signals can result in cells that continue to divide uncontrollably, which can lead to cancer.

Once a cell has completed interphase and is ready for cell division, it proceeds through four separate stages of mitosis (prophase, metaphase, anaphase, and telophase). Telophase is followed by the division of the cytoplasm (cytokinesis), which generates two daughter cells. This process takes place in all normally dividing cells of the body except for the germ cells that produce eggs and sperm.

3.6 Cellular Differentiation

One of the major areas of research in biology is that of how cells specialize to assume their unique structures and functions, since all cells essentially originate from a single fertilized egg. Cell differentiation is the process of cells becoming specialized as they body develops. A stem cell is an unspecialized cell that can divide without limit as needed and can, under specific conditions, differentiate into specialized cells. Stem cells are divided into several categories according to their potential to differentiate. While all somatic cells contain the exact same genome, different cell types only express some of those genes at any given time. These differences in gene expression ultimately dictate a cell's unique morphological and physiological characteristics. The primary mechanism that determines which genes will be expressed and which ones will not is through the use of different transcription factor proteins, which bind to DNA and promote or hinder the transcription of different genes. Through the action of these transcription factors, cells specialize into one of hundreds of different cell types in the human body.

Interactive Link Questions

1. Visit this link (http://openstax.org/l/diffusion) to see diffusion and how it is propelled by the kinetic energy of molecules in solution. How does temperature affect diffusion rate, and why?

2. Watch this video (http://openstax.org/l/endomembrane1) to learn about the endomembrane system, which includes the rough and smooth ER and the Golgi body as well as lysosomes and vesicles. What is the primary role of the endomembrane system?

3. Watch this video (http://openstax.org/l/DNArep) to learn about DNA replication. DNA replication proceeds simultaneously at several sites on the same molecule. What separates the base pair at the start of DNA replication?

4. Watch this video (http://openstax.org/l/ribosome) to learn about ribosomes. The ribosome binds to the mRNA molecule to start translation of its code into a protein. What happens to the small and large ribosomal subunits at the end of translation?

5. Visit this link (http://openstax.org/l/mitosis) to learn about mitosis. Mitosis results in two identical diploid cells. What structures form during prophase?

Review Questions

6. Because they are embedded within the membrane, ion channels are examples of _____.
   a. receptor proteins
   b. integral proteins
   c. peripheral proteins
   d. glycoproteins

7. The diffusion of substances within a solution tends to move those substances _____ their _____ gradient.
   a. up; electrical
   b. up; electrochemical
   c. down; pressure
   d. down; concentration

8. Ion pumps and phagocytosis are both examples of
   _____.
   a. endocytosis
   b. passive transport
   c. active transport
   d. facilitated diffusion

9. Choose the answer that best completes the
   following analogy: Diffusion is to _____ as
   endocytosis is to _____.
   a. filtration; phagocytosis
   b. osmosis; pinocytosis
   c. solutes; fluid
   d. gradient; chemical energy

10. Choose the term that best completes the following
    analogy: Cytoplasm is to cytosol as a swimming
    pool containing chlorine and flotation toys is to
    _____.
    a. the walls of the pool
    b. the chlorine
    c. the flotation toys
    d. the water

11. The rough ER has its name due to what associated
    structures?
    a. Golgi apparatus
    b. ribosomes
    c. lysosomes
    d. proteins

12. Which of the following is a function of the rough
    ER?
    a. production of proteins
    b. detoxification of certain substances
    c. synthesis of steroid hormones
    d. regulation of intracellular calcium
       concentration

13. Which of the following is a feature common to all
    three components of the cytoskeleton?
    a. They all serve to scaffold the organelles
       within the cell.
    b. They are all characterized by roughly the
       same diameter.
    c. They are all polymers of protein subunits.
    d. They all help the cell resist compression and
       tension.

14. Which of the following organelles produces large
    quantities of ATP when both glucose and oxygen
    are available to the cell?
    a. mitochondria
    b. peroxisomes
    c. lysosomes
    d. ER

15. The nucleus and mitochondria share which of the
    following features?
    a. protein-lined membrane pores
    b. a double cell membrane
    c. the synthesis of ribosomes
    d. the production of cellular energy

16. Which of the following structures could be found
    within the nucleolus?
    a. chromatin
    b. histones
    c. ribosomes
    d. nucleosomes

17. Which of the following sequences on a DNA
    molecule would be complementary to GCTTATAT?
    a. TAGGCGCG
    b. ATCCGCGC
    c. CGAATATA
    d. TGCCTCTC

18. Place the following structures in order from least
    to most complex organization: chromatin,
    nucleosome, DNA, chromosome
    a. DNA, nucleosome, chromatin, chromosome
    b. nucleosome, DNA, chromosome, chromatin
    c. DNA, chromatin, nucleosome, chromosome
    d. nucleosome, chromatin, DNA, chromosome

19. Which of the following is part of the elongation
    step of DNA synthesis?
    a. pulling apart the two DNA strands
    b. attaching complementary nucleotides to the
       template strand
    c. untwisting the DNA helix
    d. none of the above

20. Which of the following is *not* a difference between
    DNA and RNA?
    a. DNA contains thymine whereas RNA contains
       uracil
    b. DNA contains deoxyribose and RNA contains
       ribose
    c. DNA contains alternating sugar-phosphate
       molecules whereas RNA does not contain
       sugars
    d. RNA is single stranded and DNA is double
       stranded

21. Transcription and translation take place in the
    _____ and _____, respectively.
    a. nucleus; cytoplasm
    b. nucleolus; nucleus
    c. nucleolus; cytoplasm
    d. cytoplasm; nucleus

22. How many "letters" of an RNA molecule, in sequence, does it take to provide the code for a single amino acid?
    a. 1
    b. 2
    c. 3
    d. 4

23. Which of the following is *not* made out of RNA?
    a. the carriers that shuffle amino acids to a growing polypeptide strand
    b. the ribosome
    c. the messenger molecule that provides the code for protein synthesis
    d. the intron

24. Which of the following phases is characterized by preparation for DNA synthesis?
    a. G_0
    b. G_1
    c. G_2
    d. S

25. A mutation in the gene for a cyclin protein might result in which of the following?
    a. a cell with additional genetic material than normal
    b. cancer
    c. a cell with less genetic material than normal
    d. any of the above

26. What is a primary function of tumor suppressor genes?
    a. stop all cells from dividing
    b. stop certain cells from dividing
    c. help oncogenes produce oncoproteins
    d. allow the cell to skip certain phases of the cell cycle

27. Arrange the following terms in order of increasing specialization: oligopotency, pleuripotency, unipotency, multipotency.
    a. multipotency, pleuripotency, oligopotency, unipotency
    b. pleuripotency, oligopotency, multipotency unipotency
    c. oligopotency, pleuripotency, unipotency, multipotency
    d. pleuripotency, multipotency, oligopotency, unipotency

28. Which type of stem cell gives rise to red and white blood cells?
    a. endothelial
    b. epithelial
    c. hematopoietic
    d. mesenchymal

29. What multipotent stem cells from children sometimes banked by parents?
    a. fetal stem cells
    b. embryonic stem cells
    c. cells from the umbilical cord and from baby teeth
    d. hematopoietic stem cells from red and white blood cells

Critical Thinking Questions

30. What materials can easily diffuse through the lipid bilayer, and why?
31. Why is receptor-mediated endocytosis said to be more selective than phagocytosis or pinocytosis?
32. What do osmosis, diffusion, filtration, and the movement of ions away from like charge all have in common? In what way do they differ?
33. Explain why the structure of the ER, mitochondria, and Golgi apparatus assist their respective functions.
34. Compare and contrast lysosomes with peroxisomes: name at least two similarities and one difference.
35. Explain in your own words why DNA replication is said to be "semiconservative"?

36. Why is it important that DNA replication take place before cell division? What would happen if cell division of a body cell took place without DNA replication, or when DNA replication was incomplete?
37. Briefly explain the similarities between transcription and DNA replication.
38. Contrast transcription and translation. Name at least three differences between the two processes.
39. What would happen if anaphase proceeded even though the sister chromatids were not properly attached to their respective microtubules and lined up at the metaphase plate?
40. What are cyclins and cyclin-dependent kinases, and how do they interact?

Access for free at openstax.org

41. Explain how a transcription factor ultimately determines whether or not a protein will be present in a given cell?

42. Discuss two reasons why the therapeutic use of embryonic stem cells can present a problem.

CHAPTER 4
The Tissue Level of Organization

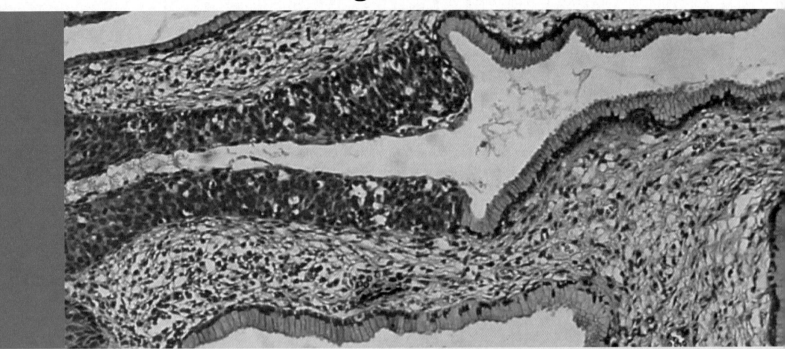

Figure 4.1 Micrograph of Cervical Tissue This figure is a view of the regular architecture of normal tissue contrasted with the irregular arrangement of cancerous cells. (credit: "Haymanj"/Wikimedia Commons)

CHAPTER OBJECTIVES

After studying this chapter, you will be able to:

- Identify the main tissue types and discuss their roles in the human body
- Identify the four types of tissue membranes and the characteristics of each that make them functional
- Explain the functions of various epithelial tissues and how their forms enable their functions
- Explain the functions of various connective tissues and how their forms enable their functions
- Describe the characteristics of muscle tissue and how these enable function
- Discuss the characteristics of nervous tissue and how these enable information processing and control of muscular and glandular activities

INTRODUCTION The body contains at least 200 distinct cell types. These cells contain essentially the same internal structures yet they vary enormously in shape and function. The different types of cells are not randomly distributed throughout the body; rather they occur in organized layers, a level of organization referred to as tissue. The micrograph that opens this chapter shows the high degree of organization among different types of cells in the tissue of the cervix. You can also see how that organization breaks down when cancer takes over the regular mitotic functioning of a cell.

The variety in shape reflects the many different roles that cells fulfill in your body. The human body starts as a single cell at fertilization. As this fertilized egg divides, it gives rise to trillions of cells, each built from the same blueprint, but organizing into tissues and becoming irreversibly committed to a developmental pathway.

4.1 Types of Tissues

LEARNING OBJECTIVES

By the end of this section, you will be able to:
- Identify the four main tissue types
- Discuss the functions of each tissue type
- Relate the structure of each tissue type to their function
- Discuss the embryonic origin of tissue
- Identify the three major germ layers
- Identify the main types of tissue membranes

The term **tissue** is used to describe a group of cells found together in the body. The cells within a tissue share a common embryonic origin. Microscopic observation reveals that the cells in a tissue share morphological features and are arranged in an orderly pattern that achieves the tissue's functions. From the evolutionary perspective, tissues appear in more complex organisms. For example, multicellular protists, ancient eukaryotes, do not have cells organized into tissues.

Although there are many types of cells in the human body, they are organized into four broad categories of tissues: epithelial, connective, muscle, and nervous. Each of these categories is characterized by specific functions that contribute to the overall health and maintenance of the body. A disruption of the structure is a sign of injury or disease. Such changes can be detected through **histology**, the microscopic study of tissue appearance, organization, and function.

The Four Types of Tissues

Epithelial tissue, also referred to as epithelium, refers to the sheets of cells that cover exterior surfaces of the body, line internal cavities and passageways, and form certain glands. **Connective tissue**, as its name implies, binds the cells and organs of the body together and functions in the protection, support, and integration of all parts of the body. **Muscle tissue** is excitable, responding to stimulation and contracting to provide movement, and occurs as three major types: skeletal (voluntary) muscle, smooth muscle, and cardiac muscle in the heart. **Nervous tissue** is also excitable, allowing the propagation of electrochemical signals in the form of nerve impulses that communicate between different regions of the body (Figure 4.2).

The next level of organization is the organ, where several types of tissues come together to form a working unit. Just as knowing the structure and function of cells helps you in your study of tissues, knowledge of tissues will help you understand how organs function. The epithelial and connective tissues are discussed in detail in this chapter. Muscle and nervous tissues will be discussed only briefly in this chapter.

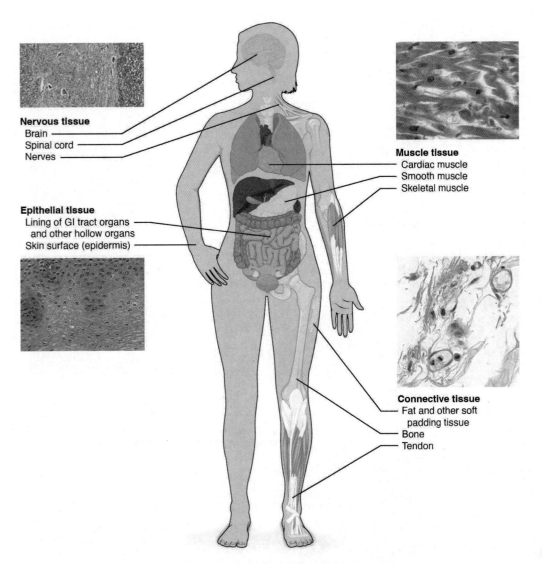

FIGURE 4.2   Four Types of Tissue: Body   The four types of tissues are exemplified in nervous tissue, stratified squamous epithelial tissue, cardiac muscle tissue, and connective tissue. (Micrographs provided by the Regents of University of Michigan Medical School © 2012)

Embryonic Origin of Tissues

The zygote, or fertilized egg, is a single cell formed by the fusion of an egg and sperm. After fertilization the zygote gives rise to rapid mitotic cycles, generating many cells to form the embryo. The first embryonic cells generated have the ability to differentiate into any type of cell in the body and, as such, are called **totipotent**, meaning each has the capacity to divide, differentiate, and develop into a new organism. As cell proliferation progresses, three major cell lineages are established within the embryo. As explained in a later chapter, each of these lineages of embryonic cells forms the distinct germ layers from which all the tissues and organs of the human body eventually form. Each germ layer is identified by its relative position: **ectoderm** (ecto- = "outer"), **mesoderm** (meso- = "middle"), and **endoderm** (endo- = "inner"). Figure 4.3 shows the types of tissues and organs associated with the each of the three germ layers. Note that epithelial tissue originates in all three layers, whereas nervous tissue derives primarily from the ectoderm and muscle tissue from mesoderm.

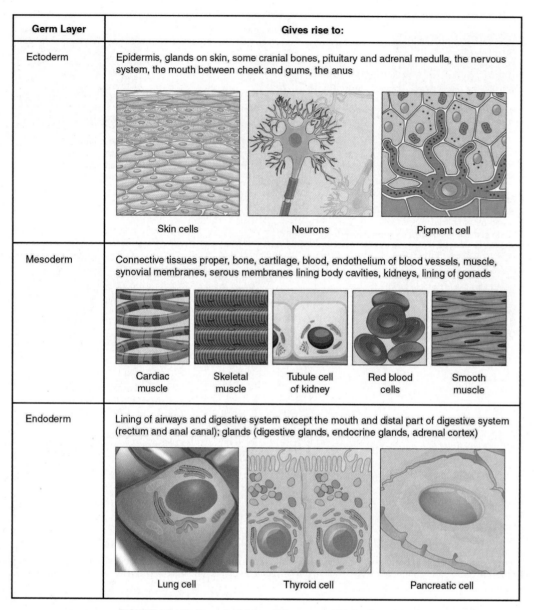

Germ Layer	Gives rise to:
Ectoderm	Epidermis, glands on skin, some cranial bones, pituitary and adrenal medulla, the nervous system, the mouth between cheek and gums, the anus
Mesoderm	Connective tissues proper, bone, cartilage, blood, endothelium of blood vessels, muscle, synovial membranes, serous membranes lining body cavities, kidneys, lining of gonads
Endoderm	Lining of airways and digestive system except the mouth and distal part of digestive system (rectum and anal canal); glands (digestive glands, endocrine glands, adrenal cortex)

FIGURE 4.3   Embryonic Origin of Tissues and Major Organs

🔗 INTERACTIVE LINK

View this slideshow (http://openstax.org/l/stemcells) to learn more about stem cells. How do somatic stem cells differ from embryonic stem cells?

Tissue Membranes

A **tissue membrane** is a thin layer or sheet of cells that covers the outside of the body (for example, skin), the organs (for example, pericardium), internal passageways that lead to the exterior of the body (for example, mucosa of stomach), and the lining of the moveable joint cavities. There are two basic types of tissue membranes: connective tissue and epithelial membranes (Figure 4.4).

Access for free at openstax.org

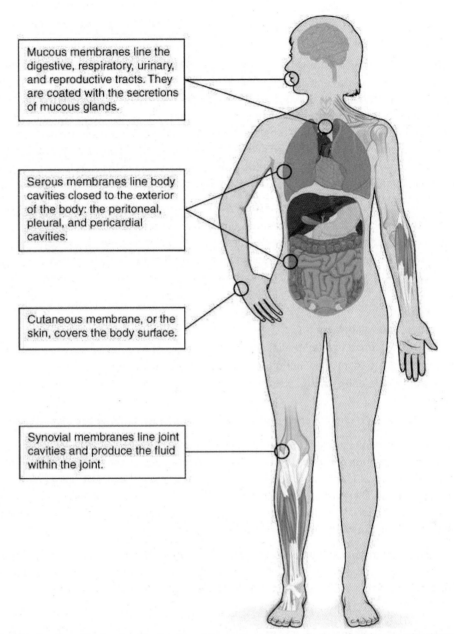

Mucous membranes line the digestive, respiratory, urinary, and reproductive tracts. They are coated with the secretions of mucous glands.

Serous membranes line body cavities closed to the exterior of the body: the peritoneal, pleural, and pericardial cavities.

Cutaneous membrane, or the skin, covers the body surface.

Synovial membranes line joint cavities and produce the fluid within the joint.

FIGURE 4.4 **Tissue Membranes** The two broad categories of tissue membranes in the body are (1) connective tissue membranes, which include synovial membranes, and (2) epithelial membranes, which include mucous membranes, serous membranes, and the cutaneous membrane, in other words, the skin.

Connective Tissue Membranes

The **connective tissue membrane** is formed solely from connective tissue. These membranes encapsulate organs, such as the kidneys, and line our movable joints. A **synovial membrane** is a type of connective tissue membrane that lines the cavity of a freely movable joint. For example, synovial membranes surround the joints of the shoulder, elbow, and knee. Fibroblasts in the inner layer of the synovial membrane release hyaluronan into the joint cavity. The hyaluronan effectively traps available water to form the synovial fluid, a natural lubricant that enables the bones of a joint to move freely against one another without much friction. This synovial fluid readily exchanges water and nutrients with blood, as do all body fluids.

Epithelial Membranes

The **epithelial membrane** is composed of epithelium attached to a layer of connective tissue, for example, your skin. The **mucous membrane** is also a composite of connective and epithelial tissues. Sometimes called mucosae, these epithelial membranes line the body cavities and hollow passageways that open to the external environment, and include the digestive, respiratory, excretory, and reproductive tracts. Mucus, produced by the epithelial exocrine glands, covers the epithelial layer. The underlying connective tissue, called the **lamina propria** (literally "own layer"), help support the fragile epithelial layer.

A **serous membrane** is an epithelial membrane composed of mesodermally derived epithelium called the mesothelium that is supported by connective tissue. These membranes line the coelomic cavities of the body, that is, those cavities that do not open to the outside, and they cover the organs located within those cavities. They are essentially membranous bags, with mesothelium lining the inside and connective tissue on the outside. Serous fluid secreted by the cells of the thin squamous mesothelium lubricates the membrane and reduces abrasion and friction between organs. Serous membranes are identified according locations. Three serous membranes line the thoracic cavity; the two pleura that cover the lungs and the pericardium that covers the heart. A fourth, the peritoneum, is the serous membrane in the abdominal cavity that covers abdominal organs and forms double sheets of mesenteries that suspend many of the digestive organs.

The skin is an epithelial membrane also called the **cutaneous membrane**. It is a stratified squamous epithelial membrane resting on top of connective tissue. The apical surface of this membrane is exposed to the external environment and is covered with dead, keratinized cells that help protect the body from desiccation and pathogens.

4.2 Epithelial Tissue

LEARNING OBJECTIVES

By the end of this section, you will be able to:

- Explain the structure and function of epithelial tissue
- Distinguish between tight junctions, anchoring junctions, and gap junctions
- Distinguish between simple epithelia and stratified epithelia, as well as between squamous, cuboidal, and columnar epithelia
- Describe the structure and function of endocrine and exocrine glands and their respective secretions

Most epithelial tissues are essentially large sheets of cells covering all the surfaces of the body exposed to the outside world and lining the outside of organs. Epithelium also forms much of the glandular tissue of the body. Skin is not the only area of the body exposed to the outside. Other areas include the airways, the digestive tract, as well as the urinary and reproductive systems, all of which are lined by an epithelium. Hollow organs and body cavities that do not connect to the exterior of the body, which includes, blood vessels and serous membranes, are lined by endothelium (plural = endothelia), which is a type of epithelium.

Epithelial cells derive from all three major embryonic layers. The epithelia lining the skin, parts of the mouth and nose, and the anus develop from the ectoderm. Cells lining the airways and most of the digestive system originate in the endoderm. The epithelium that lines vessels in the lymphatic and cardiovascular system derives from the mesoderm and is called an endothelium.

All epithelia share some important structural and functional features. This tissue is highly cellular, with little or no extracellular material present between cells. Adjoining cells form a specialized intercellular connection between their cell membranes called a **cell junction**. The epithelial cells exhibit polarity with differences in structure and function between the exposed or **apical** facing surface of the cell and the basal surface close to the underlying body structures. The **basal lamina**, a mixture of glycoproteins and collagen, provides an attachment site for the epithelium, separating it from underlying connective tissue. The basal lamina attaches to a **reticular lamina**, which is secreted by the underlying connective tissue, forming a **basement membrane** that helps hold it all together.

Epithelial tissues are nearly completely avascular. For instance, no blood vessels cross the basement membrane to enter the tissue, and nutrients must come by diffusion or absorption from underlying tissues or the surface. Many epithelial tissues are capable of rapidly replacing damaged and dead cells. Sloughing off of damaged or dead cells is a characteristic of surface epithelium and allows our airways and digestive tracts to rapidly replace damaged cells with new cells.

Generalized Functions of Epithelial Tissue

Epithelial tissues provide the body's first line of protection from physical, chemical, and biological wear and tear. The cells of an epithelium act as gatekeepers of the body controlling permeability and allowing selective transfer of materials across a physical barrier. All substances that enter the body must cross an epithelium. Some epithelia often include structural features that allow the selective transport of molecules and ions across their cell membranes.

Many epithelial cells are capable of secretion and release mucous and specific chemical compounds onto their apical surfaces. The epithelium of the small intestine releases digestive enzymes, for example. Cells lining the respiratory tract secrete mucous that traps incoming microorganisms and particles. A glandular epithelium contains many secretory cells.

The Epithelial Cell

Epithelial cells are typically characterized by the polarized distribution of organelles and membrane-bound proteins between their basal and apical surfaces. Particular structures found in some epithelial cells are an adaptation to specific functions. Certain organelles are segregated to the basal sides, whereas other organelles and extensions, such as cilia, when present, are on the apical surface.

Cilia are microscopic extensions of the apical cell membrane that are supported by microtubules. They beat in unison and move fluids as well as trapped particles. Ciliated epithelium lines the ventricles of the brain where it helps circulate the cerebrospinal fluid. The ciliated epithelium of your airway forms a mucociliary escalator that sweeps particles of dust and pathogens trapped in the secreted mucous toward the throat. It is called an escalator because it continuously pushes mucous with trapped particles upward. In contrast, nasal cilia sweep the mucous blanket down towards your throat. In both cases, the transported materials are usually swallowed, and end up in the acidic environment of your stomach.

Cell to Cell Junctions

Cells of epithelia are closely connected and are not separated by intracellular material. Three basic types of connections allow varying degrees of interaction between the cells: tight junctions, anchoring junctions, and gap junctions (Figure 4.5).

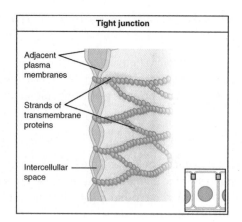

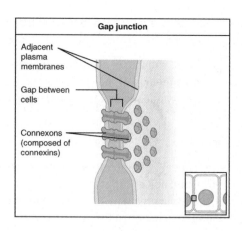

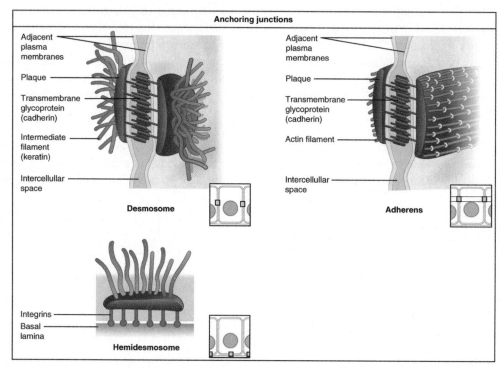

FIGURE 4.5   Types of Cell Junctions   The three basic types of cell-to-cell junctions are tight junctions, gap junctions, and anchoring junctions.

At one end of the spectrum is the **tight junction**, which separates the cells into apical and basal compartments. When two adjacent epithelial cells form a tight junction, there is no extracellular space between them and the movement of substances through the extracellular space between the cells is blocked. This enables the epithelia to act as selective barriers. An **anchoring junction** includes several types of cell junctions that help stabilize epithelial tissues. Anchoring junctions are common on the lateral and basal surfaces of cells where they provide strong and flexible connections. There are three types of anchoring junctions: desmosomes, hemidesmosomes, and adherens. Desmosomes occur in patches on the membranes of cells. The patches are structural proteins on the inner surface of the cell's membrane. The adhesion molecule, cadherin, is embedded in these patches and projects through the cell membrane to link with the cadherin molecules of adjacent cells. These connections are especially important in holding cells together. Hemidesmosomes, which look like half a desmosome, link cells to the extracellular matrix, for example, the basal lamina. While similar in appearance to desmosomes, they include the adhesion proteins called integrins rather than cadherins. Adherens junctions use either cadherins or integrins depending on whether they are linking to other cells or matrix. The junctions are characterized by the presence of the contractile protein actin located on the cytoplasmic surface of the cell membrane. The actin can connect isolated patches or form a belt-like structure inside the cell. These junctions influence the shape and folding of the epithelial tissue.

In contrast with the tight and anchoring junctions, a **gap junction** forms an intercellular passageway between the membranes of adjacent cells to facilitate the movement of small molecules and ions between the cytoplasm of adjacent cells. These junctions allow electrical and metabolic coupling of adjacent cells, which coordinates function in large groups of cells.

Classification of Epithelial Tissues

Epithelial tissues are classified according to the shape of the cells and number of the cell layers formed (Figure 4.6). Cell shapes can be squamous (flattened and thin), cuboidal (boxy, as wide as it is tall), or columnar (rectangular, taller than it is wide). Similarly, the number of cell layers in the tissue can be one—where every cell rests on the basal lamina—which is a simple epithelium, or more than one, which is a stratified epithelium and only the basal layer of cells rests on the basal lamina. Pseudostratified (pseudo- = "false") describes tissue with a single layer of irregularly shaped cells that give the appearance of more than one layer. Transitional describes a form of specialized stratified epithelium in which the shape of the cells can vary.

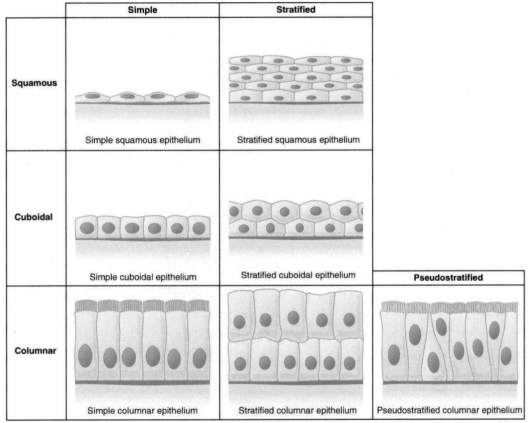

FIGURE 4.6   Cells of Epithelial Tissue   Simple epithelial tissue is organized as a single layer of cells and stratified epithelial tissue is formed by several layers of cells.

Simple Epithelium

The shape of the cells in the single cell layer of simple epithelium reflects the functioning of those cells. The cells in **simple squamous epithelium** have the appearance of thin scales. Squamous cell nuclei tend to be flat, horizontal, and elliptical, mirroring the form of the cell. The **endothelium** is the epithelial tissue that lines vessels of the lymphatic and cardiovascular system, and it is made up of a single layer of squamous cells. Simple squamous epithelium, because of the thinness of the cell, is present where rapid passage of chemical compounds is observed. The alveoli of lungs where gases diffuse, segments of kidney tubules, and the lining of capillaries are also made of simple squamous epithelial tissue. The **mesothelium** is a simple squamous epithelium that forms the surface layer of the serous membrane that lines body cavities and internal organs. Its primary function is to provide a smooth and protective surface. Mesothelial cells are squamous epithelial cells that secrete a fluid that lubricates the mesothelium.

In **simple cuboidal epithelium**, the nucleus of the box-like cells appears round and is generally located near the center of the cell. These epithelia are active in the secretion and absorptions of molecules. Simple cuboidal epithelia are observed in the lining of the kidney tubules and in the ducts of glands.

In **simple columnar epithelium**, the nucleus of the tall column-like cells tends to be elongated and located in the basal end of the cells. Like the cuboidal epithelia, this epithelium is active in the absorption and secretion of molecules. Simple columnar epithelium forms the lining of some sections of the digestive system and parts of the female reproductive tract. Ciliated columnar epithelium is composed of simple columnar epithelial cells with cilia on their apical surfaces. These epithelial cells are found in the lining of the fallopian tubes and parts of the respiratory system, where the beating of the cilia helps remove particulate matter.

Pseudostratified columnar epithelium is a type of epithelium that appears to be stratified but instead consists of a single layer of irregularly shaped and differently sized columnar cells. In pseudostratified epithelium, nuclei of neighboring cells appear at different levels rather than clustered in the basal end. The arrangement gives the appearance of stratification; but in fact all the cells are in contact with the basal lamina, although some do not reach the apical surface. Pseudostratified columnar epithelium is found in the respiratory tract, where some of these cells have cilia.

Both simple and pseudostratified columnar epithelia are heterogeneous epithelia because they include additional types of cells interspersed among the epithelial cells. For example, a **goblet cell** is a mucous-secreting unicellular "gland" interspersed between the columnar epithelial cells of mucous membranes (Figure 4.7).

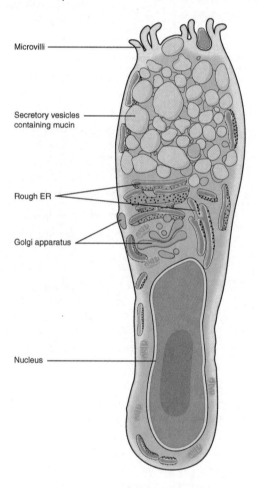

Microvilli

Secretory vesicles
containing mucin

Rough ER

Golgi apparatus

Nucleus

Access for free at openstax.org

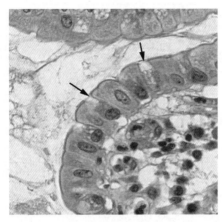

FIGURE 4.7   Goblet Cell   (a) In the lining of the small intestine, columnar epithelium cells are interspersed with goblet cells. (b) The arrows in this micrograph point to the mucous-secreting goblet cells. LM × 1600. (Micrograph provided by the Regents of University of Michigan Medical School © 2012)

INTERACTIVE LINK

View the University of Michigan WebScope (http://openstax.org/l/goblet) to explore the tissue sample in greater detail.

Stratified Epithelium

A stratified epithelium consists of several stacked layers of cells. This epithelium protects against physical and chemical wear and tear. The stratified epithelium is named by the shape of the most apical layer of cells, closest to the free space. **Stratified squamous epithelium** is the most common type of stratified epithelium in the human body. The apical cells are squamous, whereas the basal layer contains either columnar or cuboidal cells. The top layer may be covered with dead cells filled with keratin. Mammalian skin is an example of this dry, keratinized, stratified squamous epithelium. The lining of the mouth cavity is an example of an unkeratinized, stratified squamous epithelium. **Stratified cuboidal epithelium** and **stratified columnar epithelium** can also be found in certain glands and ducts, but are uncommon in the human body.

Another kind of stratified epithelium is **transitional epithelium**, so-called because of the gradual changes in the shapes of the apical cells as the bladder fills with urine. It is found only in the urinary system, specifically the ureters and urinary bladder. When the bladder is empty, this epithelium is convoluted and has cuboidal apical cells with convex, umbrella shaped, apical surfaces. As the bladder fills with urine, this epithelium loses its convolutions and the apical cells transition from cuboidal to squamous. It appears thicker and more multi-layered when the bladder is empty, and more stretched out and less stratified when the bladder is full and distended. Figure 4.8 summarizes the different categories of epithelial cell tissue cells.

Cells	Location	Function
Simple squamous epithelium 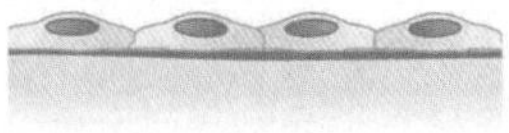	Air sacs of lungs and the lining of the heart, blood vessels, and lymphatic vessels	Allows materials to pass through by diffusion and filtration, and secretes lubricating substance
Simple cuboidal epithelium 	In ducts and secretory portions of small glands and in kidney tubules	Secretes and absorbs
Simple columnar epithelium 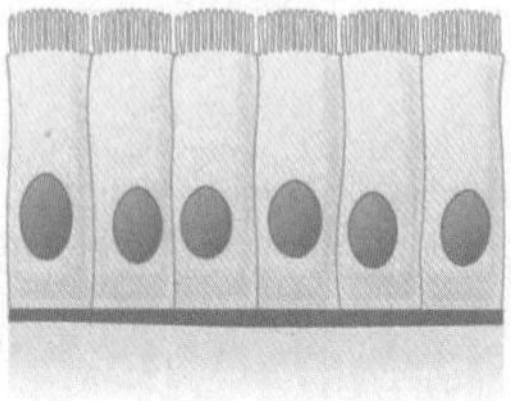	Ciliated tissues are in larger bronchioles, uterine tubes, and uterus; smooth (nonciliated tissues) are in the digestive tract, bladder	Absorbs; it also secretes mucus and enzymes
Pseudostratified columnar epithelium 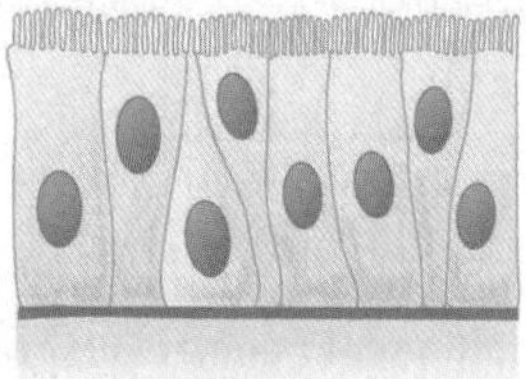	Ciliated tissue lines the bronchi, trachea, and much of the upper respiratory tract	Secretes mucus; ciliated tissue moves mucus
Stratified squamous epithelium 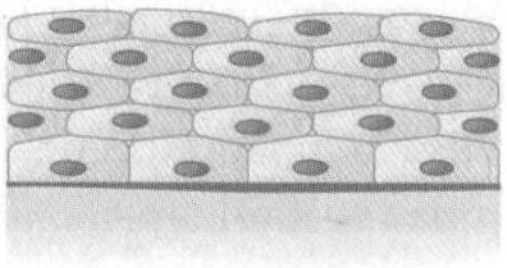	Lines the esophagus, mouth, and vagina	Protects against abrasion
Stratified cuboidal epithelium 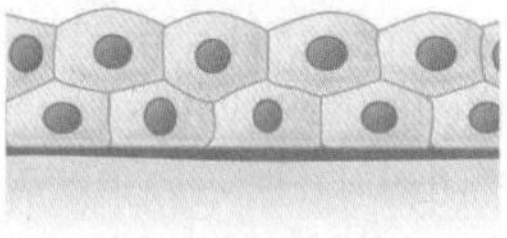	Sweat glands, salivary glands, and the mammary glands	Protective tissue
Stratified columnar epithelium 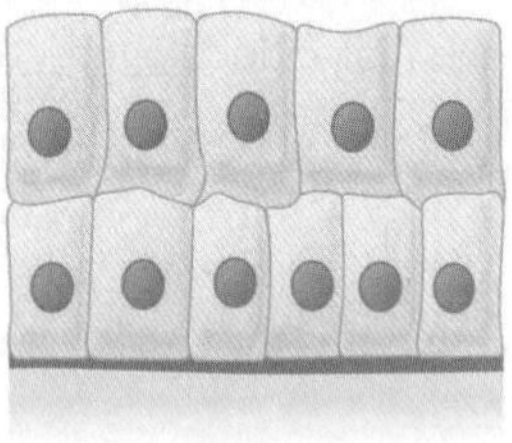	The male and female urethrae and the ducts of some glands	Secretes and protects
Transitional epithelium 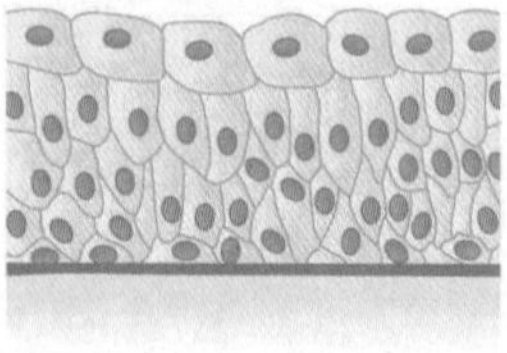	Lines the bladder, urethra, and the ureters	Allows the urinary organs to expand and stretch

FIGURE 4.8   Summary of Epithelial Tissue Cells

🔗 **INTERACTIVE LINK**

Watch this video (http://openstax.org/l/etissues) to find out more about the anatomy of epithelial tissues. Where in the body would one find non-keratinizing stratified squamous epithelium?

Glandular Epithelium

A gland is a structure made up of one or more cells modified to synthesize and secrete chemical substances. Most glands consist of groups of epithelial cells. A gland can be classified as an **endocrine gland**, a ductless gland that releases secretions directly into surrounding tissues and fluids (endo- = "inside"), or an **exocrine gland** whose secretions leave through a duct that opens directly, or indirectly, to the external environment (exo- = "outside").

Endocrine Glands

The secretions of endocrine glands are called hormones. Hormones are released into the interstitial fluid, diffused into the bloodstream, and delivered to targets, in other words, cells that have receptors to bind the hormones. The endocrine system is part of a major regulatory system coordinating the regulation and integration of body responses. A few examples of endocrine glands include the anterior pituitary, thymus, adrenal cortex, and gonads.

Exocrine Glands

Exocrine glands release their contents through a duct that leads to the epithelial surface. Mucous, sweat, saliva, and breast milk are all examples of secretions from exocrine glands. They are all discharged through tubular ducts. Secretions into the lumen of the gastrointestinal tract, technically outside of the body, are of the exocrine category.

Glandular Structure

Exocrine glands are classified as either unicellular or multicellular. The unicellular glands are scattered single cells, such as goblet cells, found in the mucous membranes of the small and large intestine.

The multicellular exocrine glands known as serous glands develop from simple epithelium to form a secretory surface that secretes directly into an inner cavity. These glands line the internal cavities of the abdomen and chest and release their secretions directly into the cavities. Other multicellular exocrine glands release their contents through a tubular duct. The duct is single in a simple gland but in compound glands is divided into one or more branches (Figure 4.9). In tubular glands, the ducts can be straight or coiled, whereas tubes that form pockets are alveolar (acinar), such as the exocrine portion of the pancreas. Combinations of tubes and pockets are known as tubuloalveolar (tubuloacinar) compound glands. In a branched gland, a duct is connected to more than one secretory group of cells.

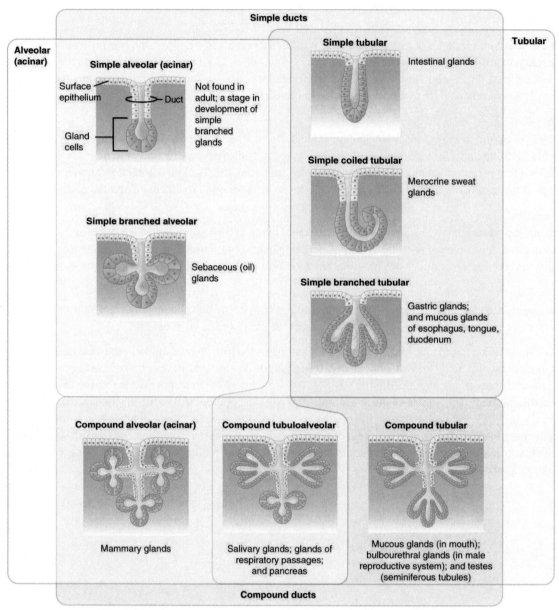

FIGURE 4.9   Types of Exocrine Glands   Exocrine glands are classified by their structure.

Methods and Types of Secretion

Exocrine glands can be classified by their mode of secretion and the nature of the substances released, as well as by the structure of the glands and shape of ducts (Figure 4.10). **Merocrine secretion** is the most common type of exocrine secretion. The secretions are enclosed in vesicles that move to the apical surface of the cell where the contents are released by exocytosis. For example, watery mucous containing the glycoprotein mucin, a lubricant that offers some pathogen protection is a merocrine secretion. The eccrine glands that produce and secrete sweat are another example.

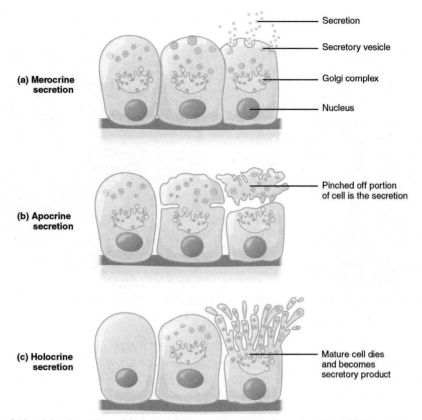

(a) Merocrine secretion

Secretion
Secretory vesicle
Golgi complex
Nucleus

(b) Apocrine secretion

Pinched off portion of cell is the secretion

(c) Holocrine secretion

Mature cell dies and becomes secretory product

FIGURE 4.10   Modes of Glandular Secretion   (a) In merocrine secretion, the cell remains intact. (b) In apocrine secretion, the apical portion of the cell is released, as well. (c) In holocrine secretion, the cell is destroyed as it releases its product and the cell itself becomes part of the secretion.

Apocrine secretion accumulates near the apical portion of the cell. That portion of the cell and its secretory contents pinch off from the cell and are released. Apocrine sweat glands in the axillary and genital areas release fatty secretions that local bacteria break down; this causes body odor. Both merocrine and apocrine glands continue to produce and secrete their contents with little damage caused to the cell because the nucleus and golgi regions remain intact after secretion.

In contrast, the process of **holocrine secretion** involves the rupture and destruction of the entire gland cell. The cell accumulates its secretory products and releases them only when it bursts. New gland cells differentiate from cells in the surrounding tissue to replace those lost by secretion. The sebaceous glands that produce the oils on the skin and hair are holocrine glands/cells (Figure 4.11).

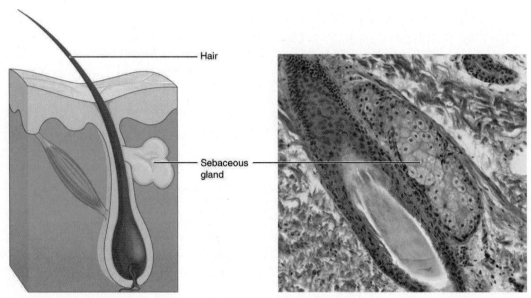

Hair

Sebaceous gland

FIGURE 4.11   Sebaceous Glands   These glands secrete oils that lubricate and protect the skin. They are holocrine glands and they are destroyed after releasing their contents. New glandular cells form to replace the cells that are lost. LM × 400. (Micrograph provided by the Regents of University of Michigan Medical School © 2012)

Glands are also named after the products they produce. The **serous gland** produces watery, blood-plasma-like secretions rich in enzymes such as alpha amylase, whereas the **mucous gland** releases watery to viscous products rich in the glycoprotein mucin. Both serous and mucous glands are common in the salivary glands of the mouth. Mixed exocrine glands contain both serous and mucous glands and release both types of secretions.

4.3 Connective Tissue Supports and Protects

LEARNING OBJECTIVES

By the end of this section, you will be able to:

- Identify and distinguish between the types of connective tissue: proper, supportive, and fluid
- Explain the functions of connective tissues

As may be obvious from its name, one of the major functions of connective tissue is to connect tissues and organs. Unlike epithelial tissue, which is composed of cells closely packed with little or no extracellular space in between, connective tissue cells are dispersed in a **matrix**. The matrix usually includes a large amount of extracellular material produced by the connective tissue cells that are embedded within it. The matrix plays a major role in the functioning of this tissue. The major component of the matrix is a **ground substance** often crisscrossed by protein fibers. This ground substance is usually a fluid, but it can also be mineralized and solid, as in bones. Connective tissues come in a vast variety of forms, yet they typically have in common three characteristic components: cells, large amounts of amorphous ground substance, and protein fibers. The amount and structure of each component correlates with the function of the tissue, from the rigid ground substance in bones supporting the body to the inclusion of specialized cells; for example, a phagocytic cell that engulfs pathogens and also rids tissue of cellular debris.

Functions of Connective Tissues

Connective tissues perform many functions in the body, but most importantly, they support and connect other tissues; from the connective tissue sheath that surrounds muscle cells, to the tendons that attach muscles to bones, and to the skeleton that supports the positions of the body. Protection is another major function of connective tissue, in the form of fibrous capsules and bones that protect delicate organs and, of course, the skeletal system. Specialized cells in connective tissue defend the body from microorganisms that enter the body. Transport of fluid, nutrients, waste, and chemical messengers is ensured by specialized fluid connective tissues, such as blood and lymph. Adipose cells store surplus energy in the form of fat and contribute to the thermal insulation of the body.

Embryonic Connective Tissue

All connective tissues derive from the mesodermal layer of the embryo (see Figure 4.3). The first connective tissue to develop in the embryo is **mesenchyme**, the stem cell line from which all connective tissues are later derived. Clusters of mesenchymal cells are scattered throughout adult tissue and supply the cells needed for replacement and repair after a connective tissue injury. A second type of embryonic connective tissue forms in the umbilical cord, called **mucous connective tissue** or Wharton's jelly. This tissue is no longer present after birth, leaving only scattered mesenchymal cells throughout the body.

Classification of Connective Tissues

The three broad categories of connective tissue are classified according to the characteristics of their ground substance and the types of fibers found within the matrix (Table 4.1). **Connective tissue proper** includes **loose connective tissue** and **dense connective tissue**. Both tissues have a variety of cell types and protein fibers suspended in a viscous ground substance. Dense connective tissue is reinforced by bundles of fibers that provide tensile strength, elasticity, and protection. In loose connective tissue, the fibers are loosely organized, leaving large spaces in between. **Supportive connective tissue**—bone and cartilage—provide structure and strength to the body and protect soft tissues. A few distinct cell types and densely packed fibers in a matrix characterize these tissues. In bone, the matrix is rigid and described as calcified because of the deposited calcium salts. In **fluid connective tissue**, in other words, lymph and blood, various specialized cells circulate in a watery fluid containing salts, nutrients, and dissolved proteins.

Connective Tissue Examples

Connective tissue proper	Supportive connective tissue	Fluid connective tissue
Loose connective tissue • Areolar • Adipose • Reticular Dense connective tissue • Dense regular • Elastic • Dense-irregular	Cartilage • Hyaline • Fibrocartilage • Elastic Bone	Blood Lymph

TABLE 4.1

Connective Tissue Proper

Fibroblasts are present in all connective tissue proper (Figure 4.12). Fibrocytes, adipocytes, and mesenchymal cells are fixed cells, which means they remain within the connective tissue. Other cells move in and out of the connective tissue in response to chemical signals. Macrophages, mast cells, lymphocytes, plasma cells, and phagocytic cells are found in connective tissue proper but are actually part of the immune system protecting the body.

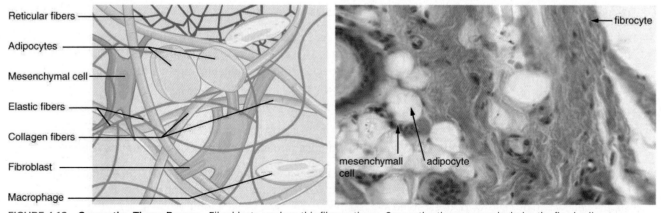

FIGURE 4.12 Connective Tissue Proper Fibroblasts produce this fibrous tissue. Connective tissue proper includes the fixed cells fibrocytes, adipocytes, and mesenchymal cells. LM × 400. (Micrograph provided by the Regents of University of Michigan Medical School ©

2012)

Cell Types

The most abundant cell in connective tissue proper is the **fibroblast**. Polysaccharides and proteins secreted by fibroblasts combine with extra-cellular fluids to produce a viscous ground substance that, with embedded fibrous proteins, forms the extra-cellular matrix. As you might expect, a **fibrocyte**, a less active form of fibroblast, is the second most common cell type in connective tissue proper.

Adipocytes are cells that store lipids as droplets that fill most of the cytoplasm. There are two basic types of adipocytes: white and brown. The brown adipocytes store lipids as many droplets, and have high metabolic activity. In contrast, white fat adipocytes store lipids as a single large drop and are metabolically less active. Their effectiveness at storing large amounts of fat is witnessed in obese individuals. The number and type of adipocytes depends on the tissue and location, and vary among individuals in the population.

The **mesenchymal cell** is a multipotent adult stem cell. These cells can differentiate into any type of connective tissue cells needed for repair and healing of damaged tissue.

The macrophage cell is a large cell derived from a monocyte, a type of blood cell, which enters the connective tissue matrix from the blood vessels. The macrophage cells are an essential component of the immune system, which is the body's defense against potential pathogens and degraded host cells. When stimulated, macrophages release cytokines, small proteins that act as chemical messengers. Cytokines recruit other cells of the immune system to infected sites and stimulate their activities. Roaming, or free, macrophages move rapidly by amoeboid movement, engulfing infectious agents and cellular debris. In contrast, fixed macrophages are permanent residents of their tissues.

The mast cell, found in connective tissue proper, has many cytoplasmic granules. These granules contain the chemical signals histamine and heparin. When irritated or damaged, mast cells release histamine, an inflammatory mediator, which causes vasodilation and increased blood flow at a site of injury or infection, along with itching, swelling, and redness you recognize as an allergic response. Like blood cells, mast cells are derived from hematopoietic stem cells and are part of the immune system.

Connective Tissue Fibers and Ground Substance

Three main types of fibers are secreted by fibroblasts: collagen fibers, elastic fibers, and reticular fibers. **Collagen fiber** is made from fibrous protein subunits linked together to form a long and straight fiber. Collagen fibers, while flexible, have great tensile strength, resist stretching, and give ligaments and tendons their characteristic resilience and strength. These fibers hold connective tissues together, even during the movement of the body.

Elastic fiber contains the protein elastin along with lesser amounts of other proteins and glycoproteins. The main property of elastin is that after being stretched or compressed, it will return to its original shape. Elastic fibers are prominent in elastic tissues found in skin and the elastic ligaments of the vertebral column.

Reticular fiber is also formed from the same protein subunits as collagen fibers; however, these fibers remain narrow and are arrayed in a branching network. They are found throughout the body, but are most abundant in the reticular tissue of soft organs, such as liver and spleen, where they anchor and provide structural support to the **parenchyma** (the functional cells, blood vessels, and nerves of the organ).

All of these fiber types are embedded in ground substance. Secreted by fibroblasts, ground substance is made of polysaccharides, specifically hyaluronic acid, and proteins. These combine to form a proteoglycan with a protein core and polysaccharide branches. The proteoglycan attracts and traps available moisture forming the clear, viscous, colorless matrix you now know as ground substance.

Loose Connective Tissue

Loose connective tissue is found between many organs where it acts both to absorb shock and bind tissues together. It allows water, salts, and various nutrients to diffuse through to adjacent or imbedded cells and tissues.

Adipose tissue consists mostly of fat storage cells, with little extracellular matrix (Figure 4.13). A large number of capillaries allow rapid storage and mobilization of lipid molecules. White adipose tissue is most abundant. It can appear yellow and owes its color to carotene and related pigments from plant food. White fat contributes mostly to lipid storage and can serve as insulation from cold temperatures and mechanical injuries. White adipose tissue can be found protecting the kidneys and cushioning the back of the eye. Brown adipose tissue is more common in infants, hence the term "baby fat." In adults, there is a reduced amount of brown fat and it is found mainly in the neck and clavicular regions of the body. The many mitochondria in the cytoplasm of brown adipose tissue help explain its efficiency at metabolizing stored fat. Brown adipose tissue is thermogenic, meaning that as it breaks down fats, it releases metabolic heat, rather than producing adenosine triphosphate (ATP), a key molecule used in metabolism.

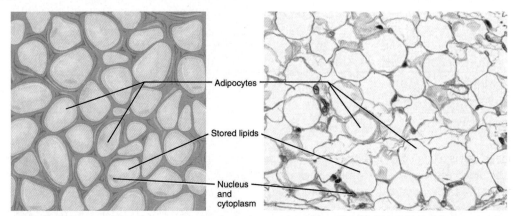

FIGURE 4.13 **Adipose Tissue** This is a loose connective tissue that consists of fat cells with little extracellular matrix. It stores fat for energy and provides insulation. LM × 800. (Micrograph provided by the Regents of University of Michigan Medical School © 2012)

Areolar tissue shows little specialization. It contains all the cell types and fibers previously described and is distributed in a random, web-like fashion. It fills the spaces between muscle fibers, surrounds blood and lymph vessels, and supports organs in the abdominal cavity. Areolar tissue underlies most epithelia and represents the connective tissue component of epithelial membranes, which are described further in a later section.

Reticular tissue is a mesh-like, supportive framework for soft organs such as lymphatic tissue, the spleen, and the liver (Figure 4.14). Reticular cells produce the reticular fibers that form the network onto which other cells attach. It derives its name from the Latin *reticulus*, which means "little net."

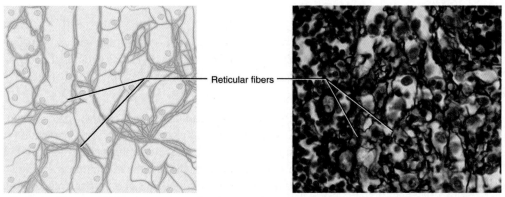

FIGURE 4.14 **Reticular Tissue** This is a loose connective tissue made up of a network of reticular fibers that provides a supportive framework for soft organs. LM × 1600. (Micrograph provided by the Regents of University of Michigan Medical School © 2012)

Dense Connective Tissue

Dense connective tissue contains more collagen fibers than does loose connective tissue. As a consequence, it displays greater resistance to stretching. There are two major categories of dense connective tissue: regular and irregular. Dense regular connective tissue fibers are parallel to each other, enhancing tensile strength and resistance to stretching in the direction of the fiber orientations. Ligaments and tendons are made of dense regular connective tissue, but in ligaments not all fibers are parallel. Dense regular elastic tissue contains elastin fibers in addition to collagen fibers, which allows the ligament to return to its original length after stretching. The ligaments in the vocal folds and between the vertebrae in the vertebral column are elastic.

In dense irregular connective tissue, the direction of fibers is random. This arrangement gives the tissue greater strength in all directions and less strength in one particular direction. In some tissues, fibers crisscross and form a mesh. In other tissues, stretching in several directions is achieved by alternating layers where fibers run in the same orientation in each layer, and it is the layers themselves that are stacked at an angle. The dermis of the skin is an example of dense irregular connective tissue rich in collagen fibers. Dense irregular elastic tissues give arterial walls the strength and the ability to regain original shape after stretching (Figure 4.15).

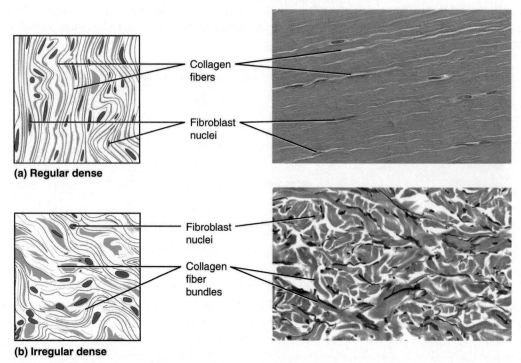

FIGURE 4.15   Dense Connective Tissue   (a) Dense regular connective tissue consists of collagenous fibers packed into parallel bundles. (b) Dense irregular connective tissue consists of collagenous fibers interwoven into a mesh-like network. From top, LM × 1000, LM × 200. (Micrographs provided by the Regents of University of Michigan Medical School © 2012)

Disorders of the...

Connective Tissue: Tendinitis

Your opponent stands ready as you prepare to hit the serve, but you are confident that you will smash the ball past your opponent. As you toss the ball high in the air, a burning pain shoots across your wrist and you drop the tennis racket. That dull ache in the wrist that you ignored through the summer is now an unbearable pain. The game is over for now.

After examining your swollen wrist, the doctor in the emergency room announces that you have developed wrist tendinitis. She recommends icing the tender area, taking non-steroidal anti-inflammatory medication to ease the pain and to reduce swelling, and complete rest for a few weeks. She interrupts your protests that you cannot stop playing. She issues a stern warning about the risk of aggravating the condition and the possibility of surgery. She consoles you by mentioning that well known tennis players such as Venus and Serena Williams and Rafael Nadal have also suffered from tendinitis related injuries.

What is tendinitis and how did it happen? Tendinitis is the inflammation of a tendon, the thick band of fibrous connective tissue that attaches a muscle to a bone. The condition causes pain and tenderness in the area around a joint. On rare occasions, a sudden serious injury will cause tendinitis. Most often, the condition results from repetitive motions over time that strain the tendons needed to perform the tasks.

Persons whose jobs and hobbies involve performing the same movements over and over again are often at the greatest risk of tendinitis. You hear of tennis and golfer's elbow, jumper's knee, and swimmer's shoulder. In all cases, overuse of the joint causes a microtrauma that initiates the inflammatory response. Tendinitis is routinely diagnosed through a clinical examination. In case of severe pain, X-rays can be examined to rule out the possibility of a bone injury. Severe cases of tendinitis can even tear loose a tendon. Surgical repair of a tendon is painful. Connective tissue in the tendon does not have abundant blood supply and heals slowly.

While older adults are at risk for tendinitis because the elasticity of tendon tissue decreases with age, active people of all ages can develop tendinitis. Young athletes, dancers, and computer operators; anyone who performs the same movements constantly is at risk for tendinitis. Although repetitive motions are unavoidable in many activities and may lead to tendinitis, precautions can be taken that can lessen the probability of developing tendinitis. For active individuals, stretches before exercising and cross training or changing exercises are recommended. For the passionate athlete, it may be time to take some lessons to improve technique. All of the preventive measures aim to increase the strength of the tendon and decrease the stress put on it. With proper rest and managed care, you will be back on the court to hit that slice-spin serve over the net.

⊘ INTERACTIVE LINK

Watch this animation (http://openstax.org/l/tendonitis) to learn more about tendonitis, a painful condition caused by swollen or injured tendons.

Supportive Connective Tissues

Two major forms of supportive connective tissue, cartilage and bone, allow the body to maintain its posture and protect internal organs.

Cartilage

The distinctive appearance of cartilage is due to polysaccharides called chondroitin sulfates, which bind with ground substance proteins to form proteoglycans. Embedded within the cartilage matrix are **chondrocytes**, or cartilage cells, and the space they occupy are called **lacunae** (singular = lacuna). A layer of dense irregular connective tissue, the perichondrium, encapsulates the cartilage. Cartilaginous tissue is avascular, thus all nutrients need to diffuse through the matrix to reach the chondrocytes. This is a factor contributing to the very slow healing of cartilaginous tissues.

The three main types of cartilage tissue are hyaline cartilage, fibrocartilage, and elastic cartilage (Figure 4.16). **Hyaline cartilage**, the most common type of cartilage in the body, consists of short and dispersed collagen fibers and contains large amounts of proteoglycans. Under the microscope, tissue samples appear clear. The surface of hyaline cartilage is smooth. Both strong and flexible, it is found in the rib cage and nose and covers bones where they meet to form moveable joints. It makes up a template of the embryonic skeleton before bone formation. A plate of hyaline cartilage at the ends of bone allows continued growth until adulthood. **Fibrocartilage** is tough because it has thick bundles of collagen fibers dispersed through its matrix. Menisci in the knee joint and the intervertebral discs are examples of fibrocartilage. **Elastic cartilage** contains elastic fibers as well as collagen and proteoglycans. This tissue gives rigid support as well as elasticity. Tug gently at your ear lobes, and notice that the lobes return to their initial shape. The external ear contains elastic cartilage.

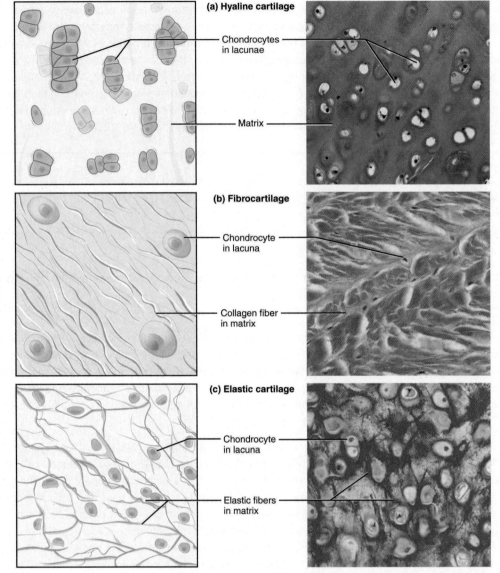

FIGURE 4.16   Types of Cartilage   Cartilage is a connective tissue consisting of collagenous fibers embedded in a firm matrix of chondroitin sulfates. (a) Hyaline cartilage provides support with some flexibility. The example is from dog tissue. (b) Fibrocartilage provides some compressibility and can absorb pressure. (c) Elastic cartilage provides firm but elastic support. From top, LM × 300, LM × 1200, LM × 1016. (Micrographs provided by the Regents of University of Michigan Medical School © 2012)

Bone

Bone is the hardest connective tissue. It provides protection to internal organs and supports the body. Bone's rigid extracellular matrix contains mostly collagen fibers embedded in a mineralized ground substance containing hydroxyapatite, a form of calcium phosphate. Both components of the matrix, organic and inorganic, contribute to the unusual properties of bone. Without collagen, bones would be brittle and shatter easily. Without mineral crystals, bones would flex and provide little support. Osteocytes, bone cells like chondrocytes, are located within lacunae. The histology of transverse tissue from long bone shows a typical arrangement of osteocytes in concentric circles around a central canal. Bone is a highly vascularized tissue. Unlike cartilage, bone tissue can recover from injuries in a relatively short time.

Cancellous bone looks like a sponge under the microscope and contains empty spaces between trabeculae, or arches of bone proper. It is lighter than compact bone and found in the interior of some bones and at the end of long bones. Compact bone is solid and has greater structural strength.

Fluid Connective Tissue

Blood and lymph are fluid connective tissues. Cells circulate in a liquid extracellular matrix. The formed elements circulating in blood are all derived from hematopoietic stem cells located in bone marrow (Figure 4.17). Erythrocytes, red blood cells, transport oxygen and some carbon dioxide. Leukocytes, white blood cells, are responsible for defending against potentially harmful microorganisms or molecules. Platelets are cell fragments involved in blood clotting. Some white blood cells have the ability to cross the endothelial layer that lines blood vessels and enter adjacent tissues. Nutrients, salts, and wastes are dissolved in the liquid matrix and transported through the body.

Lymph contains a liquid matrix and white blood cells. Lymphatic capillaries are extremely permeable, allowing larger molecules and excess fluid from interstitial spaces to enter the lymphatic vessels. Lymph drains into blood vessels, delivering molecules to the blood that could not otherwise directly enter the bloodstream. In this way, specialized lymphatic capillaries transport absorbed fats away from the intestine and deliver these molecules to the blood.

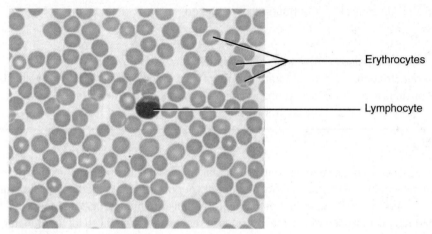

FIGURE 4.17 Blood: A Fluid Connective Tissue   Blood is a fluid connective tissue containing erythrocytes and various types of leukocytes that circulate in a liquid extracellular matrix. LM × 1600. (Micrograph provided by the Regents of University of Michigan Medical School © 2012)

🔗 INTERACTIVE LINK

View the University of Michigan Webscope (http://openstax.org/l/cardiovascular) to explore the tissue sample in greater detail.

4.4 Muscle Tissue and Motion

LEARNING OBJECTIVES

By the end of this section, you will be able to:

- Identify the three types of muscle tissue
- Compare and contrast the functions of each muscle tissue type
- Explain how muscle tissue can enable motion

Muscle tissue is characterized by properties that allow movement. Muscle cells are excitable; they respond to a stimulus. They are contractile, meaning they can shorten and generate a pulling force. When attached between two movable objects, in other words, bones, contractions of the muscles cause the bones to move. Some muscle movement is voluntary, which means it is under conscious control. For example, a person decides to open a book and read a chapter on anatomy. Other movements are involuntary, meaning they are not under conscious control, such as the contraction of your pupil in bright light. Muscle tissue is classified into three types according to structure and function: skeletal, cardiac, and smooth (Table 4.2).

Comparison of Structure and Properties of Muscle Tissue Types

Tissue	Histology	Function	Location
Skeletal	Long cylindrical fiber, striated, many peripherally located nuclei	Voluntary movement, produces heat, protects organs	Attached to bones and around entrance points to body (e.g., mouth, anus)
Cardiac	Short, branched, striated, single central nucleus	Contracts to pump blood	Heart
Smooth	Short, spindle-shaped, no evident striation, single nucleus in each fiber	Involuntary movement, moves food, involuntary control of respiration, moves secretions, regulates flow of blood in arteries by contraction	Walls of major organs and passageways

TABLE 4.2

Skeletal muscle is attached to bones and its contraction makes possible locomotion, facial expressions, posture, and other voluntary movements of the body. Forty percent of your body mass is made up of skeletal muscle. Skeletal muscles generate heat as a byproduct of their contraction and thus participate in thermal homeostasis. Shivering is an involuntary contraction of skeletal muscles in response to perceived lower than normal body temperature. The muscle cell, or **myocyte**, develops from myoblasts derived from the mesoderm. Myocytes and their numbers remain relatively constant throughout life. Skeletal muscle tissue is arranged in bundles surrounded by connective tissue. Under the light microscope, muscle cells appear striated with many nuclei squeezed along the membranes. The **striation** is due to the regular alternation of the contractile proteins actin and myosin, along with the structural proteins that couple the contractile proteins to connective tissues. The cells are multinucleated as a result of the fusion of the many myoblasts that fuse to form each long muscle fiber.

Cardiac muscle forms the contractile walls of the heart. The cells of cardiac muscle, known as cardiomyocytes, also appear striated under the microscope. Unlike skeletal muscle fibers, cardiomyocytes are single cells typically with a single centrally located nucleus. A principal characteristic of cardiomyocytes is that they contract on their own intrinsic rhythms without any external stimulation. Cardiomyocyte attach to one another with specialized cell junctions called intercalated discs. Intercalated discs have both anchoring junctions and gap junctions. Attached cells form long, branching cardiac muscle fibers that are, essentially, a mechanical and electrochemical syncytium allowing the cells to synchronize their actions. The cardiac muscle pumps blood through the body and is under involuntary control. The attachment junctions hold adjacent cells together across the dynamic pressures changes of the cardiac cycle.

Smooth muscle tissue contraction is responsible for involuntary movements in the internal organs. It forms the contractile component of the digestive, urinary, and reproductive systems as well as the airways and arteries. Each cell is spindle shaped with a single nucleus and no visible striations (Figure 4.18).

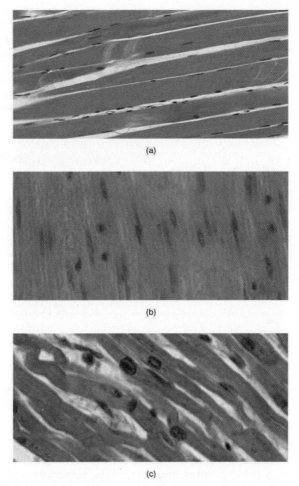

FIGURE 4.18   Muscle Tissue   (a) Skeletal muscle cells have prominent striation and nuclei on their periphery. (b) Smooth muscle cells have a single nucleus and no visible striations. (c) Cardiac muscle cells appear striated and have a single nucleus. (Micrographs provided by the Regents of University of Michigan Medical School © 2012)

⊘ INTERACTIVE LINK

Watch this video (http://openstax.org/l/musctissue) to learn more about muscle tissue. In looking through a microscope how could you distinguish skeletal muscle tissue from smooth muscle?

4.5 Nervous Tissue Mediates Perception and Response

LEARNING OBJECTIVES

By the end of this section, you will be able to:

- Identify the classes of cells that make up nervous tissue
- Discuss how nervous tissue mediates perception and response

Nervous tissue is characterized as being excitable and capable of sending and receiving electrochemical signals that provide the body with information. Two main classes of cells make up nervous tissue: the **neuron** and **neuroglia** (Figure 4.19). Neurons propagate information via electrochemical impulses, called action potentials, which are biochemically linked to the release of chemical signals. Neuroglia play an essential role in supporting neurons and modulating their information propagation.

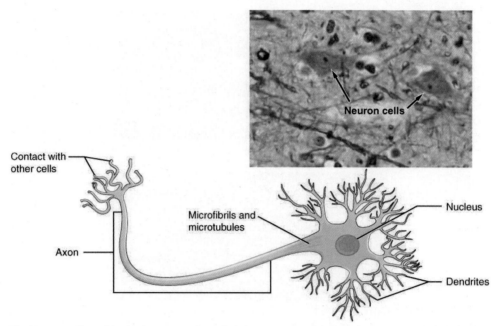

FIGURE 4.19   **The Neuron**   The cell body of a neuron, also called the soma, contains the nucleus and mitochondria. The dendrites transfer the nerve impulse to the soma. The axon carries the action potential away to another excitable cell. LM × 1600. (Micrograph provided by the Regents of University of Michigan Medical School © 2012)

🔗 INTERACTIVE LINK

Follow this link (http://openstax.org/l/nobel) to learn more about nervous tissue. What are the main parts of a nerve cell?

Neurons display distinctive morphology, well suited to their role as conducting cells, with three main parts. The cell body includes most of the cytoplasm, the organelles, and the nucleus. Dendrites branch off the cell body and appear as thin extensions. A long "tail," the axon, extends from the neuron body and can be wrapped in an insulating layer known as **myelin**, which is formed by accessory cells. The synapse is the gap between nerve cells, or between a nerve cell and its target, for example, a muscle or a gland, across which the impulse is transmitted by chemical compounds known as neurotransmitters. Neurons categorized as multipolar neurons have several dendrites and a single prominent axon. Bipolar neurons possess a single dendrite and axon with the cell body, while unipolar neurons have only a single process extending out from the cell body, which divides into a functional dendrite and into a functional axon. When a neuron is sufficiently stimulated, it generates an action potential that propagates down the axon towards the synapse. If enough neurotransmitters are released at the synapse to stimulate the next neuron or target, a response is generated.

The second class of neural cells comprises the neuroglia or glial cells, which have been characterized as having a simple support role. The word "glia" comes from the Greek word for glue. Recent research is shedding light on the more complex role of neuroglia in the function of the brain and nervous system. **Astrocyte** cells, named for their distinctive star shape, are abundant in the central nervous system. The astrocytes have many functions, including regulation of ion concentration in the intercellular space, uptake and/or breakdown of some neurotransmitters, and formation of the blood-brain barrier, the membrane that separates the circulatory system from the brain. Microglia protect the nervous system against infection but are not nervous tissue because they are related to macrophages. **Oligodendrocyte** cells produce myelin in the central nervous system (brain and spinal cord) while the **Schwann cell** produces myelin in the peripheral nervous system (Figure 4.20).

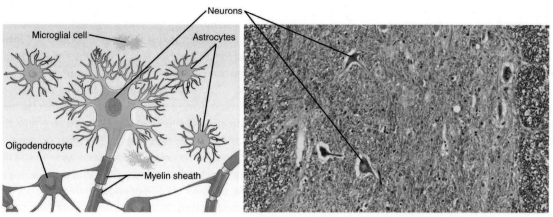

FIGURE 4.20   **Nervous Tissue**   Nervous tissue is made up of neurons and neuroglia. The cells of nervous tissue are specialized to transmit and receive impulses. LM × 872. (Micrograph provided by the Regents of University of Michigan Medical School © 2012)

4.6 Tissue Injury and Aging

LEARNING OBJECTIVES

By the end of this section, you will be able to:
- Identify the cardinal signs of inflammation
- List the body's response to tissue injury
- Explain the process of tissue repair
- Discuss the progressive impact of aging on tissue
- Describe cancerous mutations' effect on tissue

Tissues of all types are vulnerable to injury and, inevitably, aging. In the former case, understanding how tissues respond to damage can guide strategies to aid repair. In the latter case, understanding the impact of aging can help in the search for ways to diminish its effects.

Tissue Injury and Repair

Inflammation is the standard, initial response of the body to injury. Whether biological, chemical, physical, or radiation burns, all injuries lead to the same sequence of physiological events. Inflammation limits the extent of injury, partially or fully eliminates the cause of injury, and initiates repair and regeneration of damaged tissue. **Necrosis**, or accidental cell death, causes inflammation. **Apoptosis** is programmed cell death, a normal step-by-step process that destroys cells no longer needed by the body. By mechanisms still under investigation, apoptosis does not initiate the inflammatory response. Acute inflammation resolves over time by the healing of tissue. If inflammation persists, it becomes chronic and leads to diseased conditions. Arthritis and tuberculosis are examples of chronic inflammation. The suffix "-itis" denotes inflammation of a specific organ or type, for example, peritonitis is the inflammation of the peritoneum, and meningitis refers to the inflammation of the meninges, the tough membranes that surround the central nervous system

The four cardinal signs of inflammation—redness, swelling, pain, and local heat—were first recorded in antiquity. Cornelius Celsus is credited with documenting these signs during the days of the Roman Empire, as early as the first century AD. A fifth sign, loss of function, may also accompany inflammation.

Upon tissue injury, damaged cells release inflammatory chemical signals that evoke local **vasodilation**, the widening of the blood vessels. Increased blood flow results in apparent redness and heat. In response to injury, mast cells present in tissue degranulate, releasing the potent vasodilator **histamine**. Increased blood flow and inflammatory mediators recruit white blood cells to the site of inflammation. The endothelium lining the local blood vessel becomes "leaky" under the influence of histamine and other inflammatory mediators allowing neutrophils, macrophages, and fluid to move from the blood into the interstitial tissue spaces. The excess liquid in tissue causes swelling, more properly called edema. The swollen tissues squeezing pain receptors cause the sensation of pain. Prostaglandins released from injured cells also activate pain neurons. Non-steroidal anti-inflammatory drugs (NSAIDs) reduce pain because they inhibit the synthesis of prostaglandins. High levels of NSAIDs reduce inflammation. Antihistamines decrease allergies by blocking histamine receptors and as a result the histamine response.

After containment of an injury, the tissue repair phase starts with removal of toxins and waste products. **Clotting** (coagulation) reduces blood loss from damaged blood vessels and forms a network of fibrin proteins that trap blood cells and bind the edges of the wound together. A scab forms when the clot dries, reducing the risk of infection. Sometimes a mixture of dead leukocytes and fluid called pus accumulates in the wound. As healing progresses, fibroblasts from the surrounding connective tissues replace the collagen and extracellular material lost by the injury. Angiogenesis, the growth of new blood vessels, results in vascularization of the new tissue known as granulation tissue. The clot retracts pulling the edges of the wound together, and it slowly dissolves as the tissue is repaired. When a large amount of granulation tissue forms and capillaries disappear, a pale scar is often visible in the healed area. A **primary union** describes the healing of a wound where the edges are close together. When there is a gaping wound, it takes longer to refill the area with cells and collagen. The process called **secondary union** occurs as the edges of the wound are pulled together by what is called **wound contraction**. When a wound is more than one quarter of an inch deep, sutures (stitches) are recommended to promote a primary union and avoid the formation of a disfiguring scar. Regeneration is the addition of new cells of the same type as the ones that were injured (Figure 4.21).

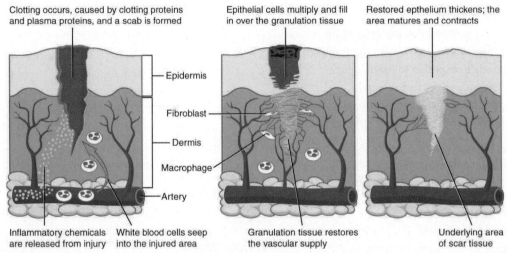

FIGURE 4.21 Tissue Healing   During wound repair, collagen fibers are laid down randomly by fibroblasts that move into repair the area.

🔗 INTERACTIVE LINK

Watch this video (http://openstax.org/l/healinghand) to see a hand heal. Over what period of time do you think these images were taken?

Tissue and Aging

According to poet Ralph Waldo Emerson, "The surest poison is time." In fact, biology confirms that many functions of the body decline with age. All the cells, tissues, and organs are affected by senescence, with noticeable variability between individuals owing to different genetic makeup and lifestyles. The outward signs of aging are easily recognizable. The skin and other tissues become thinner and drier, reducing their elasticity, contributing to wrinkles and high blood pressure. Hair turns gray because follicles produce less melanin, the brown pigment of hair and the iris of the eye. The face looks flabby because elastic and collagen fibers decrease in connective tissue and muscle tone is lost. Glasses and hearing aids may become parts of life as the senses slowly deteriorate, all due to reduced elasticity. Overall height decreases as the bones lose calcium and other minerals. With age, fluid decreases in the fibrous cartilage disks intercalated between the vertebrae in the spine. Joints lose cartilage and stiffen. Many tissues, including those in muscles, lose mass through a process called **atrophy**. Lumps and rigidity become more widespread. As a consequence, the passageways, blood vessels, and airways become more rigid. The brain and spinal cord lose mass. Nerves do not transmit impulses with the same speed and frequency as in the past. Some loss of thought clarity and memory can accompany aging. More severe problems are not necessarily associated with the aging process and may be symptoms of underlying illness.

As exterior signs of aging increase, so do the interior signs, which are not as noticeable. The incidence of heart diseases, respiratory syndromes, and type 2 diabetes increases with age, though these are not necessarily age-dependent effects. Wound healing is slower in the elderly, accompanied by a higher frequency of infection as the capacity of the immune system to fend off pathogen declines.

Aging is also apparent at the cellular level because all cells experience changes with aging. Telomeres, regions of the chromosomes necessary for cell division, shorten each time cells divide. As they do, cells are less able to divide and regenerate. Because of alterations in cell membranes, transport of oxygen and nutrients into the cell and removal of carbon dioxide and waste products from the cell are not as efficient in the elderly. Cells may begin to function abnormally, which may lead to diseases associated with aging, including arthritis, memory issues, and some cancers.

The progressive impact of aging on the body varies considerably among individuals, but Studies indicate, however, that exercise and healthy lifestyle choices can slow down the deterioration of the body that comes with old age.

HOMEOSTATIC IMBALANCES

Tissues and Cancer

Cancer is a generic term for many diseases in which cells escape regulatory signals. Uncontrolled growth, invasion into adjacent tissues, and colonization of other organs, if not treated early enough, are its hallmarks. Health suffers when tumors "rob" blood supply from the "normal" organs.

A mutation is defined as a permanent change in the DNA of a cell. Epigenetic modifications, changes that do not affect the code of the DNA but alter how the DNA is decoded, are also known to generate abnormal cells. Alterations in the genetic material may be caused by environmental agents, infectious agents, or errors in the replication of DNA that accumulate with age. Many mutations do not cause any noticeable change in the functions of a cell. However, if the modification affects key proteins that have an impact on the cell's ability to proliferate in an orderly fashion, the cell starts to divide abnormally. As changes in cells accumulate, they lose their ability to form regular tissues. A tumor, a mass of cells displaying abnormal architecture, forms in the tissue. Many tumors are benign, meaning they do not metastasize nor cause disease. A tumor becomes malignant, or cancerous, when it breaches the confines of its tissue, promotes angiogenesis, attracts the growth of capillaries, and metastasizes to other organs (Figure 4.22). The specific names of cancers reflect the tissue of origin. Cancers derived from epithelial cells are referred to as carcinomas. Cancer in myeloid tissue or blood cells form myelomas. Leukemias are cancers of white blood cells, whereas sarcomas derive from connective tissue. Cells in tumors differ both in structure and function. Some cells, called cancer stem cells, appear to be a subtype of cell responsible for uncontrolled growth. Recent research shows that contrary to what was previously assumed, tumors are not disorganized masses of cells, but have their own structures.

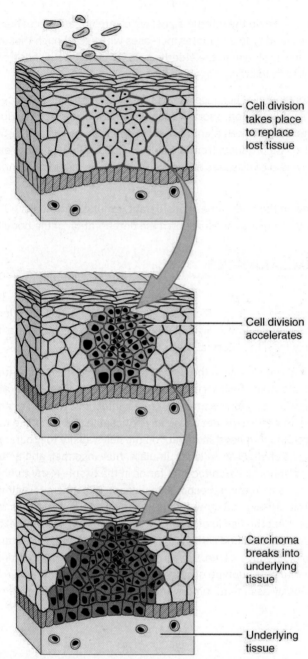

FIGURE 4.22   **Development of Cancer**   Note the change in cell size, nucleus size, and organization in the tissue.

⊘ INTERACTIVE LINK

Watch this video (http://openstax.org/l/tumor) to learn more about tumors. What is a tumor?

Cancer treatments vary depending on the disease's type and stage. Traditional approaches, including surgery, radiation, chemotherapy, and hormonal therapy, aim to remove or kill rapidly dividing cancer cells, but these strategies have their limitations. Depending on a tumor's location, for example, cancer surgeons may be unable to remove it. Radiation and chemotherapy are difficult, and it is often impossible to target only the cancer cells. The treatments inevitably destroy healthy tissue as well. To address this, researchers are working on pharmaceuticals that can target specific proteins implicated in cancer-associated molecular pathways.

Key Terms

adipocytes   lipid storage cells

adipose tissue   specialized areolar tissue rich in stored fat

anchoring junction   mechanically attaches adjacent cells to each other or to the basement membrane

apical   that part of a cell or tissue which, in general, faces an open space

apocrine secretion   release of a substance along with the apical portion of the cell

apoptosis   programmed cell death

areolar tissue   (also, loose connective tissue) a type of connective tissue proper that shows little specialization with cells dispersed in the matrix

astrocyte   star-shaped cell in the central nervous system that regulates ions and uptake and/or breakdown of some neurotransmitters and contributes to the formation of the blood-brain barrier

atrophy   loss of mass and function

basal lamina   thin extracellular layer that lies underneath epithelial cells and separates them from other tissues

basement membrane   in epithelial tissue, a thin layer of fibrous material that anchors the epithelial tissue to the underlying connective tissue; made up of the basal lamina and reticular lamina

cardiac muscle   heart muscle, under involuntary control, composed of striated cells that attach to form fibers, each cell contains a single nucleus, contracts autonomously

cell junction   point of cell-to-cell contact that connects one cell to another in a tissue

chondrocytes   cells of the cartilage

clotting   also called coagulation; complex process by which blood components form a plug to stop bleeding

collagen fiber   flexible fibrous proteins that give connective tissue tensile strength

connective tissue   type of tissue that serves to hold in place, connect, and integrate the body's organs and systems

connective tissue membrane   connective tissue that encapsulates organs and lines movable joints

connective tissue proper   connective tissue containing a viscous matrix, fibers, and cells.

cutaneous membrane   skin; epithelial tissue made up of a stratified squamous epithelial cells that cover the outside of the body

dense connective tissue   connective tissue proper that contains many fibers that provide both elasticity and protection

ectoderm   outermost embryonic germ layer from which the epidermis and the nervous tissue derive

elastic cartilage   type of cartilage, with elastin as the major protein, characterized by rigid support as well as elasticity

elastic fiber   fibrous protein within connective tissue that contains a high percentage of the protein elastin that allows the fibers to stretch and return to original size

endocrine gland   groups of cells that release chemical signals into the intercellular fluid to be picked up and transported to their target organs by blood

endoderm   innermost embryonic germ layer from which most of the digestive system and lower respiratory system derive

endothelium   tissue that lines vessels of the lymphatic and cardiovascular system, made up of a simple squamous epithelium

epithelial membrane   epithelium attached to a layer of connective tissue

epithelial tissue   type of tissue that serves primarily as a covering or lining of body parts, protecting the body; it also functions in absorption, transport, and secretion

exocrine gland   group of epithelial cells that secrete substances through ducts that open to the skin or to internal body surfaces that lead to the exterior of the body

fibroblast   most abundant cell type in connective tissue, secretes protein fibers and matrix into the extracellular space

fibrocartilage   tough form of cartilage, made of thick bundles of collagen fibers embedded in chondroitin sulfate ground substance

fibrocyte   less active form of fibroblast

fluid connective tissue   specialized cells that circulate in a watery fluid containing salts, nutrients, and dissolved proteins

gap junction   allows cytoplasmic communications to occur between cells

goblet cell   unicellular gland found in columnar epithelium that secretes mucous

ground substance   fluid or semi-fluid portion of the matrix

histamine   chemical compound released by mast cells in response to injury that causes vasodilation and endothelium permeability

histology   microscopic study of tissue architecture, organization, and function

holocrine secretion   release of a substance caused by the rupture of a gland cell, which becomes part of the secretion

hyaline cartilage   most common type of cartilage, smooth and made of short collagen fibers embedded in a chondroitin sulfate ground substance

inflammation   response of tissue to injury

lacunae   (singular = lacuna) small spaces in bone or cartilage tissue that cells occupy

lamina propria   areolar connective tissue underlying a mucous membrane

loose connective tissue   (also, areolar tissue) type of connective tissue proper that shows little specialization with cells dispersed in the matrix

matrix   extracellular material which is produced by the cells embedded in it, containing ground substance and fibers

merocrine secretion   release of a substance from a gland via exocytosis

mesenchymal cell   adult stem cell from which most connective tissue cells are derived

mesenchyme   embryonic tissue from which connective tissue cells derive

mesoderm   middle embryonic germ layer from which connective tissue, muscle tissue, and some epithelial tissue derive

mesothelium   simple squamous epithelial tissue which covers the major body cavities and is the epithelial portion of serous membranes

mucous connective tissue   specialized loose connective tissue present in the umbilical cord

mucous gland   group of cells that secrete mucous, a thick, slippery substance that keeps tissues moist and acts as a lubricant

mucous membrane   tissue membrane that is covered by protective mucous and lines tissue exposed to the outside environment

muscle tissue   type of tissue that is capable of contracting and generating tension in response to stimulation; produces movement.

myelin   layer of lipid inside some neuroglial cells that wraps around the axons of some neurons

myocyte   muscle cells

necrosis   accidental death of cells and tissues

nervous tissue   type of tissue that is capable of sending and receiving impulses through electrochemical signals.

neuroglia   supportive neural cells

neuron   excitable neural cell that transfer nerve impulses

oligodendrocyte   neuroglial cell that produces myelin in the brain

parenchyma   functional cells of a gland or organ, in contrast with the supportive or connective tissue of a gland or organ

primary union   condition of a wound where the wound edges are close enough to be brought together and fastened if necessary, allowing quicker and more thorough healing

pseudostratified columnar epithelium   tissue that consists of a single layer of irregularly shaped and sized cells that give the appearance of multiple layers; found in ducts of certain glands and the upper respiratory tract

reticular fiber   fine fibrous protein, made of collagen subunits, which cross-link to form supporting "nets" within connective tissue

reticular lamina   matrix containing collagen and elastin secreted by connective tissue; a component of the basement membrane

reticular tissue   type of loose connective tissue that provides a supportive framework to soft organs, such as lymphatic tissue, spleen, and the liver

Schwann cell   neuroglial cell that produces myelin in the peripheral nervous system

secondary union   wound healing facilitated by wound contraction

serous gland   group of cells within the serous membrane that secrete a lubricating substance onto the surface

serous membrane   type of tissue membrane that lines body cavities and lubricates them with serous fluid

simple columnar epithelium   tissue that consists of a single layer of column-like cells; promotes secretion and absorption in tissues and organs

simple cuboidal epithelium   tissue that consists of a single layer of cube-shaped cells; promotes secretion and absorption in ducts and tubules

simple squamous epithelium   tissue that consists of a single layer of flat scale-like cells; promotes diffusion and filtration across surface

skeletal muscle   usually attached to bone, under voluntary control, each cell is a fiber that is multinucleated and striated

smooth muscle   under involuntary control, moves internal organs, cells contain a single nucleus, are spindle-shaped, and do not appear striated; each cell is a fiber

stratified columnar epithelium   tissue that consists of two or more layers of column-like cells, contains glands and is found in some ducts

stratified cuboidal epithelium   tissue that consists of two or more layers of cube-shaped cells, found in some ducts

stratified squamous epithelium   tissue that consists of multiple layers of cells with the most apical being flat scale-like cells; protects surfaces from abrasion

striation   alignment of parallel actin and myosin filaments which form a banded pattern

supportive connective tissue   type of connective tissue that provides strength to the body and protects soft tissue

synovial membrane   connective tissue membrane that lines the cavities of freely movable joints, producing synovial fluid for lubrication

tight junction   forms an impermeable barrier between cells

tissue   group of cells that are similar in form and perform related functions

tissue membrane   thin layer or sheet of cells that covers the outside of the body, organs, and internal cavities

totipotent   embryonic cells that have the ability to differentiate into any type of cell and organ in the body

transitional epithelium   form of stratified epithelium found in the urinary tract, characterized by an apical layer of cells that change shape in response to the presence of urine

vasodilation   widening of blood vessels

wound contraction   process whereby the borders of a wound are physically drawn together

Chapter Review

4.1 Types of Tissues

The human body contains more than 200 types of cells that can all be classified into four types of tissues: epithelial, connective, muscle, and nervous. Epithelial tissues act as coverings controlling the movement of materials across the surface. Connective tissue integrates the various parts of the body and provides support and protection to organs. Muscle tissue allows the body to move. Nervous tissues propagate information.

The study of the shape and arrangement of cells in tissue is called histology. All cells and tissues in the body derive from three germ layers in the embryo: the ectoderm, mesoderm, and endoderm.

Different types of tissues form membranes that enclose organs, provide a friction-free interaction between organs, and keep organs together. Synovial membranes are connective tissue membranes that protect and line the joints. Epithelial membranes are formed from epithelial tissue attached to a layer of connective tissue. There are three types of epithelial membranes: mucous, which contain glands; serous, which secrete fluid; and cutaneous which makes up the skin.

4.2 Epithelial Tissue

In epithelial tissue, cells are closely packed with little or no extracellular matrix except for the basal lamina that separates the epithelium from underlying tissue. The main functions of epithelia are protection from the environment, coverage, secretion and excretion, absorption, and filtration. Cells are bound together by tight junctions that form an impermeable barrier. They can also be connected by gap junctions, which allow free exchange of soluble molecules between cells, and anchoring junctions, which attach cell to cell or cell to matrix. The different types of epithelial tissues are characterized by their cellular shapes and arrangements: squamous, cuboidal, or columnar epithelia. Single cell layers form simple epithelia, whereas stacked cells form stratified epithelia. Very few capillaries penetrate these tissues.

Glands are secretory tissues and organs that are derived from epithelial tissues. Exocrine glands release their products through ducts. Endocrine glands secrete hormones directly into the interstitial fluid and blood stream. Glands are classified both according to the type of secretion and by their structure. Merocrine glands secrete products as they are synthesized. Apocrine glands release secretions by pinching off the apical portion of the cell, whereas holocrine gland cells store their secretions until they rupture and release their contents. In this case, the cell becomes part of the secretion.

4.3 Connective Tissue Supports and Protects

Connective tissue is a heterogeneous tissue with many cell shapes and tissue architecture. Structurally, all connective tissues contain cells that are embedded in an extracellular matrix stabilized by proteins. The chemical nature and physical layout of the extracellular matrix and proteins vary enormously among tissues, reflecting the variety of functions that connective tissue fulfills in the body. Connective tissues separate and cushion organs, protecting them from shifting or traumatic injury. Connect tissues provide support and assist movement, store and transport energy molecules, protect against infections, and contribute to temperature homeostasis.

Many different cells contribute to the formation of connective tissues. They originate in the mesodermal germ layer and differentiate from mesenchyme and hematopoietic tissue in the bone marrow. Fibroblasts are the most abundant and secrete many protein fibers, adipocytes specialize in fat storage, hematopoietic cells from the bone marrow give rise to all the blood cells, chondrocytes form cartilage, and osteocytes form bone. The extracellular matrix contains fluid, proteins, polysaccharide derivatives, and, in the case of bone, mineral crystals. Protein fibers fall into three major groups: collagen fibers that are thick, strong, flexible, and resist stretch; reticular fibers that are thin and form a supportive mesh; and elastin fibers that are thin and elastic.

The major types of connective tissue are connective tissue proper, supportive tissue, and fluid tissue. Loose connective tissue proper includes adipose tissue, areolar tissue, and reticular tissue. These serve to hold organs and other tissues in place and, in the case of adipose tissue, isolate and store energy reserves. The matrix is the most abundant feature for loose tissue although adipose tissue does not have much extracellular matrix. Dense connective tissue proper is richer in fibers and may be regular, with fibers oriented in parallel as in ligaments and tendons, or irregular, with fibers oriented in several directions. Organ capsules (collagenous type) and walls of arteries (elastic type) contain dense irregular connective tissue. Cartilage and bone are supportive tissue. Cartilage contains chondrocytes and is somewhat flexible. Hyaline cartilage is smooth and clear, covers joints, and is found in the growing portion of bones. Fibrocartilage is tough because of extra collagen fibers and forms, among other things, the intervertebral discs. Elastic cartilage can stretch and recoil to its original shape because of its high content of elastic fibers. The matrix contains very few blood vessels. Bones are made of a rigid, mineralized matrix containing calcium salts, crystals, and osteocytes lodged in lacunae. Bone tissue is highly vascularized. Cancellous bone is spongy and less solid than compact bone. Fluid tissue, for example blood and lymph, is characterized by a liquid matrix and no supporting fibers.

4.4 Muscle Tissue and Motion

The three types of muscle cells are skeletal, cardiac, and smooth. Their morphologies match their specific functions in the body. Skeletal muscle is voluntary and responds to conscious stimuli. The cells are striated and multinucleated appearing as long, unbranched cylinders. Cardiac muscle is involuntary and found only in the heart. Each cell is striated with a single nucleus and they attach to one another to form long fibers.

Cells are attached to one another at intercalated disks. The cells are interconnected physically and electrochemically to act as a syncytium. Cardiac muscle cells contract autonomously and involuntarily. Smooth muscle is involuntary. Each cell is a spindle-shaped fiber and contains a single nucleus. No striations are evident because the actin and myosin filaments do not align in the cytoplasm.

4.5 Nervous Tissue Mediates Perception and Response

The most prominent cell of the nervous tissue, the neuron, is characterized mainly by its ability to receive stimuli and respond by generating an electrical signal, known as an action potential, which can travel rapidly over great distances in the body. A typical neuron displays a distinctive morphology: a large cell body branches out into short extensions called dendrites, which receive chemical signals from other neurons, and a long tail called an axon, which relays signals away from the cell to other neurons, muscles, or glands. Many axons are wrapped by a myelin sheath, a lipid derivative that acts as an insulator and speeds up the transmission of the action potential. Other cells in the nervous tissue, the neuroglia, include the astrocytes, microglia, oligodendrocytes, and Schwann cells.

4.6 Tissue Injury and Aging

Inflammation is the classic response of the body to injury and follows a common sequence of events. The area is red, feels warm to the touch, swells, and is painful. Injured cells, mast cells, and resident macrophages release chemical signals that cause vasodilation and fluid leakage in the surrounding tissue. The repair phase includes blood clotting, followed by regeneration of tissue as fibroblasts deposit collagen. Some tissues regenerate more readily than others. Epithelial and connective tissues replace damaged or dead cells from a supply of adult stem cells. Muscle and nervous tissues undergo either slow regeneration or do not repair at all.

Age affects all the tissues and organs of the body. Damaged cells do not regenerate as rapidly as in younger people. Perception of sensation and effectiveness of response are lost in the nervous system. Muscles atrophy, and bones lose mass and become brittle. Collagen decreases in some connective tissue, and joints stiffen.

Interactive Link Questions

1. View this slideshow (http://openstax.org/l/stemcells) to learn more about stem cells. How do somatic stem cells differ from embryonic stem cells?

2. Watch this video (http://openstax.org/l/etissues) to find out more about the anatomy of epithelial tissues. Where in the body would one find non-keratinizing stratified squamous epithelium?

3. Watch this video (http://openstax.org/l/musctissue) to learn more about muscle tissue. In looking through a microscope how could you distinguish skeletal muscle tissue from smooth muscle?

4. Follow this link (http://openstax.org/l/nobel) to learn more about nervous tissue. What are the main parts of a nerve cell?

5. Watch this video (http://openstax.org/l/healinghand) to see a hand heal. Over what period of time do you think these images were taken?

6. Watch this video (http://openstax.org/l/tumor) to learn more about tumors. What is a tumor?

Review Questions

7. Which of the following is not a type of tissue?
   a. muscle
   b. nervous
   c. embryonic
   d. epithelial

8. The process by which a less specialized cell matures into a more specialized cell is called _____.
   a. differentiation
   b. maturation
   c. modification
   d. specialization

9. Differentiated cells in a developing embryo derive from _____.
   a. endothelium, mesothelium, and epithelium
   b. ectoderm, mesoderm, and endoderm
   c. connective tissue, epithelial tissue, and muscle tissue
   d. epidermis, mesoderm, and endothelium

10. Which of the following lines the body cavities exposed to the external environment?
   a. mesothelium
   b. lamina propria
   c. mesenteries
   d. mucosa

11. In observing epithelial cells under a microscope, the cells are arranged in a single layer and look tall and narrow, and the nucleus is located close to the basal side of the cell. The specimen is what type of epithelial tissue?
   a. columnar
   b. stratified
   c. squamous
   d. transitional

12. Which of the following is the epithelial tissue that lines the interior of blood vessels?
   a. columnar
   b. pseudostratified
   c. simple squamous
   d. transitional

13. Which type of epithelial tissue specializes in moving particles across its surface?
   a. transitional
   b. stratified columnar
   c. pseudostratified ciliated columnar
   d. stratified squamous

14. The _____ exocrine gland stores its secretion until the glandular cell ruptures, whereas the _____ gland releases its apical region and reforms.
   a. holocrine; apocrine
   b. eccrine; endocrine
   c. apocrine; holocrine
   d. eccrine; apocrine

15. Connective tissue is made of which three essential components?
   a. cells, ground substance, and carbohydrate fibers
   b. cells, ground substance, and protein fibers
   c. collagen, ground substance, and protein fibers
   d. matrix, ground substance, and fluid

16. Under the microscope, a tissue specimen shows cells located in spaces scattered in a transparent background. This is probably _____.
   a. loose connective tissue
   b. a tendon
   c. bone
   d. hyaline cartilage

17. Which connective tissue specializes in storage of fat?
   a. tendon
   b. adipose tissue
   c. reticular tissue
   d. dense connective tissue

18. Ligaments connect bones together and withstand a lot of stress. What type of connective tissue should you expect ligaments to contain?
   a. areolar tissue
   b. adipose tissue
   c. dense regular connective tissue
   d. dense irregular connective tissue

19. In adults, new connective tissue cells originate from the _____.
   a. mesoderm
   b. mesenchyme
   c. ectoderm
   d. endoderm

20. In bone, the main cells are _____.
   a. fibroblasts
   b. chondrocytes
   c. lymphocytes
   d. osteocytes

21. Striations, cylindrical cells, and multiple nuclei are observed in _____.
   a. skeletal muscle only
   b. cardiac muscle only
   c. smooth muscle only
   d. skeletal and cardiac muscles

22. The cells of muscles, myocytes, develop from _____.
   a. myoblasts
   b. endoderm
   c. fibrocytes
   d. chondrocytes

23. Skeletal muscle is composed of very hard working cells. Which organelles do you expect to find in abundance in skeletal muscle cell?
   a. nuclei
   b. striations
   c. golgi bodies
   d. mitochondria

24. The cells responsible for the transmission of the nerve impulse are _____.
   a. neurons
   b. oligodendrocytes
   c. astrocytes
   d. microglia

25. The nerve impulse travels down a(n) _____, away from the cell body.
   a. dendrite
   b. axon
   c. microglia
   d. collagen fiber

26. Which of the following central nervous system cells regulate ions, regulate the uptake and/or breakdown of some neurotransmitters, and contribute to the formation of the blood-brain barrier?
   a. microglia
   b. neuroglia
   c. oligodendrocytes
   d. astrocytes

27. Which of the following processes is not a cardinal sign of inflammation?
   a. redness
   b. heat
   c. fever
   d. swelling

28. When a mast cell reacts to an irritation, which of the following chemicals does it release?
   a. collagen
   b. histamine
   c. hyaluronic acid
   d. meylin

29. Atrophy refers to _____.
   a. loss of elasticity
   b. loss of mass
   c. loss of rigidity
   d. loss of permeability

30. Individuals can slow the rate of aging by modifying all of these lifestyle aspects except for _____.
   a. diet
   b. exercise
   c. genetic factors
   d. stress

Critical Thinking Questions

31. Identify the four types of tissue in the body, and describe the major functions of each tissue.

32. The zygote is described as totipotent because it ultimately gives rise to all the cells in your body including the highly specialized cells of your nervous system. Describe this transition, discussing the steps and processes that lead to these specialized cells.

33. What is the function of synovial membranes?

34. The structure of a tissue usually is optimized for its function. Describe how the structure of the mucosa and its cells match its function of nutrient absorption.

35. One of the main functions of connective tissue is to integrate organs and organ systems in the body. Discuss how blood fulfills this role.

36. Why does an injury to cartilage, especially hyaline cartilage, heal much more slowly than a bone fracture?

37. You are watching cells in a dish spontaneously contract. They are all contracting at different rates; some fast, some slow. After a while, several cells link up and they begin contracting in synchrony. Discuss what is going on and what type of cells you are looking at.

38. Why does skeletal muscle look striated?

39. Which morphological adaptations of neurons make them suitable for the transmission of nerve impulse?

40. What are the functions of astrocytes?

41. Why is it important to watch for increased redness, swelling and pain after a cut or abrasion has been cleaned and bandaged?

42. Aspirin is a non-steroidal anti-inflammatory drug (NSAID) that inhibits the formation of blood clots and is taken regularly by individuals with a heart condition. Steroids such as cortisol are used to control some autoimmune diseases and severe arthritis by down-regulating the inflammatory response. After reading the role of inflammation in the body's response to infection, can you predict an undesirable consequence of taking anti-inflammatory drugs on a regular basis?

43. As an individual ages, a constellation of symptoms begins the decline to the point where an individual's functioning is compromised. Identify and discuss two factors that have a role in factors leading to the compromised situation.

44. Discuss changes that occur in cells as a person ages.

CHAPTER 5
The Integumentary System

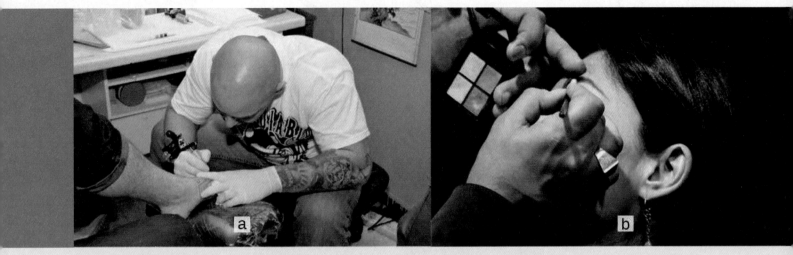

Figure 5.1 Your skin is a vital part of your life and appearance (a–b). Some people choose to embellish it with tattoos (a) or makeup (b). (credit a: Steve Teo; credit b: "spaceodissey"/flickr)

CHAPTER OBJECTIVES

After studying the chapter, you will be able to:

- Describe the integumentary system and the role it plays in homeostasis
- Describe the layers of the skin and the functions of each layer
- Describe the accessory structures of the skin and the functions of each
- Describe the changes that occur in the integumentary system during the aging process
- Discuss several common diseases, disorders, and injuries that affect the integumentary system
- Explain treatments for some common diseases, disorders, and injuries of the integumentary system

INTRODUCTION What do you think when you look at your skin in the mirror? Do you think about covering it with makeup, adding a tattoo, or maybe a body piercing? Or do you think about the fact that the skin belongs to one of the body's most essential and dynamic systems: the integumentary system? The integumentary system refers to the skin and its accessory structures, and it is responsible for much more than simply lending to your outward appearance. In the adult human body, the skin makes up about 16 percent of body weight and covers an area of 1.5 to 2 m². In fact, the skin and accessory structures are the largest organ system in the human body. As such, the skin protects your inner organs and it is in need of daily care and protection to maintain its health. This chapter will introduce the structure and functions of the integumentary system, as well as some of the diseases, disorders, and injuries that can affect this system.

5.1 Layers of the Skin

LEARNING OBJECTIVES

By the end of this section, you will be able to:

- Identify the components of the integumentary system
- Describe the layers of the skin and the functions of each layer
- Identify and describe the hypodermis and deep fascia
- Describe the role of keratinocytes and their life cycle
- Describe the role of melanocytes in skin pigmentation

Although you may not typically think of the skin as an organ, it is in fact made of tissues that work together as a single structure to perform unique and critical functions. The skin and its accessory structures make up the **integumentary system**, which provides the body with overall protection. The skin is made of multiple layers of cells and tissues, which are held to underlying structures by connective tissue (Figure 5.2). The deeper layer of skin is well vascularized (has numerous blood vessels). It also has numerous sensory, and autonomic and sympathetic nerve fibers ensuring communication to and from the brain.

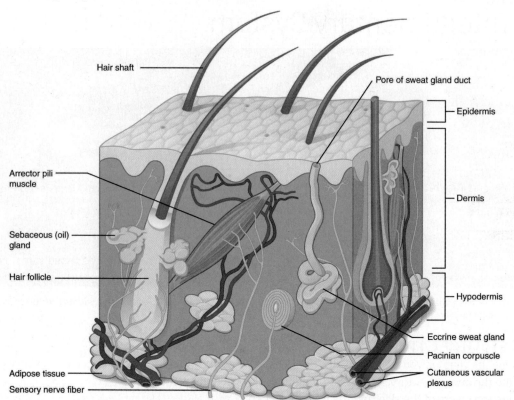

FIGURE 5.2   **Layers of Skin**   The skin is composed of two main layers: the epidermis, made of closely packed epithelial cells, and the dermis, made of dense, irregular connective tissue that houses blood vessels, hair follicles, sweat glands, and other structures. Beneath the dermis lies the hypodermis, which is composed mainly of loose connective and fatty tissues.

🔗 INTERACTIVE LINK

The skin consists of two main layers and a closely associated layer. View this animation (http://openstax.org/l/layers) to learn more about layers of the skin. What are the basic functions of each of these layers?

The Epidermis

The **epidermis** is composed of keratinized, stratified squamous epithelium. It is made of four or five layers of epithelial cells, depending on its location in the body. It does not have any blood vessels within it (i.e., it is avascular). Skin that has four layers of cells is referred to as "thin skin." From deep to superficial, these layers are the stratum basale, stratum spinosum, stratum granulosum, and stratum corneum. Most of the skin can be classified as thin skin. "Thick skin" is found only on the palms of the hands and the soles of the feet. It has a fifth layer, called the stratum lucidum, located between the stratum corneum and the stratum granulosum (Figure 5.3).

(a)   (b)

FIGURE 5.3   **Thin Skin versus Thick Skin**   These slides show cross-sections of the epidermis and dermis of (a) thin and (b) thick skin. Note the significant difference in the thickness of the epithelial layer of the thick skin. From top, LM × 40, LM × 40. (Micrographs provided by the Regents of University of Michigan Medical School © 2012)

The cells in all of the layers except the stratum basale are called keratinocytes. A **keratinocyte** is a cell that manufactures and stores the protein keratin. **Keratin** is an intracellular fibrous protein that gives hair, nails, and skin their hardness and water-resistant properties. The keratinocytes in the stratum corneum are dead and regularly slough away, being replaced by cells from the deeper layers (Figure 5.4).

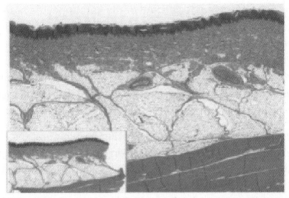

FIGURE 5.4 **Epidermis** The epidermis is epithelium composed of multiple layers of cells. The basal layer consists of cuboidal cells, whereas the outer layers are squamous, keratinized cells, so the whole epithelium is often described as being keratinized stratified squamous epithelium. LM × 40. (Micrograph provided by the Regents of University of Michigan Medical School © 2012)

⊘ INTERACTIVE LINK

View the University of Michigan WebScope (http://openstax.org/l/Epidermis) to explore the tissue sample in greater detail. If you zoom on the cells at the outermost layer of this section of skin, what do you notice about the cells?

Stratum Basale

The **stratum basale** (also called the stratum germinativum) is the deepest epidermal layer and attaches the epidermis to the basal lamina, below which lie the layers of the dermis. The cells in the stratum basale bond to the dermis via intertwining collagen fibers, referred to as the basement membrane. A finger-like projection, or fold, known as the **dermal papilla** (plural = dermal papillae) is found in the superficial portion of the dermis. Dermal papillae increase the strength of the connection between the epidermis and dermis; the greater the folding, the stronger the connections made (Figure 5.5).

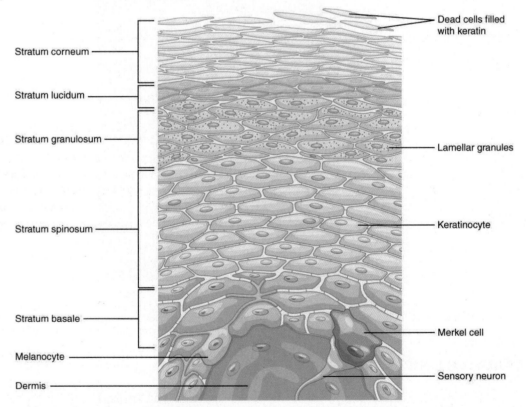

FIGURE 5.5 **Layers of the Epidermis** The epidermis of thick skin has five layers: stratum basale, stratum spinosum, stratum granulosum, stratum lucidum, and stratum corneum.

The stratum basale is a single layer of cells primarily made of basal cells. A **basal cell** is a cuboidal-shaped stem cell that is a precursor of the keratinocytes of the epidermis. All of the keratinocytes are produced from this single layer of cells, which are constantly going through mitosis to produce new cells. As new cells are formed, the existing cells are pushed superficially away from the stratum basale. Two other cell types are found dispersed among the basal cells in the stratum basale. The first is a **Merkel cell**, which functions as a receptor and is responsible for stimulating sensory nerves that the brain perceives as touch. These cells are especially abundant on the surfaces of the hands and feet. The second is a **melanocyte**, a cell that produces the pigment melanin. **Melanin** gives hair and skin its color, and also helps protect the living cells of the epidermis from ultraviolet (UV) radiation damage.

In a growing fetus, fingerprints form where the cells of the stratum basale meet the papillae of the underlying dermal layer (papillary layer), resulting in the formation of the ridges on your fingers that you recognize as fingerprints. Fingerprints are unique to each individual and are used for forensic analyses because the patterns do not change with the growth and aging processes.

Stratum Spinosum

As the name suggests, the **stratum spinosum** is spiny in appearance due to the protruding cell processes that join the cells via a structure called a **desmosome**. The desmosomes interlock with each other and strengthen the bond between the cells. It is interesting to note that the "spiny" nature of this layer is an artifact of the staining process. Unstained epidermis samples do not exhibit this characteristic appearance. The stratum spinosum is composed of eight to 10 layers of keratinocytes, formed as a result of cell division in the stratum basale (Figure 5.6). Interspersed among the keratinocytes of this layer is a type of dendritic cell called the **Langerhans cell**, which functions as a macrophage by engulfing bacteria, foreign particles, and damaged cells that occur in this layer.

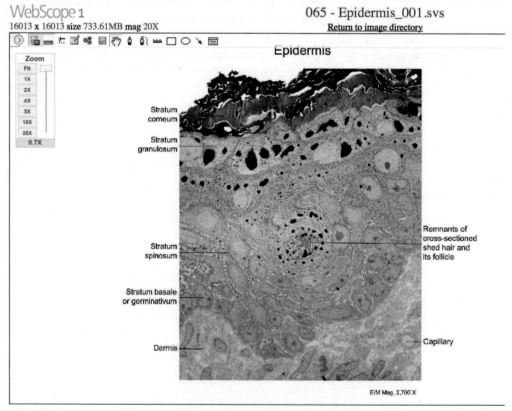

FIGURE 5.6 Cells of the Epidermis The cells in the different layers of the epidermis originate from basal cells located in the stratum basale, yet the cells of each layer are distinctively different. EM × 2700. (Micrograph provided by the Regents of University of Michigan Medical School © 2012)

🔗 INTERACTIVE LINK

View the University of Michigan WebScope (http://openstax.org/l/basal) to explore the tissue sample in greater detail. If you zoom on the cells at the outermost layer of this section of skin, what do you notice about the cells?

The keratinocytes in the stratum spinosum begin the synthesis of keratin and release a water-repelling glycolipid that helps prevent water loss from the body, making the skin relatively waterproof. As new keratinocytes are produced atop the stratum basale, the keratinocytes of the stratum spinosum are pushed into the stratum granulosum.

Stratum Granulosum

The **stratum granulosum** has a grainy appearance due to further changes to the keratinocytes as they are pushed from the stratum spinosum. The cells (three to five layers deep) become flatter, their cell membranes thicken, and they generate large amounts of the proteins keratin, which is fibrous, and **keratohyalin**, which accumulates as lamellar granules within the cells (see Figure 5.5). These two proteins make up the bulk of the keratinocyte mass in the stratum granulosum and give the layer its grainy appearance. The nuclei and other cell organelles disintegrate as the cells die, leaving behind the keratin, keratohyalin, and cell membranes that will form the stratum lucidum, the stratum corneum, and the accessory structures of hair and nails.

Stratum Lucidum

The **stratum lucidum** is a smooth, seemingly translucent layer of the epidermis located just above the stratum granulosum and below the stratum corneum. This thin layer of cells is found only in the thick skin of the palms, soles, and digits. The keratinocytes that compose the stratum lucidum are dead and flattened (see Figure 5.5). These cells are densely packed with **eleidin**, a clear protein, derived from keratohyalin, which gives these cells their transparent (i.e., lucid) appearance.

Stratum Corneum

The **stratum corneum** is the most superficial layer of the epidermis and is the layer exposed to the outside environment (see Figure 5.5). The increased keratinization (also called cornification) of the cells in this layer gives it its name. There are usually 15 to 30 layers of cells in the stratum corneum. This dry, dead layer helps prevent the penetration of microbes and the dehydration of underlying tissues, and provides a mechanical protection against abrasion for the more delicate, underlying layers. Cells in this layer are shed periodically and are replaced by cells pushed up from the stratum granulosum (or stratum lucidum in the case of the palms and soles of feet). The entire layer is replaced during a period of about 4 weeks. Cosmetic procedures, such as microdermabrasion, help remove some of the dry, upper layer and aim to keep the skin looking "fresh" and healthy.

Dermis

The **dermis** might be considered the "core" of the integumentary system (derma- = "skin"), as distinct from the epidermis (epi- = "upon" or "over") and hypodermis (hypo- = "below"). It contains blood and lymph vessels, nerves, and other structures, such as hair follicles and sweat glands. The dermis is made of two layers of connective tissue that compose an interconnected mesh of elastin and collagenous fibers, produced by fibroblasts (Figure 5.7).

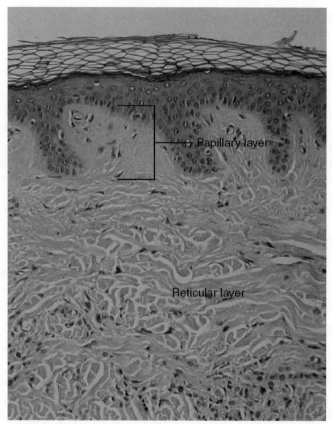

FIGURE 5.7 Layers of the Dermis This stained slide shows the two components of the dermis—the papillary layer and the reticular layer. Both are made of connective tissue with fibers of collagen extending from one to the other, making the border between the two somewhat indistinct. The dermal papillae extending into the epidermis belong to the papillary layer, whereas the dense collagen fiber bundles below belong to the reticular layer. LM × 10. (credit: modification of work by "kilbad"/Wikimedia Commons)

Papillary Layer

The **papillary layer** is made of loose, areolar connective tissue, which means the collagen and elastin fibers of this layer form a loose mesh. This superficial layer of the dermis projects into the stratum basale of the epidermis to form finger-like dermal papillae (see Figure 5.7). Within the papillary layer are fibroblasts, a small number of fat cells (adipocytes), and an abundance of small blood vessels. In addition, the papillary layer contains phagocytes, defensive cells that help fight bacteria or other infections that have breached the skin. This layer also contains lymphatic capillaries, nerve fibers, and touch receptors called the Meissner corpuscles.

Reticular Layer

Underlying the papillary layer is the much thicker **reticular layer**, composed of dense, irregular connective tissue. This layer is well vascularized and has a rich sensory and sympathetic nerve supply. The reticular layer appears reticulated (net-like) due to a tight meshwork of fibers. **Elastin fibers** provide some elasticity to the skin, enabling movement. Collagen fibers provide structure and tensile strength, with strands of collagen extending into both the papillary layer and the hypodermis. In addition, collagen binds water to keep the skin hydrated. Collagen injections and Retin-A creams help restore skin turgor by either introducing collagen externally or stimulating blood flow and repair of the dermis, respectively.

Hypodermis

The **hypodermis** (also called the subcutaneous layer or superficial fascia) is a layer directly below the dermis and serves to connect the skin to the underlying fascia (fibrous tissue) of the bones and muscles. It is not strictly a part of the skin, although the border between the hypodermis and dermis can be difficult to distinguish. The hypodermis consists of well-vascularized, loose, areolar connective tissue and adipose tissue, which functions as a mode of fat storage and provides insulation and cushioning for the integument.

Everyday Connection

Lipid Storage

The hypodermis is home to most of the fat that concerns people when they are trying to keep their weight under control. Adipose tissue present in the hypodermis consists of fat-storing cells called adipocytes. This stored fat can serve as an energy reserve, insulate the body to prevent heat loss, and act as a cushion to protect underlying structures from trauma.

Where the fat is deposited and accumulates within the hypodermis depends on hormones (testosterone, estrogen, insulin, glucagon, leptin, and others), as well as genetic factors. Fat distribution changes as our bodies mature and age. Males tend to accumulate fat in different areas (neck, arms, lower back, and abdomen) than do females (breasts, hips, thighs, and buttocks). The body mass index (BMI) is often used as a measure of fat, although this measure is, in fact, derived from a mathematical formula that compares body weight (mass) to height. Therefore, its accuracy as a health indicator can be called into question in individuals who are extremely physically fit.

In many animals, there is a pattern of storing excess calories as fat to be used in times when food is not readily available. In much of the developed world, insufficient exercise coupled with the ready availability and consumption of high-calorie foods have resulted in unwanted accumulations of adipose tissue in many people. Although periodic accumulation of excess fat may have provided an evolutionary advantage to our ancestors, who experienced unpredictable bouts of famine, it is now becoming chronic and considered a major health threat. Recent studies indicate that a distressing percentage of our population is overweight and/or clinically obese. Not only is this a problem for the individuals affected, but it also has a severe impact on our healthcare system. Changes in lifestyle, specifically in diet and exercise, are the best ways to control body fat accumulation, especially when it reaches levels that increase the risk of heart disease and diabetes.

Pigmentation

The color of skin is influenced by a number of pigments, including melanin, carotene, and hemoglobin. Recall that melanin is produced by cells called melanocytes, which are found scattered throughout the stratum basale of the epidermis. The melanin is transferred into the keratinocytes via a cellular vesicle called a **melanosome** (Figure 5.8).

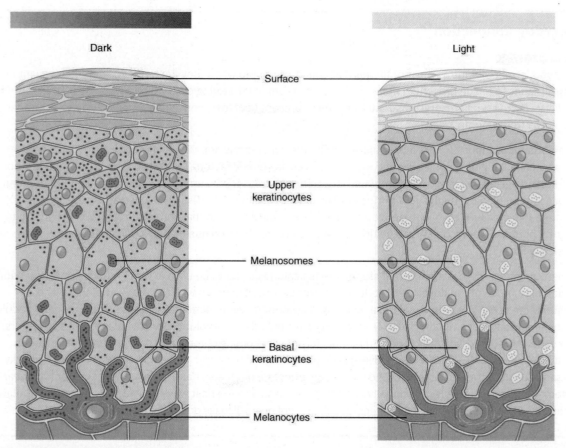

FIGURE 5.8 Skin Pigmentation   The relative coloration of the skin depends of the amount of melanin produced by melanocytes in the stratum basale and taken up by keratinocytes.

Melanin occurs in two primary forms. Eumelanin exists as black and brown, whereas pheomelanin provides a red color. Dark-skinned individuals produce more melanin than those with pale skin. Exposure to the UV rays of the sun or a tanning salon causes melanin to be manufactured and built up in keratinocytes, as sun exposure stimulates keratinocytes to secrete chemicals that stimulate melanocytes. The accumulation of melanin in keratinocytes results in the darkening of the skin, or a tan. This increased melanin accumulation protects the DNA of epidermal cells from UV ray damage and the breakdown of folic acid, a nutrient necessary for our health and well-being. In contrast, too much melanin can interfere with the production of vitamin D, an important nutrient involved in calcium absorption. Thus, the amount of melanin present in our skin is dependent on a balance between available sunlight and folic acid destruction, and protection from UV radiation and vitamin D production.

It requires about 10 days after initial sun exposure for melanin synthesis to peak, which is why pale-skinned individuals tend to suffer sunburns of the epidermis initially. Dark-skinned individuals can also get sunburns, but are more protected than are pale-skinned individuals. Melanosomes are temporary structures that are eventually destroyed by fusion with lysosomes; this fact, along with melanin-filled keratinocytes in the stratum corneum sloughing off, makes tanning impermanent.

Too much sun exposure can eventually lead to wrinkling due to the destruction of the cellular structure of the skin, and in severe cases, can cause sufficient DNA damage to result in skin cancer. When there is an irregular accumulation of melanocytes in the skin, freckles appear. Moles are larger masses of melanocytes, and although most are benign, they should be monitored for changes that might indicate the presence of cancer (Figure 5.9).

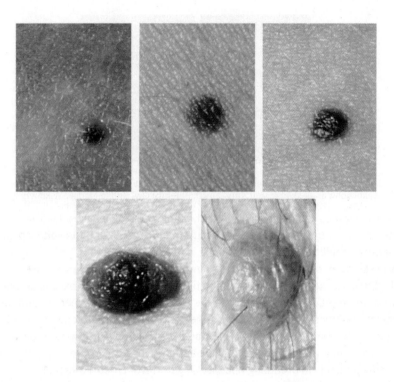

FIGURE 5.9   **Moles**   Moles range from benign accumulations of melanocytes to melanomas. These structures populate the landscape of our skin. (credit: the National Cancer Institute)

Disorders of the...

Integumentary System

The first thing a clinician sees is the skin, and so the examination of the skin should be part of any thorough physical examination. Most skin disorders are relatively benign, but a few, including melanomas, can be fatal if untreated. A couple of the more noticeable disorders, albinism and vitiligo, affect the appearance of the skin and its accessory organs. Although neither is fatal, it would be hard to claim that they are benign, at least to the individuals so afflicted.

Albinism is a genetic disorder that affects (completely or partially) the coloring of skin, hair, and eyes. The defect is primarily due to the inability of melanocytes to produce melanin. Individuals with albinism tend to appear white or very pale due to the lack of melanin in their skin and hair. Recall that melanin helps protect the skin from the harmful effects of UV radiation. Individuals with albinism tend to need more protection from UV radiation, as they are more prone to sunburns and skin cancer. They also tend to be more sensitive to light and have vision problems due to the lack of pigmentation on the retinal wall. Treatment of this disorder usually involves addressing the symptoms, such as limiting UV light exposure to the skin and eyes. In **vitiligo**, the melanocytes in certain areas lose their ability to produce melanin, possibly due to an autoimmune reaction. This leads to a loss of color in patches (Figure 5.10). Neither albinism nor vitiligo directly affects the lifespan of an individual.

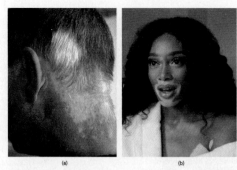

(a)   (b)

FIGURE 5.10   Vitiligo   Individuals with vitiligo experience depigmentation that results in lighter colored patches of skin. The condition is especially noticeable on darker skin. (credit: (a) Klaus D. Peter (b) Owl Bridge Media / Wikimedia.)

Other changes in the appearance of skin coloration can be indicative of diseases associated with other body systems. Liver disease or liver cancer can cause the accumulation of bile and the yellow pigment bilirubin, leading to the skin appearing yellow or jaundiced (*jaune* is the French word for "yellow"). Tumors of the pituitary gland can result in the secretion of large amounts of melanocyte-stimulating hormone (MSH), which results in a darkening of the skin. Similarly, Addison's disease can stimulate the release of excess amounts of adrenocorticotropic hormone (ACTH), which can give the skin a deep bronze color. A sudden drop in oxygenation can affect skin color, causing the skin to initially turn ashen (white). With a prolonged reduction in oxygen levels, dark red deoxyhemoglobin becomes dominant in the blood, making the skin appear blue, a condition referred to as cyanosis (*kyanos* is the Greek word for "blue"). This happens when the oxygen supply is restricted, as when someone is experiencing difficulty in breathing because of asthma or a heart attack. However, in these cases the effect on skin color has nothing do with the skin's pigmentation.

INTERACTIVE LINK

This ABC video follows the story of a pair of fraternal African-American twins, one of whom is albino. Watch this video (http://openstax.org/l/albino) to learn about the challenges these children and their family face. Which ethnicities do you think are exempt from the possibility of albinism?

5.2 Accessory Structures of the Skin

LEARNING OBJECTIVES

By the end of this section, you will be able to:

- Identify the accessory structures of the skin
- Describe the structure and function of hair and nails
- Describe the structure and function of sweat glands and sebaceous glands

Accessory structures of the skin include hair, nails, sweat glands, and sebaceous glands. These structures embryologically originate from the epidermis and can extend down through the dermis into the hypodermis.

Hair

Hair is a keratinous filament growing out of the epidermis. It is primarily made of dead, keratinized cells. Strands of hair originate in an epidermal penetration of the dermis called the **hair follicle**. The **hair shaft** is the part of the hair not anchored to the follicle, and much of this is exposed at the skin's surface. The rest of the hair, which is anchored in the follicle, lies below the surface of the skin and is referred to as the **hair root**. The hair root ends deep in the dermis at the **hair bulb**, and includes a layer of mitotically active basal cells called the **hair matrix**. The hair bulb surrounds the **hair papilla**, which is made of connective tissue and contains blood capillaries and nerve endings from the dermis (Figure 5.11).

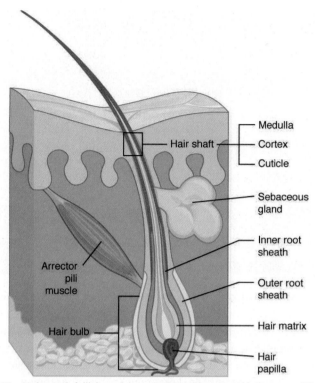

FIGURE 5.11 Hair Hair follicles originate in the epidermis and have many different parts.

Just as the basal layer of the epidermis forms the layers of epidermis that get pushed to the surface as the dead skin on the surface sheds, the basal cells of the hair bulb divide and push cells outward in the hair root and shaft as the hair grows. The **medulla** forms the central core of the hair, which is surrounded by the **cortex**, a layer of compressed, keratinized cells that is covered by an outer layer of very hard, keratinized cells known as the **cuticle**. These layers are depicted in a longitudinal cross-section of the hair follicle (Figure 5.12), although not all hair has a medullary layer. Hair texture (straight, curly) is determined by the shape and structure of the cortex, and to the extent that it is present, the medulla. The shape and structure of these layers are, in turn, determined by the shape of the hair follicle. Hair growth begins with the production of keratinocytes by the basal cells of the hair bulb. As new cells are deposited at the hair bulb, the hair shaft is pushed through the follicle toward the surface. Keratinization is completed as the cells are pushed to the skin surface to form the shaft of hair that is externally visible. The external hair is completely dead and composed entirely of keratin. For this reason, our hair does not have sensation. Furthermore, you can cut your hair or shave without damaging the hair structure because the cut is superficial. Most chemical hair removers also act superficially; however, electrolysis and yanking both attempt to destroy the hair bulb so hair cannot grow.

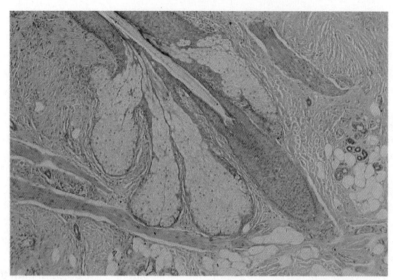

FIGURE 5.12   Hair Follicle   The slide shows a cross-section of a hair follicle. Basal cells of the hair matrix in the center differentiate into cells of the inner root sheath. Basal cells at the base of the hair root form the outer root sheath. LM × 4. (credit: modification of work by "kilbad"/Wikimedia Commons)

The wall of the hair follicle is made of three concentric layers of cells. The cells of the **internal root sheath** surround the root of the growing hair and extend just up to the hair shaft. They are derived from the basal cells of the hair matrix. The **external root sheath**, which is an extension of the epidermis, encloses the hair root. It is made of basal cells at the base of the hair root and tends to be more keratinous in the upper regions. The **glassy membrane** is a thick, clear connective tissue sheath covering the hair root, connecting it to the tissue of the dermis.

🔗 INTERACTIVE LINK

The hair follicle is made of multiple layers of cells that form from basal cells in the hair matrix and the hair root. Cells of the hair matrix divide and differentiate to form the layers of the hair. Watch this video (http://openstax.org/l/follicle) to learn more about hair follicles.

Hair serves a variety of functions, including protection, sensory input, thermoregulation, and communication. For example, hair on the head protects the skull from the sun. The hair in the nose and ears, and around the eyes (eyelashes) defends the body by trapping and excluding dust particles that may contain allergens and microbes. Hair of the eyebrows prevents sweat and other particles from dripping into and bothering the eyes. Hair also has a sensory function due to sensory innervation by a hair root plexus surrounding the base of each hair follicle. Hair is extremely sensitive to air movement or other disturbances in the environment, much more so than the skin surface. This feature is also useful for the detection of the presence of insects or other potentially damaging substances on the skin surface. Each hair root is connected to a smooth muscle called the **arrector pili** that contracts in response to nerve signals from the sympathetic nervous system, making the external hair shaft "stand up." The primary purpose for this is to trap a layer of air to add insulation. This is visible in humans as goose bumps and even more obvious in animals, such as when a frightened cat raises its fur. Of course, this is much more obvious in organisms with a heavier coat than most humans, such as dogs and cats.

Hair Growth

Hair grows and is eventually shed and replaced by new hair. This occurs in three phases. The first is the **anagen** phase, during which cells divide rapidly at the root of the hair, pushing the hair shaft up and out. The length of this phase is measured in years, typically from 2 to 7 years. The **catagen** phase lasts only 2 to 3 weeks, and marks a transition from the hair follicle's active growth. Finally, during the **telogen** phase, the hair follicle is at rest and no new growth occurs. At the end of this phase, which lasts about 2 to 4 months, another anagen phase begins. The basal cells in the hair matrix then produce a new hair follicle, which pushes the old hair out as the growth cycle repeats itself. Hair typically grows at the rate of 0.3 mm per day during the anagen phase. On average, 50 hairs are lost and replaced per day. Hair loss occurs if there is more hair shed than what is replaced and can happen due to hormonal or dietary changes. Hair loss can also result from the aging process, or the influence of hormones.

Hair Color

Similar to the skin, hair gets its color from the pigment melanin, produced by melanocytes in the hair papilla. Different hair color results from differences in the type of melanin, which is genetically determined. As a person ages, the melanin production decreases, and hair tends to lose its color and becomes gray and/or white.

Nails

The nail bed is a specialized structure of the epidermis that is found at the tips of our fingers and toes. The **nail body** is formed on the **nail bed**, and protects the tips of our fingers and toes as they are the farthest extremities and the parts of the body that experience the maximum mechanical stress (Figure 5.13). In addition, the nail body forms a back-support for picking up small objects with the fingers. The nail body is composed of densely packed dead keratinocytes. The epidermis in this part of the body has evolved a specialized structure upon which nails can form. The nail body forms at the **nail root**, which has a matrix of proliferating cells from the stratum basale that enables the nail to grow continuously. The lateral **nail fold** overlaps the nail on the sides, helping to anchor the nail body. The nail fold that meets the proximal end of the nail body forms the **nail cuticle**, also called the **eponychium**. The nail bed is rich in blood vessels, making it appear pink, except at the base, where a thick layer of epithelium over the nail matrix forms a crescent-shaped region called the **lunula** (the "little moon"). The area beneath the free edge of the nail, furthest from the cuticle, is called the **hyponychium**. It consists of a thickened layer of stratum corneum.

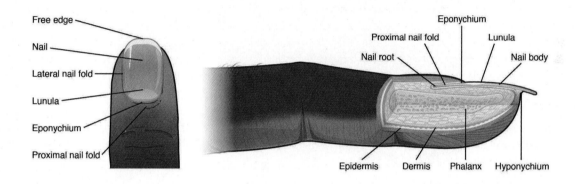

507_Nails

FIGURE 5.13   **Nails**   The nail is an accessory structure of the integumentary system.

🔗 INTERACTIVE LINK

Nails are accessory structures of the integumentary system. Visit this link (http://openstax.org/l/nails) to learn more about the origin and growth of fingernails.

Sweat Glands

When the body becomes warm, **sudoriferous glands** produce sweat to cool the body. Sweat glands develop from epidermal projections into the dermis and are classified as merocrine glands; that is, the secretions are excreted by exocytosis through a duct without affecting the cells of the gland. There are two types of sweat glands, each secreting slightly different products.

An **eccrine sweat gland** is type of gland that produces a hypotonic sweat for thermoregulation. These glands are found all over the skin's surface, but are especially abundant on the palms of the hand, the soles of the feet, and the forehead (Figure 5.14). They are coiled glands lying deep in the dermis, with the duct rising up to a pore on the skin surface, where the sweat is released. This type of sweat, released by exocytosis, is hypotonic and composed mostly of water, with some salt, antibodies, traces of metabolic waste, and dermicidin, an antimicrobial peptide. Eccrine glands are a primary component of thermoregulation in humans and thus help to maintain homeostasis.

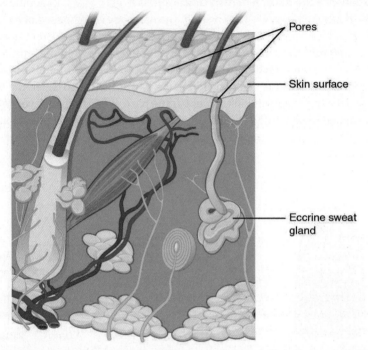

FIGURE 5.14   Eccrine Gland   Eccrine glands are coiled glands in the dermis that release sweat that is mostly water.

An **apocrine sweat gland** is usually associated with hair follicles in densely hairy areas, such as armpits and genital regions. Apocrine sweat glands are larger than eccrine sweat glands and lie deeper in the dermis, sometimes even reaching the hypodermis, with the duct normally emptying into the hair follicle. In addition to water and salts, apocrine sweat includes organic compounds that make the sweat thicker and subject to bacterial decomposition and subsequent smell. The release of this sweat is under both nervous and hormonal control, and plays a role in the poorly understood human pheromone response. Most commercial antiperspirants use an aluminum-based compound as their primary active ingredient to stop sweat. When the antiperspirant enters the sweat gland duct, the aluminum-based compounds precipitate due to a change in pH and form a physical block in the duct, which prevents sweat from coming out of the pore.

⊘ INTERACTIVE LINK

Sweating regulates body temperature. The composition of the sweat determines whether body odor is a byproduct of sweating. Visit this link (http://openstax.org/l/sweating) to learn more about sweating and body odor.

Sebaceous Glands

A **sebaceous gland** is a type of oil gland that is found all over the body and helps to lubricate and waterproof the skin and hair. Most sebaceous glands are associated with hair follicles. They generate and excrete **sebum,** a mixture of lipids, onto the skin surface, thereby naturally lubricating the dry and dead layer of keratinized cells of the stratum corneum, keeping it pliable. The fatty acids of sebum also have antibacterial properties, and prevent water loss from the skin in low-humidity environments. The secretion of sebum is stimulated by hormones, many of which do not become active until puberty. Thus, sebaceous glands are relatively inactive during childhood.

5.3 Functions of the Integumentary System

LEARNING OBJECTIVES

By the end of this section, you will be able to:
- Describe the different functions of the skin and the structures that enable them
- Explain how the skin helps maintain body temperature

The skin and accessory structures perform a variety of essential functions, such as protecting the body from invasion by microorganisms, chemicals, and other environmental factors; preventing dehydration; acting as a sensory organ; modulating body temperature and electrolyte balance; and synthesizing vitamin D. The underlying hypodermis has important roles in storing fats, forming a "cushion" over underlying structures, and providing insulation from cold temperatures.

Protection

The skin protects the rest of the body from the basic elements of nature such as wind, water, and UV sunlight. It acts as a protective barrier against water loss, due to the presence of layers of keratin and glycolipids in the stratum corneum. It also is the first line of defense against abrasive activity due to contact with grit, microbes, or harmful chemicals. Sweat excreted from sweat glands deters microbes from over-colonizing the skin surface by generating dermicidin, which has antibiotic properties.

Everyday Connection

Tattoos and Piercings

The word "armor" evokes several images. You might think of a Roman centurion or a medieval knight in a suit of armor. The skin, in its own way, functions as a form of armor—body armor. It provides a barrier between your vital, life-sustaining organs and the influence of outside elements that could potentially damage them.

For any form of armor, a breach in the protective barrier poses a danger. The skin can be breached when a child skins a knee or an adult has blood drawn—one is accidental and the other medically necessary. However, you also breach this barrier when you choose to "accessorize" your skin with a tattoo or body piercing. Because the needles involved in producing body art and piercings must penetrate the skin, there are dangers associated with the practice. These include allergic reactions; skin infections; blood-borne diseases, such as tetanus, hepatitis C, and hepatitis D; and the growth of scar tissue. Despite the risk, the practice of piercing the skin for decorative purposes has become increasingly popular. According to the American Academy of Dermatology, 24 percent of people from ages 18 to 50 have a tattoo.

🔗 INTERACTIVE LINK

Tattooing has a long history, dating back thousands of years ago. The dyes used in tattooing typically derive from metals. A person with tattoos should be cautious when having a magnetic resonance imaging (MRI) scan because an MRI machine uses powerful magnets to create images of the soft tissues of the body, which could react with the metals contained in the tattoo dyes. Watch this video (http://openstax.org/l/tattoo) to learn more about tattooing.

Sensory Function

The fact that you can feel an ant crawling on your skin, allowing you to flick it off before it bites, is because the skin, and especially the hairs projecting from hair follicles in the skin, can sense changes in the environment. The hair root plexus surrounding the base of the hair follicle senses a disturbance, and then transmits the information to the central nervous system (brain and spinal cord), which can then respond by activating the skeletal muscles of your eyes to see the ant and the skeletal muscles of the body to act against the ant.

The skin acts as a sense organ because the epidermis, dermis, and the hypodermis contain specialized sensory nerve structures that detect touch, surface temperature, and pain. These receptors are more concentrated on the tips of the fingers, which are most sensitive to touch, especially the **Meissner corpuscle** (tactile corpuscle) (Figure 5.15), which responds to light touch, and the **Pacinian corpuscle** (lamellated corpuscle), which responds to vibration. Merkel cells, seen scattered in the stratum basale, are also touch receptors. In addition to these specialized receptors, there are sensory nerves connected to each hair follicle, pain and temperature receptors scattered throughout the skin, and motor nerves innervate the arrector pili muscles and glands. This rich innervation helps us sense our environment and react accordingly.

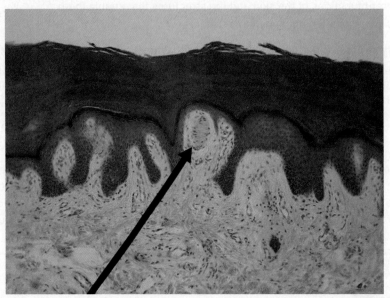

FIGURE 5.15   **Light Micrograph of a Meissner Corpuscle**   In this micrograph of a skin cross-section, you can see a Meissner corpuscle (arrow), a type of touch receptor located in a dermal papilla adjacent to the basement membrane and stratum basale of the overlying epidermis. LM × 100. (credit: "Wbensmith"/Wikimedia Commons)

Thermoregulation

The integumentary system helps regulate body temperature through its tight association with the sympathetic nervous system, the division of the nervous system involved in our fight-or-flight responses. The sympathetic nervous system is continuously monitoring body temperature and initiating appropriate motor responses. Recall that sweat glands, accessory structures to the skin, secrete water, salt, and other substances to cool the body when it becomes warm. Even when the body does not appear to be noticeably sweating, approximately 500 mL of sweat (insensible perspiration) are secreted a day. If the body becomes excessively warm due to high temperatures, vigorous activity (Figure 5.16**ac**), or a combination of the two, sweat glands will be stimulated by the sympathetic nervous system to produce large amounts of sweat, as much as 0.7 to 1.5 L per hour for an active person. When the sweat evaporates from the skin surface, the body is cooled as body heat is dissipated.

In addition to sweating, arterioles in the dermis dilate so that excess heat carried by the blood can dissipate through the skin and into the surrounding environment (Figure 5.16**b**). This accounts for the skin redness that many people experience when exercising.

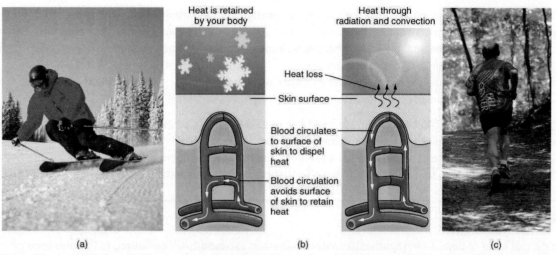

(a) (b) (c)

FIGURE 5.16 Thermoregulation During strenuous physical activities, such as skiing (a) or running (c), the dermal blood vessels dilate and sweat secretion increases (b). These mechanisms prevent the body from overheating. In contrast, the dermal blood vessels constrict to minimize heat loss in response to low temperatures (b). (credit a: "Trysil"/flickr; credit c: Ralph Daily)

When body temperatures drop, the arterioles constrict to minimize heat loss, particularly in the ends of the digits and tip of the nose. This reduced circulation can result in the skin taking on a whitish hue. Although the temperature of the skin drops as a result, passive heat loss is prevented, and internal organs and structures remain warm. If the temperature of the skin drops too much (such as environmental temperatures below freezing), the conservation of body core heat can result in the skin actually freezing, a condition called frostbite.

Aging and the...

Integumentary System

All systems in the body accumulate subtle and some not-so-subtle changes as a person ages. Among these changes are reductions in cell division, metabolic activity, blood circulation, hormonal levels, and muscle strength (Figure 5.17). In the skin, these changes are reflected in decreased mitosis in the stratum basale, leading to a thinner epidermis. The dermis, which is responsible for the elasticity and resilience of the skin, exhibits a reduced ability to regenerate, which leads to slower wound healing. The hypodermis, with its fat stores, loses structure due to the reduction and redistribution of fat, which in turn contributes to the thinning and sagging of skin.

FIGURE 5.17 Aging Generally, skin, especially on the face and hands, starts to display the first noticeable signs of aging, as it loses its elasticity over time. (credit: Janet Ramsden)

The accessory structures also have lowered activity, generating thinner hair and nails, and reduced amounts of sebum and sweat. A reduced sweating ability can cause some elderly to be intolerant to extreme heat. Other cells in the skin, such as melanocytes and dendritic cells, also become less active, leading to a paler skin tone and lowered immunity. Wrinkling of the skin occurs due to breakdown of its structure, which results from decreased collagen and elastin production in the dermis, weakening of muscles lying under the skin, and the inability of the skin to retain adequate moisture.

Many anti-aging products can be found in stores today. In general, these products try to rehydrate the skin and thereby fill out the wrinkles, and some stimulate skin growth using hormones and growth factors. Additionally, invasive techniques include collagen injections to plump the tissue and injections of BOTOX® (the name brand of the botulinum neurotoxin) that paralyze the muscles that crease the skin and cause wrinkling.

Vitamin D Synthesis

The epidermal layer of human skin synthesizes **vitamin D** when exposed to UV radiation. In the presence of sunlight, a form of vitamin D_3 called cholecalciferol is synthesized from a derivative of the steroid cholesterol in the skin. The liver converts cholecalciferol to calcidiol, which is then converted to calcitriol (the active chemical form of the vitamin) in the kidneys. Vitamin D is essential for normal absorption of calcium and phosphorous, which are required for healthy bones. The absence of sun exposure can lead to a lack of vitamin D in the body, leading to a condition called **rickets**, a painful condition in children where the bones are misshapen due to a lack of calcium, causing bowleggedness. Elderly individuals who suffer from vitamin D deficiency can develop a condition called osteomalacia, a softening of the bones. In present day society, vitamin D is added as a supplement to many foods, including milk and orange juice, compensating for the need for sun exposure.

In addition to its essential role in bone health, vitamin D is essential for general immunity against bacterial, viral, and fungal infections. Recent studies are also finding a link between insufficient vitamin D and cancer.

5.4 Diseases, Disorders, and Injuries of the Integumentary System

LEARNING OBJECTIVES

By the end of this section, you will be able to:

- Describe several different diseases and disorders of the skin
- Describe the effect of injury to the skin and the process of healing

The integumentary system is susceptible to a variety of diseases, disorders, and injuries. These range from annoying but relatively benign bacterial or fungal infections that are categorized as disorders, to skin cancer and severe burns, which can be fatal. In this section, you will learn several of the most common skin conditions.

Diseases

One of the most talked about diseases is skin cancer. Cancer is a broad term that describes diseases caused by abnormal cells in the body dividing uncontrollably. Most cancers are identified by the organ or tissue in which the cancer originates. One common form of cancer is skin cancer. The Skin Cancer Foundation reports that one in five Americans will experience some type of skin cancer in their lifetime. The degradation of the ozone layer in the atmosphere and the resulting increase in exposure to UV radiation has contributed to its rise. Overexposure to UV radiation damages DNA, which can lead to the formation of cancerous lesions. Although melanin offers some protection against DNA damage from the sun, often it is not enough. The fact that cancers can also occur on areas of the body that are normally not exposed to UV radiation suggests that there are additional factors that can lead to cancerous lesions.

In general, cancers result from an accumulation of DNA mutations. These mutations can result in cell populations that do not die when they should and uncontrolled cell proliferation that leads to tumors. Although many tumors are benign (harmless), some produce cells that can mobilize and establish tumors in other organs of the body; this process is referred to as **metastasis**. Cancers are characterized by their ability to metastasize.

Basal Cell Carcinoma

Basal cell carcinoma is a form of cancer that affects the mitotically active stem cells in the stratum basale of the epidermis. It is the most common of all cancers that occur in the United States and is frequently found on the head, neck, arms, and back, which are areas that are most susceptible to long-term sun exposure. Although UV rays are the main culprit, exposure to other agents, such as radiation and arsenic, can also lead to this type of cancer. Wounds on the skin due to open sores, tattoos, burns, etc. may be predisposing factors as well. Basal cell carcinomas start in the stratum basale and usually spread along this boundary. At some point, they begin to grow toward the surface and become an uneven patch, bump, growth, or scar on the skin surface (Figure 5.18). Like most cancers, basal cell carcinomas respond best to treatment when caught early. Treatment options include surgery, freezing (cryosurgery), and topical ointments (Mayo Clinic 2012).

FIGURE 5.18 Basal Cell Carcinoma   Basal cell carcinoma can take several different forms. Similar to other forms of skin cancer, it is readily cured if caught early and treated. (credit: John Hendrix, MD)

Squamous Cell Carcinoma

Squamous cell carcinoma is a cancer that affects the keratinocytes of the stratum spinosum and presents as lesions commonly found on the scalp, ears, and hands (Figure 5.19). It is the second most common skin cancer. The American Cancer Society reports that two of 10 skin cancers are squamous cell carcinomas, and it is more aggressive than basal cell carcinoma. If not removed, these carcinomas can metastasize. Surgery and radiation are used to cure squamous cell carcinoma.

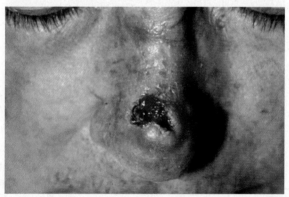

FIGURE 5.19 Squamous Cell Carcinoma   Squamous cell carcinoma presents here as a lesion on an individual's nose. (credit: the National Cancer Institute)

Melanoma

A **melanoma** is a cancer characterized by the uncontrolled growth of melanocytes, the pigment-producing cells in the epidermis. Typically, a melanoma develops from a mole. It is the most fatal of all skin cancers, as it is highly metastatic and can be difficult to detect before it has spread to other organs. Melanomas usually appear as asymmetrical brown and black patches with uneven borders and a raised surface (Figure 5.20). Treatment typically involves surgical excision and immunotherapy.

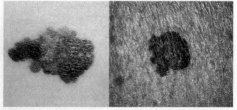

FIGURE 5.20 Melanoma   Melanomas typically present as large brown or black patches with uneven borders and a raised surface.

(credit: the National Cancer Institute / Centers for Disease Control)

Doctors often give their patients the following ABCDE mnemonic to help with the diagnosis of early-stage melanoma. If you observe a mole on your body displaying these signs, consult a doctor.

- **A**symmetry – the two sides are not symmetrical
- **B**orders – the edges are irregular in shape
- **C**olor – the color is varied shades of brown or black
- **D**iameter – it is larger than 6 mm (0.24 in)
- **E**volving – its shape has changed

Some specialists cite the following additional signs for the most serious form, nodular melanoma:

- **E**levated – it is raised on the skin surface
- **F**irm – it feels hard to the touch
- **G**rowing – it is getting larger

Skin Disorders

Two common skin disorders are eczema and acne. Eczema is an inflammatory condition and occurs in individuals of all ages. Acne involves the clogging of pores, which can lead to infection and inflammation, and is often seen in adolescents. Other disorders, not discussed here, include seborrheic dermatitis (on the scalp), psoriasis, cold sores, impetigo, scabies, hives, and warts.

Eczema

Eczema is an allergic reaction that manifests as dry, itchy patches of skin that resemble rashes (Figure 5.21). It may be accompanied by swelling of the skin, flaking, and in severe cases, bleeding. Many who suffer from eczema have antibodies against dust mites in their blood, but the link between eczema and allergy to dust mites has not been proven. Symptoms are usually managed with moisturizers, corticosteroid creams, and immunosuppressants.

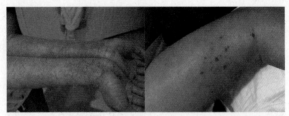

FIGURE 5.21   Eczema   Eczema is a common skin disorder that presents as a red, flaky rash. (credit: "Jambula" Wikimedia Commons / NIAID, Flickr)

Acne

Acne is a skin disturbance that typically occurs on areas of the skin that are rich in sebaceous glands (face and back). It is most common along with the onset of puberty due to associated hormonal changes, but can also occur in infants and continue into adulthood. Hormones, such as androgens, stimulate the release of sebum. An overproduction and accumulation of sebum along with keratin can block hair follicles. This plug is initially white. The sebum, when oxidized by exposure to air, turns black. Acne results from infection by acne-causing bacteria (*Propionibacterium* and *Staphylococcus*), which can lead to redness and potential scarring due to the natural wound healing process (Figure 5.22).

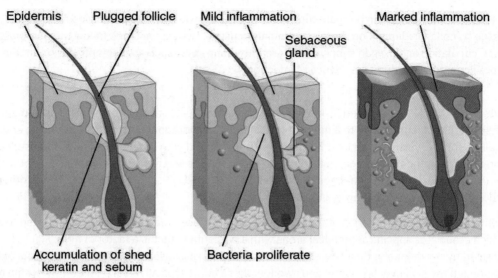

FIGURE 5.22   Acne   Acne is a result of over-productive sebaceous glands, which leads to formation of blackheads and inflammation of the skin.

 CAREER CONNECTION

Dermatologist

Have you ever had a rash that did not respond to over-the-counter creams, or a mole that you were concerned about? Dermatologists help patients with these types of problems and more, on a daily basis. Dermatologists are medical doctors who specialize in diagnosing and treating skin disorders. Like all medical doctors, dermatologists earn a medical degree and then complete several years of residency training. In addition, dermatologists may then participate in a dermatology fellowship or complete additional, specialized training in a dermatology practice. If practicing in the United States, dermatologists must pass the United States Medical Licensing Exam (USMLE), become licensed in their state of practice, and be certified by the American Board of Dermatology.

Most dermatologists work in a medical office or private-practice setting. They diagnose skin conditions and rashes, prescribe oral and topical medications to treat skin conditions, and may perform simple procedures, such as mole or wart removal. In addition, they may refer patients to an oncologist if skin cancer that has metastasized is suspected. Recently, cosmetic procedures have also become a prominent part of dermatology. Botox injections, laser treatments, and collagen and dermal filler injections are popular among patients, hoping to reduce the appearance of skin aging.

Dermatology is a competitive specialty in medicine. Limited openings in dermatology residency programs mean that many medical students compete for a few select spots. Dermatology is an appealing specialty to many prospective doctors, because unlike emergency room physicians or surgeons, dermatologists generally do not have to work excessive hours or be "on-call" weekends and holidays. Moreover, the popularity of cosmetic dermatology has made it a growing field with many lucrative opportunities. It is not unusual for dermatology clinics to market themselves exclusively as cosmetic dermatology centers, and for dermatologists to specialize exclusively in these procedures.

Consider visiting a dermatologist to talk about why they entered the field and what the field of dermatology is like. Visit this site (http://www.Diplomaguide.com) for additional information.

Injuries

Because the skin is the part of our bodies that meets the world most directly, it is especially vulnerable to injury. Injuries include burns and wounds, as well as scars and calluses. They can be caused by sharp objects, heat, or excessive pressure or friction to the skin.

Skin injuries set off a healing process that occurs in several overlapping stages. The first step to repairing damaged skin is the formation of a blood clot that helps stop the flow of blood and scabs over with time. Many different types of cells are involved in wound repair, especially if the surface area that needs repair is extensive. Before the basal stem cells of the stratum basale can recreate the epidermis, fibroblasts mobilize and divide rapidly to repair the damaged tissue by collagen deposition, forming granulation tissue. Blood capillaries follow the fibroblasts and help increase blood circulation and oxygen supply to the area. Immune cells, such as macrophages, roam the area and engulf any foreign matter to reduce the chance of infection.

Burns

A burn results when the skin is damaged by intense heat, radiation, electricity, or chemicals. The damage results in the death of skin cells, which can lead to a massive loss of fluid. Dehydration, electrolyte imbalance, and renal and circulatory failure follow, which can be fatal. Burn patients are treated with intravenous fluids to offset dehydration, as well as intravenous nutrients that enable the body to repair tissues and replace lost proteins. Another serious threat to the lives of burn patients is infection. Burned skin is extremely susceptible to bacteria and other pathogens, due to the loss of protection by intact layers of skin.

Burns are sometimes measured in terms of the size of the total surface area affected. This is referred to as the "rule of nines," which associates specific anatomical areas with a percentage that is a factor of nine (Figure 5.23). Burns are also classified by the degree of their severity. A **first-degree burn** is a superficial burn that affects only the epidermis. Although the skin may be painful and swollen, these burns typically heal on their own within a few days. Mild sunburn fits into the category of a first-degree burn. A **second-degree burn** goes deeper and affects both the epidermis and a portion of the dermis. These burns result in swelling and a painful blistering of the skin. It is important to keep the burn site clean and sterile to prevent infection. If this is done, the burn will heal within several weeks. A **third-degree burn** fully extends into the epidermis and dermis, destroying the tissue and affecting the nerve endings and sensory function. These are serious burns that may appear white, red, or black; they require medical attention and will heal slowly without it. A **fourth-degree burn** is even more severe, affecting the underlying muscle and bone. Oddly, third and fourth-degree burns are usually not as painful because the nerve endings themselves are damaged. Full-thickness burns cannot be repaired by the body, because the local tissues used for repair are damaged and require excision (debridement), or amputation in severe cases, followed by grafting of the skin from an unaffected part of the body, or from skin grown in tissue culture for grafting purposes.

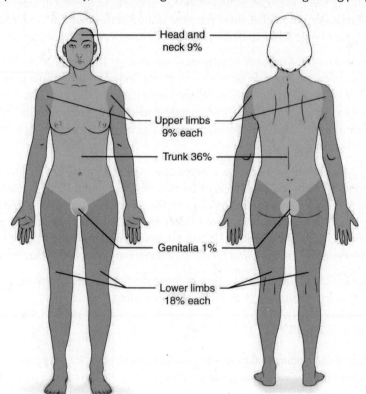

FIGURE 5.23 Calculating the Size of a Burn   The size of a burn will guide decisions made about the need for specialized treatment. Specific parts of the body are associated with a percentage of body area.

⊘ INTERACTIVE LINK

Skin grafts are required when the damage from trauma or infection cannot be closed with sutures or staples. Watch this video (http://openstax.org/l/skingraft) to learn more about skin grafting procedures.

Scars and Keloids

Most cuts or wounds, with the exception of ones that only scratch the surface (the epidermis), lead to scar formation. A **scar** is collagen-rich skin formed after the process of wound healing that differs from normal skin. Scarring occurs in cases in which there is repair of skin damage, but the skin fails to regenerate the original skin structure. Fibroblasts generate scar tissue in the form of collagen, and the bulk of repair is due to the basket-weave pattern generated by collagen fibers and does not result in regeneration of the typical cellular structure of skin. Instead, the tissue is fibrous in nature and does not allow for the regeneration of accessory structures, such as hair follicles, sweat glands, or sebaceous glands.

Sometimes, there is an overproduction of scar tissue, because the process of collagen formation does not stop when the wound is healed; this results in the formation of a raised or hypertrophic scar called a **keloid**. In contrast, scars that result from acne and chickenpox have a sunken appearance and are called atrophic scars.

Scarring of skin after wound healing is a natural process and does not need to be treated further. Application of mineral oil and lotions may reduce the formation of scar tissue. However, modern cosmetic procedures, such as dermabrasion, laser treatments, and filler injections have been invented as remedies for severe scarring. All of these procedures try to reorganize the structure of the epidermis and underlying collagen tissue to make it look more natural.

Bedsores and Stretch Marks

Skin and its underlying tissue can be affected by excessive pressure. One example of this is called a **bedsore**. Bedsores, also called decubitis ulcers, are caused by constant, long-term, unrelieved pressure on certain body parts that are bony, reducing blood flow to the area and leading to necrosis (tissue death). Bedsores are most common in elderly patients who have debilitating conditions that cause them to be immobile. Most hospitals and long-term care facilities have the practice of turning the patients every few hours to prevent the incidence of bedsores. If left untreated by removal of necrotized tissue, bedsores can be fatal if they become infected.

The skin can also be affected by pressure associated with rapid growth. A **stretch mark** results when the dermis is stretched beyond its limits of elasticity, as the skin stretches to accommodate the excess pressure. Stretch marks usually accompany rapid weight gain during puberty and pregnancy. They initially have a reddish hue, but lighten over time. Other than for cosmetic reasons, treatment of stretch marks is not required. They occur most commonly over the hips and abdomen.

Calluses

When you wear shoes that do not fit well and are a constant source of abrasion on your toes, you tend to form a **callus** at the point of contact. This occurs because the basal stem cells in the stratum basale are triggered to divide more often to increase the thickness of the skin at the point of abrasion to protect the rest of the body from further damage. This is an example of a minor or local injury, and the skin manages to react and treat the problem independent of the rest of the body. Calluses can also form on your fingers if they are subject to constant mechanical stress, such as long periods of writing, playing string instruments, or video games. A **corn** is a specialized form of callus. Corns form from abrasions on the skin that result from an elliptical-type motion.

Key Terms

acne   skin condition due to infected sebaceous glands

albinism   genetic disorder that affects the skin, in which there is no melanin production

anagen   active phase of the hair growth cycle

apocrine sweat gland   type of sweat gland that is associated with hair follicles in the armpits and genital regions

arrector pili   smooth muscle that is activated in response to external stimuli that pull on hair follicles and make the hair "stand up"

basal cell   type of stem cell found in the stratum basale and in the hair matrix that continually undergoes cell division, producing the keratinocytes of the epidermis

basal cell carcinoma   cancer that originates from basal cells in the epidermis of the skin

bedsore   sore on the skin that develops when regions of the body start necrotizing due to constant pressure and lack of blood supply; also called decubitis ulcers

callus   thickened area of skin that arises due to constant abrasion

catagen   transitional phase marking the end of the anagen phase of the hair growth cycle

corn   type of callus that is named for its shape and the elliptical motion of the abrasive force

cortex   in hair, the second or middle layer of keratinocytes originating from the hair matrix, as seen in a cross-section of the hair bulb

cuticle   in hair, the outermost layer of keratinocytes originating from the hair matrix, as seen in a cross-section of the hair bulb

dermal papilla   (plural = dermal papillae) extension of the papillary layer of the dermis that increases surface contact between the epidermis and dermis

dermis   layer of skin between the epidermis and hypodermis, composed mainly of connective tissue and containing blood vessels, hair follicles, sweat glands, and other structures

desmosome   structure that forms an impermeable junction between cells

eccrine sweat gland   type of sweat gland that is common throughout the skin surface; it produces a hypotonic sweat for thermoregulation

eczema   skin condition due to an allergic reaction, which resembles a rash

elastin fibers   fibers made of the protein elastin that increase the elasticity of the dermis

eleiden   clear protein-bound lipid found in the stratum lucidum that is derived from keratohyalin and helps to prevent water loss

epidermis   outermost tissue layer of the skin

eponychium   nail fold that meets the proximal end of the nail body, also called the cuticle

external root sheath   outer layer of the hair follicle that is an extension of the epidermis, which encloses the hair root

first-degree burn   superficial burn that injures only the epidermis

fourth-degree burn   burn in which full thickness of the skin and underlying muscle and bone is damaged

glassy membrane   layer of connective tissue that surrounds the base of the hair follicle, connecting it to the dermis

hair   keratinous filament growing out of the epidermis

hair bulb   structure at the base of the hair root that surrounds the dermal papilla

hair follicle   cavity or sac from which hair originates

hair matrix   layer of basal cells from which a strand of hair grows

hair papilla   mass of connective tissue, blood capillaries, and nerve endings at the base of the hair follicle

hair root   part of hair that is below the epidermis anchored to the follicle

hair shaft   part of hair that is above the epidermis but is not anchored to the follicle

hypodermis   connective tissue connecting the integument to the underlying bone and muscle

hyponychium   thickened layer of stratum corneum that lies below the free edge of the nail

integumentary system   skin and its accessory structures

internal root sheath   innermost layer of keratinocytes in the hair follicle that surround the hair root up to the hair shaft

keloid   type of scar that has layers raised above the skin surface

keratin   type of structural protein that gives skin, hair, and nails its hard, water-resistant properties

keratinocyte   cell that produces keratin and is the most predominant type of cell found in the epidermis

keratohyalin   granulated protein found in the stratum granulosum

Langerhans cell   specialized dendritic cell found in the stratum spinosum that functions as a macrophage

lunula   basal part of the nail body that consists of a crescent-shaped layer of thick epithelium

medulla   in hair, the innermost layer of keratinocytes originating from the hair matrix

Meissner corpuscle   (also, tactile corpuscle) receptor

in the skin that responds to light touch

melanin   pigment that determines the color of hair and skin

melanocyte   cell found in the stratum basale of the epidermis that produces the pigment melanin

melanoma   type of skin cancer that originates from the melanocytes of the skin

melanosome   intercellular vesicle that transfers melanin from melanocytes into keratinocytes of the epidermis

Merkel cell   receptor cell in the stratum basale of the epidermis that responds to the sense of touch

metastasis   spread of cancer cells from a source to other parts of the body

nail bed   layer of epidermis upon which the nail body forms

nail body   main keratinous plate that forms the nail

nail cuticle   fold of epithelium that extends over the nail bed, also called the eponychium

nail fold   fold of epithelium at that extend over the sides of the nail body, holding it in place

nail root   part of the nail that is lodged deep in the epidermis from which the nail grows

Pacinian corpuscle   (also, lamellated corpuscle) receptor in the skin that responds to vibration

papillary layer   superficial layer of the dermis, made of loose, areolar connective tissue

reticular layer   deeper layer of the dermis; it has a reticulated appearance due to the presence of abundant collagen and elastin fibers

rickets   disease in children caused by vitamin D deficiency, which leads to the weakening of bones

scar   collagen-rich skin formed after the process of wound healing that is different from normal skin

sebaceous gland   type of oil gland found in the dermis all over the body and helps to lubricate and waterproof the skin and hair by secreting sebum

sebum   oily substance that is composed of a mixture of lipids that lubricates the skin and hair

second-degree burn   partial-thickness burn that injures the epidermis and a portion of the dermis

squamous cell carcinoma   type of skin cancer that originates from the stratum spinosum of the epidermis

stratum basale   deepest layer of the epidermis, made of epidermal stem cells

stratum corneum   most superficial layer of the epidermis

stratum granulosum   layer of the epidermis superficial to the stratum spinosum

stratum lucidum   layer of the epidermis between the stratum granulosum and stratum corneum, found only in thick skin covering the palms, soles of the feet, and digits

stratum spinosum   layer of the epidermis superficial to the stratum basale, characterized by the presence of desmosomes

stretch mark   mark formed on the skin due to a sudden growth spurt and expansion of the dermis beyond its elastic limits

sudoriferous gland   sweat gland

telogen   resting phase of the hair growth cycle initiated with catagen and terminated by the beginning of a new anagen phase of hair growth

third-degree burn   burn that penetrates and destroys the full thickness of the skin (epidermis and dermis)

vitamin D   compound that aids absorption of calcium and phosphates in the intestine to improve bone health

vitiligo   skin condition in which melanocytes in certain areas lose the ability to produce melanin, possibly due an autoimmune reaction that leads to loss of color in patches

Chapter Review

5.1 Layers of the Skin

The skin is composed of two major layers: a superficial epidermis and a deeper dermis. The epidermis consists of several layers beginning with the innermost (deepest) stratum basale (germinatum), followed by the stratum spinosum, stratum granulosum, stratum lucidum (when present), and ending with the outermost layer, the stratum corneum. The topmost layer, the stratum corneum, consists of dead cells that shed periodically and is progressively replaced by cells formed from the basal layer. The stratum basale also contains melanocytes, cells that produce melanin, the pigment primarily responsible for giving skin its color. Melanin is transferred to keratinocytes in the stratum spinosum to protect cells from UV rays.

The dermis connects the epidermis to the hypodermis, and provides strength and elasticity due to the presence of collagen and elastin fibers. It has only two layers: the papillary layer with papillae that extend into the epidermis and the lower, reticular layer composed of loose connective tissue. The hypodermis, deep to the dermis of skin, is the connective tissue that connects the dermis to underlying structures; it also harbors adipose tissue for fat storage and protection.

5.2 Accessory Structures of the Skin

Accessory structures of the skin include hair, nails, sweat glands, and sebaceous glands. Hair is made of dead keratinized cells, and gets its color from melanin pigments. Nails, also made of dead keratinized cells, protect the extremities of our fingers and toes from mechanical damage. Sweat glands and sebaceous glands produce sweat and sebum, respectively. Each of these fluids has a role to play in maintaining homeostasis. Sweat cools the body surface when it gets overheated and helps excrete small amounts of metabolic waste. Sebum acts as a natural moisturizer and keeps the dead, flaky, outer keratin layer healthy.

5.3 Functions of the Integumentary System

The skin plays important roles in protection, sensing stimuli, thermoregulation, and vitamin D synthesis. It is the first layer of defense to prevent dehydration, infection, and injury to the rest of the body. Sweat glands in the skin allow the skin surface to cool when the body gets overheated. Thermoregulation is also accomplished by the dilation or constriction of heat-carrying blood vessels in the skin. Immune cells present among the skin layers patrol the areas to keep them free of foreign materials. Fat stores in the hypodermis aid in both thermoregulation and protection. Finally, the skin plays a role in the synthesis of vitamin D, which is necessary for our well-being but not easily available in natural foods.

5.4 Diseases, Disorders, and Injuries of the Integumentary System

Skin cancer is a result of damage to the DNA of skin cells, often due to excessive exposure to UV radiation. Basal cell carcinoma and squamous cell carcinoma are highly curable, and arise from cells in the stratum basale and stratum spinosum, respectively. Melanoma is the most dangerous form of skin cancer, affecting melanocytes, which can spread/metastasize to other organs. Burns are an injury to the skin that occur as a result of exposure to extreme heat, radiation, or chemicals. First-degree and second-degree burns usually heal quickly, but third-degree burns can be fatal because they penetrate the full thickness of the skin. Scars occur when there is repair of skin damage. Fibroblasts generate scar tissue in the form of collagen, which forms a basket-weave pattern that looks different from normal skin.

Bedsores and stretch marks are the result of excessive pressure on the skin and underlying tissue. Bedsores are characterized by necrosis of tissue due to immobility, whereas stretch marks result from rapid growth. Eczema is an allergic reaction that manifests as a rash, and acne results from clogged sebaceous glands. Eczema and acne are usually long-term skin conditions that may be treated successfully in mild cases. Calluses and corns are the result of abrasive pressure on the skin.

Interactive Link Questions

1. The skin consists of two layers and a closely associated layer. View this animation (http://openstax.org/l/layers) to learn more about layers of the skin. What are the basic functions of each of these layers?

2. Figure 5.4 If you zoom on the cells at the outermost layer of this section of skin, what do you notice about the cells?

3. Figure 5.6 If you zoom on the cells of the stratum spinosum, what is distinctive about them?

4. This ABC video follows the story of a pair of fraternal African-American twins, one of whom is albino. Watch this video (http://openstax.org/l/albino) to learn about the challenges these children and their family face. Which ethnicities do you think are exempt from the possibility of albinism?

Review Questions

5. The papillary layer of the dermis is most closely associated with which layer of the epidermis?
   a. stratum spinosum
   b. stratum corneum
   c. stratum granulosum
   d. stratum basale

6. Langerhans cells are commonly found in the
   _____.
   a. stratum spinosum
   b. stratum corneum
   c. stratum granulosum
   d. stratum basale

7. The papillary and reticular layers of the dermis are composed mainly of _____.
   a. melanocytes
   b. keratinocytes
   c. connective tissue
   d. adipose tissue

8. Collagen lends _____ to the skin.
   a. elasticity
   b. structure
   c. color
   d. UV protection

9. Which of the following is not a function of the hypodermis?
   a. protects underlying organs
   b. helps maintain body temperature
   c. source of blood vessels in the epidermis
   d. a site to long-term energy storage

10. In response to stimuli from the sympathetic nervous system, the arrector pili _____.
    a. are glands on the skin surface
    b. can lead to excessive sweating
    c. are responsible for goose bumps
    d. secrete sebum

11. The hair matrix contains _____.
    a. the hair follicle
    b. the hair shaft
    c. the glassy membrane
    d. a layer of basal cells

12. Eccrine sweat glands _____.
    a. are present on hair
    b. are present in the skin throughout the body and produce watery sweat
    c. produce sebum
    d. act as a moisturizer

13. Sebaceous glands _____.
    a. are a type of sweat gland
    b. are associated with hair follicles
    c. may function in response to touch
    d. release a watery solution of salt and metabolic waste

14. Similar to the hair, nails grow continuously throughout our lives. Which of the following is furthest from the nail growth center?
    a. nail bed
    b. hyponychium
    c. nail root
    d. eponychium

15. In humans, exposure of the skin to sunlight is required for _____.
    a. vitamin D synthesis
    b. arteriole constriction
    c. folate production
    d. thermoregulation

16. One of the functions of the integumentary system is protection. Which of the following does not directly contribute to that function?
    a. stratum lucidum
    b. desmosomes
    c. folic acid synthesis
    d. Merkel cells

17. An individual using a sharp knife notices a small amount of blood where he just cut himself. Which of the following layers of skin did he have to cut into in order to bleed?
    a. stratum corneum
    b. stratum basale
    c. papillary dermis
    d. stratum granulosum

18. As you are walking down the beach, you see a dead, dry, shriveled-up fish. Which layer of your epidermis keeps you from drying out?
    a. stratum corneum
    b. stratum basale
    c. stratum spinosum
    d. stratum granulosum

19. If you cut yourself and bacteria enter the wound, which of the following cells would help get rid of the bacteria?
    a. Merkel cells
    b. keratinocytes
    c. Langerhans cells
    d. melanocytes

20. In general, skin cancers _____.
    a. are easily treatable and not a major health concern
    b. occur due to poor hygiene
    c. can be reduced by limiting exposure to the sun
    d. affect only the epidermis

21. Bedsores _____.
    a. can be treated with topical moisturizers
    b. can result from deep massages
    c. are preventable by eliminating pressure points
    d. are caused by dry skin

22. An individual has spent too much time sun bathing. Not only is their skin painful to touch, but small blisters have appeared in the affected area. This indicates that they have damaged which layers of skin?
   a. epidermis only
   b. hypodermis only
   c. epidermis and hypodermis
   d. epidermis and dermis

23. After a skin injury, the body initiates a wound-healing response. The first step of this response is the formation of a blood clot to stop bleeding. Which of the following would be the next response?
   a. increased production of melanin by melanocytes
   b. increased production of connective tissue
   c. an increase in Pacinian corpuscles around the wound
   d. an increased activity in the stratum lucidum

24. Squamous cell carcinomas are the second most common of the skin cancers and are capable of metastasizing if not treated. This cancer affects which cells?
   a. basal cells of the stratum basale
   b. melanocytes of the stratum basale
   c. keratinocytes of the stratum spinosum
   d. Langerhans cells of the stratum lucidum

Critical Thinking Questions

25. What determines the color of skin, and what is the process that darkens skin when it is exposed to UV light?

26. Cells of the epidermis derive from stem cells of the stratum basale. Describe how the cells change as they become integrated into the different layers of the epidermis.

27. Explain the differences between eccrine and apocrine sweat glands.

28. Describe the structure and composition of nails.

29. Why do people sweat excessively when exercising outside on a hot day?

30. Explain your skin's response to a drop in body core temperature.

31. Why do teenagers often experience acne?

32. Why do scars look different from surrounding skin?

CHAPTER 6
Bone Tissue and the Skeletal System

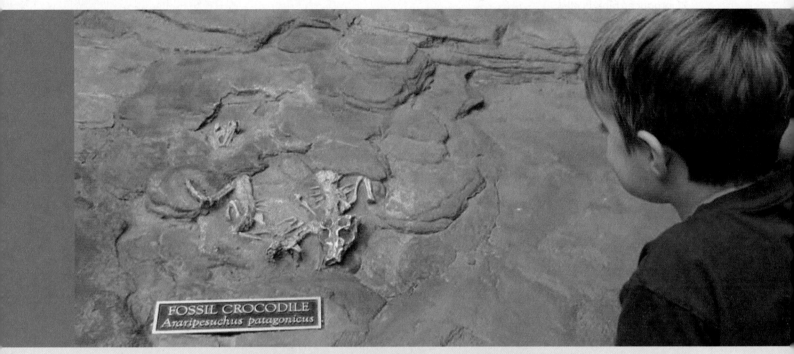

Figure 6.1 **Child Looking at Bones** Bone is a living tissue. Unlike the bones of a fossil made inert by a process of mineralization, a child's bones will continue to grow and develop while contributing to the support and function of other body systems. (credit: James Emery)

CHAPTER OBJECTIVES

After studying this chapter, you will be able to:

- List and describe the functions of bones
- Describe the classes of bones
- Discuss the process of bone formation and development
- Explain how bone repairs itself after a fracture
- Discuss the effect of exercise, nutrition, and hormones on bone tissue
- Describe how an imbalance of calcium can affect bone tissue

INTRODUCTION Bones make good fossils. While the soft tissue of a once living organism will decay and fall away over time, bone tissue will, under the right conditions, undergo a process of mineralization, effectively turning the bone to stone. A well-preserved fossil skeleton can give us a good sense of the size and shape of an organism, just as your skeleton helps to define your size and shape. Unlike a fossil skeleton, however, your skeleton is a structure of living tissue that grows, repairs, and renews itself. The bones within it are dynamic and complex organs that serve a number of important functions, including some necessary to maintain homeostasis.

6.1 The Functions of the Skeletal System

LEARNING OBJECTIVES

By the end of this section, you will be able to:

- Define bone, cartilage, and the skeletal system
- List and describe the functions of the skeletal system

Bone, or **osseous tissue**, is a hard, dense connective tissue that forms most of the adult skeleton, the support structure of the body. In the areas of the skeleton where bones move (for example, the ribcage and joints), **cartilage**, a semi-rigid form of connective tissue, provides flexibility and smooth surfaces for movement. The **skeletal system** is the body system composed of bones and cartilage and performs the following critical functions for the human body:

- supports the body
- facilitates movement
- protects internal organs
- produces blood cells
- stores and releases minerals and fat

Support, Movement, and Protection

The most apparent functions of the skeletal system are the gross functions—those visible by observation. Simply by looking at a person, you can see how the bones support, facilitate movement, and protect the human body.

Just as the steel beams of a building provide a scaffold to support its weight, the bones and cartilage of your skeletal system compose the scaffold that supports the rest of your body. Without the skeletal system, you would be a limp mass of organs, muscle, and skin.

Bones also facilitate movement by serving as points of attachment for your muscles. While some bones only serve as a support for the muscles, others also transmit the forces produced when your muscles contract. From a mechanical point of view, bones act as levers and joints serve as fulcrums (Figure 6.2). Unless a muscle spans a joint and contracts, a bone is not going to move. For information on the interaction of the skeletal and muscular systems, that is, the musculoskeletal system, seek additional content.

FIGURE 6.2   **Bones Support Movement**   Bones act as levers when muscles span a joint and contract. (credit: Benjamin J. DeLong)

Bones also protect internal organs from injury by covering or surrounding them. For example, your ribs protect your lungs and heart, the bones of your vertebral column (spine) protect your spinal cord, and the bones of your cranium (skull) protect your brain (Figure 6.3).

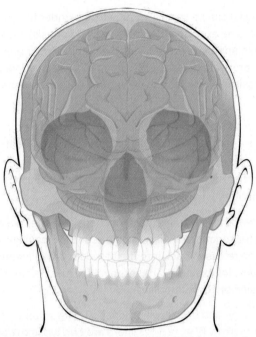

FIGURE 6.3   **Bones Protect Brain**   The cranium completely surrounds and protects the brain from non-traumatic injury.

 CAREER CONNECTION

Orthopedist

An **orthopedist** is a doctor who specializes in diagnosing and treating disorders and injuries related to the musculoskeletal system. Some orthopedic problems can be treated with medications, exercises, braces, and other devices, but others may be best treated with surgery (Figure 6.4).

FIGURE 6.4   **Complex Brace**   An orthopedist will sometimes prescribe the use of a brace that reinforces the underlying bone structure it is being used to support. (credit: Becky Stern/Flickr)

While the origin of the word "orthopedics" (ortho- = "straight"; paed- = "child"), literally means "straightening of the child," orthopedists can have patients who range from pediatric to geriatric. In recent years, orthopedists have even performed prenatal surgery to correct spina bifida, a congenital defect in which the neural canal in the spine of the fetus fails to close completely during embryologic development.

Orthopedists commonly treat bone and joint injuries but they also treat other bone conditions including curvature of the spine. Lateral curvatures (scoliosis) can be severe enough to slip under the shoulder blade (scapula) forcing it up as a hump. Spinal curvatures can also be excessive dorsoventrally (kyphosis) causing a hunch back and thoracic compression. These curvatures often appear in preteens as the result of poor posture, abnormal growth, or indeterminate causes. Mostly, they are readily treated by orthopedists. As people age, accumulated spinal column injuries and diseases like osteoporosis can also lead to curvatures of the spine, hence the stooping you sometimes see in the elderly.

Some orthopedists sub-specialize in sports medicine, which addresses both simple injuries, such as a sprained ankle, and complex injuries, such as a torn rotator cuff in the shoulder. Treatment can range from exercise to surgery.

Mineral Storage, Energy Storage, and Hematopoiesis

On a metabolic level, bone tissue performs several critical functions. For one, the bone matrix acts as a reservoir for a number of minerals important to the functioning of the body, especially calcium, and phosphorus. These minerals, incorporated into bone tissue, can be released back into the bloodstream to maintain levels needed to support physiological processes. Calcium ions, for example, are essential for muscle contractions and controlling the flow of other ions involved in the transmission of nerve impulses.

Bone also serves as a site for fat storage and blood cell production. The softer connective tissue that fills the interior of most bone is referred to as bone marrow (Figure 6.5). There are two types of bone marrow: yellow marrow and red marrow. **Yellow marrow** contains adipose tissue; the triglycerides stored in the adipocytes of the tissue can serve as a source of energy. **Red marrow** is where **hematopoiesis**—the production of blood cells—takes place. Red blood cells, white blood cells, and platelets are all produced in the red marrow.

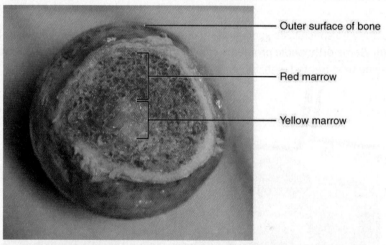

Outer surface of bone

Red marrow

Yellow marrow

FIGURE 6.5   Head of Femur Showing Red and Yellow Marrow   The head of the femur contains both yellow and red marrow. Yellow marrow stores fat. Red marrow is responsible for hematopoiesis. (credit: modification of work by "stevenfruitsmaak"/Wikimedia Commons)

6.2 Bone Classification

LEARNING OBJECTIVES

By the end of this section, you will be able to:
- Classify bones according to their shapes
- Describe the function of each category of bones

The 206 bones that compose the adult skeleton are divided into five categories based on their shapes (Figure 6.6). Their shapes and their functions are related such that each categorical shape of bone has a distinct function.

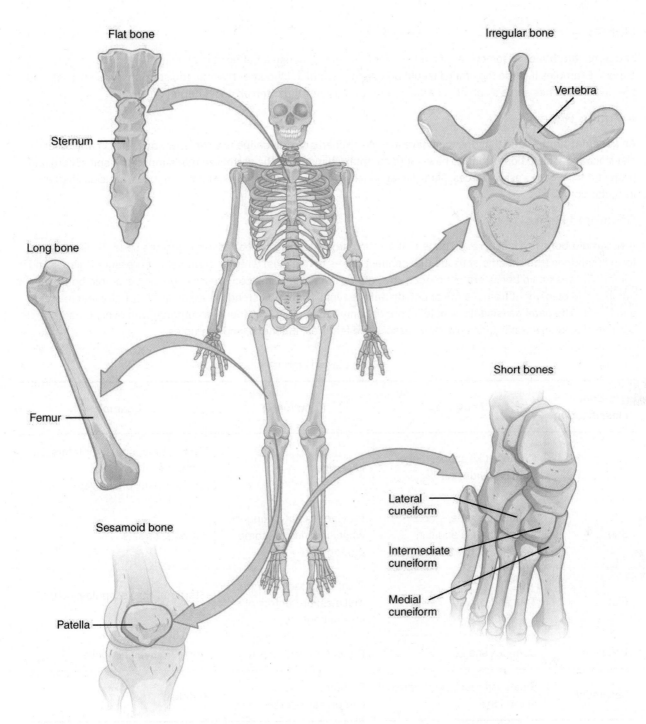

FIGURE 6.6 **Classifications of Bones** Bones are classified according to their shape.

Long Bones

A **long bone** is one that is cylindrical in shape, being longer than it is wide. Keep in mind, however, that the term describes the shape of a bone, not its size. Long bones are found in the arms (humerus, ulna, radius) and legs (femur, tibia, fibula), as well as in the fingers (metacarpals, phalanges) and toes (metatarsals, phalanges). Long bones function as levers; they move when muscles contract.

Short Bones

A **short bone** is one that is cube-like in shape, being approximately equal in length, width, and thickness. The only short bones in the human skeleton are in the carpals of the wrists and the tarsals of the ankles. Short bones provide stability and support as well as some limited motion.

Flat Bones

The term **"flat bone"** is somewhat of a misnomer because, although a flat bone is typically thin, it is also often curved. Examples include the cranial (skull) bones, the scapulae (shoulder blades), the sternum (breastbone), and the ribs. Flat bones serve as points of attachment for muscles and often protect internal organs.

Irregular Bones

An **irregular bone** is one that does not have any easily characterized shape and therefore does not fit any other classification. These bones tend to have more complex shapes, like the vertebrae that support the spinal cord and protect it from compressive forces. Many facial bones, particularly the ones containing sinuses, are classified as irregular bones.

Sesamoid Bones

A **sesamoid bone** is a small, round bone that, as the name suggests, is shaped like a sesame seed. These bones form in tendons (the sheaths of tissue that connect bones to muscles) where a great deal of pressure is generated in a joint. The sesamoid bones protect tendons by helping them overcome compressive forces. Sesamoid bones vary in number and placement from person to person but are typically found in tendons associated with the feet, hands, and knees. The patellae (singular = patella) are the only sesamoid bones found in common with every person. Table 6.1 reviews bone classifications with their associated features, functions, and examples.

Bone Classifications

Bone classification	Features	Function(s)	Examples
Long	Cylinder-like shape, longer than it is wide	Leverage	Femur, tibia, fibula, metatarsals, humerus, ulna, radius, metacarpals, phalanges
Short	Cube-like shape, approximately equal in length, width, and thickness	Provide stability, support, while allowing for some motion	Carpals, tarsals
Flat	Thin and curved	Points of attachment for muscles; protectors of internal organs	Sternum, ribs, scapulae, cranial bones
Irregular	Complex shape	Protect internal organs	Vertebrae, facial bones
Sesamoid	Small and round; embedded in tendons	Protect tendons from compressive forces	Patellae

TABLE 6.1

6.3 Bone Structure

LEARNING OBJECTIVES

By the end of this section, you will be able to:
- Identify the anatomical features of a bone
- Define and list examples of bone markings
- Describe the histology of bone tissue
- Compare and contrast compact and spongy bone
- Identify the structures that compose compact and spongy bone
- Describe how bones are nourished and innervated

Bone tissue (osseous tissue) differs greatly from other tissues in the body. Bone is hard and many of its functions depend on that characteristic hardness. Later discussions in this chapter will show that bone is also dynamic in that its shape adjusts to accommodate stresses. This section will examine the gross anatomy of bone first and then move on to its histology.

Gross Anatomy of Bone

The structure of a long bone allows for the best visualization of all of the parts of a bone (Figure 6.7). A long bone has two parts: the **diaphysis** and the **epiphysis**. The diaphysis is the tubular shaft that runs between the proximal and distal ends of the bone. The hollow region in the diaphysis is called the **medullary cavity**, which is filled with yellow marrow. The walls of the diaphysis are composed of dense and hard **compact bone**.

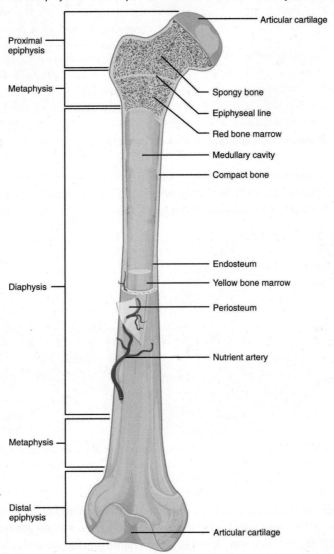

FIGURE 6.7 **Anatomy of a Long Bone**   A typical long bone shows the gross anatomical characteristics of bone.

The wider section at each end of the bone is called the epiphysis (plural = epiphyses), which is filled with spongy bone. Red marrow fills the spaces in the spongy bone. Each epiphysis meets the diaphysis at the metaphysis, the narrow area that contains the **epiphyseal plate** (growth plate), a layer of hyaline (transparent) cartilage in a growing bone. When the bone stops growing in early adulthood (approximately 18–21 years), the cartilage is replaced by osseous tissue and the epiphyseal plate becomes an epiphyseal line.

The medullary cavity has a delicate membranous lining called the **endosteum** (end- = "inside"; oste- = "bone"), where bone growth, repair, and remodeling occur. The outer surface of the bone is covered with a fibrous membrane called the **periosteum** (peri- = "around" or "surrounding"). The periosteum contains blood vessels, nerves, and lymphatic vessels that nourish compact bone. Tendons and ligaments also attach to bones at the periosteum. The periosteum covers the entire outer surface except where the epiphyses meet other bones to form joints (Figure 6.8). In this region, the epiphyses are covered with **articular cartilage**, a thin layer of cartilage that reduces friction and acts as a shock absorber.

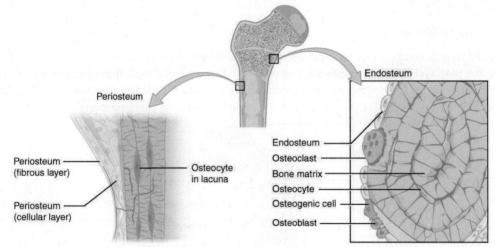

FIGURE 6.8   Periosteum and Endosteum   The periosteum forms the outer surface of bone, and the endosteum lines the medullary cavity.

Flat bones, like those of the cranium, consist of a layer of **diploë** (spongy bone), lined on either side by a layer of compact bone (Figure 6.9). The two layers of compact bone and the interior spongy bone work together to protect the internal organs. If the outer layer of a cranial bone fractures, the brain is still protected by the intact inner layer.

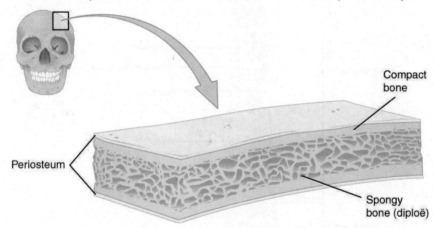

FIGURE 6.9   Anatomy of a Flat Bone   This cross-section of a flat bone shows the spongy bone (diploë) lined on either side by a layer of compact bone.

Bone Markings

The surface features of bones vary considerably, depending on the function and location in the body. Table 6.2 describes the bone markings, which are illustrated in (Figure 6.10). There are three general classes of bone markings: (1) articulations, (2) projections, and (3) holes. As the name implies, an **articulation** is where two bone surfaces come together (articulus = "joint"). These surfaces tend to conform to one another, such as one being rounded and the other cupped, to facilitate the function of the articulation. A **projection** is an area of a bone that projects above the surface of the bone. These are the attachment points for tendons and ligaments. In general, their size and shape is an indication of the forces exerted through the attachment to the bone. A **hole** is an opening or groove in the bone that allows blood vessels and nerves to enter the bone. As with the other markings, their size and shape reflect the size of the vessels and nerves that penetrate the bone at these points.

Access for free at openstax.org

Bone Markings

Marking	Description	Example
Articulations	Where two bones meet	Knee joint
Head	Prominent rounded surface	Head of femur
Facet	Flat surface	Vertebrae
Condyle	Rounded surface	Occipital condyles
Projections	Raised markings	Spinous process of the vertebrae
Protuberance	Protruding	Chin
Process	Prominence feature	Transverse process of vertebra
Spine	Sharp process	Ischial spine
Tubercle	Small, rounded process	Tubercle of humerus
Tuberosity	Rough surface	Deltoid tuberosity
Line	Slight, elongated ridge	Temporal lines of the parietal bones
Crest	Ridge	Iliac crest
Holes	Holes and depressions	Foramen (holes through which blood vessels can pass through)
Fossa	Elongated basin	Mandibular fossa
Fovea	Small pit	Fovea capitis on the head of the femur
Sulcus	Groove	Sigmoid sulcus of the temporal bones
Canal	Passage in bone	Auditory canal
Fissure	Slit through bone	Auricular fissure
Foramen	Hole through bone	Foramen magnum in the occipital bone
Meatus	Opening into canal	External auditory meatus
Sinus	Air-filled space in bone	Nasal sinus

TABLE 6.2

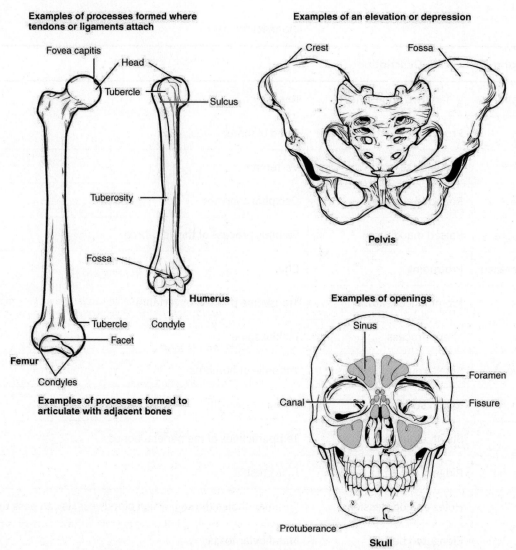

Examples of processes formed where tendons or ligaments attach

Fovea capitis

Head

Tubercle

Sulcus

Tuberosity

Fossa

Humerus

Tubercle   Condyle

Facet

Femur

Condyles

Examples of processes formed to articulate with adjacent bones

Examples of an elevation or depression

Crest   Fossa

Pelvis

Examples of openings

Sinus

Canal

Foramen

Fissure

Protuberance

Skull

FIGURE 6.10   Bone Features   The surface features of bones depend on their function, location, attachment of ligaments and tendons, or the penetration of blood vessels and nerves.

Bone Cells and Tissue

Bone contains a relatively small number of cells entrenched in a matrix of collagen fibers that provide a surface for inorganic salt crystals to adhere. These salt crystals form when calcium phosphate and calcium carbonate combine to create hydroxyapatite, which incorporates other inorganic salts like magnesium hydroxide, fluoride, and sulfate as it crystallizes, or calcifies, on the collagen fibers. The hydroxyapatite crystals give bones their hardness and strength, while the collagen fibers give them flexibility so that they are not brittle.

Although bone cells compose a small amount of the bone volume, they are crucial to the function of bones. Four types of cells are found within bone tissue: osteoblasts, osteocytes, osteogenic cells, and osteoclasts (Figure 6.11).

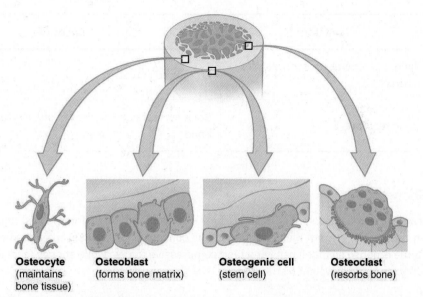

Osteocyte
(maintains
bone tissue)

Osteoblast
(forms bone matrix)

Osteogenic cell
(stem cell)

Osteoclast
(resorbs bone)

FIGURE 6.11 Bone Cells Four types of cells are found within bone tissue. Osteogenic cells are undifferentiated and develop into osteoblasts. When osteoblasts get trapped within the calcified matrix, their structure and function changes, and they become osteocytes. Osteoclasts develop from monocytes and macrophages and differ in appearance from other bone cells.

The **osteoblast** is the bone cell responsible for forming new bone and is found in the growing portions of bone, including the periosteum and endosteum. Osteoblasts, which do not divide, synthesize and secrete the collagen matrix and calcium salts. As the secreted matrix surrounding the osteoblast calcifies, the osteoblast become trapped within it; as a result, it changes in structure and becomes an **osteocyte**, the primary cell of mature bone and the most common type of bone cell. Each osteocyte is located in a space called a **lacuna** and is surrounded by bone tissue. Osteocytes maintain the mineral concentration of the matrix via the secretion of enzymes. Like osteoblasts, osteocytes lack mitotic activity. They can communicate with each other and receive nutrients via long cytoplasmic processes that extend through **canaliculi** (singular = canaliculus), channels within the bone matrix.

If osteoblasts and osteocytes are incapable of mitosis, then how are they replenished when old ones die? The answer lies in the properties of a third category of bone cells—the **osteogenic cell**. These osteogenic cells are undifferentiated with high mitotic activity and they are the only bone cells that divide. Immature osteogenic cells are found in the deep layers of the periosteum and the marrow. They differentiate and develop into osteoblasts.

The dynamic nature of bone means that new tissue is constantly formed, and old, injured, or unnecessary bone is dissolved for repair or for calcium release. The cell responsible for bone resorption, or breakdown, is the **osteoclast**. They are found on bone surfaces, are multinucleated, and originate from monocytes and macrophages, two types of white blood cells, not from osteogenic cells. Osteoclasts are continually breaking down old bone while osteoblasts are continually forming new bone. The ongoing balance between osteoblasts and osteoclasts is responsible for the constant but subtle reshaping of bone. Table 6.3 reviews the bone cells, their functions, and locations.

Bone Cells

Cell type	Function	Location
Osteogenic cells	Develop into osteoblasts	Deep layers of the periosteum and the marrow
Osteoblasts	Bone formation	Growing portions of bone, including periosteum and endosteum

TABLE 6.3

Cell type	Function	Location
Osteocytes	Maintain mineral concentration of matrix	Entrapped in matrix
Osteoclasts	Bone resorption	Bone surfaces and at sites of old, injured, or unneeded bone

TABLE 6.3

Compact and Spongy Bone

The differences between compact and spongy bone are best explored via their histology. Most bones contain compact and spongy osseous tissue, but their distribution and concentration vary based on the bone's overall function. Compact bone is dense so that it can withstand compressive forces, while spongy (cancellous) bone has open spaces and supports shifts in weight distribution.

Compact Bone

Compact bone is the denser, stronger of the two types of bone tissue (Figure 6.12). It can be found under the periosteum and in the diaphyses of long bones, where it provides support and protection.

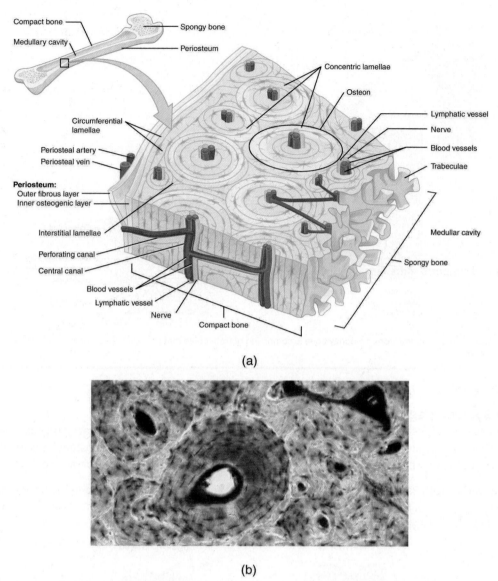

(a)

(b)

FIGURE 6.12 Diagram of Compact Bone   (a) This cross-sectional view of compact bone shows the basic structural unit, the osteon. (b) In this micrograph of the osteon, you can clearly see the concentric lamellae and central canals. LM × 40. (Micrograph provided by the Regents of University of Michigan Medical School © 2012)

The microscopic structural unit of compact bone is called an **osteon**, or Haversian system. Each osteon is composed of concentric rings of calcified matrix called lamellae (singular = lamella). Running down the center of each osteon is the **central canal**, or Haversian canal, which contains blood vessels, nerves, and lymphatic vessels. These vessels and nerves branch off at right angles through a **perforating canal**, also known as Volkmann's canals, to extend to the periosteum and endosteum.

The osteocytes are located inside spaces called lacunae (singular = lacuna), found at the borders of adjacent lamellae. As described earlier, canaliculi connect with the canaliculi of other lacunae and eventually with the central canal. This system allows nutrients to be transported to the osteocytes and wastes to be removed from them.

Spongy (Cancellous) Bone

Like compact bone, **spongy bone**, also known as cancellous bone, contains osteocytes housed in lacunae, but they are not arranged in concentric circles. Instead, the lacunae and osteocytes are found in a lattice-like network of matrix spikes called **trabeculae** (singular = trabecula) (Figure 6.13). The trabeculae may appear to be a random network, but each trabecula forms along lines of stress to provide strength to the bone. The spaces of the trabeculated network provide balance to the dense and heavy compact bone by making bones lighter so that muscles can move them more easily. In addition, the spaces in some spongy bones contain red marrow, protected by the trabeculae, where hematopoiesis occurs.

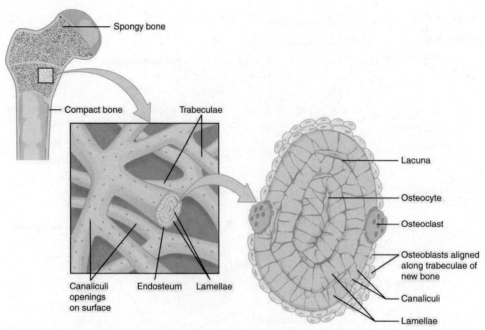

FIGURE 6.13   Diagram of Spongy Bone   Spongy bone is composed of trabeculae that contain the osteocytes. Red marrow fills the spaces in some bones.

Aging and the...

Skeletal System: Paget's Disease

Paget's disease usually occurs in adults over age 40. It is a disorder of the bone remodeling process that begins with overactive osteoclasts. This means more bone is resorbed than is laid down. The osteoblasts try to compensate but the new bone they lay down is weak and brittle and therefore prone to fracture.

While some people with Paget's disease have no symptoms, others experience pain, bone fractures, and bone deformities (Figure 6.14). Bones of the pelvis, skull, spine, and legs are the most commonly affected. When occurring in the skull, Paget's disease can cause headaches and hearing loss.

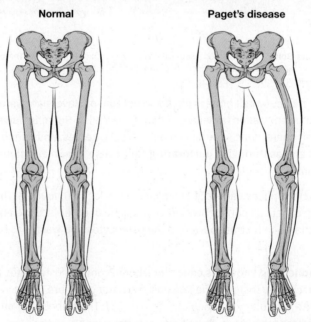

FIGURE 6.14   Paget's Disease   Normal leg bones are relatively straight, but those affected by Paget's disease are porous and curved.

What causes the osteoclasts to become overactive? The answer is still unknown, but hereditary factors seem to play a role. Some scientists believe Paget's disease is due to an as-yet-unidentified virus.

Paget's disease is diagnosed via imaging studies and lab tests. X-rays may show bone deformities or areas of bone resorption. Bone scans are also useful. In these studies, a dye containing a radioactive ion is injected into the body. Areas of bone resorption have an affinity for the ion, so they will light up on the scan if the ions are absorbed. In addition, blood levels of an enzyme called alkaline phosphatase are typically elevated in people with Paget's disease.

Bisphosphonates, drugs that decrease the activity of osteoclasts, are often used in the treatment of Paget's disease. However, in a small percentage of cases, bisphosphonates themselves have been linked to an increased risk of fractures because the old bone that is left after bisphosphonates are administered becomes worn out and brittle. Still, most doctors feel that the benefits of bisphosphonates more than outweigh the risk; the medical professional has to weigh the benefits and risks on a case-by-case basis. Bisphosphonate treatment can reduce the overall risk of deformities or fractures, which in turn reduces the risk of surgical repair and its associated risks and complications.

Blood and Nerve Supply

The spongy bone and medullary cavity receive nourishment from arteries that pass through the compact bone. The arteries enter through the **nutrient foramen** (plural = foramina), small openings in the diaphysis (Figure 6.15). The osteocytes in spongy bone are nourished by blood vessels of the periosteum that penetrate spongy bone and blood that circulates in the marrow cavities. As the blood passes through the marrow cavities, it is collected by veins, which then pass out of the bone through the foramina.

In addition to the blood vessels, nerves follow the same paths into the bone where they tend to concentrate in the more metabolically active regions of the bone. The nerves sense pain, and it appears the nerves also play roles in regulating blood supplies and in bone growth, hence their concentrations in metabolically active sites of the bone.

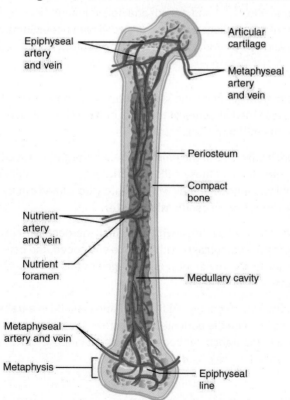

FIGURE 6.15 Diagram of Blood and Nerve Supply to Bone   Blood vessels and nerves enter the bone through the nutrient foramen.

⊘ **INTERACTIVE LINK**

Watch this video (http://openstax.org/l/microbone) to see the microscopic features of a bone.

___

6.4 Bone Formation and Development

LEARNING OBJECTIVES

By the end of this section, you will be able to:

- Explain the function of cartilage
- List the steps of intramembranous ossification
- List the steps of endochondral ossification
- Explain the growth activity at the epiphyseal plate
- Compare and contrast the processes of modeling and remodeling

In the early stages of embryonic development, the embryo's skeleton consists of fibrous membranes and hyaline cartilage. By the sixth or seventh week of embryonic life, the actual process of bone development, **ossification** (osteogenesis), begins. There are two osteogenic pathways—intramembranous ossification and endochondral ossification—but bone is the same regardless of the pathway that produces it.

Cartilage Templates

Bone is a replacement tissue; that is, it uses a model tissue on which to lay down its mineral matrix. For skeletal development, the most common template is cartilage. During fetal development, a framework is laid down that determines where bones will form. This framework is a flexible, semi-solid matrix produced by chondroblasts and consists of hyaluronic acid, chondroitin sulfate, collagen fibers, and water. As the matrix surrounds and isolates chondroblasts, they are called chondrocytes. Unlike most connective tissues, cartilage is avascular, meaning that it has no blood vessels supplying nutrients and removing metabolic wastes. All of these functions are carried on by diffusion through the matrix. This is why damaged cartilage does not repair itself as readily as most tissues do.

Throughout fetal development and into childhood growth and development, bone forms on the cartilaginous matrix. By the time a fetus is born, most of the cartilage has been replaced with bone. Some additional cartilage will be replaced throughout childhood, and some cartilage remains in the adult skeleton.

Intramembranous Ossification

During **intramembranous ossification**, compact and spongy bone develops directly from sheets of mesenchymal (undifferentiated) connective tissue. The flat bones of the face, most of the cranial bones, and the clavicles (collarbones) are formed via intramembranous ossification.

The process begins when mesenchymal cells in the embryonic skeleton gather together and begin to differentiate into specialized cells (Figure 6.16**a**). Some of these cells will differentiate into capillaries, while others will become osteogenic cells and then osteoblasts. Although they will ultimately be spread out by the formation of bone tissue, early osteoblasts appear in a cluster called an **ossification center**.

The osteoblasts secrete **osteoid**, uncalcified matrix, which calcifies (hardens) within a few days as mineral salts are deposited on it, thereby entrapping the osteoblasts within. Once entrapped, the osteoblasts become osteocytes (Figure 6.16**b**). As osteoblasts transform into osteocytes, osteogenic cells in the surrounding connective tissue differentiate into new osteoblasts.

Osteoid (unmineralized bone matrix) secreted around the capillaries results in a trabecular matrix, while osteoblasts on the surface of the spongy bone become the periosteum (Figure 6.16**c**). The periosteum then creates a protective layer of compact bone superficial to the trabecular bone. The trabecular bone crowds nearby blood vessels, which eventually condense into red marrow (Figure 6.16**d**).

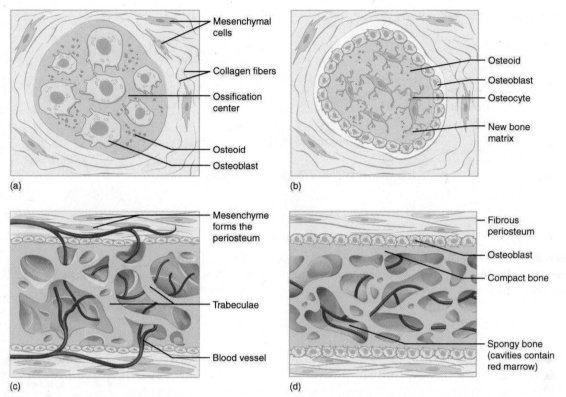

FIGURE 6.16   Intramembranous Ossification   Intramembranous ossification follows four steps. (a) Mesenchymal cells group into clusters, and ossification centers form. (b) Secreted osteoid traps osteoblasts, which then become osteocytes. (c) Trabecular matrix and periosteum form. (d) Compact bone develops superficial to the trabecular bone, and crowded blood vessels condense into red marrow.

Intramembranous ossification begins *in utero* during fetal development and continues on into adolescence. At birth, the skull and clavicles are not fully ossified nor are the sutures of the skull closed. This allows the skull and shoulders to deform during passage through the birth canal. The last bones to ossify via intramembranous ossification are the flat bones of the face, which reach their adult size at the end of the adolescent growth spurt.

Endochondral Ossification

In **endochondral ossification**, bone develops by *replacing* hyaline cartilage. Cartilage does not become bone. Instead, cartilage serves as a template to be completely replaced by new bone. Endochondral ossification takes much longer than intramembranous ossification. Bones at the base of the skull and long bones form via endochondral ossification.

In a long bone, for example, at about 6 to 8 weeks after conception, some of the mesenchymal cells differentiate into chondrocytes (cartilage cells) that form the cartilaginous skeletal precursor of the bones (Figure 6.17**a**). Soon after, the **perichondrium**, a membrane that covers the cartilage, appears Figure 6.17**b**).

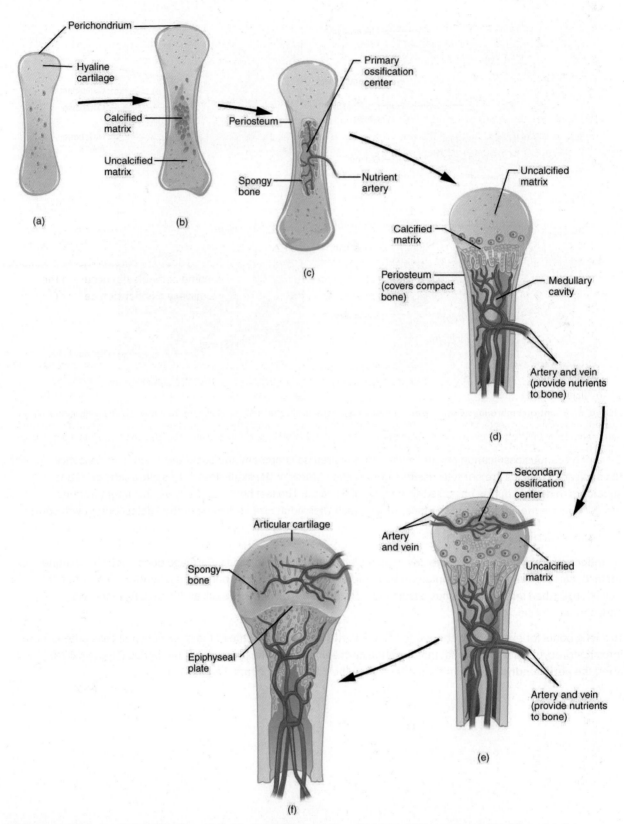

FIGURE 6.17   Endochondral Ossification   Endochondral ossification follows five steps. (a) Mesenchymal cells differentiate into chondrocytes. (b) The cartilage model of the future bony skeleton and the perichondrium form. (c) Capillaries penetrate cartilage. Perichondrium transforms into periosteum. Periosteal collar develops. Primary ossification center develops. (d) Cartilage and chondrocytes continue to grow at ends of the bone. (e) Secondary ossification centers develop. (f) Cartilage remains at epiphyseal (growth) plate and at joint surface as articular cartilage.

As more matrix is produced, the chondrocytes in the center of the cartilaginous model grow in size. As the matrix calcifies, nutrients can no longer reach the chondrocytes. This results in their death and the disintegration of the surrounding cartilage. Blood vessels invade the resulting spaces, not only enlarging the cavities but also carrying osteogenic cells with them, many of which will become osteoblasts. These enlarging spaces eventually combine to become the medullary cavity.

As the cartilage grows, capillaries penetrate it. This penetration initiates the transformation of the perichondrium into the bone-producing periosteum. Here, the osteoblasts form a periosteal collar of compact bone around the cartilage of the diaphysis. By the second or third month of fetal life, bone cell development and ossification ramps up and creates the **primary ossification center**, a region deep in the periosteal collar where ossification begins (Figure 6.17**c**).

While these deep changes are occurring, chondrocytes and cartilage continue to grow at the ends of the bone (the future epiphyses), which increases the bone's length at the same time bone is replacing cartilage in the diaphyses. By the time the fetal skeleton is fully formed, cartilage only remains at the joint surface as articular cartilage and between the diaphysis and epiphysis as the epiphyseal plate, the latter of which is responsible for the longitudinal growth of bones. After birth, this same sequence of events (matrix mineralization, death of chondrocytes, invasion of blood vessels from the periosteum, and seeding with osteogenic cells that become osteoblasts) occurs in the epiphyseal regions, and each of these centers of activity is referred to as a **secondary ossification center** (Figure 6.17**e**).

How Bones Grow in Length

The epiphyseal plate is the area of growth in a long bone. It is a layer of hyaline cartilage where ossification occurs in immature bones. On the epiphyseal side of the epiphyseal plate, cartilage is formed. On the diaphyseal side, cartilage is ossified, and the diaphysis grows in length. The epiphyseal plate is composed of four zones of cells and activity (Figure 6.18). The **reserve zone** is the region closest to the epiphyseal end of the plate and contains small chondrocytes within the matrix. These chondrocytes do not participate in bone growth but secure the epiphyseal plate to the osseous tissue of the epiphysis.

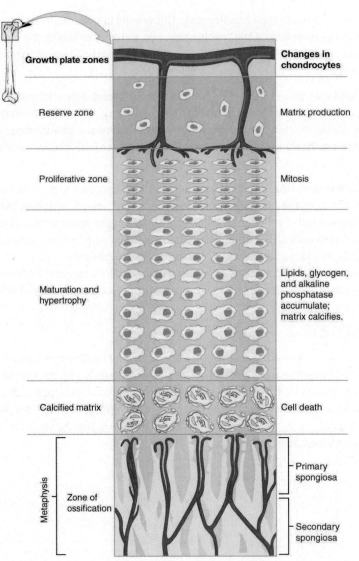

Growth plate zones

Reserve zone

Proliferative zone

Maturation and hypertrophy

Calcified matrix

Metaphysis

Zone of ossification

Changes in chondrocytes

Matrix production

Mitosis

Lipids, glycogen, and alkaline phosphatase accumulate; matrix calcifies.

Cell death

Primary spongiosa

Secondary spongiosa

FIGURE 6.18   Longitudinal Bone Growth   The epiphyseal plate is responsible for longitudinal bone growth.

The **proliferative zone** is the next layer toward the diaphysis and contains stacks of slightly larger chondrocytes. It makes new chondrocytes (via mitosis) to replace those that die at the diaphyseal end of the plate. Chondrocytes in the next layer, the **zone of maturation and hypertrophy**, are older and larger than those in the proliferative zone. The more mature cells are situated closer to the diaphyseal end of the plate. The longitudinal growth of bone is a result of cellular division in the proliferative zone and the maturation of cells in the zone of maturation and hypertrophy.

Most of the chondrocytes in the **zone of calcified matrix**, the zone closest to the diaphysis, are dead because the matrix around them has calcified. Capillaries and osteoblasts from the diaphysis penetrate this zone, and the osteoblasts secrete bone tissue on the remaining calcified cartilage. Thus, the zone of calcified matrix connects the epiphyseal plate to the diaphysis. A bone grows in length when osseous tissue is added to the diaphysis.

Bones continue to grow in length until early adulthood. The rate of growth is controlled by hormones, which will be discussed later. When the chondrocytes in the epiphyseal plate cease their proliferation and bone replaces the cartilage, longitudinal growth stops. All that remains of the epiphyseal plate is the **epiphyseal line** (Figure 6.19).

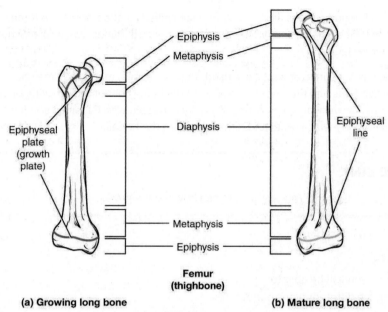

FIGURE 6.19   Progression from Epiphyseal Plate to Epiphyseal Line   As a bone matures, the epiphyseal plate progresses to an epiphyseal line. (a) Epiphyseal plates are visible in a growing bone. (b) Epiphyseal lines are the remnants of epiphyseal plates in a mature bone.

How Bones Grow in Diameter

While bones are increasing in length, they are also increasing in diameter; growth in diameter can continue even after longitudinal growth ceases. This is called appositional growth. Osteoclasts resorb old bone that lines the medullary cavity, while osteoblasts, via intramembranous ossification, produce new bone tissue beneath the periosteum. The erosion of old bone along the medullary cavity and the deposition of new bone beneath the periosteum not only increase the diameter of the diaphysis but also increase the diameter of the medullary cavity. This process is called **modeling**.

Bone Remodeling

The process in which matrix is resorbed on one surface of a bone and deposited on another is known as bone modeling. Modeling primarily takes place during a bone's growth. However, in adult life, bone undergoes **remodeling**, in which resorption of old or damaged bone takes place on the same surface where osteoblasts lay new bone to replace that which is resorbed. Injury, exercise, and other activities lead to remodeling. Those influences are discussed later in the chapter, but even without injury or exercise, about 5 to 10 percent of the skeleton is remodeled annually just by destroying old bone and renewing it with fresh bone.

Diseases of the...

Skeletal System   Osteogenesis imperfecta (OI) is a genetic disease in which bones do not form properly and therefore are fragile and break easily. It is also called brittle bone disease. The disease is present from birth and affects a person throughout life.

The genetic mutation that causes OI affects the body's production of collagen, one of the critical components of bone matrix. The severity of the disease can range from mild to severe. Those with the most severe forms of the disease sustain many more fractures than those with a mild form. Frequent and multiple fractures typically lead to bone deformities and short stature. Bowing of the long bones and curvature of the spine are also common in people afflicted with OI. Curvature of the spine makes breathing difficult because the lungs are compressed.

Because collagen is such an important structural protein in many parts of the body, people with OI may also experience fragile skin, weak muscles, loose joints, easy bruising, frequent nosebleeds, brittle teeth, blue sclera, and hearing loss. There is no known cure for OI. Treatment focuses on helping the person retain as much independence as possible while minimizing fractures and maximizing mobility. Toward that end, safe exercises, like swimming, in which the body is less likely to experience collisions or compressive forces, are recommended. Braces to support legs, ankles, knees, and wrists are used as needed. Canes, walkers, or wheelchairs can also help compensate for weaknesses.

When bones do break, casts, splints, or wraps are used. In some cases, metal rods may be surgically implanted into the long bones of the arms and legs. Research is currently being conducted on using bisphosphonates to treat OI. Smoking and being overweight are especially risky in people with OI, since smoking is known to weaken bones, and extra body weight puts additional stress on the bones.

⊘ INTERACTIVE LINK

Watch this video (http://openstax.org/l/bonegrows) to see how a bone grows.

6.5 Fractures: Bone Repair

LEARNING OBJECTIVES

By the end of this section, you will be able to:

- Differentiate among the different types of fractures
- Describe the steps involved in bone repair

A **fracture** is a broken bone. It will heal whether or not a physician resets it in its anatomical position. If the bone is not reset correctly, the healing process will keep the bone in its deformed position.

When a broken bone is manipulated and set into its natural position without surgery, the procedure is called a **closed reduction**. **Open reduction** requires surgery to expose the fracture and reset the bone. While some fractures can be minor, others are quite severe and result in grave complications. For example, a fractured diaphysis of the femur has the potential to release fat globules into the bloodstream. These can become lodged in the capillary beds of the lungs, leading to respiratory distress and if not treated quickly, death.

Types of Fractures

Fractures are classified by their complexity, location, and other features (Figure 6.20). Table 6.4 outlines common types of fractures. Some fractures may be described using more than one term because it may have the features of more than one type (e.g., an open transverse fracture).

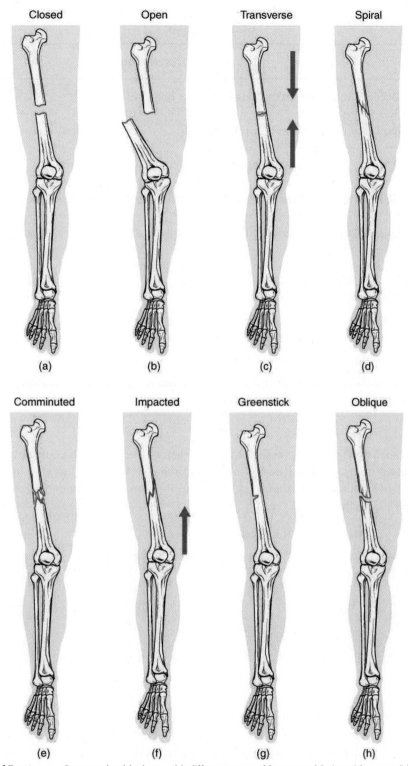

FIGURE 6.20   Types of Fractures   Compare healthy bone with different types of fractures: (a) closed fracture, (b) open fracture, (c) transverse fracture, (d) spiral fracture, (e) comminuted fracture, (f) impacted fracture, (g) greenstick fracture, and (h) oblique fracture.

Types of Fractures

Type of fracture	Description
Transverse	Occurs straight across the long axis of the bone
Oblique	Occurs at an angle that is not 90 degrees
Spiral	Bone segments are pulled apart as a result of a twisting motion
Comminuted	Several breaks result in many small pieces between two large segments
Impacted	One fragment is driven into the other, usually as a result of compression
Greenstick	A partial fracture in which only one side of the bone is broken
Open (or compound)	A fracture in which at least one end of the broken bone tears through the skin; carries a high risk of infection
Closed (or simple)	A fracture in which the skin remains intact

TABLE 6.4

Bone Repair

When a bone breaks, blood flows from any vessel torn by the fracture. These vessels could be in the periosteum, osteons, and/or medullary cavity. The blood begins to clot, and about six to eight hours after the fracture, the clotting blood has formed a **fracture hematoma** (Figure 6.21a). The disruption of blood flow to the bone results in the death of bone cells around the fracture.

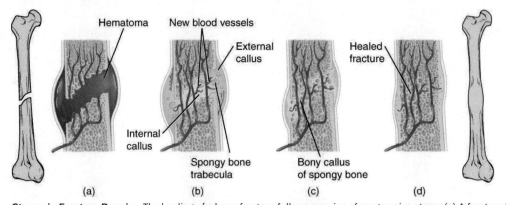

FIGURE 6.21   Stages in Fracture Repair   The healing of a bone fracture follows a series of progressive steps: (a) A fracture hematoma forms. (b) Internal and external calli form. (c) Cartilage of the calli is replaced by trabecular bone. (d) Remodeling occurs.

Within about 48 hours after the fracture, chondrocytes from the endosteum have created an **internal callus** (plural = calli) by secreting a fibrocartilaginous matrix between the two ends of the broken bone, while the periosteal chondrocytes and osteoblasts create an **external callus** of hyaline cartilage and bone, respectively, around the outside of the break (Figure 6.21b). This stabilizes the fracture.

Over the next several weeks, osteoclasts resorb the dead bone; osteogenic cells become active, divide, and differentiate into osteoblasts. The cartilage in the calli is replaced by trabecular bone via endochondral ossification (Figure 6.21c).

Eventually, the internal and external calli unite, compact bone replaces spongy bone at the outer margins of the

Access for free at openstax.org

fracture, and healing is complete. A slight swelling may remain on the outer surface of the bone, but quite often, that region undergoes remodeling (Figure 6.21**d**), and no external evidence of the fracture remains.

⊘ INTERACTIVE LINK

Visit this website (http://openstax.org/l/fracturequiz) to review different types of fractures and then take a short self-assessment quiz.

6.6 Exercise, Nutrition, Hormones, and Bone Tissue

LEARNING OBJECTIVES

By the end of this section, you will be able to:

- Describe the effect exercise has on bone tissue
- List the nutrients that affect bone health
- Discuss the role those nutrients play in bone health
- Describe the effects of hormones on bone tissue

All of the organ systems of your body are interdependent, and the skeletal system is no exception. The food you take in via your digestive system and the hormones secreted by your endocrine system affect your bones. Even using your muscles to engage in exercise has an impact on your bones.

Exercise and Bone Tissue

During long space missions, astronauts can lose approximately 1 to 2 percent of their bone mass per month. This loss of bone mass is thought to be caused by the lack of mechanical stress on astronauts' bones due to the low gravitational forces in space. Lack of mechanical stress causes bones to lose mineral salts and collagen fibers, and thus strength. Similarly, mechanical stress stimulates the deposition of mineral salts and collagen fibers. The internal and external structure of a bone will change as stress increases or decreases so that the bone is an ideal size and weight for the amount of activity it endures. That is why people who exercise regularly have thicker bones than people who are more sedentary. It is also why a broken bone in a cast atrophies while its contralateral mate maintains its concentration of mineral salts and collagen fibers. The bones undergo remodeling as a result of forces (or lack of forces) placed on them.

Numerous, controlled studies have demonstrated that people who exercise regularly have greater bone density than those who are more sedentary. Any type of exercise will stimulate the deposition of more bone tissue, but resistance training has a greater effect than cardiovascular activities. Resistance training is especially important to slow down the eventual bone loss due to aging and for preventing osteoporosis.

Nutrition and Bone Tissue

The vitamins and minerals contained in all of the food we consume are important for all of our organ systems. However, there are certain nutrients that affect bone health.

Calcium and Vitamin D

You already know that calcium is a critical component of bone, especially in the form of calcium phosphate and calcium carbonate. Since the body cannot make calcium, it must be obtained from the diet. However, calcium cannot be absorbed from the small intestine without vitamin D. Therefore, intake of vitamin D is also critical to bone health. In addition to vitamin D's role in calcium absorption, it also plays a role, though not as clearly understood, in bone remodeling.

Milk and other dairy foods are not the only sources of calcium. This important nutrient is also found in green leafy vegetables, broccoli, and intact salmon and canned sardines with their soft bones. Nuts, beans, seeds, and shellfish provide calcium in smaller quantities.

Except for fatty fish like salmon and tuna, or fortified milk or cereal, vitamin D is not found naturally in many foods. The action of sunlight on the skin triggers the body to produce its own vitamin D (Figure 6.22), but many people, especially those of darker complexion and those living in northern latitudes where the sun's rays are not as strong, are deficient in vitamin D. In cases of deficiency, a doctor can prescribe a vitamin D supplement.

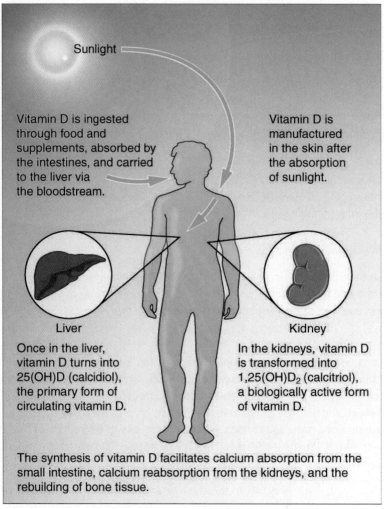

FIGURE 6.22   Synthesis of Vitamin D   Sunlight is one source of vitamin D.

Other Nutrients

Vitamin K also supports bone mineralization and may have a synergistic role with vitamin D in the regulation of bone growth. Green leafy vegetables are a good source of vitamin K.

The minerals magnesium and fluoride may also play a role in supporting bone health. While magnesium is only found in trace amounts in the human body, more than 60 percent of it is in the skeleton, suggesting it plays a role in the structure of bone. Fluoride can displace the hydroxyl group in bone's hydroxyapatite crystals and form fluorapatite. Similar to its effect on dental enamel, fluorapatite helps stabilize and strengthen bone mineral. Fluoride can also enter spaces within hydroxyapatite crystals, thus increasing their density.

Omega-3 fatty acids have long been known to reduce inflammation in various parts of the body. Inflammation can interfere with the function of osteoblasts, so consuming omega-3 fatty acids, in the diet or in supplements, may also help enhance production of new osseous tissue. Table 6.5 summarizes the role of nutrients in bone health.

Nutrients and Bone Health

Nutrient	Role in bone health
Calcium	Needed to make calcium phosphate and calcium carbonate, which form the hydroxyapatite crystals that give bone its hardness
Vitamin D	Needed for calcium absorption
Vitamin K	Supports bone mineralization; may have synergistic effect with vitamin D
Magnesium	Structural component of bone
Fluoride	Structural component of bone
Omega-3 fatty acids	Reduces inflammation that may interfere with osteoblast function

TABLE 6.5

Hormones and Bone Tissue

The endocrine system produces and secretes hormones, many of which interact with the skeletal system. These hormones are involved in controlling bone growth, maintaining bone once it is formed, and remodeling it.

Hormones That Influence Osteoblasts and/or Maintain the Matrix

Several hormones are necessary for controlling bone growth and maintaining the bone matrix. The pituitary gland secretes growth hormone (GH), which, as its name implies, controls bone growth in several ways. It triggers chondrocyte proliferation in epiphyseal plates, resulting in the increasing length of long bones. GH also increases calcium retention, which enhances mineralization, and stimulates osteoblastic activity, which improves bone density.

GH is not alone in stimulating bone growth and maintaining osseous tissue. Thyroxine, a hormone secreted by the thyroid gland promotes osteoblastic activity and the synthesis of bone matrix. During puberty, the sex hormones (estrogen and testosterone) also come into play. They too promote osteoblastic activity and production of bone matrix, and in addition, are responsible for the growth spurt that often occurs during adolescence. They also promote the conversion of the epiphyseal plate to the epiphyseal line (i.e., cartilage to its bony remnant), thus bringing an end to the longitudinal growth of bones. Additionally, calcitriol, the active form of vitamin D, is produced by the kidneys and stimulates the absorption of calcium and phosphate from the digestive tract.

Aging and the...

Skeletal System

Osteoporosis is a disease characterized by a decrease in bone mass that occurs when the rate of bone resorption exceeds the rate of bone formation, a common occurrence as the body ages. Notice how this is different from Paget's disease. In Paget's disease, new bone is formed in an attempt to keep up with the resorption by the overactive osteoclasts, but that new bone is produced haphazardly. In fact, when a physician is evaluating a patient with thinning bone, they will test for osteoporosis and Paget's disease (as well as other diseases). Osteoporosis does not have the elevated blood levels of alkaline phosphatase found in Paget's disease.

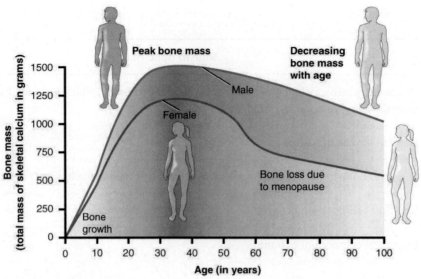

FIGURE 6.23   Graph Showing Relationship Between Age and Bone Mass   Bone density peaks at about 30 years of age. Females lose bone mass more rapidly than males.

While osteoporosis can involve any bone, it most commonly affects the proximal ends of the femur, vertebrae, and wrist. As a result of the loss of bone density, the osseous tissue may not provide adequate support for everyday functions, and something as simple as a sneeze can cause a vertebral fracture. When an elderly person falls and breaks a hip (really, the femur), it is very likely the femur that broke first, which resulted in the fall. Histologically, osteoporosis is characterized by a reduction in the thickness of compact bone and the number and size of trabeculae in cancellous bone.

Figure 6.23 shows that females lose bone mass more quickly than males starting at about 50 years of age. This occurs because 50 is the approximate age at which females go through menopause. Not only do their menstrual periods lessen and eventually cease, but their ovaries reduce in size and then cease the production of estrogen, a hormone that promotes osteoblastic activity and production of bone matrix. Thus, osteoporosis is more common in females, but males can develop it, too. Anyone with a family history of osteoporosis has a greater risk of developing the disease, so the best treatment is prevention, which should start with a childhood diet that includes adequate intake of calcium and vitamin D and a lifestyle that includes weight-bearing exercise. These actions, as discussed above, are important in building bone mass. Promoting proper nutrition and weight-bearing exercise early in life can maximize bone mass before the age of 30, thus reducing the risk of osteoporosis.

For many elderly people, a hip fracture can be life threatening. The fracture itself may not be serious, but the immobility that comes during the healing process can lead to the formation of blood clots that can lodge in the capillaries of the lungs, resulting in respiratory failure; pneumonia due to the lack of poor air exchange that accompanies immobility; pressure sores (bed sores) that allow pathogens to enter the body and cause infections; and urinary tract infections from catheterization.

Current treatments for managing osteoporosis include bisphosphonates (the same medications often used in Paget's disease), calcitonin, and estrogen (for females only). Minimizing the risk of falls, for example, by removing tripping hazards, is also an important step in managing the potential outcomes from the disease.

Hormones That Influence Osteoclasts

Bone modeling and remodeling require osteoclasts to resorb unneeded, damaged, or old bone, and osteoblasts to lay down new bone. Two hormones that affect the osteoclasts are parathyroid hormone (PTH) and calcitonin.

PTH stimulates osteoclast proliferation and activity. As a result, calcium is released from the bones into the circulation, thus increasing the calcium ion concentration in the blood. PTH also promotes the reabsorption of calcium by the kidney tubules, which can affect calcium homeostasis (see below).

The small intestine is also affected by PTH, albeit indirectly. Because another function of PTH is to stimulate the synthesis of vitamin D, and because vitamin D promotes intestinal absorption of calcium, PTH indirectly increases calcium uptake by the small intestine. Calcitonin, a hormone secreted by the thyroid gland, has some effects that counteract those of PTH. Calcitonin inhibits osteoclast activity and stimulates calcium uptake by the bones, thus reducing the concentration of calcium ions in the blood. As evidenced by their opposing functions in maintaining calcium homeostasis, PTH and calcitonin are generally *not* secreted at the same time. Table 6.6 summarizes the hormones that influence the skeletal system.

Hormones That Affect the Skeletal System

Hormone	Role
Growth hormone	Increases length of long bones, enhances mineralization, and improves bone density
Thyroxine	Stimulates bone growth and promotes synthesis of bone matrix
Sex hormones	Promote osteoblastic activity and production of bone matrix; responsible for adolescent growth spurt; promote conversion of epiphyseal plate to epiphyseal line
Calcitriol	Stimulates absorption of calcium and phosphate from digestive tract
Parathyroid hormone	Stimulates osteoclast proliferation and resorption of bone by osteoclasts; promotes reabsorption of calcium by kidney tubules; indirectly increases calcium absorption by small intestine
Calcitonin	Inhibits osteoclast activity and stimulates calcium uptake by bones

TABLE 6.6

6.7 Calcium Homeostasis: Interactions of the Skeletal System and Other Organ Systems

LEARNING OBJECTIVES

By the end of this section, you will be able to:

- Describe the effect of too much or too little calcium on the body
- Explain the process of calcium homeostasis

Calcium is not only the most abundant mineral in bone, it is also the most abundant mineral in the human body. Calcium ions are needed not only for bone mineralization but for tooth health, regulation of the heart rate and strength of contraction, blood coagulation, contraction of smooth and skeletal muscle cells, and regulation of nerve impulse conduction. The normal level of calcium in the blood is about 10 mg/dL. When the body cannot maintain this level, a person will experience hypo- or hypercalcemia.

Hypocalcemia, a condition characterized by abnormally low levels of calcium, can have an adverse effect on a number of different body systems including circulation, muscles, nerves, and bone. Without adequate calcium, blood has difficulty coagulating, the heart may skip beats or stop beating altogether, muscles may have difficulty contracting, nerves may have difficulty functioning, and bones may become brittle. The causes of hypocalcemia can range from hormonal imbalances to an improper diet. Treatments vary according to the cause, but prognoses are generally good.

Conversely, in **hypercalcemia**, a condition characterized by abnormally high levels of calcium, the nervous system is underactive, which results in lethargy, sluggish reflexes, constipation and loss of appetite, confusion, and in severe cases, coma.

Obviously, calcium homeostasis is critical. The skeletal, endocrine, and digestive systems play a role in this, but the kidneys do, too. These body systems work together to maintain a normal calcium level in the blood (Figure 6.24).

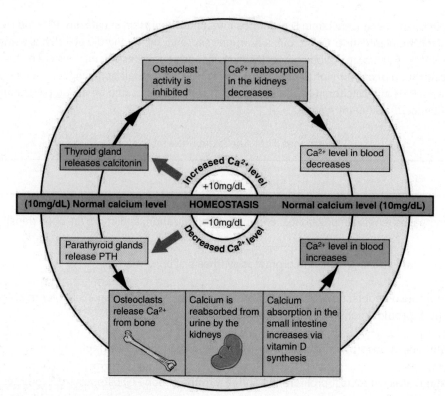

FIGURE 6.24 Pathways in Calcium Homeostasis   The body regulates calcium homeostasis with two pathways; one is signaled to turn on when blood calcium levels drop below normal and one is the pathway that is signaled to turn on when blood calcium levels are elevated.

Calcium is a chemical element that cannot be produced by any biological processes. The only way it can enter the body is through the diet. The bones act as a storage site for calcium: The body deposits calcium in the bones when blood levels get too high, and it releases calcium when blood levels drop too low. This process is regulated by PTH, vitamin D, and calcitonin.

Cells of the parathyroid gland have plasma membrane receptors for calcium. When calcium is not binding to these receptors, the cells release PTH, which stimulates osteoclast proliferation and resorption of bone by osteoclasts. This demineralization process releases calcium into the blood. PTH promotes reabsorption of calcium from the urine by the kidneys, so that the calcium returns to the blood. Finally, PTH stimulates the synthesis of vitamin D, which in turn, stimulates calcium absorption from any digested food in the small intestine.

When all these processes return blood calcium levels to normal, there is enough calcium to bind with the receptors on the surface of the cells of the parathyroid glands, and this cycle of events is turned off (Figure 6.24).

When blood levels of calcium get too high, the thyroid gland is stimulated to release calcitonin (Figure 6.24), which inhibits osteoclast activity and stimulates calcium uptake by the bones, but also decreases reabsorption of calcium by the kidneys. All of these actions lower blood levels of calcium. When blood calcium levels return to normal, the thyroid gland stops secreting calcitonin.

Key Terms

articular cartilage   thin layer of cartilage covering an epiphysis; reduces friction and acts as a shock absorber

articulation   where two bone surfaces meet

bone   hard, dense connective tissue that forms the structural elements of the skeleton

canaliculi   (singular = canaliculus) channels within the bone matrix that house one of an osteocyte's many cytoplasmic extensions that it uses to communicate and receive nutrients

cartilage   semi-rigid connective tissue found on the skeleton in areas where flexibility and smooth surfaces support movement

central canal   longitudinal channel in the center of each osteon; contains blood vessels, nerves, and lymphatic vessels; also known as the Haversian canal

closed reduction   manual manipulation of a broken bone to set it into its natural position without surgery

compact bone   dense osseous tissue that can withstand compressive forces

diaphysis   tubular shaft that runs between the proximal and distal ends of a long bone

diploë   layer of spongy bone, that is sandwiched between two the layers of compact bone found in flat bones

endochondral ossification   process in which bone forms by replacing hyaline cartilage

endosteum   delicate membranous lining of a bone's medullary cavity

epiphyseal line   completely ossified remnant of the epiphyseal plate

epiphyseal plate   (also, growth plate) sheet of hyaline cartilage in the metaphysis of an immature bone; replaced by bone tissue as the organ grows in length

epiphysis   wide section at each end of a long bone; filled with spongy bone and red marrow

external callus   collar of hyaline cartilage and bone that forms around the outside of a fracture

flat bone   thin and curved bone; serves as a point of attachment for muscles and protects internal organs

fracture   broken bone

fracture hematoma   blood clot that forms at the site of a broken bone

hematopoiesis   production of blood cells, which occurs in the red marrow of the bones

hole   opening or depression in a bone

hypercalcemia   condition characterized by abnormally high levels of calcium

hypocalcemia   condition characterized by abnormally low levels of calcium

internal callus   fibrocartilaginous matrix, in the endosteal region, between the two ends of a broken bone

intramembranous ossification   process by which bone forms directly from mesenchymal tissue

irregular bone   bone of complex shape; protects internal organs from compressive forces

lacunae   (singular = lacuna) spaces in a bone that house an osteocyte

long bone   cylinder-shaped bone that is longer than it is wide; functions as a lever

medullary cavity   hollow region of the diaphysis; filled with yellow marrow

modeling   process, during bone growth, by which bone is resorbed on one surface of a bone and deposited on another

nutrient foramen   small opening in the middle of the external surface of the diaphysis, through which an artery enters the bone to provide nourishment

open reduction   surgical exposure of a bone to reset a fracture

orthopedist   doctor who specializes in diagnosing and treating musculoskeletal disorders and injuries

osseous tissue   bone tissue; a hard, dense connective tissue that forms the structural elements of the skeleton

ossification   (also, osteogenesis) bone formation

ossification center   cluster of osteoblasts found in the early stages of intramembranous ossification

osteoblast   cell responsible for forming new bone

osteoclast   cell responsible for resorbing bone

osteocyte   primary cell in mature bone; responsible for maintaining the matrix

osteogenic cell   undifferentiated cell with high mitotic activity; the only bone cells that divide; they differentiate and develop into osteoblasts

osteoid   uncalcified bone matrix secreted by osteoblasts

osteon   (also, Haversian system) basic structural unit of compact bone; made of concentric layers of calcified matrix

osteoporosis   disease characterized by a decrease in bone mass; occurs when the rate of bone resorption exceeds the rate of bone formation, a common occurrence as the body ages

perforating canal   (also, Volkmann's canal) channel that branches off from the central canal and houses vessels and nerves that extend to the periosteum and endosteum

perichondrium   membrane that covers cartilage

periosteum   fibrous membrane covering the outer

surface of bone and continuous with ligaments

primary ossification center   region, deep in the periosteal collar, where bone development starts during endochondral ossification

projection   bone markings where part of the surface sticks out above the rest of the surface, where tendons and ligaments attach

proliferative zone   region of the epiphyseal plate that makes new chondrocytes to replace those that die at the diaphyseal end of the plate and contributes to longitudinal growth of the epiphyseal plate

red marrow   connective tissue in the interior cavity of a bone where hematopoiesis takes place

remodeling   process by which osteoclasts resorb old or damaged bone at the same time as and on the same surface where osteoblasts form new bone to replace that which is resorbed

reserve zone   region of the epiphyseal plate that anchors the plate to the osseous tissue of the epiphysis

secondary ossification center   region of bone development in the epiphyses

sesamoid bone   small, round bone embedded in a

tendon; protects the tendon from compressive forces

short bone   cube-shaped bone that is approximately equal in length, width, and thickness; provides limited motion

skeletal system   organ system composed of bones and cartilage that provides for movement, support, and protection

spongy bone   (also, cancellous bone) trabeculated osseous tissue that supports shifts in weight distribution

trabeculae   (singular = trabecula) spikes or sections of the lattice-like matrix in spongy bone

yellow marrow   connective tissue in the interior cavity of a bone where fat is stored

zone of calcified matrix   region of the epiphyseal plate closest to the diaphyseal end; functions to connect the epiphyseal plate to the diaphysis

zone of maturation and hypertrophy   region of the epiphyseal plate where chondrocytes from the proliferative zone grow and mature and contribute to the longitudinal growth of the epiphyseal plate

Chapter Review

6.1 The Functions of the Skeletal System

The major functions of the bones are body support, facilitation of movement, protection of internal organs, storage of minerals and fat, and hematopoiesis. Together, the muscular system and skeletal system are known as the musculoskeletal system.

6.2 Bone Classification

Bones can be classified according to their shapes. Long bones, such as the femur, are longer than they are wide. Short bones, such as the carpals, are approximately equal in length, width, and thickness. Flat bones are thin, but are often curved, such as the ribs. Irregular bones such as those of the face have no characteristic shape. Sesamoid bones, such as the patellae, are small and round, and are located in tendons.

6.3 Bone Structure

A hollow medullary cavity filled with yellow marrow runs the length of the diaphysis of a long bone. The walls of the diaphysis are compact bone. The epiphyses, which are wider sections at each end of a long bone, are filled with spongy bone and red marrow. The epiphyseal plate, a layer of hyaline cartilage, is replaced by osseous tissue as the organ grows in length. The medullary cavity has a delicate

membranous lining called the endosteum. The outer surface of bone, except in regions covered with articular cartilage, is covered with a fibrous membrane called the periosteum. Flat bones consist of two layers of compact bone surrounding a layer of spongy bone. Bone markings depend on the function and location of bones. Articulations are places where two bones meet. Projections stick out from the surface of the bone and provide attachment points for tendons and ligaments. Holes are openings or depressions in the bones.

Bone matrix consists of collagen fibers and organic ground substance, primarily hydroxyapatite formed from calcium salts. Osteogenic cells develop into osteoblasts. Osteoblasts are cells that make new bone. They become osteocytes, the cells of mature bone, when they get trapped in the matrix. Osteoclasts engage in bone resorption. Compact bone is dense and composed of osteons, while spongy bone is less dense and made up of trabeculae. Blood vessels and nerves enter the bone through the nutrient foramina to nourish and innervate bones.

6.4 Bone Formation and Development

All bone formation is a replacement process. Embryos develop a cartilaginous skeleton and various membranes. During development, these are replaced by bone during the ossification process. In intramembranous ossification, bone develops directly from sheets of mesenchymal connective tissue. In endochondral ossification, bone develops by replacing hyaline cartilage. Activity in the epiphyseal plate enables bones to grow in length. Modeling allows bones to grow in diameter. Remodeling occurs as bone is resorbed and replaced by new bone. Osteogenesis imperfecta is a genetic disease in which collagen production is altered, resulting in fragile, brittle bones.

6.5 Fractures: Bone Repair

Fractured bones may be repaired by closed reduction or open reduction. Fractures are classified by their complexity, location, and other features. Common types of fractures are transverse, oblique, spiral, comminuted, impacted, greenstick, open (or compound), and closed (or simple). Healing of fractures begins with the formation of a hematoma, followed by internal and external calli. Osteoclasts resorb dead bone, while osteoblasts create new bone that replaces the cartilage in the calli. The calli eventually unite, remodeling occurs, and healing is complete.

6.6 Exercise, Nutrition, Hormones, and Bone Tissue

Mechanical stress stimulates the deposition of mineral salts and collagen fibers within bones. Calcium, the predominant mineral in bone, cannot be absorbed from the small intestine if vitamin D is lacking. Vitamin K supports bone mineralization and may have a synergistic role with vitamin D. Magnesium and fluoride, as structural elements, play a supporting role in bone health. Omega-3 fatty acids reduce inflammation and may promote production of new

osseous tissue. Growth hormone increases the length of long bones, enhances mineralization, and improves bone density. Thyroxine stimulates bone growth and promotes the synthesis of bone matrix. The sex hormones (estrogen and testosterone) promote osteoblastic activity and the production of bone matrix, are responsible for the adolescent growth spurt, and promote closure of the epiphyseal plates. Osteoporosis is a disease characterized by decreased bone mass that is common in aging adults. Calcitriol stimulates the digestive tract to absorb calcium and phosphate. Parathyroid hormone (PTH) stimulates osteoclast proliferation and resorption of bone by osteoclasts. Vitamin D plays a synergistic role with PTH in stimulating the osteoclasts. Additional functions of PTH include promoting reabsorption of calcium by kidney tubules and indirectly increasing calcium absorption from the small intestine. Calcitonin inhibits osteoclast activity and stimulates calcium uptake by bones.

6.7 Calcium Homeostasis: Interactions of the Skeletal System and Other Organ Systems

Calcium homeostasis, i.e., maintaining a blood calcium level of about 10 mg/dL, is critical for normal body functions. Hypocalcemia can result in problems with blood coagulation, muscle contraction, nerve functioning, and bone strength. Hypercalcemia can result in lethargy, sluggish reflexes, constipation and loss of appetite, confusion, and coma. Calcium homeostasis is controlled by PTH, vitamin D, and calcitonin and the interactions of the skeletal, endocrine, digestive, and urinary systems.

Review Questions

1. Which function of the skeletal system would be especially important if you were in a car accident?
   a. storage of minerals
   b. protection of internal organs
   c. facilitation of movement
   d. fat storage

2. Bone tissue can be described as _____.
   a. dead calcified tissue
   b. cartilage
   c. the skeletal system
   d. dense, hard connective tissue

3. Without red marrow, bones would not be able to _____.
   a. store phosphate
   b. store calcium
   c. make blood cells
   d. move like levers

4. Yellow marrow has been identified as _____.
   a. an area of fat storage
   b. a point of attachment for muscles
   c. the hard portion of bone
   d. the cause of kyphosis

5. Which of the following can be found in areas of movement?
   a. hematopoiesis
   b. cartilage
   c. yellow marrow
   d. red marrow

6. The skeletal system is made of _____.
   a. muscles and tendons
   b. bones and cartilage
   c. vitreous humor
   d. minerals and fat

7. Most of the bones of the arms and hands are long bones; however, the bones in the wrist are categorized as _____.
   a. flat bones
   b. short bones
   c. sesamoid bones
   d. irregular bones

8. Sesamoid bones are found embedded in _____.
   a. joints
   b. muscles
   c. ligaments
   d. tendons

9. Bones that surround the spinal cord are classified as _____ bones.
   a. irregular
   b. sesamoid
   c. flat
   d. short

10. Which category of bone is among the most numerous in the skeleton?
    a. long bone
    b. sesamoid bone
    c. short bone
    d. flat bone

11. Long bones enable body movement by acting as a _____.
    a. counterweight
    b. resistive force
    c. lever
    d. fulcrum

12. Which of the following occurs in the spongy bone of the epiphysis?
    a. bone growth
    b. bone remodeling
    c. hematopoiesis
    d. shock absorption

13. The diaphysis contains _____.
    a. the metaphysis
    b. fat stores
    c. spongy bone
    d. compact bone

14. The fibrous membrane covering the outer surface of the bone is the _____.
    a. periosteum
    b. epiphysis
    c. endosteum
    d. diaphysis

15. Which of the following are incapable of undergoing mitosis?
    a. osteoblasts and osteoclasts
    b. osteocytes and osteoclasts
    c. osteoblasts and osteocytes
    d. osteogenic cells and osteoclasts

16. Which cells do not originate from osteogenic cells?
    a. osteoblasts
    b. osteoclasts
    c. osteocytes
    d. osteoprogenitor cells

17. Which of the following are found in compact bone and cancellous bone?
    a. Haversian systems
    b. Haversian canals
    c. lamellae
    d. lacunae

18. Which of the following are *only* found in cancellous bone?
    a. canaliculi
    b. Volkmann's canals
    c. trabeculae
    d. calcium salts

19. The area of a bone where the nutrient foramen passes forms what kind of bone marking?
    a. a hole
    b. a facet
    c. a canal
    d. a fissure

20. Why is cartilage slow to heal?
    a. because it eventually develops into bone
    b. because it is semi-solid and flexible
    c. because it does not have a blood supply
    d. because endochondral ossification replaces all cartilage with bone

21. Why are osteocytes spread out in bone tissue?
    a. They develop from mesenchymal cells.
    b. They are surrounded by osteoid.
    c. They travel through the capillaries.
    d. Formation of osteoid spreads out the osteoblasts that formed the ossification centers.

22. In endochondral ossification, what happens to the chondrocytes?
    a. They develop into osteocytes.
    b. They die in the calcified matrix that surrounds them and form the medullary cavity.
    c. They grow and form the periosteum.
    d. They group together to form the primary ossification center.

23. Which of the following bones is (are) formed by intramembranous ossification?
    a. the metatarsals
    b. the femur
    c. the ribs
    d. the flat bones of the cranium

24. Bones grow in length due to activity in the _____.
    a. epiphyseal plate
    b. perichondrium
    c. periosteum
    d. medullary cavity

25. Bones grow in diameter due to bone formation _____.
    a. in the medullary cavity
    b. beneath the periosteum
    c. in the epiphyseal plate
    d. within the metaphysis

26. Which of the following represents the correct sequence of zones in the epiphyseal plate?
    a. proliferation, reserved, maturation, calcification
    b. maturation, proliferation, reserved, calcification
    c. calcification, maturation, proliferation, reserved
    d. calcification, reserved, proliferation, maturation

27. A fracture can be both _____.
    a. open and closed
    b. open and transverse
    c. transverse and greenstick
    d. greenstick and comminuted

28. How can a fractured diaphysis release fat globules into the bloodstream?
    a. The bone pierces fat stores in the skin.
    b. The yellow marrow in the diaphysis is exposed and damaged.
    c. The injury triggers the body to release fat from healthy bones.
    d. The red marrow in the fractured bone releases fat to heal the fracture.

29. In a compound fracture, _____.
    a. the break occurs at an angle to the bone
    b. the broken bone does not tear the skin
    c. one fragment of broken bone is compressed into the other
    d. broken bone pierces the skin

30. The internal and external calli are replaced by _____.
    a. hyaline cartilage
    b. trabecular bone
    c. osteogenic cells
    d. osteoclasts

31. The first type of bone to form during fracture repair is _____ bone.
    a. compact
    b. lamellar
    c. spongy
    d. dense

32. Wolff's law, which describes the effect of mechanical forces in bone modeling/remodeling, would predict that _____
    a. a right-handed pitcher will have thicker bones in his right arm compared to his left.
    b. a right-handed cyclist will have thicker bones in her right leg compared to her left.
    c. a broken bone will heal thicker than it was before the fracture.
    d. a bed-ridden patient will have thicker bones than an athlete.

33. Calcium cannot be absorbed from the small intestine if _____ is lacking.
    a. vitamin D
    b. vitamin K
    c. calcitonin
    d. fluoride

34. Which one of the following foods is best for bone health?
    a. carrots
    b. liver
    c. leafy green vegetables
    d. oranges

35. Which of the following hormones are responsible for the adolescent growth spurt?
    a. estrogen and testosterone
    b. calcitonin and calcitriol
    c. growth hormone and parathyroid hormone
    d. thyroxine and progesterone

36. With respect to their direct effects on osseous tissue, which pair of hormones has actions that oppose each other?
    a. estrogen and testosterone
    b. calcitonin and calcitriol
    c. estrogen and progesterone
    d. calcitonin and parathyroid hormone

37. When calcium levels are too high or too low, which body system is primarily affected?
    a. skeletal system
    b. endocrine system
    c. digestive system
    d. nervous system

38. All of the following play a role in calcium homeostasis except
    a. thyroxine
    b. calcitonin
    c. parathyroid hormone
    d. vitamin D

39. Which of the following is most likely to be released when blood calcium levels are elevated?
    a. thyroxine
    b. calcitonin
    c. parathyroid hormone
    d. vitamin D

Critical Thinking Questions

40. The skeletal system is composed of bone and cartilage and has many functions. Choose three of these functions and discuss what features of the skeletal system allow it to accomplish these functions.

41. What are the structural and functional differences between a tarsal and a metatarsal?

42. What are the structural and functional differences between the femur and the patella?

43. If the articular cartilage at the end of one of your long bones were to degenerate, what symptoms do you think you would experience? Why?

44. In what ways is the structural makeup of compact and spongy bone well suited to their respective functions?

45. In what ways do intramembranous and endochondral ossification differ?

46. Considering how a long bone develops, what are the similarities and differences between a primary and a secondary ossification center?

47. What is the difference between closed reduction and open reduction? In what type of fracture would closed reduction most likely occur? In what type of fracture would open reduction most likely occur?

48. In terms of origin and composition, what are the differences between an internal callus and an external callus?

49. If you were a dietician who had a young female patient with a family history of osteoporosis, what foods would you suggest she include in her diet? Why?

50. During the early years of space exploration our astronauts, who had been floating in space, would return to earth showing significant bone loss dependent on how long they were in space. Discuss how this might happen and what could be done to alleviate this condition.

51. An individual with very low levels of vitamin D presents themselves to you complaining of seemingly fragile bones. Explain how these might be connected.

52. Describe the effects caused when the parathyroid gland fails to respond to calcium bound to its receptors.

CHAPTER 7
Axial Skeleton

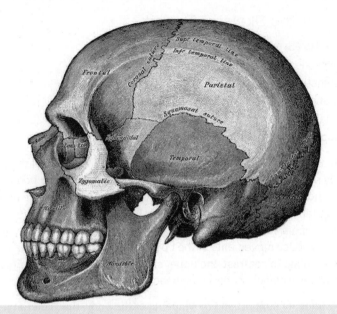

Figure 7.1   Lateral View of the Human Skull

CHAPTER OBJECTIVES

After studying this chapter, you will be able to:

- Describe the functions of the skeletal system and define its two major subdivisions
- Identify the bones and bony structures of the skull, the cranial suture lines, the cranial fossae, and the openings in the skull
- Discuss the vertebral column and regional variations in its bony components and curvatures
- Describe the components of the thoracic cage
- Discuss the embryonic development of the axial skeleton

INTRODUCTION The skeletal system forms the rigid internal framework of the body. It consists of the bones, cartilages, and ligaments. Bones support the weight of the body, allow for body movements, and protect internal organs. Cartilage provides flexible strength and support for body structures such as the thoracic cage, the external ear, and the trachea and larynx. At joints of the body, cartilage can also unite adjacent bones or provide cushioning between them. Ligaments are the strong connective tissue bands that hold the bones at a moveable joint together and serve to prevent excessive movements of the joint that would result in injury. Providing movement of the skeleton are the muscles of the body, which are firmly attached to the skeleton via connective tissue structures called tendons. As muscles contract, they pull on the bones to produce movements of the body. Thus, without a skeleton, you would not be able to stand, run, or even feed yourself!

Each bone of the body serves a particular function, and therefore bones vary in size, shape, and strength based on these functions. For example, the bones of the lower back and lower limb are thick and strong to support your body weight. Similarly, the size of a bony landmark that serves as a muscle attachment site on an individual bone is related to the strength of this muscle. Muscles can apply very strong pulling forces to the bones of the skeleton. To resist these forces, bones have enlarged bony landmarks at sites where powerful muscles attach. This means that not only the size of a bone, but also its shape, is related to its function. For this reason, the identification of bony landmarks is important during your study of the skeletal system.

Bones are also dynamic organs that can modify their strength and thickness in response to changes in muscle strength or body weight. Thus, muscle attachment sites on bones will thicken if you begin a workout program that increases muscle strength. Similarly, the walls of weight-bearing bones will thicken if you gain body weight or begin pounding the pavement as part of a new running regimen. In contrast, a reduction in muscle strength or body weight will cause bones to become thinner. This may happen during a prolonged hospital stay, following limb immobilization in a cast, or going into the weightlessness of outer space. Even a change in diet, such as eating only soft food due to the loss of teeth, will result in a noticeable decrease in the size and thickness of the jaw bones.

7.1 Divisions of the Skeletal System

LEARNING OBJECTIVES

By the end of this section, you will be able to:

- Discuss the functions of the skeletal system
- Distinguish between the axial skeleton and appendicular skeleton
- Define the axial skeleton and its components
- Define the appendicular skeleton and its components

The skeletal system includes all of the bones, cartilages, and ligaments of the body that support and give shape to the body and body structures. The **skeleton** consists of the bones of the body. For adults, there are 206 bones in the skeleton. Younger individuals have higher numbers of bones because some bones fuse together during childhood and adolescence to form an adult bone. The primary functions of the skeleton are to provide a rigid, internal structure that can support the weight of the body against the force of gravity, and to provide a structure upon which muscles can act to produce movements of the body. The lower portion of the skeleton is specialized for stability during walking or running. In contrast, the upper skeleton has greater mobility and ranges of motion, features that allow you to lift and carry objects or turn your head and trunk.

In addition to providing for support and movements of the body, the skeleton has protective and storage functions. It protects the internal organs, including the brain, spinal cord, heart, lungs, and pelvic organs. The bones of the skeleton serve as the primary storage site for important minerals such as calcium and phosphate. The bone marrow found within bones stores fat and houses the blood-cell producing tissue of the body.

The skeleton is subdivided into two major divisions—the axial and appendicular.

The Axial Skeleton

The skeleton is subdivided into two major divisions—the axial and appendicular. The **axial skeleton** forms the vertical, central axis of the body and includes all bones of the head, neck, chest, and back (Figure 7.2). It serves to protect the brain, spinal cord, heart, and lungs. It also serves as the attachment site for muscles that move the head, neck, and back, and for muscles that act across the shoulder and hip joints to move their corresponding limbs.

The axial skeleton of the adult consists of 80 bones, including the **skull**, the **vertebral column**, and the **thoracic cage**. The skull is formed by 22 bones. Also associated with the head are an additional seven bones, including the **hyoid bone** and the **ear ossicles** (three small bones found in each middle ear). The vertebral column consists of 24 bones, each called a **vertebra**, plus the **sacrum** and **coccyx**. The thoracic cage includes the 12 pairs of **ribs**, and the **sternum**, the flattened bone of the anterior chest.

Access for free at openstax.org

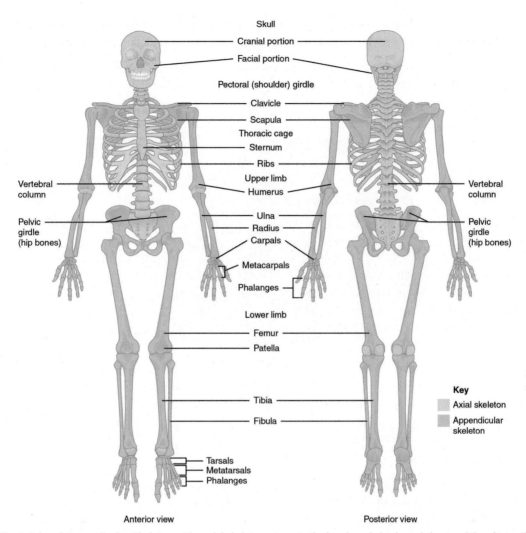

Skull

Cranial portion

Facial portion

Pectoral (shoulder) girdle

Clavicle

Scapula

Thoracic cage

Sternum

Ribs

Upper limb

Humerus

Vertebral column

Ulna

Radius

Carpals

Pelvic girdle (hip bones)

Metacarpals

Phalanges

Lower limb

Femur

Patella

Tibia

Fibula

Tarsals
Metatarsals
Phalanges

Vertebral column

Pelvic girdle (hip bones)

Key

Axial skeleton

Appendicular skeleton

Anterior view

Posterior view

FIGURE 7.2   Axial and Appendicular Skeleton   The axial skeleton supports the head, neck, back, and chest and thus forms the vertical axis of the body. It consists of the skull, vertebral column (including the sacrum and coccyx), and the thoracic cage, formed by the ribs and sternum. The appendicular skeleton is made up of all bones of the upper and lower limbs.

The Appendicular Skeleton

The **appendicular skeleton** includes all bones of the upper and lower limbs, plus the bones that attach each limb to the axial skeleton. There are 126 bones in the appendicular skeleton of an adult. The bones of the appendicular skeleton are covered in a separate chapter.

7.2 The Skull

LEARNING OBJECTIVES

By the end of this section, you will be able to:

- List and identify the bones of the brain case and face
- Locate the major suture lines of the skull and name the bones associated with each
- Locate and define the boundaries of the anterior, middle, and posterior cranial fossae, the temporal fossa, and infratemporal fossa
- Define the paranasal sinuses and identify the location of each
- Name the bones that make up the walls of the orbit and identify the openings associated with the orbit
- Identify the bones and structures that form the nasal septum and nasal conchae, and locate the hyoid bone
- Identify the bony openings of the skull

The **cranium** (skull) is the skeletal structure of the head that supports the face and protects the brain. It is subdivided into the **facial bones** and the **brain case**, or cranial vault (Figure 7.3). The facial bones underlie the facial structures, form the nasal cavity, enclose the eyeballs, and support the teeth of the upper and lower jaws. The rounded brain case surrounds and protects the brain and houses the middle and inner ear structures.

In the adult, the skull consists of 22 individual bones, 21 of which are immobile and united into a single unit. The 22nd bone is the **mandible** (lower jaw), which is the only moveable bone of the skull.

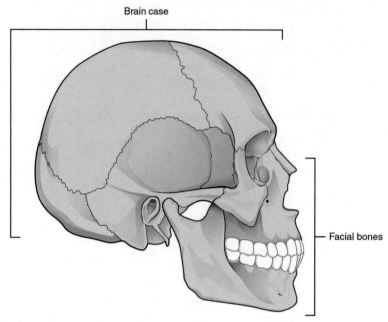

FIGURE 7.3   Parts of the Skull   The skull consists of the rounded brain case that houses the brain and the facial bones that form the upper and lower jaws, nose, orbits, and other facial structures.

⟳ INTERACTIVE LINK

Watch this video (http://openstax.org/l/skull1) to view a rotating and exploded skull, with color-coded bones. Which bone (yellow) is centrally located and joins with most of the other bones of the skull?

Anterior View of Skull

The anterior skull consists of the facial bones and provides the bony support for the eyes and structures of the face. This view of the skull is dominated by the openings of the orbits and the nasal cavity. Also seen are the upper and lower jaws, with their respective teeth (Figure 7.4).

The **orbit** is the bony socket that houses the eyeball and muscles that move the eyeball or open the upper eyelid. The upper margin of the anterior orbit is the **supraorbital margin**. Located near the midpoint of the supraorbital margin is a small opening called the **supraorbital foramen**. This provides for passage of a sensory nerve to the skin of the forehead. Below the orbit is the **infraorbital foramen**, which is the point of emergence for a sensory nerve that supplies the anterior face below the orbit.

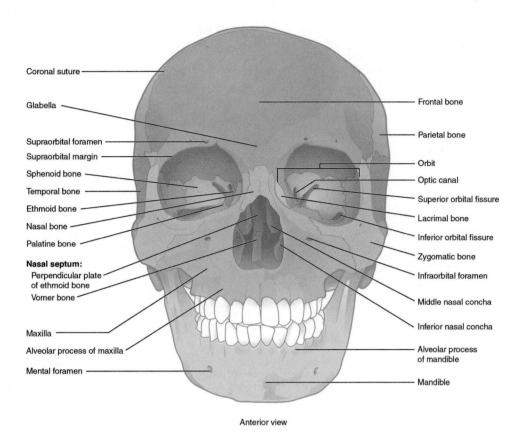

Coronal suture

Glabella

Supraorbital foramen

Supraorbital margin

Sphenoid bone

Temporal bone

Ethmoid bone

Nasal bone

Palatine bone

Nasal septum:
Perpendicular plate
of ethmoid bone

Vomer bone

Maxilla

Alveolar process of maxilla

Mental foramen

Frontal bone

Parietal bone

Orbit

Optic canal

Superior orbital fissure

Lacrimal bone

Inferior orbital fissure

Zygomatic bone

Infraorbital foramen

Middle nasal concha

Inferior nasal concha

Alveolar process
of mandible

Mandible

Anterior view

FIGURE 7.4   Anterior View of Skull   An anterior view of the skull shows the bones that form the forehead, orbits (eye sockets), nasal cavity, nasal septum, and upper and lower jaws.

Inside the nasal area of the skull, the **nasal cavity** is divided into halves by the **nasal septum**. The upper portion of the nasal septum is formed by the **perpendicular plate of the ethmoid bone** and the lower portion is the **vomer bone**. Each side of the nasal cavity is triangular in shape, with a broad inferior space that narrows superiorly. When looking into the nasal cavity from the front of the skull, two bony plates are seen projecting from each lateral wall. The larger of these is the **inferior nasal concha**, an independent bone of the skull. Located just above the inferior concha is the **middle nasal concha**, which is part of the ethmoid bone. A third bony plate, also part of the ethmoid bone, is the **superior nasal concha**. It is much smaller and out of sight, above the middle concha. The superior nasal concha is located just lateral to the perpendicular plate, in the upper nasal cavity.

Lateral View of Skull

A view of the lateral skull is dominated by the large, rounded brain case above and the upper and lower jaws with their teeth below (Figure 7.5). Separating these areas is the bridge of bone called the zygomatic arch. The **zygomatic arch** is the bony arch on the side of skull that spans from the area of the cheek to just above the ear canal. It is formed by the junction of two bony processes: a short anterior component, the **temporal process of the zygomatic bone** (the cheekbone) and a longer posterior portion, the **zygomatic process of the temporal bone**, extending forward from the temporal bone. Thus the temporal process (anteriorly) and the zygomatic process (posteriorly) join together, like the two ends of a drawbridge, to form the zygomatic arch. One of the major muscles that pulls the mandible upward during biting and chewing arises from the zygomatic arch.

On the lateral side of the brain case, above the level of the zygomatic arch, is a shallow space called the **temporal fossa**. Below the level of the zygomatic arch and deep to the vertical portion of the mandible is another space called the **infratemporal fossa**. Both the temporal fossa and infratemporal fossa contain muscles that act on the mandible during chewing.

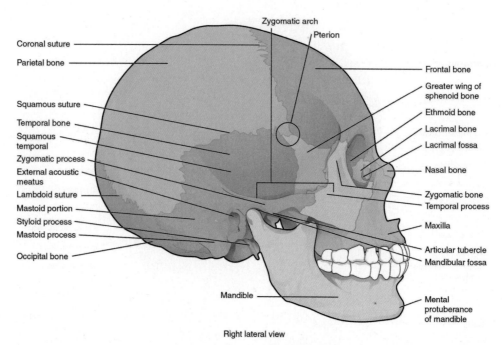

Right lateral view

FIGURE 7.5   Lateral View of Skull   The lateral skull shows the large rounded brain case, zygomatic arch, and the upper and lower jaws. The zygomatic arch is formed jointly by the zygomatic process of the temporal bone and the temporal process of the zygomatic bone. The shallow space above the zygomatic arch is the temporal fossa. The space inferior to the zygomatic arch and deep to the posterior mandible is the infratemporal fossa.

Bones of the Brain Case

The brain case contains and protects the brain. The interior space that is almost completely occupied by the brain is called the **cranial cavity**. This cavity is bounded superiorly by the rounded top of the skull, which is called the **calvaria** (skullcap), and the lateral and posterior sides of the skull. The bones that form the top and sides of the brain case are usually referred to as the "flat" bones of the skull.

The floor of the brain case is referred to as the base of the skull. This is a complex area that varies in depth and has numerous openings for the passage of cranial nerves, blood vessels, and the spinal cord. Inside the skull, the base is subdivided into three large spaces, called the **anterior cranial fossa**, **middle cranial fossa**, and **posterior cranial fossa** (fossa = "trench or ditch") (Figure 7.6). From anterior to posterior, the fossae increase in depth. The shape and depth of each fossa corresponds to the shape and size of the brain region that each houses. The boundaries and openings of the cranial fossae (singular = fossa) will be described in a later section.

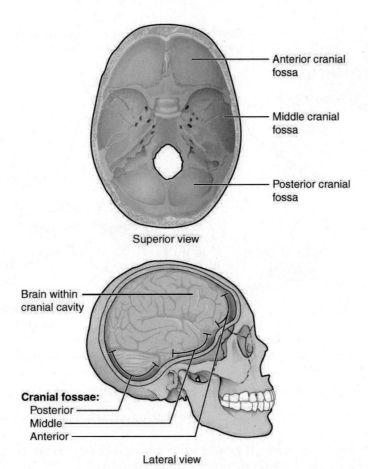

FIGURE 7.6 Cranial Fossae   The bones of the brain case surround and protect the brain, which occupies the cranial cavity. The base of the brain case, which forms the floor of cranial cavity, is subdivided into the shallow anterior cranial fossa, the middle cranial fossa, and the deep posterior cranial fossa.

The brain case consists of eight bones. These include the paired parietal and temporal bones, plus the unpaired frontal, occipital, sphenoid, and ethmoid bones.

Parietal Bone

The **parietal bone** forms most of the upper lateral side of the skull (see Figure 7.5). These are paired bones, with the right and left parietal bones joining together at the top of the skull. Each parietal bone is also bounded anteriorly by the frontal bone, inferiorly by the temporal bone, and posteriorly by the occipital bone.

Temporal Bone

The **temporal bone** forms the lower lateral side of the skull (see Figure 7.5). Common wisdom has it that the temporal bone (temporal = "time") is so named because this area of the head (the temple) is where hair typically first turns gray, indicating the passage of time.

The temporal bone is subdivided into several regions (Figure 7.7). The flattened, upper portion is the squamous portion of the temporal bone. Below this area and projecting anteriorly is the zygomatic process of the temporal bone, which forms the posterior portion of the zygomatic arch. Posteriorly is the mastoid portion of the temporal bone. Projecting inferiorly from this region is a large prominence, the **mastoid process**, which serves as a muscle attachment site. The mastoid process can easily be felt on the side of the head just behind your earlobe. On the interior of the skull, the petrous portion of each temporal bone forms the prominent, diagonally oriented **petrous ridge** in the floor of the cranial cavity. Located inside each petrous ridge are small cavities that house the structures of the middle and inner ears.

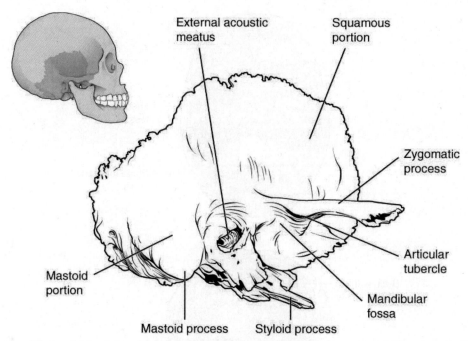

FIGURE 7.7   Temporal Bone   A lateral view of the isolated temporal bone shows the squamous, mastoid, and zygomatic portions of the temporal bone.

Important landmarks of the temporal bone, as shown in Figure 7.8, include the following:

- **External acoustic meatus** (ear canal)—This is the large opening on the lateral side of the skull that is associated with the ear.
- **Internal acoustic meatus**—This opening is located inside the cranial cavity, on the medial side of the petrous ridge. It connects to the middle and inner ear cavities of the temporal bone.
- **Mandibular fossa**—This is the deep, oval-shaped depression located on the external base of the skull, just in front of the external acoustic meatus. The mandible (lower jaw) joins with the skull at this site as part of the temporomandibular joint, which allows for movements of the mandible during opening and closing of the mouth.
- **Articular tubercle**—The smooth ridge located immediately anterior to the mandibular fossa. Both the articular tubercle and mandibular fossa contribute to the temporomandibular joint, the joint that provides for movements between the temporal bone of the skull and the mandible.
- **Styloid process**—Posterior to the mandibular fossa on the external base of the skull is an elongated, downward bony projection called the styloid process, so named because of its resemblance to a stylus (a pen or writing tool). This structure serves as an attachment site for several small muscles and for a ligament that supports the hyoid bone of the neck. (See also Figure 7.7.)
- **Stylomastoid foramen**—This small opening is located between the styloid process and mastoid process. This is the point of exit for the cranial nerve that supplies the facial muscles.
- **Carotid canal**—The carotid canal is a zig-zag shaped tunnel that provides passage through the base of the skull for one of the major arteries that supplies the brain. Its entrance is located on the outside base of the skull, anteromedial to the styloid process. The canal then runs anteromedially within the bony base of the skull, and then turns upward to its exit in the floor of the middle cranial cavity, above the foramen lacerum.

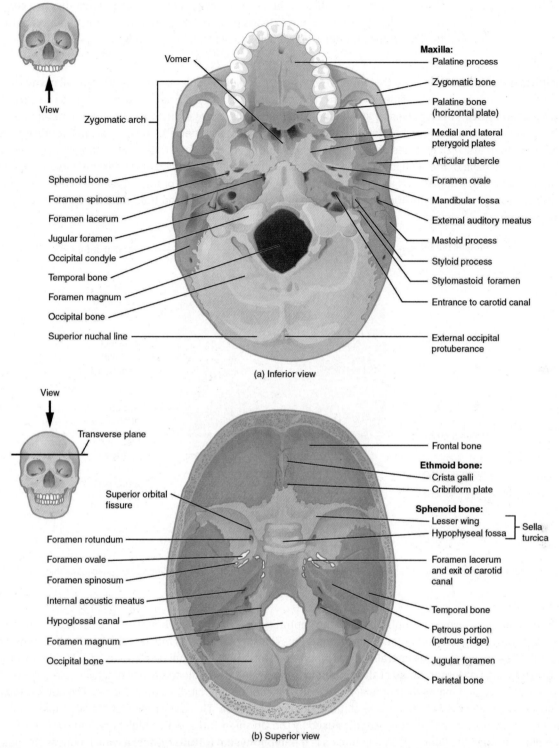

Maxilla:
— Palatine process

Vomer
— Zygomatic bone

View
— Palatine bone (horizontal plate)

Zygomatic arch
— Medial and lateral pterygoid plates

— Articular tubercle

Sphenoid bone — Foramen ovale

Foramen spinosum — Mandibular fossa

Foramen lacerum — External auditory meatus

Jugular foramen — Mastoid process

Occipital condyle — Styloid process

Temporal bone — Stylomastoid foramen

Foramen magnum — Entrance to carotid canal

Occipital bone

Superior nuchal line — External occipital protuberance

(a) Inferior view

View

Transverse plane — Frontal bone

Ethmoid bone:
— Crista galli
— Cribriform plate

Superior orbital fissure

Sphenoid bone:
— Lesser wing   ⎤ Sella
— Hypophyseal fossa   ⎦ turcica

Foramen rotundum

Foramen ovale — Foramen lacerum and exit of carotid canal

Foramen spinosum

Internal acoustic meatus — Temporal bone

Hypoglossal canal — Petrous portion (petrous ridge)

Foramen magnum — Jugular foramen

Occipital bone — Parietal bone

(b) Superior view

FIGURE 7.8   External and Internal Views of Base of Skull   (a) The hard palate is formed anteriorly by the palatine processes of the maxilla bones and posteriorly by the horizontal plate of the palatine bones. (b) The complex floor of the cranial cavity is formed by the frontal, ethmoid, sphenoid, temporal, and occipital bones. The lesser wing of the sphenoid bone separates the anterior and middle cranial fossae. The petrous ridge (petrous portion of temporal bone) separates the middle and posterior cranial fossae.

Frontal Bone

The **frontal bone** is the single bone that forms the forehead. At its anterior midline, between the eyebrows, there is a slight depression called the **glabella** (see Figure 7.5). The frontal bone also forms the supraorbital margin of the orbit. Near the middle of this margin, is the supraorbital foramen, the opening that provides passage for a sensory nerve to the forehead. The frontal bone is thickened just above each supraorbital margin, forming rounded brow ridges. These are located just behind your eyebrows and vary in size among individuals, although they are generally larger in males. Inside the cranial cavity, the frontal bone extends posteriorly. This flattened region forms both the roof of the orbit below and the floor of the anterior cranial cavity above (see Figure 7.8**b**).

Occipital Bone

The **occipital bone** is the single bone that forms the posterior skull and posterior base of the cranial cavity (Figure 7.9; see also Figure 7.8). On its outside surface, at the posterior midline, is a small protrusion called the **external occipital protuberance**, which serves as an attachment site for a ligament of the posterior neck. Lateral to either side of this bump is a **superior nuchal line** (nuchal = "nape" or "posterior neck"). The nuchal lines represent the most superior point at which muscles of the neck attach to the skull, with only the scalp covering the skull above these lines. On the base of the skull, the occipital bone contains the large opening of the **foramen magnum**, which allows for passage of the spinal cord as it exits the skull. On either side of the foramen magnum is an oval-shaped **occipital condyle**. These condyles form joints with the first cervical vertebra and thus support the skull on top of the vertebral column.

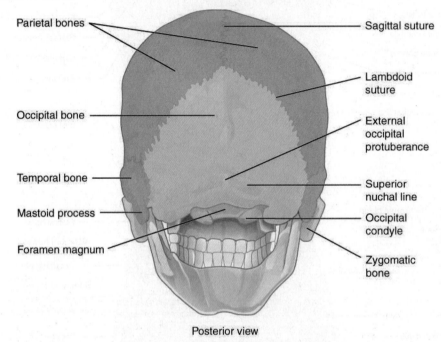

Posterior view

FIGURE 7.9   Posterior View of Skull   This view of the posterior skull shows attachment sites for muscles and joints that support the skull.

Sphenoid Bone

The **sphenoid bone** is a single, complex bone of the central skull (Figure 7.10). It serves as a "keystone" bone, because it joins with almost every other bone of the skull. The sphenoid forms much of the base of the central skull (see Figure 7.8) and also extends laterally to contribute to the sides of the skull (see Figure 7.5). Inside the cranial cavity, the right and left **lesser wings of the sphenoid bone**, which resemble the wings of a flying bird, form the lip of a prominent ridge that marks the boundary between the anterior and middle cranial fossae. The **sella turcica** ("Turkish saddle") is located at the midline of the middle cranial fossa. This bony region of the sphenoid bone is named for its resemblance to the horse saddles used by the Ottoman Turks, with a high back and a tall front. The rounded depression in the floor of the sella turcica is the **hypophyseal (pituitary) fossa**, which houses the pea-sized pituitary (hypophyseal) gland. The **greater wings of the sphenoid bone** extend laterally to either side away from the sella turcica, where they form the anterior floor of the middle cranial fossa. The greater wing is best seen on the outside of the lateral skull, where it forms a rectangular area immediately anterior to the squamous portion of the temporal bone.

On the inferior aspect of the skull, each half of the sphenoid bone forms two thin, vertically oriented bony plates. These are the **medial pterygoid plate** and **lateral pterygoid plate** (pterygoid = "wing-shaped"). The right and left medial pterygoid plates form the posterior, lateral walls of the nasal cavity. The somewhat larger lateral pterygoid plates serve as attachment sites for chewing muscles that fill the infratemporal space and act on the mandible.

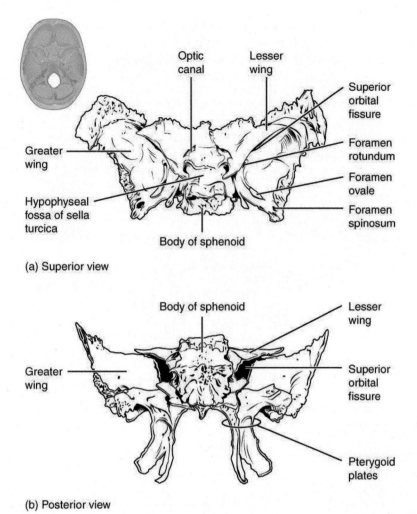

(a) Superior view

(b) Posterior view

FIGURE 7.10   Sphenoid Bone   Shown in isolation in (a) superior and (b) posterior views, the sphenoid bone is a single midline bone that forms the anterior walls and floor of the middle cranial fossa. It has a pair of lesser wings and a pair of greater wings. The sella turcica surrounds the hypophyseal fossa. Projecting downward are the medial and lateral pterygoid plates. The sphenoid has multiple openings for the passage of nerves and blood vessels, including the optic canal, superior orbital fissure, foramen rotundum, foramen ovale, and foramen spinosum.

Ethmoid Bone

The **ethmoid bone** is a single, midline bone that forms the roof and lateral walls of the upper nasal cavity, the upper portion of the nasal septum, and contributes to the medial wall of the orbit (Figure 7.11 and Figure 7.12). On the interior of the skull, the ethmoid also forms a portion of the floor of the anterior cranial cavity (see Figure 7.8**b**).

Within the nasal cavity, the perpendicular plate of the ethmoid bone forms the upper portion of the nasal septum. The ethmoid bone also forms the lateral walls of the upper nasal cavity. Extending from each lateral wall are the superior nasal concha and middle nasal concha, which are thin, curved projections that extend into the nasal cavity (Figure 7.13).

In the cranial cavity, the ethmoid bone forms a small area at the midline in the floor of the anterior cranial fossa. This region also forms the narrow roof of the underlying nasal cavity. This portion of the ethmoid bone consists of two parts, the crista galli and cribriform plates. The **crista galli** ("rooster's comb or crest") is a small upward bony projection located at the midline. It functions as an anterior attachment point for one of the covering layers of the brain. To either side of the crista galli is the **cribriform plate** (cribrum = "sieve"), a small, flattened area with numerous small openings termed olfactory foramina. Small nerve branches from the olfactory areas of the nasal cavity pass through these openings to enter the brain.

The lateral portions of the ethmoid bone are located between the orbit and upper nasal cavity, and thus form the lateral nasal cavity wall and a portion of the medial orbit wall. Located inside this portion of the ethmoid bone are several small, air-filled spaces that are part of the paranasal sinus system of the skull.

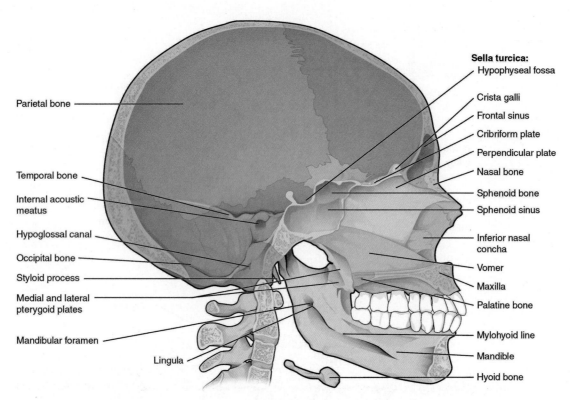

FIGURE 7.11 Sagittal Section of Skull   This midline view of the sagittally sectioned skull shows the nasal septum.

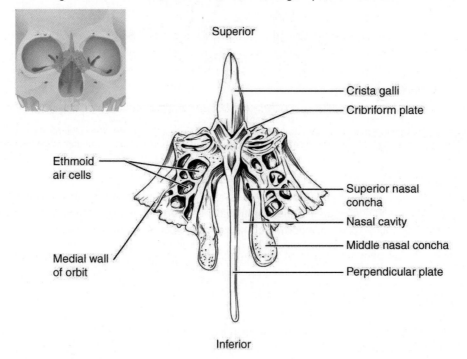

FIGURE 7.12 Ethmoid Bone   The unpaired ethmoid bone is located at the midline within the central skull. It has an upward projection, the crista galli, and a downward projection, the perpendicular plate, which forms the upper nasal septum. The cribriform plates form both the roof of the nasal cavity and a portion of the anterior cranial fossa floor. The lateral sides of the ethmoid bone form the lateral walls of the upper nasal cavity, part of the medial orbit wall, and give rise to the superior and middle nasal conchae. The ethmoid bone also contains the ethmoid air cells.

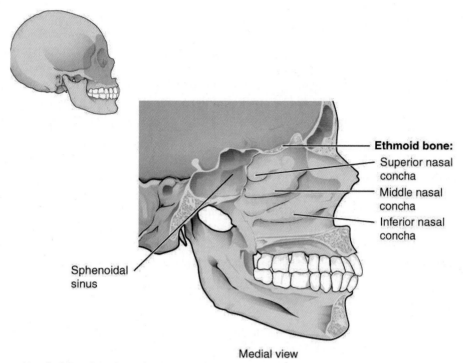

FIGURE 7.13 Lateral Wall of Nasal Cavity   The three nasal conchae are curved bones that project from the lateral walls of the nasal cavity. The superior nasal concha and middle nasal concha are parts of the ethmoid bone. The inferior nasal concha is an independent bone of the skull.

Sutures of the Skull

A **suture** is an immobile joint between adjacent bones of the skull. The narrow gap between the bones is filled with dense, fibrous connective tissue that unites the bones. The long sutures located between the bones of the brain case are not straight, but instead follow irregular, tightly twisting paths. These twisting lines serve to tightly interlock the adjacent bones, thus adding strength to the skull for brain protection.

The two suture lines seen on the top of the skull are the coronal and sagittal sutures. The **coronal suture** runs from side to side across the skull, within the coronal plane of section (see Figure 7.5). It joins the frontal bone to the right and left parietal bones. The **sagittal suture** extends posteriorly from the coronal suture, running along the midline at the top of the skull in the sagittal plane of section (see Figure 7.9). It unites the right and left parietal bones. On the posterior skull, the sagittal suture terminates by joining the lambdoid suture. The **lambdoid suture** extends downward and laterally to either side away from its junction with the sagittal suture. The lambdoid suture joins the occipital bone to the right and left parietal and temporal bones. This suture is named for its upside-down "V" shape, which resembles the capital letter version of the Greek letter lambda (Λ). The **squamous suture** is located on the lateral skull. It unites the squamous portion of the temporal bone with the parietal bone (see Figure 7.5). At the intersection of four bones is the **pterion**, a small, capital-H-shaped suture line region that unites the frontal bone, parietal bone, squamous portion of the temporal bone, and greater wing of the sphenoid bone. It is the weakest part of the skull. The pterion is located approximately two finger widths above the zygomatic arch and a thumb's width posterior to the upward portion of the zygomatic bone.

Disorders of the...

Skeletal System
Head and traumatic brain injuries are major causes of immediate death and disability, with bleeding and infections as possible additional complications. According to the Centers for Disease Control and Prevention (2010), approximately 30 percent of all injury-related deaths in the United States are caused by head injuries. The majority of head injuries involve falls. They are most common among young children (ages 0–4 years), adolescents (15–19 years), and the elderly (over 65 years). Additional causes vary, but prominent among these are automobile and motorcycle accidents.

Strong blows to the brain-case portion of the skull can produce fractures. These may result in bleeding inside the skull with subsequent injury to the brain. The most common is a linear skull fracture, in which fracture lines radiate from the point of impact. Other fracture types include a comminuted fracture, in which the bone is broken into several pieces at the point of impact, or a depressed fracture, in which the fractured bone is pushed inward. In a contrecoup (counterblow) fracture, the bone at the point of impact is not broken, but instead a fracture occurs on the opposite side of the skull. Fractures of the occipital bone at the base of the skull can occur in this manner, producing a basilar fracture that can damage the artery that passes through the carotid canal.

A blow to the lateral side of the head may fracture the bones of the pterion. The pterion is an important clinical landmark because located immediately deep to it on the inside of the skull is a major branch of an artery that supplies the skull and covering layers of the brain. A strong blow to this region can fracture the bones around the pterion. If the underlying artery is damaged, bleeding can cause the formation of a hematoma (collection of blood) between the brain and interior of the skull. As blood accumulates, it will put pressure on the brain. Symptoms associated with a hematoma may not be apparent immediately following the injury, but if untreated, blood accumulation will exert increasing pressure on the brain and can result in death within a few hours.

⊚ INTERACTIVE LINK

View this animation (http://openstax.org/l/headblow) to see how a blow to the head may produce a contrecoup (counterblow) fracture of the basilar portion of the occipital bone on the base of the skull. Why may a basilar fracture be life threatening?

Facial Bones of the Skull

The facial bones of the skull form the upper and lower jaws, the nose, nasal cavity and nasal septum, and the orbit. The facial bones include 14 bones, with six paired bones and two unpaired bones. The paired bones are the maxilla, palatine, zygomatic, nasal, lacrimal, and inferior nasal conchae bones. The unpaired bones are the vomer and mandible bones. Although classified with the brain-case bones, the ethmoid bone also contributes to the nasal septum and the walls of the nasal cavity and orbit.

Maxillary Bone

The **maxillary bone**, often referred to simply as the maxilla (plural = maxillae), is one of a pair that together form the upper jaw, much of the hard palate, the medial floor of the orbit, and the lateral base of the nose (see Figure 7.4). The curved, inferior margin of the maxillary bone that forms the upper jaw and contains the upper teeth is the **alveolar process of the maxilla** (Figure 7.14). Each tooth is anchored into a deep socket called an alveolus. On the anterior maxilla, just below the orbit, is the infraorbital foramen. This is the point of exit for a sensory nerve that supplies the nose, upper lip, and anterior cheek. On the inferior skull, the **palatine process** from each maxillary bone can be seen joining together at the midline to form the anterior three-quarters of the hard palate (see Figure 7.8a). The **hard palate** is the bony plate that forms the roof of the mouth and floor of the nasal cavity, separating the oral and nasal cavities.

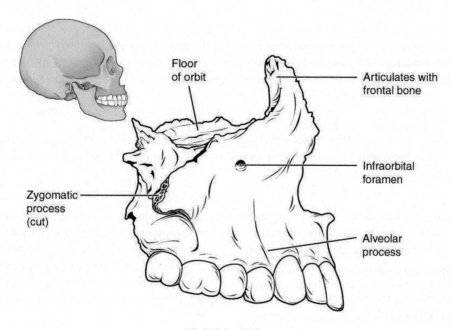

Right lateral view

FIGURE 7.14 Maxillary Bone The maxillary bone forms the upper jaw and supports the upper teeth. Each maxilla also forms the lateral floor of each orbit and the majority of the hard palate.

Palatine Bone

The **palatine bone** is one of a pair of irregularly shaped bones that contribute small areas to the lateral walls of the nasal cavity and the medial wall of each orbit. The largest region of each of the palatine bone is the **horizontal plate**. The plates from the right and left palatine bones join together at the midline to form the posterior quarter of the hard palate (see Figure 7.8**a**). Thus, the palatine bones are best seen in an inferior view of the skull and hard palate.

 HOMEOSTATIC IMBALANCES

Cleft Lip and Cleft Palate

During embryonic development, the right and left maxilla bones come together at the midline to form the upper jaw. At the same time, the muscle and skin overlying these bones join together to form the upper lip. Inside the mouth, the palatine processes of the maxilla bones, along with the horizontal plates of the right and left palatine bones, join together to form the hard palate. If an error occurs in these developmental processes, a birth defect of cleft lip or cleft palate may result.

Cleft lip is a common development defect that affects approximately 1:1000 births, most of which are male. This defect involves a partial or complete failure of the right and left portions of the upper lip to fuse together, leaving a cleft (gap).

A more severe developmental defect is cleft palate, which affects the hard palate. The hard palate is the bony structure that separates the nasal cavity from the oral cavity. It is formed during embryonic development by the midline fusion of the horizontal plates from the right and left palatine bones and the palatine processes of the maxilla bones. Cleft palate affects approximately 1:2500 births and is more common in females. It results from a failure of the two halves of the hard palate to completely come together and fuse at the midline, thus leaving a gap between them. This gap allows for communication between the nasal and oral cavities. In severe cases, the bony gap continues into the anterior upper jaw where the alveolar processes of the maxilla bones also do not properly join together above the front teeth. If this occurs, a cleft lip will also be seen. Because of the communication between the oral and nasal cavities, a cleft palate makes it very difficult for an infant to generate the suckling needed for nursing, thus leaving the infant at risk for malnutrition. Surgical repair is required to correct cleft palate defects.

Zygomatic Bone

The **zygomatic bone** is also known as the cheekbone. Each of the paired zygomatic bones forms much of the lateral wall of the orbit and the lateral-inferior margins of the anterior orbital opening (see Figure 7.4). The short temporal process of the zygomatic bone projects posteriorly, where it forms the anterior portion of the zygomatic arch (see Figure 7.5).

Nasal Bone

The **nasal bone** is one of two small bones that articulate (join) with each other to form the bony base (bridge) of the nose. They also support the cartilages that form the lateral walls of the nose (see Figure 7.11). These are the bones that are damaged when the nose is broken.

Lacrimal Bone

Each **lacrimal bone** is a small, rectangular bone that forms the anterior, medial wall of the orbit (see Figure 7.4 and Figure 7.5). The anterior portion of the lacrimal bone forms a shallow depression called the **lacrimal fossa**, and extending inferiorly from this is the **nasolacrimal canal**. The lacrimal fluid (tears of the eye), which serves to maintain the moist surface of the eye, drains at the medial corner of the eye into the nasolacrimal canal. This duct then extends downward to open into the nasal cavity, behind the inferior nasal concha. In the nasal cavity, the lacrimal fluid normally drains posteriorly, but with an increased flow of tears due to crying or eye irritation, some fluid will also drain anteriorly, thus causing a runny nose.

Inferior Nasal Conchae

The right and left inferior nasal conchae form a curved bony plate that projects into the nasal cavity space from the lower lateral wall (see Figure 7.13). The inferior concha is the largest of the nasal conchae and can easily be seen when looking into the anterior opening of the nasal cavity.

Vomer Bone

The unpaired vomer bone, often referred to simply as the vomer, is triangular-shaped and forms the posterior-inferior part of the nasal septum (see Figure 7.11). The vomer is best seen when looking from behind into the posterior openings of the nasal cavity (see Figure 7.8**a**). In this view, the vomer is seen to form the entire height of the nasal septum. A much smaller portion of the vomer can also be seen when looking into the anterior opening of the nasal cavity.

Mandible

The **mandible** forms the lower jaw and is the only moveable bone of the skull. At the time of birth, the mandible consists of paired right and left bones, but these fuse together during the first year to form the single U-shaped mandible of the adult skull. Each side of the mandible consists of a horizontal body and posteriorly, a vertically oriented **ramus of the mandible** (ramus = "branch"). The outside margin of the mandible, where the body and ramus come together is called the **angle of the mandible** (Figure 7.15).

The ramus on each side of the mandible has two upward-going bony projections. The more anterior projection is the flattened **coronoid process of the mandible**, which provides attachment for one of the biting muscles. The posterior projection is the **condylar process of the mandible**, which is topped by the oval-shaped **condyle**. The condyle of the mandible articulates (joins) with the mandibular fossa and articular tubercle of the temporal bone. Together these articulations form the temporomandibular joint, which allows for opening and closing of the mouth (see Figure 7.5). The broad U-shaped curve located between the coronoid and condylar processes is the **mandibular notch**.

Important landmarks for the mandible include the following:

- **Alveolar process of the mandible**—This is the upper border of the mandibular body and serves to anchor the lower teeth.
- **Mental protuberance**—The forward projection from the inferior margin of the anterior mandible that forms the chin (mental = "chin").
- **Mental foramen**—The opening located on each side of the anterior-lateral mandible, which is the exit site for a sensory nerve that supplies the chin.
- **Mylohyoid line**—This bony ridge extends along the inner aspect of the mandibular body (see Figure 7.11). The muscle that forms the floor of the oral cavity attaches to the mylohyoid lines on both sides of the mandible.
- **Mandibular foramen**—This opening is located on the medial side of the ramus of the mandible. The opening

leads into a tunnel that runs down the length of the mandibular body. The sensory nerve and blood vessels that supply the lower teeth enter the mandibular foramen and then follow this tunnel. Thus, to numb the lower teeth prior to dental work, the dentist must inject anesthesia into the lateral wall of the oral cavity at a point prior to where this sensory nerve enters the mandibular foramen.

*   **Lingula**—This small flap of bone is named for its shape (lingula = "little tongue"). It is located immediately next to the mandibular foramen, on the medial side of the ramus. A ligament that anchors the mandible during opening and closing of the mouth extends down from the base of the skull and attaches to the lingula.

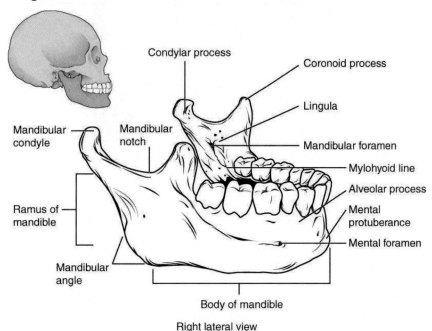

Right lateral view

FIGURE 7.15   **Isolated Mandible**   The mandible is the only moveable bone of the skull.

The Orbit

The orbit is the bony socket that houses the eyeball and contains the muscles that move the eyeball or open the upper eyelid. Each orbit is cone-shaped, with a narrow posterior region that widens toward the large anterior opening. To help protect the eye, the bony margins of the anterior opening are thickened and somewhat constricted. The medial walls of the two orbits are parallel to each other but each lateral wall diverges away from the midline at a 45° angle. This divergence provides greater lateral peripheral vision.

The walls of each orbit include contributions from seven skull bones (Figure 7.16). The frontal bone forms the roof and the zygomatic bone forms the lateral wall and lateral floor. The medial floor is primarily formed by the maxilla, with a small contribution from the palatine bone. The ethmoid bone and lacrimal bone make up much of the medial wall and the sphenoid bone forms the posterior orbit.

At the posterior apex of the orbit is the opening of the **optic canal**, which allows for passage of the optic nerve from the retina to the brain. Lateral to this is the elongated and irregularly shaped superior orbital fissure, which provides passage for the artery that supplies the eyeball, sensory nerves, and the nerves that supply the muscles involved in eye movements.

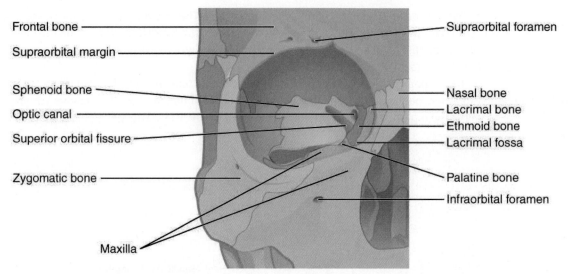

FIGURE 7.16 **Bones of the Orbit**   Seven skull bones contribute to the walls of the orbit. Opening into the posterior orbit from the cranial cavity are the optic canal and superior orbital fissure.

The Nasal Septum and Nasal Conchae

The **nasal septum** consists of both bone and cartilage components (Figure 7.17; see also Figure 7.11). The upper portion of the septum is formed by the perpendicular plate of the ethmoid bone. The lower and posterior parts of the septum are formed by the triangular-shaped vomer bone. In an anterior view of the skull, the perpendicular plate of the ethmoid bone is easily seen inside the nasal opening as the upper nasal septum, but only a small portion of the vomer is seen as the inferior septum. A better view of the vomer bone is seen when looking into the posterior nasal cavity with an inferior view of the skull, where the vomer forms the full height of the nasal septum. The anterior nasal septum is formed by the **septal cartilage**, a flexible plate that fills in the gap between the perpendicular plate of the ethmoid and vomer bones. This cartilage also extends outward into the nose where it separates the right and left nostrils. The septal cartilage is not found in the dry skull.

Attached to the lateral wall on each side of the nasal cavity are the superior, middle, and inferior **nasal conchae** (singular = concha), which are named for their positions (see Figure 7.13). These are bony plates that curve downward as they project into the space of the nasal cavity. They serve to swirl the incoming air, which helps to warm and moisturize it before the air moves into the delicate air sacs of the lungs. This also allows mucus, secreted by the tissue lining the nasal cavity, to trap incoming dust, pollen, bacteria, and viruses. The largest of the conchae is the inferior nasal concha, which is an independent bone of the skull. The middle concha and the superior conchae, which is the smallest, are both formed by the ethmoid bone. When looking into the anterior nasal opening of the skull, only the inferior and middle conchae can be seen. The small superior nasal concha is well hidden above and behind the middle concha.

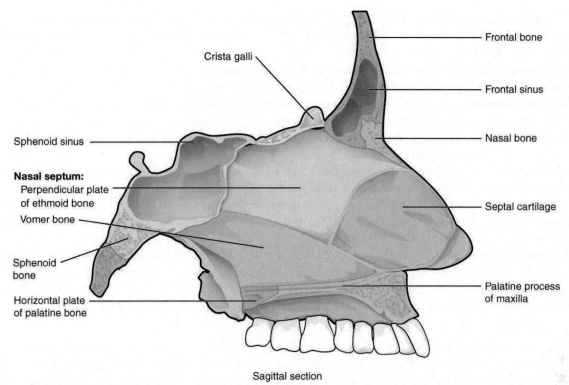

Crista galli

Frontal bone

Frontal sinus

Sphenoid sinus

Nasal bone

Nasal septum:
  Perpendicular plate
  of ethmoid bone
  Vomer bone

Septal cartilage

Sphenoid
bone

Horizontal plate
of palatine bone

Palatine process
of maxilla

Sagittal section

FIGURE 7.17 Nasal Septum The nasal septum is formed by the perpendicular plate of the ethmoid bone and the vomer bone. The septal cartilage fills the gap between these bones and extends into the nose.

Cranial Fossae

Inside the skull, the floor of the cranial cavity is subdivided into three cranial fossae (spaces), which increase in depth from anterior to posterior (see Figure 7.6, Figure 7.8**b**, and Figure 7.11). Since the brain occupies these areas, the shape of each conforms to the shape of the brain regions that it contains. Each cranial fossa has anterior and posterior boundaries and is divided at the midline into right and left areas by a significant bony structure or opening.

Anterior Cranial Fossa

The anterior cranial fossa is the most anterior and the shallowest of the three cranial fossae. It overlies the orbits and contains the frontal lobes of the brain. Anteriorly, the anterior fossa is bounded by the frontal bone, which also forms the majority of the floor for this space. The lesser wings of the sphenoid bone form the prominent ledge that marks the boundary between the anterior and middle cranial fossae. Located in the floor of the anterior cranial fossa at the midline is a portion of the ethmoid bone, consisting of the upward projecting crista galli and to either side of this, the cribriform plates.

Middle Cranial Fossa

The middle cranial fossa is deeper and situated posterior to the anterior fossa. It extends from the lesser wings of the sphenoid bone anteriorly, to the petrous ridges (petrous portion of the temporal bones) posteriorly. The large, diagonally positioned petrous ridges give the middle cranial fossa a butterfly shape, making it narrow at the midline and broad laterally. The temporal lobes of the brain occupy this fossa. The middle cranial fossa is divided at the midline by the upward bony prominence of the sella turcica, a part of the sphenoid bone. The middle cranial fossa has several openings for the passage of blood vessels and cranial nerves (see Figure 7.8).

Openings in the middle cranial fossa are as follows:

- **Optic canal**—This opening is located at the anterior lateral corner of the sella turcica. It provides for passage of the optic nerve into the orbit.
- **Superior orbital fissure**—This large, irregular opening into the posterior orbit is located on the anterior wall of the middle cranial fossa, lateral to the optic canal and under the projecting margin of the lesser wing of the sphenoid bone. Nerves to the eyeball and associated muscles, and sensory nerves to the forehead pass through this opening.

- **Foramen rotundum**—This rounded opening (rotundum = "round") is located in the floor of the middle cranial fossa, just inferior to the superior orbital fissure. It is the exit point for a major sensory nerve that supplies the cheek, nose, and upper teeth.
- **Foramen ovale of the middle cranial fossa**—This large, oval-shaped opening in the floor of the middle cranial fossa provides passage for a major sensory nerve to the lateral head, cheek, chin, and lower teeth.
- **Foramen spinosum**—This small opening, located posterior-lateral to the foramen ovale, is the entry point for an important artery that supplies the covering layers surrounding the brain. The branching pattern of this artery forms readily visible grooves on the internal surface of the skull and these grooves can be traced back to their origin at the foramen spinosum.
- **Carotid canal**—This is the zig-zag passageway through which a major artery to the brain enters the skull. The entrance to the carotid canal is located on the inferior aspect of the skull, anteromedial to the styloid process (see Figure 7.8**a**). From here, the canal runs anteromedially within the bony base of the skull. Just above the foramen lacerum, the carotid canal opens into the middle cranial cavity, near the posterior-lateral base of the sella turcica.
- **Foramen lacerum**—This irregular opening is located in the base of the skull, immediately inferior to the exit of the carotid canal. This opening is an artifact of the dry skull, because in life it is completely filled with cartilage. All the openings of the skull that provide for passage of nerves or blood vessels have smooth margins; the word lacerum ("ragged" or "torn") tells us that this opening has ragged edges and thus nothing passes through it.

Posterior Cranial Fossa

The posterior cranial fossa is the most posterior and deepest portion of the cranial cavity. It contains the cerebellum of the brain. The posterior fossa is bounded anteriorly by the petrous ridges, while the occipital bone forms the floor and posterior wall. It is divided at the midline by the large foramen magnum ("great aperture"), the opening that provides for passage of the spinal cord.

Located on the medial wall of the petrous ridge in the posterior cranial fossa is the internal acoustic meatus (see Figure 7.11). This opening provides for passage of the nerve from the hearing and equilibrium organs of the inner ear, and the nerve that supplies the muscles of the face. Located at the anterior-lateral margin of the foramen magnum is the **hypoglossal canal**. These emerge on the inferior aspect of the skull at the base of the occipital condyle and provide passage for an important nerve to the tongue.

Immediately inferior to the internal acoustic meatus is the large, irregularly shaped **jugular foramen** (see Figure 7.8**a**). Several cranial nerves from the brain exit the skull via this opening. It is also the exit point through the base of the skull for all the venous return blood leaving the brain. The venous structures that carry blood inside the skull form large, curved grooves on the inner walls of the posterior cranial fossa, which terminate at each jugular foramen.

Paranasal Sinuses

The **paranasal sinuses** are hollow, air-filled spaces located within certain bones of the skull (Figure 7.18). All of the sinuses communicate with the nasal cavity (paranasal = "next to nasal cavity") and are lined with nasal mucosa. They serve to reduce bone mass and thus lighten the skull, and they also add resonance to the voice. This second feature is most obvious when you have a cold or sinus congestion. These produce swelling of the mucosa and excess mucus production, which can obstruct the narrow passageways between the sinuses and the nasal cavity, causing your voice to sound different to yourself and others. This blockage can also allow the sinuses to fill with fluid, with the resulting pressure producing pain and discomfort.

The paranasal sinuses are named for the skull bone that each occupies. The **frontal sinus** is located just above the eyebrows, within the frontal bone (see Figure 7.17). This irregular space may be divided at the midline into bilateral spaces, or these may be fused into a single sinus space. The frontal sinus is the most anterior of the paranasal sinuses. The largest sinus is the **maxillary sinus**. These are paired and located within the right and left maxillary bones, where they occupy the area just below the orbits. The maxillary sinuses are most commonly involved during sinus infections. Because their connection to the nasal cavity is located high on their medial wall, they are difficult to drain. The **sphenoid sinus** is a single, midline sinus. It is located within the body of the sphenoid bone, just anterior and inferior to the sella turcica, thus making it the most posterior of the paranasal sinuses. The lateral aspects of the ethmoid bone contain multiple small spaces separated by very thin bony walls. Each of these spaces is called an **ethmoid air cell**. These are located on both sides of the ethmoid bone, between the upper nasal cavity and medial orbit, just behind the superior nasal conchae.

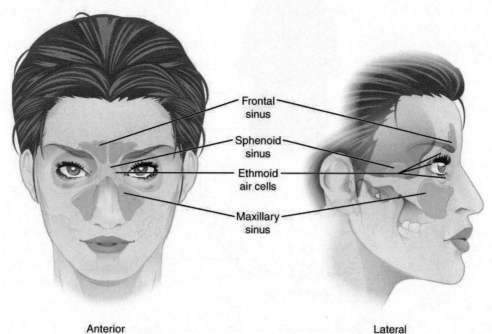

Anterior   Lateral

FIGURE 7.18 Paranasal Sinuses   The paranasal sinuses are hollow, air-filled spaces named for the skull bone that each occupies. The most anterior is the frontal sinus, located in the frontal bone above the eyebrows. The largest are the maxillary sinuses, located in the right and left maxillary bones below the orbits. The most posterior is the sphenoid sinus, located in the body of the sphenoid bone, under the sella turcica. The ethmoid air cells are multiple small spaces located in the right and left sides of the ethmoid bone, between the medial wall of the orbit and lateral wall of the upper nasal cavity.

Hyoid Bone

The hyoid bone is an independent bone that does not contact any other bone and thus is not part of the skull (Figure 7.19). It is a small U-shaped bone located in the upper neck near the level of the inferior mandible, with the tips of the "U" pointing posteriorly. The hyoid serves as the base for the tongue above, and is attached to the larynx below and the pharynx posteriorly. The hyoid is held in position by a series of small muscles that attach to it either from above or below. These muscles act to move the hyoid up/down or forward/back. Movements of the hyoid are coordinated with movements of the tongue, larynx, and pharynx during swallowing and speaking.

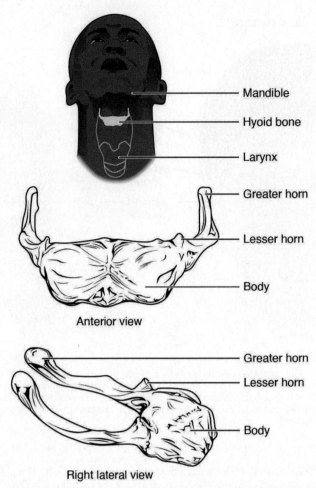

Anterior view

Right lateral view

FIGURE 7.19   Hyoid Bone   The hyoid bone is located in the upper neck and does not join with any other bone. It provides attachments for muscles that act on the tongue, larynx, and pharynx.

7.3 The Vertebral Column

LEARNING OBJECTIVES

By the end of this section, you will be able to:

- Describe each region of the vertebral column and the number of bones in each region
- Discuss the curves of the vertebral column and how these change after birth
- Describe a typical vertebra and determine the distinguishing characteristics for vertebrae in each vertebral region and features of the sacrum and the coccyx
- Define the structure of an intervertebral disc
- Determine the location of the ligaments that provide support for the vertebral column

The vertebral column is also known as the spinal column or spine (Figure 7.20). It consists of a sequence of vertebrae (singular = vertebra), each of which is separated and united by an **intervertebral disc**. Together, the vertebrae and intervertebral discs form the vertebral column. It is a flexible column that supports the head, neck, and body and allows for their movements. It also protects the spinal cord, which passes down the back through openings in the vertebrae.

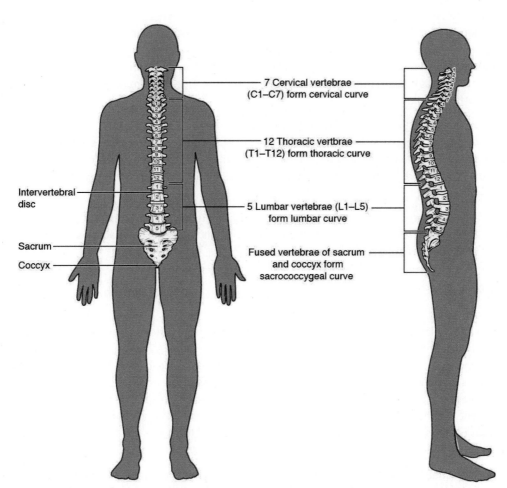

FIGURE 7.20   Vertebral Column   The adult vertebral column consists of 24 vertebrae, plus the sacrum and coccyx. The vertebrae are divided into three regions: cervical C1–C7 vertebrae, thoracic T1–T12 vertebrae, and lumbar L1–L5 vertebrae. The vertebral column is curved, with two primary curvatures (thoracic and sacrococcygeal curves) and two secondary curvatures (cervical and lumbar curves).

Regions of the Vertebral Column

The vertebral column originally develops as a series of 33 vertebrae, but this number is eventually reduced to 24 vertebrae, plus the sacrum and coccyx. The vertebral column is subdivided into five regions, with the vertebrae in each area named for that region and numbered in descending order. In the neck, there are seven cervical vertebrae, each designated with the letter "C" followed by its number. Superiorly, the C1 vertebra articulates (forms a joint) with the occipital condyles of the skull. Inferiorly, C1 articulates with the C2 vertebra, and so on. Below these are the 12 thoracic vertebrae, designated T1–T12. The lower back contains the L1–L5 lumbar vertebrae. The single sacrum, which is also part of the pelvis, is formed by the fusion of five sacral vertebrae. Similarly, the coccyx, or tailbone, results from the fusion of four small coccygeal vertebrae. However, the sacral and coccygeal fusions do not start until age 20 and are not completed until middle age.

An interesting anatomical fact is that almost all mammals have seven cervical vertebrae, regardless of body size. This means that there are large variations in the size of cervical vertebrae, ranging from the very small cervical vertebrae of a shrew to the greatly elongated vertebrae in the neck of a giraffe. In a full-grown giraffe, each cervical vertebra is 11 inches tall.

Curvatures of the Vertebral Column

The adult vertebral column does not form a straight line, but instead has four curvatures along its length (see Figure 7.20). These curves increase the vertebral column's strength, flexibility, and ability to absorb shock. When the load on the spine is increased, by carrying a heavy backpack for example, the curvatures increase in depth (become more curved) to accommodate the extra weight. They then spring back when the weight is removed. The four adult curvatures are classified as either primary or secondary curvatures. Primary curves are retained from the original fetal curvature, while secondary curvatures develop after birth.

During fetal development, the body is flexed anteriorly into the fetal position, giving the entire vertebral column a single curvature that is concave anteriorly. In the adult, this fetal curvature is retained in two regions of the vertebral column as the **thoracic curve**, which involves the thoracic vertebrae, and the **sacrococcygeal curve**, formed by the sacrum and coccyx. Each of these is thus called a **primary curve** because they are retained from the original fetal curvature of the vertebral column.

A **secondary curve** develops gradually after birth as the child learns to sit upright, stand, and walk. Secondary curves are concave posteriorly, opposite in direction to the original fetal curvature. The **cervical curve** of the neck region develops as the infant begins to hold their head upright when sitting. Later, as the child begins to stand and then to walk, the **lumbar curve** of the lower back develops. In adults, the lumbar curve is generally deeper in females.

Disorders associated with the curvature of the spine include **kyphosis** (an excessive posterior curvature of the thoracic region), **lordosis** (an excessive anterior curvature of the lumbar region), and **scoliosis** (an abnormal, lateral curvature, accompanied by twisting of the vertebral column).

Disorders of the...

Vertebral Column

Developmental anomalies, pathological changes, or obesity can enhance the normal vertebral column curves, resulting in the development of abnormal or excessive curvatures (Figure 7.21). Kyphosis, also referred to as humpback or hunchback, is an excessive posterior curvature of the thoracic region. This can develop when osteoporosis causes weakening and erosion of the anterior portions of the upper thoracic vertebrae, resulting in their gradual collapse (Figure 7.22). Lordosis, or swayback, is an excessive anterior curvature of the lumbar region and is most commonly associated with obesity or late pregnancy. The accumulation of body weight in the abdominal region results an anterior shift in the line of gravity that carries the weight of the body. This causes in an anterior tilt of the pelvis and a pronounced enhancement of the lumbar curve.

Scoliosis is an abnormal, lateral curvature, accompanied by twisting of the vertebral column. Compensatory curves may also develop in other areas of the vertebral column to help maintain the head positioned over the feet. Scoliosis is the most common vertebral abnormality among girls. The cause is usually unknown, but it may result from weakness of the back muscles, defects such as differential growth rates in the right and left sides of the vertebral column, or differences in the length of the lower limbs. When present, scoliosis tends to get worse during adolescent growth spurts. Although most individuals do not require treatment, a back brace may be recommended for growing children. In extreme cases, surgery may be required.

Excessive vertebral curves can be identified while an individual stands in the anatomical position. Observe the vertebral profile from the side and then from behind to check for kyphosis or lordosis. Then have the person bend forward. If scoliosis is present, an individual will have difficulty in bending directly forward, and the right and left sides of the back will not be level with each other in the bent position.

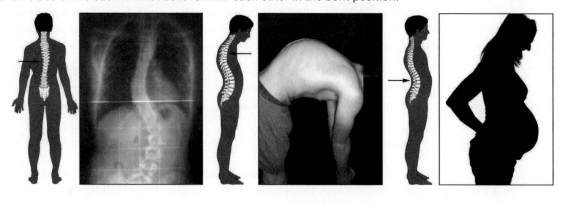

(a) Scoliosis   (b) Kyphosis   (c) Lordosis

FIGURE 7.21 Abnormal Curvatures of the Vertebral Column   (a) Scoliosis is an abnormal lateral bending of the vertebral column. (b) An excessive curvature of the upper thoracic vertebral column is called kyphosis. (c) Lordosis is an excessive curvature in the

Access for free at openstax.org

lumbar region of the vertebral column.

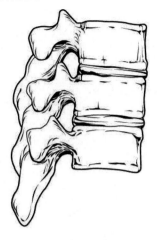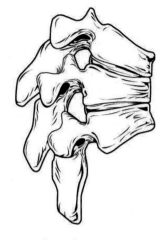

Normal vertebrae

Bone loss amplifies curvature

FIGURE 7.22 **Osteoporosis** Osteoporosis is an age-related disorder that causes the gradual loss of bone density and strength. When the thoracic vertebrae are affected, there can be a gradual collapse of the vertebrae. This results in kyphosis, an excessive curvature of the thoracic region.

🔗 INTERACTIVE LINK

Osteoporosis is a common age-related bone disease in which bone density and strength is decreased. Watch this video (http://openstax.org/l/osteoporosis) to get a better understanding of how thoracic vertebrae may become weakened and may fracture due to this disease. How may vertebral osteoporosis contribute to kyphosis?

General Structure of a Vertebra

Within the different regions of the vertebral column, vertebrae vary in size and shape, but they all follow a similar structural pattern. A typical vertebra will consist of a body, a vertebral arch, and seven processes (Figure 7.23).

The body is the anterior portion of each vertebra and is the part that supports the body weight. Because of this, the vertebral bodies progressively increase in size and thickness going down the vertebral column. The bodies of adjacent vertebrae are separated and strongly united by an intervertebral disc.

The **vertebral arch** forms the posterior portion of each vertebra. It consists of four parts, the right and left pedicles and the right and left laminae. Each **pedicle** forms one of the lateral sides of the vertebral arch. The pedicles are anchored to the posterior side of the vertebral body. Each **lamina** forms part of the posterior roof of the vertebral arch. The large opening between the vertebral arch and body is the **vertebral foramen**, which contains the spinal cord. In the intact vertebral column, the vertebral foramina of all of the vertebrae align to form the **vertebral (spinal) canal**, which serves as the bony protection and passageway for the spinal cord down the back. When the vertebrae are aligned together in the vertebral column, notches in the margins of the pedicles of adjacent vertebrae together form an **intervertebral foramen**, the opening through which a spinal nerve exits from the vertebral column (Figure 7.24).

Seven processes arise from the vertebral arch. Each paired **transverse process** projects laterally and arises from the junction point between the pedicle and lamina. The single **spinous process** (vertebral spine) projects posteriorly at the midline of the back. The vertebral spines can easily be felt as a series of bumps just under the skin down the middle of the back. The transverse and spinous processes serve as important muscle attachment sites. A **superior articular process** extends or faces upward, and an **inferior articular process** faces or projects downward on each side of a vertebrae. The paired superior articular processes of one vertebra join with the corresponding paired inferior articular processes from the next higher vertebra. These junctions form slightly moveable joints between the adjacent vertebrae. The shape and orientation of the articular processes vary in different regions of the vertebral column and play a major role in determining the type and range of motion available in each region.

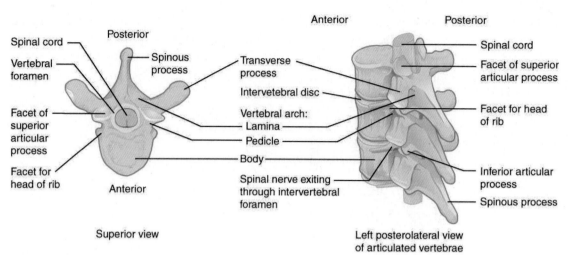

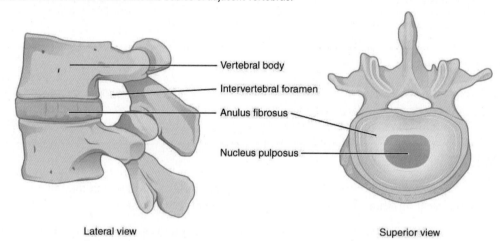

FIGURE 7.23 Parts of a Typical Vertebra A typical vertebra consists of a body and a vertebral arch. The arch is formed by the paired pedicles and paired laminae. Arising from the vertebral arch are the transverse, spinous, superior articular, and inferior articular processes. The vertebral foramen provides for passage of the spinal cord. Each spinal nerve exits through an intervertebral foramen, located between adjacent vertebrae. Intervertebral discs unite the bodies of adjacent vertebrae.

FIGURE 7.24 Intervertebral Disc The bodies of adjacent vertebrae are separated and united by an intervertebral disc, which provides padding and allows for movements between adjacent vertebrae. The disc consists of a fibrous outer layer called the anulus fibrosus and a gel-like center called the nucleus pulposus. The intervertebral foramen is the opening formed between adjacent vertebrae for the exit of a spinal nerve.

Regional Modifications of Vertebrae

In addition to the general characteristics of a typical vertebra described above, vertebrae also display characteristic size and structural features that vary between the different vertebral column regions. Thus, cervical vertebrae are smaller than lumbar vertebrae due to differences in the proportion of body weight that each supports. Thoracic vertebrae have sites for rib attachment, and the vertebrae that give rise to the sacrum and coccyx have fused together into single bones.

Cervical Vertebrae

Typical **cervical vertebrae**, such as C4 or C5, have several characteristic features that differentiate them from thoracic or lumbar vertebrae (Figure 7.25). Cervical vertebrae have a small body, reflecting the fact that they carry the least amount of body weight. Cervical vertebrae usually have a bifid (Y-shaped) spinous process. The spinous processes of the C3–C6 vertebrae are short, but the spine of C7 is much longer. You can find these vertebrae by running your finger down the midline of the posterior neck until you encounter the prominent C7 spine located at the base of the neck. The transverse processes of the cervical vertebrae are sharply curved (U-shaped) to allow for passage of the cervical spinal nerves. Each transverse process also has an opening called the **transverse foramen**. An important artery that supplies the brain ascends up the neck by passing through these openings. The superior and inferior articular processes of the cervical vertebrae are flattened and largely face upward or downward, respectively.

The first and second cervical vertebrae are further modified, giving each a distinctive appearance. The first cervical (C1) vertebra is also called the **atlas**, because this is the vertebra that supports the skull on top of the vertebral column (in Greek mythology, Atlas was the god who supported the heavens on his shoulders). The C1 vertebra does not have a body or spinous process. Instead, it is ring-shaped, consisting of an **anterior arch** and a **posterior arch**. The transverse processes of the atlas are longer and extend more laterally than do the transverse processes of any other cervical vertebrae. The superior articular processes face upward and are deeply curved for articulation with the occipital condyles on the base of the skull. The inferior articular processes are flat and face downward to join with the superior articular processes of the C2 vertebra.

The second cervical (C2) vertebra is called the **axis**, because it serves as the axis for rotation when turning the head toward the right or left. The axis resembles typical cervical vertebrae in most respects, but is easily distinguished by the **dens** (odontoid process), a bony projection that extends upward from the vertebral body. The dens joins with the inner aspect of the anterior arch of the atlas, where it is held in place by the transverse ligament.

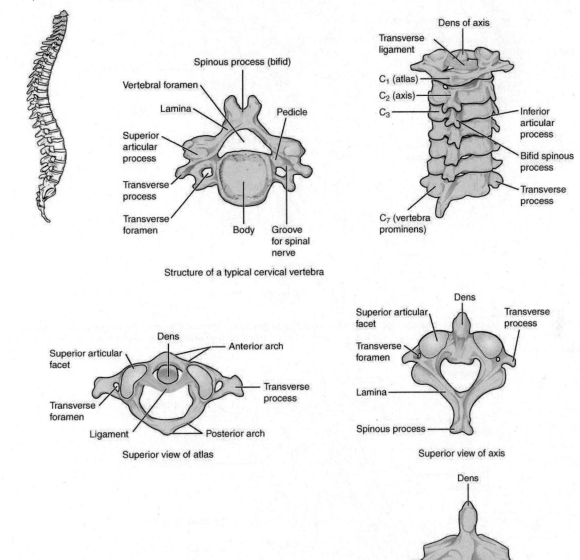

FIGURE 7.25   Cervical Vertebrae   A typical cervical vertebra has a small body, a bifid spinous process, transverse processes that have a transverse foramen and are curved for spinal nerve passage. The atlas (C1 vertebra) does not have a body or spinous process. It consists of an anterior and a posterior arch and elongated transverse processes. The axis (C2 vertebra) has the upward projecting dens, which articulates with the anterior arch of the atlas.

Thoracic Vertebrae

The bodies of the **thoracic vertebrae** are larger than those of cervical vertebrae (Figure 7.26). The characteristic feature for a typical midthoracic vertebra is the spinous process, which is long and has a pronounced downward angle that causes it to overlap the next inferior vertebra. The superior articular processes of thoracic vertebrae face anteriorly and the inferior processes face posteriorly. These orientations are important determinants for the type and range of movements available to the thoracic region of the vertebral column.

Thoracic vertebrae have several additional articulation sites, each of which is called a **facet**, where a rib is attached. Most thoracic vertebrae have two facets located on the lateral sides of the body, each of which is called a **costal facet** (costal = "rib"). These are for articulation with the head (end) of a rib. An additional facet is located on the transverse process for articulation with the tubercle of a rib.

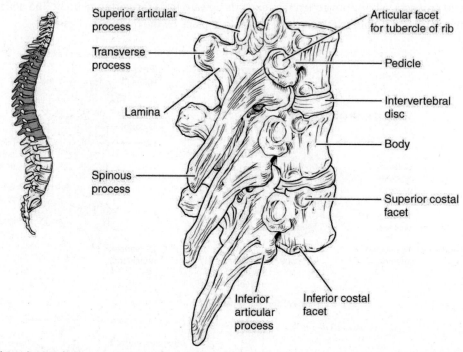

FIGURE 7.26   Thoracic Vertebrae   A typical thoracic vertebra is distinguished by the spinous process, which is long and projects downward to overlap the next inferior vertebra. It also has articulation sites (facets) on the vertebral body and a transverse process for rib attachment.

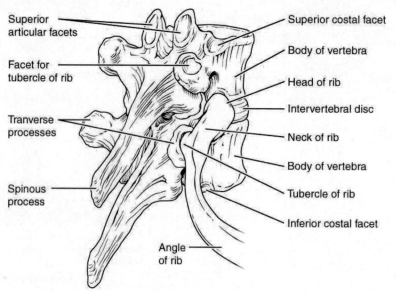

FIGURE 7.27   Rib Articulation in Thoracic Vertebrae   Thoracic vertebrae have superior and inferior articular facets on the vertebral body for articulation with the head of a rib, and a transverse process facet for articulation with the rib tubercle.

Lumbar Vertebrae

Lumbar vertebrae carry the greatest amount of body weight and are thus characterized by the large size and thickness of the vertebral body (Figure 7.28). They have short transverse processes and a short, blunt spinous process that projects posteriorly. The articular processes are large, with the superior process facing backward and the inferior facing forward.

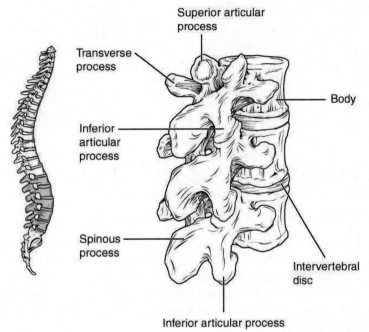

FIGURE 7.28 Lumbar Vertebrae Lumbar vertebrae are characterized by having a large, thick body and a short, rounded spinous process.

Sacrum and Coccyx

The sacrum is a triangular-shaped bone that is thick and wide across its superior base where it is weight bearing and then tapers down to an inferior, non-weight bearing apex (Figure 7.29). It is formed by the fusion of five sacral vertebrae, a process that does not begin until after the age of 20. On the anterior surface of the older adult sacrum, the lines of vertebral fusion can be seen as four transverse ridges. On the posterior surface, running down the midline, is the **median sacral crest**, a bumpy ridge that is the remnant of the fused spinous processes (median = "midline"; while medial = "toward, but not necessarily at, the midline"). Similarly, the fused transverse processes of the sacral vertebrae form the **lateral sacral crest**.

The **sacral promontory** is the anterior lip of the superior base of the sacrum. Lateral to this is the roughened auricular surface, which joins with the ilium portion of the hipbone to form the immobile sacroiliac joints of the pelvis. Passing inferiorly through the sacrum is a bony tunnel called the **sacral canal**, which terminates at the **sacral hiatus** near the inferior tip of the sacrum. The anterior and posterior surfaces of the sacrum have a series of paired openings called **sacral foramina** (singular = foramen) that connect to the sacral canal. Each of these openings is called a **posterior (dorsal) sacral foramen** or **anterior (ventral) sacral foramen**. These openings allow for the anterior and posterior branches of the sacral spinal nerves to exit the sacrum. The **superior articular process of the sacrum**, one of which is found on either side of the superior opening of the sacral canal, articulates with the inferior articular processes from the L5 vertebra.

The coccyx, or tailbone, is derived from the fusion of four very small coccygeal vertebrae (see Figure 7.29). It articulates with the inferior tip of the sacrum. It is not weight bearing in the standing position, but may receive some body weight when sitting.

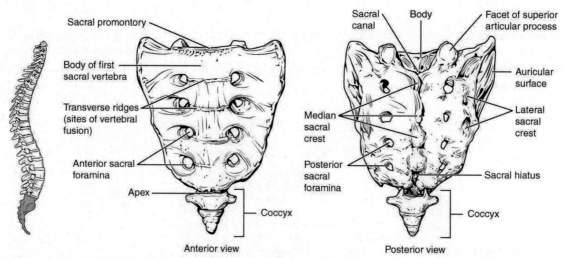

FIGURE 7.29   Sacrum and Coccyx   The sacrum is formed from the fusion of five sacral vertebrae, whose lines of fusion are indicated by the transverse ridges. The fused spinous processes form the median sacral crest, while the lateral sacral crest arises from the fused transverse processes. The coccyx is formed by the fusion of four small coccygeal vertebrae.

Intervertebral Discs and Ligaments of the Vertebral Column

The bodies of adjacent vertebrae are strongly anchored to each other by an intervertebral disc. This structure provides padding between the bones during weight bearing, and because it can change shape, also allows for movement between the vertebrae. Although the total amount of movement available between any two adjacent vertebrae is small, when these movements are summed together along the entire length of the vertebral column, large body movements can be produced. Ligaments that extend along the length of the vertebral column also contribute to its overall support and stability.

Intervertebral Disc

An **intervertebral disc** is a fibrocartilaginous pad that fills the gap between adjacent vertebral bodies (see Figure 7.24). Each disc is anchored to the bodies of its adjacent vertebrae, thus strongly uniting these. The discs also provide padding between vertebrae during weight bearing. Because of this, intervertebral discs are thin in the cervical region and thickest in the lumbar region, which carries the most body weight. In total, the intervertebral discs account for approximately 25 percent of your body height between the top of the pelvis and the base of the skull. Intervertebral discs are also flexible and can change shape to allow for movements of the vertebral column.

Each intervertebral disc consists of two parts. The **anulus fibrosus** is the tough, fibrous outer layer of the disc. It forms a circle (anulus = "ring" or "circle") and is firmly anchored to the outer margins of the adjacent vertebral bodies. Inside is the **nucleus pulposus**, consisting of a softer, more gel-like material. It has a high water content that serves to resist compression and thus is important for weight bearing. With increasing age, the water content of the nucleus pulposus gradually declines. This causes the disc to become thinner, decreasing total body height somewhat, and reduces the flexibility and range of motion of the disc, making bending more difficult.

The gel-like nature of the nucleus pulposus also allows the intervertebral disc to change shape as one vertebra rocks side to side or forward and back in relation to its neighbors during movements of the vertebral column. Thus, bending forward causes compression of the anterior portion of the disc but expansion of the posterior disc. If the posterior anulus fibrosus is weakened due to injury or increasing age, the pressure exerted on the disc when bending forward and lifting a heavy object can cause the nucleus pulposus to protrude posteriorly through the anulus fibrosus, resulting in a herniated disc ("ruptured" or "slipped" disc) (Figure 7.30). The posterior bulging of the nucleus pulposus can cause compression of a spinal nerve at the point where it exits through the intervertebral foramen, with resulting pain and/or muscle weakness in those body regions supplied by that nerve. The most common sites for disc herniation are the L4/L5 or L5/S1 intervertebral discs, which can cause sciatica, a widespread pain that radiates from the lower back down the thigh and into the leg. Similar injuries of the C5/C6 or C6/C7 intervertebral discs, following forcible hyperflexion of the neck from a collision accident or football injury, can produce pain in the neck, shoulder, and upper limb.

Access for free at openstax.org

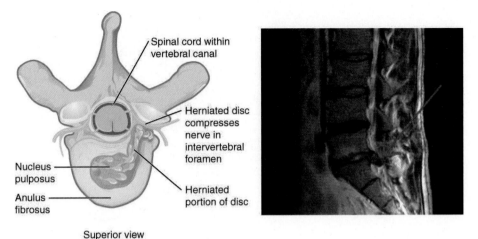

Superior view

FIGURE 7.30 Herniated Intervertebral Disc   Weakening of the anulus fibrosus can result in herniation (protrusion) of the nucleus pulposus and compression of a spinal nerve, resulting in pain and/or muscle weakness in the body regions supplied by that nerve.

⊘ INTERACTIVE LINK

Watch this video (http://openstax.org/l/herndisc1) to learn about a herniated disc. Watch this second video (http://openstax.org/l/herndisc2) to see one possible treatment for a herniated disc, removing the damaged portion of the disc. How could lifting a heavy object produce pain in a lower limb?

Ligaments of the Vertebral Column

Adjacent vertebrae are united by ligaments that run the length of the vertebral column along both its posterior and anterior aspects (Figure 7.31). These serve to resist excess forward or backward bending movements of the vertebral column, respectively.

The **anterior longitudinal ligament** runs down the anterior side of the entire vertebral column, uniting the vertebral bodies. It serves to resist excess backward bending of the vertebral column. Protection against this movement is particularly important in the neck, where extreme posterior bending of the head and neck can stretch or tear this ligament, resulting in a painful whiplash injury. Prior to the mandatory installation of seat headrests, whiplash injuries were common for passengers involved in a rear-end automobile collision.

The **supraspinous ligament** is located on the posterior side of the vertebral column, where it interconnects the spinous processes of the thoracic and lumbar vertebrae. This strong ligament supports the vertebral column during forward bending motions. In the posterior neck, where the cervical spinous processes are short, the supraspinous ligament expands to become the **nuchal ligament** (nuchae = "nape" or "back of the neck"). The nuchal ligament is attached to the cervical spinous processes and extends upward and posteriorly to attach to the midline base of the skull, out to the external occipital protuberance. It supports the skull and prevents it from falling forward. This ligament is much larger and stronger in four-legged animals such as cows, where the large skull hangs off the front end of the vertebral column. You can easily feel this ligament by first extending your head backward and pressing down on the posterior midline of your neck. Then tilt your head forward and you will fill the nuchal ligament popping out as it tightens to limit anterior bending of the head and neck.

Additional ligaments are located inside the vertebral canal, next to the spinal cord, along the length of the vertebral column. The **posterior longitudinal ligament** is found anterior to the spinal cord, where it is attached to the posterior sides of the vertebral bodies. Posterior to the spinal cord is the **ligamentum flavum** ("yellow ligament"). This consists of a series of short, paired ligaments, each of which interconnects the lamina regions of adjacent vertebrae. The ligamentum flavum has large numbers of elastic fibers, which have a yellowish color, allowing it to stretch and then pull back. Both of these ligaments provide important support for the vertebral column when bending forward.

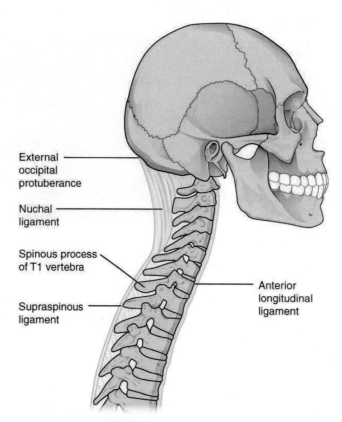

FIGURE 7.31 Ligaments of Vertebral Column   The anterior longitudinal ligament runs the length of the vertebral column, uniting the anterior sides of the vertebral bodies. The supraspinous ligament connects the spinous processes of the thoracic and lumbar vertebrae. In the posterior neck, the supraspinous ligament enlarges to form the nuchal ligament, which attaches to the cervical spinous processes and to the base of the skull.

 INTERACTIVE LINK

Use this tool (http://openstax.org/l/vertcolumn) to identify the bones, intervertebral discs, and ligaments of the vertebral column. The thickest portions of the anterior longitudinal ligament and the supraspinous ligament are found in which regions of the vertebral column?

CAREER CONNECTION

Chiropractor

Chiropractors are health professionals who use nonsurgical techniques to help patients with musculoskeletal system problems that involve the bones, muscles, ligaments, tendons, or nervous system. They treat problems such as neck pain, back pain, joint pain, or headaches. Chiropractors focus on the patient's overall health and can also provide counseling related to lifestyle issues, such as diet, exercise, or sleep problems. If needed, they will refer the patient to other medical specialists.

Chiropractors use a drug-free, hands-on approach for patient diagnosis and treatment. They will perform a physical exam, assess the patient's posture and spine, and may perform additional diagnostic tests, including taking X-ray images. They primarily use manual techniques, such as spinal manipulation, to adjust the patient's spine or other joints. They can recommend therapeutic or rehabilitative exercises, and some also include acupuncture, massage therapy, or ultrasound as part of the treatment program. In addition to those in general practice, some chiropractors specialize in sport injuries, neurology, orthopaedics, pediatrics, nutrition, internal disorders, or diagnostic imaging.

To become a chiropractor, students must have 3–4 years of undergraduate education, attend an accredited, four-year Doctor of Chiropractic (D.C.) degree program, and pass a licensure examination to be licensed for practice in their state. With the aging of the baby-boom generation, employment for chiropractors is expected to increase.

7.4 The Thoracic Cage

LEARNING OBJECTIVES

By the end of this section, you will be able to:

- Discuss the components that make up the thoracic cage
- Identify the parts of the sternum and define the sternal angle
- Discuss the parts of a rib and rib classifications

The thoracic cage (rib cage) forms the thorax (chest) portion of the body. It consists of the 12 pairs of ribs with their costal cartilages and the sternum (Figure 7.32). The ribs are anchored posteriorly to the 12 thoracic vertebrae (T1–T12). The thoracic cage protects the heart and lungs.

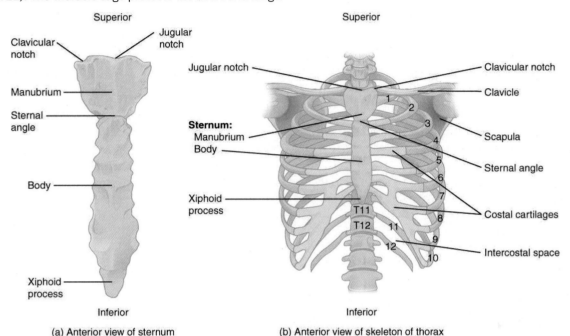

FIGURE 7.32 **Thoracic Cage** The thoracic cage is formed by the (a) sternum and (b) 12 pairs of ribs with their costal cartilages. The ribs are anchored posteriorly to the 12 thoracic vertebrae. The sternum consists of the manubrium, body, and xiphoid process. The ribs are classified as true ribs (1–7) and false ribs (8–12). The last two pairs of false ribs are also known as floating ribs (11–12).

Sternum

The sternum is the elongated bony structure that anchors the anterior thoracic cage. It consists of three parts: the manubrium, body, and xiphoid process. The **manubrium** is the wider, superior portion of the sternum. The top of the manubrium has a shallow, U-shaped border called the **jugular (suprasternal) notch**. This can be easily felt at the anterior base of the neck, between the medial ends of the clavicles. The **clavicular notch** is the shallow depression located on either side at the superior-lateral margins of the manubrium. This is the site of the sternoclavicular joint, between the sternum and clavicle. The first ribs also attach to the manubrium.

The elongated, central portion of the sternum is the body. The manubrium and body join together at the **sternal angle**, so called because the junction between these two components is not flat, but forms a slight bend. The second rib attaches to the sternum at the sternal angle. Since the first rib is hidden behind the clavicle, the second rib is the highest rib that can be identified by palpation. Thus, the sternal angle and second rib are important landmarks for the identification and counting of the lower ribs. Ribs 3–7 attach to the sternal body.

The inferior tip of the sternum is the **xiphoid process**. This small structure is cartilaginous early in life, but gradually becomes ossified starting during middle age.

Ribs

Each rib is a curved, flattened bone that contributes to the wall of the thorax. The ribs articulate posteriorly with the T1–T12 thoracic vertebrae, and most attach anteriorly via their costal cartilages to the sternum. There are 12 pairs of ribs. The ribs are numbered 1–12 in accordance with the thoracic vertebrae.

Parts of a Typical Rib

The posterior end of a typical rib is called the **head of the rib** (see Figure 7.27). This region articulates primarily with the costal facet located on the body of the same numbered thoracic vertebra and to a lesser degree, with the costal facet located on the body of the next higher vertebra. Lateral to the head is the narrowed **neck of the rib**. A small bump on the posterior rib surface is the **tubercle of the rib**, which articulates with the facet located on the transverse process of the same numbered vertebra. The remainder of the rib is the **body of the rib** (shaft). Just lateral to the tubercle is the **angle of the rib**, the point at which the rib has its greatest degree of curvature. The angles of the ribs form the most posterior extent of the thoracic cage. In the anatomical position, the angles align with the medial border of the scapula. A shallow **costal groove** for the passage of blood vessels and a nerve is found along the inferior margin of each rib.

Rib Classifications

The bony ribs do not extend anteriorly completely around to the sternum. Instead, each rib ends in a **costal cartilage**. These cartilages are made of hyaline cartilage and can extend for several inches. Most ribs are then attached, either directly or indirectly, to the sternum via their costal cartilage (see Figure 7.32). The ribs are classified into three groups based on their relationship to the sternum.

Ribs 1–7 are classified as **true ribs** (vertebrosternal ribs). The costal cartilage from each of these ribs attaches directly to the sternum. Ribs 8–12 are called **false ribs** (vertebrochondral ribs). The costal cartilages from these ribs do not attach directly to the sternum. For ribs 8–10, the costal cartilages are attached to the cartilage of the next higher rib. Thus, the cartilage of rib 10 attaches to the cartilage of rib 9, rib 9 then attaches to rib 8, and rib 8 is attached to rib 7. The last two false ribs (11–12) are also called **floating ribs** (vertebral ribs). These are short ribs that do not attach to the sternum at all. Instead, their small costal cartilages terminate within the musculature of the lateral abdominal wall.

7.5 Embryonic Development of the Axial Skeleton

LEARNING OBJECTIVES

By the end of this section, you will be able to:

- Discuss the two types of embryonic bone development within the skull
- Describe the development of the vertebral column and thoracic cage

The axial skeleton begins to form during early embryonic development. However, growth, remodeling, and ossification (bone formation) continue for several decades after birth before the adult skeleton is fully formed. Knowledge of the developmental processes that give rise to the skeleton is important for understanding the abnormalities that may arise in skeletal structures.

Development of the Skull

During the third week of embryonic development, a rod-like structure called the **notochord** develops dorsally along the length of the embryo. The tissue overlying the notochord enlarges and forms the neural tube, which will give rise to the brain and spinal cord. By the fourth week, mesoderm tissue located on either side of the notochord thickens and separates into a repeating series of block-like tissue structures, each of which is called a **somite**. As the somites enlarge, each one will split into several parts. The most medial of these parts is called a **sclerotome**. The sclerotomes consist of an embryonic tissue called mesenchyme, which will give rise to the fibrous connective tissues, cartilages, and bones of the body.

The bones of the skull arise from mesenchyme during embryonic development in two different ways. The first mechanism produces the bones that form the top and sides of the brain case. This involves the local accumulation of mesenchymal cells at the site of the future bone. These cells then differentiate directly into bone producing cells, which form the skull bones through the process of intramembranous ossification. As the brain case bones grow in the fetal skull, they remain separated from each other by large areas of dense connective tissue, each of which is called a **fontanelle** (Figure 7.33). The fontanelles are the soft spots on an infant's head. They are important during birth because these areas allow the skull to change shape as it squeezes through the birth canal. After birth, the fontanelles allow for continued growth and expansion of the skull as the brain enlarges. The largest fontanelle is located on the anterior head, at the junction of the frontal and parietal bones. The fontanelles decrease in size and disappear by age 2. However, the skull bones remained separated from each other at the sutures, which contain dense fibrous connective tissue that unites the adjacent bones. The connective tissue of the sutures allows for continued growth of the skull bones as the brain enlarges during childhood growth.

The second mechanism for bone development in the skull produces the facial bones and floor of the brain case. This also begins with the localized accumulation of mesenchymal cells. However, these cells differentiate into cartilage cells, which produce a hyaline cartilage model of the future bone. As this cartilage model grows, it is gradually converted into bone through the process of endochondral ossification. This is a slow process and the cartilage is not completely converted to bone until the skull achieves its full adult size.

At birth, the brain case and orbits of the skull are disproportionally large compared to the bones of the jaws and lower face. This reflects the relative underdevelopment of the maxilla and mandible, which lack teeth, and the small sizes of the paranasal sinuses and nasal cavity. During early childhood, the mastoid process enlarges, the two halves of the mandible and frontal bone fuse together to form single bones, and the paranasal sinuses enlarge. The jaws also expand as the teeth begin to appear. These changes all contribute to the rapid growth and enlargement of the face during childhood.

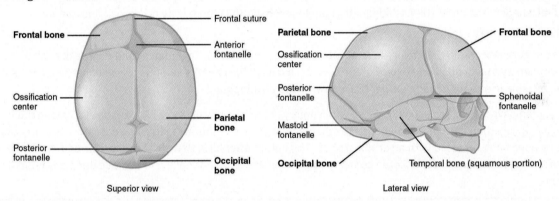

FIGURE 7.33 Newborn Skull   The bones of the newborn skull are not fully ossified and are separated by large areas called fontanelles, which are filled with fibrous connective tissue. The fontanelles allow for continued growth of the skull after birth. At the time of birth, the facial bones are small and underdeveloped, and the mastoid process has not yet formed.

Development of the Vertebral Column and Thoracic cage

Development of the vertebrae begins with the accumulation of mesenchyme cells from each sclerotome around the notochord. These cells differentiate into a hyaline cartilage model for each vertebra, which then grow and eventually ossify into bone through the process of endochondral ossification. As the developing vertebrae grow, the notochord largely disappears. However, small areas of notochord tissue persist between the adjacent vertebrae and this contributes to the formation of each intervertebral disc.

The ribs and sternum also develop from mesenchyme. The ribs initially develop as part of the cartilage model for each vertebra, but in the thorax region, the rib portion separates from the vertebra by the eighth week. The cartilage model of the rib then ossifies, except for the anterior portion, which remains as the costal cartilage. The sternum initially forms as paired hyaline cartilage models on either side of the anterior midline, beginning during the fifth week of development. The cartilage models of the ribs become attached to the lateral sides of the developing sternum. Eventually, the two halves of the cartilaginous sternum fuse together along the midline and then ossify into bone. The manubrium and body of the sternum are converted into bone first, with the xiphoid process remaining as cartilage until late in life.

🔗 INTERACTIVE LINK

View this video (http://openstax.org/l/skullbones) to review the two processes that give rise to the bones of the skull and body. What are the two mechanisms by which the bones of the body are formed and which bones are formed by each mechanism?

HOMEOSTATIC IMBALANCES

Craniosynostosis

The premature closure (fusion) of a suture line is a condition called craniosynostosis. This error in the normal developmental process results in abnormal growth of the skull and deformity of the head. It is produced either by defects in the ossification process of the skull bones or failure of the brain to properly enlarge. Genetic factors are involved, but the underlying cause is unknown. It is a relatively common condition, occurring in approximately 1:2000 births, with males being more commonly affected. Primary craniosynostosis involves the early fusion of one cranial suture, whereas complex craniosynostosis results from the premature fusion of several sutures.

The early fusion of a suture in primary craniosynostosis prevents any additional enlargement of the cranial bones and skull along this line. Continued growth of the brain and skull is therefore diverted to other areas of the head, causing an abnormal enlargement of these regions. For example, the early disappearance of the anterior fontanelle and premature closure of the sagittal suture prevents growth across the top of the head. This is compensated by upward growth by the bones of the lateral skull, resulting in a long, narrow, wedge-shaped head. This condition, known as scaphocephaly, accounts for approximately 50 percent of craniosynostosis abnormalities. Although the skull is misshapen, the brain still has adequate room to grow and thus there is no accompanying abnormal neurological development.

In cases of complex craniosynostosis, several sutures close prematurely. The amount and degree of skull deformity is determined by the location and extent of the sutures involved. This results in more severe constraints on skull growth, which can alter or impede proper brain growth and development.

Cases of craniosynostosis are usually treated with surgery. A team of physicians will open the skull along the fused suture, which will then allow the skull bones to resume their growth in this area. In some cases, parts of the skull will be removed and replaced with an artificial plate. The earlier after birth that surgery is performed, the better the outcome. After treatment, most children continue to grow and develop normally and do not exhibit any neurological problems.

Key Terms

alveolar process of the mandible   upper border of mandibular body that contains the lower teeth

alveolar process of the maxilla   curved, inferior margin of the maxilla that supports and anchors the upper teeth

angle of the mandible   rounded corner located at outside margin of the body and ramus junction

angle of the rib   portion of rib with greatest curvature; together, the rib angles form the most posterior extent of the thoracic cage

anterior (ventral) sacral foramen   one of the series of paired openings located on the anterior (ventral) side of the sacrum

anterior arch   anterior portion of the ring-like C1 (atlas) vertebra

anterior cranial fossa   shallowest and most anterior cranial fossa of the cranial base that extends from the frontal bone to the lesser wing of the sphenoid bone

anterior longitudinal ligament   ligament that runs the length of the vertebral column, uniting the anterior aspects of the vertebral bodies

anulus fibrosus   tough, fibrous outer portion of an intervertebral disc, which is strongly anchored to the bodies of the adjacent vertebrae

appendicular skeleton   all bones of the upper and lower limbs, plus the girdle bones that attach each limb to the axial skeleton

articular tubercle   smooth ridge located on the inferior skull, immediately anterior to the mandibular fossa

atlas   first cervical (C1) vertebra

axial skeleton   central, vertical axis of the body, including the skull, vertebral column, and thoracic cage

axis   second cervical (C2) vertebra

body of the rib   shaft portion of a rib

brain case   portion of the skull that contains and protects the brain, consisting of the eight bones that form the cranial base and rounded upper skull

calvaria   (also, skullcap) rounded top of the skull

carotid canal   zig-zag tunnel providing passage through the base of the skull for the internal carotid artery to the brain; begins anteromedial to the styloid process and terminates in the middle cranial cavity, near the posterior-lateral base of the sella turcica

cervical curve   posteriorly concave curvature of the cervical vertebral column region; a secondary curve of the vertebral column

cervical vertebrae   seven vertebrae numbered as C1–C7 that are located in the neck region of the vertebral column

clavicular notch   paired notches located on the superior-lateral sides of the sternal manubrium, for articulation with the clavicle

coccyx   small bone located at inferior end of the adult vertebral column that is formed by the fusion of four coccygeal vertebrae; also referred to as the "tailbone"

condylar process of the mandible   thickened upward projection from posterior margin of mandibular ramus

condyle   oval-shaped process located at the top of the condylar process of the mandible

coronal suture   joint that unites the frontal bone to the right and left parietal bones across the top of the skull

coronoid process of the mandible   flattened upward projection from the anterior margin of the mandibular ramus

costal cartilage   hyaline cartilage structure attached to the anterior end of each rib that provides for either direct or indirect attachment of most ribs to the sternum

costal facet   site on the lateral sides of a thoracic vertebra for articulation with the head of a rib

costal groove   shallow groove along the inferior margin of a rib that provides passage for blood vessels and a nerve

cranial cavity   interior space of the skull that houses the brain

cranium   skull

cribriform plate   small, flattened areas with numerous small openings, located to either side of the midline in the floor of the anterior cranial fossa; formed by the ethmoid bone

crista galli   small upward projection located at the midline in the floor of the anterior cranial fossa; formed by the ethmoid bone

dens   bony projection (odontoid process) that extends upward from the body of the C2 (axis) vertebra

ear ossicles   three small bones located in the middle ear cavity that serve to transmit sound vibrations to the inner ear

ethmoid air cell   one of several small, air-filled spaces located within the lateral sides of the ethmoid bone, between the orbit and upper nasal cavity

ethmoid bone   unpaired bone that forms the roof and upper, lateral walls of the nasal cavity, portions of the floor of the anterior cranial fossa and medial wall of orbit, and the upper portion of the nasal septum

external acoustic meatus   ear canal opening located

on the lateral side of the skull

external occipital protuberance   small bump located at the midline on the posterior skull

facet   small, flattened area on a bone for an articulation (joint) with another bone, or for muscle attachment

facial bones   fourteen bones that support the facial structures and form the upper and lower jaws and the hard palate

false ribs   vertebrochondral ribs 8–12 whose costal cartilage either attaches indirectly to the sternum via the costal cartilage of the next higher rib or does not attach to the sternum at all

floating ribs   vertebral ribs 11–12 that do not attach to the sternum or to the costal cartilage of another rib

fontanelle   expanded area of fibrous connective tissue that separates the brain case bones of the skull prior to birth and during the first year after birth

foramen lacerum   irregular opening in the base of the skull, located inferior to the exit of carotid canal

foramen magnum   large opening in the occipital bone of the skull through which the spinal cord emerges and the vertebral arteries enter the cranium

foramen ovale of the middle cranial fossa   oval-shaped opening in the floor of the middle cranial fossa

foramen rotundum   round opening in the floor of the middle cranial fossa, located between the superior orbital fissure and foramen ovale

foramen spinosum   small opening in the floor of the middle cranial fossa, located lateral to the foramen ovale

frontal bone   unpaired bone that forms forehead, roof of orbit, and floor of anterior cranial fossa

frontal sinus   air-filled space within the frontal bone; most anterior of the paranasal sinuses

glabella   slight depression of frontal bone, located at the midline between the eyebrows

greater wings of sphenoid bone   lateral projections of the sphenoid bone that form the anterior wall of the middle cranial fossa and an area of the lateral skull

hard palate   bony structure that forms the roof of the mouth and floor of the nasal cavity, formed by the palatine process of the maxillary bones and the horizontal plate of the palatine bones

head of the rib   posterior end of a rib that articulates with the bodies of thoracic vertebrae

horizontal plate   medial extension from the palatine bone that forms the posterior quarter of the hard palate

hyoid bone   small, U-shaped bone located in upper neck that does not contact any other bone

hypoglossal canal   paired openings that pass anteriorly from the anterior-lateral margins of the foramen magnum deep to the occipital condyles

hypophyseal (pituitary) fossa   shallow depression on top of the sella turcica that houses the pituitary (hypophyseal) gland

inferior articular process   bony process that extends downward from the vertebral arch of a vertebra that articulates with the superior articular process of the next lower vertebra

inferior nasal concha   one of the paired bones that project from the lateral walls of the nasal cavity to form the largest and most inferior of the nasal conchae

infraorbital foramen   opening located on anterior skull, below the orbit

infratemporal fossa   space on lateral side of skull, below the level of the zygomatic arch and deep (medial) to the ramus of the mandible

internal acoustic meatus   opening into petrous ridge, located on the lateral wall of the posterior cranial fossa

intervertebral disc   structure located between the bodies of adjacent vertebrae that strongly joins the vertebrae; provides padding, weight bearing ability, and enables vertebral column movements

intervertebral foramen   opening located between adjacent vertebrae for exit of a spinal nerve

jugular (suprasternal) notch   shallow notch located on superior surface of sternal manubrium

jugular foramen   irregularly shaped opening located in the lateral floor of the posterior cranial cavity

kyphosis   (also, humpback or hunchback) excessive posterior curvature of the thoracic vertebral column region

lacrimal bone   paired bones that contribute to the anterior-medial wall of each orbit

lacrimal fossa   shallow depression in the anterior-medial wall of the orbit, formed by the lacrimal bone that gives rise to the nasolacrimal canal

lambdoid suture   inverted V-shaped joint that unites the occipital bone to the right and left parietal bones on the posterior skull

lamina   portion of the vertebral arch on each vertebra that extends between the transverse and spinous process

lateral pterygoid plate   paired, flattened bony projections of the sphenoid bone located on the inferior skull, lateral to the medial pterygoid plate

lateral sacral crest   paired irregular ridges running down the lateral sides of the posterior sacrum that was formed by the fusion of the transverse processes from the five sacral vertebrae

lesser wings of the sphenoid bone   lateral extensions of the sphenoid bone that form the bony lip separating the anterior and middle cranial fossae

ligamentum flavum   series of short ligaments that unite the lamina of adjacent vertebrae

lingula   small flap of bone located on the inner (medial) surface of mandibular ramus, next to the mandibular foramen

lordosis   (also, swayback) excessive anterior curvature of the lumbar vertebral column region

lumbar curve   posteriorly concave curvature of the lumbar vertebral column region; a secondary curve of the vertebral column

lumbar vertebrae   five vertebrae numbered as L1–L5 that are located in lumbar region (lower back) of the vertebral column

mandible   unpaired bone that forms the lower jaw bone; the only moveable bone of the skull

mandibular foramen   opening located on the inner (medial) surface of the mandibular ramus

mandibular fossa   oval depression located on the inferior surface of the skull

mandibular notch   large U-shaped notch located between the condylar process and coronoid process of the mandible

manubrium   expanded, superior portion of the sternum

mastoid process   large bony prominence on the inferior, lateral skull, just behind the earlobe

maxillary bone   (also, maxilla) paired bones that form the upper jaw and anterior portion of the hard palate

maxillary sinus   air-filled space located with each maxillary bone; largest of the paranasal sinuses

medial pterygoid plate   paired, flattened bony projections of the sphenoid bone located on the inferior skull medial to the lateral pterygoid plate; form the posterior portion of the nasal cavity lateral wall

median sacral crest   irregular ridge running down the midline of the posterior sacrum that was formed from the fusion of the spinous processes of the five sacral vertebrae

mental foramen   opening located on the anterior-lateral side of the mandibular body

mental protuberance   inferior margin of anterior mandible that forms the chin

middle cranial fossa   centrally located cranial fossa that extends from the lesser wings of the sphenoid bone to the petrous ridge

middle nasal concha   nasal concha formed by the ethmoid bone that is located between the superior and inferior conchae

mylohyoid line   bony ridge located along the inner (medial) surface of the mandibular body

nasal bone   paired bones that form the base of the nose

nasal cavity   opening through skull for passage of air

nasal conchae   curved bony plates that project from the lateral walls of the nasal cavity; include the superior and middle nasal conchae, which are parts of the ethmoid bone, and the independent inferior nasal conchae bone

nasal septum   flat, midline structure that divides the nasal cavity into halves, formed by the perpendicular plate of the ethmoid bone, vomer bone, and septal cartilage

nasolacrimal canal   passage for drainage of tears that extends downward from the medial-anterior orbit to the nasal cavity, terminating behind the inferior nasal conchae

neck of the rib   narrowed region of a rib, next to the rib head

notochord   rod-like structure along dorsal side of the early embryo; largely disappears during later development but does contribute to formation of the intervertebral discs

nuchal ligament   expanded portion of the supraspinous ligament within the posterior neck; interconnects the spinous processes of the cervical vertebrae and attaches to the base of the skull

nucleus pulposus   gel-like central region of an intervertebral disc; provides for padding, weight-bearing, and movement between adjacent vertebrae

occipital bone   unpaired bone that forms the posterior portions of the brain case and base of the skull

occipital condyle   paired, oval-shaped bony knobs located on the inferior skull, to either side of the foramen magnum

optic canal   opening spanning between middle cranial fossa and posterior orbit

orbit   bony socket that contains the eyeball and associated muscles

palatine bone   paired bones that form the posterior quarter of the hard palate and a small area in floor of the orbit

palatine process   medial projection from the maxilla bone that forms the anterior three quarters of the hard palate

paranasal sinuses   cavities within the skull that are connected to the conchae that serve to warm and humidify incoming air, produce mucus, and lighten the weight of the skull; consist of frontal, maxillary, sphenoidal, and ethmoidal sinuses

parietal bone   paired bones that form the upper, lateral sides of the skull

pedicle   portion of the vertebral arch that extends from the vertebral body to the transverse process

perpendicular plate of the ethmoid bone   downward, midline extension of the ethmoid bone that forms the superior portion of the nasal septum

petrous ridge   petrous portion of the temporal bone that forms a large, triangular ridge in the floor of the cranial cavity, separating the middle and posterior cranial fossae; houses the middle and inner ear structures

posterior (dorsal) sacral foramen   one of the series of paired openings located on the posterior (dorsal) side of the sacrum

posterior arch   posterior portion of the ring-like C1 (atlas) vertebra

posterior cranial fossa   deepest and most posterior cranial fossa; extends from the petrous ridge to the occipital bone

posterior longitudinal ligament   ligament that runs the length of the vertebral column, uniting the posterior sides of the vertebral bodies

primary curve   anteriorly concave curvatures of the thoracic and sacrococcygeal regions that are retained from the original fetal curvature of the vertebral column

pterion   H-shaped suture junction region that unites the frontal, parietal, temporal, and sphenoid bones on the lateral side of the skull

ramus of the mandible   vertical portion of the mandible

ribs   thin, curved bones of the chest wall

sacral canal   bony tunnel that runs through the sacrum

sacral foramina   series of paired openings for nerve exit located on both the anterior (ventral) and posterior (dorsal) aspects of the sacrum

sacral hiatus   inferior opening and termination of the sacral canal

sacral promontory   anterior lip of the base (superior end) of the sacrum

sacrococcygeal curve   anteriorly concave curvature formed by the sacrum and coccyx; a primary curve of the vertebral column

sacrum   single bone located near the inferior end of the adult vertebral column that is formed by the fusion of five sacral vertebrae; forms the posterior portion of the pelvis

sagittal suture   joint that unites the right and left parietal bones at the midline along the top of the skull

sclerotome   medial portion of a somite consisting of mesenchyme tissue that will give rise to bone, cartilage, and fibrous connective tissues

scoliosis   abnormal lateral curvature of the vertebral column

secondary curve   posteriorly concave curvatures of the cervical and lumbar regions of the vertebral column that develop after the time of birth

sella turcica   elevated area of sphenoid bone located at midline of the middle cranial fossa

septal cartilage   flat cartilage structure that forms the anterior portion of the nasal septum

skeleton   bones of the body

skull   bony structure that forms the head, face, and jaws, and protects the brain; consists of 22 bones

somite   one of the paired, repeating blocks of tissue located on either side of the notochord in the early embryo

sphenoid bone   unpaired bone that forms the central base of skull

sphenoid sinus   air-filled space located within the sphenoid bone; most posterior of the paranasal sinuses

spinous process   unpaired bony process that extends posteriorly from the vertebral arch of a vertebra

squamous suture   joint that unites the parietal bone to the squamous portion of the temporal bone on the lateral side of the skull

sternal angle   junction line between manubrium and body of the sternum and the site for attachment of the second rib to the sternum

sternum   flattened bone located at the center of the anterior chest

styloid process   downward projecting, elongated bony process located on the inferior aspect of the skull

stylomastoid foramen   opening located on inferior skull, between the styloid process and mastoid process

superior articular process   bony process that extends upward from the vertebral arch of a vertebra that articulates with the inferior articular process of the next higher vertebra

superior articular process of the sacrum   paired processes that extend upward from the sacrum to articulate (join) with the inferior articular processes from the L5 vertebra

superior nasal concha   smallest and most superiorly located of the nasal conchae; formed by the ethmoid bone

superior nuchal line   paired bony lines on the posterior skull that extend laterally from the external occipital protuberance

superior orbital fissure   irregularly shaped opening

between the middle cranial fossa and the posterior orbit

supraorbital foramen   opening located on anterior skull, at the superior margin of the orbit

supraorbital margin   superior margin of the orbit

supraspinous ligament   ligament that interconnects the spinous processes of the thoracic and lumbar vertebrae

suture   junction line at which adjacent bones of the skull are united by fibrous connective tissue

temporal bone   paired bones that form the lateral, inferior portions of the skull, with squamous, mastoid, and petrous portions

temporal fossa   shallow space on the lateral side of the skull, above the level of the zygomatic arch

temporal process of the zygomatic bone   short extension from the zygomatic bone that forms the anterior portion of the zygomatic arch

thoracic cage   consists of 12 pairs of ribs and sternum

thoracic curve   anteriorly concave curvature of the thoracic vertebral column region; a primary curve of the vertebral column

thoracic vertebrae   twelve vertebrae numbered as T1–T12 that are located in the thoracic region (upper back) of the vertebral column

transverse foramen   opening found only in the transverse processes of cervical vertebrae

transverse process   paired bony processes that extends laterally from the vertebral arch of a vertebra

true ribs   vertebrosternal ribs 1–7 that attach via their costal cartilage directly to the sternum

tubercle of the rib   small bump on the posterior side of a rib for articulation with the transverse process of a thoracic vertebra

vertebra   individual bone in the neck and back regions of the vertebral column

vertebral (spinal) canal   bony passageway within the vertebral column for the spinal cord that is formed by the series of individual vertebral foramina

vertebral arch   bony arch formed by the posterior portion of each vertebra that surrounds and protects the spinal cord

vertebral column   entire sequence of bones that extend from the skull to the tailbone

vertebral foramen   opening associated with each vertebra defined by the vertebral arch that provides passage for the spinal cord

vomer bone   unpaired bone that forms the inferior and posterior portions of the nasal septum

xiphoid process   small process that forms the inferior tip of the sternum

zygomatic arch   elongated, free-standing arch on the lateral skull, formed anteriorly by the temporal process of the zygomatic bone and posteriorly by the zygomatic process of the temporal bone

zygomatic bone   cheekbone; paired bones that contribute to the lateral orbit and anterior zygomatic arch

zygomatic process of the temporal bone   extension from the temporal bone that forms the posterior portion of the zygomatic arch

Chapter Review

7.1 Divisions of the Skeletal System

The skeletal system includes all of the bones, cartilages, and ligaments of the body. It serves to support the body, protect the brain and other internal organs, and provides a rigid structure upon which muscles can pull to generate body movements. It also stores fat and the tissue responsible for the production of blood cells. The skeleton is subdivided into two parts. The axial skeleton forms a vertical axis that includes the head, neck, back, and chest. It has 80 bones and consists of the skull, vertebral column, and thoracic cage. The adult vertebral column consists of 24 vertebrae plus the sacrum and coccyx. The thoracic cage is formed by 12 pairs of ribs and the sternum. The appendicular skeleton consists of 126 bones in the adult and includes all of the bones of the upper and lower limbs plus the bones that anchor each limb to the axial skeleton.

7.2 The Skull

The skull consists of the brain case and the facial bones. The brain case surrounds and protects the brain, which occupies the cranial cavity inside the skull. It consists of the rounded calvaria and a complex base. The brain case is formed by eight bones, the paired parietal and temporal bones plus the unpaired frontal, occipital, sphenoid, and ethmoid bones. The narrow gap between the bones is filled with dense, fibrous connective tissue that unites the bones. The sagittal suture joins the right and left parietal bones. The coronal suture joins the parietal bones to the frontal bone, the lambdoid suture joins them to the occipital bone, and the squamous suture joins them to the temporal bone.

The facial bones support the facial structures and form the upper and lower jaws. These consist of 14 bones, with the paired maxillary, palatine, zygomatic, nasal, lacrimal, and inferior conchae bones and the unpaired vomer and mandible bones. The ethmoid bone also contributes to the formation of facial structures. The maxilla forms the upper jaw and the mandible forms the lower jaw. The maxilla also forms the larger anterior portion of the hard palate, which is completed by the smaller palatine bones that form the posterior portion of the hard palate.

The floor of the cranial cavity increases in depth from front to back and is divided into three cranial fossae. The anterior cranial fossa is located between the frontal bone and lesser wing of the sphenoid bone. A small area of the ethmoid bone, consisting of the crista galli and cribriform plates, is located at the midline of this fossa. The middle cranial fossa extends from the lesser wing of the sphenoid bone to the petrous ridge (petrous portion of temporal bone). The right and left sides are separated at the midline by the sella turcica, which surrounds the shallow hypophyseal fossa. Openings through the skull in the floor of the middle fossa include the optic canal and superior orbital fissure, which open into the posterior orbit, the foramen rotundum, foramen ovale, and foramen spinosum, and the exit of the carotid canal with its underlying foramen lacerum. The deep posterior cranial fossa extends from the petrous ridge to the occipital bone. Openings here include the large foramen magnum, plus the internal acoustic meatus, jugular foramina, and hypoglossal canals. Additional openings located on the external base of the skull include the stylomastoid foramen and the entrance to the carotid canal.

The anterior skull has the orbits that house the eyeballs and associated muscles. The walls of the orbit are formed by contributions from seven bones: the frontal, zygomatic, maxillary, palatine, ethmoid, lacrimal, and sphenoid. Located at the superior margin of the orbit is the supraorbital foramen, and below the orbit is the infraorbital foramen. The mandible has two openings, the mandibular foramen on its inner surface and the mental foramen on its external surface near the chin. The nasal conchae are bony projections from the lateral walls of the nasal cavity. The large inferior nasal concha is an independent bone, while the middle and superior conchae are parts of the ethmoid bone. The nasal septum is formed by the perpendicular plate of the ethmoid bone, the vomer bone, and the septal cartilage. The paranasal sinuses are air-filled spaces located within the frontal, maxillary, sphenoid, and ethmoid bones.

On the lateral skull, the zygomatic arch consists of two parts, the temporal process of the zygomatic bone anteriorly and the zygomatic process of the temporal bone posteriorly. The temporal fossa is the shallow space located on the lateral skull above the level of the zygomatic arch. The infratemporal fossa is located below the zygomatic arch and deep to the ramus of the mandible.

The hyoid bone is located in the upper neck and does not join with any other bone. It is held in position by muscles and serves to support the tongue above, the larynx below, and the pharynx posteriorly.

7.3 The Vertebral Column

The vertebral column forms the neck and back. The vertebral column originally develops as 33 vertebrae, but is eventually reduced to 24 vertebrae, plus the sacrum and coccyx. The vertebrae are divided into the cervical region (C1–C7 vertebrae), the thoracic region (T1–T12 vertebrae), and the lumbar region (L1–L5 vertebrae). The sacrum arises from the fusion of five sacral vertebrae and the coccyx from the fusion of four small coccygeal vertebrae. The vertebral column has four curvatures, the cervical, thoracic, lumbar, and sacrococcygeal curves. The thoracic and sacrococcygeal curves are primary curves retained from the original fetal curvature. The cervical and lumbar curves develop after birth and thus are secondary curves. The cervical curve develops as the infant begins to hold up the head, and the lumbar curve appears with standing and walking.

A typical vertebra consists of an enlarged anterior portion called the body, which provides weight-bearing support. Attached posteriorly to the body is a vertebral arch, which surrounds and defines the vertebral foramen for passage of the spinal cord. The vertebral arch consists of the pedicles, which attach to the vertebral body, and the laminae, which come together to form the roof of the arch. Arising from the vertebral arch are the laterally projecting transverse processes and the posteriorly oriented spinous process. The superior articular processes project upward, where they articulate with the downward projecting inferior articular processes of the next higher vertebrae.

A typical cervical vertebra has a small body, a bifid (Y-shaped) spinous process, and U-shaped transverse processes with a transverse foramen. In addition to these characteristics, the axis (C2 vertebra) also has the dens projecting upward from the vertebral body. The atlas (C1 vertebra) differs from the other cervical vertebrae in that it does not have a body, but instead consists of bony ring formed by the anterior and posterior arches. The atlas articulates with the dens from the axis. A typical thoracic vertebra is distinguished by its long, downward projecting spinous process. Thoracic vertebrae also have articulation facets on the body and transverse processes for attachment of the ribs. Lumbar vertebrae support the greatest amount of body weight and thus have a large, thick body. They also have a short, blunt spinous process. The sacrum is triangular in shape. The median sacral crest is formed by the fused vertebral spinous processes and the lateral sacral crest is derived from the fused transverse processes. Anterior (ventral) and posterior (dorsal) sacral foramina allow branches of the sacral spinal nerves to exit the sacrum. The auricular surfaces are articulation sites on the lateral sacrum that anchor the sacrum to the hipbones to form the pelvis. The coccyx is small and derived from the fusion of four small vertebrae.

The intervertebral discs fill in the gaps between the bodies of adjacent vertebrae. They provide strong attachments and padding between the vertebrae. The outer, fibrous layer of a disc is called the anulus fibrosus. The gel-like interior is called the nucleus pulposus. The disc can change shape to allow for movement between vertebrae. If the anulus fibrosus is weakened or damaged, the nucleus pulposus can protrude outward, resulting in a herniated disc.

The anterior longitudinal ligament runs along the full length of the anterior vertebral column, uniting the vertebral bodies. The supraspinous ligament is located posteriorly and interconnects the spinous processes of the thoracic and lumbar vertebrae. In the neck, this ligament expands to become the nuchal ligament. The nuchal ligament is attached to the cervical spinous processes and superiorly to the base of the skull, out to the external occipital protuberance. The posterior longitudinal ligament runs within the vertebral canal and unites the posterior sides of the vertebral bodies. The ligamentum flavum unites the lamina of adjacent vertebrae.

7.4 The Thoracic Cage

The thoracic cage protects the heart and lungs. It is composed of 12 pairs of ribs with their costal cartilages and the sternum. The ribs are anchored posteriorly to the 12 thoracic vertebrae. The sternum consists of the manubrium, body, and xiphoid process. The manubrium and body are joined at the sternal angle, which is also the site for attachment of the second ribs.

Ribs are flattened, curved bones and are numbered 1–12. Posteriorly, the head of the rib articulates with the costal facets located on the bodies of thoracic vertebrae and the rib tubercle articulates with the facet located on the vertebral transverse process. The angle

of the ribs forms the most posterior portion of the thoracic cage. The costal groove in the inferior margin of each rib carries blood vessels and a nerve. Anteriorly, each rib ends in a costal cartilage. True ribs (1–7) attach directly to the sternum via their costal cartilage. The false ribs (8–12) either attach to the sternum indirectly or not at all. Ribs 8–10 have their costal cartilages attached to the cartilage of the next higher rib. The floating ribs (11–12) are short and do not attach to the sternum or to another rib.

7.5 Embryonic Development of the Axial Skeleton

Formation of the axial skeleton begins during early embryonic development with the appearance of the rod-like notochord along the dorsal length of the early embryo. Repeating, paired blocks of tissue called somites then appear along either side of notochord. As the somites grow, they split into parts, one of which is called a sclerotome. This consists of mesenchyme, the embryonic tissue that will become the bones, cartilages, and connective tissues of the body.

Mesenchyme in the head region will produce the bones of the skull via two different mechanisms. The bones of the brain case arise via intramembranous ossification in which embryonic mesenchyme tissue converts directly into bone. At the time of birth, these bones are separated by fontanelles, wide areas of fibrous connective tissue. As the bones grow, the fontanelles are reduced to sutures, which allow for continued growth of the skull throughout childhood. In contrast, the cranial base and facial bones are produced by the process of endochondral ossification, in which mesenchyme tissue initially produces a hyaline cartilage model of the future bone. The cartilage model allows for growth of the bone and is gradually converted into bone over a period of many years.

The vertebrae, ribs, and sternum also develop via endochondral ossification. Mesenchyme accumulates around the notochord and produces hyaline cartilage models of the vertebrae. The notochord largely disappears, but remnants of the notochord contribute to formation of the intervertebral discs. In the thorax region, a portion of the vertebral cartilage model splits off to form the ribs. These then become attached anteriorly to the developing cartilage model of the sternum. Growth of the cartilage models for the vertebrae, ribs, and sternum allow for enlargement of the thoracic cage during childhood and adolescence. The cartilage models gradually undergo ossification and are converted into bone.

Interactive Link Questions

1. Watch this video (http://openstax.org/l/skull1) to view a rotating and exploded skull with color-coded bones. Which bone (yellow) is centrally located and joins with most of the other bones of the skull?

2. View this animation (http://openstax.org/l/headblow) to see how a blow to the head may produce a contrecoup (counterblow) fracture of the basilar portion of the occipital bone on the base of the skull. Why may a basilar fracture be life threatening?

3. Osteoporosis is a common age-related bone disease in which bone density and strength is decreased. Watch this video (http://openstax.org/l/osteoporosis) to get a better understanding of how thoracic vertebrae may become weakened and may fractured due to this disease. How may vertebral osteoporosis contribute to kyphosis?

4. Watch this video (http://openstax.org/l/herndisc1) to learn about a herniated disc. Watch this second video (http://openstax.org/l/herndisc2) to see one possible treatment for a herniated disc, removing the damaged portion of the disc. How could lifting a heavy object produce pain in a lower limb?

5. Use this tool (http://openstax.org/l/vertcolumn) to identify the bones, intervertebral discs, and ligaments of the vertebral column. The thickest portions of the anterior longitudinal ligament and the supraspinous ligament are found in which regions of the vertebral column?

6. View this video (http://openstax.org/l/skullbones) to review the two processes that give rise to the bones of the skull and body. What are the two mechanisms by which the bones of the body are formed and which bones are formed by each mechanism?

Review Questions

7. Which of the following is part of the axial skeleton?
   a. shoulder bones
   b. thigh bone
   c. foot bones
   d. vertebral column

8. Which of the following is a function of the axial skeleton?
   a. allows for movement of the wrist and hand
   b. protects nerves and blood vessels at the elbow
   c. supports trunk of body
   d. allows for movements of the ankle and foot

9. The axial skeleton _____.
   a. consists of 126 bones
   b. forms the vertical axis of the body
   c. includes all bones of the body trunk and limbs
   d. includes only the bones of the lower limbs

10. Which of the following is a bone of the brain case?
    a. parietal bone
    b. zygomatic bone
    c. maxillary bone
    d. lacrimal bone

11. The lambdoid suture joins the parietal bone to the _____.
    a. frontal bone
    b. occipital bone
    c. other parietal bone
    d. temporal bone

12. The middle cranial fossa _____.
    a. is bounded anteriorly by the petrous ridge
    b. is bounded posteriorly by the lesser wing of the sphenoid bone
    c. is divided at the midline by a small area of the ethmoid bone
    d. has the foramen rotundum, foramen ovale, and foramen spinosum

13. The paranasal sinuses are _____.
    a. air-filled spaces found within the frontal, maxilla, sphenoid, and ethmoid bones only
    b. air-filled spaces found within all bones of the skull
    c. not connected to the nasal cavity
    d. divided at the midline by the nasal septum

14. Parts of the sphenoid bone include the _____.
    a. sella turcica
    b. squamous portion
    c. glabella
    d. zygomatic process

15. The bony openings of the skull include the _____.
    a. carotid canal, which is located in the anterior cranial fossa
    b. superior orbital fissure, which is located at the superior margin of the anterior orbit
    c. mental foramen, which is located just below the orbit
    d. hypoglossal canal, which is located in the posterior cranial fossa

16. The cervical region of the vertebral column consists of _____.
    a. seven vertebrae
    b. 12 vertebrae
    c. five vertebrae
    d. a single bone derived from the fusion of five vertebrae

17. The primary curvatures of the vertebral column _____.
    a. include the lumbar curve
    b. are remnants of the original fetal curvature
    c. include the cervical curve
    d. develop after the time of birth

18. A typical vertebra has _____.
    a. a vertebral foramen that passes through the body
    b. a superior articular process that projects downward to articulate with the superior portion of the next lower vertebra
    c. lamina that spans between the transverse process and spinous process
    d. a pair of laterally projecting spinous processes

19. A typical lumbar vertebra has _____.
    a. a short, rounded spinous process
    b. a bifid spinous process
    c. articulation sites for ribs
    d. a transverse foramen

20. Which is found only in the cervical region of the vertebral column?
    a. nuchal ligament
    b. ligamentum flavum
    c. supraspinous ligament
    d. anterior longitudinal ligament

21. The sternum _____.
    a. consists of only two parts, the manubrium and xiphoid process
    b. has the sternal angle located between the manubrium and body
    c. receives direct attachments from the costal cartilages of all 12 pairs of ribs
    d. articulates directly with the thoracic vertebrae

22. The sternal angle is the _____.
    a. junction between the body and xiphoid process
    b. site for attachment of the clavicle
    c. site for attachment of the floating ribs
    d. junction between the manubrium and body

23. The tubercle of a rib _____.
    a. is for articulation with the transverse process of a thoracic vertebra
    b. is for articulation with the body of a thoracic vertebra
    c. provides for passage of blood vessels and a nerve
    d. is the area of greatest rib curvature

24. True ribs are _____.
    a. ribs 8–12
    b. attached via their costal cartilage to the next higher rib
    c. made entirely of bone, and thus do not have a costal cartilage
    d. attached via their costal cartilage directly to the sternum

25. Embryonic development of the axial skeleton involves _____.
    a. intramembranous ossification, which forms the facial bones.
    b. endochondral ossification, which forms the ribs and sternum
    c. the notochord, which produces the cartilage models for the vertebrae
    d. the formation of hyaline cartilage models, which give rise to the flat bones of the skull

26. A fontanelle _____.
    a. is the cartilage model for a vertebra that later is converted into bone
    b. gives rise to the facial bones and vertebrae
    c. is the rod-like structure that runs the length of the early embryo
    d. is the area of fibrous connective tissue found at birth between the brain case bones

Critical Thinking Questions

27. Define the two divisions of the skeleton.
28. Discuss the functions of the axial skeleton.
29. Define and list the bones that form the brain case or support the facial structures.
30. Identify the major sutures of the skull, their locations, and the bones united by each.

31. Describe the anterior, middle, and posterior cranial fossae and their boundaries, and give the midline structure that divides each into right and left areas.
32. Describe the parts of the nasal septum in both the dry and living skull.
33. Describe the vertebral column and define each region.
34. Describe a typical vertebra.
35. Describe the sacrum.
36. Describe the structure and function of an intervertebral disc.
37. Define the ligaments of the vertebral column.

38. Define the parts and functions of the thoracic cage.
39. Describe the parts of the sternum.
40. Discuss the parts of a typical rib.
41. Define the classes of ribs.
42. Discuss the processes by which the brain-case bones of the skull are formed and grow during skull enlargement.
43. Discuss the process that gives rise to the base and facial bones of the skull.
44. Discuss the development of the vertebrae, ribs, and sternum.

CHAPTER 8
The Appendicular Skeleton

Figure 8.1 **Dancer** The appendicular skeleton consists of the upper and lower limb bones, the bones of the hands and feet, and the bones that anchor the limbs to the axial skeleton. (credit: Melissa Dooley/flickr)

CHAPTER OBJECTIVES

After studying this chapter, you will be able to:

- Discuss the bones of the pectoral and pelvic girdles, and describe how these unite the limbs with the axial skeleton
- Describe the bones of the upper limb, including the bones of the arm, forearm, wrist, and hand
- Identify the features of the pelvis and explain how these differ between the adult male and female pelvis
- Describe the bones of the lower limb, including the bones of the thigh, leg, ankle, and foot
- Describe the embryonic formation and growth of the limb bones

INTRODUCTION Your skeleton provides the internal supporting structure of the body. The adult axial skeleton consists of 80 bones that form the head and body trunk. Attached to this are the limbs, whose 126 bones constitute the appendicular skeleton. These bones are divided into two groups: the bones that are located within the limbs themselves, and the girdle bones that attach the limbs to the axial skeleton. The bones of the shoulder region form the pectoral girdle, which anchors the upper limb to the thoracic cage of the axial skeleton. The lower limb is attached to the vertebral column by the pelvic girdle.

Because of our upright stance, different functional demands are placed upon the upper and lower limbs. Thus, the bones of the lower limbs are adapted for weight-bearing support and stability, as well as for body locomotion via walking or running. In contrast, our upper limbs are not required for these functions. Instead, our upper limbs are highly mobile and can be utilized for a wide variety of activities. The large range of upper limb movements, coupled with the ability to easily manipulate objects with our hands and opposable thumbs, has allowed humans to construct the modern world in which we live.

8.1 The Pectoral Girdle

LEARNING OBJECTIVES

By the end of this section, you will be able to:

- Describe the bones that form the pectoral girdle
- List the functions of the pectoral girdle

The appendicular skeleton includes all of the limb bones, plus the bones that unite each limb with the axial skeleton

(Figure 8.2). The bones that attach each upper limb to the axial skeleton form the pectoral girdle (shoulder girdle). This consists of two bones, the scapula and clavicle (Figure 8.3). The clavicle (collarbone) is an S-shaped bone located on the anterior side of the shoulder. It is attached on its medial end to the sternum of the thoracic cage, which is part of the axial skeleton. The lateral end of the clavicle articulates (joins) with the scapula just above the shoulder joint. You can easily palpate, or feel with your fingers, the entire length of your clavicle.

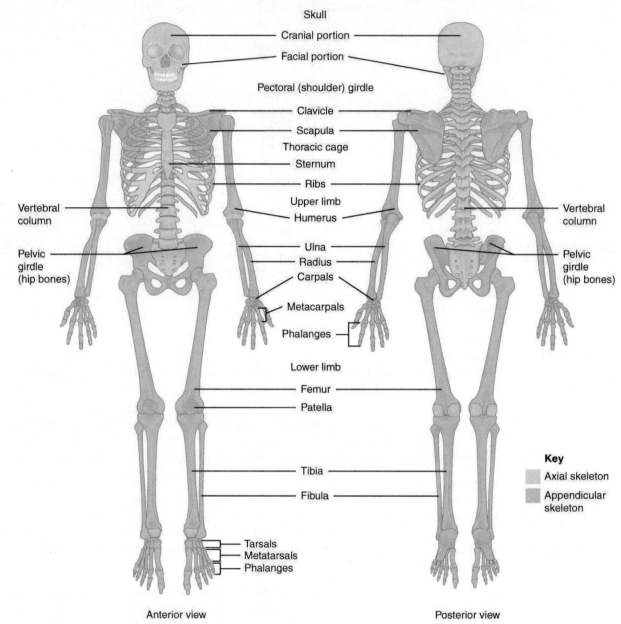

FIGURE 8.2   Axial and Appendicular Skeletons   The axial skeleton forms the central axis of the body and consists of the skull, vertebral column, and thoracic cage. The appendicular skeleton consists of the pectoral and pelvic girdles, the limb bones, and the bones of the hands and feet.

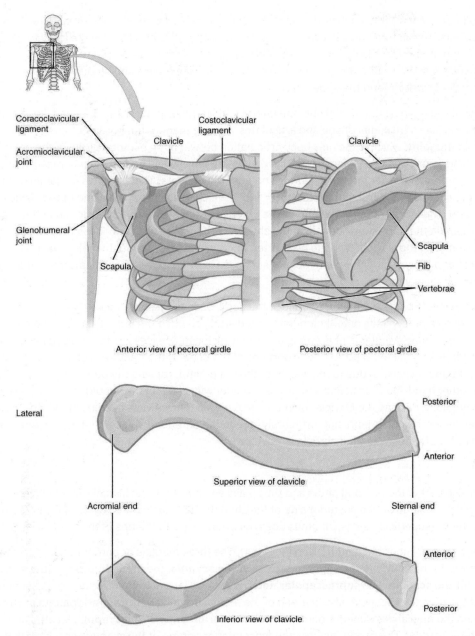

FIGURE 8.3 Pectoral Girdle   The pectoral girdle consists of the clavicle and the scapula, which serve to attach the upper limb to the sternum of the axial skeleton.

The **scapula** (shoulder blade) lies on the posterior aspect of the shoulder. It is supported by the **clavicle** and articulates with the humerus (arm bone) to form the shoulder joint. The scapula is a flat, triangular-shaped bone with a prominent ridge running across its posterior surface. This ridge extends out laterally, where it forms the bony tip of the shoulder and joins with the lateral end of the clavicle. By following along the clavicle, you can palpate out to the bony tip of the shoulder, and from there, you can move back across your posterior shoulder to follow the ridge of the scapula. Move your shoulder around and feel how the clavicle and scapula move together as a unit. Both of these bones serve as important attachment sites for muscles that aid with movements of the shoulder and arm.

The right and left pectoral girdles are not joined to each other, allowing each to operate independently. In addition, the clavicle of each **pectoral girdle** is anchored to the axial skeleton by a single, highly mobile joint. This allows for the extensive mobility of the entire pectoral girdle, which in turn enhances movements of the shoulder and upper limb.

Clavicle

The clavicle is the only long bone that lies in a horizontal position in the body (see <u>Figure 8.3</u>). The clavicle has several important functions. First, anchored by muscles from above, it serves as a strut that extends laterally to support the scapula. This in turn holds the shoulder joint superiorly and laterally from the body trunk, allowing for maximal freedom of motion for the upper limb. The clavicle also transmits forces acting on the upper limb to the sternum and axial skeleton. Finally, it serves to protect the underlying nerves and blood vessels as they pass between the trunk of the body and the upper limb.

The clavicle has three regions: the medial end, the lateral end, and the shaft. The medial end, known as the **sternal end of the clavicle**, has a triangular shape and articulates with the manubrium portion of the sternum. This forms the **sternoclavicular joint**, which is the only bony articulation between the pectoral girdle of the upper limb and the axial skeleton. This joint allows considerable mobility, enabling the clavicle and scapula to move in upward/downward and anterior/posterior directions during shoulder movements. The sternoclavicular joint is indirectly supported by the **costoclavicular ligament** (costo- = "rib"), which spans the sternal end of the clavicle and the underlying first rib. The lateral or **acromial end of the clavicle** articulates with the acromion of the scapula, the portion of the scapula that forms the bony tip of the shoulder. There are some sex differences in the morphology of the clavicle. In females, the clavicle tends to be shorter, thinner, and less curved. In males, the clavicle is heavier and longer, and has a greater curvature and rougher surfaces where muscles attach, features that are more pronounced in manual workers.

The clavicle is the most commonly fractured bone in the body. Such breaks often occur because of the force exerted on the clavicle when a person falls onto their outstretched arms, or when the lateral shoulder receives a strong blow. Because the sternoclavicular joint is strong and rarely dislocated, excessive force results in the breaking of the clavicle, usually between the middle and lateral portions of the bone. If the fracture is complete, the shoulder and lateral clavicle fragment will drop due to the weight of the upper limb, causing the person to support the sagging limb with their other hand. Muscles acting across the shoulder will also pull the shoulder and lateral clavicle anteriorly and medially, causing the clavicle fragments to override. The clavicle overlies many important blood vessels and nerves for the upper limb, but fortunately, due to the anterior displacement of a broken clavicle, these structures are rarely affected when the clavicle is fractured.

Scapula

The scapula is also part of the pectoral girdle and thus plays an important role in anchoring the upper limb to the body. The scapula is located on the posterior side of the shoulder. It is surrounded by muscles on both its anterior (deep) and posterior (superficial) sides, and thus does not articulate with the ribs of the thoracic cage.

The scapula has several important landmarks (Figure 8.4). The three margins or borders of the scapula, named for their positions within the body, are the **superior border of the scapula**, the **medial border of the scapula**, and the **lateral border of the scapula**. The **suprascapular notch** is located lateral to the midpoint of the superior border. The corners of the triangular scapula, at either end of the medial border, are the **superior angle of the scapula**, located between the medial and superior borders, and the **inferior angle of the scapula**, located between the medial and lateral borders. The inferior angle is the most inferior portion of the scapula, and is particularly important because it serves as the attachment point for several powerful muscles involved in shoulder and upper limb movements. The remaining corner of the scapula, between the superior and lateral borders, is the location of the **glenoid cavity** (glenoid fossa). This shallow depression articulates with the humerus bone of the arm to form the **glenohumeral joint** (shoulder joint). The small bony bumps located immediately above and below the glenoid cavity are the **supraglenoid tubercle** and the **infraglenoid tubercle**, respectively. These provide attachments for muscles of the arm.

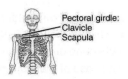

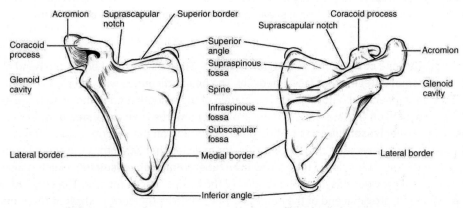

FIGURE 8.4 Scapula   The isolated scapula is shown here from its anterior (deep) side and its posterior (superficial) side.

The scapula also has two prominent projections. Toward the lateral end of the superior border, between the suprascapular notch and glenoid cavity, is the hook-like **coracoid process** (coracoid = "shaped like a crow's beak"). This process projects anteriorly and curves laterally. At the shoulder, the coracoid process is located inferior to the lateral end of the clavicle. It is anchored to the clavicle by a strong ligament, and serves as the attachment site for muscles of the anterior chest and arm. On the posterior aspect, the **spine of the scapula** is a long and prominent ridge that runs across its upper portion. Extending laterally from the spine is a flattened and expanded region called the **acromion** or **acromial process**. The acromion forms the bony tip of the superior shoulder region and articulates with the lateral end of the clavicle, forming the **acromioclavicular joint** (see Figure 8.3). Together, the clavicle, acromion, and spine of the scapula form a V-shaped bony line that provides for the attachment of neck and back muscles that act on the shoulder, as well as muscles that pass across the shoulder joint to act on the arm.

The scapula has three depressions, each of which is called a **fossa** (plural = fossae). Two of these are found on the posterior scapula, above and below the scapular spine. Superior to the spine is the narrow **supraspinous fossa**, and inferior to the spine is the broad **infraspinous fossa**. The anterior (deep) surface of the scapula forms the broad **subscapular fossa**. All of these fossae provide large surface areas for the attachment of muscles that cross the shoulder joint to act on the humerus.

The acromioclavicular joint transmits forces from the upper limb to the clavicle. The ligaments around this joint are relatively weak. A hard fall onto the elbow or outstretched hand can stretch or tear the acromioclavicular ligaments, resulting in a moderate injury to the joint. However, the primary support for the acromioclavicular joint comes from a very strong ligament called the **coracoclavicular ligament** (see Figure 8.3). This connective tissue band anchors the coracoid process of the scapula to the inferior surface of the acromial end of the clavicle and thus provides important indirect support for the acromioclavicular joint. Following a strong blow to the lateral shoulder, such as when a hockey player is driven into the boards, a complete dislocation of the acromioclavicular joint can result. In this case, the acromion is thrust under the acromial end of the clavicle, resulting in ruptures of both the acromioclavicular and coracoclavicular ligaments. The scapula then separates from the clavicle, with the weight of the upper limb pulling the shoulder downward. This dislocation injury of the acromioclavicular joint is known as a "shoulder separation" and is common in contact sports such as hockey, football, or martial arts.

8.2 Bones of the Upper Limb

LEARNING OBJECTIVES

By the end of this section, you will be able to:

- Identify the divisions of the upper limb and describe the bones in each region
- List the bones and bony landmarks that articulate at each joint of the upper limb

The upper limb is divided into three regions. These consist of the **arm**, located between the shoulder and elbow joints; the **forearm**, which is between the elbow and wrist joints; and the **hand**, which is located distal to the wrist. There are 30 bones in each upper limb (see Figure 8.2). The **humerus** is the single bone of the upper arm, and the **ulna** (medially) and the **radius** (laterally) are the paired bones of the forearm. The base of the hand contains eight bones, each called a **carpal bone**, and the palm of the hand is formed by five bones, each called a **metacarpal bone**. The fingers and thumb contain a total of 14 bones, each of which is a **phalanx bone of the hand**.

Humerus

The humerus is the single bone of the upper arm region (Figure 8.5). At its proximal end is the **head of the humerus**. This is the large, round, smooth region that faces medially. The head articulates with the glenoid cavity of the scapula to form the glenohumeral (shoulder) joint. The margin of the smooth area of the head is the **anatomical neck** of the humerus. Located on the lateral side of the proximal humerus is an expanded bony area called the **greater tubercle**. The smaller **lesser tubercle** of the humerus is found on the anterior aspect of the humerus. Both the greater and lesser tubercles serve as attachment sites for muscles that act across the shoulder joint. Passing between the greater and lesser tubercles is the narrow **intertubercular groove (sulcus)**, which is also known as the **bicipital groove** because it provides passage for a tendon of the biceps brachii muscle. The **surgical neck** is located at the base of the expanded, proximal end of the humerus, where it joins the narrow **shaft of the humerus**. The surgical neck is a common site of arm fractures. The **deltoid tuberosity** is a roughened, V-shaped region located on the lateral side in the middle of the humerus shaft. As its name indicates, it is the site of attachment for the deltoid muscle.

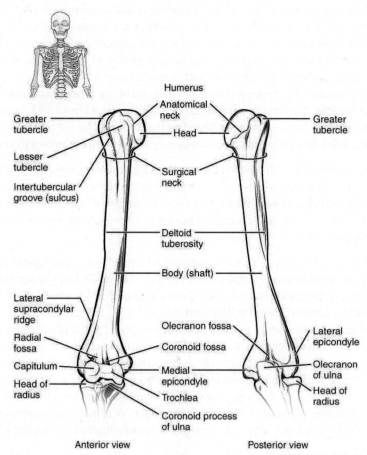

FIGURE 8.5   Humerus and Elbow Joint   The humerus is the single bone of the upper arm region. It articulates with the radius and ulna bones of the forearm to form the elbow joint.

Distally, the humerus becomes flattened. The prominent bony projection on the medial side is the **medial epicondyle of the humerus**. The much smaller **lateral epicondyle of the humerus** is found on the lateral side of the distal humerus. The roughened ridge of bone above the lateral epicondyle is the **lateral supracondylar ridge**. All of these areas are attachment points for muscles that act on the forearm, wrist, and hand. The powerful grasping muscles of the anterior forearm arise from the medial epicondyle, which is thus larger and more robust than the lateral epicondyle that gives rise to the weaker posterior forearm muscles.

The distal end of the humerus has two articulation areas, which join the ulna and radius bones of the forearm to form the **elbow joint**. The more medial of these areas is the **trochlea**, a spindle- or pulley-shaped region (trochlea = "pulley"), which articulates with the ulna bone. Immediately lateral to the trochlea is the **capitulum** ("small head"), a knob-like structure located on the anterior surface of the distal humerus. The capitulum articulates with the radius bone of the forearm. Just above these bony areas are two small depressions. These spaces accommodate the forearm bones when the elbow is fully bent (flexed). Superior to the trochlea is the **coronoid fossa**, which receives the coronoid process of the ulna, and above the capitulum is the **radial fossa**, which receives the head of the radius when the elbow is flexed. Similarly, the posterior humerus has the **olecranon fossa**, a larger depression that receives the olecranon process of the ulna when the forearm is fully extended.

Ulna

The ulna is the medial bone of the forearm. It runs parallel to the radius, which is the lateral bone of the forearm (Figure 8.6). The proximal end of the ulna resembles a crescent wrench with its large, C-shaped **trochlear notch**. This region articulates with the trochlea of the humerus as part of the elbow joint. The inferior margin of the trochlear notch is formed by a prominent lip of bone called the **coronoid process of the ulna**. Just below this on the anterior ulna is a roughened area called the **ulnar tuberosity**. To the lateral side and slightly inferior to the trochlear notch is a small, smooth area called the **radial notch of the ulna**. This area is the site of articulation between the proximal radius and the ulna, forming the **proximal radioulnar joint**. The posterior and superior portions of the proximal ulna make up the **olecranon process**, which forms the bony tip of the elbow.

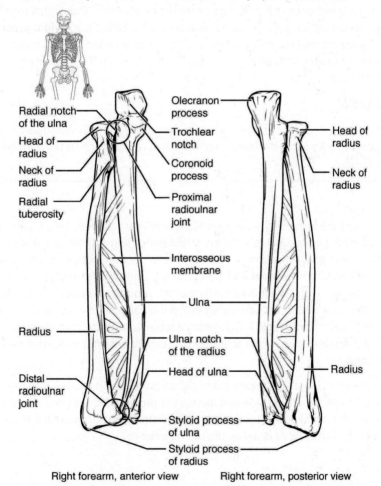

Radial notch of the ulna

Head of radius

Neck of radius

Radial tuberosity

Radius

Distal radioulnar joint

Olecranon process

Trochlear notch

Coronoid process

Proximal radioulnar joint

Interosseous membrane

Ulna

Ulnar notch of the radius

Head of ulna

Styloid process of ulna

Styloid process of radius

Head of radius

Neck of radius

Radius

Right forearm, anterior view   Right forearm, posterior view

FIGURE 8.6 Ulna and Radius The ulna is located on the medial side of the forearm, and the radius is on the lateral side. These bones are attached to each other by an interosseous membrane.

More distal is the **shaft of the ulna**. The lateral side of the shaft forms a ridge called the **interosseous border of the** ulna. This is the line of attachment for the **interosseous membrane of the forearm**, a sheet of dense connective tissue that unites the ulna and radius bones. The small, rounded area that forms the distal end is the **head of the ulna**. Projecting from the posterior side of the ulnar head is the **styloid process of the ulna**, a short bony projection. This serves as an attachment point for a connective tissue structure that unites the distal ends of the ulna and radius.

In the anatomical position, with the elbow fully extended and the palms facing forward, the arm and forearm do not form a straight line. Instead, the forearm deviates laterally by 5–15 degrees from the line of the arm. This deviation is called the carrying angle. It allows the forearm and hand to swing freely or to carry an object without hitting the hip. The carrying angle is larger in females to accommodate their wider pelvis.

Radius

The radius runs parallel to the ulna, on the lateral (thumb) side of the forearm (see Figure 8.6). The **head of the radius** is a disc-shaped structure that forms the proximal end. The small depression on the surface of the head articulates with the capitulum of the humerus as part of the elbow joint, whereas the smooth, outer margin of the head articulates with the radial notch of the ulna at the proximal radioulnar joint. The **neck of the radius** is the narrowed region immediately below the expanded head. Inferior to this point on the medial side is the **radial tuberosity**, an oval-shaped, bony protuberance that serves as a muscle attachment point. The **shaft of the radius** is slightly curved and has a small ridge along its medial side. This ridge forms the **interosseous border of the radius**, which, like the similar border of the ulna, is the line of attachment for the interosseous membrane that unites the two forearm bones. The distal end of the radius has a smooth surface for articulation with two carpal bones to form the **radiocarpal joint** or wrist joint (Figure 8.7 and Figure 8.8). On the medial side of the distal radius is the **ulnar notch of the radius**. This shallow depression articulates with the head of the ulna, which together form the **distal radioulnar joint**. The lateral end of the radius has a pointed projection called the **styloid process of the radius**. This provides attachment for ligaments that support the lateral side of the wrist joint. Compared to the styloid process of the ulna, the styloid process of the radius projects more distally, thereby limiting the range of movement for lateral deviations of the hand at the wrist joint.

⊚ INTERACTIVE LINK

Watch this video (http://openstax.org/l/fractures) to see how fractures of the distal radius bone can affect the wrist joint. Explain the problems that may occur if a fracture of the distal radius involves the joint surface of the radiocarpal joint of the wrist.

Carpal Bones

The wrist and base of the hand are formed by a series of eight small carpal bones (see Figure 8.7). The carpal bones are arranged in two rows, forming a proximal row of four carpal bones and a distal row of four carpal bones. The bones in the proximal row, running from the lateral (thumb) side to the medial side, are the **scaphoid** ("boat-shaped"), **lunate** ("moon-shaped"), **triquetrum** ("three-cornered"), and **pisiform** ("pea-shaped") bones. The small, rounded pisiform bone articulates with the anterior surface of the triquetrum bone. The pisiform thus projects anteriorly, where it forms the bony bump that can be felt at the medial base of your hand. The distal bones (lateral to medial) are the **trapezium** ("table"), **trapezoid** ("resembles a table"), **capitate** ("head-shaped"), and **hamate** ("hooked bone") bones. The hamate bone is characterized by a prominent bony extension on its anterior side called the **hook of the hamate bone**.

A helpful mnemonic for remembering the arrangement of the carpal bones is "So Long To Pinky, Here Comes The Thumb." This mnemonic starts on the lateral side and names the proximal bones from lateral to medial (scaphoid, lunate, triquetrum, pisiform), then makes a U-turn to name the distal bones from medial to lateral (hamate, capitate, trapezoid, trapezium). Thus, it starts and finishes on the lateral side.

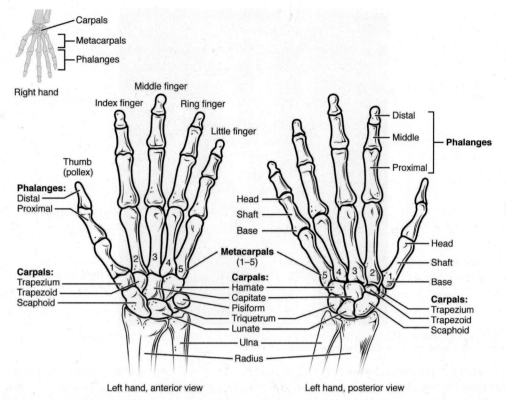

FIGURE 8.7   Bones of the Wrist and Hand   The eight carpal bones form the base of the hand. These are arranged into proximal and distal rows of four bones each. The metacarpal bones form the palm of the hand. The thumb and fingers consist of the phalanx bones.

The carpal bones form the base of the hand. This can be seen in the radiograph (X-ray image) of the hand that shows the relationships of the hand bones to the skin creases of the hand (see Figure 8.8). Within the carpal bones, the four proximal bones are united to each other by ligaments to form a unit. Only three of these bones, the scaphoid, lunate, and triquetrum, contribute to the radiocarpal joint. The scaphoid and lunate bones articulate directly with the distal end of the radius, whereas the triquetrum bone articulates with a fibrocartilaginous pad that spans the radius and styloid process of the ulna. The distal end of the ulna thus does not directly articulate with any of the carpal bones.

The four distal carpal bones are also held together as a group by ligaments. The proximal and distal rows of carpal bones articulate with each other to form the **midcarpal joint** (see Figure 8.8). Together, the radiocarpal and midcarpal joints are responsible for all movements of the hand at the wrist. The distal carpal bones also articulate with the metacarpal bones of the hand.

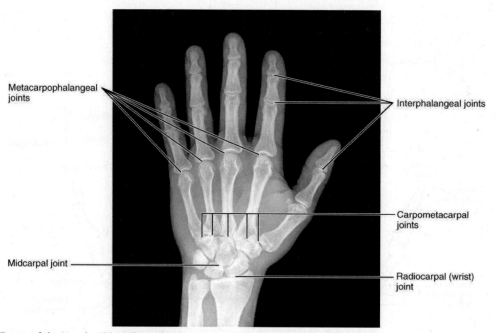

FIGURE 8.8   Bones of the Hand   This radiograph shows the position of the bones within the hand. Note the carpal bones that form the base of the hand. (credit: modification of work by Trace Meek)

In the articulated hand, the carpal bones form a U-shaped grouping. A strong ligament called the **flexor retinaculum** spans the top of this U-shaped area to maintain this grouping of the carpal bones. The flexor retinaculum is attached laterally to the trapezium and scaphoid bones, and medially to the hamate and pisiform bones. Together, the carpal bones and the flexor retinaculum form a passageway called the **carpal tunnel**, with the carpal bones forming the walls and floor, and the flexor retinaculum forming the roof of this space (Figure 8.9). The tendons of nine muscles of the anterior forearm and an important nerve pass through this narrow tunnel to enter the hand. Overuse of the muscle tendons or wrist injury can produce inflammation and swelling within this space. This produces compression of the nerve, resulting in carpal tunnel syndrome, which is characterized by pain or numbness, and muscle weakness in those areas of the hand supplied by this nerve.

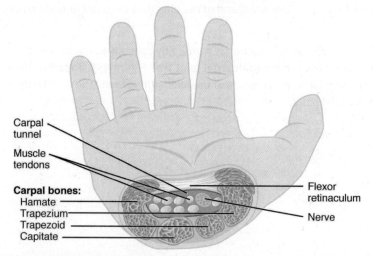

FIGURE 8.9   Carpal Tunnel   The carpal tunnel is the passageway by which nine muscle tendons and a major nerve enter the hand from the anterior forearm. The walls and floor of the carpal tunnel are formed by the U-shaped grouping of the carpal bones, and the roof is formed by the flexor retinaculum, a strong ligament that anteriorly unites the bones.

Metacarpal Bones

The palm of the hand contains five elongated metacarpal bones. These bones lie between the carpal bones of the wrist and the bones of the fingers and thumb (see Figure 8.7). The proximal end of each metacarpal bone articulates with one of the distal carpal bones. Each of these articulations is a **carpometacarpal joint** (see Figure 8.8). The expanded distal end of each metacarpal bone articulates at the **metacarpophalangeal joint** with the proximal phalanx bone of the thumb or one of the fingers. The distal end also forms the knuckles of the hand, at the base of the fingers. The metacarpal bones are numbered 1–5, beginning at the thumb.

The first metacarpal bone, at the base of the thumb, is separated from the other metacarpal bones. This allows it a freedom of motion that is independent of the other metacarpal bones, which is very important for thumb mobility. The remaining metacarpal bones are united together to form the palm of the hand. The second and third metacarpal bones are firmly anchored in place and are immobile. However, the fourth and fifth metacarpal bones have limited anterior-posterior mobility, a motion that is greater for the fifth bone. This mobility is important during power gripping with the hand (Figure 8.10). The anterior movement of these bones, particularly the fifth metacarpal bone, increases the strength of contact for the medial hand during gripping actions.

(a) Loosely held   (b) Firmly gripped

FIGURE 8.10 Hand During Gripping During tight gripping—compare (b) to (a)—the fourth and, particularly, the fifth metatarsal bones are pulled anteriorly. This increases the contact between the object and the medial side of the hand, thus improving the firmness of the grip.

Phalanx Bones

The fingers and thumb contain 14 bones, each of which is called a phalanx bone (plural = phalanges), named after the ancient Greek phalanx (a rectangular block of soldiers). The thumb (**pollex**) is digit number 1 and has two phalanges, a proximal phalanx, and a distal phalanx bone (see Figure 8.7). Digits 2 (index finger) through 5 (little finger) have three phalanges each, called the proximal, middle, and distal phalanx bones. An **interphalangeal joint** is one of the articulations between adjacent phalanges of the digits (see Figure 8.8).

🔗 INTERACTIVE LINK

Visit this site (http://openstax.org/l/handbone) to explore the bones and joints of the hand.

Disorders of the...

Appendicular System: Fractures of Upper Limb Bones

Due to our constant use of the hands and the rest of our upper limbs, an injury to any of these areas will cause a significant loss of functional ability. Many fractures result from a hard fall onto an outstretched hand. The resulting transmission of force up the limb may result in a fracture of the humerus, radius, or scaphoid bones. These injuries are especially common in elderly people whose bones are weakened due to osteoporosis.

Falls onto the hand or elbow, or direct blows to the arm, can result in fractures of the humerus (Figure 8.11). Following a fall, fractures at the surgical neck, the region at which the expanded proximal end of the humerus joins with the shaft, can result in an impacted fracture, in which the distal portion of the humerus is driven into the proximal portion. Falls or blows to the arm can also produce transverse or spiral fractures of the humeral shaft.

In children, a fall onto the tip of the elbow frequently results in a distal humerus fracture. In these, the olecranon of the ulna is driven upward, resulting in a fracture across the distal humerus, above both epicondyles (supracondylar fracture), or a fracture between the epicondyles, thus separating one or both of the epicondyles from the body of the humerus (intercondylar fracture). With these injuries, the immediate concern is possible compression of the artery to the forearm due to swelling of the surrounding tissues. If compression occurs, the resulting ischemia (lack of oxygen) due to reduced blood flow can quickly produce irreparable damage to the forearm muscles. In addition, four major nerves for shoulder and upper limb muscles are closely associated with different regions of the humerus, and thus, humeral fractures may also damage these nerves.

Another frequent injury following a fall onto an outstretched hand is a Colles fracture ("col-lees") of the distal radius (see Figure 8.11). This involves a complete transverse fracture across the distal radius that drives the separated distal fragment of the radius posteriorly and superiorly. This injury results in a characteristic "dinner fork" bend of the forearm just above the wrist due to the posterior displacement of the hand. This is the most frequent forearm fracture and is a common injury in persons over the age of 50, particularly in older people with osteoporosis. It also commonly occurs following a high-speed fall onto the hand during activities such as snowboarding or skating.

The most commonly fractured carpal bone is the scaphoid, often resulting from a fall onto the hand. Deep pain at the lateral wrist may yield an initial diagnosis of a wrist sprain, but a radiograph taken several weeks after the injury, after tissue swelling has subsided, will reveal the fracture. Due to the poor blood supply to the scaphoid bone, healing will be slow and there is the danger of bone necrosis and subsequent degenerative joint disease of the wrist.

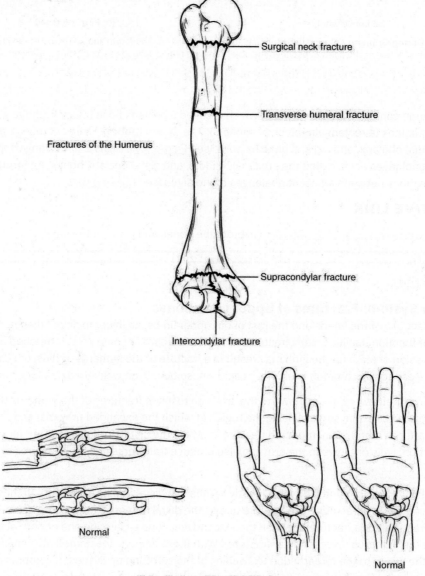

FIGURE 8.11   Fractures of the Humerus and Radius   Falls or direct blows can result in fractures of the surgical neck or shaft of the humerus. Falls onto the elbow can fracture the distal humerus. A Colles fracture of the distal radius is the most common forearm fracture.

🔗 INTERACTIVE LINK

Watch this video (http://openstax.org/l/colles) to learn about a Colles fracture, a break of the distal radius, usually caused by falling onto an outstretched hand. When would surgery be required and how would the fracture be repaired in this case?

8.3 The Pelvic Girdle and Pelvis

LEARNING OBJECTIVES

By the end of this section, you will be able to:

- Define the pelvic girdle and describe the bones and ligaments of the pelvis
- Explain the three regions of the hip bone and identify their bony landmarks
- Describe the openings of the pelvis and the boundaries of the greater and lesser pelvis

The **pelvic girdle** (hip girdle) is formed by a single bone, the **hip bone** or **coxal bone** (coxal = "hip"), which serves as the attachment point for each lower limb. Each hip bone, in turn, is firmly joined to the axial skeleton via its attachment to the sacrum of the vertebral column. The right and left hip bones also converge anteriorly to attach to each other. The bony **pelvis** is the entire structure formed by the two hip bones, the sacrum, and, attached inferiorly to the sacrum, the coccyx (Figure 8.12).

Unlike the bones of the pectoral girdle, which are highly mobile to enhance the range of upper limb movements, the bones of the pelvis are strongly united to each other to form a largely immobile, weight-bearing structure. This is important for stability because it enables the weight of the body to be easily transferred laterally from the vertebral column, through the pelvic girdle and hip joints, and into either lower limb whenever the other limb is not bearing weight. Thus, the immobility of the pelvis provides a strong foundation for the upper body as it rests on top of the mobile lower limbs.

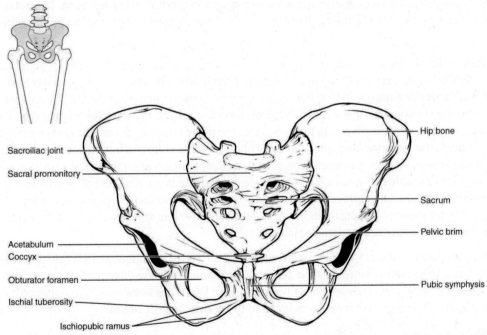

FIGURE 8.12   Pelvis   The pelvic girdle is formed by a single hip bone. The hip bone attaches the lower limb to the axial skeleton through its articulation with the sacrum. The right and left hip bones, plus the sacrum and the coccyx, together form the pelvis.

Hip Bone

The hip bone, or coxal bone, forms the pelvic girdle portion of the pelvis. The paired hip bones are the large, curved bones that form the lateral and anterior aspects of the pelvis. Each adult hip bone is formed by three separate bones that fuse together during the late teenage years. These bony components are the ilium, ischium, and pubis (Figure 8.13). These names are retained and used to define the three regions of the adult hip bone.

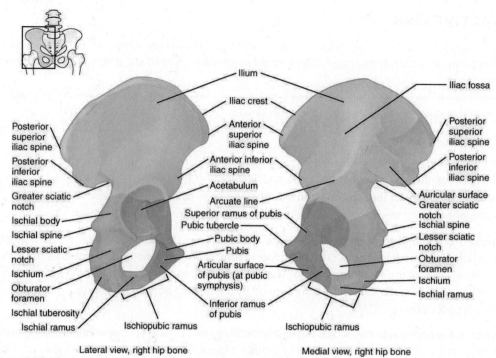

Lateral view, right hip bone   Medial view, right hip bone

FIGURE 8.13   The Hip Bone   The adult hip bone consists of three regions. The ilium forms the large, fan-shaped superior portion, the ischium forms the posteroinferior portion, and the pubis forms the anteromedial portion.

The **ilium** is the fan-like, superior region that forms the largest part of the hip bone. It is firmly united to the sacrum at the largely immobile **sacroiliac joint** (see Figure 8.12). The **ischium** forms the posteroinferior region of each hip bone. It supports the body when sitting. The **pubis** forms the anterior portion of the hip bone. The pubis curves medially, where it joins to the pubis of the opposite hip bone at a specialized joint called the **pubic symphysis**.

Ilium

When you place your hands on your waist, you can feel the arching, superior margin of the ilium along your waistline (see Figure 8.13). This curved, superior margin of the ilium is the **iliac crest**. The rounded, anterior termination of the iliac crest is the **anterior superior iliac spine**. This important bony landmark can be felt at your anterolateral hip. Inferior to the anterior superior iliac spine is a rounded protuberance called the **anterior inferior iliac spine**. Both of these iliac spines serve as attachment points for muscles of the thigh. Posteriorly, the iliac crest curves downward to terminate as the **posterior superior iliac spine**. Muscles and ligaments surround but do not cover this bony landmark, thus sometimes producing a depression seen as a "dimple" located on the lower back. More inferiorly is the **posterior inferior iliac spine**. This is located at the inferior end of a large, roughened area called the **auricular surface of the ilium**. The auricular surface articulates with the auricular surface of the sacrum to form the sacroiliac joint. Both the posterior superior and posterior inferior iliac spines serve as attachment points for the muscles and very strong ligaments that support the sacroiliac joint.

The shallow depression located on the anteromedial (internal) surface of the upper ilium is called the **iliac fossa**. The inferior margin of this space is formed by the **arcuate line of the ilium,** the ridge formed by the pronounced change in curvature between the upper and lower portions of the ilium. The large, inverted U-shaped indentation located on the posterior margin of the lower ilium is called the **greater sciatic notch**.

Ischium

The ischium forms the posterolateral portion of the hip bone (see Figure 8.13). The large, roughened area of the inferior ischium is the **ischial tuberosity**. This serves as the attachment for the posterior thigh muscles and also carries the weight of the body when sitting. You can feel the ischial tuberosity if you wiggle your pelvis against the seat of a chair. Projecting superiorly and anteriorly from the ischial tuberosity is a narrow segment of bone called the **ischial ramus**. The slightly curved posterior margin of the ischium above the ischial tuberosity is the **lesser sciatic notch**. The bony projection separating the lesser sciatic notch and greater sciatic notch is the **ischial spine**.

Access for free at openstax.org

Pubis

The pubis forms the anterior portion of the hip bone (see Figure 8.13). The enlarged medial portion of the pubis is the **pubic body**. Located superiorly on the pubic body is a small bump called the **pubic tubercle**. The **superior pubic ramus** is the segment of bone that passes laterally from the pubic body to join the ilium. The narrow ridge running along the superior margin of the superior pubic ramus is the **pectineal line** of the pubis.

The pubic body is joined to the pubic body of the opposite hip bone by the pubic symphysis. Extending downward and laterally from the body is the **inferior pubic ramus**. The **pubic arch** is the bony structure formed by the pubic symphysis, and the bodies and inferior pubic rami of the adjacent pubic bones. The inferior pubic ramus extends downward to join the ischial ramus. Together, these form the single **ischiopubic ramus**, which extends from the pubic body to the ischial tuberosity. The inverted V-shape formed as the ischiopubic rami from both sides come together at the pubic symphysis is called the **subpubic angle**.

Pelvis

The pelvis consists of four bones: the right and left hip bones, the sacrum, and the coccyx (see Figure 8.12). The pelvis has several important functions. Its primary role is to support the weight of the upper body when sitting and to transfer this weight to the lower limbs when standing. It serves as an attachment point for trunk and lower limb muscles, and also protects the internal pelvic organs. When standing in the anatomical position, the pelvis is tilted anteriorly. In this position, the anterior superior iliac spines and the pubic tubercles lie in the same vertical plane, and the anterior (internal) surface of the sacrum faces forward and downward.

The three areas of each hip bone, the ilium, pubis, and ischium, converge centrally to form a deep, cup-shaped cavity called the **acetabulum**. This is located on the lateral side of the hip bone and is part of the hip joint. The large opening in the anteroinferior hip bone between the ischium and pubis is the **obturator foramen**. This space is largely filled in by a layer of connective tissue and serves for the attachment of muscles on both its internal and external surfaces.

Several ligaments unite the bones of the pelvis (Figure 8.14). The largely immobile sacroiliac joint is supported by a pair of strong ligaments that are attached between the sacrum and ilium portions of the hip bone. These are the **anterior sacroiliac ligament** on the anterior side of the joint and the **posterior sacroiliac ligament** on the posterior side. Also spanning the sacrum and hip bone are two additional ligaments. The **sacrospinous ligament** runs from the sacrum to the ischial spine, and the **sacrotuberous ligament** runs from the sacrum to the ischial tuberosity. These ligaments help to support and immobilize the sacrum as it carries the weight of the body.

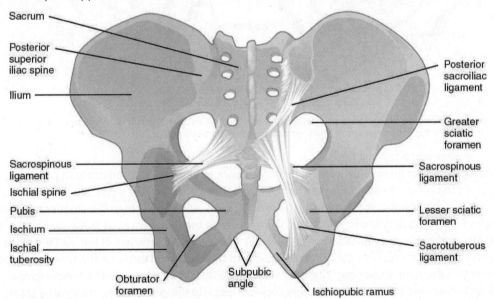

FIGURE 8.14 Ligaments of the Pelvis   The posterior sacroiliac ligament supports the sacroiliac joint. The sacrospinous ligament spans the sacrum to the ischial spine, and the sacrotuberous ligament spans the sacrum to the ischial tuberosity. The sacrospinous and sacrotuberous ligaments contribute to the formation of the greater and lesser sciatic foramina.

INTERACTIVE LINK

Watch this video (http://openstax.org/l/3Dpelvis) for a 3-D view of the pelvis and its associated ligaments. What is the large opening in the bony pelvis, located between the ischium and pubic regions, and what two parts of the pubis contribute to the formation of this opening?

The sacrospinous and sacrotuberous ligaments also help to define two openings on the posterolateral sides of the pelvis through which muscles, nerves, and blood vessels for the lower limb exit. The superior opening is the **greater sciatic foramen**. This large opening is formed by the greater sciatic notch of the hip bone, the sacrum, and the sacrospinous ligament. The smaller, more inferior **lesser sciatic foramen** is formed by the lesser sciatic notch of the hip bone, together with the sacrospinous and sacrotuberous ligaments.

The space enclosed by the bony pelvis is divided into two regions (Figure 8.15). The broad, superior region, defined laterally by the large, fan-like portion of the upper hip bone, is called the **greater pelvis** (greater pelvic cavity; false pelvis). This broad area is occupied by portions of the small and large intestines, and because it is more closely associated with the abdominal cavity, it is sometimes referred to as the false pelvis. More inferiorly, the narrow, rounded space of the **lesser pelvis** (lesser pelvic cavity; true pelvis) contains the bladder and other pelvic organs, and thus is also known as the true pelvis. The **pelvic brim** (also known as the **pelvic inlet**) forms the superior margin of the lesser pelvis, separating it from the greater pelvis. The pelvic brim is defined by a line formed by the upper margin of the pubic symphysis anteriorly, and the pectineal line of the pubis, the arcuate line of the ilium, and the sacral promontory (the anterior margin of the superior sacrum) posteriorly. The inferior limit of the lesser pelvic cavity is called the **pelvic outlet**. This large opening is defined by the inferior margin of the pubic symphysis anteriorly, and the ischiopubic ramus, the ischial tuberosity, the sacrotuberous ligament, and the inferior tip of the coccyx posteriorly. Because of the anterior tilt of the pelvis, the lesser pelvis is also angled, giving it an anterosuperior (pelvic inlet) to posteroinferior (pelvic outlet) orientation.

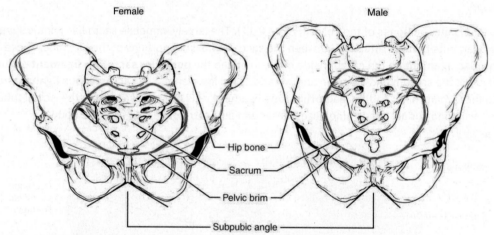

FIGURE 8.15   Male and Female Pelvis   The female pelvis is adapted for childbirth and is broader, with a larger subpubic angle, a rounder pelvic brim, and a wider and more shallow lesser pelvic cavity than the male pelvis.

Comparison of the Female and Male Pelvis

The differences between the adult female and male pelvis relate to function and body size. In general, the bones of the male pelvis are thicker and heavier, adapted for support of the male's heavier physical build and stronger muscles. The greater sciatic notch of the male hip bone is narrower and deeper than the broader notch of females. Because the female pelvis is adapted for childbirth, it is wider than the male pelvis, as evidenced by the distance between the anterior superior iliac spines (see Figure 8.15). The ischial tuberosities of females are also farther apart, which increases the size of the pelvic outlet. Because of this increased pelvic width, the subpubic angle is larger in females (greater than 80 degrees) than it is in males (less than 70 degrees). The female sacrum is wider, shorter, and less curved, and the sacral promontory projects less into the pelvic cavity, thus giving the female pelvic inlet (pelvic brim) a more rounded or oval shape compared to males. The lesser pelvic cavity of females is also wider and more shallow than the narrower, deeper, and tapering lesser pelvis of males. Because of the obvious differences between female and male hip bones, this is the one bone of the body that allows for the most accurate sex determination. Table 8.1 provides an overview of the general differences between the female and male pelvis.

Overview of Differences between the Female and Male Pelvis

	Female pelvis	Male pelvis
Pelvic weight	Bones of the pelvis are lighter and thinner	Bones of the pelvis are thicker and heavier
Pelvic inlet shape	Pelvic inlet has a round or oval shape	Pelvic inlet is heart-shaped
Lesser pelvic cavity shape	Lesser pelvic cavity is shorter and wider	Lesser pelvic cavity is longer and narrower
Subpubic angle	Subpubic angle is greater than 80 degrees	Subpubic angle is less than 70 degrees
Pelvic outlet shape	Pelvic outlet is rounded and larger	Pelvic outlet is smaller

TABLE 8.1

 CAREER CONNECTION

Forensic Pathology and Forensic Anthropology

A forensic pathologist (also known as a medical examiner) is a medically trained physician who has been specifically trained in pathology to examine the bodies of the deceased to determine the cause of death. A forensic pathologist applies understanding of disease as well as toxins, blood and DNA analysis, firearms and ballistics, and other factors to assess the cause and manner of death. At times, a forensic pathologist will be called to testify under oath in situations that involve a possible crime. Forensic pathology is a field that has received much media attention on television shows or following a high-profile death.

While forensic pathologists are responsible for determining whether the cause of someone's death was natural, by suicide, accidental, or by homicide, there are times when uncovering the cause of death is more complex, and other skills are needed. Forensic anthropology brings the tools and knowledge of physical anthropology and human osteology (the study of the skeleton) to the task of investigating a death. A forensic anthropologist assists medical and legal professionals in identifying human remains. The science behind forensic anthropology involves the study of archaeological excavation; the examination of hair; an understanding of plants, insects, and footprints; the ability to determine how much time has elapsed since the person died; the analysis of past medical history and toxicology; the ability to determine whether there are any postmortem injuries or alterations of the skeleton; and the identification of the decedent (deceased person) using skeletal and dental evidence.

Due to the extensive knowledge and understanding of excavation techniques, a forensic anthropologist is an integral and invaluable team member to have on-site when investigating a crime scene, especially when the recovery of human skeletal remains is involved. When remains are bought to a forensic anthropologist for examination, they must first determine whether the remains are in fact human. Once the remains have been identified as belonging to a person and not to an animal, the next step is to approximate the individual's age, sex, race, and height. The forensic anthropologist does not determine the cause of death, but rather provides information to the forensic pathologist, who will use all of the data collected to make a final determination regarding the cause of death.

8.4 Bones of the Lower Limb

LEARNING OBJECTIVES

By the end of this section, you will be able to:

- Identify the divisions of the lower limb and describe the bones of each region
- Describe the bones and bony landmarks that articulate at each joint of the lower limb

Like the upper limb, the lower limb is divided into three regions. The **thigh** is that portion of the lower limb located between the hip joint and knee joint. The **leg** is specifically the region between the knee joint and the ankle joint. Distal to the ankle is the **foot**. The lower limb contains 30 bones. These are the femur, patella, tibia, fibula, tarsal bones, metatarsal bones, and phalanges (see Figure 8.2). The **femur** is the single bone of the thigh. The **patella** is the kneecap and articulates with the distal femur. The **tibia** is the larger, weight-bearing bone located on the medial side of the leg, and the **fibula** is the thin bone of the lateral leg. The bones of the foot are divided into three groups. The posterior portion of the foot is formed by a group of seven bones, each of which is known as a **tarsal bone**, whereas the mid-foot contains five elongated bones, each of which is a **metatarsal bone**. The toes contain 14 small bones, each of which is a **phalanx bone of the foot**.

Femur

The femur, or thigh bone, is the single bone of the thigh region (Figure 8.16). It is the longest and strongest bone of the body, and accounts for approximately one-quarter of a person's total height. The rounded, proximal end is the **head of the femur**, which articulates with the acetabulum of the hip bone to form the **hip joint**. The **fovea capitis** is a minor indentation on the medial side of the femoral head that serves as the site of attachment for the **ligament of the head of the femur**. This ligament spans the femur and acetabulum, but is weak and provides little support for the hip joint. It does, however, carry an important artery that supplies the head of the femur.

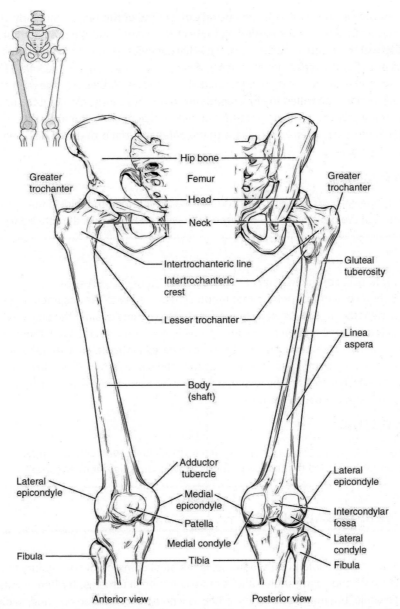

FIGURE 8.16 Femur and Patella The femur is the single bone of the thigh region. It articulates superiorly with the hip bone at the hip joint, and inferiorly with the tibia at the knee joint. The patella only articulates with the distal end of the femur.

The narrowed region below the head is the **neck of the femur**. This is a common area for fractures of the femur. The **greater trochanter** is the large, upward, bony projection located above the base of the neck. Multiple muscles that act across the hip joint attach to the greater trochanter, which, because of its projection from the femur, gives additional leverage to these muscles. The greater trochanter can be felt just under the skin on the lateral side of your upper thigh. The **lesser trochanter** is a small, bony prominence that lies on the medial aspect of the femur, just below the neck. A single, powerful muscle attaches to the lesser trochanter. Running between the greater and lesser trochanters on the anterior side of the femur is the roughened **intertrochanteric line**. The trochanters are also connected on the posterior side of the femur by the larger **intertrochanteric crest**.

The elongated **shaft of the femur** has a slight anterior bowing or curvature. At its proximal end, the posterior shaft has the **gluteal tuberosity**, a roughened area extending inferiorly from the greater trochanter. More inferiorly, the gluteal tuberosity becomes continuous with the **linea aspera** ("rough line"). This is the roughened ridge that passes distally along the posterior side of the mid-femur. Multiple muscles of the hip and thigh regions make long, thin attachments to the femur along the linea aspera.

The distal end of the femur has medial and lateral bony expansions. On the lateral side, the smooth portion that covers the distal and posterior aspects of the lateral expansion is the **lateral condyle of the femur**. The roughened area on the outer, lateral side of the condyle is the **lateral epicondyle of the femur**. Similarly, the smooth region of the distal and posterior medial femur is the **medial condyle of the femur**, and the irregular outer, medial side of this is the **medial epicondyle of the femur**. The lateral and medial condyles articulate with the tibia to form the knee joint. The epicondyles provide attachment for muscles and supporting ligaments of the knee. The **adductor tubercle** is a small bump located at the superior margin of the medial epicondyle. Posteriorly, the medial and lateral condyles are separated by a deep depression called the **intercondylar fossa**. Anteriorly, the smooth surfaces of the condyles join together to form a wide groove called the **patellar surface**, which provides for articulation with the patella bone. The combination of the medial and lateral condyles with the patellar surface gives the distal end of the femur a horseshoe (U) shape.

⊚ INTERACTIVE LINK

Watch this video (http://openstax.org/l/midfemur) to view how a fracture of the mid-femur is surgically repaired. How are the two portions of the broken femur stabilized during surgical repair of a fractured femur?

Patella

The patella (kneecap) is largest sesamoid bone of the body (see Figure 8.16). A sesamoid bone is a bone that is incorporated into the tendon of a muscle where that tendon crosses a joint. The sesamoid bone articulates with the underlying bones to prevent damage to the muscle tendon due to rubbing against the bones during movements of the joint. The patella is found in the tendon of the quadriceps femoris muscle, the large muscle of the anterior thigh that passes across the anterior knee to attach to the tibia. The patella articulates with the patellar surface of the femur and thus prevents rubbing of the muscle tendon against the distal femur. The patella also lifts the tendon away from the knee joint, which increases the leverage power of the quadriceps femoris muscle as it acts across the knee. The patella does not articulate with the tibia.

⊚ INTERACTIVE LINK

Visit this site (http://openstax.org/l/kneesurgery) to watch a virtual knee replacement surgery. The prosthetic knee components must be properly aligned to function properly. How is this alignment ensured?

HOMEOSTATIC IMBALANCES

Runner's Knee

Runner's knee, also known as patellofemoral syndrome, is the most common overuse injury among runners. It is most frequent in adolescents and young adults, and is more common in females. It often results from excessive running, particularly downhill, but may also occur in athletes who do a lot of knee bending, such as jumpers, skiers, cyclists, weight lifters, and soccer players. It is felt as a dull, aching pain around the front of the knee and deep to the patella. The pain may be felt when walking or running, going up or down stairs, kneeling or squatting, or after sitting with the knee bent for an extended period.

Patellofemoral syndrome may be initiated by a variety of causes, including individual variations in the shape and movement of the patella, a direct blow to the patella, or flat feet or improper shoes that cause excessive turning in or out of the feet or leg. These factors may cause in an imbalance in the muscle pull that acts on the patella, resulting in an abnormal tracking of the patella that allows it to deviate too far toward the lateral side of the patellar surface on the distal femur.

Because the hips are wider than the knee region, the femur has a diagonal orientation within the thigh, in contrast to the vertically oriented tibia of the leg (Figure 8.17). The Q-angle is a measure of how far the femur is angled laterally away from vertical. The Q-angle is normally 10–15 degrees, with females typically having a larger Q-angle due to their wider pelvis. During extension of the knee, the quadriceps femoris muscle pulls the patella both superiorly and laterally, with the lateral pull greater in females due to their large Q-angle. This makes females more vulnerable to developing patellofemoral syndrome than males. Normally, the large lip on the lateral side of the patellar surface of the femur compensates for the lateral pull on the patella, and thus helps to maintain its proper tracking.

However, if the pull produced by the medial and lateral sides of the quadriceps femoris muscle is not properly balanced, abnormal tracking of the patella toward the lateral side may occur. With continued use, this produces pain and could result in damage to the articulating surfaces of the patella and femur, and the possible future development of arthritis. Treatment generally involves stopping the activity that produces knee pain for a period of time, followed by a gradual resumption of activity. Proper strengthening of the quadriceps femoris muscle to correct for imbalances is also important to help prevent reoccurrence.

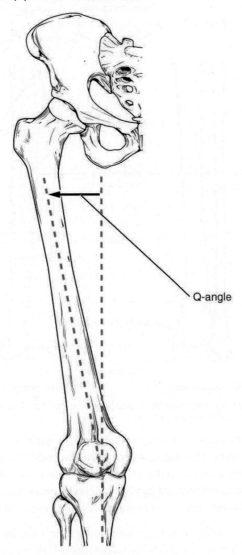

Anterior view

FIGURE 8.17   The Q-Angle   The Q-angle is a measure of the amount of lateral deviation of the femur from the vertical line of the tibia. Adult females have a larger Q-angle due to their wider pelvis than adult males.

Tibia

The tibia (shin bone) is the medial bone of the leg and is larger than the fibula, with which it is paired (Figure 8.18). The tibia is the main weight-bearing bone of the lower leg and the second longest bone of the body, after the femur. The medial side of the tibia is located immediately under the skin, allowing it to be easily palpated down the entire length of the medial leg.

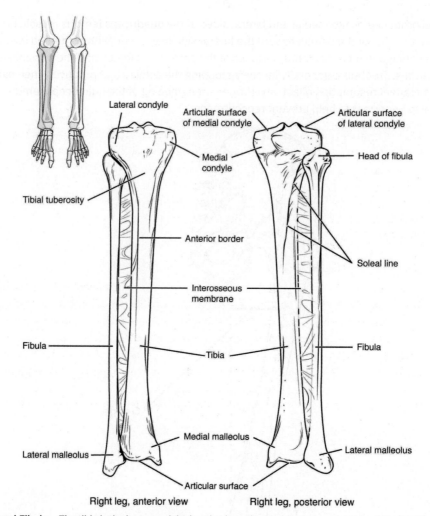

FIGURE 8.18 Tibia and Fibula   The tibia is the larger, weight-bearing bone located on the medial side of the leg. The fibula is the slender bone of the lateral side of the leg and does not bear weight.

The proximal end of the tibia is greatly expanded. The two sides of this expansion form the **medial condyle of the tibia** and the **lateral condyle of the tibia**. The tibia does not have epicondyles. The top surface of each condyle is smooth and flattened. These areas articulate with the medial and lateral condyles of the femur to form the **knee joint**. Between the articulating surfaces of the tibial condyles is the **intercondylar eminence**, an irregular, elevated area that serves as the inferior attachment point for two supporting ligaments of the knee.

The **tibial tuberosity** is an elevated area on the anterior side of the tibia, near its proximal end. It is the final site of attachment for the muscle tendon associated with the patella. More inferiorly, the **shaft of the tibia** becomes triangular in shape.

The anterior apex of this triangle forms the **anterior border of the tibia**, which begins at the tibial tuberosity and runs inferiorly along the length of the tibia. Both the anterior border and the medial side of the triangular shaft are located immediately under the skin and can be easily palpated along the entire length of the tibia. A small ridge running down the lateral side of the tibial shaft is the **interosseous border of the tibia**. This is for the attachment of the **interosseous membrane of the leg**, the sheet of dense connective tissue that unites the tibia and fibula bones. Located on the posterior side of the tibia is the **soleal line**, a diagonally running, roughened ridge that begins below the base of the lateral condyle, and runs down and medially across the proximal third of the posterior tibia. Muscles of the posterior leg attach to this line.

The large expansion found on the medial side of the distal tibia is the **medial malleolus** ("little hammer"). This forms the large bony bump found on the medial side of the ankle region. Both the smooth surface on the inside of the medial malleolus and the smooth area at the distal end of the tibia articulate with the talus bone of the foot as part of the ankle joint. On the lateral side of the distal tibia is a wide groove called the **fibular notch**. This area articulates with the distal end of the fibula, forming the **distal tibiofibular joint**.

Fibula

The fibula is the slender bone located on the lateral side of the leg (see Figure 8.18). The fibula does not bear weight. It serves primarily for muscle attachments and thus is largely surrounded by muscles. Only the proximal and distal ends of the fibula can be palpated.

The **head of the fibula** is the small, knob-like, proximal end of the fibula. It articulates with the inferior aspect of the lateral tibial condyle, forming the **proximal tibiofibular joint**. The thin **shaft of the fibula** has the **interosseous border of the fibula**, a narrow ridge running down its medial side for the attachment of the interosseous membrane that spans the fibula and tibia. The distal end of the fibula forms the **lateral malleolus**, which forms the easily palpated bony bump on the lateral side of the ankle. The deep (medial) side of the lateral malleolus articulates with the talus bone of the foot as part of the ankle joint. The distal fibula also articulates with the fibular notch of the tibia.

Tarsal Bones

The posterior half of the foot is formed by seven tarsal bones (Figure 8.19). The most superior bone is the **talus**. This has a relatively square-shaped, upper surface that articulates with the tibia and fibula to form the **ankle joint**. Three areas of articulation form the ankle joint: The superomedial surface of the talus bone articulates with the medial malleolus of the tibia, the top of the talus articulates with the distal end of the tibia, and the lateral side of the talus articulates with the lateral malleolus of the fibula. Inferiorly, the talus articulates with the **calcaneus** (heel bone), the largest bone of the foot, which forms the heel. Body weight is transferred from the tibia to the talus to the calcaneus, which rests on the ground. The medial calcaneus has a prominent bony extension called the **sustentaculum tali** ("support for the talus") that supports the medial side of the talus bone.

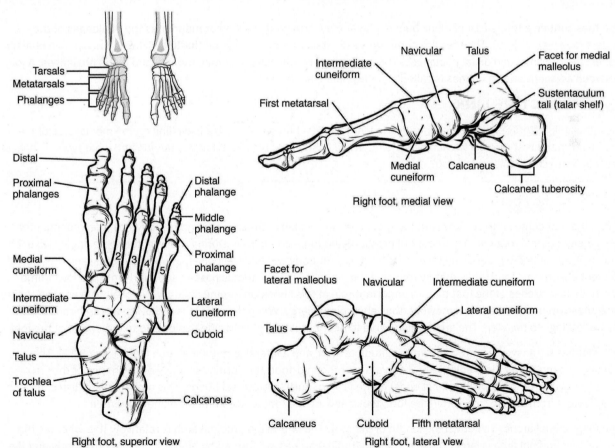

FIGURE 8.19 Bones of the Foot The bones of the foot are divided into three groups. The posterior foot is formed by the seven tarsal bones. The mid-foot has the five metatarsal bones. The toes contain the phalanges.

The **cuboid** bone articulates with the anterior end of the calcaneus bone. The cuboid has a deep groove running across its inferior surface, which provides passage for a muscle tendon. The talus bone articulates anteriorly with the **navicular** bone, which in turn articulates anteriorly with the three cuneiform ("wedge-shaped") bones. These bones are the **medial cuneiform**, the **intermediate cuneiform**, and the **lateral cuneiform**. Each of these bones has a broad superior surface and a narrow inferior surface, which together produce the transverse (medial-lateral) curvature of the foot. The navicular and lateral cuneiform bones also articulate with the medial side of the cuboid bone.

🔗 INTERACTIVE LINK

Use this tutorial (http://openstax.org/l/footbones) to review the bones of the foot. Which tarsal bones are in the proximal, intermediate, and distal groups?

Metatarsal Bones

The anterior half of the foot is formed by the five metatarsal bones, which are located between the tarsal bones of the posterior foot and the phalanges of the toes (see Figure 8.19). These elongated bones are numbered 1–5, starting with the medial side of the foot. The first metatarsal bone is shorter and thicker than the others. The second metatarsal is the longest. The **base of the metatarsal bone** is the proximal end of each metatarsal bone. These articulate with the cuboid or cuneiform bones. The base of the fifth metatarsal has a large, lateral expansion that provides for muscle attachments. This expanded base of the fifth metatarsal can be felt as a bony bump at the midpoint along the lateral border of the foot. The expanded distal end of each metatarsal is the **head of the metatarsal bone**. Each metatarsal bone articulates with the proximal phalanx of a toe to form a **metatarsophalangeal joint**. The heads of the metatarsal bones also rest on the ground and form the ball (anterior end) of the foot.

Phalanges

The toes contain a total of 14 phalanx bones (phalanges), arranged in a similar manner as the phalanges of the fingers (see Figure 8.19). The toes are numbered 1–5, starting with the big toe (**hallux**). The big toe has two phalanx bones, the proximal and distal phalanges. The remaining toes all have proximal, middle, and distal phalanges. A joint between adjacent phalanx bones is called an interphalangeal joint.

🔗 INTERACTIVE LINK

View this link (http://openstax.org/l/bunion) to learn about a bunion, a localized swelling on the medial side of the foot, next to the first metatarsophalangeal joint, at the base of the big toe. What is a bunion and what type of shoe is most likely to cause this to develop?

Arches of the Foot

When the foot comes into contact with the ground during walking, running, or jumping activities, the impact of the body weight puts a tremendous amount of pressure and force on the foot. During running, the force applied to each foot as it contacts the ground can be up to 2.5 times your body weight. The bones, joints, ligaments, and muscles of the foot absorb this force, thus greatly reducing the amount of shock that is passed superiorly into the lower limb and body. The arches of the foot play an important role in this shock-absorbing ability. When weight is applied to the foot, these arches will flatten somewhat, thus absorbing energy. When the weight is removed, the arch rebounds, giving "spring" to the step. The arches also serve to distribute body weight side to side and to either end of the foot.

The foot has a transverse arch, a medial longitudinal arch, and a lateral longitudinal arch (see Figure 8.19). The transverse arch forms the medial-lateral curvature of the mid-foot. It is formed by the wedge shapes of the cuneiform bones and bases (proximal ends) of the first to fourth metatarsal bones. This arch helps to distribute body weight from side to side within the foot, thus allowing the foot to accommodate uneven terrain.

The longitudinal arches run down the length of the foot. The lateral longitudinal arch is relatively flat, whereas the medial longitudinal arch is larger (taller). The longitudinal arches are formed by the tarsal bones posteriorly and the metatarsal bones anteriorly. These arches are supported at either end, where they contact the ground. Posteriorly, this support is provided by the calcaneus bone and anteriorly by the heads (distal ends) of the metatarsal bones. The talus bone, which receives the weight of the body, is located at the top of the longitudinal arches. Body weight is then conveyed from the talus to the ground by the anterior and posterior ends of these arches. Strong ligaments unite the adjacent foot bones to prevent disruption of the arches during weight bearing. On the bottom of the foot, additional ligaments tie together the anterior and posterior ends of the arches. These ligaments have elasticity, which allows them to stretch somewhat during weight bearing, thus allowing the longitudinal arches to spread. The stretching of these ligaments stores energy within the foot, rather than passing these forces into the leg. Contraction of the foot muscles also plays an important role in this energy absorption. When the weight is removed, the elastic ligaments recoil and pull the ends of the arches closer together. This recovery of the arches releases the stored energy and improves the energy efficiency of walking.

Stretching of the ligaments that support the longitudinal arches can lead to pain. This can occur in overweight individuals, with people who have jobs that involve standing for long periods of time (such as a waitress), or walking or running long distances. If stretching of the ligaments is prolonged, excessive, or repeated, it can result in a gradual lengthening of the supporting ligaments, with subsequent depression or collapse of the longitudinal arches, particularly on the medial side of the foot. This condition is called pes planus ("flat foot" or "fallen arches").

8.5 Development of the Appendicular Skeleton

LEARNING OBJECTIVES

By the end of this section, you will be able to:

- Describe the growth and development of the embryonic limb buds
- Discuss the appearance of primary and secondary ossification centers

Embryologically, the appendicular skeleton arises from mesenchyme, a type of embryonic tissue that can differentiate into many types of tissues, including bone or muscle tissue. Mesenchyme gives rise to the bones of the upper and lower limbs, as well as to the pectoral and pelvic girdles. Development of the limbs begins near the end of the fourth embryonic week, with the upper limbs appearing first. Thereafter, the development of the upper and lower limbs follows similar patterns, with the lower limbs lagging behind the upper limbs by a few days.

Limb Growth

Each upper and lower limb initially develops as a small bulge called a **limb bud**, which appears on the lateral side of the early embryo. The upper limb bud appears near the end of the fourth week of development, with the lower limb bud appearing shortly after (Figure 8.20).

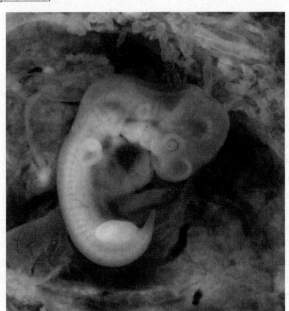

FIGURE 8.20 Embryo at Seven Weeks   Limb buds are visible in an embryo at the end of the seventh week of development (embryo derived from an ectopic pregnancy). (credit: Ed Uthman/flickr)

Initially, the limb buds consist of a core of mesenchyme covered by a layer of ectoderm. The ectoderm at the end of the limb bud thickens to form a narrow crest called the **apical ectodermal ridge**. This ridge stimulates the underlying mesenchyme to rapidly proliferate, producing the outgrowth of the developing limb. As the limb bud elongates, cells located farther from the apical ectodermal ridge slow their rates of cell division and begin to differentiate. In this way, the limb develops along a proximal-to-distal axis.

During the sixth week of development, the distal ends of the upper and lower limb buds expand and flatten into a paddle shape. This region will become the hand or foot. The wrist or ankle areas then appear as a constriction that develops at the base of the paddle. Shortly after this, a second constriction on the limb bud appears at the future site of the elbow or knee. Within the paddle, areas of tissue undergo cell death, producing separations between the growing fingers and toes. Also during the sixth week of development, mesenchyme within the limb buds begins to differentiate into hyaline cartilage that will form models of the future limb bones.

The early outgrowth of the upper and lower limb buds initially has the limbs positioned so that the regions that will become the palm of the hand or the bottom of the foot are facing medially toward the body, with the future thumb or big toe both oriented toward the head. During the seventh week of development, the upper limb rotates laterally by 90 degrees, so that the palm of the hand faces anteriorly and the thumb points laterally. In contrast, the lower limb undergoes a 90-degree medial rotation, thus bringing the big toe to the medial side of the foot.

INTERACTIVE LINK

Watch this animation (http://openstax.org/l/limbbuds) to follow the development and growth of the upper and lower limb buds. On what days of embryonic development do these events occur: (a) first appearance of the upper limb bud (limb ridge); (b) the flattening of the distal limb to form the handplate or footplate; and (c) the beginning of limb rotation?

Ossification of Appendicular Bones

All of the girdle and limb bones, except for the clavicle, develop by the process of endochondral ossification. This process begins as the mesenchyme within the limb bud differentiates into hyaline cartilage to form cartilage models for future bones. By the twelfth week, a primary ossification center will have appeared in the diaphysis (shaft) region of the long bones, initiating the process that converts the cartilage model into bone. A secondary ossification center will appear in each epiphysis (expanded end) of these bones at a later time, usually after birth. The primary and secondary ossification centers are separated by the epiphyseal plate, a layer of growing hyaline cartilage. This plate is located between the diaphysis and each epiphysis. It continues to grow and is responsible for the lengthening of the bone. The epiphyseal plate is retained for many years, until the bone reaches its final, adult size, at which time the epiphyseal plate disappears and the epiphysis fuses to the diaphysis. (Seek additional content on ossification in the chapter on bone tissue.)

Small bones, such as the phalanges, will develop only one secondary ossification center and will thus have only a single epiphyseal plate. Large bones, such as the femur, will develop several secondary ossification centers, with an epiphyseal plate associated with each secondary center. Thus, ossification of the femur begins at the end of the seventh week with the appearance of the primary ossification center in the diaphysis, which rapidly expands to ossify the shaft of the bone prior to birth. Secondary ossification centers develop at later times. Ossification of the distal end of the femur, to form the condyles and epicondyles, begins shortly before birth. Secondary ossification centers also appear in the femoral head late in the first year after birth, in the greater trochanter during the fourth year, and in the lesser trochanter between the ages of 9 and 10 years. Once these areas have ossified, their fusion to the diaphysis and the disappearance of each epiphyseal plate follow a reversed sequence. Thus, the lesser trochanter is the first to fuse, doing so at the onset of puberty (around 11 years of age), followed by the greater trochanter approximately 1 year later. The femoral head fuses between the ages of 14–17 years, whereas the distal condyles of the femur are the last to fuse, between the ages of 16–19 years. Knowledge of the age at which different epiphyseal plates disappear is important when interpreting radiographs taken of children. Since the cartilage of an epiphyseal plate is less dense than bone, the plate will appear dark in a radiograph image. Thus, a normal epiphyseal plate may be mistaken for a bone fracture.

The clavicle is the one appendicular skeleton bone that does not develop via endochondral ossification. Instead, the clavicle develops through the process of intramembranous ossification. During this process, mesenchymal cells differentiate directly into bone-producing cells, which produce the clavicle directly, without first making a cartilage model. Because of this early production of bone, the clavicle is the first bone of the body to begin ossification, with ossification centers appearing during the fifth week of development. However, ossification of the clavicle is not complete until age 25.

Disorders of the...

Appendicular System: Congenital Clubfoot

Clubfoot, also known as talipes, is a congenital (present at birth) disorder of unknown cause and is the most common deformity of the lower limb. It affects the foot and ankle, causing the foot to be twisted inward at a sharp angle, like the head of a golf club (Figure 8.21). Clubfoot has a frequency of about 1 out of every 1,000 births, and is twice as likely to occur in a male child as in a female child. In 50 percent of cases, both feet are affected.

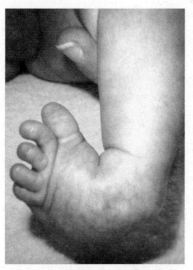

FIGURE 8.21 **Clubfoot** Clubfoot is a common deformity of the ankle and foot that is present at birth. Most cases are corrected without surgery, and affected individuals will grow up to lead normal, active lives. (credit: James W. Hanson)

At birth, children with a clubfoot have the heel turned inward and the anterior foot twisted so that the lateral side of the foot is facing inferiorly, commonly due to ligaments or leg muscles attached to the foot that are shortened or abnormally tight. These pull the foot into an abnormal position, resulting in bone deformities. Other symptoms may include bending of the ankle that lifts the heel of the foot and an extremely high foot arch. Due to the limited range of motion in the affected foot, it is difficult to place the foot into the correct position. Additionally, the affected foot may be shorter than normal, and the calf muscles are usually underdeveloped on the affected side. Despite the appearance, this is not a painful condition for newborns. However, it must be treated early to avoid future pain and impaired walking ability.

Although the cause of clubfoot is idiopathic (unknown), evidence indicates that fetal position within the uterus is not a contributing factor. Genetic factors are involved, because clubfoot tends to run within families. Cigarette smoking during pregnancy has been linked to the development of clubfoot, particularly in families with a history of clubfoot.

Previously, clubfoot required extensive surgery. Today, 90 percent of cases are successfully treated without surgery using new corrective casting techniques. The best chance for a full recovery requires that clubfoot treatment begin during the first 2 weeks after birth. Corrective casting gently stretches the foot, which is followed by the application of a holding cast to keep the foot in the proper position. This stretching and casting is repeated weekly for several weeks. In severe cases, surgery may also be required, after which the foot typically remains in a cast for 6 to 8 weeks. After the cast is removed following either surgical or nonsurgical treatment, the child will be required to wear a brace part-time (at night) for up to 4 years. In addition, special exercises will be prescribed, and the child must also wear special shoes. Close monitoring by the parents and adherence to postoperative instructions are imperative in minimizing the risk of relapse.

Despite these difficulties, treatment for clubfoot is usually successful, and the child will grow up to lead a normal, active life. Numerous examples of individuals born with a clubfoot who went on to successful careers include Dudley Moore (comedian and actor), Damon Wayans (comedian and actor), Troy Aikman (three-time Super Bowl-winning quarterback), Kristi Yamaguchi (Olympic gold medalist in figure skating), Mia Hamm (two-time Olympic gold medalist in soccer), and Charles Woodson (Heisman trophy and Super Bowl winner).

Key Terms

acetabulum   large, cup-shaped cavity located on the lateral side of the hip bone; formed by the junction of the ilium, pubis, and ischium portions of the hip bone

acromial end of the clavicle   lateral end of the clavicle that articulates with the acromion of the scapula

acromial process   acromion of the scapula

acromioclavicular joint   articulation between the acromion of the scapula and the acromial end of the clavicle

acromion   flattened bony process that extends laterally from the scapular spine to form the bony tip of the shoulder

adductor tubercle   small, bony bump located on the superior aspect of the medial epicondyle of the femur

anatomical neck   line on the humerus located around the outside margin of the humeral head

ankle joint   joint that separates the leg and foot portions of the lower limb; formed by the articulations between the talus bone of the foot inferiorly, and the distal end of the tibia, medial malleolus of the tibia, and lateral malleolus of the fibula superiorly

anterior border of the tibia   narrow, anterior margin of the tibia that extends inferiorly from the tibial tuberosity

anterior inferior iliac spine   small, bony projection located on the anterior margin of the ilium, below the anterior superior iliac spine

anterior sacroiliac ligament   strong ligament between the sacrum and the ilium portions of the hip bone that supports the anterior side of the sacroiliac joint

anterior superior iliac spine   rounded, anterior end of the iliac crest

apical ectodermal ridge   enlarged ridge of ectoderm at the distal end of a limb bud that stimulates growth and elongation of the limb

arcuate line of the ilium   smooth ridge located at the inferior margin of the iliac fossa; forms the lateral portion of the pelvic brim

arm   region of the upper limb located between the shoulder and elbow joints; contains the humerus bone

auricular surface of the ilium   roughened area located on the posterior, medial side of the ilium of the hip bone; articulates with the auricular surface of the sacrum to form the sacroiliac joint

base of the metatarsal bone   expanded, proximal end of each metatarsal bone

bicipital groove   intertubercular groove; narrow groove located between the greater and lesser tubercles of the humerus

calcaneus   heel bone; posterior, inferior tarsal bone that forms the heel of the foot

capitate   from the lateral side, the third of the four distal carpal bones; articulates with the scaphoid and lunate proximally, the trapezoid laterally, the hamate medially, and primarily with the third metacarpal distally

capitulum   knob-like bony structure located anteriorly on the lateral, distal end of the humerus

carpal bone   one of the eight small bones that form the wrist and base of the hand; these are grouped as a proximal row consisting of (from lateral to medial) the scaphoid, lunate, triquetrum, and pisiform bones, and a distal row containing (from lateral to medial) the trapezium, trapezoid, capitate, and hamate bones

carpal tunnel   passageway between the anterior forearm and hand formed by the carpal bones and flexor retinaculum

carpometacarpal joint   articulation between one of the carpal bones in the distal row and a metacarpal bone of the hand

clavicle   collarbone; elongated bone that articulates with the manubrium of the sternum medially and the acromion of the scapula laterally

coracoclavicular ligament   strong band of connective tissue that anchors the coracoid process of the scapula to the lateral clavicle; provides important indirect support for the acromioclavicular joint

coracoid process   short, hook-like process that projects anteriorly and laterally from the superior margin of the scapula

coronoid fossa   depression on the anterior surface of the humerus above the trochlea; this space receives the coronoid process of the ulna when the elbow is maximally flexed

coronoid process of the ulna   projecting bony lip located on the anterior, proximal ulna; forms the inferior margin of the trochlear notch

costoclavicular ligament   band of connective tissue that unites the medial clavicle with the first rib

coxal bone   hip bone

cuboid   tarsal bone that articulates posteriorly with the calcaneus bone, medially with the lateral cuneiform bone, and anteriorly with the fourth and fifth metatarsal bones

deltoid tuberosity   roughened, V-shaped region located laterally on the mid-shaft of the humerus

distal radioulnar joint   articulation between the head

of the ulna and the ulnar notch of the radius

distal tibiofibular joint   articulation between the distal fibula and the fibular notch of the tibia

elbow joint   joint located between the upper arm and forearm regions of the upper limb; formed by the articulations between the trochlea of the humerus and the trochlear notch of the ulna, and the capitulum of the humerus and the head of the radius

femur   thigh bone; the single bone of the thigh

fibula   thin, non-weight-bearing bone found on the lateral side of the leg

fibular notch   wide groove on the lateral side of the distal tibia for articulation with the fibula at the distal tibiofibular joint

flexor retinaculum   strong band of connective tissue at the anterior wrist that spans the top of the U-shaped grouping of the carpal bones to form the roof of the carpal tunnel

foot   portion of the lower limb located distal to the ankle joint

forearm   region of the upper limb located between the elbow and wrist joints; contains the radius and ulna bones

fossa   (plural = fossae) shallow depression on the surface of a bone

fovea capitis   minor indentation on the head of the femur that serves as the site of attachment for the ligament to the head of the femur

glenohumeral joint   shoulder joint; formed by the articulation between the glenoid cavity of the scapula and the head of the humerus

glenoid cavity   (also, glenoid fossa) shallow depression located on the lateral scapula, between the superior and lateral borders

gluteal tuberosity   roughened area on the posterior side of the proximal femur, extending inferiorly from the base of the greater trochanter

greater pelvis   (also, greater pelvic cavity or false pelvis) broad space above the pelvic brim defined laterally by the fan-like portion of the upper ilium

greater sciatic foramen   pelvic opening formed by the greater sciatic notch of the hip bone, the sacrum, and the sacrospinous ligament

greater sciatic notch   large, U-shaped indentation located on the posterior margin of the ilium, superior to the ischial spine

greater trochanter   large, bony expansion of the femur that projects superiorly from the base of the femoral neck

greater tubercle   enlarged prominence located on the lateral side of the proximal humerus

hallux   big toe; digit 1 of the foot

hamate   from the lateral side, the fourth of the four

distal carpal bones; articulates with the lunate and triquetrum proximally, the fourth and fifth metacarpals distally, and the capitate laterally

hand   region of the upper limb distal to the wrist joint

head of the femur   rounded, proximal end of the femur that articulates with the acetabulum of the hip bone to form the hip joint

head of the fibula   small, knob-like, proximal end of the fibula; articulates with the inferior aspect of the lateral condyle of the tibia

head of the humerus   smooth, rounded region on the medial side of the proximal humerus; articulates with the glenoid fossa of the scapula to form the glenohumeral (shoulder) joint

head of the metatarsal bone   expanded, distal end of each metatarsal bone

head of the radius   disc-shaped structure that forms the proximal end of the radius; articulates with the capitulum of the humerus as part of the elbow joint, and with the radial notch of the ulna as part of the proximal radioulnar joint

head of the ulna   small, rounded distal end of the ulna; articulates with the ulnar notch of the distal radius, forming the distal radioulnar joint

hip bone   coxal bone; single bone that forms the pelvic girdle; consists of three areas, the ilium, ischium, and pubis

hip joint   joint located at the proximal end of the lower limb; formed by the articulation between the acetabulum of the hip bone and the head of the femur

hook of the hamate bone   bony extension located on the anterior side of the hamate carpal bone

humerus   single bone of the upper arm

iliac crest   curved, superior margin of the ilium

iliac fossa   shallow depression found on the anterior and medial surfaces of the upper ilium

ilium   superior portion of the hip bone

inferior angle of the scapula   inferior corner of the scapula located where the medial and lateral borders meet

inferior pubic ramus   narrow segment of bone that passes inferiorly and laterally from the pubic body; joins with the ischial ramus to form the ischiopubic ramus

infraglenoid tubercle   small bump or roughened area located on the lateral border of the scapula, near the inferior margin of the glenoid cavity

infraspinous fossa   broad depression located on the posterior scapula, inferior to the spine

intercondylar eminence   irregular elevation on the superior end of the tibia, between the articulating surfaces of the medial and lateral condyles

intercondylar fossa   deep depression on the posterior side of the distal femur that separates the medial and lateral condyles

intermediate cuneiform   middle of the three cuneiform tarsal bones; articulates posteriorly with the navicular bone, medially with the medial cuneiform bone, laterally with the lateral cuneiform bone, and anteriorly with the second metatarsal bone

interosseous border of the fibula   small ridge running down the medial side of the fibular shaft; for attachment of the interosseous membrane between the fibula and tibia

interosseous border of the radius   narrow ridge located on the medial side of the radial shaft; for attachment of the interosseous membrane between the ulna and radius bones

interosseous border of the tibia   small ridge running down the lateral side of the tibial shaft; for attachment of the interosseous membrane between the tibia and fibula

interosseous border of the ulna   narrow ridge located on the lateral side of the ulnar shaft; for attachment of the interosseous membrane between the ulna and radius

interosseous membrane of the forearm   sheet of dense connective tissue that unites the radius and ulna bones

interosseous membrane of the leg   sheet of dense connective tissue that unites the shafts of the tibia and fibula bones

interphalangeal joint   articulation between adjacent phalanx bones of the hand or foot digits

intertrochanteric crest   short, prominent ridge running between the greater and lesser trochanters on the posterior side of the proximal femur

intertrochanteric line   small ridge running between the greater and lesser trochanters on the anterior side of the proximal femur

intertubercular groove (sulcus)   bicipital groove; narrow groove located between the greater and lesser tubercles of the humerus

ischial ramus   bony extension projecting anteriorly and superiorly from the ischial tuberosity; joins with the inferior pubic ramus to form the ischiopubic ramus

ischial spine   pointed, bony projection from the posterior margin of the ischium that separates the greater sciatic notch and lesser sciatic notch

ischial tuberosity   large, roughened protuberance that forms the posteroinferior portion of the hip bone; weight-bearing region of the pelvis when sitting

ischiopubic ramus   narrow extension of bone that connects the ischial tuberosity to the pubic body; formed by the junction of the ischial ramus and inferior pubic ramus

ischium   posteroinferior portion of the hip bone

knee joint   joint that separates the thigh and leg portions of the lower limb; formed by the articulations between the medial and lateral condyles of the femur, and the medial and lateral condyles of the tibia

lateral border of the scapula   diagonally oriented lateral margin of the scapula

lateral condyle of the femur   smooth, articulating surface that forms the distal and posterior sides of the lateral expansion of the distal femur

lateral condyle of the tibia   lateral, expanded region of the proximal tibia that includes the smooth surface that articulates with the lateral condyle of the femur as part of the knee joint

lateral cuneiform   most lateral of the three cuneiform tarsal bones; articulates posteriorly with the navicular bone, medially with the intermediate cuneiform bone, laterally with the cuboid bone, and anteriorly with the third metatarsal bone

lateral epicondyle of the femur   roughened area of the femur located on the lateral side of the lateral condyle

lateral epicondyle of the humerus   small projection located on the lateral side of the distal humerus

lateral malleolus   expanded distal end of the fibula

lateral supracondylar ridge   narrow, bony ridge located along the lateral side of the distal humerus, superior to the lateral epicondyle

leg   portion of the lower limb located between the knee and ankle joints

lesser pelvis   (also, lesser pelvic cavity or true pelvis) narrow space located within the pelvis, defined superiorly by the pelvic brim (pelvic inlet) and inferiorly by the pelvic outlet

lesser sciatic foramen   pelvic opening formed by the lesser sciatic notch of the hip bone, the sacrospinous ligament, and the sacrotuberous ligament

lesser sciatic notch   shallow indentation along the posterior margin of the ischium, inferior to the ischial spine

lesser trochanter   small, bony projection on the medial side of the proximal femur, at the base of the femoral neck

lesser tubercle   small, bony prominence located on anterior side of the proximal humerus

ligament of the head of the femur   ligament that spans the acetabulum of the hip bone and the fovea capitis of the femoral head

limb bud   small elevation that appears on the lateral side of the embryo during the fourth or fifth week of development, which gives rise to an upper or lower limb

linea aspera   longitudinally running bony ridge located in the middle third of the posterior femur

lunate   from the lateral side, the second of the four proximal carpal bones; articulates with the radius proximally, the capitate and hamate distally, the scaphoid laterally, and the triquetrum medially

medial border of the scapula   elongated, medial margin of the scapula

medial condyle of the femur   smooth, articulating surface that forms the distal and posterior sides of the medial expansion of the distal femur

medial condyle of the tibia   medial, expanded region of the proximal tibia that includes the smooth surface that articulates with the medial condyle of the femur as part of the knee joint

medial cuneiform   most medial of the three cuneiform tarsal bones; articulates posteriorly with the navicular bone, laterally with the intermediate cuneiform bone, and anteriorly with the first and second metatarsal bones

medial epicondyle of the femur   roughened area of the distal femur located on the medial side of the medial condyle

medial epicondyle of the humerus   enlarged projection located on the medial side of the distal humerus

medial malleolus   bony expansion located on the medial side of the distal tibia

metacarpal bone   one of the five long bones that form the palm of the hand; numbered 1–5, starting on the lateral (thumb) side of the hand

metacarpophalangeal joint   articulation between the distal end of a metacarpal bone of the hand and a proximal phalanx bone of the thumb or a finger

metatarsal bone   one of the five elongated bones that forms the anterior half of the foot; numbered 1–5, starting on the medial side of the foot

metatarsophalangeal joint   articulation between a metatarsal bone of the foot and the proximal phalanx bone of a toe

midcarpal joint   articulation between the proximal and distal rows of the carpal bones; contributes to movements of the hand at the wrist

navicular   tarsal bone that articulates posteriorly with the talus bone, laterally with the cuboid bone, and anteriorly with the medial, intermediate, and lateral cuneiform bones

neck of the femur   narrowed region located inferior to the head of the femur

neck of the radius   narrowed region immediately distal to the head of the radius

obturator foramen   large opening located in the anterior hip bone, between the pubis and ischium regions

olecranon fossa   large depression located on the posterior side of the distal humerus; this space receives the olecranon process of the ulna when the elbow is fully extended

olecranon process   expanded posterior and superior portions of the proximal ulna; forms the bony tip of the elbow

patella   kneecap; the largest sesamoid bone of the body; articulates with the distal femur

patellar surface   smooth groove located on the anterior side of the distal femur, between the medial and lateral condyles; site of articulation for the patella

pectineal line   narrow ridge located on the superior surface of the superior pubic ramus

pectoral girdle   shoulder girdle; the set of bones, consisting of the scapula and clavicle, which attaches each upper limb to the axial skeleton

pelvic brim   pelvic inlet; the dividing line between the greater and lesser pelvic regions; formed by the superior margin of the pubic symphysis, the pectineal lines of each pubis, the arcuate lines of each ilium, and the sacral promontory

pelvic girdle   hip girdle; consists of a single hip bone, which attaches a lower limb to the sacrum of the axial skeleton

pelvic inlet   pelvic brim

pelvic outlet   inferior opening of the lesser pelvis; formed by the inferior margin of the pubic symphysis, right and left ischiopubic rami and sacrotuberous ligaments, and the tip of the coccyx

pelvis   ring of bone consisting of the right and left hip bones, the sacrum, and the coccyx

phalanx bone of the foot   (plural = phalanges) one of the 14 bones that form the toes; these include the proximal and distal phalanges of the big toe, and the proximal, middle, and distal phalanx bones of toes two through five

phalanx bone of the hand   (plural = phalanges) one of the 14 bones that form the thumb and fingers; these include the proximal and distal phalanges of the thumb, and the proximal, middle, and distal phalanx bones of the fingers two through five

pisiform   from the lateral side, the fourth of the four proximal carpal bones; articulates with the anterior surface of the triquetrum

pollex   (also, thumb) digit 1 of the hand

Access for free at openstax.org

posterior inferior iliac spine   small, bony projection located at the inferior margin of the auricular surface on the posterior ilium

posterior sacroiliac ligament   strong ligament spanning the sacrum and ilium of the hip bone that supports the posterior side of the sacroiliac joint

posterior superior iliac spine   rounded, posterior end of the iliac crest

proximal radioulnar joint   articulation formed by the radial notch of the ulna and the head of the radius

proximal tibiofibular joint   articulation between the head of the fibula and the inferior aspect of the lateral condyle of the tibia

pubic arch   bony structure formed by the pubic symphysis, and the bodies and inferior pubic rami of the right and left pubic bones

pubic body   enlarged, medial portion of the pubis region of the hip bone

pubic symphysis   joint formed by the articulation between the pubic bodies of the right and left hip bones

pubic tubercle   small bump located on the superior aspect of the pubic body

pubis   anterior portion of the hip bone

radial fossa   small depression located on the anterior humerus above the capitulum; this space receives the head of the radius when the elbow is maximally flexed

radial notch of the ulna   small, smooth area on the lateral side of the proximal ulna; articulates with the head of the radius as part of the proximal radioulnar joint

radial tuberosity   oval-shaped, roughened protuberance located on the medial side of the proximal radius

radiocarpal joint   wrist joint, located between the forearm and hand regions of the upper limb; articulation formed proximally by the distal end of the radius and the fibrocartilaginous pad that unites the distal radius and ulna bone, and distally by the scaphoid, lunate, and triquetrum carpal bones

radius   bone located on the lateral side of the forearm

sacroiliac joint   joint formed by the articulation between the auricular surfaces of the sacrum and ilium

sacrospinous ligament   ligament that spans the sacrum to the ischial spine of the hip bone

sacrotuberous ligament   ligament that spans the sacrum to the ischial tuberosity of the hip bone

scaphoid   from the lateral side, the first of the four proximal carpal bones; articulates with the radius proximally, the trapezoid, trapezium, and capitate distally, and the lunate medially

scapula   shoulder blade bone located on the posterior side of the shoulder

shaft of the femur   cylindrically shaped region that forms the central portion of the femur

shaft of the fibula   elongated, slender portion located between the expanded ends of the fibula

shaft of the humerus   narrow, elongated, central region of the humerus

shaft of the radius   narrow, elongated, central region of the radius

shaft of the tibia   triangular-shaped, central portion of the tibia

shaft of the ulna   narrow, elongated, central region of the ulna

soleal line   small, diagonally running ridge located on the posterior side of the proximal tibia

spine of the scapula   prominent ridge passing mediolaterally across the upper portion of the posterior scapular surface

sternal end of the clavicle   medial end of the clavicle that articulates with the manubrium of the sternum

sternoclavicular joint   articulation between the manubrium of the sternum and the sternal end of the clavicle; forms the only bony attachment between the pectoral girdle of the upper limb and the axial skeleton

styloid process of the radius   pointed projection located on the lateral end of the distal radius

styloid process of the ulna   short, bony projection located on the medial end of the distal ulna

subpubic angle   inverted V-shape formed by the convergence of the right and left ischiopubic rami; this angle is greater than 80 degrees in females and less than 70 degrees in males

subscapular fossa   broad depression located on the anterior (deep) surface of the scapula

superior angle of the scapula   corner of the scapula between the superior and medial borders of the scapula

superior border of the scapula   superior margin of the scapula

superior pubic ramus   narrow segment of bone that passes laterally from the pubic body to join the ilium

supraglenoid tubercle   small bump located at the superior margin of the glenoid cavity

suprascapular notch   small notch located along the superior border of the scapula, medial to the coracoid process

supraspinous fossa   narrow depression located on the posterior scapula, superior to the spine

surgical neck   region of the humerus where the expanded, proximal end joins with the narrower shaft

sustentaculum tali   bony ledge extending from the medial side of the calcaneus bone

talus   tarsal bone that articulates superiorly with the tibia and fibula at the ankle joint; also articulates inferiorly with the calcaneus bone and anteriorly with the navicular bone

tarsal bone   one of the seven bones that make up the posterior foot; includes the calcaneus, talus, navicular, cuboid, medial cuneiform, intermediate cuneiform, and lateral cuneiform bones

thigh   portion of the lower limb located between the hip and knee joints

tibia   shin bone; the large, weight-bearing bone located on the medial side of the leg

tibial tuberosity   elevated area on the anterior surface of the proximal tibia

trapezium   from the lateral side, the first of the four distal carpal bones; articulates with the scaphoid proximally, the first and second metacarpals distally, and the trapezoid medially

trapezoid   from the lateral side, the second of the four distal carpal bones; articulates with the scaphoid proximally, the second metacarpal distally, the trapezium laterally, and the capitate medially

triquetrum   from the lateral side, the third of the four proximal carpal bones; articulates with the lunate laterally, the hamate distally, and has a facet for the pisiform

trochlea   pulley-shaped region located medially at the distal end of the humerus; articulates at the elbow with the trochlear notch of the ulna

trochlear notch   large, C-shaped depression located on the anterior side of the proximal ulna; articulates at the elbow with the trochlea of the humerus

ulna   bone located on the medial side of the forearm

ulnar notch of the radius   shallow, smooth area located on the medial side of the distal radius; articulates with the head of the ulna at the distal radioulnar joint

ulnar tuberosity   roughened area located on the anterior, proximal ulna inferior to the coronoid process

Chapter Review

8.1 The Pectoral Girdle

The pectoral girdle, consisting of the clavicle and the scapula, attaches each upper limb to the axial skeleton. The clavicle is an anterior bone whose sternal end articulates with the manubrium of the sternum at the sternoclavicular joint. The sternal end is also anchored to the first rib by the costoclavicular ligament. The acromial end of the clavicle articulates with the acromion of the scapula at the acromioclavicular joint. This end is also anchored to the coracoid process of the scapula by the coracoclavicular ligament, which provides indirect support for the acromioclavicular joint. The clavicle supports the scapula, transmits the weight and forces from the upper limb to the body trunk, and protects the underlying nerves and blood vessels.

The scapula lies on the posterior aspect of the pectoral girdle. It mediates the attachment of the upper limb to the clavicle, and contributes to the formation of the glenohumeral (shoulder) joint. This triangular bone has three sides called the medial, lateral, and superior borders. The suprascapular notch is located on the superior border. The scapula also has three corners, two of which are the superior and inferior angles. The third corner is occupied by the glenoid cavity. Posteriorly, the spine separates the supraspinous and infraspinous fossae, and then extends laterally as the acromion. The subscapular fossa is located on the anterior surface of the scapula. The coracoid process projects anteriorly, passing inferior to the lateral end of the clavicle.

8.2 Bones of the Upper Limb

Each upper limb is divided into three regions and contains a total of 30 bones. The upper arm is the region located between the shoulder and elbow joints. This area contains the humerus. The proximal humerus consists of the head, which articulates with the scapula at the glenohumeral joint, the greater and lesser tubercles separated by the intertubercular (bicipital) groove, and the anatomical and surgical necks. The humeral shaft has the roughened area of the deltoid tuberosity on its lateral side. The distal humerus is flattened, forming a lateral supracondylar ridge that terminates at the small lateral epicondyle. The medial side of the distal humerus has the large, medial epicondyle. The articulating surfaces of the distal humerus consist of the trochlea medially and the capitulum laterally. Depressions on the humerus that accommodate the forearm bones during bending (flexing) and straightening (extending) of the elbow include the coronoid fossa, the radial fossa, and the olecranon fossa.

The forearm is the region of the upper limb located between the elbow and wrist joints. This region contains two bones, the ulna medially and the radius on the lateral (thumb) side. The elbow joint is formed by the articulation between the trochlea of the humerus and the trochlear notch of the ulna, plus the articulation between the capitulum of the humerus and the head of the radius. The proximal radioulnar joint is the articulation between the head of the radius and the radial notch of the ulna. The proximal ulna also has the olecranon process, forming an expanded posterior region, and the coronoid process and ulnar tuberosity on its anterior aspect. On the proximal radius, the narrowed region below the head is the neck; distal to this is the radial tuberosity. The shaft portions of both the ulna and radius have an interosseous border, whereas the distal ends of each bone have a pointed styloid process. The distal radioulnar joint is found between the head of the ulna and the ulnar notch of the radius. The distal end of the radius articulates with the proximal carpal bones, but the ulna does not.

The base of the hand is formed by eight carpal bones. The carpal bones are united into two rows of bones. The proximal row contains (from lateral to medial) the scaphoid, lunate, triquetrum, and pisiform bones. The scaphoid, lunate, and triquetrum bones contribute to the formation of the radiocarpal joint. The distal row of carpal bones contains (from medial to lateral) the hamate, capitate, trapezoid, and trapezium bones ("So Long To Pinky, Here Comes The Thumb"). The anterior hamate has a prominent bony hook. The proximal and distal carpal rows articulate with each other at the midcarpal joint. The carpal bones, together with the flexor retinaculum, also form the carpal tunnel of the wrist.

The five metacarpal bones form the palm of the hand. The metacarpal bones are numbered 1–5, starting with the thumb side. The first metacarpal bone is freely mobile, but the other bones are united as a group. The digits are also numbered 1–5, with the thumb being number 1. The fingers and thumb contain a total of 14 phalanges (phalanx bones). The thumb contains a proximal and a distal phalanx, whereas the remaining digits each contain proximal, middle, and distal phalanges.

8.3 The Pelvic Girdle and Pelvis

The pelvic girdle, consisting of a hip bone, serves to attach a lower limb to the axial skeleton. The hip bone articulates posteriorly at the sacroiliac joint with the sacrum, which is part of the axial skeleton. The right and left hip bones converge anteriorly and articulate with each other at the pubic symphysis. The combination of the hip bone, the sacrum, and the coccyx forms the pelvis. The pelvis has a pronounced anterior tilt. The primary function of the pelvis is to support the upper body and transfer body weight to the lower limbs. It also serves as the site of attachment for multiple muscles.

The hip bone consists of three regions: the ilium, ischium, and pubis. The ilium forms the large, fan-like region of the hip bone. The superior margin of this area is the iliac crest. Located at either end of the iliac crest are the anterior superior and posterior superior iliac spines. Inferior to these are the anterior inferior and posterior inferior iliac spines. The auricular surface of the ilium articulates with the sacrum to form the sacroiliac joint. The medial surface of the upper ilium forms the iliac fossa, with the arcuate line marking the inferior limit of this area. The posterior margin of the ilium has the large greater sciatic notch.

The posterolateral portion of the hip bone is the ischium. It has the expanded ischial tuberosity, which supports body weight when sitting. The ischial ramus projects anteriorly and superiorly. The posterior margin of the ischium has the shallow lesser sciatic notch and the ischial spine, which separates the greater and lesser sciatic notches.

The pubis forms the anterior portion of the hip bone. The body of the pubis articulates with the pubis of the opposite hip bone at the pubic symphysis. The superior margin of the pubic body has the pubic tubercle. The pubis is joined to the ilium by the superior pubic ramus, the superior surface of which forms the pectineal line. The inferior pubic ramus projects inferiorly and laterally. The pubic arch is formed by the pubic symphysis, the bodies of the adjacent pubic bones, and the two inferior pubic rami. The inferior pubic ramus joins the ischial ramus to form the ischiopubic ramus. The subpubic angle is formed by the medial convergence of the right and left ischiopubic rami.

The lateral side of the hip bone has the cup-like acetabulum, which is part of the hip joint. The large anterior opening is the obturator foramen. The sacroiliac joint is supported by the anterior and posterior sacroiliac ligaments. The sacrum is also joined to the hip bone by the sacrospinous ligament, which attaches to the ischial spine, and the sacrotuberous ligament, which attaches to the ischial tuberosity. The sacrospinous and sacrotuberous ligaments contribute to the formation of the greater and lesser sciatic foramina.

The broad space of the upper pelvis is the greater pelvis, and the narrow, inferior space is the lesser pelvis. These areas are separated by the pelvic brim (pelvic inlet). The inferior opening of the pelvis is the pelvic outlet. Compared to the male, the female pelvis is wider to accommodate childbirth, has a larger subpubic angle, and a broader greater sciatic notch.

8.4 Bones of the Lower Limb

The lower limb is divided into three regions. These are the thigh, located between the hip and knee joints; the leg, located between the knee and ankle joints; and distal to the ankle, the foot. There are 30 bones in each lower limb. These are the femur, patella, tibia, fibula, seven tarsal bones, five metatarsal bones, and 14 phalanges.

The femur is the single bone of the thigh. Its rounded head articulates with the acetabulum of the hip bone to form the hip joint. The head has the fovea capitis for attachment of the ligament of the head of the femur. The narrow neck joins inferiorly with the greater and lesser trochanters. Passing between these bony expansions are the intertrochanteric line on the anterior femur and the larger intertrochanteric crest on the posterior femur. On the posterior shaft of the femur is the gluteal tuberosity proximally and the linea aspera in the mid-shaft region. The expanded distal end consists of three articulating surfaces: the medial and lateral condyles, and the patellar surface. The outside margins of the condyles are the medial and lateral epicondyles. The adductor tubercle is on the superior aspect of the medial epicondyle.

The patella is a sesamoid bone located within a muscle tendon. It articulates with the patellar surface on the anterior side of the distal femur, thereby protecting the muscle tendon from rubbing against the femur.

The leg contains the large tibia on the medial side and the slender fibula on the lateral side. The tibia bears the weight of the body, whereas the fibula does not bear weight. The interosseous border of each bone is the attachment site for the interosseous membrane of the leg, the connective tissue sheet that unites the tibia and fibula.

The proximal tibia consists of the expanded medial and lateral condyles, which articulate with the medial and lateral condyles of the femur to form the knee joint. Between the tibial condyles is the intercondylar eminence. On the anterior side of the proximal tibia is the tibial tuberosity, which is continuous inferiorly with the anterior border of the tibia. On the posterior side, the proximal tibia has the curved soleal line. The bony expansion on the medial side of the distal tibia is the medial malleolus. The groove on the lateral side of the distal tibia is the fibular notch.

The head of the fibula forms the proximal end and articulates with the underside of the lateral condyle of the tibia. The distal fibula articulates with the fibular notch of the tibia. The expanded distal end of the fibula is the lateral malleolus.

The posterior foot is formed by the seven tarsal bones. The talus articulates superiorly with the distal tibia, the medial malleolus of the tibia, and the lateral malleolus of the fibula to form the ankle joint. The talus articulates inferiorly with the calcaneus bone. The sustentaculum tali of the calcaneus helps to support the talus. Anterior to the talus is the navicular bone, and anterior to this are the medial, intermediate, and lateral cuneiform bones. The cuboid bone is anterior to the calcaneus.

The five metatarsal bones form the anterior foot. The base of these bones articulate with the cuboid or cuneiform bones. The metatarsal heads, at their distal ends, articulate with the proximal phalanges of the toes. The big toe (toe number 1) has proximal and distal phalanx bones. The remaining toes have proximal, middle, and distal phalanges.

8.5 Development of the Appendicular Skeleton

The bones of the appendicular skeleton arise from embryonic mesenchyme. Limb buds appear at the end of the fourth week. The apical ectodermal ridge, located at the end of the limb bud, stimulates growth and elongation of the limb. During the sixth week, the distal end of the limb bud becomes paddle-shaped, and selective cell death separates the developing fingers and toes. At the same time, mesenchyme within the limb bud begins to differentiate into hyaline cartilage, forming models for future bones. During the seventh week, the upper limbs rotate laterally and the lower limbs rotate medially, bringing the limbs into their final positions.

Endochondral ossification, the process that converts the hyaline cartilage model into bone, begins in most appendicular bones by the twelfth fetal week. This begins as a primary ossification center in the diaphysis, followed by the later appearance of one or more secondary ossifications centers in the regions of the epiphyses. Each secondary ossification center is separated from the primary ossification center by an epiphyseal plate. Continued growth of the epiphyseal plate cartilage provides for bone lengthening. Disappearance of the epiphyseal plate is followed by fusion of the bony components to form a single, adult bone.

The clavicle develops via intramembranous ossification, in which mesenchyme is converted directly into bone tissue. Ossification within the clavicle begins during the fifth week of development and continues until 25 years of age.

Interactive Link Questions

1. Watch this video (http://openstax.org/l/fractures) to see how fractures of the distal radius bone can affect the wrist joint. Explain the problems that may occur if a fracture of the distal radius involves the joint surface of the radiocarpal joint of the wrist.

2. Visit this site (http://openstax.org/l/handbone) to explore the bones and joints of the hand. What are the three arches of the hand, and what is the importance of these during the gripping of an object?

3. Watch this video (http://openstax.org/l/colles) to learn about a Colles fracture, a break of the distal radius, usually caused by falling onto an outstretched hand. When would surgery be required and how would the fracture be repaired in this case?

4. Watch this video (http://openstax.org/l/3Dpelvis) for a 3-D view of the pelvis and its associated ligaments. What is the large opening in the bony pelvis, located between the ischium and pubic regions, and what two parts of the pubis contribute to the formation of this opening?

5. Watch this video (http://openstax.org/l/midfemur) to view how a fracture of the mid-femur is surgically repaired. How are the two portions of the broken femur stabilized during surgical repair of a fractured femur?

6. Visit this site (http://openstax.org/l/kneesurgery) to watch a virtual knee replacement surgery. The prosthetic knee components must be properly aligned to function properly. How is this alignment ensured?

7. Use this tutorial (http://openstax.org/l/footbones) to review the bones of the foot. Which tarsal bones are in the proximal, intermediate, and distal groups?

8. View this link (http://openstax.org/l/bunion) to learn about a bunion, a localized swelling on the medial side of the foot, next to the first metatarsophalangeal joint, at the base of the big toe. What is a bunion and what type of shoe is most likely to cause this to develop?

9. Watch this animation (http://openstax.org/l/limbbuds) to follow the development and growth of the upper and lower limb buds. On what days of embryonic development do these events occur: (a) first appearance of the upper limb bud (limb ridge); (b) the flattening of the distal limb to form the handplate or footplate; and (c) the beginning of limb rotation?

Review Questions

10. Which part of the clavicle articulates with the manubrium?
    a. shaft
    b. sternal end
    c. acromial end
    d. coracoid process

11. A shoulder separation results from injury to the
    _____.
    a. glenohumeral joint
    b. costoclavicular joint
    c. acromioclavicular joint
    d. sternoclavicular joint

12. Which feature lies between the spine and superior border of the scapula?
    a. suprascapular notch
    b. glenoid cavity
    c. superior angle
    d. supraspinous fossa

13. What structure is an extension of the spine of the scapula?
    a. acromion
    b. coracoid process
    c. supraglenoid tubercle
    d. glenoid cavity

14. Name the short, hook-like bony process of the scapula that projects anteriorly.
    a. acromial process
    b. clavicle
    c. coracoid process
    d. glenoid fossa

15. How many bones are there in the upper limbs combined?
    a. 20
    b. 30
    c. 40
    d. 60

16. Which bony landmark is located on the lateral side of the proximal humerus?
    a. greater tubercle
    b. trochlea
    c. lateral epicondyle
    d. lesser tubercle

17. Which region of the humerus articulates with the radius as part of the elbow joint?
    a. trochlea
    b. styloid process
    c. capitulum
    d. olecranon process

18. Which is the lateral-most carpal bone of the proximal row?
    a. trapezium
    b. hamate
    c. pisiform
    d. scaphoid

19. The radius bone _____.
    a. is found on the medial side of the forearm
    b. has a head that articulates with the radial notch of the ulna
    c. does not articulate with any of the carpal bones
    d. has the radial tuberosity located near its distal end

20. How many bones fuse in adulthood to form the hip bone?
    a. 2
    b. 3
    c. 4
    d. 5

21. Which component forms the superior part of the hip bone?
    a. ilium
    b. pubis
    c. ischium
    d. sacrum

22. Which of the following supports body weight when sitting?
    a. iliac crest
    b. ischial tuberosity
    c. ischiopubic ramus
    d. pubic body

23. The ischial spine is found between which of the following structures?
    a. inferior pubic ramus and ischial ramus
    b. pectineal line and arcuate line
    c. lesser sciatic notch and greater sciatic notch
    d. anterior superior iliac spine and posterior superior iliac spine

24. The pelvis _____.
    a. has a subpubic angle that is larger in females
    b. consists of the two hip bones, but does not include the sacrum or coccyx
    c. has an obturator foramen, an opening that is defined in part by the sacrospinous and sacrotuberous ligaments
    d. has a space located inferior to the pelvic brim called the greater pelvis

25. Which bony landmark of the femur serves as a site for muscle attachments?
    a. fovea capitis
    b. lesser trochanter
    c. head
    d. medial condyle

26. What structure contributes to the knee joint?
    a. lateral malleolus of the fibula
    b. tibial tuberosity
    c. medial condyle of the tibia
    d. lateral epicondyle of the femur

27. Which tarsal bone articulates with the tibia and fibula?
    a. calcaneus
    b. cuboid
    c. navicular
    d. talus

28. What is the total number of bones found in the foot and toes?
    a. 7
    b. 14
    c. 26
    d. 30

29. The tibia _____.
    a. has an expanded distal end called the lateral malleolus
    b. is not a weight-bearing bone
    c. is firmly anchored to the fibula by an interosseous membrane
    d. can be palpated (felt) under the skin only at its proximal and distal ends

30. Which event takes place during the seventh week of development?
    a. appearance of the upper and lower limb buds
    b. flattening of the distal limb bud into a paddle shape
    c. the first appearance of hyaline cartilage models of future bones
    d. the rotation of the limbs

31. During endochondral ossification of a long bone, _____.
    a. a primary ossification center will develop within the epiphysis
    b. mesenchyme will differentiate directly into bone tissue
    c. growth of the epiphyseal plate will produce bone lengthening
    d. all epiphyseal plates will disappear before birth

32. The clavicle _____.
    a. develops via intramembranous ossification
    b. develops via endochondral ossification
    c. is the last bone of the body to begin ossification
    d. is fully ossified at the time of birth

Critical Thinking Questions

33. Describe the shape and palpable line formed by the clavicle and scapula.
34. Discuss two possible injuries of the pectoral girdle that may occur following a strong blow to the shoulder or a hard fall onto an outstretched hand.
35. Your friend runs out of gas and you have to help push their car. Discuss the sequence of bones and joints that convey the forces passing from your hand, through your upper limb and your pectoral girdle, and to your axial skeleton.
36. Name the bones in the wrist and hand, and describe or sketch out their locations and articulations.
37. Describe the articulations and ligaments that unite the four bones of the pelvis to each other.
38. Discuss the ways in which the female pelvis is adapted for childbirth.
39. Define the regions of the lower limb, name the bones found in each region, and describe the bony landmarks that articulate together to form the hip, knee, and ankle joints.
40. The talus bone of the foot receives the weight of the body from the tibia. The talus bone then distributes this weight toward the ground in two directions: one-half of the body weight is passed in a posterior direction and one-half of the weight is passed in an anterior direction. Describe the arrangement of the tarsal and metatarsal bones that are involved in both the posterior and anterior distribution of body weight.
41. How can a radiograph of a child's femur be used to determine the approximate age of that child?
42. How does the development of the clavicle differ from the development of other appendicular skeleton bones?

CHAPTER 9
Joints

Figure 9.1 **Kayaking** Without joints, body movements would be impossible. (credit: Graham Richardson/flickr.com)

CHAPTER OBJECTIVES
After this chapter, you will be able to:
- Discuss both functional and structural classifications for body joints
- Describe the characteristic features for fibrous, cartilaginous, and synovial joints and give examples of each
- Define and identify the different body movements
- Discuss the structure of specific body joints and the movements allowed by each
- Explain the development of body joints

INTRODUCTION The adult human body has 206 bones, and with the exception of the hyoid bone in the neck, each bone is connected to at least one other bone. Joints are the location where bones come together. Many joints allow for movement between the bones. At these joints, the articulating surfaces of the adjacent bones can move smoothly against each other. However, the bones of other joints may be joined to each other by connective tissue or cartilage. These joints are designed for stability and provide for little or no movement. Importantly, joint stability and movement are related to each other. This means that stable joints allow for little or no mobility between the adjacent bones. Conversely, joints that provide the most movement between bones are the least stable. Understanding the relationship between joint structure and function will help to explain why particular types of joints are found in certain areas of the body.

The articulating surfaces of bones at stable types of joints, with little or no mobility, are strongly united to each other. For example, most of the joints of the skull are held together by fibrous connective tissue and do not allow for movement between the adjacent bones. This lack of mobility is important, because the skull bones serve to protect the brain. Similarly, other joints united by fibrous connective tissue allow for very little movement, which provides stability and weight-bearing support for the body. For example, the tibia and fibula of the leg are tightly united to give stability to the body when standing. At other joints, the bones are held together by cartilage, which permits limited movements between the bones. Thus, the joints of the vertebral column only allow for small movements between adjacent vertebrae, but when added together, these movements provide the flexibility that allows your body to twist, or bend to the front, back, or side. In contrast, at joints that allow for wide ranges of motion, the articulating surfaces of the bones are not directly united to each other. Instead, these surfaces are enclosed within a space filled with lubricating fluid, which allows the bones to move smoothly against each other. These joints provide greater mobility, but since the bones are free to move in relation to each other, the joint is less stable. Most of the joints between the bones of the appendicular skeleton are this freely moveable type of joint. These joints allow the muscles of the body to pull on a bone and thereby produce movement of that body region. Your ability to kick a soccer ball, pick up a fork, and dance the tango depend on mobility at these types of joints.

9.1 Classification of Joints

LEARNING OBJECTIVES

By the end of this section, you will be able to:

- Distinguish between the functional and structural classifications for joints
- Describe the three functional types of joints and give an example of each
- List the three types of diarthrodial joints

A **joint**, also called an **articulation**, is any place where adjacent bones or bone and cartilage come together (articulate with each other) to form a connection. Joints are classified both structurally and functionally. Structural classifications of joints take into account whether the adjacent bones are strongly anchored to each other by fibrous connective tissue or cartilage, or whether the adjacent bones articulate with each other within a fluid-filled space called a **joint cavity**. Functional classifications describe the degree of movement available between the bones, ranging from immobile, to slightly mobile, to freely moveable joints. The amount of movement available at a particular joint of the body is related to the functional requirements for that joint. Thus immobile or slightly moveable joints serve to protect internal organs, give stability to the body, and allow for limited body movement. In contrast, freely moveable joints allow for much more extensive movements of the body and limbs.

Structural Classification of Joints

The structural classification of joints is based on whether the articulating surfaces of the adjacent bones are directly connected by fibrous connective tissue or cartilage, or whether the articulating surfaces contact each other within a fluid-filled joint cavity. These differences serve to divide the joints of the body into three structural classifications. A **fibrous joint** is where the adjacent bones are united by fibrous connective tissue. At a **cartilaginous joint**, the bones are joined by hyaline cartilage or fibrocartilage. At a **synovial joint**, the articulating surfaces of the bones are not directly connected, but instead come into contact with each other within a joint cavity that is filled with a lubricating fluid. Synovial joints allow for free movement between the bones and are the most common joints of the body.

Functional Classification of Joints

The functional classification of joints is determined by the amount of mobility found between the adjacent bones. Joints are thus functionally classified as a synarthrosis or immobile joint, an amphiarthrosis or slightly moveable joint, or as a diarthrosis, which is a freely moveable joint (arthroun = "to fasten by a joint"). Depending on their location, fibrous joints may be functionally classified as a synarthrosis (immobile joint) or an amphiarthrosis (slightly mobile joint). Cartilaginous joints are also functionally classified as either a synarthrosis or an amphiarthrosis joint. All synovial joints are functionally classified as a diarthrosis joint.

Synarthrosis

An immobile or nearly immobile joint is called a **synarthrosis**. The immobile nature of these joints provide for a strong union between the articulating bones. This is important at locations where the bones provide protection for internal organs. Examples include sutures, the fibrous joints between the bones of the skull that surround and protect the brain (Figure 9.2), and the manubriosternal joint, the cartilaginous joint that unites the manubrium and body of the sternum for protection of the heart.

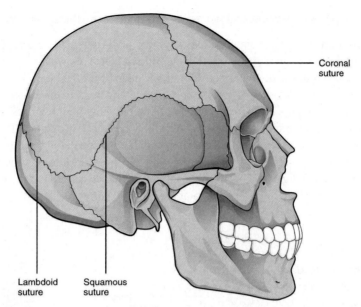

FIGURE 9.2   **Suture Joints of Skull**   The suture joints of the skull are an example of a synarthrosis, an immobile or essentially immobile joint.

Amphiarthrosis

An **amphiarthrosis** is a joint that has limited mobility. An example of this type of joint is the cartilaginous joint that unites the bodies of adjacent vertebrae. Filling the gap between the vertebrae is a thick pad of fibrocartilage called an intervertebral disc (Figure 9.3). Each intervertebral disc strongly unites the vertebrae but still allows for a limited amount of movement between them. However, the small movements available between adjacent vertebrae can sum together along the length of the vertebral column to provide for large ranges of body movements.

Another example of an amphiarthrosis is the pubic symphysis of the pelvis. This is a cartilaginous joint in which the pubic regions of the right and left hip bones are strongly anchored to each other by fibrocartilage. This joint normally has very little mobility. The strength of the pubic symphysis is important in conferring weight-bearing stability to the pelvis.

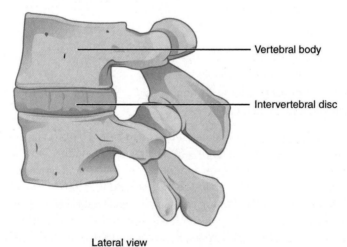

Lateral view

FIGURE 9.3   **Intervertebral Disc**   An intervertebral disc unites the bodies of adjacent vertebrae within the vertebral column. Each disc allows for limited movement between the vertebrae and thus functionally forms an amphiarthrosis type of joint. Intervertebral discs are made of fibrocartilage and thereby structurally form a symphysis type of cartilaginous joint.

Diarthrosis

A freely mobile joint is classified as a **diarthrosis**. These types of joints include all synovial joints of the body, which provide the majority of body movements. Most diarthrotic joints are found in the appendicular skeleton and thus give the limbs a wide range of motion. These joints are divided into three categories, based on the number of axes of motion provided by each. An axis in anatomy is described as the movements in reference to the three anatomical planes: transverse, frontal, and sagittal. Thus, diarthroses are classified as uniaxial (for movement in one plane), biaxial (for movement in two planes), or multiaxial joints (for movement in all three anatomical planes).

A **uniaxial joint** only allows for a motion in a single plane (around a single axis). The elbow joint, which only allows for bending or straightening, is an example of a uniaxial joint. A **biaxial joint** allows for motions within two planes. An example of a biaxial joint is a metacarpophalangeal joint (knuckle joint) of the hand. The joint allows for movement along one axis to produce bending or straightening of the finger, and movement along a second axis, which allows for spreading of the fingers away from each other and bringing them together. A joint that allows for the several directions of movement is called a **multiaxial joint** (polyaxial or triaxial joint). This type of diarthrotic joint allows for movement along three axes (Figure 9.4). The shoulder and hip joints are multiaxial joints. They allow the upper or lower limb to move in an anterior-posterior direction and a medial-lateral direction. In addition, the limb can also be rotated around its long axis. This third movement results in rotation of the limb so that its anterior surface is moved either toward or away from the midline of the body.

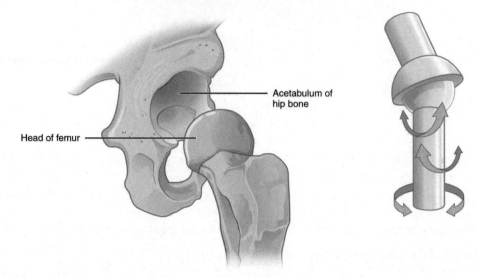

Acetabulum of hip bone

Head of femur

FIGURE 9.4   Multiaxial Joint   A multiaxial joint, such as the hip joint, allows for three types of movement: anterior-posterior, medial-lateral, and rotational.

9.2 Fibrous Joints

LEARNING OBJECTIVES

By the end of this section, you will be able to:
- Describe the structural features of fibrous joints
- Distinguish between a suture, syndesmosis, and gomphosis
- Give an example of each type of fibrous joint

At a fibrous joint, the adjacent bones are directly connected to each other by fibrous connective tissue, and thus the bones do not have a joint cavity between them (Figure 9.5). The gap between the bones may be narrow or wide. There are three types of fibrous joints. A suture is the narrow fibrous joint found between most bones of the skull. At a syndesmosis joint, the bones are more widely separated but are held together by a narrow band of fibrous connective tissue called a **ligament** or a wide sheet of connective tissue called an interosseous membrane. This type of fibrous joint is found between the shaft regions of the long bones in the forearm and in the leg. Lastly, a gomphosis is the narrow fibrous joint between the roots of a tooth and the bony socket in the jaw into which the tooth fits.

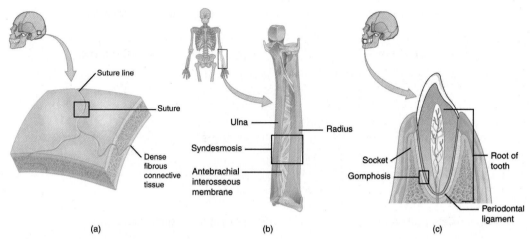

FIGURE 9.5 Fibrous Joints   Fibrous joints form strong connections between bones. (a) Sutures join most bones of the skull. (b) An interosseous membrane forms a syndesmosis between the radius and ulna bones of the forearm. (c) A gomphosis is a specialized fibrous joint that anchors a tooth to its socket in the jaw.

Suture

All the bones of the skull, except for the mandible, are joined to each other by a fibrous joint called a **suture**. The fibrous connective tissue found at a suture ("to bind or sew") strongly unites the adjacent skull bones and thus helps to protect the brain and form the face. In adults, the skull bones are closely opposed and fibrous connective tissue fills the narrow gap between the bones. The suture is frequently convoluted, forming a tight union that prevents most movement between the bones. (See Figure 9.5**a**.) Thus, skull sutures are functionally classified as a synarthrosis, although some sutures may allow for slight movements between the cranial bones.

In newborns and infants, the areas of connective tissue between the bones are much wider, especially in those areas on the top and sides of the skull that will become the sagittal, coronal, squamous, and lambdoid sutures. These broad areas of connective tissue are called **fontanelles** (Figure 9.6). During birth, the fontanelles provide flexibility to the skull, allowing the bones to push closer together or to overlap slightly, thus aiding movement of the infant's head through the birth canal. After birth, these expanded regions of connective tissue allow for rapid growth of the skull and enlargement of the brain. The fontanelles greatly decrease in width during the first year after birth as the skull bones enlarge. When the connective tissue between the adjacent bones is reduced to a narrow layer, these fibrous joints are now called sutures. At some sutures, the connective tissue will ossify and be converted into bone, causing the adjacent bones to fuse to each other. This fusion between bones is called a **synostosis** ("joined by bone"). Examples of synostosis fusions between cranial bones are found both early and late in life. At the time of birth, the frontal and maxillary bones consist of right and left halves joined together by sutures, which disappear by the eighth year as the halves fuse together to form a single bone. Late in life, the sagittal, coronal, and lambdoid sutures of the skull will begin to ossify and fuse, causing the suture line to gradually disappear.

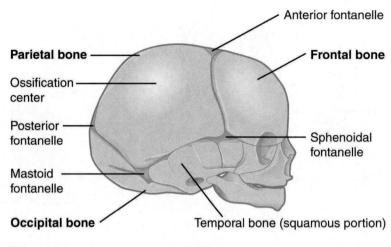

FIGURE 9.6   The Newborn Skull   The fontanelles of a newborn's skull are broad areas of fibrous connective tissue that form fibrous joints between the bones of the skull.

Syndesmosis

A **syndesmosis** ("fastened with a band") is a type of fibrous joint in which two parallel bones are united to each other by fibrous connective tissue. The gap between the bones may be narrow, with the bones joined by ligaments, or the gap may be wide and filled in by a broad sheet of connective tissue called an **interosseous membrane**.

In the forearm, the wide gap between the shaft portions of the radius and ulna bones are strongly united by an interosseous membrane (see Figure 9.5**b**). Similarly, in the leg, the shafts of the tibia and fibula are also united by an interosseous membrane. In addition, at the distal tibiofibular joint, the articulating surfaces of the bones lack cartilage and the narrow gap between the bones is anchored by fibrous connective tissue and ligaments on both the anterior and posterior aspects of the joint. Together, the interosseous membrane and these ligaments form the tibiofibular syndesmosis.

The syndesmoses found in the forearm and leg serve to unite parallel bones and prevent their separation. However, a syndesmosis does not prevent all movement between the bones, and thus this type of fibrous joint is functionally classified as an amphiarthrosis. In the leg, the syndesmosis between the tibia and fibula strongly unites the bones, allows for little movement, and firmly locks the talus bone in place between the tibia and fibula at the ankle joint. This provides strength and stability to the leg and ankle, which are important during weight bearing. In the forearm, the interosseous membrane is flexible enough to allow for rotation of the radius bone during forearm movements. Thus in contrast to the stability provided by the tibiofibular syndesmosis, the flexibility of the antebrachial interosseous membrane allows for the much greater mobility of the forearm.

The interosseous membranes of the leg and forearm also provide areas for muscle attachment. Damage to a syndesmotic joint, which usually results from a fracture of the bone with an accompanying tear of the interosseous membrane, will produce pain, loss of stability of the bones, and may damage the muscles attached to the interosseous membrane. If the fracture site is not properly immobilized with a cast or splint, contractile activity by these muscles can cause improper alignment of the broken bones during healing.

Gomphosis

A **gomphosis** ("fastened with bolts") is the specialized fibrous joint that anchors the root of a tooth into its bony socket within the maxillary bone (upper jaw) or mandible bone (lower jaw) of the skull. A gomphosis is also known as a peg-and-socket joint. Spanning between the bony walls of the socket and the root of the tooth are numerous short bands of dense connective tissue, each of which is called a **periodontal ligament** (see Figure 9.5**c**). Due to the immobility of a gomphosis, this type of joint is functionally classified as a synarthrosis.

9.3 Cartilaginous Joints

LEARNING OBJECTIVES

By the end of this section, you will be able to:
- Describe the structural features of cartilaginous joints
- Distinguish between a synchondrosis and symphysis
- Give an example of each type of cartilaginous joint

As the name indicates, at a cartilaginous joint, the adjacent bones are united by cartilage, a tough but flexible type of connective tissue. These types of joints lack a joint cavity and involve bones that are joined together by either hyaline cartilage or fibrocartilage (Figure 9.7). There are two types of cartilaginous joints. A synchondrosis is a cartilaginous joint where the bones are joined by hyaline cartilage. Also classified as a synchondrosis are places where bone is united to a cartilage structure, such as between the anterior end of a rib and the costal cartilage of the thoracic cage. The second type of cartilaginous joint is a symphysis, where the bones are joined by fibrocartilage.

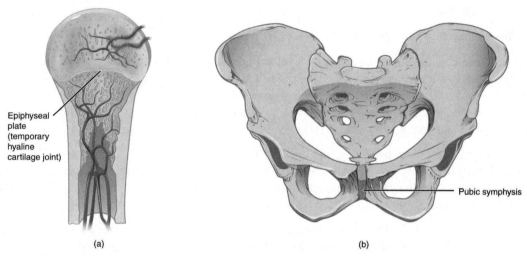

FIGURE 9.7   Cartilaginous Joints   At cartilaginous joints, bones are united by hyaline cartilage to form a synchondrosis or by fibrocartilage to form a symphysis. (a) The hyaline cartilage of the epiphyseal plate (growth plate) forms a synchondrosis that unites the shaft (diaphysis) and end (epiphysis) of a long bone and allows the bone to grow in length. (b) The pubic portions of the right and left hip bones of the pelvis are joined together by fibrocartilage, forming the pubic symphysis.

Synchondrosis

A **synchondrosis** ("joined by cartilage") is a cartilaginous joint where bones are joined together by hyaline cartilage, or where bone is united to hyaline cartilage. A synchondrosis may be temporary or permanent. A temporary synchondrosis is the epiphyseal plate (growth plate) of a growing long bone. The epiphyseal plate is the region of growing hyaline cartilage that unites the diaphysis (shaft) of the bone to the epiphysis (end of the bone). Bone lengthening involves growth of the epiphyseal plate cartilage and its replacement by bone, which adds to the diaphysis. For many years during childhood growth, the rates of cartilage growth and bone formation are equal and thus the epiphyseal plate does not change in overall thickness as the bone lengthens. During the late teens and early 20s, growth of the cartilage slows and eventually stops. The epiphyseal plate is then completely replaced by bone, and the diaphysis and epiphysis portions of the bone fuse together to form a single adult bone. This fusion of the diaphysis and epiphysis is a synostosis. Once this occurs, bone lengthening ceases. For this reason, the epiphyseal plate is considered to be a temporary synchondrosis. Because cartilage is softer than bone tissue, injury to a growing long bone can damage the epiphyseal plate cartilage, thus stopping bone growth and preventing additional bone lengthening.

Growing layers of cartilage also form synchondroses that join together the ilium, ischium, and pubic portions of the hip bone during childhood and adolescence. When body growth stops, the cartilage disappears and is replaced by bone, forming synostoses and fusing the bony components together into the single hip bone of the adult. Similarly, synostoses unite the sacral vertebrae that fuse together to form the adult sacrum.

ⓐ **INTERACTIVE LINK**

Visit this website (http://openstax.org/l/childhand) to view a radiograph (X-ray image) of a child's hand and wrist. The growing bones of child have an epiphyseal plate that forms a synchondrosis between the shaft and end of a long bone. Being less dense than bone, the area of epiphyseal cartilage is seen on this radiograph as the dark epiphyseal gaps located near the ends of the long bones, including the radius, ulna, metacarpal, and phalanx bones. Which of the bones in this image do not show an epiphyseal plate (epiphyseal gap)?

Examples of permanent synchondroses are found in the thoracic cage. One example is the first sternocostal joint, where the first rib is anchored to the manubrium by its costal cartilage. (The articulations of the remaining costal cartilages to the sternum are all synovial joints.) Additional synchondroses are formed where the anterior end of the other 11 ribs is joined to its costal cartilage. Unlike the temporary synchondroses of the epiphyseal plate, these permanent synchondroses retain their hyaline cartilage and thus do not ossify with age. Due to the lack of movement between the bone and cartilage, both temporary and permanent synchondroses are functionally classified as a synarthrosis.

Symphysis

A cartilaginous joint where the bones are joined by fibrocartilage is called a **symphysis** ("growing together"). Fibrocartilage is very strong because it contains numerous bundles of thick collagen fibers, thus giving it a much greater ability to resist pulling and bending forces when compared with hyaline cartilage. This gives symphyses the ability to strongly unite the adjacent bones, but can still allow for limited movement to occur. Thus, a symphysis is functionally classified as an amphiarthrosis.

The gap separating the bones at a symphysis may be narrow or wide. Examples in which the gap between the bones is narrow include the pubic symphysis and the manubriosternal joint. At the pubic symphysis, the pubic portions of the right and left hip bones of the pelvis are joined together by fibrocartilage across a narrow gap. Similarly, at the manubriosternal joint, fibrocartilage unites the manubrium and body portions of the sternum.

The intervertebral symphysis is a wide symphysis located between the bodies of adjacent vertebrae of the vertebral column. Here a thick pad of fibrocartilage called an intervertebral disc strongly unites the adjacent vertebrae by filling the gap between them. The width of the intervertebral symphysis is important because it allows for small movements between the adjacent vertebrae. In addition, the thick intervertebral disc provides cushioning between the vertebrae, which is important when carrying heavy objects or during high-impact activities such as running or jumping.

9.4 Synovial Joints

LEARNING OBJECTIVES

By the end of this section, you will be able to:
- Describe the structural features of a synovial joint
- Discuss the function of additional structures associated with synovial joints
- List the six types of synovial joints and give an example of each

Synovial joints are the most common type of joint in the body (Figure 9.8). A key structural characteristic for a synovial joint that is not seen at fibrous or cartilaginous joints is the presence of a joint cavity. This fluid-filled space is the site at which the articulating surfaces of the bones contact each other. Also unlike fibrous or cartilaginous joints, the articulating bone surfaces at a synovial joint are not directly connected to each other with fibrous connective tissue or cartilage. This gives the bones of a synovial joint the ability to move smoothly against each other, allowing for increased joint mobility.

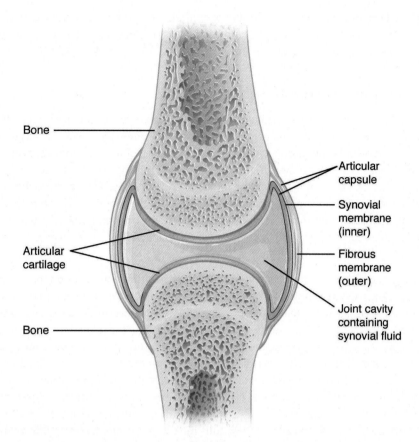

Bone

Articular
capsule

Synovial
membrane
(inner)

Articular
cartilage

Fibrous
membrane
(outer)

Joint cavity
containing
synovial fluid

Bone

FIGURE 9.8   Synovial Joints   Synovial joints allow for smooth movements between the adjacent bones. The joint is surrounded by an articular capsule that defines a joint cavity filled with synovial fluid. The articulating surfaces of the bones are covered by a thin layer of articular cartilage. Ligaments support the joint by holding the bones together and resisting excess or abnormal joint motions.

Structural Features of Synovial Joints

Synovial joints are characterized by the presence of a joint cavity. The walls of this space are formed by the **articular capsule**, a fibrous connective tissue structure that is attached to each bone just outside the area of the bone's articulating surface. The bones of the joint articulate with each other within the joint cavity.

Friction between the bones at a synovial joint is prevented by the presence of the **articular cartilage**, a thin layer of hyaline cartilage that covers the entire articulating surface of each bone. However, unlike at a cartilaginous joint, the articular cartilages of each bone are not continuous with each other. Instead, the articular cartilage acts like a Teflon® coating over the bone surface, allowing the articulating bones to move smoothly against each other without damaging the underlying bone tissue. Lining the inner surface of the articular capsule is a thin **synovial membrane**. The cells of this membrane secrete **synovial fluid** (synovia = "a thick fluid"), a thick, slimy fluid that provides lubrication to further reduce friction between the bones of the joint. This fluid also provides nourishment to the articular cartilage, which does not contain blood vessels. The ability of the bones to move smoothly against each other within the joint cavity, and the freedom of joint movement this provides, means that each synovial joint is functionally classified as a diarthrosis.

Outside of their articulating surfaces, the bones are connected together by ligaments, which are strong bands of fibrous connective tissue. These strengthen and support the joint by anchoring the bones together and preventing their separation. Ligaments allow for normal movements at a joint, but limit the range of these motions, thus preventing excessive or abnormal joint movements. Ligaments are classified based on their relationship to the fibrous articular capsule. An **extrinsic ligament** is located outside of the articular capsule, an **intrinsic ligament** is fused to or incorporated into the wall of the articular capsule, and an **intracapsular ligament** is located inside of the articular capsule.

At many synovial joints, additional support is provided by the muscles and their tendons that act across the joint. A **tendon** is the dense connective tissue structure that attaches a muscle to bone. As forces acting on a joint increase, the body will automatically increase the overall strength of contraction of the muscles crossing that joint, thus allowing the muscle and its tendon to serve as a "dynamic ligament" to resist forces and support the joint. This type of indirect support by muscles is very important at the shoulder joint, for example, where the ligaments are relatively weak.

Additional Structures Associated with Synovial Joints

A few synovial joints of the body have a fibrocartilage structure located between the articulating bones. This is called an **articular disc**, which is generally small and oval-shaped, or a **meniscus**, which is larger and C-shaped. These structures can serve several functions, depending on the specific joint. In some places, an articular disc may act to strongly unite the bones of the joint to each other. Examples of this include the articular discs found at the sternoclavicular joint or between the distal ends of the radius and ulna bones. At other synovial joints, the disc can provide shock absorption and cushioning between the bones, which is the function of each meniscus within the knee joint. Finally, an articular disc can serve to smooth the movements between the articulating bones, as seen at the temporomandibular joint. Some synovial joints also have a fat pad, which can serve as a cushion between the bones.

Additional structures located outside of a synovial joint serve to prevent friction between the bones of the joint and the overlying muscle tendons or skin. A **bursa** (plural = bursae) is a thin connective tissue sac filled with lubricating liquid. They are located in regions where skin, ligaments, muscles, or muscle tendons can rub against each other, usually near a body joint (Figure 9.9). Bursae reduce friction by separating the adjacent structures, preventing them from rubbing directly against each other. Bursae are classified by their location. A **subcutaneous bursa** is located between the skin and an underlying bone. It allows skin to move smoothly over the bone. Examples include the prepatellar bursa located over the kneecap and the olecranon bursa at the tip of the elbow. A **submuscular bursa** is found between a muscle and an underlying bone, or between adjacent muscles. These prevent rubbing of the muscle during movements. A large submuscular bursa, the trochanteric bursa, is found at the lateral hip, between the greater trochanter of the femur and the overlying gluteus maximus muscle. A **subtendinous bursa** is found between a tendon and a bone. Examples include the subacromial bursa that protects the tendon of shoulder muscle as it passes under the acromion of the scapula, and the suprapatellar bursa that separates the tendon of the large anterior thigh muscle from the distal femur just above the knee.

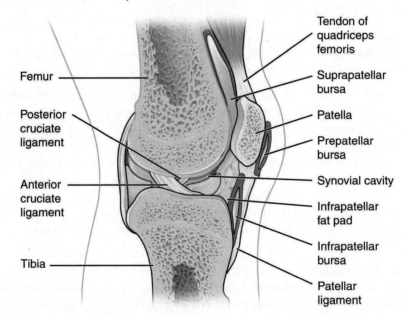

FIGURE 9.9 Bursae Bursae are fluid-filled sacs that serve to prevent friction between skin, muscle, or tendon and an underlying bone. Three major bursae and a fat pad are part of the complex joint that unites the femur and tibia of the leg.

A **tendon sheath** is similar in structure to a bursa, but smaller. It is a connective tissue sac that surrounds a muscle tendon at places where the tendon crosses a joint. It contains a lubricating fluid that allows for smooth motions of the tendon during muscle contraction and joint movements.

Access for free at openstax.org

HOMEOSTATIC IMBALANCES

Bursitis

Bursitis is the inflammation of a bursa near a joint. This will cause pain, swelling, or tenderness of the bursa and surrounding area, and may also result in joint stiffness. Bursitis is most commonly associated with the bursae found at or near the shoulder, hip, knee, or elbow joints. At the shoulder, subacromial bursitis may occur in the bursa that separates the acromion of the scapula from the tendon of a shoulder muscle as it passes deep to the acromion. In the hip region, trochanteric bursitis can occur in the bursa that overlies the greater trochanter of the femur, just below the lateral side of the hip. Ischial bursitis occurs in the bursa that separates the skin from the ischial tuberosity of the pelvis, the bony structure that is weight bearing when sitting. At the knee, inflammation and swelling of the bursa located between the skin and patella bone is prepatellar bursitis ("housemaid's knee"), a condition more commonly seen today in roofers or floor and carpet installers who do not use knee pads. At the elbow, olecranon bursitis is inflammation of the bursa between the skin and olecranon process of the ulna. The olecranon forms the bony tip of the elbow, and bursitis here is also known as "student's elbow."

Bursitis can be either acute (lasting only a few days) or chronic. It can arise from muscle overuse, trauma, excessive or prolonged pressure on the skin, rheumatoid arthritis, gout, or infection of the joint. Repeated acute episodes of bursitis can result in a chronic condition. Treatments for the disorder include antibiotics if the bursitis is caused by an infection, or anti-inflammatory agents, such as nonsteroidal anti-inflammatory drugs (NSAIDs) or corticosteroids if the bursitis is due to trauma or overuse. Chronic bursitis may require that fluid be drained, but additional surgery is usually not required.

Types of Synovial Joints

Synovial joints are subdivided based on the shapes of the articulating surfaces of the bones that form each joint. The six types of synovial joints are pivot, hinge, condyloid, saddle, plane, and ball-and socket-joints (Figure 9.10).

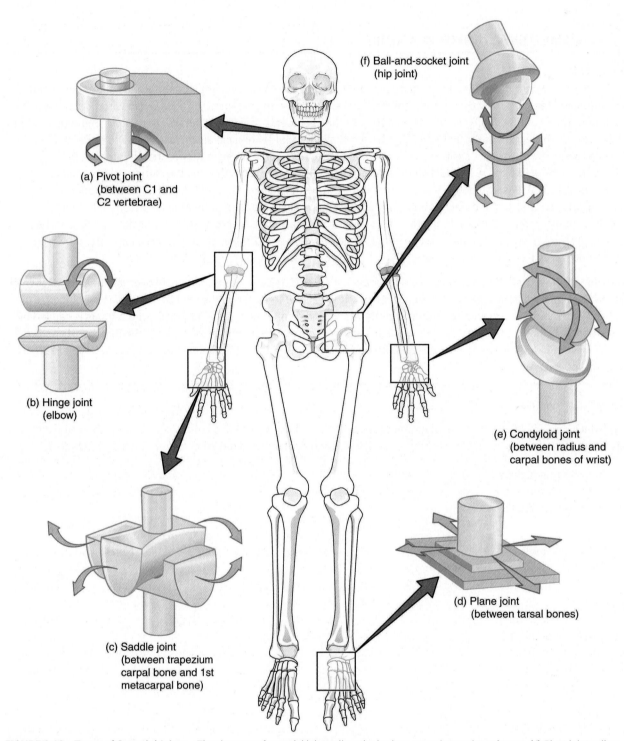

FIGURE 9.10 Types of Synovial Joints   The six types of synovial joints allow the body to move in a variety of ways. (a) Pivot joints allow for rotation around an axis, such as between the first and second cervical vertebrae, which allows for side-to-side rotation of the head. (b) The hinge joint of the elbow works like a door hinge. (c) The articulation between the trapezium carpal bone and the first metacarpal bone at the base of the thumb is a saddle joint. (d) Plane joints, such as those between the tarsal bones of the foot, allow for limited gliding movements between bones. (e) The radiocarpal joint of the wrist is a condyloid joint. (f) The hip and shoulder joints are the only ball-and-socket joints of the body.

Pivot Joint

At a **pivot joint**, a rounded portion of a bone is enclosed within a ring formed partially by the articulation with another bone and partially by a ligament (see Figure 9.10**a**). The bone rotates within this ring. Since the rotation is around a single axis, pivot joints are functionally classified as a uniaxial diarthrosis type of joint. An example of a pivot joint is the atlantoaxial joint, found between the C1 (atlas) and C2 (axis) vertebrae. Here, the upward projecting dens of the axis articulates with the inner aspect of the atlas, where it is held in place by a ligament. Rotation at this joint allows you to turn your head from side to side. A second pivot joint is found at the **proximal radioulnar joint**. Here, the head of the radius is largely encircled by a ligament that holds it in place as it articulates with the radial notch of the ulna. Rotation of the radius allows for forearm movements.

Hinge Joint

In a **hinge joint**, the convex end of one bone articulates with the concave end of the adjoining bone (see Figure 9.10**b**). This type of joint allows only for bending and straightening motions along a single axis, and thus hinge joints are functionally classified as uniaxial joints. A good example is the elbow joint, with the articulation between the trochlea of the humerus and the trochlear notch of the ulna. Other hinge joints of the body include the knee, ankle, and interphalangeal joints between the phalanx bones of the fingers and toes.

Condyloid Joint

At a **condyloid joint** (ellipsoid joint), the shallow depression at the end of one bone articulates with a rounded structure from an adjacent bone or bones (see Figure 9.10**e**). The knuckle (metacarpophalangeal) joints of the hand between the distal end of a metacarpal bone and the proximal phalanx bone are condyloid joints. Another example is the radiocarpal joint of the wrist, between the shallow depression at the distal end of the radius bone and the rounded scaphoid, lunate, and triquetrum carpal bones. In this case, the articulation area has a more oval (elliptical) shape. Functionally, condyloid joints are biaxial joints that allow for two planes of movement. One movement involves the bending and straightening of the fingers or the anterior-posterior movements of the hand. The second movement is a side-to-side movement, which allows you to spread your fingers apart and bring them together, or to move your hand in a medial-going or lateral-going direction.

Saddle Joint

At a **saddle joint**, both of the articulating surfaces for the bones have a saddle shape, which is concave in one direction and convex in the other (see Figure 9.10**c**). This allows the two bones to fit together like a rider sitting on a saddle. Saddle joints are functionally classified as biaxial joints. The primary example is the first carpometacarpal joint, between the trapezium (a carpal bone) and the first metacarpal bone at the base of the thumb. This joint provides the thumb the ability to move away from the palm of the hand along two planes. Thus, the thumb can move within the same plane as the palm of the hand, or it can jut out anteriorly, perpendicular to the palm. This movement of the first carpometacarpal joint is what gives humans their distinctive "opposable" thumbs. The sternoclavicular joint is also classified as a saddle joint.

Plane Joint

At a **plane joint** (gliding joint), the articulating surfaces of the bones are flat or slightly curved and of approximately the same size, which allows the bones to slide against each other (see Figure 9.10**d**). The motion at this type of joint is usually small and tightly constrained by surrounding ligaments. Based only on their shape, plane joints can allow multiple movements, including rotation. Thus plane joints can be functionally classified as a multiaxial joint. However, not all of these movements are available to every plane joint due to limitations placed on it by ligaments or neighboring bones. Thus, depending upon the specific joint of the body, a plane joint may exhibit only a single type of movement or several movements. Plane joints are found between the carpal bones (intercarpal joints) of the wrist or tarsal bones (intertarsal joints) of the foot, between the clavicle and acromion of the scapula (acromioclavicular joint), and between the superior and inferior articular processes of adjacent vertebrae (zygapophysial joints).

Ball-and-Socket Joint

The joint with the greatest range of motion is the **ball-and-socket joint**. At these joints, the rounded head of one bone (the ball) fits into the concave articulation (the socket) of the adjacent bone (see Figure 9.10**f**). The hip joint and the glenohumeral (shoulder) joint are the only ball-and-socket joints of the body. At the hip joint, the head of the femur articulates with the acetabulum of the hip bone, and at the shoulder joint, the head of the humerus articulates with the glenoid cavity of the scapula.

Ball-and-socket joints are classified functionally as multiaxial joints. The femur and the humerus are able to move in both anterior-posterior and medial-lateral directions and they can also rotate around their long axis. The shallow socket formed by the glenoid cavity allows the shoulder joint an extensive range of motion. In contrast, the deep socket of the acetabulum and the strong supporting ligaments of the hip joint serve to constrain movements of the femur, reflecting the need for stability and weight-bearing ability at the hip.

⊘ INTERACTIVE LINK

Watch this video (http://openstax.org/l/synjoints) to see an animation of synovial joints in action. Synovial joints are places where bones articulate with each other inside of a joint cavity. The different types of synovial joints are the ball-and-socket joint (shoulder joint), hinge joint (knee), pivot joint (atlantoaxial joint, between C1 and C2 vertebrae of the neck), condyloid joint (radiocarpal joint of the wrist), saddle joint (first carpometacarpal joint, between the trapezium carpal bone and the first metacarpal bone, at the base of the thumb), and plane joint (facet joints of vertebral column, between superior and inferior articular processes). Which type of synovial joint allows for the widest range of motion?

Aging and the...

Joints

Arthritis is a common disorder of synovial joints that involves inflammation of the joint. This often results in significant joint pain, along with swelling, stiffness, and reduced joint mobility. There are more than 100 different forms of arthritis. Arthritis may arise from aging, damage to the articular cartilage, autoimmune diseases, bacterial or viral infections, or unknown (probably genetic) causes.

The most common type of arthritis is osteoarthritis, which is associated with aging and "wear and tear" of the articular cartilage (Figure 9.11). Risk factors that may lead to osteoarthritis later in life include injury to a joint; jobs that involve physical labor; sports with running, twisting, or throwing actions; and being overweight. These factors put stress on the articular cartilage that covers the surfaces of bones at synovial joints, causing the cartilage to gradually become thinner. As the articular cartilage layer wears down, more pressure is placed on the bones. The joint responds by increasing production of the lubricating synovial fluid, but this can lead to swelling of the joint cavity, causing pain and joint stiffness as the articular capsule is stretched. The bone tissue underlying the damaged articular cartilage also responds by thickening, producing irregularities and causing the articulating surface of the bone to become rough or bumpy. Joint movement then results in pain and inflammation. In its early stages, symptoms of osteoarthritis may be reduced by mild activity that "warms up" the joint, but the symptoms may worsen following exercise. In individuals with more advanced osteoarthritis, the affected joints can become more painful and therefore are difficult to use effectively, resulting in increased immobility. There is no cure for osteoarthritis, but several treatments can help alleviate the pain. Treatments may include lifestyle changes, such as weight loss and low-impact exercise, and over-the-counter or prescription medications that help to alleviate the pain and inflammation. For severe cases, joint replacement surgery (arthroplasty) may be required.

Joint replacement is a very invasive procedure, so other treatments are always tried before surgery. However arthroplasty can provide relief from chronic pain and can enhance mobility within a few months following the surgery. This type of surgery involves replacing the articular surfaces of the bones with prosthesis (artificial components). For example, in hip arthroplasty, the worn or damaged parts of the hip joint, including the head and neck of the femur and the acetabulum of the pelvis, are removed and replaced with artificial joint components. The replacement head for the femur consists of a rounded ball attached to the end of a shaft that is inserted inside the diaphysis of the femur. The acetabulum of the pelvis is reshaped and a replacement socket is fitted into its place. The parts, which are always built in advance of the surgery, are sometimes custom made to produce the best possible fit for a patient.

Gout is a form of arthritis that results from the deposition of uric acid crystals within a body joint. Usually only one or a few joints are affected, such as the big toe, knee, or ankle. The attack may only last a few days, but may return to the same or another joint. Gout occurs when the body makes too much uric acid or the kidneys do not properly excrete it. A diet with excessive fructose has been implicated in raising the chances of a susceptible individual developing gout.

Other forms of arthritis are associated with various autoimmune diseases, bacterial infections of the joint, or unknown genetic causes. Autoimmune diseases, including rheumatoid arthritis, scleroderma, or systemic lupus erythematosus, produce arthritis because the immune system of the body attacks the body joints. In rheumatoid arthritis, the joint capsule and synovial membrane become inflamed. As the disease progresses, the articular cartilage is severely damaged or destroyed, resulting in joint deformation, loss of movement, and severe disability. The most commonly involved joints are the hands, feet, and cervical spine, with corresponding joints on both sides of the body usually affected, though not always to the same extent. Rheumatoid arthritis is also associated with lung fibrosis, vasculitis (inflammation of blood vessels), coronary heart disease, and premature mortality. With no known cure, treatments are aimed at alleviating symptoms. Exercise, anti-inflammatory and pain medications, various specific disease-modifying anti-rheumatic drugs, or surgery are used to treat rheumatoid arthritis.

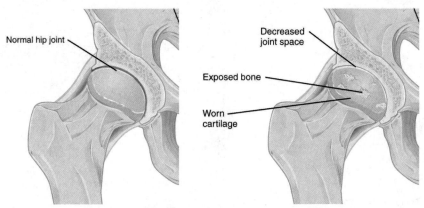

FIGURE 9.11 **Osteoarthritis** Osteoarthritis of a synovial joint results from aging or prolonged joint wear and tear. These cause erosion and loss of the articular cartilage covering the surfaces of the bones, resulting in inflammation that causes joint stiffness and pain.

⊚ INTERACTIVE LINK

Visit this website (http://openstax.org/l/gout) to learn about a patient who arrives at the hospital with joint pain and weakness in his legs. What caused this patient's weakness?

⊚ INTERACTIVE LINK

Watch this animation (http://openstax.org/l/hipreplace) to observe hip replacement surgery (total hip arthroplasty), which can be used to alleviate the pain and loss of joint mobility associated with osteoarthritis of the hip joint. What is the most common cause of hip disability?

⊚ INTERACTIVE LINK

Watch this video (http://openstax.org/l/rheuarthritis) to learn about the symptoms and treatments for rheumatoid arthritis. Which system of the body malfunctions in rheumatoid arthritis and what does this cause?

9.5 Types of Body Movements

LEARNING OBJECTIVES

By the end of this section, you will be able to:
- Define the different types of body movements
- Identify the joints that allow for these motions

Synovial joints allow the body a tremendous range of movements. Each movement at a synovial joint results from the contraction or relaxation of the muscles that are attached to the bones on either side of the articulation. The type of movement that can be produced at a synovial joint is determined by its structural type. While the ball-and-socket joint gives the greatest range of movement at an individual joint, in other regions of the body, several joints may work together to produce a particular movement. Overall, each type of synovial joint is necessary to provide the body with its great flexibility and mobility. There are many types of movement that can occur at synovial joints (Table 9.1). Movement types are generally paired, with one being the opposite of the other. Body movements are always described in relation to the anatomical position of the body: upright stance, with upper limbs to the side of body and palms facing forward. Refer to <u>Figure 9.12</u> as you go through this section.

⊘ INTERACTIVE LINK

Watch this <u>video (http://openstax.org/l/anatomical)</u> to learn about anatomical motions. What motions involve increasing or decreasing the angle of the foot at the ankle?

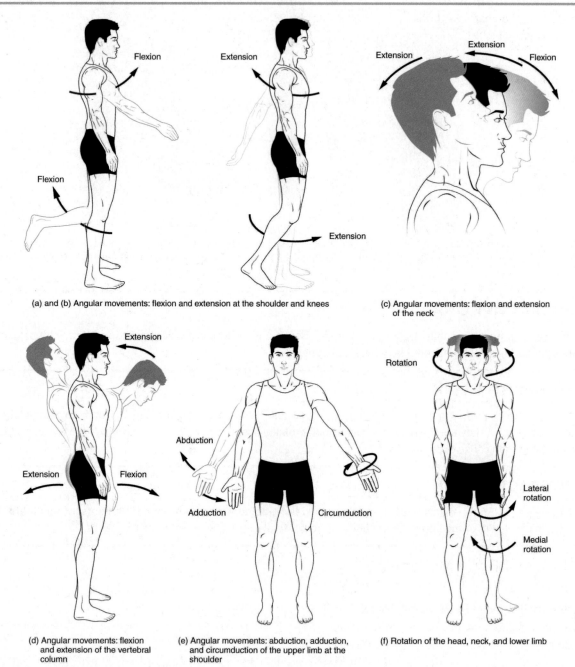

(a) and (b) Angular movements: flexion and extension at the shoulder and knees

(c) Angular movements: flexion and extension of the neck

(d) Angular movements: flexion and extension of the vertebral column

(e) Angular movements: abduction, adduction, and circumduction of the upper limb at the shoulder

(f) Rotation of the head, neck, and lower limb

FIGURE 9.12 Movements of the Body, Part 1 Synovial joints give the body many ways in which to move. (a)–(b) Flexion and extension motions are in the sagittal (anterior–posterior) plane of motion. These movements take place at the shoulder, hip, elbow, knee, wrist, metacarpophalangeal, metatarsophalangeal, and interphalangeal joints. (c)–(d) Anterior bending of the head or vertebral column is flexion, while any posterior-going movement is extension. (e) Abduction and adduction are motions of the limbs, hand, fingers, or toes in the coronal (medial–lateral) plane of movement. Moving the limb or hand laterally away from the body, or spreading the fingers or toes, is abduction. Adduction brings the limb or hand toward or across the midline of the body, or brings the fingers or toes together. Circumduction is the movement of the limb, hand, or fingers in a circular pattern, using the sequential combination of flexion, adduction, extension, and abduction motions. Adduction/abduction and circumduction take place at the shoulder, hip, wrist, metacarpophalangeal, and metatarsophalangeal joints. (f) Turning of the head side to side or twisting of the body is rotation. Medial and lateral rotation of the upper limb at the shoulder or lower limb at the hip involves turning the anterior surface of the limb toward the midline of the body (medial or internal rotation) or away from the midline (lateral or external rotation).

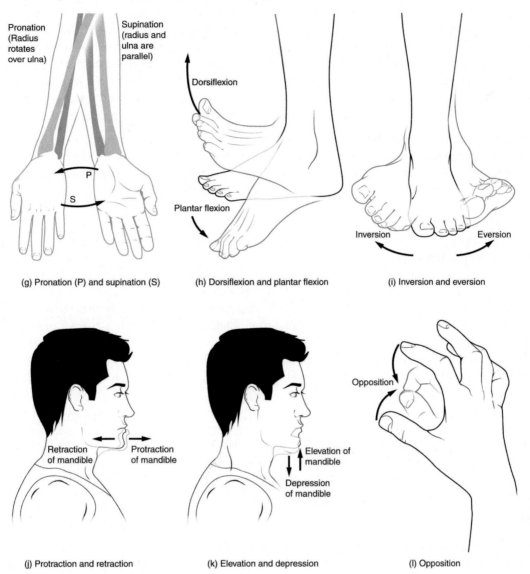

(g) Pronation (P) and supination (S)

(h) Dorsiflexion and plantar flexion

(i) Inversion and eversion

(j) Protraction and retraction

(k) Elevation and depression

(l) Opposition

FIGURE 9.13 Movements of the Body, Part 2   (g) Supination of the forearm turns the hand to the palm forward position in which the radius and ulna are parallel, while forearm pronation turns the hand to the palm backward position in which the radius crosses over the ulna to form an "X." (h) Dorsiflexion of the foot at the ankle joint moves the top of the foot toward the leg, while plantar flexion lifts the heel and points the toes. (i) Eversion of the foot moves the bottom (sole) of the foot away from the midline of the body, while foot inversion faces the sole toward the midline. (j) Protraction of the mandible pushes the chin forward, and retraction pulls the chin back. (k) Depression of the mandible opens the mouth, while elevation closes it. (l) Opposition of the thumb brings the tip of the thumb into contact with the tip of the fingers of the same hand and reposition brings the thumb back next to the index finger.

Flexion and Extension

Flexion and **extension** are typically movements that take place within the sagittal plane and involve anterior or posterior movements of the neck, trunk, or limbs. For the vertebral column, flexion (anterior flexion) is an anterior (forward) bending of the neck or trunk, while extension involves a posterior-directed motion, such as straightening from a flexed position or bending backward. **Lateral flexion** of the vertebral column occurs in the coronal plane and is defined as the bending of the neck or trunk toward the right or left side. These movements of the vertebral column involve both the symphysis joint formed by each intervertebral disc, as well as the plane type of synovial joint formed between the inferior articular processes of one vertebra and the superior articular processes of the next lower vertebra.

In the limbs, flexion decreases the angle between the bones (bending of the joint), while extension increases the angle and straightens the joint. For the upper limb, all anterior-going motions are flexion and all posterior-going motions are extension. These include anterior-posterior movements of the arm at the shoulder, the forearm at the elbow, the hand at the wrist, and the fingers at the metacarpophalangeal and interphalangeal joints. For the thumb, extension moves the thumb away from the palm of the hand, within the same plane as the palm, while flexion brings the thumb back against the index finger or into the palm. These motions take place at the first carpometacarpal joint. In the lower limb, bringing the thigh forward and upward is flexion at the hip joint, while any posterior-going motion of the thigh is extension. Note that extension of the thigh beyond the anatomical (standing) position is greatly limited by the ligaments that support the hip joint. Knee flexion is the bending of the knee to bring the foot toward the posterior thigh, and extension is the straightening of the knee. Flexion and extension movements are seen at the hinge, condyloid, saddle, and ball-and-socket joints of the limbs (see Figure 9.12**a-d**).

Hyperextension is the abnormal or excessive extension of a joint beyond its normal range of motion, thus resulting in injury. Similarly, **hyperflexion** is excessive flexion at a joint. Hyperextension injuries are common at hinge joints such as the knee or elbow. In cases of "whiplash" in which the head is suddenly moved backward and then forward, a patient may experience both hyperextension and hyperflexion of the cervical region.

Abduction and Adduction

Abduction and **adduction** motions occur within the coronal plane and involve medial-lateral motions of the limbs, fingers, toes, or thumb. Abduction moves the limb laterally away from the midline of the body, while adduction is the opposing movement that brings the limb toward the body or across the midline. For example, abduction is raising the arm at the shoulder joint, moving it laterally away from the body, while adduction brings the arm down to the side of the body. Similarly, abduction and adduction at the wrist moves the hand away from or toward the midline of the body. Spreading the fingers or toes apart is also abduction, while bringing the fingers or toes together is adduction. For the thumb, abduction is the anterior movement that brings the thumb to a 90° perpendicular position, pointing straight out from the palm. Adduction moves the thumb back to the anatomical position, next to the index finger. Abduction and adduction movements are seen at condyloid, saddle, and ball-and-socket joints (see Figure 9.12**e**).

Circumduction

Circumduction is the movement of a body region in a circular manner, in which one end of the body region being moved stays relatively stationary while the other end describes a circle. It involves the sequential combination of flexion, adduction, extension, and abduction at a joint. This type of motion is found at biaxial condyloid and saddle joints, and at multiaxial ball-and-sockets joints (see Figure 9.12**e**).

Rotation

Rotation can occur within the vertebral column, at a pivot joint, or at a ball-and-socket joint. Rotation of the neck or body is the twisting movement produced by the summation of the small rotational movements available between adjacent vertebrae. At a pivot joint, one bone rotates in relation to another bone. This is a uniaxial joint, and thus rotation is the only motion allowed at a pivot joint. For example, at the atlantoaxial joint, the first cervical (C1) vertebra (atlas) rotates around the dens, the upward projection from the second cervical (C2) vertebra (axis). This allows the head to rotate from side to side as when shaking the head "no." The proximal radioulnar joint is a pivot joint formed by the head of the radius and its articulation with the ulna. This joint allows for the radius to rotate along its length during pronation and supination movements of the forearm.

Rotation can also occur at the ball-and-socket joints of the shoulder and hip. Here, the humerus and femur rotate around their long axis, which moves the anterior surface of the arm or thigh either toward or away from the midline of the body. Movement that brings the anterior surface of the limb toward the midline of the body is called **medial (internal) rotation**. Conversely, rotation of the limb so that the anterior surface moves away from the midline is **lateral (external) rotation** (see Figure 9.12**f**). Be sure to distinguish medial and lateral rotation, which can only occur at the multiaxial shoulder and hip joints, from circumduction, which can occur at either biaxial or multiaxial joints.

Supination and Pronation

Supination and pronation are movements of the forearm. In the anatomical position, the upper limb is held next to the body with the palm facing forward. This is the **supinated position** of the forearm. In this position, the radius and ulna are parallel to each other. When the palm of the hand faces backward, the forearm is in the **pronated position**, and the radius and ulna form an X-shape.

Supination and pronation are the movements of the forearm that go between these two positions. **Pronation** is the motion that moves the forearm from the supinated (anatomical) position to the pronated (palm backward) position. This motion is produced by rotation of the radius at the proximal radioulnar joint, accompanied by movement of the radius at the distal radioulnar joint. The proximal radioulnar joint is a pivot joint that allows for rotation of the head of the radius. Because of the slight curvature of the shaft of the radius, this rotation causes the distal end of the radius to cross over the distal ulna at the distal radioulnar joint. This crossing over brings the radius and ulna into an X-shape position. **Supination** is the opposite motion, in which rotation of the radius returns the bones to their parallel positions and moves the palm to the anterior facing (supinated) position. It helps to remember that supination is the motion you use when scooping up soup with a spoon (see Figure 9.13**g**).

Dorsiflexion and Plantar Flexion

Dorsiflexion and **plantar flexion** are movements at the ankle joint, which is a hinge joint. Lifting the front of the foot, so that the top of the foot moves toward the anterior leg is dorsiflexion, while lifting the heel of the foot from the ground or pointing the toes downward is plantar flexion. These are the only movements available at the ankle joint (see Figure 9.13**h**).

Inversion and Eversion

Inversion and eversion are complex movements that involve the multiple plane joints among the tarsal bones of the posterior foot (intertarsal joints) and thus are not motions that take place at the ankle joint. **Inversion** is the turning of the foot to angle the bottom of the foot toward the midline, while **eversion** turns the bottom of the foot away from the midline. The foot has a greater range of inversion than eversion motion. These are important motions that help to stabilize the foot when walking or running on an uneven surface and aid in the quick side-to-side changes in direction used during active sports such as basketball, racquetball, or soccer (see Figure 9.13**i**).

Protraction and Retraction

Protraction and **retraction** are anterior-posterior movements of the scapula or mandible. Protraction of the scapula occurs when the shoulder is moved forward, as when pushing against something or throwing a ball. Retraction is the opposite motion, with the scapula being pulled posteriorly and medially, toward the vertebral column. For the mandible, protraction occurs when the lower jaw is pushed forward, to stick out the chin, while retraction pulls the lower jaw backward. (See Figure 9.13**j**.)

Depression and Elevation

Depression and **elevation** are downward and upward movements of the scapula or mandible. The upward movement of the scapula and shoulder is elevation, while a downward movement is depression. These movements are used to shrug your shoulders. Similarly, elevation of the mandible is the upward movement of the lower jaw used to close the mouth or bite on something, and depression is the downward movement that produces opening of the mouth (see Figure 9.13**k**).

Excursion

Excursion is the side to side movement of the mandible. **Lateral excursion** moves the mandible away from the midline, toward either the right or left side. **Medial excursion** returns the mandible to its resting position at the midline.

Superior Rotation and Inferior Rotation

Superior and inferior rotation are movements of the scapula and are defined by the direction of movement of the glenoid cavity. These motions involve rotation of the scapula around a point inferior to the scapular spine and are produced by combinations of muscles acting on the scapula. During **superior rotation**, the glenoid cavity moves upward as the medial end of the scapular spine moves downward. This is a very important motion that contributes to upper limb abduction. Without superior rotation of the scapula, the greater tubercle of the humerus would hit the acromion of the scapula, thus preventing any abduction of the arm above shoulder height. Superior rotation of the scapula is thus required for full abduction of the upper limb. Superior rotation is also used without arm abduction when carrying a heavy load with your hand or on your shoulder. You can feel this rotation when you pick up a load, such as a heavy book bag and carry it on only one shoulder. To increase its weight-bearing support for the bag, the shoulder lifts as the scapula superiorly rotates. **Inferior rotation** occurs during limb adduction and involves the downward motion of the glenoid cavity with upward movement of the medial end of the scapular spine.

Opposition and Reposition

Opposition is the thumb movement that brings the tip of the thumb in contact with the tip of a finger. This movement is produced at the first carpometacarpal joint, which is a saddle joint formed between the trapezium carpal bone and the first metacarpal bone. Thumb opposition is produced by a combination of flexion and abduction of the thumb at this joint. Returning the thumb to its anatomical position next to the index finger is called **reposition** (see Figure 9.13l).

Movements of the Joints

Type of Joint	Movement	Example
Pivot	Uniaxial joint; allows rotational movement	Atlantoaxial joint (C1–C2 vertebrae articulation); proximal radioulnar joint
Hinge	Uniaxial joint; allows flexion/extension movements	Knee; elbow; ankle; interphalangeal joints of fingers and toes
Condyloid	Biaxial joint; allows flexion/extension, abduction/adduction, and circumduction movements	Metacarpophalangeal (knuckle) joints of fingers; radiocarpal joint of wrist; metatarsophalangeal joints for toes
Saddle	Biaxial joint; allows flexion/extension, abduction/adduction, and circumduction movements	First carpometacarpal joint of the thumb; sternoclavicular joint
Plane	Multiaxial joint; allows inversion and eversion of foot, or flexion, extension, and lateral flexion of the vertebral column	Intertarsal joints of foot; superior-inferior articular process articulations between vertebrae
Ball-and-socket	Multiaxial joint; allows flexion/extension, abduction/adduction, circumduction, and medial/lateral rotation movements	Shoulder and hip joints

TABLE 9.1

9.6 Anatomy of Selected Synovial Joints

LEARNING OBJECTIVES

By the end of this section, you will be able to:
- Describe the bones that articulate together to form selected synovial joints
- Discuss the movements available at each joint
- Describe the structures that support and prevent excess movements at each joint

Each synovial joint of the body is specialized to perform certain movements. The movements that are allowed are determined by the structural classification for each joint. For example, a multiaxial ball-and-socket joint has much more mobility than a uniaxial hinge joint. However, the ligaments and muscles that support a joint may place restrictions on the total range of motion available. Thus, the ball-and-socket joint of the shoulder has little in the way of ligament support, which gives the shoulder a very large range of motion. In contrast, movements at the hip joint are restricted by strong ligaments, which reduce its range of motion but confer stability during standing and weight bearing.

This section will examine the anatomy of selected synovial joints of the body. Anatomical names for most joints are derived from the names of the bones that articulate at that joint, although some joints, such as the elbow, hip, and knee joints are exceptions to this general naming scheme.

Articulations of the Vertebral Column

In addition to being held together by the intervertebral discs, adjacent vertebrae also articulate with each other at synovial joints formed between the superior and inferior articular processes called **zygapophysial joints** (facet joints) (see Figure 9.3). These are plane joints that provide for only limited motions between the vertebrae. The orientation of the articular processes at these joints varies in different regions of the vertebral column and serves to determine the types of motions available in each vertebral region. The cervical and lumbar regions have the greatest ranges of motions.

In the neck, the articular processes of cervical vertebrae are flattened and generally face upward or downward. This orientation provides the cervical vertebral column with extensive ranges of motion for flexion, extension, lateral flexion, and rotation. In the thoracic region, the downward projecting and overlapping spinous processes, along with the attached thoracic cage, greatly limit flexion, extension, and lateral flexion. However, the flattened and vertically positioned thoracic articular processes allow for the greatest range of rotation within the vertebral column. The lumbar region allows for considerable extension, flexion, and lateral flexion, but the orientation of the articular processes largely prohibits rotation.

The articulations formed between the skull, the atlas (C1 vertebra), and the axis (C2 vertebra) differ from the articulations in other vertebral areas and play important roles in movement of the head. The **atlanto-occipital joint** is formed by the articulations between the superior articular processes of the atlas and the occipital condyles on the base of the skull. This articulation has a pronounced U-shaped curvature, oriented along the anterior-posterior axis. This allows the skull to rock forward and backward, producing flexion and extension of the head. This moves the head up and down, as when shaking your head "yes."

The **atlantoaxial joint**, between the atlas and axis, consists of three articulations. The paired superior articular processes of the axis articulate with the inferior articular processes of the atlas. These articulating surfaces are relatively flat and oriented horizontally. The third articulation is the pivot joint formed between the dens, which projects upward from the body of the axis, and the inner aspect of the anterior arch of the atlas (Figure 9.14). A strong ligament passes posterior to the dens to hold it in position against the anterior arch. These articulations allow the atlas to rotate on top of the axis, moving the head toward the right or left, as when shaking your head "no."

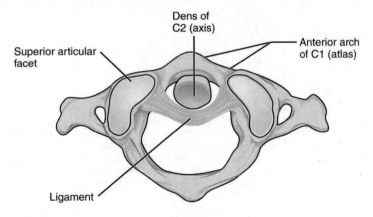

Dens of
C2 (axis)

Superior articular
facet

Anterior arch
of C1 (atlas)

Ligament

Superior view of atlas

FIGURE 9.14 Atlantoaxial Joint   The atlantoaxial joint is a pivot type of joint between the dens portion of the axis (C2 vertebra) and the anterior arch of the atlas (C1 vertebra), with the dens held in place by a ligament.

Temporomandibular Joint

The **temporomandibular joint (TMJ)** is the joint that allows for opening (mandibular depression) and closing (mandibular elevation) of the mouth, as well as side-to-side and protraction/retraction motions of the lower jaw.

This joint involves the articulation between the mandibular fossa and articular tubercle of the temporal bone, with the condyle (head) of the mandible. Located between these bony structures, filling the gap between the skull and mandible, is a flexible articular disc (Figure 9.15). This disc serves to smooth the movements between the temporal bone and mandibular condyle.

Movement at the TMJ during opening and closing of the mouth involves both gliding and hinge motions of the mandible. With the mouth closed, the mandibular condyle and articular disc are located within the mandibular fossa of the temporal bone. During opening of the mouth, the mandible hinges downward and at the same time is pulled anteriorly, causing both the condyle and the articular disc to glide forward from the mandibular fossa onto the downward projecting articular tubercle. The net result is a forward and downward motion of the condyle and mandibular depression. The temporomandibular joint is supported by an extrinsic ligament that anchors the mandible to the skull. This ligament spans the distance between the base of the skull and the lingula on the medial side of the mandibular ramus.

Dislocation of the TMJ may occur when opening the mouth too wide (such as when taking a large bite) or following a blow to the jaw, resulting in the mandibular condyle moving beyond (anterior to) the articular tubercle. In this case, the individual would not be able to close their mouth. Temporomandibular joint disorder is a painful condition that may arise due to arthritis, wearing of the articular cartilage covering the bony surfaces of the joint, muscle fatigue from overuse or grinding of the teeth, damage to the articular disc within the joint, or jaw injury. Temporomandibular joint disorders can also cause headache, difficulty chewing, or even the inability to move the jaw (lock jaw). Pharmacologic agents for pain or other therapies, including bite guards, are used as treatments.

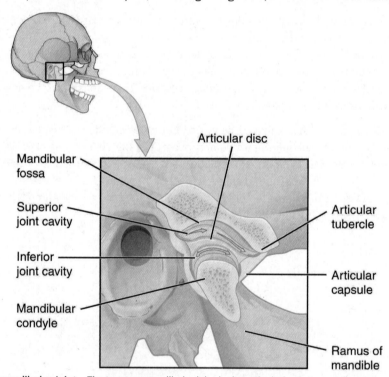

FIGURE 9.15   Temporomandibular Joint   The temporomandibular joint is the articulation between the temporal bone of the skull and the condyle of the mandible, with an articular disc located between these bones. During depression of the mandible (opening of the mouth), the mandibular condyle moves both forward and hinges downward as it travels from the mandibular fossa onto the articular tubercle.

🔗 INTERACTIVE LINK

Watch this video (http://openstax.org/l/TMJ) to learn about TMJ. Opening of the mouth requires the combination of two motions at the temporomandibular joint, an anterior gliding motion of the articular disc and mandible and the downward hinging of the mandible. What is the initial movement of the mandible during opening and how much mouth opening does this produce?

Shoulder Joint

The shoulder joint is called the **glenohumeral joint**. This is a ball-and-socket joint formed by the articulation between the head of the humerus and the glenoid cavity of the scapula (Figure 9.16). This joint has the largest range of motion of any joint in the body. However, this freedom of movement is due to the lack of structural support and thus the enhanced mobility is offset by a loss of stability.

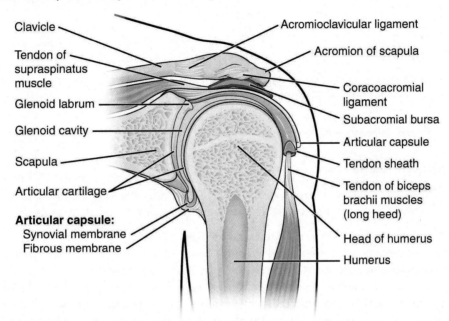

Clavicle
Tendon of supraspinatus muscle
Glenoid labrum
Glenoid cavity
Scapula
Articular cartilage
Articular capsule:
    Synovial membrane
    Fibrous membrane
Acromioclavicular ligament
Acromion of scapula
Coracoacromial ligament
Subacromial bursa
Articular capsule
Tendon sheath
Tendon of biceps brachii muscles (long heed)
Head of humerus
Humerus

FIGURE 9.16 Glenohumeral Joint The glenohumeral (shoulder) joint is a ball-and-socket joint that provides the widest range of motions. It has a loose articular capsule and is supported by ligaments and the rotator cuff muscles.

The large range of motions at the shoulder joint is provided by the articulation of the large, rounded humeral head with the small and shallow glenoid cavity, which is only about one third of the size of the humeral head. The socket formed by the glenoid cavity is deepened slightly by a small lip of fibrocartilage called the **glenoid labrum**, which extends around the outer margin of the cavity. The articular capsule that surrounds the glenohumeral joint is relatively thin and loose to allow for large motions of the upper limb. Some structural support for the joint is provided by thickenings of the articular capsule wall that form weak intrinsic ligaments. These include the **coracohumeral ligament**, running from the coracoid process of the scapula to the anterior humerus, and three ligaments, each called a **glenohumeral ligament**, located on the anterior side of the articular capsule. These ligaments help to strengthen the superior and anterior capsule walls.

However, the primary support for the shoulder joint is provided by muscles crossing the joint, particularly the four rotator cuff muscles. These muscles (supraspinatus, infraspinatus, teres minor, and subscapularis) arise from the scapula and attach to the greater or lesser tubercles of the humerus. As these muscles cross the shoulder joint, their tendons encircle the head of the humerus and become fused to the anterior, superior, and posterior walls of the articular capsule. The thickening of the capsule formed by the fusion of these four muscle tendons is called the **rotator cuff**. Two bursae, the **subacromial bursa** and the **subscapular bursa**, help to prevent friction between the rotator cuff muscle tendons and the scapula as these tendons cross the glenohumeral joint. In addition to their individual actions of moving the upper limb, the rotator cuff muscles also serve to hold the head of the humerus in position within the glenoid cavity. By constantly adjusting their strength of contraction to resist forces acting on the shoulder, these muscles serve as "dynamic ligaments" and thus provide the primary structural support for the glenohumeral joint.

Injuries to the shoulder joint are common. Repetitive use of the upper limb, particularly in abduction such as during throwing, swimming, or racquet sports, may lead to acute or chronic inflammation of the bursa or muscle tendons, a tear of the glenoid labrum, or degeneration or tears of the rotator cuff. Because the humeral head is strongly supported by muscles and ligaments around its anterior, superior, and posterior aspects, most dislocations of the humerus occur in an inferior direction. This can occur when force is applied to the humerus when the upper limb is fully abducted, as when diving to catch a baseball and landing on your hand or elbow. Inflammatory responses to any shoulder injury can lead to the formation of scar tissue between the articular capsule and surrounding structures, thus reducing shoulder mobility, a condition called adhesive capsulitis ("frozen shoulder").

🔗 INTERACTIVE LINK

Watch this video (http://openstax.org/l/shoulderjoint1) for a tutorial on the anatomy of the shoulder joint. What movements are available at the shoulder joint?

🔗 INTERACTIVE LINK

Watch this video (http://openstax.org/l/shoulderjoint2) to learn more about the anatomy of the shoulder joint, including bones, joints, muscles, nerves, and blood vessels. What is the shape of the glenoid labrum in cross-section, and what is the importance of this shape?

Elbow Joint

The **elbow joint** is a uniaxial hinge joint formed by the **humeroulnar joint**, the articulation between the trochlea of the humerus and the trochlear notch of the ulna. Also associated with the elbow are the **humeroradial joint** and the proximal radioulnar joint. All three of these joints are enclosed within a single articular capsule (Figure 9.17).

The articular capsule of the elbow is thin on its anterior and posterior aspects, but is thickened along its outside margins by strong intrinsic ligaments. These ligaments prevent side-to-side movements and hyperextension. On the medial side is the triangular **ulnar collateral ligament**. This arises from the medial epicondyle of the humerus and attaches to the medial side of the proximal ulna. The strongest part of this ligament is the anterior portion, which resists hyperextension of the elbow. The ulnar collateral ligament may be injured by frequent, forceful extensions of the forearm, as is seen in baseball pitchers. Reconstructive surgical repair of this ligament is referred to as Tommy John surgery, named for the former major league pitcher who was the first person to have this treatment.

The lateral side of the elbow is supported by the **radial collateral ligament**. This arises from the lateral epicondyle of the humerus and then blends into the lateral side of the annular ligament. The **annular ligament** encircles the head of the radius. This ligament supports the head of the radius as it articulates with the radial notch of the ulna at the proximal radioulnar joint. This is a pivot joint that allows for rotation of the radius during supination and pronation of the forearm.

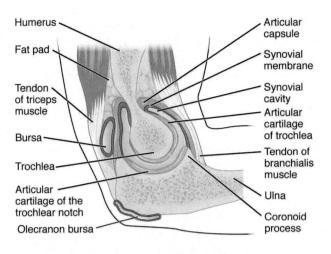

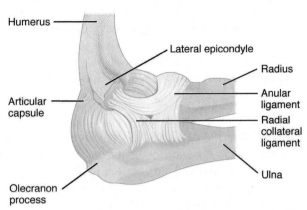

(a) Medial sagittal section through right elbow (lateral view)

(b) Lateral view of right elbow joint

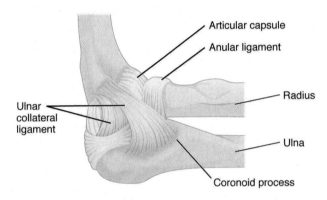

(c) Medial view of left elbow joint

FIGURE 9.17   Elbow Joint   (a) The elbow is a hinge joint that allows only for flexion and extension of the forearm. (b) It is supported by the ulnar and radial collateral ligaments. (c) The annular ligament supports the head of the radius at the proximal radioulnar joint, the pivot joint that allows for rotation of the radius.

🔗 INTERACTIVE LINK

Watch this animation (http://openstax.org/l/elbowjoint1) to learn more about the anatomy of the elbow joint. Which structures provide the main stability for the elbow?

🔗 INTERACTIVE LINK

Watch this video (http://openstax.org/l/elbowjoint2) to learn more about the anatomy of the elbow joint, including bones, joints, muscles, nerves, and blood vessels. What are the functions of the articular cartilage?

Hip Joint

The hip joint is a multiaxial ball-and-socket joint between the head of the femur and the acetabulum of the hip bone (Figure 9.18). The hip carries the weight of the body and thus requires strength and stability during standing and walking. For these reasons, its range of motion is more limited than at the shoulder joint.

The acetabulum is the socket portion of the hip joint. This space is deep and has a large articulation area for the femoral head, thus giving stability and weight bearing ability to the joint. The acetabulum is further deepened by the **acetabular labrum**, a fibrocartilage lip attached to the outer margin of the acetabulum. The surrounding articular capsule is strong, with several thickened areas forming intrinsic ligaments. These ligaments arise from the hip bone, at the margins of the acetabulum, and attach to the femur at the base of the neck. The ligaments are the **iliofemoral ligament**, **pubofemoral ligament**, and **ischiofemoral ligament**, all of which spiral around the head and neck of the femur. The ligaments are tightened by extension at the hip, thus pulling the head of the femur tightly into the acetabulum when in the upright, standing position. Very little additional extension of the thigh is permitted beyond this vertical position. These ligaments thus stabilize the hip joint and allow you to maintain an upright standing position with only minimal muscle contraction. Inside of the articular capsule, the **ligament of the head of the femur** (ligamentum teres) spans between the acetabulum and femoral head. This intracapsular ligament is normally slack and does not provide any significant joint support, but it does provide a pathway for an important artery that supplies the head of the femur.

The hip is prone to osteoarthritis, and thus was the first joint for which a replacement prosthesis was developed. A common injury in elderly individuals, particularly those with weakened bones due to osteoporosis, is a "broken hip," which is actually a fracture of the femoral neck. This may result from a fall, or it may cause the fall. This can happen as one lower limb is taking a step and all of the body weight is placed on the other limb, causing the femoral neck to break and producing a fall. Any accompanying disruption of the blood supply to the femoral neck or head can lead to necrosis of these areas, resulting in bone and cartilage death. Femoral fractures usually require surgical treatment, after which the patient will need mobility assistance for a prolonged period, either from family members or in a long-term care facility. Consequentially, the associated health care costs of "broken hips" are substantial. In addition, hip fractures are associated with increased rates of morbidity (incidences of disease) and mortality (death). Surgery for a hip fracture followed by prolonged bed rest may lead to life-threatening complications, including pneumonia, infection of pressure ulcers (bedsores), and thrombophlebitis (deep vein thrombosis; blood clot formation) that can result in a pulmonary embolism (blood clot within the lung).

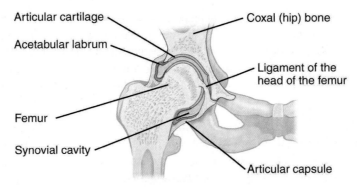

Articular cartilage

Coxal (hip) bone

Acetabular labrum

Ligament of the
head of the femur

Femur

Synovial cavity

Articular capsule

(a) Frontal section through the right hip joint

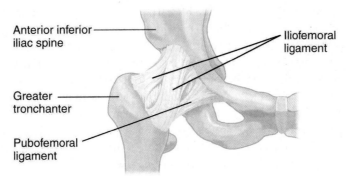

Anterior inferior
iliac spine

Iliofemoral
ligament

Greater
tronchanter

Pubofemoral
ligament

(b) Anterior view of right hip joint, capsule in place

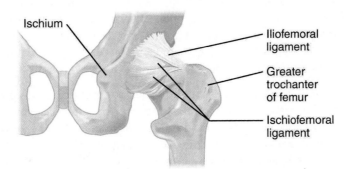

Ischium

Iliofemoral
ligament

Greater
trochanter
of femur

Ischiofemoral
ligament

(c) Posterior view of right hip joint, capsule in place

FIGURE 9.18 Hip Joint   (a) The ball-and-socket joint of the hip is a multiaxial joint that provides both stability and a wide range of motion. (b–c) When standing, the supporting ligaments are tight, pulling the head of the femur into the acetabulum.

⊘ INTERACTIVE LINK

Watch this video (http://openstax.org/l/hipjoint1) for a tutorial on the anatomy of the hip joint. What is a possible consequence following a fracture of the femoral neck within the capsule of the hip joint?

⊘ INTERACTIVE LINK

Watch this video (http://openstax.org/l/hipjoint2) to learn more about the anatomy of the hip joint, including bones, joints, muscles, nerves, and blood vessels. Where is the articular cartilage thickest within the hip joint?

Knee Joint

The knee joint is the largest joint of the body (Figure 9.19). It actually consists of three articulations. The **femoropatellar joint** is found between the patella and the distal femur. The **medial tibiofemoral joint** and **lateral tibiofemoral joint** are located between the medial and lateral condyles of the femur and the medial and lateral condyles of the tibia. All of these articulations are enclosed within a single articular capsule. The knee functions as a hinge joint, allowing flexion and extension of the leg. This action is generated by both rolling and gliding motions of the femur on the tibia. In addition, some rotation of the leg is available when the knee is flexed, but not when extended. The knee is well constructed for weight bearing in its extended position, but is vulnerable to injuries associated with hyperextension, twisting, or blows to the medial or lateral side of the joint, particularly while weight bearing.

At the femoropatellar joint, the patella slides vertically within a groove on the distal femur. The patella is a sesamoid bone incorporated into the tendon of the quadriceps femoris muscle, the large muscle of the anterior thigh. The patella serves to protect the quadriceps tendon from friction against the distal femur. Continuing from the patella to the anterior tibia just below the knee is the **patellar ligament**. Acting via the patella and patellar ligament, the quadriceps femoris is a powerful muscle that acts to extend the leg at the knee. It also serves as a "dynamic ligament" to provide very important support and stabilization for the knee joint.

The medial and lateral tibiofemoral joints are the articulations between the rounded condyles of the femur and the relatively flat condyles of the tibia. During flexion and extension motions, the condyles of the femur both roll and glide over the surfaces of the tibia. The rolling action produces flexion or extension, while the gliding action serves to maintain the femoral condyles centered over the tibial condyles, thus ensuring maximal bony, weight-bearing support for the femur in all knee positions. As the knee comes into full extension, the femur undergoes a slight medial rotation in relation to tibia. The rotation results because the lateral condyle of the femur is slightly smaller than the medial condyle. Thus, the lateral condyle finishes its rolling motion first, followed by the medial condyle. The resulting small medial rotation of the femur serves to "lock" the knee into its fully extended and most stable position. Flexion of the knee is initiated by a slight lateral rotation of the femur on the tibia, which "unlocks" the knee. This lateral rotation motion is produced by the popliteus muscle of the posterior leg.

Located between the articulating surfaces of the femur and tibia are two articular discs, the **medial meniscus** and **lateral meniscus** (see Figure 9.19**b**). Each is a C-shaped fibrocartilage structure that is thin along its inside margin and thick along the outer margin. They are attached to their tibial condyles, but do not attach to the femur. While both menisci are free to move during knee motions, the medial meniscus shows less movement because it is anchored at its outer margin to the articular capsule and tibial collateral ligament. The menisci provide padding between the bones and help to fill the gap between the round femoral condyles and flattened tibial condyles. Some areas of each meniscus lack an arterial blood supply and thus these areas heal poorly if damaged.

The knee joint has multiple ligaments that provide support, particularly in the extended position (see Figure 9.19**c**). Outside of the articular capsule, located at the sides of the knee, are two extrinsic ligaments. The **fibular collateral ligament** (lateral collateral ligament) is on the lateral side and spans from the lateral epicondyle of the femur to the head of the fibula. The **tibial collateral ligament** (medial collateral ligament) of the medial knee runs from the medial epicondyle of the femur to the medial tibia. As it crosses the knee, the tibial collateral ligament is firmly attached on its deep side to the articular capsule and to the medial meniscus, an important factor when considering knee injuries. In the fully extended knee position, both collateral ligaments are taut (tight), thus serving to stabilize and support the extended knee and preventing side-to-side or rotational motions between the femur and tibia.

The articular capsule of the posterior knee is thickened by intrinsic ligaments that help to resist knee hyperextension. Inside the knee are two intracapsular ligaments, the **anterior cruciate ligament** and **posterior cruciate ligament**. These ligaments are anchored inferiorly to the tibia at the intercondylar eminence, the roughened area between the tibial condyles. The cruciate ligaments are named for whether they are attached anteriorly or posteriorly to this tibial region. Each ligament runs diagonally upward to attach to the inner aspect of a femoral condyle. The cruciate ligaments are named for the X-shape formed as they pass each other (cruciate means "cross"). The posterior cruciate ligament is the stronger ligament. It serves to support the knee when it is flexed and weight bearing, as when walking downhill. In this position, the posterior cruciate ligament prevents the femur from sliding anteriorly off the top of the tibia. The anterior cruciate ligament becomes tight when the knee is extended, and thus resists hyperextension.

Access for free at openstax.org

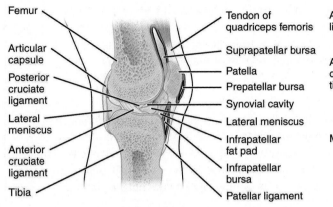

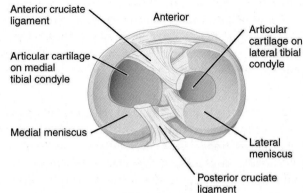

(a) Sagittal section through the right knee joint

(b) Superior view of the right tibia in the knee joint, showing the menisci and cruciate ligaments

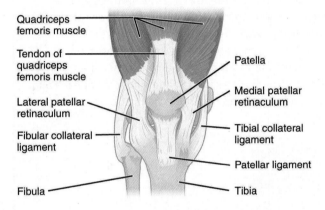

(c) Anterior view of right knee

FIGURE 9.19   **Knee Joint**   (a) The knee joint is the largest joint of the body. (b)–(c) It is supported by the tibial and fibular collateral ligaments located on the sides of the knee outside of the articular capsule, and the anterior and posterior cruciate ligaments found inside the capsule. The medial and lateral menisci provide padding and support between the femoral condyles and tibial condyles.

⊘ INTERACTIVE LINK

Watch this video (http://openstax.org/l/flexext) to learn more about the flexion and extension of the knee, as the femur both rolls and glides on the tibia to maintain stable contact between the bones in all knee positions. The patella glides along a groove on the anterior side of the distal femur. The collateral ligaments on the sides of the knee become tight in the fully extended position to help stabilize the knee. The posterior cruciate ligament supports the knee when flexed and the anterior cruciate ligament becomes tight when the knee comes into full extension to resist hyperextension. What are the ligaments that support the knee joint?

⊘ INTERACTIVE LINK

Watch this video (http://openstax.org/l/kneejoint1) to learn more about the anatomy of the knee joint, including bones, joints, muscles, nerves, and blood vessels. Which ligament of the knee keeps the tibia from sliding too far forward in relation to the femur and which ligament keeps the tibia from sliding too far backward?

Disorders of the...

Joints

Injuries to the knee are common. Since this joint is primarily supported by muscles and ligaments, injuries to any of these structures will result in pain or knee instability. Injury to the posterior cruciate ligament occurs when the knee is flexed and the tibia is driven posteriorly, such as falling and landing on the tibial tuberosity or hitting the tibia on the dashboard when not wearing a seatbelt during an automobile accident. More commonly, injuries occur when forces are applied to the extended knee, particularly when the foot is planted and unable to move. Anterior cruciate ligament injuries can result with a forceful blow to the anterior knee, producing hyperextension, or when a runner makes a quick change of direction that produces both twisting and hyperextension of the knee.

A worse combination of injuries can occur with a hit to the lateral side of the extended knee (Figure 9.20). A moderate blow to the lateral knee will cause the medial side of the joint to open, resulting in stretching or damage to the tibial collateral ligament. Because the medial meniscus is attached to the tibial collateral ligament, a stronger blow can tear the ligament and also damage the medial meniscus. This is one reason that the medial meniscus is 20 times more likely to be injured than the lateral meniscus. A powerful blow to the lateral knee produces a "terrible triad" injury, in which there is a sequential injury to the tibial collateral ligament, medial meniscus, and anterior cruciate ligament.

Arthroscopic surgery has greatly improved the surgical treatment of knee injuries and reduced subsequent recovery times. This procedure involves a small incision and the insertion into the joint of an arthroscope, a pencil-thin instrument that allows for visualization of the joint interior. Small surgical instruments are also inserted via additional incisions. These tools allow a surgeon to remove or repair a torn meniscus or to reconstruct a ruptured cruciate ligament. The current method for anterior cruciate ligament replacement involves using a portion of the patellar ligament. Holes are drilled into the cruciate ligament attachment points on the tibia and femur, and the patellar ligament graft, with small areas of attached bone still intact at each end, is inserted into these holes. The bone-to-bone sites at each end of the graft heal rapidly and strongly, thus enabling a rapid recovery.

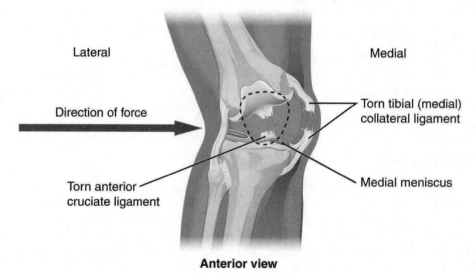

FIGURE 9.20   Knee Injury   A strong blow to the lateral side of the extended knee will cause three injuries, in sequence: tearing of the tibial collateral ligament, damage to the medial meniscus, and rupture of the anterior cruciate ligament.

🔗 INTERACTIVE LINK

Watch this video (http://openstax.org/l/kneeinjury) to learn more about different knee injuries and diagnostic testing of the knee. What are the most common causes of anterior cruciate ligament injury?

Ankle and Foot Joints

The ankle is formed by the **talocrural joint** (Figure 9.21). It consists of the articulations between the talus bone of the foot and the distal ends of the tibia and fibula of the leg (crural = "leg"). The superior aspect of the talus bone is square-shaped and has three areas of articulation. The top of the talus articulates with the inferior tibia. This is the portion of the ankle joint that carries the body weight between the leg and foot. The sides of the talus are firmly held in position by the articulations with the medial malleolus of the tibia and the lateral malleolus of the fibula, which prevent any side-to-side motion of the talus. The ankle is thus a uniaxial hinge joint that allows only for dorsiflexion and plantar flexion of the foot.

Additional joints between the tarsal bones of the posterior foot allow for the movements of foot inversion and eversion. Most important for these movements is the **subtalar joint**, located between the talus and calcaneus bones. The joints between the talus and navicular bones and the calcaneus and cuboid bones are also important contributors to these movements. All of the joints between tarsal bones are plane joints. Together, the small motions that take place at these joints all contribute to the production of inversion and eversion foot motions.

Like the hinge joints of the elbow and knee, the talocrural joint of the ankle is supported by several strong ligaments located on the sides of the joint. These ligaments extend from the medial malleolus of the tibia or lateral malleolus of the fibula and anchor to the talus and calcaneus bones. Since they are located on the sides of the ankle joint, they allow for dorsiflexion and plantar flexion of the foot. They also prevent abnormal side-to-side and twisting movements of the talus and calcaneus bones during eversion and inversion of the foot. On the medial side is the broad **deltoid ligament**. The deltoid ligament supports the ankle joint and also resists excessive eversion of the foot. The lateral side of the ankle has several smaller ligaments. These include the **anterior talofibular ligament** and the **posterior talofibular ligament**, both of which span between the talus bone and the lateral malleolus of the fibula, and the **calcaneofibular ligament**, located between the calcaneus bone and fibula. These ligaments support the ankle and also resist excess inversion of the foot.

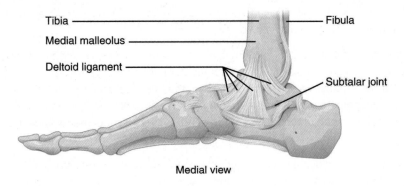

Medial view

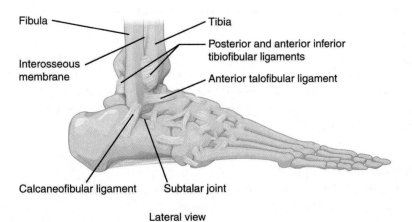

Lateral view

FIGURE 9.21 Ankle Joint   The talocrural (ankle) joint is a uniaxial hinge joint that only allows for dorsiflexion or plantar flexion of the foot. Movements at the subtalar joint, between the talus and calcaneus bones, combined with motions at other intertarsal joints, enables eversion/inversion movements of the foot. Ligaments that unite the medial or lateral malleolus with the talus and calcaneus bones serve to support the talocrural joint and to resist excess eversion or inversion of the foot.

⊘ INTERACTIVE LINK

Watch this video (http://openstax.org/l/anklejoint1) for a tutorial on the anatomy of the ankle joint. What are the three ligaments found on the lateral side of the ankle joint?

🔗 INTERACTIVE LINK

Watch this video (http://openstax.org/l/anklejoint2) to learn more about the anatomy of the ankle joint, including bones, joints, muscles, nerves, and blood vessels. Which type of joint used in woodworking does the ankle joint resemble?

Disorders of the...

Joints

The ankle is the most frequently injured joint in the body, with the most common injury being an inversion ankle sprain. A sprain is the stretching or tearing of the supporting ligaments. Excess inversion causes the talus bone to tilt laterally, thus damaging the ligaments on the lateral side of the ankle. The anterior talofibular ligament is most commonly injured, followed by the calcaneofibular ligament. In severe inversion injuries, the forceful lateral movement of the talus not only ruptures the lateral ankle ligaments, but also fractures the distal fibula.

Less common are eversion sprains of the ankle, which involve stretching of the deltoid ligament on the medial side of the ankle. Forcible eversion of the foot, for example, with an awkward landing from a jump or when a football player has a foot planted and is hit on the lateral ankle, can result in a Pott's fracture and dislocation of the ankle joint. In this injury, the very strong deltoid ligament does not tear, but instead shears off the medial malleolus of the tibia. This frees the talus, which moves laterally and fractures the distal fibula. In extreme cases, the posterior margin of the tibia may also be sheared off.

Above the ankle, the distal ends of the tibia and fibula are united by a strong syndesmosis formed by the interosseous membrane and ligaments at the distal tibiofibular joint. These connections prevent separation between the distal ends of the tibia and fibula and maintain the talus locked into position between the medial malleolus and lateral malleolus. Injuries that produce a lateral twisting of the leg on top of the planted foot can result in stretching or tearing of the tibiofibular ligaments, producing a syndesmotic ankle sprain or "high ankle sprain."

Most ankle sprains can be treated using the RICE technique: Rest, Ice, Compression, and Elevation. Reducing joint mobility using a brace or cast may be required for a period of time. More severe injuries involving ligament tears or bone fractures may require surgery.

🔗 INTERACTIVE LINK

Watch this video (http://openstax.org/l/anklejoint3) to learn more about the ligaments of the ankle joint, ankle sprains, and treatment. During an inversion ankle sprain injury, all three ligaments that resist excessive inversion of the foot may be injured. What is the sequence in which these three ligaments are injured?

9.7 Development of Joints

LEARNING OBJECTIVES

By the end of this section, you will be able to:

- Describe the two processes by which mesenchyme can give rise to bone
- Discuss the process by which joints of the limbs are formed

Joints form during embryonic development in conjunction with the formation and growth of the associated bones. The embryonic tissue that gives rise to all bones, cartilages, and connective tissues of the body is called mesenchyme. In the head, mesenchyme will accumulate at those areas that will become the bones that form the top and sides of the skull. The mesenchyme in these areas will develop directly into bone through the process of intramembranous ossification, in which mesenchymal cells differentiate into bone-producing cells that then generate bone tissue. The mesenchyme between the areas of bone production will become the fibrous connective tissue that fills the spaces between the developing bones. Initially, the connective tissue-filled gaps between the bones are wide, and are called fontanelles. After birth, as the skull bones grow and enlarge, the gaps between them decrease in width and the fontanelles are reduced to suture joints in which the bones are united by a narrow layer of fibrous connective tissue.

The bones that form the base and facial regions of the skull develop through the process of endochondral ossification. In this process, mesenchyme accumulates and differentiates into hyaline cartilage, which forms a model of the future bone. The hyaline cartilage model is then gradually, over a period of many years, displaced by bone. The mesenchyme between these developing bones becomes the fibrous connective tissue of the suture joints between the bones in these regions of the skull.

A similar process of endochondral ossification gives rises to the bones and joints of the limbs. The limbs initially develop as small limb buds that appear on the sides of the embryo around the end of the fourth week of development. Starting during the sixth week, as each limb bud continues to grow and elongate, areas of mesenchyme within the bud begin to differentiate into the hyaline cartilage that will form models for of each of the future bones. The synovial joints will form between the adjacent cartilage models, in an area called the **joint interzone**. Cells at the center of this interzone region undergo cell death to form the joint cavity, while surrounding mesenchyme cells will form the articular capsule and supporting ligaments. The process of endochondral ossification, which converts the cartilage models into bone, begins by the twelfth week of embryonic development. At birth, ossification of much of the bone has occurred, but the hyaline cartilage of the epiphyseal plate will remain throughout childhood and adolescence to allow for bone lengthening. Hyaline cartilage is also retained as the articular cartilage that covers the surfaces of the bones at synovial joints.

Key Terms

abduction   movement in the coronal plane that moves a limb laterally away from the body; spreading of the fingers

acetabular labrum   lip of fibrocartilage that surrounds outer margin of the acetabulum on the hip bone

adduction   movement in the coronal plane that moves a limb medially toward or across the midline of the body; bringing fingers together

amphiarthrosis   slightly mobile joint

annular ligament   intrinsic ligament of the elbow articular capsule that surrounds and supports the head of the radius at the proximal radioulnar joint

anterior cruciate ligament   intracapsular ligament of the knee; extends from anterior, superior surface of the tibia to the inner aspect of the lateral condyle of the femur; resists hyperextension of knee

anterior talofibular ligament   intrinsic ligament located on the lateral side of the ankle joint, between talus bone and lateral malleolus of fibula; supports talus at the talocrural joint and resists excess inversion of the foot

articular capsule   connective tissue structure that encloses the joint cavity of a synovial joint

articular cartilage   thin layer of hyaline cartilage that covers the articulating surfaces of bones at a synovial joint

articular disc   meniscus; a fibrocartilage structure found between the bones of some synovial joints; provides padding or smooths movements between the bones; strongly unites the bones together

articulation   joint of the body

atlanto-occipital joint   articulation between the occipital condyles of the skull and the superior articular processes of the atlas (C1 vertebra)

atlantoaxial joint   series of three articulations between the atlas (C1) vertebra and the axis (C2) vertebra, consisting of the joints between the inferior articular processes of C1 and the superior articular processes of C2, and the articulation between the dens of C2 and the anterior arch of C1

ball-and-socket joint   synovial joint formed between the spherical end of one bone (the ball) that fits into the depression of a second bone (the socket); found at the hip and shoulder joints; functionally classified as a multiaxial joint

biaxial joint   type of diarthrosis; a joint that allows for movements within two planes (two axes)

bursa   connective tissue sac containing lubricating fluid that prevents friction between adjacent structures, such as skin and bone, tendons and bone, or between muscles

calcaneofibular ligament   intrinsic ligament located on the lateral side of the ankle joint, between the calcaneus bone and lateral malleolus of the fibula; supports the talus bone at the ankle joint and resists excess inversion of the foot

cartilaginous joint   joint at which the bones are united by hyaline cartilage (synchondrosis) or fibrocartilage (symphysis)

circumduction   circular motion of the arm, thigh, hand, thumb, or finger that is produced by the sequential combination of flexion, abduction, extension, and adduction

condyloid joint   synovial joint in which the shallow depression at the end of one bone receives a rounded end from a second bone or a rounded structure formed by two bones; found at the metacarpophalangeal joints of the fingers or the radiocarpal joint of the wrist; functionally classified as a biaxial joint

coracohumeral ligament   intrinsic ligament of the shoulder joint; runs from the coracoid process of the scapula to the anterior humerus

deltoid ligament   broad intrinsic ligament located on the medial side of the ankle joint; supports the talus at the talocrural joint and resists excess eversion of the foot

depression   downward (inferior) motion of the scapula or mandible

diarthrosis   freely mobile joint

dorsiflexion   movement at the ankle that brings the top of the foot toward the anterior leg

elbow joint   humeroulnar joint

elevation   upward (superior) motion of the scapula or mandible

eversion   foot movement involving the intertarsal joints of the foot in which the bottom of the foot is turned laterally, away from the midline

extension   movement in the sagittal plane that increases the angle of a joint (straightens the joint); motion involving posterior bending of the vertebral column or returning to the upright position from a flexed position

extrinsic ligament   ligament located outside of the articular capsule of a synovial joint

femoropatellar joint   portion of the knee joint consisting of the articulation between the distal femur and the patella

fibrous joint   joint where the articulating areas of the adjacent bones are connected by fibrous connective tissue

fibular collateral ligament   extrinsic ligament of the knee joint that spans from the lateral epicondyle of the femur to the head of the fibula; resists hyperextension and rotation of the extended knee

flexion   movement in the sagittal plane that decreases the angle of a joint (bends the joint); motion involving anterior bending of the vertebral column

fontanelles   expanded areas of fibrous connective tissue that separate the braincase bones of the skull prior to birth and during the first year after birth

glenohumeral joint   shoulder joint; articulation between the glenoid cavity of the scapula and head of the humerus; multiaxial ball-and-socket joint that allows for flexion/extension, abduction/adduction, circumduction, and medial/lateral rotation of the humerus

glenohumeral ligament   one of the three intrinsic ligaments of the shoulder joint that strengthen the anterior articular capsule

glenoid labrum   lip of fibrocartilage located around the outside margin of the glenoid cavity of the scapula

gomphosis   type of fibrous joint in which the root of a tooth is anchored into its bony jaw socket by strong periodontal ligaments

hinge joint   synovial joint at which the convex surface of one bone articulates with the concave surface of a second bone; includes the elbow, knee, ankle, and interphalangeal joints; functionally classified as a uniaxial joint

humeroradial joint   articulation between the capitulum of the humerus and head of the radius

humeroulnar joint   articulation between the trochlea of humerus and the trochlear notch of the ulna; uniaxial hinge joint that allows for flexion/extension of the forearm

hyperextension   excessive extension of joint, beyond the normal range of movement

hyperflexion   excessive flexion of joint, beyond the normal range of movement

iliofemoral ligament   intrinsic ligament spanning from the ilium of the hip bone to the femur, on the superior-anterior aspect of the hip joint

inferior rotation   movement of the scapula during upper limb adduction in which the glenoid cavity of the scapula moves in a downward direction as the medial end of the scapular spine moves in an upward direction

interosseous membrane   wide sheet of fibrous connective tissue that fills the gap between two parallel bones, forming a syndesmosis; found between the radius and ulna of the forearm and between the tibia and fibula of the leg

intracapsular ligament   ligament that is located within the articular capsule of a synovial joint

intrinsic ligament   ligament that is fused to or incorporated into the wall of the articular capsule of a synovial joint

inversion   foot movement involving the intertarsal joints of the foot in which the bottom of the foot is turned toward the midline

ischiofemoral ligament   intrinsic ligament spanning from the ischium of the hip bone to the femur, on the posterior aspect of the hip joint

joint   site at which two or more bones or bone and cartilage come together (articulate)

joint cavity   space enclosed by the articular capsule of a synovial joint that is filled with synovial fluid and contains the articulating surfaces of the adjacent bones

joint interzone   site within a growing embryonic limb bud that will become a synovial joint

lateral (external) rotation   movement of the arm at the shoulder joint or the thigh at the hip joint that moves the anterior surface of the limb away from the midline of the body

lateral excursion   side-to-side movement of the mandible away from the midline, toward either the right or left side

lateral flexion   bending of the neck or body toward the right or left side

lateral meniscus   C-shaped fibrocartilage articular disc located at the knee, between the lateral condyle of the femur and the lateral condyle of the tibia

lateral tibiofemoral joint   portion of the knee consisting of the articulation between the lateral condyle of the tibia and the lateral condyle of the femur; allows for flexion/extension at the knee

ligament   strong band of dense connective tissue spanning between bones

ligament of the head of the femur   intracapsular ligament that runs from the acetabulum of the hip bone to the head of the femur

medial (internal) rotation   movement of the arm at the shoulder joint or the thigh at the hip joint that brings the anterior surface of the limb toward the midline of the body

medial excursion   side-to-side movement that returns the mandible to the midline

medial meniscus   C-shaped fibrocartilage articular disc located at the knee, between the medial condyle of the femur and medial condyle of the tibia

medial tibiofemoral joint   portion of the knee consisting of the articulation between the medial condyle of the tibia and the medial condyle of the femur; allows for flexion/extension at the knee

meniscus   articular disc

multiaxial joint   type of diarthrosis; a joint that allows for movements within three planes (three axes)

opposition   thumb movement that brings the tip of the thumb in contact with the tip of a finger

patellar ligament   ligament spanning from the patella to the anterior tibia; serves as the final attachment for the quadriceps femoris muscle

periodontal ligament   band of dense connective tissue that anchors the root of a tooth into the bony jaw socket

pivot joint   synovial joint at which the rounded portion of a bone rotates within a ring formed by a ligament and an articulating bone; functionally classified as uniaxial joint

plane joint   synovial joint formed between the flattened articulating surfaces of adjacent bones; functionally classified as a multiaxial joint

plantar flexion   foot movement at the ankle in which the heel is lifted off of the ground

posterior cruciate ligament   intracapsular ligament of the knee; extends from the posterior, superior surface of the tibia to the inner aspect of the medial condyle of the femur; prevents anterior displacement of the femur when the knee is flexed and weight bearing

posterior talofibular ligament   intrinsic ligament located on the lateral side of the ankle joint, between the talus bone and lateral malleolus of the fibula; supports the talus at the talocrural joint and resists excess inversion of the foot

pronated position   forearm position in which the palm faces backward

pronation   forearm motion that moves the palm of the hand from the palm forward to the palm backward position

protraction   anterior motion of the scapula or mandible

proximal radioulnar joint   articulation between head of radius and radial notch of ulna; uniaxial pivot joint that allows for rotation of radius during pronation/supination of forearm

pubofemoral ligament   intrinsic ligament spanning from the pubis of the hip bone to the femur, on the anterior-inferior aspect of the hip joint

radial collateral ligament   intrinsic ligament on the lateral side of the elbow joint; runs from the lateral epicondyle of humerus to merge with the annular ligament

reposition   movement of the thumb from opposition back to the anatomical position (next to index finger)

retraction   posterior motion of the scapula or mandible

rotation   movement of a bone around a central axis (atlantoaxial joint) or around its long axis (proximal radioulnar joint; shoulder or hip joint); twisting of the vertebral column resulting from the summation of small motions between adjacent vertebrae

rotator cuff   strong connective tissue structure formed by the fusion of four rotator cuff muscle tendons to the articular capsule of the shoulder joint; surrounds and supports superior, anterior, lateral, and posterior sides of the humeral head

saddle joint   synovial joint in which the articulating ends of both bones are convex and concave in shape, such as at the first carpometacarpal joint at the base of the thumb; functionally classified as a biaxial joint

subacromial bursa   bursa that protects the supraspinatus muscle tendon and superior end of the humerus from rubbing against the acromion of the scapula

subcutaneous bursa   bursa that prevents friction between skin and an underlying bone

submuscular bursa   bursa that prevents friction between bone and a muscle or between adjacent muscles

subscapular bursa   bursa that prevents rubbing of the subscapularis muscle tendon against the scapula

subtalar joint   articulation between the talus and calcaneus bones of the foot; allows motions that contribute to inversion/eversion of the foot

subtendinous bursa   bursa that prevents friction between bone and a muscle tendon

superior rotation   movement of the scapula during upper limb abduction in which the glenoid cavity of the scapula moves in an upward direction as the medial end of the scapular spine moves in a downward direction

supinated position   forearm position in which the palm faces anteriorly (anatomical position)

supination   forearm motion that moves the palm of the hand from the palm backward to the palm forward position

suture   fibrous joint that connects the bones of the skull (except the mandible); an immobile joint (synarthrosis)

symphysis   type of cartilaginous joint where the bones are joined by fibrocartilage

synarthrosis   immobile or nearly immobile joint

synchondrosis   type of cartilaginous joint where the bones are joined by hyaline cartilage

syndesmosis   type of fibrous joint in which two separated, parallel bones are connected by an interosseous membrane

synostosis   site at which adjacent bones or bony components have fused together

synovial fluid   thick, lubricating fluid that fills the interior of a synovial joint

synovial joint   joint at which the articulating surfaces of the bones are located within a joint cavity formed by an articular capsule

synovial membrane   thin layer that lines the inner surface of the joint cavity at a synovial joint; produces the synovial fluid

talocrural joint   ankle joint; articulation between the talus bone of the foot and medial malleolus of the tibia, distal tibia, and lateral malleolus of the fibula; a uniaxial hinge joint that allows only for dorsiflexion and plantar flexion of the foot

temporomandibular joint (TMJ)   articulation between the condyle of the mandible and the mandibular fossa and articular tubercle of the temporal bone of the skull; allows for depression/elevation (opening/closing of mouth), protraction/retraction, and side-to-side motions of the mandible

tendon   dense connective tissue structure that anchors a muscle to bone

tendon sheath   connective tissue that surrounds a tendon at places where the tendon crosses a joint; contains a lubricating fluid to prevent friction and allow smooth movements of the tendon

tibial collateral ligament   extrinsic ligament of knee joint that spans from the medial epicondyle of the femur to the medial tibia; resists hyperextension and rotation of extended knee

ulnar collateral ligament   intrinsic ligament on the medial side of the elbow joint; spans from the medial epicondyle of the humerus to the medial ulna

uniaxial joint   type of diarthrosis; joint that allows for motion within only one plane (one axis)

zygapophysial joints   facet joints; plane joints between the superior and inferior articular processes of adjacent vertebrae that provide for only limited motions between the vertebrae

Chapter Review

9.1 Classification of Joints

Structural classifications of the body joints are based on how the bones are held together and articulate with each other. At fibrous joints, the adjacent bones are directly united to each other by fibrous connective tissue. Similarly, at a cartilaginous joint, the adjacent bones are united by cartilage. In contrast, at a synovial joint, the articulating bone surfaces are not directly united to each other, but come together within a fluid-filled joint cavity.

The functional classification of body joints is based on the degree of movement found at each joint. A synarthrosis is a joint that is essentially immobile. This type of joint provides for a strong connection between the adjacent bones, which serves to protect internal structures such as the brain or heart. Examples include the fibrous joints of the skull sutures and the cartilaginous manubriosternal joint. A joint that allows for limited movement is an amphiarthrosis. An example is the pubic symphysis of the pelvis, the cartilaginous joint that strongly unites the right and left hip bones of the pelvis. The cartilaginous joints in which vertebrae are united by intervertebral discs provide for small movements between the adjacent vertebrae and are also an amphiarthrosis type of joint. Thus, based on their movement ability, both fibrous and cartilaginous joints are functionally classified as a synarthrosis or amphiarthrosis.

The most common type of joint is the diarthrosis, which is a freely moveable joint. All synovial joints are functionally classified as diarthroses. A uniaxial diarthrosis, such as the elbow, is a joint that only allows for movement within a single anatomical plane. Joints that allow for movements in two planes are biaxial joints, such as the metacarpophalangeal joints of the fingers. A multiaxial joint, such as the shoulder or hip joint, allows for three planes of motions.

9.2 Fibrous Joints

Fibrous joints are where adjacent bones are strongly united by fibrous connective tissue. The gap filled by connective tissue may be narrow or wide. The three types of fibrous joints are sutures, gomphoses, and syndesmoses. A suture is the narrow fibrous joint that unites most bones of the skull. At a gomphosis, the root of a tooth is anchored across a narrow gap by periodontal ligaments to the walls of its socket in the bony jaw. A syndesmosis is the type of fibrous joint found between parallel bones. The gap between the bones may be wide and filled with a fibrous interosseous membrane, or it may narrow with ligaments spanning between the bones. Syndesmoses are found between the bones of the forearm (radius and ulna) and the leg (tibia and fibula). Fibrous joints strongly unite adjacent bones and thus serve to provide protection for internal organs, strength to body regions, or weight-bearing stability.

9.3 Cartilaginous Joints

There are two types of cartilaginous joints. A synchondrosis is formed when the adjacent bones are united by hyaline cartilage. A temporary synchondrosis is formed by the epiphyseal plate of a growing long bone, which is lost when the epiphyseal plate ossifies as the bone reaches maturity. The synchondrosis is thus replaced by a synostosis. Permanent synchondroses that do not ossify are found at the first sternocostal joint and between the anterior ends of the bony ribs and the junction with their costal cartilage. A symphysis is where the bones are joined by fibrocartilage and the gap between the bones may be narrow or wide. A narrow symphysis is found at the manubriosternal joint and at the pubic symphysis. A wide symphysis is the intervertebral symphysis in which the bodies of adjacent vertebrae are united by an intervertebral disc.

9.4 Synovial Joints

Synovial joints are the most common type of joints in the body. They are characterized by the presence of a joint cavity, inside of which the bones of the joint articulate with each other. The articulating surfaces of the bones at a synovial joint are not directly connected to each other by connective tissue or cartilage, which allows the bones to move freely against each other. The walls of the joint cavity are formed by the articular capsule. Friction between the bones is reduced by a thin layer of articular cartilage covering the surfaces of the bones, and by a lubricating synovial fluid, which is secreted by the synovial membrane.

Synovial joints are strengthened by the presence of ligaments, which hold the bones together and resist excessive or abnormal movements of the joint. Ligaments are classified as extrinsic ligaments if they are located outside of the articular capsule, intrinsic ligaments if they are fused to the wall of the articular capsule, or intracapsular ligaments if they are located inside the articular capsule. Some synovial joints also have an articular disc (meniscus), which can provide padding between the bones, smooth their movements, or strongly join the bones together to strengthen the joint. Muscles and their tendons acting across a joint can also increase their contractile strength when needed, thus providing indirect support for the joint.

Bursae contain a lubricating fluid that serves to reduce friction between structures. Subcutaneous bursae prevent friction between the skin and an underlying bone, submuscular bursae protect muscles from rubbing against a bone or another muscle, and a subtendinous bursa prevents friction between bone and a muscle tendon. Tendon sheaths contain a lubricating fluid and surround tendons to allow for smooth movement of the tendon as it crosses a joint.

Based on the shape of the articulating bone surfaces and the types of movement allowed, synovial joints are classified into six types. At a pivot joint, one bone is held within a ring by a ligament and its articulation with a second bone. Pivot joints only allow for rotation around a single axis. These are found at the articulation between the C1 (atlas) and the dens of the C2 (axis) vertebrae, which provides the side-to-side rotation of the head, or at the proximal radioulnar joint between the head of the radius and the radial notch of the ulna, which allows for rotation of the radius during forearm movements. Hinge joints, such as at the elbow, knee, ankle, or interphalangeal joints between phalanx bones of the fingers and toes, allow only for bending and straightening of the joint. Pivot and hinge joints are functionally classified as uniaxial joints.

Condyloid joints are found where the shallow depression of one bone receives a rounded bony area formed by one or two bones. Condyloid joints are found at the base of the fingers (metacarpophalangeal joints) and at the wrist (radiocarpal joint). At a saddle joint, the articulating bones fit together like a rider and a saddle. An example is the first carpometacarpal joint located at the base of the thumb. Both condyloid and saddle joints are functionally classified as biaxial joints.

Plane joints are formed between the small, flattened surfaces of adjacent bones. These joints allow the bones to slide or rotate against each other, but the range of motion is usually slight and tightly limited by ligaments or surrounding bones. This type of joint is found between the articular processes of adjacent vertebrae, at the acromioclavicular joint, or at the intercarpal joints of the hand and intertarsal joints of the foot. Ball-and-socket joints, in which the rounded head of a bone fits into a large depression or socket, are found at the shoulder and hip joints. Both plane and ball-and-sockets joints are classified functionally as multiaxial joints. However, ball-and-socket joints allow for large movements, while the motions between bones at a plane joint are small.

9.5 Types of Body Movements

The variety of movements provided by the different types of synovial joints allows for a large range of body motions and gives you tremendous mobility. These movements allow you to flex or extend your body or limbs, medially rotate and adduct your arms and flex your elbows to hold a heavy object against your chest, raise your arms above your head, rotate or shake your head, and bend to touch the toes (with or without bending your knees).

Each of the different structural types of synovial joints also allow for specific motions. The atlantoaxial pivot joint provides side-to-side rotation of the head, while the proximal radioulnar articulation allows for rotation of the radius during pronation and supination of the forearm. Hinge joints, such as at the knee and elbow, allow only for flexion and extension. Similarly, the hinge joint of the ankle only allows for dorsiflexion and plantar flexion of the foot.

Condyloid and saddle joints are biaxial. These allow for flexion and extension, and abduction and adduction. The sequential combination of flexion, adduction, extension, and abduction produces circumduction. Multiaxial plane joints provide for only small motions, but these can add together over several adjacent joints to produce body movement, such as inversion and eversion of the foot. Similarly, plane joints allow for flexion, extension, and lateral flexion movements of the vertebral column. The multiaxial ball and socket joints allow for flexion-extension, abduction-adduction, and circumduction. In addition, these also allow for medial (internal) and lateral (external) rotation. Ball-and-socket joints have the greatest range of motion of all synovial joints.

9.6 Anatomy of Selected Synovial Joints

Although synovial joints share many common features, each joint of the body is specialized for certain movements and activities. The joints of the upper limb provide for large ranges of motion, which give the upper limb great mobility, thus enabling actions such as the throwing of a ball or typing on a keyboard. The joints of the lower limb are more robust, giving them greater strength and the stability needed to support the body weight during running, jumping, or kicking activities.

The joints of the vertebral column include the symphysis joints formed by each intervertebral disc and the plane synovial joints between the superior and inferior articular processes of adjacent vertebrae. Each of these joints provide for limited motions, but these sum together to produce flexion, extension, lateral flexion, and rotation of the neck and body. The range of motions available in each region of the vertebral column varies, with all of these motions available in the cervical region. Only rotation is allowed in the thoracic region, while the lumbar region has considerable extension, flexion, and lateral flexion, but rotation is prevented. The atlanto-occipital joint allows for flexion and extension of the head, while the atlantoaxial joint is a pivot joint that provides for rotation of the head.

The temporomandibular joint is the articulation between the condyle of the mandible and the mandibular fossa and articular tubercle of the skull temporal bone. An articular disc is located between the bony components of this joint. A combination of gliding and hinge motions of the mandibular condyle allows for elevation/depression, protraction/retraction, and side-to-side motions of the lower jaw.

The glenohumeral (shoulder) joint is a multiaxial ball-and-socket joint that provides flexion/extension, abduction/adduction, circumduction, and medial/lateral rotation of the humerus. The head of the humerus articulates with the glenoid cavity of the scapula. The glenoid labrum extends around the margin of the glenoid cavity. Intrinsic ligaments, including the coracohumeral ligament and glenohumeral ligaments, provide some support for the shoulder joint. However, the primary support comes from muscles crossing the joint whose tendons form the rotator cuff. These muscle tendons are protected from friction against the scapula by the subacromial bursa and subscapular bursa.

The elbow is a uniaxial hinge joint that allows for flexion/extension of the forearm. It includes the humeroulnar joint and the humeroradial joint. The medial elbow is supported by the ulnar collateral ligament and the radial collateral ligament supports the lateral side. These ligaments prevent side-to-side movements and resist hyperextension of the elbow. The proximal radioulnar joint is a pivot joint that allows for rotation of the radius during pronation/supination of the forearm. The annular ligament surrounds the head of the radius to hold it in place at this joint.

The hip joint is a ball-and-socket joint whose motions are more restricted than at the shoulder to provide greater stability during weight bearing. The hip joint is the articulation between the head of the femur and the acetabulum of the hip bone. The acetabulum is deepened by the acetabular labrum. The iliofemoral, pubofemoral, and ischiofemoral ligaments strongly support the hip joint in the upright, standing position. The ligament of the head of the femur provides little support but carries an important artery that supplies the femur.

The knee includes three articulations. The femoropatellar joint is between the patella and distal femur. The patella, a sesamoid bone incorporated into the tendon of the quadriceps femoris muscle of the anterior thigh, serves to protect this tendon from rubbing against the distal femur during knee movements. The medial and lateral tibiofemoral joints, between the condyles of the femur and condyles of the tibia, are modified hinge joints that allow for knee extension and flexion. During these movements, the condyles of the femur both roll and glide over the surface of the tibia. As the knee comes into full extension, a slight medial rotation of the femur serves to "lock" the knee into its most stable, weight-bearing position. The reverse motion, a small lateral rotation of the femur, is required to initiate knee flexion. When the knee is flexed, some rotation of the leg is available.

Two extrinsic ligaments, the tibial collateral ligament on the medial side and the fibular collateral ligament on the lateral side, serve to resist hyperextension or rotation of the extended knee joint. Two intracapsular ligaments, the anterior cruciate ligament and posterior cruciate ligament, span between the tibia and the inner aspects of the femoral condyles. The anterior cruciate ligament resists hyperextension of the knee, while the posterior cruciate ligament prevents anterior sliding of the femur, thus supporting the knee when it is flexed and weight bearing. The medial and lateral menisci, located between the femoral and tibial condyles, are articular discs that provide padding and improve the fit between the bones.

The talocrural joint forms the ankle. It consists of the articulation between the talus bone and the medial malleolus of the tibia, the distal end of the tibia, and the lateral malleolus of the fibula. This is a uniaxial hinge joint that allows only dorsiflexion and plantar flexion of the foot. Gliding motions at the subtalar and intertarsal joints of the foot allow for inversion/eversion of the foot. The ankle joint is supported on the medial side by the deltoid ligament, which prevents side-to-side motions of the talus at the talocrural joint and resists excessive eversion of the foot. The lateral ankle is supported by the anterior and posterior talofibular ligaments and the calcaneofibular ligament. These support the ankle joint and also resist excess inversion of the foot. An inversion ankle sprain, a common injury, will result in injury to one or more of these lateral ankle ligaments.

9.7 Development of Joints

During embryonic growth, bones and joints develop from mesenchyme, an embryonic tissue that gives rise to bone, cartilage, and fibrous connective tissues. In the skull, the bones develop either directly from mesenchyme through the process of intramembranous ossification, or indirectly through endochondral ossification, which initially forms a hyaline cartilage model of the future bone, which is later converted into bone. In both cases, the mesenchyme between the developing bones differentiates into fibrous connective tissue that will unite the skull bones at suture joints. In the limbs, mesenchyme accumulations within the growing limb bud will become a hyaline cartilage model for each of the limb bones. A joint interzone will develop between these areas of cartilage. Mesenchyme cells at the margins of the interzone will give rise to the articular capsule, while cell death at the center forms the space that will become the joint cavity of the future synovial joint. The hyaline cartilage model of each limb bone will eventually be converted into bone via the process of endochondral ossification. However, hyaline cartilage will remain, covering the ends of the adult bone as the articular cartilage.

Interactive Link Questions

1. Go to this website (http://openstax.org/l/childhand) to view a radiograph (X-ray image) of a child's hand and wrist. The growing bones of child have an epiphyseal plate that forms a synchondrosis between the shaft and end of a long bone. Being less dense than bone, the area of epiphyseal cartilage is seen on this radiograph as the dark epiphyseal gaps located near the ends of the long bones, including the radius, ulna, metacarpal, and phalanx bones. Which of the bones in this image do not show an epiphyseal plate (epiphyseal gap)?

2. Watch this video (http://openstax.org/l/synjoints) to see an animation of synovial joints in action. Synovial joints are places where bones articulate with each other inside of a joint cavity. The different types of synovial joints are the ball-and-socket joint (shoulder joint), hinge joint (knee), pivot joint (atlantoaxial joint, between C1 and C2 vertebrae of the neck), condyloid joint (radiocarpal joint of the wrist), saddle joint (first carpometacarpal joint, between the trapezium carpal bone and the first metacarpal bone, at the base of the thumb), and plane joint (facet joints of vertebral column, between superior and inferior articular processes). Which type of synovial joint allows for the widest ranges of motion?

3. Visit this website (http://openstax.org/l/gout) to read about a patient who arrives at the hospital with joint pain and weakness in his legs. What caused this patient's weakness?

4. Watch this animation (http://openstax.org/l/hipreplace) to observe hip replacement surgery (total hip arthroplasty), which can be used to alleviate the pain and loss of joint mobility associated with osteoarthritis of the hip joint. What is the most common cause of hip disability?

5. Watch this video (http://openstax.org/l/rheuarthritis) to learn about the symptoms and treatments for rheumatoid arthritis. Which system of the body malfunctions in rheumatoid arthritis and what does this cause?

6. Watch this video (http://openstax.org/l/anatomical) to learn about anatomical motions. What motions involve increasing or decreasing the angle of the foot at the ankle?

7. Watch this video (http://openstax.org/l/TMJ) to learn about TMJ. Opening of the mouth requires the combination of two motions at the temporomandibular joint, an anterior gliding motion of the articular disc and mandible and the downward hinging of the mandible. What is the initial movement of the mandible during opening and how much mouth opening does this produce?

8. Watch this video (http://openstax.org/l/shoulderjoint1) for a tutorial on the anatomy of the shoulder joint. What movements are available at the shoulder joint?

9. Watch this video (http://openstax.org/l/shoulderjoint2) to learn about the anatomy of the shoulder joint, including bones, joints, muscles, nerves, and blood vessels. What is the shape of the glenoid labrum in cross-section, and what is the importance of this shape?

10. Watch this animation (http://openstax.org/l/elbowjoint1) to learn more about the anatomy of the elbow joint. What structures provide the main stability for the elbow?

11. Watch this video (http://openstax.org/l/elbowjoint2) to learn more about the anatomy of the elbow joint, including bones, joints, muscles, nerves, and blood vessels. What are the functions of the articular cartilage?

12. Watch this video (http://openstax.org/l/hipjoint1) for a tutorial on the anatomy of the hip joint. What is a possible consequence following a fracture of the femoral neck within the capsule of the hip joint?

13. Watch this video (http://openstax.org/l/hipjoint2) to learn more about the anatomy of the hip joint, including bones, joints, muscles, nerves, and blood vessels. Where is the articular cartilage thickest within the hip joint?

14. Watch this video (http://openstax.org/l/flexext) to learn more about the flexion and extension of the knee, as the femur both rolls and glides on the tibia to maintain stable contact between the bones in all knee positions. The patella glides along a groove on the anterior side of the distal femur. The collateral ligaments on the sides of the knee become tight in the fully extended position to help stabilize the knee. The posterior cruciate ligament supports the knee when flexed and the anterior cruciate ligament becomes tight when the knee comes into full extension to resist hyperextension. What are the ligaments that support the knee joint?

15. Watch this video (http://openstax.org/l/kneejoint1) to learn more about the anatomy of the knee joint, including bones, joints, muscles, nerves, and blood vessels. Which ligament of the knee keeps the tibia from sliding too far forward in relation to the femur and which ligament keeps the tibia from sliding too far backward?

16. Watch this video (http://openstax.org/l/kneeinjury) to learn more about different knee injuries and diagnostic testing of the knee. What are the most causes of anterior cruciate ligament injury?

17. Watch this video (http://openstax.org/l/anklejoint1) for a tutorial on the anatomy of the ankle joint. What are the three ligaments found on the lateral side of the ankle joint?

18. Watch this video (http://openstax.org/l/anklejoint2) to learn more about the anatomy of the ankle joint, including bones, joints, muscles, nerves, and blood vessels. The ankle joint resembles what type of joint used in woodworking?

19. Watch this video (http://openstax.org/l/anklejoint3) to learn about the ligaments of the ankle joint, ankle sprains, and treatment. During an inversion ankle sprain injury, all three ligaments that resist excessive inversion of the foot may be injured. What is the sequence in which these three ligaments are injured?

Review Questions

20. The joint between adjacent vertebrae that includes an invertebral disc is classified as which type of joint?
   a. diarthrosis
   b. multiaxial
   c. amphiarthrosis
   d. synarthrosis

21. Which of these joints is classified as a synarthrosis?
   a. the pubic symphysis
   b. the manubriosternal joint
   c. an invertebral disc
   d. the shoulder joint

22. Which of these joints is classified as a biaxial diarthrosis?
   a. the metacarpophalangeal joint
   b. the hip joint
   c. the elbow joint
   d. the pubic symphysis

23. Synovial joints _____.
   a. may be functionally classified as a synarthrosis
   b. are joints where the bones are connected to each other by hyaline cartilage
   c. may be functionally classified as an amphiarthrosis
   d. are joints where the bones articulate with each other within a fluid-filled joint cavity

24. Which type of fibrous joint connects the tibia and fibula?
   a. syndesmosis
   b. symphysis
   c. suture
   d. gomphosis

25. An example of a wide fibrous joint is _____.
   a. the interosseous membrane of the forearm
   b. a gomphosis
   c. a suture joint
   d. a synostosis

26. A gomphosis _____.
   a. is formed by an interosseous membrane
   b. connects the tibia and fibula bones of the leg
   c. contains a joint cavity
   d. anchors a tooth to the jaw

27. A syndesmosis is _____.
   a. a narrow fibrous joint
   b. the type of joint that unites bones of the skull
   c. a fibrous joint that unites parallel bones
   d. the type of joint that anchors the teeth in the jaws

28. A cartilaginous joint _____.
   a. has a joint cavity
   b. is called a symphysis when the bones are united by fibrocartilage
   c. anchors the teeth to the jaws
   d. is formed by a wide sheet of fibrous connective tissue

29. A synchondrosis is _____.
   a. found at the pubic symphysis
   b. where bones are connected together with fibrocartilage
   c. a type of fibrous joint
   d. found at the first sternocostal joint of the thoracic cage

30. Which of the following are joined by a symphysis?
   a. adjacent vertebrae
   b. the first rib and the sternum
   c. the end and shaft of a long bone
   d. the radius and ulna bones

31. The epiphyseal plate of a growing long bone in a child is classified as a _____.
   a. synchondrosis
   b. synostosis
   c. symphysis
   d. syndesmosis

32. Which type of joint provides the greatest range of motion?
   a. ball-and-socket
   b. hinge
   c. condyloid
   d. plane

33. Which type of joint allows for only uniaxial movement?
   a. saddle joint
   b. hinge joint
   c. condyloid joint
   d. ball-and-socket joint

34. Which of the following is a type of synovial joint?
   a. a synostosis
   b. a suture
   c. a plane joint
   d. a synchondrosis

35. A bursa _____.
    a. surrounds a tendon at the point where the tendon crosses a joint
    b. secretes the lubricating fluid for a synovial joint
    c. prevents friction between skin and bone, or a muscle tendon and bone
    d. is the strong band of connective tissue that holds bones together at a synovial joint

36. At synovial joints, _____.
    a. the articulating ends of the bones are directly connected by fibrous connective tissue
    b. the ends of the bones are enclosed within a space called a subcutaneous bursa
    c. intrinsic ligaments are located entirely inside of the articular capsule
    d. the joint cavity is filled with a thick, lubricating fluid

37. At a synovial joint, the synovial membrane _____.
    a. forms the fibrous connective walls of the joint cavity
    b. is the layer of cartilage that covers the articulating surfaces of the bones
    c. forms the intracapsular ligaments
    d. secretes the lubricating synovial fluid

38. Condyloid joints _____.
    a. are a type of ball-and-socket joint
    b. include the radiocarpal joint
    c. are a uniaxial diarthrosis joint
    d. are found at the proximal radioulnar joint

39. A meniscus is _____.
    a. a fibrocartilage pad that provides padding between bones
    b. a fluid-filled space that prevents friction between a muscle tendon and underlying bone
    c. the articular cartilage that covers the ends of a bone at a synovial joint
    d. the lubricating fluid within a synovial joint

40. The joints between the articular processes of adjacent vertebrae can contribute to which movement?
    a. lateral flexion
    b. circumduction
    c. dorsiflexion
    d. abduction

41. Which motion moves the bottom of the foot away from the midline of the body?
    a. elevation
    b. dorsiflexion
    c. eversion
    d. plantar flexion

42. Movement of a body region in a circular movement at a condyloid joint is what type of motion?
    a. rotation
    b. elevation
    c. abduction
    d. circumduction

43. Supination is the motion that moves the _____.
    a. hand from the palm backward position to the palm forward position
    b. foot so that the bottom of the foot faces the midline of the body
    c. hand from the palm forward position to the palm backward position
    d. scapula in an upward direction

44. Movement at the shoulder joint that moves the upper limb laterally away from the body is called _____.
    a. elevation
    b. eversion
    c. abduction
    d. lateral rotation

45. The primary support for the glenohumeral joint is provided by the _____.
    a. coracohumeral ligament
    b. glenoid labrum
    c. rotator cuff muscles
    d. subacromial bursa

46. The proximal radioulnar joint _____.
    a. is supported by the annular ligament
    b. contains an articular disc that strongly unites the bones
    c. is supported by the ulnar collateral ligament
    d. is a hinge joint that allows for flexion/extension of the forearm

47. Which statement is true concerning the knee joint?
    a. The lateral meniscus is an intrinsic ligament located on the lateral side of the knee joint.
    b. Hyperextension is resisted by the posterior cruciate ligament.
    c. The anterior cruciate ligament supports the knee when it is flexed and weight bearing.
    d. The medial meniscus is attached to the tibial collateral ligament.

48. The ankle joint _____.
    a. is also called the subtalar joint
    b. allows for gliding movements that produce inversion/eversion of the foot
    c. is a uniaxial hinge joint
    d. is supported by the tibial collateral ligament on the lateral side

49. Which region of the vertebral column has the *greatest* range of motion for rotation?
    a. cervical
    b. thoracic
    c. lumbar
    d. sacral

50. Intramembranous ossification _____.
    a. gives rise to the bones of the limbs
    b. produces the bones of the top and sides of the skull
    c. produces the bones of the face and base of the skull
    d. involves the conversion of a hyaline cartilage model into bone

51. Synovial joints _____.
    a. are derived from fontanelles
    b. are produced by intramembranous ossification
    c. develop at an interzone site
    d. are produced by endochondral ossification

52. Endochondral ossification is _____.
    a. the process that replaces hyaline cartilage with bone tissue
    b. the process by which mesenchyme differentiates directly into bone tissue
    c. completed before birth
    d. the process that gives rise to the joint interzone and future joint cavity

Critical Thinking Questions

53. Define how joints are classified based on function. Describe and give an example for each functional type of joint.
54. Explain the reasons for why joints differ in their degree of mobility.
55. Distinguish between a narrow and wide fibrous joint and give an example of each.
56. The periodontal ligaments are made of collagen fibers and are responsible for connecting the roots of the teeth to the jaws. Describe how scurvy, a disease that inhibits collagen production, can affect the teeth.
57. Describe the two types of cartilaginous joints and give examples of each.
58. Both functional and structural classifications can be used to describe an individual joint. Define the first sternocostal joint and the pubic symphysis using both functional and structural characteristics.

59. Describe the characteristic structures found at all synovial joints.
60. Describe the structures that provide direct and indirect support for a synovial joint.
61. Briefly define the types of joint movements available at a ball-and-socket joint.
62. Discuss the joints involved and movements required for you to cross your arms together in front of your chest.
63. Discuss the structures that contribute to support of the shoulder joint.
64. Describe the sequence of injuries that may occur if the extended, weight-bearing knee receives a very strong blow to the lateral side of the knee.
65. Describe how synovial joints develop within the embryonic limb.
66. Differentiate between endochondral and intramembranous ossification.

CHAPTER 10
Muscle Tissue

Figure 10.1 **Tennis Player** Athletes rely on toned skeletal muscles to supply the force required for movement. (credit: Emmanuel Huybrechts/flickr)

CHAPTER OBJECTIVES

After studying this chapter, you will be able to:

- Explain the organization of muscle tissue
- Describe the function and structure of skeletal, cardiac muscle, and smooth muscle
- Explain how muscles work with tendons to move the body
- Describe how muscles contract and relax
- Define the process of muscle metabolism
- Explain how the nervous system controls muscle tension
- Relate the connections between exercise and muscle performance
- Explain the development and regeneration of muscle tissue

INTRODUCTION When most people think of muscles, they think of the muscles that are visible just under the skin, particularly of the limbs. These are skeletal muscles, so-named because most of them move the skeleton. But there are two other types of muscle in the body, with distinctly different jobs. Cardiac muscle, found in the heart, is concerned with pumping blood through the circulatory system. Smooth muscle is concerned with various involuntary movements, such as having one's hair stand on end when cold or frightened, or moving food through the digestive system. This chapter will examine the structure and function of these three types of muscles.

10.1 Overview of Muscle Tissues

LEARNING OBJECTIVES

By the end of this section, you will be able to:

- Describe the different types of muscle
- Explain contractibility and extensibility

Muscle is one of the four primary tissue types of the body, and the body contains three types of muscle tissue: skeletal muscle, cardiac muscle, and smooth muscle (Figure 10.2). All three muscle tissues have some properties in common; they all exhibit a quality called **excitability** as their plasma membranes can change their electrical states (from polarized to depolarized) and send an electrical wave called an action potential along the entire length of the membrane. While the nervous system can influence the excitability of cardiac and smooth muscle to some degree, skeletal muscle completely depends on signaling from the nervous system to work properly. On the other hand, both cardiac muscle and smooth muscle can respond to other stimuli, such as hormones and local stimuli.

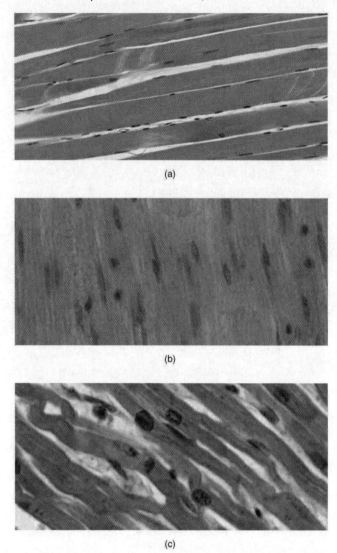

(a)

(b)

(c)

FIGURE 10.2   **The Three Types of Muscle Tissue**   The body contains three types of muscle tissue: (a) skeletal muscle, (b) smooth muscle, and (c) cardiac muscle. (Micrographs provided by the Regents of University of Michigan Medical School © 2012)

The muscles all begin the actual process of contracting (shortening) when a protein called actin is pulled by a protein called myosin. This occurs in striated muscle (skeletal and cardiac) after specific binding sites on the actin have been exposed in response to the interaction between calcium ions (Ca^{++}) and proteins (troponin and tropomyosin) that "shield" the actin-binding sites. Ca^{++} also is required for the contraction of smooth muscle, although its role is different: here Ca^{++} activates enzymes, which in turn activate myosin heads. All muscles require adenosine triphosphate (ATP) to continue the process of contracting, and they all relax when the Ca^{++} is removed and the actin-binding sites are re-shielded.

A muscle can return to its original length when relaxed due to a quality of muscle tissue called **elasticity**. It can recoil back to its original length due to elastic fibers. Muscle tissue also has the quality of **extensibility**; it can stretch or extend. **Contractility** allows muscle tissue to pull on its attachment points and shorten with force.

Differences among the three muscle types include the microscopic organization of their contractile proteins—actin and myosin. The actin and myosin proteins are arranged very regularly in the cytoplasm of individual muscle cells (referred to as fibers) in both skeletal muscle and cardiac muscle, which creates a pattern, or stripes, called striations. The striations are visible with a light microscope under high magnification (see Figure 10.2). **Skeletal**

muscle fibers are multinucleated structures that compose the skeletal muscle. **Cardiac muscle** fibers each have one to two nuclei and are physically and electrically connected to each other so that the entire heart contracts as one unit (called a syncytium).

Because the actin and myosin are not arranged in such regular fashion in **smooth muscle**, the cytoplasm of a smooth muscle fiber (which has only a single nucleus) has a uniform, nonstriated appearance (resulting in the name smooth muscle). However, the less organized appearance of smooth muscle should not be interpreted as less efficient. Smooth muscle in the walls of arteries is a critical component that regulates blood pressure necessary to push blood through the circulatory system; and smooth muscle in the skin, visceral organs, and internal passageways is essential for moving all materials through the body.

10.2 Skeletal Muscle

LEARNING OBJECTIVES

By the end of this section, you will be able to:

- Describe the layers of connective tissues packaging skeletal muscle
- Explain how muscles work with tendons to move the body
- Identify areas of the skeletal muscle fibers
- Describe excitation-contraction coupling

The best-known feature of skeletal muscle is its ability to contract and cause movement. Skeletal muscles act not only to produce movement but also to stop movement, such as resisting gravity to maintain posture. Small, constant adjustments of the skeletal muscles are needed to hold a body upright or balanced in any position. Muscles also prevent excess movement of the bones and joints, maintaining skeletal stability and preventing skeletal structure damage or deformation. Joints can become misaligned or dislocated entirely by pulling on the associated bones; muscles work to keep joints stable. Skeletal muscles are located throughout the body at the openings of internal tracts to control the movement of various substances. These muscles allow functions, such as swallowing, urination, and defecation, to be under voluntary control. Skeletal muscles also protect internal organs (particularly abdominal and pelvic organs) by acting as an external barrier or shield to external trauma and by supporting the weight of the organs.

Skeletal muscles contribute to the maintenance of homeostasis in the body by generating heat. Muscle contraction requires energy, and when ATP is broken down, heat is produced. This heat is very noticeable during exercise, when sustained muscle movement causes body temperature to rise, and in cases of extreme cold, when shivering produces random skeletal muscle contractions to generate heat.

Each skeletal muscle is an organ that consists of various integrated tissues. These tissues include the skeletal muscle fibers, blood vessels, nerve fibers, and connective tissue. Each skeletal muscle has three layers of connective tissue (called "mysia") that enclose it and provide structure to the muscle as a whole, and also compartmentalize the muscle fibers within the muscle (Figure 10.3). Each muscle is wrapped in a sheath of dense, irregular connective tissue called the **epimysium**, which allows a muscle to contract and move powerfully while maintaining its structural integrity. The epimysium also separates muscle from other tissues and organs in the area, allowing the muscle to move independently.

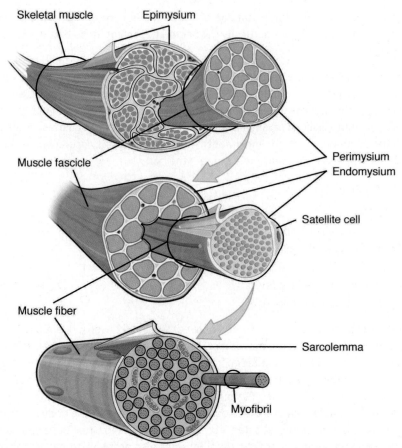

FIGURE 10.3   The Three Connective Tissue Layers   Bundles of muscle fibers, called fascicles, are covered by the perimysium. Muscle fibers are covered by the endomysium.

Inside each skeletal muscle, muscle fibers are organized into individual bundles, each called a **fascicle**, by a middle layer of connective tissue called the **perimysium**. This fascicular organization is common in muscles of the limbs; it allows the nervous system to trigger a specific movement of a muscle by activating a subset of muscle fibers within a bundle, or fascicle of the muscle. Inside each fascicle, each muscle fiber is encased in a thin connective tissue layer of collagen and reticular fibers called the **endomysium**. The endomysium contains the extracellular fluid and nutrients to support the muscle fiber. These nutrients are supplied via blood to the muscle tissue.

In skeletal muscles that work with tendons to pull on bones, the collagen in the three tissue layers (the mysia) intertwines with the collagen of a tendon. At the other end of the tendon, it fuses with the periosteum coating the bone. The tension created by contraction of the muscle fibers is then transferred though the mysia, to the tendon, and then to the periosteum to pull on the bone for movement of the skeleton. In other places, the mysia may fuse with a broad, tendon-like sheet called an **aponeurosis**, or to fascia, the connective tissue between skin and bones. The broad sheet of connective tissue in the lower back that the latissimus dorsi muscles (the "lats") fuse into is an example of an aponeurosis.

Every skeletal muscle is also richly supplied by blood vessels for nourishment, oxygen delivery, and waste removal. In addition, every muscle fiber in a skeletal muscle is supplied by the axon branch of a somatic motor neuron, which signals the fiber to contract. Unlike cardiac and smooth muscle, the only way to functionally contract a skeletal muscle is through signaling from the nervous system.

Skeletal Muscle Fibers

Because skeletal muscle cells are long and cylindrical, they are commonly referred to as muscle fibers. Skeletal muscle fibers can be quite large for human cells, with diameters up to 100 μm and lengths up to 30 cm (11.8 in) in the Sartorius of the upper leg. During early development, embryonic myoblasts, each with its own nucleus, fuse with up to hundreds of other myoblasts to form the multinucleated skeletal muscle fibers. Multiple nuclei mean multiple copies of genes, permitting the production of the large amounts of proteins and enzymes needed for muscle contraction.

Some other terminology associated with muscle fibers is rooted in the Greek *sarco*, which means "flesh." The plasma membrane of muscle fibers is called the **sarcolemma**, the cytoplasm is referred to as **sarcoplasm**, and the specialized smooth endoplasmic reticulum, which stores, releases, and retrieves calcium ions (Ca^{++}) is called the **sarcoplasmic reticulum (SR)** (Figure 10.4). As will soon be described, the functional unit of a skeletal muscle fiber is the sarcomere, a highly organized arrangement of the contractile myofilaments **actin** (thin filament) and **myosin** (thick filament), along with other support proteins.

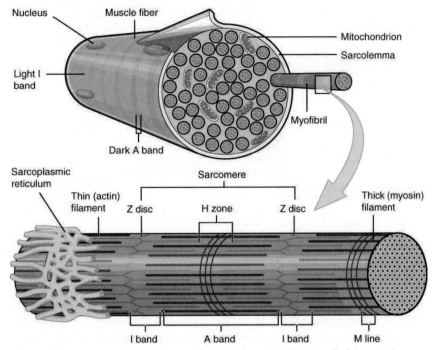

FIGURE 10.4   Muscle Fiber   A skeletal muscle fiber is surrounded by a plasma membrane called the sarcolemma, which contains sarcoplasm, the cytoplasm of muscle cells. A muscle fiber is composed of many fibrils, which give the cell its striated appearance.

The Sarcomere

The striated appearance of skeletal muscle fibers is due to the arrangement of the myofilaments of actin and myosin in sequential order from one end of the muscle fiber to the other. Each packet of these microfilaments and their regulatory proteins, **troponin** and **tropomyosin** (along with other proteins) is called a **sarcomere**.

⊘ INTERACTIVE LINK

Watch this video (http://openstax.org/l/micromacro) to learn more about macro- and microstructures of skeletal muscles. (a) What are the names of the "junction points" between sarcomeres? (b) What are the names of the "subunits" within the myofibrils that run the length of skeletal muscle fibers? (c) What is the "double strand of pearls" described in the video? (d) What gives a skeletal muscle fiber its striated appearance?

The sarcomere is the functional unit of the muscle fiber. The sarcomere itself is bundled within the myofibril that runs the entire length of the muscle fiber and attaches to the sarcolemma at its end. As myofibrils contract, the entire muscle cell contracts. Because myofibrils are only approximately 1.2 μm in diameter, hundreds to thousands (each with thousands of sarcomeres) can be found inside one muscle fiber. Each sarcomere is approximately 2 μm in length with a three-dimensional cylinder-like arrangement and is bordered by structures called Z-discs (also called Z-lines, because pictures are two-dimensional), to which the actin myofilaments are anchored (Figure 10.5). Because the actin and its troponin-tropomyosin complex (projecting from the Z-discs toward the center of the sarcomere) form strands that are thinner than the myosin, it is called the **thin filament** of the sarcomere. Likewise, because the myosin strands and their multiple heads (projecting from the center of the sarcomere, toward but not all to way to, the Z-discs) have more mass and are thicker, they are called the **thick filament** of the sarcomere.

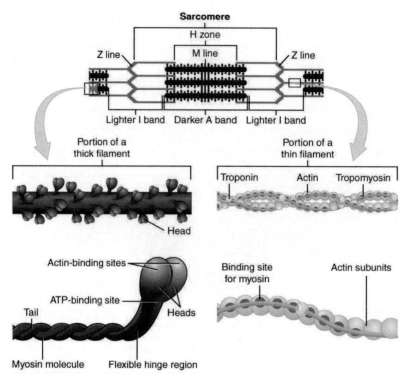

FIGURE 10.5 The Sarcomere   The sarcomere, the region from one Z-line to the next Z-line, is the functional unit of a skeletal muscle fiber.

The Neuromuscular Junction

Another specialization of the skeletal muscle is the site where a motor neuron's terminal meets the muscle fiber—called the **neuromuscular junction (NMJ)**. This is where the muscle fiber first responds to signaling by the motor neuron. Every skeletal muscle fiber in every skeletal muscle is innervated by a motor neuron at the NMJ. Excitation signals from the neuron are the only way to functionally activate the fiber to contract.

⊘ INTERACTIVE LINK

Every skeletal muscle fiber is supplied by a motor neuron at the NMJ. Watch this <u>video (http://openstax.org/l/ skelmuscfiber)</u> to learn more about what happens at the NMJ. (a) What is the definition of a motor unit? (b) What is the structural and functional difference between a large motor unit and a small motor unit? (c) Can you give an example of each? (d) Why is the neurotransmitter acetylcholine degraded after binding to its receptor?

Excitation-Contraction Coupling

All living cells have membrane potentials, or electrical gradients across their membranes. The inside of the membrane is usually around -60 to -90 mV, relative to the outside. This is referred to as a cell's membrane potential. Neurons and muscle cells can use their membrane potentials to generate electrical signals. They do this by controlling the movement of charged particles, called ions, across their membranes to create electrical currents. This is achieved by opening and closing specialized proteins in the membrane called ion channels. Although the currents generated by ions moving through these channel proteins are very small, they form the basis of both neural signaling and muscle contraction.

Both neurons and skeletal muscle cells are electrically excitable, meaning that they are able to generate action potentials. An action potential is a special type of electrical signal that can travel along a cell membrane as a wave. This allows a signal to be transmitted quickly and faithfully over long distances.

Although the term **excitation-contraction coupling** confuses or scares some students, it comes down to this: for a skeletal muscle fiber to contract, its membrane must first be "excited"—in other words, it must be stimulated to fire an action potential. The muscle fiber action potential, which sweeps along the sarcolemma as a wave, is "coupled" to the actual contraction through the release of calcium ions (Ca^{++}) from the SR. Once released, the Ca^{++} interacts with the shielding proteins, forcing them to move aside so that the actin-binding sites are available for attachment by myosin heads. The myosin then pulls the actin filaments toward the center, shortening the muscle fiber.

In skeletal muscle, this sequence begins with signals from the somatic motor division of the nervous system. In other words, the "excitation" step in skeletal muscles is always triggered by signaling from the nervous system (Figure 10.6).

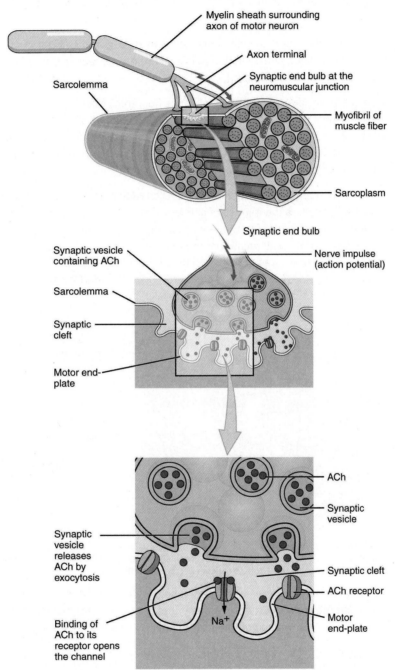

FIGURE 10.6   Motor End-Plate and Innervation   At the NMJ, the axon terminal releases ACh. The motor end-plate is the location of the ACh-receptors in the muscle fiber sarcolemma. When ACh molecules are released, they diffuse across a minute space called the synaptic cleft and bind to the receptors.

The motor neurons that tell the skeletal muscle fibers to contract originate in the spinal cord, with a smaller number located in the brainstem for activation of skeletal muscles of the face, head, and neck. These neurons have long processes, called axons, which are specialized to transmit action potentials long distances— in this case, all the way from the spinal cord to the muscle itself (which may be up to three feet away). The axons of multiple neurons bundle together to form nerves, like wires bundled together in a cable.

Signaling begins when a neuronal **action potential** travels along the axon of a motor neuron, and then along the individual branches to terminate at the NMJ. At the NMJ, the axon terminal releases a chemical messenger, or **neurotransmitter**, called **acetylcholine (ACh)**. The ACh molecules diffuse across a minute space called the **synaptic cleft** and bind to ACh receptors located within the **motor end-plate** of the sarcolemma on the other side of the synapse. Once ACh binds, a channel in the ACh receptor opens and positively charged ions can pass through into the muscle fiber, causing it to **depolarize**, meaning that the membrane potential of the muscle fiber becomes less negative (closer to zero.)

As the membrane depolarizes, another set of ion channels called **voltage-gated sodium channels** are triggered to open. Sodium ions enter the muscle fiber, and an action potential rapidly spreads (or "fires") along the entire membrane to initiate excitation-contraction coupling.

Things happen very quickly in the world of excitable membranes (just think about how quickly you can snap your fingers as soon as you decide to do it). Immediately following depolarization of the membrane, it repolarizes, re-establishing the negative membrane potential. Meanwhile, the ACh in the synaptic cleft is degraded by the enzyme acetylcholinesterase (AChE) so that the ACh cannot rebind to a receptor and reopen its channel, which would cause unwanted extended muscle excitation and contraction.

Propagation of an action potential along the sarcolemma is the excitation portion of excitation-contraction coupling. Recall that this excitation actually triggers the release of calcium ions (Ca^{++}) from its storage in the cell's SR. For the action potential to reach the membrane of the SR, there are periodic invaginations in the sarcolemma, called **T-tubules** ("T" stands for "transverse"). You will recall that the diameter of a muscle fiber can be up to 100 μm, so these T-tubules ensure that the membrane can get close to the SR in the sarcoplasm. The arrangement of a T-tubule with the membranes of SR on either side is called a **triad** (Figure 10.7). The triad surrounds the cylindrical structure called a **myofibril**, which contains actin and myosin.

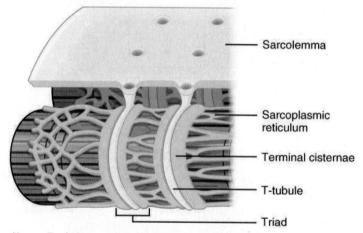

FIGURE 10.7   The T-tubule   Narrow T-tubules permit the conduction of electrical impulses. The SR functions to regulate intracellular levels of calcium. Two terminal cisternae (where enlarged SR connects to the T-tubule) and one T-tubule comprise a triad—a "threesome" of membranes, with those of SR on two sides and the T-tubule sandwiched between them.

The T-tubules carry the action potential into the interior of the cell, which triggers the opening of calcium channels in the membrane of the adjacent SR, causing Ca^{++} to diffuse out of the SR and into the sarcoplasm. It is the arrival of Ca^{++} in the sarcoplasm that initiates contraction of the muscle fiber by its contractile units, or sarcomeres.

10.3 Muscle Fiber Contraction and Relaxation

LEARNING OBJECTIVES

By the end of this section, you will be able to:

- Describe the components involved in a muscle contraction
- Explain how muscles contract and relax
- Describe the sliding filament model of muscle contraction

The sequence of events that result in the contraction of an individual muscle fiber begins with a signal—the neurotransmitter, ACh—from the motor neuron innervating that fiber. The local membrane of the fiber will depolarize

Access for free at openstax.org

as positively charged sodium ions (Na⁺) enter, triggering an action potential that spreads to the rest of the membrane which will depolarize, including the T-tubules. This triggers the release of calcium ions (Ca⁺⁺) from storage in the sarcoplasmic reticulum (SR). The Ca⁺⁺ then initiates contraction, which is sustained by ATP (Figure 10.8). As long as Ca⁺⁺ ions remain in the sarcoplasm to bind to troponin, which keeps the actin-binding sites "unshielded," and as long as ATP is available to drive the cross-bridge cycling and the pulling of actin strands by myosin, the muscle fiber will continue to shorten to an anatomical limit.

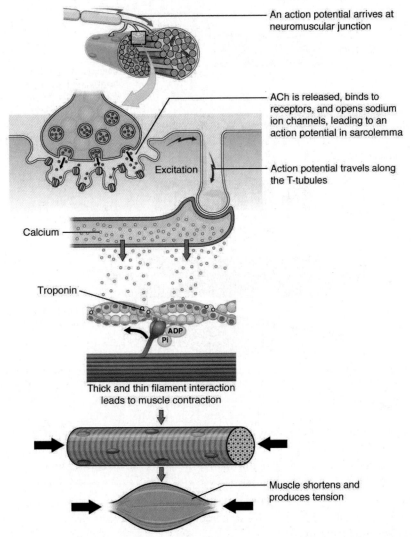

FIGURE 10.8   Contraction of a Muscle Fiber   A cross-bridge forms between actin and the myosin heads triggering contraction. As long as Ca⁺⁺ ions remain in the sarcoplasm to bind to troponin, and as long as ATP is available, the muscle fiber will continue to shorten.

Muscle contraction usually stops when signaling from the motor neuron ends, which repolarizes the sarcolemma and T-tubules, and closes the voltage-gated calcium channels in the SR. Ca⁺⁺ ions are then pumped back into the SR, which causes the tropomyosin to reshield (or re-cover) the binding sites on the actin strands. A muscle also can stop contracting when it runs out of ATP and becomes fatigued (Figure 10.9).

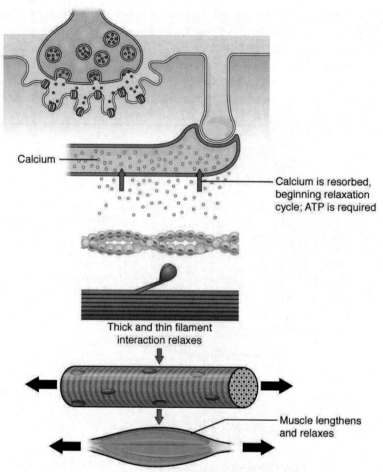

FIGURE 10.9   Relaxation of a Muscle Fiber   Ca^{++} ions are pumped back into the SR, which causes the tropomyosin to reshield the binding sites on the actin strands. A muscle may also stop contracting when it runs out of ATP and becomes fatigued.

⊘ INTERACTIVE LINK

The release of calcium ions initiates muscle contractions. Watch this video (http://openstax.org/l/calciumrole) to learn more about the role of calcium. (a) What are "T-tubules" and what is their role? (b) Please describe how actin-binding sites are made available for cross-bridging with myosin heads during contraction.

The molecular events of muscle fiber shortening occur within the fiber's sarcomeres (see Figure 10.10). The contraction of a striated muscle fiber occurs as the sarcomeres, linearly arranged within myofibrils, shorten as myosin heads pull on the actin filaments.

The region where thick and thin filaments overlap has a dense appearance, as there is little space between the filaments. This zone where thin and thick filaments overlap is very important to muscle contraction, as it is the site where filament movement starts. Thin filaments, anchored at their ends by the Z-discs, do not extend completely into the central region that only contains thick filaments, anchored at their bases at a spot called the M-line. A myofibril is composed of many sarcomeres running along its length; thus, myofibrils and muscle cells contract as the sarcomeres contract.

The Sliding Filament Model of Contraction

When signaled by a motor neuron, a skeletal muscle fiber contracts as the thin filaments are pulled and then slide past the thick filaments within the fiber's sarcomeres. This process is known as the sliding filament model of muscle contraction (Figure 10.10). The sliding can only occur when myosin-binding sites on the actin filaments are exposed by a series of steps that begins with Ca^{++} entry into the sarcoplasm.

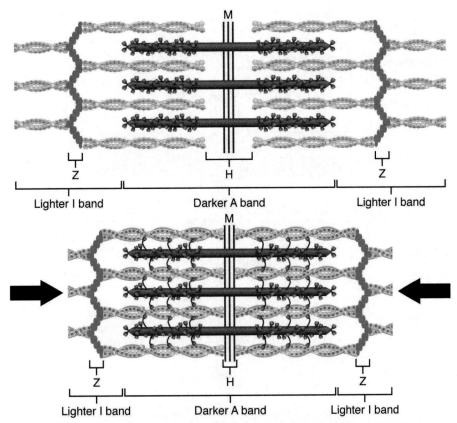

FIGURE 10.10   The Sliding Filament Model of Muscle Contraction   When a sarcomere contracts, the Z lines move closer together, and the I band becomes smaller. The A band stays the same width. At full contraction, the thin and thick filaments overlap completely.

Tropomyosin is a protein that winds around the chains of the actin filament and covers the myosin-binding sites to prevent actin from binding to myosin. Tropomyosin binds to troponin to form a troponin-tropomyosin complex. The troponin-tropomyosin complex prevents the myosin "heads" from binding to the active sites on the actin microfilaments. Troponin also has a binding site for Ca^{++} ions.

To initiate muscle contraction, tropomyosin has to expose the myosin-binding site on an actin filament to allow cross-bridge formation between the actin and myosin microfilaments. The first step in the process of contraction is for Ca^{++} to bind to troponin so that tropomyosin can slide away from the binding sites on the actin strands. This allows the myosin heads to bind to these exposed binding sites and form cross-bridges. The thin filaments are then pulled by the myosin heads to slide past the thick filaments toward the center of the sarcomere. But each head can only pull a very short distance before it has reached its limit and must be "re-cocked" before it can pull again, a step that requires ATP.

ATP and Muscle Contraction

For thin filaments to continue to slide past thick filaments during muscle contraction, myosin heads must pull the actin at the binding sites, detach, re-cock, attach to more binding sites, pull, detach, re-cock, etc. This repeated movement is known as the cross-bridge cycle. This motion of the myosin heads is similar to the oars when an individual rows a boat: The paddle of the oars (the myosin heads) pull, are lifted from the water (detach), repositioned (re-cocked) and then immersed again to pull (Figure 10.11). Each cycle requires energy, and the action of the myosin heads in the sarcomeres repetitively pulling on the thin filaments also requires energy, which is provided by ATP.

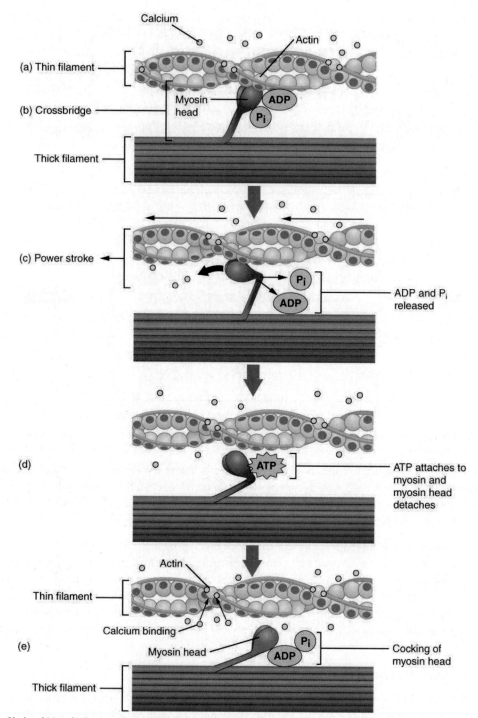

FIGURE 10.11 Skeletal Muscle Contraction   (a) The active site on actin is exposed as calcium binds to troponin. (b) The myosin head is attracted to actin, and myosin binds actin at its actin-binding site, forming the cross-bridge. (c) During the power stroke, the phosphate generated in the previous contraction cycle is released. This results in the myosin head pivoting toward the center of the sarcomere, after which the attached ADP and phosphate group are released. (d) A new molecule of ATP attaches to the myosin head, causing the cross-bridge to detach. (e) The myosin head hydrolyzes ATP to ADP and phosphate, which returns the myosin to the cocked position.

Cross-bridge formation occurs when the myosin head attaches to the actin while adenosine diphosphate (ADP) and inorganic phosphate (P_i) are still bound to myosin (Figure 10.11**a,b**). P_i is then released, causing myosin to form a stronger attachment to the actin, after which the myosin head moves toward the M-line, pulling the actin along with it. As actin is pulled, the filaments move approximately 10 nm toward the M-line. This movement is called the **power stroke**, as movement of the thin filament occurs at this step (Figure 10.11**c**). In the absence of ATP, the myosin head will not detach from actin.

One part of the myosin head attaches to the binding site on the actin, but the head has another binding site for ATP.

ATP binding causes the myosin head to detach from the actin (Figure 10.11**d**). After this occurs, ATP is converted to ADP and P$_i$ by the intrinsic **ATPase** activity of myosin. The energy released during ATP hydrolysis changes the angle of the myosin head into a cocked position (Figure 10.11**e**). The myosin head is now in position for further movement.

When the myosin head is cocked, myosin is in a high-energy configuration. This energy is expended as the myosin head moves through the power stroke, and at the end of the power stroke, the myosin head is in a low-energy position. After the power stroke, ADP is released; however, the formed cross-bridge is still in place, and actin and myosin are bound together. As long as ATP is available, it readily attaches to myosin, the cross-bridge cycle can recur, and muscle contraction can continue.

Note that each thick filament of roughly 300 myosin molecules has multiple myosin heads, and many cross-bridges form and break continuously during muscle contraction. Multiply this by all of the sarcomeres in one myofibril, all the myofibrils in one muscle fiber, and all of the muscle fibers in one skeletal muscle, and you can understand why so much energy (ATP) is needed to keep skeletal muscles working. In fact, it is the loss of ATP that results in the rigor mortis observed soon after someone dies. With no further ATP production possible, there is no ATP available for myosin heads to detach from the actin-binding sites, so the cross-bridges stay in place, causing the rigidity in the skeletal muscles.

Sources of ATP

ATP supplies the energy for muscle contraction to take place. In addition to its direct role in the cross-bridge cycle, ATP also provides the energy for the active-transport Ca^{++} pumps in the SR. Muscle contraction does not occur without sufficient amounts of ATP. The amount of ATP stored in muscle is very low, only sufficient to power a few seconds worth of contractions. As it is broken down, ATP must therefore be regenerated and replaced quickly to allow for sustained contraction. There are three mechanisms by which ATP can be regenerated in muscle cells: creatine phosphate metabolism, anaerobic glycolysis, and aerobic respiration.

Creatine phosphate is a molecule that can store energy in its phosphate bonds. In a resting muscle, excess ATP transfers its energy to creatine, producing ADP and creatine phosphate. This acts as an energy reserve that can be used to quickly create more ATP. When the muscle starts to contract and needs energy, creatine phosphate transfers its phosphate back to ADP to form ATP and creatine. This reaction is catalyzed by the enzyme creatine kinase and occurs very quickly; thus, creatine phosphate-derived ATP powers the first few seconds of muscle contraction. However, creatine phosphate can only provide approximately 15 seconds worth of energy, at which point another energy source has to be used (Figure 10.12).

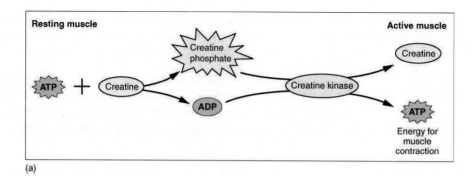

(a)

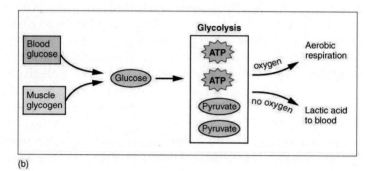

(b)

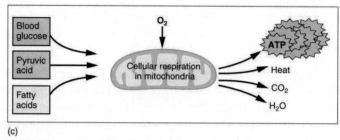

(c)

FIGURE 10.12   Muscle Metabolism   (a) Some ATP is stored in a resting muscle. As contraction starts, it is used up in seconds. More ATP is generated from creatine phosphate for about 15 seconds. (b) Each glucose molecule produces two ATP and two molecules of pyruvic acid, which can be used in aerobic respiration or converted to lactic acid. If oxygen is not available, pyruvic acid is converted to lactic acid, which may contribute to muscle fatigue. This occurs during strenuous exercise when high amounts of energy are needed but oxygen cannot be sufficiently delivered to muscle. (c) Aerobic respiration is the breakdown of glucose in the presence of oxygen (O_2) to produce carbon dioxide, water, and ATP. Approximately 95 percent of the ATP required for resting or moderately active muscles is provided by aerobic respiration, which takes place in mitochondria.

As the ATP produced by creatine phosphate is depleted, muscles turn to glycolysis as an ATP source. **Glycolysis** is an anaerobic (non-oxygen-dependent) process that breaks down glucose (sugar) to produce ATP; however, glycolysis cannot generate ATP as quickly as creatine phosphate. Thus, the switch to glycolysis results in a slower rate of ATP availability to the muscle. The sugar used in glycolysis can be provided by blood glucose or by metabolizing glycogen that is stored in the muscle. The breakdown of one glucose molecule produces two ATP and two molecules of **pyruvic acid**, which can be used in aerobic respiration or when oxygen levels are low, converted to lactic acid (Figure 10.12**b**).

If oxygen is available, pyruvic acid is used in aerobic respiration. However, if oxygen is not available, pyruvic acid is converted to **lactic acid**, which may contribute to muscle fatigue. This conversion allows the recycling of the enzyme NAD^+ from NADH, which is needed for glycolysis to continue. This occurs during strenuous exercise when high amounts of energy are needed but oxygen cannot be sufficiently delivered to muscle. Glycolysis itself cannot be sustained for very long (approximately 1 minute of muscle activity), but it is useful in facilitating short bursts of high-intensity output. This is because glycolysis does not utilize glucose very efficiently, producing a net gain of two ATPs per molecule of glucose, and the end product of lactic acid, which may contribute to muscle fatigue as it accumulates.

Aerobic respiration is the breakdown of glucose or other nutrients in the presence of oxygen (O_2) to produce carbon dioxide, water, and ATP. Approximately 95 percent of the ATP required for resting or moderately active muscles is provided by aerobic respiration, which takes place in mitochondria. The inputs for aerobic respiration include

Access for free at openstax.org

glucose circulating in the bloodstream, pyruvic acid, and fatty acids. Aerobic respiration is much more efficient than anaerobic glycolysis, producing approximately 36 ATPs per molecule of glucose versus four from glycolysis. However, aerobic respiration cannot be sustained without a steady supply of O_2 to the skeletal muscle and is much slower (Figure 10.12**c**). To compensate, muscles store small amount of excess oxygen in proteins call myoglobin, allowing for more efficient muscle contractions and less fatigue. Aerobic training also increases the efficiency of the circulatory system so that O_2 can be supplied to the muscles for longer periods of time.

Muscle fatigue occurs when a muscle can no longer contract in response to signals from the nervous system. The exact causes of muscle fatigue are not fully known, although certain factors have been correlated with the decreased muscle contraction that occurs during fatigue. ATP is needed for normal muscle contraction, and as ATP reserves are reduced, muscle function may decline. This may be more of a factor in brief, intense muscle output rather than sustained, lower intensity efforts. Lactic acid buildup may lower intracellular pH, affecting enzyme and protein activity. Imbalances in Na^+ and K^+ levels as a result of membrane depolarization may disrupt Ca^{++} flow out of the SR. Long periods of sustained exercise may damage the SR and the sarcolemma, resulting in impaired Ca^{++} regulation.

Intense muscle activity results in an **oxygen debt**, which is the amount of oxygen needed to compensate for ATP produced without oxygen during muscle contraction. Oxygen is required to restore ATP and creatine phosphate levels, convert lactic acid to pyruvic acid, and, in the liver, to convert lactic acid into glucose or glycogen. Other systems used during exercise also require oxygen, and all of these combined processes result in the increased breathing rate that occurs after exercise. Until the oxygen debt has been met, oxygen intake is elevated, even after exercise has stopped.

Relaxation of a Skeletal Muscle

Relaxing skeletal muscle fibers, and ultimately, the skeletal muscle, begins with the motor neuron, which stops releasing its chemical signal, ACh, into the synapse at the NMJ. The muscle fiber will repolarize, which closes the gates in the SR where Ca^{++} was being released. ATP-driven pumps will move Ca^{++} out of the sarcoplasm back into the SR. This results in the "reshielding" of the actin-binding sites on the thin filaments. Without the ability to form cross-bridges between the thin and thick filaments, the muscle fiber loses its tension and relaxes.

Muscle Strength

The number of skeletal muscle fibers in a given muscle is genetically determined and does not change. Muscle strength is directly related to the amount of myofibrils and sarcomeres within each fiber. Factors, such as hormones and stress (and artificial anabolic steroids), acting on the muscle can increase the production of sarcomeres and myofibrils within the muscle fibers, a change called hypertrophy, which results in the increased mass and bulk in a skeletal muscle. Likewise, decreased use of a skeletal muscle results in atrophy, where the number of sarcomeres and myofibrils disappear (but not the number of muscle fibers). It is common for a limb in a cast to show atrophied muscles when the cast is removed, and certain diseases, such as polio, show atrophied muscles.

Disorders of the...

Muscular System
Duchenne muscular dystrophy (DMD) is a progressive weakening of the skeletal muscles. It is one of several diseases collectively referred to as "muscular dystrophy." DMD is caused by a lack of the protein dystrophin, which helps the thin filaments of myofibrils bind to the sarcolemma. Without sufficient dystrophin, muscle contractions cause the sarcolemma to tear, causing an influx of Ca^{++}, leading to cellular damage and muscle fiber degradation. Over time, as muscle damage accumulates, muscle mass is lost, and greater functional impairments develop.

DMD is an inherited disorder caused by an abnormal X chromosome. It primarily affects males, and it is usually diagnosed in early childhood. DMD usually first appears as difficulty with balance and motion, and then progresses to an inability to walk. It continues progressing upward in the body from the lower extremities to the upper body, where it affects the muscles responsible for breathing and circulation. It ultimately causes death due to respiratory failure, and those afflicted do not usually live past their 20s.

Because DMD is caused by a mutation in the gene that codes for dystrophin, it was thought that introducing healthy myoblasts into patients might be an effective treatment. Myoblasts are the embryonic cells responsible for muscle development, and ideally, they would carry healthy genes that could produce the dystrophin needed for normal muscle contraction. This approach has been largely unsuccessful in humans. A recent approach has involved attempting to boost the muscle's production of utrophin, a protein similar to dystrophin that may be able to assume the role of dystrophin and prevent cellular damage from occurring.

10.4 Nervous System Control of Muscle Tension

LEARNING OBJECTIVES

By the end of this section, you will be able to:
- Explain concentric, isotonic, and eccentric contractions
- Describe the length-tension relationship
- Describe the three phases of a muscle twitch
- Define wave summation, tetanus, and treppe

To move an object, referred to as load, the sarcomeres in the muscle fibers of the skeletal muscle must shorten. The force generated by the contraction of the muscle (or shortening of the sarcomeres) is called **muscle tension**. However, muscle tension also is generated when the muscle is contracting against a load that does not move, resulting in two main types of skeletal muscle contractions: isotonic contractions and isometric contractions.

In **isotonic contractions**, where the tension in the muscle stays constant, a load is moved as the length of the muscle changes (shortens). There are two types of isotonic contractions: concentric and eccentric. A **concentric contraction** involves the muscle shortening to move a load. An example of this is the biceps brachii muscle contracting when a hand weight is brought upward with increasing muscle tension. As the biceps brachii contract, the angle of the elbow joint decreases as the forearm is brought toward the body. Here, the biceps brachii contracts as sarcomeres in its muscle fibers are shortening and cross-bridges form; the myosin heads pull the actin. An **eccentric contraction** occurs as the muscle tension diminishes and the muscle lengthens. In this case, the hand weight is lowered in a slow and controlled manner as the amount of cross-bridges being activated by nervous system stimulation decreases. In this case, as tension is released from the biceps brachii, the angle of the elbow joint increases. Eccentric contractions are also used for movement and balance of the body.

An **isometric contraction** occurs as the muscle produces tension without changing the angle of a skeletal joint. Isometric contractions involve sarcomere shortening and increasing muscle tension, but do not move a load, as the force produced cannot overcome the resistance provided by the load. For example, if one attempts to lift a hand weight that is too heavy, there will be sarcomere activation and shortening to a point, and ever-increasing muscle tension, but no change in the angle of the elbow joint. In everyday living, isometric contractions are active in maintaining posture and maintaining bone and joint stability. However, holding your head in an upright position occurs not because the muscles cannot move the head, but because the goal is to remain stationary and not produce movement. Most actions of the body are the result of a combination of isotonic and isometric contractions working together to produce a wide range of outcomes (Figure 10.13).

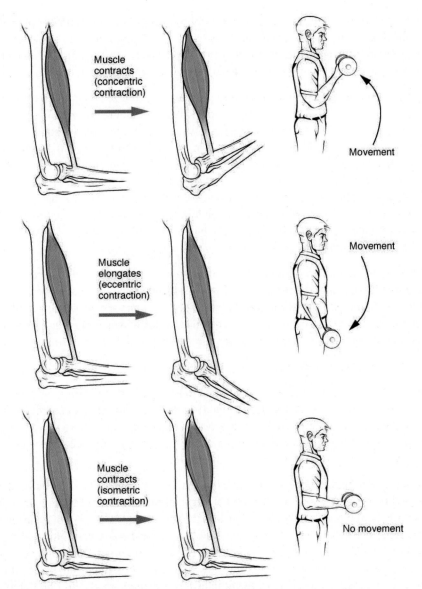

FIGURE 10.13 Types of Muscle Contractions   During isotonic contractions, muscle length changes to move a load. During isometric contractions, muscle length does not change because the load exceeds the tension the muscle can generate.

All of these muscle activities are under the exquisite control of the nervous system. Neural control regulates concentric, eccentric and isometric contractions, muscle fiber recruitment, and muscle tone. A crucial aspect of nervous system control of skeletal muscles is the role of motor units.

Motor Units

As you have learned, every skeletal muscle fiber must be innervated by the axon terminal of a motor neuron in order to contract. Each muscle fiber is innervated by only one motor neuron. The actual group of muscle fibers in a muscle innervated by a single motor neuron is called a **motor unit**. The size of a motor unit is variable depending on the nature of the muscle.

A small motor unit is an arrangement where a single motor neuron supplies a small number of muscle fibers in a muscle. Small motor units permit very fine motor control of the muscle. The best example in humans is the small motor units of the extraocular eye muscles that move the eyeballs. There are thousands of muscle fibers in each muscle, but every six or so fibers are supplied by a single motor neuron, as the axons branch to form synaptic connections at their individual NMJs. This allows for exquisite control of eye movements so that both eyes can quickly focus on the same object. Small motor units are also involved in the many fine movements of the fingers and thumb of the hand for grasping, texting, etc.

A large motor unit is an arrangement where a single motor neuron supplies a large number of muscle fibers in a muscle. Large motor units are concerned with simple, or "gross," movements, such as powerfully extending the knee joint. The best example is the large motor units of the thigh muscles or back muscles, where a single motor neuron will supply thousands of muscle fibers in a muscle, as its axon splits into thousands of branches.

There is a wide range of motor units within many skeletal muscles, which gives the nervous system a wide range of control over the muscle. The small motor units in the muscle will have smaller, lower-threshold motor neurons that are more excitable, firing first to their skeletal muscle fibers, which also tend to be the smallest. Activation of these smaller motor units, results in a relatively small degree of contractile strength (tension) generated in the muscle. As more strength is needed, larger motor units, with bigger, higher-threshold motor neurons are enlisted to activate larger muscle fibers. This increasing activation of motor units produces an increase in muscle contraction known as **recruitment**. As more motor units are recruited, the muscle contraction grows progressively stronger. In some muscles, the largest motor units may generate a contractile force of 50 times more than the smallest motor units in the muscle. This allows a feather to be picked up using the biceps brachii arm muscle with minimal force, and a heavy weight to be lifted by the same muscle by recruiting the largest motor units.

When necessary, the maximal number of motor units in a muscle can be recruited simultaneously, producing the maximum force of contraction for that muscle, but this cannot last for very long because of the energy requirements to sustain the contraction. To prevent complete muscle fatigue, motor units are generally not all simultaneously active, but instead some motor units rest while others are active, which allows for longer muscle contractions. The nervous system uses recruitment as a mechanism to efficiently utilize a skeletal muscle.

The Length-Tension Range of a Sarcomere

When a skeletal muscle fiber contracts, myosin heads attach to actin to form cross-bridges followed by the thin filaments sliding over the thick filaments as the heads pull the actin, and this results in sarcomere shortening, creating the tension of the muscle contraction. The cross-bridges can only form where thin and thick filaments already overlap, so that the length of the sarcomere has a direct influence on the force generated when the sarcomere shortens. This is called the length-tension relationship.

The ideal length of a sarcomere to produce maximal tension occurs at 80 percent to 120 percent of its resting length, with 100 percent being the state where the medial edges of the thin filaments are just at the most-medial myosin heads of the thick filaments (Figure 10.14). This length maximizes the overlap of actin-binding sites and myosin heads. If a sarcomere is stretched past this ideal length (beyond 120 percent), thick and thin filaments do not overlap sufficiently, which results in less tension produced. If a sarcomere is shortened beyond 80 percent, the zone of overlap is reduced with the thin filaments jutting beyond the last of the myosin heads and shrinks the H zone, which is normally composed of myosin tails. Eventually, there is nowhere else for the thin filaments to go and the amount of tension is diminished. If the muscle is stretched to the point where thick and thin filaments do not overlap at all, no cross-bridges can be formed, and no tension is produced in that sarcomere. This amount of stretching does not usually occur, as accessory proteins and connective tissue oppose extreme stretching.

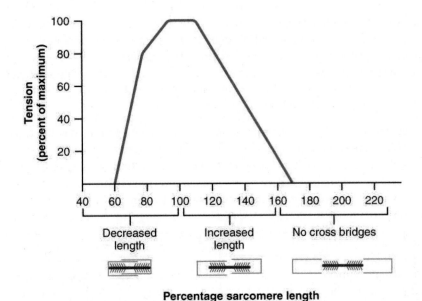

FIGURE 10.14   The Ideal Length of a Sarcomere   Sarcomeres produce maximal tension when thick and thin filaments overlap between about 80 percent to 120 percent.

The Frequency of Motor Neuron Stimulation

A single action potential from a motor neuron will produce a single contraction in the muscle fibers of its motor unit. This isolated contraction is called a **twitch**. A twitch can last for a few milliseconds or 100 milliseconds, depending on the muscle type. The tension produced by a single twitch can be measured by a **myogram**, an instrument that measures the amount of tension produced over time (Figure 10.15). Each twitch undergoes three phases. The first phase is the **latent period**, during which the action potential is being propagated along the sarcolemma and Ca⁺⁺ ions are released from the SR. This is the phase during which excitation and contraction are being coupled but contraction has yet to occur. The **contraction phase** occurs next. The Ca⁺⁺ ions in the sarcoplasm have bound to troponin, tropomyosin has shifted away from actin-binding sites, cross-bridges have formed, and sarcomeres are actively shortening to the point of peak tension. The last phase is the **relaxation phase**, when tension decreases as contraction stops. Ca⁺⁺ ions are pumped out of the sarcoplasm into the SR, and cross-bridge cycling stops, returning the muscle fibers to their resting state.

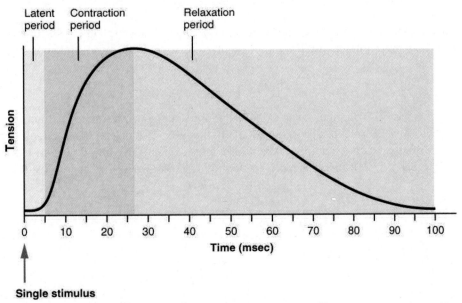

FIGURE 10.15   A Myogram of a Muscle Twitch   A single muscle twitch has a latent period, a contraction phase when tension increases, and a relaxation phase when tension decreases. During the latent period, the action potential is being propagated along the sarcolemma. During the contraction phase, Ca⁺⁺ ions in the sarcoplasm bind to troponin, tropomyosin moves from actin-binding sites, cross-bridges form, and sarcomeres shorten. During the relaxation phase, tension decreases as Ca⁺⁺ ions are pumped out of the sarcoplasm and cross-bridge cycling stops.

Although a person can experience a muscle "twitch," a single twitch does not produce any significant muscle activity in a living body. A series of action potentials to the muscle fibers is necessary to produce a muscle contraction that can produce work. Normal muscle contraction is more sustained, and it can be modified by input from the nervous system to produce varying amounts of force; this is called a **graded muscle response**. The frequency of action potentials (nerve impulses) from a motor neuron and the number of motor neurons transmitting action potentials both affect the tension produced in skeletal muscle.

The rate at which a motor neuron fires action potentials affects the tension produced in the skeletal muscle. If the fibers are stimulated while a previous twitch is still occurring, the second twitch will be stronger. This response is called **wave summation**, because the excitation-contraction coupling effects of successive motor neuron signaling is summed, or added together (Figure 10.16**a**). At the molecular level, summation occurs because the second stimulus triggers the release of more Ca^{++} ions, which become available to activate additional sarcomeres while the muscle is still contracting from the first stimulus. Summation results in greater contraction of the motor unit.

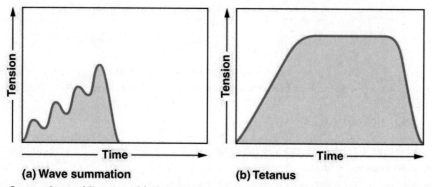

FIGURE 10.16   Wave Summation and Tetanus   (a) The excitation-contraction coupling effects of successive motor neuron signaling is added together which is referred to as wave summation. The bottom of each wave, the end of the relaxation phase, represents the point of stimulus. (b) When the stimulus frequency is so high that the relaxation phase disappears completely, the contractions become continuous; this is called tetanus.

If the frequency of motor neuron signaling increases, summation and subsequent muscle tension in the motor unit continues to rise until it reaches a peak point. The tension at this point is about three to four times greater than the tension of a single twitch, a state referred to as incomplete tetanus. During incomplete tetanus, the muscle goes through quick cycles of contraction with a short relaxation phase for each. If the stimulus frequency is so high that the relaxation phase disappears completely, contractions become continuous in a process called complete **tetanus** (Figure 10.16**b**).

During tetanus, the concentration of Ca^{++} ions in the sarcoplasm allows virtually all of the sarcomeres to form cross-bridges and shorten, so that a contraction can continue uninterrupted (until the muscle fatigues and can no longer produce tension).

Treppe

When a skeletal muscle has been dormant for an extended period and then activated to contract, with all other things being equal, the initial contractions generate about one-half the force of later contractions. The muscle tension increases in a graded manner that to some looks like a set of stairs. This tension increase is called **treppe**, a condition where muscle contractions become more efficient. It's also known as the "staircase effect" (Figure 10.17).

Access for free at openstax.org

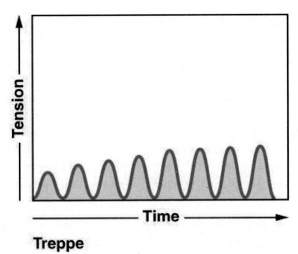

Treppe

FIGURE 10.17   Treppe   When muscle tension increases in a graded manner that looks like a set of stairs, it is called treppe. The bottom of each wave represents the point of stimulus.

It is believed that treppe results from a higher concentration of Ca^{++} in the sarcoplasm resulting from the steady stream of signals from the motor neuron. It can only be maintained with adequate ATP.

Muscle Tone

Skeletal muscles are rarely completely relaxed, or flaccid. Even if a muscle is not producing movement, it is contracted a small amount to maintain its contractile proteins and produce **muscle tone**. The tension produced by muscle tone allows muscles to continually stabilize joints and maintain posture.

Muscle tone is accomplished by a complex interaction between the nervous system and skeletal muscles that results in the activation of a few motor units at a time, most likely in a cyclical manner. In this manner, muscles never fatigue completely, as some motor units can recover while others are active.

The absence of the low-level contractions that lead to muscle tone is referred to as **hypotonia**, and can result from damage to parts of the central nervous system (CNS), such as the cerebellum, or from loss of innervations to a skeletal muscle, as in poliomyelitis. Hypotonic muscles have a flaccid appearance and display functional impairments, such as weak reflexes. Conversely, excessive muscle tone is referred to as **hypertonia**, accompanied by hyperreflexia (excessive reflex responses), often the result of damage to upper motor neurons in the CNS. Hypertonia can present with muscle rigidity (as seen in Parkinson's disease) or spasticity, a phasic change in muscle tone, where a limb will "snap" back from passive stretching (as seen in some strokes).

10.5 Types of Muscle Fibers

LEARNING OBJECTIVES

By the end of this section, you will be able to:
- Describe the types of skeletal muscle fibers
- Explain fast and slow muscle fibers

Two criteria to consider when classifying the types of muscle fibers are how fast some fibers contract relative to others, and how fibers produce ATP. Using these criteria, there are three main types of skeletal muscle fibers. **Slow oxidative (SO)** fibers contract relatively slowly and use aerobic respiration (oxygen and glucose) to produce ATP. **Fast oxidative (FO)** fibers have fast contractions and primarily use aerobic respiration, but because they may switch to anaerobic respiration (glycolysis), can fatigue more quickly than SO fibers. Lastly, **fast glycolytic (FG)** fibers have fast contractions and primarily use anaerobic glycolysis. The FG fibers fatigue more quickly than the others. Most skeletal muscles in a human contain(s) all three types, although in varying proportions.

The speed of contraction is dependent on how quickly myosin's ATPase hydrolyzes ATP to produce cross-bridge action. Fast fibers hydrolyze ATP approximately twice as quickly as slow fibers, resulting in much quicker cross-bridge cycling (which pulls the thin filaments toward the center of the sarcomeres at a faster rate). The primary metabolic pathway used by a muscle fiber determines whether the fiber is classified as oxidative or glycolytic. If a fiber primarily produces ATP through aerobic pathways it is oxidative. More ATP can be produced during each metabolic cycle, making the fiber more resistant to fatigue. Glycolytic fibers primarily create ATP through anaerobic glycolysis, which produces less ATP per cycle. As a result, glycolytic fibers fatigue at a quicker rate.

The oxidative fibers contain many more mitochondria than the glycolytic fibers, because aerobic metabolism, which uses oxygen (O_2) in the metabolic pathway, occurs in the mitochondria. The SO fibers possess a large number of mitochondria and are capable of contracting for longer periods because of the large amount of ATP they can produce, but they have a relatively small diameter and do not produce a large amount of tension. SO fibers are extensively supplied with blood capillaries to supply O_2 from the red blood cells in the bloodstream. The SO fibers also possess myoglobin, an O_2-carrying molecule similar to O_2-carrying hemoglobin in the red blood cells. The myoglobin stores some of the needed O_2 within the fibers themselves (and gives SO fibers their red color). All of these features allow SO fibers to produce large quantities of ATP, which can sustain muscle activity without fatiguing for long periods of time.

The fact that SO fibers can function for long periods without fatiguing makes them useful in maintaining posture, producing isometric contractions, stabilizing bones and joints, and making small movements that happen often but do not require large amounts of energy. They do not produce high tension, and thus they are not used for powerful, fast movements that require high amounts of energy and rapid cross-bridge cycling.

FO fibers are sometimes called intermediate fibers because they possess characteristics that are intermediate between fast fibers and slow fibers. They produce ATP relatively quickly, more quickly than SO fibers, and thus can produce relatively high amounts of tension. They are oxidative because they produce ATP aerobically, possess high amounts of mitochondria, and do not fatigue quickly. However, FO fibers do not possess significant myoglobin, giving them a lighter color than the red SO fibers. FO fibers are used primarily for movements, such as walking, that require more energy than postural control but less energy than an explosive movement, such as sprinting. FO fibers are useful for this type of movement because they produce more tension than SO fibers but they are more fatigue-resistant than FG fibers.

FG fibers primarily use anaerobic glycolysis as their ATP source. They have a large diameter and possess high amounts of glycogen, which is used in glycolysis to generate ATP quickly to produce high levels of tension. Because they do not primarily use aerobic metabolism, they do not possess substantial numbers of mitochondria or significant amounts of myoglobin and therefore have a white color. FG fibers are used to produce rapid, forceful contractions to make quick, powerful movements. These fibers fatigue quickly, permitting them to only be used for short periods. Most muscles possess a mixture of each fiber type. The predominant fiber type in a muscle is determined by the primary function of the muscle.

10.6 Exercise and Muscle Performance

LEARNING OBJECTIVES

By the end of this section, you will be able to:
- Describe hypertrophy and atrophy
- Explain how resistance exercise builds muscle
- Explain how performance-enhancing substances affect muscle

Physical training alters the appearance of skeletal muscles and can produce changes in muscle performance. Conversely, a lack of use can result in decreased performance and muscle appearance. Although muscle cells can change in size, new cells are not formed when muscles grow. Instead, structural proteins are added to muscle fibers in a process called **hypertrophy**, so cell diameter increases. The reverse, when structural proteins are lost and muscle mass decreases, is called **atrophy**. Age-related muscle atrophy is called **sarcopenia**. Cellular components of muscles can also undergo changes in response to changes in muscle use.

Endurance Exercise

Slow fibers are predominantly used in endurance exercises that require little force but involve numerous repetitions. The aerobic metabolism used by slow-twitch fibers allows them to maintain contractions over long periods. Endurance training modifies these slow fibers to make them even more efficient by producing more mitochondria to enable more aerobic metabolism and more ATP production. Endurance exercise can also increase the amount of myoglobin in a cell, as increased aerobic respiration increases the need for oxygen. Myoglobin is found in the sarcoplasm and acts as an oxygen storage supply for the mitochondria.

The training can trigger the formation of more extensive capillary networks around the fiber, a process called **angiogenesis**, to supply oxygen and remove metabolic waste. To allow these capillary networks to supply the deep portions of the muscle, muscle mass does not greatly increase in order to maintain a smaller area for the diffusion of nutrients and gases. All of these cellular changes result in the ability to sustain low levels of muscle contractions for greater periods without fatiguing.

The proportion of SO muscle fibers in muscle determines the suitability of that muscle for endurance, and may benefit those participating in endurance activities. Postural muscles have a large number of SO fibers and relatively few FO and FG fibers, to keep the back straight (Figure 10.18). Endurance athletes, like marathon-runners also would benefit from a larger proportion of SO fibers, but it is unclear if the most-successful marathoners are those with naturally high numbers of SO fibers, or whether the most successful marathon runners develop high numbers of SO fibers with repetitive training. Endurance training can result in overuse injuries such as stress fractures and joint and tendon inflammation.

FIGURE 10.18 Marathoners Long-distance runners have a large number of SO fibers and relatively few FO and FG fibers. (credit: "Tseo2"/Wikimedia Commons)

Resistance Exercise

Resistance exercises, as opposed to endurance exercise, require large amounts of FG fibers to produce short, powerful movements that are not repeated over long periods. The high rates of ATP hydrolysis and cross-bridge formation in FG fibers result in powerful muscle contractions. Muscles used for power have a higher ratio of FG to SO/FO fibers, and trained athletes possess even higher levels of FG fibers in their muscles. Resistance exercise affects muscles by increasing the formation of myofibrils, thereby increasing the thickness of muscle fibers. This added structure causes hypertrophy, or the enlargement of muscles, exemplified by the large skeletal muscles seen in body builders and other athletes (Figure 10.19). Because this muscular enlargement is achieved by the addition of structural proteins, athletes trying to build muscle mass often ingest large amounts of protein.

FIGURE 10.19 **Hypertrophy**   Body builders have a large number of FG fibers and relatively few FO and SO fibers. (credit: Lin Mei/flickr)

Except for the hypertrophy that follows an increase in the number of sarcomeres and myofibrils in a skeletal muscle, the cellular changes observed during endurance training do not usually occur with resistance training. There is usually no significant increase in mitochondria or capillary density. However, resistance training does increase the development of connective tissue, which adds to the overall mass of the muscle and helps to contain muscles as they produce increasingly powerful contractions. Tendons also become stronger to prevent tendon damage, as the force produced by muscles is transferred to tendons that attach the muscle to bone.

For effective strength training, the intensity of the exercise must continually be increased. For instance, continued weight lifting without increasing the weight of the load does not increase muscle size. To produce ever-greater results, the weights lifted must become increasingly heavier, making it more difficult for muscles to move the load. The muscle then adapts to this heavier load, and an even heavier load must be used if even greater muscle mass is desired.

If done improperly, resistance training can lead to overuse injuries of the muscle, tendon, or bone. These injuries can occur if the load is too heavy or if the muscles are not given sufficient time between workouts to recover or if joints are not aligned properly during the exercises. Cellular damage to muscle fibers that occurs after intense exercise includes damage to the sarcolemma and myofibrils. This muscle damage contributes to the feeling of soreness after strenuous exercise, but muscles gain mass as this damage is repaired, and additional structural proteins are added to replace the damaged ones. Overworking skeletal muscles can also lead to tendon damage and even skeletal damage if the load is too great for the muscles to bear.

Performance-Enhancing Substances

Some athletes attempt to boost their performance by using various agents that may enhance muscle performance. Anabolic steroids are one of the more widely known agents used to boost muscle mass and increase power output. Anabolic steroids are a form of testosterone, a male sex hormone that stimulates muscle formation, leading to increased muscle mass.

Endurance athletes may also try to boost the availability of oxygen to muscles to increase aerobic respiration by using substances such as erythropoietin (EPO), a hormone normally produced in the kidneys, which triggers the production of red blood cells. The extra oxygen carried by these blood cells can then be used by muscles for aerobic respiration. Human growth hormone (hGH) is another supplement, and although it can facilitate building muscle mass, its main role is to promote the healing of muscle and other tissues after strenuous exercise. Increased hGH may allow for faster recovery after muscle damage, reducing the rest required after exercise, and allowing for more sustained high-level performance.

Although performance-enhancing substances often do improve performance, most are banned by governing bodies in sports and are illegal for nonmedical purposes. Their use to enhance performance raises ethical issues of cheating because they give users an unfair advantage over nonusers. A greater concern, however, is that their use carries serious health risks. The side effects of these substances are often significant, nonreversible, and in some cases fatal. The physiological strain caused by these substances is often greater than what the body can handle, leading to effects that are unpredictable and dangerous. Anabolic steroid use has been linked to infertility, aggressive behavior, cardiovascular disease, and brain cancer.

Similarly, some athletes have used creatine to increase power output. Creatine phosphate provides quick bursts of ATP to muscles in the initial stages of contraction. Increasing the amount of creatine available to cells is thought to produce more ATP and therefore increase explosive power output, although its effectiveness as a supplement has been questioned.

Everyday Connection

Aging and Muscle Tissue

Although atrophy due to disuse can often be reversed with exercise, muscle atrophy with age, referred to as sarcopenia, is irreversible. This is a primary reason why even highly trained athletes succumb to declining performance with age. This decline is noticeable in athletes whose sports require strength and powerful movements, such as sprinting, whereas the effects of age are less noticeable in endurance athletes such as marathon runners or long-distance cyclists. As muscles age, muscle fibers die, and they are replaced by connective tissue and adipose tissue (Figure 10.20). Because those tissues cannot contract and generate force as muscle can, muscles lose the ability to produce powerful contractions. The decline in muscle mass causes a loss of strength, including the strength required for posture and mobility. This may be caused by a reduction in FG fibers that hydrolyze ATP quickly to produce short, powerful contractions. Muscles in older people sometimes possess greater numbers of SO fibers, which are responsible for longer contractions and do not produce powerful movements. There may also be a reduction in the size of motor units, resulting in fewer fibers being stimulated and less muscle tension being produced.

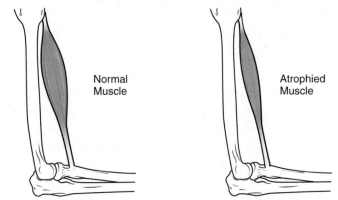

FIGURE 10.20   **Atrophy**   Muscle mass is reduced as muscles atrophy with disuse.

Sarcopenia can be delayed to some extent by exercise, as training adds structural proteins and causes cellular changes that can offset the effects of atrophy. Increased exercise can produce greater numbers of cellular mitochondria, increase capillary density, and increase the mass and strength of connective tissue. The effects of age-related atrophy are especially pronounced in people who are sedentary, as the loss of muscle cells is displayed as functional impairments such as trouble with locomotion, balance, and posture. This can lead to a decrease in quality of life and medical problems, such as joint problems because the muscles that stabilize bones and joints are weakened. Problems with locomotion and balance can also cause various injuries due to falls.

10.7 Cardiac Muscle Tissue

LEARNING OBJECTIVES

By the end of this section, you will be able to:

- Describe intercalated discs and gap junctions
- Describe a desmosome

Cardiac muscle tissue is only found in the heart. Highly coordinated contractions of cardiac muscle pump blood into the vessels of the circulatory system. Similar to skeletal muscle, cardiac muscle is striated and organized into sarcomeres, possessing the same banding organization as skeletal muscle (Figure 10.21). However, cardiac muscle fibers are shorter than skeletal muscle fibers and usually contain only one nucleus, which is located in the central region of the cell. Cardiac muscle fibers also possess many mitochondria and myoglobin, as ATP is produced primarily through aerobic metabolism. Cardiac muscle fibers cells also are extensively branched and are connected to one another at their ends by intercalated discs. An **intercalated disc** allows the cardiac muscle cells to contract in a wave-like pattern so that the heart can work as a pump.

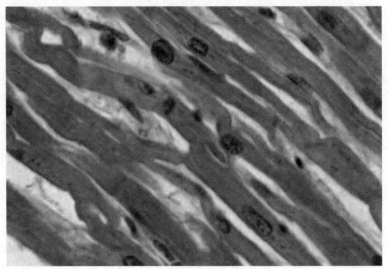

FIGURE 10.21 Cardiac Muscle Tissue   Cardiac muscle tissue is only found in the heart. LM × 1600. (Micrograph provided by the Regents of University of Michigan Medical School © 2012)

⊘ INTERACTIVE LINK

View the University of Michigan WebScope (http://openstax.org/l/cardmuscleMG) to explore the tissue sample in greater detail.

Intercalated discs are part of the sarcolemma and contain two structures important in cardiac muscle contraction: gap junctions and desmosomes. A gap junction forms channels between adjacent cardiac muscle fibers that allow the depolarizing current produced by cations to flow from one cardiac muscle cell to the next. This joining is called electric coupling, and in cardiac muscle it allows the quick transmission of action potentials and the coordinated contraction of the entire heart. This network of electrically connected cardiac muscle cells creates a functional unit of contraction called a syncytium. The remainder of the intercalated disc is composed of desmosomes. A **desmosome** is a cell structure that anchors the ends of cardiac muscle fibers together so the cells do not pull apart during the stress of individual fibers contracting (Figure 10.22).

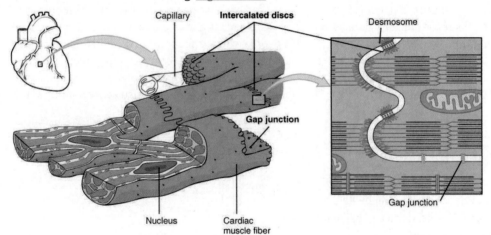

FIGURE 10.22 Cardiac Muscle   Intercalated discs are part of the cardiac muscle sarcolemma and they contain gap junctions and desmosomes.

Contractions of the heart (heartbeats) are controlled by specialized cardiac muscle cells called pacemaker cells that directly control heart rate. Although cardiac muscle cannot be consciously controlled, the pacemaker cells respond to signals from the autonomic nervous system (ANS) to speed up or slow down the heart rate. The pacemaker cells can also respond to various hormones that modulate heart rate to control blood pressure.

The wave of contraction that allows the heart to work as a unit, called a functional syncytium, begins with the pacemaker cells. This group of cells is self-excitable and able to depolarize to threshold and fire action potentials on their own, a feature called **autorhythmicity**; they do this at set intervals which determine heart rate. Because they are connected with gap junctions to surrounding muscle fibers and the specialized fibers of the heart's conduction system, the pacemaker cells are able to transfer the depolarization to the other cardiac muscle fibers in a manner that allows the heart to contract in a coordinated manner.

Another feature of cardiac muscle is its relatively long action potentials in its fibers, having a sustained depolarization "plateau." The plateau is produced by Ca^{++} entry though voltage-gated calcium channels in the sarcolemma of cardiac muscle fibers. This sustained depolarization (and Ca^{++} entry) provides for a longer contraction than is produced by an action potential in skeletal muscle. Unlike skeletal muscle, a large percentage of the Ca^{++} that initiates contraction in cardiac muscles comes from outside the cell rather than from the SR.

10.8 Smooth Muscle

LEARNING OBJECTIVES

By the end of this section, you will be able to:
- Describe a dense body
- Explain how smooth muscle works with internal organs and passageways through the body
- Explain how smooth muscles differ from skeletal and cardiac muscles
- Explain the difference between single-unit and multi-unit smooth muscle

Smooth muscle (so-named because the cells do not have striations) is present in the walls of hollow organs like the urinary bladder, uterus, stomach, intestines, and in the walls of passageways, such as the arteries and veins of the circulatory system, and the tracts of the respiratory, urinary, and reproductive systems (Figure 10.23**ab**). Smooth muscle is also present in the eyes, where it functions to change the size of the iris and alter the shape of the lens; and in the skin where it causes hair to stand erect in response to cold temperature or fear.

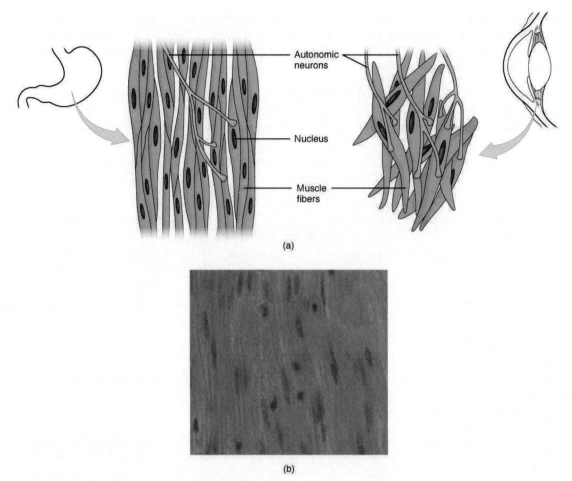

(a)

(b)

FIGURE 10.23   Smooth Muscle Tissue   Smooth muscle tissue is found around organs in the digestive, respiratory, reproductive tracts and the iris of the eye. LM × 1600. (Micrograph provided by the Regents of University of Michigan Medical School © 2012)

⊘ INTERACTIVE LINK

View the University of Michigan WebScope (http://openstax.org/l/smoothmuscMG) to explore the tissue sample in greater detail.

Smooth muscle fibers are spindle-shaped (wide in the middle and tapered at both ends, somewhat like a football) and have a single nucleus; they range from about 30 to 200 μm (thousands of times shorter than skeletal muscle fibers), and they produce their own connective tissue, endomysium. Although they do not have striations and sarcomeres, smooth muscle fibers do have actin and myosin contractile proteins, and thick and thin filaments. These thin filaments are anchored by dense bodies. A **dense body** is analogous to the Z-discs of skeletal and cardiac muscle fibers and is fastened to the sarcolemma. Calcium ions are supplied by the SR in the fibers and by sequestration from the extracellular fluid through membrane indentations called calveoli.

Because smooth muscle cells do not contain troponin, cross-bridge formation is not regulated by the troponin-tropomyosin complex but instead by the regulatory protein **calmodulin**. In a smooth muscle fiber, external Ca^{++} ions passing through opened calcium channels in the sarcolemma, and additional Ca^{++} released from SR, bind to calmodulin. The Ca^{++}-calmodulin complex then activates an enzyme called myosin (light chain) kinase, which, in turn, activates the myosin heads by phosphorylating them (converting ATP to ADP and P_i, with the P_i attaching to the head). The heads can then attach to actin-binding sites and pull on the thin filaments. The thin filaments also are anchored to the dense bodies; the structures invested in the inner membrane of the sarcolemma (at adherens junctions) that also have cord-like intermediate filaments attached to them. When the thin filaments slide past the thick filaments, they pull on the dense bodies, structures tethered to the sarcolemma, which then pull on the intermediate filaments networks throughout the sarcoplasm. This arrangement causes the entire muscle fiber to contract in a manner whereby the ends are pulled toward the center, causing the midsection to bulge in a corkscrew motion (Figure 10.24).

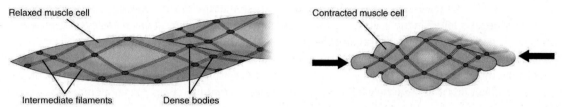

FIGURE 10.24   Muscle Contraction   The dense bodies and intermediate filaments are networked through the sarcoplasm, which cause the muscle fiber to contract.

Although smooth muscle contraction relies on the presence of Ca^{++} ions, smooth muscle fibers have a much smaller diameter than skeletal muscle cells. T-tubules are not required to reach the interior of the cell and therefore not necessary to transmit an action potential deep into the fiber. Smooth muscle fibers have a limited calcium-storing SR but have calcium channels in the sarcolemma (similar to cardiac muscle fibers) that open during the action potential along the sarcolemma. The influx of extracellular Ca^{++} ions, which diffuse into the sarcoplasm to reach the calmodulin, accounts for most of the Ca^{++} that triggers contraction of a smooth muscle cell.

Muscle contraction continues until ATP-dependent calcium pumps actively transport Ca^{++} ions back into the SR and out of the cell. However, a low concentration of calcium remains in the sarcoplasm to maintain muscle tone. This remaining calcium keeps the muscle slightly contracted, which is important in certain tracts and around blood vessels.

Because most smooth muscles must function for long periods without rest, their power output is relatively low, but contractions can continue without using large amounts of energy. Some smooth muscle can also maintain contractions even as Ca^{++} is removed and myosin kinase is inactivated/dephosphorylated. This can happen as a subset of cross-bridges between myosin heads and actin, called **latch-bridges**, keep the thick and thin filaments linked together for a prolonged period, and without the need for ATP. This allows for the maintaining of muscle "tone" in smooth muscle that lines arterioles and other visceral organs with very little energy expenditure.

Smooth muscle is not under voluntary control; thus, it is called involuntary muscle. The triggers for smooth muscle contraction include hormones, neural stimulation by the ANS, and local factors. In certain locations, such as the walls of visceral organs, stretching the muscle can trigger its contraction (the stress-relaxation response).

Axons of neurons in the ANS do not form the highly organized NMJs with smooth muscle, as seen between motor neurons and skeletal muscle fibers. Instead, there is a series of neurotransmitter-filled bulges called varicosities as an axon courses through smooth muscle, loosely forming motor units (Figure 10.25). A **varicosity** releases neurotransmitters into the synaptic cleft. Also, visceral muscle in the walls of the hollow organs (except the heart) contains pacesetter cells. A **pacesetter cell** can spontaneously trigger action potentials and contractions in the muscle.

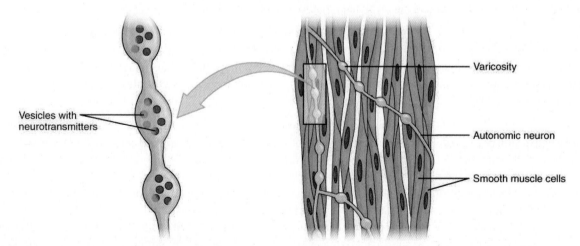

FIGURE 10.25   Motor Units   A series of axon-like swelling, called varicosities or "boutons," from autonomic neurons form motor units through the smooth muscle.

Smooth muscle is organized in two ways: as single-unit smooth muscle, which is much more common; and as multiunit smooth muscle. The two types have different locations in the body and have different characteristics. Single-unit muscle has its muscle fibers joined by gap junctions so that the muscle contracts as a single unit. This type of smooth muscle is found in the walls of all visceral organs except the heart (which has cardiac muscle in its walls), and so it is commonly called **visceral muscle**. Because the muscle fibers are not constrained by the organization and stretchability limits of sarcomeres, visceral smooth muscle has a **stress-relaxation response**. This means that as the muscle of a hollow organ is stretched when it fills, the mechanical stress of the stretching will trigger contraction, but this is immediately followed by relaxation so that the organ does not empty its contents prematurely. This is important for hollow organs, such as the stomach or urinary bladder, which continuously expand as they fill. The smooth muscle around these organs also can maintain a muscle tone when the organ empties and shrinks, a feature that prevents "flabbiness" in the empty organ. In general, visceral smooth muscle produces slow, steady contractions that allow substances, such as food in the digestive tract, to move through the body.

Multiunit smooth muscle cells rarely possess gap junctions, and thus are not electrically coupled. As a result, contraction does not spread from one cell to the next, but is instead confined to the cell that was originally stimulated. Stimuli for multiunit smooth muscles come from autonomic nerves or hormones but not from stretching. This type of tissue is found around large blood vessels, in the respiratory airways, and in the eyes.

Hyperplasia in Smooth Muscle

Similar to skeletal and cardiac muscle cells, smooth muscle can undergo hypertrophy to increase in size. Unlike other muscle, smooth muscle can also divide to produce more cells, a process called **hyperplasia**. This can most evidently be observed in the uterus at puberty, which responds to increased estrogen levels by producing more uterine smooth muscle fibers, and greatly increases the size of the myometrium.

10.9 Development and Regeneration of Muscle Tissue

LEARNING OBJECTIVES

By the end of this section, you will be able to:
- Describe the function of satellite cells
- Define fibrosis
- Explain which muscle has the greatest regeneration ability

Most muscle tissue of the body arises from embryonic mesoderm. Paraxial mesodermal cells adjacent to the neural tube form blocks of cells called **somites**. Skeletal muscles, excluding those of the head and limbs, develop from mesodermal somites, whereas skeletal muscle in the head and limbs develop from general mesoderm. Somites give rise to myoblasts. A **myoblast** is a muscle-forming stem cell that migrates to different regions in the body and then fuse(s) to form a syncytium, or **myotube**. As a myotube is formed from many different myoblast cells, it contains many nuclei, but has a continuous cytoplasm. This is why skeletal muscle cells are multinucleate, as the nucleus of each contributing myoblast remains intact in the mature skeletal muscle cell. However, cardiac and smooth muscle cells are not multinucleate because the myoblasts that form their cells do not fuse.

Gap junctions develop in the cardiac and single-unit smooth muscle in the early stages of development. In skeletal muscles, ACh receptors are initially present along most of the surface of the myoblasts, but spinal nerve innervation causes the release of growth factors that stimulate the formation of motor end-plates and NMJs. As neurons become active, electrical signals that are sent through the muscle influence the distribution of slow and fast fibers in the muscle.

Although the number of muscle cells is set during development, satellite cells help to repair skeletal muscle cells. A **satellite cell** is similar to a myoblast because it is a type of stem cell; however, satellite cells are incorporated into muscle cells and facilitate the protein synthesis required for repair and growth. These cells are located outside the sarcolemma and are stimulated to grow and fuse with muscle cells by growth factors that are released by muscle fibers under certain forms of stress. Satellite cells can regenerate muscle fibers to a very limited extent, but they primarily help to repair damage in living cells. If a cell is damaged to a greater extent than can be repaired by satellite cells, the muscle fibers are replaced by scar tissue in a process called **fibrosis**. Because scar tissue cannot contract, muscle that has sustained significant damage loses strength and cannot produce the same amount of power or endurance as it could before being damaged.

Smooth muscle tissue can regenerate from a type of stem cell called a **pericyte**, which is found in some small blood vessels. Pericytes allow smooth muscle cells to regenerate and repair much more readily than skeletal and cardiac muscle tissue. Similar to skeletal muscle tissue, cardiac muscle does not regenerate to a great extent. Dead cardiac muscle tissue is replaced by scar tissue, which cannot contract. As scar tissue accumulates, the heart loses its ability to pump because of the loss of contractile power. However, some minor regeneration may occur due to stem cells found in the blood that occasionally enter cardiac tissue.

 CAREER CONNECTION

Physical Therapist

As muscle cells die, they are not regenerated but instead are replaced by connective tissue and adipose tissue, which do not possess the contractile abilities of muscle tissue. Muscles atrophy when they are not used, and over time if atrophy is prolonged, muscle cells die. It is therefore important that those who are susceptible to muscle atrophy exercise to maintain muscle function and prevent the complete loss of muscle tissue. In extreme cases, when movement is not possible, electrical stimulation can be introduced to a muscle from an external source. This acts as a substitute for endogenous neural stimulation, stimulating the muscle to contract and preventing the loss of proteins that occurs with a lack of use.

Physiotherapists work with patients to maintain muscles. They are trained to target muscles susceptible to atrophy, and to prescribe and monitor exercises designed to stimulate those muscles. There are various causes of atrophy, including mechanical injury, disease, and age. After breaking a limb or undergoing surgery, muscle use is impaired and can lead to disuse atrophy. If the muscles are not exercised, this atrophy can lead to long-term muscle weakness. A stroke can also cause muscle impairment by interrupting neural stimulation to certain muscles. Without neural inputs, these muscles do not contract and thus begin to lose structural proteins. Exercising these muscles can help to restore muscle function and minimize functional impairments. Age-related muscle loss is also a target of physical therapy, as exercise can reduce the effects of age-related atrophy and improve muscle function.

The goal of a physiotherapist is to improve physical functioning and reduce functional impairments; this is achieved by understanding the cause of muscle impairment and assessing the capabilities of a patient, after which a program to enhance these capabilities is designed. Some factors that are assessed include strength, balance, and endurance, which are continually monitored as exercises are introduced to track improvements in muscle function. Physiotherapists can also instruct patients on the proper use of equipment, such as crutches, and assess whether someone has sufficient strength to use the equipment and when they can function without it.

Key Terms

acetylcholine (ACh)   neurotransmitter that binds at a motor end-plate to trigger depolarization

actin   protein that makes up most of the thin myofilaments in a sarcomere muscle fiber

action potential   change in voltage of a cell membrane in response to a stimulus that results in transmission of an electrical signal; unique to neurons and muscle fibers

aerobic respiration   production of ATP in the presence of oxygen

angiogenesis   formation of blood capillary networks

aponeurosis   broad, tendon-like sheet of connective tissue that attaches a skeletal muscle to another skeletal muscle or to a bone

ATPase   enzyme that hydrolyzes ATP to ADP

atrophy   loss of structural proteins from muscle fibers

autorhythmicity   heart's ability to control its own contractions

calmodulin   regulatory protein that facilitates contraction in smooth muscles

cardiac muscle   striated muscle found in the heart; joined to one another at intercalated discs and under the regulation of pacemaker cells, which contract as one unit to pump blood through the circulatory system. Cardiac muscle is under involuntary control.

concentric contraction   muscle contraction that shortens the muscle to move a load

contractility   ability to shorten (contract) forcibly

contraction phase   twitch contraction phase when tension increases

creatine phosphate   phosphagen used to store energy from ATP and transfer it to muscle

dense body   sarcoplasmic structure that attaches to the sarcolemma and shortens the muscle as thin filaments slide past thick filaments

depolarize   to reduce the voltage difference between the inside and outside of a cell's plasma membrane (the sarcolemma for a muscle fiber), making the inside less negative than at rest

desmosome   cell structure that anchors the ends of cardiac muscle fibers to allow contraction to occur

eccentric contraction   muscle contraction that lengthens the muscle as the tension is diminished

elasticity   ability to stretch and rebound

endomysium   loose, and well-hydrated connective tissue covering each muscle fiber in a skeletal muscle

epimysium   outer layer of connective tissue around a skeletal muscle

excitability   ability to undergo neural stimulation

excitation-contraction coupling   sequence of events from motor neuron signaling to a skeletal muscle fiber to contraction of the fiber's sarcomeres

extensibility   ability to lengthen (extend)

fascicle   bundle of muscle fibers within a skeletal muscle

fast glycolytic (FG)   muscle fiber that primarily uses anaerobic glycolysis

fast oxidative (FO)   intermediate muscle fiber that is between slow oxidative and fast glycolytic fibers

fibrosis   replacement of muscle fibers by scar tissue

glycolysis   anaerobic breakdown of glucose to ATP

graded muscle response   modification of contraction strength

hyperplasia   process in which one cell splits to produce new cells

hypertonia   abnormally high muscle tone

hypertrophy   addition of structural proteins to muscle fibers

hypotonia   abnormally low muscle tone caused by the absence of low-level contractions

intercalated disc   part of the sarcolemma that connects cardiac tissue, and contains gap junctions and desmosomes

isometric contraction   muscle contraction that occurs with no change in muscle length

isotonic contraction   muscle contraction that involves changes in muscle length

lactic acid   product of anaerobic glycolysis

latch-bridges   subset of a cross-bridge in which actin and myosin remain locked together

latent period   the time when a twitch does not produce contraction

motor end-plate   sarcolemma of muscle fiber at the neuromuscular junction, with receptors for the neurotransmitter acetylcholine

motor unit   motor neuron and the group of muscle fibers it innervates

muscle tension   force generated by the contraction of the muscle; tension generated during isotonic contractions and isometric contractions

muscle tone   low levels of muscle contraction that occur when a muscle is not producing movement

myoblast   muscle-forming stem cell

myofibril   long, cylindrical organelle that runs parallel within the muscle fiber and contains the sarcomeres

myogram   instrument used to measure twitch tension

myosin   protein that makes up most of the thick cylindrical myofilament within a sarcomere muscle fiber

myotube   fusion of many myoblast cells

neuromuscular junction (NMJ)   synapse between the axon terminal of a motor neuron and the section of the membrane of a muscle fiber with receptors for the acetylcholine released by the terminal

neurotransmitter   signaling chemical released by nerve terminals that bind to and activate receptors on target cells

oxygen debt   amount of oxygen needed to compensate for ATP produced without oxygen during muscle contraction

pacesetter cell   cell that triggers action potentials in smooth muscle

pericyte   stem cell that regenerates smooth muscle cells

perimysium   connective tissue that bundles skeletal muscle fibers into fascicles within a skeletal muscle

power stroke   action of myosin pulling actin inward (toward the M line)

pyruvic acid   product of glycolysis that can be used in aerobic respiration or converted to lactic acid

recruitment   increase in the number of motor units involved in contraction

relaxation phase   period after twitch contraction when tension decreases

sarcolemma   plasma membrane of a skeletal muscle fiber

sarcomere   longitudinally, repeating functional unit of skeletal muscle, with all of the contractile and associated proteins involved in contraction

sarcopenia   age-related muscle atrophy

sarcoplasm   cytoplasm of a muscle cell

sarcoplasmic reticulum (SR)   specialized smooth endoplasmic reticulum, which stores, releases, and retrieves Ca^{++}

satellite cell   stem cell that helps to repair muscle cells

skeletal muscle   striated, multinucleated muscle that requires signaling from the nervous system to trigger contraction; most skeletal muscles are referred to as voluntary muscles that move bones and produce movement

slow oxidative (SO)   muscle fiber that primarily uses aerobic respiration

smooth muscle   nonstriated, mononucleated muscle in the skin that is associated with hair follicles; assists in moving materials in the walls of internal organs, blood vessels, and internal passageways

somites   blocks of paraxial mesoderm cells

stress-relaxation response   relaxation of smooth muscle tissue after being stretched

synaptic cleft   space between a nerve (axon) terminal and a motor end-plate

T-tubule   projection of the sarcolemma into the interior of the cell

tetanus   a continuous fused contraction

thick filament   the thick myosin strands and their multiple heads projecting from the center of the sarcomere toward, but not all to way to, the Z-discs

thin filament   thin strands of actin and its troponin-tropomyosin complex projecting from the Z-discs toward the center of the sarcomere

treppe   stepwise increase in contraction tension

triad   the grouping of one T-tubule and two terminal cisternae

tropomyosin   regulatory protein that covers myosin-binding sites to prevent actin from binding to myosin

troponin   regulatory protein that binds to actin, tropomyosin, and calcium

twitch   single contraction produced by one action potential

varicosity   enlargement of neurons that release neurotransmitters into synaptic clefts

visceral muscle   smooth muscle found in the walls of visceral organs

voltage-gated sodium channels   membrane proteins that open sodium channels in response to a sufficient voltage change, and initiate and transmit the action potential as Na^+ enters through the channel

wave summation   addition of successive neural stimuli to produce greater contraction

Chapter Review

10.1 Overview of Muscle Tissues

Muscle is the tissue in animals that allows for active movement of the body or materials within the body. There are three types of muscle tissue: skeletal muscle, cardiac muscle, and smooth muscle. Most of the body's skeletal muscle produces movement by acting on the skeleton. Cardiac muscle is found in the wall of the heart and pumps blood through the circulatory system.

Smooth muscle is found in the skin, where it is associated with hair follicles; it also is found in the walls of internal organs, blood vessels, and internal passageways, where it assists in moving materials.

10.2 Skeletal Muscle

Skeletal muscles contain connective tissue, blood vessels, and nerves. There are three layers of connective tissue: epimysium, perimysium, and endomysium. Skeletal muscle fibers are organized into groups called fascicles. Blood vessels and nerves enter the connective tissue and branch in the cell. Muscles attach to bones directly or through tendons or aponeuroses. Skeletal muscles maintain posture, stabilize bones and joints, control internal movement, and generate heat.

Skeletal muscle fibers are long, multinucleated cells. The membrane of the cell is the sarcolemma; the cytoplasm of the cell is the sarcoplasm. The sarcoplasmic reticulum (SR) is a form of endoplasmic reticulum. Muscle fibers are composed of myofibrils. The striations are created by the organization of actin and myosin resulting in the banding pattern of myofibrils.

10.3 Muscle Fiber Contraction and Relaxation

A sarcomere is the smallest contractile portion of a muscle. Myofibrils are composed of thick and thin filaments. Thick filaments are composed of the protein myosin; thin filaments are composed of the protein actin. Troponin and tropomyosin are regulatory proteins.

Muscle contraction is described by the sliding filament model of contraction. ACh is the neurotransmitter that binds at the neuromuscular junction (NMJ) to trigger depolarization, and an action potential travels along the sarcolemma to trigger calcium release from SR. The actin sites are exposed after Ca^{++} enters the sarcoplasm from its SR storage to activate the troponin-tropomyosin complex so that the tropomyosin shifts away from the sites. The cross-bridging of myosin heads docking into actin-binding sites is followed by the "power stroke"—the sliding of the thin filaments by thick filaments. The power strokes are powered by ATP. Ultimately, the sarcomeres, myofibrils, and muscle fibers shorten to produce movement.

10.4 Nervous System Control of Muscle Tension

The number of cross-bridges formed between actin and myosin determines the amount of tension produced by a muscle. The length of a sarcomere is optimal when the zone of overlap between thin and thick filaments is greatest. Muscles that are stretched or compressed too greatly do not produce maximal amounts of power. A motor unit is formed by a motor neuron and all of the muscle fibers that are innervated by that same motor neuron. A single contraction is called a twitch. A muscle twitch has a latent period, a contraction phase, and a relaxation phase. A graded muscle response allows variation in muscle tension. Summation occurs as successive stimuli are added

together to produce a stronger muscle contraction. Tetanus is the fusion of contractions to produce a continuous contraction. Increasing the number of motor neurons involved increases the amount of motor units activated in a muscle, which is called recruitment. Muscle tone is the constant low-level contractions that allow for posture and stability.

10.5 Types of Muscle Fibers

ATP provides the energy for muscle contraction. The three mechanisms for ATP regeneration are creatine phosphate, anaerobic glycolysis, and aerobic metabolism. Creatine phosphate provides about the first 15 seconds of ATP at the beginning of muscle contraction. Anaerobic glycolysis produces small amounts of ATP in the absence of oxygen for a short period. Aerobic metabolism utilizes oxygen to produce much more ATP, allowing a muscle to work for longer periods. Muscle fatigue, which has many contributing factors, occurs when muscle can no longer contract. An oxygen debt is created as a result of muscle use. The three types of muscle fiber are slow oxidative (SO), fast oxidative (FO) and fast glycolytic (FG). SO fibers use aerobic metabolism to produce low power contractions over long periods and are slow to fatigue. FO fibers use aerobic metabolism to produce ATP but produce higher tension contractions than SO fibers. FG fibers use anaerobic metabolism to produce powerful, high-tension contractions but fatigue quickly.

10.6 Exercise and Muscle Performance

Hypertrophy is an increase in muscle mass due to the addition of structural proteins. The opposite of hypertrophy is atrophy, the loss of muscle mass due to the breakdown of structural proteins. Endurance exercise causes an increase in cellular mitochondria, myoglobin, and capillary networks in SO fibers. Endurance athletes have a high level of SO fibers relative to the other fiber types. Resistance exercise causes hypertrophy. Power-producing muscles have a higher number of FG fibers than of slow fibers. Strenuous exercise causes muscle cell damage that requires time to heal. Some athletes use performance-enhancing substances to enhance muscle performance. Muscle atrophy due to age is called sarcopenia and occurs as muscle fibers die and are replaced by connective and adipose tissue.

10.7 Cardiac Muscle Tissue

Cardiac muscle is striated muscle that is present only in the heart. Cardiac muscle fibers have a single nucleus, are branched, and joined to one another by intercalated discs that contain gap junctions for depolarization between cells and desmosomes to hold the fibers together when the heart contracts. Contraction in each cardiac muscle fiber is triggered by Ca^{++} ions in a similar manner as skeletal muscle, but here the Ca^{++} ions come from SR and through voltage-gated calcium channels in the sarcolemma. Pacemaker cells stimulate the spontaneous contraction of cardiac muscle as a functional unit, called a syncytium.

10.8 Smooth Muscle

Smooth muscle is found throughout the body around various organs and tracts. Smooth muscle cells have a single nucleus, and are spindle-shaped. Smooth muscle cells can undergo hyperplasia, mitotically dividing to produce new cells. The smooth cells are nonstriated, but their sarcoplasm is filled with actin and myosin, along with dense bodies in the sarcolemma to anchor the thin filaments and a network of intermediate filaments involved in pulling the sarcolemma toward the fiber's middle, shortening it in the process. Ca^{++} ions trigger contraction when they are released from SR and enter through opened voltage-gated calcium channels. Smooth muscle contraction is initiated when the Ca^{++} binds to intracellular calmodulin, which then activates an enzyme called myosin kinase that phosphorylates myosin heads so they can form the cross-bridges with actin and then pull on the thin filaments. Smooth muscle can be stimulated by pacesetter cells, by the autonomic nervous system, by hormones, spontaneously, or by stretching. The fibers in some smooth muscle have latch-bridges, cross-bridges that cycle slowly without the need for ATP; these muscles can maintain low-level contractions for long periods. Single-unit smooth muscle tissue contains gap junctions to synchronize membrane depolarization and contractions so that the muscle contracts as a single unit. Single-unit smooth muscle in the walls of the viscera, called visceral muscle, has a stress-relaxation response that permits muscle to stretch, contract, and relax as the organ expands. Multiunit smooth muscle cells do not possess gap junctions, and contraction does not spread from one cell to the next.

10.9 Development and Regeneration of Muscle Tissue

Muscle tissue arises from embryonic mesoderm. Somites give rise to myoblasts and fuse to form a myotube. The nucleus of each contributing myoblast remains intact in the mature skeletal muscle cell, resulting in a mature, multinucleate cell. Satellite cells help to repair skeletal muscle cells. Smooth muscle tissue can regenerate from stem cells called pericytes, whereas dead cardiac muscle tissue is replaced by scar tissue. Aging causes muscle mass to decrease and be replaced by noncontractile connective tissue and adipose tissue.

Interactive Link Questions

1. Watch this video (http://openstax.org/l/micromacro) to learn more about macro- and microstructures of skeletal muscles. (a) What are the names of the "junction points" between sarcomeres? (b) What are the names of the "subunits" within the myofibrils that run the length of skeletal muscle fibers? (c) What is the "double strand of pearls" described in the video? (d) What gives a skeletal muscle fiber its striated appearance?

2. Every skeletal muscle fiber is supplied by a motor neuron at the NMJ. Watch this video (http://openstax.org/l/skelmuscfiber) to learn more about what happens at the neuromuscular junction. (a) What is the definition of a motor unit? (b) What is the structural and functional difference between a large motor unit and a small motor unit? Can you give an example of each? (c) Why is the neurotransmitter acetylcholine degraded after binding to its receptor?

3. The release of calcium ions initiates muscle contractions. Watch this video (http://openstax.org/l/calciumrole) to learn more about the role of calcium. (a) What are "T-tubules" and what is their role? (b) Please also describe how actin-binding sites are made available for cross-bridging with myosin heads during contraction.

Review Questions

4. Muscle that has a striped appearance is described as being _____.
  a. elastic
  b. nonstriated
  c. excitable
  d. striated

5. Which element is important in directly triggering contraction?
  a. sodium (Na⁺)
  b. calcium (Ca⁺⁺)
  c. potassium (K⁺)
  d. chloride (Cl⁻)

6. Which of the following properties is *not* common to all three muscle tissues?
  a. excitability
  b. the need for ATP
  c. at rest, uses shielding proteins to cover actin-binding sites
  d. elasticity

7. The correct order for the smallest to the largest unit of organization in muscle tissue is _____.
  a. fascicle, filament, muscle fiber, myofibril
  b. filament, myofibril, muscle fiber, fascicle
  c. muscle fiber, fascicle, filament, myofibril
  d. myofibril, muscle fiber, filament, fascicle

8. Depolarization of the sarcolemma means _____.
  a. the inside of the membrane has become less negative as sodium ions accumulate
  b. the outside of the membrane has become less negative as sodium ions accumulate
  c. the inside of the membrane has become more negative as sodium ions accumulate
  d. the sarcolemma has completely lost any electrical charge

9. In relaxed muscle, the myosin-binding site on actin is blocked by _____.
  a. titin
  b. troponin
  c. myoglobin
  d. tropomyosin

10. According to the sliding filament model, binding sites on actin open when _____.
  a. creatine phosphate levels rise
  b. ATP levels rise
  c. acetylcholine levels rise
  d. calcium ion levels rise

11. The cell membrane of a muscle fiber is called _____.
  a. myofibril
  b. sarcolemma
  c. sarcoplasm
  d. myofilament

12. Muscle relaxation occurs when _____.
  a. calcium ions are actively transported out of the sarcoplasmic reticulum
  b. calcium ions diffuse out of the sarcoplasmic reticulum
  c. calcium ions are actively transported into the sarcoplasmic reticulum
  d. calcium ions diffuse into the sarcoplasmic reticulum

13. During muscle contraction, the cross-bridge detaches when _____.
  a. the myosin head binds to an ADP molecule
  b. the myosin head binds to an ATP molecule
  c. calcium ions bind to troponin
  d. calcium ions bind to actin

14. Thin and thick filaments are organized into functional units called _____.
  a. myofibrils
  b. myofilaments
  c. T-tubules
  d. sarcomeres

15. During which phase of a twitch in a muscle fiber is tension the greatest?
  a. resting phase
  b. repolarization phase
  c. contraction phase
  d. relaxation phase

16. Muscle fatigue is caused by _____.
  a. buildup of ATP and lactic acid levels
  b. exhaustion of energy reserves and buildup of lactic acid levels
  c. buildup of ATP and pyruvic acid levels
  d. exhaustion of energy reserves and buildup of pyruvic acid levels

17. A sprinter would experience muscle fatigue sooner than a marathon runner due to _____.
    a. anaerobic metabolism in the muscles of the sprinter
    b. anaerobic metabolism in the muscles of the marathon runner
    c. aerobic metabolism in the muscles of the sprinter
    d. glycolysis in the muscles of the marathon runner

18. What aspect of creatine phosphate allows it to supply energy to muscles?
    a. ATPase activity
    b. phosphate bonds
    c. carbon bonds
    d. hydrogen bonds

19. Drug X blocks ATP regeneration from ADP and phosphate. How will muscle cells respond to this drug?
    a. by absorbing ATP from the bloodstream
    b. by using ADP as an energy source
    c. by using glycogen as an energy source
    d. none of the above

20. The muscles of a professional sprinter are most likely to have _____.
    a. 80 percent fast-twitch muscle fibers and 20 percent slow-twitch muscle fibers
    b. 20 percent fast-twitch muscle fibers and 80 percent slow-twitch muscle fibers
    c. 50 percent fast-twitch muscle fibers and 50 percent slow-twitch muscle fibers
    d. 40 percent fast-twitch muscle fibers and 60 percent slow-twitch muscle fibers

21. The muscles of a professional marathon runner are most likely to have _____.
    a. 80 percent fast-twitch muscle fibers and 20 percent slow-twitch muscle fibers
    b. 20 percent fast-twitch muscle fibers and 80 percent slow-twitch muscle fibers
    c. 50 percent fast-twitch muscle fibers and 50 percent slow-twitch muscle fibers
    d. 40 percent fast-twitch muscle fibers and 60 percent slow-twitch muscle fibers

22. Which of the following statements is *true*?
    a. Fast fibers have a small diameter.
    b. Fast fibers contain loosely packed myofibrils.
    c. Fast fibers have large glycogen reserves.
    d. Fast fibers have many mitochondria.

23. Which of the following statements is *false*?
    a. Slow fibers have a small network of capillaries.
    b. Slow fibers contain the pigment myoglobin.
    c. Slow fibers contain a large number of mitochondria.
    d. Slow fibers contract for extended periods.

24. Cardiac muscles differ from skeletal muscles in that they _____.
    a. are striated
    b. utilize aerobic metabolism
    c. contain myofibrils
    d. contain intercalated discs

25. If cardiac muscle cells were prevented from undergoing aerobic metabolism, they ultimately would _____.
    a. undergo glycolysis
    b. synthesize ATP
    c. stop contracting
    d. start contracting

26. Smooth muscles differ from skeletal and cardiac muscles in that they _____.
    a. lack myofibrils
    b. are under voluntary control
    c. lack myosin
    d. lack actin

27. Which of the following statements describes smooth muscle cells?
    a. They are resistant to fatigue.
    b. They have a rapid onset of contractions.
    c. They cannot exhibit tetanus.
    d. They primarily use anaerobic metabolism.

28. From which embryonic cell type does muscle tissue develop?
    a. ganglion cells
    b. myotube cells
    c. myoblast cells
    d. satellite cells

29. Which cell type helps to repair injured muscle fibers?
    a. ganglion cells
    b. myotube cells
    c. myoblast cells
    d. satellite cells

Critical Thinking Questions

30. Why is elasticity an important quality of muscle tissue?

31. What would happen to skeletal muscle if the epimysium were destroyed?

32. Describe how tendons facilitate body movement.

33. What are the five primary functions of skeletal muscle?

34. What are the opposite roles of voltage-gated sodium channels and voltage-gated potassium channels?

35. How would muscle contractions be affected if skeletal muscle fibers did not have T-tubules?

36. What causes the striated appearance of skeletal muscle tissue?

37. How would muscle contractions be affected if ATP was completely depleted in a muscle fiber?

38. Why does a motor unit of the eye have few muscle fibers compared to a motor unit of the leg?

39. What factors contribute to the amount of tension produced in an individual muscle fiber?

40. Why do muscle cells use creatine phosphate instead of glycolysis to supply ATP for the first few seconds of muscle contraction?

41. Is aerobic respiration more or less efficient than glycolysis? Explain your answer.

42. What changes occur at the cellular level in response to endurance training?

43. What changes occur at the cellular level in response to resistance training?

44. What would be the drawback of cardiac contractions being the same duration as skeletal muscle contractions?

45. How are cardiac muscle cells similar to and different from skeletal muscle cells?

46. Why can smooth muscles contract over a wider range of resting lengths than skeletal and cardiac muscle?

47. Describe the differences between single-unit smooth muscle and multiunit smooth muscle.

48. Why is muscle that has sustained significant damage unable to produce the same amount of power as it could before being damaged?

49. Which muscle type(s) (skeletal, smooth, or cardiac) can regenerate new muscle cells/fibers? Explain your answer.

CHAPTER 11
The Muscular System

Figure 11.1 A Body in Motion The muscular system allows us to move, flex and contort our bodies. Practicing yoga, as pictured here, is a good example of the voluntary use of the muscular system. (credit: Dmitry Yanchylenko)

CHAPTER OBJECTIVES

After studying this chapter, you will be able to:

- Describe the actions and roles of agonists and antagonists
- Explain the structure and organization of muscle fascicles and their role in generating force
- Explain the criteria used to name skeletal muscles
- Identify the skeletal muscles and their actions on the skeleton and soft tissues of the body
- Identify the origins and insertions of skeletal muscles and the prime movements

INTRODUCTION Think about the things that you do each day—talking, walking, sitting, standing, and running—all of these activities require movement of particular skeletal muscles. Skeletal muscles are even used during sleep. The diaphragm is a sheet of skeletal muscle that has to contract and relax for you to breathe day and night. If you recall from your study of the skeletal system and joints, body movement occurs around the joints in the body. The focus of this chapter is on skeletal muscle organization. The system to name skeletal muscles will be explained; in some cases, the muscle is named by its shape, and in other cases it is named by its location or attachments to the skeleton. If you understand the meaning of the name of the muscle, often it will help you remember its location and/ or what it does. This chapter also will describe how skeletal muscles are arranged to accomplish movement, and how other muscles may assist, or be arranged on the skeleton to resist or carry out the opposite movement. The actions of the skeletal muscles will be covered in a regional manner, working from the head down to the toes.

11.1 Interactions of Skeletal Muscles, Their Fascicle Arrangement, and Their Lever Systems

LEARNING OBJECTIVES

By the end of this section, you will be able to:

- Compare and contrast agonist and antagonist muscles
- Describe how fascicles are arranged within a skeletal muscle
- Explain the major events of a skeletal muscle contraction within a muscle in generating force

To move the skeleton, the tension created by the contraction of the fibers in most skeletal muscles is transferred to the tendons. The tendons are strong bands of dense, regular connective tissue that connect muscles to bones. The bone connection is why this muscle tissue is called skeletal muscle.

Interactions of Skeletal Muscles in the Body

To pull on a bone, that is, to change the angle at its synovial joint, which essentially moves the skeleton, a skeletal muscle must also be attached to a fixed part of the skeleton. The moveable end of the muscle that attaches to the bone being pulled is called the muscle's **insertion**, and the end of the muscle attached to a fixed (stabilized) bone is called the **origin**. During forearm **flexion**—bending the elbow—the brachioradialis assists the brachialis.

Although a number of muscles may be involved in an action, the principal muscle involved is called the **prime mover**, or **agonist**. To lift a cup, a muscle called the biceps brachii is actually the prime mover; however, because it can be assisted by the brachialis, the brachialis is called a **synergist** in this action (Figure 11.2). A synergist can also be a **fixator** that stabilizes the bone that is the attachment for the prime mover's origin.

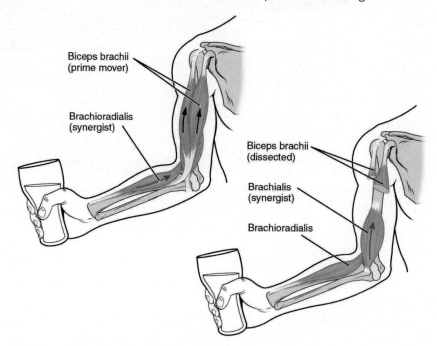

FIGURE 11.2   Prime Movers and Synergists   The biceps brachii flex the lower arm. The brachoradialis, in the forearm, and brachialis, located deep to the biceps in the upper arm, are both synergists that aid in this motion.

A muscle with the opposite action of the prime mover is called an **antagonist**. Antagonists play two important roles in muscle function: (1) they maintain body or limb position, such as holding the arm out or standing erect; and (2) they control rapid movement, as in shadow boxing without landing a punch or the ability to check the motion of a limb.

For example, to extend the knee, a group of four muscles called the quadriceps femoris in the anterior compartment of the thigh are activated (and would be called the agonists of knee extension). However, to flex the knee joint, an opposite or antagonistic set of muscles called the hamstrings is activated.

As you can see, these terms would also be reversed for the opposing action. If you consider the first action as the knee bending, the hamstrings would be called the agonists and the quadriceps femoris would then be called the antagonists. See Table 11.1 for a list of some agonists and antagonists.

Agonist and Antagonist Skeletal Muscle Pairs

Agonist	Antagonist	Movement
Biceps brachii: in the anterior compartment of the arm	Triceps brachii: in the posterior compartment of the arm	The biceps brachii flexes the forearm, whereas the triceps brachii extends it.
Hamstrings: group of three muscles in the posterior compartment of the thigh	Quadriceps femoris: group of four muscles in the anterior compartment of the thigh	The hamstrings flex the leg, whereas the quadriceps femoris extend it.
Flexor digitorum superficialis and flexor digitorum profundus: in the anterior compartment of the forearm	Extensor digitorum: in the posterior compartment of the forearm	The flexor digitorum superficialis and flexor digitorum profundus flex the fingers and the hand at the wrist, whereas the extensor digitorum extends the fingers and the hand at the wrist.

TABLE 11.1

There are also skeletal muscles that do not pull against the skeleton for movements. For example, there are the muscles that produce facial expressions. The insertions and origins of facial muscles are in the skin, so that certain individual muscles contract to form a smile or frown, form sounds or words, and raise the eyebrows. There also are skeletal muscles in the tongue, and the external urinary and anal sphincters that allow for voluntary regulation of urination and defecation, respectively. In addition, the diaphragm contracts and relaxes to change the volume of the pleural cavities but it does not move the skeleton to do this.

Everyday Connection

Exercise and Stretching

When exercising, it is important to first warm up the muscles. Stretching pulls on the muscle fibers and it also results in an increased blood flow to the muscles being worked. Without a proper warm-up, it is possible that you may either damage some of the muscle fibers or pull a tendon. A pulled tendon, regardless of location, results in pain, swelling, and diminished function; if it is moderate to severe, the injury could immobilize you for an extended period.

Recall the discussion about muscles crossing joints to create movement. Most of the joints you use during exercise are synovial joints, which have synovial fluid in the joint space between two bones. Exercise and stretching may also have a beneficial effect on synovial joints. Synovial fluid is a thin, but viscous film with the consistency of egg whites. When you first get up and start moving, your joints feel stiff for a number of reasons. After proper stretching and warm-up, the synovial fluid may become less viscous, allowing for better joint function.

Patterns of Fascicle Organization

Skeletal muscle is enclosed in connective tissue scaffolding at three levels. Each muscle fiber (cell) is covered by endomysium and the entire muscle is covered by epimysium. When a group of muscle fibers is "bundled" as a unit within the whole muscle by an additional covering of a connective tissue called perimysium, that bundled group of muscle fibers is called a **fascicle**. Fascicle arrangement by perimysia is correlated to the force generated by a muscle; it also affects the range of motion of the muscle. Based on the patterns of fascicle arrangement, skeletal muscles can be classified in several ways. What follows are the most common fascicle arrangements.

Parallel muscles have fascicles that are arranged in the same direction as the long axis of the muscle (Figure 11.3). The majority of skeletal muscles in the body have this type of organization. Some parallel muscles are flat sheets that expand at the ends to make broad attachments. Other parallel muscles are rotund with tendons at one or both ends. Muscles that seem to be plump have a large mass of tissue located in the middle of the muscle, between the insertion and the origin, which is known as the central body. A more common name for this muscle is **belly**. When a muscle contracts, the contractile fibers shorten it to an even larger bulge. For example, extend and then flex your biceps brachii muscle; the large, middle section is the belly (Figure 11.4). When a parallel muscle has a central, large belly that is spindle-shaped, meaning it tapers as it extends to its origin and insertion, it sometimes is called **fusiform**.

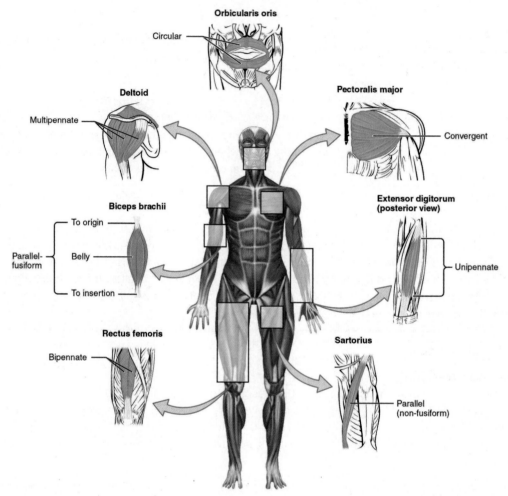

FIGURE 11.3   **Muscle Shapes and Fiber Alignment**   The skeletal muscles of the body typically come in seven different general shapes.

Access for free at openstax.org

FIGURE 11.4   Biceps Brachii Muscle Contraction   The large mass at the center of a muscle is called the belly. Tendons emerge from both ends of the belly and connect the muscle to the bones, allowing the skeleton to move. The tendons of the bicep connect to the upper arm and the forearm. (credit: Victoria Garcia)

Circular muscles are also called sphincters (see Figure 11.3). When they relax, the sphincters' concentrically arranged bundles of muscle fibers increase the size of the opening, and when they contract, the size of the opening shrinks to the point of closure. The orbicularis oris muscle is a circular muscle that goes around the mouth. When it contracts, the oral opening becomes smaller, as when puckering the lips for whistling. Another example is the orbicularis oculi, one of which surrounds each eye. Consider, for example, the names of the two orbicularis muscles (orbicularis oris and oribicularis oculi), where part of the first name of both muscles is the same. The first part of orbicularis, orb (orb = "circular"), is a reference to a round or circular structure; it may also make one think of orbit, such as the moon's path around the earth. The word oris (oris = "oral") refers to the oral cavity, or the mouth. The word oculi (ocular = "eye") refers to the eye.

There are other muscles throughout the body named by their shape or location. The deltoid is a large, triangular-shaped muscle that covers the shoulder. It is so-named because the Greek letter delta looks like a triangle. The rectus abdominis (rector = "straight") is the straight muscle in the anterior wall of the abdomen, while the rectus femoris is the straight muscle in the anterior compartment of the thigh.

When a muscle has a widespread expansion over a sizable area, but then the fascicles come to a single, common attachment point, the muscle is called **convergent**. The attachment point for a convergent muscle could be a tendon, an aponeurosis (a flat, broad tendon), or a raphe (a very slender tendon). The large muscle on the chest, the pectoralis major, is an example of a convergent muscle because it converges on the greater tubercle of the humerus via a tendon. The temporalis muscle of the cranium is another.

Pennate muscles (penna = "feathers") blend into a tendon that runs through the central region of the muscle for its whole length, somewhat like the quill of a feather with the muscle arranged similar to the feathers. Due to this design, the muscle fibers in a pennate muscle can only pull at an angle, and as a result, contracting pennate muscles do not move their tendons very far. However, because a pennate muscle generally can hold more muscle fibers within it, it can produce relatively more tension for its size. There are three subtypes of pennate muscles.

In a **unipennate** muscle, the fascicles are located on one side of the tendon. The extensor digitorum of the forearm is an example of a unipennate muscle. A **bipennate** muscle has fascicles on both sides of the tendon. In some pennate muscles, the muscle fibers wrap around the tendon, sometimes forming individual fascicles in the process. This arrangement is referred to as **multipennate**. A common example is the deltoid muscle of the shoulder, which covers the shoulder but has a single tendon that inserts on the deltoid tuberosity of the humerus.

Because of fascicles, a portion of a multipennate muscle like the deltoid can be stimulated by the nervous system to change the direction of the pull. For example, when the deltoid muscle contracts, the arm abducts (moves away from midline in the sagittal plane), but when only the anterior fascicle is stimulated, the arm will **abduct** and flex (move anteriorly at the shoulder joint).

The Lever System of Muscle and Bone Interactions

Skeletal muscles do not work by themselves. Muscles are arranged in pairs based on their functions. For muscles attached to the bones of the skeleton, the connection determines the force, speed, and range of movement. These characteristics depend on each other and can explain the general organization of the muscular and skeletal systems.

The skeleton and muscles act together to move the body. Have you ever used the back of a hammer to remove a nail from wood? The handle acts as a lever and the head of the hammer acts as a fulcrum, the fixed point that the force is applied to when you pull back or push down on the handle. The effort applied to this system is the pulling or pushing on the handle to remove the nail, which is the load, or "resistance" to the movement of the handle in the system. Our musculoskeletal system works in a similar manner, with bones being stiff levers and the articular endings of the bones—encased in synovial joints—acting as fulcrums. The load would be an object being lifted or any resistance to a movement (your head is a load when you are lifting it), and the effort, or applied force, comes from contracting skeletal muscle.

11.2 Naming Skeletal Muscles

LEARNING OBJECTIVES

By the end of this section, you will be able to:
- Describe the criteria used to name skeletal muscles
- Explain how understanding the muscle names helps describe shapes, location, and actions of various muscles

The Greeks and Romans conducted the first studies done on the human body in Western culture. The educated class of subsequent societies studied Latin and Greek, and therefore the early pioneers of anatomy continued to apply Latin and Greek terminology or roots when they named the skeletal muscles. The large number of muscles in the body and unfamiliar words can make learning the names of the muscles in the body seem daunting, but understanding the etymology can help. Etymology is the study of how the root of a particular word entered a language and how the use of the word evolved over time. Taking the time to learn the root of the words is crucial to understanding the vocabulary of anatomy and physiology. When you understand the names of muscles it will help you remember where the muscles are located and what they do (Figure 11.5, Figure 11.6, and Table 11.2). Pronunciation of words and terms will take a bit of time to master, but after you have some basic information; the correct names and pronunciations will become easier.

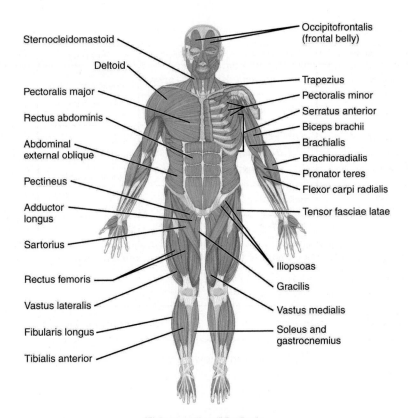

Sternocleidomastoid

Deltoid

Pectoralis major

Rectus abdominis

Abdominal
external oblique

Pectineus

Adductor
longus

Sartorius

Rectus femoris

Vastus lateralis

Fibularis longus

Tibialis anterior

Occipitofrontalis
(frontal belly)

Trapezius

Pectoralis minor

Serratus anterior

Biceps brachii

Brachialis

Brachioradialis

Pronator teres

Flexor carpi radialis

Tensor fasciae latae

Iliopsoas

Gracilis

Vastus medialis

Soleus and
gastrocnemius

Major muscles of the body.
Right side: superficial; left side: deep (anterior view)

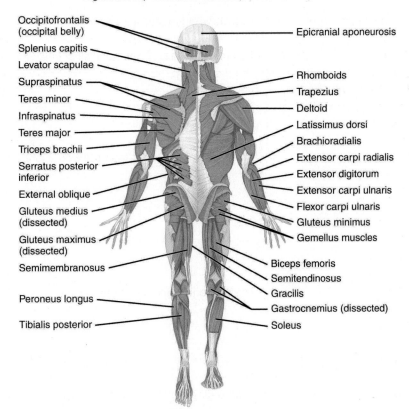

Occipitofrontalis
(occipital belly)

Splenius capitis

Levator scapulae

Supraspinatus

Teres minor

Infraspinatus

Teres major

Triceps brachii

Serratus posterior
inferior

External oblique

Gluteus medius
(dissected)

Gluteus maximus
(dissected)

Semimembranosus

Peroneus longus

Tibialis posterior

Epicranial aponeurosis

Rhomboids

Trapezius

Deltoid

Latissimus dorsi

Brachioradialis

Extensor carpi radialis

Extensor digitorum

Extensor carpi ulnaris

Flexor carpi ulnaris

Gluteus minimus

Gemellus muscles

Biceps femoris

Semitendinosus

Gracilis

Gastrocnemius (dissected)

Soleus

Major muscles of the body.
Right side: superficial; left side: deep (posterior view)

FIGURE 11.5 Overview of the Muscular System   On the anterior and posterior views of the muscular system above, superficial muscles (those at the surface) are shown on the right side of the body while deep muscles (those underneath the superficial muscles) are shown on the left half of the body. For the legs, superficial muscles are shown in the anterior view while the posterior view shows both superficial and deep muscles.

Example	Word	Latin Root 1	Latin Root 2	Meaning	Translation
abductor digiti minimi	abductor	ab = away from	duct = to move	a muscle that moves away from	A muscle that moves the little finger or toe away
	digiti	digitus = digit		refers to a finger or toe	
	minimi	minimus = mini, tiny		little	
adductor digiti minimi	adductor	ad = to, toward	duct = to move	a muscle that moves towards	A muscle that moves the little finger or toe toward
	digiti	digitus = digit		refers to a finger or toe	
	minimi	minimus = mini, tiny		little	

FIGURE 11.6   Understanding a Muscle Name from the Latin

Mnemonic Device for Latin Roots

Example	Latin or Greek Translation	Mnemonic Device
ad	to; toward	ADvance toward your goal
ab	away from	n/a
sub	under	SUBmarines move under water.
ductor	something that moves	A conDUCTOR makes a train move.
anti	against	If you are antisocial, you are against engaging in social activities.
epi	on top of	n/a
apo	to the side of	n/a
longissimus	longest	"Longissimus" is longer than the word "long."
longus	long	long
brevis	short	brief
maximus	large	max
medius	medium	"Medius" and "medium" both begin with "med."
minimus	tiny; little	mini
rectus	straight	To RECTify a situation is to straighten it out.
multi	many	If something is MULTIcolored, it has many colors.
uni	one	A UNIcorn has one horn.

TABLE 11.2

Access for free at openstax.org

Example	Latin or Greek Translation	Mnemonic Device
bi/di	two	If a ring is DIcast, it is made of two metals.
tri	three	TRIple the amount of money is three times as much.
quad	four	QUADruplets are four children born at one birth.
externus	outside	EXternal
internus	inside	INternal

TABLE 11.2

Anatomists name the skeletal muscles according to a number of criteria, each of which describes the muscle in some way. These include naming the muscle after its shape, its size compared to other muscles in the area, its location in the body or the location of its attachments to the skeleton, how many origins it has, or its action.

The skeletal muscle's anatomical location or its relationship to a particular bone often determines its name. For example, the frontalis muscle is located on top of the frontal bone of the skull. Similarly, the shapes of some muscles are very distinctive and the names, such as orbicularis, reflect the shape. For the buttocks, the size of the muscles influences the names: gluteus **maximus** (largest), gluteus **medius** (medium), and the gluteus **minimus** (smallest). Names were given to indicate length—**brevis** (short), **longus** (long)—and to identify position relative to the midline: **lateralis** (to the outside away from the midline), and **medialis** (toward the midline). The direction of the muscle fibers and fascicles are used to describe muscles relative to the midline, such as the **rectus** (straight) abdominis, or the **oblique** (at an angle) muscles of the abdomen.

Some muscle names indicate the number of muscles in a group. One example of this is the quadriceps, a group of four muscles located on the anterior (front) thigh. Other muscle names can provide information as to how many origins a particular muscle has, such as the biceps brachii. The prefix **bi** indicates that the muscle has two origins and **tri** indicates three origins.

The location of a muscle's attachment can also appear in its name. When the name of a muscle is based on the attachments, the origin is always named first. For instance, the sternocleidomastoid muscle of the neck has a dual origin on the sternum (sterno) and clavicle (cleido), and it inserts on the mastoid process of the temporal bone. The last feature by which to name a muscle is its action. When muscles are named for the movement they produce, one can find action words in their name. Some examples are **flexor** (decreases the angle at the joint), **extensor** (increases the angle at the joint), **abductor** (moves the bone away from the midline), or **adductor** (moves the bone toward the midline).

11.3 Axial Muscles of the Head, Neck, and Back

LEARNING OBJECTIVES

By the end of this section, you will be able to:
- Identify the axial muscles of the face, head, and neck
- Identify the movement and function of the face, head, and neck muscles

The skeletal muscles are divided into **axial** (muscles of the trunk and head) and **appendicular** (muscles of the arms and legs) categories. This system reflects the bones of the skeleton system, which are also arranged in this manner. The axial muscles are grouped based on location, function, or both. Some of the axial muscles may seem to blur the boundaries because they cross over to the appendicular skeleton. The first grouping of the axial muscles you will review includes the muscles of the head and neck, then you will review the muscles of the vertebral column, and finally you will review the oblique and rectus muscles.

Muscles That Create Facial Expression

The origins of the muscles of facial expression are on the surface of the skull (remember, the origin of a muscle does not move). The insertions of these muscles have fibers intertwined with connective tissue and the dermis of the skin. Because the muscles insert in the skin rather than on bone, when they contract, the skin moves to create facial expression (Figure 11.7).

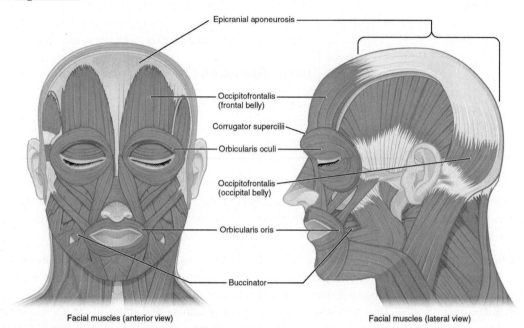

Epicranial aponeurosis

Occipitofrontalis (frontal belly)

Corrugator supercilii

Orbicularis oculi

Occipitofrontalis (occipital belly)

Orbicularis oris

Buccinator

Facial muscles (anterior view)   Facial muscles (lateral view)

FIGURE 11.7   Muscles of Facial Expression   Many of the muscles of facial expression insert into the skin surrounding the eyelids, nose and mouth, producing facial expressions by moving the skin rather than bones.

The **orbicularis oris** is a circular muscle that moves the lips, and the **orbicularis oculi** is a circular muscle that closes the eye. The **occipitofrontalis** muscle moves up the scalp and eyebrows. The muscle has a frontal belly and an occipital (near the occipital bone on the posterior part of the skull) belly. In other words, there is a muscle on the forehead (**frontalis**) and one on the back of the head (**occipitalis**), but there is no muscle across the top of the head. Instead, the two bellies are connected by a broad tendon called the **epicranial aponeurosis**, or galea aponeurosis (galea = "helmet"). The physicians originally studying human anatomy thought the skull looked like a helmet.

A large portion of the face is composed of the **buccinator** muscle, which compresses the cheek. This muscle allows you to whistle, blow, and suck; and it contributes to the action of chewing. There are several small facial muscles, one of which is the **corrugator supercilii**, which is the prime mover of the eyebrows. Place your finger on your eyebrows at the point of the bridge of the nose. Raise your eyebrows as if you were surprised and lower your eyebrows as if you were frowning. With these movements, you can feel the action of the corrugator supercilii. Additional muscles of facial expression are presented in Figure 11.8.

Movement	Target	Target motion direction	Prime mover	Origin	Insertion
Brow					
Raising eyebrows (e.g., showing surprise)	Skin of scalp	Anterior	Occipito-frontalis, frontal belly	Epicraneal aponeurosis	Underneath skin of forehead
Tensing and retracting scalp	Skin of scalp	Posterior	Occipito-frontalis, occipital belly	Occipital bone; mastoid process (temporal bone)	Epicraneal aponeurosis
Lowering eyebrows (e.g., scowling, frowning)	Skin underneath eyebrows	Inferior	Corrugator supercilii	Frontal bone	Skin underneath eyebrow
Nose					
Flaring nostrils	Nasal cartilage (pushes nostrils open when cartilage is compressed)	Inferior compression; posterior compression	Nasalis	Maxilla	Nasal bone
Mouth					
Raising upper lip	Upper lip	Elevation	Levator labii superioris	Maxilla	Underneath skin at corners of the mouth; orbicularis oris
Lowering lower lip	Lower lip	Depression	Depressor labii inferioris	Mandible	Underneath skin of lower lip
Opening mouth and sliding lower jaw left and right	Lower jaw	Depression, lateral	Depressor angulus oris	Mandible	Underneath skin at corners of mouth
Smiling	Corners of mouth	Lateral elevation	Zygomaticus major	Zygomatic bone	Underneath skin at corners of mouth (dimple area); orbicularis oris
Shaping of lips (as during speech)	Lips	Multiple	Orbicularis oris	Tissue surrounding lips	Underneath skin at corners of the mouth
Lateral movement of cheeks (e.g., sucking on a straw; also used to compress air in mouth while blowing)	Cheeks	Lateral	Buccinator	Maxilla, mandible; sphenoid bone (via pterygomandibular raphae)	Orbicularis oris
Pursing of lips by straightening them laterally	Corners of mouth	Lateral	Risorius	Fascia of parotid salivary gland	Underneath skin at corners of the mouth
Protrusion of lower lip (e.g., pouting expression)	Lower lip and skin of chin	Protraction	Mentalis	Mandible	Underneath skin of chin

FIGURE 11.8   **Muscles in Facial Expression**

Muscles That Move the Eyes

The movement of the eyeball is under the control of the **extrinsic eye muscles**, which originate outside the eye and insert onto the outer surface of the white of the eye. These muscles are located inside the eye socket and cannot be seen on any part of the visible eyeball (Figure 11.9 and Table 11.3). If you have ever been to a doctor who held up a finger and asked you to follow it up, down, and to both sides, the doctor is checking to make sure your eye muscles are acting in a coordinated pattern.

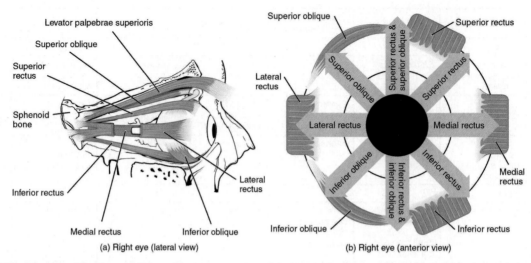

(a) Right eye (lateral view)

(b) Right eye (anterior view)

FIGURE 11.9   Muscles of the Eyes   (a) The extrinsic eye muscles originate outside of the eye on the skull. (b) Each muscle inserts onto the eyeball.

Muscles of the Eyes

Movement	Target	Target motion direction	Prime mover	Origin	Insertion
Moves eyes up and toward nose; rotates eyes from 1 o'clock to 3 o'clock	Eyeballs	Superior (elevates); medial (adducts)	Superior rectus	Common tendinous ring (ring attaches to optic foramen)	Superior surface of eyeball
Moves eyes down and toward nose; rotates eyes from 6 o'clock to 3 o'clock	Eyeballs	Inferior (depresses); medial (adducts)	Inferior rectus	Common tendinous ring (ring attaches to optic foramen)	Inferior surface of eyeball
Moves eyes away from nose	Eyeballs	Lateral (abducts)	Lateral rectus	Common tendinous ring (ring attaches to optic foramen)	Lateral surface of eyeball
Moves eyes toward nose	Eyeballs	Medial (adducts)	Medial rectus	Common tendinous ring (ring attaches to optic foramen)	Medial surface of eyeball
Moves eyes up and away from nose; rotates eyeball from 12 o'clock to 9 o'clock	Eyeballs	Superior (elevates); lateral (abducts)	Inferior oblique	Floor of orbit (maxilla)	Surface of eyeball between inferior rectus and lateral rectus

TABLE 11.3

Movement	Target	Target motion direction	Prime mover	Origin	Insertion
Moves eyes down and away from nose; rotates eyeball from 6 o'clock to 9 o'clock	Eyeballs	Inferior (depress); lateral (abducts)	Superior oblique	Sphenoid bone	Surface of eyeball between superior rectus and lateral rectus
Opens eyes	Upper eyelid	Superior (elevates)	Levator palpabrae superioris	Roof of orbit (sphenoid bone)	Skin of upper eyelids
Closes eyelids	Eyelid skin	Compression along superior–inferior axis	Orbicularis oculi	Medial bones composing the orbit	Circumference of orbit

TABLE 11.3

Muscles That Move the Lower Jaw

In anatomical terminology, chewing is called **mastication**. Muscles involved in chewing must be able to exert enough pressure to bite through and then chew food before it is swallowed (Figure 11.10 and Table 11.4). The **masseter** muscle is the main muscle used for chewing because it elevates the mandible (lower jaw) to close the mouth, and it is assisted by the **temporalis** muscle, which retracts the mandible. You can feel the temporalis move by putting your fingers to your temple as you chew.

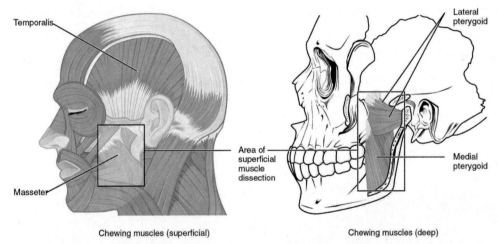

Chewing muscles (superficial)   Chewing muscles (deep)

FIGURE 11.10   Muscles That Move the Lower Jaw   The muscles that move the lower jaw are typically located within the cheek and originate from processes in the skull. This provides the jaw muscles with the large amount of leverage needed for chewing.

Muscles of the Lower Jaw

Movement	Target	Target motion direction	Prime mover	Origin	Insertion
Closes mouth; aids chewing	Mandible	Superior (elevates)	Masseter	Maxilla arch; zygomatic arch (for masseter)	Mandible
Closes mouth; pulls lower jaw in under upper jaw	Mandible	Superior (elevates); posterior (retracts)	Temporalis	Temporal bone	Mandible
Opens mouth; pushes lower jaw out under upper jaw; moves lower jaw side-to-side	Mandible	Inferior (depresses); posterior (protracts); lateral (abducts); medial (adducts)	Lateral pterygoid	Pterygoid process of sphenoid bone	Mandible
Closes mouth; pushes lower jaw out under upper jaw; moves lower jaw side-to-side	Mandible	Superior (elevates); posterior (protracts); lateral (abducts); medial (adducts)	Medial pterygoid	Sphenoid bone; maxilla	Mandible; temporo-mandibular joint

TABLE 11.4

Although the masseter and temporalis are responsible for elevating and closing the jaw to break food into digestible pieces, the **medial pterygoid** and **lateral pterygoid** muscles provide assistance in chewing and moving food within the mouth.

Muscles That Move the Tongue

Although the tongue is obviously important for tasting food, it is also necessary for mastication, **deglutition** (swallowing), and speech (Figure 11.11 and Figure 11.12). Because it is so moveable, the tongue facilitates complex speech patterns and sounds.

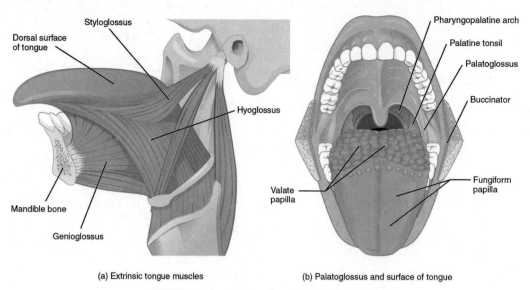

(a) Extrinsic tongue muscles   (b) Palatoglossus and surface of tongue

FIGURE 11.11   Muscles that Move the Tongue

Movement	Target	Target motion direction	Prime mover	Origin	Insertion
Tongue					
Moves tongue down; sticks tongue out of mouth	Tongue	Inferior (depresses); anterior (protracts)	Genioglossus	Mandible	Tongue undersurface; hyoid bone
Moves tongue up; retracts tongue back into mouth	Tongue	Superior (elevates); posterior (retracts)	Styloglossus	Temporal bone (styloid process)	Tongue undersurface and sides
Flattens tongue	Tongue	Inferior (depresses)	Hyoglossus	Hyoid bone	Sides of tongue
Bulges tongue	Tongue	Superior (elevation)	Palatoglossus	Soft palate	Side of tongue
Swallowing and speaking					
Raises the hyoid bone in a way that also raises the larynx, allowing the epiglottis to cover the glottis during deglutition; also assists in opening the mouth by depressing the mandible	Hyoid bone; larynx	Superior (elevates)	Digastric	Mandible; temporal bone	Hyoid bone
Raises and retracts the hyoid bone in a way that elongates the oral cavity during deglutition	Hyoid bone	Superior (elevates); posterior (retracts)	Stylohyoid	Temporal bone (styloid process)	Hyoid bone
Raises hyoid bone in a way that presses tongue against the roof of the mouth, pushing food back into the pharynx during deglutition	Hyoid bone	Superior (elevates)	Mylohyoid	Mandible	Hyoid bone; median raphe
Raises and moves hyoid bone forward, widening pharynx during deglutition	Hyoid bone	Superior (elevates); anterior (protracts)	Geniohyoid	Mandible	Hyoid bone
Retracts hyoid bone and moves it down during later phases of deglutition	Hyoid bone	Inferior (depresses); posterior (retracts)	Omohyoid	Scapula	Hyoid bone
Depresses the hyoid bone during swallowing and speaking	Hyoid bone	Inferior (depresses)	Sternohyoid	Clavicle	Hyoid bone
Shrinks distance between thyroid cartilage and hyoid bone, allowing production of high-pitch vocalizations	Hyoid bone; thyroid cartilage	Hyoid bone: inferior (depresses); thyroid cartilage: superior (elevates)	Thyrohyoid	Thyroid cartilage	Hyoid bone
Depresses larynx, thyroid cartilage, and hyoid bone to create different vocal tones	Larynx; thyroid cartilage; hyoid bone	Inferior (depresses)	Sternothyroid	Sternum	Thyroid cartilage
Rotates and tilts head to he side; tilts head forward	Skull; cervical vertebrae	Individually: medial rotation; lateral flexion; bilaterally: anterior (flexes)	Sternocleid-omastoid; semispinalis capitis	Sternum; clavicle	Temporal bone (mastoid process); occipital bone
Rotates and tilts head to the side; tilts head backwards	Skull; cervical vertebrae	Individually: lateral rotation; lateral flexion; bilaterally: anterior (flexes)	Splenius capitis; longissimus capitis		

FIGURE 11.12   **Muscles for Tongue Movement, Swallowing, and Speech**

Tongue muscles can be extrinsic or intrinsic. Extrinsic tongue muscles insert into the tongue from outside origins, and the intrinsic tongue muscles insert into the tongue from origins within it. The extrinsic muscles move the whole tongue in different directions, whereas the intrinsic muscles allow the tongue to change its shape (such as, curling the tongue in a loop or flattening it).

The extrinsic muscles all include the word root glossus (glossus = "tongue"), and the muscle names are derived from where the muscle originates. The **genioglossus** (genio = "chin") originates on the mandible and allows the tongue to move downward and forward. The **styloglossus** originates on the styloid bone, and allows upward and backward motion. The **palatoglossus** originates on the soft palate to elevate the back of the tongue, and the **hyoglossus** originates on the hyoid bone to move the tongue downward and flatten it.

Everyday Connection

Anesthesia and the Tongue Muscles

Before surgery, a patient must be made ready for general anesthesia. The normal homeostatic controls of the body are put "on hold" so that the patient can be prepped for surgery. Control of respiration must be switched from the patient's homeostatic control to the control of the anesthesiologist. The drugs used for anesthesia relax a majority of the body's muscles.

Among the muscles affected during general anesthesia are those that are necessary for breathing and moving the tongue. Under anesthesia, the tongue can relax and partially or fully block the airway, and the muscles of respiration may not move the diaphragm or chest wall. To avoid possible complications, the safest procedure to use on a patient is called endotracheal intubation. Placing a tube into the trachea allows the doctors to maintain a patient's (open) airway to the lungs and seal the airway off from the oropharynx. Post-surgery, the anesthesiologist gradually changes the mixture of the gases that keep the patient unconscious, and when the muscles of respiration begin to function, the tube is removed. It still takes about 30 minutes for a patient to wake up, and for breathing muscles to regain control of respiration. After surgery, most people have a sore or scratchy throat for a few days.

Muscles of the Anterior Neck

The muscles of the anterior neck assist in deglutition (swallowing) and speech by controlling the positions of the larynx (voice box), and the hyoid bone, a horseshoe-shaped bone that functions as a solid foundation on which the tongue can move. The muscles of the neck are categorized according to their position relative to the hyoid bone (Figure 11.13). **Suprahyoid muscles** are superior to it, and the **infrahyoid muscles** are located inferiorly.

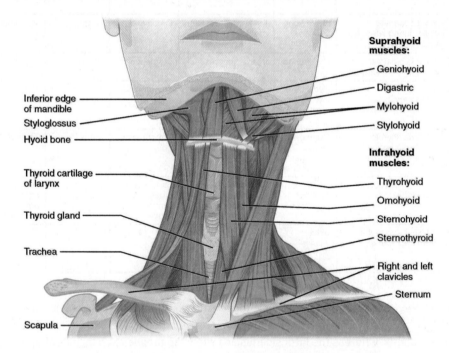

FIGURE 11.13   Muscles of the Anterior Neck   The anterior muscles of the neck facilitate swallowing and speech. The suprahyoid muscles originate from above the hyoid bone in the chin region. The infrahyoid muscles originate below the hyoid bone in the lower neck.

The suprahyoid muscles raise the hyoid bone, the floor of the mouth, and the larynx during deglutition. These include the **digastric** muscle, which has anterior and posterior bellies that work to elevate the hyoid bone and larynx when one swallows; it also depresses the mandible. The **stylohyoid** muscle moves the hyoid bone posteriorly, elevating the larynx, and the **mylohyoid** muscle lifts it and helps press the tongue to the top of the mouth. The **geniohyoid** depresses the mandible in addition to raising and pulling the hyoid bone anteriorly.

The strap-like infrahyoid muscles generally depress the hyoid bone and control the position of the larynx. The **omohyoid** muscle, which has superior and inferior bellies, depresses the hyoid bone in conjunction with the **sternohyoid** and **thyrohyoid** muscles. The thyrohyoid muscle also elevates the larynx's thyroid cartilage, whereas the **sternothyroid** depresses it to create different tones of voice.

Muscles That Move the Head

The head, attached to the top of the vertebral column, is balanced, moved, and rotated by the neck muscles (Table 11.5). When these muscles act unilaterally, the head rotates. When they contract bilaterally, the head flexes or extends. The major muscle that laterally flexes and rotates the head is the **sternocleidomastoid**. In addition, both muscles working together are the flexors of the head. Place your fingers on both sides of the neck and turn your head to the left and to the right. You will feel the movement originate there. This muscle divides the neck into anterior and posterior triangles when viewed from the side (Figure 11.14).

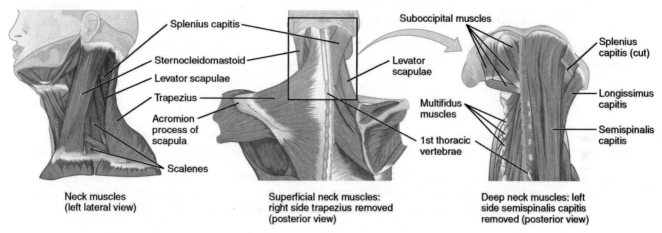

FIGURE 11.14   Posterior and Lateral Views of the Neck   The superficial and deep muscles of the neck are responsible for moving the head, cervical vertebrae, and scapulas.

Muscles That Move the Head

Movement	Target	Target motion direction	Prime mover	Origin	Insertion
Rotates and tilts head to the side; tilts head forward	Skull; vertebrae	Individually: rotates head to opposite side; bilaterally: flexion	Sternocleidomastoid	Sternum; clavicle	Temporal bone (mastoid process); occipital bone
Rotates and tilts head backward	Skull; vertebrae	Individually: laterally flexes and rotates head to same side; bilaterally: extension	Semispinalis capitis	Transverse and articular processes of cervical and thoracic vertebra	Occipital bone

TABLE 11.5

Movement	Target	Target motion direction	Prime mover	Origin	Insertion
Rotates and tilts head to the side; tilts head backward	Skull; vertebrae	Individually: laterally flexes and rotates head to same side; bilaterally: extension	Splenius capitis	Spinous processes of cervical and thoracic vertebra	Temporal bone (mastoid process); occipital bone
Rotates and tilts head to the side; tilts head backward	Skull; vertebrae	Individually: laterally flexes and rotates head to same side; bilaterally: extension	Longissimus capitis	Transverse and articular processes of cervical and thoracic vertebra	Temporal bone (mastoid process)

TABLE 11.5

Muscles of the Posterior Neck and the Back

The posterior muscles of the neck are primarily concerned with head movements, like extension. The back muscles stabilize and move the vertebral column, and are grouped according to the lengths and direction of the fascicles.

The **splenius** muscles originate at the midline and run laterally and superiorly to their insertions. From the sides and the back of the neck, the **splenius capitis** inserts onto the head region, and the **splenius cervicis** extends onto the cervical region. These muscles can extend the head, laterally flex it, and rotate it (Figure 11.15).

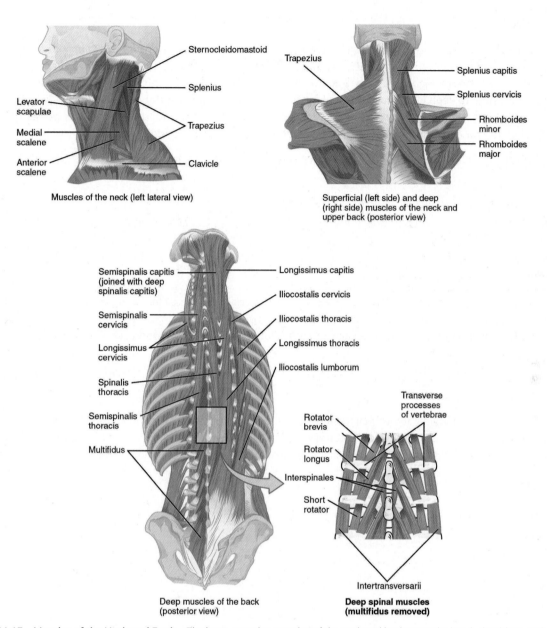

Muscles of the neck (left lateral view)

Superficial (left side) and deep (right side) muscles of the neck and upper back (posterior view)

Deep muscles of the back (posterior view)

Deep spinal muscles (multifidus removed)

FIGURE 11.15   Muscles of the Neck and Back   The large, complex muscles of the neck and back move the head, shoulders, and vertebral column.

The **erector spinae group** forms the majority of the muscle mass of the back and it is the primary extensor of the vertebral column. It controls flexion, lateral flexion, and rotation of the vertebral column, and maintains the lumbar curve. The erector spinae comprises the iliocostalis (laterally placed) group, the longissimus (intermediately placed) group, and the spinalis (medially placed) group.

The **iliocostalis group** includes the **iliocostalis cervicis**, associated with the cervical region; the **iliocostalis thoracis**, associated with the thoracic region; and the **iliocostalis lumborum**, associated with the lumbar region. The three muscles of the **longissimus group** are the **longissimus capitis**, associated with the head region; the **longissimus cervicis**, associated with the cervical region; and the **longissimus thoracis**, associated with the thoracic region. The third group, the **spinalis group**, comprises the **spinalis capitis** (head region), the **spinalis cervicis** (cervical region), and the **spinalis thoracis** (thoracic region).

The **transversospinales** muscles run from the transverse processes to the spinous processes of the vertebrae. Similar to the erector spinae muscles, the semispinalis muscles in this group are named for the areas of the body with which they are associated. The semispinalis muscles include the **semispinalis capitis**, the **semispinalis cervicis**, and the **semispinalis thoracis**. The **multifidus** muscle of the lumbar region helps extend and laterally flex the vertebral column.

Important in the stabilization of the vertebral column is the **segmental muscle group**, which includes the interspinales and intertransversarii muscles. These muscles bring together the spinous and transverse processes of each consecutive vertebra. Finally, the **scalene muscles** work together to flex, laterally flex, and rotate the head. They also contribute to deep inhalation. The scalene muscles include the **anterior scalene** muscle (anterior to the middle scalene), the **middle scalene** muscle (the longest, intermediate between the anterior and posterior scalenes), and the **posterior scalene** muscle (the smallest, posterior to the middle scalene).

11.4 Axial Muscles of the Abdominal Wall, and Thorax

LEARNING OBJECTIVES

By the end of this section, you will be able to:

- Identify the intrinsic skeletal muscles of the back and neck, and the skeletal muscles of the abdominal wall and thorax
- Identify the movement and function of the intrinsic skeletal muscles of the back and neck, and the skeletal muscles of the abdominal wall and thorax

It is a complex job to balance the body on two feet and walk upright. The muscles of the vertebral column, thorax, and abdominal wall extend, flex, and stabilize different parts of the body's trunk. The deep muscles of the core of the body help maintain posture as well as carry out other functions. The brain sends out electrical impulses to these various muscle groups to control posture by alternate contraction and relaxation. This is necessary so that no single muscle group becomes fatigued too quickly. If any one group fails to function, body posture will be compromised.

Muscles of the Abdomen

There are four pairs of abdominal muscles that cover the anterior and lateral abdominal region and meet at the anterior midline. These muscles of the anterolateral abdominal wall can be divided into four groups: the external obliques, the internal obliques, the transversus abdominis, and the rectus abdominis (Figure 11.16 and Table 11.6).

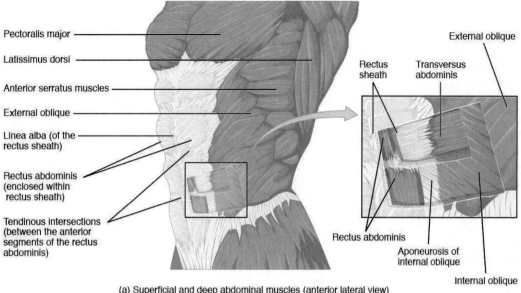

Pectoralis major

Latissimus dorsi

Anterior serratus muscles

External oblique

Linea alba (of the rectus sheath)

Rectus abdominis (enclosed within rectus sheath)

Tendinous intersections (between the anterior segments of the rectus abdominis)

External oblique

Rectus sheath

Transversus abdominis

Rectus abdominis

Aponeurosis of internal oblique

Internal oblique

(a) Superficial and deep abdominal muscles (anterior lateral view)

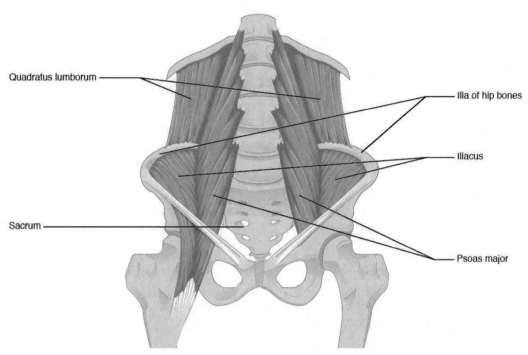

Quadratus lumborum

Sacrum

Ilia of hip bones

Iliacus

Psoas major

(b) Posterior abdominal muscles (anterior view)

FIGURE 11.16   Muscles of the Abdomen   (a) The anterior abdominal muscles include the medially located rectus abdominis, which is covered by a sheet of connective tissue called the rectus sheath. On the flanks of the body, medial to the rectus abdominis, the abdominal wall is composed of three layers. The external oblique muscles form the superficial layer, while the internal oblique muscles form the middle layer, and the transversus abdominis forms the deepest layer. (b) The muscles of the lower back move the lumbar spine but also assist in femur movements.

Muscles of the Abdomen

Movement	Target	Target motion direction	Prime mover	Origin	Insertion
Twisting at waist; also bending to the side	Vertebral column	Supination; lateral flexion	External obliques; internal obliques	Ribs 5–12; ilium	Ribs 7–10; linea alba; ilium
Squeezing abdomen during forceful exhalations, defecation, urination, and childbirth	Abdominal cavity	Compression	Transversus abdominis	Ilium; ribs 5–10	Sternum; linea alba; pubis
Sitting up	Vertebral column	Flexion	Rectus abdominis	Pubis	Sternum; ribs 5 and 7
Bending to the side	Vertebral column	Lateral flexion	Quadratus lumborum	Ilium; ribs 5–10	Rib 12; vertebrae L1–L4

TABLE 11.6

There are three flat skeletal muscles in the antero-lateral wall of the abdomen. The **external oblique**, closest to the surface, extend inferiorly and medially, in the direction of sliding one's four fingers into pants pockets. Perpendicular to it is the intermediate **internal oblique**, extending superiorly and medially, the direction the thumbs usually go when the other fingers are in the pants pocket. The deep muscle, the **transversus abdominis**, is arranged transversely around the abdomen, similar to the front of a belt on a pair of pants. This arrangement of three bands of muscles in different orientations allows various movements and rotations of the trunk. The three layers of muscle also help to protect the internal abdominal organs in an area where there is no bone.

The **linea alba** is a white, fibrous band that is made of the bilateral **rectus sheaths** that join at the anterior midline of the body. These enclose the **rectus abdominis** muscles (a pair of long, linear muscles, commonly called the "sit-up" muscles) that originate at the pubic crest and symphysis, and extend the length of the body's trunk. Each muscle is segmented by three transverse bands of collagen fibers called the **tendinous intersections**. This results in the look of "six-pack abs," as each segment hypertrophies on individuals at the gym who do many sit-ups.

The posterior abdominal wall is formed by the lumbar vertebrae, parts of the ilia of the hip bones, psoas major and iliacus muscles, and **quadratus lumborum** muscle. This part of the core plays a key role in stabilizing the rest of the body and maintaining posture.

 CAREER CONNECTION

Physical Therapists
Those who have a muscle or joint injury will most likely be sent to a physical therapist (PT) after seeing their regular doctor. PTs have a master's degree or doctorate, and are highly trained experts in the mechanics of body movements. Many PTs also specialize in sports injuries.

If you injured your shoulder while you were kayaking, the first thing a physical therapist would do during your first visit is to assess the functionality of the joint. The range of motion of a particular joint refers to the normal movements the joint performs. The PT will ask you to abduct and adduct, circumduct, and flex and extend the arm. The PT will note the shoulder's degree of function, and based on the assessment of the injury, will create an appropriate physical therapy plan.

The first step in physical therapy will probably be applying a heat pack to the injured site, which acts much like a warm-up to draw blood to the area, to enhance healing. You will be instructed to do a series of exercises to continue the therapy at home, followed by icing, to decrease inflammation and swelling, which will continue for several weeks. When physical therapy is complete, the PT will do an exit exam and send a detailed report on the improved range of motion and return of normal limb function to your doctor. Gradually, as the injury heals, the shoulder will begin to function correctly. A PT works closely with patients to help them get back to their normal level of physical activity.

Muscles of the Thorax

The muscles of the chest serve to facilitate breathing by changing the size of the thoracic cavity (Table 11.7). When you inhale, your chest rises because the cavity expands. Alternately, when you exhale, your chest falls because the thoracic cavity decreases in size.

Muscles of the Thorax

Movement	Target	Target motion direction	Prime mover	Origin	Insertion
Inhalation; exhalation	Thoracic cavity	Compression; expansion	Diaphragm	Sternum; ribs 6–12; lumbar vertebrae	Central tendon
Inhalation;exhalation	Ribs	Elevation (expands thoracic cavity)	External intercostals	Rib superior to each intercostal muscle	Rib inferior to each intercostal muscle
Forced exhalation	Ribs	Movement along superior/inferior axis to bring ribs closer together	Internal intercostals	Rib inferior to each intercostal muscle	Rib superior to each intercostal muscle

TABLE 11.7

The Diaphragm

The change in volume of the thoracic cavity during breathing is due to the alternate contraction and relaxation of the **diaphragm** (Figure 11.17). It separates the thoracic and abdominal cavities, and is dome-shaped at rest. The superior surface of the diaphragm is convex, creating the elevated floor of the thoracic cavity. The inferior surface is concave, creating the curved roof of the abdominal cavity.

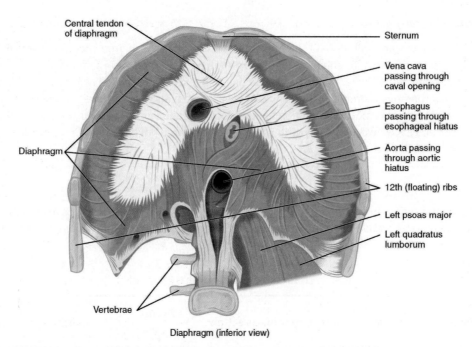

Central tendon of diaphragm

Sternum

Vena cava passing through caval opening

Esophagus passing through esophageal hiatus

Diaphragm

Aorta passing through aortic hiatus

12th (floating) ribs

Left psoas major

Left quadratus lumborum

Vertebrae

Diaphragm (inferior view)

FIGURE 11.17   Muscles of the Diaphragm   The diaphragm separates the thoracic and abdominal cavities.

Defecating, urination, and even childbirth involve cooperation between the diaphragm and abdominal muscles (this cooperation is referred to as the "Valsalva maneuver"). You hold your breath by a steady contraction of the diaphragm; this stabilizes the volume and pressure of the peritoneal cavity. When the abdominal muscles contract, the pressure cannot push the diaphragm up, so it increases pressure on the intestinal tract (defecation), urinary tract (urination), or reproductive tract (childbirth).

The inferior surface of the pericardial sac and the inferior surfaces of the pleural membranes (parietal pleura) fuse onto the central tendon of the diaphragm. To the sides of the tendon are the skeletal muscle portions of the diaphragm, which insert into the tendon while having a number of origins including the xiphoid process of the sternum anteriorly, the inferior six ribs and their cartilages laterally, and the lumbar vertebrae and 12th ribs posteriorly.

The diaphragm also includes three openings for the passage of structures between the thorax and the abdomen. The inferior vena cava passes through the **caval opening**, and the esophagus and attached nerves pass through the esophageal hiatus. The aorta, thoracic duct, and azygous vein pass through the aortic hiatus of the posterior diaphragm.

The Intercostal Muscles

There are three sets of muscles, called **intercostal muscles**, which span each of the intercostal spaces. The principal role of the intercostal muscles is to assist in breathing by changing the dimensions of the rib cage (Figure 11.18).

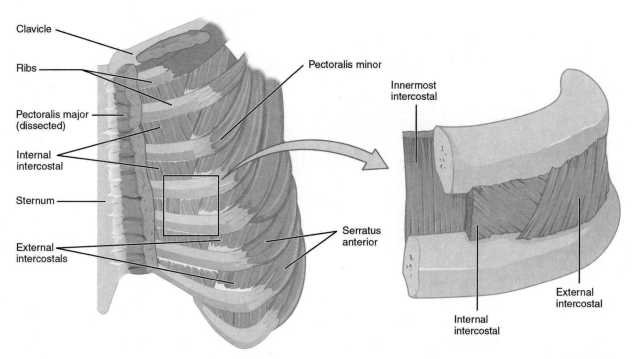

FIGURE 11.18 Intercostal Muscles The external intercostals are located laterally on the sides of the body. The internal intercostals are located medially near the sternum. The innermost intercostals are located deep to both the internal and external intercostals.

The 11 pairs of superficial **external intercostal** muscles aid in inspiration of air during breathing because when they contract, they raise the rib cage, which expands it. The 11 pairs of **internal intercostal** muscles, just under the externals, are used for expiration because they draw the ribs together to constrict the rib cage. The **innermost intercostal** muscles are the deepest, and they act as synergists for the action of the internal intercostals.

Muscles of the Pelvic Floor and Perineum

The pelvic floor is a muscular sheet that defines the inferior portion of the pelvic cavity. The **pelvic diaphragm**, spanning anteriorly to posteriorly from the pubis to the coccyx, comprises the levator ani and the ischiococcygeus. Its openings include the anal canal and urethra, and the vagina in females.

The large **levator ani** consists of two skeletal muscles, the **pubococcygeus** and the **iliococcygeus** (Figure 11.19). The levator ani is considered the most important muscle of the pelvic floor because it supports the pelvic viscera. It resists the pressure produced by contraction of the abdominal muscles so that the pressure is applied to the colon to aid in defecation and to the uterus to aid in childbirth (assisted by the **ischiococcygeus**, which pulls the coccyx anteriorly). This muscle also creates skeletal muscle sphincters at the urethra and anus.

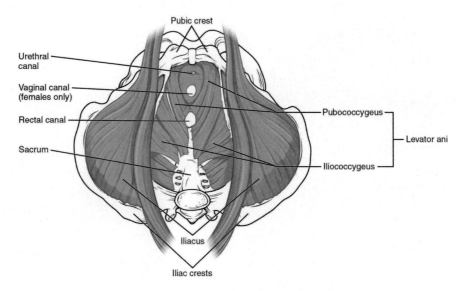

Pelvic diaphragm (superior view)

FIGURE 11.19   Muscles of the Pelvic Floor   The pelvic floor muscles support the pelvic organs, resist intra-abdominal pressure, and work as sphincters for the urethra, rectum, and vagina.

The **perineum** is the diamond-shaped space between the pubic symphysis (anteriorly), the coccyx (posteriorly), and the ischial tuberosities (laterally), lying just inferior to the pelvic diaphragm (levator ani and coccygeus). Divided transversely into triangles, the anterior is the **urogenital triangle**, which includes the external genitals. The posterior is the **anal triangle**, which contains the anus (Figure 11.20). The perineum is also divided into superficial and deep layers with some of the muscles common to people of any sex (Figure 11.21). Females also have the **compressor urethrae** and the **sphincter urethrovaginalis**, which function to close the vagina. In males, there is the **deep transverse perineal** muscle that plays a role in ejaculation.

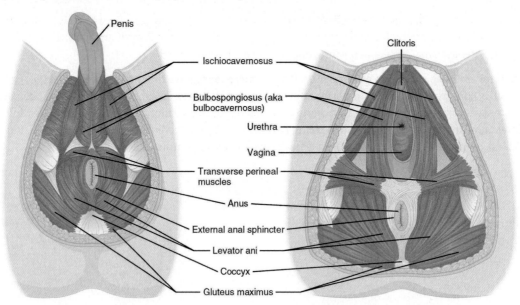

Male perineal muscles: inferior view   Female perineal muscles: inferior view

FIGURE 11.20   Muscles of the Perineum   The perineum muscles play roles in urination in both sexes, ejaculation in males, and vaginal contraction in females.

Access for free at openstax.org

Movement	Target	Target motion direction	Prime mover	Origin	Insertion
Defecation; urination; birth; coughing	Abdominal cavity	Superior (resists pressure during abdominal compression)	Levator ani pubococcygeus; levator ani iliococcygeus	Pubis; ischium	Urethra; anal canal; perineal body; coccyx
Superficial muscles					
None—supports perineal body maintaining anus at center of perineum	Perineal body	None	Superficial transverse perineal	Ischium	Perineal body
Involuntary response that compresses urethra when excreting urine in both sexes or while ejaculating in males; also aids in erection of penis in males	Urethra	Compression	Bulbospongiosus	Perineal body	Perineal membrane; corpus spongiosum of penis; deep fascia of penis; clitoris in female
Compresses veins to maintain erection of penis in males; erection of clitoris in females	Veins of penis and clitoris	Compression	Ischiocavernosus	Ischium; ischial rami; pubic rami	Pubic symphysis; corpus cavernosum of penis in male; clitoris of female
Deep muscles					
Voluntarily compresses urethra during urination	Urethra	Compression	External urethral sphincter	Ischial rami; pubic rami	Male: median raphe; female: vaginal wall
Closes anus	Anus	Sphincter	External anal sphincter	Anoccoccygeal ligament	Perineal body

FIGURE 11.21   Muscles of the Perineum Common to All Humans

11.5 Muscles of the Pectoral Girdle and Upper Limbs

LEARNING OBJECTIVES

By the end of this section, you will be able to:
- Identify the muscles of the pectoral girdle and upper limbs
- Identify the movement and function of the pectoral girdle and upper limbs

Muscles of the shoulder and upper limb can be divided into four groups: muscles that stabilize and position the pectoral girdle, muscles that move the arm, muscles that move the forearm, and muscles that move the wrists, hands, and fingers. The **pectoral girdle**, or shoulder girdle, consists of the lateral ends of the clavicle and scapula, along with the proximal end of the humerus, and the muscles covering these three bones to stabilize the shoulder joint. The girdle creates a base from which the head of the humerus, in its ball-and-socket joint with the glenoid fossa of the scapula, can move the arm in multiple directions.

Muscles That Position the Pectoral Girdle

Muscles that position the pectoral girdle are located either on the anterior thorax or on the posterior thorax (Figure 11.22 and Table 11.8). The anterior muscles include the **subclavius**, **pectoralis minor**, and **serratus anterior**. The posterior muscles include the **trapezius**, **rhomboid major**, and **rhomboid minor**. When the rhomboids are contracted, your scapula moves medially, which can pull the shoulder and upper limb posteriorly.

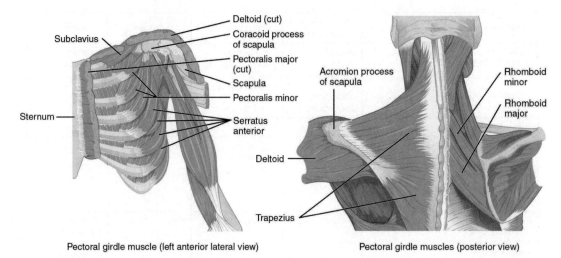

Pectoral girdle muscle (left anterior lateral view)   Pectoral girdle muscles (posterior view)

FIGURE 11.22   Muscles That Position the Pectoral Girdle   The muscles that stabilize the pectoral girdle make it a steady base on which other muscles can move the arm. Note that the pectoralis major and deltoid, which move the humerus, are cut here to show the deeper positioning muscles.

Muscles that Position the Pectoral Girdle

Position in the thorax	Movement	Target	Target motion direction	Prime mover	Origin	Insertion
Anterior thorax	Stabilizes clavicle during movement by depressing it	Clavicle	Depression	Subclavius	First rib	Inferior surface of clavicle
Anterior thorax	Rotates shoulder anteriorly (throwing motion); assists with inhalation	Scapula; ribs	Scapula: depresses; ribs: elevates	Pectoralis minor	Anterior surfaces of certain ribs (2–4 or 3–5)	Coracoid process of scapula
Anterior thorax	Moves arm from side of body to front of body; assists with inhalation	Scapula; ribs	Scapula: protracts; ribs: elevates	Serratus anterior	Muscle slips from certain ribs (1–8 or 1–9)	Anterior surface of vertebral border of scapula
Posterior thorax	Elevates shoulders (shrugging); pulls shoulder blades together; tilts head backwards	Scapula; cervical spine	Scapula: rotests inferiorly, retracts, elevates, and depresses; spine: extends	Trapezius	Skull; vertebral column	Acromion and spine of scapula; clavicle

TABLE 11.8

Position in the thorax	Movement	Target	Target motion direction	Prime mover	Origin	Insertion
Posterior thorax	Stabilizes scapula during pectoral girdle movement	Scapula	Retracts; rotates inferiorly	Rhomboid major	Thoracic vertebrae (T2–T5)	Medial border of scapula
Posterior thorax	Stabilizes scapula during pectoral girdle movement	Scapula	Retracts; rotates inferiorly	Rhomboid minor	Cervical and thoracic vertebrae (C7 and T1)	Medial border of scapula

TABLE 11.8

Muscles That Move the Humerus

Similar to the muscles that position the pectoral girdle, muscles that cross the shoulder joint and move the humerus bone of the arm include both axial and scapular muscles (Figure 11.23 and Figure 11.24). The two axial muscles are the pectoralis major and the latissimus dorsi. The **pectoralis major** is thick and fan-shaped, covering much of the superior portion of the anterior thorax. The broad, triangular **latissimus dorsi** is located on the inferior part of the back, where it inserts into a thick connective tissue sheath called an aponeurosis.

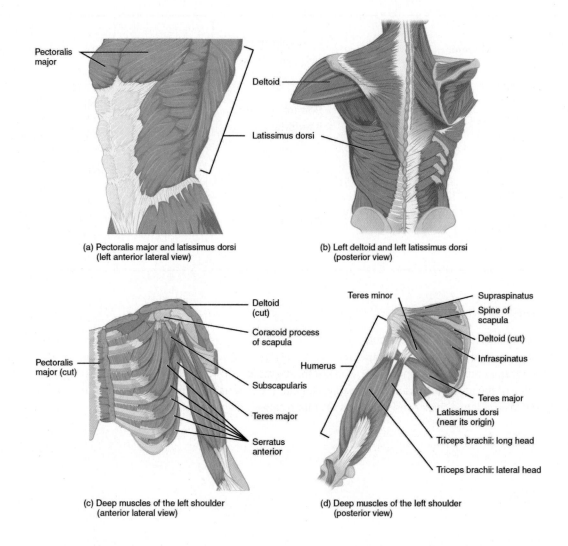

Pectoralis major

Deltoid

Latissimus dorsi

(a) Pectoralis major and latissimus dorsi
(left anterior lateral view)

(b) Left deltoid and left latissimus dorsi
(posterior view)

Deltoid (cut)

Coracoid process of scapula

Pectoralis major (cut)

Subscapularis

Teres major

Serratus anterior

(c) Deep muscles of the left shoulder
(anterior lateral view)

Teres minor

Humerus

Supraspinatus

Spine of scapula

Deltoid (cut)

Infraspinatus

Teres major

Latissimus dorsi (near its origin)

Triceps brachii: long head

Triceps brachii: lateral head

(d) Deep muscles of the left shoulder
(posterior view)

FIGURE 11.23   Muscles That Move the Humerus (a, c) The muscles that move the humerus anteriorly are generally located on the anterior side of the body and originate from the sternum (e.g., pectoralis major) or the anterior side of the scapula (e.g., subscapularis). (b) The muscles that move the humerus superiorly generally originate from the superior surfaces of the scapula and/or the clavicle (e.g., deltoids). The muscles that move the humerus inferiorly generally originate from middle or lower back (e.g., latissiumus dorsi). (d) The muscles that move the humerus posteriorly are generally located on the posterior side of the body and insert into the scapula (e.g., infraspinatus).

Movement	Target	Target motion direction	Prime mover	Origin	Insertion
Axial muscles					
Brings elbows together; moves elbow up (as during an uppercut punch)	Humerus	Flexion; adduction; medial rotation	Pectoralis major	Clavicle; sternum; cartilage of certain ribs (1–6 or 1–7); aponeurosis of external oblique muscle	Greater tubercle of humerus
Moves elbow back (as in elbowing someone standing behind you); spreads elbows apart	Humerus; scapula	Humerus: extension, adduction, and medial rotation; scapula: depression	Latissimus dorsi	Thoracic vertebrae (T7–T12); lumbar vertebrae; lower ribs (9–12); iliac crest	Intertubercular sulcus of humerus
Scapular muscles					
Lifts arms at shoulder	Humerus	Abduction; flexion; extension; medial and lateral rotation	Deltoid	Trapezius; clavicle; acromion; spine of scapula	Deltoid tuberosity of humerus
Assists pectoralis major in bringing elbows together and stabilizes shoulder joint during movement of the pectoral girdle	Humerus	Medial rotation	Subscapularis	Subscapular fossa of scapula	Lesser tubercle of humerus
Rotates elbow outwards, as during a tennis swing	Humerus	Abduction	Supraspinatus	Supraspinous fossa of scapula	Greater tubercle of humerus
Rotates elbow outwards, as during a tennis swing	Humerus	Extension; adduction	Infraspinatus	Infraspinous fossa of scapula	Greater tubercle of humerus
Assists with medial rotation at the shoulder	Humerus	Extension; adduction	Teres major	Posterior surface of scapula	Intertubercular sulcus of humerus
Assists infraspinatus in rotating elbow outwards	Humerus	Extension; adduction	Teres minor	Lateral border of dorsal scapular surface	Greater tubercle of humerus
Moves elbow up and across body, as when putting hand on chest	Humerus	Flexion; adduction	Coracobra chialis	Coracoid process of scapula	Medial surface of humerus shaft

FIGURE 11.24   Muscles That Move the Humerus

The rest of the shoulder muscles originate on the scapula. The anatomical and ligamental structure of the shoulder joint and the arrangements of the muscles covering it, allows the arm to carry out different types of movements. The **deltoid**, the thick muscle that creates the rounded lines of the shoulder is the major abductor of the arm, but it also facilitates flexing and medial rotation, as well as extension and lateral rotation. The **subscapularis** originates on the anterior scapula and medially rotates the arm. Named for their locations, the **supraspinatus** (superior to the spine of the scapula) and the **infraspinatus** (inferior to the spine of the scapula) abduct the arm, and laterally rotate the arm, respectively. The thick and flat **teres major** is inferior to the teres minor and extends the arm, and assists in adduction and medial rotation of it. The long **teres minor** laterally rotates and extends the arm. Finally, the **coracobrachialis** flexes and adducts the arm.

The tendons of the deep subscapularis, supraspinatus, infraspinatus, and teres minor connect the scapula to the humerus, forming the **rotator cuff** (musculotendinous cuff), the circle of tendons around the shoulder joint. When baseball pitchers undergo shoulder surgery it is usually on the rotator cuff, which becomes pinched and inflamed, and may tear away from the bone due to the repetitive motion of bring the arm overhead to throw a fast pitch.

Muscles That Move the Forearm

The forearm, made of the radius and ulna bones, has four main types of action at the hinge of the elbow joint:

flexion, extension, pronation, and supination. The forearm flexors include the biceps brachii, brachialis, and brachioradialis. The extensors are the **triceps brachii** and **anconeus**. The pronators are the **pronator teres** and the **pronator quadratus**, and the **supinator** is the only one that turns the forearm anteriorly. When the forearm faces anteriorly, it is supinated. When the forearm faces posteriorly, it is pronated.

The biceps brachii, brachialis, and brachioradialis flex the forearm. The two-headed **biceps brachii** crosses the shoulder and elbow joints to flex the forearm, also taking part in supinating the forearm at the radioulnar joints and flexing the arm at the shoulder joint. Deep to the biceps brachii, the **brachialis** provides additional power in flexing the forearm. Finally, the **brachioradialis** can flex the forearm quickly or help lift a load slowly. These muscles and their associated blood vessels and nerves form the **anterior compartment of the arm** (anterior flexor compartment of the arm) (Figure 11.25 and Figure 11.26).

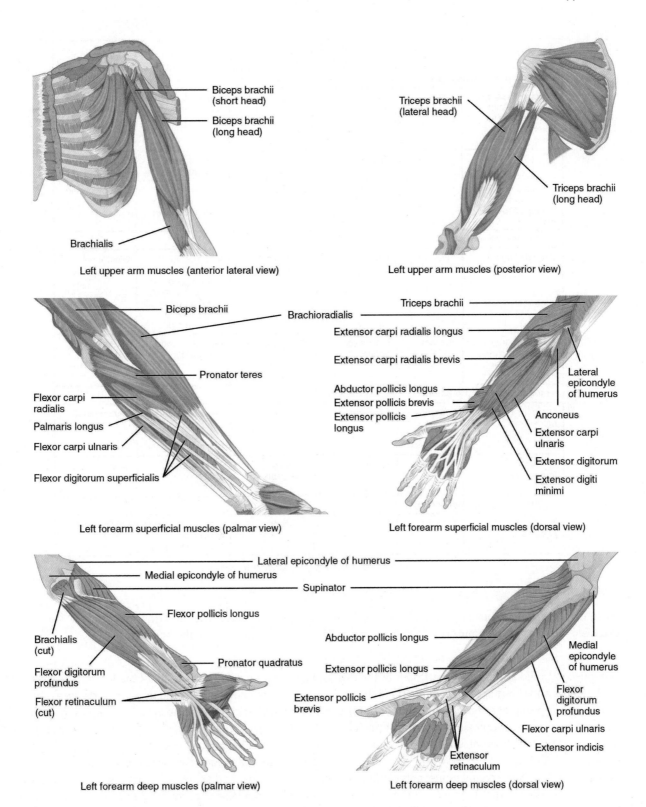

Biceps brachii (short head)

Biceps brachii (long head)

Brachialis

Left upper arm muscles (anterior lateral view)

Triceps brachii (lateral head)

Triceps brachii (long head)

Left upper arm muscles (posterior view)

Biceps brachii

Pronator teres

Flexor carpi radialis

Palmaris longus

Flexor carpi ulnaris

Flexor digitorum superficialis

Left forearm superficial muscles (palmar view)

Brachioradialis

Triceps brachii

Extensor carpi radialis longus

Extensor carpi radialis brevis

Abductor pollicis longus

Extensor pollicis brevis

Extensor pollicis longus

Lateral epicondyle of humerus

Anconeus

Extensor carpi ulnaris

Extensor digitorum

Extensor digiti minimi

Left forearm superficial muscles (dorsal view)

Lateral epicondyle of humerus

Medial epicondyle of humerus

Supinator

Flexor pollicis longus

Brachialis (cut)

Flexor digitorum profundus

Flexor retinaculum (cut)

Pronator quadratus

Left forearm deep muscles (palmar view)

Abductor pollicis longus

Extensor pollicis longus

Extensor pollicis brevis

Medial epicondyle of humerus

Flexor digitorum profundus

Flexor carpi ulnaris

Extensor indicis

Extensor retinaculum

Left forearm deep muscles (dorsal view)

FIGURE 11.25 Muscles That Move the Forearm   The muscles originating in the upper arm flex, extend, pronate, and supinate the forearm. The muscles originating in the forearm move the wrists, hands, and fingers.

Movement	Target	Target motion direction	Prime mover	Origin	Insertion
Anterior muscles (flexion)					
Performs a bicep curl; also allows palm of hand to point toward body while flexing	Forearm	Flexion; supination	Biceps brachii	Coracoid process; tubercle above glenoid cavity	Radial tuberosity
	Forearm	Flexion	Brachialis	Front of distal humerus	Coronoid process of ulna
Assists and stabilizes elbow during bicep-curl motion	Forearm	Flexion	Brachioradialis	Lateral supracondylar ridge at distal end of humerus	Base of styloid process of radius
Posterior muscles (extension)					
Extends forearm, as during a punch	Forearm	Extension	Triceps brachii	Infraglenoid tubercle of scapula; posterior shaft of humerus; posterior humeral shaft distal to radial groove	Olecranon process of ulna
Assists in extending forearm; also allows forearm to extend away from body	Forearm	Extension; abduction	Anconeus	Lateral epicondyle of humerus	Lateral aspect of olecranon process of ulna
Anterior muscles (pronation)					
Turns hand palm-down	Forearm	Pronation	Pronator teres	Medial epicondyle of humerus; coronoid process of ulna	Lateral radius
Assists in turning hand palm-down	Forearm	Pronation	Pronator quadratus	Distal portion of anterior ulnar shaft	Distal surface of anterior radius
Posterior muscles (supination)					
Turns hand palm-up	Forearm	Supination	Supinator	Lateral epicondyle of humerus; proximal ulna	Proximal end of radius

FIGURE 11.26   **Muscles That Move the Forearm**

Muscles That Move the Wrist, Hand, and Fingers

Wrist, hand, and finger movements are facilitated by two groups of muscles. The forearm is the origin of the **extrinsic muscles of the hand**. The palm is the origin of the intrinsic muscles of the hand.

Muscles of the Arm That Move the Wrists, Hands, and Fingers

The muscles in the **anterior compartment of the forearm** (anterior flexor compartment of the forearm) originate on the humerus and insert onto different parts of the hand. These make up the bulk of the forearm. From lateral to medial, the **superficial anterior compartment of the forearm** includes the **flexor carpi radialis**, **palmaris longus**, **flexor carpi ulnaris**, and **flexor digitorum superficialis**. The flexor digitorum superficialis flexes the hand as well as the digits at the knuckles, which allows for rapid finger movements, as in typing or playing a musical instrument (see Figure 11.27 and Table 11.9). However, poor ergonomics can irritate the tendons of these muscles as they slide back and forth with the carpal tunnel of the anterior wrist and pinch the median nerve, which also travels through the tunnel, causing Carpal Tunnel Syndrome. The **deep anterior compartment** produces flexion and bends fingers to make a fist. These are the **flexor pollicis longus** and the **flexor digitorum profundus**.

The muscles in the **superficial posterior compartment of the forearm** (superficial posterior extensor compartment of the forearm) originate on the humerus. These are the **extensor radialis longus**, **extensor carpi radialis brevis**, **extensor digitorum**, **extensor digiti minimi**, and the **extensor carpi ulnaris**.

The muscles of the **deep posterior compartment of the forearm** (deep posterior extensor compartment of the forearm) originate on the radius and ulna. These include the **abductor pollicis longus**, **extensor pollicis brevis**,

extensor pollicis longus, and **extensor indicis** (see Figure 11.27).

Movement	Target	Target motion direction	Prime mover	Origin	Insertion
Superficial anterior compartment of forearm					
Bends wrist toward body; tilts hand to side away from body	Wrist; hand	Flexion; abduction	Flexor carpi radialis	Medial epicondyle of humerus	Base of second and third metacarpals
Assists in bending hand up toward shoulder	Wrist	Flexion	Palmaris longus	Medial epicondyle of humerus	Palmar aponeurosis; skin and fascia of palm
Assists in bending hand up toward shoulder; tilts hand to side away from body; stabilizes wrist	Wrist; hand	Flexion, adduction	Flexor carpi ulnaris	Medial epicondyle of humerus; olecranon process; posterior surface of ulna	Pisiform, hamate bones, and base of fifth metacarpal
Bends fingers to make a fist	Wrist; fingers 2–5	Flexion	Flexor digitorum superficialis	Medial epicondyle of humerus; coronoid process of ulna; shaft of radius	Middle phalanges of fingers 2–5
Deep anterior compartment of forearm					
Bends tip of thumb	Thumb	Flexion	Flexor pollicis longus	Anterior surface of radius; interosseous membrane	Distal phalanx of thumb
Bends fingers to make a fist; also bends wrist toward body	Wrist; fingers	Flexion	Flexor digitorum profundus	Coronoid process; anteromedial surface of ulna; interosseous membrane	Distal phalanges of fingers 2–5
Superficial posterior compartment of forearm					
Straightens wrist away from body; tilts hand to side away from body	Wrist	Extension; abduction	Extensor radialis longus	Lateral supracondylar ridge of humerus	Base of second metacarpal
Assists extensor radialis longus in extending and abducting wrist; also stabilizes hand during finger flexion.	Wrist	Extension, abduction	Extensor carpi radialis brevis	Lateral epicondyle of humerus	Base of third metacarpal
Opens fingers and moves them sideways away from the body	Wrist; fingers	Extension; abduction	Extensor digitorum	Lateral epicondyle of humerus	Extensor expansions; distal phalanges of fingers
Extends little finger	Little finger	Extension	Extensor digiti minimi	Lateral epicondyle of humerus	Extensor expansion; distal phalanx of finger 5
Straightens wrist away from body; tilts hand to side toward body	Wrist	Extension; adduction	Extensor carpi ulnaris	Lateral epicondyle of humerus; posterior border of ulna	Base of fifth metacarpal
Deep posterior compartment of forearm					
Moves thumb sideways toward body; extends thumb; moves hand sideways toward body	Wrist; thumb	Thumb: abduction, extension; wrist: abduction	Abductor pollicis longus	Posterior surface of radius and ulna; interosseous membrane	Base of first metacarpal; trapezium
Extends thumb	Thumb	Extension	Extensor pollicis brevis	Dorsal shaft of radius and ulna; interosseous membrane	Base of proximal phalanx of thumb
Extends thumb	Thumb	Extension	Extensor pollicis longus	Dorsal shaft of radius and ulna; interosseous membrane	Base of distal phalanx of thumb
Extends index finger; straightens wrist away from body	Wrist; index finger	Extension	Extensor indicis	Posterior surface of distal ulna; interosseous membrane	Tendon of extensor digitorum of index finger

FIGURE 11.27   Muscles That Move the Wrist, Hands, and Forearm

The tendons of the forearm muscles attach to the wrist and extend into the hand. Fibrous bands called **retinacula** sheath the tendons at the wrist. The **flexor retinaculum** extends over the palmar surface of the hand while the **extensor retinaculum** extends over the dorsal surface of the hand.

Intrinsic Muscles of the Hand

The **intrinsic muscles of the hand** both originate and insert within it (Figure 11.28). These muscles allow your fingers to also make precise movements for actions, such as typing or writing. These muscles are divided into three groups. The **thenar** muscles are on the radial aspect of the palm. The **hypothenar** muscles are on the medial aspect of the palm, and the **intermediate** muscles are midpalmar.

The thenar muscles include the **abductor pollicis brevis**, **opponens pollicis**, **flexor pollicis brevis**, and the **adductor pollicis**. These muscles form the **thenar eminence**, the rounded contour of the base of the thumb, and all act on the thumb. The movements of the thumb play an integral role in most precise movements of the hand.

The hypothenar muscles include the **abductor digiti minimi**, **flexor digiti minimi brevis**, and the **opponens digiti minimi**. These muscles form the **hypothenar eminence**, the rounded contour of the little finger, and as such, they all act on the little finger. Finally, the intermediate muscles act on all the fingers and include the **lumbrical**, the **palmar interossei**, and the **dorsal interossei**.

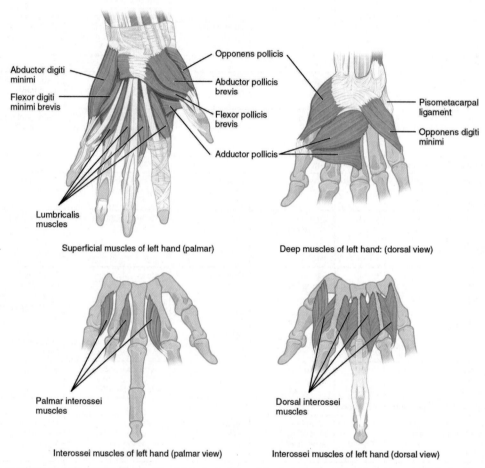

FIGURE 11.28   **Intrinsic Muscles of the Hand**   The intrinsic muscles of the hand both originate and insert within the hand. These muscles provide the fine motor control of the fingers by flexing, extending, abducting, and adducting the more distal finger and thumb segments.

Intrinsic Muscles of the Hand

Muscle	Movement	Target	Target motion direction	Prime mover	Origin	Insertion
Thenar muscles	Moves thumb toward body	Thumb	Abduction	Abductor pollicis brevis	Flexor retinaculum; and nearby carpals	Lateral base of proximal phalanx of thumb
Thenar muscles	Moves thumb across palm to touch other fingers	Thumb	Opposition	Opponens pollicis	Flexor retinaculum; trapezium	Anterior of first metacarpal
Thenar muscles	Flexes thumb	Thumb	Flexion	Flexor pollicis brevis	Flexor retinaculum; trapezium	Lateral base of proximal phalanx of thumb
Thenar muscles	Moves thumb away from body	Thumb	Adduction	Adductor pollicis	Capitate bone; bases of metacarpals 2–4; front of metacarpal 3	Medial base of proximal phalanx of thumb
Hypothenar muscles	Moves little finger toward body	Little finger	Abduction	Abductor digiti minimi	Pisiform bone	Medial side of proximal phalanx of little finger
Hypothenar muscles	Flexes little finger	Little finger	Flexion	Flexor digiti minimi brevis	Hamate bone; flexor retinaculum	Medial side of proximal phalanx of little finger
Hypothenar muscles	Moves little finger across palm to touch thumb	Little finger	Opposition	Opponens digiti minimi	Hamate bone; flexor retinaculum	Medial side of fifth metacarpal
Intermediate muscles	Flexes each finger at metacarpo-phalangeal joints; extends each finger at interphalangeal joints	Fingers	Flexion	Lumbricals	Palm (lateral sides of tendons in flexor digitorum profundus)	Fingers 2–5 (lateral edges of extensional expansions on first phalanges)

TABLE 11.9

Muscle	Movement	Target	Target motion direction	Prime mover	Origin	Insertion
Intermediate muscles	Adducts and flexes each finger at metacarpo-phalangeal joints; extends each finger at interphalangeal joints	Fingers	Adduction; flexion; extension	Palmar interossei	Side of each metacarpal that faces metacarpal 3 (absent from metacarpal 3)	Extensor expansion on first phalanx of each finger (except finger 3) on side facing finger 3
Intermediate muscles	Abducts and flexes the three middle fingers at metacarpo-phalangeal joints; extends the three middle fingers at interphalangeal joints	Fingers	Abduction; flexion; extension	Dorsal interossei	Sides of metacarpals	Both sides of finger 3; for each other finger, extensor expansion over first phalanx on side opposite finger 3

TABLE 11.9

11.6 Appendicular Muscles of the Pelvic Girdle and Lower Limbs

LEARNING OBJECTIVES

By the end of this section, you will be able to:

- Identify the appendicular muscles of the pelvic girdle and lower limb
- Identify the movement and function of the pelvic girdle and lower limb

The appendicular muscles of the lower body position and stabilize the **pelvic girdle**, which serves as a foundation for the lower limbs. Comparatively, there is much more movement at the pectoral girdle than at the pelvic girdle. There is very little movement of the pelvic girdle because of its connection with the sacrum at the base of the axial skeleton. The pelvic girdle is less range of motion because it was designed to stabilize and support the body.

Muscles of the Thigh

What would happen if the pelvic girdle, which attaches the lower limbs to the torso, were capable of the same range of motion as the pectoral girdle? For one thing, walking would expend more energy if the heads of the femurs were not secured in the acetabula of the pelvis. The body's center of gravity is in the area of the pelvis. If the center of gravity were not to remain fixed, standing up would be difficult as well. Therefore, what the leg muscles lack in range of motion and versatility, they make up for in size and power, facilitating the body's stabilization, posture, and movement.

Gluteal Region Muscles That Move the Femur

Most muscles that insert on the femur (the thigh bone) and move it, originate on the pelvic girdle. The **psoas major** and **iliacus** make up the **iliopsoas group**. Some of the largest and most powerful muscles in the body are the gluteal muscles or **gluteal group**. The **gluteus maximus** is the largest; deep to the gluteus maximus is the **gluteus medius**, and deep to the gluteus medius is the **gluteus minimus**, the smallest of the trio (Figure 11.29 and Figure 11.30).

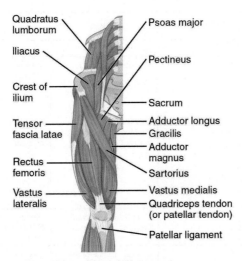

Quadratus lumborum

Iliacus

Crest of ilium

Tensor fascia latae

Rectus femoris

Vastus lateralis

Psoas major

Pectineus

Sacrum

Adductor longus

Gracilis

Adductor magnus

Sartorius

Vastus medialis

Quadriceps tendon (or patellar tendon)

Patellar ligament

Superficial pelvic and thigh muscles of right leg (anterior view)

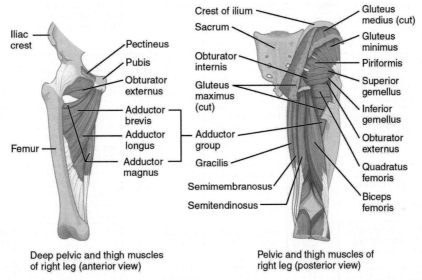

Iliac crest

Pectineus

Pubis

Obturator externus

Adductor brevis

Adductor longus

Femur

Adductor magnus

Deep pelvic and thigh muscles of right leg (anterior view)

Crest of ilium

Sacrum

Obturator internis

Gluteus maximus (cut)

Adductor group

Gracilis

Semimembranosus

Semitendinosus

Gluteus medius (cut)

Gluteus minimus

Piriformis

Superior gemellus

Inferior gemellus

Obturator externus

Quadratus femoris

Biceps femoris

Pelvic and thigh muscles of right leg (posterior view)

FIGURE 11.29   Hip and Thigh Muscles   The large and powerful muscles of the hip that move the femur generally originate on the pelvic girdle and insert into the femur. The muscles that move the lower leg typically originate on the femur and insert into the bones of the knee joint. The anterior muscles of the femur extend the lower leg but also aid in flexing the thigh. The posterior muscles of the femur flex the lower leg but also aid in extending the thigh. A combination of gluteal and thigh muscles also adduct, abduct, and rotate the thigh and lower leg.

Movement	Target	Target motion direction	Prime mover	Origin	Insertion
Iliopsoas group					
Raises knee at hip, as if performing a knee attack; assists lateral rotators in twisting thigh (and lower leg) outward; assists with bending over, maintaining posture	Femur	Thigh: flexion and lateral rotation; torso: flexion	Psoas major	Lumbar vertebrae (L1–L5); thoracic vertebra (T12)	Lesser trochanter of femur
Raises knee at hip, as if performing a knee attack; assists lateral rotators in twisting thigh (and lower leg) outward; assists with bending over, maintaining posture	Femur	Thigh: flexion and lateral rotation; torso: flexion	Iliacus	Iliac fossa; iliac crest; lateral sacrum	Lesser trochanter of femur
Gluteal group					
Lowers knee and moves thigh back, as when getting ready to kick a ball	Femur	Extension	Gluteus maximus	Dorsal ilium; sacrum; coccyx	Gluteal tuberosity of femur; iliotibial tract
Opens thighs, as when doing a split	Femur	Abduction	Gluteus medius	Lateral surface of ilium	Greater trochanter of femur
Brings the thighs back together	Femur	Abduction	Gluteus minimus	External surface of ilium	Greater trochanter of femur
Assists with raising knee at hip and opening thighs; maintains posture by stabilizing the iliotibial track, which connects to the knee	Femur	Flexion; abduction	Tensor fascia lata	Anterior aspect of iliac crest; anterior superior iliac spine	Iliotibial tract
Lateral rotators					
Twists thigh (and lower leg) outward; maintains posture by stabilizing hip joint	Femur	Lateral rotation	Piriformis	Anterolateral surface of sacrum	Greater trochanter of femur
Twists thigh (and lower leg) outward; maintains posture by stabilizing hip joint	Femur	Lateral rotation	Obuturator internus	Inner surface of obturator membrane; greater sciatic notch; margins of obturator foramen	Greater trochanter in front of piriformis
Twists thigh (and lower leg) outward; maintains posture by stabilizing hip joint	Femur	Lateral rotation	Obturator externus	Outer surfaces of obturator membrane, pubic, and ischium; margins of obturator foramen	Trochanteric fossa of posterior femur
Twists thigh (and lower leg) outward; maintains posture by stabilizing hip joint	Femur	Lateral rotation	Superior gemellus	Ischial spine	Greater trochanter of femur
Twists thigh (and lower leg) outward; maintains posture by stabilizing hip joint	Femur	Lateral rotation	Inferior gemellus	Ischial tuberosity	Greater trochanter of femur
Twists thigh (and lower leg) outward; maintains posture by stabilizing hip joint	Femur	Lateral rotation	Quadratus femoris	Ischial tuberosity	Trochanteric crest of femur
Adductors					
Brings the thighs back together; assists with raising the knee	Femur	Adduction; flexion	Adductor longus	Pubis near pubic symphysis	Linea aspera
Brings the thighs back together; assists with raising the knee	Femur	Adduction; flexion	Adductor brevis	Body of pubis; inferior ramus of pubis	Linea aspera above adductor longus
Brings the thighs back together; assists with raising the knee and moving the thigh back	Femur	Adduction; flexion; extension	Adductor magnus	Ischial rami; pubic rami; ischial tuberosity	Linea aspera; adductor tubercle of femur
Opens thighs; assists with raising the knee and turning the thigh (and lower leg) inward	Femur	Adduction; flexion; medial rotation	Pectineus	Pectineal line of pubis	Lesser trochanter to linea aspera of posterior aspect of femur

FIGURE 11.30   Gluteal Region Muscles That Move the Femur

The **tensor fascia latae** is a thick, squarish muscle in the superior aspect of the lateral thigh. It acts as a synergist of the gluteus medius and iliopsoas in flexing and abducting the thigh. It also helps stabilize the lateral aspect of the

Access for free at openstax.org

knee by pulling on the **iliotibial tract** (band), making it taut. Deep to the gluteus maximus, the **piriformis, obturator internus, obturator externus, superior gemellus, inferior gemellus**, and **quadratus femoris** laterally rotate the femur at the hip.

The **adductor longus, adductor brevis**, and **adductor magnus** can both medially and laterally rotate the thigh depending on the placement of the foot. The adductor longus flexes the thigh, whereas the adductor magnus extends it. The **pectineus** adducts and flexes the femur at the hip as well. The pectineus is located in the **femoral triangle**, which is formed at the junction between the hip and the leg and also includes the femoral nerve, the femoral artery, the femoral vein, and the deep inguinal lymph nodes.

Thigh Muscles That Move the Femur, Tibia, and Fibula

Deep fascia in the thigh separates it into medial, anterior, and posterior compartments (see Figure 11.29 and Figure 11.31). The muscles in the **medial compartment of the thigh** are responsible for adducting the femur at the hip. Along with the adductor longus, adductor brevis, adductor magnus, and pectineus, the strap-like **gracilis** adducts the thigh in addition to flexing the leg at the knee.

Movement	Target	Target motion direction	Prime mover	Origin	Insertion
Medial compartment of thigh					
Moves back of lower legs up toward buttocks, as when kneeling; assists in opening thighs	Femur; tibia/fibula	Tibia/fibula: flexion; thigh: adduction	Gracilis	Inferior ramus; body of pubis; ischial ramus	Medial surface of tibia
Anterior compartment of thigh: Quadriceps femoris group					
Moves lower leg out in front of body, as when kicking; assists in raising the knee	Femur; tibia/fibula	Tibia/fibula: extension; thigh: flexion	Rectus femoris	Anterior inferior iliac spine; superior margin of acetabulum	Patella; tibial tuberosity
Moves lower leg out in front of body, as when kicking	Tibia/fibula	Extension	Vastus lateralis	Greater trochanter; intertrochanteric line; linea aspera	Patella; tibial tuberosity
Moves lower leg out in front of body, as when kicking	Tibia/fibula	Extension	Vastus medialis	Linea aspera; intertrochanteric line	Patella; tibial tuberosity
Moves lower leg out in front of body, as when kicking	Tibia/fibula	Extension	Vastus intermedius	Proximal femur shaft	Patella; tibial tuberosity
Moves back of lower legs up and back toward the buttocks, as when kneeling; assists in moving thigh diagonally upward and outward as when mounting a bike	Femur; tibia/fibula	Tibia: flexion; thigh: flexion, abduction, lateral rotation	Sartorius	Anterior superior iliac spine	Medial aspect of proximal tibia
Posterior compartment of thigh: Hamstring group					
Moves back of lower legs up and back toward the buttocks, as when kneeling; moves thigh down and back; twists the thigh (and lower leg) outward	Femur; tibia/fibula	Tibia/fibula: flexion; thigh: extension, lateral rotation	Biceps femoris	Ischial tuberosity; linea aspera; distal femur	Head of fibula; lateral condyle of tibia
Moves back of lower legs up toward buttocks, as when kneeling; moves thigh down and back; twists the thigh (and lower leg) inward	Femur; tibia/fibula	Tibia/fibula: flexion; thigh: extension, medial rotation	Semitendinosus	Ischial tuberosity	Upper tibial shaft
Moves back of lower legs up and back toward the buttocks as when kneeling; moves thigh down and back; twists the thigh (and lower leg) inward	Femur; tibia/fibula	Tibia/fibula: flexion; thigh: extension, medial rotation	Semi-membranosus	Ischial tuberosity	Medial condyle of tibia; lateral condyle of femur

FIGURE 11.31   Thigh Muscles That Move the Femur, Tibia, and Fibula

The muscles of the **anterior compartment of the thigh** flex the thigh and extend the leg. This compartment contains the **quadriceps femoris group**, which actually comprises four muscles that extend and stabilize the knee. The **rectus femoris** is on the anterior aspect of the thigh, the **vastus lateralis** is on the lateral aspect of the thigh, the **vastus medialis** is on the medial aspect of the thigh, and the **vastus intermedius** is between the vastus lateralis and vastus medialis and deep to the rectus femoris. The tendon common to all four is the **quadriceps tendon** (patellar tendon), which inserts into the patella and continues below it as the **patellar ligament**. The patellar ligament attaches to the tibial tuberosity. In addition to the quadriceps femoris, the **sartorius** is a band-like muscle that extends from the anterior superior iliac spine to the medial side of the proximal tibia. This versatile muscle flexes the leg at the knee and flexes, abducts, and laterally rotates the leg at the hip. This muscle allows us to sit cross-legged.

The **posterior compartment of the thigh** includes muscles that flex the leg and extend the thigh. The three long muscles on the back of the knee are the **hamstring group**, which flexes the knee. These are the **biceps femoris**, **semitendinosus**, and **semimembranosus**. The tendons of these muscles form the **popliteal fossa**, the diamond-shaped space at the back of the knee.

Muscles That Move the Feet and Toes

Similar to the thigh muscles, the muscles of the leg are divided by deep fascia into compartments, although the leg has three: anterior, lateral, and posterior (Figure 11.32 and Figure 11.33).

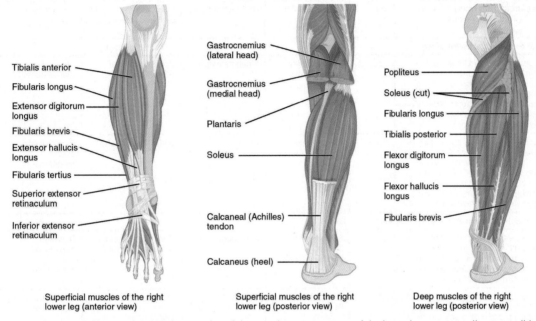

Superficial muscles of the right lower leg (anterior view)

Superficial muscles of the right lower leg (posterior view)

Deep muscles of the right lower leg (posterior view)

FIGURE 11.32   Muscles of the Lower Leg   The muscles of the anterior compartment of the lower leg are generally responsible for dorsiflexion, and the muscles of the posterior compartment of the lower leg are generally responsible for plantar flexion. The lateral and medial muscles in both compartments invert, evert, and rotate the foot.

Movement	Target	Target motion direction	Prime mover	Origin	Insertion
Anterior compartment of leg					
Raises the sole of the foot off the ground, as when preparing to foot-tap; bends the inside of the foot upwards, as when catching your balance while falling laterally toward the opposite side as the balancing foot	Foot	Dorsiflexion; inversion	Tibialis anterior	Lateral condyle and upper tibial shaft; interosseous membrane	Interior surface of medial cuneiform; First metatarsal bone
Raises the sole of the foot off the ground, as when preparing to foot-tap; extends the big toe	Foot; big toe	Foot: dorsiflexion; big toe: extension	Extensor hallucis longus	Anteromedial fibula shaft; interosseous membrane	Distal phalanx of big toe
Raises the sole of the foot off the ground, as when preparing to foot-tap; extends toes	Foot; toes 2–5	Foot: dorsiflexion; toes: extension	Extensor digitorum longus	Lateral condyle of tibia; proximal portion of fibula; interosseous membrane	Middle and distal phalanges of toes 2–5
Lateral compartment of leg					
Lowers the sole of the foot to the ground, as when foot-tapping or jumping; bends the inside of the foot downwards, as when catching your balance while falling laterally toward the same side as the balancing foot	Foot	Plantar flexion and eversion	Fibularis longus	Upper portion of lateral fibula	First metatarsal; medial cuneiform
Lowers the sole of the foot to the ground, as when foot-tapping or jumping; bends the inside of the foot downward, as when catching your balance while falling laterally toward the same side as the balancing foot	Foot	Plantar flexion and eversion	Fibularis (peroneus) brevis	Distal fibula shaft	Proximal end of fifth metatarsal
Posterior compartment of leg: Superficial muscles					
Lowers the sole of the foot to the ground, as when foot-tapping or jumping; assists in moving the back of the lower legs up and back toward the buttocks	Foot; tibia/fibula	Foot: plantar flexion; tibia/fibula: flexion	Gastrocnemius	Medial and lateral condyles of femur	Posterior calcaneus
Lowers the sole of the foot to the ground, as when foot-tapping or jumping; maintains posture while walking	Foot	Plantar flexion	Soleus	Superior tibia; fibula; interosseous membrane	Posterior calcaneus
Lowers the sole of the foot to the ground, as when foot-tapping or jumping; assists in moving the back of the lower legs up and back toward the buttocks	Foot; tibia/fibula	Foot: plantar flexion; tibia/fibula: flexion	Plantaris	Posterior femur above lateral condyle	Calcaneus or calcaneus tendon
Lowers the sole of the foot to the ground, as when foot-tapping or jumping	Foot	Plantar flexion	Tibialis posterior	Superior tibia and fibula; interosseous membrane	Several tarsals and metatarsals 2–4
Posterior compartment of leg: Deep muscles					
Moves the back of the lower legs up and back toward the buttocks; assists in rotation of the leg at the knee and thigh	Tibia/fibula	Tibia/fibula: flexion thigh and lower leg: medial and lateral rotation	Popliteus	Lateral condyle of femur; lateral meniscus	Proximal tibia
Lowers the sole of the foot to the ground, as when foot-tapping or jumping; bends the inside of the foot upward and flexes toes	Foot; toes 2–5	Foot: plantar flexion and inversion toes: flexion	Flexor digitorum longus	Posterior tibia	Distal phalanges of toes 2–5
Flexes the big toe	Big toe; foot	Big toe: flexion foot: plantar flexion	Flexor hallucis longus	Midshaft of fibula; interosseous membrane	Distal phalanx of big toe

FIGURE 11.33   Muscles That Move the Feet and Toes

The muscles in the **anterior compartment of the leg**: the **tibialis anterior**, a long and thick muscle on the lateral surface of the tibia, the **extensor hallucis longus**, deep under it, and the **extensor digitorum longus**, lateral to it, all contribute to raising the front of the foot when they contract. The **fibularis tertius**, a small muscle that originates on the anterior surface of the fibula, is associated with the extensor digitorum longus and sometimes fused to it, but is not present in all people. Thick bands of connective tissue called the **superior extensor retinaculum** (transverse ligament of the ankle) and the **inferior extensor retinaculum**, hold the tendons of these muscles in place during dorsiflexion.

The **lateral compartment of the leg** includes two muscles: the **fibularis longus** (peroneus longus) and the **fibularis brevis** (peroneus brevis). The superficial muscles in the **posterior compartment of the leg** all insert onto the **calcaneal tendon** (Achilles tendon), a strong tendon that inserts into the calcaneal bone of the ankle. The muscles in this compartment are large and strong and keep humans upright. The most superficial and visible muscle of the calf is the **gastrocnemius**. Deep to the gastrocnemius is the wide, flat **soleus**. The **plantaris** runs obliquely between the two; some people may have two of these muscles, whereas no plantaris is observed in about seven percent of other cadaver dissections. The plantaris tendon is a desirable substitute for the fascia lata in hernia repair, tendon transplants, and repair of ligaments. There are four deep muscles in the posterior compartment of the leg as well: the **popliteus, flexor digitorum longus, flexor hallucis longus**, and **tibialis posterior**.

The foot also has intrinsic muscles, which originate and insert within it (similar to the intrinsic muscles of the hand). These muscles primarily provide support for the foot and its arch, and contribute to movements of the toes (Figure 11.34 and Figure 11.35). The principal support for the longitudinal arch of the foot is a deep fascia called **plantar aponeurosis**, which runs from the calcaneus bone to the toes (inflammation of this tissue is the cause of "plantar fasciitis," which can affect runners. The intrinsic muscles of the foot consist of two groups. The **dorsal group** includes only one muscle, the **extensor digitorum brevis**. The second group is the **plantar group**, which consists of four layers, starting with the most superficial.

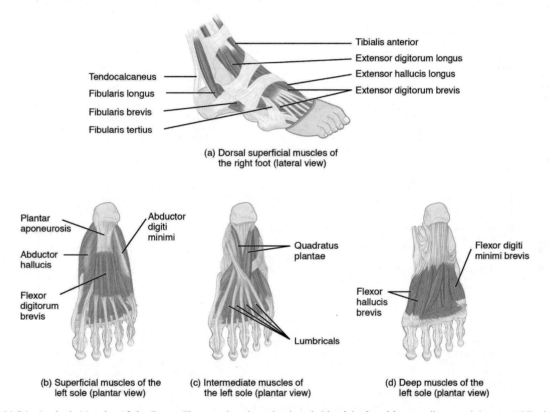

(a) Dorsal superficial muscles of
the right foot (lateral view)

(b) Superficial muscles of the
left sole (plantar view)

(c) Intermediate muscles of
the left sole (plantar view)

(d) Deep muscles of the
left sole (plantar view)

FIGURE 11.34   Intrinsic Muscles of the Foot   The muscles along the dorsal side of the foot (a) generally extend the toes while the muscles of the plantar side of the foot (b, c, d) generally flex the toes. The plantar muscles exist in three layers, providing the foot the strength to counterbalance the weight of the body. In this diagram, these three layers are shown from a plantar view beginning with the bottom-most layer just under the plantar skin of the foot (b) and ending with the top-most layer (d) located just inferior to the foot and toe bones.

Movement	Target	Target motion direction	Prime mover	Origin	Insertion
Dorsal group					
Extends toes 2–5	Toes 2–5	Extension	Extensor digitorum brevis	Calcaneus; extensor retinaculum	Base of proximal phalanx of big toe; extensor expansions on toes 2–5
Plantar group (layer 1)					
Abducts and flexes big toe	Big toe	Adduction; flexion	Abductor hallucis	Calcaneal tuberosity; flexor retinaculum	Proximal phalanx of big toe
Flexes toes 2–4	Middle toes	Flexion	Flexor digitorum brevis	Calcaneal tuberosity	Middle phalanx of toes 2–4
Abducts and flexes small toe	Toe 5	Abduction; flexion	Abductor digiti minimi	Calcaneal tuberosity	Proximal phalanx of little toe
Plantar group (layer 2)					
Assists in flexing toes 2–5	Toes 2–5	Flexion	Quadratus plantae	Medial and lateral sides of calcaneus	Tendon of flexor digitorum longus
Extends toes 2–5 at the interphalangeal joints; flexes the small toes at the metatarsophalangeal joints	Toes 2–5	Extension; flexion	Lumbricals	Tendons of flexor digitorum longus	Medial side of proximal phalanx of toes 2–5
Plantar group (layer 3)					
Flexes big toe	Big toe	Flexion	Flexor hallucis brevis	Lateral cuneiform; cuboid bones	Base of proximal phalanx of big toe
Adducts and flexes big toe	Big toe	Adduction; flexion	Adductor hallucis	Bases of metatarsals 2–4; fibularis longus tendon sheath; ligament across metatarsophalangeal joints	Base of proximal phalanx of big toe
Flexes small toe	Little toe	Flexion	Flexor digiti minimi brevis	Base of metatarsal 5; tendon sheath of fibularis longus	Base of proximal phalanx of little toe
Plantar group (layer 4)					
Abducts and flexes middle toes at metatarsophalangeal joints; extends middle toes at interphalangeal joints	Middle toes	Abduction; flexion; extension	Dorsal interossei	Sides of metatarsals	Both sides of toe 2; for each other toe, extensor expansion over first phalanx on side opposite toe 2
Abducts toes 3–5; flexes proximal phalanges and extends distal phalanges	Small toes	Abduction; flexion; extension	Plantar interossei	Side of each metatarsal that faces metatarsal 2 (absent from metatarsal 2)	Extensor expansion on first phalanx of each toe (except to 2) on side facing toe 2

FIGURE 11.35   Intrinsic Muscles in the Foot

Access for free at openstax.org

Key Terms

abduct   move away from midline in the sagittal plane

abductor   moves the bone away from the midline

abductor digiti minimi   muscle that abducts the little finger

abductor pollicis brevis   muscle that abducts the thumb

abductor pollicis longus   muscle that inserts into the first metacarpal

adductor   moves the bone toward the midline

adductor brevis   muscle that adducts and medially rotates the thigh

adductor longus   muscle that adducts, medially rotates, and flexes the thigh

adductor magnus   muscle with an anterior fascicle that adducts, medially rotates and flexes the thigh, and a posterior fascicle that assists in thigh extension

adductor pollicis   muscle that adducts the thumb

agonist   (also, prime mover) muscle whose contraction is responsible for producing a particular motion

anal triangle   posterior triangle of the perineum that includes the anus

anconeus   small muscle on the lateral posterior elbow that extends the forearm

antagonist   muscle that opposes the action of an agonist

anterior compartment of the arm   (anterior flexor compartment of the arm) the biceps brachii, brachialis, brachioradialis, and their associated blood vessels and nerves

anterior compartment of the forearm   (anterior flexor compartment of the forearm) deep and superficial muscles that originate on the humerus and insert into the hand

anterior compartment of the leg   region that includes muscles that dorsiflex the foot

anterior compartment of the thigh   region that includes muscles that flex the thigh and extend the leg

anterior scalene   a muscle anterior to the middle scalene

appendicular   of the arms and legs

axial   of the trunk and head

belly   bulky central body of a muscle

bi   two

biceps brachii   two-headed muscle that crosses the shoulder and elbow joints to flex the forearm while assisting in supinating it and flexing the arm at the shoulder

biceps femoris   hamstring muscle

bipennate   pennate muscle that has fascicles that are located on both sides of the tendon

brachialis   muscle deep to the biceps brachii that provides power in flexing the forearm.

brachioradialis   muscle that can flex the forearm quickly or help lift a load slowly

brevis   short

buccinator   muscle that compresses the cheek

calcaneal tendon   (also, Achilles tendon) strong tendon that inserts into the calcaneal bone of the ankle

caval opening   opening in the diaphragm that allows the inferior vena cava to pass through; foramen for the vena cava

circular   (also, sphincter) fascicles that are concentrically arranged around an opening

compressor urethrae   deep perineal muscle in females

convergent   fascicles that extend over a broad area and converge on a common attachment site

coracobrachialis   muscle that flexes and adducts the arm

corrugator supercilii   prime mover of the eyebrows

deep anterior compartment   flexor pollicis longus, flexor digitorum profundus, and their associated blood vessels and nerves

deep posterior compartment of the forearm   (deep posterior extensor compartment of the forearm) the abductor pollicis longus, extensor pollicis brevis, extensor pollicis longus, extensor indicis, and their associated blood vessels and nerves

deep transverse perineal   deep perineal muscle in males

deglutition   swallowing

deltoid   shoulder muscle that abducts the arm as well as flexes and medially rotates it, and extends and laterally rotates it

diaphragm   skeletal muscle that separates the thoracic and abdominal cavities and is dome-shaped at rest

digastric   muscle that has anterior and posterior bellies and elevates the hyoid bone and larynx when one swallows; it also depresses the mandible

dorsal group   region that includes the extensor digitorum brevis

dorsal interossei   muscles that abduct and flex the three middle fingers at the metacarpophalangeal joints and extend them at the interphalangeal joints

epicranial aponeurosis   (also, galea aponeurosis) flat broad tendon that connects the frontalis and occipitalis

erector spinae group   large muscle mass of the back; primary extensor of the vertebral column

extensor   muscle that increases the angle at the joint

extensor carpi radialis brevis   muscle that extends and abducts the hand at the wrist

extensor carpi ulnaris   muscle that extends and adducts the hand

extensor digiti minimi   muscle that extends the little finger

extensor digitorum   muscle that extends the hand at the wrist and the phalanges

extensor digitorum brevis   muscle that extends the toes

extensor digitorum longus   muscle that is lateral to the tibialis anterior

extensor hallucis longus   muscle that is partly deep to the tibialis anterior and extensor digitorum longus

extensor indicis   muscle that inserts onto the tendon of the extensor digitorum of the index finger

extensor pollicis brevis   muscle that inserts onto the base of the proximal phalanx of the thumb

extensor pollicis longus   muscle that inserts onto the base of the distal phalanx of the thumb

extensor radialis longus   muscle that extends and abducts the hand at the wrist

extensor retinaculum   band of connective tissue that extends over the dorsal surface of the hand

external intercostal   superficial intercostal muscles that raise the rib cage

external oblique   superficial abdominal muscle with fascicles that extend inferiorly and medially

extrinsic eye muscles   originate outside the eye and insert onto the outer surface of the white of the eye, and create eyeball movement

extrinsic muscles of the hand   muscles that move the wrists, hands, and fingers and originate on the arm

fascicle   muscle fibers bundled by perimysium into a unit

femoral triangle   region formed at the junction between the hip and the leg and includes the pectineus, femoral nerve, femoral artery, femoral vein, and deep inguinal lymph nodes

fibularis brevis   (also, peroneus brevis) muscle that plantar flexes the foot at the ankle and everts it at the intertarsal joints

fibularis longus   (also, peroneus longus) muscle that plantar flexes the foot at the ankle and everts it at the intertarsal joints

fibularis tertius   small muscle that is associated with the extensor digitorum longus

fixator   synergist that assists an agonist by preventing or reducing movement at another joint, thereby stabilizing the origin of the agonist

flexion   movement that decreases the angle of a joint

flexor   muscle that decreases the angle at the joint

flexor carpi radialis   muscle that flexes and abducts the hand at the wrist

flexor carpi ulnaris   muscle that flexes and adducts the hand at the wrist

flexor digiti minimi brevis   muscle that flexes the little finger

flexor digitorum longus   muscle that flexes the four small toes

flexor digitorum profundus   muscle that flexes the phalanges of the fingers and the hand at the wrist

flexor digitorum superficialis   muscle that flexes the hand and the digits

flexor hallucis longus   muscle that flexes the big toe

flexor pollicis brevis   muscle that flexes the thumb

flexor pollicis longus   muscle that flexes the distal phalanx of the thumb

flexor retinaculum   band of connective tissue that extends over the palmar surface of the hand

frontalis   front part of the occipitofrontalis muscle

fusiform   muscle that has fascicles that are spindle-shaped to create large bellies

gastrocnemius   most superficial muscle of the calf

genioglossus   muscle that originates on the mandible and allows the tongue to move downward and forward

geniohyoid   muscle that depresses the mandible, and raises and pulls the hyoid bone anteriorly

gluteal group   muscle group that extends, flexes, rotates, adducts, and abducts the femur

gluteus maximus   largest of the gluteus muscles that extends the femur

gluteus medius   muscle deep to the gluteus maximus that abducts the femur at the hip

gluteus minimus   smallest of the gluteal muscles and deep to the gluteus medius

gracilis   muscle that adducts the thigh and flexes the leg at the knee

hamstring group   three long muscles on the back of the leg

hyoglossus   muscle that originates on the hyoid bone to move the tongue downward and flatten it

hypothenar   group of muscles on the medial aspect of the palm

hypothenar eminence   rounded contour of muscle at the base of the little finger

iliacus   muscle that, along with the psoas major, makes up the iliopsoas

iliococcygeus   muscle that makes up the levator ani along with the pubococcygeus

iliocostalis cervicis   muscle of the iliocostalis group associated with the cervical region

iliocostalis group   laterally placed muscles of the

erector spinae

iliocostalis lumborum   muscle of the iliocostalis group associated with the lumbar region

iliocostalis thoracis   muscle of the iliocostalis group associated with the thoracic region

iliopsoas group   muscle group consisting of iliacus and psoas major muscles, that flexes the thigh at the hip, rotates it laterally, and flexes the trunk of the body onto the hip

iliotibial tract   muscle that inserts onto the tibia; made up of the gluteus maximus and connective tissues of the tensor fasciae latae

inferior extensor retinaculum   cruciate ligament of the ankle

inferior gemellus   muscle deep to the gluteus maximus on the lateral surface of the thigh that laterally rotates the femur at the hip

infrahyoid muscles   anterior neck muscles that are attached to, and inferior to the hyoid bone

infraspinatus   muscle that laterally rotates the arm

innermost intercostal   the deepest intercostal muscles that draw the ribs together

insertion   end of a skeletal muscle that is attached to the structure (usually a bone) that is moved when the muscle contracts

intercostal muscles   muscles that span the spaces between the ribs

intermediate   group of midpalmar muscles

internal intercostal   muscles the intermediate intercostal muscles that draw the ribs together

internal oblique   flat, intermediate abdominal muscle with fascicles that run perpendicular to those of the external oblique

intrinsic muscles of the hand   muscles that move the wrists, hands, and fingers and originate in the palm

ischiococcygeus   muscle that assists the levator ani and pulls the coccyx anteriorly

lateral compartment of the leg   region that includes the fibularis (peroneus) longus and the fibularis (peroneus) brevis and their associated blood vessels and nerves

lateral pterygoid   muscle that moves the mandible from side to side

lateralis   to the outside

latissimus dorsi   broad, triangular axial muscle located on the inferior part of the back

levator ani   pelvic muscle that resists intra-abdominal pressure and supports the pelvic viscera

linea alba   white, fibrous band that runs along the midline of the trunk

longissimus capitis   muscle of the longissimus group associated with the head region

longissimus cervicis   muscle of the longissimus group associated with the cervical region

longissimus group   intermediately placed muscles of the erector spinae

longissimus thoracis   muscle of the longissimus group associated with the thoracic region

longus   long

lumbrical   muscle that flexes each finger at the metacarpophalangeal joints and extend each finger at the interphalangeal joints

masseter   main muscle for chewing that elevates the mandible to close the mouth

mastication   chewing

maximus   largest

medial compartment of the thigh   a region that includes the adductor longus, adductor brevis, adductor magnus, pectineus, gracilis, and their associated blood vessels and nerves

medial pterygoid   muscle that moves the mandible from side to side

medialis   to the inside

medius   medium

middle scalene   longest scalene muscle, located between the anterior and posterior scalenes

minimus   smallest

multifidus   muscle of the lumbar region that helps extend and laterally flex the vertebral column

multipennate   pennate muscle that has a tendon branching within it

mylohyoid   muscle that lifts the hyoid bone and helps press the tongue to the top of the mouth

oblique   at an angle

obturator externus   muscle deep to the gluteus maximus on the lateral surface of the thigh that laterally rotates the femur at the hip

obturator internus   muscle deep to the gluteus maximus on the lateral surface of the thigh that laterally rotates the femur at the hip

occipitalis   posterior part of the occipitofrontalis muscle

occipitofrontalis   muscle that makes up the scalp with a frontal belly and an occipital belly

omohyoid   muscle that has superior and inferior bellies and depresses the hyoid bone

opponens digiti minimi   muscle that brings the little finger across the palm to meet the thumb

opponens pollicis   muscle that moves the thumb across the palm to meet another finger

orbicularis oculi   circular muscle that closes the eye

orbicularis oris   circular muscle that moves the lips

origin   end of a skeletal muscle that is attached to another structure (usually a bone) in a fixed position

palatoglossus   muscle that originates on the soft palate to elevate the back of the tongue

palmar interossei   muscles that abduct and flex each finger at the metacarpophalangeal joints and extend each finger at the interphalangeal joints

palmaris longus   muscle that provides weak flexion of the hand at the wrist

parallel   fascicles that extend in the same direction as the long axis of the muscle

patellar ligament   extension of the quadriceps tendon below the patella

pectineus   muscle that abducts and flexes the femur at the hip

pectoral girdle   shoulder girdle, made up of the clavicle and scapula

pectoralis major   thick, fan-shaped axial muscle that covers much of the superior thorax

pectoralis minor   muscle that moves the scapula and assists in inhalation

pelvic diaphragm   muscular sheet that comprises the levator ani and the ischiococcygeus

pelvic girdle   hips, a foundation for the lower limb

pennate   fascicles that are arranged differently based on their angles to the tendon

perineum   diamond-shaped region between the pubic symphysis, coccyx, and ischial tuberosities

piriformis   muscle deep to the gluteus maximus on the lateral surface of the thigh that laterally rotates the femur at the hip

plantar aponeurosis   muscle that supports the longitudinal arch of the foot

plantar group   four-layered group of intrinsic foot muscles

plantaris   muscle that runs obliquely between the gastrocnemius and the soleus

popliteal fossa   diamond-shaped space at the back of the knee

popliteus   muscle that flexes the leg at the knee and creates the floor of the popliteal fossa

posterior compartment of the leg   region that includes the superficial gastrocnemius, soleus, and plantaris, and the deep popliteus, flexor digitorum longus, flexor hallucis longus, and tibialis posterior

posterior compartment of the thigh   region that includes muscles that flex the leg and extend the thigh

posterior scalene   smallest scalene muscle, located posterior to the middle scalene

prime mover   (also, agonist) principle muscle involved in an action

pronator quadratus   pronator that originates on the ulna and inserts on the radius

pronator teres   pronator that originates on the humerus and inserts on the radius

psoas major   muscle that, along with the iliacus, makes up the iliopsoas

pubococcygeus   muscle that makes up the levator ani along with the iliococcygeus

quadratus femoris   muscle deep to the gluteus maximus on the lateral surface of the thigh that laterally rotates the femur at the hip

quadratus lumborum   posterior part of the abdominal wall that helps with posture and stabilization of the body

quadriceps femoris group   four muscles, that extend and stabilize the knee

quadriceps tendon   (also, patellar tendon) tendon common to all four quadriceps muscles, inserts into the patella

rectus   straight

rectus abdominis   long, linear muscle that extends along the middle of the trunk

rectus femoris   quadricep muscle on the anterior aspect of the thigh

rectus sheaths   tissue that makes up the linea alba

retinacula   fibrous bands that sheath the tendons at the wrist

rhomboid major   muscle that attaches the vertebral border of the scapula to the spinous process of the thoracic vertebrae

rhomboid minor   muscle that attaches the vertebral border of the scapula to the spinous process of the thoracic vertebrae

rotator cuff   (also, musculotendinous cuff) the circle of tendons around the shoulder joint

sartorius   band-like muscle that flexes, abducts, and laterally rotates the leg at the hip

scalene muscles   flex, laterally flex, and rotate the head; contribute to deep inhalation

segmental muscle group   interspinales and intertransversarii muscles that bring together the spinous and transverse processes of each consecutive vertebra

semimembranosus   hamstring muscle

semispinalis capitis   transversospinales muscle associated with the head region

semispinalis cervicis   transversospinales muscle associated with the cervical region

semispinalis thoracis   transversospinales muscle associated with the thoracic region

semitendinosus   hamstring muscle

serratus anterior   large and flat muscle that originates on the ribs and inserts onto the scapula

soleus   wide, flat muscle deep to the gastrocnemius

sphincter urethrovaginalis   deep perineal muscle in females

spinalis capitis   muscle of the spinalis group associated with the head region

spinalis cervicis   muscle of the spinalis group associated with the cervical region

spinalis group   medially placed muscles of the erector spinae

spinalis thoracis   muscle of the spinalis group associated with the thoracic region

splenius   posterior neck muscles; includes the splenius capitis and splenius cervicis

splenius capitis   neck muscle that inserts into the head region

splenius cervicis   neck muscle that inserts into the cervical region

sternocleidomastoid   major muscle that laterally flexes and rotates the head

sternohyoid   muscle that depresses the hyoid bone

sternothyroid   muscle that depresses the larynx's thyroid cartilage

styloglossus   muscle that originates on the styloid bone, and allows upward and backward motion of the tongue

stylohyoid   muscle that elevates the hyoid bone posteriorly

subclavius   muscle that stabilizes the clavicle during movement

subscapularis   muscle that originates on the anterior scapula and medially rotates the arm

superficial anterior compartment of the forearm   flexor carpi radialis, palmaris longus, flexor carpi ulnaris, flexor digitorum superficialis, and their associated blood vessels and nerves

superficial posterior compartment of the forearm   extensor radialis longus, extensor carpi radialis brevis, extensor digitorum, extensor digiti minimi, extensor carpi ulnaris, and their associated blood vessels and nerves

superior extensor retinaculum   transverse ligament of the ankle

superior gemellus   muscle deep to the gluteus maximus on the lateral surface of the thigh that laterally rotates the femur at the hip

supinator   muscle that moves the palm and forearm anteriorly

suprahyoid muscles   neck muscles that are superior to the hyoid bone

supraspinatus   muscle that abducts the arm

synergist   muscle whose contraction helps a prime mover in an action

temporalis   muscle that retracts the mandible

tendinous intersections   three transverse bands of collagen fibers that divide the rectus abdominis into segments

tensor fascia lata   muscle that flexes and abducts the thigh

teres major   muscle that extends the arm and assists in adduction and medial rotation of it

teres minor   muscle that laterally rotates and extends the arm

thenar   group of muscles on the lateral aspect of the palm

thenar eminence   rounded contour of muscle at the base of the thumb

thyrohyoid   muscle that depresses the hyoid bone and elevates the larynx's thyroid cartilage

tibialis anterior   muscle located on the lateral surface of the tibia

tibialis posterior   muscle that plantar flexes and inverts the foot

transversospinales   muscles that originate at the transverse processes and insert at the spinous processes of the vertebrae

transversus abdominis   deep layer of the abdomen that has fascicles arranged transversely around the abdomen

trapezius   muscle that stabilizes the upper part of the back

tri   three

triceps brachii   three-headed muscle that extends the forearm

unipennate   pennate muscle that has fascicles located on one side of the tendon

urogenital triangle   anterior triangle of the perineum that includes the external genitals

vastus intermedius   quadricep muscle that is between the vastus lateralis and vastus medialis and is deep to the rectus femoris

vastus lateralis   quadricep muscle on the lateral aspect of the thigh

vastus medialis   quadricep muscle on the medial aspect of the thigh

Chapter Review

11.1 Interactions of Skeletal Muscles, Their Fascicle Arrangement, and Their Lever Systems

Skeletal muscles each have an origin and an insertion. The end of the muscle that attaches to the bone being pulled is called the muscle's insertion and the end of the muscle attached to a fixed, or stabilized, bone is called the origin. The muscle primarily responsible for a movement is called the prime mover, and muscles that assist in this action are called synergists. A synergist that makes the insertion site more stable is called a fixator. Meanwhile, a muscle with the opposite action of the prime mover is called an antagonist. Several factors contribute to the force generated by a skeletal muscle. One is the arrangement of the fascicles in the skeletal muscle. Fascicles can be parallel, circular, convergent, pennate, fusiform, or triangular. Each arrangement has its own range of motion and ability to do work.

11.2 Naming Skeletal Muscles

Muscle names are based on many characteristics. The location of a muscle in the body is important. Some muscles are named based on their size and location, such as the gluteal muscles of the buttocks. Other muscle names can indicate the location in the body or bones with which the muscle is associated, such as the tibialis anterior. The shapes of some muscles are distinctive; for example, the direction of the muscle fibers is used to describe muscles of the body midline. The origin and/or insertion can also be features used to name a muscle; examples are the biceps brachii, triceps brachii, and the pectoralis major.

11.3 Axial Muscles of the Head, Neck, and Back

Muscles are either axial muscles or appendicular. The axial muscles are grouped based on location, function, or both. Some axial muscles cross over to the appendicular skeleton. The muscles of the head and neck are all axial. The muscles in the face create facial expression by inserting into the skin rather than onto bone. Muscles that move the eyeballs are extrinsic, meaning they originate outside of the eye and insert onto it. Tongue muscles are both extrinsic and intrinsic. The genioglossus depresses the tongue and moves it anteriorly; the styloglossus lifts the tongue and retracts it; the palatoglossus elevates the back of the tongue; and the hyoglossus depresses and flattens it. The muscles of the anterior neck facilitate swallowing and speech, stabilize the hyoid bone and position the larynx. The muscles of the neck stabilize and move the head. The sternocleidomastoid divides the neck into anterior and posterior triangles.

The muscles of the back and neck that move the vertebral column are complex, overlapping, and can be divided into five groups. The splenius group includes the splenius capitis and the splenius cervicis. The erector spinae has three subgroups. The iliocostalis group includes the iliocostalis cervicis, the iliocostalis thoracis, and the iliocostalis lumborum. The longissimus group includes the longissimus capitis, the longissimus cervicis, and the longissimus thoracis. The spinalis group includes the spinalis capitis, the spinalis

cervicis, and the spinalis thoracis. The transversospinales include the semispinalis capitis, semispinalis cervicis, semispinalis thoracis, multifidus, and rotatores. The segmental muscles include the interspinales and intertransversarii. Finally, the scalenes include the anterior scalene, middle scalene, and posterior scalene.

11.4 Axial Muscles of the Abdominal Wall, and Thorax

Made of skin, fascia, and four pairs of muscle, the anterior abdominal wall protects the organs located in the abdomen and moves the vertebral column. These muscles include the rectus abdominis, which extends through the entire length of the trunk, the external oblique, the internal oblique, and the transversus abdominis. The quadratus lumborum forms the posterior abdominal wall.

The muscles of the thorax play a large role in breathing, especially the dome-shaped diaphragm. When it contracts and flattens, the volume inside the pleural cavities increases, which decreases the pressure within them. As a result, air will flow into the lungs. The external and internal intercostal muscles span the space between the ribs and help change the shape of the rib cage and the volume-pressure ratio inside the pleural cavities during inspiration and expiration.

The perineum muscles play roles in urination in both sexes, ejaculation in males, and vaginal contraction in females. The pelvic floor muscles support the pelvic organs, resist intra-abdominal pressure, and work as sphincters for the urethra, rectum, and vagina.

11.5 Muscles of the Pectoral Girdle and Upper Limbs

The clavicle and scapula make up the pectoral girdle, which provides a stable origin for the muscles that move the humerus. The muscles that position and stabilize the pectoral girdle are located on the thorax. The anterior thoracic muscles are the subclavius, pectoralis minor, and the serratus anterior. The posterior thoracic muscles are the trapezius, levator scapulae, rhomboid major, and rhomboid minor. Nine muscles cross the shoulder joint to move the humerus. The ones that originate on the axial skeleton are the pectoralis major and the latissimus dorsi. The deltoid, subscapularis, supraspinatus, infraspinatus, teres major, teres minor, and coracobrachialis originate on the scapula.

The forearm flexors include the biceps brachii, brachialis, and brachioradialis. The extensors are the triceps brachii and anconeus. The pronators are the pronator teres and the pronator quadratus. The supinator is the only one that turns the forearm anteriorly.

The extrinsic muscles of the hands originate along the forearm and insert into the hand in order to facilitate crude movements of the wrists, hands, and fingers. The superficial anterior compartment of the forearm produces flexion. These muscles are the flexor carpi radialis, palmaris longus, flexor carpi ulnaris, and the flexor digitorum superficialis. The deep anterior compartment produces flexion as well. These are the flexor pollicis longus and the flexor digitorum profundus. The rest of the compartments produce extension. The extensor carpi radialis longus, extensor carpi radialis brevis, extensor digitorum, extensor digiti minimi, and extensor carpi ulnaris are the muscles found in the superficial posterior compartment. The deep posterior compartment includes the abductor longus, extensor pollicis brevis, extensor pollicis longus, and the extensor indicis.

Finally, the intrinsic muscles of the hands allow our fingers to make precise movements, such as typing and writing. They both originate and insert within the hand. The thenar muscles, which are located on the lateral part of the palm, are the abductor pollicis brevis, opponens pollicis, flexor pollicis brevis, and adductor pollicis. The hypothenar muscles, which are located on the medial part of the palm, are the abductor digiti minimi, flexor digiti minimi brevis, and opponens digiti minimi. The intermediate muscles, located in the middle of the palm, are the lumbricals, palmar interossei, and dorsal interossei.

11.6 Appendicular Muscles of the Pelvic Girdle and Lower Limbs

The pelvic girdle attaches the legs to the axial skeleton. The hip joint is where the pelvic girdle and the leg come together. The hip is joined to the pelvic girdle by many muscles. In the gluteal region, the psoas major and iliacus form the iliopsoas. The large and strong gluteus maximus, gluteus medius, and gluteus minimus extend and abduct the femur. Along with the gluteus maximus, the tensor fascia lata muscle forms the iliotibial tract. The lateral rotators of the femur at the hip are the piriformis, obturator internus, obturator externus, superior gemellus, inferior gemellus, and quadratus femoris. On the medial part of the thigh, the adductor longus, adductor brevis, and adductor magnus adduct the thigh and medially rotate it. The pectineus muscle adducts and flexes the femur at the hip.

The thigh muscles that move the femur, tibia, and fibula are divided into medial, anterior, and posterior compartments. The medial compartment includes the adductors, pectineus, and the gracilis. The anterior compartment comprises the quadriceps femoris, quadriceps tendon, patellar ligament, and the sartorius. The quadriceps femoris is made of four muscles: the rectus femoris, the vastus lateralis, the vastus medius, and the vastus intermedius, which together extend the knee. The posterior compartment of the thigh includes the hamstrings: the biceps femoris, semitendinosus, and the semimembranosus, which all flex the knee.

The muscles of the leg that move the foot and toes are divided into anterior, lateral, superficial- and deep-posterior compartments. The anterior compartment includes the tibialis anterior, the extensor hallucis longus, the extensor digitorum longus, and the fibularis (peroneus) tertius. The lateral compartment houses the fibularis (peroneus) longus and the fibularis (peroneus) brevis. The superficial posterior compartment has the gastrocnemius, soleus, and plantaris; and the deep posterior compartment has the popliteus, tibialis posterior, flexor digitorum longus, and flexor hallucis longus.

Review Questions

1. Which of the following is unique to the muscles of facial expression?
   a. They all originate from the scalp musculature.
   b. They insert onto the cartilage found around the face.
   c. They only insert onto the facial bones.
   d. They insert into the skin.

2. Which of the following helps an agonist work?
   a. a synergist
   b. a fixator
   c. an insertion
   d. an antagonist

3. Which of the following statements is correct about what happens during flexion?
   a. The angle between bones is increased.
   b. The angle between bones is decreased.
   c. The bone moves away from the body.
   d. The bone moves toward the center of the body.

4. Which is moved the *least* during muscle contraction?
   a. the origin
   b. the insertion
   c. the ligaments
   d. the joints

5. Which muscle has a convergent pattern of fascicles?
   a. biceps brachii
   b. gluteus maximus
   c. pectoralis major
   d. rectus femoris

6. A muscle that has a pattern of fascicles running along the long axis of the muscle has which of the following fascicle arrangements?
   a. circular
   b. pennate
   c. parallel
   d. rectus

7. Which arrangement *best* describes a bipennate muscle?
   a. The muscle fibers feed in on an angle to a long tendon from both sides.
   b. The muscle fibers feed in on an angle to a long tendon from all directions.
   c. The muscle fibers feed in on an angle to a long tendon from one side.
   d. The muscle fibers on one side of a tendon feed into it at a certain angle and muscle fibers on the other side of the tendon feed into it at the opposite angle.

8. The location of a muscle's insertion and origin can determine _____.
   a. action
   b. the force of contraction
   c. muscle name
   d. the load a muscle can carry

9. Where is the temporalis muscle located?
   a. on the forehead
   b. in the neck
   c. on the side of the head
   d. on the chin

10. Which muscle name does *not* make sense?
    a. extensor digitorum
    b. gluteus minimus
    c. biceps femoris
    d. extensor minimus longus

11. Which of the following terms would be used in the name of a muscle that moves the leg away from the body?
    a. flexor
    b. adductor
    c. extensor
    d. abductor

12. Which of the following is a prime mover in head flexion?
    a. occipitofrontalis
    b. corrugator supercilii
    c. sternocleidomastoid
    d. masseter

13. Where is the inferior oblique muscle located?
    a. in the abdomen
    b. in the eye socket
    c. in the anterior neck
    d. in the face

14. What is the action of the masseter?
    a. swallowing
    b. chewing
    c. moving the lips
    d. closing the eye

15. The names of the extrinsic tongue muscles commonly end in _____.
    a. -glottis
    b. -glossus
    c. -gluteus
    d. -hyoid

16. What is the function of the erector spinae?
    a. movement of the arms
    b. stabilization of the pelvic girdle
    c. postural support
    d. rotating of the vertebral column

17. Which of the following abdominal muscles is not a part of the anterior abdominal wall?
    a. quadratus lumborum
    b. rectus abdominis
    c. interior oblique
    d. exterior oblique

18. Which muscle pair plays a role in respiration?
    a. intertransversarii, interspinales
    b. semispinalis cervicis, semispinalis thoracis
    c. trapezius, rhomboids
    d. diaphragm, scalene

19. What is the linea alba?
    a. a small muscle that helps with compression of the abdominal organs
    b. a long tendon that runs down the middle of the rectus abdominis
    c. a long band of collagen fibers that connects the hip to the knee
    d. another name for the tendinous inscription

20. The rhomboid major and minor muscles are deep to the _____.
    a. rectus abdominis
    b. scalene muscles
    c. trapezius
    d. ligamentum nuchae

21. Which muscle extends the forearm?
    a. biceps brachii
    b. triceps brachii
    c. brachialis
    d. deltoid

22. What is the origin of the wrist flexors?
    a. the lateral epicondyle of the humerus
    b. the medial epicondyle of the humerus
    c. the carpal bones of the wrist
    d. the deltoid tuberosity of the humerus

23. Which muscles stabilize the pectoral girdle?
    a. axial and scapular
    b. axial
    c. appendicular
    d. axial and appendicular

24. The large muscle group that attaches the leg to the pelvic girdle and produces extension of the hip joint is the _____ group.
    a. gluteal
    b. obturator
    c. adductor
    d. abductor

25. Which muscle produces movement that allows you to cross your legs?
    a. the gluteus maximus
    b. the piriformis
    c. the gracilis
    d. the sartorius

26. What is the largest muscle in the lower leg?
    a. soleus
    b. gastrocnemius
    c. tibialis anterior
    d. tibialis posterior

27. The vastus intermedius muscle is deep to which of the following muscles?
    a. biceps femoris
    b. rectus femoris
    c. vastus medialis
    d. vastus lateralis

Critical Thinking Questions

28. What effect does fascicle arrangement have on a muscle's action?

29. Movements of the body occur at joints. Describe how muscles are arranged around the joints of the body.

30. Explain how a synergist assists an agonist by being a fixator.

31. Describe the different criteria that contribute to how skeletal muscles are named.

32. Explain the difference between axial and appendicular muscles.

33. Describe the muscles of the anterior neck.

34. Why are the muscles of the face different from typical skeletal muscle?

35. Describe the fascicle arrangement in the muscles of the abdominal wall. How do they relate to each other?

36. What are some similarities and differences between the diaphragm and the pelvic diaphragm?

37. The tendons of which muscles form the rotator cuff? Why is the rotator cuff important?

38. List the general muscle groups of the shoulders and upper limbs as well as their subgroups.

39. Which muscles form the hamstrings? How do they function together?

40. Which muscles form the quadriceps? How do they function together?

CHAPTER 12
The Nervous System and Nervous Tissue

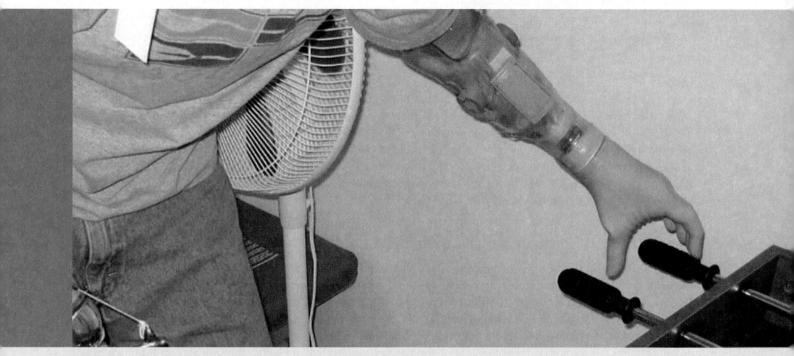

Figure 12.1   Robotic Arms Playing Foosball As the neural circuitry of the nervous system has become more fully understood and robotics more sophisticated, it is now possible to integrate technology with the body and restore abilities following traumatic events. At some point in the future, will this type of technology lead to the ability to augment our nervous systems? (credit: U.S. Army/Wikimedia Commons)

CHAPTER OBJECTIVES
After studying this chapter, you will be able to:

- Name the major divisions of the nervous system, both anatomical and functional
- Describe the functional and structural differences between gray matter and white matter structures
- Name the parts of the multipolar neuron in order of polarity
- List the types of glial cells and assign each to the proper division of the nervous system, along with their function(s)
- Distinguish the major functions of the nervous system: sensation, integration, and response
- Describe the components of the membrane that establish the resting membrane potential
- Describe the changes that occur to the membrane that result in the action potential
- Explain the differences between types of graded potentials
- Categorize the major neurotransmitters by chemical type and effect

INTRODUCTION The nervous system is a very complex organ system. In Peter D. Kramer's book *Listening to Prozac*, a pharmaceutical researcher is quoted as saying, "If the human brain were simple enough for us to understand, we would be too simple to understand it" (1994). That quote is from the early 1990s; in the two decades since, progress has continued at an amazing rate within the scientific disciplines of neuroscience. It is an interesting conundrum to consider that the complexity of the nervous system may be too complex for it (that is, for us) to completely unravel. But our current level of understanding is probably nowhere close to that limit.

One easy way to begin to understand the structure of the nervous system is to start with the large divisions and work through to a more in-depth understanding. In other chapters, the finer details of the nervous system will be explained, but first looking at an overview of the system will allow you to begin to understand how its parts work together. The focus of this chapter is on nervous (neural) tissue, both its structure and its function. But before you learn about that, you will see a big picture of the system—actually, a few big pictures.

12.1 Basic Structure and Function of the Nervous System

LEARNING OBJECTIVES

By the end of this section, you will be able to:
- Identify the anatomical and functional divisions of the nervous system
- Relate the functional and structural differences between gray matter and white matter structures of the nervous system to the structure of neurons
- List the basic functions of the nervous system

The picture you have in your mind of the nervous system probably includes the **brain**, the nervous tissue contained within the cranium, and the **spinal cord**, the extension of nervous tissue within the vertebral column. That suggests it is made of two organs—and you may not even think of the spinal cord as an organ—but the nervous system is a very complex structure. Within the brain, many different and separate regions are responsible for many different and separate functions. It is as if the nervous system is composed of many organs that all look similar and can only be differentiated using tools such as the microscope or electrophysiology. In comparison, it is easy to see that the stomach is different than the esophagus or the liver, so you can imagine the digestive system as a collection of specific organs.

The Central and Peripheral Nervous Systems

The nervous system can be divided into two major regions: the central and peripheral nervous systems. The **central nervous system (CNS)** is the brain and spinal cord, and the **peripheral nervous system (PNS)** is everything else (Figure 12.2). The brain is contained within the cranial cavity of the skull, and the spinal cord is contained within the vertebral cavity of the vertebral column. It is a bit of an oversimplification to say that the CNS is what is inside these two cavities and the peripheral nervous system is outside of them, but that is one way to start to think about it. In actuality, there are some elements of the peripheral nervous system that are within the cranial or vertebral cavities. The peripheral nervous system is so named because it is on the periphery—meaning beyond the brain and spinal cord. Depending on different aspects of the nervous system, the dividing line between central and peripheral is not necessarily universal.

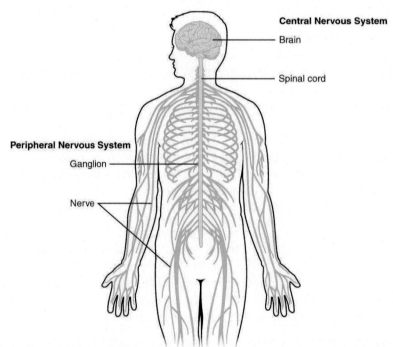

FIGURE 12.2   Central and Peripheral Nervous System   The structures of the PNS are referred to as ganglia and nerves, which can be seen as distinct structures. The equivalent structures in the CNS are not obvious from this overall perspective and are best examined in prepared tissue under the microscope.

Nervous tissue, present in both the CNS and PNS, contains two basic types of cells: neurons and glial cells. A **glial cell** is one of a variety of cells that provide a framework of tissue that supports the neurons and their activities. The

neuron is the more functionally important of the two, in terms of the communicative function of the nervous system. To describe the functional divisions of the nervous system, it is important to understand the structure of a neuron. Neurons are cells and therefore have a **soma**, or cell body, but they also have extensions of the cell; each extension is generally referred to as a **process**. There is one important process that every neuron has called an **axon**, which is the fiber that connects a neuron with its target. Another type of process that branches off from the soma is the **dendrite**. Dendrites are responsible for receiving most of the input from other neurons. Looking at nervous tissue, there are regions that predominantly contain cell bodies and regions that are largely composed of just axons. These two regions within nervous system structures are often referred to as **gray matter** (the regions with many cell bodies and dendrites) or **white matter** (the regions with many axons). Figure 12.3 demonstrates the appearance of these regions in the brain and spinal cord. The colors ascribed to these regions are what would be seen in "fresh," or unstained, nervous tissue. Gray matter is not necessarily gray. It can be pinkish because of blood content, or even slightly tan, depending on how long the tissue has been preserved. But white matter is white because axons are insulated by a lipid-rich substance called **myelin**. Lipids can appear as white ("fatty") material, much like the fat on a raw piece of chicken or beef. Actually, gray matter may have that color ascribed to it because next to the white matter, it is just darker—hence, gray.

The distinction between gray matter and white matter is most often applied to central nervous tissue, which has large regions that can be seen with the unaided eye. When looking at peripheral structures, often a microscope is used and the tissue is stained with artificial colors. That is not to say that central nervous tissue cannot be stained and viewed under a microscope, but unstained tissue is most likely from the CNS—for example, a frontal section of the brain or cross section of the spinal cord.

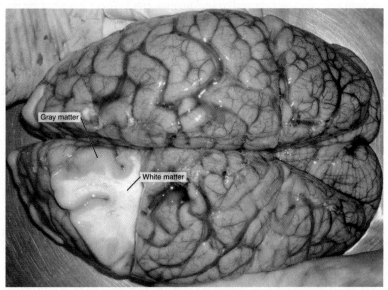

FIGURE 12.3   Gray Matter and White Matter   A brain removed during an autopsy, with a partial section removed, shows white matter surrounded by gray matter. Gray matter makes up the outer cortex of the brain. (credit: modification of work by "Suseno"/Wikimedia Commons)

Regardless of the appearance of stained or unstained tissue, the cell bodies of neurons or axons can be located in discrete anatomical structures that need to be named. Those names are specific to whether the structure is central or peripheral. A localized collection of neuron cell bodies in the CNS is referred to as a **nucleus**. In the PNS, a cluster of neuron cell bodies is referred to as a **ganglion**. Figure 12.4 indicates how the term nucleus has a few different meanings within anatomy and physiology. It is the center of an atom, where protons and neutrons are found; it is the center of a cell, where the DNA is found; and it is a center of some function in the CNS. There is also a potentially confusing use of the word ganglion (plural = ganglia) that has a historical explanation. In the central nervous system, there is a group of nuclei that are connected together and were once called the basal ganglia before "ganglion" became accepted as a description for a peripheral structure. Some sources refer to this group of nuclei as the "basal nuclei" to avoid confusion.

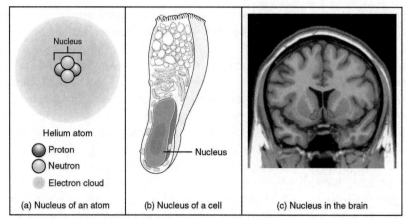

FIGURE 12.4 **What Is a Nucleus?**   (a) The nucleus of an atom contains its protons and neutrons. (b) The nucleus of a cell is the organelle that contains DNA. (c) A nucleus in the CNS is a localized center of function with the cell bodies of several neurons, shown here circled in red. (credit c: "Was a bee"/Wikimedia Commons)

Terminology applied to bundles of axons also differs depending on location. A bundle of axons, or fibers, found in the CNS is called a **tract** whereas the same thing in the PNS would be called a **nerve**. There is an important point to make about these terms, which is that they can both be used to refer to the same bundle of axons. When those axons are in the PNS, the term is nerve, but if they are CNS, the term is tract. The most obvious example of this is the axons that project from the retina into the brain. Those axons are called the optic nerve as they leave the eye, but when they are inside the cranium, they are referred to as the optic tract. There is a specific place where the name changes, which is the optic chiasm, but they are still the same axons (Figure 12.5). A similar situation outside of science can be described for some roads. Imagine a road called "Broad Street" in a town called "Anyville." The road leaves Anyville and goes to the next town over, called "Hometown." When the road crosses the line between the two towns and is in Hometown, its name changes to "Main Street." That is the idea behind the naming of the retinal axons. In the PNS, they are called the optic nerve, and in the CNS, they are the optic tract. Table 12.1 helps to clarify which of these terms apply to the central or peripheral nervous systems.

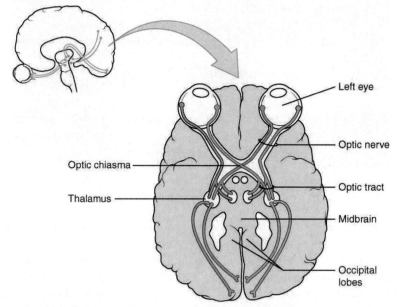

FIGURE 12.5 **Optic Nerve Versus Optic Tract**   This drawing of the connections of the eye to the brain shows the optic nerve extending from the eye to the chiasm, where the structure continues as the optic tract. The same axons extend from the eye to the brain through these two bundles of fibers, but the chiasm represents the border between peripheral and central.

🔗 INTERACTIVE LINK

In 2003, the Nobel Prize in Physiology or Medicine was awarded to Paul C. Lauterbur and Sir Peter Mansfield for discoveries related to magnetic resonance imaging (MRI). This is a tool to see the structures of the body (not just the nervous system) that depends on magnetic fields associated with certain atomic nuclei. The utility of this technique in the nervous system is that fat tissue and water appear as different shades between black and white. Because white matter is fatty (from myelin) and gray matter is not, they can be easily distinguished in MRI images. Try this PhET simulation (http://openstax.org/l/nobel_2) that demonstrates the use of this technology and compares it with other types of imaging technologies. Also, the results from an MRI session are compared with images obtained from X-ray or computed tomography. How do the imaging techniques shown in this game indicate the separation of white and gray matter compared with the freshly dissected tissue shown earlier?

Structures of the CNS and PNS

	CNS	PNS
Group of Neuron Cell Bodies (i.e., gray matter)	Nucleus	Ganglion
Bundle of Axons (i.e., white matter)	Tract	Nerve

TABLE 12.1

Functional Divisions of the Nervous System

The nervous system can also be divided on the basis of its functions, but anatomical divisions and functional divisions are different. The CNS and the PNS both contribute to the same functions, but those functions can be attributed to different regions of the brain (such as the cerebral cortex or the hypothalamus) or to different ganglia in the periphery. The problem with trying to fit functional differences into anatomical divisions is that sometimes the same structure can be part of several functions. For example, the optic nerve carries signals from the retina that are either used for the conscious perception of visual stimuli, which takes place in the cerebral cortex, or for the reflexive responses of smooth muscle tissue that are processed through the hypothalamus.

There are two ways to consider how the nervous system is divided functionally. First, the basic functions of the nervous system are sensation, integration, and response. Secondly, control of the body can be somatic or autonomic—divisions that are largely defined by the structures that are involved in the response. There is also a region of the peripheral nervous system that is called the enteric nervous system that is responsible for a specific set of the functions within the realm of autonomic control related to gastrointestinal functions.

Basic Functions

The nervous system is involved in receiving information about the environment around us (sensation) and generating responses to that information (motor responses). The nervous system can be divided into regions that are responsible for **sensation** (sensory functions) and for the **response** (motor functions). But there is a third function that needs to be included. Sensory input needs to be integrated with other sensations, as well as with memories, emotional state, or learning (cognition). Some regions of the nervous system are termed **integration** or association areas. The process of integration combines sensory perceptions and higher cognitive functions such as memories, learning, and emotion to produce a response.

Sensation. The first major function of the nervous system is sensation—receiving information about the environment to gain input about what is happening outside the body (or, sometimes, within the body). The sensory functions of the nervous system register the presence of a change from homeostasis or a particular event in the environment, known as a **stimulus**. The senses we think of most are the "big five": taste, smell, touch, sight, and hearing. The stimuli for taste and smell are both chemical substances (molecules, compounds, ions, etc.), touch is physical or mechanical stimuli that interact with the skin, sight is light stimuli, and hearing is the perception of sound, which is a physical stimulus similar to some aspects of touch. There are actually more senses than just those, but that list represents the major senses. Those five are all senses that receive stimuli from the outside world, and of which there is conscious perception. Additional sensory stimuli might be from the internal environment (inside the body), such as the stretch of an organ wall or the concentration of certain ions in the blood.

Response. The nervous system produces a response on the basis of the stimuli perceived by sensory structures. An obvious response would be the movement of muscles, such as withdrawing a hand from a hot stove, but there are broader uses of the term. The nervous system can cause the contraction of all three types of muscle tissue. For example, skeletal muscle contracts to move the skeleton, cardiac muscle is influenced as heart rate increases during exercise, and smooth muscle contracts as the digestive system moves food along the digestive tract. Responses also include the neural control of glands in the body as well, such as the production and secretion of sweat by the eccrine and merocrine sweat glands found in the skin to lower body temperature.

Responses can be divided into those that are voluntary or conscious (contraction of skeletal muscle) and those that are involuntary (contraction of smooth muscles, regulation of cardiac muscle, activation of glands). Voluntary responses are governed by the somatic nervous system and involuntary responses are governed by the autonomic nervous system, which are discussed in the next section.

Integration. Stimuli that are received by sensory structures are communicated to the nervous system where that information is processed. This is called integration. Stimuli are compared with, or integrated with, other stimuli, memories of previous stimuli, or the state of a person at a particular time. This leads to the specific response that will be generated. Seeing a baseball pitched to a batter will not automatically cause the batter to swing. The trajectory of the ball and its speed will need to be considered. Maybe the count is three balls and one strike, and the batter wants to let this pitch go by in the hope of getting a walk to first base. Or maybe the batter's team is so far ahead, it would be fun to just swing away.

Controlling the Body

The nervous system can be divided into two parts mostly on the basis of a functional difference in responses. The **somatic nervous system (SNS)** is responsible for conscious perception and voluntary motor responses. Voluntary motor response means the contraction of skeletal muscle, but those contractions are not always voluntary in the sense that you have to want to perform them. Some somatic motor responses are reflexes, and often happen without a conscious decision to perform them. If your friend jumps out from behind a corner and yells "Boo!" you will be startled and you might scream or leap back. You didn't decide to do that, and you may not have wanted to give your friend a reason to laugh at your expense, but it is a reflex involving skeletal muscle contractions. Other motor responses become automatic (in other words, unconscious) as a person learns motor skills (referred to as "habit learning" or "procedural memory").

The **autonomic nervous system (ANS)** is responsible for involuntary control of the body, usually for the sake of homeostasis (regulation of the internal environment). Sensory input for autonomic functions can be from sensory structures tuned to external or internal environmental stimuli. The motor output extends to smooth and cardiac muscle as well as glandular tissue. The role of the autonomic system is to regulate the organ systems of the body, which usually means to control homeostasis. Sweat glands, for example, are controlled by the autonomic system. When you are hot, sweating helps cool your body down. That is a homeostatic mechanism. But when you are nervous, you might start sweating also. That is not homeostatic, it is the physiological response to an emotional state.

There is another division of the nervous system that describes functional responses. The **enteric nervous system (ENS)** is responsible for controlling the smooth muscle and glandular tissue in your digestive system. It is a large part of the PNS, and is not dependent on the CNS. It is sometimes valid, however, to consider the enteric system to be a part of the autonomic system because the neural structures that make up the enteric system are a component of the autonomic output that regulates digestion. There are some differences between the two, but for our purposes here there will be a good bit of overlap. See Figure 12.6 for examples of where these divisions of the nervous system can be found.

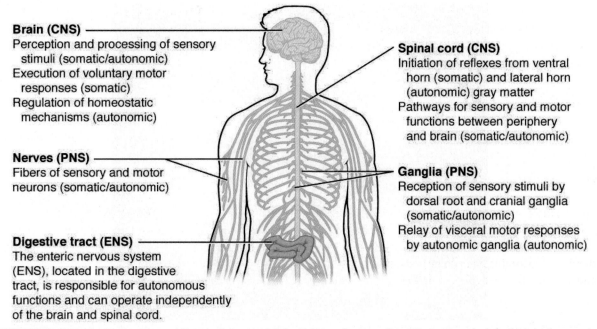

Brain (CNS)
Perception and processing of sensory
    stimuli (somatic/autonomic)
Execution of voluntary motor
    responses (somatic)
Regulation of homeostatic
    mechanisms (autonomic)

Nerves (PNS)
Fibers of sensory and motor
neurons (somatic/autonomic)

Digestive tract (ENS)
The enteric nervous system
(ENS), located in the digestive
tract, is responsible for autonomous
functions and can operate independently
of the brain and spinal cord.

Spinal cord (CNS)
Initiation of reflexes from ventral
    horn (somatic) and lateral horn
    (autonomic) gray matter
Pathways for sensory and motor
    functions between periphery
    and brain (somatic/autonomic)

Ganglia (PNS)
Reception of sensory stimuli by
    dorsal root and cranial ganglia
    (somatic/autonomic)
Relay of visceral motor responses
    by autonomic ganglia (autonomic)

FIGURE 12.6   Somatic, Autonomic, and Enteric Structures of the Nervous System   Somatic structures include the spinal nerves, both motor and sensory fibers, as well as the sensory ganglia (posterior root ganglia and cranial nerve ganglia). Autonomic structures are found in the nerves also, but include the sympathetic and parasympathetic ganglia. The enteric nervous system includes the nervous tissue within the organs of the digestive tract.

⊘ INTERACTIVE LINK

Visit this site (http://openstax.org/l/troublewstairs) to read about a woman that notices that her daughter is having trouble walking up the stairs. This leads to the discovery of a hereditary condition that affects the brain and spinal cord. The electromyography and MRI tests indicated deficiencies in the spinal cord and cerebellum, both of which are responsible for controlling coordinated movements. To what functional division of the nervous system would these structures belong?

Everyday Connection

How Much of Your Brain Do You Use?

Have you ever heard the claim that humans only use 10 percent of their brains? Maybe you have seen an advertisement on a website saying that there is a secret to unlocking the full potential of your mind—as if there were 90 percent of your brain sitting idle, just waiting for you to use it. If you see an ad like that, don't click. It isn't true.

An easy way to see how much of the brain a person uses is to take measurements of brain activity while performing a task. An example of this kind of measurement is functional magnetic resonance imaging (fMRI), which generates a map of the most active areas and can be generated and presented in three dimensions (Figure 12.7). This procedure is different from the standard MRI technique because it is measuring changes in the tissue in time with an experimental condition or event.

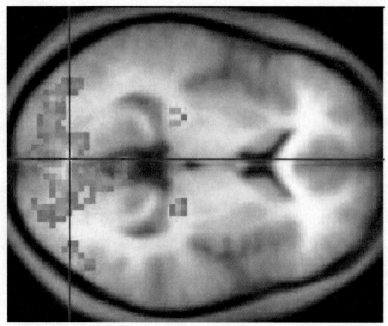

FIGURE 12.7   fMRI   This fMRI shows activation of the visual cortex in response to visual stimuli. (credit: "Superborsuk"/Wikimedia Commons)

The underlying assumption is that active nervous tissue will have greater blood flow. By having the subject perform a visual task, activity all over the brain can be measured. Consider this possible experiment: the subject is told to look at a screen with a black dot in the middle (a fixation point). A photograph of a face is projected on the screen away from the center. The subject has to look at the photograph and decipher what it is. The subject has been instructed to push a button if the photograph is of someone they recognize. The photograph might be of a celebrity, so the subject would press the button, or it might be of a random person unknown to the subject, so the subject would not press the button.

In this task, visual sensory areas would be active, integrating areas would be active, motor areas responsible for moving the eyes would be active, and motor areas for pressing the button with a finger would be active. Those areas are distributed all around the brain and the fMRI images would show activity in more than just 10 percent of the brain (some evidence suggests that about 80 percent of the brain is using energy—based on blood flow to the tissue—during well-defined tasks similar to the one suggested above). This task does not even include all of the functions the brain performs. There is no language response, the body is mostly lying still in the MRI machine, and it does not consider the autonomic functions that would be ongoing in the background.

12.2 Nervous Tissue

LEARNING OBJECTIVES

By the end of this section, you will be able to:
- Describe the basic structure of a neuron
- Identify the different types of neurons on the basis of polarity
- List the glial cells of the CNS and describe their function
- List the glial cells of the PNS and describe their function

Nervous tissue is composed of two types of cells, neurons and glial cells. Neurons are the primary type of cell that most anyone associates with the nervous system. They are responsible for the computation and communication that the nervous system provides. They are electrically active and release chemical signals to target cells. Glial cells, or glia, are known to play a supporting role for nervous tissue. Ongoing research pursues an expanded role that glial cells might play in signaling, but neurons are still considered the basis of this function. Neurons are important, but without glial support they would not be able to perform their function.

Neurons

Neurons are the cells considered to be the basis of nervous tissue. They are responsible for the electrical signals that communicate information about sensations, and that produce movements in response to those stimuli, along with inducing thought processes within the brain. An important part of the function of neurons is in their structure, or shape. The three-dimensional shape of these cells makes the immense numbers of connections within the nervous system possible.

Parts of a Neuron

As you learned in the first section, the main part of a neuron is the cell body, which is also known as the soma (soma = "body"). The cell body contains the nucleus and most of the major organelles. But what makes neurons special is that they have many extensions of their cell membranes, which are generally referred to as processes. Neurons are usually described as having one, and only one, axon—a fiber that emerges from the cell body and projects to target cells. That single axon can branch repeatedly to communicate with many target cells. It is the axon that propagates the nerve impulse, which is communicated to one or more cells. The other processes of the neuron are dendrites, which receive information from other neurons at specialized areas of contact called **synapses**. The dendrites are usually highly branched processes, providing locations for other neurons to communicate with the cell body. Information flows through a neuron from the dendrites, across the cell body, and down the axon. This gives the neuron a polarity—meaning that information flows in this one direction. Figure 12.8 shows the relationship of these parts to one another.

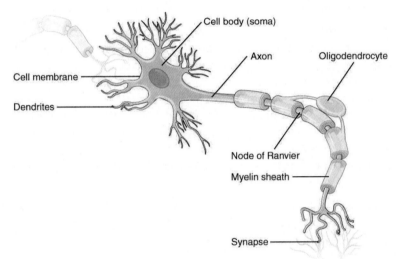

FIGURE 12.8 Parts of a Neuron   The major parts of the neuron are labeled on a multipolar neuron from the CNS.

Where the axon emerges from the cell body, there is a special region referred to as the **axon hillock**. This is a tapering of the cell body toward the axon fiber. Within the axon hillock, the cytoplasm changes to a solution of limited components called **axoplasm**. Because the axon hillock represents the beginning of the axon, it is also referred to as the **initial segment**.

Many axons are wrapped by an insulating substance called myelin, which is actually made from glial cells. Myelin acts as insulation much like the plastic or rubber that is used to insulate electrical wires. A key difference between myelin and the insulation on a wire is that there are gaps in the myelin covering of an axon. Each gap is called a **node of Ranvier** and is important to the way that electrical signals travel down the axon. The length of the axon between each gap, which is wrapped in myelin, is referred to as an **axon segment**. At the end of the axon is the **axon terminal**, where there are usually several branches extending toward the target cell, each of which ends in an enlargement called a **synaptic end bulb**. These bulbs are what make the connection with the target cell at the synapse.

Types of Neurons

There are many neurons in the nervous system—a number in the trillions. And there are many different types of neurons. They can be classified by many different criteria. The first way to classify them is by the number of processes attached to the cell body. Using the standard model of neurons, one of these processes is the axon, and the rest are dendrites. Because information flows through the neuron from dendrites or cell bodies toward the axon, these names are based on the neuron's polarity (Figure 12.9).

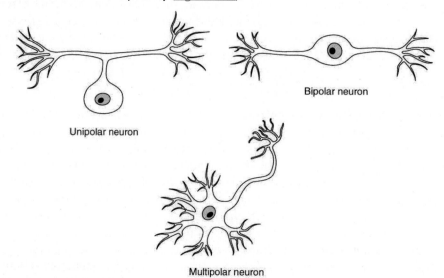

FIGURE 12.9   Neuron Classification by Shape   Unipolar cells have one process that includes both the axon and dendrite. Bipolar cells have two processes, the axon and a dendrite. Multipolar cells have more than two processes, the axon and two or more dendrites.

Unipolar cells have only one process emerging from the cell. True unipolar cells are only found in invertebrate animals, so the unipolar cells in humans are more appropriately called "pseudo-unipolar" cells. Invertebrate unipolar cells do not have dendrites. Human unipolar cells have an axon that emerges from the cell body, but it splits so that the axon can extend along a very long distance. At one end of the axon are dendrites, and at the other end, the axon forms synaptic connections with a target. Unipolar cells are exclusively sensory neurons and have two unique characteristics. First, their dendrites are receiving sensory information, sometimes directly from the stimulus itself. Secondly, the cell bodies of unipolar neurons are always found in ganglia. Sensory reception is a peripheral function (those dendrites are in the periphery, perhaps in the skin) so the cell body is in the periphery, though closer to the CNS in a ganglion. The axon projects from the dendrite endings, past the cell body in a ganglion, and into the central nervous system.

Bipolar cells have two processes, which extend from each end of the cell body, opposite to each other. One is the axon and one the dendrite. Bipolar cells are not very common. They are found mainly in the olfactory epithelium (where smell stimuli are sensed), and as part of the retina.

Multipolar neurons are all of the neurons that are not unipolar or bipolar. They have one axon and two or more dendrites (usually many more). With the exception of the unipolar sensory ganglion cells, and the two specific bipolar cells mentioned above, all other neurons are multipolar. Some cutting edge research suggests that certain neurons in the CNS do not conform to the standard model of "one, and only one" axon. Some sources describe a fourth type of neuron, called an anaxonic neuron. The name suggests that it has no axon (an- = "without"), but this is not accurate. Anaxonic neurons are very small, and if you look through a microscope at the standard resolution used in histology (approximately 400X to 1000X total magnification), you will not be able to distinguish any process specifically as an axon or a dendrite. Any of those processes can function as an axon depending on the conditions at any given time. Nevertheless, even if they cannot be easily seen, and one specific process is definitively the axon, these neurons have multiple processes and are therefore multipolar.

Neurons can also be classified on the basis of where they are found, who found them, what they do, or even what chemicals they use to communicate with each other. Some neurons referred to in this section on the nervous system are named on the basis of those sorts of classifications (Figure 12.10). For example, a multipolar neuron that has a very important role to play in a part of the brain called the cerebellum is known as a Purkinje (commonly pronounced per-KIN-gee) cell. It is named after the anatomist who discovered it (Jan Evangelista Purkinje, 1787–1869).

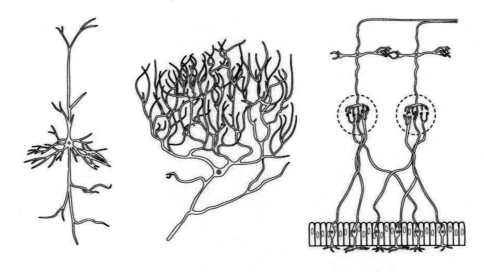

(a) Pyramidal cell of the
cerebral cortex

(b) Purkinje cell of the
cerebellar cortex

(c) Olfactory cells in the olfactory
epithelium and olfactory bulbs

FIGURE 12.10   Other Neuron Classifications   Three examples of neurons that are classified on the basis of other criteria. (a) The pyramidal cell is a multipolar cell with a cell body that is shaped something like a pyramid. (b) The Purkinje cell in the cerebellum was named after the scientist who originally described it. (c) Olfactory neurons are named for the functional group with which they belong.

Glial Cells

Glial cells, or neuroglia or simply glia, are the other type of cell found in nervous tissue. They are considered to be supporting cells, and many functions are directed at helping neurons complete their function for communication. The name glia comes from the Greek word that means "glue," and was coined by the German pathologist Rudolph Virchow, who wrote in 1856: "This connective substance, which is in the brain, the spinal cord, and the special sense nerves, is a kind of glue (neuroglia) in which the nervous elements are planted." Today, research into nervous tissue has shown that there are many deeper roles that these cells play. And research may find much more about them in the future.

There are six types of glial cells. Four of them are found in the CNS and two are found in the PNS. Table 12.2 outlines some common characteristics and functions.

Glial Cell Types by Location and Basic Function

CNS glia	PNS glia	Basic function
Astrocyte	Satellite cell	Support
Oligodendrocyte	Schwann cell	Insulation, myelination
Microglia	-	Immune surveillance and phagocytosis
Ependymal cell	-	Creating CSF

TABLE 12.2

Glial Cells of the CNS

One cell providing support to neurons of the CNS is the **astrocyte**, so named because it appears to be star-shaped under the microscope (astro- = "star"). Astrocytes have many processes extending from their main cell body (not axons or dendrites like neurons, just cell extensions). Those processes extend to interact with neurons, blood vessels, or the connective tissue covering the CNS that is called the pia mater (Figure 12.11). Generally, they are supporting cells for the neurons in the central nervous system. Some ways in which they support neurons in the central nervous system are by maintaining the concentration of chemicals in the extracellular space, removing excess signaling molecules, reacting to tissue damage, and contributing to the **blood-brain barrier (BBB)**. The blood-brain barrier is a physiological barrier that keeps many substances that circulate in the rest of the body from getting into the central nervous system, restricting what can cross from circulating blood into the CNS. Nutrient molecules, such as glucose or amino acids, can pass through the BBB, but other molecules cannot. This actually causes problems with drug delivery to the CNS. Pharmaceutical companies are challenged to design drugs that can cross the BBB as well as have an effect on the nervous system.

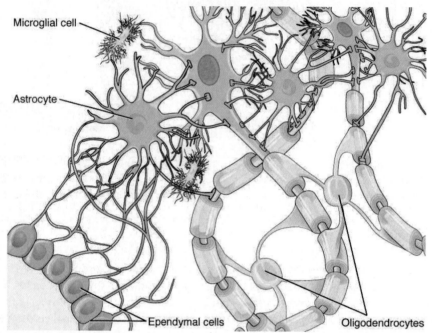

FIGURE 12.11   Glial Cells of the CNS   The CNS has astrocytes, oligodendrocytes, microglia, and ependymal cells that support the neurons of the CNS in several ways.

Like a few other parts of the body, the brain has a privileged blood supply. Very little can pass through by diffusion. Most substances that cross the wall of a blood vessel into the CNS must do so through an active transport process. Because of this, only specific types of molecules can enter the CNS. Glucose—the primary energy source—is allowed, as are amino acids. Water and some other small particles, like gases and ions, can enter. But most everything else cannot, including white blood cells, which are one of the body's main lines of defense. While this barrier protects the CNS from exposure to toxic or pathogenic substances, it also keeps out the cells that could protect the brain and spinal cord from disease and damage. The BBB also makes it harder for pharmaceuticals to be developed that can affect the nervous system. Aside from finding efficacious substances, the means of delivery is also crucial.

Also found in CNS tissue is the **oligodendrocyte**, sometimes called just "oligo," which is the glial cell type that insulates axons in the CNS. The name means "cell of a few branches" (oligo- = "few"; dendro- = "branches"; -cyte = "cell"). There are a few processes that extend from the cell body. Each one reaches out and surrounds an axon to insulate it in myelin. One oligodendrocyte will provide the myelin for multiple axon segments, either for the same axon or for separate axons. The function of myelin will be discussed below.

Microglia are, as the name implies, smaller than most of the other glial cells. Ongoing research into these cells, although not entirely conclusive, suggests that they may originate as white blood cells, called macrophages, that become part of the CNS during early development. While their origin is not conclusively determined, their function is related to what macrophages do in the rest of the body. When macrophages encounter diseased or damaged cells in the rest of the body, they ingest and digest those cells or the pathogens that cause disease. Microglia are the cells in the CNS that can do this in normal, healthy tissue, and they are therefore also referred to as CNS-resident macrophages.

The **ependymal cell** is a glial cell that filters blood to make **cerebrospinal fluid (CSF)**, the fluid that circulates through the CNS. Because of the privileged blood supply inherent in the BBB, the extracellular space in nervous tissue does not easily exchange components with the blood. Ependymal cells line each **ventricle**, one of four central

Access for free at openstax.org

cavities that are remnants of the hollow center of the neural tube formed during the embryonic development of the brain. The **choroid plexus** is a specialized structure in the ventricles where ependymal cells come in contact with blood vessels and filter and absorb components of the blood to produce cerebrospinal fluid. Because of this, ependymal cells can be considered a component of the BBB, or a place where the BBB breaks down. These glial cells appear similar to epithelial cells, making a single layer of cells with little intracellular space and tight connections between adjacent cells. They also have cilia on their apical surface to help move the CSF through the ventricular space. The relationship of these glial cells to the structure of the CNS is seen in Figure 12.11.

Glial Cells of the PNS

One of the two types of glial cells found in the PNS is the **satellite cell**. Satellite cells are found in sensory and autonomic ganglia, where they surround the cell bodies of neurons. This accounts for the name, based on their appearance under the microscope. They provide support, performing similar functions in the periphery as astrocytes do in the CNS—except, of course, for establishing the BBB.

The second type of glial cell is the **Schwann cell**, which insulate axons with myelin in the periphery. Schwann cells are different than oligodendrocytes, in that a Schwann cell wraps around a portion of only one axon segment and no others. Oligodendrocytes have processes that reach out to multiple axon segments, whereas the entire Schwann cell surrounds just one axon segment. The nucleus and cytoplasm of the Schwann cell are on the edge of the myelin sheath. The relationship of these two types of glial cells to ganglia and nerves in the PNS is seen in Figure 12.12.

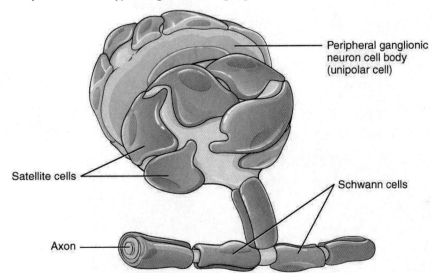

FIGURE 12.12 Glial Cells of the PNS The PNS has satellite cells and Schwann cells.

Myelin

The insulation for axons in the nervous system is provided by glial cells, oligodendrocytes in the CNS, and Schwann cells in the PNS. Whereas the manner in which either cell is associated with the axon segment, or segments, that it insulates is different, the means of myelinating an axon segment is mostly the same in the two situations. Myelin is a lipid-rich sheath that surrounds the axon and by doing so creates a **myelin sheath** that facilitates the transmission of electrical signals along the axon. The lipids are essentially the phospholipids of the glial cell membrane. Myelin, however, is more than just the membrane of the glial cell. It also includes important proteins that are integral to that membrane. Some of the proteins help to hold the layers of the glial cell membrane closely together.

The appearance of the myelin sheath can be thought of as similar to the pastry wrapped around a hot dog for "pigs in a blanket" or a similar food. The glial cell is wrapped around the axon several times with little to no cytoplasm between the glial cell layers. For oligodendrocytes, the rest of the cell is separate from the myelin sheath as a cell process extends back toward the cell body. A few other processes provide the same insulation for other axon segments in the area. For Schwann cells, the outermost layer of the cell membrane contains cytoplasm and the nucleus of the cell as a bulge on one side of the myelin sheath. During development, the glial cell is loosely or incompletely wrapped around the axon (Figure 12.13a). The edges of this loose enclosure extend toward each other, and one end tucks under the other. The inner edge wraps around the axon, creating several layers, and the other edge closes around the outside so that the axon is completely enclosed.

Myelin sheaths can extend for one or two millimeters, depending on the diameter of the axon. Axon diameters can be as small as 1 to 20 micrometers. Because a micrometer is 1/1000 of a millimeter, this means that the length of a myelin sheath can be 100–1000 times the diameter of the axon. Figure 12.8, Figure 12.11, and Figure 12.12 show the myelin sheath surrounding an axon segment, but are not to scale. If the myelin sheath were drawn to scale, the neuron would have to be immense—possibly covering an entire wall of the room in which you are sitting.

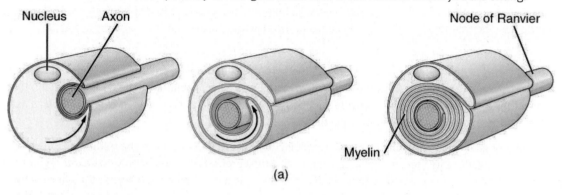

(a)

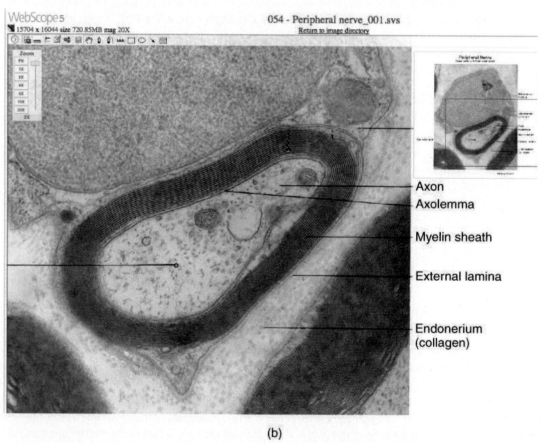

(b)

FIGURE 12.13 The Process of Myelination Myelinating glia wrap several layers of cell membrane around the cell membrane of an axon segment. A single Schwann cell insulates a segment of a peripheral nerve, whereas in the CNS, an oligodendrocyte may provide insulation for a few separate axon segments. EM × 1,460,000. (Micrograph provided by the Regents of University of Michigan Medical School © 2012)

Disorders of the...

Nervous Tissue

Several diseases can result from the demyelination of axons. The causes of these diseases are not the same; some have genetic causes, some are caused by pathogens, and others are the result of autoimmune disorders. Though the causes are varied, the results are largely similar. The myelin insulation of axons is compromised, making electrical signaling slower.

Multiple sclerosis (MS) is one such disease. It is an example of an autoimmune disease. The antibodies produced by lymphocytes (a type of white blood cell) mark myelin as something that should not be in the body. This causes inflammation and the destruction of the myelin in the central nervous system. As the insulation around the axons is destroyed by the disease, scarring becomes obvious. This is where the name of the disease comes from; sclerosis means hardening of tissue, which is what a scar is. Multiple scars are found in the white matter of the brain and spinal cord. The symptoms of MS include both somatic and autonomic deficits. Control of the musculature is compromised, as is control of organs such as the bladder.

Guillain-Barré (pronounced gee-YAN bah-RAY) syndrome is an example of a demyelinating disease of the peripheral nervous system. It is also the result of an autoimmune reaction, but the inflammation is in peripheral nerves. Sensory symptoms or motor deficits are common, and autonomic failures can lead to changes in the heart rhythm or a drop in blood pressure, especially when standing, which causes dizziness.

12.3 The Function of Nervous Tissue

LEARNING OBJECTIVES

By the end of this section, you will be able to:

- Distinguish the major functions of the nervous system: sensation, integration, and response
- List the sequence of events in a simple sensory receptor–motor response pathway

Having looked at the components of nervous tissue, and the basic anatomy of the nervous system, next comes an understanding of how nervous tissue is capable of communicating within the nervous system. Before getting to the nuts and bolts of how this works, an illustration of how the components come together will be helpful. An example is summarized in Figure 12.14.

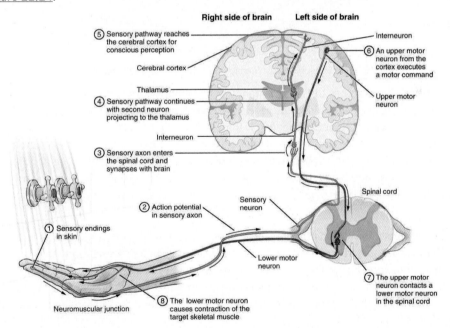

FIGURE 12.14 Testing the Water (1) The sensory neuron has endings in the skin that sense a stimulus such as water temperature. The strength of the signal that starts here is dependent on the strength of the stimulus. (2) The graded potential from the sensory endings, if strong enough, will initiate an action potential at the initial segment of the axon (which is immediately adjacent to the sensory endings in the skin). (3) The axon of the peripheral sensory neuron enters the spinal cord and contacts another neuron in the gray matter. The contact is a synapse where another graded potential is caused by the release of a chemical signal from the axon terminals. (4) An action potential is initiated at the initial segment of this neuron and travels up the sensory pathway to a region of the brain called the thalamus. Another synapse passes the information along to the next neuron. (5) The sensory pathway ends when the signal reaches the cerebral cortex. (6) After integration with neurons in other parts of the cerebral cortex, a motor command is sent from the precentral gyrus of the frontal cortex. (7) The upper motor neuron sends an action potential down to the spinal cord. The target of the upper motor neuron is the dendrites of the lower motor neuron in the gray matter of the spinal cord. (8) The axon of the lower motor neuron emerges from the spinal cord in a nerve and connects to a muscle through a neuromuscular junction to cause contraction of the target muscle.

Imagine you are about to take a shower in the morning before going to school. You have turned on the faucet to start the water as you prepare to get in the shower. After a few minutes, you expect the water to be a temperature that will be comfortable to enter. So you put your hand out into the spray of water. What happens next depends on how your nervous system interacts with the stimulus of the water temperature and what you do in response to that stimulus.

Found in the skin of your fingers or toes is a type of sensory receptor that is sensitive to temperature, called a **thermoreceptor**. When you place your hand under the shower (Figure 12.15), the cell membrane of the thermoreceptors changes its electrical state (voltage). The amount of change is dependent on the strength of the stimulus (how hot the water is). This is called a **graded potential**. If the stimulus is strong, the voltage of the cell membrane will change enough to generate an electrical signal that will travel down the axon. You have learned about this type of signaling before, with respect to the interaction of nerves and muscles at the neuromuscular junction. The voltage at which such a signal is generated is called the **threshold**, and the resulting electrical signal is called an **action potential**. In this example, the action potential travels—a process known as **propagation**—along the axon from the axon hillock to the axon terminals and into the synaptic end bulbs. When this signal reaches the end bulbs, it causes the release of a signaling molecule called a **neurotransmitter**.

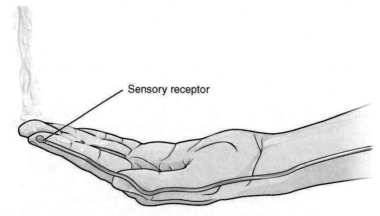

Sensory receptor

FIGURE 12.15   The Sensory Input   Receptors in the skin sense the temperature of the water.

The neurotransmitter diffuses across the short distance of the synapse and binds to a receptor protein of the target neuron. When the molecular signal binds to the receptor, the cell membrane of the target neuron changes its electrical state and a new graded potential begins. If that graded potential is strong enough to reach threshold, the second neuron generates an action potential at its axon hillock. The target of this neuron is another neuron in the **thalamus** of the brain, the part of the CNS that acts as a relay for sensory information. At another synapse, neurotransmitter is released and binds to its receptor. The thalamus then sends the sensory information to the **cerebral cortex**, the outermost layer of gray matter in the brain, where conscious perception of that water temperature begins.

Within the cerebral cortex, information is processed among many neurons, integrating the stimulus of the water temperature with other sensory stimuli, with your emotional state (you just aren't ready to wake up; the bed is calling to you), memories (perhaps of the lab notes you have to study before a quiz). Finally, a plan is developed about what to do, whether that is to turn the temperature up, turn the whole shower off and go back to bed, or step into the shower. To do any of these things, the cerebral cortex has to send a command out to your body to move muscles (Figure 12.16).

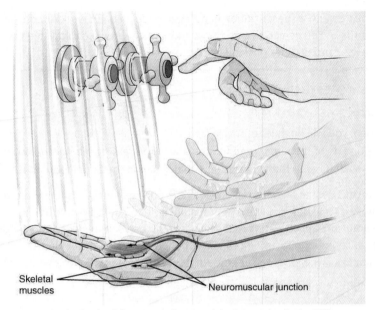

Skeletal muscles

Neuromuscular junction

FIGURE 12.16   The Motor Response   On the basis of the sensory input and the integration in the CNS, a motor response is formulated and executed.

A region of the cortex is specialized for sending signals down to the spinal cord for movement. The **upper motor neuron** is in this region, called the **precentral gyrus of the frontal cortex**, which has an axon that extends all the way down the spinal cord. At the level of the spinal cord at which this axon makes a synapse, a graded potential occurs in the cell membrane of a **lower motor neuron**. This second motor neuron is responsible for causing muscle fibers to contract. In the manner described in the chapter on muscle tissue, an action potential travels along the motor neuron axon into the periphery. The axon terminates on muscle fibers at the neuromuscular junction. Acetylcholine is released at this specialized synapse, which causes the muscle action potential to begin, following a large potential known as an end plate potential. When the lower motor neuron excites the muscle fiber, it contracts. All of this occurs in a fraction of a second, but this story is the basis of how the nervous system functions.

 CAREER CONNECTION

Neurophysiologist

Understanding how the nervous system works could be a driving force in your career. Studying neurophysiology is a very rewarding path to follow. It means that there is a lot of work to do, but the rewards are worth the effort.

The career path of a research scientist can be straightforward: college, graduate school, postdoctoral research, academic research position at a university. A Bachelor's degree in science will get you started, and for neurophysiology that might be in biology, psychology, computer science, engineering, or neuroscience. But the real specialization comes in graduate school. There are many different programs out there to study the nervous system, not just neuroscience itself. Most graduate programs are doctoral, meaning that a Master's degree is not part of the work. These are usually considered five-year programs, with the first two years dedicated to course work and finding a research mentor, and the last three years dedicated to finding a research topic and pursuing that with a near single-mindedness. The research will usually result in a few publications in scientific journals, which will make up the bulk of a doctoral dissertation. After graduating with a Ph.D., researchers will go on to find specialized work called a postdoctoral fellowship within established labs. In this position, a researcher starts to establish their own research career with the hopes of finding an academic position at a research university.

Other options are available if you are interested in how the nervous system works. Especially for neurophysiology, a medical degree might be more suitable so you can learn about the clinical applications of neurophysiology and possibly work with human subjects. An academic career is not a necessity. Biotechnology firms are eager to find motivated scientists ready to tackle the tough questions about how the nervous system works so that therapeutic chemicals can be tested on some of the most challenging disorders such as Alzheimer's disease or Parkinson's disease, or spinal cord injury.

Others with a medical degree and a specialization in neuroscience go on to work directly with patients, diagnosing and treating mental disorders. You can do this as a psychiatrist, a neuropsychologist, a neuroscience nurse, or a neurodiagnostic technician, among other possible career paths.

12.4 The Action Potential

LEARNING OBJECTIVES

By the end of this section, you will be able to:

- Describe the components of the membrane that establish the resting membrane potential
- Describe the changes that occur to the membrane that result in the action potential

The functions of the nervous system—sensation, integration, and response—depend on the functions of the neurons underlying these pathways. To understand how neurons are able to communicate, it is necessary to describe the role of an **excitable membrane** in generating these signals. The basis of this communication is the action potential, which demonstrates how changes in the membrane can constitute a signal. Looking at the way these signals work in more variable circumstances involves a look at graded potentials, which will be covered in the next section.

Electrically Active Cell Membranes

Most cells in the body make use of charged particles, ions, to build up a charge across the cell membrane. Previously, this was shown to be a part of how muscle cells work. For skeletal muscles to contract, based on excitation–contraction coupling, requires input from a neuron. Both of the cells make use of the cell membrane to regulate ion movement between the extracellular fluid and cytosol.

As you learned in the chapter on cells, the cell membrane is primarily responsible for regulating what can cross the membrane and what stays on only one side. The cell membrane is a phospholipid bilayer, so only substances that can pass directly through the hydrophobic core can diffuse through unaided. Charged particles, which are hydrophilic by definition, cannot pass through the cell membrane without assistance (Figure 12.17). Transmembrane proteins, specifically channel proteins, make this possible. Several passive transport channels, as well as active transport pumps, are necessary to generate a transmembrane potential and an action potential. Of special interest is the carrier protein referred to as the sodium/potassium pump that moves sodium ions (Na^+) out of a cell and potassium ions (K^+) into a cell, thus regulating ion concentration on both sides of the cell membrane.

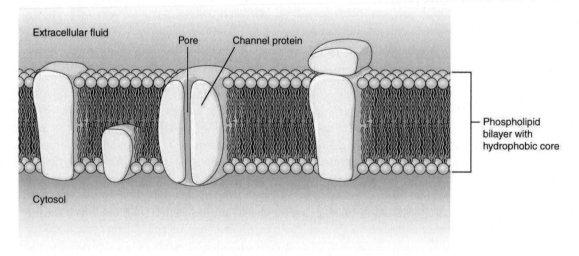

FIGURE 12.17   Cell Membrane and Transmembrane Proteins   The cell membrane is composed of a phospholipid bilayer and has many transmembrane proteins, including different types of channel proteins that serve as ion channels.

The sodium/potassium pump requires energy in the form of adenosine triphosphate (ATP), so it is also referred to as an ATPase. As was explained in the cell chapter, the concentration of Na^+ is higher outside the cell than inside, and the concentration of K^+ is higher inside the cell than outside. That means that this pump is moving the ions against the concentration gradients for sodium and potassium, which is why it requires energy. In fact, the pump basically maintains those concentration gradients.

Ion channels are pores that allow specific charged particles to cross the membrane in response to an existing concentration gradient. Proteins are capable of spanning the cell membrane, including its hydrophobic core, and can interact with the charge of ions because of the varied properties of amino acids found within specific domains or regions of the protein channel. Hydrophobic amino acids are found in the domains that are apposed to the hydrocarbon tails of the phospholipids. Hydrophilic amino acids are exposed to the fluid environments of the extracellular fluid and cytosol. Additionally, the ions will interact with the hydrophilic amino acids, which will be selective for the charge of the ion. Channels for cations (positive ions) will have negatively charged side chains in the pore. Channels for anions (negative ions) will have positively charged side chains in the pore. This is called **electrochemical exclusion**, meaning that the channel pore is charge-specific.

Ion channels can also be specified by the diameter of the pore. The distance between the amino acids will be specific for the diameter of the ion when it dissociates from the water molecules surrounding it. Because of the surrounding water molecules, larger pores are not ideal for smaller ions because the water molecules will interact, by hydrogen bonds, more readily than the amino acid side chains. This is called **size exclusion**. Some ion channels are selective for charge but not necessarily for size, and thus are called a **nonspecific channel**. These nonspecific channels allow cations—particularly Na^+, K^+, and Ca^{2+}—to cross the membrane, but exclude anions.

Ion channels do not always freely allow ions to diffuse across the membrane. Some are opened by certain events, meaning the channels are **gated**. So another way that channels can be categorized is on the basis of how they are gated. Although these classes of ion channels are found primarily in the cells of nervous or muscular tissue, they also can be found in the cells of epithelial and connective tissues.

A **ligand-gated channel** opens because a signaling molecule, a ligand, binds to the extracellular region of the channel. This type of channel is also known as an **ionotropic receptor** because when the ligand, known as a neurotransmitter in the nervous system, binds to the protein, ions cross the membrane changing its charge (Figure 12.18).

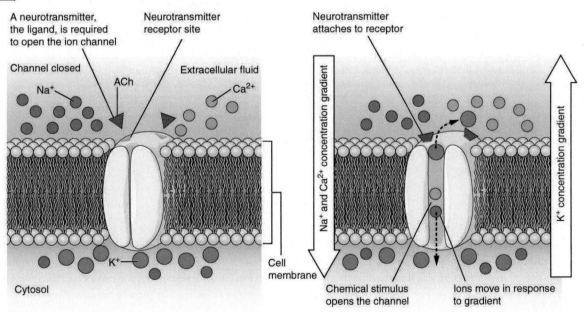

FIGURE 12.18   Ligand-Gated Channels   When the ligand, in this case the neurotransmitter acetylcholine, binds to a specific location on the extracellular surface of the channel protein, the pore opens to allow select ions through. The ions, in this case, are cations of sodium, calcium, and potassium.

A **mechanically gated channel** opens because of a physical distortion of the cell membrane. Many channels associated with the sense of touch (somatosensation) are mechanically gated. For example, as pressure is applied to the skin, these channels open and allow ions to enter the cell. Similar to this type of channel would be the channel that opens on the basis of temperature changes, as in testing the water in the shower (Figure 12.19).

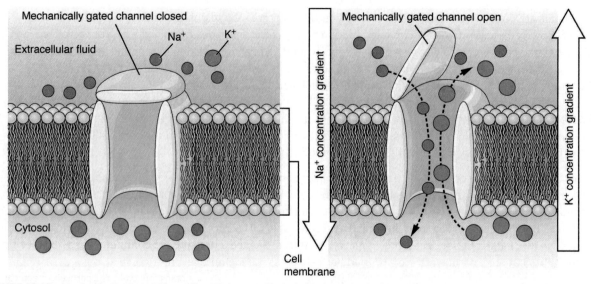

FIGURE 12.19 **Mechanically Gated Channels** When a mechanical change occurs in the surrounding tissue, such as pressure or touch, the channel is physically opened. Thermoreceptors work on a similar principle. When the local tissue temperature changes, the protein reacts by physically opening the channel.

A **voltage-gated channel** is a channel that responds to changes in the electrical properties of the membrane in which it is embedded. Normally, the inner portion of the membrane is at a negative voltage. When that voltage becomes less negative, the channel begins to allow ions to cross the membrane (Figure 12.20).

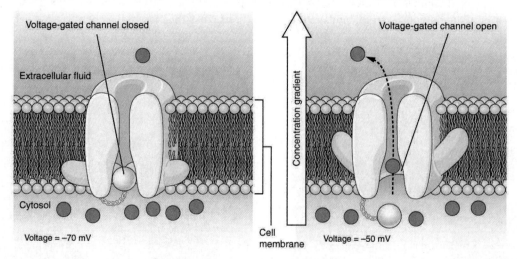

FIGURE 12.20 **Voltage-Gated Channels** Voltage-gated channels open when the transmembrane voltage changes around them. Amino acids in the structure of the protein are sensitive to charge and cause the pore to open to the selected ion.

A **leakage channel** is randomly gated, meaning that it opens and closes at random, hence the reference to leaking. There is no actual event that opens the channel; instead, it has an intrinsic rate of switching between the open and closed states. Leakage channels contribute to the resting transmembrane voltage of the excitable membrane (Figure 12.21).

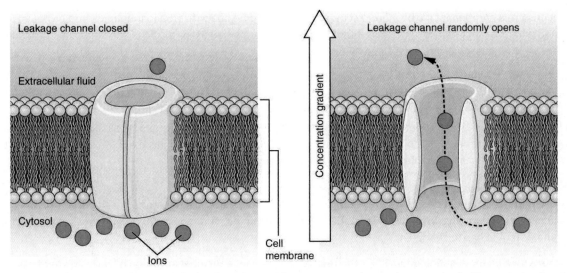

FIGURE 12.21   Leakage Channels   In certain situations, ions need to move across the membrane randomly. The particular electrical properties of certain cells are modified by the presence of this type of channel.

The Membrane Potential

The electrical state of the cell membrane can have several variations. These are all variations in the **membrane potential**. A potential is a distribution of charge across the cell membrane, measured in millivolts (mV). The standard is to compare the inside of the cell relative to the outside, so the membrane potential is a value representing the charge on the intracellular side of the membrane based on the outside being zero, relatively speaking (Figure 12.22).

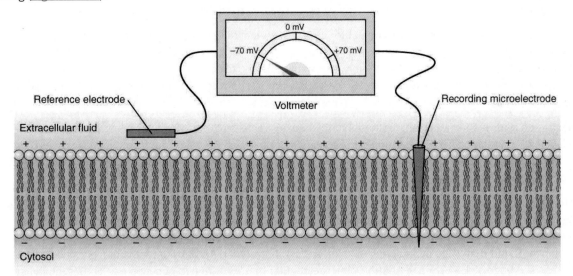

FIGURE 12.22   Measuring Charge across a Membrane with a Voltmeter   A recording electrode is inserted into the cell and a reference electrode is outside the cell. By comparing the charge measured by these two electrodes, the transmembrane voltage is determined. It is conventional to express that value for the cytosol relative to the outside.

The concentration of ions in extracellular and intracellular fluids is largely balanced, with a net neutral charge. However, a slight difference in charge occurs right at the membrane surface, both internally and externally. It is the difference in this very limited region that has all the power in neurons (and muscle cells) to generate electrical signals, including action potentials.

Before these electrical signals can be described, the resting state of the membrane must be explained. When the cell is at rest, and the ion channels are closed (except for leakage channels which randomly open), ions are distributed across the membrane in a very predictable way. The concentration of Na^+ outside the cell is 10 times greater than the concentration inside. Also, the concentration of K^+ inside the cell is greater than outside. The cytosol contains a high concentration of anions, in the form of phosphate ions and negatively charged proteins.

Large anions are a component of the inner cell membrane, including specialized phospholipids and proteins associated with the inner leaflet of the membrane (leaflet is a term used for one side of the lipid bilayer membrane). The negative charge is localized in the large anions.

With the ions distributed across the membrane at these concentrations, the difference in charge is measured at -70 mV, the value described as the **resting membrane potential**. The exact value measured for the resting membrane potential varies between cells, but -70 mV is most commonly used as this value. This voltage would actually be much lower except for the contributions of some important proteins in the membrane. Leakage channels allow Na^+ to slowly move into the cell or K^+ to slowly move out, and the Na^+/K^+ pump restores them. This may appear to be a waste of energy, but each has a role in maintaining the membrane potential.

The Action Potential

Resting membrane potential describes the steady state of the cell, which is a dynamic process that is balanced by ion leakage and ion pumping. Without any outside influence, it will not change. To get an electrical signal started, the membrane potential has to change.

This starts with a channel opening for Na^+ in the membrane. Because the concentration of Na^+ is higher outside the cell than inside the cell by a factor of 10, ions will rush into the cell that are driven largely by the concentration gradient. Because sodium is a positively charged ion, it will change the relative voltage immediately inside the cell relative to immediately outside. The resting potential is the state of the membrane at a voltage of -70 mV, so the sodium cation entering the cell will cause it to become less negative. This is known as **depolarization**, meaning the membrane potential moves toward zero.

The concentration gradient for Na^+ is so strong that it will continue to enter the cell even after the membrane potential has become zero, so that the voltage immediately around the pore begins to become positive. The electrical gradient also plays a role, as negative proteins below the membrane attract the sodium ion. The membrane potential will reach +30 mV by the time sodium has entered the cell.

As the membrane potential reaches +30 mV, other voltage-gated channels are opening in the membrane. These channels are specific for the potassium ion. A concentration gradient acts on K^+, as well. As K^+ starts to leave the cell, taking a positive charge with it, the membrane potential begins to move back toward its resting voltage. This is called **repolarization**, meaning that the membrane voltage moves back toward the -70 mV value of the resting membrane potential.

Repolarization returns the membrane potential to the -70 mV value that indicates the resting potential, but it actually overshoots that value. Potassium ions reach equilibrium when the membrane voltage is below -70 mV, so a period of hyperpolarization occurs while the K^+ channels are open. Those K^+ channels are slightly delayed in closing, accounting for this short overshoot.

What has been described here is the action potential, which is presented as a graph of voltage over time in Figure 12.23. It is the electrical signal that nervous tissue generates for communication. The change in the membrane voltage from -70 mV at rest to +30 mV at the end of depolarization is a 100 mV change. That can also be written as a 0.1 V change. To put that value in perspective, think about a battery. An AA battery that you might find in a television remote has a voltage of 1.5 V, or a 9 V battery (the rectangular battery with two posts on one end) is, obviously, 9 V. The change seen in the action potential is one or two orders of magnitude less than the charge in these batteries. In fact, the membrane potential can be described as a battery. A charge is stored across the membrane that can be released under the correct conditions. A battery in your remote has stored a charge that is "released" when you push a button.

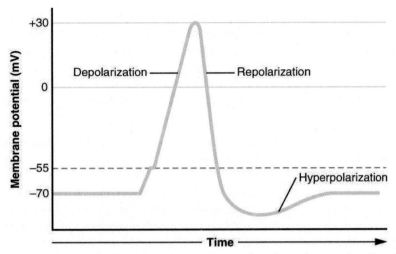

FIGURE 12.23 Graph of Action Potential Plotting voltage measured across the cell membrane against time, the action potential begins with depolarization, followed by repolarization, which goes past the resting potential into hyperpolarization, and finally the membrane returns to rest.

🔗 INTERACTIVE LINK

What happens across the membrane of an electrically active cell is a dynamic process that is hard to visualize with static images or through text descriptions. View this animation (http://openstax.org/l/dynamic1) to learn more about this process. What is the difference between the driving force for Na⁺ and K⁺? And what is similar about the movement of these two ions?

The question is, now, what initiates the action potential? The description above conveniently glosses over that point. But it is vital to understanding what is happening. The membrane potential will stay at the resting voltage until something changes. The description above just says that a Na⁺ channel opens. Now, to say "a channel opens" does not mean that one individual transmembrane protein changes. Instead, it means that one kind of channel opens. There are a few different types of channels that allow Na⁺ to cross the membrane. A ligand-gated Na⁺ channel will open when a neurotransmitter binds to it and a mechanically gated Na⁺ channel will open when a physical stimulus affects a sensory receptor (like pressure applied to the skin compresses a touch receptor). Whether it is a neurotransmitter binding to its receptor protein or a sensory stimulus activating a sensory receptor cell, some stimulus gets the process started. Sodium starts to enter the cell and the membrane becomes less negative.

A third type of channel that is an important part of depolarization in the action potential is the voltage-gated Na⁺ channel. The channels that start depolarizing the membrane because of a stimulus help the cell to depolarize from -70 mV to -55 mV. Once the membrane reaches that voltage, the voltage-gated Na⁺ channels open. This is what is known as the threshold. Any depolarization that does not change the membrane potential to -55 mV or higher will not reach threshold and thus will not result in an action potential. Also, any stimulus that depolarizes the membrane to -55 mV or beyond will cause a large number of channels to open and an action potential will be initiated.

Because of the threshold, the action potential can be likened to a digital event—it either happens or it does not. If the threshold is not reached, then no action potential occurs. If depolarization reaches -55 mV, then the action potential continues and runs all the way to +30 mV, at which K⁺ causes repolarization, including the hyperpolarizing overshoot. Also, those changes are the same for every action potential, which means that once the threshold is reached, the exact same thing happens. A stronger stimulus, which might depolarize the membrane well past threshold, will not make a "bigger" action potential. Action potentials are "all or none." Either the membrane reaches the threshold and everything occurs as described above, or the membrane does not reach the threshold and nothing else happens. All action potentials peak at the same voltage (+30 mV), so one action potential is not bigger than another. Stronger stimuli will initiate multiple action potentials more quickly, but the individual signals are not bigger. Thus, for example, you will not feel a greater sensation of pain, or have a stronger muscle contraction, because of the size of the action potential because they are not different sizes.

As we have seen, the depolarization and repolarization of an action potential are dependent on two types of channels (the voltage-gated Na⁺ channel and the voltage-gated K⁺ channel). The voltage-gated Na⁺ channel actually has two gates. One is the **activation gate**, which opens when the membrane potential crosses -55 mV. The other gate is the **inactivation gate**, which closes after a specific period of time—on the order of a fraction of a millisecond. When a cell is at rest, the activation gate is closed and the inactivation gate is open. However, when the threshold is reached, the activation gate opens, allowing Na⁺ to rush into the cell. Timed with the peak of depolarization, the inactivation gate closes. During repolarization, no more sodium can enter the cell. When the membrane potential passes -55 mV again, the activation gate closes. After that, the inactivation gate re-opens, making the channel ready to start the whole process over again.

The voltage-gated K⁺ channel has only one gate, which is sensitive to a membrane voltage of -50 mV. However, it does not open as quickly as the voltage-gated Na⁺ channel does. It might take a fraction of a millisecond for the channel to open once that voltage has been reached. The timing of this coincides exactly with when the Na⁺ flow peaks, so voltage-gated K⁺ channels open just as the voltage-gated Na⁺ channels are being inactivated. As the membrane potential repolarizes and the voltage passes -50 mV again, the channel closes—again, with a little delay. Potassium continues to leave the cell for a short while and the membrane potential becomes more negative, resulting in the hyperpolarizing overshoot. Then the channel closes again and the membrane can return to the resting potential because of the ongoing activity of the non-gated channels and the Na⁺/K⁺ pump.

All of this takes place within approximately 2 milliseconds (Figure 12.24). While an action potential is in progress, another one cannot be initiated. That effect is referred to as the **refractory period**. There are two phases of the refractory period: the **absolute refractory period** and the **relative refractory period**. During the absolute phase, another action potential will not start. This is because of the inactivation gate of the voltage-gated Na⁺ channel. Once that channel is back to its resting conformation (less than -55 mV), a new action potential could be started, but only by a stronger stimulus than the one that initiated the current action potential. This is because of the flow of K⁺ out of the cell. Because that ion is rushing out, any Na⁺ that tries to enter will not depolarize the cell, but will only keep the cell from hyperpolarizing.

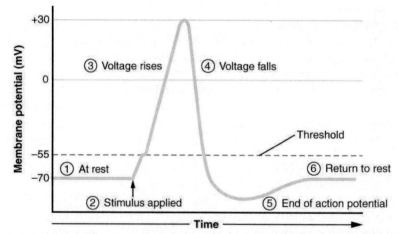

FIGURE 12.24 Stages of an Action Potential Plotting voltage measured across the cell membrane against time, the events of the action potential can be related to specific changes in the membrane voltage. (1) At rest, the membrane voltage is -70 mV. (2) The membrane begins to depolarize when an external stimulus is applied. (3) The membrane voltage begins a rapid rise toward +30 mV. (4) The membrane voltage starts to return to a negative value. (5) Repolarization continues past the resting membrane voltage, resulting in hyperpolarization. (6) The membrane voltage returns to the resting value shortly after hyperpolarization.

Propagation of the Action Potential

The action potential is initiated at the beginning of the axon, at what is called the initial segment. There is a high density of voltage-gated Na⁺ channels so that rapid depolarization can take place here. Going down the length of the axon, the action potential is propagated because more voltage-gated Na⁺ channels are opened as the depolarization spreads. This spreading occurs because Na⁺ enters through the channel and moves along the inside of the cell membrane. As the Na⁺ moves, or flows, a short distance along the cell membrane, its positive charge depolarizes a little more of the cell membrane. As that depolarization spreads, new voltage-gated Na⁺ channels open and more ions rush into the cell, spreading the depolarization a little farther.

Because voltage-gated Na⁺ channels are inactivated at the peak of the depolarization, they cannot be opened again for a brief time—the absolute refractory period. Because of this, depolarization spreading back toward previously opened channels has no effect. The action potential must propagate toward the axon terminals; as a result, the polarity of the neuron is maintained, as mentioned above.

Propagation, as described above, applies to unmyelinated axons. When myelination is present, the action potential propagates differently. Sodium ions that enter the cell at the initial segment start to spread along the length of the axon segment, but there are no voltage-gated Na^+ channels until the first node of Ranvier. Because there is not constant opening of these channels along the axon segment, the depolarization spreads at an optimal speed. The distance between nodes is the optimal distance to keep the membrane still depolarized above threshold at the next node. As Na^+ spreads along the inside of the membrane of the axon segment, the charge starts to dissipate. If the node were any farther down the axon, that depolarization would have fallen off too much for voltage-gated Na^+ channels to be activated at the next node of Ranvier. If the nodes were any closer together, the speed of propagation would be slower.

Propagation along an unmyelinated axon is referred to as **continuous conduction**; along the length of a myelinated axon, it is **saltatory conduction**. Continuous conduction is slow because there are always voltage-gated Na^+ channels opening, and more and more Na^+ is rushing into the cell. Saltatory conduction is faster because the action potential basically jumps from one node to the next (saltare = "to leap"), and the new influx of Na^+ renews the depolarized membrane. Along with the myelination of the axon, the diameter of the axon can influence the speed of conduction. Much as water runs faster in a wide river than in a narrow creek, Na^+-based depolarization spreads faster down a wide axon than down a narrow one. This concept is known as **resistance** and is generally true for electrical wires or plumbing, just as it is true for axons, although the specific conditions are different at the scales of electrons or ions versus water in a river.

 ## HOMEOSTATIC IMBALANCES

Potassium Concentration

Glial cells, especially astrocytes, are responsible for maintaining the chemical environment of the CNS tissue. The concentrations of ions in the extracellular fluid are the basis for how the membrane potential is established and changes in electrochemical signaling. If the balance of ions is upset, drastic outcomes are possible.

Normally the concentration of K^+ is higher inside the neuron than outside. After the repolarizing phase of the action potential, K^+ leakage channels and the Na^+/K^+ pump ensure that the ions return to their original locations. Following a stroke or other ischemic event, extracellular K^+ levels are elevated. The astrocytes in the area are equipped to clear excess K^+ to aid the pump. But when the level is far out of balance, the effects can be irreversible.

Astrocytes can become reactive in cases such as these, which impairs their ability to maintain the local chemical environment. The glial cells enlarge and their processes swell. They lose their K^+ buffering ability and the function of the pump is affected, or even reversed. One of the early signs of cell disease is this "leaking" of sodium ions into the body cells. This sodium/potassium imbalance negatively affects the internal chemistry of cells, preventing them from functioning normally.

 ## INTERACTIVE LINK

Visit this site (http://openstax.org/l/neurolab) to see a virtual neurophysiology lab, and to observe electrophysiological processes in the nervous system, where scientists directly measure the electrical signals produced by neurons. Often, the action potentials occur so rapidly that watching a screen to see them occur is not helpful. A speaker is powered by the signals recorded from a neuron and it "pops" each time the neuron fires an action potential. These action potentials are firing so fast that it sounds like static on the radio. Electrophysiologists can recognize the patterns within that static to understand what is happening. Why is the leech model used for measuring the electrical activity of neurons instead of using humans?

12.5 Communication Between Neurons

LEARNING OBJECTIVES

By the end of this section, you will be able to:

• Explain the differences between the types of graded potentials
• Categorize the major neurotransmitters by chemical type and effect

The electrical changes taking place within a neuron, as described in the previous section, are similar to a light switch being turned on. A stimulus starts the depolarization, but the action potential runs on its own once a threshold has been reached. The question is now, "What flips the light switch on?" Temporary changes to the cell membrane voltage can result from neurons receiving information from the environment, or from the action of one neuron on another. These special types of potentials influence a neuron and determine whether an action potential will occur or not. Many of these transient signals originate at the synapse.

Graded Potentials

Local changes in the membrane potential are called graded potentials and are usually associated with the dendrites of a neuron. The amount of change in the membrane potential is determined by the size of the stimulus that causes it. In the example of testing the temperature of the shower, slightly warm water would only initiate a small change in a thermoreceptor, whereas hot water would cause a large amount of change in the membrane potential.

Graded potentials can be of two sorts, either they are depolarizing or hyperpolarizing (Figure 12.25). For a membrane at the resting potential, a graded potential represents a change in that voltage either above -70 mV or below -70 mV. Depolarizing graded potentials are often the result of Na^+ or Ca^{2+} entering the cell. Both of these ions have higher concentrations outside the cell than inside; because they have a positive charge, they will move into the cell causing it to become less negative relative to the outside. Hyperpolarizing graded potentials can be caused by K^+ leaving the cell or Cl^- entering the cell. If a positive charge moves out of a cell, the cell becomes more negative; if a negative charge enters the cell, the same thing happens.

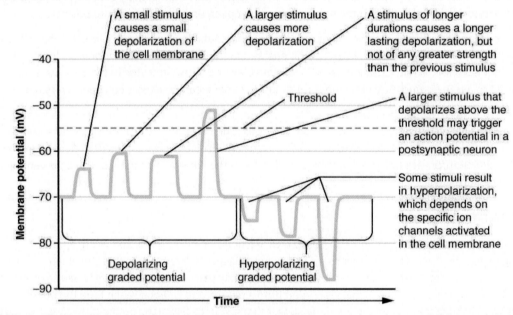

FIGURE 12.25 Graded Potentials   Graded potentials are temporary changes in the membrane voltage, the characteristics of which depend on the size of the stimulus. Some types of stimuli cause depolarization of the membrane, whereas others cause hyperpolarization. It depends on the specific ion channels that are activated in the cell membrane.

Types of Graded Potentials

For the unipolar cells of sensory neurons—both those with free nerve endings and those within encapsulations—graded potentials develop in the dendrites that influence the generation of an action potential in the axon of the same cell. This is called a **generator potential**. For other sensory receptor cells, such as taste cells or photoreceptors of the retina, graded potentials in their membranes result in the release of neurotransmitters at synapses with sensory neurons. This is called a **receptor potential**.

A **postsynaptic potential (PSP)** is the graded potential in the dendrites of a neuron that is receiving synapses from other cells. Postsynaptic potentials can be depolarizing or hyperpolarizing. Depolarization in a postsynaptic potential is called an **excitatory postsynaptic potential (EPSP)** because it causes the membrane potential to move toward threshold. Hyperpolarization in a postsynaptic potential is an **inhibitory postsynaptic potential (IPSP)** because it causes the membrane potential to move away from threshold.

Summation

All types of graded potentials will result in small changes of either depolarization or hyperpolarization in the voltage of a membrane. These changes can lead to the neuron reaching threshold if the changes add together, or **summate**. The combined effects of different types of graded potentials are illustrated in Figure 12.26. If the total change in voltage in the membrane is a positive 15 mV, meaning that the membrane depolarizes from -70 mV to -55 mV, then the graded potentials will result in the membrane reaching threshold.

For receptor potentials, threshold is not a factor because the change in membrane potential for receptor cells directly causes neurotransmitter release. However, generator potentials can initiate action potentials in the sensory neuron axon, and postsynaptic potentials can initiate an action potential in the axon of other neurons. Graded potentials summate at a specific location at the beginning of the axon to initiate the action potential, namely the initial segment. For sensory neurons, which do not have a cell body between the dendrites and the axon, the initial segment is directly adjacent to the dendritic endings. For all other neurons, the axon hillock is essentially the initial segment of the axon, and it is where summation takes place. These locations have a high density of voltage-gated Na^+ channels that initiate the depolarizing phase of the action potential.

Summation can be spatial or temporal, meaning it can be the result of multiple graded potentials at different locations on the neuron, or all at the same place but separated in time. **Spatial summation** is related to associating the activity of multiple inputs to a neuron with each other. **Temporal summation** is the relationship of multiple action potentials from a single cell resulting in a significant change in the membrane potential. Spatial and temporal summation can act together, as well.

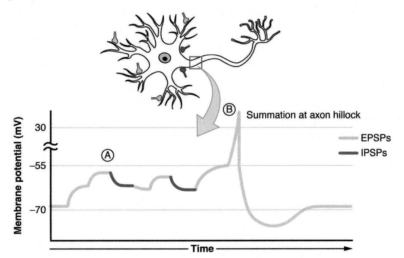

FIGURE 12.26   Postsynaptic Potential Summation   The result of summation of postsynaptic potentials is the overall change in the membrane potential. At point A, several different excitatory postsynaptic potentials add up to a large depolarization. At point B, a mix of excitatory and inhibitory postsynaptic potentials result in a different end result for the membrane potential.

🔗 INTERACTIVE LINK

Watch this video (http://openstax.org/l/summation) to learn about summation. The process of converting electrical signals to chemical signals and back requires subtle changes that can result in transient increases or decreases in membrane voltage. To cause a lasting change in the target cell, multiple signals are usually added together, or summated. Does spatial summation have to happen all at once, or can the separate signals arrive on the postsynaptic neuron at slightly different times? Explain your answer.

Synapses

There are two types of connections between electrically active cells, chemical synapses and electrical synapses. In a **chemical synapse**, a chemical signal—namely, a neurotransmitter—is released from one cell and it affects the other cell. In an **electrical synapse**, there is a direct connection between the two cells so that ions can pass directly from one cell to the next. If one cell is depolarized in an electrical synapse, the joined cell also depolarizes because the ions pass between the cells. Chemical synapses involve the transmission of chemical information from one cell to the next. This section will concentrate on the chemical type of synapse.

An example of a chemical synapse is the neuromuscular junction (NMJ) described in the chapter on muscle tissue. In the nervous system, there are many more synapses that are essentially the same as the NMJ. All synapses have common characteristics, which can be summarized in this list:

- presynaptic element
- neurotransmitter (packaged in vesicles)
- synaptic cleft
- receptor proteins
- postsynaptic element
- neurotransmitter elimination or re-uptake

For the NMJ, these characteristics are as follows: the presynaptic element is the motor neuron's axon terminals, the neurotransmitter is acetylcholine, the synaptic cleft is the space between the cells where the neurotransmitter diffuses, the receptor protein is the nicotinic acetylcholine receptor, the postsynaptic element is the sarcolemma of the muscle cell, and the neurotransmitter is eliminated by acetylcholinesterase. Other synapses are similar to this, and the specifics are different, but they all contain the same characteristics.

Neurotransmitter Release

When an action potential reaches the axon terminals, voltage-gated Ca^{2+} channels in the membrane of the synaptic end bulb open. The concentration of Ca^{2+} increases inside the end bulb, and the Ca^{2+} ion associates with proteins in the outer surface of neurotransmitter vesicles. The Ca^{2+} facilitates the merging of the vesicle with the presynaptic membrane so that the neurotransmitter is released through exocytosis into the small gap between the cells, known as the **synaptic cleft**.

Once in the synaptic cleft, the neurotransmitter diffuses the short distance to the postsynaptic membrane and can interact with neurotransmitter receptors. Receptors are specific for the neurotransmitter, and the two fit together like a key and lock. One neurotransmitter binds to its receptor and will not bind to receptors for other neurotransmitters, making the binding a specific chemical event (Figure 12.27).

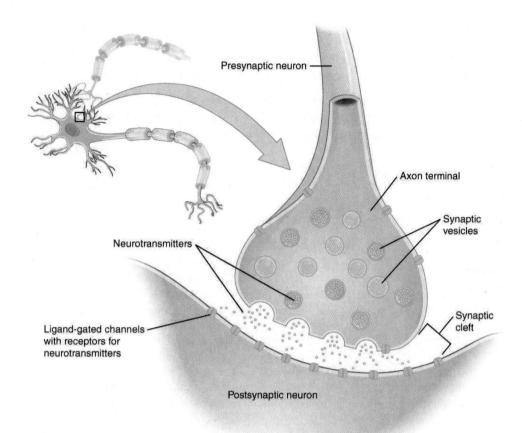

FIGURE 12.27   The Synapse   The synapse is a connection between a neuron and its target cell (which is not necessarily a neuron). The presynaptic element is the synaptic end bulb of the axon where Ca^{2+} enters the bulb to cause vesicle fusion and neurotransmitter release. The neurotransmitter diffuses across the synaptic cleft to bind to its receptor. The neurotransmitter is cleared from the synapse either by enzymatic degradation, neuronal reuptake, or glial reuptake.

Neurotransmitter Systems

There are several systems of neurotransmitters that are found at various synapses in the nervous system. These groups refer to the chemicals that are the neurotransmitters, and within the groups are specific systems.

The first group, which is a neurotransmitter system of its own, is the **cholinergic system**. It is the system based on acetylcholine. This includes the NMJ as an example of a cholinergic synapse, but cholinergic synapses are found in other parts of the nervous system. They are in the autonomic nervous system, as well as distributed throughout the brain.

The cholinergic system has two types of receptors, the **nicotinic receptor** is found in the NMJ as well as other synapses. There is also an acetylcholine receptor known as the **muscarinic receptor**. Both of these receptors are named for drugs that interact with the receptor in addition to acetylcholine. Nicotine will bind to the nicotinic receptor and activate it similar to acetylcholine. Muscarine, a product of certain mushrooms, will bind to the muscarinic receptor. However, nicotine will not bind to the muscarinic receptor and muscarine will not bind to the nicotinic receptor.

Another group of neurotransmitters are amino acids. This includes glutamate (Glu), GABA (gamma-aminobutyric acid, a derivative of glutamate), and glycine (Gly). These amino acids have an amino group and a carboxyl group in their chemical structures. Glutamate is one of the 20 amino acids that are used to make proteins. Each amino acid neurotransmitter would be part of its own system, namely the glutamatergic, GABAergic, and glycinergic systems. They each have their own receptors and do not interact with each other. Amino acid neurotransmitters are eliminated from the synapse by reuptake. A pump in the cell membrane of the presynaptic element, or sometimes a neighboring glial cell, will clear the amino acid from the synaptic cleft so that it can be recycled, repackaged in vesicles, and released again.

Another class of neurotransmitter is the **biogenic amine**, a group of neurotransmitters that are enzymatically made from amino acids. They have amino groups in them, but no longer have carboxyl groups and are therefore no longer classified as amino acids. Serotonin is made from tryptophan. It is the basis of the serotonergic system, which has its own specific receptors. Serotonin is transported back into the presynaptic cell for repackaging.

Other biogenic amines are made from tyrosine, and include dopamine, norepinephrine, and epinephrine. Dopamine is part of its own system, the dopaminergic system, which has dopamine receptors. Dopamine is removed from the synapse by transport proteins in the presynaptic cell membrane. Norepinephrine and epinephrine belong to the adrenergic neurotransmitter system. The two molecules are very similar and bind to the same receptors, which are referred to as alpha and beta receptors. Norepinephrine and epinephrine are also transported back into the presynaptic cell. The chemical epinephrine (epi- = "on"; "-nephrine" = kidney) is also known as adrenaline (renal = "kidney"), and norepinephrine is sometimes referred to as noradrenaline. The adrenal gland produces epinephrine and norepinephrine to be released into the blood stream as hormones.

A **neuropeptide** is a neurotransmitter molecule made up of chains of amino acids connected by peptide bonds. This is what a protein is, but the term protein implies a certain length to the molecule. Some neuropeptides are quite short, such as met-enkephalin, which is five amino acids long. Others are long, such as beta-endorphin, which is 31 amino acids long. Neuropeptides are often released at synapses in combination with another neurotransmitter, and they often act as hormones in other systems of the body, such as vasoactive intestinal peptide (VIP) or substance P.

The effect of a neurotransmitter on the postsynaptic element is entirely dependent on the receptor protein. First, if there is no receptor protein in the membrane of the postsynaptic element, then the neurotransmitter has no effect. The depolarizing or hyperpolarizing effect is also dependent on the receptor. When acetylcholine binds to the nicotinic receptor, the postsynaptic cell is depolarized. This is because the receptor is a cation channel and positively charged Na^+ will rush into the cell. However, when acetylcholine binds to the muscarinic receptor, of which there are several variants, it might cause depolarization or hyperpolarization of the target cell.

The amino acid neurotransmitters, glutamate, glycine, and GABA, are almost exclusively associated with just one effect. Glutamate is considered an excitatory amino acid, but only because Glu receptors in the adult cause depolarization of the postsynaptic cell. Glycine and GABA are considered inhibitory amino acids, again because their receptors cause hyperpolarization.

The biogenic amines have mixed effects. For example, the dopamine receptors that are classified as D1 receptors are excitatory whereas D2-type receptors are inhibitory. Biogenic amine receptors and neuropeptide receptors can have even more complex effects because some may not directly affect the membrane potential, but rather have an effect on gene transcription or other metabolic processes in the neuron. The characteristics of the various neurotransmitter systems presented in this section are organized in Table 12.3.

The important thing to remember about neurotransmitters, and signaling chemicals in general, is that the effect is entirely dependent on the receptor. Neurotransmitters bind to one of two classes of receptors at the cell surface, ionotropic or metabotropic (Figure 12.28). Ionotropic receptors are ligand-gated ion channels, such as the nicotinic receptor for acetylcholine or the glycine receptor. A **metabotropic receptor** involves a complex of proteins that result in metabolic changes within the cell. The receptor complex includes the transmembrane receptor protein, a G protein, and an effector protein. The neurotransmitter, referred to as the first messenger, binds to the receptor protein on the extracellular surface of the cell, and the intracellular side of the protein initiates activity of the G protein. The **G protein** is a guanosine triphosphate (GTP) hydrolase that physically moves from the receptor protein to the effector protein to activate the latter. An **effector protein** is an enzyme that catalyzes the generation of a new molecule, which acts as the intracellular mediator of the signal that binds to the receptor. This intracellular mediator is called the second messenger.

Different receptors use different second messengers. Two common examples of second messengers are cyclic adenosine monophosphate (cAMP) and inositol triphosphate (IP_3). The enzyme adenylate cyclase (an example of an effector protein) makes cAMP, and phospholipase C is the enzyme that makes IP_3. Second messengers, after they are produced by the effector protein, cause metabolic changes within the cell. These changes are most likely the activation of other enzymes in the cell. In neurons, they often modify ion channels, either opening or closing them. These enzymes can also cause changes in the cell, such as the activation of genes in the nucleus, and therefore the increased synthesis of proteins. In neurons, these kinds of changes are often the basis of stronger connections

Access for free at openstax.org

between cells at the synapse and may be the basis of learning and memory.

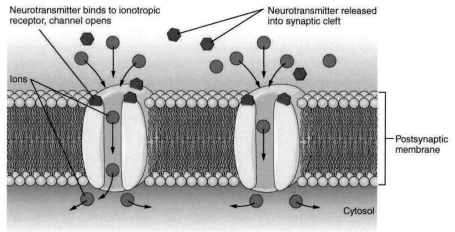

(a) Direct activation brings about immediate response

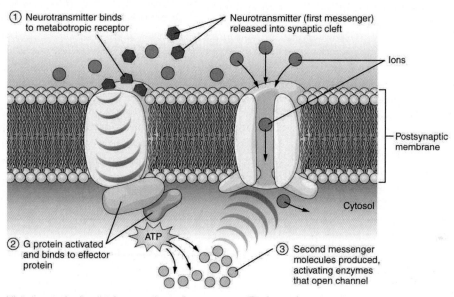

(b) Indirect activation involves a prolonged response, amplified over time

FIGURE 12.28 **Receptor Types**   (a) An ionotropic receptor is a channel that opens when the neurotransmitter binds to it. (b) A metabotropic receptor is a complex that causes metabolic changes in the cell when the neurotransmitter binds to it (1). After binding, the G protein hydrolyzes ATP and moves to the effector protein (2). When the G protein contacts the effector protein, the latter is activated. In the case shown, the effector protein then acts on ATP to generate a second messenger, cAMP (3). The second messenger can then go on to cause changes in the neuron, such as opening or closing ion channels, metabolic changes, and changes in gene transcription.

⊘ INTERACTIVE LINK

Watch this video (http://openstax.org/l/neurotrans) to learn about the release of a neurotransmitter. The action potential reaches the end of the axon, called the axon terminal, and a chemical signal is released to tell the target cell to do something—either to initiate a new action potential, or to suppress that activity. In a very short space, the electrical signal of the action potential is changed into the chemical signal of a neurotransmitter and then back to electrical changes in the target cell membrane. What is the importance of voltage-gated calcium channels in the release of neurotransmitters?

Characteristics of Neurotransmitter Systems

System	Cholinergic	Amino acids	Biogenic amines	Neuropeptides
Neurotransmitters	Acetylcholine	Glutamate, glycine, GABA	Serotonin (5-HT), dopamine, norepinephrine, (epinephrine)	Met-enkephalin, beta-endorphin, VIP, Substance P, etc.
Receptors	Nicotinic and muscarinic receptors	Glu receptors, gly receptors, GABA receptors	5-HT receptors, D1 and D2 receptors, α-adrenergic and β-adrenergic receptors	Receptors are too numerous to list, but are specific to the peptides.
Elimination	Degradation by acetylcholinesterase	Reuptake by neurons or glia	Reuptake by neurons	Degradation by enzymes called peptidases
Postsynaptic effect	Nicotinic receptor causes depolarization. Muscarinic receptors can cause both depolarization or hyperpolarization depending on the subtype.	Glu receptors cause depolarization. Gly and GABA receptors cause hyperpolarization.	Depolarization or hyperpolarization depends on the specific receptor. For example, D1 receptors cause depolarization and D2 receptors cause hyperpolarization.	Depolarization or hyperpolarization depends on the specific receptor.

TABLE 12.3

Disorders of the...

Nervous System

The underlying cause of some neurodegenerative diseases, such as Alzheimer's and Parkinson's, appears to be related to proteins—specifically, to proteins behaving badly. One of the strongest theories of what causes Alzheimer's disease is based on the accumulation of beta-amyloid plaques, dense conglomerations of a protein that is not functioning correctly. Parkinson's disease is linked to an increase in a protein known as alpha-synuclein that is toxic to the cells of the substantia nigra nucleus in the midbrain.

For proteins to function correctly, they are dependent on their three-dimensional shape. The linear sequence of amino acids folds into a three-dimensional shape that is based on the interactions between and among those amino acids. When the folding is disturbed, and proteins take on a different shape, they stop functioning correctly. But the disease is not necessarily the result of functional loss of these proteins; rather, these altered proteins start to accumulate and may become toxic. For example, in Alzheimer's, the hallmark of the disease is the accumulation of these amyloid plaques in the cerebral cortex. The term coined to describe this sort of disease is "proteopathy" and it includes other diseases. Creutzfeld-Jacob disease, the human variant of the prion disease known as mad cow disease in the bovine, also involves the accumulation of amyloid plaques, similar to Alzheimer's. Diseases of other organ systems can fall into this group as well, such as cystic fibrosis or type 2 diabetes. Recognizing the relationship between these diseases has suggested new therapeutic possibilities. Interfering with the accumulation of the proteins, and possibly as early as their original production within the cell, may unlock new ways to alleviate these devastating diseases.

Key Terms

absolute refractory period   time during an action period when another action potential cannot be generated because the voltage-gated Na⁺ channel is inactivated

action potential   change in voltage of a cell membrane in response to a stimulus that results in transmission of an electrical signal; unique to neurons and muscle fibers

activation gate   part of the voltage-gated Na⁺ channel that opens when the membrane voltage reaches threshold

astrocyte   glial cell type of the CNS that provides support for neurons and maintains the blood-brain barrier

autonomic nervous system (ANS)   functional division of the nervous system that is responsible for homeostatic reflexes that coordinate control of cardiac and smooth muscle, as well as glandular tissue

axon   single process of the neuron that carries an electrical signal (action potential) away from the cell body toward a target cell

axon hillock   tapering of the neuron cell body that gives rise to the axon

axon segment   single stretch of the axon insulated by myelin and bounded by nodes of Ranvier at either end (except for the first, which is after the initial segment, and the last, which is followed by the axon terminal)

axon terminal   end of the axon, where there are usually several branches extending toward the target cell

axoplasm   cytoplasm of an axon, which is different in composition than the cytoplasm of the neuronal cell body

biogenic amine   class of neurotransmitters that are enzymatically derived from amino acids but no longer contain a carboxyl group

bipolar   shape of a neuron with two processes extending from the neuron cell body—the axon and one dendrite

blood-brain barrier (BBB)   physiological barrier between the circulatory system and the central nervous system that establishes a privileged blood supply, restricting the flow of substances into the CNS

brain   the large organ of the central nervous system composed of white and gray matter, contained within the cranium and continuous with the spinal cord

central nervous system (CNS)   anatomical division of the nervous system located within the cranial and vertebral cavities, namely the brain and spinal cord

cerebral cortex   outermost layer of gray matter in the brain, where conscious perception takes place

cerebrospinal fluid (CSF)   circulatory medium within the CNS that is produced by ependymal cells in the choroid plexus filtering the blood

chemical synapse   connection between two neurons, or between a neuron and its target, where a neurotransmitter diffuses across a very short distance

cholinergic system   neurotransmitter system of acetylcholine, which includes its receptors and the enzyme acetylcholinesterase

choroid plexus   specialized structure containing ependymal cells that line blood capillaries and filter blood to produce CSF in the four ventricles of the brain

continuous conduction   slow propagation of an action potential along an unmyelinated axon owing to voltage-gated Na⁺ channels located along the entire length of the cell membrane

dendrite   one of many branchlike processes that extends from the neuron cell body and functions as a contact for incoming signals (synapses) from other neurons or sensory cells

depolarization   change in a cell membrane potential from rest toward zero

effector protein   enzyme that catalyzes the generation of a new molecule, which acts as the intracellular mediator of the signal that binds to the receptor

electrical synapse   connection between two neurons, or any two electrically active cells, where ions flow directly through channels spanning their adjacent cell membranes

electrochemical exclusion   principle of selectively allowing ions through a channel on the basis of their charge

enteric nervous system (ENS)   neural tissue associated with the digestive system that is responsible for nervous control through autonomic connections

ependymal cell   glial cell type in the CNS responsible for producing cerebrospinal fluid

excitable membrane   cell membrane that regulates the movement of ions so that an electrical signal can be generated

excitatory postsynaptic potential (EPSP)   graded potential in the postsynaptic membrane that is the result of depolarization and makes an action potential more likely to occur

G protein   guanosine triphosphate (GTP) hydrolase

that physically moves from the receptor protein to the effector protein to activate the latter

ganglion   localized collection of neuron cell bodies in the peripheral nervous system

gated   property of a channel that determines how it opens under specific conditions, such as voltage change or physical deformation

generator potential   graded potential from dendrites of a unipolar cell which generates the action potential in the initial segment of that cell's axon

glial cell   one of the various types of neural tissue cells responsible for maintenance of the tissue, and largely responsible for supporting neurons

graded potential   change in the membrane potential that varies in size, depending on the size of the stimulus that elicits it

gray matter   regions of the nervous system containing cell bodies of neurons with few or no myelinated axons; actually may be more pink or tan in color, but called gray in contrast to white matter

inactivation gate   part of a voltage-gated Na^+ channel that closes when the membrane potential reaches +30 mV

inhibitory postsynaptic potential (IPSP)   graded potential in the postsynaptic membrane that is the result of hyperpolarization and makes an action potential less likely to occur

initial segment   first part of the axon as it emerges from the axon hillock, where the electrical signals known as action potentials are generated

integration   nervous system function that combines sensory perceptions and higher cognitive functions (memories, learning, emotion, etc.) to produce a response

ionotropic receptor   neurotransmitter receptor that acts as an ion channel gate, and opens by the binding of the neurotransmitter

leakage channel   ion channel that opens randomly and is not gated to a specific event, also known as a non-gated channel

ligand-gated channels   another name for an ionotropic receptor for which a neurotransmitter is the ligand

lower motor neuron   second neuron in the motor command pathway that is directly connected to the skeletal muscle

mechanically gated channel   ion channel that opens when a physical event directly affects the structure of the protein

membrane potential   distribution of charge across the cell membrane, based on the charges of ions

metabotropic receptor   neurotransmitter receptor that involves a complex of proteins that cause

metabolic changes in a cell

microglia   glial cell type in the CNS that serves as the resident component of the immune system

multipolar   shape of a neuron that has multiple processes—the axon and two or more dendrites

muscarinic receptor   type of acetylcholine receptor protein that is characterized by also binding to muscarine and is a metabotropic receptor

myelin   lipid-rich insulating substance surrounding the axons of many neurons, allowing for faster transmission of electrical signals

myelin sheath   lipid-rich layer of insulation that surrounds an axon, formed by oligodendrocytes in the CNS and Schwann cells in the PNS; facilitates the transmission of electrical signals

nerve   cord-like bundle of axons located in the peripheral nervous system that transmits sensory input and response output to and from the central nervous system

neuron   neural tissue cell that is primarily responsible for generating and propagating electrical signals into, within, and out of the nervous system

neuropeptide   neurotransmitter type that includes protein molecules and shorter chains of amino acids

neurotransmitter   chemical signal that is released from the synaptic end bulb of a neuron to cause a change in the target cell

nicotinic receptor   type of acetylcholine receptor protein that is characterized by also binding to nicotine and is an ionotropic receptor

node of Ranvier   gap between two myelinated regions of an axon, allowing for strengthening of the electrical signal as it propagates down the axon

nonspecific channel   channel that is not specific to one ion over another, such as a nonspecific cation channel that allows any positively charged ion across the membrane

nucleus   in the nervous system, a localized collection of neuron cell bodies that are functionally related; a "center" of neural function

oligodendrocyte   glial cell type in the CNS that provides the myelin insulation for axons in tracts

peripheral nervous system (PNS)   anatomical division of the nervous system that is largely outside the cranial and vertebral cavities, namely all parts except the brain and spinal cord

postsynaptic potential (PSP)   graded potential in the postsynaptic membrane caused by the binding of neurotransmitter to protein receptors

precentral gyrus of the frontal cortex   region of the cerebral cortex responsible for generating motor commands, where the upper motor neuron cell body is located

process   in cells, an extension of a cell body; in the case of neurons, this includes the axon and dendrites

propagation   movement of an action potential along the length of an axon

receptor potential   graded potential in a specialized sensory cell that directly causes the release of neurotransmitter without an intervening action potential

refractory period   time after the initiation of an action potential when another action potential cannot be generated

relative refractory period   time during the refractory period when a new action potential can only be initiated by a stronger stimulus than the current action potential because voltage-gated K^+ channels are not closed

repolarization   return of the membrane potential to its normally negative voltage at the end of the action potential

resistance   property of an axon that relates to the ability of particles to diffuse through the cytoplasm; this is inversely proportional to the fiber diameter

response   nervous system function that causes a target tissue (muscle or gland) to produce an event as a consequence to stimuli

resting membrane potential   the difference in voltage measured across a cell membrane under steady-state conditions, typically -70 mV

saltatory conduction   quick propagation of the action potential along a myelinated axon owing to voltage-gated Na^+ channels being present only at the nodes of Ranvier

satellite cell   glial cell type in the PNS that provides support for neurons in the ganglia

Schwann cell   glial cell type in the PNS that provides the myelin insulation for axons in nerves

sensation   nervous system function that receives information from the environment and translates it into the electrical signals of nervous tissue

size exclusion   principle of selectively allowing ions through a channel on the basis of their relative size

soma   in neurons, that portion of the cell that contains the nucleus; the cell body, as opposed to the cell processes (axons and dendrites)

somatic nervous system (SNS)   functional division of the nervous system that is concerned with conscious perception, voluntary movement, and skeletal muscle reflexes

spatial summation   combination of graded potentials across the neuronal cell membrane caused by signals from separate presynaptic elements that add up to initiate an action potential

spinal cord   organ of the central nervous system found within the vertebral cavity and connected with the periphery through spinal nerves; mediates reflex behaviors

stimulus   an event in the external or internal environment that registers as activity in a sensory neuron

summate   to add together, as in the cumulative change in postsynaptic potentials toward reaching threshold in the membrane, either across a span of the membrane or over a certain amount of time

synapse   narrow junction across which a chemical signal passes from neuron to the next, initiating a new electrical signal in the target cell

synaptic cleft   small gap between cells in a chemical synapse where neurotransmitter diffuses from the presynaptic element to the postsynaptic element

synaptic end bulb   swelling at the end of an axon where neurotransmitter molecules are released onto a target cell across a synapse

temporal summation   combination of graded potentials at the same location on a neuron resulting in a strong signal from one input

thalamus   region of the central nervous system that acts as a relay for sensory pathways

thermoreceptor   type of sensory receptor capable of transducing temperature stimuli into neural action potentials

threshold   membrane voltage at which an action potential is initiated

tract   bundle of axons in the central nervous system having the same function and point of origin

unipolar   shape of a neuron which has only one process that includes both the axon and dendrite

upper motor neuron   first neuron in the motor command pathway with its cell body in the cerebral cortex that synapses on the lower motor neuron in the spinal cord

ventricle   central cavity within the brain where CSF is produced and circulates

voltage-gated channel   ion channel that opens because of a change in the charge distributed across the membrane where it is located

white matter   regions of the nervous system containing mostly myelinated axons, making the tissue appear white because of the high lipid content of myelin

Chapter Review

12.1 Basic Structure and Function of the Nervous System

The nervous system can be separated into divisions on the basis of anatomy and physiology. The anatomical divisions are the central and peripheral nervous systems. The CNS is the brain and spinal cord. The PNS is everything else. Functionally, the nervous system can be divided into those regions that are responsible for sensation, those that are responsible for integration, and those that are responsible for generating responses. All of these functional areas are found in both the central and peripheral anatomy.

Considering the anatomical regions of the nervous system, there are specific names for the structures within each division. A localized collection of neuron cell bodies is referred to as a nucleus in the CNS and as a ganglion in the PNS. A bundle of axons is referred to as a tract in the CNS and as a nerve in the PNS. Whereas nuclei and ganglia are specifically in the central or peripheral divisions, axons can cross the boundary between the two. A single axon can be part of a nerve and a tract. The name for that specific structure depends on its location.

Nervous tissue can also be described as gray matter and white matter on the basis of its appearance in unstained tissue. These descriptions are more often used in the CNS. Gray matter is where nuclei are found and white matter is where tracts are found. In the PNS, ganglia are basically gray matter and nerves are white matter.

The nervous system can also be divided on the basis of how it controls the body. The somatic nervous system (SNS) is responsible for functions that result in moving skeletal muscles. Any sensory or integrative functions that result in the movement of skeletal muscle would be considered somatic. The autonomic nervous system (ANS) is responsible for functions that affect cardiac or smooth muscle tissue, or that cause glands to produce their secretions. Autonomic functions are distributed between central and peripheral regions of the nervous system. The sensations that lead to autonomic functions can be the same sensations that are part of initiating somatic responses. Somatic and autonomic integrative functions may overlap as well.

A special division of the nervous system is the enteric nervous system, which is responsible for controlling the digestive organs. Parts of the autonomic nervous system overlap with the enteric nervous system. The enteric nervous system is exclusively found in the periphery because it is the nervous tissue in the organs of the digestive system.

12.2 Nervous Tissue

Nervous tissue contains two major cell types, neurons and glial cells. Neurons are the cells responsible for communication through electrical signals. Glial cells are supporting cells, maintaining the environment around the neurons.

Neurons are polarized cells, based on the flow of electrical signals along their membrane. Signals are received at the dendrites, are passed along the cell body, and propagate along the axon towards the target, which may be another neuron, muscle tissue, or a gland. Many axons are insulated by a lipid-rich substance called myelin. Specific types of glial cells provide this insulation.

Several types of glial cells are found in the nervous system, and they can be categorized by the anatomical division in which they are found. In the CNS, astrocytes, oligodendrocytes, microglia, and ependymal cells are found. Astrocytes are important for maintaining the chemical environment around the neuron and are crucial for regulating the blood-brain barrier. Oligodendrocytes are the myelinating glia in the CNS. Microglia act as phagocytes and play a role in immune surveillance. Ependymal cells are responsible for filtering the blood to produce cerebrospinal fluid, which is a circulatory fluid that performs some of the functions of blood in the brain and spinal cord because of the BBB. In the PNS, satellite cells are supporting cells for the neurons, and Schwann cells insulate peripheral axons.

12.3 The Function of Nervous Tissue

Sensation starts with the activation of a sensory ending, such as the thermoreceptor in the skin sensing the temperature of the water. The sensory endings in the skin initiate an electrical signal that travels along the sensory axon within a nerve into the spinal cord, where it synapses with a neuron in the gray matter of the spinal cord. The temperature information represented in that electrical signal is passed to the next neuron by a chemical signal that diffuses across the small gap of the synapse and initiates a new electrical signal in the target cell. That signal travels through the sensory pathway to the brain, passing through the thalamus, where conscious perception of the water temperature is made possible by the cerebral cortex. Following integration of that information with other cognitive processes and sensory information, the brain sends a command back down to the spinal cord to initiate a motor response by controlling a skeletal muscle. The motor pathway is composed of two cells, the upper motor neuron and the lower motor neuron. The upper motor neuron has its cell body in the cerebral cortex and synapses on a cell in the gray matter of the spinal cord. The lower motor neuron is that cell in the gray matter of the spinal cord and its axon extends into the periphery where it synapses with a skeletal muscle in a neuromuscular junction.

12.4 The Action Potential

The nervous system is characterized by electrical signals that are sent from one area to another. Whether those areas are close or very far apart, the signal must travel along an axon. The basis of the electrical signal is the controlled distribution of ions across the membrane. Transmembrane ion channels regulate when ions can move in or out of the cell, so that a precise signal is generated. This signal is the action potential which has a very characteristic shape based on voltage changes across the membrane in a given time period.

The membrane is normally at rest with established Na^+ and K^+ concentrations on either side. A stimulus will start the depolarization of the membrane, and voltage-gated channels will result in further depolarization followed by repolarization of the membrane. A slight overshoot of hyperpolarization marks the end of the action potential. While an action potential is in progress, another cannot be generated under the same conditions. While the voltage-gated Na^+ channel is inactivated, absolutely no action potentials can be generated. Once that channel has returned to its resting state, a new action potential is possible, but it must be started by a relatively stronger stimulus to overcome the K^+ leaving the cell.

The action potential travels down the axon as voltage-gated ion channels are opened by the spreading depolarization. In unmyelinated axons, this happens in a continuous fashion because there are voltage-gated channels throughout the membrane. In myelinated axons, propagation is described as saltatory because voltage-gated channels are only found at the nodes of Ranvier and the electrical events seem to "jump" from one node to the next. Saltatory conduction is faster than continuous conduction, meaning that myelinated axons propagate their signals faster. The diameter of the axon also makes a difference as ions diffusing within the cell have less resistance in a wider space.

12.5 Communication Between Neurons

The basis of the electrical signal within a neuron is the action potential that propagates down the axon. For a neuron to generate an action potential, it needs to receive input from another source, either another neuron or a sensory stimulus. That input will result in opening ion channels in the neuron, resulting in a graded potential based on the strength of the stimulus. Graded potentials can be depolarizing or hyperpolarizing and can summate to affect the probability of the neuron reaching threshold.

Graded potentials can be the result of sensory stimuli. If the sensory stimulus is received by the dendrites of a unipolar sensory neuron, such as the sensory neuron ending in the skin, the graded potential is called a generator potential because it can directly generate the action potential in the initial segment of the axon. If the sensory stimulus is received by a specialized sensory receptor cell, the graded potential is called a receptor potential. Graded potentials produced by interactions between neurons at synapses are called postsynaptic potentials (PSPs). A depolarizing graded potential at a synapse is called an excitatory PSP, and a hyperpolarizing graded potential at a synapse is called an inhibitory PSP.

Synapses are the contacts between neurons, which can either be chemical or electrical in nature. Chemical synapses are far more common. At a chemical synapse, neurotransmitter is released from the presynaptic element and diffuses across the synaptic cleft. The neurotransmitter binds to a receptor protein and causes a change in the postsynaptic membrane (the PSP). The neurotransmitter must be inactivated or removed from the synaptic cleft so that the stimulus is limited in time.

The particular characteristics of a synapse vary based on the neurotransmitter system produced by that neuron. The cholinergic system is found at the neuromuscular junction and in certain places within the nervous system. Amino acids, such as glutamate, glycine, and gamma-aminobutyric acid (GABA) are used as neurotransmitters. Other neurotransmitters are the result of amino acids being enzymatically changed, as in the biogenic amines, or being covalently bonded together, as in the neuropeptides.

Interactive Link Questions

1. In 2003, the Nobel Prize in Physiology or Medicine was awarded to Paul C. Lauterbur and Sir Peter Mansfield for discoveries related to magnetic resonance imaging (MRI). This is a tool to see the structures of the body (not just the nervous system) that depends on magnetic fields associated with certain atomic nuclei. The utility of this technique in the nervous system is that fat tissue and water appear as different shades between black and white. Because white matter is fatty (from myelin) and gray matter is not, they can be easily distinguished in MRI images. Visit the Nobel Prize website (http://openstax.org/l/nobel_2) to play an interactive game that demonstrates the use of this technology and compares it with other types of imaging technologies. Also, the results from an MRI session are compared with images obtained from x-ray or computed tomography. How do the imaging techniques shown in this game indicate the separation of white and gray matter compared with the freshly dissected tissue shown earlier?

2. Visit this site (http://openstax.org/l/troublewstairs) to read about a woman that notices that her daughter is having trouble walking up the stairs. This leads to the discovery of a hereditary condition that affects the brain and spinal cord. The electromyography and MRI tests indicated deficiencies in the spinal cord and cerebellum, both of which are responsible for controlling coordinated movements. To what functional division of the nervous system would these structures belong?

3. The neurons are dynamic cells with the ability to make a vast number of connections and to respond incredibly quickly to stimuli and to initiate movements based on those stimuli. They are the focus of intense research as failures in physiology can lead to devastating illnesses. Why are neurons only found in animals? Why wouldn't they be helpful for plants or microorganisms?

4. View the University of Michigan Webscope (http://openstax.org/l/nervefiber) to see an electron micrograph of a cross-section of a myelinated nerve fiber. The axon contains microtubules and neurofilaments, bounded by a plasma membrane known as the axolemma. Outside the plasma membrane of the axon is the myelin sheath, which is composed of the tightly wrapped plasma membrane of a Schwann cell. What aspects of the cells in this image react with the stain that makes them the deep, dark, black color, such as the multiple layers that are the myelin sheath?

5. What happens across the membrane of an electrically active cell is a dynamic process that is hard to visualize with static images or through text descriptions. View this animation (http://openstax.org/l/dynamic1) to really understand the process. What is the difference between the driving force for Na^+ and K^+? And what is similar about the movement of these two ions?

6. Visit this site (http://openstax.org/l/neurolab) to see a virtual neurophysiology lab, and to observe electrophysiological processes in the nervous system, where scientists directly measure the electrical signals produced by neurons. Often, the action potentials occur so rapidly that watching a screen to see them occur is not helpful. A speaker is powered by the signals recorded from a neuron and it "pops" each time the neuron fires an action potential. These action potentials are firing so fast that it sounds like static on the radio. Electrophysiologists can recognize the patterns within that static to understand what is happening. Why is the leech model used for measuring the electrical activity of neurons instead of using humans?

7. Watch this video (http://openstax.org/l/summation) to learn about summation. The process of converting electrical signals to chemical signals and back requires subtle changes that can result in transient increases or decreases in membrane voltage. To cause a lasting change in the target cell, multiple signals are usually added together, or summated. Does spatial summation have to happen all at once, or can the separate signals arrive on the postsynaptic neuron at slightly different times? Explain your answer.

8. Watch this video (http://openstax.org/l/neurotrans) to learn about the release of a neurotransmitter. The action potential reaches the end of the axon, called the axon terminal, and a chemical signal is released to tell the target cell to do something, either initiate a new action potential, or to suppress that activity. In a very short space, the electrical signal of the action potential is changed into the chemical signal of a neurotransmitter, and then back to electrical changes in the target cell membrane. What is the importance of voltage-gated calcium channels in the release of neurotransmitters?

Review Questions

9. Which of the following cavities contains a component of the central nervous system?
   a. abdominal
   b. pelvic
   c. cranial
   d. thoracic

10. Which structure predominates in the white matter of the brain?
    a. myelinated axons
    b. neuronal cell bodies
    c. ganglia of the parasympathetic nerves
    d. bundles of dendrites from the enteric nervous system

11. Which part of a neuron transmits an electrical signal to a target cell?
    a. dendrites
    b. soma
    c. cell body
    d. axon

12. Which term describes a bundle of axons in the peripheral nervous system?
    a. nucleus
    b. ganglion
    c. tract
    d. nerve

13. Which functional division of the nervous system would be responsible for the physiological changes seen during exercise (e.g., increased heart rate and sweating)?
    a. somatic
    b. autonomic
    c. enteric
    d. central

14. What type of glial cell provides myelin for the axons in a tract?
    a. oligodendrocyte
    b. astrocyte
    c. Schwann cell
    d. satellite cell

15. Which part of a neuron contains the nucleus?
    a. dendrite
    b. soma
    c. axon
    d. synaptic end bulb

16. Which of the following substances is least able to cross the blood-brain barrier?
    a. water
    b. sodium ions
    c. glucose
    d. white blood cells

17. What type of glial cell is the resident macrophage behind the blood-brain barrier?
    a. microglia
    b. astrocyte
    c. Schwann cell
    d. satellite cell

18. What two types of macromolecules are the main components of myelin?
    a. carbohydrates and lipids
    b. proteins and nucleic acids
    c. lipids and proteins
    d. carbohydrates and nucleic acids

19. If a thermoreceptor is sensitive to temperature sensations, what would a chemoreceptor be sensitive to?
    a. light
    b. sound
    c. molecules
    d. vibration

20. Which of these locations is where the greatest level of integration is taking place in the example of testing the temperature of the shower?
    a. skeletal muscle
    b. spinal cord
    c. thalamus
    d. cerebral cortex

21. How long does all the signaling through the sensory pathway, within the central nervous system, and through the motor command pathway take?
    a. 1 to 2 minutes
    b. 1 to 2 seconds
    c. fraction of a second
    d. varies with graded potential

22. What is the target of an upper motor neuron?
    a. cerebral cortex
    b. lower motor neuron
    c. skeletal muscle
    d. thalamus

23. What ion enters a neuron causing depolarization of the cell membrane?
    a. sodium
    b. chloride
    c. potassium
    d. phosphate

24. Voltage-gated Na$^+$ channels open upon reaching what state?
    a. resting potential
    b. threshold
    c. repolarization
    d. overshoot

25. What does a ligand-gated channel require in order to open?
    a. increase in concentration of Na$^+$ ions
    b. binding of a neurotransmitter
    c. increase in concentration of K$^+$ ions
    d. depolarization of the membrane

26. What does a mechanically gated channel respond to?
    a. physical stimulus
    b. chemical stimulus
    c. increase in resistance
    d. decrease in resistance

27. Which of the following voltages would most likely be measured during the relative refractory period?
    a. +30 mV
    b. 0 mV
    c. -45 mV
    d. -80 mv

28. Which of the following is probably going to propagate an action potential fastest?
    a. a thin, unmyelinated axon
    b. a thin, myelinated axon
    c. a thick, unmyelinated axon
    d. a thick, myelinated axon

29. How much of a change in the membrane potential is necessary for the summation of postsynaptic potentials to result in an action potential being generated?
    a. +30 mV
    b. +15 mV
    c. +10 mV
    d. -15 mV

30. A channel opens on a postsynaptic membrane that causes a negative ion to enter the cell. What type of graded potential is this?
    a. depolarizing
    b. repolarizing
    c. hyperpolarizing
    d. non-polarizing

31. What neurotransmitter is released at the neuromuscular junction?
    a. norepinephrine
    b. serotonin
    c. dopamine
    d. acetylcholine

32. What type of receptor requires an effector protein to initiate a signal?
    a. biogenic amine
    b. ionotropic receptor
    c. cholinergic system
    d. metabotropic receptor

33. Which of the following neurotransmitters is associated with inhibition exclusively?
    a. GABA
    b. acetylcholine
    c. glutamate
    d. norepinephrine

Critical Thinking Questions

34. What responses are generated by the nervous system when you run on a treadmill? Include an example of each type of tissue that is under nervous system control.

35. When eating food, what anatomical and functional divisions of the nervous system are involved in the perceptual experience?

36. Multiple sclerosis is a demyelinating disease affecting the central nervous system. What type of cell would be the most likely target of this disease? Why?

37. Which type of neuron, based on its shape, is best suited for relaying information directly from one neuron to another? Explain why.

38. Sensory fibers, or pathways, are referred to as "afferent." Motor fibers, or pathways, are referred to as "efferent." What can you infer about the meaning of these two terms (afferent and efferent) in a structural or anatomical context?

39. If a person has a motor disorder and cannot move their arm voluntarily, but their muscles have tone, which motor neuron—upper or lower—is probably affected? Explain why.

40. What does it mean for an action potential to be an "all or none" event?

41. The conscious perception of pain is often delayed because of the time it takes for the sensations to reach the cerebral cortex. Why would this be the case based on propagation of the axon potential?

42. If a postsynaptic cell has synapses from five different cells, and three cause EPSPs and two of them cause IPSPs, give an example of a series of depolarizations and hyperpolarizations that would result in the neuron reaching threshold.

43. Why is the receptor the important element determining the effect a neurotransmitter has on a target cell?

CHAPTER 13
Anatomy of the Nervous System

Figure 13.1 Human Nervous System The ability to balance like an acrobat combines functions throughout the nervous system. The central and peripheral divisions coordinate control of the body using the senses of balance, body position, and touch on the soles of the feet. (credit: Rhett Sutphin)

CHAPTER OBJECTIVES
After studying this chapter, you will be able to:
- Relate the developmental processes of the embryonic nervous system to the adult structures
- Name the major regions of the adult nervous system
- Locate regions of the cerebral cortex on the basis of anatomical landmarks common to all human brains
- Describe the regions of the spinal cord in cross-section
- List the cranial nerves in order of anatomical location and provide the central and peripheral connections
- List the spinal nerves by vertebral region and by which nerve plexus each supplies

INTRODUCTION The nervous system is responsible for controlling much of the body, both through somatic (voluntary) and autonomic (involuntary) functions. The structures of the nervous system must be described in detail to understand how many of these functions are possible. There is a physiological concept known as localization of function that states that certain structures are specifically responsible for prescribed functions. It is an underlying concept in all of anatomy and physiology, but the nervous system illustrates the concept very well.

Fresh, unstained nervous tissue can be described as gray or white matter, and within those two types of tissue it can be very hard to see any detail. However, as specific regions and structures have been described, they were related to specific functions. Understanding these structures and the functions they perform requires a detailed description of the anatomy of the nervous system, delving deep into what the central and peripheral structures are.

The place to start this study of the nervous system is the beginning of the individual human life, within the womb. The embryonic development of the nervous system allows for a simple framework on which progressively more complicated structures can be built. With this framework in place, a thorough investigation of the nervous system is possible.

13.1 The Embryologic Perspective

LEARNING OBJECTIVES

By the end of this section, you will be able to:

- Describe the growth and differentiation of the neural tube
- Relate the different stages of development to the adult structures of the central nervous system
- Explain the expansion of the ventricular system of the adult brain from the central canal of the neural tube
- Describe the connections of the diencephalon and cerebellum on the basis of patterns of embryonic development

The brain is a complex organ composed of gray parts and white matter, which can be hard to distinguish. Starting from an embryologic perspective allows you to understand more easily how the parts relate to each other. The embryonic nervous system begins as a very simple structure—essentially just a straight line, which then gets increasingly complex. Looking at the development of the nervous system with a couple of early snapshots makes it easier to understand the whole complex system.

Many structures that appear to be adjacent in the adult brain are not connected, and the connections that exist may seem arbitrary. But there is an underlying order to the system that comes from how different parts develop. By following the developmental pattern, it is possible to learn what the major regions of the nervous system are.

The Neural Tube

To begin, a sperm cell and an egg cell fuse to become a fertilized egg. The fertilized egg cell, or zygote, starts dividing to generate the cells that make up an entire organism. Sixteen days after fertilization, the developing embryo's cells belong to one of three germ layers that give rise to the different tissues in the body. The endoderm, or inner tissue, is responsible for generating the lining tissues of various spaces within the body, such as the mucosae of the digestive and respiratory systems. The mesoderm, or middle tissue, gives rise to most of the muscle and connective tissues. Finally the ectoderm, or outer tissue, develops into the integumentary system (the skin) and the nervous system. It is probably not difficult to see that the outer tissue of the embryo becomes the outer covering of the body. But how is it responsible for the nervous system?

As the embryo develops, a portion of the ectoderm differentiates into a specialized region of neuroectoderm, which is the precursor for the tissue of the nervous system. Molecular signals induce cells in this region to differentiate into the neuroepithelium, forming a **neural plate**. The cells then begin to change shape, causing the tissue to buckle and fold inward (Figure 13.2). A **neural groove** forms, visible as a line along the dorsal surface of the embryo. The ridge-like edge on either side of the neural groove is referred as the **neural fold**. As the neural folds come together and converge, the underlying structure forms into a tube just beneath the ectoderm called the **neural tube**. Cells from the neural folds then separate from the ectoderm to form a cluster of cells referred to as the **neural crest**, which runs lateral to the neural tube. The neural crest migrates away from the nascent, or embryonic, central nervous system (CNS) that will form along the neural groove and develops into several parts of the peripheral nervous system (PNS), including the enteric nervous tissue. Many tissues that are not part of the nervous system also arise from the neural crest, such as craniofacial cartilage and bone, and melanocytes.

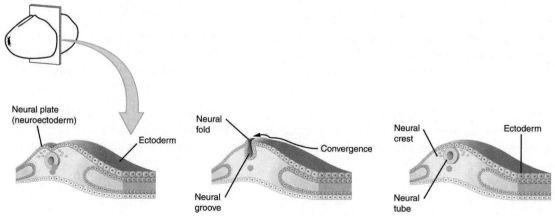

FIGURE 13.2 Early Embryonic Development of Nervous System   The neuroectoderm begins to fold inward to form the neural groove.

Access for free at openstax.org

As the two sides of the neural groove converge, they form the neural tube, which lies beneath the ectoderm. The anterior end of the neural tube will develop into the brain, and the posterior portion will become the spinal cord. The neural crest develops into peripheral structures.

At this point, the early nervous system is a simple, hollow tube. It runs from the anterior end of the embryo to the posterior end. Beginning at 25 days, the anterior end develops into the brain, and the posterior portion becomes the spinal cord. This is the most basic arrangement of tissue in the nervous system, and it gives rise to the more complex structures by the fourth week of development.

Primary Vesicles

As the anterior end of the neural tube starts to develop into the brain, it undergoes a couple of enlargements; the result is the production of sac-like vesicles. Similar to a child's balloon animal, the long, straight neural tube begins to take on a new shape. Three vesicles form at the first stage, which are called **primary vesicles**. These vesicles are given names that are based on Greek words, the main root word being *enkephalon*, which means "brain" (en- = "inside"; kephalon = "head"). The prefix to each generally corresponds to its position along the length of the developing nervous system.

The **prosencephalon** (pros- = "in front") is the forward-most vesicle, and the term can be loosely translated to mean **forebrain**. The **mesencephalon** (mes- = "middle") is the next vesicle, which can be called the **midbrain**. The third vesicle at this stage is the **rhombencephalon**. The first part of this word is also the root of the word rhombus, which is a geometrical figure with four sides of equal length (a square is a rhombus with 90° angles). Whereas prosencephalon and mesencephalon translate into the English words forebrain and midbrain, there is not a word for "four-sided-figure-brain." However, the third vesicle can be called the **hindbrain**. One way of thinking about how the brain is arranged is to use these three regions—forebrain, midbrain, and hindbrain—which are based on the primary vesicle stage of development (Figure 13.3**a**).

Secondary Vesicles

The brain continues to develop, and the vesicles differentiate further (see Figure 13.3**b**). The three primary vesicles become five **secondary vesicles**. The prosencephalon enlarges into two new vesicles called the **telencephalon** and the **diencephalon**. The telecephalon will become the cerebrum. The diencephalon gives rise to several adult structures; two that will be important are the thalamus and the hypothalamus. In the embryonic diencephalon, a structure known as the eye cup develops, which will eventually become the retina, the nervous tissue of the eye called the retina. This is a rare example of nervous tissue developing as part of the CNS structures in the embryo, but becoming a peripheral structure in the fully formed nervous system.

The mesencephalon does not differentiate into any finer divisions. The midbrain is an established region of the brain at the primary vesicle stage of development and remains that way. The rest of the brain develops around it and constitutes a large percentage of the mass of the brain. Dividing the brain into forebrain, midbrain, and hindbrain is useful in considering its developmental pattern, but the midbrain is a small proportion of the entire brain, relatively speaking.

The rhombencephalon develops into the **metencephalon** and **myelencephalon**. The metencephalon corresponds to the adult structure known as the pons and also gives rise to the cerebellum. The cerebellum (from the Latin meaning "little brain") accounts for about 10 percent of the mass of the brain and is an important structure in itself. The most significant connection between the cerebellum and the rest of the brain is at the pons, because the pons and cerebellum develop out of the same vesicle. The myelencephalon corresponds to the adult structure known as the medulla oblongata. The structures that come from the mesencephalon and rhombencephalon, except for the cerebellum, are collectively considered the **brain stem**, which specifically includes the midbrain, pons, and medulla.

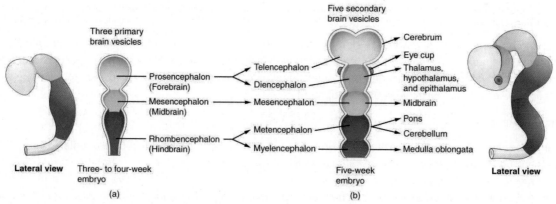

FIGURE 13.3 Primary and Secondary Vesicle Stages of Development   The embryonic brain develops complexity through enlargements of the neural tube called vesicles; (a) The primary vesicle stage has three regions, and (b) the secondary vesicle stage has five regions.

🔗 INTERACTIVE LINK

Watch this animation (http://openstax.org/l/braindevel) to examine the development of the brain, starting with the neural tube. As the anterior end of the neural tube develops, it enlarges into the primary vesicles that establish the forebrain, midbrain, and hindbrain. Those structures continue to develop throughout the rest of embryonic development and into adolescence. They are the basis of the structure of the fully developed adult brain. How would you describe the difference in the relative sizes of the three regions of the brain when comparing the early (25th embryonic day) brain and the adult brain?

Spinal Cord Development

While the brain is developing from the anterior neural tube, the spinal cord is developing from the posterior neural tube. However, its structure does not differ from the basic layout of the neural tube. It is a long, straight cord with a small, hollow space down the center. The neural tube is defined in terms of its anterior versus posterior portions, but it also has a dorsal–ventral dimension. As the neural tube separates from the rest of the ectoderm, the side closest to the surface is dorsal, and the deeper side is ventral.

As the spinal cord develops, the cells making up the wall of the neural tube proliferate and differentiate into the neurons and glia of the spinal cord. The dorsal tissues will be associated with sensory functions, and the ventral tissues will be associated with motor functions.

Relating Embryonic Development to the Adult Brain

Embryonic development can help in understanding the structure of the adult brain because it establishes a framework on which more complex structures can be built. First, the neural tube establishes the anterior–posterior dimension of the nervous system, which is called the **neuraxis**. The embryonic nervous system in mammals can be said to have a standard arrangement. Humans (and other primates, to some degree) make this complicated by standing up and walking on two legs. The anterior–posterior dimension of the neuraxis overlays the superior–inferior dimension of the body. However, there is a major curve between the brain stem and forebrain, which is called the **cephalic flexure**. Because of this, the neuraxis starts in an inferior position—the end of the spinal cord—and ends in an anterior position, the front of the cerebrum. If this is confusing, just imagine a four-legged animal standing up on two legs. Without the flexure in the brain stem, and at the top of the neck, that animal would be looking straight up instead of straight in front (Figure 13.4).

Access for free at openstax.org

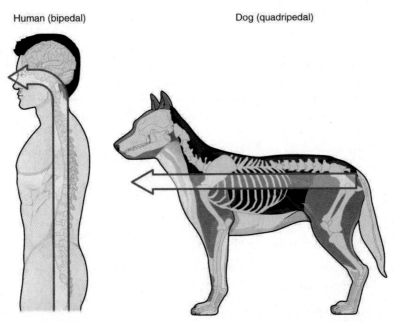

FIGURE 13.4 Human Neuraxis The mammalian nervous system is arranged with the neural tube running along an anterior to posterior axis, from nose to tail for a four-legged animal like a dog. Humans, as two-legged animals, have a bend in the neuraxis between the brain stem and the diencephalon, along with a bend in the neck, so that the eyes and the face are oriented forward.

In summary, the primary vesicles help to establish the basic regions of the nervous system: forebrain, midbrain, and hindbrain. These divisions are useful in certain situations, but they are not equivalent regions. The midbrain is small compared with the hindbrain and particularly the forebrain. The secondary vesicles go on to establish the major regions of the adult nervous system that will be followed in this text. The telencephalon is the cerebrum, which is the major portion of the human brain. The diencephalon continues to be referred to by this Greek name, because there is no better term for it (dia- = "through"). The diencephalon is between the cerebrum and the rest of the nervous system and can be described as the region through which all projections have to pass between the cerebrum and everything else. The brain stem includes the midbrain, pons, and medulla, which correspond to the mesencephalon, metencephalon, and myelencephalon. The cerebellum, being a large portion of the brain, is considered a separate region. Table 13.1 connects the different stages of development to the adult structures of the CNS.

One other benefit of considering embryonic development is that certain connections are more obvious because of how these adult structures are related. The retina, which began as part of the diencephalon, is primarily connected to the diencephalon. The eyes are just inferior to the anterior-most part of the cerebrum, but the optic nerve extends back to the thalamus as the optic tract, with branches into a region of the hypothalamus. There is also a connection of the optic tract to the midbrain, but the mesencephalon is adjacent to the diencephalon, so that is not difficult to imagine. The cerebellum originates out of the metencephalon, and its largest white matter connection is to the pons, also from the metencephalon. There are connections between the cerebellum and both the medulla and midbrain, which are adjacent structures in the secondary vesicle stage of development. In the adult brain, the cerebellum seems close to the cerebrum, but there is no direct connection between them.

Another aspect of the adult CNS structures that relates to embryonic development is the ventricles—open spaces within the CNS where cerebrospinal fluid circulates. They are the remnant of the hollow center of the neural tube. The four ventricles and the tubular spaces associated with them can be linked back to the hollow center of the embryonic brain (see Table 13.1).

Stages of Embryonic Development

Neural tube	Primary vesicle stage	Secondary vesicle stage	Adult structures	Ventricles
Anterior neural tube	Prosencephalon	Telencephalon	Cerebrum	Lateral ventricles
Anterior neural tube	Prosencephalon	Diencephalon	Diencephalon	Third ventricle
Anterior neural tube	Mesencephalon	Mesencephalon	Midbrain	Cerebral aqueduct
Anterior neural tube	Rhombencephalon	Metencephalon	Pons cerebellum	Fourth ventricle
Anterior neural tube	Rhombencephalon	Myelencephalon	Medulla	Fourth ventricle
Posterior neural tube			Spinal cord	Central canal

TABLE 13.1

Disorders of the...

Nervous System

Early formation of the nervous system depends on the formation of the neural tube. A groove forms along the dorsal surface of the embryo, which becomes deeper until its edges meet and close off to form the tube. If this fails to happen, especially in the posterior region where the spinal cord forms, a developmental defect called spina bifida occurs. The closing of the neural tube is important for more than just the proper formation of the nervous system. The surrounding tissues are dependent on the correct development of the tube. The connective tissues surrounding the CNS can be involved as well.

There are three classes of this disorder: occulta, meningocele, and myelomeningocele (Figure 13.5). The first type, spina bifida occulta, is the mildest because the vertebral bones do not fully surround the spinal cord, but the spinal cord itself is not affected. No functional differences may be noticed, which is what the word occulta means; it is hidden spina bifida. The other two types both involve the formation of a cyst—a fluid-filled sac of the connective tissues that cover the spinal cord called the meninges. "Meningocele" means that the meninges protrude through the spinal column but nerves may not be involved and few symptoms are present, though complications may arise later in life. "Myelomeningocele" means that the meninges protrude and spinal nerves are involved, and therefore severe neurological symptoms can be present.

Often surgery to close the opening or to remove the cyst is necessary. The earlier that surgery can be performed, the better the chances of controlling or limiting further damage or infection at the opening. For many children with meningocele, surgery will alleviate the pain, although they may experience some functional loss. Because the myelomeningocele form of spina bifida involves more extensive damage to the nervous tissue, neurological damage may persist, but symptoms can often be handled. Complications of the spinal cord may present later in life, but overall life expectancy is not reduced.

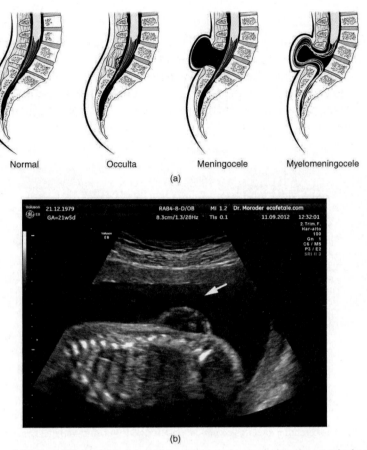

FIGURE 13.5   **Spinal Bifida**   (a) Spina bifida is a birth defect of the spinal cord caused when the neural tube does not completely close, but the rest of development continues. The result is the emergence of meninges and neural tissue through the vertebral column. (b) Fetal myelomeningocele is evident in this ultrasound taken at 21 weeks.

🔗 INTERACTIVE LINK

Watch this video (http://openstax.org/l/whitematter) to learn about the white matter in the cerebrum that develops during childhood and adolescence. This is a composite of MRI images taken of the brains of people from 5 years of age through 20 years of age, demonstrating how the cerebrum changes. As the color changes to blue, the ratio of gray matter to white matter changes. The caption for the video describes it as "less gray matter," which is another way of saying "more white matter." If the brain does not finish developing until approximately 20 years of age, can teenagers be held responsible for behaving badly?

13.2 The Central Nervous System

LEARNING OBJECTIVES

By the end of this section, you will be able to:
- Name the major regions of the adult brain
- Describe the connections between the cerebrum and brain stem through the diencephalon, and from those regions into the spinal cord
- Recognize the complex connections within the subcortical structures of the basal nuclei
- Explain the arrangement of gray and white matter in the spinal cord

The brain and the spinal cord are the central nervous system, and they represent the main organs of the nervous system. The spinal cord is a single structure, whereas the adult brain is described in terms of four major regions: the cerebrum, the diencephalon, the brain stem, and the cerebellum. A person's conscious experiences are based on neural activity in the brain. The regulation of homeostasis is governed by a specialized region in the brain. The coordination of reflexes depends on the integration of sensory and motor pathways in the spinal cord.

The Cerebrum

The iconic gray mantle of the human brain, which appears to make up most of the mass of the brain, is the **cerebrum** (Figure 13.6). The wrinkled portion is the **cerebral cortex**, and the rest of the structure is beneath that outer covering. There is a large separation between the two sides of the cerebrum called the **longitudinal fissure**. It separates the cerebrum into two distinct halves, a right and left **cerebral hemisphere**. Deep within the cerebrum, the white matter of the **corpus callosum** provides the major pathway for communication between the two hemispheres of the cerebral cortex.

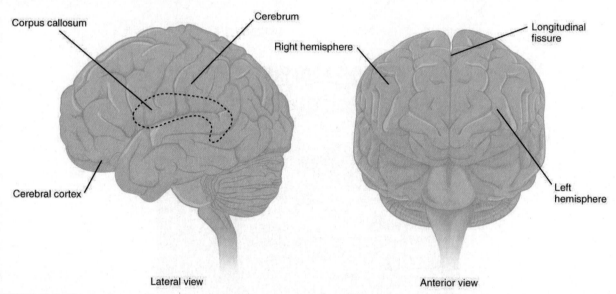

FIGURE 13.6   The Cerebrum   The cerebrum is a large component of the CNS in humans, and the most obvious aspect of it is the folded surface called the cerebral cortex.

Many of the higher neurological functions, such as memory, emotion, and consciousness, are the result of cerebral function. The complexity of the cerebrum is different across vertebrate species. The cerebrum of the most primitive vertebrates is not much more than the connection for the sense of smell. In mammals, the cerebrum comprises the outer gray matter that is the cortex (from the Latin word meaning "bark of a tree") and several deep nuclei that belong to three important functional groups. The **basal nuclei** are responsible for cognitive processing, the most important function being that associated with planning movements. The **basal forebrain** contains nuclei that are important in learning and memory. The **limbic cortex** is the region of the cerebral cortex that is part of the **limbic system**, a collection of structures involved in emotion, memory, and behavior.

Cerebral Cortex

The cerebrum is covered by a continuous layer of gray matter that wraps around either side of the forebrain—the cerebral cortex. This thin, extensive region of wrinkled gray matter is responsible for the higher functions of the nervous system. A **gyrus** (plural = gyri) is the ridge of one of those wrinkles, and a **sulcus** (plural = sulci) is the groove between two gyri. The pattern of these folds of tissue indicates specific regions of the cerebral cortex.

The head is limited by the size of the birth canal, and the brain must fit inside the cranial cavity of the skull. Extensive folding in the cerebral cortex enables more gray matter to fit into this limited space. If the gray matter of the cortex were peeled off of the cerebrum and laid out flat, its surface area would be roughly equal to one square meter.

The folding of the cortex maximizes the amount of gray matter in the cranial cavity. During embryonic development, as the telencephalon expands within the skull, the brain goes through a regular course of growth that results in everyone's brain having a similar pattern of folds. The surface of the brain can be mapped on the basis of the locations of large gyri and sulci. Using these landmarks, the cortex can be separated into four major regions, or lobes (Figure 13.7). The **lateral sulcus** that separates the **temporal lobe** from the other regions is one such landmark. Superior to the lateral sulcus are the **parietal lobe** and **frontal lobe**, which are separated from each other by the **central sulcus**. The posterior region of the cortex is the **occipital lobe**, which has no obvious anatomical border between it and the parietal or temporal lobes on the lateral surface of the brain. From the medial surface, an obvious landmark separating the parietal and occipital lobes is called the **parieto-occipital sulcus**. The fact that there is no obvious anatomical border between these lobes is consistent with the functions of these regions being interrelated.

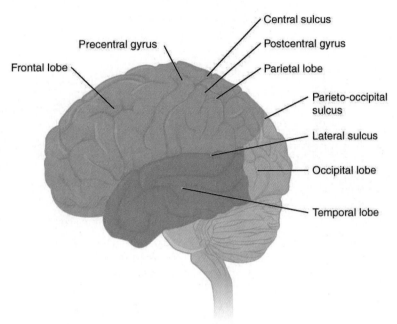

FIGURE 13.7   Lobes of the Cerebral Cortex   The cerebral cortex is divided into four lobes. Extensive folding increases the surface area available for cerebral functions.

Different regions of the cerebral cortex can be associated with particular functions, a concept known as localization of function. In the early 1900s, a German neuroscientist named Korbinian Brodmann performed an extensive study of the microscopic anatomy—the cytoarchitecture—of the cerebral cortex and divided the cortex into 52 separate regions on the basis of the histology of the cortex. His work resulted in a system of classification known as **Brodmann's areas**, which is still used today to describe the anatomical distinctions within the cortex (Figure 13.8). The results from Brodmann's work on the anatomy align very well with the functional differences within the cortex. Areas 17 and 18 in the occipital lobe are responsible for primary visual perception. That visual information is complex, so it is processed in the temporal and parietal lobes as well.

The temporal lobe is associated with primary auditory sensation, known as Brodmann's areas 41 and 42 in the superior temporal lobe. Because regions of the temporal lobe are part of the limbic system, memory is an important function associated with that lobe. Memory is essentially a sensory function; memories are recalled sensations such as the smell of Mom's baking or the sound of a barking dog. Even memories of movement are really the memory of sensory feedback from those movements, such as stretching muscles or the movement of the skin around a joint. Structures in the temporal lobe are responsible for establishing long-term memory, but the ultimate location of those memories is usually in the region in which the sensory perception was processed.

The main sensation associated with the parietal lobe is **somatosensation**, meaning the general sensations associated with the body. Posterior to the central sulcus is the **postcentral gyrus**, the primary somatosensory cortex, which is identified as Brodmann's areas 1, 2, and 3. All of the tactile senses are processed in this area, including touch, pressure, tickle, pain, itch, and vibration, as well as more general senses of the body such as **proprioception** and **kinesthesia**, which are the senses of body position and movement, respectively.

Anterior to the central sulcus is the frontal lobe, which is primarily associated with motor functions. The **precentral gyrus** is the primary motor cortex. Cells from this region of the cerebral cortex are the upper motor neurons that instruct cells in the spinal cord to move skeletal muscles. Anterior to this region are a few areas that are associated with planned movements. The **premotor area** is responsible for thinking of a movement to be made. The **frontal eye fields** are important in eliciting eye movements and in attending to visual stimuli. **Broca's area** is responsible for the production of language, or controlling movements responsible for speech; in the vast majority of people, it is located only on the left side. Anterior to these regions is the **prefrontal lobe**, which serves cognitive functions that can be the basis of personality, short-term memory, and consciousness. The prefrontal lobotomy is an outdated mode of treatment for personality disorders (psychiatric conditions) that profoundly affected the personality of the patient.

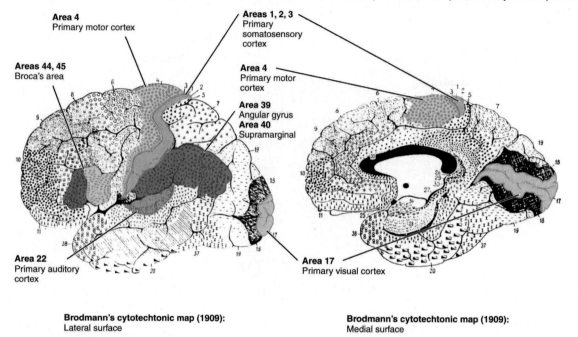

FIGURE 13.8 Brodmann's Areas of the Cerebral Cortex   Brodmann mapping of functionally distinct regions of the cortex was based on its cytoarchitecture at a microscopic level.

Subcortical structures

Beneath the cerebral cortex are sets of nuclei known as **subcortical nuclei** that augment cortical processes. The nuclei of the basal forebrain serve as the primary location for acetylcholine production, which modulates the overall activity of the cortex, possibly leading to greater attention to sensory stimuli. Alzheimer's disease is associated with a loss of neurons in the basal forebrain. The **hippocampus** and **amygdala** are medial-lobe structures that, along with the adjacent cortex, are involved in long-term memory formation and emotional responses. The basal nuclei are a set of nuclei in the cerebrum responsible for comparing cortical processing with the general state of activity in the nervous system to influence the likelihood of movement taking place. For example, while a student is sitting in a classroom listening to a lecture, the basal nuclei will keep the urge to jump up and scream from actually happening. (The basal nuclei are also referred to as the basal ganglia, although that is potentially confusing because the term ganglia is typically used for peripheral structures.)

The major structures of the basal nuclei that control movement are the **caudate**, **putamen**, and **globus pallidus**, which are located deep in the cerebrum. The caudate is a long nucleus that follows the basic C-shape of the cerebrum from the frontal lobe, through the parietal and occipital lobes, into the temporal lobe. The putamen is mostly deep in the anterior regions of the frontal and parietal lobes. Together, the caudate and putamen are called the **striatum**. The globus pallidus is a layered nucleus that lies just medial to the putamen; they are called the lenticular nuclei because they look like curved pieces fitting together like lenses. The globus pallidus has two subdivisions, the external and internal segments, which are lateral and medial, respectively. These nuclei are depicted in a frontal section of the brain in <u>Figure 13.9</u>.

Access for free at openstax.org

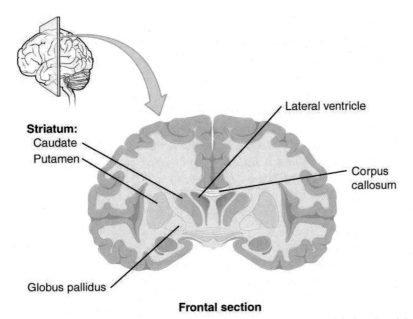

Frontal section

FIGURE 13.9   Frontal Section of Cerebral Cortex and Basal Nuclei   The major components of the basal nuclei, shown in a frontal section of the brain, are the caudate (just lateral to the lateral ventricle), the putamen (inferior to the caudate and separated by the large white-matter structure called the internal capsule), and the globus pallidus (medial to the putamen).

The basal nuclei in the cerebrum are connected with a few more nuclei in the brain stem that together act as a functional group that forms a motor pathway. Two streams of information processing take place in the basal nuclei. All input to the basal nuclei is from the cortex into the striatum (Figure 13.10). The **direct pathway** is the projection of axons from the striatum to the globus pallidus internal segment (GPi) and the **substantia nigra pars reticulata** (SNr). The GPi/SNr then projects to the thalamus, which projects back to the cortex. The **indirect pathway** is the projection of axons from the striatum to the globus pallidus external segment (GPe), then to the subthalamic nucleus (STN), and finally to GPi/SNr. The two streams both target the GPi/SNr, but one has a direct projection and the other goes through a few intervening nuclei. The direct pathway causes the **disinhibition** of the thalamus (inhibition of one cell on a target cell that then inhibits the first cell), whereas the indirect pathway causes, or reinforces, the normal inhibition of the thalamus. The thalamus then can either excite the cortex (as a result of the direct pathway) or fail to excite the cortex (as a result of the indirect pathway).

Basal nuclei

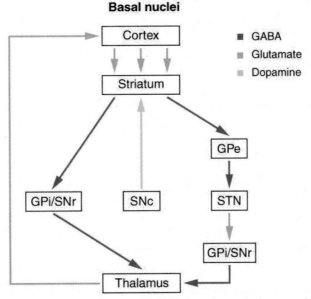

FIGURE 13.10   Connections of Basal Nuclei   Input to the basal nuclei is from the cerebral cortex, which is an excitatory connection releasing glutamate as a neurotransmitter. This input is to the striatum, or the caudate and putamen. In the direct pathway, the striatum projects to the internal segment of the globus pallidus and the substantia nigra pars reticulata (GPi/SNr). This is an inhibitory pathway, in which GABA is released at the synapse, and the target cells are hyperpolarized and less likely to fire. The output from the basal nuclei is to the thalamus, which is an inhibitory projection using GABA. The diagram also includes the substantia nigra compacta (SNc), globus pallidus

external segment (GPe), and subthalamic nucleus (STN).

The switch between the two pathways is the **substantia nigra pars compacta**, which projects to the striatum and releases the neurotransmitter dopamine. Dopamine receptors are either excitatory (D1-type receptors) or inhibitory (D2-type receptors). The direct pathway is activated by dopamine, and the indirect pathway is inhibited by dopamine. When the substantia nigra pars compacta is firing, it signals to the basal nuclei that the body is in an active state, and movement will be more likely. When the substantia nigra pars compacta is silent, the body is in a passive state, and movement is inhibited. To illustrate this situation, while a student is sitting listening to a lecture, the substantia nigra pars compacta would be silent and the student less likely to get up and walk around. Likewise, while the professor is lecturing, and walking around at the front of the classroom, the professor's substantia nigra pars compacta would be active, in keeping with their activity level.

⊘ INTERACTIVE LINK

Watch this video (http://openstax.org/l/basalnuclei1) to learn about the basal nuclei (also known as the basal ganglia), which have two pathways that process information within the cerebrum. As shown in this video, the direct pathway is the shorter pathway through the system that results in increased activity in the cerebral cortex and increased motor activity. The direct pathway is described as resulting in "disinhibition" of the thalamus. What does disinhibition mean? What are the two neurons doing individually to cause this?

⊘ INTERACTIVE LINK

Watch this video (http://openstax.org/l/basalnuclei2) to learn about the basal nuclei (also known as the basal ganglia), which have two pathways that process information within the cerebrum. As shown in this video, the indirect pathway is the longer pathway through the system that results in decreased activity in the cerebral cortex, and therefore less motor activity. The indirect pathway has an extra couple of connections in it, including disinhibition of the subthalamic nucleus. What is the end result on the thalamus, and therefore on movement initiated by the cerebral cortex?

Everyday Connection

The Myth of Left Brain/Right Brain

There is a persistent myth that people are "right-brained" or "left-brained," which is an oversimplification of an important concept about the cerebral hemispheres. There is some lateralization of function, in which the left side of the brain is devoted to language function and the right side is devoted to spatial and nonverbal reasoning. Whereas these functions are predominantly associated with those sides of the brain, there is no monopoly by either side on these functions. Many pervasive functions, such as language, are distributed globally around the cerebrum.

Some of the support for this misconception has come from studies of split brains. A drastic way to deal with a rare and devastating neurological condition (intractable epilepsy) is to separate the two hemispheres of the brain. After sectioning the corpus callosum, a split-brained patient will have trouble producing verbal responses on the basis of sensory information processed on the right side of the cerebrum, leading to the idea that the left side is responsible for language function.

However, there are well-documented cases of language functions lost from damage to the right side of the brain. The deficits seen in damage to the left side of the brain are classified as aphasia, a loss of speech function; damage on the right side can affect the use of language. Right-side damage can result in a loss of ability to understand figurative aspects of speech, such as jokes, irony, or metaphors. Nonverbal aspects of speech can be affected by damage to the right side, such as facial expression or body language, and right-side damage can lead to a "flat affect" in speech, or a loss of emotional expression in speech—sounding like a robot when talking.

The Diencephalon

The diencephalon is the one region of the adult brain that retains its name from embryologic development. The etymology of the word diencephalon translates to "through brain." It is the connection between the cerebrum and the rest of the nervous system, with one exception. The rest of the brain, the spinal cord, and the PNS all send information to the cerebrum through the diencephalon. Output from the cerebrum passes through the diencephalon. The single exception is the system associated with **olfaction**, or the sense of smell, which connects directly with the cerebrum. In the earliest vertebrate species, the cerebrum was not much more than olfactory bulbs that received peripheral information about the chemical environment (to call it smell in these organisms is imprecise because they lived in the ocean).

The diencephalon is deep beneath the cerebrum and constitutes the walls of the third ventricle. The diencephalon can be described as any region of the brain with "thalamus" in its name. The two major regions of the diencephalon are the thalamus itself and the hypothalamus (Figure 13.11). There are other structures, such as the **epithalamus**, which contains the pineal gland, or the **subthalamus**, which includes the subthalamic nucleus that is part of the basal nuclei.

Thalamus

The **thalamus** is a collection of nuclei that relay information between the cerebral cortex and the periphery, spinal cord, or brain stem. All sensory information, except for the sense of smell, passes through the thalamus before processing by the cortex. Axons from the peripheral sensory organs, or intermediate nuclei, synapse in the thalamus, and thalamic neurons project directly to the cerebrum. It is a requisite synapse in any sensory pathway, except for olfaction. The thalamus does not just pass the information on, it also processes that information. For example, the portion of the thalamus that receives visual information will influence what visual stimuli are important, or what receives attention.

The cerebrum also sends information down to the thalamus, which usually communicates motor commands. This involves interactions with the cerebellum and other nuclei in the brain stem. The cerebrum interacts with the basal nuclei, which involves connections with the thalamus. The primary output of the basal nuclei is to the thalamus, which relays that output to the cerebral cortex. The cortex also sends information to the thalamus that will then influence the effects of the basal nuclei.

Hypothalamus

Inferior and slightly anterior to the thalamus is the **hypothalamus**, the other major region of the diencephalon. The hypothalamus is a collection of nuclei that are largely involved in regulating homeostasis. The hypothalamus is the executive region in charge of the autonomic nervous system and the endocrine system through its regulation of the anterior pituitary gland. Other parts of the hypothalamus are involved in memory and emotion as part of the limbic system.

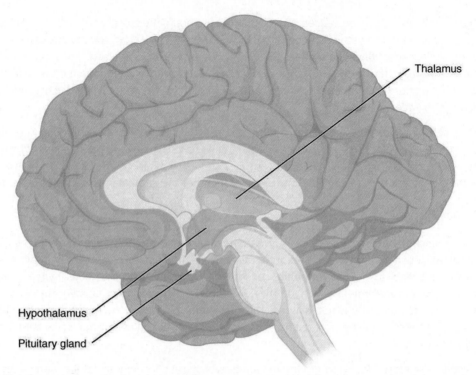

FIGURE 13.11   The Diencephalon   The diencephalon is composed primarily of the thalamus and hypothalamus, which together define the walls of the third ventricle. The thalami are two elongated, ovoid structures on either side of the midline that make contact in the middle. The hypothalamus is inferior and anterior to the thalamus, culminating in a sharp angle to which the pituitary gland is attached.

Brain Stem

The midbrain and hindbrain (composed of the pons and the medulla) are collectively referred to as the brain stem (Figure 13.12). The structure emerges from the ventral surface of the forebrain as a tapering cone that connects the brain to the spinal cord. Attached to the brain stem, but considered a separate region of the adult brain, is the cerebellum. The midbrain coordinates sensory representations of the visual, auditory, and somatosensory perceptual spaces. The pons is the main connection with the cerebellum. The pons and the medulla regulate several crucial functions, including the cardiovascular and respiratory systems and rates.

The cranial nerves connect through the brain stem and provide the brain with the sensory input and motor output associated with the head and neck, including most of the special senses. The major ascending and descending pathways between the spinal cord and brain, specifically the cerebrum, pass through the brain stem.

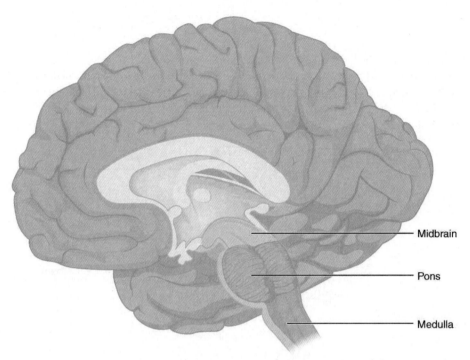

FIGURE 13.12 The Brain Stem The brain stem comprises three regions: the midbrain, the pons, and the medulla.

Midbrain

One of the original regions of the embryonic brain, the midbrain is a small region between the thalamus and pons. It is separated into the **tectum** and **tegmentum**, from the Latin words for roof and floor, respectively. The cerebral aqueduct passes through the center of the midbrain, such that these regions are the roof and floor of that canal.

The tectum is composed of four bumps known as the colliculi (singular = colliculus), which means "little hill" in Latin. The **inferior colliculus** is the inferior pair of these enlargements and is part of the auditory brain stem pathway. Neurons of the inferior colliculus project to the thalamus, which then sends auditory information to the cerebrum for the conscious perception of sound. The **superior colliculus** is the superior pair and combines sensory information about visual space, auditory space, and somatosensory space. Activity in the superior colliculus is related to orienting the eyes to a sound or touch stimulus. If you are walking along the sidewalk on campus and you hear chirping, the superior colliculus coordinates that information with your awareness of the visual location of the tree right above you. That is the correlation of auditory and visual maps. If you suddenly feel something wet fall on your head, your superior colliculus integrates that with the auditory and visual maps and you know that the chirping bird just relieved itself on you. You want to look up to see the culprit, but do not.

The tegmentum is continuous with the gray matter of the rest of the brain stem. Throughout the midbrain, pons, and medulla, the tegmentum contains the nuclei that receive and send information through the cranial nerves, as well as regions that regulate important functions such as those of the cardiovascular and respiratory systems.

Pons

The word pons comes from the Latin word for bridge. It is visible on the anterior surface of the brain stem as the thick bundle of white matter attached to the cerebellum. The pons is the main connection between the cerebellum and the brain stem. The bridge-like white matter is only the anterior surface of the pons; the gray matter beneath that is a continuation of the tegmentum from the midbrain. Gray matter in the tegmentum region of the pons contains neurons receiving descending input from the forebrain that is sent to the cerebellum.

Medulla

The medulla is the region known as the myelencephalon in the embryonic brain. The initial portion of the name, "myel," refers to the significant white matter found in this region—especially on its exterior, which is continuous with the white matter of the spinal cord. The tegmentum of the midbrain and pons continues into the medulla because this gray matter is responsible for processing cranial nerve information. A diffuse region of gray matter throughout the brain stem, known as the **reticular formation**, is related to sleep and wakefulness, such as general brain activity and attention.

The Cerebellum

The **cerebellum**, as the name suggests, is the "little brain." It is covered in gyri and sulci like the cerebrum, and looks like a miniature version of that part of the brain (Figure 13.13). The cerebellum is largely responsible for comparing information from the cerebrum with sensory feedback from the periphery through the spinal cord. It accounts for approximately 10 percent of the mass of the brain.

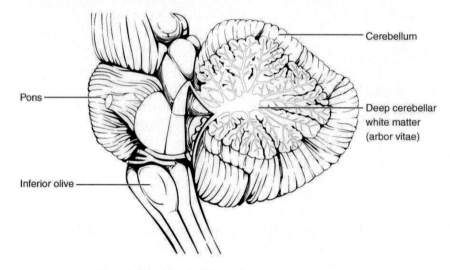

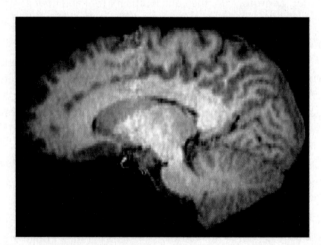

FIGURE 13.13   The Cerebellum   The cerebellum is situated on the posterior surface of the brain stem. Descending input from the cerebellum enters through the large white matter structure of the pons. Ascending input from the periphery and spinal cord enters through the fibers of the inferior olive. Output goes to the midbrain, which sends a descending signal to the spinal cord.

Descending fibers from the cerebrum have branches that connect to neurons in the pons. Those neurons project into the cerebellum, providing a copy of motor commands sent to the spinal cord. Sensory information from the periphery, which enters through spinal or cranial nerves, is copied to a nucleus in the medulla known as the **inferior olive**. Fibers from this nucleus enter the cerebellum and are compared with the descending commands from the cerebrum. If the primary motor cortex of the frontal lobe sends a command down to the spinal cord to initiate walking, a copy of that instruction is sent to the cerebellum. Sensory feedback from the muscles and joints, proprioceptive information about the movements of walking, and sensations of balance are sent to the cerebellum through the inferior olive and the cerebellum compares them. If walking is not coordinated, perhaps because the ground is uneven or a strong wind is blowing, then the cerebellum sends out a corrective command to compensate for the difference between the original cortical command and the sensory feedback. The output of the cerebellum is into the midbrain, which then sends a descending input to the spinal cord to correct the messages going to skeletal muscles.

The Spinal Cord

The description of the CNS is concentrated on the structures of the brain, but the spinal cord is another major organ of the system. Whereas the brain develops out of expansions of the neural tube into primary and then secondary vesicles, the spinal cord maintains the tube structure and is only specialized into certain regions. As the spinal cord continues to develop in the newborn, anatomical features mark its surface. The anterior midline is marked by the **anterior median fissure**, and the posterior midline is marked by the **posterior median sulcus**. Axons enter the posterior side through the **dorsal (posterior) nerve root**, which marks the **posterolateral sulcus** on either side. The axons emerging from the anterior side do so through the **ventral (anterior) nerve root**. Note that it is common to see the terms dorsal (dorsal = "back") and ventral (ventral = "belly") used interchangeably with posterior and anterior, particularly in reference to nerves and the structures of the spinal cord. You should learn to be comfortable with both.

On the whole, the posterior regions are responsible for sensory functions and the anterior regions are associated with motor functions. This comes from the initial development of the spinal cord, which is divided into the **basal plate** and the **alar plate**. The basal plate is closest to the ventral midline of the neural tube, which will become the anterior face of the spinal cord and gives rise to motor neurons. The alar plate is on the dorsal side of the neural tube and gives rise to neurons that will receive sensory input from the periphery.

The length of the spinal cord is divided into regions that correspond to the regions of the vertebral column. The name of a spinal cord region corresponds to the level at which spinal nerves pass through the intervertebral foramina. Immediately adjacent to the brain stem is the cervical region, followed by the thoracic, then the lumbar, and finally the sacral region. The spinal cord is not the full length of the vertebral column because the spinal cord does not grow significantly longer after the first or second year, but the skeleton continues to grow. The nerves that emerge from the spinal cord pass through the intervertebral foramina at the respective levels. As the vertebral column grows, these nerves grow with it and result in a long bundle of nerves that resembles a horse's tail and is named the **cauda equina**. The sacral spinal cord is at the level of the upper lumbar vertebral bones. The spinal nerves extend from their various levels to the proper level of the vertebral column.

Gray Horns

In cross-section, the gray matter of the spinal cord has the appearance of an ink-blot test, with the spread of the gray matter on one side replicated on the other—a shape reminiscent of a bulbous capital "H." As shown in <u>Figure 13.14</u>, the gray matter is subdivided into regions that are referred to as horns. The **posterior horn** is responsible for sensory processing. The **anterior horn** sends out motor signals to the skeletal muscles. The **lateral horn**, which is only found in the thoracic, upper lumbar, and sacral regions, contains cell bodies of motor neurons of the autonomic nervous system.

Some of the largest neurons of the spinal cord are the multipolar motor neurons in the anterior horn. The fibers that cause contraction of skeletal muscles are the axons of these neurons. The motor neuron that causes contraction of the big toe, for example, is located in the sacral spinal cord. The axon that has to reach all the way to the belly of that muscle may be a meter in length. The neuronal cell body that maintains that long fiber must be quite large, possibly several hundred micrometers in diameter, making it one of the largest cells in the body.

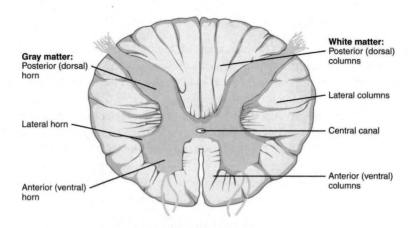

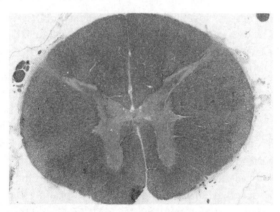

FIGURE 13.14   Cross-section of Spinal Cord   The cross-section of a thoracic spinal cord segment shows the posterior, anterior, and lateral horns of gray matter, as well as the posterior, anterior, and lateral columns of white matter. LM × 40. (Micrograph provided by the Regents of University of Michigan Medical School © 2012)

White Columns

Just as the gray matter is separated into horns, the white matter of the spinal cord is separated into columns. **Ascending tracts** of nervous system fibers in these columns carry sensory information up to the brain, whereas **descending tracts** carry motor commands from the brain. Looking at the spinal cord longitudinally, the columns extend along its length as continuous bands of white matter. Between the two posterior horns of gray matter are the **posterior columns**. Between the two anterior horns, and bounded by the axons of motor neurons emerging from that gray matter area, are the **anterior columns**. The white matter on either side of the spinal cord, between the posterior horn and the axons of the anterior horn neurons, are the **lateral columns**. The posterior columns are composed of axons of ascending tracts. The anterior and lateral columns are composed of many different groups of axons of both ascending and descending tracts—the latter carrying motor commands down from the brain to the spinal cord to control output to the periphery.

⊚ INTERACTIVE LINK

Watch this video (http://openstax.org/l/graymatter) to learn about the gray matter of the spinal cord that receives input from fibers of the dorsal (posterior) root and sends information out through the fibers of the ventral (anterior) root. As discussed in this video, these connections represent the interactions of the CNS with peripheral structures for both sensory and motor functions. The cervical and lumbar spinal cords have enlargements as a result of larger populations of neurons. What are these enlargements responsible for?

Disorders of the...

Basal Nuclei

Parkinson's disease is a disorder of the basal nuclei, specifically of the substantia nigra, that demonstrates the effects of the direct and indirect pathways. Parkinson's disease is the result of neurons in the substantia nigra pars compacta dying. These neurons release dopamine into the striatum. Without that modulatory influence, the basal nuclei are stuck in the indirect pathway, without the direct pathway being activated. The direct pathway is responsible for increasing cortical movement commands. The increased activity of the indirect pathway results in the hypokinetic disorder of Parkinson's disease.

Parkinson's disease is neurodegenerative, meaning that neurons die that cannot be replaced, so there is no cure for the disorder. Treatments for Parkinson's disease are aimed at increasing dopamine levels in the striatum. Currently, the most common way of doing that is by providing the amino acid L-DOPA, which is a precursor to the neurotransmitter dopamine and can cross the blood-brain barrier. With levels of the precursor elevated, the remaining cells of the substantia nigra pars compacta can make more neurotransmitter and have a greater effect. Unfortunately, the patient will become less responsive to L-DOPA treatment as time progresses, and it can cause increased dopamine levels elsewhere in the brain, which are associated with psychosis or schizophrenia.

⊘ INTERACTIVE LINK

Visit this site (http://openstax.org/l/parkinsons) for a thorough explanation of Parkinson's disease.

⊘ INTERACTIVE LINK

Compared with the nearest evolutionary relative, the chimpanzee, the human has a brain that is huge. At a point in the past, a common ancestor gave rise to the two species of humans and chimpanzees. That evolutionary history is long and is still an area of intense study. But something happened to increase the size of the human brain relative to the chimpanzee. Read this article (http://openstax.org/l/hugebrain) in which the author explores the current understanding of why this happened.

According to one hypothesis about the expansion of brain size, what tissue might have been sacrificed so energy was available to grow our larger brain? Based on what you know about that tissue and nervous tissue, why would there be a trade-off between them in terms of energy use?

13.3 Circulation and the Central Nervous System

LEARNING OBJECTIVES

By the end of this section, you will be able to:
- Describe the vessels that supply the CNS with blood
- Name the components of the ventricular system and the regions of the brain in which each is located
- Explain the production of cerebrospinal fluid and its flow through the ventricles
- Explain how a disruption in circulation would result in a stroke

The CNS is crucial to the operation of the body, and any compromise in the brain and spinal cord can lead to severe difficulties. The CNS has a privileged blood supply, as suggested by the blood-brain barrier. The function of the tissue in the CNS is crucial to the survival of the organism, so the contents of the blood cannot simply pass into the central nervous tissue. To protect this region from the toxins and pathogens that may be traveling through the blood stream, there is strict control over what can move out of the general systems and into the brain and spinal cord. Because of this privilege, the CNS needs specialized structures for the maintenance of circulation. This begins with a unique arrangement of blood vessels carrying fresh blood into the CNS. Beyond the supply of blood, the CNS filters that blood into cerebrospinal fluid (CSF), which is then circulated through the cavities of the brain and spinal cord called ventricles.

Blood Supply to the Brain

A lack of oxygen to the CNS can be devastating, and the cardiovascular system has specific regulatory reflexes to ensure that the blood supply is not interrupted. There are multiple routes for blood to get into the CNS, with specializations to protect that blood supply and to maximize the ability of the brain to get an uninterrupted perfusion.

Arterial Supply

The major artery carrying recently oxygenated blood away from the heart is the aorta. The very first branches off the aorta supply the heart with nutrients and oxygen. The next branches give rise to the **common carotid arteries**, which further branch into the **internal carotid arteries**. The external carotid arteries supply blood to the tissues on the surface of the cranium. The bases of the common carotids contain stretch receptors that immediately respond to the drop in blood pressure upon standing. The **orthostatic reflex** is a reaction to this change in body position, so that blood pressure is maintained against the increasing effect of gravity (orthostatic means "standing up"). Heart rate increases—a reflex of the sympathetic division of the autonomic nervous system—and this raises blood pressure.

The internal carotid artery enters the cranium through the **carotid canal** in the temporal bone. A second set of vessels that supply the CNS are the **vertebral arteries**, which are protected as they pass through the neck region by the transverse foramina of the cervical vertebrae. The vertebral arteries enter the cranium through the **foramen magnum** of the occipital bone. Branches off the left and right vertebral arteries merge into the **anterior spinal artery** supplying the anterior aspect of the spinal cord, found along the anterior median fissure. The two vertebral arteries then merge into the **basilar artery**, which gives rise to branches to the brain stem and cerebellum. The left and right internal carotid arteries and branches of the basilar artery all become the **circle of Willis**, a confluence of arteries that can maintain perfusion of the brain even if narrowing or a blockage limits flow through one part (Figure 13.15).

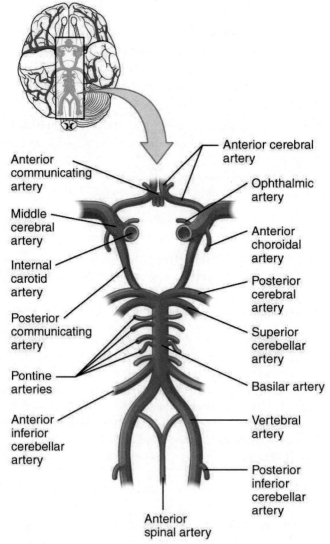

Anterior cerebral artery

Anterior communicating artery

Ophthalmic artery

Middle cerebral artery

Anterior choroidal artery

Internal carotid artery

Posterior cerebral artery

Posterior communicating artery

Superior cerebellar artery

Pontine arteries

Basilar artery

Anterior inferior cerebellar artery

Vertebral artery

Posterior inferior cerebellar artery

Anterior spinal artery

FIGURE 13.15   Circle of Willis   The blood supply to the brain enters through the internal carotid arteries and the vertebral arteries, eventually giving rise to the circle of Willis.

⊘ INTERACTIVE LINK

Watch this animation (http://openstax.org/l/bloodflow1) to see how blood flows to the brain and passes through the circle of Willis before being distributed through the cerebrum. The circle of Willis is a specialized arrangement of arteries that ensure constant perfusion of the cerebrum even in the event of a blockage of one of the arteries in the circle. The animation shows the normal direction of flow through the circle of Willis to the middle cerebral artery. Where would the blood come from if there were a blockage just posterior to the middle cerebral artery on the left?

Venous Return

After passing through the CNS, blood returns to the circulation through a series of **dural sinuses** and veins (Figure 13.16). The **superior sagittal sinus** runs in the groove of the longitudinal fissure, where it absorbs CSF from the meninges. The superior sagittal sinus drains to the confluence of sinuses, along with the **occipital sinuses** and **straight sinus**, to then drain into the **transverse sinuses**. The transverse sinuses connect to the **sigmoid sinuses**, which then connect to the **jugular veins**. From there, the blood continues toward the heart to be pumped to the lungs for reoxygenation.

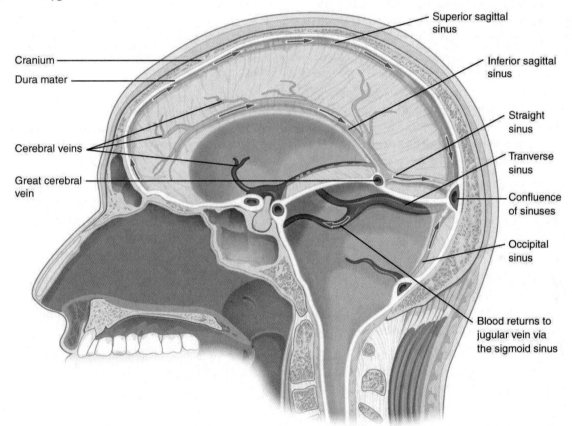

FIGURE 13.16   Dural Sinuses and Veins   Blood drains from the brain through a series of sinuses that connect to the jugular veins.

Protective Coverings of the Brain and Spinal Cord

The outer surface of the CNS is covered by a series of membranes composed of connective tissue called the **meninges,** which protect the brain. The **dura mater** is a thick fibrous layer and a strong protective sheath over the entire brain and spinal cord. It is anchored to the inner surface of the cranium and vertebral cavity. The **arachnoid mater** is a membrane of thin fibrous tissue that forms a loose sac around the CNS. Beneath the arachnoid is a thin, filamentous mesh called the **arachnoid trabeculae,** which looks like a spider web, giving this layer its name. Directly adjacent to the surface of the CNS is the **pia mater**, a thin fibrous membrane that follows the convolutions of gyri and sulci in the cerebral cortex and fits into other grooves and indentations (Figure 13.17).

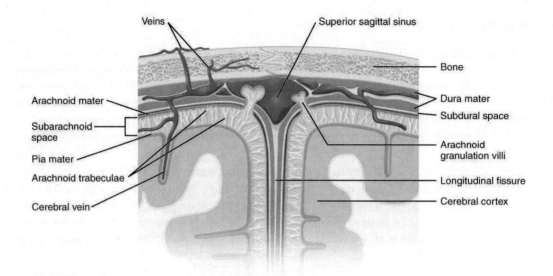

FIGURE 13.17   Meningeal Layers of Superior Sagittal Sinus   The layers of the meninges in the longitudinal fissure of the superior sagittal sinus are shown, with the dura mater adjacent to the inner surface of the cranium, the pia mater adjacent to the surface of the brain, and the arachnoid and subarachnoid space between them. An arachnoid villus is shown emerging into the dural sinus to allow CSF to filter back into the blood for drainage.

Dura Mater

Like a thick cap covering the brain, the dura mater is a tough outer covering. The name comes from the Latin for "tough mother" to represent its physically protective role. It encloses the entire CNS and the major blood vessels that enter the cranium and vertebral cavity. It is directly attached to the inner surface of the bones of the cranium and to the very end of the vertebral cavity.

There are infoldings of the dura that fit into large crevasses of the brain. Two infoldings go through the midline separations of the cerebrum and cerebellum; one forms a shelf-like tent between the occipital lobes of the cerebrum and the cerebellum, and the other surrounds the pituitary gland. The dura also surrounds and supports the venous sinuses.

Arachnoid Mater

The middle layer of the meninges is the arachnoid, named for the spider-web–like trabeculae between it and the pia mater. The arachnoid defines a sac-like enclosure around the CNS. The trabeculae are found in the **subarachnoid space**, which is filled with circulating CSF. The arachnoid emerges into the dural sinuses as the **arachnoid granulations**, where the CSF is filtered back into the blood for drainage from the nervous system.

The subarachnoid space is filled with circulating CSF, which also provides a liquid cushion to the brain and spinal cord. Similar to clinical blood work, a sample of CSF can be withdrawn to find chemical evidence of neuropathology or metabolic traces of the biochemical functions of nervous tissue.

Pia Mater

The outer surface of the CNS is covered in the thin fibrous membrane of the pia mater. It is thought to have a continuous layer of cells providing a fluid-impermeable membrane. The name pia mater comes from the Latin for "tender mother," suggesting the thin membrane is a gentle covering for the brain. The pia extends into every convolution of the CNS, lining the inside of the sulci in the cerebral and cerebellar cortices. At the end of the spinal cord, a thin filament extends from the inferior end of CNS at the upper lumbar region of the vertebral column to the sacral end of the vertebral column. Because the spinal cord does not extend through the lower lumbar region of the vertebral column, a needle can be inserted through the dura and arachnoid layers to withdraw CSF. This procedure is called a **lumbar puncture** and avoids the risk of damaging the central tissue of the spinal cord. Blood vessels that are nourishing the central nervous tissue are between the pia mater and the nervous tissue.

Disorders of the...

Meninges

Meningitis is an inflammation of the meninges, the three layers of fibrous membrane that surround the CNS. Meningitis can be caused by infection by bacteria or viruses. The particular pathogens are not special to meningitis; it is just an inflammation of that specific set of tissues from what might be a broader infection. Bacterial meningitis can be caused by *Streptococcus*, *Staphylococcus*, or the tuberculosis pathogen, among many others. Viral meningitis is usually the result of common enteroviruses (such as those that cause intestinal disorders), but may be the result of the herpes virus or West Nile virus. Bacterial meningitis tends to be more severe.

The symptoms associated with meningitis can be fever, chills, nausea, vomiting, light sensitivity, soreness of the neck, or severe headache. More important are the neurological symptoms, such as changes in mental state (confusion, memory deficits, and other dementia-type symptoms). A serious risk of meningitis can be damage to peripheral structures because of the nerves that pass through the meninges. Hearing loss is a common result of meningitis.

The primary test for meningitis is a lumbar puncture. A needle inserted into the lumbar region of the spinal column through the dura mater and arachnoid membrane into the subarachnoid space can be used to withdraw the fluid for chemical testing. Fatality occurs in 5 to 40 percent of children and 20 to 50 percent of adults with bacterial meningitis. Treatment of bacterial meningitis is through antibiotics, but viral meningitis cannot be treated with antibiotics because viruses do not respond to that type of drug. Fortunately, the viral forms are milder.

⊘ INTERACTIVE LINK

Watch this video (http://openstax.org/l/lumbarpuncture) that describes the procedure known as the lumbar puncture, a medical procedure used to sample the CSF. Because of the anatomy of the CNS, it is a relative safe location to insert a needle. Why is the lumbar puncture performed in the lower lumbar area of the vertebral column?

The Ventricular System

Cerebrospinal fluid (CSF) circulates throughout and around the CNS. In other tissues, water and small molecules are filtered through capillaries as the major contributor to the interstitial fluid. In the brain, CSF is produced in special structures to perfuse through the nervous tissue of the CNS and is continuous with the interstitial fluid. Specifically, CSF circulates to remove metabolic wastes from the interstitial fluids of nervous tissues and return them to the blood stream. The **ventricles** are the open spaces within the brain where CSF circulates. In some of these spaces, CSF is produced by filtering of the blood that is performed by a specialized membrane known as a choroid plexus. The CSF circulates through all of the ventricles to eventually emerge into the subarachnoid space where it will be reabsorbed into the blood.

The Ventricles

There are four ventricles within the brain, all of which developed from the original hollow space within the neural tube, the **central canal**. The first two are named the **lateral ventricles** and are deep within the cerebrum. These ventricles are connected to the **third ventricle** by two openings called the **interventricular foramina**. The third ventricle is the space between the left and right sides of the diencephalon, which opens into the **cerebral aqueduct** that passes through the midbrain. The aqueduct opens into the **fourth ventricle**, which is the space between the cerebellum and the pons and upper medulla (Figure 13.18).

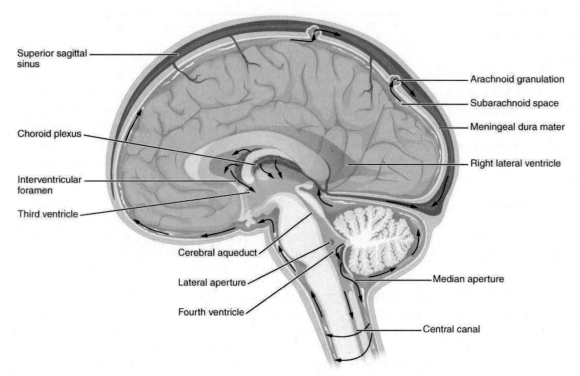

FIGURE 13.18   Cerebrospinal Fluid Circulation   The choroid plexus in the four ventricles produce CSF, which is circulated through the ventricular system and then enters the subarachnoid space through the median and lateral apertures. The CSF is then reabsorbed into the blood at the arachnoid granulations, where the arachnoid membrane emerges into the dural sinuses.

As the telencephalon enlarges and grows into the cranial cavity, it is limited by the space within the skull. The telencephalon is the most anterior region of what was the neural tube, but cannot grow past the limit of the frontal bone of the skull. Because the cerebrum fits into this space, it takes on a C-shaped formation, through the frontal, parietal, occipital, and finally temporal regions. The space within the telencephalon is stretched into this same C-shape. The two ventricles are in the left and right sides, and were at one time referred to as the first and second ventricles. The interventricular foramina connect the frontal region of the lateral ventricles with the third ventricle.

The third ventricle is the space bounded by the medial walls of the hypothalamus and thalamus. The two thalami touch in the center in most brains as the massa intermedia, which is surrounded by the third ventricle. The cerebral aqueduct opens just inferior to the epithalamus and passes through the midbrain. The tectum and tegmentum of the midbrain are the roof and floor of the cerebral aqueduct, respectively. The aqueduct opens up into the fourth ventricle. The floor of the fourth ventricle is the dorsal surface of the pons and upper medulla (that gray matter making a continuation of the tegmentum of the midbrain). The fourth ventricle then narrows into the central canal of the spinal cord.

The ventricular system opens up to the subarachnoid space from the fourth ventricle. The single **median aperture** and the pair of **lateral apertures** connect to the subarachnoid space so that CSF can flow through the ventricles and around the outside of the CNS. Cerebrospinal fluid is produced within the ventricles by a type of specialized membrane called a **choroid plexus**. Ependymal cells (one of the types of glial cells described in the introduction to the nervous system) surround blood capillaries and filter the blood to make CSF. The fluid is a clear solution with a limited amount of the constituents of blood. It is essentially water, small molecules, and electrolytes. Oxygen and carbon dioxide are dissolved into the CSF, as they are in blood, and can diffuse between the fluid and the nervous tissue.

Cerebrospinal Fluid Circulation

The choroid plexuses are found in all four ventricles. Observed in dissection, they appear as soft, fuzzy structures that may still be pink, depending on how well the circulatory system is cleared in preparation of the tissue. The CSF is produced from components extracted from the blood, so its flow out of the ventricles is tied to the pulse of cardiovascular circulation.

From the lateral ventricles, the CSF flows into the third ventricle, where more CSF is produced, and then through the cerebral aqueduct into the fourth ventricle where even more CSF is produced. A very small amount of CSF is filtered at any one of the plexuses, for a total of about 500 milliliters daily, but it is continuously made and pulses through the ventricular system, keeping the fluid moving. From the fourth ventricle, CSF can continue down the central canal of the spinal cord, but this is essentially a cul-de-sac, so more of the fluid leaves the ventricular system and moves into the subarachnoid space through the median and lateral apertures.

Within the subarachnoid space, the CSF flows around all of the CNS, providing two important functions. As with elsewhere in its circulation, the CSF picks up metabolic wastes from the nervous tissue and moves it out of the CNS. It also acts as a liquid cushion for the brain and spinal cord. By surrounding the entire system in the subarachnoid space, it provides a thin buffer around the organs within the strong, protective dura mater. The arachnoid granulations are outpocketings of the arachnoid membrane into the dural sinuses so that CSF can be reabsorbed into the blood, along with the metabolic wastes. From the dural sinuses, blood drains out of the head and neck through the jugular veins, along with the rest of the circulation for blood, to be reoxygenated by the lungs and wastes to be filtered out by the kidneys (Table 13.2).

⊚ INTERACTIVE LINK

Watch this animation (http://openstax.org/l/CSFflow) that shows the flow of CSF through the brain and spinal cord, and how it originates from the ventricles and then spreads into the space within the meninges, where the fluids then move into the venous sinuses to return to the cardiovascular circulation. What are the structures that produce CSF and where are they found? How are the structures indicated in this animation?

Components of CSF Circulation

	Lateral ventricles	Third ventricle	Cerebral aqueduct	Fourth ventricle	Central canal	Subarachnoid space
Location in CNS	Cerebrum	Diencephalon	Midbrain	Between pons/upper medulla and cerebellum	Spinal cord	External to entire CNS
Blood vessel structure	Choroid plexus	Choroid plexus	None	Choroid plexus	None	Arachnoid granulations

TABLE 13.2

Disorders of the...

Central Nervous System

The supply of blood to the brain is crucial to its ability to perform many functions. Without a steady supply of oxygen, and to a lesser extent glucose, the nervous tissue in the brain cannot keep up its extensive electrical activity. These nutrients get into the brain through the blood, and if blood flow is interrupted, neurological function is compromised.

The common name for a disruption of blood supply to the brain is a stroke. It is caused by a blockage to an artery in the brain. The blockage is from some type of embolus: a blood clot, a fat embolus, or an air bubble. When the blood cannot travel through the artery, the surrounding tissue that is deprived starves and dies. Strokes will often result in the loss of very specific functions. A stroke in the lateral medulla, for example, can cause a loss in the ability to swallow. Sometimes, seemingly unrelated functions will be lost because they are dependent on structures in the same region. Along with the swallowing in the previous example, a stroke in that region could affect sensory functions from the face or extremities because important white matter pathways also pass through the lateral medulla. Loss of blood flow to specific regions of the cortex can lead to the loss of specific higher functions, from the ability to recognize faces to the ability to move a particular region of the body.

Severe or limited memory loss can be the result of a temporal lobe stroke.

Related to strokes are transient ischemic attacks (TIAs), which can also be called "mini-strokes." These are events in which a physical blockage may be temporary, cutting off the blood supply and oxygen to a region, but not to the extent that it causes cell death in that region. While the neurons in that area are recovering from the event, neurological function may be lost. Function can return if the area is able to recover from the event.

Recovery from a stroke (or TIA) is strongly dependent on the speed of treatment. Often, the person who is present and notices something is wrong must then make a decision. The mnemonic **FAST** helps people remember what to look for when someone is dealing with sudden losses of neurological function. If someone complains of feeling "funny," check these things quickly: Look at the person's face. Do they have problems moving **F**ace muscles and making regular facial expressions? Ask the person to raise their **A**rms above the head. Can the person lift one arm but not the other? Has the person's **S**peech changed? Are they slurring words or having trouble saying things? If any of these things have happened, then it is **T**ime to call for help.

Sometimes, treatment with blood-thinning drugs can alleviate the problem, and recovery is possible. If the tissue is damaged, the amazing thing about the nervous system is that it is adaptable. With physical, occupational, and speech therapy, victims of strokes can recover, or more accurately relearn, functions.

13.4 The Peripheral Nervous System

LEARNING OBJECTIVES

By the end of this section, you will be able to:

- Describe the structures found in the PNS
- Distinguish between somatic and autonomic structures, including the special peripheral structures of the enteric nervous system
- Name the twelve cranial nerves and explain the functions associated with each
- Describe the sensory and motor components of spinal nerves and the plexuses that they pass through

The PNS is not as contained as the CNS because it is defined as everything that is not the CNS. Some peripheral structures are incorporated into the other organs of the body. In describing the anatomy of the PNS, it is necessary to describe the common structures, the nerves and the ganglia, as they are found in various parts of the body. Many of the neural structures that are incorporated into other organs are features of the digestive system; these structures are known as the **enteric nervous system** and are a special subset of the PNS.

Ganglia

A ganglion is a group of neuron cell bodies in the periphery. Ganglia can be categorized, for the most part, as either sensory ganglia or autonomic ganglia, referring to their primary functions. The most common type of sensory ganglion is a **dorsal (posterior) root ganglion**. These ganglia are the cell bodies of neurons with axons that are sensory endings in the periphery, such as in the skin, and that extend into the CNS through the dorsal nerve root. The ganglion is an enlargement of the nerve root. Under microscopic inspection, it can be seen to include the cell bodies of the neurons, as well as bundles of fibers that are the posterior nerve root (Figure 13.19). The cells of the dorsal root ganglion are unipolar cells, classifying them by shape. Also, the small round nuclei of satellite cells can be seen surrounding—as if they were orbiting—the neuron cell bodies.

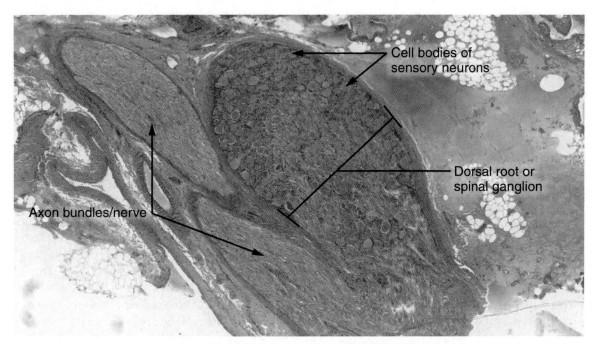

FIGURE 13.19 Dorsal Root Ganglion   The cell bodies of sensory neurons, which are unipolar neurons by shape, are seen in this photomicrograph. Also, the fibrous region is composed of the axons of these neurons that are passing through the ganglion to be part of the dorsal nerve root (tissue source: canine). LM × 40. (Micrograph provided by the Regents of University of Michigan Medical School © 2012)

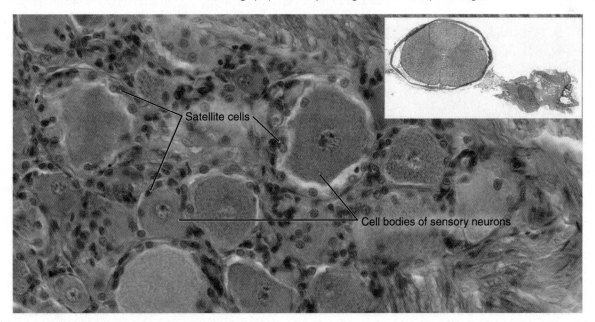

FIGURE 13.20 Spinal Cord and Root Ganglion   The slide includes both a cross-section of the lumbar spinal cord and a section of the dorsal root ganglion (see also Figure 13.19) (tissue source: canine). LM × 1600. (Micrograph provided by the Regents of University of Michigan Medical School © 2012)

⊘ INTERACTIVE LINK

View the University of Michigan WebScope (http://openstax.org/l/spinalroot) to explore the tissue sample in greater detail. If you zoom in on the dorsal root ganglion, you can see smaller satellite glial cells surrounding the large cell bodies of the sensory neurons. From what structure do satellite cells derive during embryologic development?

Another type of sensory ganglion is a **cranial nerve ganglion**. This is analogous to the dorsal root ganglion, except that it is associated with a **cranial nerve** instead of a **spinal nerve**. The roots of cranial nerves are within the cranium, whereas the ganglia are outside the skull. For example, the **trigeminal ganglion** is superficial to the temporal bone whereas its associated nerve is attached to the mid-pons region of the brain stem. The neurons of cranial nerve ganglia are also unipolar in shape with associated satellite cells.

The other major category of ganglia are those of the autonomic nervous system, which is divided into the sympathetic and parasympathetic nervous systems. The **sympathetic chain ganglia** constitute a row of ganglia along the vertebral column that receive central input from the lateral horn of the thoracic and upper lumbar spinal cord. Superior to the chain ganglia are three **paravertebral ganglia** in the cervical region. Three other autonomic ganglia that are related to the sympathetic chain are the **prevertebral ganglia**, which are located outside of the chain but have similar functions. They are referred to as prevertebral because they are anterior to the vertebral column. The neurons of these autonomic ganglia are multipolar in shape, with dendrites radiating out around the cell body where synapses from the spinal cord neurons are made. The neurons of the chain, paravertebral, and prevertebral ganglia then project to organs in the head and neck, thoracic, abdominal, and pelvic cavities to regulate the sympathetic aspect of homeostatic mechanisms.

Another group of autonomic ganglia are the **terminal ganglia** that receive input from cranial nerves or sacral spinal nerves and are responsible for regulating the parasympathetic aspect of homeostatic mechanisms. These two sets of ganglia, sympathetic and parasympathetic, often project to the same organs—one input from the chain ganglia and one input from a terminal ganglion—to regulate the overall function of an organ. For example, the heart receives two inputs such as these; one increases heart rate, and the other decreases it. The terminal ganglia that receive input from cranial nerves are found in the head and neck, as well as the thoracic and upper abdominal cavities, whereas the terminal ganglia that receive sacral input are in the lower abdominal and pelvic cavities.

Terminal ganglia below the head and neck are often incorporated into the wall of the target organ as a **plexus**. A plexus, in a general sense, is a network of fibers or vessels. This can apply to nervous tissue (as in this instance) or structures containing blood vessels (such as a choroid plexus). For example, the **enteric plexus** is the extensive network of axons and neurons in the wall of the small and large intestines. The enteric plexus is actually part of the enteric nervous system, along with the **gastric plexuses** and the **esophageal plexus**. Though the enteric nervous system receives input originating from central neurons of the autonomic nervous system, it does not require CNS input to function. In fact, it operates independently to regulate the digestive system.

Nerves

Bundles of axons in the PNS are referred to as nerves. These structures in the periphery are different than the central counterpart, called a tract. Nerves are composed of more than just nervous tissue. They have connective tissues invested in their structure, as well as blood vessels supplying the tissues with nourishment. The outer surface of a nerve is a surrounding layer of fibrous connective tissue called the **epineurium**. Within the nerve, axons are further bundled into **fascicles**, which are each surrounded by their own layer of fibrous connective tissue called **perineurium**. Finally, individual axons are surrounded by loose connective tissue called the **endoneurium** (Figure 13.21). These three layers are similar to the connective tissue sheaths for muscles. Nerves are associated with the region of the CNS to which they are connected, either as cranial nerves connected to the brain or spinal nerves connected to the spinal cord.

Access for free at openstax.org

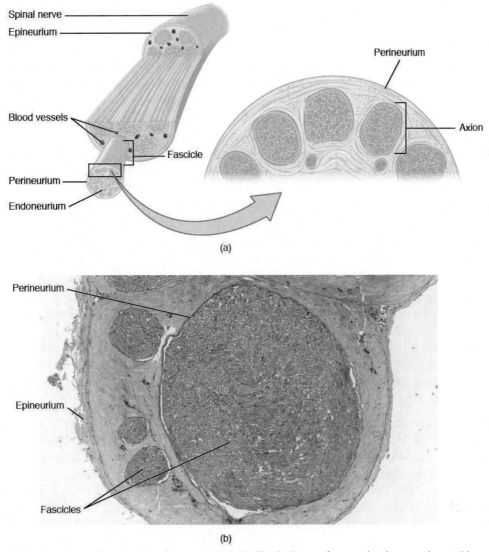

(a)

(b)

FIGURE 13.21   Nerve Structure   The structure of a nerve is organized by the layers of connective tissue on the outside, around each fascicle, and surrounding the individual nerve fibers (tissue source: simian). LM × 40. (Micrograph provided by the Regents of University of Michigan Medical School © 2012)

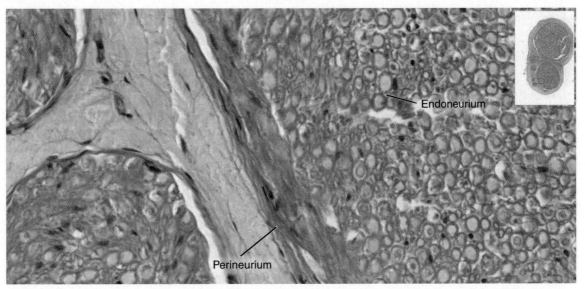

FIGURE 13.22   Close-Up of Nerve Trunk   Zoom in on this slide of a nerve trunk to examine the endoneurium, perineurium, and

epineurium in greater detail (tissue source: simian). LM × 1600. (Micrograph provided by the Regents of University of Michigan Medical School © 2012)

⊚ INTERACTIVE LINK

View the University of Michigan WebScope (http://openstax.org/l/nervetrunk) to explore the tissue sample in greater detail. With what structures in a skeletal muscle are the endoneurium, perineurium, and epineurium comparable?

Cranial Nerves

The nerves attached to the brain are the cranial nerves, which are primarily responsible for the sensory and motor functions of the head and neck (one of these nerves targets organs in the thoracic and abdominal cavities as part of the parasympathetic nervous system). There are twelve cranial nerves, which are designated CNI through CNXII for "Cranial Nerve," using Roman numerals for 1 through 12. They can be classified as sensory nerves, motor nerves, or a combination of both, meaning that the axons in these nerves originate out of sensory ganglia external to the cranium or motor nuclei within the brain stem. Sensory axons enter the brain to synapse in a nucleus. Motor axons connect to skeletal muscles of the head or neck. Three of the nerves are solely composed of sensory fibers; five are strictly motor; and the remaining four are mixed nerves.

Learning the cranial nerves is a tradition in anatomy courses, and students have always used mnemonic devices to remember the nerve names. A traditional mnemonic is the rhyming couplet, "On Old Olympus' Towering Tops/A Finn And German Viewed Some Hops," in which the initial letter of each word corresponds to the initial letter in the name of each nerve. The names of the nerves have changed over the years to reflect current usage and more accurate naming. An exercise to help learn this sort of information is to generate a mnemonic using words that have personal significance. The names of the cranial nerves are listed in Table 13.3 along with a brief description of their function, their source (sensory ganglion or motor nucleus), and their target (sensory nucleus or skeletal muscle). They are listed here with a brief explanation of each nerve (Figure 13.23).

The **olfactory nerve** and **optic nerve** are responsible for the sense of smell and vision, respectively. The **oculomotor nerve** is responsible for eye movements by controlling four of the **extraocular muscles**. It is also responsible for lifting the upper eyelid when the eyes point up, and for pupillary constriction. The **trochlear nerve** and the **abducens nerve** are both responsible for eye movement, but do so by controlling different extraocular muscles. The **trigeminal nerve** is responsible for cutaneous sensations of the face and controlling the muscles of mastication. The **facial nerve** is responsible for the muscles involved in facial expressions, as well as part of the sense of taste and the production of saliva. The **vestibulocochlear nerve** is responsible for the senses of hearing and balance. The **glossopharyngeal nerve** is responsible for controlling muscles in the oral cavity and upper throat, as well as part of the sense of taste and the production of saliva. The **vagus nerve** is responsible for contributing to homeostatic control of the organs of the thoracic and upper abdominal cavities. The **spinal accessory nerve** is responsible for controlling the muscles of the neck, along with cervical spinal nerves. The **hypoglossal nerve** is responsible for controlling the muscles of the lower throat and tongue.

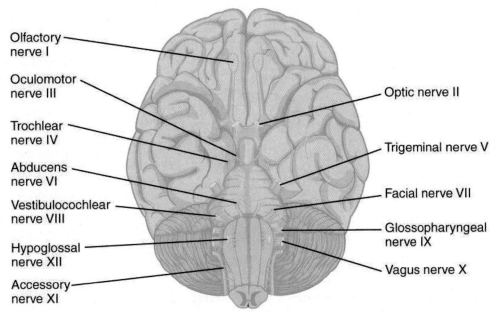

FIGURE 13.23   The Cranial Nerves   The anatomical arrangement of the roots of the cranial nerves observed from an inferior view of the brain.

Three of the cranial nerves also contain autonomic fibers, and a fourth is almost purely a component of the autonomic system. The oculomotor, facial, and glossopharyngeal nerves contain fibers that contact autonomic ganglia. The oculomotor fibers initiate pupillary constriction, whereas the facial and glossopharyngeal fibers both initiate salivation. The vagus nerve primarily targets autonomic ganglia in the thoracic and upper abdominal cavities.

🔗 INTERACTIVE LINK

Visit this site (http://openstax.org/l/NYTmeningitis) to read about a man who wakes with a headache and a loss of vision. His regular doctor sent him to an ophthalmologist to address the vision loss. The ophthalmologist recognizes a greater problem and immediately sends him to the emergency room. Once there, the patient undergoes a large battery of tests, but a definite cause cannot be found. A specialist recognizes the problem as meningitis, but the question is what caused it originally. How can that be cured? The loss of vision comes from swelling around the optic nerve, which probably presented as a bulge on the inside of the eye. Why is swelling related to meningitis going to push on the optic nerve?

Another important aspect of the cranial nerves that lends itself to a mnemonic is the functional role each nerve plays. The nerves fall into one of three basic groups. They are sensory, motor, or both (see Table 13.3). The sentence, "Some Say Marry Money But My Brother Says Brains Beauty Matter More," corresponds to the basic function of each nerve. The first, second, and eighth nerves are purely sensory: the olfactory (CNI), optic (CNII), and vestibulocochlear (CNVIII) nerves. The three eye-movement nerves are all motor: the oculomotor (CNIII), trochlear (CNIV), and abducens (CNVI). The spinal accessory (CNXI) and hypoglossal (CNXII) nerves are also strictly motor. The remainder of the nerves contain both sensory and motor fibers. They are the trigeminal (CNV), facial (CNVII), glossopharyngeal (CNIX), and vagus (CNX) nerves. The nerves that convey both are often related to each other. The trigeminal and facial nerves both concern the face; one concerns the sensations and the other concerns the muscle movements. The facial and glossopharyngeal nerves are both responsible for conveying gustatory, or taste, sensations as well as controlling salivary glands. The vagus nerve is involved in visceral responses to taste, namely the gag reflex. This is not an exhaustive list of what these combination nerves do, but there is a thread of relation between them.

Cranial Nerves

Mnemonic	#	Name	Function (S/M/B)	Central connection (nuclei)	Peripheral connection (ganglion or muscle)
On	I	Olfactory	Smell (S)	Olfactory bulb	Olfactory epithelium
Old	II	Optic	Vision (S)	Hypothalamus/thalamus/midbrain	Retina (retinal ganglion cells)
Olympus'	III	Oculomotor	Eye movements (M)	Oculomotor nucleus	Extraocular muscles (other 4), levator palpebrae superioris, ciliary ganglion (autonomic)
Towering	IV	Trochlear	Eye movements (M)	Trochlear nucleus	Superior oblique muscle
Tops	V	Trigeminal	Sensory/motor – face (B)	Trigeminal nuclei in the midbrain, pons, and medulla	Trigeminal
A	VI	Abducens	Eye movements (M)	Abducens nucleus	Lateral rectus muscle
Finn	VII	Facial	Motor – face, Taste (B)	Facial nucleus, solitary nucleus, superior salivatory nucleus	Facial muscles, Geniculate ganglion, Pterygopalatine ganglion (autonomic)
And	VIII	Auditory (Vestibulocochlear)	Hearing/balance (S)	Cochlear nucleus, Vestibular nucleus/cerebellum	Spiral ganglion (hearing), Vestibular ganglion (balance)
German	IX	Glossopharyngeal	Motor – throat Taste (B)	Solitary nucleus, inferior salivatory nucleus, nucleus ambiguus	Pharyngeal muscles, Geniculate ganglion, Otic ganglion (autonomic)
Viewed	X	Vagus	Motor/sensory – viscera (autonomic) (B)	Medulla	Terminal ganglia serving thoracic and upper abdominal organs (heart and small intestines)

TABLE 13.3

Mnemonic	#	Name	Function (S/M/B)	Central connection (nuclei)	Peripheral connection (ganglion or muscle)
Some	XI	Spinal Accessory	Motor – head and neck (M)	Spinal accessory nucleus	Neck muscles
Hops	XII	Hypoglossal	Motor – lower throat (M)	Hypoglossal nucleus	Muscles of the larynx and lower pharynx

TABLE 13.3

Spinal Nerves

The nerves connected to the spinal cord are the spinal nerves. The arrangement of these nerves is much more regular than that of the cranial nerves. All of the spinal nerves are combined sensory and motor axons that separate into two nerve roots. The sensory axons enter the spinal cord as the dorsal nerve root. The motor fibers, both somatic and autonomic, emerge as the ventral nerve root. The dorsal root ganglion for each nerve is an enlargement of the spinal nerve.

There are 31 spinal nerves, named for the level of the spinal cord at which each one emerges. There are eight pairs of cervical nerves designated C1 to C8, twelve thoracic nerves designated T1 to T12, five pairs of lumbar nerves designated L1 to L5, five pairs of sacral nerves designated S1 to S5, and one pair of coccygeal nerves. The nerves are numbered from the superior to inferior positions, and each emerges from the vertebral column through the intervertebral foramen at its level. The first nerve, C1, emerges between the first cervical vertebra and the occipital bone. The second nerve, C2, emerges between the first and second cervical vertebrae. The same occurs for C3 to C7, but C8 emerges between the seventh cervical vertebra and the first thoracic vertebra. For the thoracic and lumbar nerves, each one emerges between the vertebra that has the same designation and the next vertebra in the column. The sacral nerves emerge from the sacral foramina along the length of that unique vertebra.

Spinal nerves extend outward from the vertebral column to innervate the periphery. The nerves in the periphery are not straight continuations of the spinal nerves, but rather the reorganization of the axons in those nerves to follow different courses. Axons from different spinal nerves will come together into a **systemic nerve**. This occurs at four places along the length of the vertebral column, each identified as a **nerve plexus**, whereas the other spinal nerves directly correspond to nerves at their respective levels. In this instance, the word plexus is used to describe networks of nerve fibers with no associated cell bodies.

Of the four nerve plexuses, two are found at the cervical level, one at the lumbar level, and one at the sacral level (Figure 13.24). The **cervical plexus** is composed of axons from spinal nerves C1 through C5 and branches into nerves in the posterior neck and head, as well as the **phrenic nerve**, which connects to the diaphragm at the base of the thoracic cavity. The other plexus from the cervical level is the **brachial plexus**. Spinal nerves C4 through T1 reorganize through this plexus to give rise to the nerves of the arms, as the name brachial suggests. A large nerve from this plexus is the **radial nerve** from which the **axillary nerve** branches to go to the armpit region. The radial nerve continues through the arm and is paralleled by the **ulnar nerve** and the **median nerve**. The **lumbar plexus** arises from all the lumbar spinal nerves and gives rise to nerves enervating the pelvic region and the anterior leg. The **femoral nerve** is one of the major nerves from this plexus, which gives rise to the **saphenous nerve** as a branch that extends through the anterior lower leg. The **sacral plexus** comes from the lower lumbar nerves L4 and L5 and the sacral nerves S1 to S4. The most significant systemic nerve to come from this plexus is the **sciatic nerve**, which is a combination of the **tibial nerve** and the **fibular nerve**. The sciatic nerve extends across the hip joint and is most commonly associated with the condition **sciatica**, which is the result of compression or irritation of the nerve or any of the spinal nerves giving rise to it.

These plexuses are described as arising from spinal nerves and giving rise to certain systemic nerves, but they contain fibers that serve sensory functions or fibers that serve motor functions. This means that some fibers extend from cutaneous or other peripheral sensory surfaces and send action potentials into the CNS. Those are axons of sensory neurons in the dorsal root ganglia that enter the spinal cord through the dorsal nerve root. Other fibers are the axons of motor neurons of the anterior horn of the spinal cord, which emerge in the ventral nerve root and send action potentials to cause skeletal muscles to contract in their target regions. For example, the radial nerve contains fibers of cutaneous sensation in the arm, as well as motor fibers that move muscles in the arm.

Spinal nerves of the thoracic region, T2 through T11, are not part of the plexuses but rather emerge and give rise to the **intercostal nerves** found between the ribs, which articulate with the vertebrae surrounding the spinal nerve.

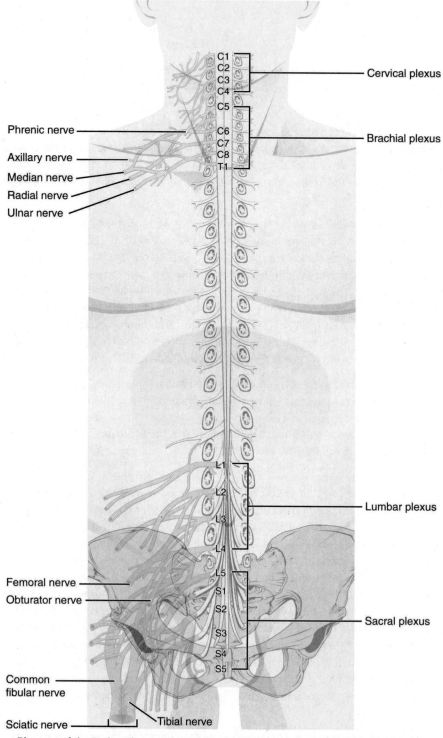

FIGURE 13.24   Nerve Plexuses of the Body   There are four main nerve plexuses in the human body. The cervical plexus supplies nerves to the posterior head and neck, as well as to the diaphragm. The brachial plexus supplies nerves to the arm. The lumbar plexus supplies nerves to the anterior leg. The sacral plexus supplies nerves to the posterior leg.

Aging and the...

Nervous System

Anosmia is the loss of the sense of smell. It is often the result of the olfactory nerve being severed, usually because of blunt force trauma to the head. The sensory neurons of the olfactory epithelium have a limited lifespan of approximately one to four months, and new ones are made on a regular basis. The new neurons extend their axons into the CNS by growing along the existing fibers of the olfactory nerve. The ability of these neurons to be replaced is lost with age. Age-related anosmia is not the result of impact trauma to the head, but rather a slow loss of the sensory neurons with no new neurons born to replace them.

Smell is an important sense, especially for the enjoyment of food. There are only five tastes sensed by the tongue, and two of them are generally thought of as unpleasant tastes (sour and bitter). The rich sensory experience of food is the result of odor molecules associated with the food, both as food is moved into the mouth, and therefore passes under the nose, and when it is chewed and molecules are released to move up the pharynx into the posterior nasal cavity. Anosmia results in a loss of the enjoyment of food.

As the replacement of olfactory neurons declines with age, anosmia can set in. Without the sense of smell, many sufferers complain of food tasting bland. Often, the only way to enjoy food is to add seasoning that can be sensed on the tongue, which usually means adding table salt. The problem with this solution, however, is that this increases sodium intake, which can lead to cardiovascular problems through water retention and the associated increase in blood pressure.

Key Terms

abducens nerve   sixth cranial nerve; responsible for contraction of one of the extraocular muscles

alar plate   developmental region of the spinal cord that gives rise to the posterior horn of the gray matter

amygdala   nucleus deep in the temporal lobe of the cerebrum that is related to memory and emotional behavior

anterior column   white matter between the anterior horns of the spinal cord composed of many different groups of axons of both ascending and descending tracts

anterior horn   gray matter of the spinal cord containing multipolar motor neurons, sometimes referred to as the ventral horn

anterior median fissure   deep midline feature of the anterior spinal cord, marking the separation between the right and left sides of the cord

anterior spinal artery   blood vessel from the merged branches of the vertebral arteries that runs along the anterior surface of the spinal cord

arachnoid granulation   outpocket of the arachnoid membrane into the dural sinuses that allows for reabsorption of CSF into the blood

arachnoid mater   middle layer of the meninges named for the spider-web–like trabeculae that extend between it and the pia mater

arachnoid trabeculae   filaments between the arachnoid and pia mater within the subarachnoid space

ascending tract   central nervous system fibers carrying sensory information from the spinal cord or periphery to the brain

axillary nerve   systemic nerve of the arm that arises from the brachial plexus

basal forebrain   nuclei of the cerebrum related to modulation of sensory stimuli and attention through broad projections to the cerebral cortex, loss of which is related to Alzheimer's disease

basal nuclei   nuclei of the cerebrum (with a few components in the upper brain stem and diencephalon) that are responsible for assessing cortical movement commands and comparing them with the general state of the individual through broad modulatory activity of dopamine neurons; largely related to motor functions, as evidenced through the symptoms of Parkinson's and Huntington's diseases

basal plate   developmental region of the spinal cord that gives rise to the lateral and anterior horns of gray matter

basilar artery   blood vessel from the merged vertebral arteries that runs along the dorsal surface of the brain stem

brachial plexus   nerve plexus associated with the lower cervical spinal nerves and first thoracic spinal nerve

brain stem   region of the adult brain that includes the midbrain, pons, and medulla oblongata and develops from the mesencephalon, metencephalon, and myelencephalon of the embryonic brain

Broca's area   region of the frontal lobe associated with the motor commands necessary for speech production and located only in the cerebral hemisphere responsible for language production, which is the left side in approximately 95 percent of the population

Brodmann's areas   mapping of regions of the cerebral cortex based on microscopic anatomy that relates specific areas to functional differences, as described by Brodmann in the early 1900s

carotid canal   opening in the temporal bone through which the internal carotid artery enters the cranium

cauda equina   bundle of spinal nerve roots that descend from the lower spinal cord below the first lumbar vertebra and lie within the vertebral cavity; has the appearance of a horse's tail

caudate   nucleus deep in the cerebrum that is part of the basal nuclei; along with the putamen, it is part of the striatum

central canal   hollow space within the spinal cord that is the remnant of the center of the neural tube

central sulcus   surface landmark of the cerebral cortex that marks the boundary between the frontal and parietal lobes

cephalic flexure   curve in midbrain of the embryo that positions the forebrain ventrally

cerebellum   region of the adult brain connected primarily to the pons that developed from the metencephalon (along with the pons) and is largely responsible for comparing information from the cerebrum with sensory feedback from the periphery through the spinal cord

cerebral aqueduct   connection of the ventricular system between the third and fourth ventricles located in the midbrain

cerebral cortex   outer gray matter covering the forebrain, marked by wrinkles and folds known as gyri and sulci

cerebral hemisphere   one half of the bilaterally symmetrical cerebrum

cerebrum   region of the adult brain that develops from the telencephalon and is responsible for higher neurological functions such as memory, emotion, and consciousness

cervical plexus   nerve plexus associated with the upper cervical spinal nerves

choroid plexus   specialized structures containing ependymal cells lining blood capillaries that filter blood to produce CSF in the four ventricles of the brain

circle of Willis   unique anatomical arrangement of blood vessels around the base of the brain that maintains perfusion of blood into the brain even if one component of the structure is blocked or narrowed

common carotid artery   blood vessel that branches off the aorta (or the brachiocephalic artery on the right) and supplies blood to the head and neck

corpus callosum   large white matter structure that connects the right and left cerebral hemispheres

cranial nerve   one of twelve nerves connected to the brain that are responsible for sensory or motor functions of the head and neck

cranial nerve ganglion   sensory ganglion of cranial nerves

descending tract   central nervous system fibers carrying motor commands from the brain to the spinal cord or periphery

diencephalon   region of the adult brain that retains its name from embryonic development and includes the thalamus and hypothalamus

direct pathway   connections within the basal nuclei from the striatum to the globus pallidus internal segment and substantia nigra pars reticulata that disinhibit the thalamus to increase cortical control of movement

disinhibition   disynaptic connection in which the first synapse inhibits the second cell, which then stops inhibiting the final target

dorsal (posterior) nerve root   axons entering the posterior horn of the spinal cord

dorsal (posterior) root ganglion   sensory ganglion attached to the posterior nerve root of a spinal nerve

dura mater   tough, fibrous, outer layer of the meninges that is attached to the inner surface of the cranium and vertebral column and surrounds the entire CNS

dural sinus   any of the venous structures surrounding the brain, enclosed within the dura mater, which drain blood from the CNS to the common venous return of the jugular veins

endoneurium   innermost layer of connective tissue that surrounds individual axons within a nerve

enteric nervous system   peripheral structures, namely ganglia and nerves, that are incorporated into the digestive system organs

enteric plexus   neuronal plexus in the wall of the intestines, which is part of the enteric nervous system

epineurium   outermost layer of connective tissue that surrounds an entire nerve

epithalamus   region of the diecephalon containing the pineal gland

esophageal plexus   neuronal plexus in the wall of the esophagus that is part of the enteric nervous system

extraocular muscles   six skeletal muscles that control eye movement within the orbit

facial nerve   seventh cranial nerve; responsible for contraction of the facial muscles and for part of the sense of taste, as well as causing saliva production

fascicle   small bundles of nerve or muscle fibers enclosed by connective tissue

femoral nerve   systemic nerve of the anterior leg that arises from the lumbar plexus

fibular nerve   systemic nerve of the posterior leg that begins as part of the sciatic nerve

foramen magnum   large opening in the occipital bone of the skull through which the spinal cord emerges and the vertebral arteries enter the cranium

forebrain   anterior region of the adult brain that develops from the prosencephalon and includes the cerebrum and diencephalon

fourth ventricle   the portion of the ventricular system that is in the region of the brain stem and opens into the subarachnoid space through the median and lateral apertures

frontal eye field   region of the frontal lobe associated with motor commands to orient the eyes toward an object of visual attention

frontal lobe   region of the cerebral cortex directly beneath the frontal bone of the cranium

gastric plexuses   neuronal networks in the wall of the stomach that are part of the enteric nervous system

globus pallidus   nuclei deep in the cerebrum that are part of the basal nuclei and can be divided into the internal and external segments

glossopharyngeal nerve   ninth cranial nerve; responsible for contraction of muscles in the tongue and throat and for part of the sense of taste, as well as causing saliva production

gyrus   ridge formed by convolutions on the surface of the cerebrum or cerebellum

hindbrain   posterior region of the adult brain that develops from the rhombencephalon and includes the pons, medulla oblongata, and cerebellum

hippocampus   gray matter deep in the temporal lobe that is very important for long-term memory formation

hypoglossal nerve   twelfth cranial nerve; responsible for contraction of muscles of the tongue

hypothalamus   major region of the diencephalon that is responsible for coordinating autonomic and endocrine control of homeostasis

indirect pathway   connections within the basal nuclei from the striatum through the globus pallidus external segment and subthalamic nucleus to the globus pallidus internal segment/substantia nigra pars compacta that result in inhibition of the thalamus to decrease cortical control of movement

inferior colliculus   half of the midbrain tectum that is part of the brain stem auditory pathway

inferior olive   nucleus in the medulla that is involved in processing information related to motor control

intercostal nerve   systemic nerve in the thoracic cavity that is found between two ribs

internal carotid artery   branch from the common carotid artery that enters the cranium and supplies blood to the brain

interventricular foramina   openings between the lateral ventricles and third ventricle allowing for the passage of CSF

jugular veins   blood vessels that return "used" blood from the head and neck

kinesthesia   general sensory perception of movement of the body

lateral apertures   pair of openings from the fourth ventricle to the subarachnoid space on either side and between the medulla and cerebellum

lateral column   white matter of the spinal cord between the posterior horn on one side and the axons from the anterior horn on the same side; composed of many different groups of axons, of both ascending and descending tracts, carrying motor commands to and from the brain

lateral horn   region of the spinal cord gray matter in the thoracic, upper lumbar, and sacral regions that is the central component of the sympathetic division of the autonomic nervous system

lateral sulcus   surface landmark of the cerebral cortex that marks the boundary between the temporal lobe and the frontal and parietal lobes

lateral ventricles   portions of the ventricular system that are in the region of the cerebrum

limbic cortex   collection of structures of the cerebral cortex that are involved in emotion, memory, and behavior and are part of the larger limbic system

limbic system   structures at the edge (limit) of the boundary between the forebrain and hindbrain that are most associated with emotional behavior and memory formation

longitudinal fissure   large separation along the midline between the two cerebral hemispheres

lumbar plexus   nerve plexus associated with the lumbar spinal nerves

lumbar puncture   procedure used to withdraw CSF from the lower lumbar region of the vertebral column that avoids the risk of damaging CNS tissue because the spinal cord ends at the upper lumbar vertebrae

median aperture   singular opening from the fourth ventricle into the subarachnoid space at the midline between the medulla and cerebellum

median nerve   systemic nerve of the arm, located between the ulnar and radial nerves

meninges   protective outer coverings of the CNS composed of connective tissue

mesencephalon   primary vesicle of the embryonic brain that does not significantly change through the rest of embryonic development and becomes the midbrain

metencephalon   secondary vesicle of the embryonic brain that develops into the pons and the cerebellum

midbrain   middle region of the adult brain that develops from the mesencephalon

myelencephalon   secondary vesicle of the embryonic brain that develops into the medulla

nerve plexus   network of nerves without neuronal cell bodies included

neural crest   tissue that detaches from the edges of the neural groove and migrates through the embryo to develop into peripheral structures of both nervous and non-nervous tissues

neural fold   elevated edge of the neural groove

neural groove   region of the neural plate that folds into the dorsal surface of the embryo and closes off to become the neural tube

neural plate   thickened layer of neuroepithelium that runs longitudinally along the dorsal surface of an embryo and gives rise to nervous system tissue

neural tube   precursor to structures of the central nervous system, formed by the invagination and separation of neuroepithelium

neuraxis   central axis to the nervous system, from the posterior to anterior ends of the neural tube; the inferior tip of the spinal cord to the anterior surface of the cerebrum

occipital lobe   region of the cerebral cortex directly beneath the occipital bone of the cranium

occipital sinuses   dural sinuses along the edge of the occipital lobes of the cerebrum

oculomotor nerve   third cranial nerve; responsible for contraction of four of the extraocular muscles, the muscle in the upper eyelid, and pupillary constriction

olfaction   special sense responsible for smell, which has a unique, direct connection to the cerebrum

olfactory nerve   first cranial nerve; responsible for the sense of smell

optic nerve   second cranial nerve; responsible for visual sensation

orthostatic reflex   sympathetic function that maintains blood pressure when standing to offset the increased effect of gravity

paravertebral ganglia   autonomic ganglia superior to the sympathetic chain ganglia

parietal lobe   region of the cerebral cortex directly beneath the parietal bone of the cranium

parieto-occipital sulcus   groove in the cerebral cortex representing the border between the parietal and occipital cortices

perineurium   layer of connective tissue surrounding fascicles within a nerve

phrenic nerve   systemic nerve from the cervical plexus that innervates the diaphragm

pia mater   thin, innermost membrane of the meninges that directly covers the surface of the CNS

plexus   network of nerves or nervous tissue

postcentral gyrus   primary motor cortex located in the frontal lobe of the cerebral cortex

posterior columns   white matter of the spinal cord that lies between the posterior horns of the gray matter, sometimes referred to as the dorsal column; composed of axons of ascending tracts that carry sensory information up to the brain

posterior horn   gray matter region of the spinal cord in which sensory input arrives, sometimes referred to as the dorsal horn

posterior median sulcus   midline feature of the posterior spinal cord, marking the separation between right and left sides of the cord

posterolateral sulcus   feature of the posterior spinal cord marking the entry of posterior nerve roots and the separation between the posterior and lateral columns of the white matter

precentral gyrus   ridge just posterior to the central sulcus, in the parietal lobe, where somatosensory processing initially takes place in the cerebrum

prefrontal lobe   specific region of the frontal lobe anterior to the more specific motor function areas, which can be related to the early planning of movements and intentions to the point of being personality-type functions

premotor area   region of the frontal lobe responsible for planning movements that will be executed through the primary motor cortex

prevertebral ganglia   autonomic ganglia that are anterior to the vertebral column and functionally related to the sympathetic chain ganglia

primary vesicle   initial enlargements of the anterior neural tube during embryonic development that develop into the forebrain, midbrain, and hindbrain

proprioception   general sensory perceptions providing information about location and movement of body parts; the "sense of the self"

prosencephalon   primary vesicle of the embryonic brain that develops into the forebrain, which includes the cerebrum and diencephalon

putamen   nucleus deep in the cerebrum that is part of the basal nuclei; along with the caudate, it is part of the striatum

radial nerve   systemic nerve of the arm, the distal component of which is located near the radial bone

reticular formation   diffuse region of gray matter throughout the brain stem that regulates sleep, wakefulness, and states of consciousness

rhombencephalon   primary vesicle of the embryonic brain that develops into the hindbrain, which includes the pons, cerebellum, and medulla

sacral plexus   nerve plexus associated with the lower lumbar and sacral spinal nerves

saphenous nerve   systemic nerve of the lower anterior leg that is a branch from the femoral nerve

sciatic nerve   systemic nerve from the sacral plexus that is a combination of the tibial and fibular nerves and extends across the hip joint and gluteal region into the upper posterior leg

sciatica   painful condition resulting from inflammation or compression of the sciatic nerve or any of the spinal nerves that contribute to it

secondary vesicle   five vesicles that develop from primary vesicles, continuing the process of differentiation of the embryonic brain

sigmoid sinuses   dural sinuses that drain directly into the jugular veins

somatosensation   general senses related to the body, usually thought of as the senses of touch, which would include pain, temperature, and proprioception

spinal accessory nerve   eleventh cranial nerve; responsible for contraction of neck muscles

spinal nerve   one of 31 nerves connected to the spinal cord

straight sinus   dural sinus that drains blood from the deep center of the brain to collect with the other sinuses

striatum   the caudate and putamen collectively, as part of the basal nuclei, which receive input from the cerebral cortex

subarachnoid space   space between the arachnoid

mater and pia mater that contains CSF and the fibrous connections of the arachnoid trabeculae

subcortical nucleus   all the nuclei beneath the cerebral cortex, including the basal nuclei and the basal forebrain

substantia nigra pars compacta   nuclei within the basal nuclei that release dopamine to modulate the function of the striatum; part of the motor pathway

substantia nigra pars reticulata   nuclei within the basal nuclei that serve as an output center of the nuclei; part of the motor pathway

subthalamus   nucleus within the basal nuclei that is part of the indirect pathway

sulcus   groove formed by convolutions in the surface of the cerebral cortex

superior colliculus   half of the midbrain tectum that is responsible for aligning visual, auditory, and somatosensory spatial perceptions

superior sagittal sinus   dural sinus that runs along the top of the longitudinal fissure and drains blood from the majority of the outer cerebrum

sympathetic chain ganglia   autonomic ganglia in a chain along the anterolateral aspect of the vertebral column that are responsible for contributing to homeostatic mechanisms of the autonomic nervous system

systemic nerve   nerve in the periphery distal to a nerve plexus or spinal nerve

tectum   region of the midbrain, thought of as the roof of the cerebral aqueduct, which is subdivided into the inferior and superior colliculi

tegmentum   region of the midbrain, thought of as the floor of the cerebral aqueduct, which continues into the pons and medulla as the floor of the fourth ventricle

telencephalon   secondary vesicle of the embryonic brain that develops into the cerebrum

temporal lobe   region of the cerebral cortex directly beneath the temporal bone of the cranium

terminal ganglion   autonomic ganglia that are near or within the walls of organs that are responsible for contributing to homeostatic mechanisms of the autonomic nervous system

thalamus   major region of the diencephalon that is responsible for relaying information between the cerebrum and the hindbrain, spinal cord, and periphery

third ventricle   portion of the ventricular system that is in the region of the diencephalon

tibial nerve   systemic nerve of the posterior leg that begins as part of the sciatic nerve

transverse sinuses   dural sinuses that drain along either side of the occipital–cerebellar space

trigeminal ganglion   sensory ganglion that contributes sensory fibers to the trigeminal nerve

trigeminal nerve   fifth cranial nerve; responsible for cutaneous sensation of the face and contraction of the muscles of mastication

trochlear nerve   fourth cranial nerve; responsible for contraction of one of the extraocular muscles

ulnar nerve   systemic nerve of the arm located close to the ulna, a bone of the forearm

vagus nerve   tenth cranial nerve; responsible for the autonomic control of organs in the thoracic and upper abdominal cavities

ventral (anterior) nerve root   axons emerging from the anterior or lateral horns of the spinal cord

ventricles   remnants of the hollow center of the neural tube that are spaces for cerebrospinal fluid to circulate through the brain

vertebral arteries   arteries that ascend along either side of the vertebral column through the transverse foramina of the cervical vertebrae and enter the cranium through the foramen magnum

vestibulocochlear nerve   eighth cranial nerve; responsible for the sensations of hearing and balance

Chapter Review

13.1 The Embryologic Perspective

The development of the nervous system starts early in embryonic development. The outer layer of the embryo, the ectoderm, gives rise to the skin and the nervous system. A specialized region of this layer, the neuroectoderm, becomes a groove that folds in and becomes the neural tube beneath the dorsal surface of the embryo. The anterior end of the neural tube develops into the brain, and the posterior region becomes the spinal cord. Tissues at the edges of the neural groove, when it closes off, are called the neural crest and migrate through the embryo to give rise to

PNS structures as well as some non-nervous tissues.

The brain develops from this early tube structure and gives rise to specific regions of the adult brain. As the neural tube grows and differentiates, it enlarges into three vesicles that correspond to the forebrain, midbrain, and hindbrain regions of the adult brain. Later in development, two of these three vesicles differentiate further, resulting in five vesicles. Those five vesicles can be aligned with the four major regions of the adult brain. The cerebrum is formed directly from the telencephalon. The diencephalon is the only region that keeps its embryonic name. The

Access for free at openstax.org

mesencephalon, metencephalon, and myelencephalon become the brain stem. The cerebellum also develops from the metencephalon and is a separate region of the adult brain.

The spinal cord develops out of the rest of the neural tube and retains the tube structure, with the nervous tissue thickening and the hollow center becoming a very small central canal through the cord. The rest of the hollow center of the neural tube corresponds to open spaces within the brain called the ventricles, where cerebrospinal fluid is found.

13.2 The Central Nervous System

The adult brain is separated into four major regions: the cerebrum, the diencephalon, the brain stem, and the cerebellum. The cerebrum is the largest portion and contains the cerebral cortex and subcortical nuclei. It is divided into two halves by the longitudinal fissure.

The cortex is separated into the frontal, parietal, temporal, and occipital lobes. The frontal lobe is responsible for motor functions, from planning movements through executing commands to be sent to the spinal cord and periphery. The most anterior portion of the frontal lobe is the prefrontal cortex, which is associated with aspects of personality through its influence on motor responses in decision-making.

The other lobes are responsible for sensory functions. The parietal lobe is where somatosensation is processed. The occipital lobe is where visual processing begins, although the other parts of the brain can contribute to visual function. The temporal lobe contains the cortical area for auditory processing, but also has regions crucial for memory formation.

Nuclei beneath the cerebral cortex, known as the subcortical nuclei, are responsible for augmenting cortical functions. The basal nuclei receive input from cortical areas and compare it with the general state of the individual through the activity of a dopamine-releasing nucleus. The output influences the activity of part of the thalamus that can then increase or decrease cortical activity that often results in changes to motor commands. The basal forebrain is responsible for modulating cortical activity in attention and memory. The limbic system includes deep cerebral nuclei that are responsible for emotion and memory.

The diencephalon includes the thalamus and the hypothalamus, along with some other structures. The thalamus is a relay between the cerebrum and the rest of the nervous system. The hypothalamus coordinates homeostatic functions through the autonomic and endocrine systems.

The brain stem is composed of the midbrain, pons, and medulla. It controls the head and neck region of the body through the cranial nerves. There are control centers in the brain stem that regulate the cardiovascular and respiratory systems.

The cerebellum is connected to the brain stem, primarily at the pons, where it receives a copy of the descending input from the cerebrum to the spinal cord. It can compare this with sensory feedback input through the medulla and send output through the midbrain that can correct motor commands for coordination.

13.3 Circulation and the Central Nervous System

The CNS has a privileged blood supply established by the blood-brain barrier. Establishing this barrier are anatomical structures that help to protect and isolate the CNS. The arterial blood to the brain comes from the internal carotid and vertebral arteries, which both contribute to the unique circle of Willis that provides constant perfusion of the brain even if one of the blood vessels is blocked or narrowed. That blood is eventually filtered to make a separate medium, the CSF, that circulates within the spaces of the brain and then into the surrounding space defined by the meninges, the protective covering of the brain and spinal cord.

The blood that nourishes the brain and spinal cord is behind the glial-cell–enforced blood-brain barrier, which limits the exchange of material from blood vessels with the interstitial fluid of the nervous tissue. Thus, metabolic wastes are collected in cerebrospinal fluid that circulates through the CNS. This fluid is produced by filtering blood at the choroid plexuses in the four ventricles of the brain. It then circulates through the ventricles and into the subarachnoid space, between the pia mater and the arachnoid mater. From the arachnoid granulations, CSF is reabsorbed into the blood, removing the waste from the privileged central nervous tissue.

The blood, now with the reabsorbed CSF, drains out of the cranium through the dural sinuses. The dura mater is the tough outer covering of the CNS, which is anchored to the inner surface of the cranial and vertebral cavities. It surrounds the venous space known as the dural sinuses, which connect to the jugular veins, where blood drains from the head and neck.

13.4 The Peripheral Nervous System

The PNS is composed of the groups of neurons

(ganglia) and bundles of axons (nerves) that are outside of the brain and spinal cord. Ganglia are of two types, sensory or autonomic. Sensory ganglia contain unipolar sensory neurons and are found on the dorsal root of all spinal nerves as well as associated with many of the cranial nerves. Autonomic ganglia are in the sympathetic chain, the associated paravertebral or prevertebral ganglia, or in terminal ganglia near or within the organs controlled by the autonomic nervous system.

Nerves are classified as cranial nerves or spinal nerves on the basis of their connection to the brain or spinal cord, respectively. The twelve cranial nerves can be

strictly sensory in function, strictly motor in function, or a combination of the two functions. Sensory fibers are axons of sensory ganglia that carry sensory information into the brain and target sensory nuclei. Motor fibers are axons of motor neurons in motor nuclei of the brain stem and target skeletal muscles of the head and neck. Spinal nerves are all mixed nerves with both sensory and motor fibers. Spinal nerves emerge from the spinal cord and reorganize through plexuses, which then give rise to systemic nerves. Thoracic spinal nerves are not part of any plexus, but give rise to the intercostal nerves directly.

Interactive Link Questions

1. Watch this animation (http://openstax.org/l/braindevel) to examine the development of the brain, starting with the neural tube. As the anterior end of the neural tube develops, it enlarges into the primary vesicles that establish the forebrain, midbrain, and hindbrain. Those structures continue to develop throughout the rest of embryonic development and into adolescence. They are the basis of the structure of the fully developed adult brain. How would you describe the difference in the relative sizes of the three regions of the brain when comparing the early (25th embryonic day) brain and the adult brain?

2. Watch this video (http://openstax.org/l/whitematter) to learn about the white matter in the cerebrum that develops during childhood and adolescence. This is a composite of MRI images taken of the brains of people from 5 years of age through 20 years of age, demonstrating how the cerebrum changes. As the color changes to blue, the ratio of gray matter to white matter changes. The caption for the video describes it as "less gray matter," which is another way of saying "more white matter." If the brain does not finish developing until approximately 20 years of age, can teenagers be held responsible for behaving badly?

3. Watch this video (http://openstax.org/l/basalnuclei1) to learn about the basal nuclei (also known as the basal ganglia), which have two pathways that process information within the cerebrum. As shown in this video, the direct pathway is the shorter pathway through the system that results in increased activity in the cerebral cortex and increased motor activity. The direct pathway is described as resulting in "disinhibition" of the thalamus. What does disinhibition mean? What are the two neurons doing individually to cause this?

4. Watch this video (http://openstax.org/l/basalnuclei2) to learn about the basal nuclei (also known as the basal ganglia), which have two pathways that process information within the cerebrum. As shown in this video, the indirect pathway is the longer pathway through the system that results in decreased activity in the cerebral cortex, and therefore less motor activity. The indirect pathway has an extra couple of connections in it, including disinhibition of the subthalamic nucleus. What is the end result on the thalamus, and therefore on movement initiated by the cerebral cortex?

5. Watch this video (http://openstax.org/l/graymatter) to learn about the gray matter of the spinal cord that receives input from fibers of the dorsal (posterior) root and sends information out through the fibers of the ventral (anterior) root. As discussed in this video, these connections represent the interactions of the CNS with peripheral structures for both sensory and motor functions. The cervical and lumbar spinal cords have enlargements as a result of larger populations of neurons. What are these enlargements responsible for?

6. Compared with the nearest evolutionary relative, the chimpanzee, the human has a brain that is huge. At a point in the past, a common ancestor gave rise to the two species of humans and chimpanzees. That evolutionary history is long and is still an area of intense study. But something happened to increase the size of the human brain relative to the chimpanzee. Read this article (http://openstax.org/l/hugebrain) in which the author explores the current understanding of why this happened.
According to one hypothesis about the expansion of brain size, what tissue might have been sacrificed so energy was available to grow our larger brain? Based on what you know about that tissue and nervous tissue, why would there be a trade-off between them in terms of energy use?

7. Watch this animation (http://openstax.org/l/bloodflow1) to see how blood flows to the brain and passes through the circle of Willis before being distributed through the cerebrum. The circle of Willis is a specialized arrangement of arteries that ensure constant perfusion of the cerebrum even in the event of a blockage of one of the arteries in the circle. The animation shows the normal direction of flow through the circle of Willis to the middle cerebral artery. Where would the blood come from if there were a blockage just posterior to the middle cerebral artery on the left?

8. Watch this video (http://openstax.org/l/lumbarpuncture) that describes the procedure known as the lumbar puncture, a medical procedure used to sample the CSF. Because of the anatomy of the CNS, it is a relative safe location to insert a needle. Why is the lumbar puncture performed in the lower lumbar area of the vertebral column?

9. Watch this animation (http://openstax.org/l/CSFflow) that shows the flow of CSF through the brain and spinal cord, and how it originates from the ventricles and then spreads into the space within the meninges, where the fluids then move into the venous sinuses to return to the cardiovascular circulation. What are the structures that produce CSF and where are they found? How are the structures indicated in this animation?

10. Figure 13.20 If you zoom in on the DRG, you can see smaller satellite glial cells surrounding the large cell bodies of the sensory neurons. From what structure do satellite cells derive during embryologic development?

11. Figure 13.22 To what structures in a skeletal muscle are the endoneurium, perineurium, and epineurium comparable?

12. Visit this site (http://openstax.org/l/NYTmeningitis) to read about a man who wakes with a headache and a loss of vision. His regular doctor sent him to an ophthalmologist to address the vision loss. The ophthalmologist recognizes a greater problem and immediately sends him to the emergency room. Once there, the patient undergoes a large battery of tests, but a definite cause cannot be found. A specialist recognizes the problem as meningitis, but the question is what caused it originally. How can that be cured? The loss of vision comes from swelling around the optic nerve, which probably presented as a bulge on the inside of the eye. Why is swelling related to meningitis going to push on the optic nerve?

Review Questions

13. Aside from the nervous system, which other organ system develops out of the ectoderm?
    a. digestive
    b. respiratory
    c. integumentary
    d. urinary

14. Which primary vesicle of the embryonic nervous system does not differentiate into more vesicles at the secondary stage?
    a. prosencephalon
    b. mesencephalon
    c. diencephalon
    d. rhombencephalon

15. Which adult structure(s) arises from the diencephalon?
    a. thalamus, hypothalamus, retina
    b. midbrain, pons, medulla
    c. pons and cerebellum
    d. cerebrum

16. Which non-nervous tissue develops from the neuroectoderm?
    a. respiratory mucosa
    b. vertebral bone
    c. digestive lining
    d. craniofacial bone

17. Which structure is associated with the embryologic development of the peripheral nervous system?
    a. neural crest
    b. neuraxis
    c. rhombencephalon
    d. neural tube

18. Which lobe of the cerebral cortex is responsible for generating motor commands?
    a. temporal
    b. parietal
    c. occipital
    d. frontal

19. What region of the diencephalon coordinates homeostasis?
    a. thalamus
    b. epithalamus
    c. hypothalamus
    d. subthalamus

20. What level of the brain stem is the major input to the cerebellum?
    a. midbrain
    b. pons
    c. medulla
    d. spinal cord

21. What region of the spinal cord contains motor neurons that direct the movement of skeletal muscles?
    a. anterior horn
    b. posterior horn
    c. lateral horn
    d. alar plate

22. Brodmann's areas map different regions of the _____ to particular functions.
    a. cerebellum
    b. cerebral cortex
    c. basal forebrain
    d. corpus callosum

23. What blood vessel enters the cranium to supply the brain with fresh, oxygenated blood?
    a. common carotid artery
    b. jugular vein
    c. internal carotid artery
    d. aorta

24. Which layer of the meninges surrounds and supports the sinuses that form the route through which blood drains from the CNS?
    a. dura mater
    b. arachnoid mater
    c. subarachnoid
    d. pia mater

25. What type of glial cell is responsible for filtering blood to produce CSF at the choroid plexus?
    a. ependymal cell
    b. astrocyte
    c. oligodendrocyte
    d. Schwann cell

26. Which portion of the ventricular system is found within the diencephalon?
    a. lateral ventricles
    b. third ventricle
    c. cerebral aqueduct
    d. fourth ventricle

27. What condition causes a stroke?
    a. inflammation of meninges
    b. lumbar puncture
    c. infection of cerebral spinal fluid
    d. disruption of blood to the brain

28. What type of ganglion contains neurons that control homeostatic mechanisms of the body?
    a. sensory ganglion
    b. dorsal root ganglion
    c. autonomic ganglion
    d. cranial nerve ganglion

29. Which ganglion is responsible for cutaneous sensations of the face?
    a. otic ganglion
    b. vestibular ganglion
    c. geniculate ganglion
    d. trigeminal ganglion

30. What is the name for a bundle of axons within a nerve?
    a. fascicle
    b. tract
    c. nerve root
    d. epineurium

31. Which cranial nerve does not control functions in the head and neck?
    a. olfactory
    b. trochlear
    c. glossopharyngeal
    d. vagus

32. Which of these structures is not under direct control of the peripheral nervous system?
  a. trigeminal ganglion
  b. gastric plexus
  c. sympathetic chain ganglia
  d. cervical plexus

Critical Thinking Questions

33. Studying the embryonic development of the nervous system makes it easier to understand the complexity of the adult nervous system. Give one example of how development in the embryonic nervous system explains a more complex structure in the adult nervous system.

34. What happens in development that suggests that there is a special relationship between the skeletal structure of the head and the nervous system?

35. Damage to specific regions of the cerebral cortex, such as through a stroke, can result in specific losses of function. What functions would likely be lost by a stroke in the temporal lobe?

36. Why do the anatomical inputs to the cerebellum suggest that it can compare motor commands and sensory feedback?

37. Why can the circle of Willis maintain perfusion of the brain even if there is a blockage in one part of the structure?

38. Meningitis is an inflammation of the meninges that can have severe effects on neurological function. Why is infection of this structure potentially so dangerous?

39. Why are ganglia and nerves not surrounded by protective structures like the meninges of the CNS?

40. Testing for neurological function involves a series of tests of functions associated with the cranial nerves. What functions, and therefore which nerves, are being tested by asking a patient to follow the tip of a pen with their eyes?

CHAPTER 14
The Somatic Nervous System

Figure 14.1   Too Hot to Touch When high temperature is sensed in the skin, a reflexive withdrawal is initiated by the muscles of the arm. Sensory neurons are activated by a stimulus, which is sent to the central nervous system, and a motor response is sent out to the skeletal muscles that control this movement.

CHAPTER OBJECTIVES

After studying this chapter, you will be able to:

- Describe the components of the somatic nervous system
- Name the modalities and submodalities of the sensory systems
- Distinguish between general and special senses
- Describe regions of the central nervous system that contribute to somatic functions
- Explain the stimulus-response motor pathway

INTRODUCTION The somatic nervous system is traditionally considered a division within the peripheral nervous system. However, this misses an important point: somatic refers to a functional division, whereas peripheral refers to an anatomic division. The somatic nervous system is responsible for our conscious perception of the environment and for our voluntary responses to that perception by means of skeletal muscles. Peripheral sensory neurons receive input from environmental stimuli, but the neurons that produce motor responses originate in the central nervous system. The distinction between the structures (i.e., anatomy) of the peripheral and central nervous systems and functions (i.e., physiology) of the somatic and autonomic systems can most easily be demonstrated through a simple reflex action. When you touch a hot stove, you pull your hand away. Sensory receptors in the skin sense extreme temperature and the early signs of tissue damage. This triggers an action potential, which travels along the sensory fiber from the skin, through the dorsal spinal root to the spinal cord, and directly activates a ventral horn motor neuron. That neuron sends a signal along its axon to excite the biceps brachii, causing contraction of the muscle and flexion of the forearm at the elbow to withdraw the hand from the hot stove. The withdrawal reflex has more components, such as inhibiting the opposing muscle and balancing posture while the arm is forcefully withdrawn, which will be further explored at the end of this chapter.

The basic withdrawal reflex explained above includes sensory input (the painful stimulus), central processing (the synapse in the spinal cord), and motor output (activation of a ventral motor neuron that causes contraction of the biceps brachii). Expanding the explanation of the withdrawal reflex can include inhibition of the opposing muscle, or cross extension, either of which increase the complexity of the example by involving more central neurons. A collateral branch of the sensory axon would inhibit another ventral horn motor neuron so that the triceps brachii do not contract and slow the withdrawal down. The cross extensor reflex provides a counterbalancing movement on the other side of the body, which requires another collateral of the sensory axon to activate contraction of the extensor muscles in the contralateral limb.

A more complex example of somatic function is conscious muscle movement. For example, reading of this text starts with visual sensory input to the retina, which then projects to the thalamus, and on to the cerebral cortex. A sequence of regions of the cerebral cortex process the visual information, starting in the primary visual cortex of the occipital lobe, and resulting in the conscious perception of these letters. Subsequent cognitive processing results in understanding of the content. As you continue reading, regions of the cerebral cortex in the frontal lobe plan how to move the eyes to follow the lines of text. The output from the cortex causes activity in motor neurons in the brain stem that cause movement of the extraocular muscles through the third, fourth, and sixth cranial nerves. This example also includes sensory input (the retinal projection to the thalamus), central processing (the thalamus and subsequent cortical activity), and motor output (activation of neurons in the brain stem that lead to coordinated contraction of extraocular muscles).

14.1 Sensory Perception

LEARNING OBJECTIVES

By the end of this section, you will be able to:
- Describe different types of sensory receptors
- Describe the structures responsible for the special senses of taste, smell, hearing, balance, and vision
- Distinguish how different tastes are transduced
- Describe the means of mechanoreception for hearing and balance
- List the supporting structures around the eye and describe the structure of the eyeball
- Describe the processes of phototransduction

A major role of sensory receptors is to help us learn about the environment around us, or about the state of our internal environment. Stimuli from varying sources, and of different types, are received and changed into the electrochemical signals of the nervous system. This occurs when a stimulus changes the cell membrane potential of a sensory neuron. The stimulus causes the sensory cell to produce an action potential that is relayed into the central nervous system (CNS), where it is integrated with other sensory information—or sometimes higher cognitive functions—to become a conscious perception of that stimulus. The central integration may then lead to a motor response.

Describing sensory function with the term sensation or perception is a deliberate distinction. Sensation is the activation of sensory receptor cells at the level of the stimulus. Perception is the central processing of sensory stimuli into a meaningful pattern. Perception is dependent on sensation, but not all sensations are perceived. Receptors are the cells or structures that detect sensations. A receptor cell is changed directly by a stimulus. A transmembrane protein receptor is a protein in the cell membrane that mediates a physiological change in a neuron, most often through the opening of ion channels or changes in the cell signaling processes. Transmembrane receptors are activated by chemicals called ligands. For example, a molecule in food can serve as a ligand for taste receptors. Other transmembrane proteins, which are not accurately called receptors, are sensitive to mechanical or thermal changes. Physical changes in these proteins increase ion flow across the membrane, and can generate an action potential or a graded potential in the sensory neurons.

Sensory Receptors

Stimuli in the environment activate specialized receptor cells in the peripheral nervous system. Different types of stimuli are sensed by different types of receptor cells. Receptor cells can be classified into types on the basis of three different criteria: cell type, position, and function. Receptors can be classified structurally on the basis of cell type and their position in relation to stimuli they sense. They can also be classified functionally on the basis of the **transduction** of stimuli, or how the mechanical stimulus, light, or chemical changed the cell membrane potential.

Structural Receptor Types

The cells that interpret information about the environment can be either (1) a neuron that has a **free nerve ending**, with dendrites embedded in tissue that would receive a sensation; (2) a neuron that has an **encapsulated ending** in which the sensory nerve endings are encapsulated in connective tissue that enhances their sensitivity; or (3) a specialized **receptor cell**, which has distinct structural components that interpret a specific type of stimulus (Figure 14.2). The pain and temperature receptors in the dermis of the skin are examples of neurons that have free nerve endings. Also located in the dermis of the skin are lamellated corpuscles, neurons with encapsulated nerve endings that respond to pressure and touch. The cells in the retina that respond to light stimuli are an example of a specialized receptor, a **photoreceptor**.

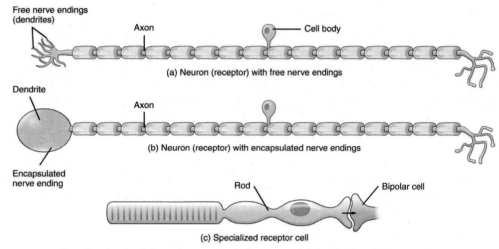

FIGURE 14.2   Receptor Classification by Cell Type   Receptor cell types can be classified on the basis of their structure. Sensory neurons can have either (a) free nerve endings or (b) encapsulated endings. Photoreceptors in the eyes, such as rod cells, are examples of (c) specialized receptor cells. These cells release neurotransmitters onto a bipolar cell, which then synapses with the optic nerve neurons.

Another way that receptors can be classified is based on their location relative to the stimuli. An **exteroceptor** is a receptor that is located near a stimulus in the external environment, such as the somatosensory receptors that are located in the skin. An **interoceptor** is one that interprets stimuli from internal organs and tissues, such as the receptors that sense the increase in blood pressure in the aorta or carotid sinus. Finally, a **proprioceptor** is a receptor located near a moving part of the body, such as a muscle, that interprets the positions of the tissues as they move.

Functional Receptor Types

A third classification of receptors is by how the receptor transduces stimuli into membrane potential changes. Stimuli are of three general types. Some stimuli are ions and macromolecules that affect transmembrane receptor proteins when these chemicals diffuse across the cell membrane. Some stimuli are physical variations in the environment that affect receptor cell membrane potentials. Other stimuli include the electromagnetic radiation from visible light. For humans, the only electromagnetic energy that is perceived by our eyes is visible light. Some other organisms have receptors that humans lack, such as the heat sensors of snakes, the ultraviolet light sensors of bees, or magnetic receptors in migratory birds.

Receptor cells can be further categorized on the basis of the type of stimuli they transduce. Chemical stimuli can be interpreted by a **chemoreceptor** that interprets chemical stimuli, such as an object's taste or smell. **Osmoreceptors** respond to solute concentrations of body fluids. Additionally, pain is primarily a chemical sense that interprets the presence of chemicals from tissue damage, or similar intense stimuli, through a **nociceptor**. Physical stimuli, such as pressure and vibration, as well as the sensation of sound and body position (balance), are interpreted through a **mechanoreceptor**. Another physical stimulus that has its own type of receptor is temperature, which is sensed through a **thermoreceptor** that is either sensitive to temperatures above (heat) or below (cold) normal body temperature.

Sensory Modalities

Ask anyone what the senses are, and they are likely to list the five major senses—taste, smell, touch, hearing, and sight. However, these are not all of the senses. The most obvious omission from this list is balance. Also, what is referred to simply as touch can be further subdivided into pressure, vibration, stretch, and hair-follicle position, on the basis of the type of mechanoreceptors that perceive these touch sensations. Other overlooked senses include temperature perception by thermoreceptors and pain perception by nociceptors.

Within the realm of physiology, senses can be classified as either general or specific. A **general sense** is one that is distributed throughout the body and has receptor cells within the structures of other organs. Mechanoreceptors in the skin, muscles, or the walls of blood vessels are examples of this type. General senses often contribute to the sense of touch, as described above, or to **proprioception** (body movement) and **kinesthesia** (body movement), or to a **visceral sense**, which is most important to autonomic functions. A **special sense** is one that has a specific organ devoted to it, namely the eye, inner ear, tongue, or nose.

Each of the senses is referred to as a **sensory modality**. Modality refers to the way that information is encoded, which is similar to the idea of transduction. The main sensory modalities can be described on the basis of how each is transduced. The chemical senses are taste and smell. The general sense that is usually referred to as touch includes chemical sensation in the form of nociception, or pain. Pressure, vibration, muscle stretch, and the movement of hair by an external stimulus, are all sensed by mechanoreceptors. Hearing and balance are also sensed by mechanoreceptors. Finally, vision involves the activation of photoreceptors.

Listing all the different sensory modalities, which can number as many as 17, involves separating the five major senses into more specific categories, or **submodalities**, of the larger sense. An individual sensory modality represents the sensation of a specific type of stimulus. For example, the general sense of touch, which is known as **somatosensation**, can be separated into light pressure, deep pressure, vibration, itch, pain, temperature, or hair movement.

Gustation (Taste)

Only a few recognized submodalities exist within the sense of taste, or **gustation**. Until recently, only four tastes were recognized: sweet, salty, sour, and bitter. Research at the turn of the 20th century led to recognition of the fifth taste, umami, during the mid-1980s. **Umami** is a Japanese word that means "delicious taste," and is often translated to mean savory. Very recent research has suggested that there may also be a sixth taste for fats, or lipids.

Gustation is the special sense associated with the tongue. The surface of the tongue, along with the rest of the oral cavity, is lined by a stratified squamous epithelium. Raised bumps called **papillae** (singular = papilla) contain the structures for gustatory transduction. There are four types of papillae, based on their appearance (Figure 14.3): circumvallate, foliate, filiform, and fungiform. Within the structure of the papillae are **taste buds** that contain specialized **gustatory receptor cells** for the transduction of taste stimuli. These receptor cells are sensitive to the chemicals contained within foods that are ingested, and they release neurotransmitters based on the amount of the chemical in the food. Neurotransmitters from the gustatory cells can activate sensory neurons in the facial, glossopharyngeal, and vagus cranial nerves.

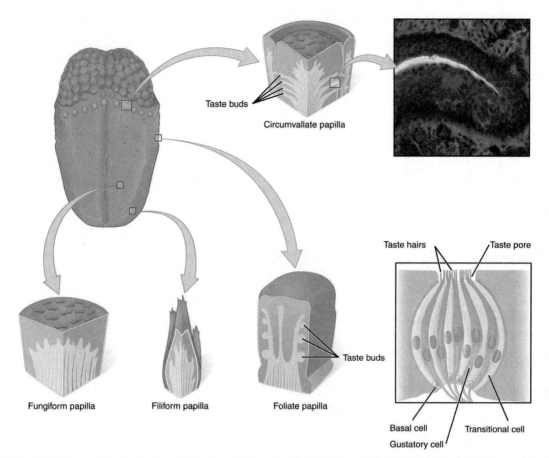

FIGURE 14.3   The Tongue   The tongue is covered with small bumps, called papillae, which contain taste buds that are sensitive to chemicals in ingested food or drink. Different types of papillae are found in different regions of the tongue. The taste buds contain specialized gustatory receptor cells that respond to chemical stimuli dissolved in the saliva. These receptor cells activate sensory neurons that are part of the facial and glossopharyngeal nerves. LM × 1600. (Micrograph provided by the Regents of University of Michigan Medical School © 2012)

Salty taste is simply the perception of sodium ions (Na^+) in the saliva. When you eat something salty, the salt crystals dissociate into the component ions Na^+ and Cl^-, which dissolve into the saliva in your mouth. The Na^+ concentration becomes high outside the gustatory cells, creating a strong concentration gradient that drives the diffusion of the ion into the cells. The entry of Na^+ into these cells results in the depolarization of the cell membrane and the generation of a receptor potential.

Sour taste is the perception of H^+ concentration. Just as with sodium ions in salty flavors, these hydrogen ions enter the cell and trigger depolarization. Sour flavors are, essentially, the perception of acids in our food. Increasing hydrogen ion concentrations in the saliva (lowering saliva pH) triggers progressively stronger graded potentials in the gustatory cells. For example, orange juice—which contains citric acid—will taste sour because it has a pH value of approximately 3. Of course, it is often sweetened so that the sour taste is masked.

The first two tastes (salty and sour) are triggered by the cations Na^+ and H^+. The other tastes result from food molecules binding to a G protein–coupled receptor. A G protein signal transduction system ultimately leads to depolarization of the gustatory cell. The sweet taste is the sensitivity of gustatory cells to the presence of glucose dissolved in the saliva. Other monosaccharides such as fructose, or artificial sweeteners such as aspartame (NutraSweet™), saccharine, or sucralose (Splenda™) also activate the sweet receptors. The affinity for each of these molecules varies, and some will taste sweeter than glucose because they bind to the G protein–coupled receptor differently.

Bitter taste is similar to sweet in that food molecules bind to G protein–coupled receptors. However, there are a number of different ways in which this can happen because there are a large diversity of bitter-tasting molecules. Some bitter molecules depolarize gustatory cells, whereas others hyperpolarize gustatory cells. Likewise, some bitter molecules increase G protein activation within the gustatory cells, whereas other bitter molecules decrease G protein activation. The specific response depends on which molecule is binding to the receptor.

One major group of bitter-tasting molecules are alkaloids. **Alkaloids** are nitrogen containing molecules that are commonly found in bitter-tasting plant products, such as coffee, hops (in beer), tannins (in wine), tea, and aspirin. By containing toxic alkaloids, the plant is less susceptible to microbe infection and less attractive to herbivores.

Therefore, the function of bitter taste may primarily be related to stimulating the gag reflex to avoid ingesting poisons. Because of this, many bitter foods that are normally ingested are often combined with a sweet component to make them more palatable (cream and sugar in coffee, for example). The highest concentration of bitter receptors appear to be in the posterior tongue, where a gag reflex could still spit out poisonous food.

The taste known as umami is often referred to as the savory taste. Like sweet and bitter, it is based on the activation of G protein–coupled receptors by a specific molecule. The molecule that activates this receptor is the amino acid L-glutamate. Therefore, the umami flavor is often perceived while eating protein-rich foods. Not surprisingly, dishes that contain meat are often described as savory.

Once the gustatory cells are activated by the taste molecules, they release neurotransmitters onto the dendrites of sensory neurons. These neurons are part of the facial and glossopharyngeal cranial nerves, as well as a component within the vagus nerve dedicated to the gag reflex. The facial nerve connects to taste buds in the anterior third of the tongue. The glossopharyngeal nerve connects to taste buds in the posterior two thirds of the tongue. The vagus nerve connects to taste buds in the extreme posterior of the tongue, verging on the pharynx, which are more sensitive to noxious stimuli such as bitterness.

⊘ INTERACTIVE LINK

Watch this video (http://openstax.org/l/DanielleReed) to learn about Dr. Danielle Reed of the Monell Chemical Senses Center in Philadelphia, Pennsylvania, who became interested in science at an early age because of her sensory experiences. She recognized that her sense of taste was unique compared with other people she knew. Now, she studies the genetic differences between people and their sensitivities to taste stimuli. In the video, there is a brief image of a person sticking out their tongue, which has been covered with a colored dye. This is how Dr. Reed is able to visualize and count papillae on the surface of the tongue. People fall into two groups known as "tasters" and "non-tasters" based on the density of papillae on their tongue, which also indicates the number of taste buds. Non-tasters can taste food, but they are not as sensitive to certain tastes, such as bitterness. Dr. Reed discovered that she is a non-taster, which explains why she perceived bitterness differently than other people she knew. Are you very sensitive to tastes? Can you see any similarities among the members of your family?

Olfaction (Smell)

Like taste, the sense of smell, or **olfaction**, is also responsive to chemical stimuli. The olfactory receptor neurons are located in a small region within the superior nasal cavity (Figure 14.4). This region is referred to as the **olfactory epithelium** and contains bipolar sensory neurons. Each **olfactory sensory neuron** has dendrites that extend from the apical surface of the epithelium into the mucus lining the cavity. As airborne molecules are inhaled through the nose, they pass over the olfactory epithelial region and dissolve into the mucus. These **odorant molecules** bind to proteins that keep them dissolved in the mucus and help transport them to the olfactory dendrites. The odorant–protein complex binds to a receptor protein within the cell membrane of an olfactory dendrite. These receptors are G protein–coupled, and will produce a graded membrane potential in the olfactory neurons.

The axon of an olfactory neuron extends from the basal surface of the epithelium, through an olfactory foramen in the cribriform plate of the ethmoid bone, and into the brain. The group of axons called the olfactory tract connect to the **olfactory bulb** on the ventral surface of the frontal lobe. From there, the axons split to travel to several brain regions. Some travel to the cerebrum, specifically to the primary olfactory cortex that is located in the inferior and medial areas of the temporal lobe. Others project to structures within the limbic system and hypothalamus, where smells become associated with long-term memory and emotional responses. This is how certain smells trigger emotional memories, such as the smell of food associated with one's birthplace. Smell is the one sensory modality that does not synapse in the thalamus before connecting to the cerebral cortex. This intimate connection between the olfactory system and the cerebral cortex is one reason why smell can be a potent trigger of memories and emotion.

The nasal epithelium, including the olfactory cells, can be harmed by airborne toxic chemicals. Therefore, the olfactory neurons are regularly replaced within the nasal epithelium, after which the axons of the new neurons must find their appropriate connections in the olfactory bulb. These new axons grow along the axons that are already in place in the cranial nerve.

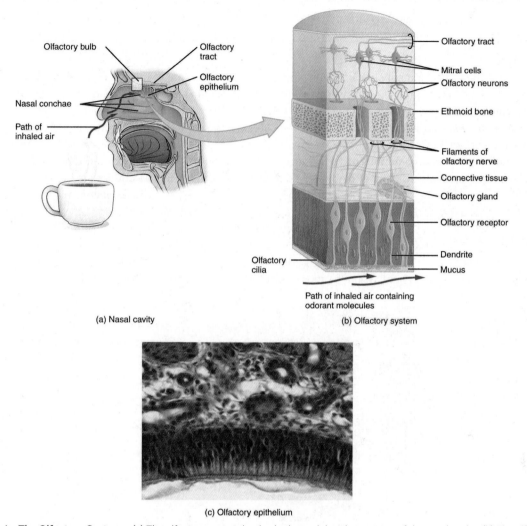

(a) Nasal cavity

(b) Olfactory system

(c) Olfactory epithelium

FIGURE 14.4 **The Olfactory System**   (a) The olfactory system begins in the peripheral structures of the nasal cavity. (b) The olfactory receptor neurons are within the olfactory epithelium. (c) Axons of the olfactory receptor neurons project through the cribriform plate of the ethmoid bone and synapse with the neurons of the olfactory bulb (tissue source: simian). LM × 812. (Micrograph provided by the Regents of University of Michigan Medical School © 2012)

Disorders of the...

Olfactory System: Anosmia

Blunt force trauma to the face, such as that common in many car accidents, can lead to the loss of the olfactory nerve, and subsequently, loss of the sense of smell. This condition is known as **anosmia**. When the frontal lobe of the brain moves relative to the ethmoid bone, the olfactory tract axons may be sheared apart. Professional fighters often experience anosmia because of repeated trauma to face and head. In addition, certain pharmaceuticals, such as antibiotics, can cause anosmia by killing all the olfactory neurons at once. If no axons are in place within the olfactory nerve, then the axons from newly formed olfactory neurons have no guide to lead them to their connections within the olfactory bulb. There are temporary causes of anosmia, as well, such as those caused by inflammatory responses related to respiratory infections or allergies.

Loss of the sense of smell can result in food tasting bland. A person with an impaired sense of smell may require additional spice and seasoning levels for food to be tasted. Anosmia may also be related to some presentations of mild depression, because the loss of enjoyment of food may lead to a general sense of despair.

The ability of olfactory neurons to replace themselves decreases with age, leading to age-related anosmia. This explains why some elderly people salt their food more than younger people do. However, this increased sodium intake can increase blood volume and blood pressure, increasing the risk of cardiovascular diseases in the elderly.

Audition (Hearing)

Hearing, or **audition**, is the transduction of sound waves into a neural signal that is made possible by the structures of the ear (Figure 14.5). The large, fleshy structure on the lateral aspect of the head is known as the **auricle**. Some sources will also refer to this structure as the pinna, though that term is more appropriate for a structure that can be moved, such as the external ear of a cat. The C-shaped curves of the auricle direct sound waves toward the auditory canal. The canal enters the skull through the external auditory meatus of the temporal bone. At the end of the auditory canal is the **tympanic membrane**, or ear drum, which vibrates after it is struck by sound waves. The auricle, ear canal, and tympanic membrane are often referred to as the **external ear**. The **middle ear** consists of a space spanned by three small bones called the **ossicles**. The three ossicles are the **malleus**, **incus**, and **stapes**, which are Latin names that roughly translate to hammer, anvil, and stirrup. The malleus is attached to the tympanic membrane and articulates with the incus. The incus, in turn, articulates with the stapes. The stapes is then attached to the **inner ear**, where the sound waves will be transduced into a neural signal. The middle ear is connected to the pharynx through the Eustachian tube, which helps equilibrate air pressure across the tympanic membrane. The tube is normally closed but will pop open when the muscles of the pharynx contract during swallowing or yawning.

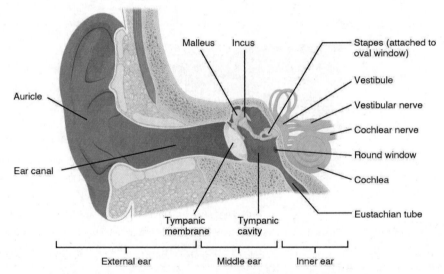

FIGURE 14.5   Structures of the Ear   The external ear contains the auricle, ear canal, and tympanic membrane. The middle ear contains the ossicles and is connected to the pharynx by the Eustachian tube. The inner ear contains the cochlea and vestibule, which are responsible for audition and equilibrium, respectively.

The inner ear is often described as a bony labyrinth, as it is composed of a series of canals embedded within the temporal bone. It has two separate regions, the **cochlea** and the **vestibule**, which are responsible for hearing and balance, respectively. The neural signals from these two regions are relayed to the brain stem through separate fiber bundles. However, these two distinct bundles travel together from the inner ear to the brain stem as the vestibulocochlear nerve. Sound is transduced into neural signals within the cochlear region of the inner ear, which contains the sensory neurons of the **spiral ganglia**. These ganglia are located within the spiral-shaped cochlea of the inner ear. The cochlea is attached to the stapes through the **oval window**.

The oval window is located at the beginning of a fluid-filled tube within the cochlea called the **scala vestibuli**. The scala vestibuli extends from the oval window, travelling above the **cochlear duct**, which is the central cavity of the cochlea that contains the sound-transducing neurons. At the uppermost tip of the cochlea, the scala vestibuli curves over the top of the cochlear duct. The fluid-filled tube, now called the **scala tympani**, returns to the base of the cochlea, this time travelling under the cochlear duct. The scala tympani ends at the **round window**, which is

Access for free at openstax.org

covered by a membrane that contains the fluid within the scala. As vibrations of the ossicles travel through the oval window, the fluid of the scala vestibuli and scala tympani moves in a wave-like motion. The frequency of the fluid waves match the frequencies of the sound waves (Figure 14.6). The membrane covering the round window will bulge out or pucker in with the movement of the fluid within the scala tympani.

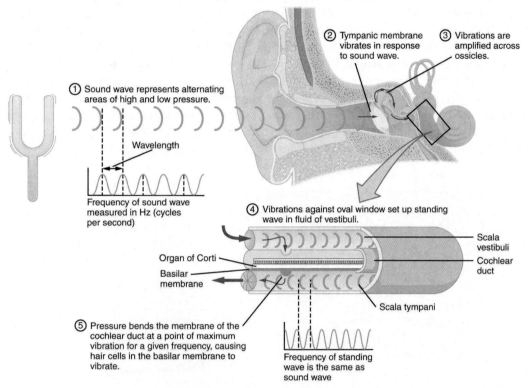

FIGURE 14.6 **Transmission of Sound Waves to Cochlea** A sound wave causes the tympanic membrane to vibrate. This vibration is amplified as it moves across the malleus, incus, and stapes. The amplified vibration is picked up by the oval window causing pressure waves in the fluid of the scala vestibuli and scala tympani. The complexity of the pressure waves is determined by the changes in amplitude and frequency of the sound waves entering the ear.

A cross-sectional view of the cochlea shows that the scala vestibuli and scala tympani run along both sides of the cochlear duct (Figure 14.7). The cochlear duct contains several **organs of Corti**, which transduce the wave motion of the two scala into neural signals. The organs of Corti lie on top of the **basilar membrane**, which is the side of the cochlear duct located between the organs of Corti and the scala tympani. As the fluid waves move through the scala vestibuli and scala tympani, the basilar membrane moves at a specific spot, depending on the frequency of the waves. Higher frequency waves move the region of the basilar membrane that is close to the base of the cochlea. Lower frequency waves move the region of the basilar membrane that is near the tip of the cochlea.

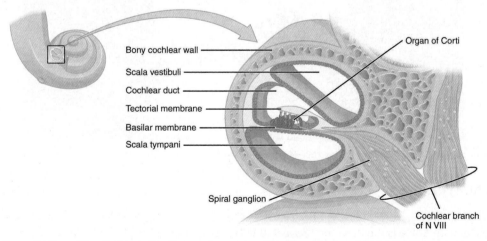

FIGURE 14.7 **Cross Section of the Cochlea** The three major spaces within the cochlea are highlighted. The scala tympani and scala

vestibuli lie on either side of the cochlear duct. The organ of Corti, containing the mechanoreceptor hair cells, is adjacent to the scala tympani, where it sits atop the basilar membrane.

The organs of Corti contain **hair cells**, which are named for the hair-like **stereocilia** extending from the cell's apical surfaces (Figure 14.8). The stereocilia are an array of microvilli-like structures arranged from tallest to shortest. Protein fibers tether adjacent hairs together within each array, such that the array will bend in response to movements of the basilar membrane. The stereocilia extend up from the hair cells to the overlying **tectorial membrane**, which is attached medially to the organ of Corti. When the pressure waves from the scala move the basilar membrane, the tectorial membrane slides across the stereocilia. This bends the stereocilia either toward or away from the tallest member of each array. When the stereocilia bend toward the tallest member of their array, tension in the protein tethers opens ion channels in the hair cell membrane. This will depolarize the hair cell membrane, triggering nerve impulses that travel down the afferent nerve fibers attached to the hair cells. When the stereocilia bend toward the shortest member of their array, the tension on the tethers slackens and the ion channels close. When no sound is present, and the stereocilia are standing straight, a small amount of tension still exists on the tethers, keeping the membrane potential of the hair cell slightly depolarized.

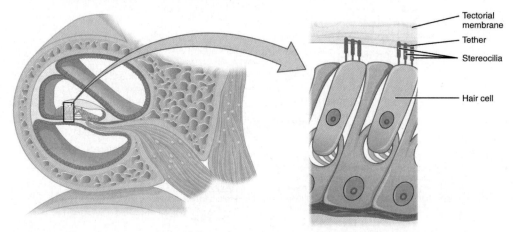

FIGURE 14.8   Hair Cell   The hair cell is a mechanoreceptor with an array of stereocilia emerging from its apical surface. The stereocilia are tethered together by proteins that open ion channels when the array is bent toward the tallest member of their array, and closed when the array is bent toward the shortest member of their array.

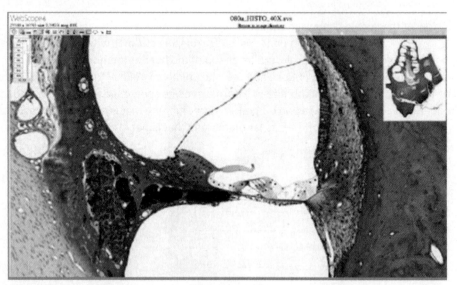

FIGURE 14.9   Cochlea and Organ of Corti   LM × 412. (Micrograph provided by the Regents of University of Michigan Medical School © 2012)

⊘ INTERACTIVE LINK

View the University of Michigan WebScope (http://openstax.org/l/cochleaMG) to explore the tissue sample in greater detail. The basilar membrane is the thin membrane that extends from the central core of the cochlea to the edge.

What is anchored to this membrane so that they can be activated by movement of the fluids within the cochlea?

As stated above, a given region of the basilar membrane will only move if the incoming sound is at a specific frequency. Because the tectorial membrane only moves where the basilar membrane moves, the hair cells in this region will also only respond to sounds of this specific frequency. Therefore, as the frequency of a sound changes, different hair cells are activated all along the basilar membrane. The cochlea encodes auditory stimuli for frequencies between 20 and 20,000 Hz, which is the range of sound that human ears can detect. The unit of Hertz measures the frequency of sound waves in terms of cycles produced per second. Frequencies as low as 20 Hz are detected by hair cells at the apex, or tip, of the cochlea. Frequencies in the higher ranges of 20 KHz are encoded by hair cells at the base of the cochlea, close to the round and oval windows (Figure 14.10). Most auditory stimuli contain a mixture of sounds at a variety of frequencies and intensities (represented by the amplitude of the sound wave). The hair cells along the length of the cochlear duct, which are each sensitive to a particular frequency, allow the cochlea to separate auditory stimuli by frequency, just as a prism separates visible light into its component colors.

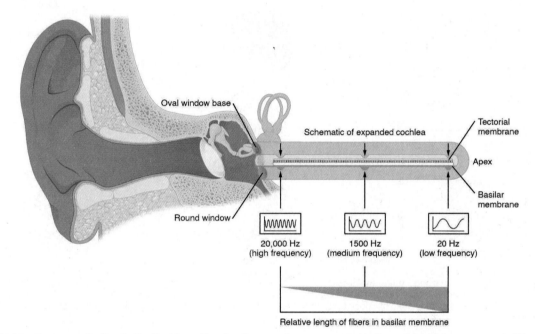

FIGURE 14.10   **Frequency Coding in the Cochlea**   The standing sound wave generated in the cochlea by the movement of the oval window deflects the basilar membrane on the basis of the frequency of sound. Therefore, hair cells at the base of the cochlea are activated only by high frequencies, whereas those at the apex of the cochlea are activated only by low frequencies.

🔗 INTERACTIVE LINK

Watch this video (http://openstax.org/l/ear1) to learn more about how the structures of the ear convert sound waves into a neural signal by moving the "hairs," or stereocilia, of the cochlear duct. Specific locations along the length of the duct encode specific frequencies, or pitches. The brain interprets the meaning of the sounds we hear as music, speech, noise, etc. Which ear structures are responsible for the amplification and transfer of sound from the external ear to the inner ear?

🔗 INTERACTIVE LINK

Watch this animation (http://openstax.org/l/ear2) to learn more about the inner ear and to see the cochlea unroll, with the base at the back of the image and the apex at the front. Specific wavelengths of sound cause specific regions of the basilar membrane to vibrate, much like the keys of a piano produce sound at different frequencies. Based on the animation, where do frequencies—from high to low pitches—cause activity in the hair cells within the cochlear duct?

Equilibrium (Balance)

Along with audition, the inner ear is responsible for encoding information about **equilibrium**, the sense of balance. A similar mechanoreceptor—a hair cell with stereocilia—senses head position, head movement, and whether our bodies are in motion. These cells are located within the vestibule of the inner ear. Head position is sensed by the **utricle** and **saccule**, whereas head movement is sensed by the **semicircular canals**. The neural signals generated in the **vestibular ganglion** are transmitted through the vestibulocochlear nerve to the brain stem and cerebellum.

The utricle and saccule are both largely composed of **macula** tissue (plural = maculae). The macula is composed of hair cells surrounded by support cells. The stereocilia of the hair cells extend into a viscous gel called the **otolithic membrane** (Figure 14.11). On top of the otolithic membrane is a layer of calcium carbonate crystals, called otoliths. The otoliths essentially make the otolithic membrane top-heavy. The otolithic membrane moves separately from the macula in response to head movements. Tilting the head causes the otolithic membrane to slide over the macula in the direction of gravity. The moving otolithic membrane, in turn, bends the sterocilia, causing some hair cells to depolarize as others hyperpolarize. The exact position of the head is interpreted by the brain based on the pattern of hair-cell depolarization.

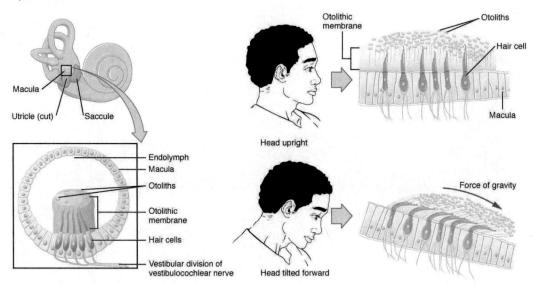

FIGURE 14.11   Linear Acceleration Coding by Maculae   The maculae are specialized for sensing linear acceleration, such as when gravity acts on the tilting head, or if the head starts moving in a straight line. The difference in inertia between the hair cell stereocilia and the otolithic membrane in which they are embedded leads to a shearing force that causes the stereocilia to bend in the direction of that linear acceleration.

The semicircular canals are three ring-like extensions of the vestibule. One is oriented in the horizontal plane, whereas the other two are oriented in the vertical plane. The anterior and posterior vertical canals are oriented at approximately 45 degrees relative to the sagittal plane (Figure 14.12). The base of each semicircular canal, where it meets with the vestibule, connects to an enlarged region known as the **ampulla**. The ampulla contains the hair cells that respond to rotational movement, such as turning the head while saying "no." The stereocilia of these hair cells extend into the **cupula**, a membrane that attaches to the top of the ampulla. As the head rotates in a plane parallel to the semicircular canal, the fluid lags, deflecting the cupula in the direction opposite to the head movement. The semicircular canals contain several ampullae, with some oriented horizontally and others oriented vertically. By comparing the relative movements of both the horizontal and vertical ampullae, the vestibular system can detect the direction of most head movements within three-dimensional (3-D) space.

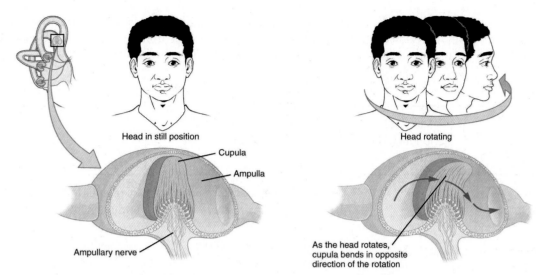

FIGURE 14.12   Rotational Coding by Semicircular Canals   Rotational movement of the head is encoded by the hair cells in the base of the semicircular canals. As one of the canals moves in an arc with the head, the internal fluid moves in the opposite direction, causing the cupula and stereocilia to bend. The movement of two canals within a plane results in information about the direction in which the head is moving, and activation of all six canals can give a very precise indication of head movement in three dimensions.

Somatosensation (Touch)

Somatosensation is considered a general sense, as opposed to the special senses discussed in this section. Somatosensation is the group of sensory modalities that are associated with touch, proprioception, and interoception. These modalities include pressure, vibration, light touch, tickle, itch, temperature, pain, proprioception, and kinesthesia. This means that its receptors are not associated with a specialized organ, but are instead spread throughout the body in a variety of organs. Many of the somatosensory receptors are located in the skin, but receptors are also found in muscles, tendons, joint capsules, ligaments, and in the walls of visceral organs.

Two types of somatosensory signals that are transduced by free nerve endings are pain and temperature. These two modalities use thermoreceptors and nociceptors to transduce temperature and pain stimuli, respectively. Temperature receptors are stimulated when local temperatures differ from body temperature. Some thermoreceptors are sensitive to just cold and others to just heat. Nociception is the sensation of potentially damaging stimuli. Mechanical, chemical, or thermal stimuli beyond a set threshold will elicit painful sensations. Stressed or damaged tissues release chemicals that activate receptor proteins in the nociceptors. For example, the sensation of heat associated with spicy foods involves **capsaicin**, the active molecule in hot peppers. Capsaicin molecules bind to a transmembrane ion channel in nociceptors that is sensitive to temperatures above 37°C. The dynamics of capsaicin binding with this transmembrane ion channel is unusual in that the molecule remains bound for a long time. Because of this, it will decrease the ability of other stimuli to elicit pain sensations through the activated nociceptor. For this reason, capsaicin can be used as a topical analgesic, such as in products such as Icy Hot™.

If you drag your finger across a textured surface, the skin of your finger will vibrate. Such low frequency vibrations are sensed by mechanoreceptors called Merkel cells, also known as type I cutaneous mechanoreceptors. Merkel cells are located in the stratum basale of the epidermis. Deep pressure and vibration is transduced by lamellated (Pacinian) corpuscles, which are receptors with encapsulated endings found deep in the dermis, or subcutaneous tissue. Light touch is transduced by the encapsulated endings known as tactile (Meissner) corpuscles. Follicles are also wrapped in a plexus of nerve endings known as the hair follicle plexus. These nerve endings detect the movement of hair at the surface of the skin, such as when an insect may be walking along the skin. Stretching of the skin is transduced by stretch receptors known as bulbous corpuscles. Bulbous corpuscles are also known as Ruffini corpuscles, or type II cutaneous mechanoreceptors.

Other somatosensory receptors are found in the joints and muscles. Stretch receptors monitor the stretching of tendons, muscles, and the components of joints. For example, have you ever stretched your muscles before or after exercise and noticed that you can only stretch so far before your muscles spasm back to a less stretched state? This spasm is a reflex that is initiated by stretch receptors to avoid muscle tearing. Such stretch receptors can also prevent over-contraction of a muscle. In skeletal muscle tissue, these stretch receptors are called muscle spindles.

Golgi tendon organs similarly transduce the stretch levels of tendons. Bulbous corpuscles are also present in joint capsules, where they measure stretch in the components of the skeletal system within the joint. The types of nerve endings, their locations, and the stimuli they transduce are presented in Table 14.1.

Mechanoreceptors of Somatosensation

Name	Historical (eponymous) name	Location(s)	Stimuli
Free nerve endings	*	Dermis, cornea, tongue, joint capsules, visceral organs	Pain, temperature, mechanical deformation
Mechanoreceptors	Merkel's discs	Epidermal–dermal junction, mucosal membranes	Low frequency vibration (5–15 Hz)
Bulbous corpuscle	Ruffini's corpuscle	Dermis, joint capsules	Stretch
Tactile corpuscle	Meissner's corpuscle	Papillary dermis, especially in the fingertips and lips	Light touch, vibrations below 50 Hz
Lamellated corpuscle	Pacinian corpuscle	Deep dermis, subcutaneous tissue	Deep pressure, high-frequency vibration (around 250 Hz)
Hair follicle plexus	*	Wrapped around hair follicles in the dermis	Movement of hair
Muscle spindle	*	In line with skeletal muscle fibers	Muscle contraction and stretch
Tendon stretch organ	Golgi tendon organ	In line with tendons	Stretch of tendons

TABLE 14.1 *No corresponding eponymous name.

Vision

Vision is the special sense of sight that is based on the transduction of light stimuli received through the eyes. The eyes are located within either orbit in the skull. The bony orbits surround the eyeballs, protecting them and anchoring the soft tissues of the eye (Figure 14.13). The eyelids, with lashes at their leading edges, help to protect the eye from abrasions by blocking particles that may land on the surface of the eye. The inner surface of each lid is a thin membrane known as the **palpebral conjunctiva**. The conjunctiva extends over the white areas of the eye (the sclera), connecting the eyelids to the eyeball. Tears are produced by the **lacrimal gland**, located just inside the orbit, superior and lateral to the eyeball. Tears produced by this gland flow through the **lacrimal duct** to the medial corner of the eye, where the tears flow over the conjunctiva, washing away foreign particles.

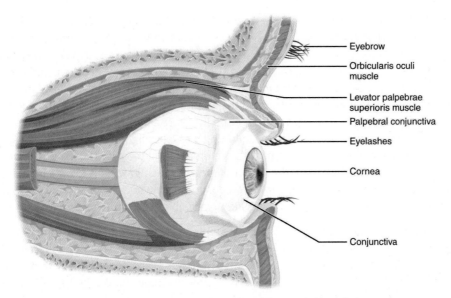

FIGURE 14.13 **The Eye in the Orbit**   The eye is located within the orbit and surrounded by soft tissues that protect and support its function. The orbit is surrounded by cranial bones of the skull.

Movement of the eye within the orbit is accomplished by the contraction of six **extraocular muscles** that originate from the bones of the orbit and insert into the surface of the eyeball (Figure 14.14). Four of the muscles are arranged at the cardinal points around the eye and are named for those locations. They are the **superior rectus**, **medial rectus**, **inferior rectus**, and **lateral rectus**. When each of these muscles contract, the eye moves toward the contracting muscle. For example, when the superior rectus contracts, the eye rotates to look up. The **superior oblique** originates at the posterior orbit, near the origin of the four rectus muscles. However, the tendon of the oblique muscles threads through a pulley-like piece of cartilage known as the **trochlea**. The tendon inserts obliquely into the superior surface of the eye. The angle of the tendon through the trochlea means that contraction of the superior oblique rotates the eye laterally. The **inferior oblique** muscle originates from the floor of the orbit and inserts into the inferolateral surface of the eye. When it contracts, it laterally rotates the eye, in opposition to the superior oblique. Rotation of the eye by the two oblique muscles is necessary because the eye is not perfectly aligned on the sagittal plane. When the eye looks up or down, the eye must also rotate slightly to compensate for the superior rectus pulling at approximately a 20-degree angle, rather than straight up. The same is true for the inferior rectus, which is compensated by contraction of the inferior oblique. A seventh muscle in the orbit is the **levator palpebrae superioris**, which is responsible for elevating and retracting the upper eyelid, a movement that usually occurs in concert with elevation of the eye by the superior rectus (see Figure 14.13).

The extraocular muscles are innervated by three cranial nerves. The lateral rectus, which causes abduction of the eye, is innervated by the abducens nerve. The superior oblique is innervated by the trochlear nerve. All of the other muscles are innervated by the oculomotor nerve, as is the levator palpebrae superioris. The motor nuclei of these cranial nerves connect to the brain stem, which coordinates eye movements.

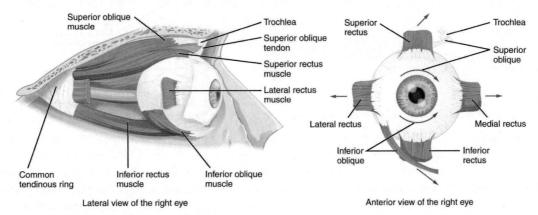

FIGURE 14.14 **Extraocular Muscles**   The extraocular muscles move the eye within the orbit.

The eye itself is a hollow sphere composed of three layers of tissue. The outermost layer is the **fibrous tunic**, which includes the white **sclera** and clear **cornea**. The sclera accounts for five sixths of the surface of the eye, most of which is not visible, though humans are unique compared with many other species in having so much of the "white of the eye" visible (Figure 14.15). The transparent cornea covers the anterior tip of the eye and allows light to enter the eye. The middle layer of the eye is the **vascular tunic**, which is mostly composed of the choroid, ciliary body, and iris. The **choroid** is a layer of highly vascularized connective tissue that provides a blood supply to the eyeball. The choroid is posterior to the **ciliary body**, a muscular structure that is attached to the **lens** by suspensory ligaments, or **zonule fibers**. These two structures bend the lens, allowing it to focus light on the back of the eye. Overlaying the ciliary body, and visible in the anterior eye, is the **iris**—the colored part of the eye. The iris is a smooth muscle that opens or closes the **pupil**, which is the hole at the center of the eye that allows light to enter. The iris constricts the pupil in response to bright light and dilates the pupil in response to dim light. The innermost layer of the eye is the **neural tunic**, or **retina**, which contains the nervous tissue responsible for photoreception.

The eye is also divided into two cavities: the anterior cavity and the posterior cavity. The anterior cavity is the space between the cornea and lens, including the iris and ciliary body. It is filled with a watery fluid called the **aqueous humor**. The posterior cavity is the space behind the lens that extends to the posterior side of the interior eyeball, where the retina is located. The posterior cavity is filled with a more viscous fluid called the **vitreous humor**.

The retina is composed of several layers and contains specialized cells for the initial processing of visual stimuli. The photoreceptors (rods and cones) change their membrane potential when stimulated by light energy. The change in membrane potential alters the amount of neurotransmitter that the photoreceptor cells release onto **bipolar cells** in the **outer synaptic layer**. It is the bipolar cell in the retina that connects a photoreceptor to a **retinal ganglion cell (RGC)** in the **inner synaptic layer**. There, **amacrine cells** additionally contribute to retinal processing before an action potential is produced by the RGC. The axons of RGCs, which lie at the innermost layer of the retina, collect at the **optic disc** and leave the eye as the **optic nerve** (see Figure 14.15). Because these axons pass through the retina, there are no photoreceptors at the very back of the eye, where the optic nerve begins. This creates a "blind spot" in the retina, and a corresponding blind spot in our visual field.

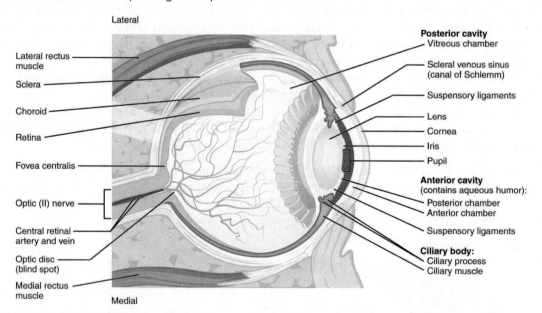

FIGURE 14.15 Structure of the Eye   The sphere of the eye can be divided into anterior and posterior chambers. The wall of the eye is composed of three layers: the fibrous tunic, vascular tunic, and neural tunic. Within the neural tunic is the retina, with three layers of cells and two synaptic layers in between. The center of the retina has a small indentation known as the fovea.

Note that the photoreceptors in the retina (rods and cones) are located behind the axons, RGCs, bipolar cells, and retinal blood vessels. A significant amount of light is absorbed by these structures before the light reaches the photoreceptor cells. However, at the exact center of the retina is a small area known as the **fovea**. At the fovea, the retina lacks the supporting cells and blood vessels, and only contains photoreceptors. Therefore, **visual acuity**, or the sharpness of vision, is greatest at the fovea. This is because the fovea is where the least amount of incoming light is absorbed by other retinal structures (see Figure 14.15). As one moves in either direction from this central point of the retina, visual acuity drops significantly. In addition, each photoreceptor cell of the fovea is connected to a single RGC. Therefore, this RGC does not have to integrate inputs from multiple photoreceptors, which reduces the accuracy of visual transduction. Toward the edges of the retina, several photoreceptors converge on RGCs (through the bipolar cells) up to a ratio of 50 to 1. The difference in visual acuity between the fovea and peripheral retina is easily evidenced by looking directly at a word in the middle of this paragraph. The visual stimulus in the middle of the field of view falls on the fovea and is in the sharpest focus. Without moving your eyes off that word, notice that words at the beginning or end of the paragraph are not in focus. The images in your peripheral vision are focused by the peripheral retina, and have vague, blurry edges and words that are not as clearly identified. As a result, a large part of the neural function of the eyes is concerned with moving the eyes and head so that important visual stimuli are centered on the fovea.

Light falling on the retina causes chemical changes to pigment molecules in the photoreceptors, ultimately leading to a change in the activity of the RGCs. Photoreceptor cells have two parts, the **inner segment** and the **outer segment** (Figure 14.16). The inner segment contains the nucleus and other common organelles of a cell, whereas the outer segment is a specialized region in which photoreception takes place. There are two types of photoreceptors—rods and cones—which differ in the shape of their outer segment. The rod-shaped outer segments of the **rod photoreceptor** contain a stack of membrane-bound discs that contain the photosensitive pigment **rhodopsin**. The cone-shaped outer segments of the **cone photoreceptor** contain their photosensitive pigments in infoldings of the cell membrane. There are three cone photopigments, called **opsins**, which are each sensitive to a particular wavelength of light. The wavelength of visible light determines its color. The pigments in human eyes are specialized in perceiving three different primary colors: red, green, and blue.

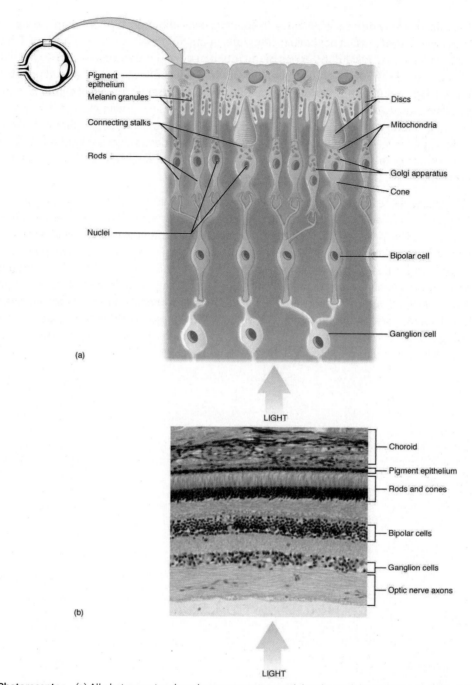

FIGURE 14.16 Photoreceptor   (a) All photoreceptors have inner segments containing the nucleus and other important organelles and outer segments with membrane arrays containing the photosensitive opsin molecules. Rod outer segments are long columnar shapes with stacks of membrane-bound discs that contain the rhodopsin pigment. Cone outer segments are short, tapered shapes with folds of membrane in place of the discs in the rods. (b) Tissue of the retina shows a dense layer of nuclei of the rods and cones. LM × 800. (Micrograph provided by the Regents of University of Michigan Medical School © 2012)

At the molecular level, visual stimuli cause changes in the photopigment molecule that lead to changes in membrane potential of the photoreceptor cell. A single unit of light is called a **photon**, which is described in physics as a packet of energy with properties of both a particle and a wave. The energy of a photon is represented by its wavelength, with each wavelength of visible light corresponding to a particular color. Visible light is electromagnetic radiation with a wavelength between 380 and 720 nm. Wavelengths of electromagnetic radiation longer than 720 nm fall into the infrared range, whereas wavelengths shorter than 380 nm fall into the ultraviolet range. Light with a wavelength of 380 nm is blue whereas light with a wavelength of 720 nm is dark red. All other colors fall between red and blue at various points along the wavelength scale.

Opsin pigments are actually transmembrane proteins that contain a cofactor known as **retinal**. Retinal is a

Access for free at openstax.org

hydrocarbon molecule related to vitamin A. When a photon hits retinal, the long hydrocarbon chain of the molecule is biochemically altered. Specifically, photons cause some of the double-bonded carbons within the chain to switch from a *cis* to a *trans* conformation. This process is called **photoisomerization**. Before interacting with a photon, retinal's flexible double-bonded carbons are in the *cis* conformation. This molecule is referred to as 11-*cis*-retinal. A photon interacting with the molecule causes the flexible double-bonded carbons to change to the *trans*-conformation, forming all-*trans*-retinal, which has a straight hydrocarbon chain (Figure 14.17).

The shape change of retinal in the photoreceptors initiates visual transduction in the retina. Activation of retinal and the opsin proteins result in activation of a G protein. The G protein changes the membrane potential of the photoreceptor cell, which then releases less neurotransmitter into the outer synaptic layer of the retina. Until the retinal molecule is changed back to the 11-*cis*-retinal shape, the opsin cannot respond to light energy, which is called bleaching. When a large group of photopigments is bleached, the retina will send information as if opposing visual information is being perceived. After a bright flash of light, afterimages are usually seen in negative. The photoisomerization is reversed by a series of enzymatic changes so that the retinal responds to more light energy.

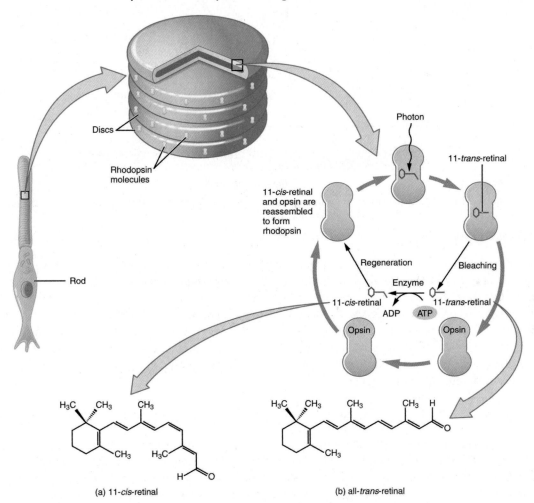

(a) 11-*cis*-retinal   (b) all-*trans*-retinal

FIGURE 14.17   Retinal Isomers   The retinal molecule has two isomers, (a) one before a photon interacts with it and (b) one that is altered through photoisomerization.

The opsins are sensitive to limited wavelengths of light. Rhodopsin, the photopigment in rods, is most sensitive to light at a wavelength of 498 nm. The three color opsins have peak sensitivities of 564 nm, 534 nm, and 420 nm corresponding roughly to the primary colors of red, green, and blue (Figure 14.18). The absorbance of rhodopsin in the rods is much more sensitive than in the cone opsins; specifically, rods are sensitive to vision in low light conditions, and cones are sensitive to brighter conditions. In normal sunlight, rhodopsin will be constantly bleached while the cones are active. In a darkened room, there is not enough light to activate cone opsins, and vision is entirely dependent on rods. Rods are so sensitive to light that a single photon can result in an action potential from a rod's corresponding RGC.

The three types of cone opsins, being sensitive to different wavelengths of light, provide us with color vision. By comparing the activity of the three different cones, the brain can extract color information from visual stimuli. For example, a bright blue light that has a wavelength of approximately 450 nm would activate the "red" cones minimally, the "green" cones marginally, and the "blue" cones predominantly. The relative activation of the three different cones is calculated by the brain, which perceives the color as blue. However, cones cannot react to low-intensity light, and rods do not sense the color of light. Therefore, our low-light vision is—in essence—in grayscale. In other words, in a dark room, everything appears as a shade of gray. If you think that you can see colors in the dark, it is most likely because your brain knows what color something is and is relying on that memory.

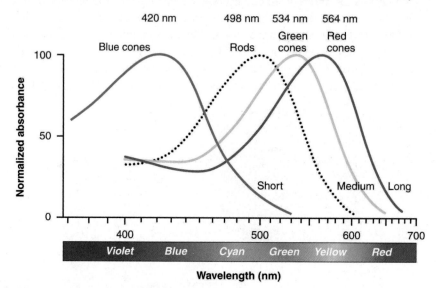

FIGURE 14.18 **Comparison of Color Sensitivity of Photopigments** Comparing the peak sensitivity and absorbance spectra of the four photopigments suggests that they are most sensitive to particular wavelengths.

⊚ INTERACTIVE LINK

Watch this video (http://openstax.org/l/occipital) to learn more about a transverse section through the brain that depicts the visual pathway from the eye to the occipital cortex. The first half of the pathway is the projection from the RGCs through the optic nerve to the lateral geniculate nucleus in the thalamus on either side. This first fiber in the pathway synapses on a thalamic cell that then projects to the visual cortex in the occipital lobe where "seeing," or visual perception, takes place. This video gives an abbreviated overview of the visual system by concentrating on the pathway from the eyes to the occipital lobe. The video makes the statement (at 0:45) that "specialized cells in the retina called ganglion cells convert the light rays into electrical signals." What aspect of retinal processing is simplified by that statement? Explain your answer.

Sensory Nerves

Once any sensory cell transduces a stimulus into a nerve impulse, that impulse has to travel along axons to reach the CNS. In many of the special senses, the axons leaving the sensory receptors have a **topographical** arrangement, meaning that the location of the sensory receptor relates to the location of the axon in the nerve. For example, in the retina, axons from RGCs in the fovea are located at the center of the optic nerve, where they are surrounded by axons from the more peripheral RGCs.

Spinal Nerves

Generally, spinal nerves contain afferent axons from sensory receptors in the periphery, such as from the skin, mixed with efferent axons travelling to the muscles or other effector organs. As the spinal nerve nears the spinal cord, it splits into dorsal and ventral roots. The dorsal root contains only the axons of sensory neurons, whereas the ventral roots contain only the axons of the motor neurons. Some of the branches will synapse with local neurons in the dorsal root ganglion, posterior (dorsal) horn, or even the anterior (ventral) horn, at the level of the spinal cord where they enter. Other branches will travel a short distance up or down the spine to interact with neurons at other levels of the spinal cord. A branch may also turn into the posterior (dorsal) column of the white matter to connect with the brain. For the sake of convenience, we will use the terms ventral and dorsal in reference to structures within the spinal cord that are part of these pathways. This will help to underscore the relationships between the different components. Typically, spinal nerve systems that connect to the brain are **contralateral**, in that the right side of the body is connected to the left side of the brain and the left side of the body to the right side of the brain.

Cranial Nerves

Cranial nerves convey specific sensory information from the head and neck directly to the brain. Whereas spinal information is contralateral, cranial nerve systems, with some exceptions, are mostly **ipsilateral**, meaning that a cranial nerve on the right side of the head is connected to the right side of the brain. Some cranial nerves contain only sensory axons, such as the olfactory, optic, and vestibulocochlear nerves. Other cranial nerves contain both sensory and motor axons, including the trigeminal, facial, glossopharyngeal, and vagus nerves (however, the vagus nerve is not associated with the somatic nervous system). The general senses of somatosensation for the face travel through the trigeminal system.

14.2 Central Processing

LEARNING OBJECTIVES

By the end of this section, you will be able to:

- Describe the pathways that sensory systems follow into the central nervous system
- Differentiate between the two major ascending pathways in the spinal cord
- Describe the pathway of somatosensory input from the face and compare it to the ascending pathways in the spinal cord
- Explain topographical representations of sensory information in at least two systems
- Describe two pathways of visual processing and the functions associated with each

Sensory Pathways

Specific regions of the CNS coordinate different somatic processes using sensory inputs and motor outputs of peripheral nerves. A simple case is a reflex caused by a synapse between a dorsal sensory neuron axon and a motor neuron in the ventral horn. More complex arrangements are possible to integrate peripheral sensory information with higher processes. The important regions of the CNS that play a role in somatic processes can be separated into the spinal cord brain stem, diencephalon, cerebral cortex, and subcortical structures.

Spinal Cord and Brain Stem

A sensory pathway that carries peripheral sensations to the brain is referred to as an **ascending pathway**, or ascending tract. The various sensory modalities each follow specific pathways through the CNS. Tactile and other somatosensory stimuli activate receptors in the skin, muscles, tendons, and joints throughout the entire body. However, the somatosensory pathways are divided into two separate systems on the basis of the location of the receptor neurons. Somatosensory stimuli from below the neck pass along the sensory pathways of the spinal cord, whereas somatosensory stimuli from the head and neck travel through the cranial nerves—specifically, the trigeminal system.

The **dorsal column system** (sometimes referred to as the dorsal column–medial lemniscus) and the **spinothalamic tract** are two major pathways that bring sensory information to the brain (Figure 14.19). The sensory pathways in each of these systems are composed of three successive neurons.

The dorsal column system begins with the axon of a dorsal root ganglion neuron entering the dorsal root and joining the dorsal column white matter in the spinal cord. As axons of this pathway enter the dorsal column, they take on a positional arrangement so that axons from lower levels of the body position themselves medially, whereas axons from upper levels of the body position themselves laterally. The dorsal column is separated into two component tracts, the **fasciculus gracilis** that contains axons from the legs and lower body, and the **fasciculus cuneatus** that contains axons from the upper body and arms.

The axons in the dorsal column terminate in the nuclei of the medulla, where each synapses with the second neuron in their respective pathway. The **nucleus gracilis** is the target of fibers in the fasciculus gracilis, whereas the **nucleus cuneatus** is the target of fibers in the fasciculus cuneatus. The second neuron in the system projects from one of the two nuclei and then **decussates**, or crosses the midline of the medulla. These axons then continue to ascend the brain stem as a bundle called the **medial lemniscus**. These axons terminate in the thalamus, where each synapses with the third neuron in their respective pathway. The third neuron in the system projects its axons to the postcentral gyrus of the cerebral cortex, where somatosensory stimuli are initially processed and the conscious perception of the stimulus occurs.

The spinothalamic tract also begins with neurons in a dorsal root ganglion. These neurons extend their axons to the dorsal horn, where they synapse with the second neuron in their respective pathway. The name "spinothalamic" comes from this second neuron, which has its cell body in the spinal cord gray matter and connects to the thalamus. Axons from these second neurons then decussate within the spinal cord and ascend to the brain and enter the thalamus, where each synapses with the third neuron in its respective pathway. The neurons in the thalamus then project their axons to the spinothalamic tract, which synapses in the postcentral gyrus of the cerebral cortex.

These two systems are similar in that they both begin with dorsal root ganglion cells, as with most general sensory information. The dorsal column system is primarily responsible for touch sensations and proprioception, whereas the spinothalamic tract pathway is primarily responsible for pain and temperature sensations. Another similarity is that the second neurons in both of these pathways are contralateral, because they project across the midline to the other side of the brain or spinal cord. In the dorsal column system, this decussation takes place in the brain stem; in the spinothalamic pathway, it takes place in the spinal cord at the same spinal cord level at which the information entered. The third neurons in the two pathways are essentially the same. In both, the second neuron synapses in the thalamus, and the thalamic neuron projects to the somatosensory cortex.

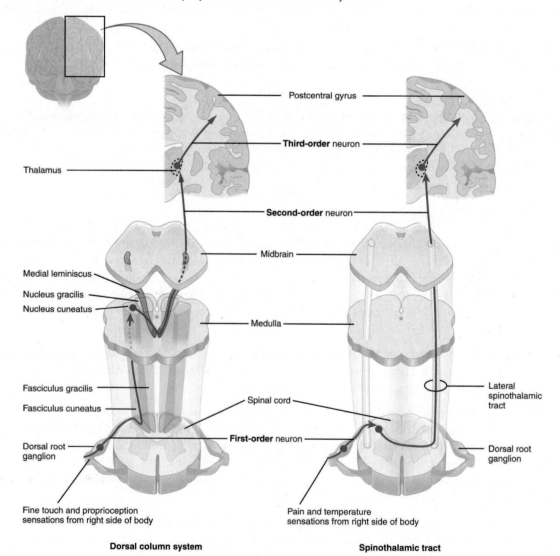

FIGURE 14.19 Anterior View of Ascending Sensory Pathways of the Spinal Cord   The dorsal column system and spinothalamic tract are the major ascending pathways that connect the periphery with the brain.

The trigeminal pathway carries somatosensory information from the face, head, mouth, and nasal cavity. As with the previously discussed nerve tracts, the sensory pathways of the trigeminal pathway each involve three successive neurons. First, axons from the trigeminal ganglion enter the brain stem at the level of the pons. These axons project to one of three locations. The **spinal trigeminal nucleus** of the medulla receives information similar to that carried by spinothalamic tract, such as pain and temperature sensations. Other axons go to either the **chief sensory nucleus** in the pons or the **mesencephalic nuclei** in the midbrain. These nuclei receive information like that carried by the dorsal column system, such as touch, pressure, vibration, and proprioception. Axons from the second neuron decussate and ascend to the thalamus along the trigeminothalamic tract. In the thalamus, each axon synapses with the third neuron in its respective pathway. Axons from the third neuron then project from the thalamus to the primary somatosensory cortex of the cerebrum.

The sensory pathway for gustation travels along the facial and glossopharyngeal cranial nerves, which synapse with neurons of the **solitary nucleus** in the brain stem. Axons from the solitary nucleus then project to the **ventral posterior nucleus** of the thalamus. Finally, axons from the ventral posterior nucleus project to the gustatory cortex of the cerebral cortex, where taste is processed and consciously perceived.

The sensory pathway for audition travels along the vestibulocochlear nerve, which synapses with neurons in the cochlear nuclei of the superior medulla. Within the brain stem, input from either ear is combined to extract location information from the auditory stimuli. Whereas the initial auditory stimuli received at the cochlea strictly represent the frequency—or pitch—of the stimuli, the locations of sounds can be determined by comparing information arriving at both ears.

Sound localization is a feature of central processing in the auditory nuclei of the brain stem. Sound localization is achieved by the brain calculating the **interaural time difference** and the **interaural intensity difference**. A sound originating from a specific location will arrive at each ear at different times, unless the sound is directly in front of the listener. If the sound source is slightly to the left of the listener, the sound will arrive at the left ear microseconds before it arrives at the right ear (Figure 14.20). This time difference is an example of an interaural time difference. Also, the sound will be slightly louder in the left ear than in the right ear because some of the sound waves reaching the opposite ear are blocked by the head. This is an example of an interaural intensity difference.

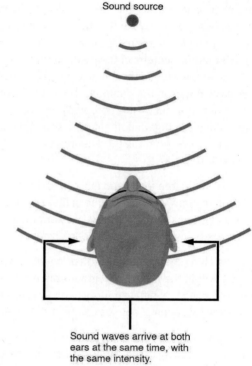

Sound source

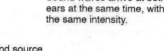

Sound waves arrive at both ears at the same time, with the same intensity.

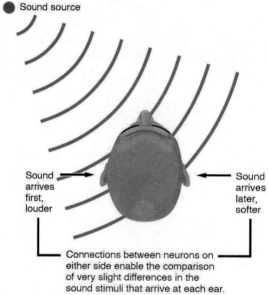

Sound source

Sound arrives first, louder

Sound arrives later, softer

Connections between neurons on either side enable the comparison of very slight differences in the sound stimuli that arrive at each ear.

FIGURE 14.20   Auditory Brain Stem Mechanisms of Sound Localization   Localizing sound in the horizontal plane is achieved by processing in the medullary nuclei of the auditory system. Connections between neurons on either side are able to compare very slight differences in sound stimuli that arrive at either ear and represent interaural time and intensity differences.

Auditory processing continues on to a nucleus in the midbrain called the **inferior colliculus**. Axons from the inferior colliculus project to two locations, the thalamus and the **superior colliculus**. The **medial geniculate nucleus** of the thalamus receives the auditory information and then projects that information to the auditory cortex in the temporal lobe of the cerebral cortex. The superior colliculus receives input from the visual and somatosensory systems, as well as the ears, to initiate stimulation of the muscles that turn the head and neck toward the auditory stimulus.

Balance is coordinated through the vestibular system, the nerves of which are composed of axons from the vestibular ganglion that carries information from the utricle, saccule, and semicircular canals. The system contributes to controlling head and neck movements in response to vestibular signals. An important function of the vestibular system is coordinating eye and head movements to maintain visual attention. Most of the axons terminate in the **vestibular nuclei** of the medulla. Some axons project from the vestibular ganglion directly to the cerebellum, with no intervening synapse in the vestibular nuclei. The cerebellum is primarily responsible for initiating movements on the basis of equilibrium information.

Neurons in the vestibular nuclei project their axons to targets in the brain stem. One target is the reticular formation, which influences respiratory and cardiovascular functions in relation to body movements. A second target of the axons of neurons in the vestibular nuclei is the spinal cord, which initiates the spinal reflexes involved with posture and balance. To assist the visual system, fibers of the vestibular nuclei project to the oculomotor, trochlear, and abducens nuclei to influence signals sent along the cranial nerves. These connections constitute the pathway of the **vestibulo-ocular reflex (VOR)**, which compensates for head and body movement by stabilizing images on the retina (Figure 14.21). Finally, the vestibular nuclei project to the thalamus to join the proprioceptive pathway of the dorsal column system, allowing conscious perception of equilibrium.

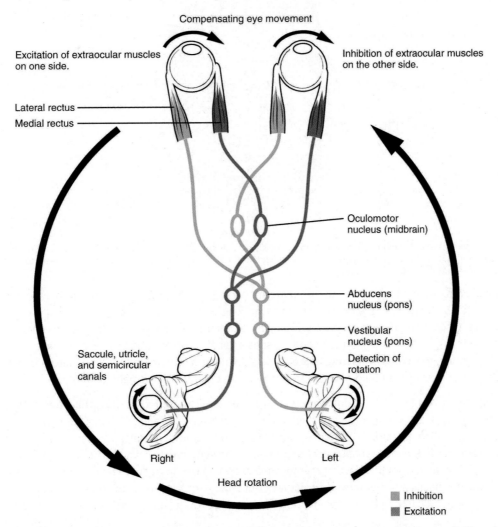

FIGURE 14.21   Vestibulo-ocular Reflex   Connections between the vestibular system and the cranial nerves controlling eye movement keep the eyes centered on a visual stimulus, even though the head is moving. During head movement, the eye muscles move the eyes in the opposite direction as the head movement, keeping the visual stimulus centered in the field of view.

The connections of the optic nerve are more complicated than those of other cranial nerves. Instead of the connections being between each eye and the brain, visual information is segregated between the left and right sides of the visual field. In addition, some of the information from one side of the visual field projects to the opposite side of the brain. Within each eye, the axons projecting from the medial side of the retina decussate at the **optic chiasm**. For example, the axons from the medial retina of the left eye cross over to the right side of the brain at the optic chiasm. However, within each eye, the axons projecting from the lateral side of the retina do not decussate. For example, the axons from the lateral retina of the right eye project back to the right side of the brain. Therefore the left field of view of each eye is processed on the right side of the brain, whereas the right field of view of each eye is processed on the left side of the brain (Figure 14.22).

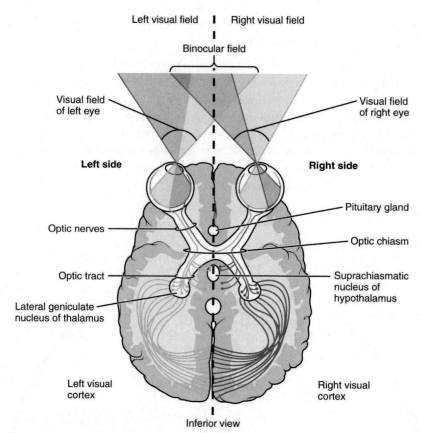

FIGURE 14.22 Segregation of Visual Field Information at the Optic Chiasm   Contralateral visual field information from the lateral retina projects to the ipsilateral brain, whereas ipsilateral visual field information has to decussate at the optic chiasm to reach the opposite side of the brain. (Note that this is an inferior view.)

A unique clinical presentation that relates to this anatomic arrangement is the loss of lateral peripheral vision, known as bilateral hemianopia. This is different from "tunnel vision" because the superior and inferior peripheral fields are not lost. Visual field deficits can be disturbing for a patient, but in this case, the cause is not within the visual system itself. A growth of the pituitary gland presses against the optic chiasm and interferes with signal transmission. However, the axons projecting to the same side of the brain are unaffected. Therefore, the patient loses the outermost areas of their field of vision and cannot see objects to their right and left.

Extending from the optic chiasm, the axons of the visual system are referred to as the **optic tract** instead of the optic nerve. The optic tract has three major targets, two in the diencephalon and one in the midbrain. The connection between the eyes and diencephalon is demonstrated during development, in which the neural tissue of the retina differentiates from that of the diencephalon by the growth of the secondary vesicles. The connections of the retina into the CNS are a holdover from this developmental association. The majority of the connections of the optic tract are to the thalamus—specifically, the **lateral geniculate nucleus**. Axons from this nucleus then project to the visual cortex of the cerebrum, located in the occipital lobe. Another target of the optic tract is the superior colliculus.

In addition, a very small number of RGC axons project from the optic chiasm to the **suprachiasmatic nucleus** of the hypothalamus. These RGCs are photosensitive, in that they respond to the presence or absence of light. Unlike the photoreceptors, however, these photosensitive RGCs cannot be used to perceive images. By simply responding to the absence or presence of light, these RGCs can send information about day length. The perceived proportion of sunlight to darkness establishes the **circadian rhythm** of our bodies, allowing certain physiological events to occur at approximately the same time every day.

Diencephalon

The diencephalon is beneath the cerebrum and includes the thalamus and hypothalamus. In the somatic nervous system, the thalamus is an important relay for communication between the cerebrum and the rest of the nervous system. The hypothalamus has both somatic and autonomic functions. In addition, the hypothalamus communicates with the limbic system, which controls emotions and memory functions.

Sensory input to the thalamus comes from most of the special senses and ascending somatosensory tracts. Each sensory system is relayed through a particular nucleus in the thalamus. The thalamus is a required transfer point for most sensory tracts that reach the cerebral cortex, where conscious sensory perception begins. The one exception to this rule is the olfactory system. The olfactory tract axons from the olfactory bulb project directly to the cerebral cortex, along with the limbic system and hypothalamus.

The thalamus is a collection of several nuclei that can be categorized into three anatomical groups. White matter running through the thalamus defines the three major regions of the thalamus, which are an anterior nucleus, a medial nucleus, and a lateral group of nuclei. The anterior nucleus serves as a relay between the hypothalamus and the emotion and memory-producing limbic system. The medial nuclei serve as a relay for information from the limbic system and basal ganglia to the cerebral cortex. This allows memory creation during learning, but also determines alertness. The special and somatic senses connect to the lateral nuclei, where their information is relayed to the appropriate sensory cortex of the cerebrum.

Cortical Processing

As described earlier, many of the sensory axons are positioned in the same way as their corresponding receptor cells in the body. This allows identification of the position of a stimulus on the basis of which receptor cells are sending information. The cerebral cortex also maintains this sensory topography in the particular areas of the cortex that correspond to the position of the receptor cells. The somatosensory cortex provides an example in which, in essence, the locations of the somatosensory receptors in the body are mapped onto the somatosensory cortex. This mapping is often depicted using a **sensory homunculus** (Figure 14.23).

The term homunculus comes from the Latin word for "little man" and refers to a map of the human body that is laid across a portion of the cerebral cortex. In the somatosensory cortex, the external genitals, feet, and lower legs are represented on the medial face of the gyrus within the longitudinal fissure. As the gyrus curves out of the fissure and along the surface of the parietal lobe, the body map continues through the thighs, hips, trunk, shoulders, arms, and hands. The head and face are just lateral to the fingers as the gyrus approaches the lateral sulcus. The representation of the body in this topographical map is medial to lateral from the lower to upper body. It is a continuation of the topographical arrangement seen in the dorsal column system, where axons from the lower body are carried in the fasciculus gracilis, whereas axons from the upper body are carried in the fasciculus cuneatus. As the dorsal column system continues into the medial lemniscus, these relationships are maintained. Also, the head and neck axons running from the trigeminal nuclei to the thalamus run adjacent to the upper body fibers. The connections through the thalamus maintain topography such that the anatomic information is preserved. Note that this correspondence does not result in a perfectly miniature scale version of the body, but rather exaggerates the more sensitive areas of the body, such as the fingers and lower face. Less sensitive areas of the body, such as the shoulders and back, are mapped to smaller areas on the cortex.

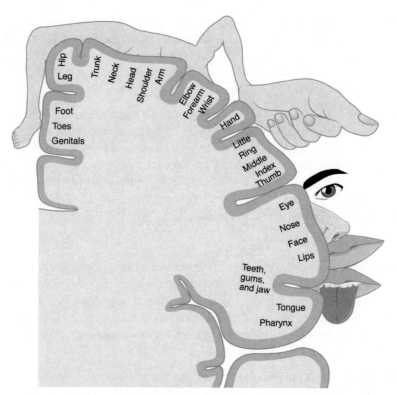

FIGURE 14.23 The Sensory Homunculus   A cartoon representation of the sensory homunculus arranged adjacent to the cortical region in which the processing takes place.

Likewise, the topographic relationship between the retina and the visual cortex is maintained throughout the visual pathway. The visual field is projected onto the two retinae, as described above, with sorting at the optic chiasm. The right peripheral visual field falls on the medial portion of the right retina and the lateral portion of the left retina. The right medial retina then projects across the midline through the optic chiasm. This results in the right visual field being processed in the left visual cortex. Likewise, the left visual field is processed in the right visual cortex (see Figure 14.22). Though the chiasm is helping to sort right and left visual information, superior and inferior visual information is maintained topographically in the visual pathway. Light from the superior visual field falls on the inferior retina, and light from the inferior visual field falls on the superior retina. This topography is maintained such that the superior region of the visual cortex processes the inferior visual field and vice versa. Therefore, the visual field information is inverted and reversed as it enters the visual cortex—up is down, and left is right. However, the cortex processes the visual information such that the final conscious perception of the visual field is correct. The topographic relationship is evident in that information from the foveal region of the retina is processed in the center of the primary visual cortex. Information from the peripheral regions of the retina are correspondingly processed toward the edges of the visual cortex. Similar to the exaggerations in the sensory homunculus of the somatosensory cortex, the foveal-processing area of the visual cortex is disproportionately larger than the areas processing peripheral vision.

In an experiment performed in the 1960s, subjects wore prism glasses so that the visual field was inverted before reaching the eye. On the first day of the experiment, subjects would duck when walking up to a table, thinking it was suspended from the ceiling. However, after a few days of acclimation, the subjects behaved as if everything were represented correctly. Therefore, the visual cortex is somewhat flexible in adapting to the information it receives from our eyes (Figure 14.24).

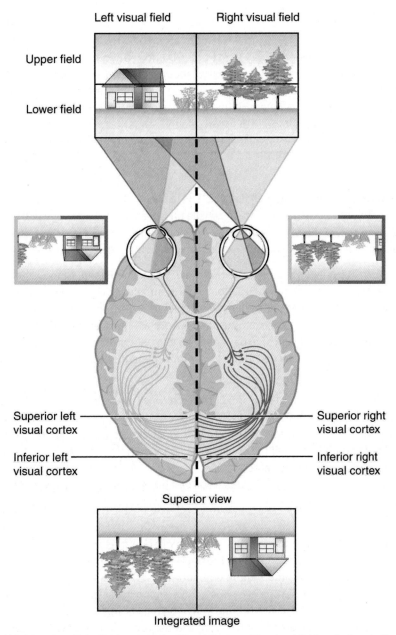

FIGURE 14.24 Topographic Mapping of the Retina onto the Visual Cortex   The visual field projects onto the retina through the lenses and falls on the retinae as an inverted, reversed image. The topography of this image is maintained as the visual information travels through the visual pathway to the cortex.

The cortex has been described as having specific regions that are responsible for processing specific information; there is the visual cortex, somatosensory cortex, gustatory cortex, etc. However, our experience of these senses is not divided. Instead, we experience what can be referred to as a seamless percept. Our perceptions of the various sensory modalities—though distinct in their content—are integrated by the brain so that we experience the world as a continuous whole.

In the cerebral cortex, sensory processing begins at the **primary sensory cortex**, then proceeds to an **association area**, and finally, into a **multimodal integration area**. For example, the visual pathway projects from the retinae through the thalamus to the primary visual cortex in the occipital lobe. This area is primarily in the medial wall within the longitudinal fissure. Here, visual stimuli begin to be recognized as basic shapes. Edges of objects are recognized and built into more complex shapes. Also, inputs from both eyes are compared to extract depth information. Because of the overlapping field of view between the two eyes, the brain can begin to estimate the distance of stimuli based on **binocular depth cues**.

🔗 INTERACTIVE LINK

Watch this video (http://openstax.org/l/l_3-D1) to learn more about how the brain perceives 3-D motion. Similar to how retinal disparity offers 3-D moviegoers a way to extract 3-D information from the two-dimensional visual field projected onto the retina, the brain can extract information about movement in space by comparing what the two eyes see. If movement of a visual stimulus is leftward in one eye and rightward in the opposite eye, the brain interprets this as movement toward (or away) from the face along the midline. If both eyes see an object moving in the same direction, but at different rates, what would that mean for spatial movement?

Everyday Connection

Depth Perception, 3-D Movies, and Optical Illusions

The visual field is projected onto the retinal surface, where photoreceptors transduce light energy into neural signals for the brain to interpret. The retina is a two-dimensional surface, so it does not encode three-dimensional information. However, we can perceive depth. How is that accomplished?

Two ways in which we can extract depth information from the two-dimensional retinal signal are based on monocular cues and binocular cues, respectively. Monocular depth cues are those that are the result of information within the two-dimensional visual field. One object that overlaps another object has to be in front. Relative size differences are also a cue. For example, if a basketball appears larger than the basket, then the basket must be further away. On the basis of experience, we can estimate how far away the basket is. Binocular depth cues compare information represented in the two retinae because they do not see the visual field exactly the same.

The centers of the two eyes are separated by a small distance, which is approximately 6 to 6.5 cm in most people. Because of this offset, visual stimuli do not fall on exactly the same spot on both retinae unless we are fixated directly on them and they fall on the fovea of each retina. All other objects in the visual field, either closer or farther away than the fixated object, will fall on different spots on the retina. When vision is fixed on an object in space, closer objects will fall on the lateral retina of each eye, and more distant objects will fall on the medial retina of either eye (Figure 14.25). This is easily observed by holding a finger up in front of your face as you look at a more distant object. You will see two images of your finger that represent the two disparate images that are falling on either retina.

These depth cues, both monocular and binocular, can be exploited to make the brain think there are three dimensions in two-dimensional information. This is the basis of 3-D movies. The projected image on the screen is two dimensional, but it has disparate information embedded in it. The 3-D glasses that are available at the theater filter the information so that only one eye sees one version of what is on the screen, and the other eye sees the other version. If you take the glasses off, the image on the screen will have varying amounts of blur because both eyes are seeing both layers of information, and the third dimension will not be evident. Some optical illusions can take advantage of depth cues as well, though those are more often using monocular cues to fool the brain into seeing different parts of the scene as being at different depths.

FIGURE 14.25 Retinal Disparity Because of the interocular distance, which results in objects of different distances falling on different spots of the two retinae, the brain can extract depth perception from the two-dimensional information of the visual field.

There are two main regions that surround the primary cortex that are usually referred to as areas V2 and V3 (the primary visual cortex is area V1). These surrounding areas are the visual association cortex. The visual association regions develop more complex visual perceptions by adding color and motion information. The information processed in these areas is then sent to regions of the temporal and parietal lobes. Visual processing has two separate streams of processing: one into the temporal lobe and one into the parietal lobe. These are the ventral and dorsal streams, respectively (Figure 14.26). The **ventral stream** identifies visual stimuli and their significance. Because the ventral stream uses temporal lobe structures, it begins to interact with the non-visual cortex and may be important in visual stimuli becoming part of memories. The **dorsal stream** locates objects in space and helps in guiding movements of the body in response to visual inputs. The dorsal stream enters the parietal lobe, where it interacts with somatosensory cortical areas that are important for our perception of the body and its movements. The dorsal stream can then influence frontal lobe activity where motor functions originate.

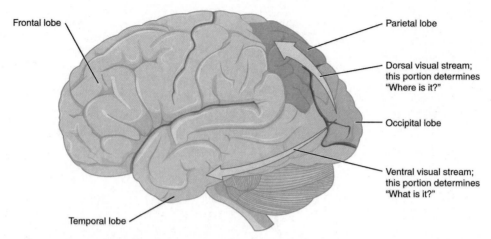

Labels: Frontal lobe, Parietal lobe, Dorsal visual stream; this portion determines "Where is it?", Occipital lobe, Ventral visual stream; this portion determines "What is it?", Temporal lobe

FIGURE 14.26 Ventral and Dorsal Visual Streams   From the primary visual cortex in the occipital lobe, visual processing continues in two streams—one into the temporal lobe and one into the parietal lobe.

Disorders of the...

Brain: Prosopagnosia

The failures of sensory perception can be unusual and debilitating. A particular sensory deficit that inhibits an important social function of humans is prosopagnosia, or face blindness. The word comes from the Greek words prosopa, that means "faces," and agnosia, that means "not knowing." Some people may feel that they cannot recognize people easily by their faces. However, a person with prosopagnosia cannot recognize the most recognizable people in their respective cultures. They would not recognize the face of a celebrity, an important historical figure, or even a family member like their mother. They may not even recognize their own face.

Prosopagnosia can be caused by trauma to the brain, or it can be present from birth. The exact cause of proposagnosia and the reason that it happens to some people is unclear. A study of the brains of people born with the deficit found that a specific region of the brain, the anterior fusiform gyrus of the temporal lobe, is often underdeveloped. This region of the brain is concerned with the recognition of visual stimuli and its possible association with memories. Though the evidence is not yet definitive, this region is likely to be where facial recognition occurs.

Though this can be a devastating condition, people who suffer from it can get by—often by using other cues to recognize the people they see. Often, the sound of a person's voice, or the presence of unique cues such as distinct facial features (a mole, for example) or hair color can help the sufferer recognize a familiar person. In the video on prosopagnosia provided in this section, a woman is shown having trouble recognizing celebrities, family members, and herself. In some situations, she can use other cues to help her recognize faces.

🔗 INTERACTIVE LINK

The inability to recognize people by their faces is a troublesome problem. It can be caused by trauma, or it may be inborn. Watch this video (http://openstax.org/l/faces) to learn more about a person who lost the ability to recognize faces as the result of an injury. She cannot recognize the faces of close family members or herself. What other information can a person suffering from prosopagnosia use to figure out whom they are seeing?

14.3 Motor Responses

LEARNING OBJECTIVES

By the end of this section, you will be able to:
- List the components of the basic processing stream for the motor system
- Describe the pathway of descending motor commands from the cortex to the skeletal muscles
- Compare different descending pathways, both by structure and function
- Explain the initiation of movement from the neurological connections
- Describe several reflex arcs and their functional roles

The defining characteristic of the somatic nervous system is that it controls skeletal muscles. Somatic senses inform the nervous system about the external environment, but the response to that is through voluntary muscle movement. The term "voluntary" suggests that there is a conscious decision to make a movement. However, some aspects of the somatic system use voluntary muscles without conscious control. One example is the ability of our breathing to switch to unconscious control while we are focused on another task. However, the muscles that are responsible for the basic process of breathing are also utilized for speech, which is entirely voluntary.

Cortical Responses

Let's start with sensory stimuli that have been registered through receptor cells and the information relayed to the CNS along ascending pathways. In the cerebral cortex, the initial processing of sensory perception progresses to associative processing and then integration in multimodal areas of cortex. These levels of processing can lead to the incorporation of sensory perceptions into memory, but more importantly, they lead to a response. The completion of cortical processing through the primary, associative, and integrative sensory areas initiates a similar progression of motor processing, usually in different cortical areas.

Whereas the sensory cortical areas are located in the occipital, temporal, and parietal lobes, motor functions are largely controlled by the frontal lobe (See Figure 13.7). The most anterior regions of the frontal lobe—the prefrontal areas—are important for **executive functions**, which are those cognitive functions that lead to goal-directed behaviors. These higher cognitive processes include **working memory**, which has been called a "mental scratch pad," that can help organize and represent information that is not in the immediate environment. The prefrontal lobe is responsible for aspects of attention, such as inhibiting distracting thoughts and actions so that a person can focus on a goal and direct behavior toward achieving that goal.

The functions of the prefrontal cortex are integral to the personality of an individual, because it is largely responsible for what a person intends to do and how they accomplish those plans. A famous case of damage to the prefrontal cortex is that of Phineas Gage, dating back to 1848. He was a railroad worker who had a metal spike impale his prefrontal cortex (Figure 14.27). He survived the accident, but according to second-hand accounts, his personality changed drastically. Friends described him as no longer acting like himself. Whereas he was a hardworking, amiable man before the accident, he turned into an irritable, temperamental, and lazy man after the accident. Many of the accounts of his change may have been inflated in the retelling, and some behavior was likely attributable to alcohol used as a pain medication. However, the accounts suggest that some aspects of his personality did change. Also, there is new evidence that though his life changed dramatically, he was able to become a functioning stagecoach driver, suggesting that the brain has the ability to recover even from major trauma such as this.

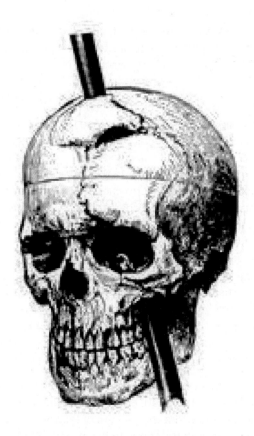

FIGURE 14.27 **Phineas Gage** The victim of an accident while working on a railroad in 1848, Phineas Gage had a large iron rod impaled through the prefrontal cortex of his frontal lobe. After the accident, his personality appeared to change, but he eventually learned to cope with the trauma and lived as a coach driver even after such a traumatic event. (credit b: John M. Harlow, MD)

Secondary Motor Cortices

In generating motor responses, the executive functions of the prefrontal cortex will need to initiate actual movements. One way to define the prefrontal area is any region of the frontal lobe that does not elicit movement when electrically stimulated. These are primarily in the anterior part of the frontal lobe. The regions of the frontal lobe that remain are the regions of the cortex that produce movement. The prefrontal areas project into the secondary motor cortices, which include the **premotor cortex** and the **supplemental motor area**.

Two important regions that assist in planning and coordinating movements are located adjacent to the primary motor cortex. The premotor cortex is more lateral, whereas the supplemental motor area is more medial and superior. The premotor area aids in controlling movements of the core muscles to maintain posture during movement, whereas the supplemental motor area is hypothesized to be responsible for planning and coordinating movement. The supplemental motor area also manages sequential movements that are based on prior experience (that is, learned movements). Neurons in these areas are most active leading up to the initiation of movement. For example, these areas might prepare the body for the movements necessary to drive a car in anticipation of a traffic light changing.

Adjacent to these two regions are two specialized motor planning centers. The **frontal eye fields** are responsible for moving the eyes in response to visual stimuli. There are direct connections between the frontal eye fields and the superior colliculus. Also, anterior to the premotor cortex and primary motor cortex is **Broca's area**. This area is responsible for controlling movements of the structures of speech production. The area is named after a French surgeon and anatomist who studied patients who could not produce speech. They did not have impairments to understanding speech, only to producing speech sounds, suggesting a damaged or underdeveloped Broca's area.

Primary Motor Cortex

The primary motor cortex is located in the precentral gyrus of the frontal lobe. A neurosurgeon, Walter Penfield, described much of the basic understanding of the primary motor cortex by electrically stimulating the surface of the cerebrum. Penfield would probe the surface of the cortex while the patient was only under local anesthesia so that he could observe responses to the stimulation. This led to the belief that the precentral gyrus directly stimulated muscle movement. We now know that the primary motor cortex receives input from several areas that aid in planning movement, and its principle output stimulates spinal cord neurons to stimulate skeletal muscle contraction.

The primary motor cortex is arranged in a similar fashion to the primary somatosensory cortex, in that it has a topographical map of the body, creating a motor homunculus (see Figure 14.23). The neurons responsible for musculature in the feet and lower legs are in the medial wall of the precentral gyrus, with the thighs, trunk, and shoulder at the crest of the longitudinal fissure. The hand and face are in the lateral face of the gyrus. Also, the relative space allotted for the different regions is exaggerated in muscles that have greater enervation. The greatest amount of cortical space is given to muscles that perform fine, agile movements, such as the muscles of the fingers and the lower face. The "power muscles" that perform coarser movements, such as the buttock and back muscles, occupy much less space on the motor cortex.

Descending Pathways

The motor output from the cortex descends into the brain stem and to the spinal cord to control the musculature through motor neurons. Neurons located in the primary motor cortex, named **Betz cells**, are large cortical neurons that synapse with lower motor neurons in the brain stem or in the spinal cord. The two descending pathways travelled by the axons of Betz cells are the **corticobulbar tract** and the **corticospinal tract**, respectively. Both tracts are named for their origin in the cortex and their targets—either the brain stem (the term "bulbar" refers to the brain stem as the bulb, or enlargement, at the top of the spinal cord) or the spinal cord.

These two descending pathways are responsible for the conscious or voluntary movements of skeletal muscles. Any motor command from the primary motor cortex is sent down the axons of the Betz cells to activate lower motor neurons in either the cranial motor nuclei or in the ventral horn of the spinal cord. The axons of the corticobulbar tract are ipsilateral, meaning they project from the cortex to the motor nucleus on the same side of the nervous system. Conversely, the axons of the corticospinal tract are largely contralateral, meaning that they cross the midline of the brain stem or spinal cord and synapse on the opposite side of the body. Therefore, the right motor cortex of the cerebrum controls muscles on the left side of the body, and vice versa.

The corticospinal tract descends from the cortex through the deep white matter of the cerebrum. It then passes between the caudate nucleus and putamen of the basal nuclei as a bundle called the **internal capsule**. The tract then passes through the midbrain as the **cerebral peduncles**, after which it burrows through the pons. Upon entering the medulla, the tracts make up the large white matter tract referred to as the **pyramids** (Figure 14.28). The defining landmark of the medullary-spinal border is the **pyramidal decussation**, which is where most of the fibers in the corticospinal tract cross over to the opposite side of the brain. At this point, the tract separates into two parts, which have control over different domains of the musculature.

Access for free at openstax.org

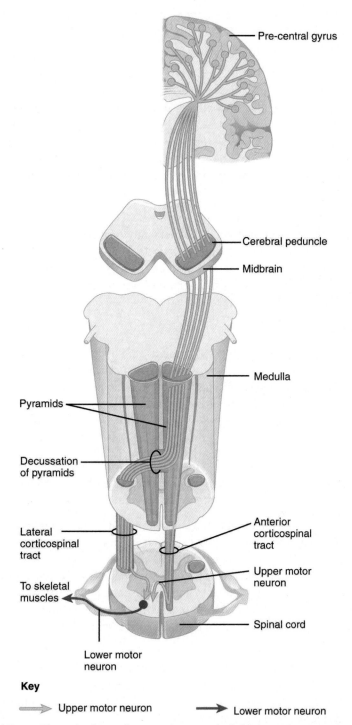

Pre-central gyrus

Cerebral peduncle

Midbrain

Medulla

Pyramids

Decussation of pyramids

Lateral corticospinal tract

Anterior corticospinal tract

Upper motor neuron

To skeletal muscles

Lower motor neuron

Spinal cord

Key

⟶ Upper motor neuron   ⟶ Lower motor neuron

FIGURE 14.28 Corticospinal Tract The major descending tract that controls skeletal muscle movements is the corticospinal tract. It is composed of two neurons, the upper motor neuron and the lower motor neuron. The upper motor neuron has its cell body in the primary motor cortex of the frontal lobe and synapses on the lower motor neuron, which is in the ventral horn of the spinal cord and projects to the skeletal muscle in the periphery.

Appendicular Control

The **lateral corticospinal tract** is composed of the fibers that cross the midline at the pyramidal decussation (see Figure 14.28). The axons cross over from the anterior position of the pyramids in the medulla to the lateral column of the spinal cord. These axons are responsible for controlling appendicular muscles.

This influence over the appendicular muscles means that the lateral corticospinal tract is responsible for moving the muscles of the arms and legs. The ventral horn in both the lower cervical spinal cord and the lumbar spinal cord both have wider ventral horns, representing the greater number of muscles controlled by these motor neurons. The

cervical enlargement is particularly large because there is greater control over the fine musculature of the upper limbs, particularly of the fingers. The **lumbar enlargement** is not as significant in appearance because there is less fine motor control of the lower limbs.

Axial Control

The **anterior corticospinal tract** is responsible for controlling the muscles of the body trunk (see Figure 14.28). These axons do not decussate in the medulla. Instead, they remain in an anterior position as they descend the brain stem and enter the spinal cord. These axons then travel to the spinal cord level at which they synapse with a lower motor neuron. Upon reaching the appropriate level, the axons decussate, entering the ventral horn on the opposite side of the spinal cord from which they entered. In the ventral horn, these axons synapse with their corresponding lower motor neurons. The lower motor neurons are located in the medial regions of the ventral horn, because they control the axial muscles of the trunk.

Because movements of the body trunk involve both sides of the body, the anterior corticospinal tract is not entirely contralateral. Some collateral branches of the tract will project into the ipsilateral ventral horn to control synergistic muscles on that side of the body, or to inhibit antagonistic muscles through interneurons within the ventral horn. Through the influence of both sides of the body, the anterior corticospinal tract can coordinate postural muscles in broad movements of the body. These coordinating axons in the anterior corticospinal tract are often considered bilateral, as they are both ipsilateral and contralateral.

⊚ **INTERACTIVE LINK**

Watch this video (http://openstax.org/l/motorpathway) to learn more about the descending motor pathway for the somatic nervous system. The autonomic connections are mentioned, which are covered in another chapter. From this brief video, only some of the descending motor pathway of the somatic nervous system is described. Which division of the pathway is described and which division is left out?

Extrapyramidal Controls

Other descending connections between the brain and the spinal cord are called the **extrapyramidal system**. The name comes from the fact that this system is outside the corticospinal pathway, which includes the pyramids in the medulla. A few pathways originating from the brain stem contribute to this system.

The **tectospinal tract** projects from the midbrain to the spinal cord and is important for postural movements that are driven by the superior colliculus. The name of the tract comes from an alternate name for the superior colliculus, which is the tectum. The **reticulospinal tract** connects the reticular system, a diffuse region of gray matter in the brain stem, with the spinal cord. This tract influences trunk and proximal limb muscles related to posture and locomotion. The reticulospinal tract also contributes to muscle tone and influences autonomic functions. The **vestibulospinal tract** connects the brain stem nuclei of the vestibular system with the spinal cord. This allows posture, movement, and balance to be modulated on the basis of equilibrium information provided by the vestibular system.

The pathways of the extrapyramidal system are influenced by subcortical structures. For example, connections between the secondary motor cortices and the extrapyramidal system modulate spine and cranium movements. The basal nuclei, which are important for regulating movement initiated by the CNS, influence the extrapyramidal system as well as its thalamic feedback to the motor cortex.

The conscious movement of our muscles is more complicated than simply sending a single command from the precentral gyrus down to the proper motor neurons. During the movement of any body part, our muscles relay information back to the brain, and the brain is constantly sending "revised" instructions back to the muscles. The cerebellum is important in contributing to the motor system because it compares cerebral motor commands with proprioceptive feedback. The corticospinal fibers that project to the ventral horn of the spinal cord have branches that also synapse in the pons, which project to the cerebellum. Also, the proprioceptive sensations of the dorsal column system have a collateral projection to the medulla that projects to the cerebellum. These two streams of information are compared in the cerebellar cortex. Conflicts between the motor commands sent by the cerebrum and body position information provided by the proprioceptors cause the cerebellum to stimulate the **red nucleus** of the midbrain. The red nucleus then sends corrective commands to the spinal cord along the **rubrospinal tract**. The name of this tract comes from the word for red that is seen in the English word "ruby."

A good example of how the cerebellum corrects cerebral motor commands can be illustrated by walking in water. An original motor command from the cerebrum to walk will result in a highly coordinated set of learned movements. However, in water, the body cannot actually perform a typical walking movement as instructed. The cerebellum can alter the motor command, stimulating the leg muscles to take larger steps to overcome the water resistance. The cerebellum can make the necessary changes through the rubrospinal tract. Modulating the basic command to walk also relies on spinal reflexes, but the cerebellum is responsible for calculating the appropriate response. When the cerebellum does not work properly, coordination and balance are severely affected. The most dramatic example of this is during the overconsumption of alcohol. Alcohol inhibits the ability of the cerebellum to interpret proprioceptive feedback, making it more difficult to coordinate body movements, such as walking a straight line, or guide the movement of the hand to touch the tip of the nose.

⊛ INTERACTIVE LINK

Visit this site (http://openstax.org/l/NYTmotor) to read about an elderly woman who starts to lose the ability to control fine movements, such as speech and the movement of limbs. Many of the usual causes were ruled out. It was not a stroke, Parkinson's disease, diabetes, or thyroid dysfunction. The next most obvious cause was medication, so her pharmacist had to be consulted. The side effect of a drug meant to help her sleep had resulted in changes in motor control. What regions of the nervous system are likely to be the focus of haloperidol side effects?

Ventral Horn Output

The somatic nervous system provides output strictly to skeletal muscles. The lower motor neurons, which are responsible for the contraction of these muscles, are found in the ventral horn of the spinal cord. These large, multipolar neurons have a corona of dendrites surrounding the cell body and an axon that extends out of the ventral horn. This axon travels through the ventral nerve root to join the emerging spinal nerve. The axon is relatively long because it needs to reach muscles in the periphery of the body. The diameters of cell bodies may be on the order of hundreds of micrometers to support the long axon; some axons are a meter in length, such as the lumbar motor neurons that innervate muscles in the first digits of the feet.

The axons will also branch to innervate multiple muscle fibers. Together, the motor neuron and all the muscle fibers that it controls make up a motor unit. Motor units vary in size. Some may contain up to 1000 muscle fibers, such as in the quadriceps, or they may only have 10 fibers, such as in an extraocular muscle. The number of muscle fibers that are part of a motor unit corresponds to the precision of control of that muscle. Also, muscles that have finer motor control have more motor units connecting to them, and this requires a larger topographical field in the primary motor cortex.

Motor neuron axons connect to muscle fibers at a neuromuscular junction. This is a specialized synaptic structure at which multiple axon terminals synapse with the muscle fiber sarcolemma. The synaptic end bulbs of the motor neurons secrete acetylcholine, which binds to receptors on the sarcolemma. The binding of acetylcholine opens ligand-gated ion channels, increasing the movement of cations across the sarcolemma. This depolarizes the sarcolemma, initiating muscle contraction. Whereas other synapses result in graded potentials that must reach a threshold in the postsynaptic target, activity at the neuromuscular junction reliably leads to muscle fiber contraction with every nerve impulse received from a motor neuron. However, the strength of contraction and the number of fibers that contract can be affected by the frequency of the motor neuron impulses.

Reflexes

This chapter began by introducing reflexes as an example of the basic elements of the somatic nervous system. Simple somatic reflexes do not include the higher centers discussed for conscious or voluntary aspects of movement. Reflexes can be spinal or cranial, depending on the nerves and central components that are involved. The example described at the beginning of the chapter involved heat and pain sensations from a hot stove causing withdrawal of the arm through a connection in the spinal cord that leads to contraction of the biceps brachii. The description of this withdrawal reflex was simplified, for the sake of the introduction, to emphasize the parts of the somatic nervous system. But to consider reflexes fully, more attention needs to be given to this example.

As you withdraw your hand from the stove, you do not want to slow that reflex down. As the biceps brachii contracts, the antagonistic triceps brachii needs to relax. Because the neuromuscular junction is strictly excitatory, the biceps will contract when the motor nerve is active. Skeletal muscles do not actively relax. Instead the motor neuron needs to "quiet down," or be inhibited. In the hot-stove withdrawal reflex, this occurs through an interneuron in the spinal cord. The interneuron's cell body is located in the dorsal horn of the spinal cord. The interneuron receives a synapse from the axon of the sensory neuron that detects that the hand is being burned. In response to this stimulation from the sensory neuron, the interneuron then inhibits the motor neuron that controls the triceps brachii. This is done by releasing a neurotransmitter or other signal that hyperpolarizes the motor neuron connected to the triceps brachii, making it less likely to initiate an action potential. With this motor neuron being inhibited, the triceps brachii relaxes. Without the antagonistic contraction, withdrawal from the hot stove is faster and keeps further tissue damage from occurring.

Another example of a withdrawal reflex occurs when you step on a painful stimulus, like a tack or a sharp rock. The nociceptors that are activated by the painful stimulus activate the motor neurons responsible for contraction of the tibialis anterior muscle. This causes dorsiflexion of the foot. An inhibitory interneuron, activated by a collateral branch of the nociceptor fiber, will inhibit the motor neurons of the gastrocnemius and soleus muscles to cancel plantar flexion. An important difference in this reflex is that plantar flexion is most likely in progress as the foot is pressing down onto the tack. Contraction of the tibialis anterior is not the most important aspect of the reflex, as continuation of plantar flexion will result in further damage from stepping onto the tack.

Another type of reflex is a **stretch reflex**. In this reflex, when a skeletal muscle is stretched, a muscle spindle receptor is activated. The axon from this receptor structure will cause direct contraction of the muscle. A collateral of the muscle spindle fiber will also inhibit the motor neuron of the antagonist muscles. The reflex helps to maintain muscles at a constant length. A common example of this reflex is the knee jerk that is elicited by a rubber hammer struck against the patellar ligament in a physical exam.

A specialized reflex to protect the surface of the eye is the **corneal reflex**, or the eye blink reflex. When the cornea is stimulated by a tactile stimulus, or even by bright light in a related reflex, blinking is initiated. The sensory component travels through the trigeminal nerve, which carries somatosensory information from the face, or through the optic nerve, if the stimulus is bright light. The motor response travels through the facial nerve and innervates the orbicularis oculi on the same side. This reflex is commonly tested during a physical exam using an air puff or a gentle touch of a cotton-tipped applicator.

⊘ • INTERACTIVE LINK

Watch this video (http://openstax.org/l/reflexarc) to learn more about the reflex arc of the corneal reflex. When the right cornea senses a tactile stimulus, what happens to the left eye? Explain your answer.

⊘ • INTERACTIVE LINK

Watch this video (http://openstax.org/l/newreflex) to learn more about newborn reflexes. Newborns have a set of reflexes that are expected to have been crucial to survival before the modern age. These reflexes disappear as the baby grows, as some of them may be unnecessary as they age. The video demonstrates a reflex called the Babinski reflex, in which the foot flexes dorsally and the toes splay out when the sole of the foot is lightly scratched. This is normal for newborns, but it is a sign of reduced myelination of the spinal tract in adults. Why would this reflex be a problem for an adult?

Key Terms

alkaloid substance, usually from a plant source, that is chemically basic with respect to pH and will stimulate bitter receptors

amacrine cell type of cell in the retina that connects to the bipolar cells near the outer synaptic layer and provides the basis for early image processing within the retina

ampulla in the ear, the structure at the base of a semicircular canal that contains the hair cells and cupula for transduction of rotational movement of the head

anosmia loss of the sense of smell; usually the result of physical disruption of the first cranial nerve

anterior corticospinal tract division of the corticospinal pathway that travels through the ventral (anterior) column of the spinal cord and controls axial musculature through the medial motor neurons in the ventral (anterior) horn

aqueous humor watery fluid that fills the anterior chamber containing the cornea, iris, ciliary body, and lens of the eye

ascending pathway fiber structure that relays sensory information from the periphery through the spinal cord and brain stem to other structures of the brain

association area region of cortex connected to a primary sensory cortical area that further processes the information to generate more complex sensory perceptions

audition sense of hearing

auricle fleshy external structure of the ear

basilar membrane in the ear, the floor of the cochlear duct on which the organ of Corti sits

Betz cells output cells of the primary motor cortex that cause musculature to move through synapses on cranial and spinal motor neurons

binocular depth cues indications of the distance of visual stimuli on the basis of slight differences in the images projected onto either retina

bipolar cell cell type in the retina that connects the photoreceptors to the RGCs

Broca's area region of the frontal lobe associated with the motor commands necessary for speech production

capsaicin molecule that activates nociceptors by interacting with a temperature-sensitive ion channel and is the basis for "hot" sensations in spicy food

cerebral peduncles segments of the descending motor pathway that make up the white matter of the ventral midbrain

cervical enlargement region of the ventral (anterior) horn of the spinal cord that has a larger population of motor neurons for the greater number of and finer control of muscles of the upper limb

chemoreceptor sensory receptor cell that is sensitive to chemical stimuli, such as in taste, smell, or pain

chief sensory nucleus component of the trigeminal nuclei that is found in the pons

choroid highly vascular tissue in the wall of the eye that supplies the outer retina with blood

ciliary body smooth muscle structure on the interior surface of the iris that controls the shape of the lens through the zonule fibers

circadian rhythm internal perception of the daily cycle of light and dark based on retinal activity related to sunlight

cochlea auditory portion of the inner ear containing structures to transduce sound stimuli

cochlear duct space within the auditory portion of the inner ear that contains the organ of Corti and is adjacent to the scala tympani and scala vestibuli on either side

cone photoreceptor one of the two types of retinal receptor cell that is specialized for color vision through the use of three photopigments distributed through three separate populations of cells

contralateral word meaning "on the opposite side," as in axons that cross the midline in a fiber tract

cornea fibrous covering of the anterior region of the eye that is transparent so that light can pass through it

corneal reflex protective response to stimulation of the cornea causing contraction of the orbicularis oculi muscle resulting in blinking of the eye

corticobulbar tract connection between the cortex and the brain stem responsible for generating movement

corticospinal tract connection between the cortex and the spinal cord responsible for generating movement

cupula specialized structure within the base of a semicircular canal that bends the stereocilia of hair cells when the head rotates by way of the relative movement of the enclosed fluid

decussate to cross the midline, as in fibers that project from one side of the body to the other

dorsal column system ascending tract of the spinal cord associated with fine touch and proprioceptive sensations

dorsal stream connections between cortical areas from the occipital to parietal lobes that are responsible for the perception of visual motion and guiding movement of the body in relation to that motion

encapsulated ending   configuration of a sensory receptor neuron with dendrites surrounded by specialized structures to aid in transduction of a particular type of sensation, such as the lamellated corpuscles in the deep dermis and subcutaneous tissue

equilibrium   sense of balance that includes sensations of position and movement of the head

executive functions   cognitive processes of the prefrontal cortex that lead to directing goal-directed behavior, which is a precursor to executing motor commands

external ear   structures on the lateral surface of the head, including the auricle and the ear canal back to the tympanic membrane

exteroceptor   sensory receptor that is positioned to interpret stimuli from the external environment, such as photoreceptors in the eye or somatosensory receptors in the skin

extraocular muscle   one of six muscles originating out of the bones of the orbit and inserting into the surface of the eye which are responsible for moving the eye

extrapyramidal system   pathways between the brain and spinal cord that are separate from the corticospinal tract and are responsible for modulating the movements generated through that primary pathway

fasciculus cuneatus   lateral division of the dorsal column system composed of fibers from sensory neurons in the upper body

fasciculus gracilis   medial division of the dorsal column system composed of fibers from sensory neurons in the lower body

fibrous tunic   outer layer of the eye primarily composed of connective tissue known as the sclera and cornea

fovea   exact center of the retina at which visual stimuli are focused for maximal acuity, where the retina is thinnest, at which there is nothing but photoreceptors

free nerve ending   configuration of a sensory receptor neuron with dendrites in the connective tissue of the organ, such as in the dermis of the skin, that are most often sensitive to chemical, thermal, and mechanical stimuli

frontal eye fields   area of the prefrontal cortex responsible for moving the eyes to attend to visual stimuli

general sense   any sensory system that is distributed throughout the body and incorporated into organs of multiple other systems, such as the walls of the digestive organs or the skin

gustation   sense of taste

gustatory receptor cells   sensory cells in the taste bud that transduce the chemical stimuli of gustation

hair cells   mechanoreceptor cells found in the inner ear that transduce stimuli for the senses of hearing and balance

incus   (also, anvil) ossicle of the middle ear that connects the malleus to the stapes

inferior colliculus   last structure in the auditory brainstem pathway that projects to the thalamus and superior colliculus

inferior oblique   extraocular muscle responsible for lateral rotation of the eye

inferior rectus   extraocular muscle responsible for looking down

inner ear   structure within the temporal bone that contains the sensory apparati of hearing and balance

inner segment   in the eye, the section of a photoreceptor that contains the nucleus and other major organelles for normal cellular functions

inner synaptic layer   layer in the retina where bipolar cells connect to RGCs

interaural intensity difference   cue used to aid sound localization in the horizontal plane that compares the relative loudness of sounds at the two ears, because the ear closer to the sound source will hear a slightly more intense sound

interaural time difference   cue used to help with sound localization in the horizontal plane that compares the relative time of arrival of sounds at the two ears, because the ear closer to the sound source will receive the stimulus microseconds before the other ear

internal capsule   segment of the descending motor pathway that passes between the caudate nucleus and the putamen

interoceptor   sensory receptor that is positioned to interpret stimuli from internal organs, such as stretch receptors in the wall of blood vessels

ipsilateral   word meaning on the same side, as in axons that do not cross the midline in a fiber tract

iris   colored portion of the anterior eye that surrounds the pupil

kinesthesia   sense of body movement based on sensations in skeletal muscles, tendons, joints, and the skin

lacrimal duct   duct in the medial corner of the orbit that drains tears into the nasal cavity

lacrimal gland   gland lateral to the orbit that produces tears to wash across the surface of the eye

lateral corticospinal tract   division of the

corticospinal pathway that travels through the lateral column of the spinal cord and controls appendicular musculature through the lateral motor neurons in the ventral (anterior) horn

lateral geniculate nucleus   thalamic target of the RGCs that projects to the visual cortex

lateral rectus   extraocular muscle responsible for abduction of the eye

lens   component of the eye that focuses light on the retina

levator palpebrae superioris   muscle that causes elevation of the upper eyelid, controlled by fibers in the oculomotor nerve

lumbar enlargement   region of the ventral (anterior) horn of the spinal cord that has a larger population of motor neurons for the greater number of muscles of the lower limb

macula   enlargement at the base of a semicircular canal at which transduction of equilibrium stimuli takes place within the ampulla

malleus   (also, hammer) ossicle that is directly attached to the tympanic membrane

mechanoreceptor   receptor cell that transduces mechanical stimuli into an electrochemical signal

medial geniculate nucleus   thalamic target of the auditory brain stem that projects to the auditory cortex

medial lemniscus   fiber tract of the dorsal column system that extends from the nuclei gracilis and cuneatus to the thalamus, and decussates

medial rectus   extraocular muscle responsible for adduction of the eye

mesencephalic nucleus   component of the trigeminal nuclei that is found in the midbrain

middle ear   space within the temporal bone between the ear canal and bony labyrinth where the ossicles amplify sound waves from the tympanic membrane to the oval window

multimodal integration area   region of the cerebral cortex in which information from more than one sensory modality is processed to arrive at higher level cortical functions such as memory, learning, or cognition

neural tunic   layer of the eye that contains nervous tissue, namely the retina

nociceptor   receptor cell that senses pain stimuli

nucleus cuneatus   medullary nucleus at which first-order neurons of the dorsal column system synapse specifically from the upper body and arms

nucleus gracilis   medullary nucleus at which first-order neurons of the dorsal column system synapse specifically from the lower body and legs

odorant molecules   volatile chemicals that bind to receptor proteins in olfactory neurons to stimulate the sense of smell

olfaction   sense of smell

olfactory bulb   central target of the first cranial nerve; located on the ventral surface of the frontal lobe in the cerebrum

olfactory epithelium   region of the nasal epithelium where olfactory neurons are located

olfactory sensory neuron   receptor cell of the olfactory system, sensitive to the chemical stimuli of smell, the axons of which compose the first cranial nerve

opsin   protein that contains the photosensitive cofactor retinal for phototransduction

optic chiasm   decussation point in the visual system at which medial retina fibers cross to the other side of the brain

optic disc   spot on the retina at which RGC axons leave the eye and blood vessels of the inner retina pass

optic nerve   second cranial nerve, which is responsible visual sensation

optic tract   name for the fiber structure containing axons from the retina posterior to the optic chiasm representing their CNS location

organ of Corti   structure in the cochlea in which hair cells transduce movements from sound waves into electrochemical signals

osmoreceptor   receptor cell that senses differences in the concentrations of bodily fluids on the basis of osmotic pressure

ossicles   three small bones in the middle ear

otolith   layer of calcium carbonate crystals located on top of the otolithic membrane

otolithic membrane   gelatinous substance in the utricle and saccule of the inner ear that contains calcium carbonate crystals and into which the stereocilia of hair cells are embedded

outer segment   in the eye, the section of a photoreceptor that contains opsin molecules that transduce light stimuli

outer synaptic layer   layer in the retina at which photoreceptors connect to bipolar cells

oval window   membrane at the base of the cochlea where the stapes attaches, marking the beginning of the scala vestibuli

palpebral conjunctiva   membrane attached to the inner surface of the eyelids that covers the anterior surface of the cornea

papilla   for gustation, a bump-like projection on the surface of the tongue that contains taste buds

photoisomerization   chemical change in the retinal molecule that alters the bonding so that it switches from the 11-*cis*-retinal isomer to the all-*trans*-retinal isomer

photon   individual "packet" of light

photoreceptor   receptor cell specialized to respond to light stimuli

premotor cortex   cortical area anterior to the primary motor cortex that is responsible for planning movements

primary sensory cortex   region of the cerebral cortex that initially receives sensory input from an ascending pathway from the thalamus and begins the processing that will result in conscious perception of that modality

proprioception   sense of position and movement of the body

proprioceptor   receptor cell that senses changes in the position and kinesthetic aspects of the body

pupil   open hole at the center of the iris that light passes through into the eye

pyramidal decussation   location at which corticospinal tract fibers cross the midline and segregate into the anterior and lateral divisions of the pathway

pyramids   segment of the descending motor pathway that travels in the anterior position of the medulla

receptor cell   cell that transduces environmental stimuli into neural signals

red nucleus   midbrain nucleus that sends corrective commands to the spinal cord along the rubrospinal tract, based on disparity between an original command and the sensory feedback from movement

reticulospinal tract   extrapyramidal connections between the brain stem and spinal cord that modulate movement, contribute to posture, and regulate muscle tone

retina   nervous tissue of the eye at which phototransduction takes place

retinal   cofactor in an opsin molecule that undergoes a biochemical change when struck by a photon (pronounced with a stress on the last syllable)

retinal ganglion cell (RGC)   neuron of the retina that projects along the second cranial nerve

rhodopsin   photopigment molecule found in the rod photoreceptors

rod photoreceptor   one of the two types of retinal receptor cell that is specialized for low-light vision

round window   membrane that marks the end of the scala tympani

rubrospinal tract   descending motor control pathway, originating in the red nucleus, that mediates control of the limbs on the basis of cerebellar processing

saccule   structure of the inner ear responsible for

transducing linear acceleration in the vertical plane

scala tympani   portion of the cochlea that extends from the apex to the round window

scala vestibuli   portion of the cochlea that extends from the oval window to the apex

sclera   white of the eye

semicircular canals   structures within the inner ear responsible for transducing rotational movement information

sensory homunculus   topographic representation of the body within the somatosensory cortex demonstrating the correspondence between neurons processing stimuli and sensitivity

sensory modality   a particular system for interpreting and perceiving environmental stimuli by the nervous system

solitary nucleus   medullar nucleus that receives taste information from the facial and glossopharyngeal nerves

somatosensation   general sense associated with modalities lumped together as touch

special sense   any sensory system associated with a specific organ structure, namely smell, taste, sight, hearing, and balance

spinal trigeminal nucleus   component of the trigeminal nuclei that is found in the medulla

spinothalamic tract   ascending tract of the spinal cord associated with pain and temperature sensations

spiral ganglion   location of neuronal cell bodies that transmit auditory information along the eighth cranial nerve

stapes   (also, stirrup) ossicle of the middle ear that is attached to the inner ear

stereocilia   array of apical membrane extensions in a hair cell that transduce movements when they are bent

stretch reflex   response to activation of the muscle spindle stretch receptor that causes contraction of the muscle to maintain a constant length

submodality   specific sense within a broader major sense such as sweet as a part of the sense of taste, or color as a part of vision

superior colliculus   structure in the midbrain that combines visual, auditory, and somatosensory input to coordinate spatial and topographic representations of the three sensory systems

superior oblique   extraocular muscle responsible for medial rotation of the eye

superior rectus   extraocular muscle responsible for looking up

supplemental motor area   cortical area anterior to the primary motor cortex that is responsible for planning movements

suprachiasmatic nucleus   hypothalamic target of the retina that helps to establish the circadian rhythm of the body on the basis of the presence or absence of daylight

taste buds   structures within a papilla on the tongue that contain gustatory receptor cells

tectorial membrane   component of the organ of Corti that lays over the hair cells, into which the stereocilia are embedded

tectospinal tract   extrapyramidal connections between the superior colliculus and spinal cord

thermoreceptor   sensory receptor specialized for temperature stimuli

topographical   relating to positional information

transduction   process of changing an environmental stimulus into the electrochemical signals of the nervous system

trochlea   cartilaginous structure that acts like a pulley for the superior oblique muscle

tympanic membrane   ear drum

umami   taste submodality for sensitivity to the concentration of amino acids; also called the savory sense

utricle   structure of the inner ear responsible for transducing linear acceleration in the horizontal plane

vascular tunic   middle layer of the eye primarily composed of connective tissue with a rich blood supply

ventral posterior nucleus   nucleus in the thalamus that is the target of gustatory sensations and projects to the cerebral cortex

ventral stream   connections between cortical areas from the occipital lobe to the temporal lobe that are responsible for identification of visual stimuli

vestibular ganglion   location of neuronal cell bodies that transmit equilibrium information along the eighth cranial nerve

vestibular nuclei   targets of the vestibular component of the eighth cranial nerve

vestibule   in the ear, the portion of the inner ear responsible for the sense of equilibrium

vestibulo-ocular reflex (VOR)   reflex based on connections between the vestibular system and the cranial nerves of eye movements that ensures images are stabilized on the retina as the head and body move

vestibulospinal tract   extrapyramidal connections between the vestibular nuclei in the brain stem and spinal cord that modulate movement and contribute to balance on the basis of the sense of equilibrium

visceral sense   sense associated with the internal organs

vision   special sense of sight based on transduction of light stimuli

visual acuity   property of vision related to the sharpness of focus, which varies in relation to retinal position

vitreous humor   viscous fluid that fills the posterior chamber of the eye

working memory   function of the prefrontal cortex to maintain a representation of information that is not in the immediate environment

zonule fibers   fibrous connections between the ciliary body and the lens

Chapter Review

14.1 Sensory Perception

The senses are olfaction (smell), gustation (taste), somatosensation (sensations associated with the skin and body), audition (hearing), equilibrium (balance), and vision. With the exception of somatosensation, this list represents the special senses, or those systems of the body that are associated with specific organs such as the tongue or eye. Somatosensation belongs to the general senses, which are those sensory structures that are distributed throughout the body and in the walls of various organs. The special senses are all primarily part of the somatic nervous system in that they are consciously perceived through cerebral processes, though some special senses contribute to autonomic function. The general senses can be divided into somatosensation, which is commonly considered touch, but includes tactile, pressure, vibration, temperature, and pain perception. The general senses

also include the visceral senses, which are separate from the somatic nervous system function in that they do not normally rise to the level of conscious perception.

The cells that transduce sensory stimuli into the electrochemical signals of the nervous system are classified on the basis of structural or functional aspects of the cells. The structural classifications are either based on the anatomy of the cell that is interacting with the stimulus (free nerve endings, encapsulated endings, or specialized receptor cell), or where the cell is located relative to the stimulus (interoceptor, exteroceptor, proprioceptor). Thirdly, the functional classification is based on how the cell transduces the stimulus into a neural signal. Chemoreceptors respond to chemical stimuli and are the basis for olfaction and gustation. Related to chemoreceptors are osmoreceptors and nociceptors for fluid balance and pain reception, respectively. Mechanoreceptors respond to mechanical stimuli and are the basis for most aspects of somatosensation, as well as being the basis of audition and equilibrium in the inner ear. Thermoreceptors are sensitive to temperature changes, and photoreceptors are sensitive to light energy.

The nerves that convey sensory information from the periphery to the CNS are either spinal nerves, connected to the spinal cord, or cranial nerves, connected to the brain. Spinal nerves have mixed populations of fibers; some are motor fibers and some are sensory. The sensory fibers connect to the spinal cord through the dorsal root, which is attached to the dorsal root ganglion. Sensory information from the body that is conveyed through spinal nerves will project to the opposite side of the brain to be processed by the cerebral cortex. The cranial nerves can be strictly sensory fibers, such as the olfactory, optic, and vestibulocochlear nerves, or mixed sensory and motor nerves, such as the trigeminal, facial, glossopharyngeal, and vagus nerves. The cranial nerves are connected to the same side of the brain from which the sensory information originates.

14.2 Central Processing

Sensory input to the brain enters through pathways that travel through either the spinal cord (for somatosensory input from the body) or the brain stem (for everything else, except the visual and olfactory systems) to reach the diencephalon. In the diencephalon, sensory pathways reach the thalamus. This is necessary for all sensory systems to reach the cerebral cortex, except for the olfactory system that is directly connected to the frontal and temporal lobes.

The two major tracts in the spinal cord, originating from sensory neurons in the dorsal root ganglia, are the dorsal column system and the spinothalamic tract. The major differences between the two are in the type of information that is relayed to the brain and where the tracts decussate. The dorsal column system primarily carries information about touch and proprioception and crosses the midline in the medulla. The spinothalamic tract is primarily responsible for pain and temperature sensation and crosses the midline in the spinal cord at the level at which it enters. The trigeminal nerve adds similar sensation information from the head to these pathways.

The auditory pathway passes through multiple nuclei in the brain stem in which additional information is extracted from the basic frequency stimuli processed by the cochlea. Sound localization is made possible

through the activity of these brain stem structures. The vestibular system enters the brain stem and influences activity in the cerebellum, spinal cord, and cerebral cortex.

The visual pathway segregates information from the two eyes so that one half of the visual field projects to the other side of the brain. Within visual cortical areas, the perception of the stimuli and their location is passed along two streams, one ventral and one dorsal. The ventral visual stream connects to structures in the temporal lobe that are important for long-term memory formation. The dorsal visual stream interacts with the somatosensory cortex in the parietal lobe, and together they can influence the activity in the frontal lobe to generate movements of the body in relation to visual information.

14.3 Motor Responses

The motor components of the somatic nervous system begin with the frontal lobe of the brain, where the prefrontal cortex is responsible for higher functions such as working memory. The integrative and associate functions of the prefrontal lobe feed into the secondary motor areas, which help plan movements. The premotor cortex and supplemental motor area then feed into the primary motor cortex that initiates movements. Large Betz cells project through the corticobulbar and corticospinal tracts to synapse on lower motor neurons in the brain stem and ventral horn of the spinal cord, respectively. These connections are responsible for generating movements of skeletal muscles.

The extrapyramidal system includes projections from the brain stem and higher centers that influence movement, mostly to maintain balance and posture, as well as to maintain muscle tone. The superior colliculus and red nucleus in the midbrain, the vestibular nuclei in the medulla, and the reticular formation throughout the brain stem each have tracts projecting to the spinal cord in this system. Descending input from the secondary motor cortices, basal nuclei, and cerebellum connect to the origins of these tracts in the brain stem.

All of these motor pathways project to the spinal cord to synapse with motor neurons in the ventral horn of the spinal cord. These lower motor neurons are the cells that connect to skeletal muscle and cause contractions. These neurons project through the spinal nerves to connect to the muscles at neuromuscular junctions. One motor neuron connects to multiple muscle fibers within a target muscle. The number of fibers that are innervated by a single motor neuron varies on the basis of the precision necessary for that muscle and the amount of force necessary for that motor unit. The quadriceps, for example, have many fibers controlled by single motor neurons for powerful contractions that do not need to be precise. The extraocular muscles have only a small number of fibers controlled by each motor neuron because moving the eyes does not require much force, but needs to be very precise.

Reflexes are the simplest circuits within the somatic nervous system. A withdrawal reflex from a painful stimulus only requires the sensory fiber that enters the spinal cord and the motor neuron that projects to a muscle. Antagonist and postural muscles can be coordinated with the withdrawal, making the connections more complex. The simple, single neuronal connection is the basis of somatic reflexes. The corneal reflex is contraction of the orbicularis oculi muscle to blink the eyelid when something touches the surface of the eye. Stretch reflexes maintain a constant length of muscles by causing a contraction of a muscle to compensate for a stretch that can be sensed by a specialized receptor called a muscle spindle.

Interactive Link Questions

1. Watch this video (http://openstax.org/l/DanielleReed) to learn about Dr. Danielle Reed of the Monell Chemical Senses Center in Philadelphia, PA, who became interested in science at an early age because of her sensory experiences. She recognized that her sense of taste was unique compared with other people she knew. Now, she studies the genetic differences between people and their sensitivities to taste stimuli. In the video, there is a brief image of a person sticking out their tongue, which has been covered with a colored dye. This is how Dr. Reed is able to visualize and count papillae on the surface of the tongue. People fall into two large groups known as "tasters" and "non-tasters" on the basis of the density of papillae on their tongue, which also indicates the number of taste buds. Non-tasters can taste food, but they are not as sensitive to certain tastes, such as bitterness. Dr. Reed discovered that she is a non-taster, which explains why she perceived bitterness differently than other people she knew. Are you very sensitive to tastes? Can you see any similarities among the members of your family?

2. Figure 14.9 The basilar membrane is the thin membrane that extends from the central core of the cochlea to the edge. What is anchored to this membrane so that they can be activated by movement of the fluids within the cochlea?

3. Watch this video (http://openstax.org/l/ear1) to learn more about how the structures of the ear convert sound waves into a neural signal by moving the "hairs," or stereocilia, of the cochlear duct. Specific locations along the length of the duct encode specific frequencies, or pitches. The brain interprets the meaning of the sounds we hear as music, speech, noise, etc. Which ear structures are responsible for the amplification and transfer of sound from the external ear to the inner ear?

4. Watch this animation (http://openstax.org/l/ear2) to learn more about the inner ear and to see the cochlea unroll, with the base at the back of the image and the apex at the front. Specific wavelengths of sound cause specific regions of the basilar membrane to vibrate, much like the keys of a piano produce sound at different frequencies. Based on the animation, where do frequencies—from high to low pitches—cause activity in the hair cells within the cochlear duct?

5. Watch this video (http://openstax.org/l/occipital) to learn more about a transverse section through the brain that depicts the visual pathway from the eye to the occipital cortex. The first half of the pathway is the projection from the RGCs through the optic nerve to the lateral geniculate nucleus in the thalamus on either side. This first fiber in the pathway synapses on a thalamic cell that then projects to the visual cortex in the occipital lobe where "seeing," or visual perception, takes place. This video gives an abbreviated overview of the visual system by concentrating on the pathway from the eyes to the occipital lobe. The video makes the statement (at 0:45) that "specialized cells in the retina called ganglion cells convert the light rays into electrical signals." What aspect of retinal processing is simplified by that statement? Explain your answer.

6. Watch this video (http://openstax.org/l/l_3-D1) to learn more about how the brain perceives 3-D motion. Similar to how retinal disparity offers 3-D moviegoers a way to extract 3-D information from the two-dimensional visual field projected onto the retina, the brain can extract information about movement in space by comparing what the two eyes see. If movement of a visual stimulus is leftward in one eye and rightward in the opposite eye, the brain interprets this as movement toward (or away) from the face along the midline. If both eyes see an object moving in the same direction, but at different rates, what would that mean for spatial movement?

7. The inability to recognize people by their faces is a troublesome problem. It can be caused by trauma, or it may be inborn. Watch this video (http://openstax.org/l/faces) to learn more about a person who lost the ability to recognize faces as the result of an injury. She cannot recognize the faces of close family members or herself. What other information can a person suffering from prosopagnosia use to figure out whom they are seeing?

8. Watch this video (http://openstax.org/l/motorpathway) to learn more about the descending motor pathway for the somatic nervous system. The autonomic connections are mentioned, which are covered in another chapter. From this brief video, only some of the descending motor pathway of the somatic nervous system is described. Which division of the pathway is described and which division is left out?

9. Visit this site (http://openstax.org/l/NYTmotor) to read about an elderly woman who starts to lose the ability to control fine movements, such as speech and the movement of limbs. Many of the usual causes were ruled out. It was not a stroke, Parkinson's disease, diabetes, or thyroid dysfunction. The next most obvious cause was medication, so her pharmacist had to be consulted. The side effect of a drug meant to help her sleep had resulted in changes in motor control. What regions of the nervous system are likely to be the focus of haloperidol side effects?

10. Watch this video (http://openstax.org/l/reflexarc) to learn more about the reflex arc of the corneal reflex. When the right cornea senses a tactile stimulus, what happens to the left eye? Explain your answer.

11. Watch this video (http://openstax.org/l/newreflex) to learn more about newborn reflexes. Newborns have a set of reflexes that are expected to have been crucial to survival before the modern age. These reflexes disappear as the baby grows, as some of them may be unnecessary as they age. The video demonstrates a reflex called the Babinski reflex, in which the foot flexes dorsally and the toes splay out when the sole of the foot is lightly scratched. This is normal for newborns, but it is a sign of reduced myelination of the spinal tract in adults. Why would this reflex be a problem for an adult?

Review Questions

12. What type of receptor cell is responsible for transducing pain stimuli?
    a. mechanoreceptor
    b. nociceptor
    c. osmoreceptor
    d. photoreceptor

13. Which of these cranial nerves is part of the gustatory system?
    a. olfactory
    b. trochlear
    c. trigeminal
    d. facial

14. Which submodality of taste is sensitive to the pH of saliva?
    a. umami
    b. sour
    c. bitter
    d. sweet

15. Axons from which neuron in the retina make up the optic nerve?
    a. amacrine cells
    b. photoreceptors
    c. bipolar cells
    d. retinal ganglion cells

16. What type of receptor cell is involved in the sensations of sound and balance?
    a. photoreceptor
    b. chemoreceptor
    c. mechanoreceptor
    d. nociceptor

17. Which of these sensory modalities does *not* pass through the ventral posterior thalamus?
    a. gustatory
    b. proprioception
    c. audition
    d. nociception

18. Which nucleus in the medulla is connected to the inferior colliculus?
    a. solitary nucleus
    b. vestibular nucleus
    c. chief sensory nucleus
    d. cochlear nucleus

19. Visual stimuli in the upper-left visual field will be processed in what region of the primary visual cortex?
    a. inferior right
    b. inferior left
    c. superior right
    d. superior left

20. Which location on the body has the largest region of somatosensory cortex representing it, according to the sensory homunculus?
    a. lips
    b. thigh
    c. elbow
    d. neck

21. Which of the following is a direct target of the vestibular ganglion?
    a. superior colliculus
    b. cerebellum
    c. thalamus
    d. optic chiasm

22. Which region of the frontal lobe is responsible for initiating movement by directly connecting to cranial and spinal motor neurons?
    a. prefrontal cortex
    b. supplemental motor area
    c. premotor cortex
    d. primary motor cortex

23. Which extrapyramidal tract incorporates equilibrium sensations with motor commands to aid in posture and movement?
    a. tectospinal tract
    b. vestibulospinal tract
    c. reticulospinal tract
    d. corticospinal tract

24. Which region of gray matter in the spinal cord contains motor neurons that innervate skeletal muscles?
    a. ventral horn
    b. dorsal horn
    c. lateral horn
    d. lateral column

25. What type of reflex can protect the foot when a painful stimulus is sensed?
    a. stretch reflex
    b. gag reflex
    c. withdrawal reflex
    d. corneal reflex

26. What is the name for the topographical representation of the sensory input to the somatosensory cortex?
    a. homunculus
    b. homo sapiens
    c. postcentral gyrus
    d. primary cortex

Critical Thinking Questions

27. The sweetener known as stevia can replace glucose in food. What does the molecular similarity of stevia to glucose mean for the gustatory sense?

28. Why does the blind spot from the optic disc in either eye not result in a blind spot in the visual field?

29. Following a motorcycle accident, the victim loses the ability to move the right leg but has normal control over the left one, suggesting a hemisection somewhere in the thoracic region of the spinal cord. What sensory deficits would be expected in terms of touch versus pain? Explain your answer.

30. A pituitary tumor can cause perceptual losses in the lateral visual field. The pituitary gland is located directly inferior to the hypothalamus. Why would this happen?

31. The prefrontal lobotomy is a drastic—and largely out-of-practice—procedure used to disconnect that portion of the cerebral cortex from the rest of the frontal lobe and the diencephalon as a psychiatric therapy. Why would this have been thought necessary for someone with a potentially uncontrollable behavior?

32. If a reflex is a limited circuit within the somatic system, why do physical and neurological exams include them to test the health of an individual?

CHAPTER 15
The Autonomic Nervous System

Figure 15.1 **Fight or Flight?** Though the threats that modern humans face are not large predators, the autonomic nervous system is adapted to this type of stimulus. The modern world presents stimuli that trigger the same response. (credit: Vernon Swanepoel)

CHAPTER OBJECTIVES
After studying this chapter, you will be able to:
- Describe the components of the autonomic nervous system
- Differentiate between the structures of the sympathetic and parasympathetic divisions in the autonomic nervous system
- Name the components of a visceral reflex specific to the autonomic division to which it belongs
- Predict the response of a target effector to autonomic input on the basis of the released signaling molecule
- Describe how the central nervous system coordinates and contributes to autonomic functions

INTRODUCTION The autonomic nervous system is often associated with the "fight-or-flight response," which refers to the preparation of the body to either run away from a threat or to stand and fight in the face of that threat. To suggest what this means, consider the (very unlikely) situation of seeing a lioness hunting out on the savannah. Though this is not a common threat that humans deal with in the modern world, it represents the type of environment in which the human species thrived and adapted. The spread of humans around the world to the present state of the modern age occurred much more quickly than any species would adapt to environmental pressures such as predators. However, the reactions modern humans have in the modern world are based on these prehistoric situations. If your boss is walking down the hallway on Friday afternoon looking for "volunteers" to come in on the weekend, your response is the same as the prehistoric human seeing the lioness running across the savannah: fight or flight.

Most likely, your response to your boss—not to mention the lioness—would be flight. Run away! The autonomic system is responsible for the physiological response to make that possible, and hopefully successful. Adrenaline starts to flood your circulatory system. Your heart rate increases. Sweat glands become active. The bronchi of the lungs dilate to allow more air exchange. Pupils dilate to increase visual information. Blood pressure increases in general, and blood vessels dilate in skeletal muscles. Time to run. Similar physiological responses would occur in preparation for fighting off the threat.

This response should sound a bit familiar. The autonomic nervous system is tied into emotional responses as well, and the fight-or-flight response probably sounds like a panic attack. In the modern world, these sorts of reactions are associated with anxiety as much as with response to a threat. It is engrained in the nervous system to respond like this. In fact, the adaptations of the autonomic nervous system probably predate the human species and are likely to be common to all mammals, and perhaps shared by many animals. That lioness might herself be threatened in some other situation.

However, the autonomic nervous system is not just about responding to threats. Besides the fight-or-flight response, there are the responses referred to as "rest and digest." If that lioness is successful in her hunting, then she is going to rest from the exertion. Her heart rate will slow. Breathing will return to normal. The digestive system has a big job to do. Much of the function of the autonomic system is based on the connections within an autonomic, or visceral, reflex.

15.1 Divisions of the Autonomic Nervous System

LEARNING OBJECTIVES

By the end of this section, you will be able to:

- Name the components that generate the sympathetic and parasympathetic responses of the autonomic nervous system
- Explain the differences in output connections within the two divisions of the autonomic nervous system
- Describe the signaling molecules and receptor proteins involved in communication within the two divisions of the autonomic nervous system

The nervous system can be divided into two functional parts: the somatic nervous system and the autonomic nervous system. The major differences between the two systems are evident in the responses that each produces. The somatic nervous system causes contraction of skeletal muscles. The autonomic nervous system controls cardiac and smooth muscle, as well as glandular tissue. The somatic nervous system is associated with voluntary responses (though many can happen without conscious awareness, like breathing), and the autonomic nervous system is associated with involuntary responses, such as those related to homeostasis.

The autonomic nervous system regulates many of the internal organs through a balance of two aspects, or divisions. In addition to the endocrine system, the autonomic nervous system is instrumental in homeostatic mechanisms in the body. The two divisions of the autonomic nervous system are the **sympathetic division** and the **parasympathetic division**. The sympathetic system is associated with the **fight-or-flight response**, and parasympathetic activity is referred to by the epithet of **rest and digest**. Homeostasis is the balance between the two systems. At each target effector, dual innervation determines activity. For example, the heart receives connections from both the sympathetic and parasympathetic divisions. One causes heart rate to increase, whereas the other causes heart rate to decrease.

⊘ INTERACTIVE LINK

Watch this video (http://openstax.org/l/fightflight) to learn more about adrenaline and the fight-or-flight response. When someone is said to have a rush of adrenaline, the image of bungee jumpers or skydivers usually comes to mind. But adrenaline, also known as epinephrine, is an important chemical in coordinating the body's fight-or-flight response. In this video, you look inside the physiology of the fight-or-flight response, as envisioned for a firefighter. His body's reaction is the result of the sympathetic division of the autonomic nervous system causing system-wide changes as it prepares for extreme responses. What two changes does adrenaline bring about to help the skeletal muscle response?

Sympathetic Division of the Autonomic Nervous System

To respond to a threat—to fight or to run away—the sympathetic system causes divergent effects as many different effector organs are activated together for a common purpose. More oxygen needs to be inhaled and delivered to skeletal muscle. The respiratory, cardiovascular, and musculoskeletal systems are all activated together. Additionally, sweating keeps the excess heat that comes from muscle contraction from causing the body to overheat. The digestive system shuts down so that blood is not absorbing nutrients when it should be delivering oxygen to skeletal muscles. To coordinate all these responses, the connections in the sympathetic system diverge from a limited region of the central nervous system (CNS) to a wide array of ganglia that project to the many effector organs simultaneously. The complex set of structures that compose the output of the sympathetic system make it possible for these disparate effectors to come together in a coordinated, systemic change.

The sympathetic division of the autonomic nervous system influences the various organ systems of the body through connections emerging from the thoracic and upper lumbar spinal cord. It is referred to as the **thoracolumbar system** to reflect this anatomical basis. A **central neuron** in the lateral horn of any of these spinal regions projects to ganglia adjacent to the vertebral column through the ventral spinal roots. The majority of ganglia of the sympathetic system belong to a network of **sympathetic chain ganglia** that runs alongside the vertebral column. The ganglia appear as a series of clusters of neurons linked by axonal bridges. There are typically 23 ganglia in the chain on either side of the spinal column. Three correspond to the cervical region, 12 are in the thoracic region, four are in the lumbar region, and four correspond to the sacral region. The cervical and sacral levels are not connected to the spinal cord directly through the spinal roots, but through ascending or descending connections through the bridges within the chain.

A diagram that shows the connections of the sympathetic system is somewhat like a circuit diagram that shows the electrical connections between different receptacles and devices. In Figure 15.2, the "circuits" of the sympathetic system are intentionally simplified.

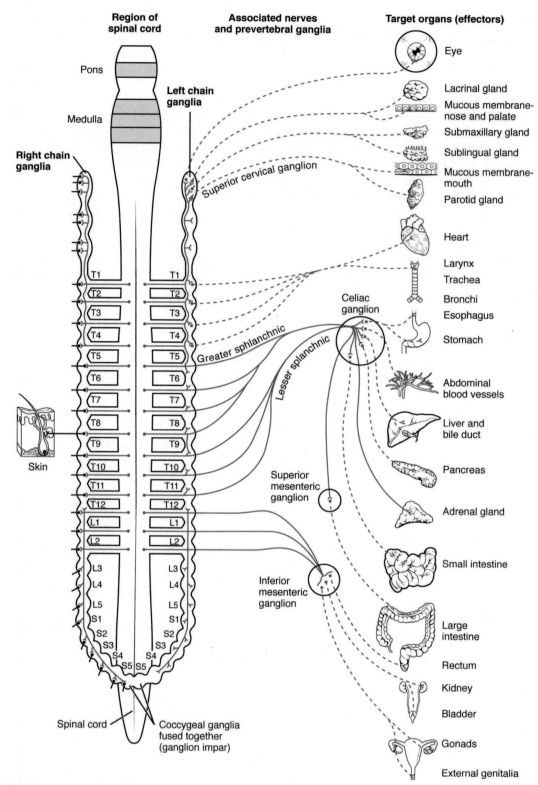

FIGURE 15.2 Connections of Sympathetic Division of the Autonomic Nervous System   Neurons from the lateral horn of the spinal cord (preganglionic nerve fibers - solid lines)) project to the chain ganglia on either side of the vertebral column or to collateral (prevertebral) ganglia that are anterior to the vertebral column in the abdominal cavity. Axons from these ganglionic neurons (postganglionic nerve fibers - dotted lines) then project to target effectors throughout the body.

To continue with the analogy of the circuit diagram, there are three different types of "junctions" that operate within the sympathetic system (Figure 15.3). The first type is most direct: the sympathetic nerve projects to the chain ganglion at the same level as the **target effector** (the organ, tissue, or gland to be innervated). An example of this type is spinal nerve T1 that synapses with the T1 chain ganglion to innervate the trachea. The fibers of this branch are called **white rami communicantes** (singular = ramus communicans); they are myelinated and therefore referred to as white (see Figure 15.3**a**). The axon from the central neuron (the preganglionic fiber shown as a solid line) synapses with the **ganglionic neuron** (with the postganglionic fiber shown as a dashed line). This neuron then projects to a target effector—in this case, the trachea—via **gray rami communicantes**, which are unmyelinated axons.

In some cases, the target effectors are located superior or inferior to the spinal segment at which the preganglionic fiber emerges. With respect to the "wiring" involved, the synapse with the ganglionic neuron occurs at chain ganglia superior or inferior to the location of the central neuron. An example of this is spinal nerve T1 that innervates the eye. The spinal nerve tracks up through the chain until it reaches the **superior cervical ganglion**, where it synapses with the postganglionic neuron (see Figure 15.3**b**). The cervical ganglia are referred to as **paravertebral ganglia**, given their location adjacent to prevertebral ganglia in the sympathetic chain.

Not all axons from the central neurons terminate in the chain ganglia. Additional branches from the ventral nerve root continue through the chain and on to one of the collateral ganglia as the **greater splanchnic nerve** or **lesser splanchnic nerve**. For example, the greater splanchnic nerve at the level of T5 synapses with a collateral ganglion outside the chain before making the connection to the postganglionic nerves that innervate the stomach (see Figure 15.3**c**).

Collateral ganglia, also called **prevertebral ganglia**, are situated anterior to the vertebral column and receive inputs from splanchnic nerves as well as central sympathetic neurons. They are associated with controlling organs in the abdominal cavity, and are also considered part of the enteric nervous system. The three collateral ganglia are the **celiac ganglion**, the **superior mesenteric ganglion**, and the **inferior mesenteric ganglion** (see Figure 15.2). The word celiac is derived from the Latin word "coelom," which refers to a body cavity (in this case, the abdominal cavity), and the word mesenteric refers to the digestive system.

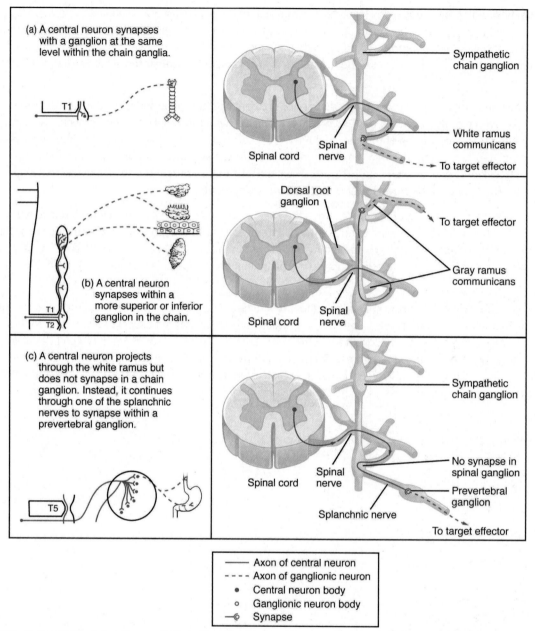

FIGURE 15.3 Sympathetic Connections and Chain Ganglia The axon from a central sympathetic neuron in the spinal cord can project to the periphery in a number of different ways. (a) The fiber can project out to the ganglion at the same level and synapse on a ganglionic neuron. (b) A branch can project to more superior or inferior ganglion in the chain. (c) A branch can project through the white ramus communicans, but not terminate on a ganglionic neuron in the chain. Instead, it projects through one of the splanchnic nerves to a collateral ganglion or the adrenal medulla (not pictured).

An axon from the central neuron that projects to a sympathetic ganglion is referred to as a **preganglionic fiber** or neuron, and represents the output from the CNS to the ganglion. Because the sympathetic ganglia are adjacent to the vertebral column, preganglionic sympathetic fibers are relatively short, and they are myelinated. A **postganglionic fiber**—the axon from a ganglionic neuron that projects to the target effector—represents the output of a ganglion that directly influences the organ. Compared with the preganglionic fibers, postganglionic sympathetic fibers are long because of the relatively greater distance from the ganglion to the target effector. These fibers are unmyelinated. (Note that the term "postganglionic neuron" may be used to describe the projection from a ganglion to the target. The problem with that usage is that the cell body is in the ganglion, and only the fiber is postganglionic. Typically, the term neuron applies to the entire cell.)

One type of preganglionic sympathetic fiber does not terminate in a ganglion. These are the axons from central sympathetic neurons that project to the **adrenal medulla**, the interior portion of the adrenal gland. These axons are still referred to as preganglionic fibers, but the target is not a ganglion. The adrenal medulla releases signaling molecules into the bloodstream, rather than using axons to communicate with target structures. The cells in the adrenal medulla that are contacted by the preganglionic fibers are called **chromaffin cells**. These cells are neurosecretory cells that develop from the neural crest along with the sympathetic ganglia, reinforcing the idea that the gland is, functionally, a sympathetic ganglion.

The projections of the sympathetic division of the autonomic nervous system diverge widely, resulting in a broad influence of the system throughout the body. As a response to a threat, the sympathetic system would increase heart rate and breathing rate and cause blood flow to the skeletal muscle to increase and blood flow to the digestive system to decrease. Sweat gland secretion should also increase as part of an integrated response. All of those physiological changes are going to be required to occur together to run away from the hunting lioness, or the modern equivalent. This divergence is seen in the branching patterns of preganglionic sympathetic neurons—a single preganglionic sympathetic neuron may have 10–20 targets. An axon that leaves a central neuron of the lateral horn in the thoracolumbar spinal cord will pass through the white ramus communicans and enter the sympathetic chain, where it will branch toward a variety of targets. At the level of the spinal cord at which the preganglionic sympathetic fiber exits the spinal cord, a branch will synapse on a neuron in the adjacent chain ganglion. Some branches will extend up or down to a different level of the chain ganglia. Other branches will pass through the chain ganglia and project through one of the splanchnic nerves to a collateral ganglion. Finally, some branches may project through the splanchnic nerves to the adrenal medulla. All of these branches mean that one preganglionic neuron can influence different regions of the sympathetic system very broadly, by acting on widely distributed organs.

Parasympathetic Division of the Autonomic Nervous System

The parasympathetic system can also be referred to as the **craniosacral system** (or outflow) because the preganglionic neurons are located in nuclei of the brain stem and the lateral horn of the sacral spinal cord.

The connections, or "circuits," of the parasympathetic division are similar to the general layout of the sympathetic division with a few specific differences (Figure 15.4). The preganglionic fibers from the cranial region travel in cranial nerves, whereas preganglionic fibers from the sacral region travel in spinal nerves. The targets of these fibers are **terminal ganglia**, which are located near—or even within—the target effector. These ganglia are often referred to as **intramural ganglia** when they are found within the walls of the target organ. The postganglionic fiber projects from the terminal ganglia a short distance to the target effector, or to the specific target tissue within the organ. Comparing the relative lengths of axons in the parasympathetic system, the preganglionic fibers are long and the postganglionic fibers are short because the ganglia are close to—and sometimes within—the target effectors.

The cranial component of the parasympathetic system is based in particular nuclei of the brain stem. In the midbrain, the **Edinger–Westphal nucleus** is part of the oculomotor complex, and axons from those neurons travel with the fibers in the oculomotor nerve (cranial nerve III) that innervate the extraocular muscles. The preganglionic parasympathetic fibers within cranial nerve III terminate in the **ciliary ganglion**, which is located in the posterior orbit. The postganglionic parasympathetic fibers then project to the smooth muscle of the iris to control pupillary size. In the upper medulla, the salivatory nuclei contain neurons with axons that project through the facial and glossopharyngeal nerves to ganglia that control salivary glands. Tear production is influenced by parasympathetic fibers in the facial nerve, which activate a ganglion, and ultimately the lacrimal (tear) gland. Neurons in the **dorsal nucleus of the vagus nerve** and the **nucleus ambiguus** project through the vagus nerve (cranial nerve X) to the terminal ganglia of the thoracic and abdominal cavities. Parasympathetic preganglionic fibers primarily influence the heart, bronchi, and esophagus in the thoracic cavity and the stomach, liver, pancreas, gall bladder, and small intestine of the abdominal cavity. The postganglionic fibers from the ganglia activated by the vagus nerve are often incorporated into the structure of the organ, such as the **mesenteric plexus** of the digestive tract organs and the intramural ganglia.

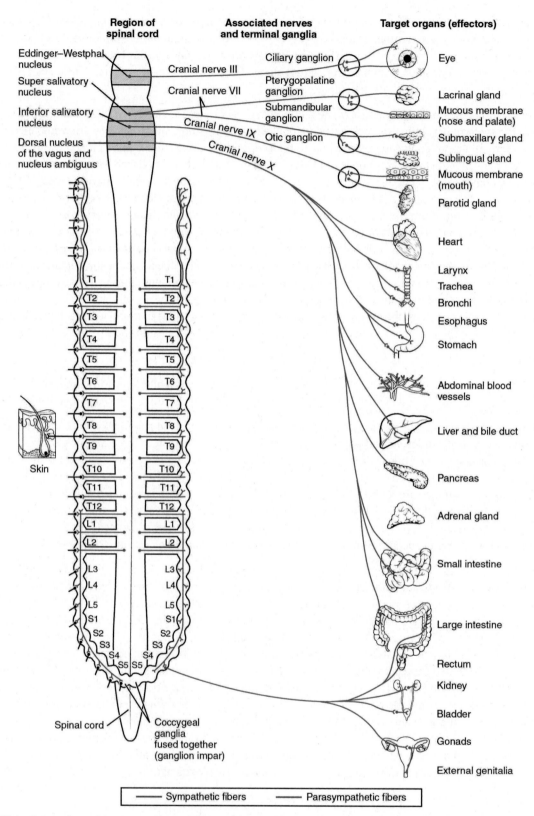

FIGURE 15.4   Connections of Parasympathetic Division of the Autonomic Nervous System   Neurons from brain-stem nuclei, or from the lateral horn of the sacral spinal cord, project to terminal ganglia near or within the various organs of the body. Axons from these ganglionic neurons then project the short distance to those target effectors.

Chemical Signaling in the Autonomic Nervous System

Where an autonomic neuron connects with a target, there is a synapse. The electrical signal of the action potential

Access for free at openstax.org

causes the release of a signaling molecule, which will bind to receptor proteins on the target cell. Synapses of the autonomic system are classified as either **cholinergic**, meaning that **acetylcholine (ACh)** is released, or **adrenergic**, meaning that **norepinephrine** is released. The terms cholinergic and adrenergic refer not only to the signaling molecule that is released but also to the class of receptors that each binds.

The cholinergic system includes two classes of receptor: the **nicotinic receptor** and the **muscarinic receptor**. Both receptor types bind to ACh and cause changes in the target cell. The nicotinic receptor is a **ligand-gated cation channel** and the muscarinic receptor is a **G protein–coupled receptor**. The receptors are named for, and differentiated by, other molecules that bind to them. Whereas nicotine will bind to the nicotinic receptor, and muscarine will bind to the muscarinic receptor, there is no cross-reactivity between the receptors. The situation is similar to locks and keys. Imagine two locks—one for a classroom and the other for an office—that are opened by two separate keys. The classroom key will not open the office door and the office key will not open the classroom door. This is similar to the specificity of nicotine and muscarine for their receptors. However, a master key can open multiple locks, such as a master key for the Biology Department that opens both the classroom and the office doors. This is similar to ACh that binds to both types of receptors. The molecules that define these receptors are not crucial—they are simply tools for researchers to use in the laboratory. These molecules are **exogenous**, meaning that they are made outside of the human body, so a researcher can use them without any confounding **endogenous** results (results caused by the molecules produced in the body).

The adrenergic system also has two types of receptors, named the **alpha (α)-adrenergic receptor** and **beta (β)-adrenergic receptor**. Unlike cholinergic receptors, these receptor types are not classified by which drugs can bind to them. All of them are G protein–coupled receptors. There are two types of α-adrenergic receptors, termed α_1, and α_2, and there are three types of β-adrenergic receptors, termed β_1, β_2 and β_3. An additional aspect of the adrenergic system is that there is a second signaling molecule called **epinephrine**. The chemical difference between norepinephrine and epinephrine is the addition of a methyl group (CH_3) in epinephrine. The prefix "nor-" actually refers to this chemical difference, in which a methyl group is missing.

The term adrenergic should remind you of the word adrenaline, which is associated with the fight-or-flight response described at the beginning of the chapter. Adrenaline and epinephrine are two names for the same molecule. The adrenal gland (in Latin, ad- = "on top of"; renal = "kidney") secretes adrenaline. The ending "-ine" refers to the chemical being derived, or extracted, from the adrenal gland. A similar construction from Greek instead of Latin results in the word epinephrine (epi- = "above"; nephr- = "kidney"). In scientific usage, epinephrine is preferred in the United States, whereas adrenaline is preferred in Great Britain, because "adrenalin" was once a registered, proprietary drug name in the United States. Though the drug is no longer sold, the convention of referring to this molecule by the two different names persists. Similarly, norepinephrine and noradrenaline are two names for the same molecule.

Having understood the cholinergic and adrenergic systems, their role in the autonomic system is relatively simple to understand. All preganglionic fibers, both sympathetic and parasympathetic, release ACh. All ganglionic neurons—the targets of these preganglionic fibers—have nicotinic receptors in their cell membranes. The nicotinic receptor is a ligand-gated cation channel that results in depolarization of the postsynaptic membrane. The postganglionic parasympathetic fibers also release ACh, but the receptors on their targets are muscarinic receptors, which are G protein–coupled receptors and do not exclusively cause depolarization of the postsynaptic membrane. Postganglionic sympathetic fibers release norepinephrine, except for fibers that project to sweat glands and to blood vessels associated with skeletal muscles, which release ACh (Table 15.1).

Autonomic System Signaling Molecules

	Sympathetic	Parasympathetic
Preganglionic	Acetylcholine → nicotinic receptor	Acetylcholine → nicotinic receptor
Postganglionic	Norepinephrine → α- or β-adrenergic receptors Acetylcholine → muscarinic receptor (associated with sweat glands and the blood vessels associated with skeletal muscles only	Acetylcholine → muscarinic receptor

TABLE 15.1

Signaling molecules can belong to two broad groups. Neurotransmitters are released at synapses, whereas hormones are released into the bloodstream. These are simplistic definitions, but they can help to clarify this point. Acetylcholine can be considered a neurotransmitter because it is released by axons at synapses. The adrenergic system, however, presents a challenge. Postganglionic sympathetic fibers release norepinephrine, which can be considered a neurotransmitter. But the adrenal medulla releases epinephrine and norepinephrine into circulation, so they should be considered hormones.

What are referred to here as synapses may not fit the strictest definition of synapse. Some sources will refer to the connection between a postganglionic fiber and a target effector as neuroeffector junctions; neurotransmitters, as defined above, would be called neuromodulators. The structure of postganglionic connections are not the typical synaptic end bulb that is found at the neuromuscular junction, but rather are chains of swellings along the length of a postganglionic fiber called a **varicosity** (Figure 15.5).

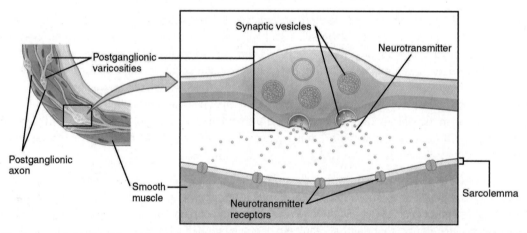

FIGURE 15.5 **Autonomic Varicosities** The connection between autonomic fibers and target effectors is not the same as the typical synapse, such as the neuromuscular junction. Instead of a synaptic end bulb, a neurotransmitter is released from swellings along the length of a fiber that makes an extended network of connections in the target effector.

Everyday Connection

Fight or Flight? What About Fright and Freeze?

The original usage of the epithet "fight or flight" comes from a scientist named Walter Cannon who worked at Harvard in 1915. The concept of homeostasis and the functioning of the sympathetic system had been introduced in France in the previous century. Cannon expanded the idea, and introduced the idea that an animal responds to a threat by preparing to stand and fight or run away. The nature of this response was thoroughly explained in a book on the physiology of pain, hunger, fear, and rage.

When students learn about the sympathetic system and the fight-or-flight response, they often stop and wonder about other responses. If you were faced with a lioness running toward you as pictured at the beginning of this chapter, would you run or would you stand your ground? Some people would say that they would freeze and not know what to do. So isn't there really more to what the autonomic system does than fight, flight, rest, or digest. What about fear and paralysis in the face of a threat?

The common epithet of "fight or flight" is being enlarged to be "fight, flight, or fright" or even "fight, flight, fright, or freeze." Cannon's original contribution was a catchy phrase to express some of what the nervous system does in response to a threat, but it is incomplete. The sympathetic system is responsible for the physiological responses to emotional states. The name "sympathetic" can be said to mean that (sym- = "together"; -pathos = "pain," "suffering," or "emotion").

⊘ INTERACTIVE LINK

Watch this video (http://openstax.org/l/nervsystem1) to learn more about the nervous system. As described in this video, the nervous system has a way to deal with threats and stress that is separate from the conscious control of the somatic nervous system. The system comes from a time when threats were about survival, but in the modern age, these responses become part of stress and anxiety. This video describes how the autonomic system is only part of the response to threats, or stressors. What other organ system gets involved, and what part of the brain coordinates the two systems for the entire response, including epinephrine (adrenaline) and cortisol?

15.2 Autonomic Reflexes and Homeostasis

LEARNING OBJECTIVES

By the end of this section, you will be able to:
- Compare the structure of somatic and autonomic reflex arcs
- Explain the differences in sympathetic and parasympathetic reflexes
- Differentiate between short and long reflexes
- Determine the effect of the autonomic nervous system on the regulation of the various organ systems on the basis of the signaling molecules involved
- Describe the effects of drugs that affect autonomic function

The autonomic nervous system regulates organ systems through circuits that resemble the reflexes described in the somatic nervous system. The main difference between the somatic and autonomic systems is in what target tissues are effectors. Somatic responses are solely based on skeletal muscle contraction. The autonomic system, however, targets cardiac and smooth muscle, as well as glandular tissue. Whereas the basic circuit is a **reflex arc**, there are differences in the structure of those reflexes for the somatic and autonomic systems.

The Structure of Reflexes

One difference between a **somatic reflex**, such as the withdrawal reflex, and a **visceral reflex**, which is an autonomic reflex, is in the **efferent branch**. The output of a somatic reflex is the lower motor neuron in the ventral horn of the spinal cord that projects directly to a skeletal muscle to cause its contraction. The output of a visceral reflex is a two-step pathway starting with the preganglionic fiber emerging from a lateral horn neuron in the spinal cord, or a cranial nucleus neuron in the brain stem, to a ganglion—followed by the postganglionic fiber projecting to a target effector. The other part of a reflex, the **afferent branch**, is often the same between the two systems. Sensory neurons receiving input from the periphery—with cell bodies in the sensory ganglia, either of a cranial nerve or a dorsal root ganglion adjacent to the spinal cord—project into the CNS to initiate the reflex (Figure 15.6). The Latin root "effere" means "to carry." Adding the prefix "ef-" suggests the meaning "to carry away," whereas adding the prefix "af-" suggests "to carry toward or inward."

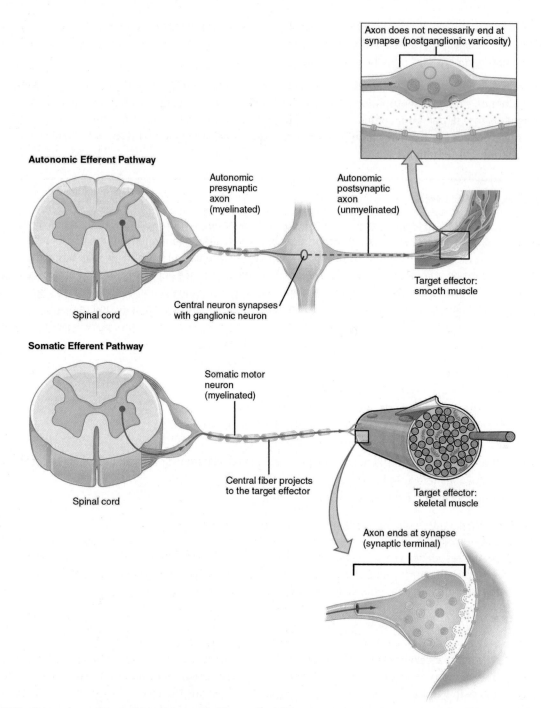

FIGURE 15.6　Comparison of Somatic and Visceral Reflexes　The afferent inputs to somatic and visceral reflexes are essentially the same, whereas the efferent branches are different. Somatic reflexes, for instance, involve a direct connection from the ventral horn of the spinal cord to the skeletal muscle. Visceral reflexes involve a projection from the central neuron to a ganglion, followed by a second projection from the ganglion to the target effector.

Afferent Branch

The afferent branch of a reflex arc does differ between somatic and visceral reflexes in some instances. Many of the inputs to visceral reflexes are from special or somatic senses, but particular senses are associated with the viscera that are not part of the conscious perception of the environment through the somatic nervous system. For example, there is a specific type of mechanoreceptor, called a **baroreceptor**, in the walls of the aorta and carotid sinuses that senses the stretch of those organs when blood volume or pressure increases. You do not have a conscious perception of having high blood pressure, but that is an important afferent branch of the cardiovascular and, particularly, vasomotor reflexes. The sensory neuron is essentially the same as any other general sensory neuron. The baroreceptor apparatus is part of the ending of a unipolar neuron that has a cell body in a sensory ganglion. The baroreceptors from the carotid arteries have axons in the glossopharyngeal nerve, and those from the aorta have axons in the vagus nerve.

Though visceral senses are not primarily a part of conscious perception, those sensations sometimes make it to conscious awareness. If a visceral sense is strong enough, it will be perceived. The sensory homunculus—the representation of the body in the primary somatosensory cortex—only has a small region allotted for the perception of internal stimuli. If you swallow a large bolus of food, for instance, you will probably feel the lump of that food as it pushes through your esophagus, or even if your stomach is distended after a large meal. If you inhale especially cold air, you can feel it as it enters your larynx and trachea. These sensations are not the same as feeling high blood pressure or blood sugar levels.

When particularly strong visceral sensations rise to the level of conscious perception, the sensations are often felt in unexpected places. For example, strong visceral sensations of the heart will be felt as pain in the left shoulder and left arm. This irregular pattern of projection of conscious perception of visceral sensations is called **referred pain**. Depending on the organ system affected, the referred pain will project to different areas of the body (Figure 15.7). The location of referred pain is not random, but a definitive explanation of the mechanism has not been established. The most broadly accepted theory for this phenomenon is that the visceral sensory fibers enter into the same level of the spinal cord as the somatosensory fibers of the referred pain location. By this explanation, the visceral sensory fibers from the mediastinal region, where the heart is located, would enter the spinal cord at the same level as the spinal nerves from the shoulder and arm, so the brain misinterprets the sensations from the mediastinal region as being from the axillary and brachial regions. Projections from the medial and inferior divisions of the cervical ganglia do enter the spinal cord at the middle to lower cervical levels, which is where the somatosensory fibers enter.

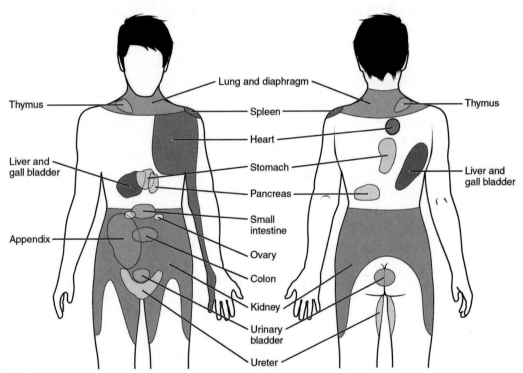

FIGURE 15.7   Referred Pain Chart   Conscious perception of visceral sensations map to specific regions of the body, as shown in this chart. Some sensations are felt locally, whereas others are perceived as affecting areas that are quite distant from the involved organ.

Disorders of the...

Nervous System: Kehr's Sign

Kehr's sign is the presentation of pain in the left shoulder, chest, and neck regions following rupture of the spleen. The spleen is in the upper-left abdominopelvic quadrant, but the pain is more in the shoulder and neck. How can this be? The sympathetic fibers connected to the spleen are from the celiac ganglion, which would be from the mid-thoracic to lower thoracic region whereas parasympathetic fibers are found in the vagus nerve, which connects in the medulla of the brain stem. However, the neck and shoulder would connect to the spinal cord at the mid-cervical level of the spinal cord. These connections do not fit with the expected correspondence of visceral and somatosensory fibers entering at the same level of the spinal cord.

The incorrect assumption would be that the visceral sensations are coming from the spleen directly. In fact, the visceral fibers are coming from the diaphragm. The nerve connecting to the diaphragm takes a special route. The phrenic nerve is connected to the spinal cord at cervical levels 3 to 5. The motor fibers that make up this nerve are responsible for the muscle contractions that drive ventilation. These fibers have left the spinal cord to enter the phrenic nerve, meaning that spinal cord damage below the mid-cervical level is not fatal by making ventilation impossible. Therefore, the visceral fibers from the diaphragm enter the spinal cord at the same level as the somatosensory fibers from the neck and shoulder.

The diaphragm plays a role in Kehr's sign because the spleen is just inferior to the diaphragm in the upper-left quadrant of the abdominopelvic cavity. When the spleen ruptures, blood spills into this region. The accumulating hemorrhage then puts pressure on the diaphragm. The visceral sensation is actually in the diaphragm, so the referred pain is in a region of the body that corresponds to the diaphragm, not the spleen.

Efferent Branch

The efferent branch of the visceral reflex arc begins with the projection from the central neuron along the preganglionic fiber. This fiber then makes a synapse on the ganglionic neuron that projects to the target effector.

The effector organs that are the targets of the autonomic system range from the iris and ciliary body of the eye to the urinary bladder and reproductive organs. The thoracolumbar output, through the various sympathetic ganglia, reaches all of these organs. The cranial component of the parasympathetic system projects from the eye to part of the intestines. The sacral component picks up with the majority of the large intestine and the pelvic organs of the urinary and reproductive systems.

Short and Long Reflexes

Somatic reflexes involve sensory neurons that connect sensory receptors to the CNS and motor neurons that project back out to the skeletal muscles. Visceral reflexes that involve the thoracolumbar or craniosacral systems share similar connections. However, there are reflexes that do not need to involve any CNS components. A **long reflex** has afferent branches that enter the spinal cord or brain and involve the efferent branches, as previously explained. A **short reflex** is completely peripheral and only involves the local integration of sensory input with motor output (Figure 15.8).

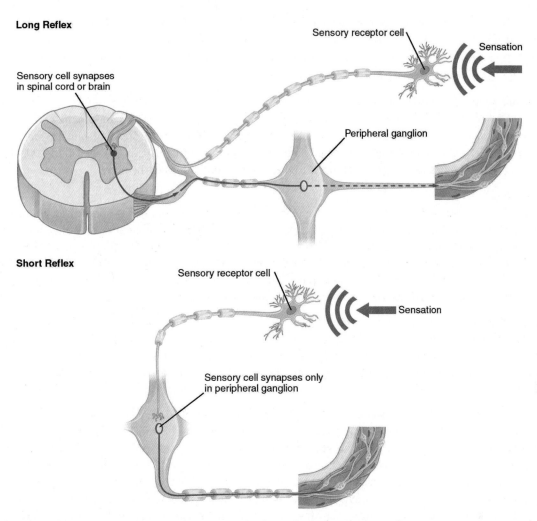

FIGURE 15.8 Short and Long Reflexes   Sensory input can stimulate either a short or a long reflex. A sensory neuron can project to the CNS or to an autonomic ganglion. The short reflex involves the direct stimulation of a postganglionic fiber by the sensory neuron, whereas the long reflex involves integration in the spinal cord or brain.

The difference between short and long reflexes is in the involvement of the CNS. Somatic reflexes always involve the CNS, even in a monosynaptic reflex in which the sensory neuron directly activates the motor neuron. That synapse is in the spinal cord or brain stem, so it has to involve the CNS. However, in the autonomic system there is the possibility that the CNS is not involved. Because the efferent branch of a visceral reflex involves two neurons—the central neuron and the ganglionic neuron—a "short circuit" can be possible. If a sensory neuron projects directly to the ganglionic neuron and causes it to activate the effector target, then the CNS is not involved.

A division of the nervous system that is related to the autonomic nervous system is the enteric nervous system. The word enteric refers to the digestive organs, so this represents the nervous tissue that is part of the digestive system. There are a few myenteric plexuses in which the nervous tissue in the wall of the digestive tract organs can directly influence digestive function. If stretch receptors in the stomach are activated by the filling and distension of the stomach, a short reflex will directly activate the smooth muscle fibers of the stomach wall to increase motility to digest the excessive food in the stomach. No CNS involvement is needed because the stretch receptor is directly activating a neuron in the wall of the stomach that causes the smooth muscle to contract. That neuron, connected to the smooth muscle, is a postganglionic parasympathetic neuron that can be controlled by a fiber found in the vagus nerve.

🔗 INTERACTIVE LINK

Read this article (http://openstax.org/l/strokespell) to learn about a teenager who experiences a series of spells that suggest a stroke. He undergoes endless tests and seeks input from multiple doctors. In the end, one expert, one question, and a simple blood pressure cuff answers the question. Why would the heart have to beat faster when the teenager changes his body position from lying down to sitting, and then to standing?

Balance in Competing Autonomic Reflex Arcs

The autonomic nervous system is important for homeostasis because its two divisions compete at the target effector. The balance of homeostasis is attributable to the competing inputs from the sympathetic and parasympathetic divisions (dual innervation). At the level of the target effector, the signal of which system is sending the message is strictly chemical. A signaling molecule binds to a receptor that causes changes in the target cell, which in turn causes the tissue or organ to respond to the changing conditions of the body.

Competing Neurotransmitters

The postganglionic fibers of the sympathetic and parasympathetic divisions both release neurotransmitters that bind to receptors on their targets. Postganglionic sympathetic fibers release norepinephrine, with a minor exception, whereas postganglionic parasympathetic fibers release ACh. For any given target, the difference in which division of the autonomic nervous system is exerting control is just in what chemical binds to its receptors. The target cells will have adrenergic and muscarinic receptors. If norepinephrine is released, it will bind to the adrenergic receptors present on the target cell, and if ACh is released, it will bind to the muscarinic receptors on the target cell.

In the sympathetic system, there are exceptions to this pattern of dual innervation. The postganglionic sympathetic fibers that contact the blood vessels within skeletal muscle and that contact sweat glands do not release norepinephrine, they release ACh. This does not create any problem because there is no parasympathetic input to the sweat glands. Sweat glands have muscarinic receptors and produce and secrete sweat in response to the presence of ACh.

At most of the other targets of the autonomic system, the effector response is based on which neurotransmitter is released and what receptor is present. For example, regions of the heart that establish heart rate are contacted by postganglionic fibers from both systems. If norepinephrine is released onto those cells, it binds to an adrenergic receptor that causes the cells to depolarize faster, and the heart rate increases. If ACh is released onto those cells, it binds to a muscarinic receptor that causes the cells to hyperpolarize so that they cannot reach threshold as easily, and the heart rate slows. Without this parasympathetic input, the heart would work at a rate of approximately 100 beats per minute (bpm). The sympathetic system speeds that up, as it would during exercise, to 120–140 bpm, for example. The parasympathetic system slows it down to the resting heart rate of 60–80 bpm.

Another example is in the control of pupillary size (Figure 15.9). The afferent branch responds to light hitting the retina. Photoreceptors are activated, and the signal is transferred to the retinal ganglion cells that send an action potential along the optic nerve into the diencephalon. If light levels are low, the sympathetic system sends a signal out through the upper thoracic spinal cord to the superior cervical ganglion of the sympathetic chain. The postganglionic fiber then projects to the iris, where it releases norepinephrine onto the radial fibers of the iris (a smooth muscle). When those fibers contract, the pupil dilates—increasing the amount of light hitting the retina. If light levels are too high, the parasympathetic system sends a signal out from the Edinger–Westphal nucleus through the oculomotor nerve. This fiber synapses in the ciliary ganglion in the posterior orbit. The postganglionic fiber then projects to the iris, where it releases ACh onto the circular fibers of the iris—another smooth muscle. When those fibers contract, the pupil constricts to limit the amount of light hitting the retina.

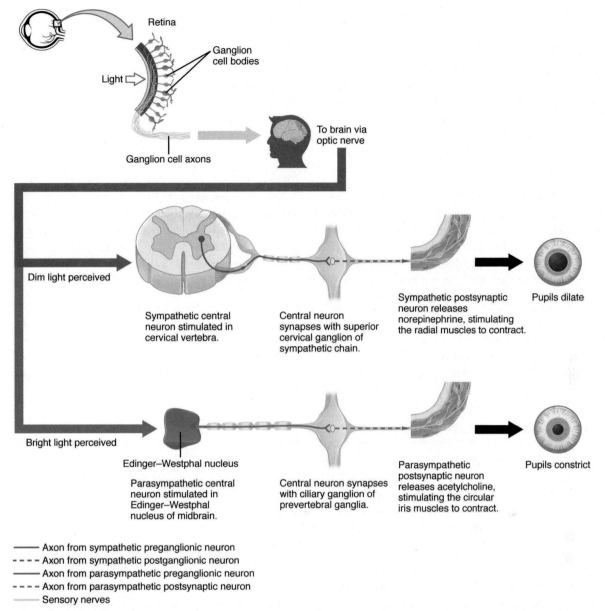

- ——— Axon from sympathetic preganglionic neuron
- - - - - Axon from sympathetic postganglionic neuron
- ——— Axon from parasympathetic preganglionic neuron
- - - - - Axon from parasympathetic postsynaptic neuron
- ——— Sensory nerves

FIGURE 15.9   Autonomic Control of Pupillary Size   Activation of the pupillary reflex comes from the amount of light activating the retinal ganglion cells, as sent along the optic nerve. The output of the sympathetic system projects through the superior cervical ganglion, whereas the parasympathetic system originates out of the midbrain and projects through the oculomotor nerve to the ciliary ganglion, which then projects to the iris. The postganglionic fibers of either division release neurotransmitters onto the smooth muscles of the iris to cause changes in the pupillary size. Norepinephrine results in dilation and ACh results in constriction.

In this example, the autonomic system is controlling how much light hits the retina. It is a homeostatic reflex mechanism that keeps the activation of photoreceptors within certain limits. In the context of avoiding a threat like the lioness on the savannah, the sympathetic response for fight or flight will increase pupillary diameter so that more light hits the retina and more visual information is available for running away. Likewise, the parasympathetic response of rest reduces the amount of light reaching the retina, allowing the photoreceptors to cycle through bleaching and be regenerated for further visual perception; this is what the homeostatic process is attempting to maintain.

INTERACTIVE LINK

Watch this video (http://openstax.org/l/pupillary) to learn about the pupillary reflexes. The pupillary light reflex involves sensory input through the optic nerve and motor response through the oculomotor nerve to the ciliary ganglion, which projects to the circular fibers of the iris. As shown in this short animation, pupils will constrict to limit the amount of light falling on the retina under bright lighting conditions. What constitutes the afferent and efferent branches of the competing reflex (dilation)?

Autonomic Tone

Organ systems are balanced between the input from the sympathetic and parasympathetic divisions. When something upsets that balance, the homeostatic mechanisms strive to return it to its regular state. For each organ system, there may be more of a sympathetic or parasympathetic tendency to the resting state, which is known as the **autonomic tone** of the system. For example, the heart rate was described above. Because the resting heart rate is the result of the parasympathetic system slowing the heart down from its intrinsic rate of 100 bpm, the heart can be said to be in parasympathetic tone.

In a similar fashion, another aspect of the cardiovascular system is primarily under sympathetic control. Blood pressure is partially determined by the contraction of smooth muscle in the walls of blood vessels. These tissues have adrenergic receptors that respond to the release of norepinephrine from postganglionic sympathetic fibers by constricting and increasing blood pressure. The hormones released from the adrenal medulla—epinephrine and norepinephrine—will also bind to these receptors. Those hormones travel through the bloodstream where they can easily interact with the receptors in the vessel walls. The parasympathetic system has no significant input to the systemic blood vessels, so the sympathetic system determines their tone.

There are a limited number of blood vessels that respond to sympathetic input in a different fashion. Blood vessels in skeletal muscle, particularly those in the lower limbs, are more likely to dilate. It does not have an overall effect on blood pressure to alter the tone of the vessels, but rather allows for blood flow to increase for those skeletal muscles that will be active in the fight-or-flight response. The blood vessels that have a parasympathetic projection are limited to those in the erectile tissue of the reproductive organs. Acetylcholine released by these postganglionic parasympathetic fibers cause the vessels to dilate, leading to the engorgement of the erectile tissue.

 HOMEOSTATIC IMBALANCES

Orthostatic Hypotension

Have you ever stood up quickly and felt dizzy for a moment? This is because, for one reason or another, blood is not getting to your brain so it is briefly deprived of oxygen. When you change position from sitting or lying down to standing, your cardiovascular system has to adjust for a new challenge, keeping blood pumping up into the head while gravity is pulling more and more blood down into the legs.

The reason for this is a sympathetic reflex that maintains the output of the heart in response to postural change. When a person stands up, proprioceptors indicate that the body is changing position. A signal goes to the CNS, which then sends a signal to the upper thoracic spinal cord neurons of the sympathetic division. The sympathetic system then causes the heart to beat faster and the blood vessels to constrict. Both changes will make it possible for the cardiovascular system to maintain the rate of blood delivery to the brain. Blood is being pumped superiorly through the internal branch of the carotid arteries into the brain, against the force of gravity. Gravity is not increasing while standing, but blood is more likely to flow down into the legs as they are extended for standing. This sympathetic reflex keeps the brain well oxygenated so that cognitive and other neural processes are not interrupted.

Sometimes this does not work properly. If the sympathetic system cannot increase cardiac output, then blood pressure into the brain will decrease, and a brief neurological loss can be felt. This can be brief, as a slight "wooziness" when standing up too quickly, or a loss of balance and neurological impairment for a period of time. The name for this is orthostatic hypotension, which means that blood pressure goes below the homeostatic set point when standing. It can be the result of standing up faster than the reflex can occur, which may be referred to as a benign "head rush," or it may be the result of an underlying cause.

There are two basic reasons that orthostatic hypotension can occur. First, blood volume is too low and the sympathetic reflex is not effective. This hypovolemia may be the result of dehydration or medications that affect fluid balance, such as diuretics or vasodilators. Both of these medications are meant to lower blood pressure, which may be necessary in the case of systemic hypertension, and regulation of the medications may alleviate the problem. Sometimes increasing fluid intake or water retention through salt intake can improve the situation.

The second underlying cause of orthostatic hypotension is autonomic failure. There are several disorders that result in compromised sympathetic functions. The disorders range from diabetes to multiple system atrophy (a loss of control over many systems in the body), and addressing the underlying condition can improve the hypotension. For example, with diabetes, peripheral nerve damage can occur, which would affect the postganglionic sympathetic fibers. Getting blood glucose levels under control can improve neurological deficits associated with diabetes.

15.3 Central Control

LEARNING OBJECTIVES

By the end of this section, you will be able to:

- Describe the role of higher centers of the brain in autonomic regulation
- Explain the connection of the hypothalamus to homeostasis
- Describe the regions of the CNS that link the autonomic system with emotion
- Describe the pathways important to descending control of the autonomic system

The pupillary light reflex (Figure 15.10) begins when light hits the retina and causes a signal to travel along the optic nerve. This is visual sensation, because the afferent branch of this reflex is simply sharing the special sense pathway. Bright light hitting the retina leads to the parasympathetic response, through the oculomotor nerve, followed by the postganglionic fiber from the ciliary ganglion, which stimulates the circular fibers of the iris to contract and constrict the pupil. When light hits the retina in one eye, both pupils contract. When that light is removed, both pupils dilate again back to the resting position. When the stimulus is unilateral (presented to only one eye), the response is bilateral (both eyes). The same is not true for somatic reflexes. If you touch a hot radiator, you only pull that arm back, not both. Central control of autonomic reflexes is different than for somatic reflexes. The hypothalamus, along with other CNS locations, controls the autonomic system.

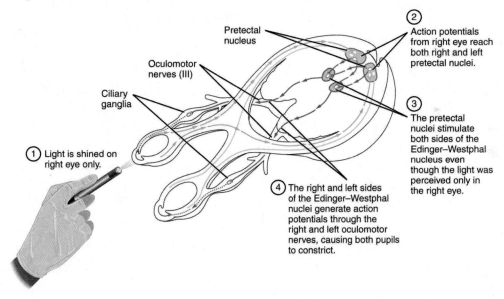

FIGURE 15.10 Pupillary Reflex Pathways   The pupil is under competing autonomic control in response to light levels hitting the retina. The sympathetic system will dilate the pupil when the retina is not receiving enough light, and the parasympathetic system will constrict the pupil when too much light hits the retina.

Forebrain Structures

Autonomic control is based on the visceral reflexes, composed of the afferent and efferent branches. These homeostatic mechanisms are based on the balance between the two divisions of the autonomic system, which results in tone for various organs that is based on the predominant input from the sympathetic or parasympathetic systems. Coordinating that balance requires integration that begins with forebrain structures like the hypothalamus and continues into the brain stem and spinal cord.

The Hypothalamus

The hypothalamus is the control center for many homeostatic mechanisms. It regulates both autonomic function and endocrine function. The roles it plays in the pupillary reflexes demonstrates the importance of this control center. The optic nerve projects primarily to the thalamus, which is the necessary relay to the occipital cortex for conscious visual perception. Another projection of the optic nerve, however, goes to the hypothalamus.

The hypothalamus then uses this visual system input to drive the pupillary reflexes. If the retina is activated by high levels of light, the hypothalamus stimulates the parasympathetic response. If the optic nerve message shows that low levels of light are falling on the retina, the hypothalamus activates the sympathetic response. Output from the hypothalamus follows two main tracts, the **dorsal longitudinal fasciculus** and the **medial forebrain bundle** (Figure 15.11). Along these two tracts, the hypothalamus can influence the Edinger–Westphal nucleus of the oculomotor complex or the lateral horns of the thoracic spinal cord.

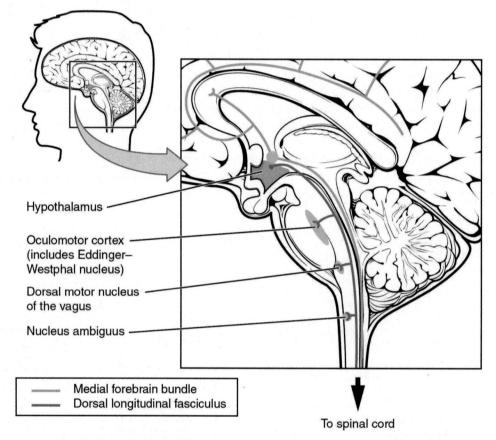

FIGURE 15.11   Fiber Tracts of the Central Autonomic System   The hypothalamus is the source of most of the central control of autonomic function. It receives input from cerebral structures and projects to brain stem and spinal cord structures to regulate the balance of sympathetic and parasympathetic input to the organ systems of the body. The main pathways for this are the medial forebrain bundle and the dorsal longitudinal fasciculus.

These two tracts connect the hypothalamus with the major parasympathetic nuclei in the brain stem and the preganglionic (central) neurons of the thoracolumbar spinal cord. The hypothalamus also receives input from other areas of the forebrain through the medial forebrain bundle. The olfactory cortex, the septal nuclei of the basal forebrain, and the amygdala project into the hypothalamus through the medial forebrain bundle. These forebrain structures inform the hypothalamus about the state of the nervous system and can influence the regulatory processes of homeostasis. A good example of this is found in the amygdala, which is found beneath the cerebral cortex of the temporal lobe and plays a role in our ability to remember and feel emotions.

The Amygdala

The amygdala is a group of nuclei in the medial region of the temporal lobe that is part of the **limbic lobe** (Figure 15.12). The limbic lobe includes structures that are involved in emotional responses, as well as structures that contribute to memory function. The limbic lobe has strong connections with the hypothalamus and influences the

Access for free at openstax.org

state of its activity on the basis of emotional state. For example, when you are anxious or scared, the amygdala will send signals to the hypothalamus along the medial forebrain bundle that will stimulate the sympathetic fight-or-flight response. The hypothalamus will also stimulate the release of stress hormones through its control of the endocrine system in response to amygdala input.

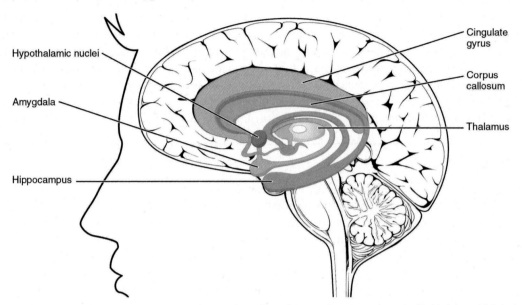

FIGURE 15.12   The Limbic Lobe   Structures arranged around the edge of the cerebrum constitute the limbic lobe, which includes the amygdala, hippocampus, and cingulate gyrus, and connects to the hypothalamus.

The Medulla

The medulla contains nuclei referred to as the **cardiovascular center**, which controls the smooth and cardiac muscle of the cardiovascular system through autonomic connections. When the homeostasis of the cardiovascular system shifts, such as when blood pressure changes, the coordination of the autonomic system can be accomplished within this region. Furthermore, when descending inputs from the hypothalamus stimulate this area, the sympathetic system can increase activity in the cardiovascular system, such as in response to anxiety or stress. The preganglionic sympathetic fibers that are responsible for increasing heart rate are referred to as the **cardiac accelerator nerves**, whereas the preganglionic sympathetic fibers responsible for constricting blood vessels compose the **vasomotor nerves**.

Several brain stem nuclei are important for the visceral control of major organ systems. One brain stem nucleus involved in cardiovascular function is the solitary nucleus. It receives sensory input about blood pressure and cardiac function from the glossopharyngeal and vagus nerves, and its output will activate sympathetic stimulation of the heart or blood vessels through the upper thoracic lateral horn. Another brain stem nucleus important for visceral control is the dorsal motor nucleus of the vagus nerve, which is the motor nucleus for the parasympathetic functions ascribed to the vagus nerve, including decreasing the heart rate, relaxing bronchial tubes in the lungs, and activating digestive function through the enteric nervous system. The nucleus ambiguus, which is named for its ambiguous histology, also contributes to the parasympathetic output of the vagus nerve and targets muscles in the pharynx and larynx for swallowing and speech, as well as contributing to the parasympathetic tone of the heart along with the dorsal motor nucleus of the vagus.

Everyday Connection

Exercise and the Autonomic System
In addition to its association with the fight-or-flight response and rest-and-digest functions, the autonomic system is responsible for certain everyday functions. For example, it comes into play when homeostatic mechanisms dynamically change, such as the physiological changes that accompany exercise. Getting on the treadmill and putting in a good workout will cause the heart rate to increase, breathing to be stronger and

deeper, sweat glands to activate, and the digestive system to suspend activity. These are the same physiological changes associated with the fight-or-flight response, but there is nothing chasing you on that treadmill.

This is not a simple homeostatic mechanism at work because "maintaining the internal environment" would mean getting all those changes back to their set points. Instead, the sympathetic system has become active during exercise so that your body can cope with what is happening. A homeostatic mechanism is dealing with the conscious decision to push the body away from a resting state. The heart, actually, is moving away from its homeostatic set point. Without any input from the autonomic system, the heart would beat at approximately 100 bpm, and the parasympathetic system slows that down to the resting rate of approximately 70 bpm. But in the middle of a good workout, you should see your heart rate at 120–140 bpm. You could say that the body is stressed because of what you are doing to it. Homeostatic mechanisms are trying to keep blood pH in the normal range, or to keep body temperature under control, but those are in response to the choice to exercise.

(@) INTERACTIVE LINK

Watch this video (http://openstax.org/l/emotions) to learn about physical responses to emotion. The autonomic system, which is important for regulating the homeostasis of the organ systems, is also responsible for our physiological responses to emotions such as fear. The video summarizes the extent of the body's reactions and describes several effects of the autonomic system in response to fear. On the basis of what you have already studied about autonomic function, which effect would you expect to be associated with parasympathetic, rather than sympathetic, activity?

15.4 Drugs that Affect the Autonomic System

LEARNING OBJECTIVES

By the end of this section, you will be able to:
- List the classes of pharmaceuticals that interact with the autonomic nervous system
- Differentiate between cholinergic and adrenergic compounds
- Differentiate between sympathomimetic and sympatholytic drugs
- Relate the consequences of nicotine abuse with respect to autonomic control of the cardiovascular system

An important way to understand the effects of native neurochemicals in the autonomic system is in considering the effects of pharmaceutical drugs. This can be considered in terms of how drugs change autonomic function. These effects will primarily be based on how drugs act at the receptors of the autonomic system neurochemistry. The signaling molecules of the nervous system interact with proteins in the cell membranes of various target cells. In fact, no effect can be attributed to just the signaling molecules themselves without considering the receptors. A chemical that the body produces to interact with those receptors is called an **endogenous chemical**, whereas a chemical introduced to the system from outside is an **exogenous chemical**. Exogenous chemicals may be of a natural origin, such as a plant extract, or they may be synthetically produced in a pharmaceutical laboratory.

Broad Autonomic Effects

One important drug that affects the autonomic system broadly is not a pharmaceutical therapeutic agent associated with the system. This drug is nicotine. The effects of nicotine on the autonomic nervous system are important in considering the role smoking can play in health.

All ganglionic neurons of the autonomic system, in both sympathetic and parasympathetic ganglia, are activated by ACh released from preganglionic fibers. The ACh receptors on these neurons are of the nicotinic type, meaning that they are ligand-gated ion channels. When the neurotransmitter released from the preganglionic fiber binds to the receptor protein, a channel opens to allow positive ions to cross the cell membrane. The result is depolarization of the ganglia. Nicotine acts as an ACh analog at these synapses, so when someone takes in the drug, it binds to these ACh receptors and activates the ganglionic neurons, causing them to depolarize.

Ganglia of both divisions are activated equally by the drug. For many target organs in the body, this results in no net change. The competing inputs to the system cancel each other out and nothing significant happens. For example, the sympathetic system will cause sphincters in the digestive tract to contract, limiting digestive propulsion, but the parasympathetic system will cause the contraction of other muscles in the digestive tract, which will try to push the contents of the digestive system along. The end result is that the food does not really move along and the digestive system has not appreciably changed.

The system in which this can be problematic is in the cardiovascular system, which is why smoking is a risk factor for cardiovascular disease. First, there is no significant parasympathetic regulation of blood pressure. Only a limited number of blood vessels are affected by parasympathetic input, so nicotine will preferentially cause the vascular tone to become more sympathetic, which means blood pressure will be increased. Second, the autonomic control of the heart is special. Unlike skeletal or smooth muscles, cardiac muscle is intrinsically active, meaning that it generates its own action potentials. The autonomic system does not cause the heart to beat, it just speeds it up (sympathetic) or slows it down (parasympathetic). The mechanisms for this are not mutually exclusive, so the heart receives conflicting signals, and the rhythm of the heart can be affected (Figure 15.13).

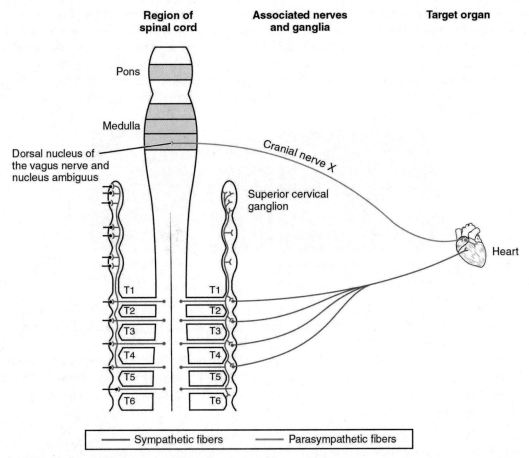

FIGURE 15.13   Autonomic Connections to Heart and Blood Vessels   The nicotinic receptor is found on all autonomic ganglia, but the cardiovascular connections are particular, and do not conform to the usual competitive projections that would just cancel each other out when stimulated by nicotine. The opposing signals to the heart would both depolarize and hyperpolarize the heart cells that establish the rhythm of the heartbeat, likely causing arrhythmia. Only the sympathetic system governs systemic blood pressure so nicotine would cause an increase.

Sympathetic Effect

The neurochemistry of the sympathetic system is based on the adrenergic system. Norepinephrine and epinephrine influence target effectors by binding to the α-adrenergic or β-adrenergic receptors. Drugs that affect the sympathetic system affect these chemical systems. The drugs can be classified by whether they enhance the functions of the sympathetic system or interrupt those functions. A drug that enhances adrenergic function is known as a **sympathomimetic drug**, whereas a drug that interrupts adrenergic function is a **sympatholytic drug**.

Sympathomimetic Drugs

When the sympathetic system is not functioning correctly or the body is in a state of homeostatic imbalance, these drugs act at postganglionic terminals and synapses in the sympathetic efferent pathway. These drugs either bind to particular adrenergic receptors and mimic norepinephrine at the synapses between sympathetic postganglionic fibers and their targets, or they increase the production and release of norepinephrine from postganglionic fibers. Also, to increase the effectiveness of adrenergic chemicals released from the fibers, some of these drugs may block the removal or reuptake of the neurotransmitter from the synapse.

A common sympathomimetic drug is phenylephrine, which is a common component of decongestants. It can also be used to dilate the pupil and to raise blood pressure. Phenylephrine is known as an α_1-adrenergic **agonist**, meaning that it binds to a specific adrenergic receptor, stimulating a response. In this role, phenylephrine will bind to the adrenergic receptors in bronchioles of the lungs and cause them to dilate. By opening these structures, accumulated mucus can be cleared out of the lower respiratory tract. Phenylephrine is often paired with other pharmaceuticals, such as analgesics, as in the "sinus" version of many over-the-counter drugs, such as Tylenol Sinus® or Excedrin Sinus®, or in expectorants for chest congestion such as in Robitussin CF®.

A related molecule, called pseudoephedrine, was much more commonly used in these applications than was phenylephrine, until the molecule became useful in the illicit production of amphetamines. Phenylephrine is not as effective as a drug because it can be partially broken down in the digestive tract before it is ever absorbed. Like the adrenergic agents, phenylephrine is effective in dilating the pupil, known as **mydriasis** (Figure 15.14). Phenylephrine is used during an eye exam in an ophthalmologist's or optometrist's office for this purpose. It can also be used to increase blood pressure in situations in which cardiac function is compromised, such as under anesthesia or during septic shock.

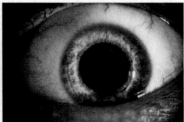

FIGURE 15.14 Mydriasis   The sympathetic system causes pupillary dilation when norepinephrine binds to an adrenergic receptor in the radial fibers of the iris smooth muscle. Phenylephrine mimics this action by binding to the same receptor when drops are applied onto the surface of the eye in a doctor's office. (credit: Corey Theiss / Vulegenda/Wikimedia Commons)

Other drugs that enhance adrenergic function are not associated with therapeutic uses, but affect the functions of the sympathetic system in a similar fashion. Cocaine primarily interferes with the uptake of dopamine at the synapse and can also increase adrenergic function. Caffeine is an antagonist to a different neurotransmitter receptor, called the adenosine receptor. Adenosine will suppress adrenergic activity, specifically the release of norepinephrine at synapses, so caffeine indirectly increases adrenergic activity. There is some evidence that caffeine can aid in the therapeutic use of drugs, perhaps by potentiating (increasing) sympathetic function, as is suggested by the inclusion of caffeine in over-the-counter analgesics such as Excedrin®.

Sympatholytic Drugs

Drugs that interfere with sympathetic function are referred to as sympatholytic, or sympathoplegic, drugs. They primarily work as an **antagonist** to the adrenergic receptors. They block the ability of norepinephrine or epinephrine to bind to the receptors so that the effect is "cut" or "takes a blow," to refer to the endings "-lytic" and "-plegic," respectively. The various drugs of this class will be specific to α-adrenergic or β-adrenergic receptors, or to their receptor subtypes.

Possibly the most familiar type of sympatholytic drug are the β-blockers. These drugs are often used to treat cardiovascular disease because they block the β-receptors associated with vasoconstriction and cardioacceleration. By allowing blood vessels to dilate, or keeping heart rate from increasing, these drugs can improve cardiac function in a compromised system, such as for a person with congestive heart failure or who has previously suffered a heart attack. A couple of common versions of β-blockers are metoprolol, which specifically blocks the β_1-receptor, and propanolol, which nonspecifically blocks β-receptors. There are other drugs that are α-blockers and can affect the sympathetic system in a similar way.

Other uses for sympatholytic drugs are as antianxiety medications. A common example of this is clonidine, which is an α-agonist. The sympathetic system is tied to anxiety to the point that the sympathetic response can be referred to as "fight, flight, or fright." Clonidine is used for other treatments aside from hypertension and anxiety, including pain conditions and attention deficit hyperactivity disorder.

Parasympathetic Effects

Drugs affecting parasympathetic functions can be classified into those that increase or decrease activity at postganglionic terminals. Parasympathetic postganglionic fibers release ACh, and the receptors on the targets are muscarinic receptors. There are several types of muscarinic receptors, M1–M5, but the drugs are not usually specific to the specific types. Parasympathetic drugs can be either muscarinic agonists or antagonists, or have indirect effects on the cholinergic system. Drugs that enhance cholinergic effects are called **parasympathomimetic drugs**, whereas those that inhibit cholinergic effects are referred to as **anticholinergic drugs**.

Pilocarpine is a nonspecific muscarinic agonist commonly used to treat disorders of the eye. It reverses mydriasis, such as is caused by phenylephrine, and can be administered after an eye exam. Along with constricting the pupil through the smooth muscle of the iris, pilocarpine will also cause the ciliary muscle to contract. This will open perforations at the base of the cornea, allowing for the drainage of aqueous humor from the anterior compartment of the eye and, therefore, reducing intraocular pressure related to glaucoma.

Atropine and scopolamine are part of a class of muscarinic antagonists that come from the *Atropa* genus of plants that include belladonna or deadly nightshade (Figure 15.15). The name of one of these plants, belladonna, refers to the fact that extracts from this plant were used cosmetically for dilating the pupil. The active chemicals from this plant block the muscarinic receptors in the iris and allow the pupil to dilate, which is considered attractive because it makes the eyes appear larger. Humans are instinctively attracted to anything with larger eyes, which comes from the fact that the ratio of eye-to-head size is different in infants (or baby animals) and can elicit an emotional response. The cosmetic use of belladonna extract was essentially acting on this response. Atropine is no longer used in this cosmetic capacity for reasons related to the other name for the plant, which is deadly nightshade. Suppression of parasympathetic function, especially when it becomes systemic, can be fatal. Autonomic regulation is disrupted and anticholinergic symptoms develop. The berries of this plant are highly toxic, but can be mistaken for other berries. The antidote for atropine or scopolamine poisoning is pilocarpine.

FIGURE 15.15   Belladonna Plant   The plant from the genus *Atropa*, which is known as belladonna or deadly nightshade, was used cosmetically to dilate pupils, but can be fatal when ingested. The berries on the plant may seem attractive as a fruit, but they contain the same anticholinergic compounds as the rest of the plant.

Sympathetic and Parasympathetic Effects of Different Drug Types

Drug type	Example(s)	Sympathetic effect	Parasympathetic effect	Overall result
Nicotinic agonists	Nicotine	Mimic ACh at preganglionic synapses, causing activation of postganglionic fibers and the release of norepinephrine onto the target organ	Mimic ACh at preganglionic synapses, causing activation of postganglionic fibers and the release of ACh onto the target organ	Most conflicting signals cancel each other out, but cardiovascular system is susceptible to hypertension and arrhythmias
Sympathomimetic drugs	Phenylephrine	Bind to adrenergic receptors or mimics sympathetic action in some other way	No effect	Increase sympathetic tone
Sympatholytic drugs	β-blockers such as propanolol or metoprolol; α-agonists such as clonidine	Block binding to adrenergic drug or decrease adrenergic signals	No effect	Increase parasympathetic tone
Parasymphatho-mimetics/ muscarinic agonists	Pilocarpine	No effect, except on sweat glands	Bind to muscarinic receptor, similar to ACh	Increase parasympathetic tone
Anticholinergics/ muscarinic antagonists	Atropine, scopolamine, dimenhydrinate	No effect	Block muscarinic receptors and parasympathetic function	Increase sympathetic tone

TABLE 15.2

Disorders of the...

Autonomic Nervous System

Approximately 33 percent of people experience a mild problem with motion sickness, whereas up to 66 percent experience motion sickness under extreme conditions, such as being on a tossing boat with no view of the horizon. Connections between regions in the brain stem and the autonomic system result in the symptoms of nausea, cold sweats, and vomiting.

The part of the brain responsible for vomiting, or emesis, is known as the area postrema. It is located next to the fourth ventricle and is not restricted by the blood–brain barrier, which allows it to respond to chemicals in the bloodstream—namely, toxins that will stimulate emesis. There are significant connections between this area, the solitary nucleus, and the dorsal motor nucleus of the vagus nerve. These autonomic system and nuclei connections are associated with the symptoms of motion sickness.

Motion sickness is the result of conflicting information from the visual and vestibular systems. If motion is perceived by the visual system without the complementary vestibular stimuli, or through vestibular stimuli without visual confirmation, the brain stimulates emesis and the associated symptoms. The area postrema, by itself, appears to be able to stimulate emesis in response to toxins in the blood, but it is also connected to the autonomic system and can trigger a similar response to motion.

Autonomic drugs are used to combat motion sickness. Though it is often described as a dangerous and deadly drug, scopolamine is used to treat motion sickness. A popular treatment for motion sickness is the transdermal scopolamine patch. Scopolamine is one of the substances derived from the *Atropa* genus along with atropine. At higher doses, those substances are thought to be poisonous and can lead to an extreme sympathetic syndrome. However, the transdermal patch regulates the release of the drug, and the concentration is kept very low so that the dangers are avoided. For those who are concerned about using "The Most Dangerous Drug," as some websites will call it, antihistamines such as dimenhydrinate (Dramamine®) can be used.

⊘ INTERACTIVE LINK

Watch this video (http://openstax.org/l/3Dmovies) to learn about the side effects of 3-D movies. As discussed in this video, movies that are shot in 3-D can cause motion sickness, which elicits the autonomic symptoms of nausea and sweating. The disconnection between the perceived motion on the screen and the lack of any change in equilibrium stimulates these symptoms. Why do you think sitting close to the screen or right in the middle of the theater makes motion sickness during a 3-D movie worse?

Key Terms

acetylcholine (ACh)   neurotransmitter that binds at a motor end-plate to trigger depolarization

adrenal medulla   interior portion of the adrenal (or suprarenal) gland that releases epinephrine and norepinephrine into the bloodstream as hormones

adrenergic   synapse where norepinephrine is released, which binds to α- or β-adrenergic receptors

afferent branch   component of a reflex arc that represents the input from a sensory neuron, for either a special or general sense

agonist   any exogenous substance that binds to a receptor and produces a similar effect to the endogenous ligand

alpha (α)-adrenergic receptor   one of the receptors to which epinephrine and norepinephrine bind, which comes in two subtypes: α_1 and α_2

antagonist   any exogenous substance that binds to a receptor and produces an opposing effect to the endogenous ligand

anticholinergic drugs   drugs that interrupt or reduce the function of the parasympathetic system

autonomic tone   tendency of an organ system to be governed by one division of the autonomic nervous system over the other, such as heart rate being lowered by parasympathetic input at rest

baroreceptor   mechanoreceptor that senses the stretch of blood vessels to indicate changes in blood pressure

beta (β)-adrenergic receptor   one of the receptors to which epinephrine and norepinephrine bind, which comes in three subtypes: β_1, β_2, and β_3

cardiac accelerator nerves   preganglionic sympathetic fibers that cause the heart rate to increase when the cardiovascular center in the medulla initiates a signal

cardiovascular center   region in the medulla that controls the cardiovascular system through cardiac accelerator nerves and vasomotor nerves, which are components of the sympathetic division of the autonomic nervous system

celiac ganglion   one of the collateral ganglia of the sympathetic system that projects to the digestive system

central neuron   specifically referring to the cell body of a neuron in the autonomic system that is located in the central nervous system, specifically the lateral horn of the spinal cord or a brain stem nucleus

cholinergic   synapse at which acetylcholine is released and binds to the nicotinic or muscarinic receptor

chromaffin cells   neuroendocrine cells of the adrenal medulla that release epinephrine and norepinephrine into the bloodstream as part of sympathetic system activity

ciliary ganglion   one of the terminal ganglia of the parasympathetic system, located in the posterior orbit, axons from which project to the iris

collateral ganglia   ganglia outside of the sympathetic chain that are targets of sympathetic preganglionic fibers, which are the celiac, inferior mesenteric, and superior mesenteric ganglia

craniosacral system   alternate name for the parasympathetic division of the autonomic nervous system that is based on the anatomical location of central neurons in brain-stem nuclei and the lateral horn of the sacral spinal cord; also referred to as craniosacral outflow

dorsal longitudinal fasciculus   major output pathway of the hypothalamus that descends through the gray matter of the brain stem and into the spinal cord

dorsal nucleus of the vagus nerve   location of parasympathetic neurons that project through the vagus nerve to terminal ganglia in the thoracic and abdominal cavities

Edinger–Westphal nucleus   location of parasympathetic neurons that project to the ciliary ganglion

efferent branch   component of a reflex arc that represents the output, with the target being an effector, such as muscle or glandular tissue

endogenous   describes substance made in the human body

endogenous chemical   substance produced and released within the body to interact with a receptor protein

epinephrine   signaling molecule released from the adrenal medulla into the bloodstream as part of the sympathetic response

exogenous   describes substance made outside of the human body

exogenous chemical   substance from a source outside the body, whether it be another organism such as a plant or from the synthetic processes of a laboratory, that binds to a transmembrane receptor protein

fight-or-flight response   set of responses induced by sympathetic activity that lead to either fleeing a threat or standing up to it, which in the modern world is often associated with anxious feelings

G protein–coupled receptor   membrane protein complex that consists of a receptor protein that binds to a signaling molecule—a G protein—that is

Access for free at openstax.org

activated by that binding and in turn activates an effector protein (enzyme) that creates a second-messenger molecule in the cytoplasm of the target cell

ganglionic neuron   specifically refers to the cell body of a neuron in the autonomic system that is located in a ganglion

gray rami communicantes   (singular = ramus communicans) unmyelinated structures that provide a short connection from a sympathetic chain ganglion to the spinal nerve that contains the postganglionic sympathetic fiber

greater splanchnic nerve   nerve that contains fibers of the central sympathetic neurons that do not synapse in the chain ganglia but project onto the celiac ganglion

inferior mesenteric ganglion   one of the collateral ganglia of the sympathetic system that projects to the digestive system

intramural ganglia   terminal ganglia of the parasympathetic system that are found within the walls of the target effector

lesser splanchnic nerve   nerve that contains fibers of the central sympathetic neurons that do not synapse in the chain ganglia but project onto the inferior mesenteric ganglion

ligand-gated cation channel   ion channel, such as the nicotinic receptor, that is specific to positively charged ions and opens when a molecule such as a neurotransmitter binds to it

limbic lobe   structures arranged around the edges of the cerebrum that are involved in memory and emotion

long reflex   reflex arc that includes the central nervous system

medial forebrain bundle   fiber pathway that extends anteriorly into the basal forebrain, passes through the hypothalamus, and extends into the brain stem and spinal cord

mesenteric plexus   nervous tissue within the wall of the digestive tract that contains neurons that are the targets of autonomic preganglionic fibers and that project to the smooth muscle and glandular tissues in the digestive organ

muscarinic receptor   type of acetylcholine receptor protein that is characterized by also binding to muscarine and is a metabotropic receptor

mydriasis   dilation of the pupil; typically the result of disease, trauma, or drugs

nicotinic receptor   type of acetylcholine receptor protein that is characterized by also binding to nicotine and is an ionotropic receptor

norepinephrine   signaling molecule released as a neurotransmitter by most postganglionic sympathetic fibers as part of the sympathetic response, or as a hormone into the bloodstream from the adrenal medulla

nucleus ambiguus   brain-stem nucleus that contains neurons that project through the vagus nerve to terminal ganglia in the thoracic cavity; specifically associated with the heart

parasympathetic division   division of the autonomic nervous system responsible for restful and digestive functions

parasympathomimetic drugs   drugs that enhance or mimic the function of the parasympathetic system

paravertebral ganglia   autonomic ganglia superior to the sympathetic chain ganglia

postganglionic fiber   axon from a ganglionic neuron in the autonomic nervous system that projects to and synapses with the target effector; sometimes referred to as a postganglionic neuron

preganglionic fiber   axon from a central neuron in the autonomic nervous system that projects to and synapses with a ganglionic neuron; sometimes referred to as a preganglionic neuron

prevertebral ganglia   autonomic ganglia that are anterior to the vertebral column and functionally related to the sympathetic chain ganglia

referred pain   the conscious perception of visceral sensation projected to a different region of the body, such as the left shoulder and arm pain as a sign for a heart attack

reflex arc   circuit of a reflex that involves a sensory input and motor output, or an afferent branch and an efferent branch, and an integrating center to connect the two branches

rest and digest   set of functions associated with the parasympathetic system that lead to restful actions and digestion

short reflex   reflex arc that does not include any components of the central nervous system

somatic reflex   reflex involving skeletal muscle as the effector, under the control of the somatic nervous system

superior cervical ganglion   one of the paravertebral ganglia of the sympathetic system that projects to the head

superior mesenteric ganglion   one of the collateral ganglia of the sympathetic system that projects to the digestive system

sympathetic chain ganglia   series of ganglia adjacent to the vertebral column that receive input from central sympathetic neurons

sympathetic division   division of the autonomic nervous system associated with the fight-or-flight response

sympatholytic drug   drug that interrupts, or "lyses," the function of the sympathetic system

sympathomimetic drug   drug that enhances or mimics the function of the sympathetic system

target effector   organ, tissue, or gland that will respond to the control of an autonomic or somatic or endocrine signal

terminal ganglia   ganglia of the parasympathetic division of the autonomic system, which are located near or within the target effector, the latter also known as intramural ganglia

thoracolumbar system   alternate name for the sympathetic division of the autonomic nervous system that is based on the anatomical location of central neurons in the lateral horn of the thoracic

and upper lumbar spinal cord

varicosity   structure of some autonomic connections that is not a typical synaptic end bulb, but a string of swellings along the length of a fiber that makes a network of connections with the target effector

vasomotor nerves   preganglionic sympathetic fibers that cause the constriction of blood vessels in response to signals from the cardiovascular center

visceral reflex   reflex involving an internal organ as the effector, under the control of the autonomic nervous system

white rami communicantes   (singular = ramus communicans) myelinated structures that provide a short connection from a sympathetic chain ganglion to the spinal nerve that contains the preganglionic sympathetic fiber

Chapter Review

15.1 Divisions of the Autonomic Nervous System

The primary responsibilities of the autonomic nervous system are to regulate homeostatic mechanisms in the body, which is also part of what the endocrine system does. The key to understanding the autonomic system is to explore the response pathways—the output of the nervous system. The way we respond to the world around us, to manage the internal environment on the basis of the external environment, is divided between two parts of the autonomic nervous system. The sympathetic division responds to threats and produces a readiness to confront the threat or to run away: the fight-or-flight response. The parasympathetic division plays the opposite role. When the external environment does not present any immediate danger, a restful mode descends on the body, and the digestive system is more active.

The sympathetic output of the nervous system originates out of the lateral horn of the thoracolumbar spinal cord. An axon from one of these central neurons projects by way of the ventral spinal nerve root and spinal nerve to a sympathetic ganglion, either in the sympathetic chain ganglia or one of the collateral locations, where it synapses on a ganglionic neuron. These preganglionic fibers release ACh, which excites the ganglionic neuron through the nicotinic receptor. The axon from the ganglionic neuron—the postganglionic fiber—then projects to a target effector where it will release norepinephrine to bind to an adrenergic receptor, causing a change in the physiology of that organ in keeping with the broad, divergent sympathetic response. The postganglionic connections to sweat glands in the skin and blood vessels supplying

skeletal muscle are, however, exceptions; those fibers release ACh onto muscarinic receptors. The sympathetic system has a specialized preganglionic connection to the adrenal medulla that causes epinephrine and norepinephrine to be released into the bloodstream rather than exciting a neuron that contacts an organ directly. This hormonal component means that the sympathetic chemical signal can spread throughout the body very quickly and affect many organ systems at once.

The parasympathetic output is based in the brain stem and sacral spinal cord. Neurons from particular nuclei in the brain stem or from the lateral horn of the sacral spinal cord (preganglionic neurons) project to terminal (intramural) ganglia located close to or within the wall of target effectors. These preganglionic fibers also release ACh onto nicotinic receptors to excite the ganglionic neurons. The postganglionic fibers then contact the target tissues within the organ to release ACh, which binds to muscarinic receptors to induce rest-and-digest responses.

Signaling molecules utilized by the autonomic nervous system are released from axons and can be considered as either neurotransmitters (when they directly interact with the effector) or as hormones (when they are released into the bloodstream). The same molecule, such as norepinephrine, could be considered either a neurotransmitter or a hormone on the basis of whether it is released from a postganglionic sympathetic axon or from the adrenal gland. The synapses in the autonomic system are not always the typical type of connection first described in the neuromuscular junction. Instead of having synaptic end bulbs at the very end of an axonal fiber, they may have swellings—called varicosities—along the length of a fiber so that it makes a network of connections within the target tissue.

15.2 Autonomic Reflexes and Homeostasis

Autonomic nervous system function is based on the visceral reflex. This reflex is similar to the somatic reflex, but the efferent branch is composed of two neurons. The central neuron projects from the spinal cord or brain stem to synapse on the ganglionic neuron that projects to the effector. The afferent branch of the somatic and visceral reflexes is very similar, as many somatic and special senses activate autonomic responses. However, there are visceral senses that do not form part of conscious perception. If a visceral sensation, such as cardiac pain, is strong enough, it will rise to the level of consciousness. However, the sensory homunculus does not provide a representation of the internal structures to the same degree as the surface of the body, so visceral sensations are often experienced as referred pain, such as feelings of pain in the left shoulder and arm in connection with a heart attack.

The role of visceral reflexes is to maintain a balance of function in the organ systems of the body. The two divisions of the autonomic system each play a role in effecting change, usually in competing directions. The sympathetic system increases heart rate, whereas the parasympathetic system decreases heart rate. The sympathetic system dilates the pupil of the eye, whereas the parasympathetic system constricts the pupil. The competing inputs can contribute to the resting tone of the organ system. Heart rate is normally under parasympathetic tone, whereas blood pressure is normally under sympathetic tone. The heart rate is slowed by the autonomic system at rest, whereas blood vessels retain a slight constriction at rest.

In a few systems of the body, the competing input from the two divisions is not the norm. The sympathetic tone of blood vessels is caused by the lack of parasympathetic input to the systemic circulatory system. Only certain regions receive parasympathetic input that relaxes the smooth muscle wall of the blood vessels. Sweat glands are another example, which only receive input from the sympathetic system.

15.3 Central Control

The autonomic system integrates sensory information and higher cognitive processes to generate output, which balances homeostatic mechanisms. The central autonomic structure is the hypothalamus, which coordinates sympathetic and parasympathetic efferent pathways to regulate activities of the organ systems of the body. The majority of hypothalamic output travels through the medial forebrain bundle and the dorsal longitudinal fasciculus to influence brain stem and spinal components of the autonomic nervous system. The medial forebrain bundle also connects the hypothalamus with higher centers of the limbic system where emotion can influence visceral responses. The amygdala is a structure within the limbic system that influences the hypothalamus in the regulation of the autonomic system, as well as the endocrine system.

These higher centers have descending control of the autonomic system through brain stem centers, primarily in the medulla, such as the cardiovascular center. This collection of medullary nuclei regulates cardiac function, as well as blood pressure. Sensory input from the heart, aorta, and carotid sinuses project to these regions of the medulla. The solitary nucleus increases sympathetic tone of the cardiovascular system through the cardiac accelerator and vasomotor nerves. The nucleus ambiguus and the dorsal motor nucleus both contribute fibers to the vagus nerve, which exerts parasympathetic control of the heart by decreasing heart rate.

15.4 Drugs that Affect the Autonomic System

The autonomic system is affected by a number of exogenous agents, including some that are therapeutic and some that are illicit. These drugs affect the autonomic system by mimicking or interfering with the endogenous agents or their receptors. A survey of how different drugs affect autonomic function illustrates the role that the neurotransmitters and hormones play in autonomic function. Drugs can be thought of as chemical tools to effect changes in the system with some precision, based on where those drugs are effective.

Nicotine is not a drug that is used therapeutically, except for smoking cessation. When it is introduced into the body via products, it has broad effects on the autonomic system. Nicotine carries a risk for cardiovascular disease because of these broad effects. The drug stimulates both sympathetic and parasympathetic ganglia at the preganglionic fiber synapse. For most organ systems in the body, the competing input from the two postganglionic fibers will essentially cancel each other out. However, for the cardiovascular system, the results are different. Because there is essentially no parasympathetic influence on blood pressure for the entire body, the sympathetic input is increased by nicotine, causing an increase in blood pressure. Also, the influence that the autonomic system has on the heart is not the same as for other systems. Other organs have smooth muscle or glandular tissue that is activated or inhibited by the autonomic system. Cardiac muscle is intrinsically active and is modulated by the autonomic system. The contradictory signals do not just cancel each other out, they alter the regularity of the heart rate and can cause arrhythmias. Both hypertension and arrhythmias are risk factors for heart disease.

Other drugs affect one division of the autonomic system or the other. The sympathetic system is affected by drugs that mimic the actions of adrenergic molecules (norepinephrine and epinephrine) and are

called sympathomimetic drugs. Drugs such as phenylephrine bind to the adrenergic receptors and stimulate target organs just as sympathetic activity would. Other drugs are sympatholytic because they block adrenergic activity and cancel the sympathetic influence on the target organ. Drugs that act on the parasympathetic system also work by either enhancing the postganglionic signal or blocking it. A muscarinic agonist (or parasympathomimetic drug) acts just like ACh released by the parasympathetic postganglionic fiber. Anticholinergic drugs block muscarinic receptors, suppressing parasympathetic interaction with the organ.

Interactive Link Questions

1. Watch this video (http://openstax.org/l/fightflight) to learn more about adrenaline and the fight-or-flight response. When someone is said to have a rush of adrenaline, the image of bungee jumpers or skydivers usually comes to mind. But adrenaline, also known as epinephrine, is an important chemical in coordinating the body's fight-or-flight response. In this video, you look inside the physiology of the fight-or-flight response, as envisioned for a firefighter. His body's reaction is the result of the sympathetic division of the autonomic nervous system causing system-wide changes as it prepares for extreme responses. What two changes does adrenaline bring about to help the skeletal muscle response?

2. Watch this video (http://openstax.org/l/nervsystem1) to learn more about the nervous system. As described in this video, the nervous system has a way to deal with threats and stress that is separate from the conscious control of the somatic nervous system. The system comes from a time when threats were about survival, but in the modern age, these responses become part of stress and anxiety. This video describes how the autonomic system is only part of the response to threats, or stressors. What other organ system gets involved, and what part of the brain coordinates the two systems for the entire response, including epinephrine (adrenaline) and cortisol?

3. Read this article (http://openstax.org/l/strokespell) to learn about a teenager who experiences a series of spells that suggest a stroke. He undergoes endless tests and seeks input from multiple doctors. In the end, one expert, one question, and a simple blood pressure cuff answers the question. Why would the heart have to beat faster when the teenager changes his body position from lying down to sitting, and then to standing?

4. Watch this video (http://openstax.org/l/pupillary) to learn about the pupillary reflexes. The pupillary light reflex involves sensory input through the optic nerve and motor response through the oculomotor nerve to the ciliary ganglion, which projects to the circular fibers of the iris. As shown in this short animation, pupils will constrict to limit the amount of light falling on the retina under bright lighting conditions. What constitutes the afferent and efferent branches of the competing reflex (dilation)?

5. Watch this video (http://openstax.org/l/emotions) to learn about physical responses to emotion. The autonomic system, which is important for regulating the homeostasis of the organ systems, is also responsible for our physiological responses to emotions such as fear. The video summarizes the extent of the body's reactions and describes several effects of the autonomic system in response to fear. On the basis of what you have already studied about autonomic function, which effect would you expect to be associated with parasympathetic, rather than sympathetic, activity?

6. Watch this video (http://openstax.org/l/3Dmovies) to learn about the side effects of 3-D movies. As discussed in this video, movies that are shot in 3-D can cause motion sickness, which elicits the autonomic symptoms of nausea and sweating. The disconnection between the perceived motion on the screen and the lack of any change in equilibrium stimulates these symptoms. Why do you think sitting close to the screen or right in the middle of the theater makes motion sickness during a 3-D movie worse?

Review Questions

7. Which of these physiological changes would *not* be considered part of the sympathetic fight-or-flight response?
  a. increased heart rate
  b. increased sweating
  c. dilated pupils
  d. increased stomach motility

8. Which type of fiber could be considered the longest?
  a. preganglionic parasympathetic
  b. preganglionic sympathetic
  c. postganglionic parasympathetic
  d. postganglionic sympathetic

9. Which signaling molecule is *most likely* responsible for an increase in digestive activity?
  a. epinephrine
  b. norepinephrine
  c. acetylcholine
  d. adrenaline

10. Which of these cranial nerves contains preganglionic parasympathetic fibers?
  a. optic, CN II
  b. facial, CN VII
  c. trigeminal, CN V
  d. hypoglossal, CN XII

11. Which of the following is *not* a target of a sympathetic preganglionic fiber?
  a. intermural ganglion
  b. collateral ganglion
  c. adrenal gland
  d. chain ganglion

12. Which of the following represents a sensory input that is *not* part of both the somatic and autonomic systems?
  a. vision
  b. taste
  c. baroreception
  d. proprioception

13. What is the term for a reflex that does *not* include a CNS component?
  a. long reflex
  b. visceral reflex
  c. somatic reflex
  d. short reflex

14. What neurotransmitter will result in constriction of the pupil?
  a. norepinephrine
  b. acetylcholine
  c. epinephrine
  d. serotonin

15. What gland produces a secretion that causes fight-or-flight responses in effectors?
  a. adrenal medulla
  b. salivatory gland
  c. reproductive gland
  d. thymus

16. Which of the following is an incorrect pairing?
  a. norepinephrine dilates the pupil
  b. epinephrine increases blood pressure
  c. acetylcholine decreases digestion
  d. norepinephrine increases heart rate

17. Which of these locations in the forebrain is the master control center for homeostasis through the autonomic and endocrine systems?
  a. hypothalamus
  b. thalamus
  c. amygdala
  d. cerebral cortex

18. Which nerve projects to the hypothalamus to indicate the level of light stimuli in the retina?
   a. glossopharyngeal
   b. oculomotor
   c. optic
   d. vagus

19. What region of the limbic lobe is responsible for generating stress responses via the hypothalamus?
   a. hippocampus
   b. amygdala
   c. mammillary bodies
   d. prefrontal cortex

20. What is another name for the preganglionic sympathetic fibers that project to the heart?
   a. solitary tract
   b. vasomotor nerve
   c. vagus nerve
   d. cardiac accelerator nerve

21. What central fiber tract connects forebrain and brain stem structures with the hypothalamus?
   a. cardiac accelerator nerve
   b. medial forebrain bundle
   c. dorsal longitudinal fasciculus
   d. corticospinal tract

22. A drug that affects both divisions of the autonomic system is going to bind to, or block, which type of neurotransmitter receptor?
   a. nicotinic
   b. muscarinic
   c. α-adrenergic
   d. β-adrenergic

23. A drug is called an agonist if it _____.
   a. blocks a receptor
   b. interferes with neurotransmitter reuptake
   c. acts like the endogenous neurotransmitter by binding to its receptor
   d. blocks the voltage-gated calcium ion channel

24. Which type of drug would be an antidote to atropine poisoning?
   a. nicotinic agonist
   b. anticholinergic
   c. muscarinic agonist
   d. α-blocker

25. Which kind of drug would have anti-anxiety effects?
   a. nicotinic agonist
   b. anticholinergic
   c. muscarinic agonist
   d. α-blocker

26. Which type of drug could be used to treat asthma by opening airways wider?
   a. sympatholytic drug
   b. sympathomimetic drug
   c. anticholinergic drug
   d. parasympathomimetic drug

Critical Thinking Questions

27. In the context of a lioness hunting on the savannah, why would the sympathetic system *not* activate the digestive system?

28. A target effector, such as the heart, receives input from the sympathetic and parasympathetic systems. What is the actual difference between the sympathetic and parasympathetic divisions at the level of those connections (i.e., at the synapse)?

29. Damage to internal organs will present as pain associated with a particular surface area of the body. Why would something like irritation to the diaphragm, which is between the thoracic and abdominal cavities, feel like pain in the shoulder or neck?

30. Medical practice is paying more attention to the autonomic system in considering disease states. Why would autonomic tone be important in considering cardiovascular disease?

31. Horner's syndrome is a condition that presents with changes in one eye, such as pupillary constriction and dropping of eyelids, as well as decreased sweating in the face. Why could a tumor in the thoracic cavity have an effect on these autonomic functions?

32. The cardiovascular center is responsible for regulating the heart and blood vessels through homeostatic mechanisms. What tone does each component of the cardiovascular system have? What connections does the cardiovascular center invoke to keep these two systems in their resting tone?

33. Why does smoking increase the risk of heart disease? Provide two reasons based on autonomic function.

34. Why might topical, cosmetic application of atropine or scopolamine from the belladonna plant not cause fatal poisoning, as would occur with ingestion of the plant?

CHAPTER 16
The Neurological Exam

Figure 16.1 Neurological Exam Health care professionals, such as this air force nurse, can rapidly assess the neurological functions of a patient using the neurological exam. One part of the exam is the inspection of the oral cavity and pharynx, which enables the doctor to not only inspect the tissues for signs of infection, but also provides a means to test the functions of the cranial nerves associated with the oral cavity. (credit: U.S. Department of Defense / AMISOM Public Information/Flickr)

CHAPTER OBJECTIVES
After studying this chapter, you will be able to:
- Describe the major sections of the neurological exam
- Outline the benefits of rapidly assessing neurological function
- Relate anatomical structures of the nervous system to specific functions
- Diagram the connections of the nervous system to the musculature and integument involved in primary sensorimotor responses
- Compare and contrast the somatic and visceral reflexes with respect to how they are assessed through the neurological exam

INTRODUCTION A man arrives at the hospital after feeling faint and complaining of a "pins-and-needles" feeling all along one side of his body. The most likely explanation is that he has suffered a stroke, which has caused a loss of oxygen to a particular part of the central nervous system (CNS). The problem is finding where in the entire nervous system the stroke has occurred. By checking reflexes, sensory responses, and motor control, a health care provider can focus on what abilities the patient may have lost as a result of the stroke and can use this information to determine where the injury occurred. In the emergency department of the hospital, this kind of rapid assessment of neurological function is key to treating trauma to the nervous system. In the classroom, the neurological exam is a valuable tool for learning the anatomy and physiology of the nervous system because it allows you to relate the functions of the system to particular locations in the nervous system.

As a student of anatomy and physiology, you may be planning to go into an allied health field, perhaps nursing or physical therapy. You could be in the emergency department treating a patient such as the one just described. An important part of this course is to understand the nervous system. This can be especially challenging because you need to learn about the nervous system using your own nervous system. The first chapter in this unit about the nervous system began with a quote: "If the human brain were simple enough for us to understand, we would be too simple to understand it." However, you are being asked to understand aspects of it. A healthcare provider can pinpoint problems with the nervous system in minutes by running through the series of tasks to test neurological function that are described in this chapter. You can use the same approach, though not as quickly, to learn about neurological function and its relationship to the structures of the nervous system.

Nervous tissue is different from other tissues in that it is not classified into separate tissue types. It does contain two types of cells, neurons and glia, but it is all just nervous tissue. White matter and gray matter are not types of nervous tissue, but indications of different specializations within the nervous tissue. However, not all nervous tissue performs the same function. Furthermore, specific functions are not wholly localized to individual brain structures in the way that other bodily functions occur strictly within specific organs. In the CNS, we must consider the connections between cells over broad areas, not just the function of cells in one particular nucleus or region. In a broad sense, the nervous system is responsible for the majority of electrochemical signaling in the body, but the use of those signals is different in various regions.

The nervous system is made up of the brain and spinal cord as the central organs, and the ganglia and nerves as organs in the periphery. The brain and spinal cord can be thought of as a collection of smaller organs, most of which would be the nuclei (such as the oculomotor nuclei), but white matter structures play an important role (such as the corpus callosum). Studying the nervous system requires an understanding of the varied physiology of the nervous system. For example, the hypothalamus plays a very different role than the visual cortex. The neurological exam provides a way to elicit behavior that represents those varied functions.

16.1 Overview of the Neurological Exam

LEARNING OBJECTIVES

By the end of this section, you will be able to:

- List the major sections of the neurological exam
- Explain the connection between location and function in the nervous system
- Explain the benefit of a rapid assessment for neurological function in a clinical setting
- List the causes of neurological deficits
- Describe the different ischemic events in the nervous system

The **neurological exam** is a clinical assessment tool used to determine what specific parts of the CNS are affected by damage or disease. It can be performed in a short time—sometimes as quickly as 5 minutes—to establish neurological function. In the emergency department, this rapid assessment can make the difference with respect to proper treatment and the extent of recovery that is possible.

The exam is a series of subtests separated into five major sections. The first of these is the **mental status exam**, which assesses the higher cognitive functions such as memory, orientation, and language. Then there is the **cranial nerve exam**, which tests the function of the 12 cranial nerves and, therefore, the central and peripheral structures associated with them. The cranial nerve exam tests the sensory and motor functions of each of the nerves, as applicable. Two major sections, the **sensory exam** and the **motor exam**, test the sensory and motor functions associated with spinal nerves. Finally, the **coordination exam** tests the ability to perform complex and coordinated movements. The **gait exam**, which is often considered a sixth major exam, specifically assesses the motor function of walking and can be considered part of the coordination exam because walking is a coordinated movement.

Neuroanatomy and the Neurological Exam

Localization of function is the concept that circumscribed locations are responsible for specific functions. The neurological exam highlights this relationship. For example, the cognitive functions that are assessed in the mental status exam are based on functions in the cerebrum, mostly in the cerebral cortex. Several of the subtests examine language function. Deficits in neurological function uncovered by these examinations usually point to damage to the left cerebral cortex. In the majority of individuals, language function is localized to the left hemisphere between the superior temporal lobe and the posterior frontal lobe, including the intervening connections through the inferior parietal lobe.

The five major sections of the neurological exam are related to the major regions of the CNS (Figure 16.2). The mental status exam assesses functions related to the cerebrum. The cranial nerve exam is for the nerves that connect to the diencephalon and brain stem (as well as the olfactory connections to the forebrain). The coordination exam and the related gait exam primarily assess the functions of the cerebellum. The motor and sensory exams are associated with the spinal cord and its connections through the spinal nerves.

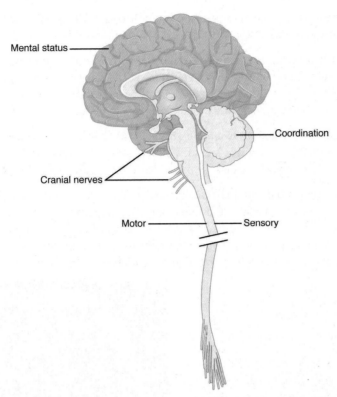

Mental status

Coordination

Cranial nerves

Motor   Sensory

FIGURE 16.2   Anatomical Underpinnings of the Neurological Exam   The different regions of the CNS relate to the major sections of the neurological exam: the mental status exam, cranial nerve exam, sensory exam, motor exam, and coordination exam (including the gait exam).

Part of the power of the neurological exam is this link between structure and function. Testing the various functions represented in the exam allows an accurate estimation of where the nervous system may be damaged. Consider the patient described in the chapter introduction. In the emergency department, he is given a quick exam to find where the deficit may be localized. Knowledge of where the damage occurred will lead to the most effective therapy.

In rapid succession, he is asked to smile, raise his eyebrows, stick out his tongue, and shrug his shoulders. The doctor tests muscular strength by providing resistance against his arms and legs while he tries to lift them. With his eyes closed, he has to indicate when he feels the tip of a pen touch his legs, arms, fingers, and face. He follows the tip of a pen as the doctor moves it through the visual field and finally toward his face. A formal mental status exam is not needed at this point; the patient will demonstrate any possible deficits in that area during normal interactions with the interviewer. If cognitive or language deficits are apparent, the interviewer can pursue mental status in more depth. All of this takes place in less than 5 minutes. The patient reports that he feels pins and needles in his left arm and leg, and has trouble feeling the tip of the pen when he is touched on those limbs. This suggests a problem with the sensory systems between the spinal cord and the brain. The emergency department has a lead to follow before a CT scan is performed. He is put on aspirin therapy to limit the possibility of blood clots forming, in case the cause is an **embolus**—an obstruction such as a blood clot that blocks the flow of blood in an artery or vein.

🔗 INTERACTIVE LINK

Watch this video (http://openstax.org/l/neuroexam) to see a demonstration of the neurological exam—a series of tests that can be performed rapidly when a patient is initially brought into an emergency department. The exam can be repeated on a regular basis to keep a record of how and if neurological function changes over time. In what order were the sections of the neurological exam tested in this video, and which section seemed to be left out?

Causes of Neurological Deficits

Damage to the nervous system can be limited to individual structures or can be distributed across broad areas of the brain and spinal cord. Localized, limited injury to the nervous system is most often the result of circulatory problems. Neurons are very sensitive to oxygen deprivation and will start to deteriorate within 1 or 2 minutes, and permanent damage (cell death) could result within a few hours. The loss of blood flow to part of the brain is known as a **stroke**, or a cerebrovascular accident (CVA).

There are two main types of stroke, depending on how the blood supply is compromised: ischemic and hemorrhagic. An **ischemic stroke** is the loss of blood flow to an area because vessels are blocked or narrowed. This is often caused by an embolus, which may be a blood clot or fat deposit. Ischemia may also be the result of thickening of the blood vessel wall, or a drop in blood volume in the brain known as **hypovolemia**.

A related type of CVA is known as a **transient ischemic attack (TIA)**, which is similar to a stroke although it does not last as long. The diagnostic definition of a stroke includes effects that last at least 24 hours. Any stroke symptoms that are resolved within a 24-hour period because of restoration of adequate blood flow are classified as a TIA.

A **hemorrhagic stroke** is bleeding into the brain because of a damaged blood vessel. Accumulated blood fills a region of the cranial vault and presses against the tissue in the brain (Figure 16.3). Physical pressure on the brain can cause the loss of function, as well as the squeezing of local arteries resulting in compromised blood flow beyond the site of the hemorrhage. As blood pools in the nervous tissue and the vasculature is damaged, the blood-brain barrier can break down and allow additional fluid to accumulate in the region, which is known as **edema**.

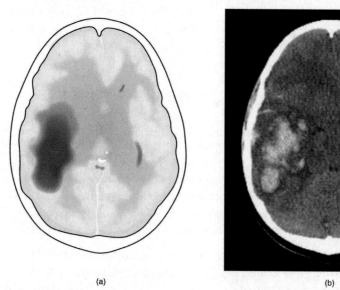

(a)   (b)

FIGURE 16.3   Hemorrhagic Stroke   (a) A hemorrhage into the tissue of the cerebrum results in a large accumulation of blood with an additional edema in the adjacent tissue. The hemorrhagic area causes the entire brain to be disfigured as suggested here by the lateral ventricles being squeezed into the opposite hemisphere. (b) A CT scan shows an intraparenchymal hemorrhage within the parietal lobe. (credit b: James Heilman)

Whereas hemorrhagic stroke may involve bleeding into a large region of the CNS, such as into the deep white matter of a cerebral hemisphere, other events can cause widespread damage and loss of neurological functions. Infectious diseases can lead to loss of function throughout the CNS as components of nervous tissue, specifically astrocytes and microglia, react to the disease. Blunt force trauma, such as from a motor vehicle accident, can physically damage the CNS.

A class of disorders that affect the nervous system are the neurodegenerative diseases: Alzheimer's disease, Parkinson's disease, Huntington's disease, amyotrophic lateral sclerosis (ALS), Creutzfeld–Jacob disease, multiple sclerosis (MS), and other disorders that are the result of nervous tissue degeneration. In diseases like Alzheimer's, Parkinson's, or ALS, neurons die; in diseases like MS, myelin is affected. Some of these disorders affect motor function, and others present with dementia. How patients with these disorders perform in the neurological exam varies, but is often broad in its effects, such as memory deficits that compromise many aspects of the mental status exam, or movement deficits that compromise aspects of the cranial nerve exam, the motor exam, or the coordination exam. The causes of these disorders are also varied. Some are the result of genetics, such as Huntington's disease, or the result of autoimmunity, such as MS; others are not entirely understood, such as Alzheimer's and Parkinson's diseases. Current research suggests that many of these diseases are related in how the degeneration takes place and may be treated by common therapies.

Finally, a common cause of neurological changes is observed in developmental disorders. Whether the result of genetic factors or the environment during development, there are certain situations that result in neurological functions being different from the expected norms. Developmental disorders are difficult to define because they are caused by defects that existed in the past and disrupted the normal development of the CNS. These defects probably involve multiple environmental and genetic factors—most of the time, we don't know what the cause is other than that it is more complex than just one factor. Furthermore, each defect on its own may not be a problem, but when several are added together, they can disrupt growth processes that are not well understand in the first place. For instance, it is possible for a stroke to damage a specific region of the brain and lead to the loss of the ability to recognize faces (prosopagnosia). The link between cell death in the fusiform gyrus and the symptom is relatively easy to understand. In contrast, similar deficits can be seen in children with the developmental disorder, autism spectrum disorder (ASD). However, these children do not lack a fusiform gyrus, nor is there any damage or defect visible to this brain region. We conclude, rather poorly, that this brain region is not connected properly to other brain regions.

Infection, trauma, and congenital disorders can all lead to significant signs, as identified through the neurological exam. It is important to differentiate between an acute event, such as stroke, and a chronic or global condition such as blunt force trauma. Responses seen in the neurological exam can help. A loss of language function observed in all its aspects is more likely a global event as opposed to a discrete loss of one function, such as not being able to say certain types of words. A concern, however, is that a specific function—such as controlling the muscles of speech—may mask other language functions. The various subtests within the mental status exam can address these finer points and help clarify the underlying cause of the neurological loss.

⊘ INTERACTIVE LINK

Watch this video (http://openstax.org/l/neuroexam2) for an introduction to the neurological exam. Studying the neurological exam can give insight into how structure and function in the nervous system are interdependent. This is a tool both in the clinic and in the classroom, but for different reasons. In the clinic, this is a powerful but simple tool to assess a patient's neurological function. In the classroom, it is a different way to think about the nervous system. Though medical technology provides noninvasive imaging and real-time functional data, the presenter says these cannot replace the history at the core of the medical examination. What does history mean in the context of medical practice?

16.2 The Mental Status Exam

LEARNING OBJECTIVES

By the end of this section, you will be able to:

- Describe the relationship of mental status exam results to cerebral functions
- Explain the categorization of regions of the cortex based on anatomy and physiology
- Differentiate between primary, association, and integration areas of the cerebral cortex
- Provide examples of localization of function related to the cerebral cortex

In the clinical setting, the set of subtests known as the mental status exam helps us understand the relationship of the brain to the body. Ultimately, this is accomplished by assessing behavior. Tremors related to intentional movements, incoordination, or the neglect of one side of the body can be indicative of failures of the connections of the cerebrum either within the hemispheres, or from the cerebrum to other portions of the nervous system. There is no strict test for what the cerebrum does alone, but rather in what it does through its control of the rest of the CNS, the peripheral nervous system (PNS), and the musculature.

Sometimes eliciting a behavior is as simple as asking a question. Asking a patient to state their name is not only to verify that the file folder in a health care provider's hands is the correct one, but also to be sure that the patient is aware, oriented, and capable of interacting with another person. If the answer to "What is your name?" is "Santa Claus," the person may have a problem understanding reality. If the person just stares at the examiner with a confused look on their face, the person may have a problem understanding or producing speech.

Functions of the Cerebral Cortex

The cerebrum is the seat of many of the higher mental functions, such as memory and learning, language, and conscious perception, which are the subjects of subtests of the mental status exam. The cerebral cortex is the thin layer of gray matter on the outside of the cerebrum. On average, it is approximately 2.55 mm thick and highly folded to fit within the limited space of the cranial vault. These higher functions are distributed across various regions of the cortex, and specific locations can be said to be responsible for particular functions. There is a limited set of regions, for example, that are involved in language function, and they can be subdivided on the basis of the particular part of language function that each governs.

The basis for parceling out areas of the cortex and attributing them to various functions has its root in pure anatomical underpinnings. The German neurologist and histologist Korbinian Brodmann, who made a careful study of the **cytoarchitecture** of the cerebrum around the turn of the nineteenth century, described approximately 50 regions of the cortex that differed enough from each other to be considered separate areas (Figure 16.4). Brodmann made preparations of many different regions of the cerebral cortex to view with a microscope. He compared the size, shape, and number of neurons to find anatomical differences in the various parts of the cerebral cortex. Continued investigation into these anatomical areas over the subsequent 100 or more years has demonstrated a strong correlation between the structures and the functions attributed to those structures. For example, the first three areas in Brodmann's list—which are in the postcentral gyrus—compose the primary somatosensory cortex. Within this area, finer separation can be made on the basis of the concept of the sensory homunculus, as well as the different submodalities of somatosensation such as touch, vibration, pain, temperature, or proprioception. Today, we more frequently refer to these regions by their function (i.e., primary sensory cortex) than by the number Brodmann assigned to them, but in some situations the use of Brodmann numbers persists.

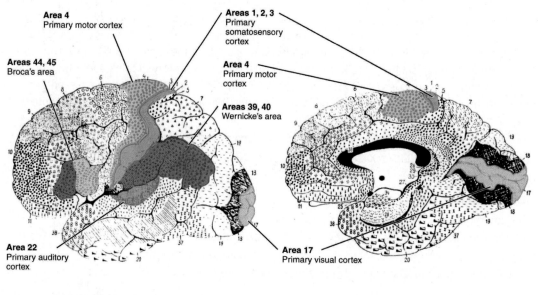

Brodmann's cytotechtonic map (1909):
Lateral surface

Brodmann's cytotechtonic map (1909):
Medial surface

FIGURE 16.4   **Brodmann's Areas of the Cerebral Cortex**   On the basis of cytoarchitecture, the anatomist Korbinian Brodmann described the extensive array of cortical regions, as illustrated in this figure. Subsequent investigations found that these areas corresponded very well to functional differences in the cerebral cortex. (credit: modification of work by "Looie496"/Wikimedia Commons, based on original work by Korvinian Brodmann)

Area 17, as Brodmann described it, is also known as the primary visual cortex. Adjacent to that are areas 18 and 19, which constitute subsequent regions of visual processing. Area 22 is the primary auditory cortex, and it is followed by area 23, which further processes auditory information. Area 4 is the primary motor cortex in the precentral gyrus, whereas area 6 is the premotor cortex. These areas suggest some specialization within the cortex for functional processing, both in sensory and motor regions. The fact that Brodmann's areas correlate so closely to functional localization in the cerebral cortex demonstrates the strong link between structure and function in these regions.

Areas 1, 2, 3, 4, 17, and 22 are each described as primary cortical areas. The adjoining regions are each referred to as association areas. Primary areas are where sensory information is initially received from the thalamus for conscious perception, or—in the case of the primary motor cortex—where descending commands are sent down to the brain stem or spinal cord to execute movements (Figure 16.5).

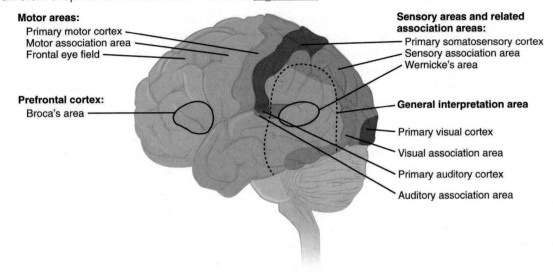

Motor areas:
Primary motor cortex
Motor association area
Frontal eye field

Prefrontal cortex:
Broca's area

Sensory areas and related association areas:
Primary somatosensory cortex
Sensory association area
Wernicke's area

General interpretation area

Primary visual cortex

Visual association area

Primary auditory cortex

Auditory association area

FIGURE 16.5   Types of Cortical Areas   The cerebral cortex can be described as containing three types of processing regions: primary, association, and integration areas. The primary cortical areas are where sensory information is initially processed, or where motor commands emerge to go to the brain stem or spinal cord. Association areas are adjacent to primary areas and further process the modality-specific input. Multimodal integration areas are found where the modality-specific regions meet; they can process multiple modalities together or different modalities on the basis of similar functions, such as spatial processing in vision or somatosensation.

A number of other regions, which extend beyond these primary or association areas of the cortex, are referred to as integrative areas. These areas are found in the spaces between the domains for particular sensory or motor functions, and they integrate multisensory information, or process sensory or motor information in more complex ways. Consider, for example, the posterior parietal cortex that lies between the somatosensory cortex and visual cortex regions. This has been ascribed to the coordination of visual and motor functions, such as reaching to pick up a glass. The somatosensory function that would be part of this is the proprioceptive feedback from moving the arm and hand. The weight of the glass, based on what it contains, will influence how those movements are executed.

Cognitive Abilities

Assessment of cerebral functions is directed at cognitive abilities. The abilities assessed through the mental status exam can be separated into four groups: orientation and memory, language and speech, sensorium, and judgment and abstract reasoning.

Orientation and Memory

Orientation is the patient's awareness of their immediate circumstances. It is awareness of time, not in terms of the clock, but of the date and what is occurring around the patient. It is awareness of place, such that a patient should know where they are and why. It is also awareness of who the patient is—recognizing personal identity and being able to relate that to the examiner. The initial tests of orientation are based on the questions, "Do you know what the date is?" or "Do you know where you are?" or "What is your name?" Further understanding of a patient's awareness of orientation can come from questions that address remote memory, such as "Who is the President of the United States?", or asking what happened on a specific date.

There are also specific tasks to address memory. One is the three-word recall test. The patient is given three words to recall, such as book, clock, and shovel. After a short interval, during which other parts of the interview continue, the patient is asked to recall the three words. Other tasks that assess memory—aside from those related to orientation—have the patient recite the months of the year in reverse order to avoid the overlearned sequence and focus on the memory of the months in an order, or to spell common words backwards, or to recite a list of numbers back.

Memory is largely a function of the temporal lobe, along with structures beneath the cerebral cortex such as the hippocampus and the amygdala. The storage of memory requires these structures of the medial temporal lobe. A famous case of a man who had both medial temporal lobes removed to treat intractable epilepsy provided insight into the relationship between the structures of the brain and the function of memory.

Henry Molaison, who was referred to as patient HM when he was alive, had epilepsy localized to both of his medial temporal lobes. In 1953, a bilateral lobectomy was performed that alleviated the epilepsy but resulted in the inability for HM to form new memories—a condition called **anterograde amnesia**. HM was able to recall most events from before his surgery, although there was a partial loss of earlier memories, which is referred to as **retrograde amnesia**. HM became the subject of extensive studies into how memory works. What he was unable to do was form new memories of what happened to him, what are now called **episodic memory**. Episodic memory is autobiographical in nature, such as remembering riding a bicycle as a child around the neighborhood, as opposed to the **procedural memory** of how to ride a bike. HM also retained his **short-term memory**, such as what is tested by the three-word task described above. After a brief period, those memories would dissipate or decay and not be stored in the long-term because the medial temporal lobe structures were removed.

The difference in short-term, procedural, and episodic memory, as evidenced by patient HM, suggests that there are different parts of the brain responsible for those functions. The long-term storage of episodic memory requires the hippocampus and related medial temporal structures, and the location of those memories is in the multimodal integration areas of the cerebral cortex. However, short-term memory—also called working or active memory—is localized to the prefrontal lobe. Because patient HM had only lost his medial temporal lobe—and lost very little of his previous memories, and did not lose the ability to form new short-term memories—it was concluded that the function of the hippocampus, and adjacent structures in the medial temporal lobe, is to move (or consolidate) short-term memories (in the pre-frontal lobe) to long-term memory (in the temporal lobe).

The prefrontal cortex can also be tested for the ability to organize information. In one subtest of the mental status exam called set generation, the patient is asked to generate a list of words that all start with the same letter, but not to include proper nouns or names. The expectation is that a person can generate such a list of at least 10 words within 1 minute. Many people can likely do this much more quickly, but the standard separates the accepted normal from those with compromised prefrontal cortices.

⊘ INTERACTIVE LINK

Read this article (http://openstax.org/l/3word) to learn about a young man who texts his fiancée in a panic as he finds that he is having trouble remembering things. At the hospital, a neurologist administers the mental status exam, which is mostly normal except for the three-word recall test. The young man could not recall them even 30 seconds after hearing them and repeating them back to the doctor. An undiscovered mass in the mediastinum region was found to be Hodgkin's lymphoma, a type of cancer that affects the immune system and likely caused antibodies to attack the nervous system. The patient eventually regained his ability to remember, though the events in the hospital were always elusive. Considering that the effects on memory were temporary, but resulted in the loss of the specific events of the hospital stay, what regions of the brain were likely to have been affected by the antibodies and what type of memory does that represent?

Language and Speech

Language is, arguably, a very human aspect of neurological function. There are certainly strides being made in understanding communication in other species, but much of what makes the human experience seemingly unique is its basis in language. Any understanding of our species is necessarily reflective, as suggested by the question "What am I?" And the fundamental answer to this question is suggested by the famous quote by René Descartes: "Cogito Ergo Sum" (translated from Latin as "I think, therefore I am"). Formulating an understanding of yourself is largely describing who you are to yourself. It is a confusing topic to delve into, but language is certainly at the core of what it means to be self-aware.

The neurological exam has two specific subtests that address language. One measures the ability of the patient to understand language by asking them to follow a set of instructions to perform an action, such as "touch your right finger to your left elbow and then to your right knee." Another subtest assesses the fluency and coherency of language by having the patient generate descriptions of objects or scenes depicted in drawings, and by reciting sentences or explaining a written passage. Language, however, is important in so many ways in the neurological exam. The patient needs to know what to do, whether it is as simple as explaining how the knee-jerk reflex is going to be performed, or asking a question such as "What is your name?" Often, language deficits can be determined without specific subtests; if a person cannot reply to a question properly, there may be a problem with the reception of language.

An important example of multimodal integrative areas is associated with language function (Figure 16.6). Adjacent to the auditory association cortex, at the end of the lateral sulcus just anterior to the visual cortex, is **Wernicke's area**. In the lateral aspect of the frontal lobe, just anterior to the region of the motor cortex associated with the head and neck, is Broca's area. Both regions were originally described on the basis of losses of speech and language, which is called **aphasia**. The aphasia associated with Broca's area is known as an **expressive aphasia**, which means that speech production is compromised. This type of aphasia is often described as non-fluency because the ability to say some words leads to broken or halting speech. Grammar can also appear to be lost. The aphasia associated with Wernicke's area is known as a **receptive aphasia**, which is not a loss of speech production, but a loss of understanding of content. Patients, after recovering from acute forms of this aphasia, report not being able to understand what is said to them or what they are saying themselves, but they often cannot keep from talking.

The two regions are connected by white matter tracts that run between the posterior temporal lobe and the lateral aspect of the frontal lobe. **Conduction aphasia** associated with damage to this connection refers to the problem of connecting the understanding of language to the production of speech. This is a very rare condition, but is likely to present as an inability to faithfully repeat spoken language.

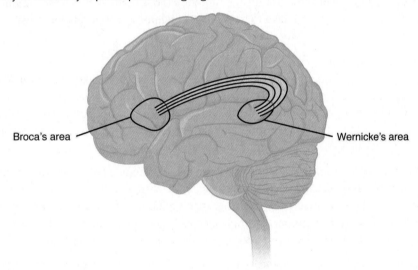

Broca's area   Wernicke's area

FIGURE 16.6 Broca's and Wernicke's Areas   Two important integration areas of the cerebral cortex associated with language function are Broca's and Wernicke's areas. The two areas are connected through the deep white matter running from the posterior temporal lobe to the frontal lobe.

Sensorium

Those parts of the brain involved in the reception and interpretation of sensory stimuli are referred to collectively as the sensorium. The cerebral cortex has several regions that are necessary for sensory perception. From the primary cortical areas of the somatosensory, visual, auditory, and gustatory senses to the association areas that process information in these modalities, the cerebral cortex is the seat of conscious sensory perception. In contrast, sensory information can also be processed by deeper brain regions, which we may vaguely describe as subconscious—for instance, we are not constantly aware of the proprioceptive information that the cerebellum uses to maintain balance. Several of the subtests can reveal activity associated with these sensory modalities, such as being able to hear a question or see a picture. Two subtests assess specific functions of these cortical areas.

The first is **praxis**, a practical exercise in which the patient performs a task completely on the basis of verbal description without any demonstration from the examiner. For example, the patient can be told to take their left hand and place it palm down on their left thigh, then flip it over so the palm is facing up, and then repeat this four times. The examiner describes the activity without any movements on their part to suggest how the movements are to be performed. The patient needs to understand the instructions, transform them into movements, and use sensory feedback, both visual and proprioceptive, to perform the movements correctly.

The second subtest for sensory perception is **gnosis**, which involves two tasks. The first task, known as **stereognosis**, involves the naming of objects strictly on the basis of the somatosensory information that comes from manipulating them. The patient keeps their eyes closed and is given a common object, such as a coin, that they have to identify. The patient should be able to indicate the particular type of coin, such as a dime versus a penny, or a nickel versus a quarter, on the basis of the sensory cues involved. For example, the size, thickness, or weight of the coin may be an indication, or to differentiate the pairs of coins suggested here, the smooth or corrugated edge of the coin will correspond to the particular denomination. The second task, **graphesthesia**, is to recognize numbers or letters written on the palm of the hand with a dull pointer, such as a pen cap.

Praxis and gnosis are related to the conscious perception and cortical processing of sensory information. Being able to transform verbal commands into a sequence of motor responses, or to manipulate and recognize a common object and associate it with a name for that object. Both subtests have language components because language function is integral to these functions. The relationship between the words that describe actions, or the nouns that represent objects, and the cerebral location of these concepts is suggested to be localized to particular cortical areas. Certain aphasias can be characterized by a deficit of verbs or nouns, known as V impairment or N impairment, or may be classified as V–N dissociation. Patients have difficulty using one type of word over the other. To describe what is happening in a photograph as part of the expressive language subtest, a patient will use active- or image-based language. The lack of one or the other of these components of language can relate to the ability to use verbs or nouns. Damage to the region at which the frontal and temporal lobes meet, including the region known as the insula, is associated with V impairment; damage to the middle and inferior temporal lobe is associated with N impairment.

Judgment and Abstract Reasoning

Planning and producing responses requires an ability to make sense of the world around us. Making judgments and reasoning in the abstract are necessary to produce movements as part of larger responses. For example, when your alarm goes off, do you hit the snooze button or jump out of bed? Is 10 extra minutes in bed worth the extra rush to get ready for your day? Will hitting the snooze button multiple times lead to feeling more rested or result in a panic as you run late? How you mentally process these questions can affect your whole day.

The prefrontal cortex is responsible for the functions responsible for planning and making decisions. In the mental status exam, the subtest that assesses judgment and reasoning is directed at three aspects of frontal lobe function. First, the examiner asks questions about problem solving, such as "If you see a house on fire, what would you do?" The patient is also asked to interpret common proverbs, such as "Don't look a gift horse in the mouth." Additionally, pairs of words are compared for similarities, such as apple and orange, or lamp and cabinet.

The prefrontal cortex is composed of the regions of the frontal lobe that are not directly related to specific motor functions. The most posterior region of the frontal lobe, the precentral gyrus, is the primary motor cortex. Anterior to that are the premotor cortex, Broca's area, and the frontal eye fields, which are all related to planning certain types of movements. Anterior to what could be described as motor association areas are the regions of the prefrontal cortex. They are the regions in which judgment, abstract reasoning, and working memory are localized. The antecedents to planning certain movements are judging whether those movements should be made, as in the example of deciding whether to hit the snooze button.

To an extent, the prefrontal cortex may be related to personality. The neurological exam does not necessarily assess personality, but it can be within the realm of neurology or psychiatry. A clinical situation that suggests this link between the prefrontal cortex and personality comes from the story of Phineas Gage, the railroad worker from the mid-1800s who had a metal spike impale his prefrontal cortex. There are suggestions that the steel rod led to changes in his personality. A man who was a quiet, dependable railroad worker became a raucous, irritable drunkard. Later anecdotal evidence from his life suggests that he was able to support himself, although he had to relocate and take on a different career as a stagecoach driver.

A psychiatric practice to deal with various disorders was the prefrontal lobotomy. This procedure was common in the 1940s and early 1950s, until antipsychotic drugs became available. The connections between the prefrontal cortex and other regions of the brain were severed. The disorders associated with this procedure included some aspects of what are now referred to as personality disorders, but also included mood disorders and psychoses. Depictions of lobotomies in popular media suggest a link between cutting the white matter of the prefrontal cortex and changes in a patient's mood and personality, though this correlation is not well understood.

Everyday Connection

Left Brain, Right Brain

Popular media often refer to right-brained and left-brained people, as if the brain were two independent halves that work differently for different people. This is a popular misinterpretation of an important neurological phenomenon. As an extreme measure to deal with a debilitating condition, the corpus callosum may be sectioned to overcome intractable epilepsy. When the connections between the two cerebral hemispheres are cut, interesting effects can be observed.

If a person with an intact corpus callosum is asked to put their hands in their pockets and describe what is there on the basis of what their hands feel, they might say that they have keys in their right pocket and loose change in the left. They may even be able to count the coins in their pocket and say if they can afford to buy a candy bar from the vending machine. If a person with a sectioned corpus callosum is given the same instructions, they will do something quite peculiar. They will only put their right hand in their pocket and say they have keys there. They will not even move their left hand, much less report that there is loose change in the left pocket.

The reason for this is that the language functions of the cerebral cortex are localized to the left hemisphere in 95 percent of the population. Additionally, the left hemisphere is connected to the right side of the body through the corticospinal tract and the ascending tracts of the spinal cord. Motor commands from the precentral gyrus control the opposite side of the body, whereas sensory information processed by the postcentral gyrus is received from the opposite side of the body. For a verbal command to initiate movement of the right arm and hand, the left side of the brain needs to be connected by the corpus callosum. Language is processed in the left side of the brain and directly influences the left brain and right arm motor functions, but is sent to influence the right brain and left arm motor functions through the corpus callosum. Likewise, the left-handed sensory perception of what is in the left pocket travels across the corpus callosum from the right brain, so no verbal report on those contents would be possible if the hand happened to be in the pocket.

INTERACTIVE LINK

Watch the video (http://openstax.org/l/2brains) titled "The Man With Two Brains" to see the neuroscientist Michael Gazzaniga introduce a patient he has worked with for years who has had his corpus callosum cut, separating his two cerebral hemispheres. A few tests are run to demonstrate how this manifests in tests of cerebral function. Unlike normal people, this patient can perform two independent tasks at the same time because the lines of communication between the right and left sides of his brain have been removed. Whereas a person with an intact corpus callosum cannot overcome the dominance of one hemisphere over the other, this patient can. If the left cerebral hemisphere is dominant in the majority of people, why would right-handedness be most common?

16.3 The Cranial Nerve Exam

LEARNING OBJECTIVES

By the end of this section, you will be able to:

- Describe the functional grouping of cranial nerves
- Match the regions of the forebrain and brain stem that are connected to each cranial nerve
- Suggest diagnoses that would explain certain losses of function in the cranial nerves
- Relate cranial nerve deficits to damage of adjacent, unrelated structures

The twelve cranial nerves are typically covered in introductory anatomy courses, and memorizing their names is facilitated by numerous mnemonics developed by students over the years of this practice. But knowing the names of the nerves in order often leaves much to be desired in understanding what the nerves do. The nerves can be categorized by functions, and subtests of the cranial nerve exam can clarify these functional groupings.

Three of the nerves are strictly responsible for special senses whereas four others contain fibers for special and general senses. Three nerves are connected to the extraocular muscles resulting in the control of gaze. Four nerves connect to muscles of the face, oral cavity, and pharynx, controlling facial expressions, mastication, swallowing, and speech. Four nerves make up the cranial component of the parasympathetic nervous system responsible for pupillary constriction, salivation, and the regulation of the organs of the thoracic and upper abdominal cavities. Finally, one nerve controls the muscles of the neck, assisting with spinal control of the movement of the head and neck.

The cranial nerve exam allows directed tests of forebrain and brain stem structures. The twelve cranial nerves serve the head and neck. The vagus nerve (cranial nerve X) has autonomic functions in the thoracic and superior abdominal cavities. The special senses are served through the cranial nerves, as well as the general senses of the head and neck. The movement of the eyes, face, tongue, throat, and neck are all under the control of cranial nerves. Preganglionic parasympathetic nerve fibers that control pupillary size, salivary glands, and the thoracic and upper abdominal viscera are found in four of the nerves. Tests of these functions can provide insight into damage to specific regions of the brain stem and may uncover deficits in adjacent regions.

Sensory Nerves

The olfactory, optic, and vestibulocochlear nerves (cranial nerves I, II, and VIII) are dedicated to four of the special senses: smell, vision, equilibrium, and hearing, respectively. Taste sensation is relayed to the brain stem through fibers of the facial and glossopharyngeal nerves. The trigeminal nerve is a mixed nerve that carries the general somatic senses from the head, similar to those coming through spinal nerves from the rest of the body.

Testing smell is straightforward, as common smells are presented to one nostril at a time. The patient should be able to recognize the smell of coffee or mint, indicating the proper functioning of the olfactory system. Loss of the sense of smell is called anosmia and can be lost following blunt trauma to the head or through aging. The short axons of the first cranial nerve regenerate on a regular basis. The neurons in the olfactory epithelium have a limited life span, and new cells grow to replace the ones that die off. The axons from these neurons grow back into the CNS by following the existing axons—representing one of the few examples of such growth in the mature nervous system. If all of the fibers are sheared when the brain moves within the cranium, such as in a motor vehicle accident, then no axons can find their way back to the olfactory bulb to re-establish connections. If the nerve is not completely severed, the anosmia may be temporary as new neurons can eventually reconnect.

Olfaction is not the pre-eminent sense, but its loss can be quite detrimental. The enjoyment of food is largely based on our sense of smell. Anosmia means that food will not seem to have the same taste, though the gustatory sense is intact, and food will often be described as being bland. However, the taste of food can be improved by adding ingredients (e.g., salt) that stimulate the gustatory sense.

Testing vision relies on the tests that are common in an optometry office. The **Snellen chart** (Figure 16.7) demonstrates visual acuity by presenting standard Roman letters in a variety of sizes. The result of this test is a rough generalization of the acuity of a person based on the normal accepted acuity, such that a letter that subtends a visual angle of 5 minutes of an arc at 20 feet can be seen. To have 20/60 vision, for example, means that the smallest letters that a person can see at a 20-foot distance could be seen by a person with normal acuity from 60 feet away. Testing the extent of the visual field means that the examiner can establish the boundaries of peripheral vision as simply as holding their hands out to either side and asking the patient when the fingers are no longer visible without moving the eyes to track them. If it is necessary, further tests can establish the perceptions in the visual fields. Physical inspection of the optic disk, or where the optic nerve emerges from the eye, can be accomplished by looking through the pupil with an ophthalmoscope.

Access for free at openstax.org

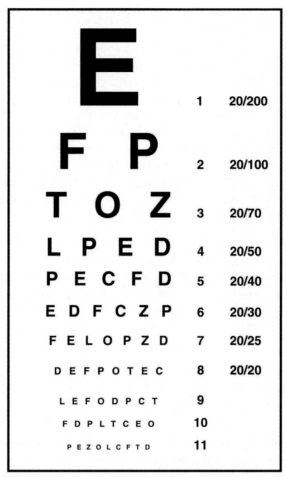

FIGURE 16.7 The Snellen Chart   The Snellen chart for visual acuity presents a limited number of Roman letters in lines of decreasing size. The line with letters that subtend 5 minutes of an arc from 20 feet represents the smallest letters that a person with normal acuity should be able to read at that distance. The different sizes of letters in the other lines represent rough approximations of what a person of normal acuity can read at different distances. For example, the line that represents 20/200 vision would have larger letters so that they are legible to the person with normal acuity at 200 feet.

The optic nerves from both sides enter the cranium through the respective optic canals and meet at the optic chiasm at which fibers sort such that the two halves of the visual field are processed by the opposite sides of the brain. Deficits in visual field perception often suggest damage along the length of the optic pathway between the orbit and the diencephalon. For example, loss of peripheral vision may be the result of a pituitary tumor pressing on the optic chiasm (Figure 16.8). The pituitary, seated in the sella turcica of the sphenoid bone, is directly inferior to the optic chiasm. The axons that decussate in the chiasm are from the medial retinae of either eye, and therefore carry information from the peripheral visual field.

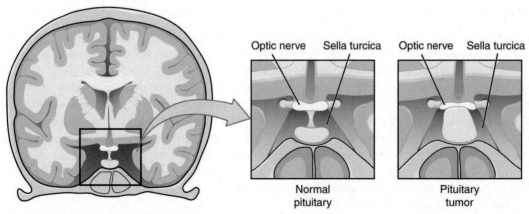

FIGURE 16.8 Pituitary Tumor   The pituitary gland is located in the sella turcica of the sphenoid bone within the cranial floor, placing it immediately inferior to the optic chiasm. If the pituitary gland develops a tumor, it can press against the fibers crossing in the chiasm.

Those fibers are conveying peripheral visual information to the opposite side of the brain, so the patient will experience "tunnel vision"—meaning that only the central visual field will be perceived.

The vestibulocochlear nerve (CN VIII) carries both equilibrium and auditory sensations from the inner ear to the medulla. Though the two senses are not directly related, anatomy is mirrored in the two systems. Problems with balance, such as vertigo, and deficits in hearing may both point to problems with the inner ear. Within the petrous region of the temporal bone is the bony labyrinth of the inner ear. The vestibule is the portion for equilibrium, composed of the utricle, saccule, and the three semicircular canals. The cochlea is responsible for transducing sound waves into a neural signal. The sensory nerves from these two structures travel side-by-side as the vestibulocochlear nerve, though they are really separate divisions. They both emerge from the inner ear, pass through the internal auditory meatus, and synapse in nuclei of the superior medulla. Though they are part of distinct sensory systems, the vestibular nuclei and the cochlear nuclei are close neighbors with adjacent inputs. Deficits in one or both systems could occur from damage that encompasses structures close to both. Damage to structures near the two nuclei can result in deficits to one or both systems.

Balance or hearing deficits may be the result of damage to the middle or inner ear structures. Ménière's disease is a disorder that can affect both equilibrium and audition in a variety of ways. The patient can suffer from vertigo, a low-frequency ringing in the ears, or a loss of hearing. From patient to patient, the exact presentation of the disease can be different. Additionally, within a single patient, the symptoms and signs may change as the disease progresses. Use of the neurological exam subtests for the vestibulocochlear nerve illuminates the changes a patient may go through. The disease appears to be the result of accumulation, or over-production, of fluid in the inner ear, in either the vestibule or cochlea.

Tests of equilibrium are important for coordination and gait and are related to other aspects of the neurological exam. The vestibulo-ocular reflex involves the cranial nerves for gaze control. Balance and equilibrium, as tested by the Romberg test, are part of spinal and cerebellar processes and involved in those components of the neurological exam, as discussed later.

Hearing is tested by using a tuning fork in a couple of different ways. The **Rinne test** involves using a tuning fork to distinguish between **conductive hearing** and **sensorineural hearing**. Conductive hearing relies on vibrations being conducted through the ossicles of the middle ear. Sensorineural hearing is the transmission of sound stimuli through the neural components of the inner ear and cranial nerve. A vibrating tuning fork is placed on the mastoid process and the patient indicates when the sound produced from this is no longer present. Then the fork is immediately moved to just next to the ear canal so the sound travels through the air. If the sound is not heard through the ear, meaning the sound is conducted better through the temporal bone than through the ossicles, a conductive hearing deficit is present. The **Weber test** also uses a tuning fork to differentiate between conductive versus sensorineural hearing loss. In this test, the tuning fork is placed at the top of the skull, and the sound of the tuning fork reaches both inner ears by travelling through bone. In a healthy patient, the sound would appear equally loud in both ears. With unilateral conductive hearing loss, however, the tuning fork sounds louder in the ear with hearing loss. This is because the sound of the tuning fork has to compete with background noise coming from the outer ear, but in conductive hearing loss, the background noise is blocked in the damaged ear, allowing the tuning fork to sound relatively louder in that ear. With unilateral sensorineural hearing loss, however, damage to the cochlea or associated nervous tissue means that the tuning fork sounds quieter in that ear.

The trigeminal system of the head and neck is the equivalent of the ascending spinal cord systems of the dorsal column and the spinothalamic pathways. Somatosensation of the face is conveyed along the nerve to enter the brain stem at the level of the pons. Synapses of those axons, however, are distributed across nuclei found throughout the brain stem. The mesencephalic nucleus processes proprioceptive information of the face, which is the movement and position of facial muscles. It is the sensory component of the **jaw-jerk reflex**, a stretch reflex of the masseter muscle. The chief nucleus, located in the pons, receives information about light touch as well as proprioceptive information about the mandible, which are both relayed to the thalamus and, ultimately, to the postcentral gyrus of the parietal lobe. The spinal trigeminal nucleus, located in the medulla, receives information about crude touch, pain, and temperature to be relayed to the thalamus and cortex. Essentially, the projection through the chief nucleus is analogous to the dorsal column pathway for the body, and the projection through the spinal trigeminal nucleus is analogous to the spinothalamic pathway.

Subtests for the sensory component of the trigeminal system are the same as those for the sensory exam targeting the spinal nerves. The primary sensory subtest for the trigeminal system is sensory discrimination. A cotton-tipped applicator, which is cotton attached to the end of a thin wooden stick, can be used easily for this. The wood of the applicator can be snapped so that a pointed end is opposite the soft cotton-tipped end. The cotton end provides a touch stimulus, while the pointed end provides a painful, or sharp, stimulus. While the patient's eyes are closed, the examiner touches the two ends of the applicator to the patient's face, alternating randomly between them. The patient must identify whether the stimulus is sharp or dull. These stimuli are processed by the trigeminal system separately. Contact with the cotton tip of the applicator is a light touch, relayed by the chief nucleus, but contact with the pointed end of the applicator is a painful stimulus relayed by the spinal trigeminal nucleus. Failure to discriminate these stimuli can localize problems within the brain stem. If a patient cannot recognize a painful stimulus, that might indicate damage to the spinal trigeminal nucleus in the medulla. The medulla also contains important regions that regulate the cardiovascular, respiratory, and digestive systems, as well as being the pathway for ascending and descending tracts between the brain and spinal cord. Damage, such as a stroke, that results in changes in sensory discrimination may indicate these unrelated regions are affected as well.

Gaze Control

The three nerves that control the extraocular muscles are the oculomotor, trochlear, and abducens nerves, which are the third, fourth, and sixth cranial nerves. As the name suggests, the abducens nerve is responsible for abducting the eye, which it controls through contraction of the lateral rectus muscle. The trochlear nerve controls the superior oblique muscle to rotate the eye along its axis in the orbit medially, which is called **intorsion**, and is a component of focusing the eyes on an object close to the face. The oculomotor nerve controls all the other extraocular muscles, as well as a muscle of the upper eyelid. Movements of the two eyes need to be coordinated to locate and track visual stimuli accurately. When moving the eyes to locate an object in the horizontal plane, or to track movement horizontally in the visual field, the lateral rectus muscle of one eye and medial rectus muscle of the other eye are both active. The lateral rectus is controlled by neurons of the abducens nucleus in the superior medulla, whereas the medial rectus is controlled by neurons in the oculomotor nucleus of the midbrain.

Coordinated movement of both eyes through different nuclei requires integrated processing through the brain stem. In the midbrain, the superior colliculus integrates visual stimuli with motor responses to initiate eye movements. The **paramedian pontine reticular formation (PPRF)** will initiate a rapid eye movement, or **saccade**, to bring the eyes to bear on a visual stimulus quickly. These areas are connected to the oculomotor, trochlear, and abducens nuclei by the **medial longitudinal fasciculus (MLF)** that runs through the majority of the brain stem. The MLF allows for **conjugate gaze**, or the movement of the eyes in the same direction, during horizontal movements that require the lateral and medial rectus muscles. Control of conjugate gaze strictly in the vertical direction is contained within the oculomotor complex. To elevate the eyes, the oculomotor nerve on either side stimulates the contraction of both superior rectus muscles; to depress the eyes, the oculomotor nerve on either side stimulates the contraction of both inferior rectus muscles.

Purely vertical movements of the eyes are not very common. Movements are often at an angle, so some horizontal components are necessary, adding the medial and lateral rectus muscles to the movement. The rapid movement of the eyes used to locate and direct the fovea onto visual stimuli is called a saccade. Notice that the paths that are traced in Figure 16.9 are not strictly vertical. The movements between the nose and the mouth are closest, but still have a slant to them. Also, the superior and inferior rectus muscles are not perfectly oriented with the line of sight. The origin for both muscles is medial to their insertions, so elevation and depression may require the lateral rectus muscles to compensate for the slight adduction inherent in the contraction of those muscles, requiring MLF activity as well.

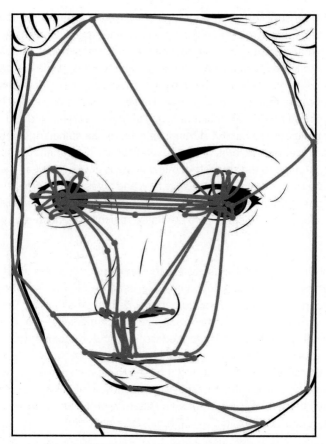

FIGURE 16.9 Saccadic Eye Movements   Saccades are rapid, conjugate movements of the eyes to survey a complicated visual stimulus, or to follow a moving visual stimulus. This image represents the shifts in gaze typical of a person studying a face. Notice the concentration of gaze on the major features of the face and the large number of paths traced between the eyes or around the mouth.

Testing eye movement is simply a matter of having the patient track the tip of a pen as it is passed through the visual field. This may appear similar to testing visual field deficits related to the optic nerve, but the difference is that the patient is asked to not move the eyes while the examiner moves a stimulus into the peripheral visual field. Here, the extent of movement is the point of the test. The examiner is watching for conjugate movements representing proper function of the related nuclei and the MLF. Failure of one eye to abduct while the other adducts in a horizontal movement is referred to as **internuclear ophthalmoplegia**. When this occurs, the patient will experience **diplopia**, or double vision, as the two eyes are temporarily pointed at different stimuli. Diplopia is not restricted to failure of the lateral rectus, because any of the extraocular muscles may fail to move one eye in perfect conjugation with the other.

The final aspect of testing eye movements is to move the tip of the pen in toward the patient's face. As visual stimuli move closer to the face, the two medial recti muscles cause the eyes to move in the one nonconjugate movement that is part of gaze control. When the two eyes move to look at something closer to the face, they both adduct, which is referred to as **convergence**. To keep the stimulus in focus, the eye also needs to change the shape of the lens, which is controlled through the parasympathetic fibers of the oculomotor nerve. The change in focal power of the eye is referred to as **accommodation**. Accommodation ability changes with age; focusing on nearer objects, such as the written text of a book or on a computer screen, may require corrective lenses later in life. Coordination of the skeletal muscles for convergence and coordination of the smooth muscles of the ciliary body for accommodation are referred to as the **accommodation–convergence reflex**.

A crucial function of the cranial nerves is to keep visual stimuli centered on the fovea of the retina. The **vestibulo-ocular reflex (VOR)** coordinates all of the components (Figure 16.10), both sensory and motor, that make this possible. If the head rotates in one direction—for example, to the right—the horizontal pair of semicircular canals in the inner ear indicate the movement by increased activity on the right and decreased activity on the left. The information is sent to the abducens nuclei and oculomotor nuclei on either side to coordinate the lateral and medial rectus muscles. The left lateral rectus and right medial rectus muscles will contract, rotating the eyes in the opposite direction of the head, while nuclei controlling the right lateral rectus and left medial rectus muscles will be inhibited to reduce antagonism of the contracting muscles. These actions stabilize the visual field by compensating for the head rotation with opposite rotation of the eyes in the orbits. Deficits in the VOR may be related to vestibular damage, such as in Ménière's disease, or from dorsal brain stem damage that would affect the eye movement nuclei or their connections through the MLF.

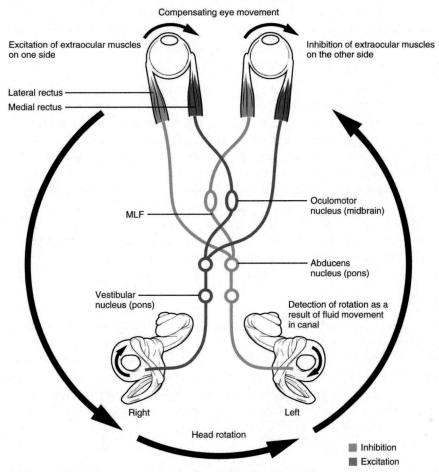

FIGURE 16.10   Vestibulo-ocular Reflex   If the head is turned in one direction, the coordination of that movement with the fixation of the eyes on a visual stimulus involves a circuit that ties the vestibular sense with the eye movement nuclei through the MLF.

Nerves of the Face and Oral Cavity

An iconic part of a doctor's visit is the inspection of the oral cavity and pharynx, suggested by the directive to "open your mouth and say 'ah.'" This is followed by inspection, with the aid of a tongue depressor, of the back of the mouth, or the opening of the oral cavity into the pharynx known as the **fauces**. Whereas this portion of a medical exam inspects for signs of infection, such as in tonsillitis, it is also the means to test the functions of the cranial nerves that are associated with the oral cavity.

The facial and glossopharyngeal nerves convey gustatory stimulation to the brain. Testing this is as simple as introducing salty, sour, bitter, or sweet stimuli to either side of the tongue. The patient should respond to the taste stimulus before retracting the tongue into the mouth. Stimuli applied to specific locations on the tongue will dissolve into the saliva and may stimulate taste buds connected to either the left or right of the nerves, masking any lateral deficits. Along with taste, the glossopharyngeal nerve relays general sensations from the pharyngeal walls. These sensations, along with certain taste stimuli, can stimulate the gag reflex. If the examiner moves the tongue depressor to contact the lateral wall of the fauces, this should elicit the gag reflex. Stimulation of either side of the fauces should elicit an equivalent response. The motor response, through contraction of the muscles of the pharynx, is mediated through the vagus nerve. Normally, the vagus nerve is considered autonomic in nature. The vagus nerve directly stimulates the contraction of skeletal muscles in the pharynx and larynx to contribute to the swallowing and speech functions. Further testing of vagus motor function has the patient repeating consonant sounds that require movement of the muscles around the fauces. The patient is asked to say "lah-kah-pah" or a similar set of alternating sounds while the examiner observes the movements of the soft palate and arches between the palate and tongue.

The facial and glossopharyngeal nerves are also responsible for the initiation of salivation. Neurons in the salivary nuclei of the medulla project through these two nerves as preganglionic fibers, and synapse in ganglia located in the head. The parasympathetic fibers of the facial nerve synapse in the pterygopalatine ganglion, which projects to the submandibular gland and sublingual gland. The parasympathetic fibers of the glossopharyngeal nerve synapse in the otic ganglion, which projects to the parotid gland. Salivation in response to food in the oral cavity is based on a visceral reflex arc within the facial or glossopharyngeal nerves. Other stimuli that stimulate salivation are coordinated through the hypothalamus, such as the smell and sight of food.

The hypoglossal nerve is the motor nerve that controls the muscles of the tongue, except for the palatoglossus muscle, which is controlled by the vagus nerve. There are two sets of muscles of the tongue. The **extrinsic muscles of the tongue** are connected to other structures, whereas the **intrinsic muscles of the tongue** are completely contained within the lingual tissues. While examining the oral cavity, movement of the tongue will indicate whether hypoglossal function is impaired. The test for hypoglossal function is the "stick out your tongue" part of the exam. The genioglossus muscle is responsible for protrusion of the tongue. If the hypoglossal nerves on both sides are working properly, then the tongue will stick straight out. If the nerve on one side has a deficit, the tongue will stick out to that side—pointing to the side with damage. Loss of function of the tongue can interfere with speech and swallowing. Additionally, because the location of the hypoglossal nerve and nucleus is near the cardiovascular center, inspiratory and expiratory areas for respiration, and the vagus nuclei that regulate digestive functions, a tongue that protrudes incorrectly can suggest damage in adjacent structures that have nothing to do with controlling the tongue.

⊘ INTERACTIVE LINK

Watch this short video (http://openstax.org/l/facialnerve) to see an examination of the facial nerve using some simple tests. The facial nerve controls the muscles of facial expression. Severe deficits will be obvious in watching someone use those muscles for normal control. One side of the face might not move like the other side. But directed tests, especially for contraction against resistance, require a formal testing of the muscles. The muscles of the upper and lower face need to be tested. The strength test in this video involves the patient squeezing her eyes shut and the examiner trying to pry her eyes open. Why does the examiner ask her to try a second time?

Motor Nerves of the Neck

The accessory nerve, also referred to as the spinal accessory nerve, innervates the sternocleidomastoid and trapezius muscles (Figure 16.11). When both the sternocleidomastoids contract, the head flexes forward; individually, they cause rotation to the opposite side. The trapezius can act as an antagonist, causing extension and hyperextension of the neck. These two superficial muscles are important for changing the position of the head. Both muscles also receive input from cervical spinal nerves. Along with the spinal accessory nerve, these nerves contribute to elevating the scapula and clavicle through the trapezius, which is tested by asking the patient to shrug both shoulders, and watching for asymmetry. For the sternocleidomastoid, those spinal nerves are primarily sensory projections, whereas the trapezius also has lateral insertions to the clavicle and scapula, and receives motor input from the spinal cord. Calling the nerve the spinal accessory nerve suggests that it is aiding the spinal nerves. Though that is not precisely how the name originated, it does help make the association between the function of this nerve in controlling these muscles and the role these muscles play in movements of the trunk or shoulders.

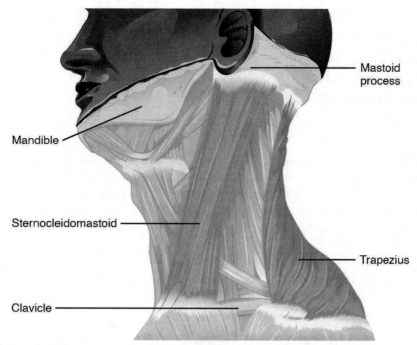

- Mastoid process
- Mandible
- Sternocleidomastoid
- Trapezius
- Clavicle

FIGURE 16.11   Muscles Controlled by the Accessory Nerve   The accessory nerve innervates the sternocleidomastoid and trapezius muscles, both of which attach to the head and to the trunk and shoulders. They can act as antagonists in head flexion and extension, and as synergists in lateral flexion toward the shoulder.

To test these muscles, the patient is asked to flex and extend the neck or shrug the shoulders against resistance, testing the strength of the muscles. Lateral flexion of the neck toward the shoulder tests both at the same time. Any difference on one side versus the other would suggest damage on the weaker side. These strength tests are common for the skeletal muscles controlled by spinal nerves and are a significant component of the motor exam. Deficits associated with the accessory nerve may have an effect on orienting the head, as described with the VOR.

 HOMEOSTATIC IMBALANCES

The Pupillary Light Response

The autonomic control of pupillary size in response to a bright light involves the sensory input of the optic nerve and the parasympathetic motor output of the oculomotor nerve. When light hits the retina, specialized photosensitive ganglion cells send a signal along the optic nerve to the pretectal nucleus in the superior midbrain. A neuron from this nucleus projects to the Edinger–Westphal nuclei in the oculomotor complex in both sides of the midbrain. Neurons in this nucleus give rise to the preganglionic parasympathetic fibers that project through the oculomotor nerve to the ciliary ganglion in the posterior orbit. The postganglionic parasympathetic fibers from the ganglion project to the iris, where they release acetylcholine onto circular fibers that constrict the pupil to reduce the amount of light hitting the retina. The sympathetic nervous system is responsible for dilating the pupil when light levels are low.

Shining light in one eye will elicit constriction of both pupils. The efferent limb of the pupillary light reflex is bilateral. Light shined in one eye causes a constriction of that pupil, as well as constriction of the contralateral pupil. Shining a penlight in the eye of a patient is a very artificial situation, as both eyes are normally exposed to the same light sources. Testing this reflex can illustrate whether the optic nerve or the oculomotor nerve is damaged. If shining the light in one eye results in no changes in pupillary size but shining light in the opposite eye elicits a normal, bilateral response, the damage is associated with the optic nerve on the nonresponsive side. If light in either eye elicits a response in only one eye, the problem is with the oculomotor system.

If light in the right eye only causes the left pupil to constrict, the direct reflex is lost and the consensual reflex is intact, which means that the right oculomotor nerve (or Edinger–Westphal nucleus) is damaged. Damage to the right oculomotor connections will be evident when light is shined in the left eye. In that case, the direct reflex is intact but the consensual reflex is lost, meaning that the left pupil will constrict while the right does not.

16.4 The Sensory and Motor Exams

LEARNING OBJECTIVES

By the end of this section, you will be able to:

- Describe the arrangement of sensory and motor regions in the spinal cord
- Relate damage in the spinal cord to sensory or motor deficits
- Differentiate between upper motor neuron and lower motor neuron diseases
- Describe the clinical indications of common reflexes

Connections between the body and the CNS occur through the spinal cord. The cranial nerves connect the head and neck directly to the brain, but the spinal cord receives sensory input and sends motor commands out to the body through the spinal nerves. Whereas the brain develops into a complex series of nuclei and fiber tracts, the spinal cord remains relatively simple in its configuration (Figure 16.12). From the initial neural tube early in embryonic development, the spinal cord retains a tube-like structure with gray matter surrounding the small central canal and white matter on the surface in three columns. The dorsal, or posterior, horns of the gray matter are mainly devoted to sensory functions whereas the ventral, or anterior, and lateral horns are associated with motor functions. In the white matter, the dorsal column relays sensory information to the brain, and the anterior column is almost exclusively relaying motor commands to the ventral horn motor neurons. The lateral column, however, conveys both sensory and motor information between the spinal cord and brain.

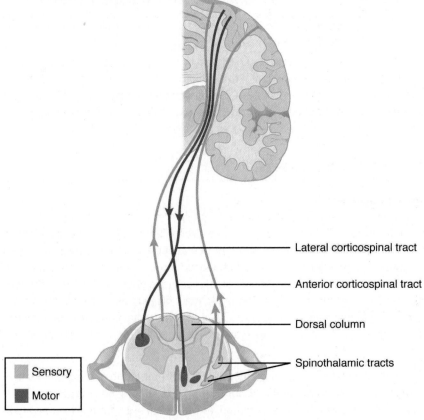

Lateral corticospinal tract

Anterior corticospinal tract

Dorsal column

Spinothalamic tracts

Sensory

Motor

FIGURE 16.12   Locations of Spinal Fiber Tracts

Sensory Modalities and Location

The general senses are distributed throughout the body, relying on nervous tissue incorporated into various organs. Somatic senses are incorporated mostly into the skin, muscles, or tendons, whereas the visceral senses come from nervous tissue incorporated into the majority of organs such as the heart or stomach. The somatic senses are those that usually make up the conscious perception of the how the body interacts with the environment. The visceral senses are most often below the limit of conscious perception because they are involved in homeostatic regulation through the autonomic nervous system.

The sensory exam tests the somatic senses, meaning those that are consciously perceived. Testing of the senses begins with examining the regions known as dermatomes that connect to the cortical region where somatosensation is perceived in the postcentral gyrus. To test the sensory fields, a simple stimulus of the light touch of the soft end of a cotton-tipped applicator is applied at various locations on the skin. The spinal nerves, which contain sensory fibers with dendritic endings in the skin, connect with the skin in a topographically organized manner, illustrated as dermatomes (Figure 16.13). For example, the fibers of eighth cervical nerve innervate the medial surface of the forearm and extend out to the fingers. In addition to testing perception at different positions on the skin, it is necessary to test sensory perception within the dermatome from distal to proximal locations in the appendages, or lateral to medial locations in the trunk. In testing the eighth cervical nerve, the patient would be asked if the touch of the cotton to the fingers or the medial forearm was perceptible, and whether there were any differences in the sensations.

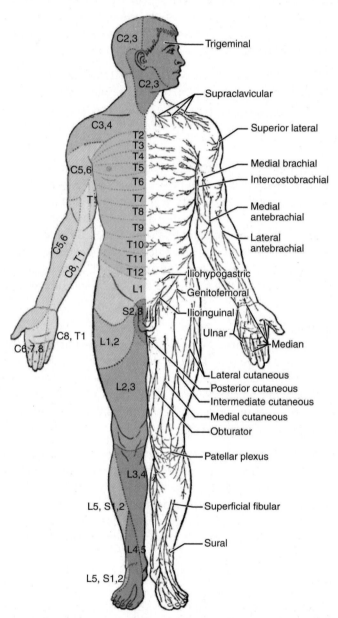

FIGURE 16.13 Dermatomes The surface of the skin can be divided into topographic regions that relate to the location of sensory endings in the skin based on the spinal nerve that contains those fibers. (credit: modification of work by Mikael Häggström)

Other modalities of somatosensation can be tested using a few simple tools. The perception of pain can be tested using the broken end of the cotton-tipped applicator. The perception of vibratory stimuli can be testing using an oscillating tuning fork placed against prominent bone features such as the distal head of the ulna on the medial aspect of the elbow. When the tuning fork is still, the metal against the skin can be perceived as a cold stimulus.

Using the cotton tip of the applicator, or even just a fingertip, the perception of tactile movement can be assessed as the stimulus is drawn across the skin for approximately 2–3 cm. The patient would be asked in what direction the stimulus is moving. All of these tests are repeated in distal and proximal locations and for different dermatomes to assess the spatial specificity of perception. The sense of position and motion, proprioception, is tested by moving the fingers or toes and asking the patient if they sense the movement. If the distal locations are not perceived, the test is repeated at increasingly proximal joints.

The various stimuli used to test sensory input assess the function of the major ascending tracts of the spinal cord. The dorsal column pathway conveys fine touch, vibration, and proprioceptive information, whereas the spinothalamic pathway primarily conveys pain and temperature. Testing these stimuli provides information about whether these two major ascending pathways are functioning properly. Within the spinal cord, the two systems are segregated. The dorsal column information ascends ipsilateral to the source of the stimulus and decussates in the medulla, whereas the spinothalamic pathway decussates at the level of entry and ascends contralaterally. The differing sensory stimuli are segregated in the spinal cord so that the various subtests for these stimuli can distinguish which ascending pathway may be damaged in certain situations.

Whereas the basic sensory stimuli are assessed in the subtests directed at each submodality of somatosensation, testing the ability to discriminate sensations is important. Pairing the light touch and pain subtests together makes it possible to compare the two submodalities at the same time, and therefore the two major ascending tracts at the same time. Mistaking painful stimuli for light touch, or vice versa, may point to errors in ascending projections, such as in a **hemisection** of the spinal cord that might come from a motor vehicle accident.

Another issue of sensory discrimination is not distinguishing between different submodalities, but rather location. The two-point discrimination subtest highlights the density of sensory endings, and therefore receptive fields in the skin. The sensitivity to fine touch, which can give indications of the texture and detailed shape of objects, is highest in the fingertips. To assess the limit of this sensitivity, two-point discrimination is measured by simultaneously touching the skin in two locations, such as could be accomplished with a pair of forceps. Specialized calipers for precisely measuring the distance between points are also available. The patient is asked to indicate whether one or two stimuli are present while keeping their eyes closed. The examiner will switch between using the two points and a single point as the stimulus. Failure to recognize two points may be an indication of a dorsal column pathway deficit.

Similar to two-point discrimination, but assessing laterality of perception, is double simultaneous stimulation. Two stimuli, such as the cotton tips of two applicators, are touched to the same position on both sides of the body. If one side is not perceived, this may indicate damage to the contralateral posterior parietal lobe. Because there is one of each pathway on either side of the spinal cord, they are not likely to interact. If none of the other subtests suggest particular deficits with the pathways, the deficit is likely to be in the cortex where conscious perception is based. The mental status exam contains subtests that assess other functions that are primarily localized to the parietal cortex, such as stereognosis and graphesthesia.

A final subtest of sensory perception that concentrates on the sense of proprioception is known as the **Romberg test**. The patient is asked to stand straight with feet together. Once the patient has achieved their balance in that position, they are asked to close their eyes. Without visual feedback that the body is in a vertical orientation relative to the surrounding environment, the patient must rely on the proprioceptive stimuli of joint and muscle position, as well as information from the inner ear, to maintain balance. This test can indicate deficits in dorsal column pathway proprioception, as well as problems with proprioceptive projections to the cerebellum through the **spinocerebellar tract**.

🔗 INTERACTIVE LINK

Watch this video (http://openstax.org/l/2point) to see a quick demonstration of two-point discrimination. Touching a specialized caliper to the surface of the skin will measure the distance between two points that are perceived as distinct stimuli versus a single stimulus. The patient keeps their eyes closed while the examiner switches between using both points of the caliper or just one. The patient then must indicate whether one or two stimuli are in contact with the skin. Why is the distance between the caliper points closer on the fingertips as opposed to the palm of the hand? And what do you think the distance would be on the arm, or the shoulder?

Muscle Strength and Voluntary Movement

The skeletomotor system is largely based on the simple, two-cell projection from the precentral gyrus of the frontal lobe to the skeletal muscles. The corticospinal tract represents the neurons that send output from the primary motor cortex. These fibers travel through the deep white matter of the cerebrum, then through the midbrain and pons, into the medulla where most of them decussate, and finally through the spinal cord white matter in the lateral (crossed fibers) or anterior (uncrossed fibers) columns. These fibers synapse on motor neurons in the ventral horn. The ventral horn motor neurons then project to skeletal muscle and cause contraction. These two cells are termed the upper motor neuron (UMN) and the lower motor neuron (LMN). Voluntary movements require these two cells to be active.

The motor exam tests the function of these neurons and the muscles they control. First, the muscles are inspected and palpated for signs of structural irregularities. Movement disorders may be the result of changes to the muscle tissue, such as scarring, and these possibilities need to be ruled out before testing function. Along with this inspection, muscle tone is assessed by moving the muscles through a passive range of motion. The arm is moved at the elbow and wrist, and the leg is moved at the knee and ankle. Skeletal muscle should have a resting tension representing a slight contraction of the fibers. The lack of muscle tone, known as **hypotonicity** or **flaccidity**, may indicate that the LMN is not conducting action potentials that will keep a basal level of acetylcholine in the neuromuscular junction.

If muscle tone is present, muscle strength is tested by having the patient contract muscles against resistance. The examiner will ask the patient to lift the arm, for example, while the examiner is pushing down on it. This is done for both limbs, including shrugging the shoulders. Lateral differences in strength—being able to push against resistance with the right arm but not the left—would indicate a deficit in one corticospinal tract versus the other. An overall loss of strength, without laterality, could indicate a global problem with the motor system. Diseases that result in UMN lesions include cerebral palsy or MS, or it may be the result of a stroke. A sign of UMN lesion is a negative result in the subtest for **pronator drift**. The patient is asked to extend both arms in front of the body with the palms facing up. While keeping the eyes closed, if the patient unconsciously allows one or the other arm to slowly relax, toward the pronated position, this could indicate a failure of the motor system to maintain the supinated position.

Reflexes

Reflexes combine the spinal sensory and motor components with a sensory input that directly generates a motor response. The reflexes that are tested in the neurological exam are classified into two groups. A **deep tendon reflex** is commonly known as a stretch reflex, and is elicited by a strong tap to a tendon, such as in the knee-jerk reflex. A **superficial reflex** is elicited through gentle stimulation of the skin and causes contraction of the associated muscles.

For the arm, the common reflexes to test are of the biceps, brachioradialis, triceps, and flexors for the digits. For the leg, the knee-jerk reflex of the quadriceps is common, as is the ankle reflex for the gastrocnemius and soleus. The tendon at the insertion for each of these muscles is struck with a rubber mallet. The muscle is quickly stretched, resulting in activation of the muscle spindle that sends a signal into the spinal cord through the dorsal root. The fiber synapses directly on the ventral horn motor neuron that activates the muscle, causing contraction. The reflexes are physiologically useful for stability. If a muscle is stretched, it reflexively contracts to return the muscle to compensate for the change in length. In the context of the neurological exam, reflexes indicate that the LMN is functioning properly.

The most common superficial reflex in the neurological exam is the **plantar reflex** that tests for the **Babinski sign** on the basis of the extension or flexion of the toes at the plantar surface of the foot. The plantar reflex is commonly tested in newborn infants to establish the presence of neuromuscular function. To elicit this reflex, an examiner brushes a stimulus, usually the examiner's fingertip, along the plantar surface of the infant's foot. An infant would present a positive Babinski sign, meaning the foot dorsiflexes and the toes extend and splay out. As a person learns to walk, the plantar reflex changes to cause curling of the toes and a moderate plantar flexion. If superficial stimulation of the sole of the foot caused extension of the foot, keeping one's balance would be harder. The descending input of the corticospinal tract modifies the response of the plantar reflex, meaning that a negative Babinski sign is the expected response in testing the reflex. Other superficial reflexes are not commonly tested, though a series of abdominal reflexes can target function in the lower thoracic spinal segments.

🔗 INTERACTIVE LINK

Watch this video (http://openstax.org/l/reflextest) to see how to test reflexes in the abdomen. Testing reflexes of the trunk is not commonly performed in the neurological exam, but if findings suggest a problem with the thoracic segments of the spinal cord, a series of superficial reflexes of the abdomen can localize function to those segments. If contraction is not observed when the skin lateral to the umbilicus (belly button) is stimulated, what level of the spinal cord may be damaged?

Comparison of Upper and Lower Motor Neuron Damage

Many of the tests of motor function can indicate differences that will address whether damage to the motor system is in the upper or lower motor neurons. Signs that suggest a UMN lesion include muscle weakness, strong deep tendon reflexes, decreased control of movement or slowness, pronator drift, a positive Babinski sign, **spasticity**, and the **clasp-knife response**. Spasticity is an excess contraction in resistance to stretch. It can result in **hyperflexia**, which is when joints are overly flexed. The clasp-knife response occurs when the patient initially resists movement, but then releases, and the joint will quickly flex like a pocket knife closing.

A lesion on the LMN would result in paralysis, or at least partial loss of voluntary muscle control, which is known as **paresis**. The paralysis observed in LMN diseases is referred to as **flaccid paralysis**, referring to a complete or partial loss of muscle tone, in contrast to the loss of control in UMN lesions in which tone is retained and spasticity is exhibited. Other signs of an LMN lesion are **fibrillation**, **fasciculation**, and compromised or lost reflexes resulting from the denervation of the muscle fibers.

Disorders of the...

Spinal Cord

In certain situations, such as a motorcycle accident, only half of the spinal cord may be damaged in what is known as a hemisection. Forceful trauma to the trunk may cause ribs or vertebrae to fracture, and debris can crush or section through part of the spinal cord. The full section of a spinal cord would result in paraplegia, or loss of voluntary motor control of the lower body, as well as loss of sensations from that point down. A hemisection, however, will leave spinal cord tracts intact on one side. The resulting condition would be hemiplegia on the side of the trauma—one leg would be paralyzed. The sensory results are more complicated.

The ascending tracts in the spinal cord are segregated between the dorsal column and spinothalamic pathways. This means that the sensory deficits will be based on the particular sensory information each pathway conveys. Sensory discrimination between touch and painful stimuli will illustrate the difference in how these pathways divide these functions.

On the paralyzed leg, a patient will acknowledge painful stimuli, but not fine touch or proprioceptive sensations. On the functional leg, the opposite is true. The reason for this is that the dorsal column pathway ascends ipsilateral to the sensation, so it would be damaged the same way as the lateral corticospinal tract. The spinothalamic pathway decussates immediately upon entering the spinal cord and ascends contralateral to the source; it would therefore bypass the hemisection.

The motor system can indicate the loss of input to the ventral horn in the lumbar enlargement where motor neurons to the leg are found, but motor function in the trunk is less clear. The left and right anterior corticospinal tracts are directly adjacent to each other. The likelihood of trauma to the spinal cord resulting in a hemisection that affects one anterior column, but not the other, is very unlikely. Either the axial musculature will not be affected at all, or there will be bilateral losses in the trunk.

Sensory discrimination can pinpoint the level of damage in the spinal cord. Below the hemisection, pain stimuli will be perceived in the damaged side, but not fine touch. The opposite is true on the other side. The pain fibers on the side with motor function cross the midline in the spinal cord and ascend in the contralateral lateral column as far as the hemisection. The dorsal column will be intact ipsilateral to the source on the intact side and reach the brain for conscious perception. The trauma would be at the level just before sensory discrimination returns to normal, helping to pinpoint the trauma. Whereas imaging technology, like magnetic resonance

Access for free at openstax.org

imaging (MRI) or computed tomography (CT) scanning, could localize the injury as well, nothing more complicated than a cotton-tipped applicator can localize the damage. That may be all that is available on the scene when moving the victim requires crucial decisions be made.

16.5 The Coordination and Gait Exams

LEARNING OBJECTIVES

By the end of this section, you will be able to:

- Explain the relationship between the location of the cerebellum and its function in movement
- Chart the major divisions of the cerebellum
- List the major connections of the cerebellum
- Describe the relationship of the cerebellum to axial and appendicular musculature
- Explain the prevalent causes of cerebellar ataxia

The role of the cerebellum is a subject of debate. There is an obvious connection to motor function based on the clinical implications of cerebellar damage. There is also strong evidence of the cerebellar role in procedural memory. The two are not incompatible; in fact, procedural memory is motor memory, such as learning to ride a bicycle. Significant work has been performed to describe the connections within the cerebellum that result in learning. A model for this learning is classical conditioning, as shown by the famous dogs from the physiologist Ivan Pavlov's work. This classical conditioning, which can be related to motor learning, fits with the neural connections of the cerebellum. The cerebellum is 10 percent of the mass of the brain and has varied functions that all point to a role in the motor system.

Location and Connections of the Cerebellum

The cerebellum is located in apposition to the dorsal surface of the brain stem, centered on the pons. The name of the pons is derived from its connection to the cerebellum. The word means "bridge" and refers to the thick bundle of myelinated axons that form a bulge on its ventral surface. Those fibers are axons that project from the gray matter of the pons into the contralateral cerebellar cortex. These fibers make up the **middle cerebellar peduncle (MCP)** and are the major physical connection of the cerebellum to the brain stem (Figure 16.14). Two other white matter bundles connect the cerebellum to the other regions of the brain stem. The **superior cerebellar peduncle (SCP)** is the connection of the cerebellum to the midbrain and forebrain. The **inferior cerebellar peduncle (ICP)** is the connection to the medulla.

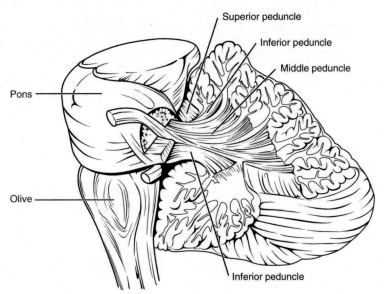

FIGURE 16.14 Cerebellar Peduncles   The connections to the cerebellum are the three cerebellar peduncles, which are close to each other. The ICP arises from the medulla—specifically from the inferior olive, which is visible as a bulge on the ventral surface of the brain stem. The MCP is the ventral surface of the pons. The SCP projects into the midbrain.

These connections can also be broadly described by their functions. The ICP conveys sensory input to the cerebellum, partially from the spinocerebellar tract, but also through fibers of the **inferior olive**. The MCP is part of the **cortico-ponto-cerebellar pathway** that connects the cerebral cortex with the cerebellum and preferentially targets the lateral regions of the cerebellum. It includes a copy of the motor commands sent from the precentral gyrus through the corticospinal tract, arising from collateral branches that synapse in the gray matter of the pons, along with input from other regions such as the visual cortex. The SCP is the major output of the cerebellum, divided between the **red nucleus** in the midbrain and the thalamus, which will return cerebellar processing to the motor cortex. These connections describe a circuit that compares motor commands and sensory feedback to generate a new output. These comparisons make it possible to coordinate movements. If the cerebral cortex sends a motor command to initiate walking, that command is copied by the pons and sent into the cerebellum through the MCP. Sensory feedback in the form of proprioception from the spinal cord, as well as vestibular sensations from the inner ear, enters through the ICP. If you take a step and begin to slip on the floor because it is wet, the output from the cerebellum—through the SCP—can correct for that and keep you balanced and moving. The red nucleus sends new motor commands to the spinal cord through the **rubrospinal tract**.

The cerebellum is divided into regions that are based on the particular functions and connections involved. The midline regions of the cerebellum, the **vermis** and **flocculonodular lobe**, are involved in comparing visual information, equilibrium, and proprioceptive feedback to maintain balance and coordinate movements such as walking, or **gait**, through the descending output of the red nucleus (Figure 16.15). The lateral hemispheres are primarily concerned with planning motor functions through frontal lobe inputs that are returned through the thalamic projections back to the premotor and motor cortices. Processing in the midline regions targets movements of the axial musculature, whereas the lateral regions target movements of the appendicular musculature. The vermis is referred to as the **spinocerebellum** because it primarily receives input from the dorsal columns and spinocerebellar pathways. The flocculonodular lobe is referred to as the **vestibulocerebellum** because of the vestibular projection into that region. Finally, the lateral cerebellum is referred to as the **cerebrocerebellum**, reflecting the significant input from the cerebral cortex through the cortico-ponto-cerebellar pathway.

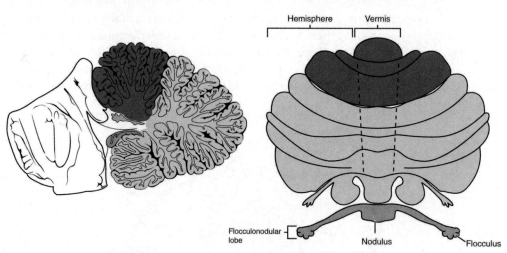

FIGURE 16.15   Major Regions of the Cerebellum   The cerebellum can be divided into two basic regions: the midline and the hemispheres. The midline is composed of the vermis and the flocculonodular lobe, and the hemispheres are the lateral regions.

Coordination and Alternating Movement

Testing for cerebellar function is the basis of the coordination exam. The subtests target appendicular musculature, controlling the limbs, and axial musculature for posture and gait. The assessment of cerebellar function will depend on the normal functioning of other systems addressed in previous sections of the neurological exam. Motor control from the cerebrum, as well as sensory input from somatic, visual, and vestibular senses, are important to cerebellar function.

The subtests that address appendicular musculature, and therefore the lateral regions of the cerebellum, begin with a check for tremor. The patient extends their arms in front of them and holds the position. The examiner watches for the presence of tremors that would not be present if the muscles are relaxed. By pushing down on the arms in this position, the examiner can check for the rebound response, which is when the arms are automatically brought back to the extended position. The extension of the arms is an ongoing motor process, and the tap or push on the arms presents a change in the proprioceptive feedback. The cerebellum compares the cerebral motor command with the proprioceptive feedback and adjusts the descending input to correct. The red nucleus would send an additional signal to the LMN for the arm to increase contraction momentarily to overcome the change and regain the original position.

The **check reflex** depends on cerebellar input to keep increased contraction from continuing after the removal of resistance. The patient flexes the elbow against resistance from the examiner to extend the elbow. When the examiner releases the arm, the patient should be able to stop the increased contraction and keep the arm from moving. A similar response would be seen if you try to pick up a coffee mug that you believe to be full but turns out to be empty. Without checking the contraction, the mug would be thrown from the overexertion of the muscles expecting to lift a heavier object.

Several subtests of the cerebellum assess the ability to alternate movements, or switch between muscle groups that may be antagonistic to each other. In the finger-to-nose test, the patient touches their finger to the examiner's finger and then to their nose, and then back to the examiner's finger, and back to the nose. The examiner moves the target finger to assess a range of movements. A similar test for the lower extremities has the patient touch their toe to a moving target, such as the examiner's finger. Both of these tests involve flexion and extension around a joint—the elbow or the knee and the shoulder or hip—as well as movements of the wrist and ankle. The patient must switch between the opposing muscles, like the biceps and triceps brachii, to move their finger from the target to their nose. Coordinating these movements involves the motor cortex communicating with the cerebellum through the pons and feedback through the thalamus to plan the movements. Visual cortex information is also part of the processing that occurs in the cerebrocerebellum while it is involved in guiding movements of the finger or toe.

Rapid, alternating movements are tested for the upper and lower extremities. The patient is asked to touch each finger to their thumb, or to pat the palm of one hand on the back of the other, and then flip that hand over and alternate back-and-forth. To test similar function in the lower extremities, the patient touches their heel to their shin near the knee and slides it down toward the ankle, and then back again, repetitively. Rapid, alternating movements are part of speech as well. A patient is asked to repeat the nonsense consonants "lah-kah-pah" to alternate movements of the tongue, lips, and palate. All of these rapid alternations require planning from the cerebrocerebellum to coordinate movement commands that control the coordination.

Posture and Gait

Gait can either be considered a separate part of the neurological exam or a subtest of the coordination exam that addresses walking and balance. Testing posture and gait addresses functions of the spinocerebellum and the vestibulocerebellum because both are part of these activities. A subtest called station begins with the patient standing in a normal position to check for the placement of the feet and balance. The patient is asked to hop on one foot to assess the ability to maintain balance and posture during movement. Though the station subtest appears to be similar to the Romberg test, the difference is that the patient's eyes are open during station. The Romberg test has the patient stand still with the eyes closed. Any changes in posture would be the result of proprioceptive deficits, and the patient is able to recover when they open their eyes.

Subtests of walking begin with having the patient walk normally for a distance away from the examiner, and then turn and return to the starting position. The examiner watches for abnormal placement of the feet and the movement of the arms relative to the movement. The patient is then asked to walk with a few different variations. Tandem gait is when the patient places the heel of one foot against the toe of the other foot and walks in a straight line in that manner. Walking only on the heels or only on the toes will test additional aspects of balance.

Ataxia

A movement disorder of the cerebellum is referred to as **ataxia**. It presents as a loss of coordination in voluntary movements. Ataxia can also refer to sensory deficits that cause balance problems, primarily in proprioception and equilibrium. When the problem is observed in movement, it is ascribed to cerebellar damage. Sensory and vestibular ataxia would likely also present with problems in gait and station.

Ataxia is often the result of exposure to exogenous substances, focal lesions, or a genetic disorder. Focal lesions include strokes affecting the cerebellar arteries, tumors that may impinge on the cerebellum, trauma to the back of the head and neck, or MS. Alcohol intoxication or drugs such as ketamine cause ataxia, but it is often reversible. Mercury in fish can cause ataxia as well. Hereditary conditions can lead to degeneration of the cerebellum or spinal cord, as well as malformation of the brain, or the abnormal accumulation of copper seen in Wilson's disease.

🔗 INTERACTIVE LINK

Watch this short video (http://openstax.org/l/stationtest) to see a test for station. Station refers to the position a person adopts when they are standing still. The examiner would look for issues with balance, which coordinates proprioceptive, vestibular, and visual information in the cerebellum. To test the ability of a subject to maintain balance, asking them to stand or hop on one foot can be more demanding. The examiner may also push the subject to see if they can maintain balance. An abnormal finding in the test of station is if the feet are placed far apart. Why would a wide stance suggest problems with cerebellar function?

Everyday Connection

The Field Sobriety Test

The neurological exam has been described as a clinical tool throughout this chapter. It is also useful in other ways. A variation of the coordination exam is the Field Sobriety Test (FST) used to assess whether drivers are under the influence of alcohol. The cerebellum is crucial for coordinated movements such as keeping balance while walking, or moving appendicular musculature on the basis of proprioceptive feedback. The cerebellum is also very sensitive to ethanol, the particular type of alcohol found in beer, wine, and liquor.

Walking in a straight line involves comparing the motor command from the primary motor cortex to the proprioceptive and vestibular sensory feedback, as well as following the visual guide of the white line on the side of the road. When the cerebellum is compromised by alcohol, the cerebellum cannot coordinate these movements effectively, and maintaining balance becomes difficult.

Another common aspect of the FST is to have the driver extend their arms out wide and touch their fingertip to their nose, usually with their eyes closed. The point of this is to remove the visual feedback for the movement and force the driver to rely just on proprioceptive information about the movement and position of their fingertip relative to their nose. With eyes open, the corrections to the movement of the arm might be so small as to be hard to see, but proprioceptive feedback is not as immediate and broader movements of the arm will probably be needed, particularly if the cerebellum is affected by alcohol.

Reciting the alphabet backwards is not always a component of the FST, but its relationship to neurological function is interesting. There is a cognitive aspect to remembering how the alphabet goes and how to recite it backwards. That is actually a variation of the mental status subtest of repeating the months backwards. However, the cerebellum is important because speech production is a coordinated activity. The speech rapid alternating movement subtest is specifically using the consonant changes of "lah-kah-pah" to assess coordinated movements of the lips, tongue, pharynx, and palate. But the entire alphabet, especially in the nonrehearsed backwards order, pushes this type of coordinated movement quite far. It is related to the reason that speech becomes slurred when a person is intoxicated.

Key Terms

accommodation   in vision, a change in the ability of the eye to focus on objects at different distances

accommodation–convergence reflex   coordination of somatic control of the medial rectus muscles of either eye with the parasympathetic control of the ciliary bodies to maintain focus while the eyes converge on visual stimuli near to the face

anterograde amnesia   inability to form new memories from a particular time forward

aphasia   loss of language function

ataxia   movement disorder related to damage of the cerebellum characterized by loss of coordination in voluntary movements

Babinski sign   dorsiflexion of the foot with extension and splaying of the toes in response to the plantar reflex, normally suppressed by corticospinal input

cerebrocerebellum   lateral regions of the cerebellum; named for the significant input from the cerebral cortex

check reflex   response to a release in resistance so that the contractions stop, or check, movement

clasp-knife response   sign of UMN disease when a patient initially resists passive movement of a muscle but will quickly release to a lower state of resistance

conduction aphasia   loss of language function related to connecting the understanding of speech with the production of speech, without either specific function being lost

conductive hearing   hearing dependent on the conduction of vibrations of the tympanic membrane through the ossicles of the middle ear

conjugate gaze   coordinated movement of the two eyes simultaneously in the same direction

convergence   in vision, the movement of the eyes so that they are both pointed at the same point in space, which increases for stimuli that are closer to the subject

coordination exam   major section of the neurological exam that assesses complex, coordinated motor functions of the cerebellum and associated motor pathways

cortico-ponto-cerebellar pathway   projection from the cerebral cortex to the cerebellum by way of the gray matter of the pons

cranial nerve exam   major section of the neurological exam that assesses sensory and motor functions of the cranial nerves and their associated central and peripheral structures

cytoarchitecture   study of a tissue based on the structure and organization of its cellular components; related to the broader term, histology

deep tendon reflex   another term for stretch reflex, based on the elicitation through deep stimulation of the tendon at the insertion

diplopia   double vision resulting from a failure in conjugate gaze

edema   fluid accumulation in tissue; often associated with circulatory deficits

embolus   obstruction in a blood vessel such as a blood clot, fatty mass, air bubble, or other foreign matter that interrupts the flow of blood to an organ or some part of the body

episodic memory   memory of specific events in an autobiographical sense

expressive aphasia   loss of the ability to produce language; usually associated with damage to Broca's area in the frontal lobe

extrinsic muscles of the tongue   muscles that are connected to other structures, such as the hyoid bone or the mandible, and control the position of the tongue

fasciculation   small muscle twitch as a result of spontaneous activity from an LMN

fauces   opening from the oral cavity into the pharynx

fibrillation   in motor responses, a spontaneous muscle action potential that occurs in the absence of neuromuscular input, resulting from LMN lesions

flaccid paralysis   loss of voluntary muscle control and muscle tone, as the result of LMN disease

flaccidity   presentation of a loss of muscle tone, observed as floppy limbs or a lack of resistance to passive movement

flocculonodular lobe   lobe of the cerebellum that receives input from the vestibular system to help with balance and posture

gait   rhythmic pattern of alternating movements of the lower limbs during locomotion

gait exam   major section of the neurological exam that assesses the cerebellum and descending pathways in the spinal cord through the coordinated motor functions of walking; a portion of the coordination exam

gnosis   in a neurological exam, intuitive experiential knowledge tested by interacting with common objects or symbols

graphesthesia   perception of symbols, such as letters or numbers, traced in the palm of the hand

hemisection   cut through half of a structure, such as the spinal cord

hemorrhagic stroke   disruption of blood flow to the brain caused by bleeding within the cranial vault

hyperflexia   overly flexed joints

hypotonicity   low muscle tone, a sign of LMN disease

hypovolemia   decrease in blood volume

inferior cerebellar peduncle (ICP)   input to the cerebellum, largely from the inferior olive, that represents sensory feedback from the periphery

inferior olive   large nucleus in the medulla that receives input from sensory systems and projects into the cerebellar cortex

internuclear ophthalmoplegia   deficit of conjugate lateral gaze because the lateral rectus muscle of one eye does not contract resulting from damage to the abducens nerve or the MLF

intorsion   medial rotation of the eye around its axis

intrinsic muscles of the tongue   muscles that originate out of, and insert into, other tissues within the tongue and control the shape of the tongue

ischemic stroke   disruption of blood flow to the brain because blood cannot flow through blood vessels as a result of a blockage or narrowing of the vessel

jaw-jerk reflex   stretch reflex of the masseter muscle

localization of function   principle that circumscribed anatomical locations are responsible for specific functions in an organ system

medial longitudinal fasciculus (MLF)   fiber pathway that connects structures involved in the control of eye and head position, from the superior colliculus to the vestibular nuclei and cerebellum

mental status exam   major section of the neurological exam that assesses cognitive functions of the cerebrum

middle cerebellar peduncle (MCP)   large, white-matter bridge from the pons that constitutes the major input to the cerebellar cortex

motor exam   major section of the neurological exam that assesses motor functions of the spinal cord and spinal nerves

neurological exam   clinical assessment tool that can be used to quickly evaluate neurological function and determine if specific parts of the nervous system have been affected by damage or disease

paramedian pontine reticular formation (PPRF)   region of the brain stem adjacent to the motor nuclei for gaze control that coordinates rapid, conjugate eye movements

paresis   partial loss of, or impaired, voluntary muscle control

plantar reflex   superficial reflex initiated by gentle stimulation of the sole of the foot

praxis   in a neurological exam, the act of doing something using ready knowledge or skills in response to verbal instruction

procedural memory   memory of how to perform a specific task

pronator drift   sign of contralateral corticospinal lesion when the one arm will drift into a pronated position when held straight out with the palms facing upward

receptive aphasia   loss of the ability to understand received language, such as what is spoken to the subject or given in written form

red nucleus   nucleus in the midbrain that receives output from the cerebellum and projects onto the spinal cord in the rubrospinal tract

retrograde amnesia   loss of memories before a particular event

Rinne test   use of a tuning fork to test conductive hearing loss versus sensorineural hearing loss

Romberg test   test of equilibrium that requires the patient to maintain a straight, upright posture without visual feedback of position

rubrospinal tract   descending tract from the red nucleus of the midbrain that results in modification of ongoing motor programs

saccade   small, rapid movement of the eyes used to locate and direct the fovea onto visual stimuli

sensorineural hearing   hearing dependent on the transduction and propagation of auditory information through the neural components of the peripheral auditory structures

sensory exam   major section of the neurological exam that assesses sensory functions of the spinal cord and spinal nerves

short-term memory   capacity to retain information actively in the brain for a brief period of time

Snellen chart   standardized arrangement of letters in decreasing size presented to a subject at a distance of 20 feet to test visual acuity

spasticity   increased contraction of a muscle in response to resistance, often resulting in hyperflexia

spinocerebellar tract   ascending fibers that carry proprioceptive input to the cerebellum used in maintaining balance and coordinated movement

spinocerebellum   midline region of the cerebellum known as the vermis that receives proprioceptive input from the spinal cord

stereognosis   perception of common objects placed in the hand solely on the basis of manipulation of that object in the hand

stroke   (also, cerebrovascular accident (CVA)) loss of neurological function caused by an interruption of blood flow to a region of the central nervous system

superficial reflex   reflexive contraction initiated by gentle stimulation of the skin

superior cerebellar peduncle (SCP)   white-matter tract representing output of the cerebellum to the red nucleus of the midbrain

transient ischemic attack (TIA)   temporary

disruption of blood flow to the brain in which symptoms occur rapidly but last only a short time

vermis   prominent ridge along the midline of the cerebellum that is referred to as the spinocerebellum

vestibulo-ocular reflex (VOR)   reflex based on connections between the vestibular system and the cranial nerves of eye movements that ensures that images are stabilized on the retina as the head and body move

vestibulocerebellum   flocculonodular lobe of the cerebellum named for the vestibular input from the eighth cranial nerve

Weber test   use of a tuning fork to test the laterality of hearing loss by placing it at several locations on the midline of the skull

Wernicke's area   region at the posterior end of the lateral sulcus in which speech comprehension is localized

Chapter Review

16.1 Overview of the Neurological Exam

The neurological exam is a clinical assessment tool to determine the extent of function from the nervous system. It is divided into five major sections that each deal with a specific region of the CNS. The mental status exam is concerned with the cerebrum and assesses higher functions such as memory, language, and emotion. The cranial nerve exam tests the functions of all of the cranial nerves and, therefore, their connections to the CNS through the forebrain and brain stem. The sensory and motor exams assess those functions as they relate to the spinal cord, as well as the combination of the functions in spinal reflexes. The coordination exam targets cerebellar function in coordinated movements, including those functions associated with gait.

Damage to and disease of the nervous system lead to loss of function. The location of the injury will correspond to the functional loss, as suggested by the principle of localization of function. The neurological exam provides the opportunity for a clinician to determine where damage has occurred on the basis of the function that is lost. Damage from acute injuries such as strokes may result in specific functions being lost, whereas broader effects in infection or developmental disorders may result in general losses across an entire section of the neurological exam.

16.2 The Mental Status Exam

The cerebrum, particularly the cerebral cortex, is the location of important cognitive functions that are the focus of the mental status exam. The regionalization of the cortex, initially described on the basis of anatomical evidence of cytoarchitecture, reveals the distribution of functionally distinct areas. Cortical regions can be described as primary sensory or motor areas, association areas, or multimodal integration areas. The functions attributed to these regions include attention, memory, language, speech, sensation, judgment, and abstract reasoning.

The mental status exam addresses these cognitive abilities through a series of subtests designed to elicit particular behaviors ascribed to these functions. The loss of neurological function can illustrate the location of damage to the cerebrum. Memory functions are attributed to the temporal lobe, particularly the medial temporal lobe structures known as the hippocampus and amygdala, along with the adjacent cortex. Evidence of the importance of these structures comes from the side effects of a bilateral temporal lobectomy that were studied in detail in patient HM.

Losses of language and speech functions, known as aphasias, are associated with damage to the important integration areas in the left hemisphere known as Broca's or Wernicke's areas, as well as the connections in the white matter between them. Different types of aphasia are named for the particular structures that are damaged. Assessment of the functions of the sensorium includes praxis and gnosis. The subtests related to these functions depend on multimodal integration, as well as language-dependent processing.

The prefrontal cortex contains structures important for planning, judgment, reasoning, and working memory. Damage to these areas can result in changes to personality, mood, and behavior. The famous case of Phineas Gage suggests a role for this cortex in personality, as does the outdated practice of prefrontal lobectomy.

16.3 The Cranial Nerve Exam

The cranial nerves can be separated into four major groups associated with the subtests of the cranial nerve exam. First are the sensory nerves, then the nerves that control eye movement, the nerves of the oral cavity and superior pharynx, and the nerve that controls movements of the neck.

The olfactory, optic, and vestibulocochlear nerves are strictly sensory nerves for smell, sight, and balance and hearing, whereas the trigeminal, facial, and glossopharyngeal nerves carry somatosensation of the face, and taste—separated between the anterior two-thirds of the tongue and the posterior one-third. Special senses are tested by presenting the particular stimuli to each receptive organ. General senses can be tested through sensory discrimination of touch versus painful stimuli.

The oculomotor, trochlear, and abducens nerves control the extraocular muscles and are connected by the medial longitudinal fasciculus to coordinate gaze. Testing conjugate gaze is as simple as having the patient follow a visual target, like a pen tip, through the visual field ending with an approach toward the face to test convergence and accommodation. Along with the vestibular functions of the eighth nerve, the vestibulo-ocular reflex stabilizes gaze during head movements by coordinating equilibrium sensations with the eye movement systems.

The trigeminal nerve controls the muscles of chewing, which are tested for stretch reflexes. Motor functions of the facial nerve are usually obvious if facial expressions are compromised, but can be tested by having the patient raise their eyebrows, smile, and frown. Movements of the tongue, soft palate, or superior pharynx can be observed directly while the patient swallows, while the gag reflex is elicited, or while the patient says repetitive consonant sounds. The motor control of the gag reflex is largely controlled by fibers in the vagus nerve and constitutes a test of that nerve because the parasympathetic functions of that nerve are involved in visceral regulation, such as regulating the heartbeat and digestion.

Movement of the head and neck using the sternocleidomastoid and trapezius muscles is controlled by the accessory nerve. Flexing of the neck and strength testing of those muscles reviews the function of that nerve.

16.4 The Sensory and Motor Exams

The sensory and motor exams assess function related to the spinal cord and the nerves connected to it. Sensory functions are associated with the dorsal regions of the spinal cord, whereas motor function is associated with the ventral side. Localizing damage to the spinal cord is related to assessments of the peripheral projections mapped to dermatomes.

Sensory tests address the various submodalities of the somatic senses: touch, temperature, vibration, pain, and proprioception. Results of the subtests can point to trauma in the spinal cord gray matter, white matter, or

even in connections to the cerebral cortex.

Motor tests focus on the function of the muscles and the connections of the descending motor pathway. Muscle tone and strength are tested for upper and lower extremities. Input to the muscles comes from the descending cortical input of upper motor neurons and the direct innervation of lower motor neurons.

Reflexes can either be based on deep stimulation of tendons or superficial stimulation of the skin. The presence of reflexive contractions helps to differentiate motor disorders between the upper and lower motor neurons. The specific signs associated with motor disorders can establish the difference further, based on the type of paralysis, the state of muscle tone, and specific indicators such as pronator drift or the Babinski sign.

16.5 The Coordination and Gait Exams

The cerebellum is an important part of motor function in the nervous system. It apparently plays a role in procedural learning, which would include motor skills such as riding a bike or throwing a football. The basis for these roles is likely to be tied into the role the cerebellum plays as a comparator for voluntary movement.

The motor commands from the cerebral hemispheres travel along the corticospinal pathway, which passes through the pons. Collateral branches of these fibers synapse on neurons in the pons, which then project into the cerebellar cortex through the middle cerebellar peduncles. Ascending sensory feedback, entering through the inferior cerebellar peduncles, provides information about motor performance. The cerebellar cortex compares the command to the actual performance and can adjust the descending input to compensate for any mismatch. The output from deep cerebellar nuclei projects through the superior cerebellar peduncles to initiate descending signals from the red nucleus to the spinal cord.

The primary role of the cerebellum in relation to the spinal cord is through the spinocerebellum; it controls posture and gait with significant input from the vestibular system. Deficits in cerebellar function result in ataxias, or a specific kind of movement disorder. The root cause of the ataxia may be the sensory input—either the proprioceptive input from the spinal cord or the equilibrium input from the vestibular system, or direct damage to the cerebellum by stroke, trauma, hereditary factors, or toxins.

Access for free at openstax.org

Interactive Link Questions

1. Watch this video (http://openstax.org/l/neuroexam) that provides a demonstration of the neurological exam—a series of tests that can be performed rapidly when a patient is initially brought into an emergency department. The exam can be repeated on a regular basis to keep a record of how and if neurological function changes over time. In what order were the sections of the neurological exam tested in this video, and which section seemed to be left out?

2. Watch this video (http://openstax.org/l/neuroexam2) for an introduction to the neurological exam. Studying the neurological exam can give insight into how structure and function in the nervous system are interdependent. This is a tool both in the clinic and in the classroom, but for different reasons. In the clinic, this is a powerful but simple tool to assess a patient's neurological function. In the classroom, it is a different way to think about the nervous system. Though medical technology provides noninvasive imaging and real-time functional data, the presenter says these cannot replace the history at the core of the medical examination. What does history mean in the context of medical practice?

3. Read this article (http://openstax.org/l/3word) to learn about a young man who texts his fiancée in a panic as he finds that he is having trouble remembering things. At the hospital, a neurologist administers the mental status exam, which is mostly normal except for the three-word recall test. The young man could not recall them even 30 seconds after hearing them and repeating them back to the doctor. An undiscovered mass in the mediastinum region was found to be Hodgkin's lymphoma, a type of cancer that affects the immune system and likely caused antibodies to attack the nervous system. The patient eventually regained his ability to remember, though the events in the hospital were always elusive. Considering that the effects on memory were temporary, but resulted in the loss of the specific events of the hospital stay, what regions of the brain were likely to have been affected by the antibodies and what type of memory does that represent?

4. Watch the video (http://openstax.org/l/2brains) titled "The Man With Two Brains" to see the neuroscientist Michael Gazzaniga introduce a patient he has worked with for years who has had his corpus callosum cut, separating his two cerebral hemispheres. A few tests are run to demonstrate how this manifests in tests of cerebral function. Unlike normal people, this patient can perform two independent tasks at the same time because the lines of communication between the right and left sides of his brain have been removed. Whereas a person with an intact corpus callosum cannot overcome the dominance of one hemisphere over the other, this patient can. If the left cerebral hemisphere is dominant in the majority of people, why would right-handedness be most common?

5. Watch this short video (http://openstax.org/l/facialnerve) to see an examination of the facial nerve using some simple tests. The facial nerve controls the muscles of facial expression. Severe deficits will be obvious in watching someone use those muscles for normal control. One side of the face might not move like the other side. But directed tests, especially for contraction against resistance, require a formal testing of the muscles. The muscles of the upper and lower face need to be tested. The strength test in this video involves the patient squeezing her eyes shut and the examiner trying to pry her eyes open. Why does the examiner ask her to try a second time?

6. Watch this video (http://openstax.org/l/2point) to see a quick demonstration of two-point discrimination. Touching a specialized caliper to the surface of the skin will measure the distance between two points that are perceived as distinct stimuli versus a single stimulus. The patient keeps their eyes closed while the examiner switches between using both points of the caliper or just one. The patient then must indicate whether one or two stimuli are in contact with the skin. Why is the distance between the caliper points closer on the fingertips as opposed to the palm of the hand? And what do you think the distance would be on the arm, or the shoulder?

7. Watch this video (http://openstax.org/l/reflextest) to see how to test reflexes in the abdomen. Testing reflexes of the trunk is not commonly performed in the neurological exam, but if findings suggest a problem with the thoracic segments of the spinal cord, a series of superficial reflexes of the abdomen can localize function to those segments. If contraction is not observed when the skin lateral to the umbilicus (belly button) is stimulated, what level of the spinal cord may be damaged?

8. Watch this short video (http://openstax.org/l/stationtest) to see a test for station. Station refers to the position a person adopts when they are standing still. The examiner would look for issues with balance, which coordinates proprioceptive, vestibular, and visual information in the cerebellum. To test the ability of a subject to maintain balance, asking them to stand or hop on one foot can be more demanding. The examiner may also push the subject to see if they can maintain balance. An abnormal finding in the test of station is if the feet are placed far apart. Why would a wide stance suggest problems with cerebellar function?

Review Questions

9. Which major section of the neurological exam is *most likely* to reveal damage to the cerebellum?
   a.   cranial nerve exam
   b.   mental status exam
   c.   sensory exam
   d.   coordination exam

10. What function would *most likely* be affected by a restriction of a blood vessel in the cerebral cortex?
   a.   language
   b.   gait
   c.   facial expressions
   d.   knee-jerk reflex

11. Which major section of the neurological exam includes subtests that are sometimes considered a separate set of tests concerned with walking?
   a.   mental status exam
   b.   cranial nerve exam
   c.   coordination exam
   d.   sensory exam

12. Memory, emotional, language, and sensorimotor deficits together are *most likely* the result of what kind of damage?
   a.   stroke
   b.   developmental disorder
   c.   whiplash
   d.   gunshot wound

13. Where is language function localized in the majority of people?
   a.   cerebellum
   b.   right cerebral hemisphere
   c.   hippocampus
   d.   left cerebral hemisphere

14. Which of the following could be elements of cytoarchitecture, as related to Brodmann's microscopic studies of the cerebral cortex?
   a.   connections to the cerebellum
   b.   activation by visual stimuli
   c.   number of neurons per square millimeter
   d.   number of gyri or sulci

15. Which of the following could be a multimodal integrative area?
   a.   primary visual cortex
   b.   premotor cortex
   c.   hippocampus
   d.   Wernicke's area

16. Which is an example of episodic memory?
   a.   how to bake a cake
   b.   your last birthday party
   c.   how old you are
   d.   needing to wear an oven mitt to take a cake out of the oven

17. Which type of aphasia is more like hearing a foreign language spoken?
   a.   receptive aphasia
   b.   expressive aphasia
   c.   conductive aphasia
   d.   Broca's aphasia

18. What region of the cerebral cortex is associated with understanding language, both from another person and the language a person generates himself or herself?
   a.   medial temporal lobe
   b.   ventromedial prefrontal cortex
   c.   superior temporal gyrus
   d.   postcentral gyrus

19. Without olfactory sensation to complement gustatory stimuli, food will taste bland unless it is seasoned with which substance?
    a. salt
    b. thyme
    c. garlic
    d. olive oil

20. Which of the following cranial nerves is *not* part of the VOR?
    a. optic
    b. oculomotor
    c. abducens
    d. vestibulocochlear

21. Which nerve is responsible for controlling the muscles that result in the gag reflex?
    a. trigeminal
    b. facial
    c. glossopharyngeal
    d. vagus

22. Which nerve is responsible for taste, as well as salivation, in the anterior oral cavity?
    a. facial
    b. glossopharyngeal
    c. vagus
    d. hypoglossal

23. Which of the following nerves controls movements of the neck?
    a. oculomotor
    b. vestibulocochlear
    c. spinal accessory
    d. hypoglossal

24. Which of the following is *not* part of the corticospinal pathway?
    a. cerebellar deep white matter
    b. midbrain
    c. medulla
    d. lateral column

25. Which subtest is directed at proprioceptive sensation?
    a. two-point discrimination
    b. tactile movement
    c. vibration
    d. Romberg test

26. What term describes the inability to lift the arm above the level of the shoulder?
    a. paralysis
    b. paresis
    c. fasciculation
    d. fibrillation

27. Which type of reflex is the jaw-jerk reflex that is part of the cranial nerve exam for the vestibulocochlear nerve?
    a. visceral reflex
    b. withdrawal reflex
    c. stretch reflex
    d. superficial reflex

28. Which of the following is a feature of both somatic and visceral senses?
    a. requires cerebral input
    b. causes skeletal muscle contraction
    c. projects to a ganglion near the target effector
    d. involves an axon in the ventral nerve root

29. Which white matter structure carries information from the cerebral cortex to the cerebellum?
    a. cerebral peduncle
    b. superior cerebellar peduncle
    c. middle cerebellar peduncle
    d. inferior cerebellar peduncle

30. Which region of the cerebellum receives proprioceptive input from the spinal cord?
    a. vermis
    b. left hemisphere
    c. flocculonodular lobe
    d. right hemisphere

31. Which of the following tests cerebellar function related to gait?
    a. toe-to-finger
    b. station
    c. lah-kah-pah
    d. finger-to-nose

32. Which of the following is *not* a cause of cerebellar ataxia?
    a. mercury from fish
    b. drinking alcohol
    c. antibiotics
    d. hereditary degeneration of the cerebellum

33. Which of the following functions *cannot* be attributed to the cerebellum?
    a. comparing motor commands and sensory feedback
    b. associating sensory stimuli with learned behavior
    c. coordinating complex movements
    d. processing visual information

Critical Thinking Questions

34. Why is a rapid assessment of neurological function important in an emergency situation?

35. How is the diagnostic category of TIA different from a stroke?

36. A patient's performance of the majority of the mental status exam subtests is in line with the expected norms, but the patient cannot repeat a string of numbers given by the examiner. What is a likely explanation?

37. A patient responds to the question "What is your name?" with a look of incomprehension. Which of the two major language areas is most likely affected and what is the name for that type of aphasia?

38. As a person ages, their ability to focus on near objects (accommodation) changes. If a person is already myopic (near-sighted), why would corrective lenses not be necessary to read a book or computer screen?

39. When a patient flexes their neck, the head tips to the right side. Also, their tongue sticks out slightly to the left when they try to stick it straight out. Where is the damage to the brain stem most likely located?

40. The location of somatosensation is based on the topographical map of sensory innervation. What does this mean?

41. Why are upper motor neuron lesions characterized by "spastic paralysis"?

42. Learning to ride a bike is a motor function dependent on the cerebellum. Why are the different regions of the cerebellum involved in this complex motor learning?

43. Alcohol intoxication can produce slurred speech. How is this related to cerebellar function?

CHAPTER 17
The Endocrine System

Figure 17.1   A Child Catches a Falling Leaf Hormones of the endocrine system coordinate and control growth, metabolism, temperature regulation, the stress response, reproduction, and many other functions. (credit: "seenthroughmylense"/flickr.com)

CHAPTER OBJECTIVES
After studying this chapter, you will be able to:
- Identify the contributions of the endocrine system to homeostasis
- Discuss the chemical composition of hormones and the mechanisms of hormone action
- Summarize the site of production, regulation, and effects of the hormones of the pituitary, thyroid, parathyroid, adrenal, and pineal glands
- Discuss the hormonal regulation of the reproductive system
- Explain the role of the pancreatic endocrine cells in the regulation of blood glucose
- Identify the hormones released by the heart, kidneys, and other organs with secondary endocrine functions
- Discuss several common diseases associated with endocrine system dysfunction
- Discuss the embryonic development of, and the effects of aging on, the endocrine system

INTRODUCTION You may never have thought of it this way, but when you send a text message to two friends to meet you at the dining hall at six, you're sending digital signals that (you hope) will affect their behavior—even though they are some distance away. Similarly, certain cells send chemical signals to other cells in the body that influence their behavior. This long-distance intercellular communication, coordination, and control is critical for homeostasis, and it is the fundamental function of the endocrine system.

17.1 An Overview of the Endocrine System

LEARNING OBJECTIVES

By the end of this section, you will be able to:
- Distinguish the types of intercellular communication, their importance, mechanisms, and effects
- Identify the major organs and tissues of the endocrine system and their location in the body

Communication is a process in which a sender transmits signals to one or more receivers to control and coordinate actions. In the human body, two major organ systems participate in relatively "long distance" communication: the nervous system and the endocrine system. Together, these two systems are primarily responsible for maintaining homeostasis in the body.

Neural and Endocrine Signaling

The nervous system uses two types of intercellular communication—electrical and chemical signaling—either by the direct action of an electrical potential, or in the latter case, through the action of chemical neurotransmitters such as serotonin or norepinephrine. Neurotransmitters act locally and rapidly. When an electrical signal in the form of an action potential arrives at the synaptic terminal, they diffuse across the synaptic cleft (the gap between a sending neuron and a receiving neuron or muscle cell). Once the neurotransmitters interact (bind) with receptors on the receiving (post-synaptic) cell, the receptor stimulation is transduced into a response such as continued electrical signaling or modification of cellular response. The target cell responds within milliseconds of receiving the chemical "message"; this response then ceases very quickly once the neural signaling ends. In this way, neural communication enables body functions that involve quick, brief actions, such as movement, sensation, and cognition.In contrast, the **endocrine system** uses just one method of communication: chemical signaling. These signals are sent by the endocrine organs, which secrete chemicals—the **hormone**—into the extracellular fluid. Hormones are transported primarily via the bloodstream throughout the body, where they bind to receptors on target cells, inducing a characteristic response. As a result, endocrine signaling requires more time than neural signaling to prompt a response in target cells, though the precise amount of time varies with different hormones. For example, the hormones released when you are confronted with a dangerous or frightening situation, called the fight-or-flight response, occur by the release of adrenal hormones—epinephrine and norepinephrine—within seconds. In contrast, it may take up to 48 hours for target cells to respond to certain reproductive hormones.

Ⓐ INTERACTIVE LINK

Visit this link (http://openstax.org/l/hormonebind) to watch an animation of the events that occur when a hormone binds to a cell membrane receptor. What is the secondary messenger made by adenylyl cyclase during the activation of liver cells by epinephrine?

In addition, endocrine signaling is typically less specific than neural signaling. The same hormone may play a role in a variety of different physiological processes depending on the target cells involved. For example, the hormone oxytocin promotes uterine contractions in people in labor. It is also important in breastfeeding, and may be involved in the sexual response and in feelings of emotional attachment in humans.

In general, the nervous system involves quick responses to rapid changes in the external environment, and the endocrine system is usually slower acting—taking care of the internal environment of the body, maintaining homeostasis, and controlling reproduction (Table 17.1). So how does the fight-or-flight response that was mentioned earlier happen so quickly if hormones are usually slower acting? It is because the two systems are connected. It is the fast action of the nervous system in response to the danger in the environment that stimulates the adrenal glands to secrete their hormones. As a result, the nervous system can cause rapid endocrine responses to keep up with sudden changes in both the external and internal environments when necessary.

Endocrine and Nervous Systems

	Endocrine system	Nervous system
Signaling mechanism(s)	Chemical	Chemical/electrical
Primary chemical signal	Hormones	Neurotransmitters
Distance traveled	Long or short	Always short

TABLE 17.1

	Endocrine system	Nervous system
Response time	Fast or slow	Always fast
Environment targeted	Internal	Internal and external

TABLE 17.1

Structures of the Endocrine System

The endocrine system consists of cells, tissues, and organs that secrete hormones as a primary or secondary function. The **endocrine gland** is the major player in this system. The primary function of these ductless glands is to secrete their hormones directly into the surrounding fluid. The interstitial fluid and the blood vessels then transport the hormones throughout the body. The endocrine system includes the pituitary, thyroid, parathyroid, adrenal, and pineal glands (Figure 17.2). Some of these glands have both endocrine and non-endocrine functions. For example, the pancreas contains cells that function in digestion as well as cells that secrete the hormones insulin and glucagon, which regulate blood glucose levels. The hypothalamus, thymus, heart, kidneys, stomach, small intestine, liver, skin, ovaries, and testes are other organs that contain cells with endocrine function. Moreover, adipose tissue has long been known to produce hormones, and recent research has revealed that even bone tissue has endocrine functions.

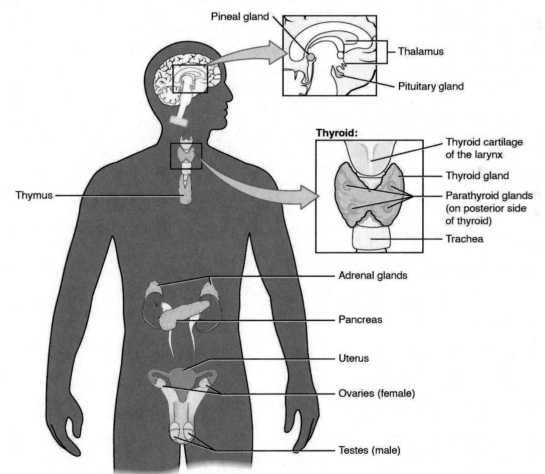

FIGURE 17.2 Endocrine System Endocrine glands and cells are located throughout the body and play an important role in homeostasis.

The ductless endocrine glands are not to be confused with the body's **exocrine system**, whose glands release their secretions through ducts. Examples of exocrine glands include the sebaceous and sweat glands of the skin. As just noted, the pancreas also has an exocrine function: most of its cells secrete pancreatic juice through the pancreatic and accessory ducts to the lumen of the small intestine.

Other Types of Chemical Signaling

In endocrine signaling, hormones secreted into the extracellular fluid diffuse into the blood or lymph, and can then travel great distances throughout the body. In contrast, autocrine signaling takes place within the same cell. An **autocrine** (auto- = "self") is a chemical that elicits a response in the same cell that secreted it. Interleukin-1, or IL-1, is a signaling molecule that plays an important role in inflammatory response. The cells that secrete IL-1 have receptors on their cell surface that bind these molecules, resulting in autocrine signaling.

Local intercellular communication is the province of the **paracrine**, also called a paracrine factor, which is a chemical that induces a response in neighboring cells. Although paracrines may enter the bloodstream, their concentration is generally too low to elicit a response from distant tissues. A familiar example to those with asthma is histamine, a paracrine that is released by immune cells in the bronchial tree. Histamine causes the smooth muscle cells of the bronchi to constrict, narrowing the airways. Another example is the neurotransmitters of the nervous system, which act only locally within the synaptic cleft.

 CAREER CONNECTION

Endocrinologist

Endocrinology is a specialty in the field of medicine that focuses on the treatment of endocrine system disorders. Endocrinologists—medical doctors who specialize in this field—are experts in treating diseases associated with hormonal systems, ranging from thyroid disease to diabetes mellitus. Endocrine surgeons treat endocrine disease through the removal, or resection, of the affected endocrine gland.

Patients who are referred to endocrinologists may have signs and symptoms or blood test results that suggest excessive or impaired functioning of an endocrine gland or endocrine cells. The endocrinologist may order additional blood tests to determine whether the patient's hormonal levels are abnormal, or they may stimulate or suppress the function of the suspect endocrine gland and then have blood taken for analysis. Treatment varies according to the diagnosis. Some endocrine disorders, such as type 2 diabetes, may respond to lifestyle changes such as modest weight loss, adoption of a healthy diet, and regular physical activity. Other disorders may require medication, such as hormone replacement, and routine monitoring by the endocrinologist. These include disorders of the pituitary gland that can affect growth and disorders of the thyroid gland that can result in a variety of metabolic problems.

Some patients experience health problems as a result of the normal decline in hormones that can accompany aging. These patients can consult with an endocrinologist to weigh the risks and benefits of hormone replacement therapy intended to boost their natural levels of reproductive hormones.

In addition to treating patients, endocrinologists may be involved in research to improve the understanding of endocrine system disorders and develop new treatments for these diseases.

17.2 Hormones

LEARNING OBJECTIVES

By the end of this section, you will be able to:
- Identify the three major classes of hormones on the basis of chemical structure
- Compare and contrast intracellular and cell membrane hormone receptors
- Describe signaling pathways that involve cAMP and IP3
- Identify several factors that influence a target cell's response
- Discuss the role of feedback loops and humoral, hormonal, and neural stimuli in hormone control

Although a given hormone may travel throughout the body in the bloodstream, it will affect the activity only of its target cells; that is, cells with receptors for that particular hormone. Once the hormone binds to the receptor, a chain of events is initiated that leads to the target cell's response. Hormones play a critical role in the regulation of physiological processes because of the target cell responses they regulate. These responses contribute to human reproduction, growth and development of body tissues, metabolism, fluid, and electrolyte balance, sleep, and many other body functions. The major hormones of the human body and their effects are identified in Table 17.2.

Endocrine Glands and Their Major Hormones

Endocrine gland	Associated hormones	Chemical class	Effect
Pituitary (anterior)	Growth hormone (GH)	Protein	Promotes growth of body tissues
Pituitary (anterior)	Prolactin (PRL)	Peptide	Promotes milk production
Pituitary (anterior)	Thyroid-stimulating hormone (TSH)	Glycoprotein	Stimulates thyroid hormone release
Pituitary (anterior)	Adrenocorticotropic hormone (ACTH)	Peptide	Stimulates hormone release by adrenal cortex
Pituitary (anterior)	Follicle-stimulating hormone (FSH)	Glycoprotein	Stimulates gamete production
Pituitary (anterior)	Luteinizing hormone (LH)	Glycoprotein	Stimulates androgen production by gonads
Pituitary (posterior)	Antidiuretic hormone (ADH)	Peptide	Stimulates water reabsorption by kidneys
Pituitary (posterior)	Oxytocin	Peptide	Stimulates uterine contractions during childbirth
Thyroid	Thyroxine (T_4), triiodothyronine (T_3)	Amine	Stimulate basal metabolic rate
Thyroid	Calcitonin	Peptide	Reduces blood Ca^{2+} levels
Parathyroid	Parathyroid hormone (PTH)	Peptide	Increases blood Ca^{2+} levels
Adrenal (cortex)	Aldosterone	Steroid	Increases blood Na^+ levels
Adrenal (cortex)	Cortisol, corticosterone, cortisone	Steroid	Increase blood glucose levels
Adrenal (medulla)	Epinephrine, norepinephrine	Amine	Stimulate fight-or-flight response
Pineal	Melatonin	Amine	Regulates sleep cycles

TABLE 17.2

Endocrine gland	Associated hormones	Chemical class	Effect
Pancreas	Insulin	Protein	Reduces blood glucose levels
Pancreas	Glucagon	Protein	Increases blood glucose levels
Testes	Testosterone	Steroid	Stimulates development of sex characteristics including a deeper voice, increased muscle mass, development of body hair, and sperm production
Ovaries	Estrogens and progesterone	Steroid	Stimulate development of sex characteristics including the development of adipose and breast tissue, and prepare the body for childbirth

TABLE 17.2

Types of Hormones

The hormones of the human body can be divided into two major groups on the basis of their chemical structure. Hormones derived from amino acids include amines, peptides, and proteins. Those derived from lipids include steroids (Figure 17.3). These chemical groups affect a hormone's distribution, the type of receptors it binds to, and other aspects of its function.

Hormone Class	Components	Example(s)
Amine Hormone	Amino acids with modified groups (e.g. norepinephrine's carboxyl group is replaced with a benzene ring)	**Norepinephrine** 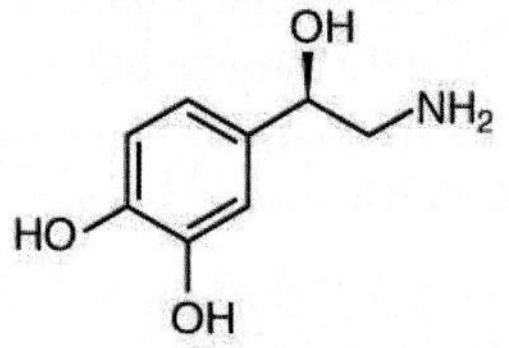
Peptide Hormone	Short chains of linked amino acids	**Oxytocin** 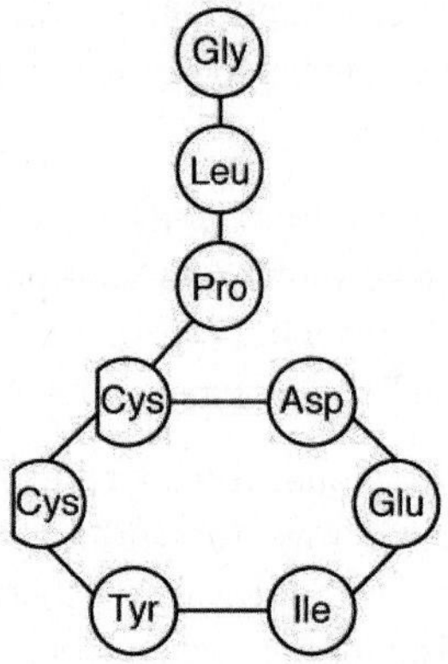
Protein Hormone	Long chains of linked amino acids	**Human Growth Hormone** 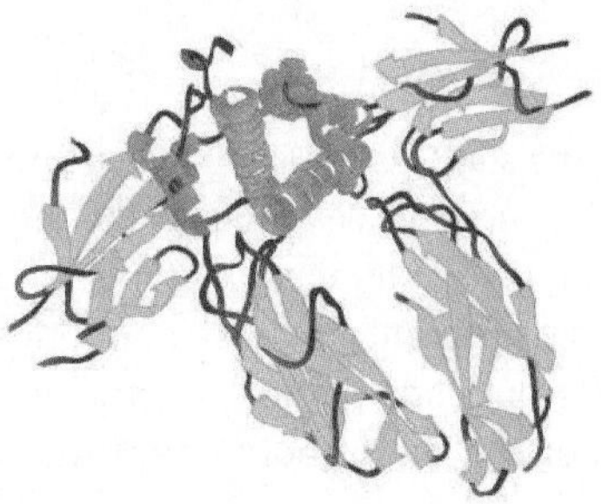
Steroid Hormones	Derived from the lipid cholesterol	**Testosterone** 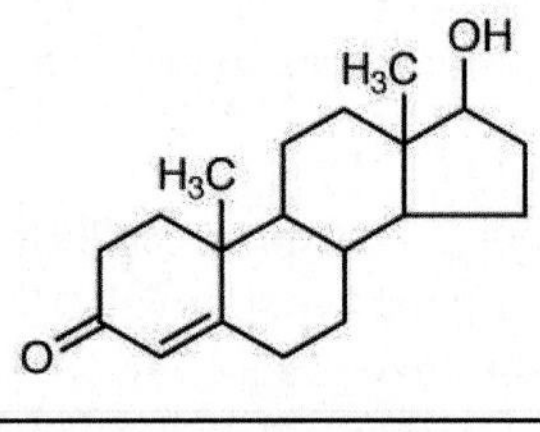 **Progesterone** 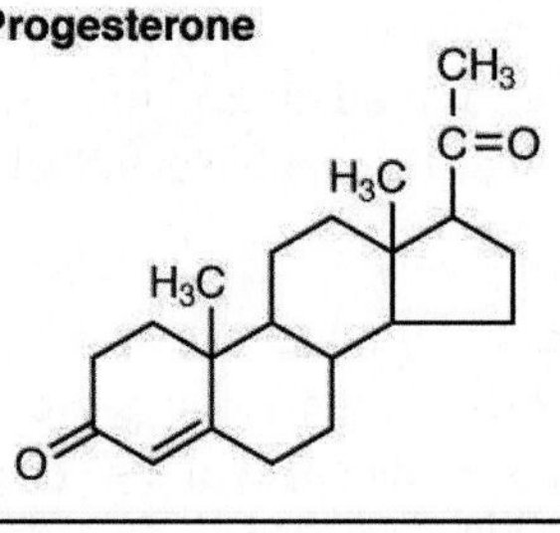

FIGURE 17.3   Amine, Peptide, Protein, and Steroid Hormone Structure

Amine Hormones

Hormones derived from the modification of amino acids are referred to as amine hormones. Typically, the original structure of the amino acid is modified such that a –COOH, or carboxyl, group is removed, whereas the $-NH_3^+$, or amine, group remains.

Amine hormones are synthesized from the amino acids tryptophan or tyrosine. An example of a hormone derived from tryptophan is melatonin, which is secreted by the pineal gland and helps regulate circadian rhythm. Tyrosine derivatives include the metabolism-regulating thyroid hormones, as well as the catecholamines, such as epinephrine, norepinephrine, and dopamine. Epinephrine and norepinephrine are secreted by the adrenal medulla and play a role in the fight-or-flight response, whereas dopamine is secreted by the hypothalamus and inhibits the release of certain anterior pituitary hormones.

Peptide and Protein Hormones

Whereas the amine hormones are derived from a single amino acid, peptide and protein hormones consist of multiple amino acids that link to form an amino acid chain. Peptide hormones consist of short chains of amino acids, whereas protein hormones are longer polypeptides. Both types are synthesized like other body proteins: DNA is transcribed into mRNA, which is translated into an amino acid chain.

Examples of peptide hormones include antidiuretic hormone (ADH), a pituitary hormone important in fluid balance, and atrial-natriuretic peptide, which is produced by the heart and helps to decrease blood pressure. Some examples of protein hormones include growth hormone, which is produced by the pituitary gland, and follicle-stimulating hormone (FSH), which has an attached carbohydrate group and is thus classified as a glycoprotein. FSH helps stimulate the maturation of eggs in the ovaries and sperm in the testes.

Steroid Hormones

The primary hormones derived from lipids are steroids. Steroid hormones are derived from the lipid cholesterol. For example, the reproductive hormones testosterone and the estrogens—which are produced by the gonads (testes and ovaries)—are steroid hormones. The adrenal glands produce the steroid hormone aldosterone, which is involved in osmoregulation, and cortisol, which plays a role in metabolism.

Like cholesterol, steroid hormones are not soluble in water (they are hydrophobic). Because blood is water-based, lipid-derived hormones must travel to their target cell bound to a transport protein. This more complex structure extends the half-life of steroid hormones much longer than that of hormones derived from amino acids. A hormone's half-life is the time required for half the concentration of the hormone to be degraded. For example, the lipid-derived hormone cortisol has a half-life of approximately 60 to 90 minutes. In contrast, the amino acid–derived hormone epinephrine has a half-life of approximately one minute.

Pathways of Hormone Action

The message a hormone sends is received by a **hormone receptor**, a protein located either inside the cell or within the cell membrane. The receptor will process the message by initiating other signaling events or cellular mechanisms that result in the target cell's response. Hormone receptors recognize molecules with specific shapes and side groups, and respond only to those hormones that are recognized. The same type of receptor may be located on cells in different body tissues, and trigger somewhat different responses. Thus, the response triggered by a hormone depends not only on the hormone, but also on the target cell.

Once the target cell receives the hormone signal, it can respond in a variety of ways. The response may include the stimulation of protein synthesis, activation or deactivation of enzymes, alteration in the permeability of the cell membrane, altered rates of mitosis and cell growth, and stimulation of the secretion of products. Moreover, a single hormone may be capable of inducing different responses in a given cell.

Pathways Involving Intracellular Hormone Receptors

Intracellular hormone receptors are located inside the cell. Hormones that bind to this type of receptor must be able to cross the cell membrane. Steroid hormones are derived from cholesterol and therefore can readily diffuse through the lipid bilayer of the cell membrane to reach the intracellular receptor (Figure 17.4). Thyroid hormones, cross the cell membrane by a specific carrier-mediated mechanism that is energy and Na^+ dependent.

The location of steroid and thyroid hormone binding differs slightly: a steroid hormone may bind to its receptor within the cytosol or within the nucleus. In either case, this binding generates a hormone-receptor complex that moves toward the chromatin in the cell nucleus and binds to a particular segment of the cell's DNA. In contrast, thyroid hormones bind to receptors already bound to DNA. For both steroid and thyroid hormones, binding of the hormone-receptor complex with DNA triggers transcription of a target gene to mRNA, which moves to the cytosol and directs protein synthesis by ribosomes.

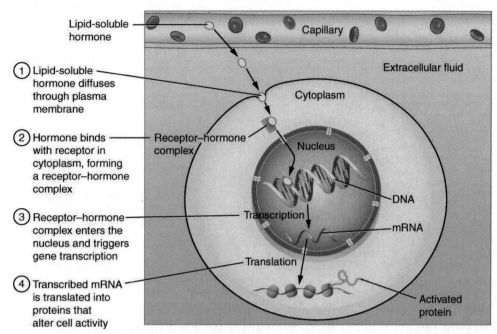

① Lipid-soluble hormone diffuses through plasma membrane

② Hormone binds with receptor in cytoplasm, forming a receptor–hormone complex

③ Receptor–hormone complex enters the nucleus and triggers gene transcription

④ Transcribed mRNA is translated into proteins that alter cell activity

Lipid-soluble hormone

Capillary

Extracellular fluid

Cytoplasm

Receptor–hormone complex

Nucleus

DNA

Transcription

mRNA

Translation

Activated protein

FIGURE 17.4   Binding of Lipid-Soluble Hormones   A steroid hormone directly initiates the production of proteins within a target cell. Steroid hormones easily diffuse through the cell membrane. The hormone binds to its receptor in the cytosol, forming a receptor–hormone complex. The receptor–hormone complex then enters the nucleus and binds to the target gene on the DNA. Transcription of the gene creates a messenger RNA that is translated into the desired protein within the cytoplasm.

Pathways Involving Cell Membrane Hormone Receptors

Hydrophilic, or water-soluble, hormones are unable to diffuse through the lipid bilayer of the cell membrane and must therefore pass on their message to a receptor located at the surface of the cell. Except for thyroid hormones, which are lipid-soluble, all amino acid–derived hormones bind to cell membrane receptors that are located, at least in part, on the extracellular surface of the cell membrane. Therefore, they do not directly affect the transcription of target genes, but instead initiate a signaling cascade that is carried out by a molecule called a **second messenger**. In this case, the hormone is called a **first messenger**.

The second messenger used by most hormones is **cyclic adenosine monophosphate (cAMP)**. In the cAMP second messenger system, a water-soluble hormone binds to its receptor in the cell membrane (Step 1 in <ins>Figure 17.5</ins>). This receptor is associated with an intracellular component called a **G protein**, and binding of the hormone activates the G-protein component (Step 2). The activated G protein in turn activates an enzyme called **adenylyl cyclase**, also known as adenylate cyclase (Step 3), which converts adenosine triphosphate (ATP) to cAMP (Step 4). As the second messenger, cAMP activates a type of enzyme called a **protein kinase** that is present in the cytosol (Step 5). Activated protein kinases initiate a **phosphorylation cascade**, in which multiple protein kinases phosphorylate (add a phosphate group to) numerous and various cellular proteins, including other enzymes (Step 6).

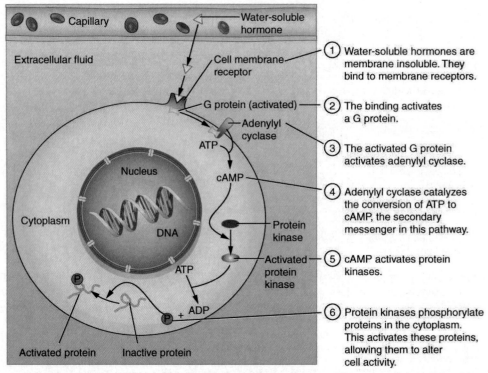

FIGURE 17.5 Binding of Water-Soluble Hormones   Water-soluble hormones cannot diffuse through the cell membrane. These hormones must bind to a surface cell-membrane receptor. The receptor then initiates a cell-signaling pathway within the cell involving G proteins, adenylyl cyclase, the secondary messenger cyclic AMP (cAMP), and protein kinases. In the final step, these protein kinases phosphorylate proteins in the cytoplasm. This activates proteins in the cell that carry out the changes specified by the hormone.

The phosphorylation of cellular proteins can trigger a wide variety of effects, from nutrient metabolism to the synthesis of different hormones and other products. The effects vary according to the type of target cell, the G proteins and kinases involved, and the phosphorylation of proteins. Examples of hormones that use cAMP as a second messenger include calcitonin, which is important for bone construction and regulating blood calcium levels; glucagon, which plays a role in blood glucose levels; and thyroid-stimulating hormone, which causes the release of T_3 and T_4 from the thyroid gland.

Overall, the phosphorylation cascade significantly increases the efficiency, speed, and specificity of the hormonal response, as thousands of signaling events can be initiated simultaneously in response to a very low concentration of hormone in the bloodstream. However, the duration of the hormone signal is short, as cAMP is quickly deactivated by the enzyme **phosphodiesterase (PDE)**, which is located in the cytosol. The action of PDE helps to ensure that a target cell's response ceases quickly unless new hormones arrive at the cell membrane.

Importantly, there are also G proteins that decrease the levels of cAMP in the cell in response to hormone binding. For example, when growth hormone–inhibiting hormone (GHIH), also known as somatostatin, binds to its receptors in the pituitary gland, the level of cAMP decreases, thereby inhibiting the secretion of human growth hormone.

Not all water-soluble hormones initiate the cAMP second messenger system. One common alternative system uses calcium ions as a second messenger. In this system, G proteins activate the enzyme phospholipase C (PLC), which functions similarly to adenylyl cyclase. Once activated, PLC cleaves a membrane-bound phospholipid into two molecules: **diacylglycerol (DAG)** and **inositol triphosphate (IP$_3$)**. Like cAMP, DAG activates protein kinases that initiate a phosphorylation cascade. At the same time, IP$_3$ causes calcium ions to be released from storage sites within the cytosol, such as from within the smooth endoplasmic reticulum. The calcium ions then act as second messengers in two ways: they can influence enzymatic and other cellular activities directly, or they can bind to calcium-binding proteins, the most common of which is calmodulin. Upon binding calcium, calmodulin is able to modulate protein kinase within the cell. Examples of hormones that use calcium ions as a second messenger system include angiotensin II, which helps regulate blood pressure through vasoconstriction, and growth hormone–releasing hormone (GHRH), which causes the pituitary gland to release growth hormones.

Factors Affecting Target Cell Response

You will recall that target cells must have receptors specific to a given hormone if that hormone is to trigger a response. But several other factors influence the target cell response. For example, the presence of a significant level of a hormone circulating in the bloodstream can cause its target cells to decrease their number of receptors for that hormone. This process is called **downregulation**, and it allows cells to become less reactive to the excessive hormone levels. When the level of a hormone is chronically reduced, target cells engage in **upregulation** to increase their number of receptors. This process allows cells to be more sensitive to the hormone that is present. Cells can also alter the sensitivity of the receptors themselves to various hormones.

Two or more hormones can interact to affect the response of cells in a variety of ways. The three most common types of interaction are as follows:

- The permissive effect, in which the presence of one hormone enables another hormone to act. For example, thyroid hormones have complex permissive relationships with certain reproductive hormones. A dietary deficiency of iodine, a component of thyroid hormones, can therefore affect reproductive system development and functioning.
- The synergistic effect, in which two hormones with similar effects produce an amplified response. In some cases, two hormones are required for an adequate response. For example, two different reproductive hormones—FSH from the pituitary gland and estrogens from the ovaries—are required for the maturation of female ova (egg cells).
- The antagonistic effect, in which two hormones have opposing effects. A familiar example is the effect of two pancreatic hormones, insulin and glucagon. Insulin increases the liver's storage of glucose as glycogen, decreasing blood glucose, whereas glucagon stimulates the breakdown of glycogen stores, increasing blood glucose.

Regulation of Hormone Secretion

To prevent abnormal hormone levels and a potential disease state, hormone levels must be tightly controlled. The body maintains this control by balancing hormone production and degradation. Feedback loops govern the initiation and maintenance of most hormone secretion in response to various stimuli.

Role of Feedback Loops

The contribution of feedback loops to homeostasis will only be briefly reviewed here. Positive feedback loops are characterized by the release of additional hormone in response to an original hormone release. The release of oxytocin during childbirth is a positive feedback loop. The initial release of oxytocin begins to signal the uterine muscles to contract, which pushes the fetus toward the cervix, causing it to stretch. This, in turn, signals the pituitary gland to release more oxytocin, causing labor contractions to intensify. The release of oxytocin decreases after the birth of the child.

The more common method of hormone regulation is the negative feedback loop. Negative feedback is characterized by the inhibition of further secretion of a hormone in response to adequate levels of that hormone. This allows blood levels of the hormone to be regulated within a narrow range. An example of a negative feedback loop is the release of glucocorticoid hormones from the adrenal glands, as directed by the hypothalamus and pituitary gland. As glucocorticoid concentrations in the blood rise, the hypothalamus and pituitary gland reduce their signaling to the adrenal glands to prevent additional glucocorticoid secretion (Figure 17.6).

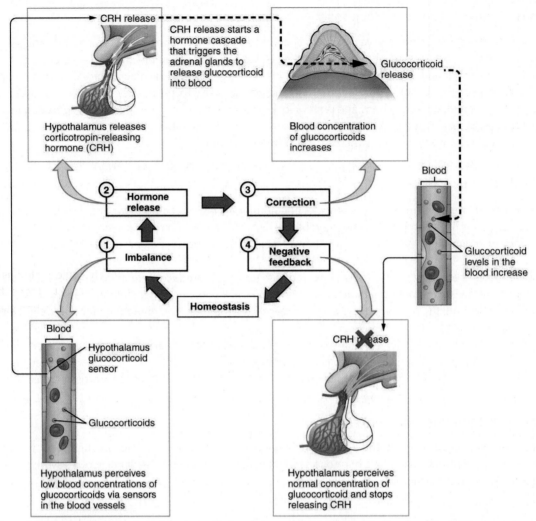

FIGURE 17.6 Negative Feedback Loop   The release of adrenal glucocorticoids is stimulated by the release of hormones from the hypothalamus and pituitary gland. This signaling is inhibited when glucocorticoid levels become elevated by causing negative signals to the pituitary gland and hypothalamus.

Role of Endocrine Gland Stimuli

Reflexes triggered by both chemical and neural stimuli control endocrine activity. These reflexes may be simple, involving only one hormone response, or they may be more complex and involve many hormones, as is the case with the hypothalamic control of various anterior pituitary–controlled hormones.

Humoral stimuli are changes in blood levels of non-hormone chemicals, such as nutrients or ions, which cause the release or inhibition of a hormone to, in turn, maintain homeostasis. For example, osmoreceptors in the hypothalamus detect changes in blood osmolarity (the concentration of solutes in the blood plasma). If blood osmolarity is too high, meaning that the blood is not dilute enough, osmoreceptors signal the hypothalamus to release ADH. The hormone causes the kidneys to reabsorb more water and reduce the volume of urine produced. This reabsorption causes a reduction of the osmolarity of the blood, diluting the blood to the appropriate level. The regulation of blood glucose is another example. High blood glucose levels cause the release of insulin from the pancreas, which increases glucose uptake by cells and liver storage of glucose as glycogen.

An endocrine gland may also secrete a hormone in response to the presence of another hormone produced by a different endocrine gland. Such hormonal stimuli often involve the hypothalamus, which produces releasing and inhibiting hormones that control the secretion of a variety of pituitary hormones.

In addition to these chemical signals, hormones can also be released in response to neural stimuli. A common example of neural stimuli is the activation of the fight-or-flight response by the sympathetic nervous system. When an individual perceives danger, sympathetic neurons signal the adrenal glands to secrete norepinephrine and epinephrine. The two hormones dilate blood vessels, increase the heart and respiratory rate, and suppress the digestive and immune systems. These responses boost the body's transport of oxygen to the brain and muscles, thereby improving the body's ability to fight or flee.

Everyday Connection

Bisphenol A and Endocrine Disruption

You may have heard news reports about the effects of a chemical called bisphenol A (BPA) in various types of food packaging. BPA is used in the manufacturing of hard plastics and epoxy resins. Common food-related items that may contain BPA include the lining of aluminum cans, plastic food-storage containers, drinking cups, as well as baby bottles and "sippy" cups. Other uses of BPA include medical equipment, dental fillings, and the lining of water pipes.

Research suggests that BPA is an endocrine disruptor, meaning that it negatively interferes with the endocrine system, particularly during the prenatal and postnatal development period. In particular, BPA mimics the hormonal effects of estrogens and has the opposite effect—that of androgens. The U.S. Food and Drug Administration (FDA) notes in their statement about BPA safety that although traditional toxicology studies have supported the safety of low levels of exposure to BPA, recent studies using novel approaches to test for subtle effects have led to some concern about the potential effects of BPA on the brain, behavior, and prostate gland in fetuses, infants, and young children. The FDA is currently facilitating decreased use of BPA in food-related materials. Many US companies have voluntarily removed BPA from baby bottles, "sippy" cups, and the linings of infant formula cans, and most plastic reusable water bottles sold today boast that they are "BPA free." In contrast, both Canada and the European Union have completely banned the use of BPA in baby products.

The potential harmful effects of BPA have been studied in both animal models and humans and include a large variety of health effects, such as developmental delay and disease. For example, prenatal exposure to BPA during the first trimester of human pregnancy may be associated with wheezing and aggressive behavior during childhood. Adults exposed to high levels of BPA may experience altered thyroid signaling and male sexual dysfunction. BPA exposure during the prenatal or postnatal period of development in animal models has been observed to cause neurological delays, changes in brain structure and function, sexual dysfunction, asthma, and increased risk for multiple cancers. In vitro studies have also shown that BPA exposure causes molecular changes that initiate the development of cancers of the breast, prostate, and brain. Although these studies have implicated BPA in numerous ill health effects, some experts caution that some of these studies may be flawed and that more research needs to be done. In the meantime, the FDA recommends that consumers take precautions to limit their exposure to BPA. In addition to purchasing foods in packaging free of BPA, consumers should avoid carrying or storing foods or liquids in bottles with the recycling code 3 or 7. Foods and liquids should not be microwave-heated in any form of plastic: use paper, glass, or ceramics instead.

17.3 The Pituitary Gland and Hypothalamus

LEARNING OBJECTIVES

By the end of this section, you will be able to:

- Explain the interrelationships of the anatomy and functions of the hypothalamus and the posterior and anterior lobes of the pituitary gland
- Identify the two hormones released from the posterior pituitary, their target cells, and their principal actions
- Identify the six hormones produced by the anterior lobe of the pituitary gland, their target cells, their principal actions, and their regulation by the hypothalamus

The hypothalamus–pituitary complex can be thought of as the "command center" of the endocrine system. This complex secretes several hormones that directly produce responses in target tissues, as well as hormones that regulate the synthesis and secretion of hormones of other glands. In addition, the hypothalamus–pituitary complex coordinates the messages of the endocrine and nervous systems. In many cases, a stimulus received by the nervous system must pass through the hypothalamus–pituitary complex to be translated into hormones that can initiate a response.

The **hypothalamus** is a structure of the diencephalon of the brain located anterior and inferior to the thalamus (Figure 17.7). It has both neural and endocrine functions, producing and secreting many hormones. In addition, the hypothalamus is anatomically and functionally related to the **pituitary gland** (or hypophysis), a bean-sized organ suspended from it by a stem called the **infundibulum** (or pituitary stalk). The pituitary gland is cradled within the sellaturcica of the sphenoid bone of the skull. It consists of two lobes that arise from distinct parts of embryonic tissue: the posterior pituitary (neurohypophysis) is neural tissue, whereas the anterior pituitary (also known as the adenohypophysis) is glandular tissue that develops from the primitive digestive tract. The hormones secreted by the posterior and anterior pituitary, and the intermediate zone between the lobes are summarized in Table 17.3.

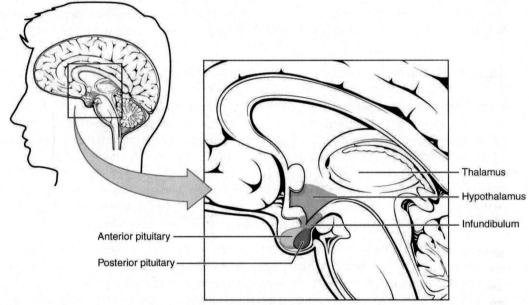

FIGURE 17.7   Hypothalamus–Pituitary Complex   The hypothalamus region lies inferior and anterior to the thalamus. It connects to the pituitary gland by the stalk-like infundibulum. The pituitary gland consists of an anterior and posterior lobe, with each lobe secreting different hormones in response to signals from the hypothalamus.

Pituitary Hormones

Pituitary lobe	Associated hormones	Chemical class	Effect
Anterior	Growth hormone (GH)	Protein	Promotes growth of body tissues
Anterior	Prolactin (PRL)	Peptide	Promotes milk production from mammary glands
Anterior	Thyroid-stimulating hormone (TSH)	Glycoprotein	Stimulates thyroid hormone release from thyroid
Anterior	Adrenocorticotropic hormone (ACTH)	Peptide	Stimulates hormone release by adrenal cortex
Anterior	Follicle-stimulating hormone (FSH)	Glycoprotein	Stimulates gamete production in gonads
Anterior	Luteinizing hormone (LH)	Glycoprotein	Stimulates androgen production by gonads

TABLE 17.3

Pituitary lobe	Associated hormones	Chemical class	Effect
Posterior	Antidiuretic hormone (ADH)	Peptide	Stimulates water reabsorption by kidneys
Posterior	Oxytocin	Peptide	Stimulates uterine contractions during childbirth
Intermediate zone	Melanocyte-stimulating hormone	Peptide	Stimulates melanin formation in melanocytes

TABLE 17.3

Posterior Pituitary

The posterior pituitary is actually an extension of the neurons of the paraventricular and supraoptic nuclei of the hypothalamus. The cell bodies of these regions rest in the hypothalamus, but their axons descend as the hypothalamic–hypophyseal tract within the infundibulum, and end in axon terminals that comprise the posterior pituitary (Figure 17.8).

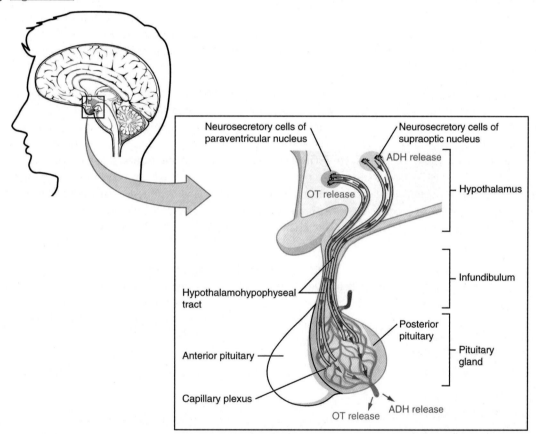

FIGURE 17.8 Posterior Pituitary   Neurosecretory cells in the hypothalamus release oxytocin (OT) or ADH into the posterior lobe of the pituitary gland. These hormones are stored or released into the blood via the capillary plexus.

The posterior pituitary gland does not produce hormones, but rather stores and secretes hormones produced by the hypothalamus. The paraventricular nuclei produce the hormone oxytocin, whereas the supraoptic nuclei produce ADH. These hormones travel along the axons into storage sites in the axon terminals of the posterior pituitary. In response to signals from the same hypothalamic neurons, the hormones are released from the axon terminals into the bloodstream.

Oxytocin

When fetal development is complete, the peptide-derived hormone **oxytocin** (tocia- = "childbirth") stimulates uterine contractions and dilation of the cervix. Throughout most of pregnancy, oxytocin hormone receptors are not expressed at high levels in the uterus. Toward the end of pregnancy, the synthesis of oxytocin receptors in the uterus increases, and the smooth muscle cells of the uterus become more sensitive to its effects. Oxytocin is continually released throughout childbirth through a positive feedback mechanism. As noted earlier, oxytocin prompts uterine contractions that push the fetal head toward the cervix. In response, cervical stretching stimulates additional oxytocin to be synthesized by the hypothalamus and released from the pituitary. This increases the intensity and effectiveness of uterine contractions and prompts additional dilation of the cervix. The feedback loop continues until birth.

Although the high blood levels of oxytocin begin to decrease immediately following birth, oxytocin continues to play a role in female and newborn health. First, oxytocin is necessary for the milk ejection reflex (commonly referred to as "let-down") in breastfeeding people. As the newborn begins suckling, sensory receptors in the nipples transmit signals to the hypothalamus. In response, oxytocin is secreted and released into the bloodstream. Within seconds, cells in the milk ducts contract, ejecting milk into the infant's mouth. Secondly, in ball people, oxytocin is thought to contribute to parent–newborn bonding, known as attachment. Oxytocin is also thought to be involved in feelings of love and closeness, as well as in the sexual response.

Antidiuretic Hormone (ADH)

The solute concentration of the blood, or blood osmolarity, may change in response to the consumption of certain foods and fluids, as well as in response to disease, injury, medications, or other factors. Blood osmolarity is constantly monitored by **osmoreceptors**—specialized cells within the hypothalamus that are particularly sensitive to the concentration of sodium ions and other solutes.

In response to high blood osmolarity, which can occur during dehydration or following a very salty meal, the osmoreceptors signal the posterior pituitary to release **antidiuretic hormone (ADH)**. The target cells of ADH are located in the tubular cells of the kidneys. Its effect is to increase epithelial permeability to water, allowing increased water reabsorption. The more water reabsorbed from the filtrate, the greater the amount of water that is returned to the blood and the less that is excreted in the urine. A greater concentration of water results in a reduced concentration of solutes. ADH is also known as vasopressin because, in very high concentrations, it causes constriction of blood vessels, which increases blood pressure by increasing peripheral resistance. The release of ADH is controlled by a negative feedback loop. As blood osmolarity decreases, the hypothalamic osmoreceptors sense the change and prompt a corresponding decrease in the secretion of ADH. As a result, less water is reabsorbed from the urine filtrate.

Interestingly, drugs can affect the secretion of ADH. For example, alcohol consumption inhibits the release of ADH, resulting in increased urine production that can eventually lead to dehydration and a hangover. A disease called diabetes insipidus is characterized by chronic underproduction of ADH that causes chronic dehydration. Because little ADH is produced and secreted, not enough water is reabsorbed by the kidneys. Although patients feel thirsty, and increase their fluid consumption, this doesn't effectively decrease the solute concentration in their blood because ADH levels are not high enough to trigger water reabsorption in the kidneys. Electrolyte imbalances can occur in severe cases of diabetes insipidus.

Anterior Pituitary

The anterior pituitary originates from the digestive tract in the embryo and migrates toward the brain during fetal development. There are three regions: the pars distalis is the most anterior, the pars intermedia is adjacent to the posterior pituitary, and the pars tuberalis is a slender "tube" that wraps the infundibulum.

Recall that the posterior pituitary does not synthesize hormones, but merely stores them. In contrast, the anterior pituitary does manufacture hormones. However, the secretion of hormones from the anterior pituitary is regulated by two classes of hormones. These hormones—secreted by the hypothalamus—are the releasing hormones that stimulate the secretion of hormones from the anterior pituitary and the inhibiting hormones that inhibit secretion.

Hypothalamic hormones are secreted by neurons, but enter the anterior pituitary through blood vessels (Figure 17.9). Within the infundibulum is a bridge of capillaries that connects the hypothalamus to the anterior pituitary.

This network, called the **hypophyseal portal system**, allows hypothalamic hormones to be transported to the anterior pituitary without first entering the systemic circulation. The system originates from the superior hypophyseal artery, which branches off the carotid arteries and transports blood to the hypothalamus. The branches of the superior hypophyseal artery form the hypophyseal portal system (see Figure 17.9). Hypothalamic releasing and inhibiting hormones travel through a primary capillary plexus to the portal veins, which carry them into the anterior pituitary. Hormones produced by the anterior pituitary (in response to releasing hormones) enter a secondary capillary plexus, and from there drain into the circulation.

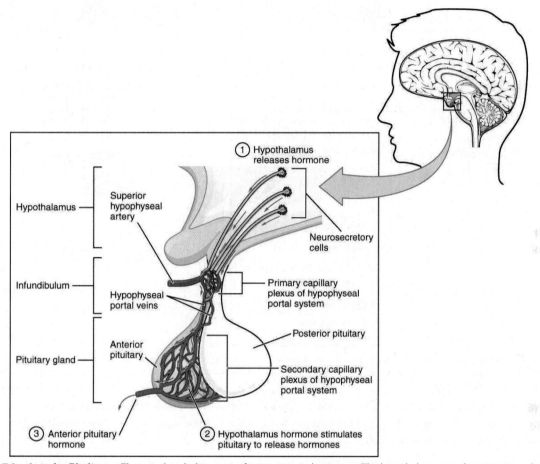

FIGURE 17.9 Anterior Pituitary The anterior pituitary manufactures seven hormones. The hypothalamus produces separate hormones that stimulate or inhibit hormone production in the anterior pituitary. Hormones from the hypothalamus reach the anterior pituitary via the hypophyseal portal system.

The anterior pituitary produces seven hormones. These are the growth hormone (GH), thyroid-stimulating hormone (TSH), adrenocorticotropic hormone (ACTH), follicle-stimulating hormone (FSH), luteinizing hormone (LH), beta endorphin, and prolactin. Of the hormones of the anterior pituitary, TSH, ACTH, FSH, and LH are collectively referred to as tropic hormones (trope- = "turning") because they turn on or off the function of other endocrine glands.

Growth Hormone

The endocrine system regulates the growth of the human body, protein synthesis, and cellular replication. A major hormone involved in this process is **growth hormone (GH)**, also called somatotropin—a protein hormone produced and secreted by the anterior pituitary gland. Its primary function is anabolic; it promotes protein synthesis and tissue building through direct and indirect mechanisms (Figure 17.10). GH levels are controlled by the release of GHRH and GHIH (also known as somatostatin) from the hypothalamus.

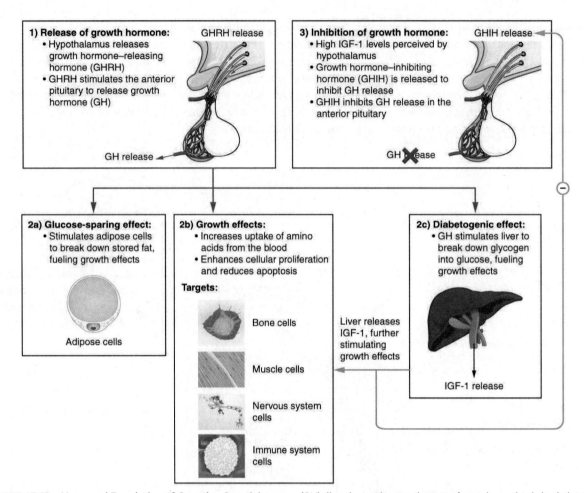

1) Release of growth hormone:
- Hypothalamus releases growth hormone–releasing hormone (GHRH)
- GHRH stimulates the anterior pituitary to release growth hormone (GH)

GHRH release

GH release

3) Inhibition of growth hormone:
- High IGF-1 levels perceived by hypothalamus
- Growth hormone–inhibiting hormone (GHIH) is released to inhibit GH release
- GHIH inhibits GH release in the anterior pituitary

GHIH release

GH release

2a) Glucose-sparing effect:
- Stimulates adipose cells to break down stored fat, fueling growth effects

Adipose cells

2b) Growth effects:
- Increases uptake of amino acids from the blood
- Enhances cellular proliferation and reduces apoptosis

Targets:

Bone cells

Muscle cells

Nervous system cells

Immune system cells

Liver releases IGF-1, further stimulating growth effects

2c) Diabetogenic effect:
- GH stimulates liver to break down glycogen into glucose, fueling growth effects

IGF-1 release

FIGURE 17.10 Hormonal Regulation of Growth   Growth hormone (GH) directly accelerates the rate of protein synthesis in skeletal muscle and bones. Insulin-like growth factor 1 (IGF-1) is activated by growth hormone and indirectly supports the formation of new proteins in muscle cells and bone.

A glucose-sparing effect occurs when GH stimulates lipolysis, or the breakdown of adipose tissue, releasing fatty acids into the blood. As a result, many tissues switch from glucose to fatty acids as their main energy source, which means that less glucose is taken up from the bloodstream.

GH also initiates the diabetogenic effect in which GH stimulates the liver to break down glycogen to glucose, which is then deposited into the blood. The name "diabetogenic" is derived from the similarity in elevated blood glucose levels observed between individuals with untreated diabetes mellitus and individuals experiencing GH excess. Blood glucose levels rise as the result of a combination of glucose-sparing and diabetogenic effects.

GH indirectly mediates growth and protein synthesis by triggering the liver and other tissues to produce a group of proteins called **insulin-like growth factors (IGFs)**. These proteins enhance cellular proliferation and inhibit apoptosis, or programmed cell death. IGFs stimulate cells to increase their uptake of amino acids from the blood for protein synthesis. Skeletal muscle and cartilage cells are particularly sensitive to stimulation from IGFs.

Dysfunction of the endocrine system's control of growth can result in several disorders. For example, **gigantism** is a disorder in children that is caused by the secretion of abnormally large amounts of GH, resulting in excessive growth. A similar condition in adults is **acromegaly**, a disorder that results in the growth of bones in the face, hands, and feet in response to excessive levels of GH in individuals who have stopped growing. Abnormally low levels of GH in children can cause growth impairment—a disorder called **pituitary dwarfism** (also known as growth hormone deficiency).

Thyroid-Stimulating Hormone

The activity of the thyroid gland is regulated by **thyroid-stimulating hormone (TSH)**, also called thyrotropin. TSH is released from the anterior pituitary in response to thyrotropin-releasing hormone (TRH) from the hypothalamus. As

Access for free at openstax.org

discussed shortly, it triggers the secretion of thyroid hormones by the thyroid gland. In a classic negative feedback loop, elevated levels of thyroid hormones in the bloodstream then trigger a drop in production of TRH and subsequently TSH.

Adrenocorticotropic Hormone

The **adrenocorticotropic hormone (ACTH)**, also called corticotropin, stimulates the adrenal cortex (the more superficial "bark" of the adrenal glands) to secrete corticosteroid hormones such as cortisol. ACTH come from a precursor molecule known as pro-opiomelanocortin (POMC) which produces several biologically active molecules when cleaved, including ACTH, melanocyte-stimulating hormone, and the brain opioid peptides known as endorphins.

The release of ACTH is regulated by the corticotropin-releasing hormone (CRH) from the hypothalamus in response to normal physiologic rhythms. A variety of stressors can also influence its release, and the role of ACTH in the stress response is discussed later in this chapter.

Follicle-Stimulating Hormone and Luteinizing Hormone

The endocrine glands secrete a variety of hormones that control the development and regulation of the reproductive system (these glands include the anterior pituitary, the adrenal cortex, and the gonads—the testes and the ovaries). Much of the development of the reproductive system occurs during puberty and is marked by the development of sex-specific characteristics in adolescents. Puberty is initiated by gonadotropin-releasing hormone (GnRH), a hormone produced and secreted by the hypothalamus. GnRH stimulates the anterior pituitary to secrete **gonadotropins**—hormones that regulate the function of the gonads. The levels of GnRH are regulated through a negative feedback loop; high levels of reproductive hormones inhibit the release of GnRH. Throughout life, gonadotropins regulate reproductive function and, in the case of females, the onset and cessation of reproductive capacity.

The gonadotropins include two glycoprotein hormones: **follicle-stimulating hormone (FSH)** stimulates the production and maturation of sex cells, or gametes, including ova and sperm. FSH also promotes follicular growth; these follicles then release estrogens in ovaries. **Luteinizing hormone (LH)** triggers ovulation, as well as the production of estrogens and progesterone by the ovaries. LH stimulates production of testosterone by the testes.

Prolactin

As its name implies, **prolactin (PRL)** promotes lactation (milk production). During pregnancy, it contributes to development of the mammary glands, and after birth, it stimulates the mammary glands to produce breast milk. However, the effects of prolactin depend heavily upon the permissive effects of estrogens, progesterone, and other hormones. And as noted earlier, the let-down of milk occurs in response to stimulation from oxytocin.

In non-pregnant females, prolactin secretion is inhibited by prolactin-inhibiting hormone (PIH), which is actually the neurotransmitter dopamine, and is released from neurons in the hypothalamus. Only during pregnancy do prolactin levels rise in response to prolactin-releasing hormone (PRH) from the hypothalamus.

Intermediate Pituitary: Melanocyte-Stimulating Hormone

The cells in the zone between the pituitary lobes secrete a hormone known as melanocyte-stimulating hormone (MSH) that is formed by cleavage of the pro-opiomelanocortin (POMC) precursor protein. Local production of MSH in the skin is responsible for melanin production in response to UV light exposure. The role of MSH made by the pituitary is more complicated. For instance, people with lighter skin generally have the same amount of MSH as people with darker skin. Nevertheless, this hormone is capable of darkening of the skin by inducing melanin production in the skin's melanocytes. People also show increased MSH production during pregnancy; in combination with estrogens, it can lead to darker skin pigmentation, especially the skin of the areolas and labia minora. Figure 17.11 is a summary of the pituitary hormones and their principal effects.

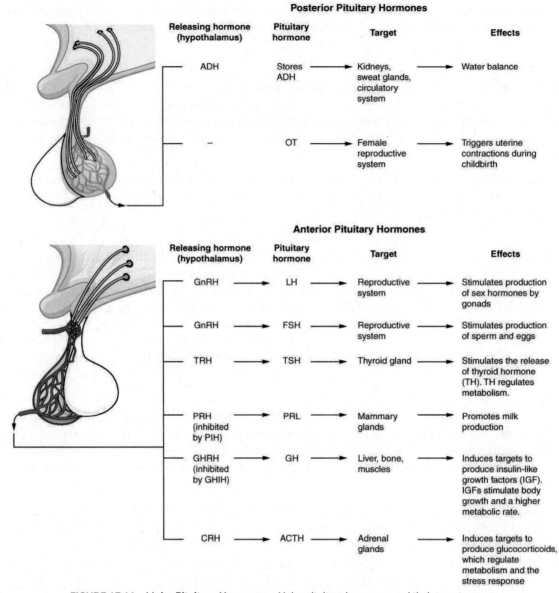

Posterior Pituitary Hormones

Releasing hormone (hypothalamus)	Pituitary hormone	Target	Effects
ADH	Stores ADH	Kidneys, sweat glands, circulatory system	Water balance
–	OT	Female reproductive system	Triggers uterine contractions during childbirth

Anterior Pituitary Hormones

Releasing hormone (hypothalamus)	Pituitary hormone	Target	Effects
GnRH	LH	Reproductive system	Stimulates production of sex hormones by gonads
GnRH	FSH	Reproductive system	Stimulates production of sperm and eggs
TRH	TSH	Thyroid gland	Stimulates the release of thyroid hormone (TH). TH regulates metabolism.
PRH (inhibited by PIH)	PRL	Mammary glands	Promotes milk production
GHRH (inhibited by GHIH)	GH	Liver, bone, muscles	Induces targets to produce insulin-like growth factors (IGF). IGFs stimulate body growth and a higher metabolic rate.
CRH	ACTH	Adrenal glands	Induces targets to produce glucocorticoids, which regulate metabolism and the stress response

FIGURE 17.11   **Major Pituitary Hormones**   Major pituitary hormones and their target organs.

⊘ INTERACTIVE LINK

Visit this link (http://openstax.org/l/roleofhypo) to watch an animation showing the role of the hypothalamus and the pituitary gland. Which hormone is released by the pituitary to stimulate the thyroid gland?

17.4 The Thyroid Gland

LEARNING OBJECTIVES

By the end of this section, you will be able to:

- Describe the location and anatomy of the thyroid gland
- Discuss the synthesis of triiodothyronine and thyroxine
- Explain the role of thyroid hormones in the regulation of basal metabolism
- Identify the hormone produced by the parafollicular cells of the thyroid

A butterfly-shaped organ, the **thyroid gland** is located anterior to the trachea, just inferior to the larynx (Figure 17.12). The medial region, called the isthmus, is flanked by wing-shaped left and right lobes. Each of the thyroid lobes are embedded with parathyroid glands, primarily on their posterior surfaces. The tissue of the thyroid gland is composed mostly of thyroid follicles. The follicles are made up of a central cavity filled with a sticky fluid called

colloid. Surrounded by a wall of epithelial follicle cells, the colloid is the center of thyroid hormone production, and that production is dependent on the hormones' essential and unique component: iodine.

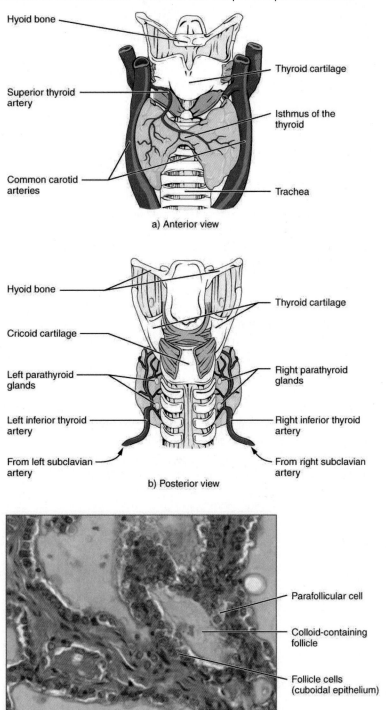

a) Anterior view

b) Posterior view

c) Thyroid follicle cells

FIGURE 17.12   Thyroid Gland   The thyroid gland is located in the neck where it wraps around the trachea. (a) Anterior view of the thyroid gland. (b) Posterior view of the thyroid gland. (c) The glandular tissue is composed primarily of thyroid follicles. The larger parafollicular cells often appear within the matrix of follicle cells. LM × 1332. (Micrograph provided by the Regents of University of Michigan Medical School © 2012)

Synthesis and Release of Thyroid Hormones

Hormones are produced in the colloid when atoms of the mineral iodine attach to a glycoprotein, called thyroglobulin, that is secreted into the colloid by the follicle cells. The following steps outline the hormones' assembly:

1. Binding of TSH to its receptors in the follicle cells of the thyroid gland causes the cells to actively transport iodide ions (I^-) across their cell membrane, from the bloodstream into the cytosol. As a result, the concentration of iodide ions "trapped" in the follicular cells is many times higher than the concentration in the bloodstream.
2. Iodide ions then move to the lumen of the follicle cells that border the colloid. There, the ions undergo oxidation (their negatively charged electrons are removed). The oxidation of two iodide ions ($2\ I^-$) results in iodine (I_2), which passes through the follicle cell membrane into the colloid.
3. In the colloid, peroxidase enzymes link the iodine to the tyrosine amino acids in thyroglobulin to produce two intermediaries: a tyrosine attached to one iodine and a tyrosine attached to two iodines. When one of each of these intermediaries is linked by covalent bonds, the resulting compound is **triiodothyronine** (T_3), a thyroid hormone with three iodines. Much more commonly, two copies of the second intermediary bond, forming tetraiodothyronine, also known as **thyroxine** (T_4), a thyroid hormone with four iodines.

These hormones remain in the colloid center of the thyroid follicles until TSH stimulates endocytosis of colloid back into the follicle cells. There, lysosomal enzymes break apart the thyroglobulin colloid, releasing free T_3 and T_4, which diffuse across the follicle cell membrane and enter the bloodstream.

In the bloodstream, less than one percent of the circulating T_3 and T_4 remains unbound. This free T_3 and T_4 can cross the lipid bilayer of cell membranes and be taken up by cells. The remaining 99 percent of circulating T_3 and T_4 is bound to specialized transport proteins called thyroxine-binding globulins (TBGs), to albumin, or to other plasma proteins. This "packaging" prevents their free diffusion into body cells. When blood levels of T_3 and T_4 begin to decline, bound T_3 and T_4 are released from these plasma proteins and readily cross the membrane of target cells. T_3 is more potent than T_4, and many cells convert T_4 to T_3 through the removal of an iodine atom.

Regulation of TH Synthesis

The release of T_3 and T_4 from the thyroid gland is regulated by thyroid-stimulating hormone (TSH). As shown in Figure 17.13, low blood levels of T_3 and T_4 stimulate the release of thyrotropin-releasing hormone (TRH) from the hypothalamus, which triggers secretion of TSH from the anterior pituitary. In turn, TSH stimulates the thyroid gland to secrete T_3 and T_4. The levels of TRH, TSH, T_3, and T_4 are regulated by a negative feedback system in which increasing levels of T_3 and T_4 decrease the production and secretion of TSH.

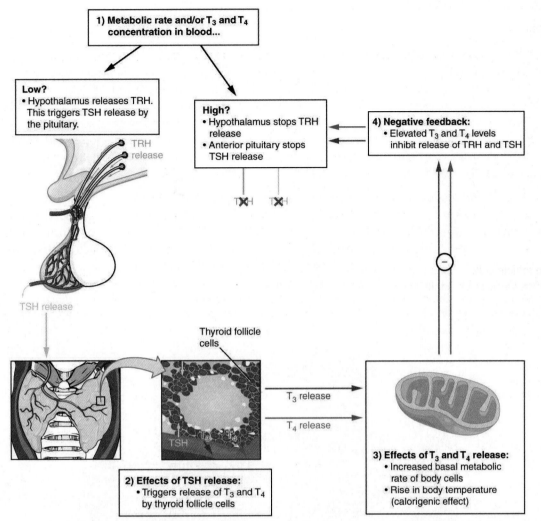

FIGURE 17.13   Classic Negative Feedback Loop   A classic negative feedback loop controls the regulation of thyroid hormone levels.

Functions of Thyroid Hormones

The thyroid hormones, T_3 and T_4, are often referred to as metabolic hormones because their levels influence the body's basal metabolic rate, the amount of energy used by the body at rest. When T_3 and T_4 bind to intracellular receptors located on the mitochondria, they cause an increase in nutrient breakdown and the use of oxygen to produce ATP. In addition, T_3 and T_4 initiate the transcription of genes involved in glucose oxidation. Although these mechanisms prompt cells to produce more ATP, the process is inefficient, and an abnormally increased level of heat is released as a byproduct of these reactions. This so-called calorigenic effect (calor- = "heat") raises body temperature.

Adequate levels of thyroid hormones are also required for protein synthesis and for fetal and childhood tissue development and growth. They are especially critical for normal development of the nervous system both in utero and in early childhood, and they continue to support neurological function in adults. As noted earlier, these thyroid hormones have a complex interrelationship with reproductive hormones, and deficiencies can influence libido, fertility, and other aspects of reproductive function. Finally, thyroid hormones increase the body's sensitivity to catecholamines (epinephrine and norepinephrine) from the adrenal medulla by upregulation of receptors in the blood vessels. When levels of T_3 and T_4 hormones are excessive, this effect accelerates the heart rate, strengthens the heartbeat, and increases blood pressure. Because thyroid hormones regulate metabolism, heat production, protein synthesis, and many other body functions, thyroid disorders can have severe and widespread consequences.

Disorders of the...

Endocrine System: Iodine Deficiency, Hypothyroidism, and Hyperthyroidism

As discussed above, dietary iodine is required for the synthesis of T_3 and T_4. But for much of the world's population, foods do not provide adequate levels of this mineral, because the amount varies according to the level in the soil in which the food was grown, as well as the irrigation and fertilizers used. Marine fish and shrimp tend to have high levels because they concentrate iodine from seawater, but many people in landlocked regions lack access to seafood. Thus, the primary source of dietary iodine in many countries is iodized salt. Fortification of salt with iodine began in the United States in 1924, and international efforts to iodize salt in the world's poorest nations continue today.

Dietary iodine deficiency can result in the impaired ability to synthesize T_3 and T_4, leading to a variety of severe disorders. When T_3 and T_4 cannot be produced, TSH is secreted in increasing amounts. As a result of this hyperstimulation, thyroglobulin accumulates in the thyroid gland follicles, increasing their deposits of colloid. The accumulation of colloid increases the overall size of the thyroid gland, a condition called a **goiter** (Figure 17.14). A goiter is only a visible indication of the deficiency. Other iodine deficiency disorders include impaired growth and development, decreased fertility, and prenatal and infant death. Moreover, iodine deficiency is the primary cause of preventable intellectual disabilities worldwide. **Neonatal hypothyroidism** (cretinism) is characterized by cognitive deficits, short stature, and sometimes deafness and muteness in children and adults born to mothers who were iodine-deficient during pregnancy.

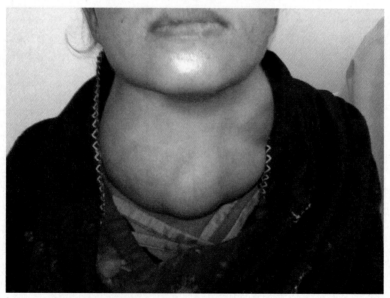

FIGURE 17.14   Goiter   (credit: "Almazi"/Wikimedia Commons)

In areas of the world with access to iodized salt, dietary deficiency is rare. Instead, inflammation of the thyroid gland is the more common cause of low blood levels of thyroid hormones. Called **hypothyroidism**, the condition is characterized by a low metabolic rate, weight gain, cold extremities, constipation, reduced libido, menstrual irregularities, and reduced mental activity. In contrast, **hyperthyroidism**—an abnormally elevated blood level of thyroid hormones—is often caused by a pituitary or thyroid tumor. In Graves' disease, the hyperthyroid state results from an autoimmune reaction in which antibodies overstimulate the follicle cells of the thyroid gland. Hyperthyroidism can lead to an increased metabolic rate, excessive body heat and sweating, diarrhea, weight loss, tremors, and increased heart rate. The person's eyes may bulge (called exophthalmos) as antibodies produce inflammation in the soft tissues of the orbits. The person may also develop a goiter.

Calcitonin

The thyroid gland also secretes a hormone called **calcitonin** that is produced by the parafollicular cells (also called C cells) that stud the tissue between distinct follicles. Calcitonin is released in response to a rise in blood calcium levels. It appears to have a function in decreasing blood calcium concentrations by:

- Inhibiting the activity of osteoclasts, bone cells that release calcium into the circulation by degrading bone matrix
- Increasing osteoblastic activity
- Decreasing calcium absorption in the intestines
- Increasing calcium loss in the urine

However, these functions are usually not significant in maintaining calcium homeostasis, so the importance of calcitonin is not entirely understood. Pharmaceutical preparations of calcitonin are sometimes prescribed to reduce osteoclast activity in people with osteoporosis and to reduce the degradation of cartilage in people with osteoarthritis. The hormones secreted by thyroid are summarized in Table 17.4.

Thyroid Hormones

Associated hormones	Chemical class	Effect
Thyroxine (T_4), triiodothyronine (T_3)	Amine	Stimulate basal metabolic rate
Calcitonin	Peptide	Reduces blood Ca^{2+} levels

TABLE 17.4

Of course, calcium is critical for many other biological processes. It is a second messenger in many signaling pathways, and is essential for muscle contraction, nerve impulse transmission, and blood clotting. Given these roles, it is not surprising that blood calcium levels are tightly regulated by the endocrine system. The organs involved in the regulation are the parathyroid glands.

17.5 The Parathyroid Glands

LEARNING OBJECTIVES

By the end of this section, you will be able to:
- Describe the location and structure of the parathyroid glands
- Describe the hormonal control of blood calcium levels
- Discuss the physiological response of parathyroid dysfunction

The **parathyroid glands** are tiny, round structures usually found embedded in the posterior surface of the thyroid gland (Figure 17.15). A thick connective tissue capsule separates the glands from the thyroid tissue. Most people have four parathyroid glands, but occasionally there are more in tissues of the neck or chest. The function of one type of parathyroid cells, the oxyphil cells, is not clear. The primary functional cells of the parathyroid glands are the chief cells. These epithelial cells produce and secrete the **parathyroid hormone (PTH)**, the major hormone involved in the regulation of blood calcium levels.

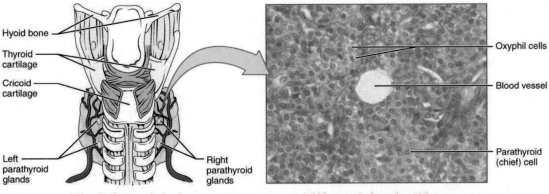

a) Thyroid gland, posterior view   b) Micrograph of parathyroid tissue

FIGURE 17.15 Parathyroid Glands   The small parathyroid glands are embedded in the posterior surface of the thyroid gland. LM × 760.

(Micrograph provided by the Regents of University of Michigan Medical School © 2012)

 **INTERACTIVE LINK**

View the University of Michigan WebScope (http://openstax.org/l/parathyroid) to explore the tissue sample in greater detail.

The parathyroid glands produce and secrete PTH, a peptide hormone, in response to low blood calcium levels (Figure 17.16). PTH secretion causes the release of calcium from the bones by stimulating osteoclasts, which secrete enzymes that degrade bone and release calcium into the interstitial fluid. PTH also inhibits osteoblasts, the cells involved in bone deposition, thereby sparing blood calcium. PTH causes increased reabsorption of calcium (and magnesium) in the kidney tubules from the urine filtrate. In addition, PTH initiates the production of the steroid hormone calcitriol (also known as 1,25-dihydroxyvitamin D), which is the active form of vitamin D_3, in the kidneys. Calcitriol then stimulates increased absorption of dietary calcium by the intestines. A negative feedback loop regulates the levels of PTH, with rising blood calcium levels inhibiting further release of PTH.

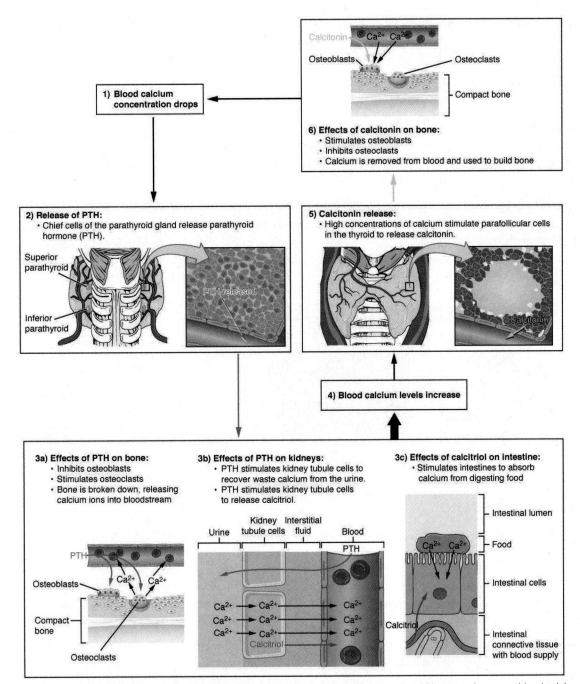

FIGURE 17.16 Parathyroid Hormone in Maintaining Blood Calcium Homeostasis Parathyroid hormone increases blood calcium levels when they drop too low. Conversely, calcitonin, which is released from the thyroid gland, decreases blood calcium levels when they become too high. These two mechanisms constantly maintain blood calcium concentration at homeostasis.

Abnormally high activity of the parathyroid gland can cause **hyperparathyroidism**, a disorder caused by an overproduction of PTH that results in excessive calcium reabsorption from bone. Hyperparathyroidism can significantly decrease bone density, leading to spontaneous fractures or deformities. As blood calcium levels rise, cell membrane permeability to sodium is decreased, and the responsiveness of the nervous system is reduced. At the same time, calcium deposits may collect in the body's tissues and organs, impairing their functioning.

In contrast, abnormally low blood calcium levels may be caused by parathyroid hormone deficiency, called **hypoparathyroidism**, which may develop following injury or surgery involving the thyroid gland. Low blood calcium increases membrane permeability to sodium, resulting in muscle twitching, cramping, spasms, or convulsions. Severe deficits can paralyze muscles, including those involved in breathing, and can be fatal.

When blood calcium levels are high, calcitonin is produced and secreted by the parafollicular cells of the thyroid gland. As discussed earlier, calcitonin inhibits the activity of osteoclasts, reduces the absorption of dietary calcium in the intestine, and signals the kidneys to reabsorb less calcium, resulting in larger amounts of calcium excreted in the urine.

17.6 The Adrenal Glands

LEARNING OBJECTIVES

By the end of this section, you will be able to:

- Describe the location and structure of the adrenal glands
- Identify the hormones produced by the adrenal cortex and adrenal medulla, and summarize their target cells and effects

The **adrenal glands** are wedges of glandular and neuroendocrine tissue adhering to the top of the kidneys by a fibrous capsule (Figure 17.17). The adrenal glands have a rich blood supply and experience one of the highest rates of blood flow in the body. They are served by several arteries branching off the aorta, including the suprarenal and renal arteries. Blood flows to each adrenal gland at the adrenal cortex and then drains into the adrenal medulla. Adrenal hormones are released into the circulation via the left and right suprarenal veins.

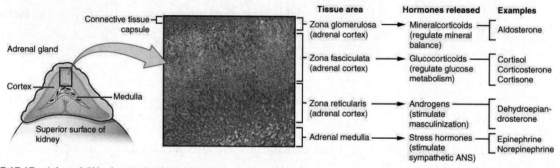

FIGURE 17.17   Adrenal Glands   Both adrenal glands sit atop the kidneys and are composed of an outer cortex and an inner medulla, all surrounded by a connective tissue capsule. The cortex can be subdivided into additional zones, all of which produce different types of hormones. LM × 204. (Micrograph provided by the Regents of University of Michigan Medical School © 2012)

🔗 INTERACTIVE LINK

View the University of Michigan WebScope (http://openstax.org/l/adrenal) to explore the tissue sample in greater detail.

The adrenal gland consists of an outer cortex of glandular tissue and an inner medulla of nervous tissue. The cortex itself is divided into three zones: the **zona glomerulosa**, the **zona fasciculata**, and the **zona reticularis**. Each region secretes its own set of hormones.

The **adrenal cortex**, as a component of the hypothalamic-pituitary-adrenal (HPA) axis, secretes steroid hormones important for the regulation of the long-term stress response, blood pressure and blood volume, nutrient uptake and storage, fluid and electrolyte balance, and inflammation. The HPA axis involves the stimulation of hormone release of adrenocorticotropic hormone (ACTH) from the pituitary by the hypothalamus. ACTH then stimulates the adrenal cortex to produce the hormone cortisol. This pathway will be discussed in more detail below.

The **adrenal medulla** is neuroendocrine tissue composed of postganglionic sympathetic nervous system (SNS) neurons. It is really an extension of the autonomic nervous system, which regulates homeostasis in the body. The sympathomedullary (SAM) pathway involves the stimulation of the medulla by impulses from the hypothalamus via neurons from the thoracic spinal cord. The medulla is stimulated to secrete the amine hormones epinephrine and norepinephrine.

One of the major functions of the adrenal gland is to respond to stress. Stress can be either physical or psychological or both. Physical stresses include exposing the body to injury, walking outside in cold and wet conditions without a coat on, or malnutrition. Psychological stresses include the perception of a physical threat, a fight with a loved one, or just a bad day at school.

The body responds in different ways to short-term stress and long-term stress following a pattern known as the

general adaptation syndrome (GAS). Stage one of GAS is called the **alarm reaction**. This is short-term stress, the fight-or-flight response, mediated by the hormones epinephrine and norepinephrine from the adrenal medulla via the SAM pathway. Their function is to prepare the body for extreme physical exertion. Once this stress is relieved, the body quickly returns to normal. The section on the adrenal medulla covers this response in more detail.

If the stress is not soon relieved, the body adapts to the stress in the second stage called the **stage of resistance**. If a person is starving for example, the body may send signals to the gastrointestinal tract to maximize the absorption of nutrients from food.

If the stress continues for a longer term however, the body responds with symptoms quite different than the fight-or-flight response. During the **stage of exhaustion**, individuals may begin to suffer depression, the suppression of their immune response, severe fatigue, or even a fatal heart attack. These symptoms are mediated by the hormones of the adrenal cortex, especially cortisol, released as a result of signals from the HPA axis.

Adrenal hormones also have several non–stress-related functions, including the increase of blood sodium and glucose levels, which will be described in detail below.

Adrenal Cortex

The adrenal cortex consists of multiple layers of lipid-storing cells that occur in three structurally distinct regions. Each of these regions produces different hormones.

⊘ INTERACTIVE LINK

Visit this link (http://openstax.org/l/adrenalglands) to view an animation describing the location and function of the adrenal glands. Which hormone produced by the adrenal glands is responsible for the mobilization of energy stores?

Hormones of the Zona Glomerulosa

The most superficial region of the adrenal cortex is the zona glomerulosa, which produces a group of hormones collectively referred to as **mineralocorticoids** because of their effect on body minerals, especially sodium and potassium. These hormones are essential for fluid and electrolyte balance.

Aldosterone is the major mineralocorticoid. It is important in the regulation of the concentration of sodium and potassium ions in urine, sweat, and saliva. For example, it is released in response to elevated blood K^+, low blood Na^+, low blood pressure, or low blood volume. In response, aldosterone increases the excretion of K^+ and the retention of Na^+, which in turn increases blood volume and blood pressure. Its secretion is prompted when CRH from the hypothalamus triggers ACTH release from the anterior pituitary.

Aldosterone is also a key component of the renin-angiotensin-aldosterone system (RAAS) in which specialized cells of the kidneys secrete the enzyme renin in response to low blood volume or low blood pressure. Renin then catalyzes the conversion of the blood protein angiotensinogen, produced by the liver, to the hormone angiotensin I. Angiotensin I is converted in the lungs to angiotensin II by **angiotensin-converting enzyme** (ACE). Angiotensin II has three major functions:

1. Initiating vasoconstriction of the arterioles, decreasing blood flow
2. Stimulating kidney tubules to reabsorb NaCl and water, increasing blood volume
3. Signaling the adrenal cortex to secrete aldosterone, the effects of which further contribute to fluid retention, restoring blood pressure and blood volume

For individuals with hypertension, or high blood pressure, drugs are available that block the production of angiotensin II. These drugs, known as ACE inhibitors, block the ACE enzyme from converting angiotensin I to angiotensin II, thus mitigating the latter's ability to increase blood pressure.

Hormones of the Zona Fasciculata

The intermediate region of the adrenal cortex is the zona fasciculata, named as such because the cells form small fascicles (bundles) separated by tiny blood vessels. The cells of the zona fasciculata produce hormones called **glucocorticoids** because of their role in glucose metabolism. The most important of these is **cortisol**, some of which the liver converts to cortisone. A glucocorticoid produced in much smaller amounts is corticosterone. In response to long-term stressors, the hypothalamus secretes CRH, which in turn triggers the release of ACTH by the anterior pituitary. ACTH triggers the release of the glucocorticoids. Their overall effect is to inhibit tissue building while stimulating the breakdown of stored nutrients to maintain adequate fuel supplies. In conditions of long-term stress, for example, cortisol promotes the catabolism of glycogen to glucose, the catabolism of stored triglycerides into fatty acids and glycerol, and the catabolism of muscle proteins into amino acids. These raw materials can then be used to synthesize additional glucose and ketones for use as body fuels. The hippocampus, which is part of the temporal lobe of the cerebral cortices and important in memory formation, is highly sensitive to stress levels because of its many glucocorticoid receptors.

You are probably familiar with prescription and over-the-counter medications containing glucocorticoids, such as cortisone injections into inflamed joints, prednisone tablets and steroid-based inhalers used to manage severe asthma, and hydrocortisone creams applied to relieve itchy rashes. These drugs reflect another role of cortisol—the downregulation of the immune system, which inhibits the inflammatory response.

Hormones of the Zona Reticularis

The deepest region of the adrenal cortex is the zona reticularis, which produces small amounts of a class of steroid sex hormones called androgens. During puberty and most of adulthood, androgens are produced in the gonads. The androgens produced in the zona reticularis supplement the gonadal androgens. They are produced in response to ACTH from the anterior pituitary and are converted in the tissues to testosterone or estrogens. In adult females, they may contribute to the sex drive, but their function in adult males is not well understood. In post-menopausal people, as the functions of the ovaries decline, the main source of estrogens becomes the androgens produced by the zona reticularis.

Adrenal Medulla

As noted earlier, the adrenal cortex releases glucocorticoids in response to long-term stress such as severe illness. In contrast, the adrenal medulla releases its hormones in response to acute, short-term stress mediated by the sympathetic nervous system (SNS).

The medullary tissue is composed of unique postganglionic SNS neurons called **chromaffin** cells, which are large and irregularly shaped, and produce the neurotransmitters **epinephrine** (also called adrenaline) and **norepinephrine** (or noradrenaline). Epinephrine is produced in greater quantities—approximately a 4 to 1 ratio with norepinephrine—and is the more powerful hormone. Because the chromaffin cells release epinephrine and norepinephrine into the systemic circulation, where they travel widely and exert effects on distant cells, they are considered hormones. Derived from the amino acid tyrosine, they are chemically classified as catecholamines.

The secretion of medullary epinephrine and norepinephrine is controlled by a neural pathway that originates from the hypothalamus in response to danger or stress (the SAM pathway). Both epinephrine and norepinephrine signal the liver and skeletal muscle cells to convert glycogen into glucose, resulting in increased blood glucose levels. These hormones increase the heart rate, pulse, and blood pressure to prepare the body to fight the perceived threat or flee from it. In addition, the pathway dilates the airways, raising blood oxygen levels. It also prompts vasodilation, further increasing the oxygenation of important organs such as the lungs, brain, heart, and skeletal muscle. At the same time, it triggers vasoconstriction to blood vessels serving less essential organs such as the gastrointestinal tract, kidneys, and skin, and downregulates some components of the immune system. Other effects include a dry mouth, loss of appetite, pupil dilation, and a loss of peripheral vision. The major hormones of the adrenal glands are summarized in Table 17.5.

Hormones of the Adrenal Glands

Adrenal gland	Associated hormones	Chemical class	Effect
Adrenal cortex	Aldosterone	Steroid	Increases blood Na^+ levels
Adrenal cortex	Cortisol, corticosterone, cortisone	Steroid	Increase blood glucose levels
Adrenal medulla	Epinephrine, norepinephrine	Amine	Stimulate fight-or-flight response

TABLE 17.5

Disorders Involving the Adrenal Glands

Several disorders are caused by the dysregulation of the hormones produced by the adrenal glands. For example, Cushing's disease is a disorder characterized by high blood glucose levels and the accumulation of lipid deposits on the face and neck. It is caused by hypersecretion of cortisol. The most common source of Cushing's disease is a pituitary tumor that secretes cortisol or ACTH in abnormally high amounts. Other common signs of Cushing's disease include the development of a moon-shaped face, a buffalo hump on the back of the neck, rapid weight gain, and hair loss. Chronically elevated glucose levels are also associated with an elevated risk of developing type 2 diabetes. In addition to hyperglycemia, chronically elevated glucocorticoids compromise immunity, resistance to infection, and memory, and can result in rapid weight gain and hair loss.

In contrast, the hyposecretion of corticosteroids can result in Addison's disease, a rare disorder that causes low blood glucose levels and low blood sodium levels. The signs and symptoms of Addison's disease are vague and are typical of other disorders as well, making diagnosis difficult. They may include general weakness, abdominal pain, weight loss, nausea, vomiting, sweating, and cravings for salty food.

17.7 The Pineal Gland

LEARNING OBJECTIVES

By the end of this section, you will be able to:
- Describe the location and structure of the pineal gland
- Discuss the function of melatonin

Recall that the hypothalamus, part of the diencephalon of the brain, sits inferior and somewhat anterior to the thalamus. Inferior but somewhat posterior to the thalamus is the **pineal gland**, a tiny endocrine gland whose functions are not entirely clear. The **pinealocyte** cells that make up the pineal gland are known to produce and secrete the amine hormone **melatonin**, which is derived from serotonin.

The secretion of melatonin varies according to the level of light received from the environment. When photons of light stimulate the retinas of the eyes, a nerve impulse is sent to a region of the hypothalamus called the suprachiasmatic nucleus (SCN), which is important in regulating biological rhythms. From the SCN, the nerve signal is carried to the spinal cord and eventually to the pineal gland, where the production of melatonin is inhibited. As a result, blood levels of melatonin fall, promoting wakefulness. In contrast, as light levels decline—such as during the evening—melatonin production increases, boosting blood levels and causing drowsiness.

⊚ INTERACTIVE LINK

Visit this link (http://openstax.org/l/melatonin) to view an animation describing the function of the hormone melatonin. What should you avoid doing in the middle of your sleep cycle that would lower melatonin?

The secretion of melatonin may influence the body's circadian rhythms, the dark-light fluctuations that affect not only sleepiness and wakefulness, but also appetite and body temperature. Interestingly, children have higher melatonin levels than adults, which may prevent the release of gonadotropins from the anterior pituitary, thereby inhibiting the onset of puberty. Finally, an antioxidant role of melatonin is the subject of current research.

Jet lag occurs when a person travels across several time zones and feels sleepy during the day or wakeful at night. Traveling across multiple time zones significantly disturbs the light-dark cycle regulated by melatonin. It can take up to several days for melatonin synthesis to adjust to the light-dark patterns in the new environment, resulting in jet lag. Some air travelers take melatonin supplements to induce sleep.

17.8 Gonadal and Placental Hormones

LEARNING OBJECTIVES

By the end of this section, you will be able to:

- Identify the most important hormones produced by the testes and ovaries
- Name the hormones produced by the placenta and state their functions

This section briefly discusses the hormonal role of the gonads—the testes and ovaries—which produce the sex cells (sperm and ova) and secrete the gonadal hormones. The roles of the gonadotropins released from the anterior pituitary (FSH and LH) were discussed earlier.

The primary hormone produced by the testes is **testosterone**, a steroid hormone important in the development of the testicular reproductive system, the maturation of sperm cells, and the development of secondary sex characteristics such as a deepened voice, body hair, and increased muscle mass. Interestingly, testosterone is also produced in the ovaries, but at a much reduced level. In addition, the testes produce the peptide hormone **inhibin**, which inhibits the secretion of FSH from the anterior pituitary gland. FSH stimulates spermatogenesis.

The primary hormones produced by the ovaries are **estrogens**, which include estradiol, estriol, and estrone. Estrogens play an important role in a larger number of physiological processes, including the development of the ovarian reproductive system, regulation of the menstrual cycle, the development of secondary sex characteristics such as increased adipose tissue and the development of breast tissue, and the maintenance of pregnancy. Another significant ovarian hormone is **progesterone**, which contributes to regulation of the menstrual cycle and is important in preparing the body for pregnancy as well as maintaining pregnancy. In addition, the granulosa cells of the ovarian follicles produce inhibin, which inhibits the secretion of FSH.During the initial stages of pregnancy, an organ called the placenta develops within the uterus. The placenta supplies oxygen and nutrients to the fetus, excretes waste products, and produces and secretes estrogens and progesterone. The placenta produces human chorionic gonadotropin (hCG) as well. The hCG hormone promotes progesterone synthesis and reduces the mother's immune function to protect the fetus from immune rejection. It also secretes human placental lactogen (hPL), which plays a role in preparing the breasts for lactation, and relaxin, which is thought to help soften and widen the pubic symphysis in preparation for childbirth. The hormones controlling reproduction are summarized in Table 17.6.

Reproductive Hormones

Gonad	Associated hormones	Chemical class	Effect
Testes	Testosterone	Steroid	Stimulates development of secondary sex characteristics and sperm production
Testes	Inhibin	Protein	Inhibits FSH release from pituitary
Ovaries	Estrogens and progesterone	Steroid	Stimulate development of secondary sex characteristics and prepare the body for childbirth
Placenta	Human chorionic gonadotropin	Protein	Promotes progesterone synthesis during pregnancy and inhibits immune response against fetus

TABLE 17.6

Everyday Connection

Anabolic Steroids

The endocrine system can be exploited for illegal or unethical purposes. A prominent example of this is the use of steroid drugs by professional athletes.

Commonly used for performance enhancement, anabolic steroids are synthetic versions of the sex hormone, testosterone. By boosting natural levels of this hormone, athletes experience increased muscle mass. Synthetic versions of human growth hormone are also used to build muscle mass.

The use of performance-enhancing drugs is banned by all major collegiate and professional sports organizations in the United States because they impart an unfair advantage to athletes who take them. In addition, the drugs can cause significant and dangerous side effects. For example, anabolic steroid use can increase cholesterol levels, raise blood pressure, and damage the liver. Altered testosterone levels (both too low or too high) have been implicated in causing structural damage to the heart, and increasing the risk for cardiac arrhythmias, heart attacks, congestive heart failure, and sudden death. Paradoxically, steroids can have effects, including shriveled testicles and enlarged breast tissue. In females, their use can cause effects such as an enlarged clitoris and growth of facial hair. In all people, their use can promote increased aggression (commonly known as "roid-rage"), depression, sleep disturbances, severe acne, and infertility.

17.9 The Endocrine Pancreas

LEARNING OBJECTIVES

By the end of this section, you will be able to:

- Describe the location and structure of the pancreas, and the morphology and function of the pancreatic islets
- Compare and contrast the functions of insulin and glucagon

The **pancreas** is a long, slender organ, most of which is located posterior to the bottom half of the stomach (Figure 17.18). Although it is primarily an exocrine gland, secreting a variety of digestive enzymes, the pancreas has an endocrine function. Its **pancreatic islets**—clusters of cells formerly known as the islets of Langerhans—secrete the hormones glucagon, insulin, somatostatin, and pancreatic polypeptide (PP).

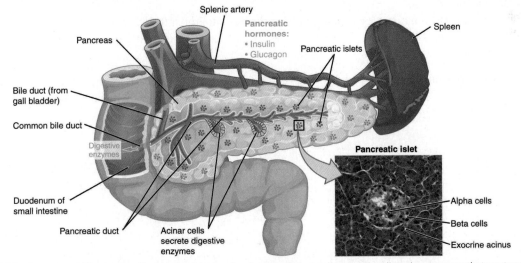

FIGURE 17.18 Pancreas   The pancreatic exocrine function involves the acinar cells secreting digestive enzymes that are transported into the small intestine by the pancreatic duct. Its endocrine function involves the secretion of insulin (produced by beta cells) and glucagon (produced by alpha cells) within the pancreatic islets. These two hormones regulate the rate of glucose metabolism in the body. The micrograph reveals pancreatic islets. LM × 760. (Micrograph provided by the Regents of University of Michigan Medical School © 2012)

🔗 INTERACTIVE LINK

View the University of Michigan WebScope (http://openstax.org/l/pancreaticislet) to explore the tissue sample in greater detail.

Cells and Secretions of the Pancreatic Islets

The pancreatic islets each contain four varieties of cells:

- The **alpha cell** produces the hormone glucagon and makes up approximately 20 percent of each islet. Glucagon plays an important role in blood glucose regulation; low blood glucose levels stimulate its release.
- The **beta cell** produces the hormone insulin and makes up approximately 75 percent of each islet. Elevated blood glucose levels stimulate the release of insulin.
- The **delta cell** accounts for four percent of the islet cells and secretes the peptide hormone somatostatin. Recall that somatostatin is also released by the hypothalamus (as GHIH), and the stomach and intestines also secrete it. An inhibiting hormone, pancreatic somatostatin inhibits the release of both glucagon and insulin.
- The **PP cell** accounts for about one percent of islet cells and secretes the pancreatic polypeptide hormone. It is thought to play a role in appetite, as well as in the regulation of pancreatic exocrine and endocrine secretions. Pancreatic polypeptide released following a meal may reduce further food consumption; however, it is also released in response to fasting.

Regulation of Blood Glucose Levels by Insulin and Glucagon

Glucose is required for cellular respiration and is the preferred fuel for all body cells. The body derives glucose from the breakdown of the carbohydrate-containing foods and drinks we consume. Glucose not immediately taken up by cells for fuel can be stored by the liver and muscles as glycogen, or converted to triglycerides and stored in the adipose tissue. Hormones regulate both the storage and the utilization of glucose as required. Receptors located in the pancreas sense blood glucose levels, and subsequently the pancreatic cells secrete glucagon or insulin to maintain normal levels.

Glucagon

Receptors in the pancreas can sense the decline in blood glucose levels, such as during periods of fasting or during prolonged labor or exercise (Figure 17.19). In response, the alpha cells of the pancreas secrete the hormone **glucagon**, which has several effects:

- It stimulates the liver to convert its stores of glycogen back into glucose. This response is known as glycogenolysis. The glucose is then released into the circulation for use by body cells.
- It stimulates the liver to take up amino acids from the blood and convert them into glucose. This response is known as gluconeogenesis.
- It stimulates lipolysis, the breakdown of stored triglycerides into free fatty acids and glycerol. Some of the free glycerol released into the bloodstream travels to the liver, which converts it into glucose. This is also a form of gluconeogenesis.

Taken together, these actions increase blood glucose levels. The activity of glucagon is regulated through a negative feedback mechanism; rising blood glucose levels inhibit further glucagon production and secretion.

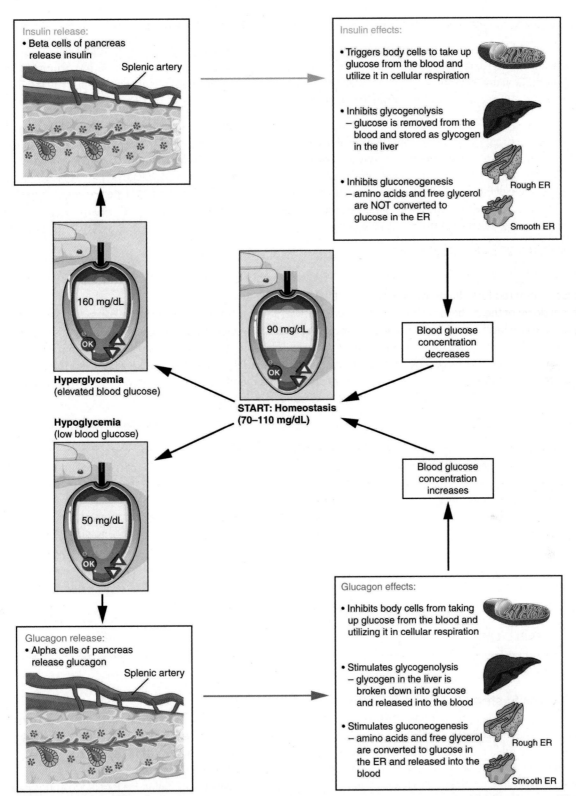

FIGURE 17.19   Homeostatic Regulation of Blood Glucose Levels   Blood glucose concentration is tightly maintained between 70 mg/dL and 110 mg/dL. If blood glucose concentration rises above this range, insulin is released, which stimulates body cells to remove glucose from the blood. If blood glucose concentration drops below this range, glucagon is released, which stimulates body cells to release glucose into the blood.

Insulin

The primary function of **insulin** is to facilitate the uptake of glucose into body cells. Red blood cells, as well as cells of the brain, liver, kidneys, and the lining of the small intestine, do not have insulin receptors on their cell membranes and do not require insulin for glucose uptake. Although all other body cells do require insulin if they are to take glucose from the bloodstream, skeletal muscle cells and adipose cells are the primary targets of insulin.

The presence of food in the intestine triggers the release of gastrointestinal tract hormones such as glucose-dependent insulinotropic peptide (previously known as gastric inhibitory peptide). This is in turn the initial trigger for insulin production and secretion by the beta cells of the pancreas. Once nutrient absorption occurs, the resulting surge in blood glucose levels further stimulates insulin secretion.

Precisely how insulin facilitates glucose uptake is not entirely clear. However, insulin appears to activate a tyrosine kinase receptor, triggering the phosphorylation of many substrates within the cell. These multiple biochemical reactions converge to support the movement of intracellular vesicles containing facilitative glucose transporters to the cell membrane. In the absence of insulin, these transport proteins are normally recycled slowly between the cell membrane and cell interior. Insulin triggers the rapid movement of a pool of glucose transporter vesicles to the cell membrane, where they fuse and expose the glucose transporters to the extracellular fluid. The transporters then move glucose by facilitated diffusion into the cell interior.

INTERACTIVE LINK

Visit this link (http://openstax.org/l/pancreas1) to view an animation describing the location and function of the pancreas. What goes wrong in the function of insulin in type 2 diabetes?

Insulin also reduces blood glucose levels by stimulating glycolysis, the metabolism of glucose for generation of ATP. Moreover, it stimulates the liver to convert excess glucose into glycogen for storage, and it inhibits enzymes involved in glycogenolysis and gluconeogenesis. Finally, insulin promotes triglyceride and protein synthesis. The secretion of insulin is regulated through a negative feedback mechanism. As blood glucose levels decrease, further insulin release is inhibited. The pancreatic hormones are summarized in Table 17.7.

Hormones of the Pancreas

Associated hormones	Chemical class	Effect
Insulin (beta cells)	Protein	Reduces blood glucose levels
Glucagon (alpha cells)	Protein	Increases blood glucose levels
Somatostatin (delta cells)	Protein	Inhibits insulin and glucagon release
Pancreatic polypeptide (PP cells)	Protein	Role in appetite

TABLE 17.7

Disorders of the...

Endocrine System: Diabetes Mellitus

Dysfunction of insulin production and secretion, as well as the target cells' responsiveness to insulin, can lead to a condition called **diabetes mellitus**. An increasingly common disease, diabetes mellitus has been diagnosed in more than 18 million adults in the United States, and more than 200,000 children. It is estimated that up to 7 million more adults have the condition but have not been diagnosed. In addition, approximately 79 million people in the US are estimated to have pre-diabetes, a condition in which blood glucose levels are abnormally high, but not yet high enough to be classified as diabetes.

There are two main forms of diabetes mellitus. Type 1 diabetes is an autoimmune disease affecting the beta cells of the pancreas. Certain genes are recognized to increase susceptibility. The beta cells of people with type 1 diabetes do not produce insulin; thus, synthetic insulin must be administered by injection or infusion. This form of diabetes accounts for less than five percent of all diabetes cases.

Type 2 diabetes accounts for approximately 95 percent of all cases. It is acquired, and lifestyle factors such as poor diet, inactivity, and the presence of pre-diabetes greatly increase a person's risk. About 80 to 90 percent of people with type 2 diabetes are overweight or obese. In type 2 diabetes, cells become resistant to the effects of insulin. In response, the pancreas increases its insulin secretion, but over time, the beta cells become exhausted. In many cases, type 2 diabetes can be reversed by moderate weight loss, regular physical activity, and consumption of a healthy diet; however, if blood glucose levels cannot be controlled, the person with diabetes will eventually require insulin.

Two of the early manifestations of diabetes are excessive urination and excessive thirst. They demonstrate how the out-of-control levels of glucose in the blood affect kidney function. The kidneys are responsible for filtering glucose from the blood. Excessive blood glucose draws water into the urine, and as a result the person eliminates an abnormally large quantity of sweet urine. The use of body water to dilute the urine leaves the body dehydrated, and so the person is unusually and continually thirsty. The person may also experience persistent hunger because the body cells are unable to access the glucose in the bloodstream.

Over time, persistently high levels of glucose in the blood injure tissues throughout the body, especially those of the blood vessels and nerves. Inflammation and injury of the lining of arteries lead to atherosclerosis and an increased risk of heart attack and stroke. Damage to the microscopic blood vessels of the kidney impairs kidney function and can lead to kidney failure. Damage to blood vessels that serve the eyes can lead to blindness. Blood vessel damage also reduces circulation to the limbs, whereas nerve damage leads to a loss of sensation, called neuropathy, particularly in the hands and feet. Together, these changes increase the risk of injury, infection, and tissue death (necrosis), contributing to a high rate of toe, foot, and lower leg amputations in people with diabetes. Uncontrolled diabetes can also lead to a dangerous form of metabolic acidosis called ketoacidosis. Deprived of glucose, cells increasingly rely on fat stores for fuel. However, in a glucose-deficient state, the liver is forced to use an alternative lipid metabolism pathway that results in the increased production of ketone bodies (or ketones), which are acidic. The build-up of ketones in the blood causes ketoacidosis, which—if left untreated—may lead to a life-threatening "diabetic coma." Together, these complications make diabetes the seventh leading cause of death in the United States.

Diabetes is diagnosed when lab tests reveal that blood glucose levels are higher than normal, a condition called **hyperglycemia**. The treatment of diabetes depends on the type, the severity of the condition, and the ability of the patient to make lifestyle changes. As noted earlier, moderate weight loss, regular physical activity, and consumption of a healthful diet can reduce blood glucose levels. Some patients with type 2 diabetes may be unable to control their disease with these lifestyle changes, and will require medication. Historically, the first-line treatment of type 2 diabetes was insulin. Research advances have resulted in alternative options, including medications that enhance pancreatic function.

INTERACTIVE LINK

Visit this link (http://openstax.org/l/insulin) to view an animation describing the role of insulin and the pancreas in diabetes.

17.10 Organs with Secondary Endocrine Functions

LEARNING OBJECTIVES

By the end of this section, you will be able to:

- Identify the organs with a secondary endocrine function, the hormone they produce, and its effects

In your study of anatomy and physiology, you have already encountered a few of the many organs of the body that have secondary endocrine functions. Here, you will learn about the hormone-producing activities of the heart, gastrointestinal tract, kidneys, skeleton, adipose tissue, skin, and thymus.

Heart

When the body experiences an increase in blood volume or pressure, the cells of the heart's atrial wall stretch. In response, specialized cells in the wall of the atria produce and secrete the peptide hormone **atrial natriuretic**

peptide (ANP). ANP signals the kidneys to reduce sodium reabsorption, thereby decreasing the amount of water reabsorbed from the urine filtrate and reducing blood volume. Other actions of ANP include the inhibition of renin secretion, thus inhibition of the renin-angiotensin-aldosterone system (RAAS) and vasodilation. Therefore, ANP aids in decreasing blood pressure, blood volume, and blood sodium levels.

Gastrointestinal Tract

The endocrine cells of the GI tract are located in the mucosa of the stomach and small intestine. Some of these hormones are secreted in response to eating a meal and aid in digestion. An example of a hormone secreted by the stomach cells is gastrin, a peptide hormone secreted in response to stomach distention that stimulates the release of hydrochloric acid. Secretin is a peptide hormone secreted by the small intestine as acidic chyme (partially digested food and fluid) moves from the stomach. It stimulates the release of bicarbonate from the pancreas, which buffers the acidic chyme, and inhibits the further secretion of hydrochloric acid by the stomach. Cholecystokinin (CCK) is another peptide hormone released from the small intestine. It promotes the secretion of pancreatic enzymes and the release of bile from the gallbladder, both of which facilitate digestion. Other hormones produced by the intestinal cells aid in glucose metabolism, such as by stimulating the pancreatic beta cells to secrete insulin, reducing glucagon secretion from the alpha cells, or enhancing cellular sensitivity to insulin.

Kidneys

The kidneys participate in several complex endocrine pathways and produce certain hormones. A decline in blood flow to the kidneys stimulates them to release the enzyme renin, triggering the renin-angiotensin-aldosterone (RAAS) system, and stimulating the reabsorption of sodium and water. The reabsorption increases blood flow and blood pressure. The kidneys also play a role in regulating blood calcium levels through the production of calcitriol from vitamin D_3, which is released in response to the secretion of parathyroid hormone (PTH). In addition, the kidneys produce the hormone **erythropoietin (EPO)** in response to low oxygen levels. EPO stimulates the production of red blood cells (erythrocytes) in the bone marrow, thereby increasing oxygen delivery to tissues. You may have heard of EPO as a performance-enhancing drug (in a synthetic form).

Skeleton

Although bone has long been recognized as a target for hormones, only recently have researchers recognized that the skeleton itself produces at least two hormones. Fibroblast growth factor 23 (FGF23) is produced by bone cells in response to increased blood levels of vitamin D_3 or phosphate. It triggers the kidneys to inhibit the formation of calcitriol from vitamin D_3 and to increase phosphorus excretion. Osteocalcin, produced by osteoblasts, stimulates the pancreatic beta cells to increase insulin production. It also acts on peripheral tissues to increase their sensitivity to insulin and their utilization of glucose.

Adipose Tissue

Adipose tissue produces and secretes several hormones involved in lipid metabolism and storage. One important example is **leptin**, a protein manufactured by adipose cells that circulates in amounts directly proportional to levels of body fat. Leptin is released in response to food consumption and acts by binding to brain neurons involved in energy intake and expenditure. Binding of leptin produces a feeling of satiety after a meal, thereby reducing appetite. It also appears that the binding of leptin to brain receptors triggers the sympathetic nervous system to regulate bone metabolism, increasing deposition of cortical bone. Adiponectin—another hormone synthesized by adipose cells—appears to reduce cellular insulin resistance and to protect blood vessels from inflammation and atherosclerosis. Its levels are lower in people who are obese, and rise following weight loss.

Skin

The skin functions as an endocrine organ in the production of the inactive form of vitamin D_3, cholecalciferol. When cholesterol present in the epidermis is exposed to ultraviolet radiation, it is converted to cholecalciferol, which then enters the blood. In the liver, cholecalciferol is converted to an intermediate that travels to the kidneys and is further converted to calcitriol, the active form of vitamin D_3. Vitamin D is important in a variety of physiological processes, including intestinal calcium absorption and immune system function. In some studies, low levels of vitamin D have been associated with increased risks of cancer, severe asthma, and multiple sclerosis. Vitamin D deficiency in children causes rickets, and in adults, osteomalacia—both of which are characterized by bone deterioration.

Thymus

The **thymus** is an organ of the immune system that is larger and more active during infancy and early childhood, and begins to atrophy as we age. Its endocrine function is the production of a group of hormones called **thymosins** that contribute to the development and differentiation of T lymphocytes, which are immune cells. Although the role of thymosins is not yet well understood, it is clear that they contribute to the immune response. Thymosins have been found in tissues other than the thymus and have a wide variety of functions, so the thymosins cannot be strictly categorized as thymic hormones.

Liver

The liver is responsible for secreting at least four important hormones or hormone precursors: insulin-like growth factor (somatomedin), angiotensinogen, thrombopoietin, and hepcidin. Insulin-like growth factor-1 is the immediate stimulus for growth in the body, especially of the bones. Angiotensinogen is the precursor to angiotensin, mentioned earlier, which increases blood pressure. Thrombopoietin stimulates the production of the blood's platelets. Hepcidins block the release of iron from cells in the body, helping to regulate iron homeostasis in our body fluids. The major hormones of these other organs are summarized in Table 17.8.

Organs with Secondary Endocrine Functions and Their Major Hormones

Organ	Major hormones	Effects
Heart	Atrial natriuretic peptide (ANP)	Reduces blood volume, blood pressure, and Na^+ concentration
Gastrointestinal tract	Gastrin, secretin, and cholecystokinin	Aid digestion of food and buffering of stomach acids
Gastrointestinal tract	Glucose-dependent insulinotropic peptide (GIP) and glucagon-like peptide 1 (GLP-1)	Stimulate beta cells of the pancreas to release insulin
Kidneys	Renin	Stimulates release of aldosterone
Kidneys	Calcitriol	Aids in the absorption of Ca^{2+}
Kidneys	Erythropoietin	Triggers the formation of red blood cells in the bone marrow
Skeleton	FGF23	Inhibits production of calcitriol and increases phosphate excretion
Skeleton	Osteocalcin	Increases insulin production
Adipose tissue	Leptin	Promotes satiety signals in the brain
Adipose tissue	Adiponectin	Reduces insulin resistance
Skin	Cholecalciferol	Modified to form vitamin D
Thymus (and other organs)	Thymosins	Among other things, aids in the development of T lymphocytes of the immune system

TABLE 17.8

Organ	Major hormones	Effects
Liver	Insulin-like growth factor-1	Stimulates bodily growth
Liver	Angiotensinogen	Raises blood pressure
Liver	Thrombopoietin	Causes increase in platelets
Liver	Hepcidin	Blocks release of iron into body fluids

TABLE 17.8

17.11 Development and Aging of the Endocrine System

LEARNING OBJECTIVES

By the end of this section, you will be able to:
- Describe the embryonic origins of the endocrine system
- Discuss the effects of aging on the endocrine system

The endocrine system arises from all three embryonic germ layers. The endocrine glands that produce the steroid hormones, such as the gonads and adrenal cortex, arise from the mesoderm. In contrast, endocrine glands that arise from the endoderm and ectoderm produce the amine, peptide, and protein hormones. The pituitary gland arises from two distinct areas of the ectoderm: the anterior pituitary gland arises from the oral ectoderm, whereas the posterior pituitary gland arises from the neural ectoderm at the base of the hypothalamus. The pineal gland also arises from the ectoderm. The two structures of the adrenal glands arise from two different germ layers: the adrenal cortex from the mesoderm and the adrenal medulla from ectoderm neural cells. The endoderm gives rise to the thyroid and parathyroid glands, as well as the pancreas and the thymus.

As the body ages, changes occur that affect the endocrine system, sometimes altering the production, secretion, and catabolism of hormones. For example, the structure of the anterior pituitary gland changes as vascularization decreases and the connective tissue content increases with increasing age. This restructuring affects the gland's hormone production. For example, the amount of human growth hormone that is produced declines with age, resulting in the reduced muscle mass commonly observed in the elderly.

The adrenal glands also undergo changes as the body ages; as fibrous tissue increases, the production of cortisol and aldosterone decreases. Interestingly, the production and secretion of epinephrine and norepinephrine remain normal throughout the aging process.

A well-known example of the aging process affecting an endocrine gland is menopause and the decline of ovarian function. With increasing age, the ovaries decrease in both size and weight and become progressively less sensitive to gonadotropins. This gradually causes a decrease in estrogen and progesterone levels, leading to menopause and the inability to reproduce. Low levels of estrogens and progesterone are also associated with some disease states, such as osteoporosis, atherosclerosis, and hyperlipidemia, or abnormal blood lipid levels.

Testosterone levels also decline with age, a condition called andropause (or viropause); however, this decline is much less dramatic than the decline of estrogens, and much more gradual, rarely affecting sperm production until very old age. Although this means that males maintain their ability to produce offspring for decades longer than females, the quantity, quality, and motility of their sperm is often reduced.

As the body ages, the thyroid gland produces less of the thyroid hormones, causing a gradual decrease in the basal metabolic rate. The lower metabolic rate reduces the production of body heat and increases levels of body fat. Parathyroid hormones, on the other hand, increase with age. This may be because of reduced dietary calcium levels, causing a compensatory increase in parathyroid hormone. However, increased parathyroid hormone levels combined with decreased levels of calcitonin (and estrogens in females) can lead to osteoporosis as PTH stimulates demineralization of bones to increase blood calcium levels. Notice that osteoporosis is common in all elderly people regardless of sex.

Access for free at openstax.org

Increasing age also affects glucose metabolism, as blood glucose levels spike more rapidly and take longer to return to normal in the elderly. In addition, increasing glucose intolerance may occur because of a gradual decline in cellular insulin sensitivity. Almost 27 percent of Americans aged 65 and older have diabetes.

Key Terms

acromegaly   disorder in adults caused when abnormally high levels of GH trigger growth of bones in the face, hands, and feet

adenylyl cyclase   membrane-bound enzyme that converts ATP to cyclic AMP, creating cAMP, as a result of G-protein activation

adrenal cortex   outer region of the adrenal glands consisting of multiple layers of epithelial cells and capillary networks that produces mineralocorticoids and glucocorticoids

adrenal glands   endocrine glands located at the top of each kidney that are important for the regulation of the stress response, blood pressure and blood volume, water homeostasis, and electrolyte levels

adrenal medulla   inner layer of the adrenal glands that plays an important role in the stress response by producing epinephrine and norepinephrine

adrenocorticotropic hormone (ACTH)   anterior pituitary hormone that stimulates the adrenal cortex to secrete corticosteroid hormones (also called corticotropin)

alarm reaction   the short-term stress, or the fight-or-flight response, of stage one of the general adaptation syndrome mediated by the hormones epinephrine and norepinephrine

aldosterone   hormone produced and secreted by the adrenal cortex that stimulates sodium and fluid retention and increases blood volume and blood pressure

alpha cell   pancreatic islet cell type that produces the hormone glucagon

angiotensin-converting enzyme   the enzyme that converts angiotensin I to angiotensin II

antidiuretic hormone (ADH)   hypothalamic hormone that is stored by the posterior pituitary and that signals the kidneys to reabsorb water

atrial natriuretic peptide (ANP)   peptide hormone produced by the walls of the atria in response to high blood pressure, blood volume, or blood sodium that reduces the reabsorption of sodium and water in the kidneys and promotes vasodilation

autocrine   chemical signal that elicits a response in the same cell that secreted it

beta cell   pancreatic islet cell type that produces the hormone insulin

calcitonin   peptide hormone produced and secreted by the parafollicular cells (C cells) of the thyroid gland that functions to decrease blood calcium levels

chromaffin   neuroendocrine cells of the adrenal medulla

colloid   viscous fluid in the central cavity of thyroid follicles, containing the glycoprotein thyroglobulin

cortisol   glucocorticoid important in gluconeogenesis, the catabolism of glycogen, and downregulation of the immune system

cyclic adenosine monophosphate (cAMP)   second messenger that, in response to adenylyl cyclase activation, triggers a phosphorylation cascade

delta cell   minor cell type in the pancreas that secretes the hormone somatostatin

diabetes mellitus   condition caused by destruction or dysfunction of the beta cells of the pancreas or cellular resistance to insulin that results in abnormally high blood glucose levels

diacylglycerol (DAG)   molecule that, like cAMP, activates protein kinases, thereby initiating a phosphorylation cascade

downregulation   decrease in the number of hormone receptors, typically in response to chronically excessive levels of a hormone

endocrine gland   tissue or organ that secretes hormones into the blood and lymph without ducts such that they may be transported to organs distant from the site of secretion

endocrine system   cells, tissues, and organs that secrete hormones as a primary or secondary function and play an integral role in normal bodily processes

epinephrine   primary and most potent catecholamine hormone secreted by the adrenal medulla in response to short-term stress; also called adrenaline

erythropoietin (EPO)   protein hormone secreted in response to low oxygen levels that triggers the bone marrow to produce red blood cells

estrogens   class of predominantly female sex hormones important for the development and growth of the female reproductive tract, secondary sex characteristics, the female reproductive cycle, and the maintenance of pregnancy

exocrine system   cells, tissues, and organs that secrete substances directly to target tissues via glandular ducts

first messenger   hormone that binds to a cell membrane hormone receptor and triggers activation of a second messenger system

follicle-stimulating hormone (FSH)   anterior pituitary hormone that stimulates the production and maturation of sex cells

G protein   protein associated with a cell membrane hormone receptor that initiates the next step in a second messenger system upon activation by hormone–receptor binding

general adaptation syndrome (GAS)   the human body's three-stage response pattern to short- and long-term stress

gigantism   disorder in children caused when abnormally high levels of GH prompt excessive growth

glucagon   pancreatic hormone that stimulates the catabolism of glycogen to glucose, thereby increasing blood glucose levels

glucocorticoids   hormones produced by the zona fasciculata of the adrenal cortex that influence glucose metabolism

goiter   enlargement of the thyroid gland either as a result of iodine deficiency or hyperthyroidism

gonadotropins   hormones that regulate the function of the gonads

growth hormone (GH)   anterior pituitary hormone that promotes tissue building and influences nutrient metabolism (also called somatotropin)

hormone   secretion of an endocrine organ that travels via the bloodstream or lymphatics to induce a response in target cells or tissues in another part of the body

hormone receptor   protein within a cell or on the cell membrane that binds a hormone, initiating the target cell response

hyperglycemia   abnormally high blood glucose levels

hyperparathyroidism   disorder caused by overproduction of PTH that results in abnormally elevated blood calcium

hyperthyroidism   clinically abnormal, elevated level of thyroid hormone in the blood; characterized by an increased metabolic rate, excess body heat, sweating, diarrhea, weight loss, and increased heart rate

hypoparathyroidism   disorder caused by underproduction of PTH that results in abnormally low blood calcium

hypophyseal portal system   network of blood vessels that enables hypothalamic hormones to travel into the anterior lobe of the pituitary without entering the systemic circulation

hypothalamus   region of the diencephalon inferior to the thalamus that functions in neural and endocrine signaling

hypothyroidism   clinically abnormal, low level of thyroid hormone in the blood; characterized by low metabolic rate, weight gain, cold extremities, constipation, and reduced mental activity

infundibulum   stalk containing vasculature and neural tissue that connects the pituitary gland to the hypothalamus (also called the pituitary stalk)

inhibin   hormone secreted by the male and female gonads that inhibits FSH production by the anterior pituitary

inositol triphosphate (IP$_3$)   molecule that initiates the release of calcium ions from intracellular stores

insulin   pancreatic hormone that enhances the cellular uptake and utilization of glucose, thereby decreasing blood glucose levels

insulin-like growth factors (IGF)   protein that enhances cellular proliferation, inhibits apoptosis, and stimulates the cellular uptake of amino acids for protein synthesis

leptin   protein hormone secreted by adipose tissues in response to food consumption that promotes satiety

luteinizing hormone (LH)   anterior pituitary hormone that triggers ovulation and the production of ovarian hormones, and the production of testosterone

melatonin   amino acid–derived hormone that is secreted in response to low light and causes drowsiness

mineralocorticoids   hormones produced by the zona glomerulosa cells of the adrenal cortex that influence fluid and electrolyte balance

neonatal hypothyroidism   condition characterized by cognitive deficits, short stature, and other signs and symptoms in people born to people who were iodine-deficient during pregnancy

norepinephrine   secondary catecholamine hormone secreted by the adrenal medulla in response to short-term stress; also called noradrenaline

osmoreceptor   hypothalamic sensory receptor that is stimulated by changes in solute concentration (osmotic pressure) in the blood

oxytocin   hypothalamic hormone stored in the posterior pituitary gland and important in stimulating uterine contractions in labor, milk ejection during breastfeeding, and feelings of attachment (produced by males and females)

pancreas   organ with both exocrine and endocrine functions located posterior to the stomach that is important for digestion and the regulation of blood glucose

pancreatic islets   specialized clusters of pancreatic cells that have endocrine functions; also called islets of Langerhans

paracrine   chemical signal that elicits a response in neighboring cells; also called paracrine factor

parathyroid glands   small, round glands embedded in the posterior thyroid gland that produce parathyroid hormone (PTH)

parathyroid hormone (PTH)   peptide hormone produced and secreted by the parathyroid glands in response to low blood calcium levels

phosphodiesterase (PDE)   cytosolic enzyme that deactivates and degrades cAMP

phosphorylation cascade   signaling event in which multiple protein kinases phosphorylate the next protein substrate by transferring a phosphate group from ATP to the protein

pineal gland   endocrine gland that secretes melatonin, which is important in regulating the sleep-wake cycle

pinealocyte   cell of the pineal gland that produces and secretes the hormone melatonin

pituitary dwarfism   disorder in children caused when abnormally low levels of GH result in growth retardation

pituitary gland   bean-sized organ suspended from the hypothalamus that produces, stores, and secretes hormones in response to hypothalamic stimulation (also called hypophysis)

PP cell   minor cell type in the pancreas that secretes the hormone pancreatic polypeptide

progesterone   predominantly female sex hormone important in regulating the female reproductive cycle and the maintenance of pregnancy

prolactin (PRL)   anterior pituitary hormone that promotes development of the mammary glands and the production of breast milk

protein kinase   enzyme that initiates a phosphorylation cascade upon activation

second messenger   molecule that initiates a signaling cascade in response to hormone binding on a cell membrane receptor and activation of a G protein

stage of exhaustion   stage three of the general adaptation syndrome; the body's long-term response to stress mediated by the hormones of the adrenal cortex

stage of resistance   stage two of the general adaptation syndrome; the body's continued

response to stress after stage one diminishes

testosterone   steroid hormone secreted by the testes and important in the maturation of sperm cells, growth and development of the reproductive system, and the development of secondary sex characteristics

thymosins   hormones produced and secreted by the thymus that play an important role in the development and differentiation of T cells

thymus   organ that is involved in the development and maturation of T-cells and is particularly active during infancy and childhood

thyroid gland   large endocrine gland responsible for the synthesis of thyroid hormones

thyroid-stimulating hormone (TSH)   anterior pituitary hormone that triggers secretion of thyroid hormones by the thyroid gland (also called thyrotropin)

thyroxine   (also, tetraiodothyronine, T_4) amino acid–derived thyroid hormone that is more abundant but less potent than T_3 and often converted to T_3 by target cells

triiodothyronine   (also, T_3) amino acid–derived thyroid hormone that is less abundant but more potent than T_4

upregulation   increase in the number of hormone receptors, typically in response to chronically reduced levels of a hormone

zona fasciculata   intermediate region of the adrenal cortex that produce hormones called glucocorticoids

zona glomerulosa   most superficial region of the adrenal cortex, which produces the hormones collectively referred to as mineralocorticoids

zona reticularis   deepest region of the adrenal cortex, which produces the steroid sex hormones called androgens

Chapter Review

17.1 An Overview of the Endocrine System

The endocrine system consists of cells, tissues, and organs that secrete hormones critical to homeostasis. The body coordinates its functions through two major types of communication: neural and endocrine. Neural communication includes both electrical and chemical signaling between neurons and target cells. Endocrine communication involves chemical signaling via the release of hormones into the extracellular fluid. From there, hormones diffuse into the bloodstream and may travel to distant body regions, where they elicit a response in target cells. Endocrine glands are ductless glands that secrete hormones. Many organs of the body with other primary functions—such as the heart,

stomach, and kidneys—also have hormone-secreting cells.

17.2 Hormones

Hormones are derived from amino acids or lipids. Amine hormones originate from the amino acids tryptophan or tyrosine. Larger amino acid hormones include peptides and protein hormones. Steroid hormones are derived from cholesterol.

Steroid hormones and thyroid hormone are lipid soluble. All other amino acid–derived hormones are water soluble. Hydrophobic hormones are able to diffuse through the membrane and interact with an intracellular receptor. In contrast, hydrophilic hormones must interact with cell membrane receptors. These are typically associated with a G protein, which becomes activated when the hormone binds the receptor. This initiates a signaling cascade that involves a second messenger, such as cyclic adenosine monophosphate (cAMP). Second messenger systems greatly amplify the hormone signal, creating a broader, more efficient, and faster response.

Hormones are released upon stimulation that is of either chemical or neural origin. Regulation of hormone release is primarily achieved through negative feedback. Various stimuli may cause the release of hormones, but there are three major types. Humoral stimuli are changes in ion or nutrient levels in the blood. Hormonal stimuli are changes in hormone levels that initiate or inhibit the secretion of another hormone. Finally, a neural stimulus occurs when a nerve impulse prompts the secretion or inhibition of a hormone.

17.3 The Pituitary Gland and Hypothalamus

The hypothalamus–pituitary complex is located in the diencephalon of the brain. The hypothalamus and the pituitary gland are connected by a structure called the infundibulum, which contains vasculature and nerve axons. The pituitary gland is divided into two distinct structures with different embryonic origins. The posterior lobe houses the axon terminals of hypothalamic neurons. It stores and releases into the bloodstream two hypothalamic hormones: oxytocin and antidiuretic hormone (ADH). The anterior lobe is connected to the hypothalamus by vasculature in the infundibulum and produces and secretes six hormones. Their secretion is regulated, however, by releasing and inhibiting hormones from the hypothalamus. The six anterior pituitary hormones are: growth hormone (GH), thyroid-stimulating hormone (TSH), adrenocorticotropic hormone (ACTH), follicle-stimulating hormone (FSH), luteinizing hormone (LH), and prolactin (PRL).

17.4 The Thyroid Gland

The thyroid gland is a butterfly-shaped organ located in the neck anterior to the trachea. Its hormones regulate basal metabolism, oxygen use, nutrient metabolism, the production of ATP, and calcium homeostasis. They also contribute to protein synthesis and the normal growth and development of body tissues, including maturation of the nervous system, and they increase the body's sensitivity to catecholamines. The thyroid hormones triiodothyronine (T_3) and thyroxine (T_4) are produced and secreted by the thyroid gland in response to thyroid-stimulating hormone (TSH) from the anterior pituitary. Synthesis of the amino acid–derived T_3 and T_4 hormones requires iodine. Insufficient amounts of iodine in the diet can lead to goiter, cretinism, and many other disorders.

17.5 The Parathyroid Glands

Calcium is required for a variety of important physiologic processes, including neuromuscular functioning; thus, blood calcium levels are closely regulated. The parathyroid glands are small structures located on the posterior thyroid gland that produce parathyroid hormone (PTH), which regulates blood calcium levels. Low blood calcium levels cause the production and secretion of PTH. In contrast, elevated blood calcium levels inhibit secretion of PTH and trigger secretion of the thyroid hormone calcitonin. Underproduction of PTH can result in hypoparathyroidism. In contrast, overproduction of PTH can result in hyperparathyroidism.

17.6 The Adrenal Glands

The adrenal glands, located superior to each kidney, consist of two regions: the adrenal cortex and adrenal medulla. The adrenal cortex—the outer layer of the gland—produces mineralocorticoids, glucocorticoids, and androgens. The adrenal medulla at the core of the gland produces epinephrine and norepinephrine.

The adrenal glands mediate a short-term stress response and a long-term stress response. A perceived threat results in the secretion of epinephrine and norepinephrine from the adrenal medulla, which mediate the fight-or-flight response. The long-term stress response is mediated by the secretion of CRH from the hypothalamus, which triggers ACTH, which in turn stimulates the secretion of corticosteroids from the adrenal cortex. The mineralocorticoids, chiefly aldosterone, cause sodium and fluid retention, which increases blood volume and blood pressure.

17.7 The Pineal Gland

The pineal gland is an endocrine structure of the diencephalon of the brain, and is located inferior and posterior to the thalamus. It is made up of pinealocytes. These cells produce and secrete the hormone melatonin in response to low light levels. High blood levels of melatonin induce drowsiness. Jet lag, caused by traveling across several time zones, occurs because melatonin synthesis takes several days to readjust to the light-dark patterns in the new environment.

17.8 Gonadal and Placental Hormones

The reproductive system is regulated by follicle-stimulating hormone (FSH) and luteinizing hormone (LH) produced by the anterior lobe of the pituitary gland in response to gonadotropin-releasing hormone (GnRH) from the hypothalamus. FSH stimulates sperm maturation, which is inhibited by the hormone inhibin. The steroid hormone testosterone, a type of androgen, is released in response to LH and is responsible for the maturation and maintenance of the testicular reproductive system, as well as the development of secondary sex characteristics. FSH also promotes egg maturation and LH signals the secretion of the sex hormones, the estrogens and progesterone. Both of these hormones are important in the development and maintenance of the ovarian reproductive system, as well as maintaining pregnancy. The placenta develops during early pregnancy, and secretes several hormones important for maintaining the pregnancy.

17.9 The Endocrine Pancreas

The pancreas has both exocrine and endocrine functions. The pancreatic islet cell types include alpha cells, which produce glucagon; beta cells, which produce insulin; delta cells, which produce somatostatin; and PP cells, which produce pancreatic polypeptide. Insulin and glucagon are involved in the regulation of glucose metabolism. Insulin is produced by the beta cells in response to high blood glucose levels. It enhances glucose uptake and utilization by target cells, as well as the storage of excess glucose for later use. Dysfunction of the production of insulin or target cell resistance to the effects of insulin causes diabetes mellitus, a disorder characterized by high blood glucose levels. The hormone glucagon is produced and secreted by the alpha cells of the pancreas in response to low blood glucose levels. Glucagon stimulates mechanisms that increase blood glucose levels, such as the catabolism of glycogen into glucose.

17.10 Organs with Secondary Endocrine Functions

Some organs have a secondary endocrine function. For example, the walls of the atria of the heart produce the hormone atrial natriuretic peptide (ANP), the gastrointestinal tract produces the hormones gastrin, secretin, and cholecystokinin, which aid in digestion, and the kidneys produce erythropoietin (EPO), which stimulates the formation of red blood cells. Even bone, adipose tissue, and the skin have secondary endocrine functions.

17.11 Development and Aging of the Endocrine System

The endocrine system originates from all three germ layers of the embryo, including the endoderm, ectoderm, and mesoderm. In general, different hormone classes arise from distinct germ layers. Aging affects the endocrine glands, potentially affecting hormone production and secretion, and can cause disease. The production of hormones, such as human growth hormone, cortisol, aldosterone, sex hormones, and the thyroid hormones, decreases with age.

Interactive Link Questions

1. Visit this link (http://openstax.org/l/hormonebind) to watch an animation of the events that occur when a hormone binds to a cell membrane receptor. What is the secondary messenger made by adenylyl cyclase during the activation of liver cells by epinephrine?

2. Visit this link (http://openstax.org/l/roleofhypo) to watch an animation showing the role of the hypothalamus and the pituitary gland. Which hormone is released by the pituitary to stimulate the thyroid gland?

3. Visit this link (http://openstax.org/l/adrenalglands) to view an animation describing the location and function of the adrenal glands. Which hormone produced by the adrenal glands is responsible for mobilization of energy stores?

4. Visit this link (http://openstax.org/l/melatonin) to view an animation describing the function of the hormone melatonin. What should you avoid doing in the middle of your sleep cycle that would lower melatonin?

5. Visit this link (http://openstax.org/l/pancreas1) to view an animation describing the location and function of the pancreas. What goes wrong in the function of insulin in type 2 diabetes?

Review Questions

6. Endocrine glands _____.
   a. secrete hormones that travel through a duct to the target organs
   b. release neurotransmitters into the synaptic cleft
   c. secrete chemical messengers that travel in the bloodstream
   d. include sebaceous glands and sweat glands

7. Chemical signaling that affects neighboring cells is called _____.
   a. autocrine
   b. paracrine
   c. endocrine
   d. neuron

8. A newly developed pesticide has been observed to bind to an intracellular hormone receptor. If ingested, residue from this pesticide could disrupt levels of _____.
   a. melatonin
   b. thyroid hormone
   c. growth hormone
   d. insulin

9. A small molecule binds to a G protein, preventing its activation. What direct effect will this have on signaling that involves cAMP?
   a. The hormone will not be able to bind to the hormone receptor.
   b. Adenylyl cyclase will not be activated.
   c. Excessive quantities of cAMP will be produced.
   d. The phosphorylation cascade will be initiated.

10. A student is in a car accident, and although not hurt, immediately experiences pupil dilation, increased heart rate, and rapid breathing. What type of endocrine system stimulus did the student receive?
    a. humoral
    b. hormonal
    c. neural
    d. positive feedback

11. The hypothalamus is functionally and anatomically connected to the posterior pituitary lobe by a bridge of _____.
    a. blood vessels
    b. nerve axons
    c. cartilage
    d. bone

12. Which of the following is an anterior pituitary hormone?
    a. ADH
    b. oxytocin
    c. TSH
    d. cortisol

13. How many hormones are produced by the posterior pituitary?
    a. 0
    b. 1
    c. 2
    d. 6

14. Which of the following hormones contributes to the regulation of the body's fluid and electrolyte balance?
    a. adrenocorticotropic hormone
    b. antidiuretic hormone
    c. luteinizing hormone
    d. all of the above

15. Which of the following statements about the thyroid gland is true?
    a. It is located anterior to the trachea and inferior to the larynx.
    b. The parathyroid glands are embedded within it.
    c. It manufactures three hormones.
    d. all of the above

16. The secretion of thyroid hormones is controlled by _____.
    a. TSH from the hypothalamus
    b. TSH from the anterior pituitary
    c. thyroxine from the anterior pituitary
    d. thyroglobulin from the thyroid's parafollicular cells

17. The development of a goiter indicates that _____.
    a. the anterior pituitary is abnormally enlarged
    b. there is hypertrophy of the thyroid's follicle cells
    c. there is an excessive accumulation of colloid in the thyroid follicles
    d. the anterior pituitary is secreting excessive growth hormone

18. Iodide ions cross from the bloodstream into follicle cells via _____.
    a. simple diffusion
    b. facilitated diffusion
    c. active transport
    d. osmosis

19. When blood calcium levels are low, PTH stimulates _____.
    a. urinary excretion of calcium by the kidneys
    b. a reduction in calcium absorption from the intestines
    c. the activity of osteoblasts
    d. the activity of osteoclasts

20. Which of the following can result from hyperparathyroidism?
    a. increased bone deposition
    b. fractures
    c. convulsions
    d. all of the above

21. The adrenal glands are attached superiorly to which organ?
    a. thyroid
    b. liver
    c. kidneys
    d. hypothalamus

22. What secretory cell type is found in the adrenal medulla?
    a. chromaffin cells
    b. neuroglial cells
    c. follicle cells
    d. oxyphil cells

23. Cushing's disease is a disorder caused by _____.
    a. abnormally low levels of cortisol
    b. abnormally high levels of cortisol
    c. abnormally low levels of aldosterone
    d. abnormally high levels of aldosterone

24. Which of the following responses s not part of the fight-or-flight response?
    a. pupil dilation
    b. increased oxygen supply to the lungs
    c. suppressed digestion
    d. reduced mental activity

25. What cells secrete melatonin?
    a. melanocytes
    b. pinealocytes
    c. suprachiasmatic nucleus cells
    d. retinal cells

26. The production of melatonin is inhibited by _____.
    a. declining levels of light
    b. exposure to bright light
    c. the secretion of serotonin
    d. the activity of pinealocytes

27. The gonads produce what class of hormones?
    a. amine hormones
    b. peptide hormones
    c. steroid hormones
    d. catecholamines

28. The production of FSH by the anterior pituitary is reduced by which hormone?
    a. estrogens
    b. progesterone
    c. relaxin
    d. inhibin

29. The function of the placental hormone human placental lactogen (hPL) is to _____.
    a. prepare the breasts for lactation
    b. nourish the placenta
    c. regulate the menstrual cycle
    d. all of the above

30. If an autoimmune disorder targets the alpha cells, production of which hormone would be directly affected?
    a. somatostatin
    b. pancreatic polypeptide
    c. insulin
    d. glucagon

31. Which of the following statements about insulin is true?
    a. Insulin acts as a transport protein, carrying glucose across the cell membrane.
    b. Insulin facilitates the movement of intracellular glucose transporters to the cell membrane.
    c. Insulin stimulates the breakdown of stored glycogen into glucose.
    d. Insulin stimulates the kidneys to reabsorb glucose into the bloodstream.

32. The walls of the atria produce which hormone?
    a. cholecystokinin
    b. atrial natriuretic peptide
    c. renin
    d. calcitriol

33. The end result of the RAAS is to _____.
    a. reduce blood volume
    b. increase blood glucose
    c. reduce blood pressure
    d. increase blood pressure

34. Athletes may take synthetic EPO to boost their _____.
    a. blood calcium levels
    b. secretion of growth hormone
    c. blood oxygen levels
    d. muscle mass

35. Hormones produced by the thymus play a role in the _____.
    a. development of T cells
    b. preparation of the body for childbirth
    c. regulation of appetite
    d. release of hydrochloric acid in the stomach

36. The anterior pituitary gland develops from which embryonic germ layer?
    a. oral ectoderm
    b. neural ectoderm
    c. mesoderm
    d. endoderm

37. In the elderly, decreased thyroid function causes _____.
    a. increased tolerance for cold
    b. decreased basal metabolic rate
    c. decreased body fat
    d. osteoporosis

Critical Thinking Questions

38. Describe several main differences in the communication methods used by the endocrine system and the nervous system.
39. Compare and contrast endocrine and exocrine glands.
40. True or false: Neurotransmitters are a special class of paracrines. Explain your answer.
41. Compare and contrast the signaling events involved with the second messengers cAMP and IP$_3$.
42. Describe the mechanism of hormone response resulting from the binding of a hormone with an intracellular receptor.
43. Compare and contrast the anatomical relationship of the anterior and posterior lobes of the pituitary gland to the hypothalamus.
44. Name the target tissues for prolactin.
45. Explain why maternal iodine deficiency might lead to neurological impairment in the fetus.
46. Define hyperthyroidism and explain why one of its symptoms is weight loss.
47. Describe the role of negative feedback in the function of the parathyroid gland.
48. Explain why someone with a parathyroid gland tumor might develop kidney stones.
49. What are the three regions of the adrenal cortex and what hormones do they produce?
50. If innervation to the adrenal medulla were disrupted, what would be the physiological outcome?
51. Compare and contrast the short-term and long-term stress response.
52. Seasonal affective disorder (SAD) is a mood disorder characterized by, among other symptoms, increased appetite, sluggishness, and increased sleepiness. It occurs most commonly during the winter months, especially in regions with long winter nights. Propose a role for melatonin in SAD and a possible non-drug therapy.
53. Retinitis pigmentosa (RP) is a disease that causes deterioration of the retinas of the eyes. Describe the impact RP would have on melatonin levels.
54. Compare and contrast the role of estrogens and progesterone.
55. Describe the role of placental secretion of relaxin in preparation for childbirth.
56. What would be the physiological consequence of a disease that destroyed the beta cells of the pancreas?
57. Why is foot care extremely important for people with diabetes mellitus?
58. Summarize the role of GI tract hormones following a meal.
59. Compare and contrast the thymus gland in infancy and adulthood.
60. Distinguish between the effects of menopause and andropause on fertility.

CHAPTER 18
The Cardiovascular System: Blood

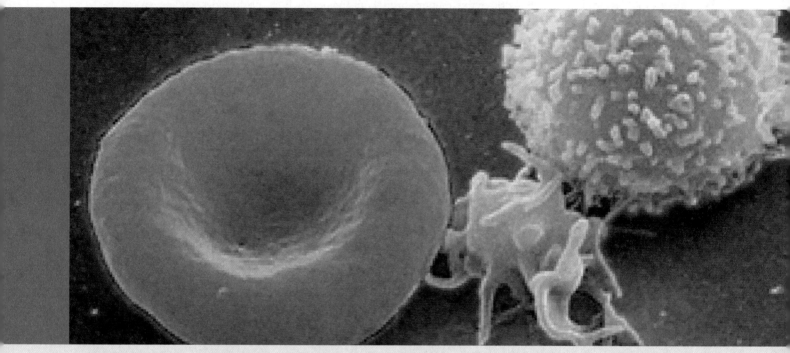

Figure 18.1 **Blood Cells** A single drop of blood contains millions of red blood cells, white blood cells, and platelets. One of each type is shown here, isolated from a scanning electron micrograph.

CHAPTER OBJECTIVES

After studying this chapter, you will be able to:

- Identify the primary functions of blood, its fluid and cellular components, and its physical characteristics
- Identify the most important proteins and other solutes present in blood plasma
- Describe the formation of the formed element components of blood
- Discuss the structure and function of red blood cells and hemoglobin
- Classify and characterize white blood cells
- Describe the structure of platelets and explain the process of hemostasis
- Explain the significance of AB and Rh blood groups in blood transfusions
- Discuss a variety of blood disorders

INTRODUCTION Single-celled organisms do not need blood. They obtain nutrients directly from and excrete wastes directly into their environment. The human organism cannot do that. Our large, complex bodies need blood to deliver nutrients to and remove wastes from our trillions of cells. The heart pumps blood throughout the body in a network of blood vessels. Together, these three components—blood, heart, and vessels—makes up the cardiovascular system. This chapter focuses on the medium of transport: blood.

18.1 An Overview of Blood

LEARNING OBJECTIVES

By the end of this section, you will be able to:

- Identify the primary functions of blood in transportation, defense, and maintenance of homeostasis
- Name the fluid component of blood and the three major types of formed elements, and identify their relative proportions in a blood sample
- Discuss the unique physical characteristics of blood
- Identify the composition of blood plasma, including its most important solutes and plasma proteins

Recall that **blood** is a connective tissue. Like all connective tissues, it is made up of cellular elements and an extracellular matrix. The cellular elements—referred to as the **formed elements**—include **red blood cells (RBCs)**, **white blood cells (WBCs)**, and cell fragments called **platelets**. The extracellular matrix, called **plasma**, makes blood unique among connective tissues because it is fluid. This fluid, which is mostly water, perpetually suspends the formed elements and enables them to circulate throughout the body within the cardiovascular system.

Functions of Blood

The primary function of blood is to deliver oxygen and nutrients to and remove wastes from body cells, but that is only the beginning of the story. The specific functions of blood also include defense, distribution of heat, and maintenance of homeostasis.

Transportation

Nutrients from the foods you eat are absorbed in the digestive tract. Most of these travel in the bloodstream directly to the liver, where they are processed and released back into the bloodstream for delivery to body cells. Oxygen from the air you breathe diffuses into the blood, which moves from the lungs to the heart, which then pumps it out to the rest of the body. Moreover, endocrine glands scattered throughout the body release their products, called hormones, into the bloodstream, which carries them to distant target cells. Blood also picks up cellular wastes and byproducts, and transports them to various organs for removal. For instance, blood moves carbon dioxide to the lungs for exhalation from the body, and various waste products are transported to the kidneys and liver for excretion from the body in the form of urine or bile.

Defense

Many types of WBCs protect the body from external threats, such as disease-causing bacteria that have entered the bloodstream in a wound. Other WBCs seek out and destroy internal threats, such as cells with mutated DNA that could multiply to become cancerous, or body cells infected with viruses.

When damage to the vessels results in bleeding, blood platelets and certain proteins dissolved in the plasma, the fluid portion of the blood, interact to block the ruptured areas of the blood vessels involved. This protects the body from further blood loss.

Maintenance of Homeostasis

Recall that body temperature is regulated via a classic negative-feedback loop. If you were exercising on a warm day, your rising core body temperature would trigger several homeostatic mechanisms, including increased transport of blood from your core to your body periphery, which is typically cooler. As blood passes through the vessels of the skin, heat would be dissipated to the environment, and the blood returning to your body core would be cooler. In contrast, on a cold day, blood is diverted away from the skin to maintain a warmer body core. In extreme cases, this may result in frostbite.

Blood also helps to maintain the chemical balance of the body. Proteins and other compounds in blood act as buffers, which thereby help to regulate the pH of body tissues. Blood also helps to regulate the water content of body cells.

Composition of Blood

You have probably had blood drawn from a superficial vein in your arm, which was then sent to a lab for analysis. Some of the most common blood tests—for instance, those measuring lipid or glucose levels in plasma—determine which substances are present within blood and in what quantities. Other blood tests check for the composition of the blood itself, including the quantities and types of formed elements.

One such test, called a **hematocrit**, measures the percentage of RBCs, clinically known as erythrocytes, in a blood sample. It is performed by spinning the blood sample in a specialized centrifuge, a process that causes the heavier elements suspended within the blood sample to separate from the lightweight, liquid plasma (Figure 18.2). Because the heaviest elements in blood are the erythrocytes, these settle at the very bottom of the hematocrit tube. Located above the erythrocytes is a pale, thin layer composed of the remaining formed elements of blood. These are the WBCs, clinically known as leukocytes, and the platelets, cell fragments also called thrombocytes. This layer is referred to as the **buffy coat** because of its color; it normally constitutes less than 1 percent of a blood sample. Above the buffy coat is the blood plasma, normally a pale, straw-colored fluid, which constitutes the remainder of the sample.

The volume of erythrocytes after centrifugation is also commonly referred to as **packed cell volume (PCV)**. In normal blood, about 45 percent of a sample is erythrocytes. The hematocrit of any one sample can vary significantly, however, about 36–50 percent, according to gender and other factors. Normal hematocrit values for females range from 37 to 47, with a mean value of 41; for males, hematocrit ranges from 42 to 52, with a mean of 47. The percentage of other formed elements, the WBCs and platelets, is extremely small so it is not normally considered with the hematocrit. So the mean plasma percentage is the percent of blood that is not erythrocytes: for females, it is approximately 59 (or 100 minus 41), and for males, it is approximately 53 (or 100 minus 47).

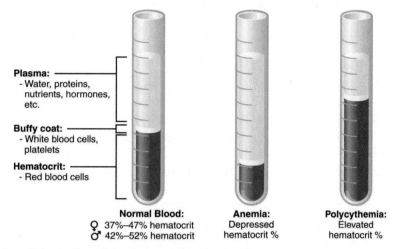

FIGURE 18.2   Composition of Blood   The cellular elements of blood include a vast number of erythrocytes and comparatively fewer leukocytes and platelets. Plasma is the fluid in which the formed elements are suspended. A sample of blood spun in a centrifuge reveals that plasma is the lightest component. It floats at the top of the tube separated from the heaviest elements, the erythrocytes, by a buffy coat of leukocytes and platelets. Hematocrit is the percentage of the total sample that is comprised of erythrocytes. Depressed and elevated hematocrit levels are shown for comparison.

Characteristics of Blood

When you think about blood, the first characteristic that probably comes to mind is its color. Blood that has just taken up oxygen in the lungs is bright red, and blood that has released oxygen in the tissues is a more dusky red. This is because hemoglobin is a pigment that changes color, depending upon the degree of oxygen saturation.

Blood is viscous and somewhat sticky to the touch. It has a viscosity approximately five times greater than water. Viscosity is a measure of a fluid's thickness or resistance to flow, and is influenced by the presence of the plasma proteins and formed elements within the blood. The viscosity of blood has a dramatic impact on blood pressure and flow. Consider the difference in flow between water and honey. The more viscous honey would demonstrate a greater resistance to flow than the less viscous water. The same principle applies to blood.

The normal temperature of blood is slightly higher than normal body temperature—about 38 °C (or 100.4 °F), compared to 37 °C (or 98.6 °F) for an internal body temperature reading, although daily variations of 0.5 °C are normal. Although the surface of blood vessels is relatively smooth, as blood flows through them, it experiences some friction and resistance, especially as vessels age and lose their elasticity, thereby producing heat. This accounts for its slightly higher temperature.

The pH of blood averages about 7.4; however, it can range from 7.35 to 7.45 in a healthy person. Blood is therefore somewhat more basic (alkaline) on a chemical scale than pure water, which has a pH of 7.0. Blood contains numerous buffers that actually help to regulate pH.

Blood constitutes approximately 8 percent of adult body weight. Adult males typically average about 5 to 6 liters of blood. Females average 4–5 liters.

Blood Plasma

Like other fluids in the body, plasma is composed primarily of water: In fact, it is about 92 percent water. Dissolved or suspended within this water is a mixture of substances, most of which are proteins. There are literally hundreds of substances dissolved or suspended in the plasma, although many of them are found only in very small quantities.

⊘ INTERACTIVE LINK

Visit this site (http://openstax.org/l/normallevels) for a list of normal levels established for many of the substances found in a sample of blood. Serum, one of the specimen types included, refers to a sample of plasma after clotting factors have been removed. What types of measurements are given for levels of glucose in the blood?

Plasma Proteins

About 7 percent of the volume of plasma—nearly all that is not water—is made of proteins. These include several plasma proteins (proteins that are unique to the plasma), plus a much smaller number of regulatory proteins, including enzymes and some hormones. The major components of plasma are summarized in Figure 18.3.

The three major groups of plasma proteins are as follows:

- **Albumin** is the most abundant of the plasma proteins. Manufactured by the liver, albumin molecules serve as binding proteins—transport vehicles for fatty acids and steroid hormones. Recall that lipids are hydrophobic; however, their binding to albumin enables their transport in the watery plasma. Albumin is also the most significant contributor to the osmotic pressure of blood; that is, its presence holds water inside the blood vessels and draws water from the tissues, across blood vessel walls, and into the bloodstream. This in turn helps to maintain both blood volume and blood pressure. Albumin normally accounts for approximately 54 percent of the total plasma protein content, in clinical levels of 3.5–5.0 g/dL blood.
- The second most common plasma proteins are the **globulins**. A heterogeneous group, there are three main subgroups known as alpha, beta, and gamma globulins. The alpha and beta globulins transport iron, lipids, and the fat-soluble vitamins A, D, E, and K to the cells; like albumin, they also contribute to osmotic pressure. The gamma globulins are proteins involved in immunity and are better known as an **antibodies** or **immunoglobulins**. Although other plasma proteins are produced by the liver, immunoglobulins are produced by specialized leukocytes known as plasma cells. (Seek additional content for more information about immunoglobulins.) Globulins make up approximately 38 percent of the total plasma protein volume, in clinical levels of 1.0–1.5 g/dL blood.
- **Fibrinogen** is the third of the three major groups of plasma proteins. Like albumin and the alpha and beta globulins, fibrinogen is produced by the liver. It is essential for blood clotting, a process described later in this chapter. Fibrinogen accounts for about 7 percent of the total plasma protein volume, in clinical levels of 0.2–0.45 g/dL blood.

Other Plasma Solutes

In addition to proteins, plasma contains a wide variety of other substances. These include various electrolytes, such as sodium, potassium, and calcium ions; dissolved gases, such as oxygen, carbon dioxide, and nitrogen; various organic nutrients, such as vitamins, lipids, glucose, and amino acids; and metabolic wastes. All of these nonprotein solutes combined contribute approximately 1 percent to the total volume of plasma.

Component and % of blood	Subcomponent and % of component	Type and % (where appropriate)	Site of production	Major function(s)
Plasma 46–63 percent	Water 92 percent	Fluid	Absorbed by intestinal tract or produced by metabolism	Transport medium
	Plasma proteins 7 percent	Albumin 54–60 percent	Liver	Maintain osmotic concentration, transport lipid molecules
		Globulins 35–38 percent	Alpha globulins— liver	Transport, maintain osmotic concentration
			Beta globulins— liver	Transport, maintain osmotic concentration
			Gamma globulins (immunoglobulins) —plasma cells	Immune responses
		Fibrinogen 4–7 percent	Liver	Blood clotting in hemostasis
	Regulatory proteins <1 percent	Hormones and enzymes	Various sources	Regulate various body functions
	Other solutes 1 percent	Nutrients, gases, and wastes	Absorbed by intestinal tract, exchanged in respiratory system, or produced by cells	Numerous and varied
Formed elements 37–54 percent	Erythrocytes 99 percent	Erythrocytes	Red bone marrow	Transport gases, primarily oxygen and some carbon dioxide
	Leukocytes <1 percent Platelets <1 percent	Granular leukocytes: neutrophils eosinophils basophils	Red bone marrow	Nonspecific immunity
		Agranular leukocytes: lymphocytes monocytes	Lymphocytes: bone marrow and lymphatic tissue	Lymphocytes: specific immunity
			Monocytes: red bone marrow	Monocytes: nonspecific immunity
	Platelets <1 percent		Megakaryocytes: red bone marrow	Hemostasis

FIGURE 18.3   Major Blood Components

 CAREER CONNECTION

Phlebotomy and Medical Lab Technology

Phlebotomists are professionals trained to draw blood (phleb- = "a blood vessel"; -tomy = "to cut"). When more than a few drops of blood are required, phlebotomists perform a venipuncture, typically of a surface vein in the arm. They perform a capillary stick on a finger, an earlobe, or the heel of an infant when only a small quantity of blood is required. An arterial stick is collected from an artery and used to analyze blood gases. After collection, the blood may be analyzed by medical laboratories or perhaps used for transfusions, donations, or research. While many allied health professionals practice phlebotomy, the American Society of Phlebotomy Technicians issues certificates to individuals passing a national examination, and some large labs and hospitals hire individuals expressly for their skill in phlebotomy.

Medical or clinical laboratories employ a variety of individuals in technical positions:

- Medical technologists (MT), also known as clinical laboratory technologists (CLT), typically hold a bachelor's degree and certification from an accredited training program. They perform a wide variety of tests on various body fluids, including blood. The information they provide is essential to the primary care providers in determining a diagnosis and in monitoring the course of a disease and response to treatment.
- Medical laboratory technicians (MLT) typically have an associate's degree but may perform duties similar to those of an MT.
- Medical laboratory assistants (MLA) spend the majority of their time processing samples and carrying out routine assignments within the lab. Clinical training is required, but a degree may not be essential to obtaining a position.

18.2 Production of the Formed Elements

LEARNING OBJECTIVES

By the end of this section, you will be able to:

- Trace the generation of the formed elements of blood from bone marrow stem cells
- Discuss the role of hemopoietic growth factors in promoting the production of the formed elements

The lifespan of the formed elements is very brief. Although one type of leukocyte called memory cells can survive for years, most erythrocytes, leukocytes, and platelets normally live only a few hours to a few weeks. Thus, the body must form new blood cells and platelets quickly and continuously. When you donate a unit of blood during a blood drive (approximately 475 mL, or about 1 pint), your body typically replaces the donated plasma within 24 hours, but it takes about 4 to 6 weeks to replace the blood cells. This restricts the frequency with which donors can contribute their blood. The process by which this replacement occurs is called **hemopoiesis**, or hematopoiesis (from the Greek root haima- = "blood"; -poiesis = "production").

Sites of Hemopoiesis

Prior to birth, hemopoiesis occurs in a number of tissues, beginning with the yolk sac of the developing embryo, and continuing in the fetal liver, spleen, lymphatic tissue, and eventually the red bone marrow. Following birth, most hemopoiesis occurs in the red marrow, a connective tissue within the spaces of spongy (cancellous) bone tissue. In children, hemopoiesis can occur in the medullary cavity of long bones; in adults, the process is largely restricted to the cranial and pelvic bones, the vertebrae, the sternum, and the proximal epiphyses of the femur and humerus.

Throughout adulthood, the liver and spleen maintain their ability to generate the formed elements. This process is referred to as extramedullary hemopoiesis (meaning hemopoiesis outside the medullary cavity of adult bones). When a disease such as bone cancer destroys the bone marrow, causing hemopoiesis to fail, extramedullary hemopoiesis may be initiated.

Differentiation of Formed Elements from Stem Cells

All formed elements arise from stem cells of the red bone marrow. Recall that stem cells undergo mitosis plus cytokinesis (cellular division) to give rise to new daughter cells: One of these remains a stem cell and the other differentiates into one of any number of diverse cell types. Stem cells may be viewed as occupying a hierarchal system, with some loss of the ability to diversify at each step. The **totipotent stem cell** is the zygote, or fertilized egg. The totipotent (toti- = "all") stem cell gives rise to all cells of the human body. The next level is the **pluripotent stem cell**, which gives rise to multiple types of cells of the body and some of the supporting fetal membranes. Beneath this level, the mesenchymal cell is a stem cell that develops only into types of connective tissue, including fibrous connective tissue, bone, cartilage, and blood, but not epithelium, muscle, and nervous tissue. One step lower on the hierarchy of stem cells is the **hematopoietic stem cell**, or **hemocytoblast**. All of the formed elements of blood originate from this specific type of cell.

Hemopoiesis begins when the hematopoietic stem cell is exposed to appropriate chemical stimuli collectively called **hemopoietic growth factors**, which prompt it to divide and differentiate. One daughter cell remains a hematopoietic stem cell, allowing hemopoiesis to continue. The other daughter cell becomes either of two types of more specialized stem cells (Figure 18.4):

- **Lymphoid stem cells** give rise to a class of leukocytes known as lymphocytes, which include the various T cells, B cells, and natural killer (NK) cells, all of which function in immunity. However, hemopoiesis of lymphocytes progresses somewhat differently from the process for the other formed elements. In brief, lymphoid stem cells quickly migrate from the bone marrow to lymphatic tissues, including the lymph nodes, spleen, and thymus, where their production and differentiation continues. B cells are so named since they mature in the bone marrow, while T cells mature in the thymus.
- **Myeloid stem cells** give rise to all the other formed elements, including the erythrocytes; megakaryocytes that produce platelets; and a myeloblast lineage that gives rise to monocytes and three forms of granular leukocytes: neutrophils, eosinophils, and basophils.

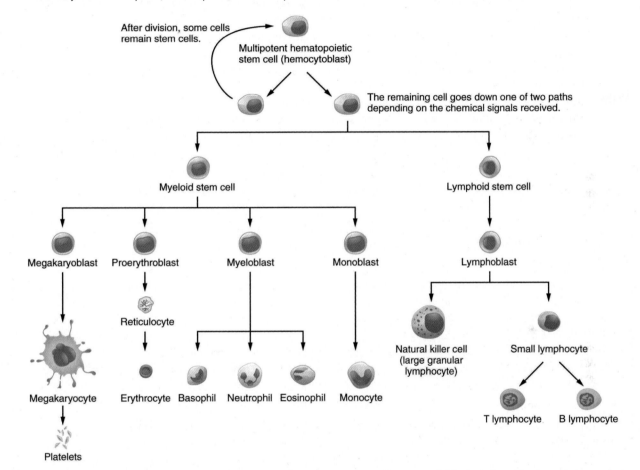

FIGURE 18.4   Hematopoietic System of Bone Marrow   Hemopoiesis is the proliferation and differentiation of the formed elements of blood.

Lymphoid and myeloid stem cells do not immediately divide and differentiate into mature formed elements. As you can see in Figure 18.4, there are several intermediate stages of precursor cells (literally, forerunner cells), many of which can be recognized by their names, which have the suffix -blast. For instance, megakaryoblasts are the precursors of megakaryocytes, and proerythroblasts become reticulocytes, which eject their nucleus and most other organelles before maturing into erythrocytes.

Hemopoietic Growth Factors

Development from stem cells to precursor cells to mature cells is again initiated by hemopoietic growth factors. These include the following:

- **Erythropoietin (EPO)** is a glycoprotein hormone secreted by the interstitial fibroblast cells of the kidneys in response to low oxygen levels. It prompts the production of erythrocytes. Some athletes use synthetic EPO as a performance-enhancing drug (called blood doping) to increase RBC counts and subsequently increase oxygen delivery to tissues throughout the body. EPO is a banned substance in most organized sports, but it is also used medically in the treatment of certain anemia, specifically those triggered by certain types of cancer, and other disorders in which increased erythrocyte counts and oxygen levels are desirable.

- **Thrombopoietin**, another glycoprotein hormone, is produced by the liver and kidneys. It triggers the development of megakaryocytes into platelets.
- **Cytokines** are glycoproteins secreted by a wide variety of cells, including red bone marrow, leukocytes, macrophages, fibroblasts, and endothelial cells. They act locally as autocrine or paracrine factors, stimulating the proliferation of progenitor cells and helping to stimulate both nonspecific and specific resistance to disease. There are two major subtypes of cytokines known as colony-stimulating factors and interleukins.
  - ◦ **Colony-stimulating factors (CSFs)** are glycoproteins that act locally, as autocrine or paracrine factors. Some trigger the differentiation of myeloblasts into granular leukocytes, namely, neutrophils, eosinophils, and basophils. These are referred to as granulocyte CSFs. A different CSF induces the production of monocytes, called monocyte CSFs. Both granulocytes and monocytes are stimulated by GM-CSF; granulocytes, monocytes, platelets, and erythrocytes are stimulated by multi-CSF. Synthetic forms of these hormones are often administered to patients with various forms of cancer who are receiving chemotherapy to revive their WBC counts.
  - ◦ **Interleukins** are another class of cytokine signaling molecules important in hemopoiesis. They were initially thought to be secreted uniquely by leukocytes and to communicate only with other leukocytes, and were named accordingly, but are now known to be produced by a variety of cells including bone marrow and endothelium. Researchers now suspect that interleukins may play other roles in body functioning, including differentiation and maturation of cells, producing immunity and inflammation. To date, more than a dozen interleukins have been identified, with others likely to follow. They are generally numbered IL-1, IL-2, IL-3, etc.

Everyday Connection

Blood Doping

In its original intent, the term blood doping was used to describe the practice of injecting by transfusion supplemental RBCs into an individual, typically to enhance performance in a sport. Additional RBCs would deliver more oxygen to the tissues, providing extra aerobic capacity, clinically referred to as VO_2 max. The source of the cells was either from the recipient (autologous) or from a donor with compatible blood (homologous). This practice was aided by the well-developed techniques of harvesting, concentrating, and freezing of the RBCs that could be later thawed and injected, yet still retain their functionality. These practices are considered illegal in virtually all sports and run the risk of infection, significantly increasing the viscosity of the blood and the potential for transmission of blood-borne pathogens if the blood was collected from another individual.

With the development of synthetic EPO in the 1980s, it became possible to provide additional RBCs by artificially stimulating RBC production in the bone marrow. Originally developed to treat patients suffering from anemia, renal failure, or cancer treatment, large quantities of EPO can be generated by recombinant DNA technology. Synthetic EPO is injected under the skin and can increase hematocrit for many weeks. It may also induce polycythemia and raise hematocrit to 70 or greater. This increased viscosity raises the resistance of the blood and forces the heart to pump more powerfully; in extreme cases, it has resulted in death. Other drugs such as cobalt II chloride have been shown to increase natural EPO gene expression. Blood doping has become problematic in many sports, especially cycling. Lance Armstrong, winner of seven Tour de France and many other cycling titles, was stripped of his victories and admitted to blood doping in 2013.

⊘ INTERACTIVE LINK

Watch this video (http://openstax.org/l/doping) to see doctors discuss the dangers of blood doping in sports. What are the some potential side effects of blood doping?

Bone Marrow Sampling and Transplants

Sometimes, a healthcare provider will order a **bone marrow biopsy**, a diagnostic test of a sample of red bone marrow, or a **bone marrow transplant**, a treatment in which a donor's healthy bone marrow—and its stem cells—replaces the faulty bone marrow of a patient. These tests and procedures are often used to assist in the diagnosis and treatment of various severe forms of anemia, such as thalassemia major and sickle cell anemia, as well as some types of cancer, specifically leukemia.

In the past, when a bone marrow sample or transplant was necessary, the procedure would have required inserting a large-bore needle into the region near the iliac crest of the pelvic bones (os coxae). This location was preferred, since its location close to the body surface makes it more accessible, and it is relatively isolated from most vital organs. Unfortunately, the procedure is quite painful.

Now, direct sampling of bone marrow can often be avoided. In many cases, stem cells can be isolated in just a few hours from a sample of a patient's blood. The isolated stem cells are then grown in culture using the appropriate hemopoietic growth factors, and analyzed or sometimes frozen for later use.

For an individual requiring a transplant, a matching donor is essential to prevent the immune system from destroying the donor cells—a phenomenon known as tissue rejection. To treat patients with bone marrow transplants, it is first necessary to destroy the patient's own diseased marrow through radiation and/or chemotherapy. Donor bone marrow stem cells are then intravenously infused. From the bloodstream, they establish themselves in the recipient's bone marrow.

18.3 Erythrocytes

LEARNING OBJECTIVES

By the end of this section, you will be able to:

- Describe the anatomy of erythrocytes
- Discuss the various steps in the lifecycle of an erythrocyte
- Explain the composition and function of hemoglobin

The **erythrocyte**, commonly known as a red blood cell (or RBC), is by far the most common formed element: A single drop of blood contains millions of erythrocytes and just thousands of leukocytes. Specifically, males have about 5.4 million erythrocytes per microliter (μL) of blood, and females have approximately 4.8 million per μL. In fact, erythrocytes are estimated to make up about 25 percent of the total cells in the body. As you can imagine, they are quite small cells, with a mean diameter of only about 7–8 micrometers (μm) (Figure 18.5). The primary functions of erythrocytes are to pick up inhaled oxygen from the lungs and transport it to the body's tissues, and to pick up some (about 24 percent) carbon dioxide waste at the tissues and transport it to the lungs for exhalation. Erythrocytes remain within the vascular network. Although leukocytes typically leave the blood vessels to perform their defensive functions, movement of erythrocytes from the blood vessels is abnormal.

Formed element	Major subtypes	Numbers present per microliter (μL) and mean (range)	Appearance in a standard blood smear	Summary of functions	Comments
Erythrocytes (red blood cells)		5.2 million (4.4–6.0 million)	Flattened biconcave disk; no nucleus; pale red color	Transport oxygen and some carbon dioxide between tissues and lungs	Lifespan of approximately 120 days
Leukocytes (white blood cells)		7000 (5000–10,000)	Obvious dark-staining nucleus	All function in body defenses	Exit capillaries and move into tissues; lifespan of usually a few hours or days
	Granulocytes including neutrophils, eosinophils, and basophils	4360 (1800–9950)	Abundant granules in cytoplasm; nucleus normally lobed	Nonspecific (innate) resistance to disease	Classified according to membrane-bound granules in cytoplasm
	Neutrophils	4150 (1800–7300)	Nuclear lobes increase with age; pale lilac granules	Phagocytic; particularly effective against bacteria. Release cytotoxic chemicals from granules	Most common leukocyte; lifespan of minutes to days
	Eosinophils	165 (0–700)	Nucleus generally two-lobed; bright red-orange granules	Phagocytic cells; particularly effective with antigen- antibody complexes. Release antihistamines. Increase in allergies and parasitic infections	Lifespan of minutes to days
	Basophils	44 (0–150)	Nucleus generally two-lobed but difficult to see due to presence of heavy, dense, dark purple granules	Promotes inflammation	Least common leukocyte; lifespan unknown
	Agranulocytes including lymphocytes and monocytes	2640 (1700–4950)	Lack abundant granules in cytoplasm; have a simple-shaped nucleus that may be indented	Body defenses	Group consists of two major cell types from different lineages
	Lymphocytes	2185 (1500–4000)	Spherical cells with a single often large nucleus occupying much of the cell's volume; stains purple; seen in large (natural killer cells) and small (B and T cells) variants	Primarily specific (adaptive) immunity: T cells directly attack other cells (cellular immunity); B cells release antibodies (humoral immunity); natural killer cells are similar to T cells but nonspecific	Initial cells originate in bone marrow, but secondary production occurs in lymphatic tissue; several distinct subtypes; memory cells form after exposure to a pathogen and rapidly increase responses to subsequent exposure; lifespan of many years
	Monocytes	455 (200–950)	Largest leukocyte with an indented or horseshoe-shaped nucleus	Very effective phagocytic cells engulfing pathogens or worn out cells; also serve as antigen-presenting cells (APCs) for other components of the immune system	Produced in red bone marrow; referred to as macrophages after leaving circulation
Platelets		350,000 (150,000–500,000)	Cellular fragments surrounded by a plasma membrane and containing granules; purple stain	Hemostasis plus release growth factors for repair and healing of tissue	Formed from megakaryocytes that remain in the red bone marrow and shed platelets into circulation

Access for free at openstax.org

FIGURE 18.5   **Summary of Formed Elements in Blood**

Shape and Structure of Erythrocytes

As an erythrocyte matures in the red bone marrow, it extrudes its nucleus and most of its other organelles. During the first day or two that it is in the circulation, an immature erythrocyte, known as a **reticulocyte**, will still typically contain remnants of organelles. Reticulocytes should comprise approximately 1–2 percent of the erythrocyte count and provide a rough estimate of the rate of RBC production, with abnormally low or high rates indicating deviations in the production of these cells. These remnants, primarily of networks (reticulum) of ribosomes, are quickly shed, however, and mature, circulating erythrocytes have few internal cellular structural components. Lacking mitochondria, for example, they rely on anaerobic respiration. This means that they do not utilize any of the oxygen they are transporting, so they can deliver it all to the tissues. They also lack endoplasmic reticula and do not synthesize proteins. Erythrocytes do, however, contain some structural proteins that help the blood cells maintain their unique structure and enable them to change their shape to squeeze through capillaries. This includes the protein spectrin, a cytoskeletal protein element.

Erythrocytes are biconcave disks; that is, they are plump at their periphery and very thin in the center (Figure 18.6). Since they lack most organelles, there is more interior space for the presence of the hemoglobin molecules that, as you will see shortly, transport gases. The biconcave shape also provides a greater surface area across which gas exchange can occur, relative to its volume; a sphere of a similar diameter would have a lower surface area-to-volume ratio. In the capillaries, the oxygen carried by the erythrocytes can diffuse into the plasma and then through the capillary walls to reach the cells, whereas some of the carbon dioxide produced by the cells as a waste product diffuses into the capillaries to be picked up by the erythrocytes. Capillary beds are extremely narrow, slowing the passage of the erythrocytes and providing an extended opportunity for gas exchange to occur. However, the space within capillaries can be so minute that, despite their own small size, erythrocytes may have to fold in on themselves if they are to make their way through. Fortunately, their structural proteins like spectrin are flexible, allowing them to bend over themselves to a surprising degree, then spring back again when they enter a wider vessel. In wider vessels, erythrocytes may stack up much like a roll of coins, forming a rouleaux, from the French word for "roll."

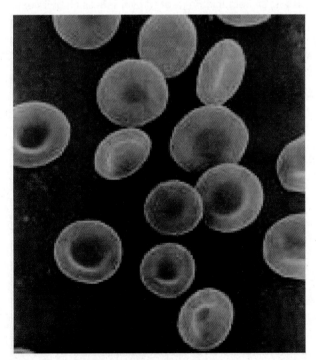

FIGURE 18.6   **Shape of Red Blood Cells**   Erythrocytes are biconcave discs with very shallow centers. This shape optimizes the ratio of surface area to volume, facilitating gas exchange. It also enables them to fold up as they move through narrow blood vessels.

Hemoglobin

Hemoglobin is a large molecule made up of proteins and iron. It consists of four folded chains of a protein called

globin, designated alpha 1 and 2, and beta 1 and 2 (Figure 18.7**a**). Each of these globin molecules is bound to a red pigment molecule called **heme**, which contains an ion of iron (Fe^{2+}) (Figure 18.7**b**).

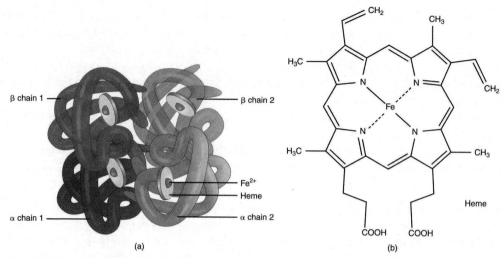

FIGURE 18.7   Hemoglobin   (a) A molecule of hemoglobin contains four globin proteins, each of which is bound to one molecule of the iron-containing pigment heme. (b) A single erythrocyte can contain 300 million hemoglobin molecules, and thus more than 1 billion oxygen molecules.

Each iron ion in the heme can bind to one oxygen molecule; therefore, each hemoglobin molecule can transport four oxygen molecules. An individual erythrocyte may contain about 300 million hemoglobin molecules, and therefore can bind to and transport up to 1.2 billion oxygen molecules (see Figure 18.7**b**).

In the lungs, hemoglobin picks up oxygen, which binds to the iron ions, forming **oxyhemoglobin**. The bright red, oxygenated hemoglobin travels to the body tissues, where it releases some of the oxygen molecules, becoming darker red **deoxyhemoglobin**, sometimes referred to as reduced hemoglobin. Oxygen release depends on the need for oxygen in the surrounding tissues, so hemoglobin rarely if ever leaves all of its oxygen behind. In the capillaries, carbon dioxide enters the bloodstream. About 76 percent dissolves in the plasma, some of it remaining as dissolved CO_2, and the remainder forming bicarbonate ion. About 23–24 percent of it binds to the amino acids in hemoglobin, forming a molecule known as **carbaminohemoglobin**. From the capillaries, the hemoglobin carries carbon dioxide back to the lungs, where it releases it for exchange of oxygen.

Changes in the levels of RBCs can have significant effects on the body's ability to effectively deliver oxygen to the tissues. Ineffective hematopoiesis results in insufficient numbers of RBCs and results in one of several forms of anemia. An overproduction of RBCs produces a condition called polycythemia. The primary drawback with polycythemia is not a failure to directly deliver enough oxygen to the tissues, but rather the increased viscosity of the blood, which makes it more difficult for the heart to circulate the blood.

In patients with insufficient hemoglobin, the tissues may not receive sufficient oxygen, resulting in another form of anemia. In determining oxygenation of tissues, the value of greatest interest in healthcare is the percent saturation; that is, the percentage of hemoglobin sites occupied by oxygen in a patient's blood. Clinically this value is commonly referred to simply as "percent sat."

Percent saturation is normally monitored using a device known as a pulse oximeter, which is applied to a thin part of the body, typically the tip of the patient's finger. The device works by sending two different wavelengths of light (one red, the other infrared) through the finger and measuring the light with a photodetector as it exits. Hemoglobin absorbs light differentially depending upon its saturation with oxygen. The machine calibrates the amount of light received by the photodetector against the amount absorbed by the partially oxygenated hemoglobin and presents the data as percent saturation. Normal pulse oximeter readings range from 95–100 percent. Lower percentages reflect **hypoxemia**, or low blood oxygen. The term hypoxia is more generic and simply refers to low oxygen levels. Oxygen levels are also directly monitored from free oxygen in the plasma typically following an arterial stick. When this method is applied, the amount of oxygen present is expressed in terms of partial pressure of oxygen or simply P_{O2} or PO2 and is typically recorded in units of millimeters of mercury, mm Hg.

Access for free at openstax.org

The kidneys filter about 180 liters (~380 pints) of blood in an average adult each day, or about 20 percent of the total resting volume, and thus serve as ideal sites for receptors that determine oxygen saturation. In response to hypoxemia, less oxygen will exit the vessels supplying the kidney, resulting in hypoxia (low oxygen concentration) in the tissue fluid of the kidney where oxygen concentration is actually monitored. Interstitial fibroblasts within the kidney secrete EPO, thereby increasing erythrocyte production and restoring oxygen levels. In a classic negative-feedback loop, as oxygen saturation rises, EPO secretion falls, and vice versa, thereby maintaining homeostasis. Populations dwelling at high elevations, with inherently lower levels of oxygen in the atmosphere, naturally maintain a hematocrit higher than people living at sea level. Consequently, people traveling to high elevations may experience symptoms of hypoxemia, such as fatigue, headache, and shortness of breath, for a few days after their arrival. In response to the hypoxemia, the kidneys secrete EPO to step up the production of erythrocytes until homeostasis is achieved once again. To avoid the symptoms of hypoxemia, or altitude sickness, mountain climbers typically rest for several days to a week or more at a series of camps situated at increasing elevations to allow EPO levels and, consequently, erythrocyte counts to rise. When climbing the tallest peaks, such as Mt. Everest and K2 in the Himalayas, many mountain climbers rely upon bottled oxygen as they near the summit.

Lifecycle of Erythrocytes

Production of erythrocytes in the marrow occurs at the staggering rate of more than 2 million cells per second. For this production to occur, a number of raw materials must be present in adequate amounts. These include the same nutrients that are essential to the production and maintenance of any cell, such as glucose, lipids, and amino acids. However, erythrocyte production also requires several trace elements:

- Iron. We have said that each heme group in a hemoglobin molecule contains an ion of the trace mineral iron. On average, less than 20 percent of the iron we consume is absorbed. Heme iron, from animal foods such as meat, poultry, and fish, is absorbed more efficiently than non-heme iron from plant foods. Upon absorption, iron becomes part of the body's total iron pool. The bone marrow, liver, and spleen can store iron in the protein compounds **ferritin** and **hemosiderin**. Ferroportin transports the iron across the intestinal cell plasma membranes and from its storage sites into tissue fluid where it enters the blood. When EPO stimulates the production of erythrocytes, iron is released from storage, bound to transferrin, and carried to the red marrow where it attaches to erythrocyte precursors.
- Copper. A trace mineral, copper is a component of two plasma proteins, hephaestin and ceruloplasmin. Without these, hemoglobin could not be adequately produced. Located in intestinal villi, hephaestin enables iron to be absorbed by intestinal cells. Ceruloplasmin transports copper. Both enable the oxidation of iron from Fe^{2+} to Fe^{3+}, a form in which it can be bound to its transport protein, **transferrin**, for transport to body cells. In a state of copper deficiency, the transport of iron for heme synthesis decreases, and iron can accumulate in tissues, where it can eventually lead to organ damage.
- Zinc. The trace mineral zinc functions as a co-enzyme that facilitates the synthesis of the heme portion of hemoglobin.
- B vitamins. The B vitamins folate and vitamin B_{12} function as co-enzymes that facilitate DNA synthesis. Thus, both are critical for the synthesis of new cells, including erythrocytes.

Erythrocytes live up to 120 days in the circulation, after which the worn-out cells are removed by a type of myeloid phagocytic cell called a **macrophage**, located primarily within the bone marrow, liver, and spleen. The components of the degraded erythrocytes' hemoglobin are further processed as follows:

- Globin, the protein portion of hemoglobin, is broken down into amino acids, which can be sent back to the bone marrow to be used in the production of new erythrocytes. Hemoglobin that is not phagocytized is broken down in the circulation, releasing alpha and beta chains that are removed from circulation by the kidneys.
- The iron contained in the heme portion of hemoglobin may be stored in the liver or spleen, primarily in the form of ferritin or hemosiderin, or carried through the bloodstream by transferrin to the red bone marrow for recycling into new erythrocytes.
- The non-iron portion of heme is degraded into the waste product **biliverdin**, a green pigment, and then into another waste product, **bilirubin**, a yellow pigment. Bilirubin binds to albumin and travels in the blood to the liver, which uses it in the manufacture of bile, a compound released into the intestines to help emulsify dietary fats. In the large intestine, bacteria breaks the bilirubin apart from the bile and converts it to urobilinogen and then into stercobilin. It is then eliminated from the body in the feces. Broad-spectrum antibiotics typically

eliminate these bacteria as well and may alter the color of feces. The kidneys also remove any circulating bilirubin and other related metabolic byproducts such as urobilins and secrete them into the urine.

The breakdown pigments formed from the destruction of hemoglobin can be seen in a variety of situations. At the site of an injury, biliverdin from damaged RBCs produces some of the dramatic colors associated with a **bruise**. With a failing liver, bilirubin cannot be removed effectively from circulation and causes the body to assume a yellowish tinge associated with **jaundice**. Stercobilins within the feces produce the typical brown color associated with this waste. And the yellow of urine is associated with the urobilins.

The erythrocyte lifecycle is summarized in Figure 18.8.

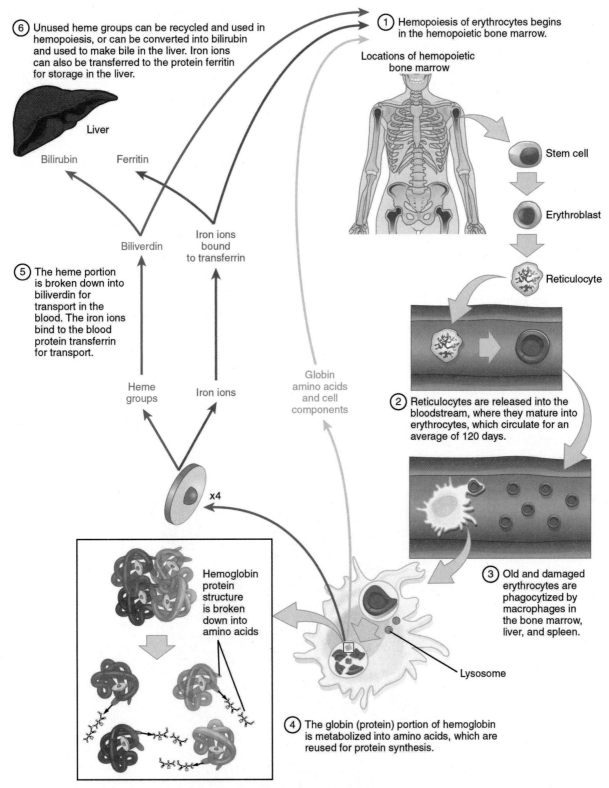

⑥ Unused heme groups can be recycled and used in hemopoiesis, or can be converted into bilirubin and used to make bile in the liver. Iron ions can also be transferred to the protein ferritin for storage in the liver.

Liver

Bilirubin   Ferritin

Biliverdin   Iron ions bound to transferrin

⑤ The heme portion is broken down into biliverdin for transport in the blood. The iron ions bind to the blood protein transferrin for transport.

Heme groups   Iron ions

Globin amino acids and cell components

Hemoglobin protein structure is broken down into amino acids

x4

① Hemopoiesis of erythrocytes begins in the hemopoietic bone marrow.

Locations of hemopoietic bone marrow

Stem cell

Erythroblast

Reticulocyte

② Reticulocytes are released into the bloodstream, where they mature into erythrocytes, which circulate for an average of 120 days.

③ Old and damaged erythrocytes are phagocytized by macrophages in the bone marrow, liver, and spleen.

Lysosome

④ The globin (protein) portion of hemoglobin is metabolized into amino acids, which are reused for protein synthesis.

FIGURE 18.8   **Erythrocyte Lifecycle**   Erythrocytes are produced in the bone marrow and sent into the circulation. At the end of their lifecycle, they are destroyed by macrophages, and their components are recycled.

Disorders of Erythrocytes

The size, shape, and number of erythrocytes, and the number of hemoglobin molecules can have a major impact on a person's health. When the number of RBCs or hemoglobin is deficient, the general condition is called **anemia**. There are more than 400 types of anemia and more than 3.5 million Americans suffer from this condition. Anemia can be broken down into three major groups: those caused by blood loss, those caused by faulty or decreased RBC production, and those caused by excessive destruction of RBCs. Clinicians often use two groupings in diagnosis: The kinetic approach focuses on evaluating the production, destruction, and removal of RBCs, whereas the morphological approach examines the RBCs themselves, paying particular emphasis to their size. A common test is the mean corpuscle volume (MCV), which measures size. Normal-sized cells are referred to as normocytic, smaller-than-normal cells are referred to as microcytic, and larger-than-normal cells are referred to as macrocytic. Reticulocyte counts are also important and may reveal inadequate production of RBCs. The effects of the various anemias are widespread, because reduced numbers of RBCs or hemoglobin will result in lower levels of oxygen being delivered to body tissues. Since oxygen is required for tissue functioning, anemia produces fatigue, lethargy, and an increased risk for infection. An oxygen deficit in the brain impairs the ability to think clearly, and may prompt headaches and irritability. Lack of oxygen leaves the patient short of breath, even as the heart and lungs work harder in response to the deficit.

Blood loss anemias are fairly straightforward. In addition to bleeding from wounds or other lesions, these forms of anemia may be due to ulcers, hemorrhoids, inflammation of the stomach (gastritis), and some cancers of the gastrointestinal tract. The excessive use of aspirin or other nonsteroidal anti-inflammatory drugs such as ibuprofen can trigger ulceration and gastritis. Excessive menstruation and loss of blood during childbirth are also potential causes.

Anemias caused by faulty or decreased RBC production include sickle cell anemia, iron deficiency anemia, vitamin deficiency anemia, and diseases of the bone marrow and stem cells.

- A characteristic change in the shape of erythrocytes is seen in **sickle cell disease** (also referred to as sickle cell anemia). A genetic disorder, it is caused by production of an abnormal type of hemoglobin, called hemoglobin S, which delivers less oxygen to tissues and causes erythrocytes to assume a sickle (or crescent) shape, especially at low oxygen concentrations (Figure 18.9). These abnormally shaped cells can then become lodged in narrow capillaries because they are unable to fold in on themselves to squeeze through, blocking blood flow to tissues and causing a variety of serious problems from painful joints to delayed growth and even blindness and cerebrovascular accidents (strokes). Sickle cell anemia is a genetic condition particularly found in individuals of African descent.

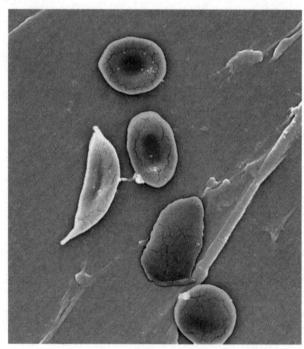

FIGURE 18.9 Sickle Cells   Sickle cell anemia is caused by a mutation in one of the hemoglobin genes. Erythrocytes produce an abnormal type of hemoglobin, which causes the cell to take on a sickle or crescent shape. (credit: Janice Haney Carr)

- Iron deficiency anemia is the most common type and results when the amount of available iron is insufficient to allow production of sufficient heme. This condition can occur in individuals with a deficiency of iron in the diet

and is especially common in teens and children as well as in vegans and vegetarians. Additionally, iron deficiency anemia may be caused by either an inability to absorb and transport iron or slow, chronic bleeding.
- Vitamin-deficient anemias generally involve insufficient vitamin B12 and folate.
  ◦ Megaloblastic anemia involves a deficiency of vitamin B12 and/or folate, and often involves diets deficient in these essential nutrients. Lack of meat or a viable alternate source, and overcooking or eating insufficient amounts of vegetables may lead to a lack of folate.
  ◦ Pernicious anemia is caused by poor absorption of vitamin B12 and is often seen in patients with Crohn's disease (a severe intestinal disorder often treated by surgery), surgical removal of the intestines or stomach (common in some weight loss surgeries), intestinal parasites, and AIDS.
  ◦ Pregnancies, some medications, excessive alcohol consumption, and some diseases such as celiac disease are also associated with vitamin deficiencies. It is essential to provide sufficient folic acid during the early stages of pregnancy to reduce the risk of neurological defects, including spina bifida, a failure of the neural tube to close.

- Assorted disease processes can also interfere with the production and formation of RBCs and hemoglobin. If myeloid stem cells are defective or replaced by cancer cells, there will be insufficient quantities of RBCs produced.
  ◦ Aplastic anemia is the condition in which there are deficient numbers of RBC stem cells. Aplastic anemia is often inherited, or it may be triggered by radiation, medication, chemotherapy, or infection.
  ◦ **Thalassemia** is an inherited condition typically occurring in individuals from the Middle East, the Mediterranean, African, and Southeast Asia, in which maturation of the RBCs does not proceed normally. The most severe form is called Cooley's anemia.
  ◦ Lead exposure from industrial sources or even dust from paint chips of iron-containing paints or pottery that has not been properly glazed may also lead to destruction of the red marrow.

- Various disease processes also can lead to anemias. These include chronic kidney diseases often associated with a decreased production of EPO, hypothyroidism, some forms of cancer, lupus, and rheumatoid arthritis.

In contrast to anemia, an elevated RBC count is called **polycythemia** and is detected in a patient's elevated hematocrit. It can occur transiently in a person who is dehydrated; when water intake is inadequate or water losses are excessive, the plasma volume falls. As a result, the hematocrit rises. For reasons mentioned earlier, a mild form of polycythemia is chronic but normal in people living at high altitudes. Some elite athletes train at high elevations specifically to induce this phenomenon. Finally, a type of bone marrow disease called polycythemia vera (from the Greek vera = "true") causes an excessive production of immature erythrocytes. Polycythemia vera can dangerously elevate the viscosity of blood, raising blood pressure and making it more difficult for the heart to pump blood throughout the body. It is a relatively rare disease that occurs more often in males than in females, and is more likely to be present in elderly patients those over 60 years of age.

18.4 Leukocytes and Platelets

LEARNING OBJECTIVES

By the end of this section, you will be able to:
- Describe the general characteristics of leukocytes
- Classify leukocytes according to their lineage, their main structural features, and their primary functions
- Discuss the most common malignancies involving leukocytes
- Identify the lineage, basic structure, and function of platelets

The **leukocyte**, commonly known as a white blood cell (or WBC), is a major component of the body's defenses against disease. Leukocytes protect the body against invading microorganisms and body cells with mutated DNA, and they clean up debris. Platelets are essential for the repair of blood vessels when damage to them has occurred; they also provide growth factors for healing and repair. See Figure 18.5 for a summary of leukocytes and platelets.

Characteristics of Leukocytes

Although leukocytes and erythrocytes both originate from hematopoietic stem cells in the bone marrow, they are very different from each other in many significant ways. For instance, leukocytes are far less numerous than erythrocytes: Typically there are only 5000 to 10,000 per μL. They are also larger than erythrocytes and are the only formed elements that are complete cells, possessing a nucleus and organelles. And although there is just one type of erythrocyte, there are many types of leukocytes. Most of these types have a much shorter lifespan than that of erythrocytes, some as short as a few hours or even a few minutes in the case of acute infection.

One of the most distinctive characteristics of leukocytes is their movement. Whereas erythrocytes spend their days circulating within the blood vessels, leukocytes routinely leave the bloodstream to perform their defensive functions in the body's tissues. For leukocytes, the vascular network is simply a highway they travel and soon exit to reach their true destination. When they arrive, they are often given distinct names, such as macrophage or microglia, depending on their function. As shown in Figure 18.10, they leave the capillaries—the smallest blood vessels—or other small vessels through a process known as **emigration** (from the Latin for "removal") or **diapedesis** (dia- = "through"; -pedan = "to leap") in which they squeeze through adjacent cells in a blood vessel wall.

Once they have exited the capillaries, some leukocytes will take up fixed positions in lymphatic tissue, bone marrow, the spleen, the thymus, or other organs. Others will move about through the tissue spaces very much like amoebas, continuously extending their plasma membranes, sometimes wandering freely, and sometimes moving toward the direction in which they are drawn by chemical signals. This attracting of leukocytes occurs because of **positive chemotaxis** (literally "movement in response to chemicals"), a phenomenon in which injured or infected cells and nearby leukocytes emit the equivalent of a chemical "911" call, attracting more leukocytes to the site. In clinical medicine, the differential counts of the types and percentages of leukocytes present are often key indicators in making a diagnosis and selecting a treatment.

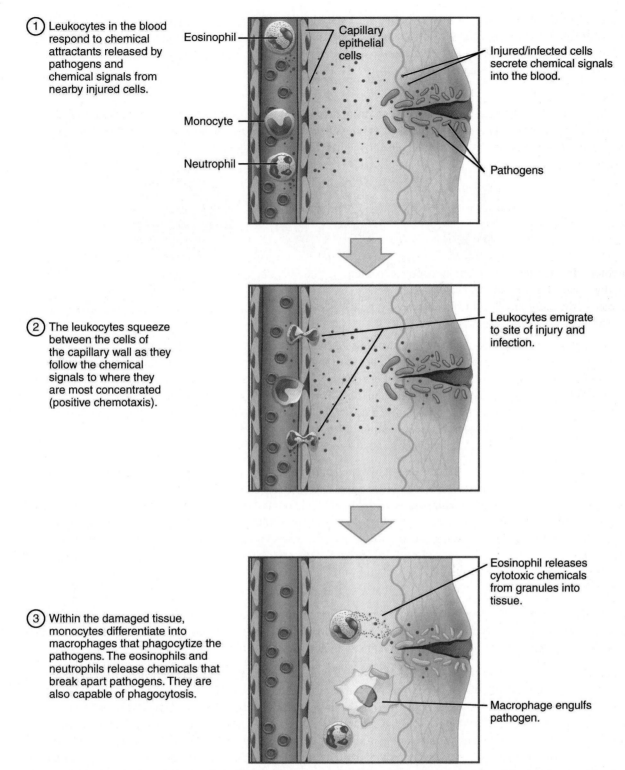

① Leukocytes in the blood respond to chemical attractants released by pathogens and chemical signals from nearby injured cells.

Eosinophil

Capillary epithelial cells

Injured/infected cells secrete chemical signals into the blood.

Monocyte

Neutrophil

Pathogens

② The leukocytes squeeze between the cells of the capillary wall as they follow the chemical signals to where they are most concentrated (positive chemotaxis).

Leukocytes emigrate to site of injury and infection.

③ Within the damaged tissue, monocytes differentiate into macrophages that phagocytize the pathogens. The eosinophils and neutrophils release chemicals that break apart pathogens. They are also capable of phagocytosis.

Eosinophil releases cytotoxic chemicals from granules into tissue.

Macrophage engulfs pathogen.

FIGURE 18.10   Emigration   Leukocytes exit the blood vessel and then move through the connective tissue of the dermis toward the site of a wound. Some leukocytes, such as the eosinophil and neutrophil, are characterized as granular leukocytes. They release chemicals from their granules that destroy pathogens; they are also capable of phagocytosis. The monocyte, an agranular leukocyte, differentiates into a macrophage that then phagocytizes the pathogens.

Classification of Leukocytes

When scientists first began to observe stained blood slides, it quickly became evident that leukocytes could be divided into two groups, according to whether their cytoplasm contained highly visible granules:

- **Granular leukocytes** contain abundant granules within the cytoplasm. They include neutrophils, eosinophils, and basophils (you can view their lineage from myeloid stem cells in <u>Figure 18.4</u>).

- While granules are not totally lacking in **agranular leukocytes**, they are far fewer and less obvious. Agranular leukocytes include monocytes, which mature into macrophages that are phagocytic, and lymphocytes, which arise from the lymphoid stem cell line.

Granular Leukocytes

We will consider the granular leukocytes in order from most common to least common. All of these are produced in the red bone marrow and have a short lifespan of hours to days. They typically have a lobed nucleus and are classified according to which type of stain best highlights their granules (<u>Figure 18.11</u>).

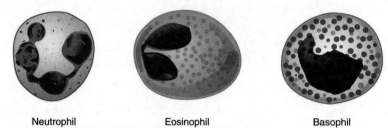

Neutrophil   Eosinophil   Basophil

FIGURE 18.11   Granular Leukocytes   A neutrophil has small granules that stain light lilac and a nucleus with two to five lobes. An eosinophil's granules are slightly larger and stain reddish-orange, and its nucleus has two to three lobes. A basophil has large granules that stain dark blue to purple and a two-lobed nucleus.

The most common of all the leukocytes, **neutrophils** will normally comprise 50–70 percent of total leukocyte count. They are 10–12 μm in diameter, significantly larger than erythrocytes. They are called neutrophils because their granules show up most clearly with stains that are chemically neutral (neither acidic nor basic). The granules are numerous but quite fine and normally appear light lilac. The nucleus has a distinct lobed appearance and may have two to five lobes, the number increasing with the age of the cell. Older neutrophils have increasing numbers of lobes and are often referred to as **polymorphonuclear** (a nucleus with many forms), or simply "polys." Younger and immature neutrophils begin to develop lobes and are known as "bands."

Neutrophils are rapid responders to the site of infection and are efficient phagocytes with a preference for bacteria. Their granules include **lysozyme**, an enzyme capable of lysing, or breaking down, bacterial cell walls; oxidants such as hydrogen peroxide; and **defensins**, proteins that bind to and puncture bacterial and fungal plasma membranes, so that the cell contents leak out. Abnormally high counts of neutrophils indicate infection and/or inflammation, particularly triggered by bacteria, but are also found in burn patients and others experiencing unusual stress. A burn injury increases the proliferation of neutrophils in order to fight off infection that can result from the destruction of the barrier of the skin. Low counts may be caused by drug toxicity and other disorders, and may increase an individual's susceptibility to infection.

Eosinophils typically represent 2–4 percent of total leukocyte count. They are also 10–12 μm in diameter. The granules of eosinophils stain best with an acidic stain known as eosin. The nucleus of the eosinophil will typically have two to three lobes and, if stained properly, the granules will have a distinct red to orange color.

The granules of eosinophils include antihistamine molecules, which counteract the activities of histamines, inflammatory chemicals produced by basophils and mast cells. Some eosinophil granules contain molecules toxic to parasitic worms, which can enter the body through the integument, or when an individual consumes raw or undercooked fish or meat. Eosinophils are also capable of phagocytosis and are particularly effective when antibodies bind to the target and form an antigen-antibody complex. High counts of eosinophils are typical of patients experiencing allergies, parasitic worm infestations, and some autoimmune diseases. Low counts may be due to drug toxicity and stress.

Basophils are the least common leukocytes, typically comprising less than one percent of the total leukocyte count. They are slightly smaller than neutrophils and eosinophils at 8–10 μm in diameter. The granules of basophils stain best with basic (alkaline) stains. Basophils contain large granules that pick up a dark blue stain and are so common they may make it difficult to see the two-lobed nucleus.

In general, basophils intensify the inflammatory response. They share this trait with mast cells. In the past, mast cells were considered to be basophils that left the circulation. However, this appears not to be the case, as the two cell types develop from different lineages.

The granules of basophils release histamines, which contribute to inflammation, and heparin, which opposes blood clotting. High counts of basophils are associated with allergies, parasitic infections, and hypothyroidism. Low counts are associated with pregnancy, stress, and hyperthyroidism.

Agranular Leukocytes

Agranular leukocytes contain smaller, less-visible granules in their cytoplasm than do granular leukocytes. The nucleus is simple in shape, sometimes with an indentation but without distinct lobes. There are two major types of agranulocytes: lymphocytes and monocytes (see Figure 18.4).

Lymphocytes are the only formed element of blood that arises from lymphoid stem cells. Although they form initially in the bone marrow, much of their subsequent development and reproduction occurs in the lymphatic tissues. Lymphocytes are the second most common type of leukocyte, accounting for about 20–30 percent of all leukocytes, and are essential for the immune response. The size range of lymphocytes is quite extensive, with some authorities recognizing two size classes and others three. Typically, the large cells are 10–14 μm and have a smaller nucleus-to-cytoplasm ratio and more granules. The smaller cells are typically 6–9 μm with a larger volume of nucleus to cytoplasm, creating a "halo" effect. A few cells may fall outside these ranges, at 14–17 μm. This finding has led to the three size range classification.

The three major groups of lymphocytes include natural killer cells, B cells, and T cells. **Natural killer (NK) cells** are capable of recognizing cells that do not express "self" proteins on their plasma membrane or that contain foreign or abnormal markers. These "nonself" cells include cancer cells, cells infected with a virus, and other cells with atypical surface proteins. Thus, they provide generalized, nonspecific immunity. The larger lymphocytes are typically NK cells.

B cells and T cells, also called **B lymphocytes** and **T lymphocytes**, play prominent roles in defending the body against specific pathogens (disease-causing microorganisms) and are involved in specific immunity. One form of B cells (plasma cells) produces the antibodies or immunoglobulins that bind to specific foreign or abnormal components of plasma membranes. This is also referred to as humoral (body fluid) immunity. T cells provide cellular-level immunity by physically attacking foreign or diseased cells. A **memory cell** is a variety of both B and T cells that forms after exposure to a pathogen and mounts rapid responses upon subsequent exposures. Unlike other leukocytes, memory cells live for many years. B cells undergo a maturation process in the bone marrow, whereas T cells undergo maturation in the thymus. This site of the maturation process gives rise to the name B and T cells. The functions of lymphocytes are complex and will be covered in detail in the chapter covering the lymphatic system and immunity. Smaller lymphocytes are either B or T cells, although they cannot be differentiated in a normal blood smear.

Abnormally high lymphocyte counts are characteristic of viral infections as well as some types of cancer. Abnormally low lymphocyte counts are characteristic of prolonged (chronic) illness or immunosuppression, including that caused by HIV infection and drug therapies that often involve steroids.

Monocytes originate from myeloid stem cells. They normally represent 2–8 percent of the total leukocyte count. They are typically easily recognized by their large size of 12–20 μm and indented or horseshoe-shaped nuclei. Macrophages are monocytes that have left the circulation and phagocytize debris, foreign pathogens, worn-out erythrocytes, and many other dead, worn out, or damaged cells. Macrophages also release antimicrobial defensins and chemotactic chemicals that attract other leukocytes to the site of an infection. Some macrophages occupy fixed locations, whereas others wander through the tissue fluid.

Abnormally high counts of monocytes are associated with viral or fungal infections, tuberculosis, and some forms of leukemia and other chronic diseases. Abnormally low counts are typically caused by suppression of the bone marrow.

Lifecycle of Leukocytes

Most leukocytes have a relatively short lifespan, typically measured in hours or days. Production of all leukocytes begins in the bone marrow under the influence of CSFs and interleukins. Secondary production and maturation of lymphocytes occurs in specific regions of lymphatic tissue known as germinal centers. Lymphocytes are fully capable of mitosis and may produce clones of cells with identical properties. This capacity enables an individual to maintain immunity throughout life to many threats that have been encountered in the past.

Disorders of Leukocytes

Leukopenia is a condition in which too few leukocytes are produced. If this condition is pronounced, the individual may be unable to ward off disease. Excessive leukocyte proliferation is known as **leukocytosis**. Although leukocyte counts are high, the cells themselves are often nonfunctional, leaving the individual at increased risk for disease.

Leukemia is a cancer involving an abundance of leukocytes. It may involve only one specific type of leukocyte from either the myeloid line (myelocytic leukemia) or the lymphoid line (lymphocytic leukemia). In chronic leukemia, mature leukocytes accumulate and fail to die. In acute leukemia, there is an overproduction of young, immature leukocytes. In both conditions the cells do not function properly.

Lymphoma is a form of cancer in which masses of malignant T and/or B lymphocytes collect in lymph nodes, the spleen, the liver, and other tissues. As in leukemia, the malignant leukocytes do not function properly, and the patient is vulnerable to infection. Some forms of lymphoma tend to progress slowly and respond well to treatment. Others tend to progress quickly and require aggressive treatment, without which they are rapidly fatal.

Platelets

You may occasionally see platelets referred to as **thrombocytes**, but because this name suggests they are a type of cell, it is not accurate. A platelet is not a cell but rather a fragment of the cytoplasm of a cell called a **megakaryocyte** that is surrounded by a plasma membrane. Megakaryocytes are descended from myeloid stem cells (see Figure 18.4) and are large, typically 50–100 μm in diameter, and contain an enlarged, lobed nucleus. As noted earlier, thrombopoietin, a glycoprotein secreted by the kidneys and liver, stimulates the proliferation of megakaryoblasts, which mature into megakaryocytes. These remain within bone marrow tissue (Figure 18.12) and ultimately form platelet-precursor extensions that extend through the walls of bone marrow capillaries to release into the circulation thousands of cytoplasmic fragments, each enclosed by a bit of plasma membrane. These enclosed fragments are platelets. Each megakarocyte releases 2000–3000 platelets during its lifespan. Following platelet release, megakaryocyte remnants, which are little more than a cell nucleus, are consumed by macrophages.

Platelets are relatively small, 2–4 μm in diameter, but numerous, with typically 150,000–160,000 per μL of blood. After entering the circulation, approximately one-third migrate to the spleen for storage for later release in response to any rupture in a blood vessel. They then become activated to perform their primary function, which is to limit blood loss. Platelets remain only about 10 days, then are phagocytized by macrophages.

Platelets are critical to hemostasis, the stoppage of blood flow following damage to a vessel. They also secrete a variety of growth factors essential for growth and repair of tissue, particularly connective tissue. Infusions of concentrated platelets are now being used in some therapies to stimulate healing.

Disorders of Platelets

Thrombocytosis is a condition in which there are too many platelets. This may trigger formation of unwanted blood clots (thrombosis), a potentially fatal disorder. If there is an insufficient number of platelets, called **thrombocytopenia**, blood may not clot properly, and excessive bleeding may result.

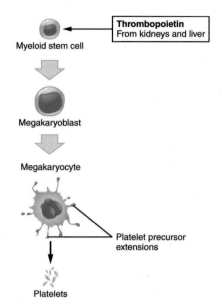

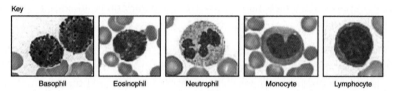

FIGURE 18.12 Platelets Platelets are derived from cells called megakaryocytes.

⊘ INTERACTIVE LINK

FIGURE 18.13 Leukocytes (Micrographs provided by the Regents of University of Michigan Medical School © 2012)

View University of Michigan Webscopes (https://openstax.org/r/bloodsmear) and explore the blood slides in greater detail. The Webscope feature allows you to move the slides as you would with a mechanical stage. You can increase and decrease the magnification. There is a chance to review each of the leukocytes individually after you have attempted to identify them from the first two blood smears. In addition, there are a few multiple choice questions.

Are you able to recognize and identify the various formed elements? You will need to do this is a systematic manner, scanning along the image. The standard method is to use a grid, but this is not possible with this resource. Try constructing a simple table with each leukocyte type and then making a mark for each cell type you identify. Attempt to classify at least 50 and perhaps as many as 100 different cells. Based on the percentage of cells that you count, do the numbers represent a normal blood smear or does something appear to be abnormal?

18.5 Hemostasis

LEARNING OBJECTIVES

By the end of this section, you will be able to:
- Describe the three mechanisms involved in hemostasis
- Explain how the extrinsic and intrinsic coagulation pathways lead to the common pathway, and the coagulation factors involved in each
- Discuss disorders affecting hemostasis

Platelets are key players in **hemostasis**, the process by which the body seals a ruptured blood vessel and prevents further loss of blood. Although rupture of larger vessels usually requires medical intervention, hemostasis is quite effective in dealing with small, simple wounds. There are three steps to the process: vascular spasm, the formation of a platelet plug, and coagulation (blood clotting). Failure of any of these steps will result in **hemorrhage**—excessive bleeding.

Vascular Spasm

When a vessel is severed or punctured, or when the wall of a vessel is damaged, vascular spasm occurs. In **vascular spasm**, the smooth muscle in the walls of the vessel contracts dramatically. This smooth muscle has both circular layers; larger vessels also have longitudinal layers. The circular layers tend to constrict the flow of blood, whereas the longitudinal layers, when present, draw the vessel back into the surrounding tissue, often making it more difficult for a surgeon to locate, clamp, and tie off a severed vessel. The vascular spasm response is believed to be triggered by several chemicals called endothelins that are released by vessel-lining cells and by pain receptors in response to vessel injury. This phenomenon typically lasts for up to 30 minutes, although it can last for hours.

Formation of the Platelet Plug

In the second step, platelets, which normally float free in the plasma, encounter the area of vessel rupture with the exposed underlying connective tissue and collagenous fibers. The platelets begin to clump together, become spiked and sticky, and bind to the exposed collagen and endothelial lining. This process is assisted by a glycoprotein in the blood plasma called von Willebrand factor, which helps stabilize the growing **platelet plug**. As platelets collect, they simultaneously release chemicals from their granules into the plasma that further contribute to hemostasis. Among the substances released by the platelets are:

- adenosine diphosphate (ADP), which helps additional platelets to adhere to the injury site, reinforcing and expanding the platelet plug
- serotonin, which maintains vasoconstriction
- prostaglandins and phospholipids, which also maintain vasoconstriction and help to activate further clotting chemicals, as discussed next

A platelet plug can temporarily seal a small opening in a blood vessel. Plug formation, in essence, buys the body time while more sophisticated and durable repairs are being made. In a similar manner, even modern naval warships still carry an assortment of wooden plugs to temporarily repair small breaches in their hulls until permanent repairs can be made.

Coagulation

Those more sophisticated and more durable repairs are collectively called **coagulation**, the formation of a blood clot. The process is sometimes characterized as a cascade, because one event prompts the next as in a multi-level waterfall. The result is the production of a gelatinous but robust clot made up of a mesh of **fibrin**—an insoluble filamentous protein derived from fibrinogen, the plasma protein introduced earlier—in which platelets and blood cells are trapped. Figure 18.14 summarizes the three steps of hemostasis.

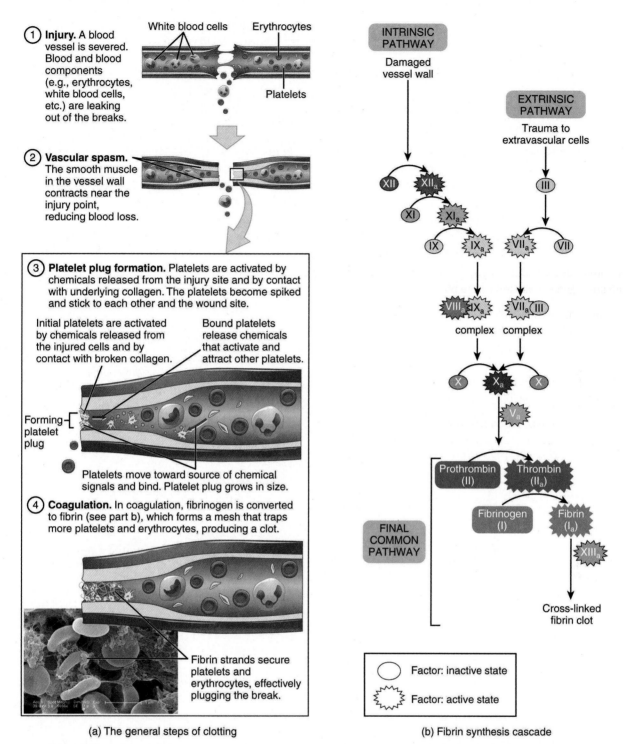

FIGURE 18.14 **Hemostasis** (a) An injury to a blood vessel initiates the process of hemostasis. Blood clotting involves three steps. First, vascular spasm constricts the flow of blood. Next, a platelet plug forms to temporarily seal small openings in the vessel. Coagulation then enables the repair of the vessel wall once the leakage of blood has stopped. (b) The synthesis of fibrin in blood clots involves either an intrinsic pathway or an extrinsic pathway, both of which lead to a common pathway. (credit a: Kevin MacKenzie)

Clotting Factors Involved in Coagulation

In the coagulation cascade, chemicals called **clotting factors** (or coagulation factors) prompt reactions that activate still more coagulation factors. The process is complex, but is initiated along two basic pathways:

- The extrinsic pathway, which normally is triggered by trauma.
- The intrinsic pathway, which begins in the bloodstream and is triggered by internal damage to the wall of the vessel.

Both of these merge into a third pathway, referred to as the common pathway (see Figure 18.14**b**). All three pathways are dependent upon the 12 known clotting factors, including Ca^{2+} and vitamin K (Table 18.1). Clotting factors are secreted primarily by the liver and the platelets. The liver requires the fat-soluble vitamin K to produce many of them. Vitamin K (along with biotin and folate) is somewhat unusual among vitamins in that it is not only consumed in the diet but is also synthesized by bacteria residing in the large intestine. The calcium ion, considered factor IV, is derived from the diet and from the breakdown of bone. Some recent evidence indicates that activation of various clotting factors occurs on specific receptor sites on the surfaces of platelets.

The 12 clotting factors are numbered I through XIII according to the order of their discovery. Factor VI was once believed to be a distinct clotting factor, but is now thought to be identical to factor V. Rather than renumber the other factors, factor VI was allowed to remain as a placeholder and also a reminder that knowledge changes over time.

Clotting Factors

Factor number	Name	Type of molecule	Source	Pathway(s)
I	Fibrinogen	Plasma protein	Liver	Common; converted into fibrin
II	Prothrombin	Plasma protein	Liver*	Common; converted into thrombin
III	Tissue thromboplastin or tissue factor	Lipoprotein mixture	Damaged cells and platelets	Extrinsic
IV	Calcium ions	Inorganic ions in plasma	Diet, platelets, bone matrix	Entire process
V	Proaccelerin	Plasma protein	Liver, platelets	Extrinsic and intrinsic
VI	Not used	Not used	Not used	Not used
VII	Proconvertin	Plasma protein	Liver *	Extrinsic
VIII	Antihemolytic factor A	Plasma protein factor	Platelets and endothelial cells	Intrinsic; deficiency results in hemophilia A
IX	Antihemolytic factor B (plasma thromboplastin component)	Plasma protein	Liver*	Intrinsic; deficiency results in hemophilia B
X	Stuart–Prower factor (thrombokinase)	Protein	Liver*	Extrinsic and intrinsic
XI	Antihemolytic factor C (plasma thromboplastin antecedent)	Plasma protein	Liver	Intrinsic; deficiency results in hemophilia C

TABLE 18.1 *Vitamin K required.

Factor number	Name	Type of molecule	Source	Pathway(s)
XII	Hageman factor	Plasma protein	Liver	Intrinsic; initiates clotting in vitro also activates plasmin
XIII	Fibrin-stabilizing factor	Plasma protein	Liver, platelets	Stabilizes fibrin; slows fibrinolysis

TABLE 18.1 *Vitamin K required.

Extrinsic Pathway

The quicker responding and more direct **extrinsic pathway** (also known as the **tissue factor** pathway) begins when damage occurs to the surrounding tissues, such as in a traumatic injury. Upon contact with blood plasma, the damaged extravascular cells, which are extrinsic to the bloodstream, release factor III (thromboplastin). Sequentially, Ca^{2+} then factor VII (proconvertin), which is activated by factor III, are added, forming an enzyme complex. This enzyme complex leads to activation of factor X (Stuart–Prower factor), which activates the common pathway discussed below. The events in the extrinsic pathway are completed in a matter of seconds.

Intrinsic Pathway

The **intrinsic pathway** (also known as the contact activation pathway) is longer and more complex. In this case, the factors involved are intrinsic to (present within) the bloodstream. The pathway can be prompted by damage to the tissues, resulting from internal factors such as arterial disease; however, it is most often initiated when factor XII (Hageman factor) comes into contact with foreign materials, such as when a blood sample is put into a glass test tube. Within the body, factor XII is typically activated when it encounters negatively charged molecules, such as inorganic polymers and phosphate produced earlier in the series of intrinsic pathway reactions. Factor XII sets off a series of reactions that in turn activates factor XI (antihemolytic factor C or plasma thromboplastin antecedent) then factor IX (antihemolytic factor B or plasma thromboplasmin). In the meantime, chemicals released by the platelets increase the rate of these activation reactions. Finally, factor VIII (antihemolytic factor A) from the platelets and endothelial cells combines with factor IX (antihemolytic factor B or plasma thromboplasmin) to form an enzyme complex that activates factor X (Stuart–Prower factor or thrombokinase), leading to the common pathway. The events in the intrinsic pathway are completed in a few minutes.

Common Pathway

Both the intrinsic and extrinsic pathways lead to the **common pathway**, in which fibrin is produced to seal off the vessel. Once factor X has been activated by either the intrinsic or extrinsic pathway, the enzyme prothrombinase converts factor II, the inactive enzyme prothrombin, into the active enzyme **thrombin**. (Note that if the enzyme thrombin were not normally in an inactive form, clots would form spontaneously, a condition not consistent with life.) Then, thrombin converts factor I, the soluble fibrinogen, into the insoluble fibrin protein strands. Factor XIII then stabilizes the fibrin clot.

Fibrinolysis

The stabilized clot is acted upon by contractile proteins within the platelets. As these proteins contract, they pull on the fibrin threads, bringing the edges of the clot more tightly together, somewhat as we do when tightening loose shoelaces (see Figure 18.14**a**). This process also wrings out of the clot a small amount of fluid called **serum**, which is blood plasma without its clotting factors.

To restore normal blood flow as the vessel heals, the clot must eventually be removed. **Fibrinolysis** is the gradual degradation of the clot. Again, there is a fairly complicated series of reactions that involves factor XII and protein-catabolizing enzymes. During this process, the inactive protein plasminogen is converted into the active **plasmin**, which gradually breaks down the fibrin of the clot. Additionally, bradykinin, a vasodilator, is released, reversing the effects of the serotonin and prostaglandins from the platelets. This allows the smooth muscle in the walls of the vessels to relax and helps to restore the circulation.

Plasma Anticoagulants

An **anticoagulant** is any substance that opposes coagulation. Several circulating plasma anticoagulants play a role in limiting the coagulation process to the region of injury and restoring a normal, clot-free condition of blood. For instance, a cluster of proteins collectively referred to as the protein C system inactivates clotting factors involved in the intrinsic pathway. TFPI (tissue factor pathway inhibitor) inhibits the conversion of the inactive factor VII to the active form in the extrinsic pathway. **Antithrombin** inactivates factor X and opposes the conversion of prothrombin (factor II) to thrombin in the common pathway. And as noted earlier, basophils release **heparin**, a short-acting anticoagulant that also opposes prothrombin. Heparin is also found on the surfaces of cells lining the blood vessels. A pharmaceutical form of heparin is often administered therapeutically, for example, in surgical patients at risk for blood clots.

⊘ INTERACTIVE LINK

View these animations (http://openstax.org/l/coagulation) to explore the intrinsic, extrinsic, and common pathways that are involved the process of coagulation. The coagulation cascade restores hemostasis by activating coagulation factors in the presence of an injury. How does the endothelium of the blood vessel walls prevent the blood from coagulating as it flows through the blood vessels?

Disorders of Clotting

Either an insufficient or an excessive production of platelets can lead to severe disease or death. As discussed earlier, an insufficient number of platelets, called thrombocytopenia, typically results in the inability of blood to form clots. This can lead to excessive bleeding, even from minor wounds.

Another reason for failure of the blood to clot is the inadequate production of functional amounts of one or more clotting factors. This is the case in the genetic disorder **hemophilia**, which is actually a group of related disorders, the most common of which is hemophilia A, accounting for approximately 80 percent of cases. This disorder results in the inability to synthesize sufficient quantities of factor VIII. Hemophilia B is the second most common form, accounting for approximately 20 percent of cases. In this case, there is a deficiency of factor IX. Both of these defects are linked to the X chromosome and are typically passed from a healthy (carrier) female to their male offspring, since males are XY. Females would need to inherit a defective gene from each parent to manifest the disease, since they are XX. Patients with hemophilia bleed from even minor internal and external wounds, and leak blood into joint spaces after exercise and into urine and stool. Hemophilia C is a rare condition that is triggered by an autosomal (not sex) chromosome that renders factor XI nonfunctional. It is not a true recessive condition, since even individuals with a single copy of the mutant gene show a tendency to bleed. Regular infusions of clotting factors isolated from healthy donors can help prevent bleeding in hemophiliac patients. At some point, genetic therapy will become a viable option.

In contrast to the disorders characterized by coagulation failure is thrombocytosis, also mentioned earlier, a condition characterized by excessive numbers of platelets that increases the risk for excessive clot formation, a condition known as **thrombosis**. A **thrombus** (plural = thrombi) is an aggregation of platelets, erythrocytes, and even WBCs typically trapped within a mass of fibrin strands. While the formation of a clot is normal following the hemostatic mechanism just described, thrombi can form within an intact or only slightly damaged blood vessel. In a large vessel, a thrombus will adhere to the vessel wall and decrease the flow of blood, and is referred to as a mural thrombus. In a small vessel, it may actually totally block the flow of blood and is termed an occlusive thrombus. Thrombi are most commonly caused by vessel damage to the endothelial lining, which activates the clotting mechanism. These may include venous stasis, when blood in the veins, particularly in the legs, remains stationary for long periods. This is one of the dangers of long airplane flights in crowded conditions and may lead to deep vein thrombosis. Thrombophilia, also called hypercoagulation, is a condition in which there is a tendency to form thrombosis. This may be familial (genetic) or acquired. Acquired forms include the autoimmune disease lupus, immune reactions to heparin, polycythemia vera, thrombocytosis, sickle cell disease, pregnancy, and even obesity. A thrombus can seriously impede blood flow to or from a region and will cause a local increase in blood pressure. If flow is to be maintained, the heart will need to generate a greater pressure to overcome the resistance.

When a portion of a thrombus breaks free from the vessel wall and enters the circulation, it is referred to as an

Access for free at openstax.org

embolus. An embolus that is carried through the bloodstream can be large enough to block a vessel critical to a major organ. When it becomes trapped, an embolus is called an embolism. In the heart, brain, or lungs, an embolism may accordingly cause a heart attack, a stroke, or a pulmonary embolism. These are medical emergencies.

Among the many known biochemical activities of aspirin is its role as an anticoagulant. Aspirin (acetylsalicylic acid) is very effective at inhibiting the aggregation of platelets. It is routinely administered during a heart attack or stroke to reduce the adverse effects. Physicians sometimes recommend that patients at risk for cardiovascular disease take a low dose of aspirin on a daily basis as a preventive measure. However, aspirin can also lead to serious side effects, including increasing the risk of ulcers. A patient is well advised to consult a physician before beginning any aspirin regimen.

A class of drugs collectively known as thrombolytic agents can help speed up the degradation of an abnormal clot. If a thrombolytic agent is administered to a patient within 3 hours following a thrombotic stroke, the patient's prognosis improves significantly. However, some strokes are not caused by thrombi, but by hemorrhage. Thus, the cause must be determined before treatment begins. Tissue plasminogen activator is an enzyme that catalyzes the conversion of plasminogen to plasmin, the primary enzyme that breaks down clots. It is released naturally by endothelial cells but is also used in clinical medicine. New research is progressing using compounds isolated from the venom of some species of snakes, particularly vipers and cobras, which may eventually have therapeutic value as thrombolytic agents.

18.6 Blood Typing

LEARNING OBJECTIVES

By the end of this section, you will be able to:

- Describe the two basic physiological consequences of transfusion of incompatible blood
- Compare and contrast ABO and Rh blood groups
- Identify which blood groups may be safely transfused into patients with different ABO types
- Discuss the pathophysiology of hemolytic disease of the newborn

Blood transfusions in humans were risky procedures until the discovery of the major human blood groups by Karl Landsteiner, an Austrian biologist and physician, in 1900. Until that point, physicians did not understand that death sometimes followed blood transfusions, when the type of donor blood infused into the patient was incompatible with the patient's own blood. Blood groups are determined by the presence or absence of specific marker molecules on the plasma membranes of erythrocytes. With their discovery, it became possible for the first time to match patient-donor blood types and prevent transfusion reactions and deaths.

Antigens, Antibodies, and Transfusion Reactions

Antigens are substances that the body does not recognize as belonging to the "self" and that therefore trigger a defensive response from the leukocytes of the immune system. (Seek more content for additional information on immunity.) Here, we will focus on the role of immunity in blood transfusion reactions. With RBCs in particular, you may see the antigens referred to as isoantigens or agglutinogens (surface antigens) and the antibodies referred to as isoantibodies or agglutinins. In this chapter, we will use the more common terms antigens and antibodies.

Antigens are generally large proteins, but may include other classes of organic molecules, including carbohydrates, lipids, and nucleic acids. Following an infusion of incompatible blood, erythrocytes with foreign antigens appear in the bloodstream and trigger an immune response. Proteins called antibodies (immunoglobulins), which are produced by certain B lymphocytes called plasma cells, attach to the antigens on the plasma membranes of the infused erythrocytes and cause them to adhere to one another.

- Because the arms of the Y-shaped antibodies attach randomly to more than one nonself erythrocyte surface, they form clumps of erythrocytes. This process is called **agglutination**.
- The clumps of erythrocytes block small blood vessels throughout the body, depriving tissues of oxygen and nutrients.
- As the erythrocyte clumps are degraded, in a process called **hemolysis**, their hemoglobin is released into the bloodstream. This hemoglobin travels to the kidneys, which are responsible for filtration of the blood. However,

the load of hemoglobin released can easily overwhelm the kidney's capacity to clear it, and the patient can quickly develop kidney failure.

More than 50 antigens have been identified on erythrocyte membranes, but the most significant in terms of their potential harm to patients are classified in two groups: the ABO blood group and the Rh blood group.

The ABO Blood Group

Although the **ABO blood group** name consists of three letters, ABO blood typing designates the presence or absence of just two antigens, A and B. Both are glycoproteins. People whose erythrocytes have A antigens on their erythrocyte membrane surfaces are designated blood type A, and those whose erythrocytes have B antigens are blood type B. People can also have both A and B antigens on their erythrocytes, in which case they are blood type AB. People with neither A nor B antigens are designated blood type O. ABO blood types are genetically determined.

The body must be exposed to a foreign antigen before an antibody can be produced. ABO blood group antigens are found in foods and microbes throughout nature. Thus, the human immune system is exposed to A and B antigens at an early age and antibodies are formed naturally. Individuals with type A blood—without any prior exposure to incompatible blood—have naturally-formed antibodies to the B antigen circulating in their blood plasma. These antibodies, referred to as anti-B antibodies, will cause agglutination and hemolysis if they ever encounter erythrocytes with B antigens. Similarly, an individual with type B blood has naturally-formed anti-A antibodies. Individuals with type AB blood, which has both antigens, do not have naturally-formed antibodies to either of these. People with type O blood lack antigens A and B on their erythrocytes, but both anti-A and anti-B antibodies circulate in their blood plasma.

Rh Blood Groups

The **Rh blood group** is classified according to the presence or absence of a second erythrocyte antigen identified as Rh. (It was first discovered in a type of primate known as a rhesus macaque, which is often used in research, because its blood is similar to that of humans.) Although dozens of Rh antigens have been identified, only one, designated D, is clinically important. Those who have the Rh D antigen present on their erythrocytes—about 85 percent of Americans—are described as Rh positive (Rh^+) and those who lack it are Rh negative (Rh^-). Note that the Rh group is distinct from the ABO group, so any individual, no matter their ABO blood type, may have or lack this Rh antigen. When identifying a patient's blood type, the Rh group is designated by adding the word positive or negative to the ABO type. For example, A positive (A^+) means ABO group A blood with the Rh antigen present, and AB negative (AB^-) means ABO group AB blood without the Rh antigen.

Table 18.2 summarizes the distribution of the ABO and Rh blood types within the United States.

Summary of ABO and Rh Blood Types within the United States

Blood Type	Asian	Black non-Hispanic	Hispanic	North American Indian	White non-Hispanic
A^+	27.3	24.0	28.7	31.3	33.0
A^-	0.5	1.9	2.4	3.8	6.8
B^+	25.0	18.4	9.2	7.0	9.1
B^-	0.4	1.3	0.7	0.9	1.8
AB^+	7.0	4.0	2.3	2.2	3.4
AB^-	0.1	0.3	0.2	0.3	0.7

TABLE 18.2

Blood Type	Asian	Black non-Hispanic	Hispanic	North American Indian	White non-Hispanic
O⁺	39.0	46.6	52.6	50.0	37.2
O⁻	0.7	3.6	3.9	4.7	8.0

TABLE 18.2

In contrast to the ABO group antibodies, which are preformed, antibodies to the Rh antigen are produced only in Rh⁻ individuals after exposure to the antigen. This process, called sensitization, occurs following a transfusion with Rh-incompatible blood or, more commonly, with the birth of an Rh⁺ baby to an Rh⁻ person. Problems are rare in a first pregnancy, since the baby's Rh⁺ cells rarely cross the placenta (the organ of gas and nutrient exchange between the fetus and the pregnant person). However, during or immediately after birth, the Rh⁻ parent can be exposed to the baby's Rh⁺ cells (Figure 18.15). Research has shown that this occurs in about 13–14 percent of such pregnancies. After exposure, the immune system of the person who has given birth begins to generate anti-Rh antibodies. If the same person should then become pregnant with another Rh⁺ baby, the Rh antibodies they have produced can cross the placenta into the fetal bloodstream and destroy the fetal RBCs. This condition, known as **hemolytic disease of the newborn (HDN)** or erythroblastosis fetalis, may cause anemia in mild cases, but the agglutination and hemolysis can be so severe that without treatment the fetus may die in the womb or shortly after birth.

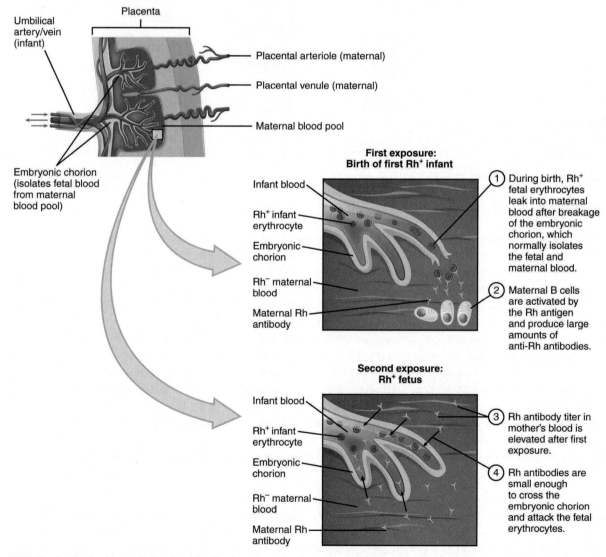

FIGURE 18.15 Erythroblastosis Fetalis The first exposure of an Rh⁻ person to Rh⁺ erythrocytes during pregnancy induces

sensitization. Anti-Rh antibodies begin to circulate in the pregnant person's bloodstream. A second exposure occurs with a subsequent pregnancy with an Rh⁺ fetus in the uterus. During that subsequent pregnancy, the pregnant person's anti-Rh antibodies may cross the placenta and enter the fetal bloodstream, causing agglutination and hemolysis of fetal erythrocytes.

A drug known as RhoGAM, short for Rh immune globulin, can temporarily prevent the development of Rh antibodies in the Rh⁻ parent, thereby averting this potentially serious disease for the fetus. RhoGAM antibodies destroy any fetal Rh⁺ erythrocytes that may cross the placental barrier. RhoGAM is normally administered to Rh⁻ pregnant people during weeks 26–28 of pregnancy and within 72 hours following birth. It has proven remarkably effective in decreasing the incidence of HDN. Earlier we noted that the incidence of HDN in an Rh⁺ subsequent pregnancy to an Rh⁻ person is about 13–14 percent without preventive treatment. Since the introduction of RhoGAM in 1968, the incidence has dropped to about 0.1 percent in the United States.

Determining ABO Blood Types

Clinicians are able to determine a patient's blood type quickly and easily using commercially prepared antibodies. An unknown blood sample is allocated into separate wells. Into one well a small amount of anti-A antibody is added, and to another a small amount of anti-B antibody. If the antigen is present, the antibodies will cause visible agglutination of the cells (Figure 18.16). The blood should also be tested for Rh antibodies.

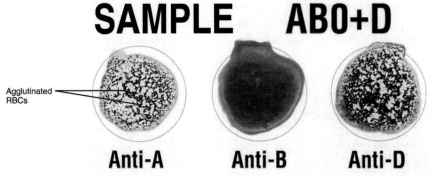

FIGURE 18.16   Cross Matching Blood Types   This sample of a commercially produced "bedside" card enables quick typing of both a recipient's and donor's blood before transfusion. The card contains three reaction sites or wells. One is coated with an anti-A antibody, one with an anti-B antibody, and one with an anti-D antibody (tests for the presence of Rh factor D). Mixing a drop of blood and saline into each well enables the blood to interact with a preparation of type-specific antibodies, also called anti-seras. Agglutination of RBCs in a given site indicates a positive identification of the blood antigens, in this case A and Rh antigens for blood type A⁺. For the purpose of transfusion, the donor's and recipient's blood types must match.

ABO Transfusion Protocols

To avoid transfusion reactions, it is best to transfuse only matching blood types; that is, a type B⁺ recipient should ideally receive blood only from a type B⁺ donor and so on. That said, in emergency situations, when acute hemorrhage threatens the patient's life, there may not be time for cross matching to identify blood type. In these cases, blood from a **universal donor**—an individual with type O⁻ blood—may be transfused. Recall that type O erythrocytes do not display A or B antigens. Thus, anti-A or anti-B antibodies that might be circulating in the patient's blood plasma will not encounter any erythrocyte surface antigens on the donated blood and therefore will not be provoked into a response. One problem with this designation of universal donor is if the O⁻ individual had prior exposure to Rh antigen, Rh antibodies may be present in the donated blood. Also, introducing type O blood into an individual with type A, B, or AB blood will nevertheless introduce antibodies against both A and B antigens, as these are always circulating in the type O blood plasma. This may cause problems for the recipient, but because the volume of blood transfused is much lower than the volume of the patient's own blood, the adverse effects of the relatively few infused plasma antibodies are typically limited. Rh factor also plays a role. If Rh⁻ individuals receiving blood have had prior exposure to Rh antigen, antibodies for this antigen may be present in the blood and trigger agglutination to some degree. Although it is always preferable to cross match a patient's blood before transfusing, in a true life-threatening emergency situation, this is not always possible, and these procedures may be implemented.

A patient with blood type AB⁺ is known as the **universal recipient**. This patient can theoretically receive any type of blood, because the patient's own blood—having both A and B antigens on the erythrocyte surface—does not produce anti-A or anti-B antibodies. In addition, an Rh⁺ patient can receive both Rh⁺ and Rh⁻ blood. However, keep in mind that the donor's blood will contain circulating antibodies, again with possible negative implications. Figure 18.17 summarizes the blood types and compatibilities.

Access for free at openstax.org

At the scene of multiple-vehicle accidents, military engagements, and natural or human-caused disasters, many victims may suffer simultaneously from acute hemorrhage, yet type O blood may not be immediately available. In these circumstances, medics may at least try to replace some of the volume of blood that has been lost. This is done by intravenous administration of a saline solution that provides fluids and electrolytes in proportions equivalent to those of normal blood plasma. Research is ongoing to develop a safe and effective artificial blood that would carry out the oxygen-carrying function of blood without the RBCs, enabling transfusions in the field without concern for incompatibility. These blood substitutes normally contain hemoglobin- as well as perfluorocarbon-based oxygen carriers.

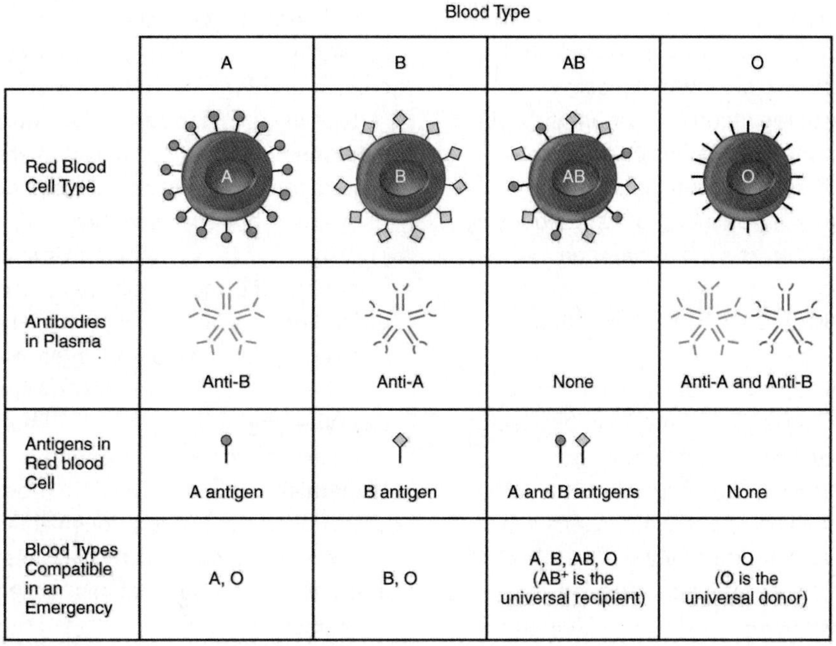

	Blood Type			
	A	B	AB	O
Red Blood Cell Type				
Antibodies in Plasma	Anti-B	Anti-A	None	Anti-A and Anti-B
Antigens in Red blood Cell	A antigen	B antigen	A and B antigens	None
Blood Types Compatible in an Emergency	A, O	B, O	A, B, AB, O (AB⁺ is the universal recipient)	O (O is the universal donor)

FIGURE 18.17   **ABO Blood Group**   This chart summarizes the characteristics of the blood types in the ABO blood group. See the text for more on the concept of a universal donor or recipient.

Key Terms

ABO blood group   blood-type classification based on the presence or absence of A and B glycoproteins on the erythrocyte membrane surface

agglutination   clustering of cells into masses linked by antibodies

agranular leukocytes   leukocytes with few granules in their cytoplasm; specifically, monocytes, lymphocytes, and NK cells

albumin   most abundant plasma protein, accounting for most of the osmotic pressure of plasma

anemia   deficiency of red blood cells or hemoglobin

antibodies   (also, immunoglobulins or gamma globulins) antigen-specific proteins produced by specialized B lymphocytes that protect the body by binding to foreign objects such as bacteria and viruses

anticoagulant   substance such as heparin that opposes coagulation

antithrombin   anticoagulant that inactivates factor X and opposes the conversion of prothrombin (factor II) into thrombin in the common pathway

B lymphocytes   (also, B cells) lymphocytes that defend the body against specific pathogens and thereby provide specific immunity

basophils   granulocytes that stain with a basic (alkaline) stain and store histamine and heparin

bilirubin   yellowish bile pigment produced when iron is removed from heme and is further broken down into waste products

biliverdin   green bile pigment produced when the non-iron portion of heme is degraded into a waste product; converted to bilirubin in the liver

blood   liquid connective tissue composed of formed elements—erythrocytes, leukocytes, and platelets—and a fluid extracellular matrix called plasma; component of the cardiovascular system

bone marrow biopsy   diagnostic test of a sample of red bone marrow

bone marrow transplant   treatment in which a donor's healthy bone marrow with its stem cells replaces diseased or damaged bone marrow of a patient

bruise   localized bleeding under the skin due to damaged blood vessels

buffy coat   thin, pale layer of leukocytes and platelets that separates the erythrocytes from the plasma in a sample of centrifuged blood

carbaminohemoglobin   compound of carbon dioxide and hemoglobin, and one of the ways in which carbon dioxide is carried in the blood

clotting factors   group of 12 identified substances active in coagulation

coagulation   formation of a blood clot; part of the process of hemostasis

colony-stimulating factors (CSFs)   glycoproteins that trigger the proliferation and differentiation of myeloblasts into granular leukocytes (basophils, neutrophils, and eosinophils)

common pathway   final coagulation pathway activated either by the intrinsic or the extrinsic pathway, and ending in the formation of a blood clot

cross matching   blood test for identification of blood type using antibodies and small samples of blood

cytokines   class of proteins that act as autocrine or paracrine signaling molecules; in the cardiovascular system, they stimulate the proliferation of progenitor cells and help to stimulate both nonspecific and specific resistance to disease

defensins   antimicrobial proteins released from neutrophils and macrophages that create openings in the plasma membranes to kill cells

deoxyhemoglobin   molecule of hemoglobin without an oxygen molecule bound to it

diapedesis   (also, emigration) process by which leukocytes squeeze through adjacent cells in a blood vessel wall to enter tissues

embolus   thrombus that has broken free from the blood vessel wall and entered the circulation

emigration   (also, diapedesis) process by which leukocytes squeeze through adjacent cells in a blood vessel wall to enter tissues

eosinophils   granulocytes that stain with eosin; they release antihistamines and are especially active against parasitic worms

erythrocyte   (also, red blood cell) mature myeloid blood cell that is composed mostly of hemoglobin and functions primarily in the transportation of oxygen and carbon dioxide

erythropoietin (EPO)   glycoprotein that triggers the bone marrow to produce RBCs; secreted by the kidney in response to low oxygen levels

extrinsic pathway   initial coagulation pathway that begins with tissue damage and results in the activation of the common pathway

ferritin   protein-containing storage form of iron found in the bone marrow, liver, and spleen

fibrin   insoluble, filamentous protein that forms the structure of a blood clot

fibrinogen   plasma protein produced in the liver and involved in blood clotting

fibrinolysis   gradual degradation of a blood clot

formed elements   cellular components of blood; that is, erythrocytes, leukocytes, and platelets

globin   heme-containing globular protein that is a

constituent of hemoglobin

globulins   heterogeneous group of plasma proteins that includes transport proteins, clotting factors, immune proteins, and others

granular leukocytes   leukocytes with abundant granules in their cytoplasm; specifically, neutrophils, eosinophils, and basophils

hematocrit   (also, packed cell volume) volume percentage of erythrocytes in a sample of centrifuged blood

hematopoietic stem cell   type of pluripotent stem cell that gives rise to the formed elements of blood (hemocytoblast)

heme   red, iron-containing pigment to which oxygen binds in hemoglobin

hemocytoblast   hematopoietic stem cell that gives rise to the formed elements of blood

hemoglobin   oxygen-carrying compound in erythrocytes

hemolysis   destruction (lysis) of erythrocytes and the release of their hemoglobin into circulation

hemolytic disease of the newborn (HDN)   (also, erythroblastosis fetalis) disorder causing agglutination and hemolysis in an Rh⁺ fetus or newborn of an Rh⁻ person

hemophilia   genetic disorder characterized by inadequate synthesis of clotting factors

hemopoiesis   production of the formed elements of blood

hemopoietic growth factors   chemical signals including erythropoietin, thrombopoietin, colony-stimulating factors, and interleukins that regulate the differentiation and proliferation of particular blood progenitor cells

hemorrhage   excessive bleeding

hemosiderin   protein-containing storage form of iron found in the bone marrow, liver, and spleen

hemostasis   physiological process by which bleeding ceases

heparin   short-acting anticoagulant stored in mast cells and released when tissues are injured, opposes prothrombin

hypoxemia   below-normal level of oxygen saturation of blood (typically <95 percent)

immunoglobulins   (also, antibodies or gamma globulins) antigen-specific proteins produced by specialized B lymphocytes that protect the body by binding to foreign objects such as bacteria and viruses

interleukins   signaling molecules that may function in hemopoiesis, inflammation, and specific immune responses

intrinsic pathway   initial coagulation pathway that begins with vascular damage or contact with foreign substances, and results in the activation of the common pathway

jaundice   yellowing of the skin or whites of the eyes due to excess bilirubin in the blood

leukemia   cancer involving leukocytes

leukocyte   (also, white blood cell) colorless, nucleated blood cell, the chief function of which is to protect the body from disease

leukocytosis   excessive leukocyte proliferation

leukopenia   below-normal production of leukocytes

lymphocytes   agranular leukocytes of the lymphoid stem cell line, many of which function in specific immunity

lymphoid stem cells   type of hematopoietic stem cells that gives rise to lymphocytes, including various T cells, B cells, and NK cells, all of which function in immunity

lymphoma   form of cancer in which masses of malignant T and/or B lymphocytes collect in lymph nodes, the spleen, the liver, and other tissues

lysozyme   digestive enzyme with bactericidal properties

macrophage   phagocytic cell of the myeloid lineage; a matured monocyte

megakaryocyte   bone marrow cell that produces platelets

memory cell   type of B or T lymphocyte that forms after exposure to a pathogen

monocytes   agranular leukocytes of the myeloid stem cell line that circulate in the bloodstream; tissue monocytes are macrophages

myeloid stem cells   type of hematopoietic stem cell that gives rise to some formed elements, including erythrocytes, megakaryocytes that produce platelets, and a myeloblast lineage that gives rise to monocytes and three forms of granular leukocytes (neutrophils, eosinophils, and basophils)

natural killer (NK) cells   cytotoxic lymphocytes capable of recognizing cells that do not express "self" proteins on their plasma membrane or that contain foreign or abnormal markers; provide generalized, nonspecific immunity

neutrophils   granulocytes that stain with a neutral dye and are the most numerous of the leukocytes; especially active against bacteria

oxyhemoglobin   molecule of hemoglobin to which oxygen is bound

packed cell volume (PCV)   (also, hematocrit) volume percentage of erythrocytes present in a sample of centrifuged blood

plasma   in blood, the liquid extracellular matrix composed mostly of water that circulates the formed elements and dissolved materials throughout the cardiovascular system

plasmin   blood protein active in fibrinolysis

platelet plug   accumulation and adhesion of platelets at the site of blood vessel injury

platelets   (also, thrombocytes) one of the formed elements of blood that consists of cell fragments broken off from megakaryocytes

pluripotent stem cell   stem cell that derives from totipotent stem cells and is capable of differentiating into many, but not all, cell types

polycythemia   elevated level of hemoglobin, whether adaptive or pathological

polymorphonuclear   having a lobed nucleus, as seen in some leukocytes

positive chemotaxis   process in which a cell is attracted to move in the direction of chemical stimuli

red blood cells (RBCs)   (also, erythrocytes) one of the formed elements of blood that transports oxygen

reticulocyte   immature erythrocyte that may still contain fragments of organelles

Rh blood group   blood-type classification based on the presence or absence of the antigen Rh on the erythrocyte membrane surface

serum   blood plasma that does not contain clotting factors

sickle cell disease   (also, sickle cell anemia) inherited blood disorder in which hemoglobin molecules are malformed, leading to the breakdown of RBCs that take on a characteristic sickle shape

T lymphocytes   (also, T cells) lymphocytes that provide cellular-level immunity by physically attacking foreign or diseased cells

thalassemia   inherited blood disorder in which maturation of RBCs does not proceed normally,

leading to abnormal formation of hemoglobin and the destruction of RBCs

thrombin   enzyme essential for the final steps in formation of a fibrin clot

thrombocytes   platelets, one of the formed elements of blood that consists of cell fragments broken off from megakaryocytes

thrombocytopenia   condition in which there are too few platelets, resulting in abnormal bleeding (hemophilia)

thrombocytosis   condition in which there are too many platelets, resulting in abnormal clotting (thrombosis)

thrombopoietin   hormone secreted by the liver and kidneys that prompts the development of megakaryocytes into thrombocytes (platelets)

thrombosis   excessive clot formation

thrombus   aggregation of fibrin, platelets, and erythrocytes in an intact artery or vein

tissue factor   protein thromboplastin, which initiates the extrinsic pathway when released in response to tissue damage

totipotent stem cell   embryonic stem cell that is capable of differentiating into any and all cells of the body; enabling the full development of an organism

transferrin   plasma protein that binds reversibly to iron and distributes it throughout the body

universal donor   individual with type O⁻ blood

universal recipient   individual with type AB⁺ blood

vascular spasm   initial step in hemostasis, in which the smooth muscle in the walls of the ruptured or damaged blood vessel contracts

white blood cells (WBCs)   (also, leukocytes) one of the formed elements of blood that provides defense against disease agents and foreign materials

Chapter Review

18.1 An Overview of Blood

Blood is a fluid connective tissue critical to the transportation of nutrients, gases, and wastes throughout the body; to defend the body against infection and other threats; and to the homeostatic regulation of pH, temperature, and other internal conditions. Blood is composed of formed elements—erythrocytes, leukocytes, and cell fragments called platelets—and a fluid extracellular matrix called plasma. More than 90 percent of plasma is water. The remainder is mostly plasma proteins—mainly albumin, globulins, and fibrinogen—and other dissolved solutes such as glucose, lipids, electrolytes, and dissolved gases. Because of the formed elements and the plasma proteins and other solutes, blood is sticky and

more viscous than water. It is also slightly alkaline, and its temperature is slightly higher than normal body temperature.

18.2 Production of the Formed Elements

Through the process of hemopoiesis, the formed elements of blood are continually produced, replacing the relatively short-lived erythrocytes, leukocytes, and platelets. Hemopoiesis begins in the red bone marrow, with hematopoietic stem cells that differentiate into myeloid and lymphoid lineages. Myeloid stem cells give rise to most of the formed elements. Lymphoid stem cells give rise only to the various lymphocytes designated as B and T cells, and NK cells. Hemopoietic growth factors, including erythropoietin, thrombopoietin, colony-stimulating factors, and interleukins, promote the proliferation and differentiation of formed elements.

18.3 Erythrocytes

The most abundant formed elements in blood, erythrocytes are red, biconcave disks packed with an oxygen-carrying compound called hemoglobin. The hemoglobin molecule contains four globin proteins bound to a pigment molecule called heme, which contains an ion of iron. In the bloodstream, iron picks up oxygen in the lungs and drops it off in the tissues; the amino acids in hemoglobin then transport carbon dioxide from the tissues back to the lungs. Erythrocytes live only 120 days on average, and thus must be continually replaced. Worn-out erythrocytes are phagocytized by macrophages and their hemoglobin is broken down. The breakdown products are recycled or removed as wastes: Globin is broken down into amino acids for synthesis of new proteins; iron is stored in the liver or spleen or used by the bone marrow for production of new erythrocytes; and the remnants of heme are converted into bilirubin, or other waste products that are taken up by the liver and excreted in the bile or removed by the kidneys. Anemia is a deficiency of RBCs or hemoglobin, whereas polycythemia is an excess of RBCs.

18.4 Leukocytes and Platelets

Leukocytes function in body defenses. They squeeze out of the walls of blood vessels through emigration or diapedesis, then may move through tissue fluid or become attached to various organs where they fight against pathogenic organisms, diseased cells, or other threats to health. Granular leukocytes, which include neutrophils, eosinophils, and basophils, originate with myeloid stem cells, as do the agranular monocytes. The other agranular leukocytes, NK cells, B cells, and T cells, arise from the lymphoid stem cell line. The most abundant leukocytes are the neutrophils, which are first responders to infections, especially with bacteria. About 20–30 percent of all leukocytes are lymphocytes, which are critical to the body's defense against specific threats. Leukemia and lymphoma are malignancies involving leukocytes. Platelets are fragments of cells known as megakaryocytes that dwell within the bone marrow. While many platelets are stored in the spleen, others enter the circulation and are essential for hemostasis; they also produce several growth factors important for repair and healing.

18.5 Hemostasis

Hemostasis is the physiological process by which bleeding ceases. Hemostasis involves three basic steps: vascular spasm, the formation of a platelet plug, and coagulation, in which clotting factors promote the formation of a fibrin clot. Fibrinolysis is the process in which a clot is degraded in a healing vessel. Anticoagulants are substances that oppose coagulation. They are important in limiting the extent and duration of clotting. Inadequate clotting can result from too few platelets, or inadequate production of clotting factors, for instance, in the genetic disorder hemophilia. Excessive clotting, called thrombosis, can be caused by excessive numbers of platelets. A thrombus is a collection of fibrin, platelets, and erythrocytes that has accumulated along the lining of a blood vessel, whereas an embolus is a thrombus that has broken free from the vessel wall and is circulating in the bloodstream.

18.6 Blood Typing

Antigens are nonself molecules, usually large proteins, which provoke an immune response. In transfusion reactions, antibodies attach to antigens on the surfaces of erythrocytes and cause agglutination and hemolysis. ABO blood group antigens are designated A and B. People with type A blood have A antigens on their erythrocytes, whereas those with type B blood have B antigens. Those with AB blood have both A and B antigens, and those with type O blood have neither A nor B antigens. The blood plasma contains preformed antibodies against the antigens not present on a person's erythrocytes.

A second group of blood antigens is the Rh group, the most important of which is Rh D. People with Rh⁻ blood do not have this antigen on their erythrocytes, whereas those who are Rh⁺ do. About 85 percent of Americans are Rh⁺. When a person who is Rh⁻ becomes pregnant with an Rh⁺ fetus, their body may begin to produce anti-Rh antibodies. If the person subsequently becomes pregnant with a second Rh⁺ fetus and is not treated preventively with RhoGAM, the fetus will be at risk for an antigen-antibody reaction, including agglutination and hemolysis. This is known as hemolytic disease of the newborn.

Cross matching to determine blood type is necessary before transfusing blood, unless the patient is experiencing hemorrhage that is an immediate threat to life, in which case type O⁻ blood may be transfused.

Interactive Link Questions

1. Visit this site (http://openstax.org/l/normallevels) for a list of normal levels established for many of the substances found in a sample of blood. Serum, one of the specimen types included, refers to a sample of plasma after clotting factors have been removed. What types of measurements are given for levels of glucose in the blood?

2. Watch this video (http://openstax.org/l/doping) to see doctors discuss the dangers of blood doping in sports. What are the some potential side effects of blood doping?

3. Figure 18.13 Are you able to recognize and identify the various formed elements? You will need to do this is a systematic manner, scanning along the image. The standard method is to use a grid, but this is not possible with this resource. Try constructing a simple table with each leukocyte type and then making a mark for each cell type you identify. Attempt to classify at least 50 and perhaps as many as 100 different cells. Based on the percentage of cells that you count, do the numbers represent a normal blood smear or does something appear to be abnormal?

4. View these animations (http://openstax.org/l/coagulation) to explore the intrinsic, extrinsic, and common pathways that are involved the process of coagulation. The coagulation cascade restores hemostasis by activating coagulation factors in the presence of an injury. How does the endothelium of the blood vessel walls prevent the blood from coagulating as it flows through the blood vessels?

Review Questions

5. Which of the following statements about blood is true?
   a. Blood is about 92 percent water.
   b. Blood is slightly more acidic than water.
   c. Blood is slightly more viscous than water.
   d. Blood is slightly more salty than seawater.

6. Which of the following statements about albumin is true?
   a. It draws water out of the blood vessels and into the body's tissues.
   b. It is the most abundant plasma protein.
   c. It is produced by specialized leukocytes called plasma cells.
   d. All of the above are true.

7. Which of the following plasma proteins is *not* produced by the liver?
   a. fibrinogen
   b. alpha globulin
   c. beta globulin
   d. immunoglobulin

8. Which of the formed elements arise from myeloid stem cells?
   a. B cells
   b. natural killer cells
   c. platelets
   d. all of the above

9. Which of the following statements about erythropoietin is true?
   a. It facilitates the proliferation and differentiation of the erythrocyte lineage.
   b. It is a hormone produced by the thyroid gland.
   c. It is a hemopoietic growth factor that prompts lymphoid stem cells to leave the bone marrow.
   d. Both a and b are true.

10. Interleukins are associated primarily with which of the following?
    a. production of various lymphocytes
    b. immune responses
    c. inflammation
    d. all of the above

11. Which of the following statements about mature, circulating erythrocytes is true?
    a. They have no nucleus.
    b. They are packed with mitochondria.
    c. They survive for an average of 4 days.
    d. All of the above

12. A molecule of hemoglobin _____.
    a. is shaped like a biconcave disk packed almost entirely with iron
    b. contains four glycoprotein units studded with oxygen
    c. consists of four globin proteins, each bound to a molecule of heme
    d. can carry up to 120 molecules of oxygen

13. The production of healthy erythrocytes depends upon the availability of _____.
    a. copper
    b. zinc
    c. vitamin B_{12}
    d. copper, zinc, and vitamin B_{12}

14. Aging and damaged erythrocytes are removed from the circulation by _____.
    a. myeoblasts
    b. monocytes
    c. macrophages
    d. mast cells

15. A patient has been suffering for 2 months with a chronic, watery diarrhea. A blood test is likely to reveal _____.
    a. a hematocrit below 30 percent
    b. hypoxemia
    c. anemia
    d. polycythemia

16. The process by which leukocytes squeeze through adjacent cells in a blood vessel wall is called _____.
    a. leukocytosis
    b. positive chemotaxis
    c. emigration
    d. cytoplasmic extending

17. Which of the following describes a neutrophil?
    a. abundant, agranular, especially effective against cancer cells
    b. abundant, granular, especially effective against bacteria
    c. rare, agranular, releases antimicrobial defensins
    d. rare, granular, contains multiple granules packed with histamine

18. T and B lymphocytes _____.
    a. are polymorphonuclear
    b. are involved with specific immune function
    c. proliferate excessively in leukopenia
    d. are most active against parasitic worms

19. A patient has been experiencing severe, persistent allergy symptoms that are reduced when she takes an antihistamine. Before the treatment, this patient was likely to have had increased activity of which leukocyte?
    a. basophils
    b. neutrophils
    c. monocytes
    d. natural killer cells

20. Thrombocytes are more accurately called _____.
    a. clotting factors
    b. megakaryoblasts
    c. megakaryocytes
    d. platelets

21. The first step in hemostasis is _____.
    a. vascular spasm
    b. conversion of fibrinogen to fibrin
    c. activation of the intrinsic pathway
    d. activation of the common pathway

22. Prothrombin is converted to thrombin during the _____.
    a. intrinsic pathway
    b. extrinsic pathway
    c. common pathway
    d. formation of the platelet plug

23. Hemophilia is characterized by _____.
    a. inadequate production of heparin
    b. inadequate production of clotting factors
    c. excessive production of fibrinogen
    d. excessive production of platelets

24. The process in which antibodies attach to antigens, causing the formation of masses of linked cells, is called _____.
    a. sensitization
    b. coagulation
    c. agglutination
    d. hemolysis

25. People with ABO blood type O _____.
    a. have both antigens A and B on their erythrocytes
    b. lack both antigens A and B on their erythrocytes
    c. have neither anti-A nor anti-B antibodies circulating in their blood plasma
    d. are considered universal recipients

26. Hemolytic disease of the newborn is a risk during a subsequent pregnancy in which _____.
    a. a type AB person is carrying a type O fetus
    b. a type O person is carrying a type AB fetus
    c. an Rh$^+$ person is carrying an Rh$^-$ fetus
    d. an Rh$^-$ person is carrying a second Rh$^+$ fetus

Critical Thinking Questions

27. A patient's hematocrit is 42 percent. Approximately what percentage of the patient's blood is plasma?

28. Why would it be incorrect to refer to the formed elements as cells?

29. True or false: The buffy coat is the portion of a blood sample that is made up of its proteins.

30. Myelofibrosis is a disorder in which inflammation and scar tissue formation in the bone marrow impair hemopoiesis. One sign is an enlarged spleen. Why?

31. Would you expect a patient with a form of cancer called acute myelogenous leukemia to experience impaired production of erythrocytes, or impaired production of lymphocytes? Explain your choice.

32. A young person has been experiencing unusually heavy menstrual bleeding for several years. They follow a strict vegan diet (no animal foods). They are is at risk for what disorder, and why?

33. A patient has thalassemia, a genetic disorder characterized by abnormal synthesis of globin proteins and excessive destruction of erythrocytes. This patient is jaundiced and is found to have an excessive level of bilirubin in their blood. Explain the connection.

34. One of the more common adverse effects of cancer chemotherapy is the destruction of leukocytes. Before his next scheduled chemotherapy treatment, a patient undergoes a blood test called an absolute neutrophil count (ANC), which reveals that his neutrophil count is 1900 cells per microliter. Would his healthcare team be likely to proceed with his chemotherapy treatment? Why?

35. A patient was admitted to the burn unit the previous evening suffering from a severe burn involving their left upper extremity and shoulder. A blood test reveals that they are experiencing leukocytosis. Why is this an expected finding?

36. A lab technician collects a blood sample in a glass tube. After about an hour, she harvests serum to continue her blood analysis. Explain what has happened during the hour that the sample was in the glass tube.

37. Explain why administration of a thrombolytic agent is a first intervention for someone who has suffered a thrombotic stroke.

38. Following a motor vehicle accident, a patient is rushed to the emergency department with multiple traumatic injuries, causing severe bleeding. The patient's condition is critical, and there is no time for determining their blood type. What type of blood is transfused, and why?

39. In preparation for a scheduled surgery, a patient visits the hospital lab for a blood draw. The technician collects a blood sample and performs a test to determine its type. She places a sample of the patient's blood in two wells. To the first well she adds anti-A antibody. To the second she adds anti-B antibody. Both samples visibly agglutinate. Has the technician made an error, or is this a normal response? If normal, what blood type does this indicate?

CHAPTER 19
The Cardiovascular System: The Heart

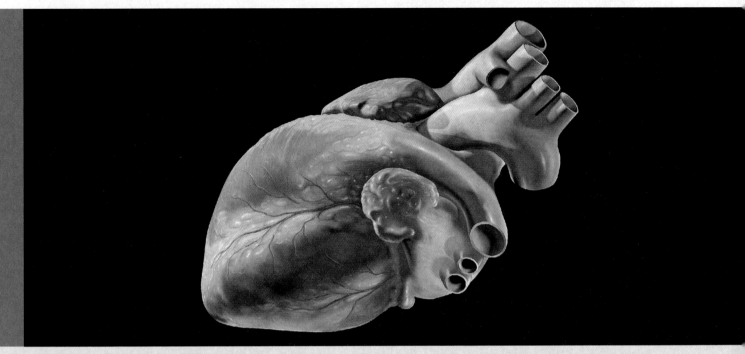

Figure 19.1 Human Heart This artist's conception of the human heart suggests a powerful engine—not inappropriate for a muscular pump that keeps the body continually supplied with blood. (credit: Patrick J. Lynch)

CHAPTER OBJECTIVES
After studying this chapter, you will be able to:

- Identify and describe the interior and exterior parts of the human heart
- Describe the path of blood through the cardiac circuits
- Describe the size, shape, and location of the heart
- Compare cardiac muscle to skeletal and smooth muscle
- Explain the cardiac conduction system
- Describe the process and purpose of an electrocardiogram
- Explain the cardiac cycle
- Calculate cardiac output
- Describe the effects of exercise on cardiac output and heart rate
- Name the centers of the brain that control heart rate and describe their function
- Identify other factors affecting heart rate
- Describe fetal heart development

INTRODUCTION In this chapter, you will explore the remarkable pump that propels the blood into the vessels. There is no single better word to describe the function of the heart other than "pump," since its contraction develops the pressure that ejects blood into the major vessels: the aorta and pulmonary trunk. From these vessels, the blood is distributed to the remainder of the body. Although the connotation of the term "pump" suggests a mechanical device made of steel and plastic, the anatomical structure is a living, sophisticated muscle. As you read this chapter, try to keep these twin concepts in mind: pump and muscle.

Although the term "heart" is an English word, cardiac (heart-related) terminology can be traced back to the Latin term, "kardia." Cardiology is the study of the heart, and cardiologists are the physicians who deal primarily with the heart.

19.1 Heart Anatomy

LEARNING OBJECTIVES

By the end of this section, you will be able to:

- Describe the location and position of the heart within the body cavity
- Describe the internal and external anatomy of the heart
- Identify the tissue layers of the heart
- Relate the structure of the heart to its function as a pump
- Compare systemic circulation to pulmonary circulation
- Identify the veins and arteries of the coronary circulation system
- Trace the pathway of oxygenated and deoxygenated blood thorough the chambers of the heart

The vital importance of the heart is obvious. If one assumes an average rate of contraction of 75 contractions per minute, a human heart would contract approximately 108,000 times in one day, more than 39 million times in one year, and nearly 3 billion times during a 75-year lifespan. Each of the major pumping chambers of the heart ejects approximately 70 mL blood per contraction in a resting adult. This would be equal to 5.25 liters of fluid per minute and approximately 14,000 liters per day. Over one year, that would equal 10,000,000 liters or 2.6 million gallons of blood sent through roughly 60,000 miles of vessels. In order to understand how that happens, it is necessary to understand the anatomy and physiology of the heart.

Location of the Heart

The human heart is located within the thoracic cavity, medially between the lungs in the space known as the mediastinum. Figure 19.2 shows the position of the heart within the thoracic cavity. Within the mediastinum, the heart is separated from the other mediastinal structures by a tough membrane known as the pericardium, or pericardial sac, and sits in its own space called the **pericardial cavity**. The dorsal surface of the heart lies near the bodies of the vertebrae, and its anterior surface sits deep to the sternum and costal cartilages. The great veins, the superior and inferior venae cavae, and the great arteries, the aorta and pulmonary trunk, are attached to the superior surface of the heart, called the base. The base of the heart is located at the level of the third costal cartilage, as seen in Figure 19.2. The inferior tip of the heart, the apex, lies just to the left of the sternum between the junction of the fourth and fifth ribs near their articulation with the costal cartilages. The right side of the heart is deflected anteriorly, and the left side is deflected posteriorly. It is important to remember the position and orientation of the heart when placing a stethoscope on the chest of a patient and listening for heart sounds, and also when looking at images taken from a midsagittal perspective. The slight deviation of the apex to the left is reflected in a depression in the medial surface of the inferior lobe of the left lung, called the **cardiac notch**.

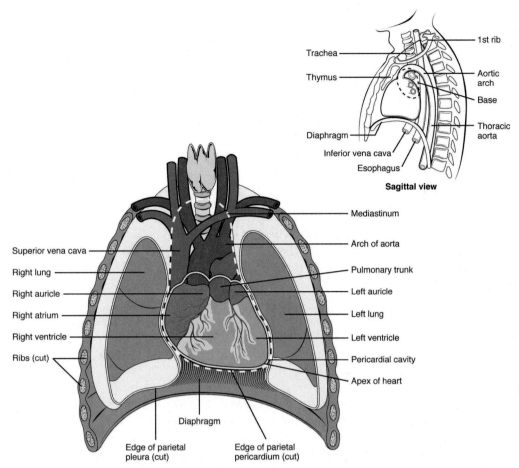

FIGURE 19.2 Position of the Heart in the Thorax   The heart is located within the thoracic cavity, medially between the lungs in the mediastinum. It is about the size of a fist, is broad at the top, and tapers toward the base.

Everyday Connection

CPR

The position of the heart in the torso between the vertebrae and sternum (see Figure 19.2 for the position of the heart within the thorax) allows for individuals to apply an emergency technique known as cardiopulmonary resuscitation (CPR) if the heart of a patient should stop. By applying pressure with the flat portion of one hand on the sternum in the area between the line at T4 and T9 (Figure 19.3), it is possible to manually compress the blood within the heart enough to push some of the blood within it into the pulmonary and systemic circuits. This is particularly critical for the brain, as irreversible damage and death of neurons occur within minutes of loss of blood flow. Current standards call for compression of the chest at least 5 cm deep and at a rate of 100 compressions per minute, a rate equal to the beat in "Staying Alive," recorded in 1977 by the Bee Gees. If you are unfamiliar with this song, a version is available on www.youtube.com. At this stage, the emphasis is on performing high-quality chest compressions, rather than providing artificial respiration. CPR is generally performed until the patient regains spontaneous contraction or is declared dead by an experienced healthcare professional.

When performed by untrained or overzealous individuals, CPR can result in broken ribs or a broken sternum, and can inflict additional severe damage on the patient. It is also possible, if the hands are placed too low on the sternum, to manually drive the xiphoid process into the liver, a consequence that may prove fatal for the patient. Proper training is essential. This proven life-sustaining technique is so valuable that virtually all medical personnel as well as concerned members of the public should be certified and routinely recertified in its application. CPR courses are offered at a variety of locations, including colleges, hospitals, the American Red Cross, and some commercial companies. They normally include practice of the compression technique on a mannequin.

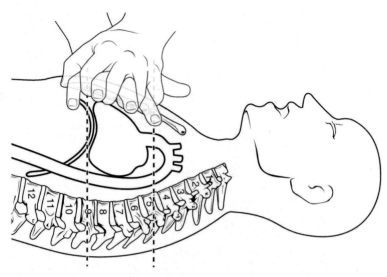

FIGURE 19.3   CPR Technique   If the heart should stop, CPR can maintain the flow of blood until the heart resumes beating. By applying pressure to the sternum, the blood within the heart will be squeezed out of the heart and into the circulation. Proper positioning of the hands on the sternum to perform CPR would be between the lines at T4 and T9.

🔗 INTERACTIVE LINK

Visit the American Heart Association website (http://openstax.org/l/AHA) to help locate a course near your home in the United States. There are also many other national and regional heart associations that offer the same service, depending upon the location.

Shape and Size of the Heart

The shape of the heart is similar to a pinecone, rather broad at the superior surface and tapering to the apex (see Figure 19.2). A typical heart is approximately the size of your fist: 12 cm (5 in) in length, 8 cm (3.5 in) wide, and 6 cm (2.5 in) in thickness. Given the size difference between most members of the sexes, the weight of a female heart is approximately 250–300 grams (9 to 11 ounces), and the weight of a male heart is approximately 300–350 grams (11 to 12 ounces). The heart of a well-trained athlete, especially one specializing in aerobic sports, can be considerably larger than this. Cardiac muscle responds to exercise in a manner similar to that of skeletal muscle. That is, exercise results in the addition of protein myofilaments that increase the size of the individual cells without increasing their numbers, a concept called hypertrophy. Hearts of athletes can pump blood more effectively at lower rates than those of nonathletes. Enlarged hearts are not always a result of exercise; they can result from pathologies, such as **hypertrophic cardiomyopathy**. The cause of an abnormally enlarged heart muscle is unknown, but the condition is often undiagnosed and can cause sudden death in apparently otherwise healthy young people.

Chambers and Circulation through the Heart

The human heart consists of four chambers: The left side and the right side each have one **atrium** and one **ventricle**. Each of the upper chambers, the right atrium (plural = atria) and the left atrium, acts as a receiving chamber and contracts to push blood into the lower chambers, the right ventricle and the left ventricle. The ventricles serve as the primary pumping chambers of the heart, propelling blood to the lungs or to the rest of the body.

There are two distinct but linked circuits in the human circulation called the pulmonary and systemic circuits. Although both circuits transport blood and everything it carries, we can initially view the circuits from the point of view of gases. The **pulmonary circuit** transports blood to and from the lungs, where it picks up oxygen and delivers carbon dioxide for exhalation. The **systemic circuit** transports oxygenated blood to virtually all of the tissues of the body and returns relatively deoxygenated blood and carbon dioxide to the heart to be sent back to the pulmonary circulation.

The right ventricle pumps deoxygenated blood into the **pulmonary trunk**, which leads toward the lungs and bifurcates into the left and right **pulmonary arteries**. These vessels in turn branch many times before reaching the **pulmonary capillaries**, where gas exchange occurs: Carbon dioxide exits the blood and oxygen enters. The pulmonary trunk arteries and their branches are the only arteries in the post-natal body that carry relatively deoxygenated blood. Highly oxygenated blood returning from the pulmonary capillaries in the lungs passes through a series of vessels that join together to form the **pulmonary veins**—the only post-natal veins in the body that carry highly oxygenated blood. The pulmonary veins conduct blood into the left atrium, which pumps the blood into the left ventricle, which in turn pumps oxygenated blood into the aorta and on to the many branches of the systemic circuit. Eventually, these vessels will lead to the systemic capillaries, where exchange with the tissue fluid and cells of the body occurs. In this case, oxygen and nutrients exit the systemic capillaries to be used by the cells in their metabolic processes, and carbon dioxide and waste products will enter the blood.

The blood exiting the systemic capillaries is lower in oxygen concentration than when it entered. The capillaries will ultimately unite to form venules, joining to form ever-larger veins, eventually flowing into the two major systemic veins, the **superior vena cava** and the **inferior vena cava**, which return blood to the right atrium. The blood in the superior and inferior venae cavae flows into the right atrium, which pumps blood into the right ventricle. This process of blood circulation continues as long as the individual remains alive. Understanding the flow of blood through the pulmonary and systemic circuits is critical to all health professions (Figure 19.4).

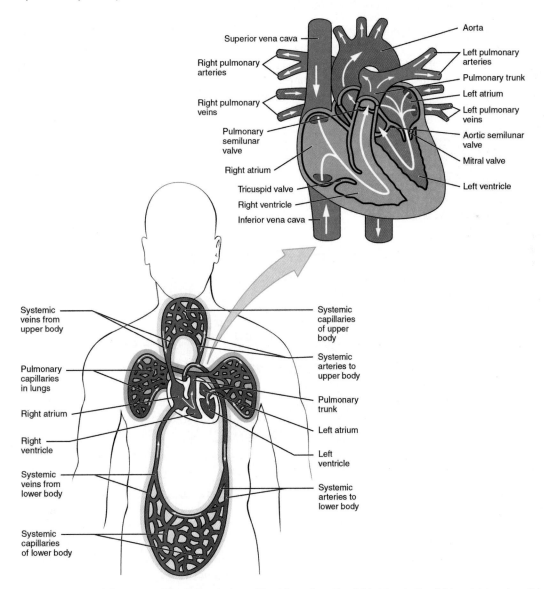

FIGURE 19.4   Dual System of the Human Blood Circulation   Blood flows from the right atrium to the right ventricle, where it is

pumped into the pulmonary circuit. The blood in the pulmonary artery branches is low in oxygen but relatively high in carbon dioxide. Gas exchange occurs in the pulmonary capillaries (oxygen into the blood, carbon dioxide out), and blood high in oxygen and low in carbon dioxide is returned to the left atrium. From here, blood enters the left ventricle, which pumps it into the systemic circuit. Following exchange in the systemic capillaries (oxygen and nutrients out of the capillaries and carbon dioxide and wastes in), blood returns to the right atrium and the cycle is repeated.

Membranes, Surface Features, and Layers

Our exploration of more in-depth heart structures begins by examining the membrane that surrounds the heart, the prominent surface features of the heart, and the layers that form the wall of the heart. Each of these components plays its own unique role in terms of function.

Membranes

The membrane that directly surrounds the heart and defines the pericardial cavity is called the **pericardium** or **pericardial sac**. It also surrounds the "roots" of the major vessels, or the areas of closest proximity to the heart. The pericardium, which literally translates as "around the heart," consists of two distinct sublayers: the sturdy outer fibrous pericardium and the inner serous pericardium. The fibrous pericardium is made of tough, dense connective tissue that protects the heart and maintains its position in the thorax. The more delicate serous pericardium consists of two layers: the parietal pericardium, which is fused to the fibrous pericardium, and an inner visceral pericardium, or **epicardium**, which is fused to the heart and is part of the heart wall. The pericardial cavity, filled with lubricating serous fluid, lies between the epicardium and the pericardium.

In most organs within the body, visceral serous membranes such as the epicardium are microscopic. However, in the case of the heart, it is not a microscopic layer but rather a macroscopic layer, consisting of a simple squamous epithelium called a **mesothelium**, reinforced with loose, irregular, or areolar connective tissue that attaches to the pericardium. This mesothelium secretes the lubricating serous fluid that fills the pericardial cavity and reduces friction as the heart contracts. Figure 19.5 illustrates the pericardial membrane and the layers of the heart.

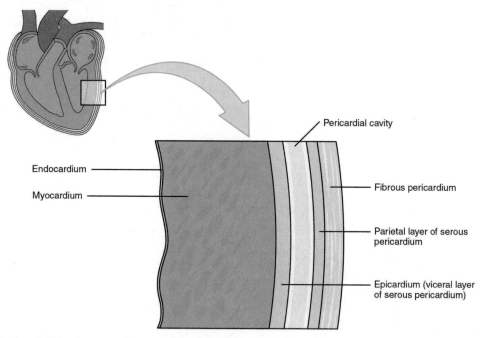

FIGURE 19.5   Pericardial Membranes and Layers of the Heart Wall   The pericardial membrane that surrounds the heart consists of three layers and the pericardial cavity. The heart wall also consists of three layers. The pericardial membrane and the heart wall share the epicardium.

Disorders of the...

Heart: Cardiac Tamponade

If excess fluid builds within the pericardial space, it can lead to a condition called cardiac tamponade, or pericardial tamponade. With each contraction of the heart, more fluid—in most instances, blood—accumulates within the pericardial cavity. In order to fill with blood for the next contraction, the heart must relax. However, the excess fluid in the pericardial cavity puts pressure on the heart and prevents full relaxation, so the chambers within the heart contain slightly less blood as they begin each heart cycle. Over time, less and less blood is ejected from the heart. If the fluid builds up slowly, as in hypothyroidism, the pericardial cavity may be able to expand gradually to accommodate this extra volume. Some cases of fluid in excess of one liter within the pericardial cavity have been reported. Rapid accumulation of as little as 100 mL of fluid following trauma may trigger cardiac tamponade. Other common causes include myocardial rupture, pericarditis, cancer, or even cardiac surgery. Removal of this excess fluid requires insertion of drainage tubes into the pericardial cavity. Premature removal of these drainage tubes, for example, following cardiac surgery, or clot formation within these tubes are causes of this condition. Untreated, cardiac tamponade can lead to death.

Surface Features of the Heart

Inside the pericardium, the surface features of the heart are visible, including the four chambers. There is a superficial leaf-like extension of the atria near the superior surface of the heart, one on each side, called an **auricle**—a name that means "ear like"—because its shape resembles the external ear of a human (Figure 19.6). Auricles are relatively thin-walled structures that can fill with blood and empty into the atria or upper chambers of the heart. You may also hear them referred to as atrial appendages. Also prominent is a series of fat-filled grooves, each of which is known as a **sulcus** (plural = sulci), along the superior surfaces of the heart. Major coronary blood vessels are located in these sulci. The deep **coronary sulcus** is located between the atria and ventricles. Located between the left and right ventricles are two additional sulci that are not as deep as the coronary sulcus. The **anterior interventricular sulcus** is visible on the anterior surface of the heart, whereas the **posterior interventricular sulcus** is visible on the posterior surface of the heart. Figure 19.6 illustrates anterior and posterior views of the surface of the heart.

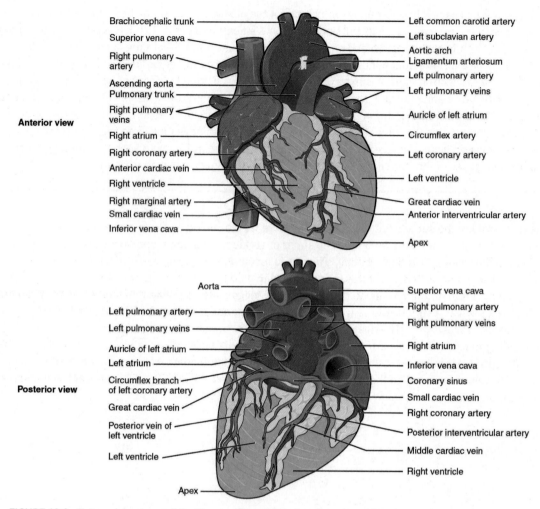

Anterior view

Brachiocephalic trunk
Superior vena cava
Right pulmonary artery
Ascending aorta
Pulmonary trunk
Right pulmonary veins
Right atrium
Right coronary artery
Anterior cardiac vein
Right ventricle
Right marginal artery
Small cardiac vein
Inferior vena cava

Left common carotid artery
Left subclavian artery
Aortic arch
Ligamentum arteriosum
Left pulmonary artery
Left pulmonary veins
Auricle of left atrium
Circumflex artery
Left coronary artery
Left ventricle
Great cardiac vein
Anterior interventricular artery
Apex

Posterior view

Aorta
Left pulmonary artery
Left pulmonary veins
Auricle of left atrium
Left atrium
Circumflex branch of left coronary artery
Great cardiac vein
Posterior vein of left ventricle
Left ventricle
Apex

Superior vena cava
Right pulmonary artery
Right pulmonary veins
Right atrium
Inferior vena cava
Coronary sinus
Small cardiac vein
Right coronary artery
Posterior interventricular artery
Middle cardiac vein
Right ventricle

FIGURE 19.6   External Anatomy of the Heart   Inside the pericardium, the surface features of the heart are visible.

Layers

The wall of the heart is composed of three layers of unequal thickness. From superficial to deep, these are the epicardium, the myocardium, and the endocardium (see Figure 19.5). The outermost layer of the wall of the heart is also the innermost layer of the pericardium, the epicardium, or the visceral pericardium discussed earlier.

The middle and thickest layer is the **myocardium**, made largely of cardiac muscle cells. It is built upon a framework of collagenous fibers, plus the blood vessels that supply the myocardium and the nerve fibers that help regulate the heart. It is the contraction of the myocardium that pumps blood through the heart and into the major arteries. The muscle pattern is elegant and complex, as the muscle cells swirl and spiral around the chambers of the heart. They form a figure 8 pattern around the atria and around the bases of the great vessels. Deeper ventricular muscles also form a figure 8 around the two ventricles and proceed toward the apex. More superficial layers of ventricular muscle wrap around both ventricles. This complex swirling pattern allows the heart to pump blood more effectively than a simple linear pattern would. Figure 19.7 illustrates the arrangement of muscle cells.

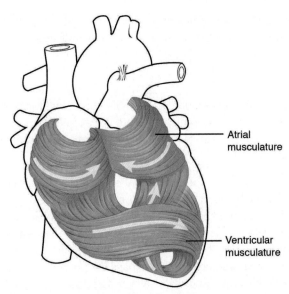

FIGURE 19.7   Heart Musculature   The swirling pattern of cardiac muscle tissue contributes significantly to the heart's ability to pump blood effectively.

Although the ventricles on the right and left sides pump the same amount of blood per contraction, the muscle of the left ventricle is much thicker and better developed than that of the right ventricle. In order to overcome the high resistance required to pump blood into the long systemic circuit, the left ventricle must generate a great amount of pressure. The right ventricle does not need to generate as much pressure, since the pulmonary circuit is shorter and provides less resistance. Figure 19.8 illustrates the differences in muscular thickness needed for each of the ventricles.

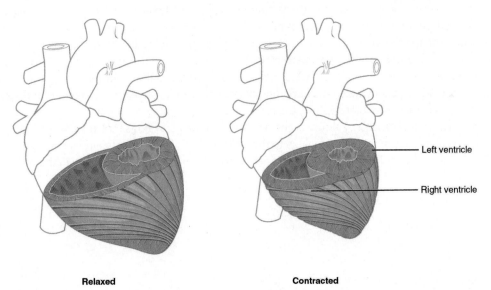

FIGURE 19.8   Differences in Ventricular Muscle Thickness   The myocardium in the left ventricle is significantly thicker than that of the right ventricle. Both ventricles pump the same amount of blood, but the left ventricle must generate a much greater pressure to overcome greater resistance in the systemic circuit. The ventricles are shown in both relaxed and contracting states. Note the differences in the relative size of the lumens, the region inside each ventricle where the blood is contained.

The innermost layer of the heart wall, the **endocardium**, is joined to the myocardium with a thin layer of connective tissue. The endocardium lines the chambers where the blood circulates and covers the heart valves. It is made of simple squamous epithelium called **endothelium**, which is continuous with the endothelial lining of the blood vessels (see Figure 19.5).

Once regarded as a simple lining layer, recent evidence indicates that the endothelium of the endocardium and the coronary capillaries may play active roles in regulating the contraction of the muscle within the myocardium. The endothelium may also regulate the growth patterns of the cardiac muscle cells throughout life, and the endothelins it secretes create an environment in the surrounding tissue fluids that regulates ionic concentrations and states of contractility. Endothelins are potent vasoconstrictors and, in a normal individual, establish a homeostatic balance with other vasoconstrictors and vasodilators.

Internal Structure of the Heart

Recall that the heart's contraction cycle follows a dual pattern of circulation—the pulmonary and systemic circuits—because of the pairs of chambers that pump blood into the circulation. In order to develop a more precise understanding of cardiac function, it is first necessary to explore the internal anatomical structures in more detail.

Septa of the Heart

The word septum is derived from the Latin for "something that encloses;" in this case, a **septum** (plural = septa) refers to a wall or partition that divides the heart into chambers. The septa are physical extensions of the myocardium lined with endocardium. Located between the two atria is the **interatrial septum**. Normally in an adult heart, the interatrial septum bears an oval-shaped depression known as the **fossa ovalis**, a remnant of an opening in the fetal heart known as the **foramen ovale**. The foramen ovale allowed blood in the fetal heart to pass directly from the right atrium to the left atrium, allowing some blood to bypass the pulmonary circuit. Within seconds after birth, a flap of tissue known as the **septum primum** that previously acted as a valve closes the foramen ovale and establishes the typical cardiac circulation pattern.

Between the two ventricles is a second septum known as the **interventricular septum**. Unlike the interatrial septum, the interventricular septum is normally intact after its formation during fetal development. It is substantially thicker than the interatrial septum, since the ventricles generate far greater pressure when they contract.

The septum between the atria and ventricles is known as the **atrioventricular septum**. It is marked by the presence of four openings that allow blood to move from the atria into the ventricles and from the ventricles into the pulmonary trunk and aorta. Located in each of these openings between the atria and ventricles is a **valve**, a specialized structure that ensures one-way flow of blood. The valves between the atria and ventricles are known generically as **atrioventricular valves**. The valves at the openings that lead to the pulmonary trunk and aorta are known generically as **semilunar valves**. The interventricular septum is visible in <u>Figure 19.9</u>. In this figure, the atrioventricular septum has been removed to better show the bicuspid and tricuspid valves; the interatrial septum is not visible, since its location is covered by the aorta and pulmonary trunk. Since these openings and valves structurally weaken the atrioventricular septum, the remaining tissue is heavily reinforced with dense connective tissue called the **cardiac skeleton**, or skeleton of the heart. It includes four rings that surround the openings between the atria and ventricles, and the openings to the pulmonary trunk and aorta, and serve as the point of attachment for the heart valves. The cardiac skeleton also provides an important boundary in the heart electrical conduction system.

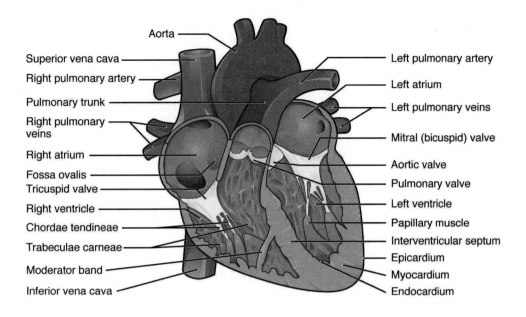

Anterior view

FIGURE 19.9 **Internal Structures of the Heart** This anterior view of the heart shows the four chambers, the major vessels and their early branches, as well as the valves. The presence of the pulmonary trunk and aorta covers the interatrial septum, and the atrioventricular septum is cut away to show the atrioventricular valves.

Disorders of the...

Heart: Heart Defects

One very common form of interatrial septum pathology is patent foramen ovale, which occurs when the septum primum does not close at birth, and the fossa ovalis is unable to fuse. The word patent is from the Latin root patens for "open." It may be benign or asymptomatic, perhaps never being diagnosed, or in extreme cases, it may require surgical repair to close the opening permanently. As much as 20–25 percent of the general population may have a patent foramen ovale, but fortunately, most have the benign, asymptomatic version. Patent foramen ovale is normally detected by auscultation of a heart murmur (an abnormal heart sound) and confirmed by imaging with an echocardiogram. Despite its prevalence in the general population, the causes of patent ovale are unknown, and there are no known risk factors. In nonlife-threatening cases, it is better to monitor the condition than to risk heart surgery to repair and seal the opening.

Coarctation of the aorta is a congenital abnormal narrowing of the aorta that is normally located at the insertion of the ligamentum arteriosum, the remnant of the fetal shunt called the ductus arteriosus. If severe, this condition drastically restricts blood flow through the primary systemic artery, which is life threatening. In some individuals, the condition may be fairly benign and not detected until later in life. Detectable symptoms in an infant include difficulty breathing, poor appetite, trouble feeding, or failure to thrive. In older individuals, symptoms include dizziness, fainting, shortness of breath, chest pain, fatigue, headache, and nosebleeds. Treatment involves surgery to resect (remove) the affected region or angioplasty to open the abnormally narrow passageway. Studies have shown that the earlier the surgery is performed, the better the chance of survival.

A patent ductus arteriosus is a congenital condition in which the ductus arteriosus fails to close. The condition may range from severe to benign. Failure of the ductus arteriosus to close results in blood flowing from the higher pressure aorta into the lower pressure pulmonary trunk. This additional fluid moving toward the lungs increases pulmonary pressure and makes respiration difficult. Symptoms include shortness of breath (dyspnea), tachycardia, enlarged heart, a widened pulse pressure, and poor weight gain in infants. Treatments include surgical closure (ligation), manual closure using platinum coils or specialized mesh inserted via the femoral artery or vein, or nonsteroidal anti-inflammatory drugs to block the synthesis of prostaglandin E2, which maintains the vessel in an open position. If untreated, the condition can result in congestive heart failure.

Septal defects are not uncommon in individuals and may be congenital or caused by various disease processes. Tetralogy of Fallot is a congenital condition that may also occur from exposure to unknown environmental factors; it occurs when there is an opening in the interventricular septum caused by blockage of the pulmonary trunk, normally at the pulmonary semilunar valve. This allows blood that is relatively low in oxygen from the right ventricle to flow into the left ventricle and mix with the blood that is relatively high in oxygen. Symptoms include a distinct heart murmur, low blood oxygen percent saturation, dyspnea or difficulty in breathing, polycythemia, broadening (clubbing) of the fingers and toes, and in children, difficulty in feeding or failure to grow and develop. It is the most common cause of cyanosis following birth. The term "tetralogy" is derived from the four components of the condition, although only three may be present in an individual patient: pulmonary infundibular stenosis (rigidity of the pulmonary valve), overriding aorta (the aorta is shifted above both ventricles), ventricular septal defect (opening), and right ventricular hypertrophy (enlargement of the right ventricle). Other heart defects may also accompany this condition, which is typically confirmed by echocardiography imaging. Tetralogy of Fallot occurs in approximately 400 out of one million live births. Normal treatment involves extensive surgical repair, including the use of stents to redirect blood flow and replacement of valves and patches to repair the septal defect, but the condition has a relatively high mortality. Survival rates are currently 75 percent during the first year of life; 60 percent by 4 years of age; 30 percent by 10 years; and 5 percent by 40 years.

In the case of severe septal defects, including both tetralogy of Fallot and patent foramen ovale, failure of the heart to develop properly can lead to a condition commonly known as a "blue baby." Regardless of normal skin pigmentation, individuals with this condition have an insufficient supply of oxygenated blood, which leads to cyanosis, a blue or purple coloration of the skin, especially when active.

Septal defects are commonly first detected through auscultation, listening to the chest using a stethoscope. In this case, instead of hearing normal heart sounds attributed to the flow of blood and closing of heart valves, unusual heart sounds may be detected. This is often followed by medical imaging to confirm or rule out a diagnosis. In many cases, treatment may not be needed. Some common congenital heart defects are illustrated in Figure 19.10.

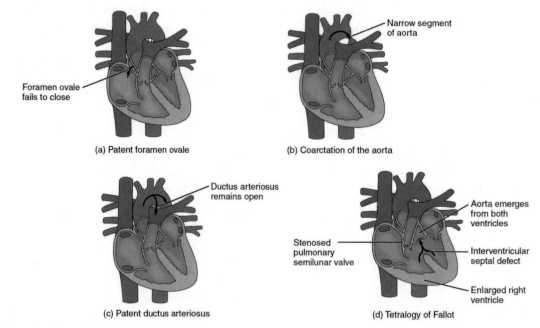

FIGURE 19.10   Congenital Heart Defects   (a) A patent foramen ovale defect is an abnormal opening in the interatrial septum, or more commonly, a failure of the foramen ovale to close. (b) Coarctation of the aorta is an abnormal narrowing of the aorta. (c) A patent ductus arteriosus is the failure of the ductus arteriosus to close. (d) Tetralogy of Fallot includes an abnormal opening in the interventricular septum.

Right Atrium

The right atrium serves as the receiving chamber for blood returning to the heart from the systemic circulation. The two major systemic veins, the superior and inferior venae cavae, and the large coronary vein called the **coronary sinus** that drains the heart myocardium empty into the right atrium. The superior vena cava drains blood from regions superior to the diaphragm: the head, neck, upper limbs, and the thoracic region. It empties into the superior and posterior portions of the right atrium. The inferior vena cava drains blood from areas inferior to the diaphragm: the lower limbs and abdominopelvic region of the body. It, too, empties into the posterior portion of the atria, but inferior to the opening of the superior vena cava. Immediately superior and slightly medial to the opening of the inferior vena cava on the posterior surface of the atrium is the opening of the coronary sinus. This thin-walled vessel drains most of the coronary veins that return systemic blood from the heart. The majority of the internal heart structures discussed in this and subsequent sections are illustrated in Figure 19.9.

While the bulk of the internal surface of the right atrium is smooth, the depression of the fossa ovalis is medial, and the anterior surface demonstrates prominent ridges of muscle called the **pectinate muscles**. The right auricle also has pectinate muscles. The left atrium does not have pectinate muscles except in the auricle.

The atria receive venous blood on a nearly continuous basis, preventing venous flow from stopping while the ventricles are contracting. While most ventricular filling occurs while the atria are relaxed, they do demonstrate a contractile phase and actively pump blood into the ventricles just prior to ventricular contraction. The opening between the atrium and ventricle is guarded by the tricuspid valve.

Right Ventricle

The right ventricle receives blood from the right atrium through the tricuspid valve. Each flap of the valve is attached to strong strands of connective tissue, the **chordae tendineae**, literally "tendinous cords," or sometimes more poetically referred to as "heart strings." There are several chordae tendineae associated with each of the flaps. They are composed of approximately 80 percent collagenous fibers with the remainder consisting of elastic fibers and endothelium. They connect each of the flaps to a **papillary muscle** that extends from the inferior ventricular surface. There are three papillary muscles in the right ventricle, called the anterior, posterior, and septal muscles, which correspond to the three sections of the valves.

When the myocardium of the ventricle contracts, pressure within the ventricular chamber rises. Blood, like any fluid, flows from higher pressure to lower pressure areas, in this case, toward the pulmonary trunk and the atrium. To prevent any potential backflow, the papillary muscles also contract, generating tension on the chordae tendineae. This prevents the flaps of the valves from being forced into the atria and regurgitation of the blood back into the atria during ventricular contraction. Figure 19.11 shows papillary muscles and chordae tendineae attached to the tricuspid valve.

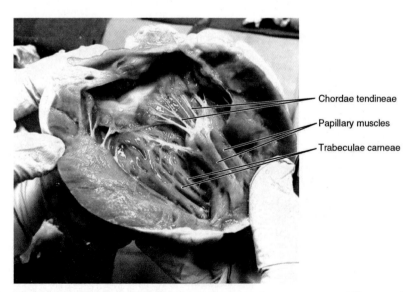

FIGURE 19.11 Chordae Tendineae and Papillary Muscles   In this frontal section, you can see papillary muscles attached to the tricuspid valve on the right as well as the mitral valve on the left via chordae tendineae. (credit: modification of work by "PV KS"/flickr.com)

The walls of the ventricle are lined with **trabeculae carneae**, ridges of cardiac muscle covered by endocardium. In addition to these muscular ridges, a band of cardiac muscle, also covered by endocardium, known as the **moderator**

band (see Figure 19.9) reinforces the thin walls of the right ventricle and plays a crucial role in cardiac conduction. It arises from the inferior portion of the interventricular septum and crosses the interior space of the right ventricle to connect with the inferior papillary muscle.

When the right ventricle contracts, it ejects blood into the pulmonary trunk, which branches into the left and right pulmonary arteries that carry it to each lung. The superior surface of the right ventricle begins to taper as it approaches the pulmonary trunk. At the base of the pulmonary trunk is the pulmonary semilunar valve that prevents backflow from the pulmonary trunk.

Left Atrium

After exchange of gases in the pulmonary capillaries, blood returns to the left atrium high in oxygen via one of the four pulmonary veins. While the left atrium does not contain pectinate muscles, it does have an auricle that includes these pectinate ridges. Blood flows nearly continuously from the pulmonary veins back into the atrium, which acts as the receiving chamber, and from here through an opening into the left ventricle. Most blood flows passively into the heart while both the atria and ventricles are relaxed, but toward the end of the ventricular relaxation period, the left atrium will contract, pumping blood into the ventricle. This atrial contraction accounts for approximately 20 percent of ventricular filling. The opening between the left atrium and ventricle is guarded by the mitral valve.

Left Ventricle

Recall that, although both sides of the heart will pump the same amount of blood, the muscular layer is much thicker in the left ventricle compared to the right (see Figure 19.8). Like the right ventricle, the left also has trabeculae carneae, but there is no moderator band. The mitral valve is connected to papillary muscles via chordae tendineae. There are two papillary muscles on the left—the anterior and posterior—as opposed to three on the right.

The left ventricle is the major pumping chamber for the systemic circuit; it ejects blood into the aorta through the aortic semilunar valve.

Heart Valve Structure and Function

A transverse section through the heart slightly above the level of the atrioventricular septum reveals all four heart valves along the same plane (Figure 19.12). The valves ensure unidirectional blood flow through the heart. Between the right atrium and the right ventricle is the **right atrioventricular valve**, or **tricuspid valve**. It typically consists of three flaps, or leaflets, made of endocardium reinforced with additional connective tissue. The flaps are connected by chordae tendineae to the papillary muscles, which control the opening and closing of the valves.

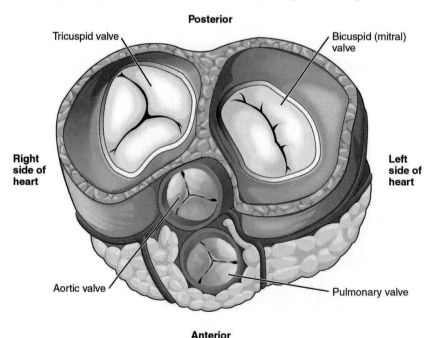

FIGURE 19.12   Heart Valves   With the atria and major vessels removed, all four valves are clearly visible, although it is difficult to distinguish the three separate cusps of the tricuspid valve.

Emerging from the right ventricle at the base of the pulmonary trunk is the pulmonary semilunar valve, or the **pulmonary valve**; it is also known as the pulmonic valve or the right semilunar valve. The pulmonary valve is comprised of three small flaps of endothelium reinforced with connective tissue. When the ventricle relaxes, the pressure differential causes blood to flow back into the ventricle from the pulmonary trunk. This flow of blood fills the pocket-like flaps of the pulmonary valve, causing the valve to close and producing an audible sound. Unlike the atrioventricular valves, there are no papillary muscles or chordae tendineae associated with the pulmonary valve.

Located at the opening between the left atrium and left ventricle is the **mitral valve**, also called the **bicuspid valve** or the **left atrioventricular valve**. Structurally, this valve consists of two cusps, compared to the three cusps of the tricuspid valve. In a clinical setting, the valve is referred to as the mitral valve, rather than the bicuspid valve. The two cusps of the mitral valve are attached by chordae tendineae to two papillary muscles that project from the wall of the ventricle.

At the base of the aorta is the aortic semilunar valve, or the **aortic valve**, which prevents backflow from the aorta. It normally is composed of three flaps. When the ventricle relaxes and blood attempts to flow back into the ventricle from the aorta, blood will fill the cusps of the valve, causing it to close and producing an audible sound.

In Figure 19.13**a**, the two atrioventricular valves are open and the two semilunar valves are closed. This occurs when both atria and ventricles are relaxed and when the atria contract to pump blood into the ventricles. Figure 19.13**b** shows a frontal view. Although only the left side of the heart is illustrated, the process is virtually identical on the right.

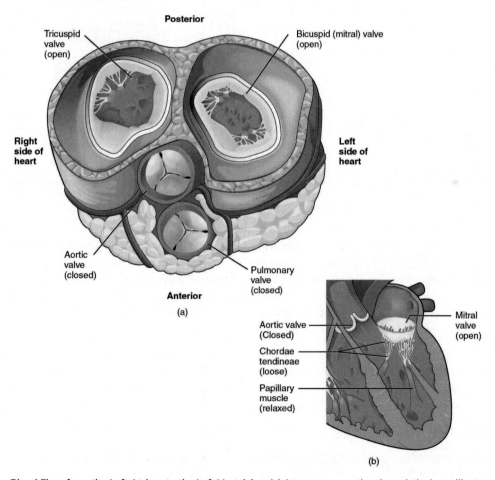

FIGURE 19.13   Blood Flow from the Left Atrium to the Left Ventricle   (a) A transverse section through the heart illustrates the four heart valves. The two atrioventricular valves are open; the two semilunar valves are closed. The atria and vessels have been removed. (b) A frontal section through the heart illustrates blood flow through the mitral valve. When the mitral valve is open, it allows blood to move from the left atrium to the left ventricle. The aortic semilunar valve is closed to prevent backflow of blood from the aorta to the left ventricle.

Figure 19.14**a** shows the atrioventricular valves closed while the two semilunar valves are open. This occurs when the ventricles contract to eject blood into the pulmonary trunk and aorta. Closure of the two atrioventricular valves prevents blood from being forced back into the atria. This stage can be seen from a frontal view in Figure 19.14**b**.

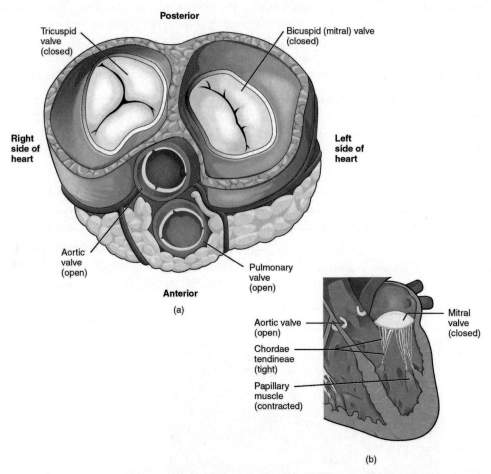

FIGURE 19.14 **Blood Flow from the Left Ventricle into the Great Vessels** (a) A transverse section through the heart illustrates the four heart valves during ventricular contraction. The two atrioventricular valves are closed, but the two semilunar valves are open. The atria and vessels have been removed. (b) A frontal view shows the closed mitral (bicuspid) valve that prevents backflow of blood into the left atrium. The aortic semilunar valve is open to allow blood to be ejected into the aorta.

When the ventricles begin to contract, pressure within the ventricles rises and blood flows toward the area of lowest pressure, which is initially in the atria. This backflow causes the cusps of the tricuspid and mitral (bicuspid) valves to close. These valves are tied down to the papillary muscles by chordae tendineae. During the relaxation phase of the cardiac cycle, the papillary muscles are also relaxed and the tension on the chordae tendineae is slight (see Figure 19.13**b**). However, as the myocardium of the ventricle contracts, so do the papillary muscles. This creates tension on the chordae tendineae (see Figure 19.14**b**), helping to hold the cusps of the atrioventricular valves in place and preventing them from being blown back into the atria.

The aortic and pulmonary semilunar valves lack the chordae tendineae and papillary muscles associated with the atrioventricular valves. Instead, they consist of pocket-like folds of endocardium reinforced with additional connective tissue. When the ventricles relax and the change in pressure forces the blood toward the ventricles, the blood presses against these cusps and seals the openings.

🔗 INTERACTIVE LINK

Visit this site (http://openstax.org/l/heartvalve) to observe an echocardiogram of actual heart valves opening and closing. Although much of the heart has been "removed" from this gif loop so the chordae tendineae are not visible, why is their presence more critical for the atrioventricular valves (tricuspid and mitral) than the semilunar (aortic and pulmonary) valves?

Disorders of the...

Heart Valves

When heart valves do not function properly, they are often described as incompetent and result in valvular heart disease, which can range from benign to lethal. Some of these conditions are congenital, that is, the individual was born with the defect, whereas others may be attributed to disease processes or trauma. Some malfunctions are treated with medications, others require surgery, and still others may be mild enough that the condition is merely monitored since treatment might trigger more serious consequences.

Valvular disorders are often caused by carditis, or inflammation of the heart. One common trigger for this inflammation is rheumatic fever, or scarlet fever, an autoimmune response to the presence of a bacterium, *Streptococcus pyogenes*, normally a disease of childhood.

While any of the heart valves may be involved in valve disorders, mitral regurgitation is the most common, detected in approximately 2 percent of the population, and the pulmonary semilunar valve is the least frequently involved. When a valve malfunctions, the flow of blood to a region will often be disrupted. The resulting inadequate flow of blood to this region will be described in general terms as an insufficiency. The specific type of insufficiency is named for the valve involved: aortic insufficiency, mitral insufficiency, tricuspid insufficiency, or pulmonary insufficiency.

If one of the cusps of the valve is forced backward by the force of the blood, the condition is referred to as a prolapsed valve. Prolapse may occur if the chordae tendineae are damaged or broken, causing the closure mechanism to fail. The failure of the valve to close properly disrupts the normal one-way flow of blood and results in regurgitation, when the blood flows backward from its normal path. Using a stethoscope, the disruption to the normal flow of blood produces a heart murmur.

Stenosis is a condition in which the heart valves become rigid and may calcify over time. The loss of flexibility of the valve interferes with normal function and may cause the heart to work harder to propel blood through the valve, which eventually weakens the heart. Aortic stenosis affects approximately 2 percent of the population over 65 years of age, and the percentage increases to approximately 4 percent in individuals over 85 years. Occasionally, one or more of the chordae tendineae will tear or the papillary muscle itself may die as a component of a myocardial infarction (heart attack). In this case, the patient's condition will deteriorate dramatically and rapidly, and immediate surgical intervention may be required.

Auscultation, or listening to a patient's heart sounds, is one of the most useful diagnostic tools, since it is proven, safe, and inexpensive. The term auscultation is derived from the Latin for "to listen," and the technique has been used for diagnostic purposes as far back as the ancient Egyptians. Valve and septal disorders will trigger abnormal heart sounds. If a valvular disorder is detected or suspected, a test called an echocardiogram, or simply an "echo," may be ordered. Echocardiograms are sonograms of the heart and can help in the diagnosis of valve disorders as well as a wide variety of heart pathologies.

🔗 INTERACTIVE LINK

Visit this site (http://openstax.org/l/heartsounds) for a free download, including excellent animations and audio of heart sounds.

CAREER CONNECTION

Cardiologist

Cardiologists are medical doctors that specialize in the diagnosis and treatment of diseases of the heart. After completing 4 years of medical school, cardiologists complete a three-year residency in internal medicine followed by an additional three or more years in cardiology. Following this 10-year period of medical training and clinical experience, they qualify for a rigorous two-day examination administered by the Board of Internal Medicine that tests their academic training and clinical abilities, including diagnostics and treatment. After successful completion of this examination, a physician becomes a board-certified cardiologist. Some board-certified cardiologists may be invited to become a Fellow of the American College of Cardiology (FACC). This professional recognition is awarded to outstanding physicians based upon merit, including outstanding credentials, achievements, and community contributions to cardiovascular medicine.

 INTERACTIVE LINK

Visit this site (http://openstax.org/l/cardiologist) to learn more about cardiologists.

 CAREER CONNECTION

Cardiovascular Technologist/Technician

Cardiovascular technologists/technicians are trained professionals who perform a variety of imaging techniques, such as sonograms or echocardiograms, used by physicians to diagnose and treat diseases of the heart. Nearly all of these positions require an associate degree, and these technicians earn a median salary of $49,410 as of May 2010, according to the U.S. Bureau of Labor Statistics. Growth within the field is fast, projected at 29 percent from 2010 to 2020.

There is a considerable overlap and complementary skills between cardiac technicians and vascular technicians, and so the term cardiovascular technician is often used. Special certifications within the field require documenting appropriate experience and completing additional and often expensive certification examinations. These subspecialties include Certified Rhythm Analysis Technician (CRAT), Certified Cardiographic Technician (CCT), Registered Congenital Cardiac Sonographer (RCCS), Registered Cardiac Electrophysiology Specialist (RCES), Registered Cardiovascular Invasive Specialist (RCIS), Registered Cardiac Sonographer (RCS), Registered Vascular Specialist (RVS), and Registered Phlebology Sonographer (RPhS).

 INTERACTIVE LINK

Visit this site (http://openstax.org/l/cardiotech) for more information on cardiovascular technologists/technicians.

Coronary Circulation

You will recall that the heart is a remarkable pump composed largely of cardiac muscle cells that are incredibly active throughout life. Like all other cells, a **cardiomyocyte** requires a reliable supply of oxygen and nutrients, and a way to remove wastes, so it needs a dedicated, complex, and extensive coronary circulation. And because of the critical and nearly ceaseless activity of the heart throughout life, this need for a blood supply is even greater than for a typical cell. However, coronary circulation is not continuous; rather, it cycles, reaching a peak when the heart muscle is relaxed and nearly ceasing while it is contracting.

Coronary Arteries

Coronary arteries supply blood to the myocardium and other components of the heart. The first portion of the aorta after it arises from the left ventricle gives rise to the coronary arteries. There are three dilations in the wall of the aorta just superior to the aortic semilunar valve. Two of these, the left posterior aortic sinus and anterior aortic sinus, give rise to the left and right coronary arteries, respectively. The third sinus, the right posterior aortic sinus, typically does not give rise to a vessel. Coronary vessel branches that remain on the surface of the artery and follow the sulci are called **epicardial coronary arteries**.

The left coronary artery distributes blood to the left side of the heart, the left atrium and ventricle, and the interventricular septum. The **circumflex artery** arises from the left coronary artery and follows the coronary sulcus to the left. Eventually, it will fuse with the small branches of the right coronary artery. The larger **anterior interventricular artery**, also known as the left anterior descending artery (LAD), is the second major branch arising from the left coronary artery. It follows the anterior interventricular sulcus around the pulmonary trunk. Along the way it gives rise to numerous smaller branches that interconnect with the branches of the posterior interventricular artery, forming anastomoses. An **anastomosis** is an area where vessels unite to form interconnections that normally allow blood to circulate to a region even if there may be partial blockage in another branch. The anastomoses in the heart are very small. Therefore, this ability is somewhat restricted in the heart so a coronary artery blockage often results in death of the cells (myocardial infarction) supplied by the particular vessel.

The right coronary artery proceeds along the coronary sulcus and distributes blood to the right atrium, portions of both ventricles, and the heart conduction system. Normally, one or more marginal arteries arise from the right coronary artery inferior to the right atrium. The **marginal arteries** supply blood to the superficial portions of the right ventricle. On the posterior surface of the heart, the right coronary artery gives rise to the **posterior interventricular artery**, also known as the posterior descending artery. It runs along the posterior portion of the interventricular sulcus toward the apex of the heart, giving rise to branches that supply the interventricular septum and portions of both ventricles. Figure 19.15 presents views of the coronary circulation from both the anterior and posterior views.

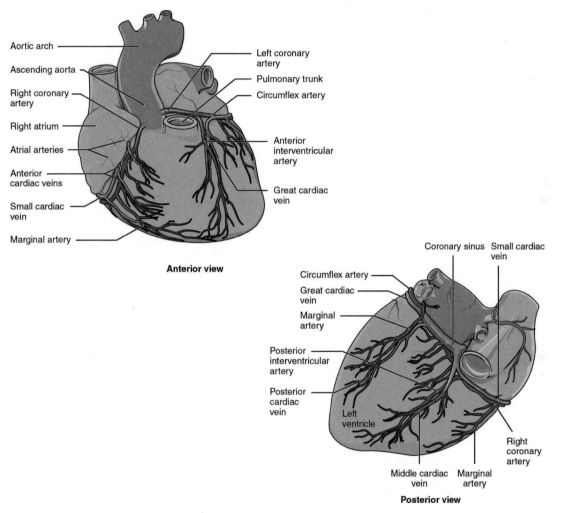

Anterior view

Posterior view

FIGURE 19.15 **Coronary Circulation**   The anterior view of the heart shows the prominent coronary surface vessels. The posterior view of the heart shows the prominent coronary surface vessels.

Diseases of the...

Heart: Myocardial Infarction   Myocardial infarction (MI) is the formal term for what is commonly referred to as a heart attack. It normally results from a lack of blood flow (ischemia) and oxygen (hypoxia) to a region of the heart, resulting in death of the cardiac muscle cells. An MI often occurs when a coronary artery is blocked by the buildup of atherosclerotic plaque consisting of lipids, cholesterol and fatty acids, and white blood cells, primarily macrophages. It can also occur when a portion of an unstable atherosclerotic plaque travels through the coronary arterial system and lodges in one of the smaller vessels. The resulting blockage restricts the flow of blood and oxygen to the myocardium and causes death of the tissue. MIs may be triggered by excessive exercise, in which the partially occluded artery is no longer able to pump sufficient quantities of blood, or severe stress, which may induce spasm of the smooth muscle in the walls of the vessel.

In the case of acute MI, there is often sudden pain beneath the sternum (retrosternal pain) called angina pectoris, often radiating down the left arm in males but not in female patients. Until this anomaly between the sexes was discovered, many female patients suffering MIs were misdiagnosed and sent home. In addition, patients typically present with difficulty breathing and shortness of breath (dyspnea), irregular heartbeat (palpations), nausea and vomiting, sweating (diaphoresis), anxiety, and fainting (syncope), although not all of these symptoms may be present. Many of the symptoms are shared with other medical conditions, including anxiety attacks and simple indigestion, so differential diagnosis is critical. It is estimated that between 22 and 64 percent of MIs present without any symptoms.

An MI can be confirmed by examining the patient's ECG, which frequently reveals alterations in the ST and Q components. Some classification schemes of MI are referred to as ST-elevated MI (STEMI) and non-elevated MI (non-STEMI). In addition, echocardiography or cardiac magnetic resonance imaging may be employed. Common blood tests indicating an MI include elevated levels of creatine kinase MB (an enzyme that catalyzes the conversion of creatine to phosphocreatine, consuming ATP) and cardiac troponin (the regulatory protein for muscle contraction), both of which are released by damaged cardiac muscle cells.

Immediate treatments for MI are essential and include administering supplemental oxygen, aspirin that helps to break up clots, and nitroglycerine administered sublingually (under the tongue) to facilitate its absorption. Despite its unquestioned success in treatments and use since the 1880s, the mechanism of nitroglycerine is still incompletely understood but is believed to involve the release of nitric oxide, a known vasodilator, and endothelium-derived releasing factor, which also relaxes the smooth muscle in the tunica media of coronary vessels. Longer-term treatments include injections of thrombolytic agents such as streptokinase that dissolve the clot, the anticoagulant heparin, balloon angioplasty and stents to open blocked vessels, and bypass surgery to allow blood to pass around the site of blockage. If the damage is extensive, coronary replacement with a donor heart or coronary assist device, a sophisticated mechanical device that supplements the pumping activity of the heart, may be employed. Despite the attention, development of artificial hearts to augment the severely limited supply of heart donors has proven less than satisfactory but will likely improve in the future.

MIs may trigger cardiac arrest, but the two are not synonymous. Important risk factors for MI include cardiovascular disease, age, smoking, high blood levels of the low-density lipoprotein (LDL, often referred to as "bad" cholesterol), low levels of high-density lipoprotein (HDL, or "good" cholesterol), hypertension, diabetes mellitus, obesity, lack of physical exercise, chronic kidney disease, excessive alcohol consumption, and use of illegal drugs.

Coronary Veins

Coronary veins drain the heart and generally parallel the large surface arteries (see Figure 19.15). The **great cardiac vein** can be seen initially on the surface of the heart following the interventricular sulcus, but it eventually flows along the coronary sulcus into the coronary sinus on the posterior surface. The great cardiac vein initially parallels the anterior interventricular artery and drains the areas supplied by this vessel. It receives several major branches, including the posterior cardiac vein, the middle cardiac vein, and the small cardiac vein. The **posterior cardiac vein** parallels and drains the areas supplied by the marginal artery branch of the circumflex artery. The **middle cardiac vein** parallels and drains the areas supplied by the posterior interventricular artery. The **small cardiac vein** parallels the right coronary artery and drains the blood from the posterior surfaces of the right atrium and ventricle. The coronary sinus is a large, thin-walled vein on the posterior surface of the heart lying within the atrioventricular sulcus and emptying directly into the right atrium. The **anterior cardiac veins** parallel the small cardiac arteries and drain the anterior surface of the right ventricle. Unlike these other cardiac veins, it bypasses the coronary sinus and drains directly into the right atrium.

Disorders of the...

Diseases of the...

Heart: Coronary Artery Disease

Coronary artery disease is the leading cause of death worldwide. It occurs when the buildup of plaque—a fatty material including cholesterol, connective tissue, white blood cells, and some smooth muscle cells—within the walls of the arteries obstructs the flow of blood and decreases the flexibility or compliance of the vessels. This condition is called atherosclerosis, a hardening of the arteries that involves the accumulation of plaque. As the coronary blood vessels become occluded, the flow of blood to the tissues will be restricted, a condition called ischemia that causes the cells to receive insufficient amounts of oxygen, called hypoxia. Figure 19.16 shows the blockage of coronary arteries highlighted by the injection of dye. Some individuals with coronary artery disease report pain radiating from the chest called angina pectoris, but others remain asymptomatic. If untreated, coronary artery disease can lead to MI or a heart attack.

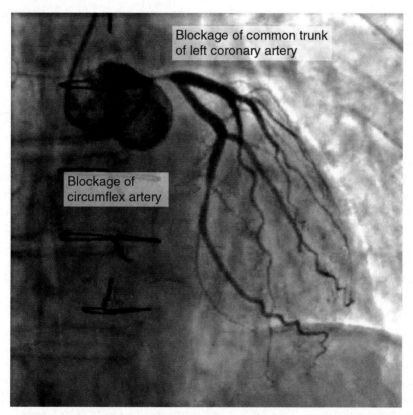

FIGURE 19.16   Atherosclerotic Coronary Arteries   In this coronary angiogram (X-ray), the dye makes visible two occluded coronary arteries. Such blockages can lead to decreased blood flow (ischemia) and insufficient oxygen (hypoxia) delivered to the cardiac tissues. If uncorrected, this can lead to cardiac muscle death (myocardial infarction).

The disease progresses slowly and often begins in children and can be seen as fatty "streaks" in the vessels. It then gradually progresses throughout life. Well-documented risk factors include smoking, family history, hypertension, obesity, diabetes, high alcohol consumption, lack of exercise, stress, and hyperlipidemia or high circulating levels of lipids in the blood. Treatments may include medication, changes to diet and exercise, angioplasty with a balloon catheter, insertion of a stent, or coronary bypass procedure.

Angioplasty is a procedure in which the occlusion is mechanically widened with a balloon. A specialized catheter with an expandable tip is inserted into a superficial vessel, normally in the leg, and then directed to the site of the occlusion. At this point, the balloon is inflated to compress the plaque material and to open the vessel to increase blood flow. Then, the balloon is deflated and retracted. A stent consisting of a specialized mesh is typically inserted at the site of occlusion to reinforce the weakened and damaged walls. Stent insertions have been routine in cardiology for more than 40 years.

Coronary bypass surgery may also be performed. This surgical procedure grafts a replacement vessel obtained from another, less vital portion of the body to bypass the occluded area. This procedure is clearly effective in treating patients experiencing a MI, but overall does not increase longevity. Nor does it seem advisable in patients with stable although diminished cardiac capacity since frequently loss of mental acuity occurs following the procedure. Long-term changes to behavior, emphasizing diet and exercise plus a medicine regime tailored to lower blood pressure, lower cholesterol and lipids, and reduce clotting are equally as effective.

19.2 Cardiac Muscle and Electrical Activity

LEARNING OBJECTIVES

By the end of this section, you will be able to:
- Describe the structure of cardiac muscle
- Identify and describe the components of the conducting system that distributes electrical impulses through the heart
- Compare the effect of ion movement on membrane potential of cardiac conductive and contractile cells
- Relate characteristics of an electrocardiogram to events in the cardiac cycle
- Identify blocks that can interrupt the cardiac cycle

Recall that cardiac muscle shares a few characteristics with both skeletal muscle and smooth muscle, but it has some unique properties of its own. Not the least of these exceptional properties is its ability to initiate an electrical potential at a fixed rate that spreads rapidly from cell to cell to trigger the contractile mechanism. This property is known as **autorhythmicity**. Neither smooth nor skeletal muscle can do this. Even though cardiac muscle has autorhythmicity, heart rate is modulated by the endocrine and nervous systems.

There are two major types of cardiac muscle cells: myocardial contractile cells and myocardial conducting cells. The **myocardial contractile cells** constitute the bulk (99 percent) of the cells in the atria and ventricles. Contractile cells conduct impulses and are responsible for contractions that pump blood through the body. The **myocardial conducting cells** (1 percent of the cells) form the conduction system of the heart. Except for Purkinje cells, they are generally much smaller than the contractile cells and have few of the myofibrils or filaments needed for contraction. Their function is similar in many respects to neurons, although they are specialized muscle cells. Myocardial conduction cells initiate and propagate the action potential (the electrical impulse) that travels throughout the heart and triggers the contractions that propel the blood.

Structure of Cardiac Muscle

Compared to the giant cylinders of skeletal muscle, cardiac muscle cells, or cardiomyocytes, are considerably shorter with much smaller diameters. Cardiac muscle also demonstrates striations, the alternating pattern of dark A bands and light I bands attributed to the precise arrangement of the myofilaments and fibrils that are organized in sarcomeres along the length of the cell (Figure 19.17**a**). These contractile elements are virtually identical to skeletal muscle. T (transverse) tubules penetrate from the surface plasma membrane, the sarcolemma, to the interior of the cell, allowing the electrical impulse to reach the interior. The T tubules are only found at the Z discs, whereas in skeletal muscle, they are found at the junction of the A and I bands. Therefore, there are one-half as many T tubules in cardiac muscle as in skeletal muscle. In addition, the sarcoplasmic reticulum stores few calcium ions, so most of the calcium ions must come from outside the cells. The result is a slower onset of contraction. Mitochondria are plentiful, providing energy for the contractions of the heart. Typically, cardiomyocytes have a single, central nucleus, but two or more nuclei may be found in some cells.

Cardiac muscle cells branch freely. A junction between two adjoining cells is marked by a critical structure called an **intercalated disc**, which helps support the synchronized contraction of the muscle (Figure 19.17**b**). The sarcolemmas from adjacent cells bind together at the intercalated discs. They consist of desmosomes, specialized linking proteoglycans, tight junctions, and large numbers of gap junctions that allow the passage of ions between the cells and help to synchronize the contraction (Figure 19.17**c**). Intercellular connective tissue also helps to bind the cells together. The importance of strongly binding these cells together is necessitated by the forces exerted by contraction.

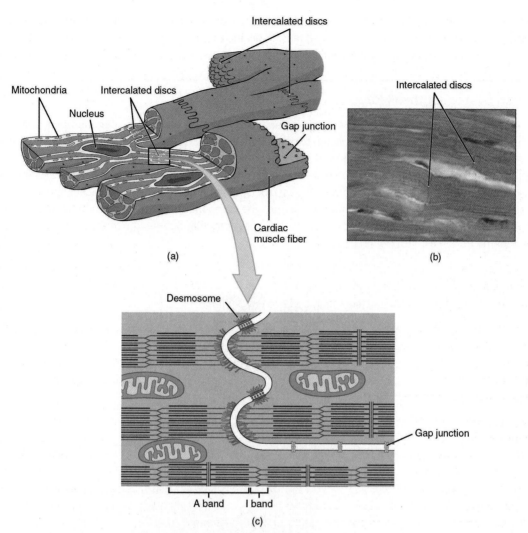

FIGURE 19.17 Cardiac Muscle (a) Cardiac muscle cells have myofibrils composed of myofilaments arranged in sarcomeres, T tubules to transmit the impulse from the sarcolemma to the interior of the cell, numerous mitochondria for energy, and intercalated discs that are found at the junction of different cardiac muscle cells. (b) A photomicrograph of cardiac muscle cells shows the nuclei and intercalated discs. (c) An intercalated disc connects cardiac muscle cells and consists of desmosomes and gap junctions. LM × 1600. (Micrograph provided by the Regents of the University of Michigan Medical School © 2012)

Cardiac muscle undergoes aerobic respiration patterns, primarily metabolizing lipids and carbohydrates. Myoglobin, lipids, and glycogen are all stored within the cytoplasm. Cardiac muscle cells undergo twitch-type contractions with long refractory periods followed by brief relaxation periods. The relaxation is essential so the heart can fill with blood for the next cycle. The refractory period is very long to prevent the possibility of tetany, a condition in which muscle remains involuntarily contracted. In the heart, tetany is not compatible with life, since it would prevent the heart from pumping blood.

Everyday Connection

Repair and Replacement

Damaged cardiac muscle cells have extremely limited abilities to repair themselves or to replace dead cells via mitosis. Recent evidence indicates that at least some stem cells remain within the heart that continue to divide and at least potentially replace these dead cells. However, newly formed or repaired cells are rarely as functional as the original cells, and cardiac function is reduced. In the event of a heart attack or MI, dead cells are often replaced by patches of scar tissue. Autopsies performed on individuals who had successfully received heart transplants show some proliferation of original cells. If researchers can unlock the mechanism that generates new cells and restore full mitotic capabilities to heart muscle, the prognosis for heart attack survivors will be greatly enhanced. To date, myocardial cells produced within the patient (*in situ*) by cardiac stem cells seem to be nonfunctional, although those grown in Petri dishes (*in vitro*) do beat. Perhaps soon this mystery will be solved, and new advances in treatment will be commonplace.

Conduction System of the Heart

If embryonic heart cells are separated into a Petri dish and kept alive, each is capable of generating its own electrical impulse followed by contraction. When two independently beating embryonic cardiac muscle cells are placed together, the cell with the higher inherent rate sets the pace, and the impulse spreads from the faster to the slower cell to trigger a contraction. As more cells are joined together, the fastest cell continues to assume control of the rate. A fully developed adult heart maintains the capability of generating its own electrical impulse, triggered by the fastest cells, as part of the cardiac conduction system. The components of the cardiac conduction system include the sinoatrial node, the atrioventricular node, the atrioventricular bundle, the atrioventricular bundle branches, and the Purkinje cells (Figure 19.18).

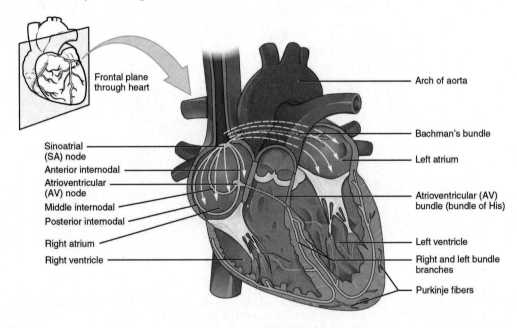

Anterior view of frontal section

FIGURE 19.18   Conduction System of the Heart   Specialized conducting components of the heart include the sinoatrial node, the internodal pathways, the atrioventricular node, the atrioventricular bundle, the right and left bundle branches, and the Purkinje fibers.

Sinoatrial (SA) Node

Normal cardiac rhythm is established by the **sinoatrial (SA) node**, a specialized clump of myocardial conducting cells located in the superior and posterior walls of the right atrium in close proximity to the orifice of the superior vena cava. The SA node has the highest inherent rate of depolarization and is known as the **pacemaker** of the heart. It initiates the **sinus rhythm**, or normal electrical pattern followed by contraction of the heart.

This impulse spreads from its initiation in the SA node throughout the atria through specialized **internodal pathways**, to the atrial myocardial contractile cells and the atrioventricular node. The internodal pathways consist of three bands (anterior, middle, and posterior) that lead directly from the SA node to the next node in the conduction system, the atrioventricular node (see Figure 19.18). The impulse takes approximately 50 ms (milliseconds) to travel between these two nodes. The relative importance of this pathway has been debated since the impulse would reach the atrioventricular node simply following the cell-by-cell pathway through the contractile cells of the myocardium in the atria. In addition, there is a specialized pathway called **Bachmann's bundle** or the **interatrial band** that conducts the impulse directly from the right atrium to the left atrium. Regardless of the pathway, as the impulse reaches the atrioventricular septum, the connective tissue of the cardiac skeleton prevents the impulse from spreading into the myocardial cells in the ventricles except at the atrioventricular node. Figure 19.19 illustrates the initiation of the impulse in the SA node that then spreads the impulse throughout the atria to the atrioventricular node.

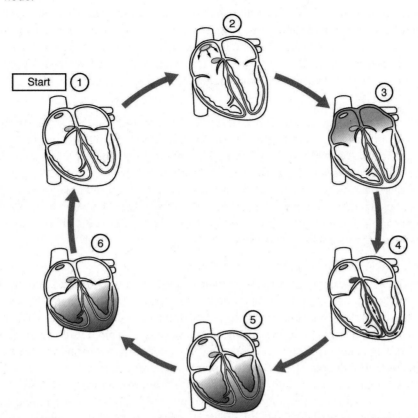

FIGURE 19.19   Cardiac Conduction   (1) The sinoatrial (SA) node and the remainder of the conduction system are at rest. (2) The SA node initiates the action potential, which sweeps across the atria. (3) After reaching the atrioventricular node, there is a delay of approximately 100 ms that allows the atria to complete pumping blood before the impulse is transmitted to the atrioventricular bundle. (4) Following the delay, the impulse travels through the atrioventricular bundle and bundle branches to the Purkinje fibers, and also reaches the right papillary muscle via the moderator band. (5) The impulse spreads to the contractile fibers of the ventricle. (6) Ventricular contraction begins.

The electrical event, the wave of depolarization, is the trigger for muscular contraction. The wave of depolarization begins in the right atrium, and the impulse spreads across the superior portions of both atria and then down through the contractile cells. The contractile cells then begin contraction from the superior to the inferior portions of the atria, efficiently pumping blood into the ventricles.

Atrioventricular (AV) Node

The **atrioventricular (AV) node** is a second clump of specialized myocardial conductive cells, located in the inferior portion of the right atrium within the atrioventricular septum. The septum prevents the impulse from spreading directly to the ventricles without passing through the AV node. There is a critical pause before the AV node depolarizes and transmits the impulse to the atrioventricular bundle (see Figure 19.19, step 3). This delay in transmission is partially attributable to the small diameter of the cells of the node, which slow the impulse. Also, conduction between nodal cells is less efficient than between conducting cells. These factors mean that it takes the impulse approximately 100 ms to pass through the node. This pause is critical to heart function, as it allows the atrial cardiomyocytes to complete their contraction that pumps blood into the ventricles before the impulse is transmitted to the cells of the ventricle itself. With extreme stimulation by the SA node, the AV node can transmit impulses maximally at 220 per minute. This establishes the typical maximum heart rate in a healthy young individual. Damaged hearts or those stimulated by drugs can contract at higher rates, but at these rates, the heart can no longer effectively pump blood.

Atrioventricular Bundle (Bundle of His), Bundle Branches, and Purkinje Fibers

Arising from the AV node, the **atrioventricular bundle**, or **bundle of His**, proceeds through the interventricular septum before dividing into two **atrioventricular bundle branches**, commonly called the left and right bundle branches. The left bundle branch has two fascicles. The left bundle branch supplies the left ventricle, and the right bundle branch the right ventricle. Since the left ventricle is much larger than the right, the left bundle branch is also considerably larger than the right. Portions of the right bundle branch are found in the moderator band and supply the right papillary muscles. Because of this connection, each papillary muscle receives the impulse at approximately the same time, so they begin to contract simultaneously just prior to the remainder of the myocardial contractile cells of the ventricles. This is believed to allow tension to develop on the chordae tendineae prior to right ventricular contraction. There is no corresponding moderator band on the left. Both bundle branches descend and reach the apex of the heart where they connect with the Purkinje fibers (see Figure 19.19, step 4). This passage takes approximately 25 ms.

The **Purkinje fibers** are additional myocardial conductive fibers that spread the impulse to the myocardial contractile cells in the ventricles. They extend throughout the myocardium from the apex of the heart toward the atrioventricular septum and the base of the heart. The Purkinje fibers have a fast inherent conduction rate, and the electrical impulse reaches all of the ventricular muscle cells in about 75 ms (see Figure 19.19, step 5). Since the electrical stimulus begins at the apex, the contraction also begins at the apex and travels toward the base of the heart, similar to squeezing a tube of toothpaste from the bottom. This allows the blood to be pumped out of the ventricles and into the aorta and pulmonary trunk. The total time elapsed from the initiation of the impulse in the SA node until depolarization of the ventricles is approximately 225 ms.

Membrane Potentials and Ion Movement in Cardiac Conductive Cells

Action potentials are considerably different between cardiac conductive cells and cardiac contractive cells. While Na^+ and K^+ play essential roles, Ca^{2+} is also critical for both types of cells. Unlike skeletal muscles and neurons, cardiac conductive cells do not have a stable resting potential. Conductive cells contain a series of sodium ion channels that allow a normal and slow influx of sodium ions that causes the membrane potential to rise slowly from an initial value of −60 mV up to about −40 mV. The resulting movement of sodium ions creates **spontaneous depolarization** (or **prepotential depolarization**). At this point, calcium ion channels open and Ca^{2+} enters the cell, further depolarizing it at a more rapid rate until it reaches a value of approximately +15 mV. At this point, the calcium ion channels close and K^+ channels open, allowing outflux of K^+ and resulting in repolarization. When the membrane potential reaches approximately −60 mV, the K^+ channels close and Na^+ channels open, and the prepotential phase begins again. This phenomenon explains the autorhythmicity properties of cardiac muscle (Figure 19.20).

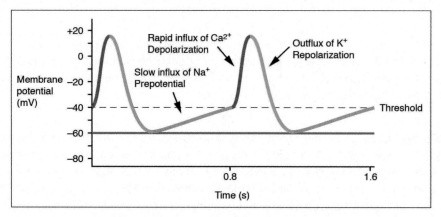

FIGURE 19.20   Action Potential at the SA Node   The prepotential is due to a slow influx of sodium ions until the threshold is reached followed by a rapid depolarization and repolarization. The prepotential accounts for the membrane reaching threshold and initiates the spontaneous depolarization and contraction of the cell. Note the lack of a resting potential.

Membrane Potentials and Ion Movement in Cardiac Contractile Cells

There is a distinctly different electrical pattern involving the contractile cells. In this case, there is a rapid depolarization, followed by a plateau phase and then repolarization. This phenomenon accounts for the long refractory periods required for the cardiac muscle cells to pump blood effectively before they are capable of firing for a second time. These cardiac myocytes normally do not initiate their own electrical potential but rather wait for an impulse to reach them.

Contractile cells demonstrate a much more stable resting phase than conductive cells at approximately −80 mV for cells in the atria and −90 mV for cells in the ventricles. Despite this initial difference, the other components of their action potentials are virtually identical. In both cases, when stimulated by an action potential, voltage-gated channels rapidly open, beginning the positive-feedback mechanism of depolarization. This rapid influx of positively charged ions raises the membrane potential to approximately +30 mV, at which point the sodium channels close. The rapid depolarization period typically lasts 3–5 ms. Depolarization is followed by the plateau phase, in which membrane potential declines relatively slowly. This is due in large part to the opening of the slow Ca^{2+} channels, allowing Ca^{2+} to enter the cell while few K^+ channels are open, allowing K^+ to exit the cell. The relatively long plateau phase lasts approximately 175 ms. Once the membrane potential reaches approximately zero, the Ca^{2+} channels close and K^+ channels open, allowing K^+ to exit the cell. The repolarization lasts approximately 75 ms. At this point, membrane potential drops until it reaches resting levels once more and the cycle repeats. The entire event lasts between 250 and 300 ms (Figure 19.21).

The absolute refractory period for cardiac contractile muscle lasts approximately 200 ms, and the relative refractory period lasts approximately 50 ms, for a total of 250 ms. This extended period is critical, since the heart muscle must contract to pump blood effectively and the contraction must follow the electrical events. Without extended refractory periods, premature contractions would occur in the heart and would not be compatible with life.

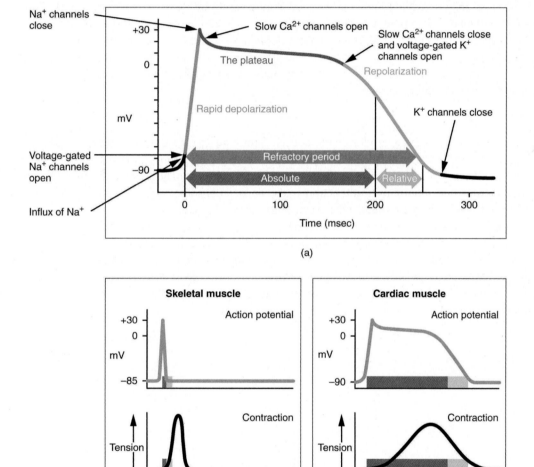

FIGURE 19.21   Action Potential in Cardiac Contractile Cells   (a) Note the long plateau phase due to the influx of calcium ions. The extended refractory period allows the cell to fully contract before another electrical event can occur. (b) The action potential for heart muscle is compared to that of skeletal muscle.

Calcium Ions

Calcium ions play two critical roles in the physiology of cardiac muscle. Their influx through slow calcium channels accounts for the prolonged plateau phase and absolute refractory period that enable cardiac muscle to function properly. Calcium ions also combine with the regulatory protein troponin in the troponin-tropomyosin complex; this complex removes the inhibition that prevents the heads of the myosin molecules from forming cross bridges with the active sites on actin that provide the power stroke of contraction. This mechanism is virtually identical to that of skeletal muscle. Approximately 20 percent of the calcium required for contraction is supplied by the influx of Ca^{2+} during the plateau phase. The remaining Ca^{2+} for contraction is released from storage in the sarcoplasmic reticulum.

Comparative Rates of Conduction System Firing

The pattern of prepotential or spontaneous depolarization, followed by rapid depolarization and repolarization just described, are seen in the SA node and a few other conductive cells in the heart. Since the SA node is the pacemaker, it reaches threshold faster than any other component of the conduction system. It will initiate the impulses spreading to the other conducting cells. The SA node, without nervous or endocrine control, would initiate a heart impulse approximately 80–100 times per minute. Although each component of the conduction system is capable of generating its own impulse, the rate progressively slows as you proceed from the SA node to the Purkinje fibers. Without the SA node, the AV node would generate a heart rate of 40–60 beats per minute. If the AV node were blocked, the atrioventricular bundle would fire at a rate of approximately 30–40 impulses per minute. The bundle branches would have an inherent rate of 20–30 impulses per minute, and the Purkinje fibers would fire at 15–20 impulses per minute. While a few exceptionally trained aerobic athletes demonstrate resting heart rates in the range of 30–40 beats per minute (the lowest recorded figure is 28 beats per minute for Miguel Indurain, a cyclist), for most individuals, rates lower than 50 beats per minute would indicate a condition called bradycardia. Depending upon the specific individual, as rates fall much below this level, the heart would be unable to maintain adequate flow of blood to vital tissues, initially resulting in decreasing loss of function across the systems, unconsciousness, and ultimately death.

Electrocardiogram

By careful placement of surface electrodes on the body, it is possible to record the complex, compound electrical signal of the heart. This tracing of the electrical signal is the **electrocardiogram (ECG)**, also commonly abbreviated EKG (K coming kardiology, from the German term for cardiology). Careful analysis of the ECG reveals a detailed picture of both normal and abnormal heart function, and is an indispensable clinical diagnostic tool. The standard electrocardiograph (the instrument that generates an ECG) uses 3, 5, or 12 leads. The greater the number of leads an electrocardiograph uses, the more information the ECG provides. The term "lead" may be used to refer to the cable from the electrode to the electrical recorder, but it typically describes the voltage difference between two of the electrodes. The 12-lead electrocardiograph uses 10 electrodes placed in standard locations on the patient's skin (Figure 19.22). In continuous ambulatory electrocardiographs, the patient wears a small, portable, battery-operated device known as a Holter monitor, or simply a Holter, that continuously monitors heart electrical activity, typically for a period of 24 hours during the patient's normal routine.

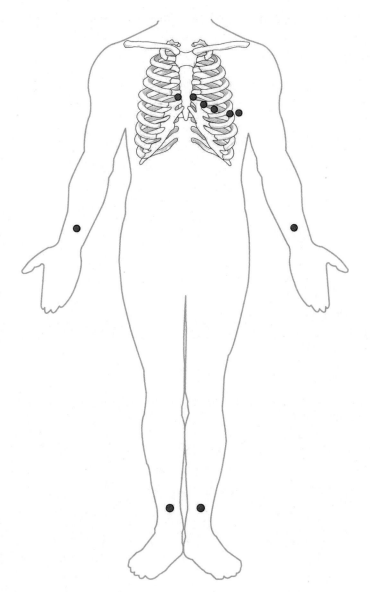

FIGURE 19.22 Standard Placement of ECG Leads In a 12-lead ECG, six electrodes are placed on the chest, and four electrodes are placed on the limbs.

A normal ECG tracing is presented in Figure 19.23. Each component, segment, and interval is labeled and corresponds to important electrical events, demonstrating the relationship between these events and contraction in the heart.

There are five prominent points on the ECG: the P wave, the QRS complex, and the T wave. The small **P wave** represents the depolarization of the atria. The atria begin contracting approximately 25 ms after the start of the P wave. The large **QRS complex** represents the depolarization of the ventricles, which requires a much stronger electrical signal because of the larger size of the ventricular cardiac muscle. The ventricles begin to contract as the QRS reaches the peak of the R wave. Lastly, the **T wave** represents the repolarization of the ventricles. The repolarization of the atria occurs during the QRS complex, which masks it on an ECG.

The major segments and intervals of an ECG tracing are indicated in Figure 19.23. Segments are defined as the regions between two waves. Intervals include one segment plus one or more waves. For example, the PR segment begins at the end of the P wave and ends at the beginning of the QRS complex. The PR interval starts at the beginning of the P wave and ends with the beginning of the QRS complex. The PR interval is more clinically relevant, as it measures the duration from the beginning of atrial depolarization (the P wave) to the initiation of the QRS complex. Since the Q wave may be difficult to view in some tracings, the measurement is often extended to the R that is more easily visible. Should there be a delay in passage of the impulse from the SA node to the AV node, it would be visible in the PR interval. Figure 19.24 correlates events of heart contraction to the corresponding segments and intervals of an ECG.

⊘ INTERACTIVE LINK

Visit this site (http://openstax.org/l/ECG) for a more detailed analysis of ECGs.

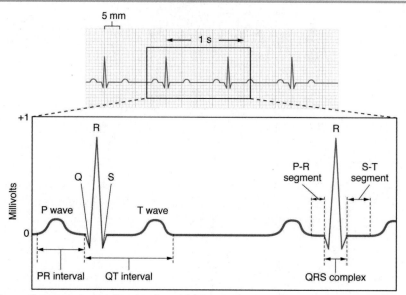

FIGURE 19.23   Electrocardiogram   A normal tracing shows the P wave, QRS complex, and T wave. Also indicated are the PR, QT, QRS, and ST intervals, plus the P-R and S-T segments.

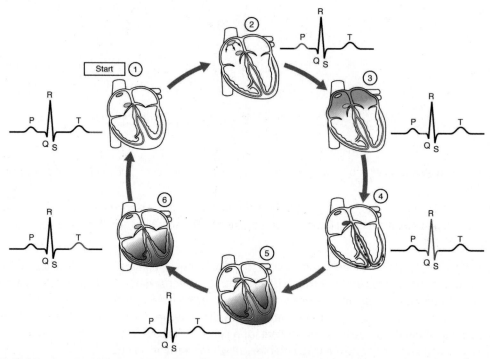

FIGURE 19.24   ECG Tracing Correlated to the Cardiac Cycle   This diagram correlates an ECG tracing with the electrical and mechanical events of a heart contraction. Each segment of an ECG tracing corresponds to one event in the cardiac cycle.

Everyday Connection

ECG Abnormalities

Occassionally, an area of the heart other than the SA node will initiate an impulse that will be followed by a premature contraction. Such an area, which may actually be a component of the conduction system or some other contractile cells, is known as an ectopic focus or ectopic pacemaker. An ectopic focus may be stimulated by localized ischemia; exposure to certain drugs, including caffeine, digitalis, or acetylcholine; elevated stimulation by both sympathetic or parasympathetic divisions of the autonomic nervous system; or a number of disease or pathological conditions. Occasional occurences are generally transitory and nonlife threatening, but if the condition becomes chronic, it may lead to either an arrhythmia, a deviation from the normal pattern of impulse conduction and contraction, or to fibrillation, an uncoordinated beating of the heart.

While interpretation of an ECG is possible and extremely valuable after some training, a full understanding of the complexities and intricacies generally requires several years of experience. In general, the size of the electrical variations, the duration of the events, and detailed vector analysis provide the most comprehensive picture of cardiac function. For example, an amplified P wave may indicate enlargement of the atria, an enlarged Q wave may indicate a MI, and an enlarged suppressed or inverted Q wave often indicates enlarged ventricles. T waves often appear flatter when insufficient oxygen is being delivered to the myocardium. An elevation of the ST segment above baseline is often seen in patients with an acute MI, and may appear depressed below the baseline when hypoxia is occurring.

As useful as analyzing these electrical recordings may be, there are limitations. For example, not all areas suffering a MI may be obvious on the ECG. Additionally, it will not reveal the effectiveness of the pumping, which requires further testing, such as an ultrasound test called an echocardiogram or nuclear medicine imaging. It is also possible for there to be pulseless electrical activity, which will show up on an ECG tracing, although there is no corresponding pumping action. Common abnormalities that may be detected by the ECGs are shown in Figure 19.25.

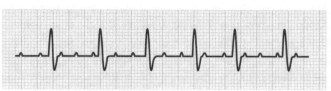

Note how half of the P waves are not followed by the QRS complex and T waves while the other half are.
Question: What would you expect to happen to heart rate (pulse)?

(a)   Second-degree (partial) block

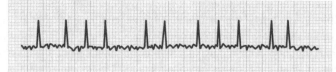

Note the abnormal electrical pattern prior to the QRS complexes. Also note how the frequency between the QRS complexes has increased.
Question: What would you expect to happen to heart rate (pulse)?

(b)   Atrial fibrillation

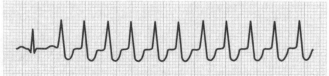

Note the unusual shape of the QRS complex, focusing on the "S" component.
Question: What would you expect to happen to heart rate (pulse)?

(c)   Ventricular tachycardia

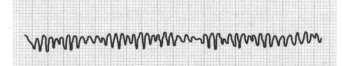

Note the total lack of normal electrical activity.
Question: What would you expect to happen to heart rate (pulse)?

(d)   Ventricular fibrillation

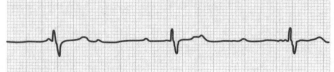

Note that in a third-degree block some of the impulses initiated by the SA node do not reach the AV node while others do. Also note that the P waves are not followed by the QRS complex.
Question: What would you expect to happen to heart rate (pulse)?

(e)   Third-degree block

FIGURE 19.25   Common ECG Abnormalities   (a) In a second-degree or partial block, one-half of the P waves are not followed by the QRS complex and T waves while the other half are. (b) In atrial fibrillation, the electrical pattern is abnormal prior to the QRS complex, and the frequency between the QRS complexes has increased. (c) In ventricular tachycardia, the shape of the QRS complex is abnormal. (d) In ventricular fibrillation, there is no normal electrical activity. (e) In a third-degree block, there is no correlation between atrial activity (the P wave) and ventricular activity (the QRS complex).

🔗 INTERACTIVE LINK

Visit this site (http://openstax.org/l/abnormalECG) for a more complete library of abnormal ECGs.

Everyday Connection

External Automated Defibrillators

In the event that the electrical activity of the heart is severely disrupted, cessation of electrical activity or fibrillation may occur. In fibrillation, the heart beats in a wild, uncontrolled manner, which prevents it from being able to pump effectively. Atrial fibrillation (see Figure 19.25**b**) is a serious condition, but as long as the ventricles continue to pump blood, the patient's life may not be in immediate danger. Ventricular fibrillation (see Figure 19.25**d**) is a medical emergency that requires life support, because the ventricles are not effectively pumping blood. In a hospital setting, it is often described as "code blue." If untreated for as little as a few minutes, ventricular fibrillation may lead to brain death. The most common treatment is defibrillation, which uses special paddles to apply a charge to the heart from an external electrical source in an attempt to establish a normal sinus rhythm (Figure 19.26). A defibrillator effectively stops the heart so that the SA node can trigger a normal conduction cycle. Because of their effectiveness in reestablishing a normal sinus rhythm, external automated defibrillators (EADs) are being placed in areas frequented by large numbers of people, such as schools, restaurants, and airports. These devices contain simple and direct verbal instructions that can be followed by nonmedical personnel in an attempt to save a life.

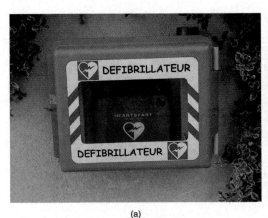
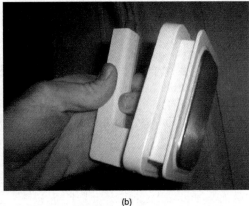

(a)   (b)

FIGURE 19.26   **Defibrillators**   (a) An external automatic defibrillator can be used by nonmedical personnel to reestablish a normal sinus rhythm in a person with fibrillation. (b) Defibrillator paddles are more commonly used in hospital settings. (credit b: "widerider107"/flickr.com)

A **heart block** refers to an interruption in the normal conduction pathway. The nomenclature for these is very straightforward. SA nodal blocks occur within the SA node. AV nodal blocks occur within the AV node. Infra-Hisian blocks involve the bundle of His. Bundle branch blocks occur within either the left or right atrioventricular bundle branches. Hemiblocks are partial and occur within one or more fascicles of the atrioventricular bundle branch. Clinically, the most common types are the AV nodal and infra-Hisian blocks.

AV blocks are often described by degrees. A first-degree or partial block indicates a delay in conduction between the SA and AV nodes. This can be recognized on the ECG as an abnormally long PR interval. A second-degree or incomplete block occurs when some impulses from the SA node reach the AV node and continue, while others do not. In this instance, the ECG would reveal some P waves not followed by a QRS complex, while others would appear normal. In the third-degree or complete block, there is no correlation between atrial activity (the P wave) and ventricular activity (the QRS complex). Even in the event of a total SA block, the AV node will assume the role of pacemaker and continue initiating contractions at 40–60 contractions per minute, which is adequate to maintain consciousness. Second- and third-degree blocks are demonstrated on the ECG presented in Figure 19.25.

When arrhythmias become a chronic problem, the heart maintains a junctional rhythm, which originates in the AV node. In order to speed up the heart rate and restore full sinus rhythm, a cardiologist can implant an **artificial pacemaker**, which delivers electrical impulses to the heart muscle to ensure that the heart continues to contract and pump blood effectively. These artificial pacemakers are programmable by the cardiologists and can either provide stimulation temporarily upon demand or on a continuous basis. Some devices also contain built-in defibrillators.

Cardiac Muscle Metabolism

Normally, cardiac muscle metabolism is entirely aerobic. Oxygen from the lungs is brought to the heart, and every other organ, attached to the hemoglobin molecules within the erythrocytes. Heart cells also store appreciable amounts of oxygen in myoglobin. Normally, these two mechanisms, circulating oxygen and oxygen attached to myoglobin, can supply sufficient oxygen to the heart, even during peak performance.

Fatty acids and glucose from the circulation are broken down within the mitochondria to release energy in the form of ATP. Both fatty acid droplets and glycogen are stored within the sarcoplasm and provide additional nutrient supply. (Seek additional content for more detail about metabolism.)

19.3 Cardiac Cycle

LEARNING OBJECTIVES

By the end of this section, you will be able to:

- Describe the relationship between blood pressure and blood flow
- Summarize the events of the cardiac cycle
- Compare atrial and ventricular systole and diastole
- Relate heart sounds detected by auscultation to action of heart's valves

The period of time that begins with contraction of the atria and ends with ventricular relaxation is known as the **cardiac cycle** (Figure 19.27). The period of contraction that the heart undergoes while it pumps blood into circulation is called **systole**. The period of relaxation that occurs as the chambers fill with blood is called **diastole**. Both the atria and ventricles undergo systole and diastole, and it is essential that these components be carefully regulated and coordinated to ensure blood is pumped efficiently to the body.

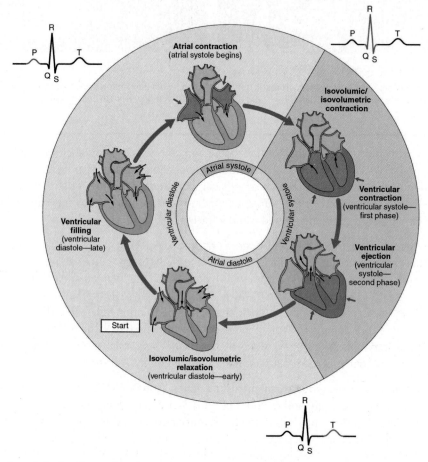

FIGURE 19.27   Overview of the Cardiac Cycle   The cardiac cycle begins with atrial systole and progresses to ventricular systole, atrial diastole, and ventricular diastole, when the cycle begins again. Correlations to the ECG are highlighted.

Pressures and Flow

Fluids, whether gases or liquids, are materials that flow according to pressure gradients—that is, they move from regions that are higher in pressure to regions that are lower in pressure. Accordingly, when the heart chambers are relaxed (diastole), blood will flow into the atria from the veins, which are higher in pressure. As blood flows into the atria, the pressure will rise, so the blood will initially move passively from the atria into the ventricles. When the action potential triggers the muscles in the atria to contract (atrial systole), the pressure within the atria rises further, pumping blood into the ventricles. During ventricular systole, pressure rises in the ventricles, pumping blood into the pulmonary trunk from the right ventricle and into the aorta from the left ventricle. Again, as you consider this flow and relate it to the conduction pathway, the elegance of the system should become apparent.

Access for free at openstax.org

Phases of the Cardiac Cycle

At the beginning of the cardiac cycle, both the atria and ventricles are relaxed (diastole). Blood is flowing into the right atrium from the superior and inferior venae cavae and the coronary sinus. Blood flows into the left atrium from the four pulmonary veins. The two atrioventricular valves, the tricuspid and mitral valves, are both open, so blood flows unimpeded from the atria and into the ventricles. Approximately 70–80 percent of ventricular filling occurs by this method. The two semilunar valves, the pulmonary and aortic valves, are closed, preventing backflow of blood into the right and left ventricles from the pulmonary trunk on the right and the aorta on the left.

Atrial Systole and Diastole

Contraction of the atria follows depolarization, represented by the P wave of the ECG. As the atrial muscles contract from the superior portion of the atria toward the atrioventricular septum, pressure rises within the atria and blood is pumped into the ventricles through the open atrioventricular (tricuspid, and mitral or bicuspid) valves. At the start of atrial systole, the ventricles are normally filled with approximately 70–80 percent of their capacity due to inflow during diastole. Atrial contraction, also referred to as the "atrial kick," contributes the remaining 20–30 percent of filling (see Figure 19.27). Atrial systole lasts approximately 100 ms and ends prior to ventricular systole, as the atrial muscle returns to diastole.

Ventricular Systole

Ventricular systole (see Figure 19.27) follows the depolarization of the ventricles and is represented by the QRS complex in the ECG. It may be conveniently divided into two phases, lasting a total of 270 ms. At the end of atrial systole and just prior to ventricular contraction, the ventricles contain approximately 130 mL blood in a resting adult in a standing position. This volume is known as the **end diastolic volume (EDV)** or **preload**.

Initially, as the muscles in the ventricle contract, the pressure of the blood within the chamber rises, but it is not yet high enough to open the semilunar (pulmonary and aortic) valves and be ejected from the heart. However, blood pressure quickly rises above that of the atria that are now relaxed and in diastole. This increase in pressure causes blood to flow back toward the atria, closing the tricuspid and mitral valves. Since blood is not being ejected from the ventricles at this early stage, the volume of blood within the chamber remains constant. Consequently, this initial phase of ventricular systole is known as **isovolumic contraction**, also called isovolumetric contraction (see Figure 19.27).

In the second phase of ventricular systole, the **ventricular ejection phase**, the contraction of the ventricular muscle has raised the pressure within the ventricle to the point that it is greater than the pressures in the pulmonary trunk and the aorta. Blood is pumped from the heart, pushing open the pulmonary and aortic semilunar valves. Pressure generated by the left ventricle will be appreciably greater than the pressure generated by the right ventricle, since the existing pressure in the aorta will be so much higher. Nevertheless, both ventricles pump the same amount of blood. This quantity is referred to as stroke volume. Stroke volume will normally be in the range of 70–80 mL. Since ventricular systole began with an EDV of approximately 130 mL of blood, this means that there is still 50–60 mL of blood remaining in the ventricle following contraction. This volume of blood is known as the **end systolic volume (ESV)**.

Ventricular Diastole

Ventricular relaxation, or diastole, follows repolarization of the ventricles and is represented by the T wave of the ECG. It too is divided into two distinct phases and lasts approximately 430 ms.

During the early phase of ventricular diastole, as the ventricular muscle relaxes, pressure on the remaining blood within the ventricle begins to fall. When pressure within the ventricles drops below pressure in both the pulmonary trunk and aorta, blood flows back toward the heart, producing the dicrotic notch (small dip) seen in blood pressure tracings. The semilunar valves close to prevent backflow into the heart. Since the atrioventricular valves remain closed at this point, there is no change in the volume of blood in the ventricle, so the early phase of ventricular diastole is called the **isovolumic ventricular relaxation phase**, also called isovolumetric ventricular relaxation phase (see Figure 19.27).

In the second phase of ventricular diastole, called late ventricular diastole, as the ventricular muscle relaxes, pressure on the blood within the ventricles drops even further. Eventually, it drops below the pressure in the atria. When this occurs, blood flows from the atria into the ventricles, pushing open the tricuspid and mitral valves. As pressure drops within the ventricles, blood flows from the major veins into the relaxed atria and from there into the ventricles. Both chambers are in diastole, the atrioventricular valves are open, and the semilunar valves remain closed (see Figure 19.27). The cardiac cycle is complete.

Figure 19.28 illustrates the relationship between the cardiac cycle and the ECG.

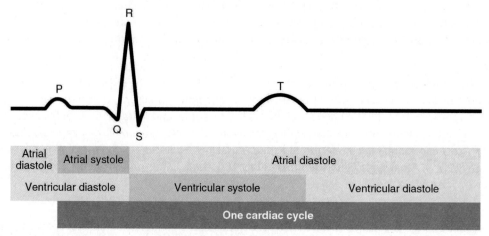

FIGURE 19.28   Relationship between the Cardiac Cycle and ECG   Initially, both the atria and ventricles are relaxed (diastole). The P wave represents depolarization of the atria and is followed by atrial contraction (systole). Atrial systole extends until the QRS complex, at which point, the atria relax. The QRS complex represents depolarization of the ventricles and is followed by ventricular contraction. The T wave represents the repolarization of the ventricles and marks the beginning of ventricular relaxation.

Heart Sounds

One of the simplest, yet effective, diagnostic techniques applied to assess the state of a patient's heart is auscultation using a stethoscope.

In a normal, healthy heart, there are only two audible **heart sounds**: S_1 and S_2. S_1 is the sound created by the closing of the atrioventricular valves during ventricular contraction and is normally described as a "lub," or first heart sound. The second heart sound, S_2, is the sound of the closing of the semilunar valves during ventricular diastole and is described as a "dub" (Figure 19.29). In both cases, as the valves close, the openings within the atrioventricular septum guarded by the valves will become reduced, and blood flow through the opening will become more turbulent until the valves are fully closed. There is a third heart sound, S_3, but it is rarely heard in healthy individuals. It may be the sound of blood flowing into the atria, or blood sloshing back and forth in the ventricle, or even tensing of the chordae tendineae. S_3 may be heard in youth, some athletes, and pregnant people. If the sound is heard later in life, it may indicate congestive heart failure, warranting further tests. Some cardiologists refer to the collective S_1, S_2, and S_3 sounds as the "Kentucky gallop," because they mimic those produced by a galloping horse. The fourth heart sound, S_4, results from the contraction of the atria pushing blood into a stiff or hypertrophic ventricle, indicating failure of the left ventricle. S_4 occurs prior to S_1 and the collective sounds S_4, S_1, and S_2 are referred to by some cardiologists as the "Tennessee gallop," because of their similarity to the sound produced by a galloping horse with a different gait. A few individuals may have both S_3 and S_4, and this combined sound is referred to as S_7.

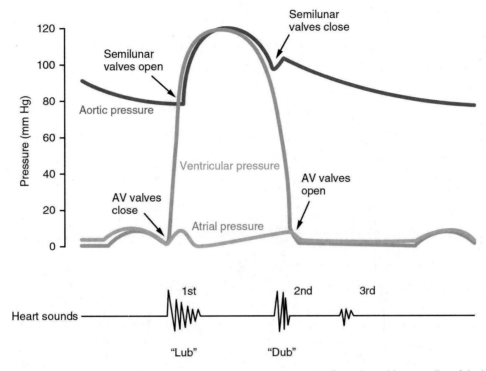

FIGURE 19.29   Heart Sounds and the Cardiac Cycle   In this illustration, the x-axis reflects time with a recording of the heart sounds. The y-axis represents pressure.

The term **murmur** is used to describe an unusual sound coming from the heart that is caused by the turbulent flow of blood. Murmurs are graded on a scale of 1 to 6, with 1 being the most common, the most difficult sound to detect, and the least serious. The most severe is a 6. Phonocardiograms or auscultograms can be used to record both normal and abnormal sounds using specialized electronic stethoscopes.

During auscultation, it is common practice for the clinician to ask the patient to breathe deeply. This procedure not only allows for listening to airflow, but it may also amplify heart murmurs. Inhalation increases blood flow into the right side of the heart and may increase the amplitude of right-sided heart murmurs. Expiration partially restricts blood flow into the left side of the heart and may amplify left-sided heart murmurs. Figure 19.30 indicates proper placement of the bell of the stethoscope to facilitate auscultation.

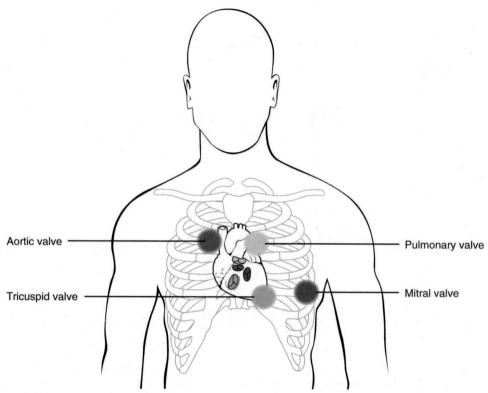

FIGURE 19.30   Stethoscope Placement for Auscultation   Proper placement of the bell of the stethoscope facilitates auscultation. At each of the four locations on the chest, a different valve can be heard.

19.4 Cardiac Physiology

LEARNING OBJECTIVES

By the end of this section, you will be able to:

- Relate heart rate to cardiac output
- Describe the effect of exercise on heart rate
- Identify cardiovascular centers and cardiac reflexes that regulate heart function
- Describe factors affecting heart rate
- Distinguish between positive and negative factors that affect heart contractility
- Summarize factors affecting stroke volume and cardiac output
- Describe the cardiac response to variations in blood flow and pressure

The autorhythmicity inherent in cardiac cells keeps the heart beating at a regular pace; however, the heart is regulated by and responds to outside influences as well. Neural and endocrine controls are vital to the regulation of cardiac function. In addition, the heart is sensitive to several environmental factors, including electrolytes.

Resting Cardiac Output

Cardiac output (CO) is a measurement of the amount of blood pumped by each ventricle in one minute. To calculate this value, multiply **stroke volume (SV)**, the amount of blood pumped by each ventricle, by **heart rate (HR)**, in contractions per minute (or beats per minute, bpm). It can be represented mathematically by the following equation:

$$CO = HR \times SV$$

SV is normally measured using an echocardiogram to record EDV and ESV, and calculating the difference: SV = EDV − ESV. SV can also be measured using a specialized catheter, but this is an invasive procedure and far more dangerous to the patient. A mean SV for a resting 70-kg (150-lb) individual would be approximately 70 mL. There are several important variables, including size of the heart, physical and mental condition of the individual, sex, contractility, duration of contraction, preload or EDV, and afterload or resistance. Normal range for SV would be 55–100 mL. An average resting HR would be approximately 75 bpm but could range from 60–100 in some

Access for free at openstax.org

individuals.

Using these numbers, the mean CO is 5.25 L/min, with a range of 4.0–8.0 L/min. Remember, however, that these numbers refer to CO from each ventricle separately, not the total for the heart. Factors influencing CO are summarized in Figure 19.31.

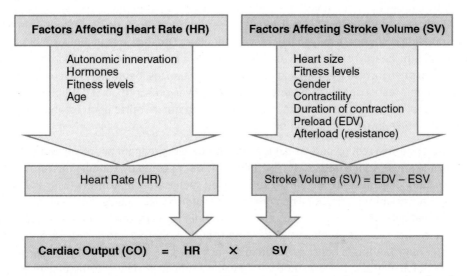

FIGURE 19.31   Major Factors Influencing Cardiac Output   Cardiac output is influenced by heart rate and stroke volume, both of which are also variable.

SVs are also used to calculate **ejection fraction**, which is the portion of the blood that is pumped or ejected from the heart with each contraction. To calculate ejection fraction, SV is divided by EDV. Despite the name, the ejection fraction is normally expressed as a percentage. Ejection fractions range from approximately 55–70 percent, with a mean of 58 percent.

Exercise and Maximum Cardiac Output

In healthy young individuals, HR may increase to 150 bpm during exercise. SV can also increase from 70 to approximately 130 mL due to increased strength of contraction. This would increase CO to approximately 19.5 L/min, 4–5 times the resting rate. Top cardiovascular athletes can achieve even higher levels. At their peak performance, they may increase resting CO by 7–8 times.

Since the heart is a muscle, exercising it increases its efficiency. The difference between maximum and resting CO is known as the **cardiac reserve**. It measures the residual capacity of the heart to pump blood.

Heart Rates

HRs vary considerably, not only with exercise and fitness levels, but also with age. Newborn resting HRs may be 120 bpm. HR gradually decreases until young adulthood and then gradually increases again with age.

Maximum HRs are normally in the range of 200–220 bpm, although there are some extreme cases in which they may reach higher levels. As one ages, the ability to generate maximum rates decreases. This may be estimated by taking the maximal value of 220 bpm and subtracting the individual's age. So a 40-year-old individual would be expected to hit a maximum rate of approximately 180, and a 60-year-old person would achieve a HR of 160.

Disorders of the...

Heart: Abnormal Heart Rates

For an adult, normal resting HR will be in the range of 60–100 bpm. Bradycardia is the condition in which resting rate drops below 60 bpm, and tachycardia is the condition in which the resting rate is above 100 bpm. Trained athletes typically have very low HRs. If the patient is not exhibiting other symptoms, such as weakness, fatigue, dizziness, fainting, chest discomfort, palpitations, or respiratory distress, bradycardia is not considered clinically significant. However, if any of these symptoms are present, they may indicate that the heart is not providing sufficient oxygenated blood to the tissues. The term relative bradycardia may be used with a patient who has a HR in the normal range but is still suffering from these symptoms. Most patients remain asymptomatic as long as the HR remains above 50 bpm.

Bradycardia may be caused by either inherent factors or causes external to the heart. While the condition may be inherited, typically it is acquired in older individuals. Inherent causes include abnormalities in either the SA or AV node. If the condition is serious, a pacemaker may be required. Other causes include ischemia to the heart muscle or diseases of the heart vessels or valves. External causes include metabolic disorders, pathologies of the endocrine system often involving the thyroid, electrolyte imbalances, neurological disorders including inappropriate autonomic responses, autoimmune pathologies, over-prescription of beta blocker drugs that reduce HR, recreational drug use, or even prolonged bed rest. Treatment relies upon establishing the underlying cause of the disorder and may necessitate supplemental oxygen.

Tachycardia is not normal in a resting patient but may be detected in pregnant people or individuals experiencing extreme stress. In the latter case, it would likely be triggered by stimulation from the limbic system or disorders of the autonomic nervous system. In some cases, tachycardia may involve only the atria. Some individuals may remain asymptomatic, but when present, symptoms may include dizziness, shortness of breath, lightheadedness, rapid pulse, heart palpations, chest pain, or fainting (syncope). While tachycardia is defined as a HR above 100 bpm, there is considerable variation among people. Further, the normal resting HRs of children are often above 100 bpm, but this is not considered to be tachycardia Many causes of tachycardia may be benign, but the condition may also be correlated with fever, anemia, hypoxia, hyperthyroidism, hypersecretion of catecholamines, some cardiomyopathies, some disorders of the valves, and acute exposure to radiation. Elevated rates in an exercising or resting patient are normal and expected. Resting rate should always be taken after recovery from exercise. Treatment depends upon the underlying cause but may include medications, implantable cardioverter defibrillators, ablation, or surgery.

Correlation Between Heart Rates and Cardiac Output

Initially, physiological conditions that cause HR to increase also trigger an increase in SV. During exercise, the rate of blood returning to the heart increases. However as the HR rises, there is less time spent in diastole and consequently less time for the ventricles to fill with blood. Even though there is less filling time, SV will initially remain high. However, as HR continues to increase, SV gradually decreases due to decreased filling time. CO will initially stabilize as the increasing HR compensates for the decreasing SV, but at very high rates, CO will eventually decrease as increasing rates are no longer able to compensate for the decreasing SV. Consider this phenomenon in a healthy young individual. Initially, as HR increases from resting to approximately 120 bpm, CO will rise. As HR increases from 120 to 160 bpm, CO remains stable, since the increase in rate is offset by decreasing ventricular filling time and, consequently, SV. As HR continues to rise above 160 bpm, CO actually decreases as SV falls faster than HR increases. So although aerobic exercises are critical to maintain the health of the heart, individuals are cautioned to monitor their HR to ensure they stay within the **target heart rate** range of between 120 and 160 bpm, so CO is maintained. The target HR is loosely defined as the range in which both the heart and lungs receive the maximum benefit from the aerobic workout and is dependent upon age.

Cardiovascular Centers

Nervous control over HR is centralized within the two paired cardiovascular centers of the medulla oblongata (Figure 19.32). The cardioaccelerator regions stimulate activity via sympathetic stimulation of the cardioaccelerator nerves, and the cardioinhibitory centers decrease heart activity via parasympathetic stimulation as one component of the vagus nerve, cranial nerve X. During rest, both centers provide slight stimulation to the heart, contributing to **autonomic tone**. This is a similar concept to tone in skeletal muscles. Normally, vagal stimulation predominates as, left unregulated, the SA node would initiate a sinus rhythm of approximately 100 bpm.

Both sympathetic and parasympathetic stimulations flow through a paired complex network of nerve fibers known as the **cardiac plexus** near the base of the heart. The cardioaccelerator center also sends additional fibers, forming the cardiac nerves via sympathetic ganglia (the cervical ganglia plus superior thoracic ganglia T1–T4) to both the SA and AV nodes, plus additional fibers to the atria and ventricles. The ventricles are more richly innervated by sympathetic fibers than parasympathetic fibers. Sympathetic stimulation causes the release of the neurotransmitter norepinephrine (NE) at the neuromuscular junction of the cardiac nerves. NE shortens the repolarization period, thus speeding the rate of depolarization and contraction, which results in an increase in HR. It opens chemical- or ligand-gated sodium and calcium ion channels, allowing an influx of positively charged ions.

NE binds to the beta-1 receptor. Some cardiac medications (for example, beta blockers) work by blocking these receptors, thereby slowing HR and are one possible treatment for hypertension. Overprescription of these drugs may lead to bradycardia and even stoppage of the heart.

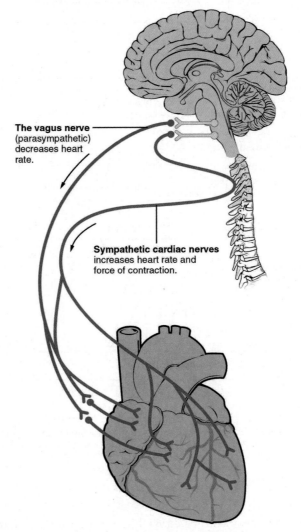

The vagus nerve (parasympathetic) decreases heart rate.

Sympathetic cardiac nerves increases heart rate and force of contraction.

FIGURE 19.32 Autonomic Innervation of the Heart Cardioaccelerator and cardioinhibitory areas are components of the paired cardiac centers located in the medulla oblongata of the brain. They innervate the heart via sympathetic cardiac nerves that increase cardiac activity and vagus (parasympathetic) nerves that slow cardiac activity.

Parasympathetic stimulation originates from the cardioinhibitory region with impulses traveling via the vagus nerve (cranial nerve X). The vagus nerve sends branches to both the SA and AV nodes, and to portions of both the atria and ventricles. Parasympathetic stimulation releases the neurotransmitter acetylcholine (ACh) at the neuromuscular junction. ACh slows HR by opening chemical- or ligand-gated potassium ion channels to slow the rate of spontaneous depolarization, which extends repolarization and increases the time before the next spontaneous depolarization occurs. Without any nervous stimulation, the SA node would establish a sinus rhythm of approximately 100 bpm. Since resting rates are considerably less than this, it becomes evident that parasympathetic stimulation normally slows HR. This is similar to an individual driving a car with one foot on the brake pedal. To speed up, one need merely remove one's foot from the break and let the engine increase speed. In the case of the heart, decreasing parasympathetic stimulation decreases the release of ACh, which allows HR to increase up to approximately 100 bpm. Any increases beyond this rate would require sympathetic stimulation. Figure 19.33 illustrates the effects of parasympathetic and sympathetic stimulation on the normal sinus rhythm.

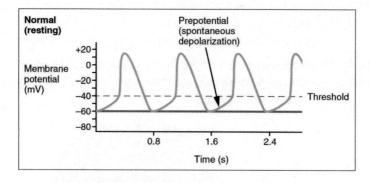

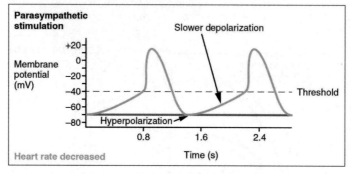

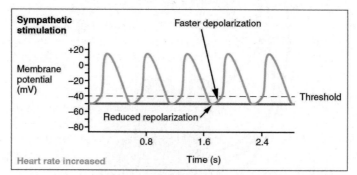

FIGURE 19.33   Effects of Parasympathetic and Sympathetic Stimulation on Normal Sinus Rhythm   The wave of depolarization in a normal sinus rhythm shows a stable resting HR. Following parasympathetic stimulation, HR slows. Following sympathetic stimulation, HR increases.

Input to the Cardiovascular Center

The cardiovascular center receives input from a series of visceral receptors with impulses traveling through visceral sensory fibers within the vagus and sympathetic nerves via the cardiac plexus. Among these receptors are various proprioreceptors, baroreceptors, and chemoreceptors, plus stimuli from the limbic system. Collectively, these inputs normally enable the cardiovascular centers to regulate heart function precisely, a process known as **cardiac reflexes**. Increased physical activity results in increased rates of firing by various proprioreceptors located in muscles, joint capsules, and tendons. Any such increase in physical activity would logically warrant increased blood flow. The cardiac centers monitor these increased rates of firing, and suppress parasympathetic stimulation and increase sympathetic stimulation as needed in order to increase blood flow.

Similarly, baroreceptors are stretch receptors located in the aortic sinus, carotid bodies, the venae cavae, and other locations, including pulmonary vessels and the right side of the heart itself. Rates of firing from the baroreceptors represent blood pressure, level of physical activity, and the relative distribution of blood. The cardiac centers monitor baroreceptor firing to maintain cardiac homeostasis, a mechanism called the **baroreceptor reflex**. With increased pressure and stretch, the rate of baroreceptor firing increases, and the cardiac centers decrease sympathetic stimulation and increase parasympathetic stimulation. As pressure and stretch decrease, the rate of

Access for free at openstax.org

baroreceptor firing decreases, and the cardiac centers increase sympathetic stimulation and decrease parasympathetic stimulation.

There is a similar reflex, called the **atrial reflex** or **Bainbridge reflex**, associated with varying rates of blood flow to the atria. Increased venous return stretches the walls of the atria where specialized baroreceptors are located. However, as the atrial baroreceptors increase their rate of firing and as they stretch due to the increased blood pressure, the cardiac center responds by increasing sympathetic stimulation and inhibiting parasympathetic stimulation to increase HR. The opposite is also true.

Increased metabolic byproducts associated with increased activity, such as carbon dioxide, hydrogen ions, and lactic acid, plus falling oxygen levels, are detected by a suite of chemoreceptors innervated by the glossopharyngeal and vagus nerves. These chemoreceptors provide feedback to the cardiovascular centers about the need for increased or decreased blood flow, based on the relative levels of these substances.

The limbic system can also significantly impact HR related to emotional state. During periods of stress, it is not unusual to identify higher than normal HRs, often accompanied by a surge in the stress hormone cortisol. Individuals experiencing extreme anxiety may manifest panic attacks with symptoms that resemble those of heart attacks. These events are typically transient and treatable. Meditation techniques have been developed to ease anxiety and have been shown to lower HR effectively. Doing simple deep and slow breathing exercises with one's eyes closed can also significantly reduce this anxiety and HR.

Disorders of the...

Heart: Broken Heart Syndrome

Extreme stress from such life events as the death of a loved one, an emotional break up, loss of income, or foreclosure of a home may lead to a condition commonly referred to as broken heart syndrome. This condition may also be called Takotsubo cardiomyopathy, transient apical ballooning syndrome, apical ballooning cardiomyopathy, stress-induced cardiomyopathy, Gebrochenes-Herz syndrome, and stress cardiomyopathy. The recognized effects on the heart include congestive heart failure due to a profound weakening of the myocardium not related to lack of oxygen. This may lead to acute heart failure, lethal arrhythmias, or even the rupture of a ventricle. The exact etiology is not known, but several factors have been suggested, including transient vasospasm, dysfunction of the cardiac capillaries, or thickening of the myocardium—particularly in the left ventricle—that may lead to the critical circulation of blood to this region. While many patients survive the initial acute event with treatment to restore normal function, there is a strong correlation with death. Careful statistical analysis by the Jaap Spreeuw and Iqbal Owadally of Bayes Business School in London, revealed that within one year of the death of a loved one, women are more than twice as likely to die and men are six times as likely to die as would otherwise be expected. The same study indicated that longer relationships also had a greater incidence of a person dying soon after the death of their spouse.

Other Factors Influencing Heart Rate

Using a combination of autorhythmicity and innervation, the cardiovascular center is able to provide relatively precise control over HR. However, there are a number of other factors that have an impact on HR as well, including epinephrine, NE, and thyroid hormones; levels of various ions including calcium, potassium, and sodium; body temperature; hypoxia; and pH balance (Table 19.1 and Table 19.2). After reading this section, the importance of maintaining homeostasis should become even more apparent.

Major Factors Increasing Heart Rate and Force of Contraction

Factor	Effect
Cardioaccelerator nerves	Release of norepinephrine by cardioaccelerator nerves
Proprioreceptors	Increased firing rates of proprioreceptors (e.g. during exercise)
Chemoreceptors	Chemoreceptors sensing decreased levels of O_2 or increased levels of H^+, CO_2 and lactic acid
Baroreceptors	Decreased firing rates of baroreceptors (indicating falling blood volume/pressure)
Limbic system	Anticipation of physical exercise or strong emotions by the limbic system
Catecholamines	Decreased epinephrine and norepinephrine release by the adrenal glands
Thyroid hormones	Increased T_3 and T_4 in the blood (released by thyroid)
Calcium	Decrease in calcium ions in the blood
Potassium	Decrease in potassium ions in the blood
Sodium	Decrease in sodium ions in the blood
Body temperature	Increase in body temperature
Nicotine and caffeine	Presence of nicotine, caffeine or other stimulants

TABLE 19.1

Factors Decreasing Heart Rate and Force of Contraction

Factor	Effect
Cardioinhibitor nerves (vagus)	Release of acetylcholine by cardioinhibitor nerves
Proprioreceptors	Decreased firing rates of proprioreceptors (e.g. during rest)
Chemoreceptors	Chemoreceptors sensing increased levels of O_2 or decreased levels of H^+, CO_2 and lactic acid
Baroreceptors	Increased firing rates of baroreceptors (indicating rising blood volume/pressure)
Limbic system	Anticipation of relaxation by the limbic system
Catecholamines	Decreased epinephrine and norepinephrine release by the adrenal glands

TABLE 19.2

Factor	Effect
Thyroid hormones	Decreased T_3 and T_4 in the blood (released by thyroid)
Calcium	Decrease in calcium ions in the blood
Potassium	Increase in potassium ions in the blood
Sodium	Increase in sodium ions in the blood
Body temperature	Decrease in body temperature
Opiates and tranquilizers	Presence of opiates (heroin), tranquilizers or other depressants

TABLE 19.2

Epinephrine and Norepinephrine

The catecholamines, epinephrine and NE, secreted by the adrenal medulla form one component of the extended fight-or-flight mechanism. The other component is sympathetic stimulation. Epinephrine and NE have similar effects: binding to the beta-1 receptors, and opening sodium and calcium ion chemical- or ligand-gated channels. The rate of depolarization is increased by this additional influx of positively charged ions, so the threshold is reached more quickly and the period of repolarization is shortened. However, massive releases of these hormones coupled with sympathetic stimulation may actually lead to arrhythmias. There is no parasympathetic stimulation to the adrenal medulla.

Thyroid Hormones

In general, increased levels of thyroid hormone, or thyroxin, increase cardiac rate and contractility. The impact of thyroid hormone is typically of a much longer duration than that of the catecholamines. The physiologically active form of thyroid hormone, T_3 or triiodothyronine, has been shown to directly enter cardiomyocytes and alter activity at the level of the genome. It also impacts the beta adrenergic response similar to epinephrine and NE described above. Excessive levels of thyroxin may trigger tachycardia.

Calcium

Calcium ion levels have great impacts upon both HR and contractility; as the levels of calcium ions increase, so do HR and contractility. High levels of calcium ions (hypercalcemia) may be implicated in a short QT interval and a widened T wave in the ECG. The QT interval represents the time from the start of depolarization to repolarization of the ventricles, and includes the period of ventricular systole. Extremely high levels of calcium may induce cardiac arrest. Drugs known as calcium channel blockers slow HR by binding to these channels and blocking or slowing the inward movement of calcium ions.

Caffeine and Nicotine

Caffeine and nicotine are not found naturally within the body. Both of these nonregulated drugs have an excitatory effect on membranes of neurons in general and have a stimulatory effect on the cardiac centers specifically, causing an increase in HR. Caffeine works by increasing the rates of depolarization at the SA node, whereas nicotine stimulates the activity of the sympathetic neurons that deliver impulses to the heart.

Although it is the world's most widely consumed psychoactive drug, caffeine is legal and not regulated. While precise quantities have not been established, "normal" consumption is not considered harmful to most people, although it may cause disruptions to sleep and acts as a diuretic. Its consumption by pregnant people is cautioned against, although no evidence of negative effects has been confirmed. Tolerance and even physical and mental addiction to the drug result in individuals who routinely consume the substance.

Nicotine, too, is a stimulant and produces addiction. While legal and nonregulated, concerns about nicotine's safety and documented links to respiratory and cardiac disease have resulted in warning labels on cigarette packages.

Factors Decreasing Heart Rate

HR can be slowed when a person experiences altered sodium and potassium levels, hypoxia, acidosis, alkalosis, and hypothermia (see Table 19.1). The relationship between electrolytes and HR is complex, but maintaining electrolyte balance is critical to the normal wave of depolarization. Of the two ions, potassium has the greater clinical significance. Initially, both hyponatremia (low sodium levels) and hypernatremia (high sodium levels) may lead to tachycardia. Severely high hypernatremia may lead to fibrillation, which may cause CO to cease. Severe hyponatremia leads to both bradycardia and other arrhythmias. Hypokalemia (low potassium levels) also leads to arrhythmias, whereas hyperkalemia (high potassium levels) causes the heart to become weak and flaccid, and ultimately to fail.

Acidosis is a condition in which excess hydrogen ions are present, and the patient's blood expresses a low pH value. Alkalosis is a condition in which there are too few hydrogen ions, and the patient's blood has an elevated pH. Normal blood pH falls in the range of 7.35–7.45, so a number lower than this range represents acidosis and a higher number represents alkalosis. Recall that enzymes are the regulators or catalysts of virtually all biochemical reactions; they are sensitive to pH and will change shape slightly with values outside their normal range. These variations in pH and accompanying slight physical changes to the active site on the enzyme decrease the rate of formation of the enzyme-substrate complex, subsequently decreasing the rate of many enzymatic reactions, which can have complex effects on HR. Severe changes in pH will lead to denaturation of the enzyme.

The last variable is body temperature. Elevated body temperature is called hyperthermia, and suppressed body temperature is called hypothermia. Slight hyperthermia results in increasing HR and strength of contraction. Hypothermia slows the rate and strength of heart contractions. This distinct slowing of the heart is one component of the larger diving reflex that diverts blood to essential organs while submerged. If sufficiently chilled, the heart will stop beating, a technique that may be employed during open heart surgery. In this case, the patient's blood is normally diverted to an artificial heart-lung machine to maintain the body's blood supply and gas exchange until the surgery is complete, and sinus rhythm can be restored. Excessive hyperthermia and hypothermia will both result in death, as enzymes drive the body systems to cease normal function, beginning with the central nervous system.

Stroke Volume

Many of the same factors that regulate HR also impact cardiac function by altering SV. While a number of variables are involved, SV is ultimately dependent upon the difference between EDV and ESV. The three primary factors to consider are preload, or the stretch on the ventricles prior to contraction; the contractility, or the force or strength of the contraction itself; and afterload, the force the ventricles must generate to pump blood against the resistance in the vessels. These factors are summarized in Table 19.1 and Table 19.2.

Preload

Preload is another way of expressing EDV. Therefore, the greater the EDV is, the greater the preload is. One of the primary factors to consider is **filling time**, or the duration of ventricular diastole during which filling occurs. The more rapidly the heart contracts, the shorter the filling time becomes, and the lower the EDV and preload are. This effect can be partially overcome by increasing the second variable, contractility, and raising SV, but over time, the heart is unable to compensate for decreased filling time, and preload also decreases.

With increasing ventricular filling, both EDV or preload increase, and the cardiac muscle itself is stretched to a greater degree. At rest, there is little stretch of the ventricular muscle, and the sarcomeres remain short. With increased ventricular filling, the ventricular muscle is increasingly stretched and the sarcomere length increases. As the sarcomeres reach their optimal lengths, they will contract more powerfully, because more of the myosin heads can bind to the actin on the thin filaments, forming cross bridges and increasing the strength of contraction and SV. If this process were to continue and the sarcomeres stretched beyond their optimal lengths, the force of contraction would decrease. However, due to the physical constraints of the location of the heart, this excessive stretch is not a concern.

The relationship between ventricular stretch and contraction has been stated in the well-known **Frank-Starling mechanism** or simply Starling's Law of the Heart. This principle states that, within physiological limits, the force of heart contraction is directly proportional to the initial length of the muscle fiber. This means that the greater the stretch of the ventricular muscle (within limits), the more powerful the contraction is, which in turn increases SV. Therefore, by increasing preload, you increase the second variable, contractility.

Otto Frank (1865–1944) was a German physiologist; among his many published works are detailed studies of this important heart relationship. Ernest Starling (1866–1927) was an important English physiologist who also studied the heart. Although they worked largely independently, their combined efforts and similar conclusions have been recognized in the name "Frank-Starling mechanism."

Any sympathetic stimulation to the venous system will increase venous return to the heart, which contributes to ventricular filling, and EDV and preload. While much of the ventricular filling occurs while both atria and ventricles are in diastole, the contraction of the atria, the atrial kick, plays a crucial role by providing the last 20–30 percent of ventricular filling.

Contractility

It is virtually impossible to consider preload or ESV without including an early mention of the concept of contractility. Indeed, the two parameters are intimately linked. Contractility refers to the force of the contraction of the heart muscle, which controls SV, and is the primary parameter for impacting ESV. The more forceful the contraction is, the greater the SV and smaller the ESV are. Less forceful contractions result in smaller SVs and larger ESVs. Factors that increase contractility are described as **positive inotropic factors**, and those that decrease contractility are described as **negative inotropic factors** (ino- = "fiber;" -tropic = "turning toward").

Not surprisingly, sympathetic stimulation is a positive inotrope, whereas parasympathetic stimulation is a negative inotrope. Sympathetic stimulation triggers the release of NE at the neuromuscular junction from the cardiac nerves and also stimulates the adrenal cortex to secrete epinephrine and NE. In addition to their stimulatory effects on HR, they also bind to both alpha and beta receptors on the cardiac muscle cell membrane to increase metabolic rate and the force of contraction. This combination of actions has the net effect of increasing SV and leaving a smaller residual ESV in the ventricles. In comparison, parasympathetic stimulation releases ACh at the neuromuscular junction from the vagus nerve. The membrane hyperpolarizes and inhibits contraction to decrease the strength of contraction and SV, and to raise ESV. Since parasympathetic fibers are more widespread in the atria than in the ventricles, the primary site of action is in the upper chambers. Parasympathetic stimulation in the atria decreases the atrial kick and reduces EDV, which decreases ventricular stretch and preload, thereby further limiting the force of ventricular contraction. Stronger parasympathetic stimulation also directly decreases the force of contraction of the ventricles.

Several synthetic drugs, including dopamine and isoproterenol, have been developed that mimic the effects of epinephrine and NE by stimulating the influx of calcium ions from the extracellular fluid. Higher concentrations of intracellular calcium ions increase the strength of contraction. Excess calcium (hypercalcemia) also acts as a positive inotropic agent. The drug digitalis lowers HR and increases the strength of the contraction, acting as a positive inotropic agent by blocking the sequestering of calcium ions into the sarcoplasmic reticulum. This leads to higher intracellular calcium levels and greater strength of contraction. In addition to the catecholamines from the adrenal medulla, other hormones also demonstrate positive inotropic effects. These include thyroid hormones and glucagon from the pancreas.

Negative inotropic agents include hypoxia, acidosis, hyperkalemia, and a variety of synthetic drugs. These include numerous beta blockers and calcium channel blockers. Early beta blocker drugs include propranolol and pronethalol, and are credited with revolutionizing treatment of cardiac patients experiencing angina pectoris. There is also a large class of dihydropyridine, phenylalkylamine, and benzothiazepine calcium channel blockers that may be administered decreasing the strength of contraction and SV.

Afterload

Afterload refers to the tension that the ventricles must develop to pump blood effectively against the resistance in the vascular system. Any condition that increases resistance requires a greater afterload to force open the semilunar valves and pump the blood. Damage to the valves, such as stenosis, which makes them harder to open will also increase afterload. Any decrease in resistance decreases the afterload. Figure 19.34 summarizes the major factors influencing SV, Figure 19.35 summarizes the major factors influencing CO, and Table 19.3 and Table 19.4 summarize cardiac responses to increased and decreased blood flow and pressure in order to restore homeostasis.

Factors Affecting Stroke Volume (SV)		
Preload	**Contractility**	**Afterload**
Raised due to: • fast filling time • increased venous return **Increases end diastolic volume,** Increases stroke volume	• sympathetic stimulation • epinephrine and norepinephrine • high intracellular calcium ions • high blood calcium level • thyroid hormones • glucagon **Decreases end systolic volume,** Increases stroke volume	• increased vascular resistance • semilunar valve damage **Increases end systolic volume** Decreases stroke volume
Lowered due to: • decreased thyroid hormones • decreased calcium ions • high or low potassium ions • high or low sodium • low body temperature • hypoxia • abnormal pH balance • drugs (i.e., calcium channel blockers) **Decreases end diastolic volume,** Decreases stroke volume	• parasympathetic stimulation • acetylcholine • hypoxia • hyperkalemia **Increases end systolic volume** Decreases stroke volume	• decreased vascular resistance **Decreases end systolic volume** Increases stroke volume

FIGURE 19.34   Major Factors Influencing Stroke Volume   Multiple factors impact preload, afterload, and contractility, and are the major considerations influencing SV.

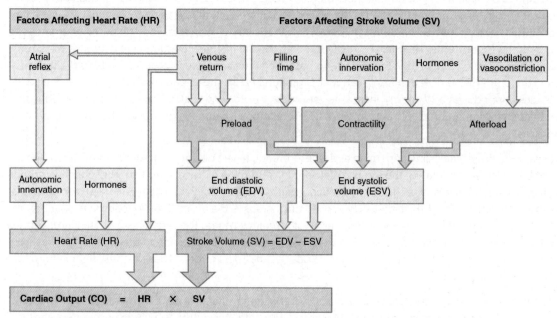

FIGURE 19.35   Summary of Major Factors Influencing Cardiac Output   The primary factors influencing HR include autonomic innervation plus endocrine control. Not shown are environmental factors, such as electrolytes, metabolic products, and temperature. The primary factors controlling SV include preload, contractility, and afterload. Other factors such as electrolytes may be classified as either positive or negative inotropic agents.

Cardiac Response to Decreasing Blood Flow and Pressure Due to Decreasing Cardiac Output

	Baroreceptors (aorta, carotid arteries, venae cavae, and atria)	Chemoreceptors (both central nervous system and in proximity to baroreceptors)
Sensitive to	Decreasing stretch	Decreasing O_2 and increasing CO_2, H^+, and lactic acid
Target	Parasympathetic stimulation suppressed	Sympathetic stimulation increased
Response of heart	Increasing heart rate and increasing stroke volume	Increasing heart rate and increasing stroke volume
Overall effect	Increasing blood flow and pressure due to increasing cardiac output; homeostasis restored	Increasing blood flow and pressure due to increasing cardiac output; homeostasis restored

TABLE 19.3

Cardiac Response to Increasing Blood Flow and Pressure Due to Increasing Cardiac Output

	Baroreceptors (aorta, carotid arteries, venae cavae, and atria)	Chemoreceptors (both central nervous system and in proximity to baroreceptors)
Sensitive to	Increasing stretch	Increasing O_2 and decreasing CO_2, H^+, and lactic acid
Target	Parasympathetic stimulation increased	Sympathetic stimulation suppressed
Response of heart	Decreasing heart rate and decreasing stroke volume	Decreasing heart rate and decreasing stroke volume
Overall effect	Decreasing blood flow and pressure due to decreasing cardiac output; homeostasis restored	Decreasing blood flow and pressure due to decreasing cardiac output; homeostasis restored

TABLE 19.4

19.5 Development of the Heart

LEARNING OBJECTIVES

By the end of this section, you will be able to:
- Describe the embryological development of heart structures
- Identify five regions of the fetal heart
- Relate fetal heart structures to adult counterparts

The human heart is the first functional organ to develop. It begins beating and pumping blood around day 21 or 22, a mere three weeks after fertilization. This emphasizes the critical nature of the heart in distributing blood through the vessels and the vital exchange of nutrients, oxygen, and wastes both to and from the developing baby. The critical early development of the heart is reflected by the prominent **heart bulge** that appears on the anterior surface of the embryo.

The heart forms from an embryonic tissue called **mesoderm** around 18 to 19 days after fertilization. Mesoderm is one of the three primary germ layers that differentiates early in development that collectively gives rise to all subsequent tissues and organs. The heart begins to develop near the head of the embryo in a region known as the

cardiogenic area. Following chemical signals called factors from the underlying endoderm (another of the three primary germ layers), the cardiogenic area begins to form two strands called the **cardiogenic cords** (Figure 19.36). As the cardiogenic cords develop, a lumen rapidly develops within them. At this point, they are referred to as **endocardial tubes**. The two tubes migrate together and fuse to form a single **primitive heart tube**. The primitive heart tube quickly forms five distinct regions. From head to tail, these include the truncus arteriosus, bulbus cordis, primitive ventricle, primitive atrium, and the sinus venosus. Initially, all venous blood flows into the sinus venosus, and contractions propel the blood from tail to head, or from the sinus venosus to the truncus arteriosus. This is a very different pattern from that of an adult.

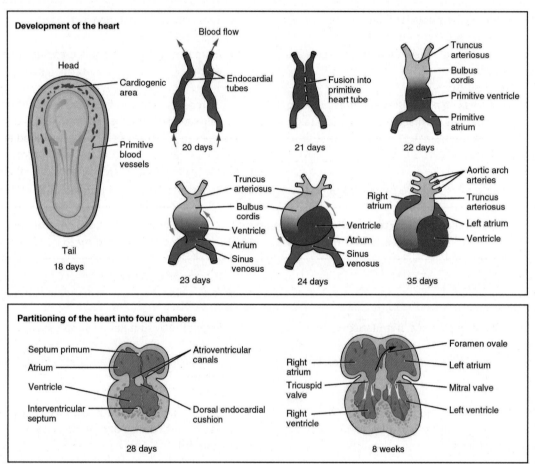

FIGURE 19.36   Development of the Human Heart   This diagram outlines the embryological development of the human heart during the first eight weeks and the subsequent formation of the four heart chambers.

The five regions of the primitive heart tube develop into recognizable structures in a fully developed heart. The **truncus arteriosus** will eventually divide and give rise to the ascending aorta and pulmonary trunk. The **bulbus cordis** develops into the right ventricle. The **primitive ventricle** forms the left ventricle. The **primitive atrium** becomes the anterior portions of both the right and left atria, and the two auricles. The **sinus venosus** develops into the posterior portion of the right atrium, the SA node, and the coronary sinus.

As the primitive heart tube elongates, it begins to fold within the pericardium, eventually forming an S shape, which places the chambers and major vessels into an alignment similar to the adult heart. This process occurs between days 23 and 28. The remainder of the heart development pattern includes development of septa and valves, and remodeling of the actual chambers. Partitioning of the atria and ventricles by the interatrial septum, interventricular septum, and atrioventricular septum is complete by the end of the fifth week, although the fetal blood shunts remain until birth or shortly after. The atrioventricular valves form between weeks five and eight, and the semilunar valves form between weeks five and nine.

Access for free at openstax.org

Key Terms

afterload   force the ventricles must develop to effectively pump blood against the resistance in the vessels

anastomosis   (plural = anastomoses) area where vessels unite to allow blood to circulate even if there may be partial blockage in another branch

anterior cardiac veins   vessels that parallel the small cardiac arteries and drain the anterior surface of the right ventricle; bypass the coronary sinus and drain directly into the right atrium

anterior interventricular artery   (also, left anterior descending artery or LAD) major branch of the left coronary artery that follows the anterior interventricular sulcus

anterior interventricular sulcus   sulcus located between the left and right ventricles on the anterior surface of the heart

aortic valve   (also, aortic semilunar valve) valve located at the base of the aorta

artificial pacemaker   medical device that transmits electrical signals to the heart to ensure that it contracts and pumps blood to the body

atrial reflex   (also, called Bainbridge reflex) autonomic reflex that responds to stretch receptors in the atria that send impulses to the cardioaccelerator area to increase HR when venous flow into the atria increases

atrioventricular (AV) node   clump of myocardial cells located in the inferior portion of the right atrium within the atrioventricular septum; receives the impulse from the SA node, pauses, and then transmits it into specialized conducting cells within the interventricular septum

atrioventricular bundle   (also, bundle of His) group of specialized myocardial conductile cells that transmit the impulse from the AV node through the interventricular septum; form the left and right atrioventricular bundle branches

atrioventricular bundle branches   (also, left or right bundle branches) specialized myocardial conductile cells that arise from the bifurcation of the atrioventricular bundle and pass through the interventricular septum; lead to the Purkinje fibers and also to the right papillary muscle via the moderator band

atrioventricular septum   cardiac septum located between the atria and ventricles; atrioventricular valves are located here

atrioventricular valves   one-way valves located between the atria and ventricles; the valve on the right is called the tricuspid valve, and the one on the left is the mitral or bicuspid valve

atrium   (plural = atria) upper or receiving chamber of the heart that pumps blood into the lower chambers just prior to their contraction; the right atrium receives blood from the systemic circuit that flows into the right ventricle; the left atrium receives blood from the pulmonary circuit that flows into the left ventricle

auricle   extension of an atrium visible on the superior surface of the heart

autonomic tone   contractile state during resting cardiac activity produced by mild sympathetic and parasympathetic stimulation

autorhythmicity   ability of cardiac muscle to initiate its own electrical impulse that triggers the mechanical contraction that pumps blood at a fixed pace without nervous or endocrine control

Bachmann's bundle   (also, interatrial band) group of specialized conducting cells that transmit the impulse directly from the SA node in the right atrium to the left atrium

Bainbridge reflex   (also, called atrial reflex) autonomic reflex that responds to stretch receptors in the atria that send impulses to the cardioaccelerator area to increase HR when venous flow into the atria increases

baroreceptor reflex   autonomic reflex in which the cardiac centers monitor signals from the baroreceptor stretch receptors and regulate heart function based on blood flow

bicuspid valve   (also, mitral valve or left atrioventricular valve) valve located between the left atrium and ventricle; consists of two flaps of tissue

bulbus cordis   portion of the primitive heart tube that will eventually develop into the right ventricle

bundle of His   (also, atrioventricular bundle) group of specialized myocardial conductile cells that transmit the impulse from the AV node through the interventricular septum; form the left and right atrioventricular bundle branches

cardiac cycle   period of time between the onset of atrial contraction (atrial systole) and ventricular relaxation (ventricular diastole)

cardiac notch   depression in the medial surface of the inferior lobe of the left lung where the apex of the heart is located

cardiac output (CO)   amount of blood pumped by each ventricle during one minute; equals HR multiplied by SV

cardiac plexus   paired complex network of nerve fibers near the base of the heart that receive sympathetic and parasympathetic stimulations to regulate HR

cardiac reflexes   series of autonomic reflexes that enable the cardiovascular centers to regulate heart function based upon sensory information from a variety of visceral sensors

cardiac reserve   difference between maximum and resting CO

cardiac skeleton   (also, skeleton of the heart) reinforced connective tissue located within the atrioventricular septum; includes four rings that surround the openings between the atria and ventricles, and the openings to the pulmonary trunk and aorta; the point of attachment for the heart valves

cardiogenic area   area near the head of the embryo where the heart begins to develop 18–19 days after fertilization

cardiogenic cords   two strands of tissue that form within the cardiogenic area

cardiomyocyte   muscle cell of the heart

chordae tendineae   string-like extensions of tough connective tissue that extend from the flaps of the atrioventricular valves to the papillary muscles

circumflex artery   branch of the left coronary artery that follows coronary sulcus

coronary arteries   branches of the ascending aorta that supply blood to the heart; the left coronary artery feeds the left side of the heart, the left atrium and ventricle, and the interventricular septum; the right coronary artery feeds the right atrium, portions of both ventricles, and the heart conduction system

coronary sinus   large, thin-walled vein on the posterior surface of the heart that lies within the atrioventricular sulcus and drains the heart myocardium directly into the right atrium

coronary sulcus   sulcus that marks the boundary between the atria and ventricles

coronary veins   vessels that drain the heart and generally parallel the large surface arteries

diastole   period of time when the heart muscle is relaxed and the chambers fill with blood

ejection fraction   portion of the blood that is pumped or ejected from the heart with each contraction; mathematically represented by SV divided by EDV

electrocardiogram (ECG)   surface recording of the electrical activity of the heart that can be used for diagnosis of irregular heart function; also abbreviated as EKG

end diastolic volume (EDV)   (also, preload) the amount of blood in the ventricles at the end of atrial systole just prior to ventricular contraction

end systolic volume (ESV)   amount of blood remaining in each ventricle following systole

endocardial tubes   stage in which lumens form within the expanding cardiogenic cords, forming hollow structures

endocardium   innermost layer of the heart lining the heart chambers and heart valves; composed of endothelium reinforced with a thin layer of connective tissue that binds to the myocardium

endothelium   layer of smooth, simple squamous epithelium that lines the endocardium and blood vessels

epicardial coronary arteries   surface arteries of the heart that generally follow the sulci

epicardium   innermost layer of the serous pericardium and the outermost layer of the heart wall

filling time   duration of ventricular diastole during which filling occurs

foramen ovale   opening in the fetal heart that allows blood to flow directly from the right atrium to the left atrium, bypassing the fetal pulmonary circuit

fossa ovalis   oval-shaped depression in the interatrial septum that marks the former location of the foramen ovale

Frank-Starling mechanism   relationship between ventricular stretch and contraction in which the force of heart contraction is directly proportional to the initial length of the muscle fiber

great cardiac vein   vessel that follows the interventricular sulcus on the anterior surface of the heart and flows along the coronary sulcus into the coronary sinus on the posterior surface; parallels the anterior interventricular artery and drains the areas supplied by this vessel

heart block   interruption in the normal conduction pathway

heart bulge   prominent feature on the anterior surface of the heart, reflecting early cardiac development

heart rate (HR)   number of times the heart contracts (beats) per minute

heart sounds   sounds heard via auscultation with a stethoscope of the closing of the atrioventricular valves ("lub") and semilunar valves ("dub")

hypertrophic cardiomyopathy   pathological enlargement of the heart, generally for no known reason

inferior vena cava   large systemic vein that returns blood to the heart from the inferior portion of the body

interatrial band   (also, Bachmann's bundle) group of specialized conducting cells that transmit the impulse directly from the SA node in the right atrium to the left atrium

interatrial septum   cardiac septum located between

the two atria; contains the fossa ovalis after birth

intercalated disc   physical junction between adjacent cardiac muscle cells; consisting of desmosomes, specialized linking proteoglycans, and gap junctions that allow passage of ions between the two cells

internodal pathways   specialized conductile cells within the atria that transmit the impulse from the SA node throughout the myocardial cells of the atrium and to the AV node

interventricular septum   cardiac septum located between the two ventricles

isovolumic contraction   (also, isovolumetric contraction) initial phase of ventricular contraction in which tension and pressure in the ventricle increase, but no blood is pumped or ejected from the heart

isovolumic ventricular relaxation phase   initial phase of the ventricular diastole when pressure in the ventricles drops below pressure in the two major arteries, the pulmonary trunk, and the aorta, and blood attempts to flow back into the ventricles, producing the dicrotic notch of the ECG and closing the two semilunar valves

left atrioventricular valve   (also, mitral valve or bicuspid valve) valve located between the left atrium and ventricle; consists of two flaps of tissue

marginal arteries   branches of the right coronary artery that supply blood to the superficial portions of the right ventricle

mesoderm   one of the three primary germ layers that differentiate early in embryonic development

mesothelium   simple squamous epithelial portion of serous membranes, such as the superficial portion of the epicardium (the visceral pericardium) and the deepest portion of the pericardium (the parietal pericardium)

middle cardiac vein   vessel that parallels and drains the areas supplied by the posterior interventricular artery; drains into the great cardiac vein

mitral valve   (also, left atrioventricular valve or bicuspid valve) valve located between the left atrium and ventricle; consists of two flaps of tissue

moderator band   band of myocardium covered by endocardium that arises from the inferior portion of the interventricular septum in the right ventricle and crosses to the anterior papillary muscle; contains conductile fibers that carry electrical signals followed by contraction of the heart

murmur   unusual heart sound detected by auscultation; typically related to septal or valve defects

myocardial conducting cells   specialized cells that transmit electrical impulses throughout the heart

and trigger contraction by the myocardial contractile cells

myocardial contractile cells   bulk of the cardiac muscle cells in the atria and ventricles that conduct impulses and contract to propel blood

myocardium   thickest layer of the heart composed of cardiac muscle cells built upon a framework of primarily collagenous fibers and blood vessels that supply it and the nervous fibers that help to regulate it

negative inotropic factors   factors that negatively impact or lower heart contractility

P wave   component of the electrocardiogram that represents the depolarization of the atria

pacemaker   cluster of specialized myocardial cells known as the SA node that initiates the sinus rhythm

papillary muscle   extension of the myocardium in the ventricles to which the chordae tendineae attach

pectinate muscles   muscular ridges seen on the anterior surface of the right atrium

pericardial cavity   cavity surrounding the heart filled with a lubricating serous fluid that reduces friction as the heart contracts

pericardial sac   (also, pericardium) membrane that separates the heart from other mediastinal structures; consists of two distinct, fused sublayers: the fibrous pericardium and the parietal pericardium

pericardium   (also, pericardial sac) membrane that separates the heart from other mediastinal structures; consists of two distinct, fused sublayers: the fibrous pericardium and the parietal pericardium

positive inotropic factors   factors that positively impact or increase heart contractility

posterior cardiac vein   vessel that parallels and drains the areas supplied by the marginal artery branch of the circumflex artery; drains into the great cardiac vein

posterior interventricular artery   (also, posterior descending artery) branch of the right coronary artery that runs along the posterior portion of the interventricular sulcus toward the apex of the heart and gives rise to branches that supply the interventricular septum and portions of both ventricles

posterior interventricular sulcus   sulcus located between the left and right ventricles on the posterior surface of the heart

preload   (also, end diastolic volume) amount of blood in the ventricles at the end of atrial systole just prior to ventricular contraction

prepotential depolarization   (also, spontaneous depolarization) mechanism that accounts for the autorhythmic property of cardiac muscle; the membrane potential increases as sodium ions diffuse through the always-open sodium ion channels and causes the electrical potential to rise

primitive atrium   portion of the primitive heart tube that eventually becomes the anterior portions of both the right and left atria, and the two auricles

primitive heart tube   singular tubular structure that forms from the fusion of the two endocardial tubes

primitive ventricle   portion of the primitive heart tube that eventually forms the left ventricle

pulmonary arteries   left and right branches of the pulmonary trunk that carry deoxygenated blood from the heart to each of the lungs

pulmonary capillaries   capillaries surrounding the alveoli of the lungs where gas exchange occurs: carbon dioxide exits the blood and oxygen enters

pulmonary circuit   blood flow to and from the lungs

pulmonary trunk   large arterial vessel that carries blood ejected from the right ventricle; divides into the left and right pulmonary arteries

pulmonary valve   (also, pulmonary semilunar valve, the pulmonic valve, or the right semilunar valve) valve at the base of the pulmonary trunk that prevents backflow of blood into the right ventricle; consists of three flaps

pulmonary veins   veins that carry highly oxygenated blood into the left atrium, which pumps the blood into the left ventricle, which in turn pumps oxygenated blood into the aorta and to the many branches of the systemic circuit

Purkinje fibers   specialized myocardial conduction fibers that arise from the bundle branches and spread the impulse to the myocardial contraction fibers of the ventricles

QRS complex   component of the electrocardiogram that represents the depolarization of the ventricles and includes, as a component, the repolarization of the atria

right atrioventricular valve   (also, tricuspid valve) valve located between the right atrium and ventricle; consists of three flaps of tissue

semilunar valves   valves located at the base of the pulmonary trunk and at the base of the aorta

septum   (plural = septa) walls or partitions that divide the heart into chambers

septum primum   flap of tissue in the fetus that covers the foramen ovale within a few seconds after birth

sinoatrial (SA) node   known as the pacemaker, a specialized clump of myocardial conducting cells located in the superior portion of the right atrium that has the highest inherent rate of depolarization that then spreads throughout the heart

sinus rhythm   normal contractile pattern of the heart

sinus venosus   develops into the posterior portion of the right atrium, the SA node, and the coronary sinus

small cardiac vein   parallels the right coronary artery and drains blood from the posterior surfaces of the right atrium and ventricle; drains into the coronary sinus, middle cardiac vein, or right atrium

spontaneous depolarization   (also, prepotential depolarization) the mechanism that accounts for the autorhythmic property of cardiac muscle; the membrane potential increases as sodium ions diffuse through the always-open sodium ion channels and causes the electrical potential to rise

stroke volume (SV)   amount of blood pumped by each ventricle per contraction; also, the difference between EDV and ESV

sulcus   (plural = sulci) fat-filled groove visible on the surface of the heart; coronary vessels are also located in these areas

superior vena cava   large systemic vein that returns blood to the heart from the superior portion of the body

systemic circuit   blood flow to and from virtually all of the tissues of the body

systole   period of time when the heart muscle is contracting

T wave   component of the electrocardiogram that represents the repolarization of the ventricles

target heart rate   range in which both the heart and lungs receive the maximum benefit from an aerobic workout

trabeculae carneae   ridges of muscle covered by endocardium located in the ventricles

tricuspid valve   term used most often in clinical settings for the right atrioventricular valve

truncus arteriosus   portion of the primitive heart that will eventually divide and give rise to the ascending aorta and pulmonary trunk

valve   in the cardiovascular system, a specialized structure located within the heart or vessels that ensures one-way flow of blood

ventricle   one of the primary pumping chambers of the heart located in the lower portion of the heart; the left ventricle is the major pumping chamber on the lower left side of the heart that ejects blood into the systemic circuit via the aorta and receives blood from the left atrium; the right ventricle is the major pumping chamber on the lower right side of the heart that ejects blood into the pulmonary circuit via the pulmonary trunk and receives blood from the right atrium

ventricular ejection phase   second phase of

ventricular systole during which blood is pumped

from the ventricle

Chapter Review

19.1 Heart Anatomy

The heart resides within the pericardial sac and is located in the mediastinal space within the thoracic cavity. The pericardial sac consists of two fused layers: an outer fibrous capsule and an inner parietal pericardium lined with a serous membrane. Between the pericardial sac and the heart is the pericardial cavity, which is filled with lubricating serous fluid. The walls of the heart are composed of an outer epicardium, a thick myocardium, and an inner lining layer of endocardium. The human heart consists of a pair of atria, which receive blood and pump it into a pair of ventricles, which pump blood into the vessels. The right atrium receives systemic blood relatively low in oxygen and pumps it into the right ventricle, which pumps it into the pulmonary circuit. Exchange of oxygen and carbon dioxide occurs in the lungs, and blood high in oxygen returns to the left atrium, which pumps blood into the left ventricle, which in turn pumps blood into the aorta and the remainder of the systemic circuit. The septa are the partitions that separate the chambers of the heart. They include the interatrial septum, the interventricular septum, and the atrioventricular septum. Two of these openings are guarded by the atrioventricular valves, the right tricuspid valve and the left mitral valve, which prevent the backflow of blood. Each is attached to chordae tendineae that extend to the papillary muscles, which are extensions of the myocardium, to prevent the valves from being blown back into the atria. The pulmonary valve is located at the base of the pulmonary trunk, and the left semilunar valve is located at the base of the aorta. The right and left coronary arteries are the first to branch off the aorta and arise from two of the three sinuses located near the base of the aorta and are generally located in the sulci. Cardiac veins parallel the small cardiac arteries and generally drain into the coronary sinus.

19.2 Cardiac Muscle and Electrical Activity

The heart is regulated by both neural and endocrine control, yet it is capable of initiating its own action potential followed by muscular contraction. The conductive cells within the heart establish the heart rate and transmit it through the myocardium. The contractile cells contract and propel the blood. The normal path of transmission for the conductive cells is the sinoatrial (SA) node, internodal pathways, atrioventricular (AV) node, atrioventricular (AV) bundle of His, bundle branches, and Purkinje fibers. The action potential for the conductive cells consists of a prepotential phase with a slow influx of Na^+ followed by a rapid influx of Ca^{2+} and outflux of K^+. Contractile cells have an action potential with an extended plateau phase that results in an extended refractory period to allow complete contraction for the heart to pump blood effectively. Recognizable points on the ECG include the P wave that corresponds to atrial depolarization, the QRS complex that corresponds to ventricular depolarization, and the T wave that corresponds to ventricular repolarization.

19.3 Cardiac Cycle

The cardiac cycle comprises a complete relaxation and contraction of both the atria and ventricles, and lasts approximately 0.8 seconds. Beginning with all chambers in diastole, blood flows passively from the veins into the atria and past the atrioventricular valves into the ventricles. The atria begin to contract (atrial systole), following depolarization of the atria, and pump blood into the ventricles. The ventricles begin to contract (ventricular systole), raising pressure within the ventricles. When ventricular pressure rises above the pressure in the atria, blood flows toward the atria, producing the first heart sound, S_1 or lub. As pressure in the ventricles rises above two major arteries, blood pushes open the two semilunar valves and moves into the pulmonary trunk and aorta in the ventricular ejection phase. Following ventricular repolarization, the ventricles begin to relax (ventricular diastole), and pressure within the ventricles drops. As ventricular pressure drops, there is a tendency for blood to flow back into the atria from the major arteries, producing the dicrotic notch in the ECG and closing the two semilunar valves. The second heart sound, S_2 or dub, occurs when the semilunar valves close. When the pressure falls below that of the atria, blood moves from the atria into the ventricles, opening the atrioventricular valves and marking one complete heart cycle. The valves prevent backflow of blood. Failure of the valves to operate properly produces turbulent blood flow within the heart; the resulting heart murmur can often be heard with a stethoscope.

19.4 Cardiac Physiology

Many factors affect HR and SV, and together, they contribute to cardiac function. HR is largely determined and regulated by autonomic stimulation and hormones. There are several feedback loops that contribute to maintaining homeostasis dependent upon activity levels, such as the atrial reflex, which is determined by venous return.

SV is regulated by autonomic innervation and hormones, but also by filling time and venous return. Venous return is determined by activity of the skeletal muscles, blood volume, and changes in peripheral circulation. Venous return determines preload and the atrial reflex. Filling time directly related to HR also determines preload. Preload then impacts both EDV and ESV. Autonomic innervation and hormones largely regulate contractility. Contractility impacts EDV as does afterload. CO is the product of HR multiplied by SV. SV is the difference between EDV and ESV.

19.5 Development of the Heart

The heart is the first organ to form and become functional, emphasizing the importance of transport of material to and from the developing infant. It originates about day 18 or 19 from the mesoderm and begins beating and pumping blood about day 21 or 22. It forms from the cardiogenic region near the head and is visible as a prominent heart bulge on the surface of the embryo. Originally, it consists of a pair of strands called cardiogenic cords that quickly form a hollow lumen and are referred to as endocardial tubes. These then fuse into a single heart tube and differentiate into the truncus arteriosus, bulbus cordis, primitive ventricle, primitive atrium, and sinus venosus, starting about day 22. The primitive heart begins to form an S shape within the pericardium between days 23 and 28. The internal septa begin to form about day 28, separating the heart into the atria and ventricles, although the foramen ovale persists until shortly after birth. Between weeks five and eight, the atrioventricular valves form. The semilunar valves form between weeks five and nine.

Interactive Link Questions

1. Visit this site (http://openstax.org/l/heartvalve) to observe an echocardiogram of actual heart valves opening and closing. Although much of the heart has been "removed" from this gif loop so the chordae tendineae are not visible, why is their presence more critical for the atrioventricular valves (tricuspid and mitral) than the semilunar (aortic and pulmonary) valves?

Review Questions

2. Which of the following is not important in preventing backflow of blood?
   a. chordae tendineae
   b. papillary muscles
   c. AV valves
   d. endocardium

3. Which valve separates the left atrium from the left ventricle?
   a. mitral
   b. tricuspid
   c. pulmonary
   d. aortic

4. Which of the following lists the valves in the order through which the blood flows from the vena cava through the heart?
   a. tricuspid, pulmonary semilunar, bicuspid, aortic semilunar
   b. mitral, pulmonary semilunar, bicuspid, aortic semilunar
   c. aortic semilunar, pulmonary semilunar, tricuspid, bicuspid
   d. bicuspid, aortic semilunar, tricuspid, pulmonary semilunar

5. Which chamber initially receives blood from the systemic circuit?
   a. left atrium
   b. left ventricle
   c. right atrium
   d. right ventricle

6. The _____ layer secretes chemicals that help to regulate ionic environments and strength of contraction and serve as powerful vasoconstrictors.
   a. pericardial sac
   b. endocardium
   c. myocardium
   d. epicardium

7. The myocardium would be the thickest in the _____.
   a. left atrium
   b. left ventricle
   c. right atrium
   d. right ventricle

8. In which septum is it normal to find openings in the adult?
   a. interatrial septum
   b. interventricular septum
   c. atrioventricular septum
   d. all of the above

9. Which of the following is unique to cardiac muscle cells?
   a. Only cardiac muscle contains a sarcoplasmic reticulum.
   b. Only cardiac muscle has gap junctions.
   c. Only cardiac muscle is capable of autorhythmicity
   d. Only cardiac muscle has a high concentration of mitochondria.

10. The influx of which ion accounts for the plateau phase?
   a. sodium
   b. potassium
   c. chloride
   d. calcium

11. Which portion of the ECG corresponds to repolarization of the atria?
   a. P wave
   b. QRS complex
   c. T wave
   d. none of the above: atrial repolarization is masked by ventricular depolarization

12. Which component of the heart conduction system would have the slowest rate of firing?
   a. atrioventricular node
   b. atrioventricular bundle
   c. bundle branches
   d. Purkinje fibers

13. The cardiac cycle consists of a distinct relaxation and contraction phase. Which term is typically used to refer ventricular contraction while no blood is being ejected?
   a. systole
   b. diastole
   c. quiescent
   d. isovolumic contraction

14. Most blood enters the ventricle during _____.
   a. atrial systole
   b. atrial diastole
   c. ventricular systole
   d. isovolumic contraction

15. The first heart sound represents which portion of the cardiac cycle?
   a. atrial systole
   b. ventricular systole
   c. closing of the atrioventricular valves
   d. closing of the semilunar valves

16. Ventricular relaxation immediately follows _____.
   a. atrial depolarization
   b. ventricular repolarization
   c. ventricular depolarization
   d. atrial repolarization

17. The force the heart must overcome to pump blood is known as _____.
   a. preload
   b. afterload
   c. cardiac output
   d. stroke volume

18. The cardiovascular centers are located in which area of the brain?
   a. medulla oblongata
   b. pons
   c. mesencephalon (midbrain)
   d. cerebrum

19. In a healthy young adult, what happens to cardiac output when heart rate increases above 160 bpm?
   a. It increases.
   b. It decreases.
   c. It remains constant.
   d. There is no way to predict.

20. What happens to preload when there is venous constriction in the veins?
   a. It increases.
   b. It decreases.
   c. It remains constant.
   d. There is no way to predict.

21. Which of the following is a positive inotrope?
    a. Na^+
    b. K^+
    c. Ca^{2+}
    d. both Na^+ and K^+

22. The earliest organ to form and begin function within the developing human is the _____.
    a. brain
    b. stomach
    c. lungs
    d. heart

23. Of the three germ layers that give rise to all adult tissues and organs, which gives rise to the heart?
    a. ectoderm
    b. endoderm
    c. mesoderm
    d. placenta

24. The two tubes that eventually fuse to form the heart are referred to as the _____.
    a. primitive heart tubes
    b. endocardial tubes
    c. cardiogenic region
    d. cardiogenic tubes

25. Which primitive area of the heart will give rise to the right ventricle?
    a. bulbus cordis
    b. primitive ventricle
    c. sinus venosus
    d. truncus arteriosus

26. The pulmonary trunk and aorta are derived from which primitive heart structure?
    a. bulbus cordis
    b. primitive ventricle
    c. sinus venosus
    d. truncus arteriosus

Critical Thinking Questions

27. Describe how the valves keep the blood moving in one direction.
28. Why is the pressure in the pulmonary circulation lower than in the systemic circulation?
29. Why is the plateau phase so critical to cardiac muscle function?
30. How does the delay of the impulse at the atrioventricular node contribute to cardiac function?
31. How do gap junctions and intercalated disks aid contraction of the heart?

32. Why do the cardiac muscles cells demonstrate autorhythmicity?
33. Describe one cardiac cycle, beginning with both atria and ventricles relaxed.
34. Why does increasing EDV increase contractility?
35. Why is afterload important to cardiac function?
36. Why is it so important for the human heart to develop early and begin functioning within the developing embryo?
37. Describe how the major pumping chambers, the ventricles, form within the developing heart.

CHAPTER 20
The Cardiovascular System: Blood Vessels and Circulation

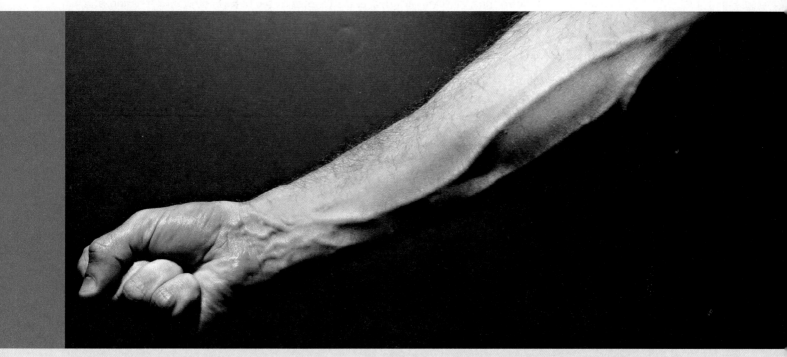

Figure 20.1 Blood Vessels While most blood vessels are located deep from the surface and are not visible, the superficial veins of the upper limb provide an indication of the extent, prominence, and importance of these structures to the body. (credit: Colin Davis)

CHAPTER OBJECTIVES
After studying this chapter, you will be able to:

- Compare and contrast the anatomical structure of arteries, arterioles, capillaries, venules, and veins
- Accurately describe the forces that account for capillary exchange
- List the major factors affecting blood flow, blood pressure, and resistance
- Describe how blood flow, blood pressure, and resistance interrelate
- Discuss how the neural and endocrine mechanisms maintain homeostasis within the blood vessels
- Describe the interaction of the cardiovascular system with other body systems
- Label the major blood vessels of the pulmonary and systemic circulations
- Identify and describe the hepatic portal system
- Describe the development of blood vessels and fetal circulation
- Compare fetal circulation to that of an individual after birth

INTRODUCTION In this chapter, you will learn about the vascular part of the cardiovascular system, that is, the vessels that transport blood throughout the body and provide the physical site where gases, nutrients, and other substances are exchanged with body cells. When vessel functioning is reduced, blood-borne substances do not circulate effectively throughout the body. As a result, tissue injury occurs, metabolism is impaired, and the functions of every bodily system are threatened.

20.1 Structure and Function of Blood Vessels

LEARNING OBJECTIVES

By the end of this section, you will be able to:

- Compare and contrast the three tunics that make up the walls of most blood vessels
- Distinguish between elastic arteries, muscular arteries, and arterioles on the basis of structure, location, and function
- Describe the basic structure of a capillary bed, from the supplying metarteriole to the venule into which it drains
- Explain the structure and function of venous valves in the large veins of the extremities

Blood is carried through the body via blood vessels. An artery is a blood vessel that carries blood away from the heart, where it branches into ever-smaller vessels. Eventually, the smallest arteries, vessels called arterioles, further branch into tiny capillaries, where nutrients and wastes are exchanged, and then combine with other vessels that exit capillaries to form venules, small blood vessels that carry blood to a vein, a larger blood vessel that returns blood to the heart.

Arteries and veins transport blood in two distinct circuits: the systemic circuit and the pulmonary circuit (Figure 20.2). Systemic arteries provide blood rich in oxygen to the body's tissues. The blood returned to the heart through systemic veins has less oxygen, since much of the oxygen carried by the arteries has been delivered to the cells. In contrast, in the pulmonary circuit, arteries carry blood low in oxygen exclusively to the lungs for gas exchange. Pulmonary veins then return freshly oxygenated blood from the lungs to the heart to be pumped back out into systemic circulation. Although arteries and veins differ structurally and functionally, they share certain features.

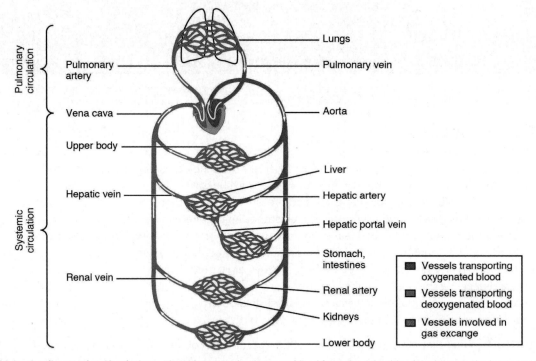

FIGURE 20.2 Cardiovascular Circulation   The pulmonary circuit moves blood from the right side of the heart to the lungs and back to the heart. The systemic circuit moves blood from the left side of the heart to the head and body and returns it to the right side of the heart to repeat the cycle. The arrows indicate the direction of blood flow, and the colors show the relative levels of oxygen concentration.

Shared Structures

Different types of blood vessels vary slightly in their structures, but they share the same general features. Arteries and arterioles have thicker walls than veins and venules because they are closer to the heart and receive blood that is surging at a far greater pressure (Figure 20.3). Each type of vessel has a **lumen**—a hollow passageway through which blood flows. Arteries have smaller lumens than veins, a characteristic that helps to maintain the pressure of blood moving through the system. Together, their thicker walls and smaller diameters give arterial lumens a more rounded appearance in cross section than the lumens of veins.

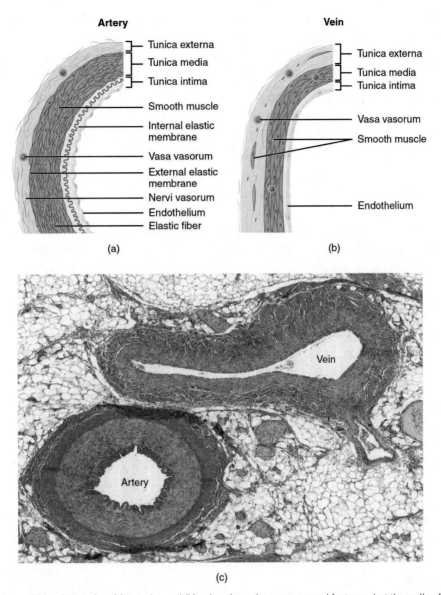

(a)

(b)

(c)

FIGURE 20.3   Structure of Blood Vessels   (a) Arteries and (b) veins share the same general features, but the walls of arteries are much thicker because of the higher pressure of the blood that flows through them. (c) A micrograph shows the relative differences in thickness. LM × 160. (Micrograph provided by the Regents of the University of Michigan Medical School © 2012)

By the time blood has passed through capillaries and entered venules, the pressure initially exerted upon it by heart contractions has diminished. In other words, in comparison to arteries, venules and veins withstand a much lower pressure from the blood that flows through them. Their walls are considerably thinner and their lumens are correspondingly larger in diameter, allowing more blood to flow with less vessel resistance. In addition, many veins of the body, particularly those of the limbs, contain valves that assist the unidirectional flow of blood toward the heart. This is critical because blood flow becomes sluggish in the extremities, as a result of the lower pressure and the effects of gravity.

The walls of arteries and veins are largely composed of living cells and their products (including collagenous and elastic fibers); the cells require nourishment and produce waste. Since blood passes through the larger vessels relatively quickly, there is limited opportunity for blood in the lumen of the vessel to provide nourishment to or remove waste from the vessel's cells. Further, the walls of the larger vessels are too thick for nutrients to diffuse through to all of the cells. Larger arteries and veins contain small blood vessels within their walls known as the **vasa vasorum**—literally "vessels of the vessel"—to provide them with this critical exchange. Since the pressure within arteries is relatively high, the vasa vasorum must function in the outer layers of the vessel (see Figure 20.3) or the pressure exerted by the blood passing through the vessel would collapse it, preventing any exchange from occurring. The lower pressure within veins allows the vasa vasorum to be located closer to the lumen. The restriction of the vasa vasorum to the outer layers of arteries is thought to be one reason that arterial diseases are more common than venous diseases, since its location makes it more difficult to nourish the cells of the arteries and remove waste products. There are also minute nerves within the walls of both types of vessels that control the contraction and dilation of smooth muscle. These minute nerves are known as the nervi vasorum.

Both arteries and veins have the same three distinct tissue layers, called tunics (from the Latin term tunica), for the garments first worn by ancient Romans; the term tunic is also used for some modern garments. From the most interior layer to the outer, these tunics are the tunica intima, the tunica media, and the tunica externa (see Figure 20.3). Table 20.1 compares and contrasts the tunics of the arteries and veins.

Comparison of Tunics in Arteries and Veins

	Arteries	Veins
General appearance	Thick walls with small lumens Generally appear rounded	Thin walls with large lumens Generally appear flattened
Tunica intima	Endothelium usually appears wavy due to constriction of smooth muscle Internal elastic membrane present in larger vessels	Endothelium appears smooth Internal elastic membrane absent
Tunica media	Normally the thickest layer in arteries Smooth muscle cells and elastic fibers predominate (the proportions of these vary with distance from the heart) External elastic membrane present in larger vessels	Normally thinner than the tunica externa Smooth muscle cells and collagenous fibers predominate Nervi vasorum and vasa vasorum present External elastic membrane absent
Tunica externa	Normally thinner than the tunica media in all but the largest arteries Collagenous and elastic fibers Nervi vasorum and vasa vasorum present	Normally the thickest layer in veins Collagenous and smooth fibers predominate Some smooth muscle fibers Nervi vasorum and vasa vasorum present

TABLE 20.1

Tunica Intima

The **tunica intima** (also called the tunica interna) is composed of epithelial and connective tissue layers. Lining the tunica intima is the specialized simple squamous epithelium called the endothelium, which is continuous throughout the entire vascular system, including the lining of the chambers of the heart. Damage to this endothelial lining and exposure of blood to the collagenous fibers beneath is one of the primary causes of clot formation. Until recently, the endothelium was viewed simply as the boundary between the blood in the lumen and the walls of the vessels. Recent studies, however, have shown that it is physiologically critical to such activities as helping to regulate capillary exchange and altering blood flow. The endothelium releases local chemicals called endothelins that can constrict the smooth muscle within the walls of the vessel to increase blood pressure. Uncompensated overproduction of endothelins may contribute to hypertension (high blood pressure) and cardiovascular disease.

Next to the endothelium is the basement membrane, or basal lamina, that effectively binds the endothelium to the connective tissue. The basement membrane provides strength while maintaining flexibility, and it is permeable, allowing materials to pass through it. The thin outer layer of the tunica intima contains a small amount of areolar connective tissue that consists primarily of elastic fibers to provide the vessel with additional flexibility; it also contains some collagenous fibers to provide additional strength.

In larger arteries, there is also a thick, distinct layer of elastic fibers known as the **internal elastic membrane** (also called the internal elastic lamina) at the boundary with the tunica media. Like the other components of the tunica intima, the internal elastic membrane provides structure while allowing the vessel to stretch. It is permeated with small openings that allow exchange of materials between the tunics. The internal elastic membrane is not apparent in veins. In addition, many veins, particularly in the lower limbs, contain valves formed by sections of thickened endothelium that are reinforced with connective tissue, extending into the lumen.

Under the microscope, the lumen and the entire tunica intima of a vein will appear smooth, whereas those of an artery will normally appear wavy because of the partial constriction of the smooth muscle in the tunica media, the next layer of blood vessel walls.

Tunica Media

The **tunica media** is the substantial middle layer of the vessel wall (see Figure 20.3). It is generally the thickest layer in arteries, and it is much thicker in arteries than it is in veins. The tunica media consists of layers of smooth muscle supported by connective tissue that is primarily made up of elastic fibers, most of which are arranged in circular sheets. Toward the outer portion of the tunic, there are also layers of longitudinal muscle. Contraction and relaxation of the circular muscles decrease and increase the diameter of the vessel lumen, respectively. Specifically in arteries, **vasoconstriction** decreases blood flow as the smooth muscle in the walls of the tunica media contracts, making the lumen narrower and increasing blood pressure. Similarly, **vasodilation** increases blood flow as the smooth muscle relaxes, allowing the lumen to widen and blood pressure to drop. Both vasoconstriction and vasodilation are regulated in part by small vascular nerves, known as **nervi vasorum**, or "nerves of the vessel," that run within the walls of blood vessels. These are generally all sympathetic fibers, although some trigger vasodilation and others induce vasoconstriction, depending upon the nature of the neurotransmitter and receptors located on the target cell. Parasympathetic stimulation does trigger vasodilation as well as erection during sexual arousal in the external genitalia of both sexes. Nervous control over vessels tends to be more generalized than the specific targeting of individual blood vessels. Local controls, discussed later, account for this phenomenon. (Seek additional content for more information on these dynamic aspects of the autonomic nervous system.) Hormones and local chemicals also control blood vessels. Together, these neural and chemical mechanisms reduce or increase blood flow in response to changing body conditions, from exercise to hydration. Regulation of both blood flow and blood pressure is discussed in detail later in this chapter.

The smooth muscle layers of the tunica media are supported by a framework of collagenous fibers that also binds the tunica media to the inner and outer tunics. Along with the collagenous fibers are large numbers of elastic fibers that appear as wavy lines in prepared slides. Separating the tunica media from the outer tunica externa in larger arteries is the **external elastic membrane** (also called the external elastic lamina), which also appears wavy in slides. This structure is not usually seen in smaller arteries, nor is it seen in veins.

Tunica Externa

The outer tunic, the **tunica externa** (also called the tunica adventitia), is a substantial sheath of connective tissue composed primarily of collagenous fibers. Some bands of elastic fibers are found here as well. The tunica externa in veins also contains groups of smooth muscle fibers. This is normally the thickest tunic in veins and may be thicker than the tunica media in some larger arteries. The outer layers of the tunica externa are not distinct but rather blend with the surrounding connective tissue outside the vessel, helping to hold the vessel in relative position. If you are able to palpate some of the superficial veins on your upper limbs and try to move them, you will find that the tunica externa prevents this. If the tunica externa did not hold the vessel in place, any movement would likely result in disruption of blood flow.

Arteries

An **artery** is a blood vessel that conducts blood away from the heart. All arteries have relatively thick walls that can withstand the high pressure of blood ejected from the heart. However, those close to the heart have the thickest walls, containing a high percentage of elastic fibers in all three of their tunics. This type of artery is known as an **elastic artery** (Figure 20.4). Vessels larger than 10 mm in diameter are typically elastic. Their abundant elastic fibers allow them to expand, as blood pumped from the ventricles passes through them, and then to recoil after the surge has passed. If artery walls were rigid and unable to expand and recoil, their resistance to blood flow would greatly increase and blood pressure would rise to even higher levels, which would in turn require the heart to pump harder to increase the volume of blood expelled by each pump (the stroke volume) and maintain adequate pressure and flow. Artery walls would have to become even thicker in response to this increased pressure. The elastic recoil of the vascular wall helps to maintain the pressure gradient that drives the blood through the arterial system. An elastic artery is also known as a conducting artery, because the large diameter of the lumen enables it to accept a large volume of blood from the heart and conduct it to smaller branches.

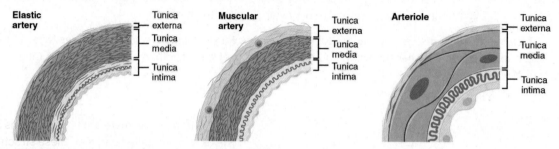

FIGURE 20.4   Types of Arteries and Arterioles   Comparison of the walls of an elastic artery, a muscular artery, and an arteriole is shown. In terms of scale, the diameter of an arteriole is measured in micrometers compared to millimeters for elastic and muscular arteries.

Farther from the heart, where the surge of blood has dampened, the percentage of elastic fibers in an artery's tunica intima decreases and the amount of smooth muscle in its tunica media increases. The artery at this point is described as a **muscular artery**. The diameter of muscular arteries typically ranges from 0.1 mm to 10 mm. Their thick tunica media allows muscular arteries to play a leading role in vasoconstriction. In contrast, their decreased quantity of elastic fibers limits their ability to expand. Fortunately, because the blood pressure has eased by the time it reaches these more distant vessels, elasticity has become less important.

Notice that although the distinctions between elastic and muscular arteries are important, there is no "line of demarcation" where an elastic artery suddenly becomes muscular. Rather, there is a gradual transition as the vascular tree repeatedly branches. In turn, muscular arteries branch to distribute blood to the vast network of arterioles. For this reason, a muscular artery is also known as a distributing artery.

Arterioles

An **arteriole** is a very small artery that leads to a capillary. Arterioles have the same three tunics as the larger vessels, but the thickness of each is greatly diminished. The critical endothelial lining of the tunica intima is intact. The tunica media is restricted to one or two smooth muscle cell layers in thickness. The tunica externa remains but is very thin (see Figure 20.4).

With a lumen averaging 30 micrometers or less in diameter, arterioles are critical in slowing down—or resisting—blood flow and, thus, causing a substantial drop in blood pressure. Because of this, you may see them referred to as resistance vessels. The muscle fibers in arterioles are normally slightly contracted, causing arterioles to maintain a consistent muscle tone—in this case referred to as vascular tone—in a similar manner to the muscular tone of skeletal muscle. In reality, all blood vessels exhibit vascular tone due to the partial contraction of smooth muscle. The importance of the arterioles is that they will be the primary site of both resistance and regulation of blood pressure. The precise diameter of the lumen of an arteriole at any given moment is determined by neural and chemical controls, and vasoconstriction and vasodilation in the arterioles are the primary mechanisms for distribution of blood flow.

Capillaries

A **capillary** is a microscopic channel that supplies blood to the tissues, a process called **perfusion**. Exchange of gases and other substances occurs between the blood in capillaries and the surrounding cells and their tissue fluid (interstitial fluid). The diameter of a capillary lumen ranges from 5–10 micrometers; the smallest are just barely wide enough for an erythrocyte to squeeze through. Flow through capillaries is often described as **microcirculation**.

The wall of a capillary consists of the endothelial layer surrounded by a basement membrane with occasional

Access for free at openstax.org

smooth muscle fibers. There is some variation in wall structure: In a large capillary, several endothelial cells bordering each other may line the lumen; in a small capillary, there may be only a single cell layer that wraps around to contact itself.

For capillaries to function, their walls must be leaky, allowing substances to pass through. There are three major types of capillaries, which differ according to their degree of "leakiness:" continuous, fenestrated, and sinusoid capillaries (Figure 20.5).

Continuous Capillaries

The most common type of capillary, the **continuous capillary**, is found in almost all vascularized tissues. Continuous capillaries are characterized by a complete endothelial lining with tight junctions between endothelial cells. Although a tight junction is usually impermeable and only allows for the passage of water and ions, they are often incomplete in capillaries, leaving intercellular clefts that allow for exchange of water and other very small molecules between the blood plasma and the interstitial fluid. Substances that can pass between cells include metabolic products, such as glucose, water, and small hydrophobic molecules like gases and hormones, as well as various leukocytes. Continuous capillaries not associated with the brain are rich in transport vesicles, contributing to either endocytosis or exocytosis. Those in the brain are part of the blood-brain barrier. Here, there are tight junctions and no intercellular clefts, plus a thick basement membrane and astrocyte extensions called end feet; these structures combine to prevent the movement of nearly all substances.

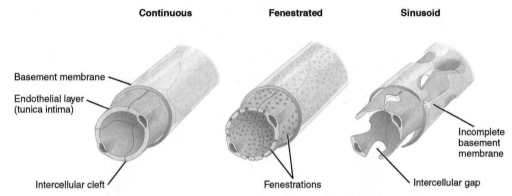

FIGURE 20.5   Types of Capillaries   The three major types of capillaries: continuous, fenestrated, and sinusoid.

Fenestrated Capillaries

A **fenestrated capillary** is one that has pores (or fenestrations) in addition to tight junctions in the endothelial lining. These make the capillary permeable to larger molecules. The number of fenestrations and their degree of permeability vary, however, according to their location. Fenestrated capillaries are common in the small intestine, which is the primary site of nutrient absorption, as well as in the kidneys, which filter the blood. They are also found in the choroid plexus of the brain and many endocrine structures, including the hypothalamus, pituitary, pineal, and thyroid glands.

Sinusoid Capillaries

A **sinusoid capillary** (or sinusoid) is the least common type of capillary. Sinusoid capillaries are flattened, and they have extensive intercellular gaps and incomplete basement membranes, in addition to intercellular clefts and fenestrations. This gives them an appearance not unlike Swiss cheese. These very large openings allow for the passage of the largest molecules, including plasma proteins and even cells. Blood flow through sinusoids is very slow, allowing more time for exchange of gases, nutrients, and wastes. Sinusoids are found in the liver and spleen, bone marrow, lymph nodes (where they carry lymph, not blood), and many endocrine glands including the pituitary and adrenal glands. Without these specialized capillaries, these organs would not be able to provide their myriad of functions. For example, when bone marrow forms new blood cells, the cells must enter the blood supply and can only do so through the large openings of a sinusoid capillary; they cannot pass through the small openings of continuous or fenestrated capillaries. The liver also requires extensive specialized sinusoid capillaries in order to process the materials brought to it by the hepatic portal vein from both the digestive tract and spleen, and to release plasma proteins into circulation.

Metarterioles and Capillary Beds

A **metarteriole** is a type of vessel that has structural characteristics of both an arteriole and a capillary. Slightly larger than the typical capillary, the smooth muscle of the tunica media of the metarteriole is not continuous but forms rings of smooth muscle (sphincters) prior to the entrance to the capillaries. Each metarteriole arises from a terminal arteriole and branches to supply blood to a **capillary bed** that may consist of 10–100 capillaries.

The **precapillary sphincters**, circular smooth muscle cells that surround the capillary at its origin with the metarteriole, tightly regulate the flow of blood from a metarteriole to the capillaries it supplies. Their function is critical: If all of the capillary beds in the body were to open simultaneously, they would collectively hold every drop of blood in the body and there would be none in the arteries, arterioles, venules, veins, or the heart itself. Normally, the precapillary sphincters are closed. When the surrounding tissues need oxygen and have excess waste products, the precapillary sphincters open, allowing blood to flow through and exchange to occur before closing once more (Figure 20.6). If all of the precapillary sphincters in a capillary bed are closed, blood will flow from the metarteriole directly into a **thoroughfare channel** and then into the venous circulation, bypassing the capillary bed entirely. This creates what is known as a **vascular shunt**. In addition, an **arteriovenous anastomosis** may bypass the capillary bed and lead directly to the venous system.

Although you might expect blood flow through a capillary bed to be smooth, in reality, it moves with an irregular, pulsating flow. This pattern is called **vasomotion** and is regulated by chemical signals that are triggered in response to changes in internal conditions, such as oxygen, carbon dioxide, hydrogen ion, and lactic acid levels. For example, during strenuous exercise when oxygen levels decrease and carbon dioxide, hydrogen ion, and lactic acid levels all increase, the capillary beds in skeletal muscle are open, as they would be in the digestive system when nutrients are present in the digestive tract. During sleep or rest periods, vessels in both areas are largely closed; they open only occasionally to allow oxygen and nutrient supplies to travel to the tissues to maintain basic life processes.

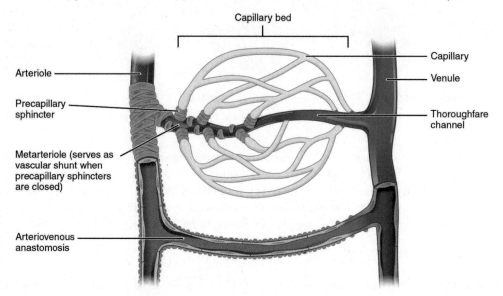

FIGURE 20.6 Capillary Bed   In a capillary bed, arterioles give rise to metarterioles. Precapillary sphincters located at the junction of a metarteriole with a capillary regulate blood flow. A thoroughfare channel connects the metarteriole to a venule. An arteriovenous anastomosis, which directly connects the arteriole with the venule, is shown at the bottom.

Venules

A **venule** is an extremely small vein, generally 8–100 micrometers in diameter. Postcapillary venules join multiple capillaries exiting from a capillary bed. Multiple venules join to form veins. The walls of venules consist of endothelium, a thin middle layer with a few muscle cells and elastic fibers, plus an outer layer of connective tissue fibers that constitute a very thin tunica externa (Figure 20.7). Venules as well as capillaries are the primary sites of emigration or diapedesis, in which the white blood cells adhere to the endothelial lining of the vessels and then squeeze through adjacent cells to enter the tissue fluid.

Veins

A **vein** is a blood vessel that conducts blood toward the heart. Compared to arteries, veins are thin-walled vessels with large and irregular lumens (see Figure 20.7). Because they are low-pressure vessels, larger veins are commonly equipped with valves that promote the unidirectional flow of blood toward the heart and prevent backflow toward the capillaries caused by the inherent low blood pressure in veins as well as the pull of gravity. Table 20.2 compares the features of arteries and veins.

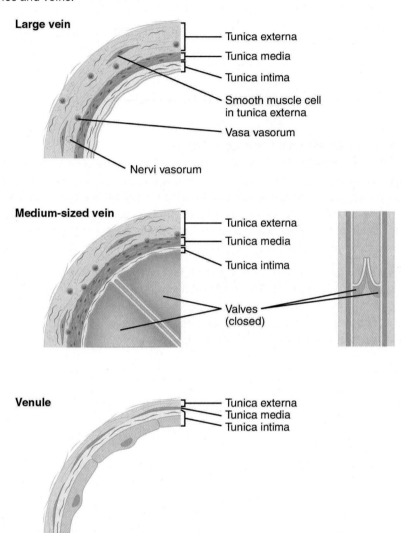

FIGURE 20.7   Comparison of Veins and Venules   Many veins have valves to prevent back flow of blood, whereas venules do not. In terms of scale, the diameter of a venule is measured in micrometers compared to millimeters for veins.

Comparison of Arteries and Veins

	Arteries	Veins
Direction of blood flow	Conducts blood away from the heart	Conducts blood toward the heart
General appearance	Rounded	Irregular, often collapsed
Pressure	High	Low

TABLE 20.2

	Arteries	**Veins**
Wall thickness	Thick	Thin
Relative oxygen concentration	Higher in systemic arteries Lower in pulmonary arteries	Lower in systemic veins Higher in pulmonary veins
Valves	Not present	Present most commonly in limbs and in veins inferior to the heart

TABLE 20.2

Disorders of the...

Cardiovascular System: Edema and Varicose Veins

Despite the presence of valves and the contributions of other anatomical and physiological adaptations we will cover shortly, over the course of a day, some blood will inevitably pool, especially in the lower limbs, due to the pull of gravity. Any blood that accumulates in a vein will increase the pressure within it, which can then be reflected back into the smaller veins, venules, and eventually even the capillaries. Increased pressure will promote the flow of fluids out of the capillaries and into the interstitial fluid. The presence of excess tissue fluid around the cells leads to a condition called edema.

Most people experience a daily accumulation of tissue fluid, especially if they spend much of their work life on their feet (like most health professionals). However, clinical edema goes beyond normal swelling and requires medical treatment. Edema has many potential causes, including hypertension and heart failure, severe protein deficiency, renal failure, and many others. In order to treat edema, which is a sign rather than a discrete disorder, the underlying cause must be diagnosed and alleviated.

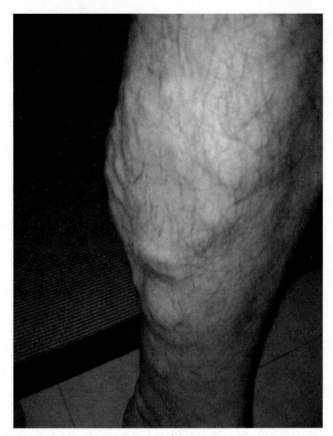

FIGURE 20.8   **Varicose Veins**   Varicose veins are commonly found in the lower limbs. (credit: Thomas Kriese)

Edema may be accompanied by varicose veins, especially in the superficial veins of the legs (Figure 20.8). This disorder arises when defective valves allow blood to accumulate within the veins, causing them to distend, twist, and become visible on the surface of the integument. Varicose veins may occur in all people, but are more common in females and are often related to pregnancy. More than simple cosmetic blemishes, varicose veins are often painful and sometimes itchy or throbbing. Without treatment, they tend to grow worse over time. The use of support hose, as well as elevating the feet and legs whenever possible, may be helpful in alleviating this condition. Laser surgery and interventional radiologic procedures can reduce the size and severity of varicose veins. Severe cases may require conventional surgery to remove the damaged vessels. As there are typically redundant circulation patterns, that is, anastomoses, for the smaller and more superficial veins, removal does not typically impair the circulation. There is evidence that patients with varicose veins suffer a greater risk of developing a thrombus or clot.

Veins as Blood Reservoirs

In addition to their primary function of returning blood to the heart, veins may be considered blood reservoirs, since systemic veins contain approximately 64 percent of the blood volume at any given time (Figure 20.9). Their ability to hold this much blood is due to their high **capacitance**, that is, their capacity to distend (expand) readily to store a high volume of blood, even at a low pressure. The large lumens and relatively thin walls of veins make them far more distensible than arteries; thus, they are said to be **capacitance vessels**.

Systemic circulation 84%	Systemic veins 64%	Large veins 18%
		Large venous networks (liver, bone marrow, and integument) 21%
		Venules and medium-sized veins 25%
	Systemic arteries 13%	Arterioles 2%
		Muscular arteries 5%
		Elastic arteries 4%
		Aorta 2%
	Systemic capillaries 7%	Systemic capillaries 7%
Pulmonary circulation 9%	Pulmonary veins 4%	
	Pulmonary capillaries 2%	
	Pulmonary arteries 3%	
Heart 7%		

FIGURE 20.9   Distribution of Blood Flow

When blood flow needs to be redistributed to other portions of the body, the vasomotor center located in the medulla oblongata sends sympathetic stimulation to the smooth muscles in the walls of the veins, causing constriction—or in this case, venoconstriction. Less dramatic than the vasoconstriction seen in smaller arteries and arterioles, venoconstriction may be likened to a "stiffening" of the vessel wall. This increases pressure on the blood within the veins, speeding its return to the heart. As you will note in Figure 20.9, approximately 21 percent of the venous blood is located in venous networks within the liver, bone marrow, and integument. This volume of blood is referred to as **venous reserve**. Through venoconstriction, this "reserve" volume of blood can get back to the heart more quickly for redistribution to other parts of the circulation.

 CAREER CONNECTION

Vascular Surgeons and Technicians

Vascular surgery is a specialty in which the physician deals primarily with diseases of the vascular portion of the cardiovascular system. This includes repair and replacement of diseased or damaged vessels, removal of plaque from vessels, minimally invasive procedures including the insertion of venous catheters, and traditional surgery. Following completion of medical school, the physician generally completes a 5-year surgical residency followed by an additional 1 to 2 years of vascular specialty training. In the United States, most vascular surgeons are members of the Society of Vascular Surgery.

Vascular technicians are specialists in imaging technologies that provide information on the health of the vascular system. They may also assist physicians in treating disorders involving the arteries and veins. This profession often overlaps with cardiovascular technology, which would also include treatments involving the heart. Although recognized by the American Medical Association, there are currently no licensing requirements for vascular technicians, and licensing is voluntary. Vascular technicians typically have an Associate's degree or certificate, involving 18 months to 2 years of training. The United States Bureau of Labor projects this profession to grow by 29 percent from 2010 to 2020.

⊘ **INTERACTIVE LINK**

Visit this site (http://openstax.org/l/vascsurgery) to learn more about vascular surgery.

⊘ **INTERACTIVE LINK**

Visit this site (http://openstax.org/l/vasctechs) to learn more about vascular technicians.

20.2 Blood Flow, Blood Pressure, and Resistance

LEARNING OBJECTIVES

By the end of this section, you will be able to:

- Distinguish between systolic pressure, diastolic pressure, pulse pressure, and mean arterial pressure
- Describe the clinical measurement of pulse and blood pressure
- Identify and discuss five variables affecting arterial blood flow and blood pressure
- Discuss several factors affecting blood flow in the venous system

Blood flow refers to the movement of blood through a vessel, tissue, or organ, and is usually expressed in terms of volume of blood per unit of time. It is initiated by the contraction of the ventricles of the heart. Ventricular contraction ejects blood into the major arteries, resulting in flow from regions of higher pressure to regions of lower pressure, as blood encounters smaller arteries and arterioles, then capillaries, then the venules and veins of the venous system. This section discusses a number of critical variables that contribute to blood flow throughout the body. It also discusses the factors that impede or slow blood flow, a phenomenon known as **resistance**.

As noted earlier, hydrostatic pressure is the force exerted by a fluid due to gravitational pull, usually against the wall of the container in which it is located. One form of hydrostatic pressure is **blood pressure**, the force exerted by blood upon the walls of the blood vessels or the chambers of the heart. Blood pressure may be measured in capillaries and veins, as well as the vessels of the pulmonary circulation; however, the term blood pressure without any specific descriptors typically refers to systemic arterial blood pressure—that is, the pressure of blood flowing in the arteries of the systemic circulation. In clinical practice, this pressure is measured in mm Hg and is usually obtained using the brachial artery of the arm.

Components of Arterial Blood Pressure

Arterial blood pressure in the larger vessels consists of several distinct components (Figure 20.10): systolic and diastolic pressures, pulse pressure, and mean arterial pressure.

Systolic and Diastolic Pressures

When systemic arterial blood pressure is measured, it is recorded as a ratio of two numbers (e.g., 120/80 is a normal adult blood pressure), expressed as systolic pressure over diastolic pressure. The **systolic pressure** is the higher value (typically around 120 mm Hg) and reflects the arterial pressure resulting from the ejection of blood during ventricular contraction, or systole. The **diastolic pressure** is the lower value (usually about 80 mm Hg) and represents the arterial pressure of blood during ventricular relaxation, or diastole.

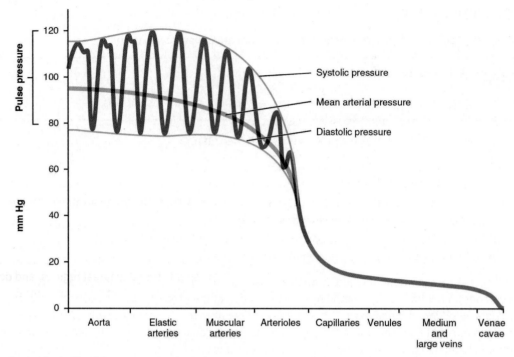

FIGURE 20.10   Systemic Blood Pressure   The graph shows the components of blood pressure throughout the blood vessels, including systolic, diastolic, mean arterial, and pulse pressures.

Pulse Pressure

As shown in Figure 20.10, the difference between the systolic pressure and the diastolic pressure is the **pulse pressure**. For example, an individual with a systolic pressure of 120 mm Hg and a diastolic pressure of 80 mm Hg would have a pulse pressure of 40 mmHg.

Generally, a pulse pressure should be at least 25 percent of the systolic pressure. A pulse pressure below this level is described as low or narrow. This may occur, for example, in patients with a low stroke volume, which may be seen in congestive heart failure, stenosis of the aortic valve, or significant blood loss following trauma. In contrast, a high or wide pulse pressure is common in healthy people following strenuous exercise, when their resting pulse pressure of 30–40 mm Hg may increase temporarily to 100 mm Hg as stroke volume increases. A persistently high pulse pressure at or above 100 mm Hg may indicate excessive resistance in the arteries and can be caused by a variety of disorders. Chronic high resting pulse pressures can degrade the heart, brain, and kidneys, and warrant medical treatment.

Mean Arterial Pressure

Mean arterial pressure (MAP) represents the "average" pressure of blood in the arteries, that is, the average force driving blood into vessels that serve the tissues. Mean is a statistical concept and is calculated by taking the sum of the values divided by the number of values. Although complicated to measure directly and complicated to calculate, MAP can be approximated by adding the diastolic pressure to one-third of the pulse pressure or systolic pressure minus the diastolic pressure:

$$MAP = \text{diastolic BP} + \frac{(\text{systolic-diastolic BP})}{3}$$

In Figure 20.10, this value is approximately 80 + (120 − 80) / 3, or 93.33. Normally, the MAP falls within the range of 70–110 mm Hg. If the value falls below 60 mm Hg for an extended time, blood pressure will not be high enough to ensure circulation to and through the tissues, which results in **ischemia**, or insufficient blood flow. A condition called **hypoxia**, inadequate oxygenation of tissues, commonly accompanies ischemia. The term hypoxemia refers to low levels of oxygen in systemic arterial blood. Neurons are especially sensitive to hypoxia and may die or be damaged if blood flow and oxygen supplies are not quickly restored.

Pulse

After blood is ejected from the heart, elastic fibers in the arteries help maintain a high-pressure gradient as they expand to accommodate the blood, then recoil. This expansion and recoiling effect, known as the **pulse**, can be palpated manually or measured electronically. Although the effect diminishes over distance from the heart, elements of the systolic and diastolic components of the pulse are still evident down to the level of the arterioles.

Because pulse indicates heart rate, it is measured clinically to provide clues to a patient's state of health. It is recorded as beats per minute. Both the rate and the strength of the pulse are important clinically. A high or irregular pulse rate can be caused by physical activity or other temporary factors, but it may also indicate a heart condition. The pulse strength indicates the strength of ventricular contraction and cardiac output. If the pulse is strong, then systolic pressure is high. If it is weak, systolic pressure has fallen, and medical intervention may be warranted.

Pulse can be palpated manually by placing the tips of the fingers across an artery that runs close to the body surface and pressing lightly. While this procedure is normally performed using the radial artery in the wrist or the common carotid artery in the neck, any superficial artery that can be palpated may be used (Figure 20.11). Common sites to find a pulse include temporal and facial arteries in the head, brachial arteries in the upper arm, femoral arteries in the thigh, popliteal arteries behind the knees, posterior tibial arteries near the medial tarsal regions, and dorsalis pedis arteries in the feet. A variety of commercial electronic devices are also available to measure pulse.

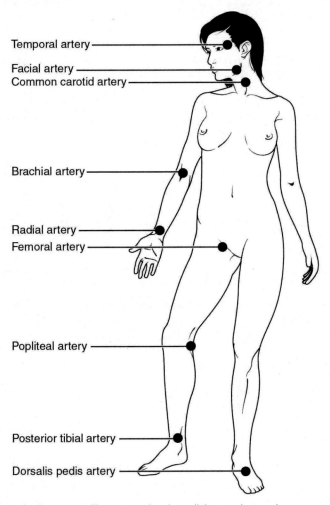

Temporal artery
Facial artery
Common carotid artery
Brachial artery
Radial artery
Femoral artery
Popliteal artery
Posterior tibial artery
Dorsalis pedis artery

FIGURE 20.11   Pulse Sites   The pulse is most readily measured at the radial artery, but can be measured at any of the pulse points shown.

Measurement of Blood Pressure

Blood pressure is one of the critical parameters measured on virtually every patient in every healthcare setting. The technique used today was developed more than 100 years ago by a pioneering Russian physician, Dr. Nikolai

Korotkoff. Turbulent blood flow through the vessels can be heard as a soft ticking while measuring blood pressure; these sounds are known as **Korotkoff sounds**. The technique of measuring blood pressure requires the use of a **sphygmomanometer** (a blood pressure cuff attached to a measuring device) and a stethoscope. The technique is as follows:

- The clinician wraps an inflatable cuff tightly around the patient's arm at about the level of the heart.
- The clinician squeezes a rubber pump to inject air into the cuff, raising pressure around the artery and temporarily cutting off blood flow into the patient's arm.
- The clinician places the stethoscope on the patient's antecubital region and, while gradually allowing air within the cuff to escape, listens for the Korotkoff sounds.

Although there are five recognized Korotkoff sounds, only two are normally recorded. Initially, no sounds are heard since there is no blood flow through the vessels, but as air pressure drops, the cuff relaxes, and blood flow returns to the arm. As shown in Figure 20.12, the first sound heard through the stethoscope—the first Korotkoff sound—indicates systolic pressure. As more air is released from the cuff, blood is able to flow freely through the brachial artery and all sounds disappear. The point at which the last sound is heard is recorded as the patient's diastolic pressure.

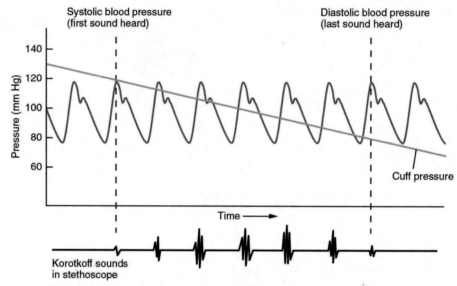

FIGURE 20.12   Blood Pressure Measurement   When pressure in a sphygmomanometer cuff is released, a clinician can hear the Korotkoff sounds. In this graph, a blood pressure tracing is aligned to a measurement of systolic and diastolic pressures.

The majority of hospitals and clinics have automated equipment for measuring blood pressure that work on the same principles. An even more recent innovation is a small instrument that wraps around a patient's wrist. The patient then holds the wrist over the heart while the device measures blood flow and records pressure.

Variables Affecting Blood Flow and Blood Pressure

Five variables influence blood flow and blood pressure:

- Cardiac output
- Compliance
- Volume of the blood
- Viscosity of the blood
- Blood vessel length and diameter

Recall that blood moves from higher pressure to lower pressure. It is pumped from the heart into the arteries at high pressure. If you increase pressure in the arteries (afterload), and cardiac function does not compensate, blood flow will actually decrease. In the venous system, the opposite relationship is true. Increased pressure in the veins does not decrease flow as it does in arteries, but actually increases flow. Since pressure in the veins is normally relatively low, for blood to flow back into the heart, the pressure in the atria during atrial diastole must be even lower. It normally approaches zero, except when the atria contract (see Figure 20.10).

Cardiac Output

Cardiac output is the measurement of blood flow from the heart through the ventricles, and is usually measured in liters per minute. Any factor that causes cardiac output to increase, by elevating heart rate or stroke volume or both, will elevate blood pressure and promote blood flow. These factors include sympathetic stimulation, the catecholamines epinephrine and norepinephrine, thyroid hormones, and increased calcium ion levels. Conversely, any factor that decreases cardiac output, by decreasing heart rate or stroke volume or both, will decrease arterial pressure and blood flow. These factors include parasympathetic stimulation, elevated or decreased potassium ion levels, decreased calcium levels, anoxia, and acidosis.

Compliance

Compliance is the ability of any compartment to expand to accommodate increased content. A metal pipe, for example, is not compliant, whereas a balloon is. The greater the compliance of an artery, the more effectively it is able to expand to accommodate surges in blood flow without increased resistance or blood pressure. Veins are more compliant than arteries and can expand to hold more blood. When vascular disease causes stiffening of arteries, compliance is reduced and resistance to blood flow is increased. The result is more turbulence, higher pressure within the vessel, and reduced blood flow. This increases the work of the heart.

A Mathematical Approach to Factors Affecting Blood Flow

Jean Louis Marie Poiseuille was a French physician and physiologist who devised a mathematical equation describing blood flow and its relationship to known parameters. The same equation also applies to engineering studies of the flow of fluids. Although understanding the math behind the relationships among the factors affecting blood flow is not necessary to understand blood flow, it can help solidify an understanding of their relationships. Please note that even if the equation looks intimidating, breaking it down into its components and following the relationships will make these relationships clearer, even if you are weak in math. Focus on the three critical variables: radius (r), vessel length (λ), and viscosity (η).

Poiseuille's equation:

$$\text{Blood flow} = \frac{\pi \, \Delta P \, r^4}{8\eta\lambda}$$

- π is the Greek letter pi, used to represent the mathematical constant that is the ratio of a circle's circumference to its diameter. It may commonly be represented as 3.14, although the actual number extends to infinity.
- ΔP represents the difference in pressure.
- r^4 is the radius (one-half of the diameter) of the vessel to the fourth power.
- η is the Greek letter eta and represents the viscosity of the blood.
- λ is the Greek letter lambda and represents the length of a blood vessel.

One of several things this equation allows us to do is calculate the resistance in the vascular system. Normally this value is extremely difficult to measure, but it can be calculated from this known relationship:

$$\text{Blood flow} = \frac{\Delta P}{\text{Resistance}}$$

If we rearrange this slightly,

$$\text{Resistance} = \frac{\Delta P}{\text{Blood flow}}$$

Then by substituting Pouseille's equation for blood flow:

$$\text{Resistance} = \frac{8\eta\lambda}{\pi r^4}$$

By examining this equation, you can see that there are only three variables: viscosity, vessel length, and radius, since 8 and π are both constants. The important thing to remember is this: Two of these variables, viscosity and vessel length, will change slowly in the body. Only one of these factors, the radius, can be changed rapidly by vasoconstriction and vasodilation, thus dramatically impacting resistance and flow. Further, small changes in the radius will greatly affect flow, since it is raised to the fourth power in the equation.

We have briefly considered how cardiac output and blood volume impact blood flow and pressure; the next step is to see how the other variables (contraction, vessel length, and viscosity) articulate with Pouseille's equation and what they can teach us about the impact on blood flow.

Blood Volume

The relationship between blood volume, blood pressure, and blood flow is intuitively obvious. Water may merely trickle along a creek bed in a dry season, but rush quickly and under great pressure after a heavy rain. Similarly, as blood volume decreases, pressure and flow decrease. As blood volume increases, pressure and flow increase.

Under normal circumstances, blood volume varies little. Low blood volume, called **hypovolemia**, may be caused by bleeding, dehydration, vomiting, severe burns, or some medications used to treat hypertension. It is important to recognize that other regulatory mechanisms in the body are so effective at maintaining blood pressure that an individual may be asymptomatic until 10–20 percent of the blood volume has been lost. Treatment typically includes intravenous fluid replacement.

Hypervolemia, excessive fluid volume, may be caused by retention of water and sodium, as seen in patients with heart failure, liver cirrhosis, some forms of kidney disease, hyperaldosteronism, and some glucocorticoid steroid treatments. Restoring homeostasis in these patients depends upon reversing the condition that triggered the hypervolemia.

Blood Viscosity

Viscosity is the thickness of fluids that affects their ability to flow. Clean water, for example, is less viscous than mud. The viscosity of blood is directly proportional to resistance and inversely proportional to flow; therefore, any condition that causes viscosity to increase will also increase resistance and decrease flow. For example, imagine sipping milk, then a milkshake, through the same size straw. You experience more resistance and therefore less flow from the milkshake. Conversely, any condition that causes viscosity to decrease (such as when the milkshake melts) will decrease resistance and increase flow.

Normally the viscosity of blood does not change over short periods of time. The two primary determinants of blood viscosity are the formed elements and plasma proteins. Since the vast majority of formed elements are erythrocytes, any condition affecting erythropoiesis, such as polycythemia or anemia, can alter viscosity. Since most plasma proteins are produced by the liver, any condition affecting liver function can also change the viscosity slightly and therefore alter blood flow. Liver abnormalities such as hepatitis, cirrhosis, alcohol damage, and drug toxicities result in decreased levels of plasma proteins, which decrease blood viscosity. While leukocytes and platelets are normally a small component of the formed elements, there are some rare conditions in which severe overproduction can impact viscosity as well.

Vessel Length and Diameter

The length of a vessel is directly proportional to its resistance: the longer the vessel, the greater the resistance and the lower the flow. As with blood volume, this makes intuitive sense, since the increased surface area of the vessel will impede the flow of blood. Likewise, if the vessel is shortened, the resistance will decrease and flow will increase.

The length of our blood vessels increases throughout childhood as we grow, of course, but is unchanging in adults under normal physiological circumstances. Further, the distribution of vessels is not the same in all tissues. Adipose tissue does not have an extensive vascular supply. One pound of adipose tissue contains approximately 200 miles of vessels, whereas skeletal muscle contains more than twice that. Overall, vessels decrease in length only during loss of mass or amputation. An individual weighing 150 pounds has approximately 60,000 miles of vessels in the body. Gaining about 10 pounds adds from 2000 to 4000 miles of vessels, depending upon the nature of the gained tissue. One of the great benefits of weight reduction is the reduced stress to the heart, which does not have to overcome the resistance of as many miles of vessels.

In contrast to length, the diameter of blood vessels changes throughout the body, according to the type of vessel, as we discussed earlier. The diameter of any given vessel may also change frequently throughout the day in response to neural and chemical signals that trigger vasodilation and vasoconstriction. The **vascular tone** of the vessel is the contractile state of the smooth muscle and the primary determinant of diameter, and thus of resistance and flow. The effect of vessel diameter on resistance is inverse: Given the same volume of blood, an increased diameter means there is less blood contacting the vessel wall, thus lower friction and lower resistance, subsequently increasing flow. A decreased diameter means more of the blood contacts the vessel wall, and resistance increases, subsequently decreasing flow.

The influence of lumen diameter on resistance is dramatic: A slight increase or decrease in diameter causes a huge decrease or increase in resistance. This is because resistance is inversely proportional to the radius of the blood vessel (one-half of the vessel's diameter) raised to the fourth power ($R = 1/r^4$). This means, for example, that if an artery or arteriole constricts to one-half of its original radius, the resistance to flow will increase 16 times. And if an artery or arteriole dilates to twice its initial radius, then resistance in the vessel will decrease to 1/16 of its original value and flow will increase 16 times.

The Roles of Vessel Diameter and Total Area in Blood Flow and Blood Pressure

Recall that we classified arterioles as resistance vessels, because given their small lumen, they dramatically slow the flow of blood from arteries. In fact, arterioles are the site of greatest resistance in the entire vascular network. This may seem surprising, given that capillaries have a smaller size. How can this phenomenon be explained?

Figure 20.13 compares vessel diameter, total cross-sectional area, average blood pressure, and blood velocity through the systemic vessels. Notice in parts (a) and (b) that the total cross-sectional area of the body's capillary beds is far greater than any other type of vessel. Although the diameter of an individual capillary is significantly smaller than the diameter of an arteriole, there are vastly more capillaries in the body than there are other types of blood vessels. Part (c) shows that blood pressure drops unevenly as blood travels from arteries to arterioles, capillaries, venules, and veins, and encounters greater resistance. However, the site of the most precipitous drop, and the site of greatest resistance, is the arterioles. This explains why vasodilation and vasoconstriction of arterioles play more significant roles in regulating blood pressure than do the vasodilation and vasoconstriction of other vessels.

Part (d) shows that the velocity (speed) of blood flow decreases dramatically as the blood moves from arteries to arterioles to capillaries. This slow flow rate allows more time for exchange processes to occur. As blood flows through the veins, the rate of velocity increases, as blood is returned to the heart.

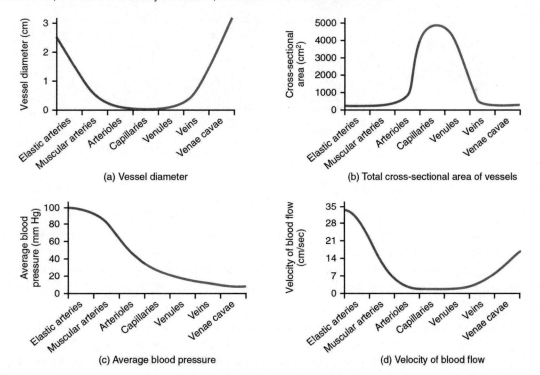

(a) Vessel diameter

(b) Total cross-sectional area of vessels

(c) Average blood pressure

(d) Velocity of blood flow

FIGURE 20.13 Relationships among Vessels in the Systemic Circuit The relationships among blood vessels that can be compared include (a) vessel diameter, (b) total cross-sectional area, (c) average blood pressure, and (d) velocity of blood flow.

Disorders of the...

Cardiovascular System: Arteriosclerosis

Compliance allows an artery to expand when blood is pumped through it from the heart, and then to recoil after the surge has passed. This helps promote blood flow. In arteriosclerosis, compliance is reduced, and pressure and resistance within the vessel increase. This is a leading cause of hypertension and coronary heart disease, as it causes the heart to work harder to generate a pressure great enough to overcome the resistance.

Arteriosclerosis begins with injury to the endothelium of an artery, which may be caused by irritation from high blood glucose, infection, tobacco use, excessive blood lipids, and other factors. Artery walls that are constantly stressed by blood flowing at high pressure are also more likely to be injured—which means that hypertension can promote arteriosclerosis, as well as result from it.

Recall that tissue injury causes inflammation. As inflammation spreads into the artery wall, it weakens and scars it, leaving it stiff (sclerotic). As a result, compliance is reduced. Moreover, circulating triglycerides and cholesterol can seep between the damaged lining cells and become trapped within the artery wall, where they are frequently joined by leukocytes, calcium, and cellular debris. Eventually, this buildup, called plaque, can narrow arteries enough to impair blood flow. The term for this condition, atherosclerosis (athero- = "porridge") describes the mealy deposits (Figure 20.14).

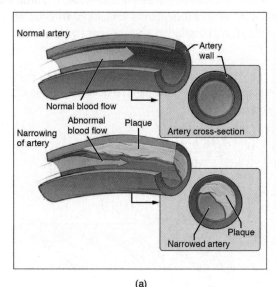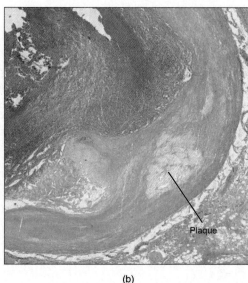

(a)   (b)

FIGURE 20.14   Atherosclerosis   (a) Atherosclerosis can result from plaques formed by the buildup of fatty, calcified deposits in an artery. (b) Plaques can also take other forms, as shown in this micrograph of a coronary artery that has a buildup of connective tissue within the artery wall. LM × 40. (Micrograph provided by the Regents of University of Michigan Medical School © 2012)

Sometimes a plaque can rupture, causing microscopic tears in the artery wall that allow blood to leak into the tissue on the other side. When this happens, platelets rush to the site to clot the blood. This clot can further obstruct the artery and—if it occurs in a coronary or cerebral artery—cause a sudden heart attack or stroke. Alternatively, plaque can break off and travel through the bloodstream as an embolus until it blocks a more distant, smaller artery.

Even without total blockage, vessel narrowing leads to ischemia—reduced blood flow—to the tissue region "downstream" of the narrowed vessel. Ischemia in turn leads to hypoxia—decreased supply of oxygen to the tissues. Hypoxia involving cardiac muscle or brain tissue can lead to cell death and severe impairment of brain or heart function.

A major risk factor for both arteriosclerosis and atherosclerosis is advanced age, as the conditions tend to progress over time. Arteriosclerosis is normally defined as the more generalized loss of compliance, "hardening of the arteries," whereas atherosclerosis is a more specific term for the build-up of plaque in the walls of the vessel and is a specific type of arteriosclerosis. There is also a distinct genetic component, and pre-existing hypertension and/or diabetes also greatly increase the risk. However, obesity, poor nutrition, lack of physical activity, and tobacco use all are major risk factors.

Treatment includes lifestyle changes, such as weight loss, smoking cessation, regular exercise, and adoption of a diet low in sodium and saturated fats. Medications to reduce cholesterol and blood pressure may be prescribed. For blocked coronary arteries, surgery is warranted. In angioplasty, a catheter is inserted into the vessel at the point of narrowing, and a second catheter with a balloon-like tip is inflated to widen the opening. To prevent subsequent collapse of the vessel, a small mesh tube called a stent is often inserted. In an endarterectomy, plaque is surgically removed from the walls of a vessel. This operation is typically performed on the carotid arteries of the neck, which are a prime source of oxygenated blood for the brain. In a coronary bypass procedure, a non-vital superficial vessel from another part of the body (often the great saphenous vein) or a synthetic vessel is inserted to create a path around the blocked area of a coronary artery.

Venous System

The pumping action of the heart propels the blood into the arteries, from an area of higher pressure toward an area of lower pressure. If blood is to flow from the veins back into the heart, the pressure in the veins must be greater than the pressure in the atria of the heart. Two factors help maintain this pressure gradient between the veins and the heart. First, the pressure in the atria during diastole is very low, often approaching zero when the atria are relaxed (atrial diastole). Second, two physiologic "pumps" increase pressure in the venous system. The use of the term "pump" implies a physical device that speeds flow. These physiological pumps are less obvious.

Skeletal Muscle Pump

In many body regions, the pressure within the veins can be increased by the contraction of the surrounding skeletal muscle. This mechanism, known as the **skeletal muscle pump** (Figure 20.15), helps the lower-pressure veins counteract the force of gravity, increasing pressure to move blood back to the heart. As leg muscles contract, for example during walking or running, they exert pressure on nearby veins with their numerous one-way valves. This increased pressure causes blood to flow upward, opening valves superior to the contracting muscles so blood flows through. Simultaneously, valves inferior to the contracting muscles close; thus, blood should not seep back downward toward the feet. Military recruits are trained to flex their legs slightly while standing at attention for prolonged periods. Failure to do so may allow blood to pool in the lower limbs rather than returning to the heart. Consequently, the brain will not receive enough oxygenated blood, and the individual may lose consciousness.

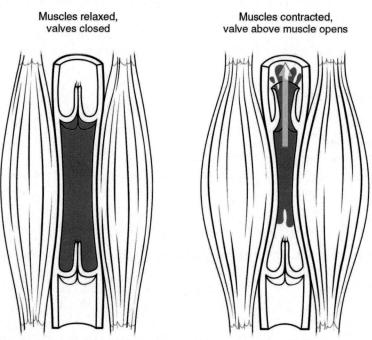

Muscles relaxed, valves closed

Muscles contracted, valve above muscle opens

FIGURE 20.15   Skeletal Muscle Pump   The contraction of skeletal muscles surrounding a vein compresses the blood and increases the pressure in that area. This action forces blood closer to the heart where venous pressure is lower. Note the importance of the one-way valves to assure that blood flows only in the proper direction.

Respiratory Pump

The **respiratory pump** aids blood flow through the veins of the thorax and abdomen. During inhalation, the volume of the thorax increases, largely through the contraction of the diaphragm, which moves downward and compresses the abdominal cavity. The elevation of the chest caused by the contraction of the external intercostal muscles also contributes to the increased volume of the thorax. The volume increase causes air pressure within the thorax to decrease, allowing us to inhale. Additionally, as air pressure within the thorax drops, blood pressure in the thoracic veins also decreases, falling below the pressure in the abdominal veins. This causes blood to flow along its pressure gradient from veins outside the thorax, where pressure is higher, into the thoracic region, where pressure is now lower. This in turn promotes the return of blood from the thoracic veins to the atria. During exhalation, when air pressure increases within the thoracic cavity, pressure in the thoracic veins increases, speeding blood flow into the heart while valves in the veins prevent blood from flowing backward from the thoracic and abdominal veins.

Pressure Relationships in the Venous System

Although vessel diameter increases from the smaller venules to the larger veins and eventually to the venae cavae (singular = vena cava), the total cross-sectional area actually decreases (see Figure 20.15**a** and **b**). The individual veins are larger in diameter than the venules, but their total number is much lower, so their total cross-sectional area is also lower.

Also notice that, as blood moves from venules to veins, the average blood pressure drops (see Figure 20.15**c**), but the blood velocity actually increases (see Figure 20.15). This pressure gradient drives blood back toward the heart. Again, the presence of one-way valves and the skeletal muscle and respiratory pumps contribute to this increased flow. Since approximately 64 percent of the total blood volume resides in systemic veins, any action that increases the flow of blood through the veins will increase venous return to the heart. Maintaining vascular tone within the veins prevents the veins from merely distending, dampening the flow of blood, and as you will see, vasoconstriction actually enhances the flow.

The Role of Venoconstriction in Resistance, Blood Pressure, and Flow

As previously discussed, vasoconstriction of an artery or arteriole decreases the radius, increasing resistance and pressure, but decreasing flow. Venoconstriction, on the other hand, has a very different outcome. The walls of veins are thin but irregular; thus, when the smooth muscle in those walls constricts, the lumen becomes more rounded. The more rounded the lumen, the less surface area the blood encounters, and the less resistance the vessel offers. Vasoconstriction increases pressure within a vein as it does in an artery, but in veins, the increased pressure increases flow. Recall that the pressure in the atria, into which the venous blood will flow, is very low, approaching zero for at least part of the relaxation phase of the cardiac cycle. Thus, venoconstriction increases the return of blood to the heart. Another way of stating this is that venoconstriction increases the preload or stretch of the cardiac muscle and increases contraction.

20.3 Capillary Exchange

LEARNING OBJECTIVES

By the end of this section, you will be able to:

- Identify the primary mechanisms of capillary exchange
- Distinguish between capillary hydrostatic pressure and blood colloid osmotic pressure, explaining the contribution of each to net filtration pressure
- Compare filtration and reabsorption
- Explain the fate of fluid that is not reabsorbed from the tissues into the vascular capillaries

The primary purpose of the cardiovascular system is to circulate gases, nutrients, wastes, and other substances to and from the cells of the body. Small molecules, such as gases, lipids, and lipid-soluble molecules, can diffuse directly through the membranes of the endothelial cells of the capillary wall. Glucose, amino acids, and ions—including sodium, potassium, calcium, and chloride—use transporters to move through specific channels in the membrane by facilitated diffusion. Glucose, ions, and larger molecules may also leave the blood through intercellular clefts. Larger molecules can pass through the pores of fenestrated capillaries, and even large plasma proteins can pass through the great gaps in the sinusoids. Some large proteins in blood plasma can move into and out of the endothelial cells packaged within vesicles by endocytosis and exocytosis. Water moves by osmosis.

Bulk Flow

The mass movement of fluids into and out of capillary beds requires a transport mechanism far more efficient than mere diffusion. This movement, often referred to as bulk flow, involves two pressure-driven mechanisms: Volumes of fluid move from an area of higher pressure in a capillary bed to an area of lower pressure in the tissues via **filtration**. In contrast, the movement of fluid from an area of higher pressure in the tissues into an area of lower pressure in the capillaries is **reabsorption**. Two types of pressure interact to drive each of these movements: hydrostatic pressure and osmotic pressure.

Hydrostatic Pressure

The primary force driving fluid transport between the capillaries and tissues is hydrostatic pressure, which can be defined as the pressure of any fluid enclosed in a space. **Blood hydrostatic pressure** is the force exerted by the blood confined within blood vessels or heart chambers. Even more specifically, the pressure exerted by blood against the wall of a capillary is called **capillary hydrostatic pressure (CHP)**, and is the same as capillary blood pressure. CHP is the force that drives fluid out of capillaries and into the tissues.

As fluid exits a capillary and moves into tissues, the hydrostatic pressure in the interstitial fluid correspondingly rises. This opposing hydrostatic pressure is called the **interstitial fluid hydrostatic pressure (IFHP)**. Generally, the CHP originating from the arterial pathways is considerably higher than the IFHP, because lymphatic vessels are continually absorbing excess fluid from the tissues. Thus, fluid generally moves out of the capillary and into the interstitial fluid. This process is called filtration.

Osmotic Pressure

The net pressure that drives reabsorption—the movement of fluid from the interstitial fluid back into the capillaries—is called osmotic pressure (sometimes referred to as oncotic pressure). Whereas hydrostatic pressure forces fluid out of the capillary, osmotic pressure draws fluid back in. Osmotic pressure is determined by osmotic concentration gradients, that is, the difference in the solute-to-water concentrations in the blood and tissue fluid. A region higher in solute concentration (and lower in water concentration) draws water across a semipermeable membrane from a region higher in water concentration (and lower in solute concentration).

As we discuss osmotic pressure in blood and tissue fluid, it is important to recognize that the formed elements of blood do not contribute to osmotic concentration gradients. Rather, it is the plasma proteins that play the key role. Solutes also move across the capillary wall according to their concentration gradient, but overall, the concentrations should be similar and not have a significant impact on osmosis. Because of their large size and chemical structure, plasma proteins are not truly solutes, that is, they do not dissolve but are dispersed or suspended in their fluid medium, forming a colloid rather than a solution.

The pressure created by the concentration of colloidal proteins in the blood is called the **blood colloidal osmotic pressure (BCOP)**. Its effect on capillary exchange accounts for the reabsorption of water. The plasma proteins suspended in blood cannot move across the semipermeable capillary cell membrane, and so they remain in the plasma. As a result, blood has a higher colloidal concentration and lower water concentration than tissue fluid. It therefore attracts water. We can also say that the BCOP is higher than the **interstitial fluid colloidal osmotic pressure (IFCOP)**, which is always very low because interstitial fluid contains few proteins. Thus, water is drawn from the tissue fluid back into the capillary, carrying dissolved molecules with it. This difference in colloidal osmotic pressure accounts for reabsorption.

Interaction of Hydrostatic and Osmotic Pressures

The normal unit used to express pressures within the cardiovascular system is millimeters of mercury (mm Hg). When blood leaving an arteriole first enters a capillary bed, the CHP is quite high—about 35 mm Hg. Gradually, this initial CHP declines as the blood moves through the capillary so that by the time the blood has reached the venous end, the CHP has dropped to approximately 18 mm Hg. In comparison, the plasma proteins remain suspended in the blood, so the BCOP remains fairly constant at about 25 mm Hg throughout the length of the capillary and considerably above the osmotic pressure in the interstitial fluid.

The **net filtration pressure (NFP)** represents the interaction of the hydrostatic and osmotic pressures, driving fluid out of the capillary. It is equal to the difference between the CHP and the BCOP. Since filtration is, by definition, the movement of fluid out of the capillary, when reabsorption is occurring, the NFP is a negative number.

NFP changes at different points in a capillary bed (Figure 20.16). Close to the arterial end of the capillary, it is approximately 10 mm Hg, because the CHP of 35 mm Hg minus the BCOP of 25 mm Hg equals 10 mm Hg. Recall that the hydrostatic and osmotic pressures of the interstitial fluid are essentially negligible. Thus, the NFP of 10 mm Hg drives a net movement of fluid out of the capillary at the arterial end. At approximately the middle of the capillary, the CHP is about the same as the BCOP of 25 mm Hg, so the NFP drops to zero. At this point, there is no net change of volume: Fluid moves out of the capillary at the same rate as it moves into the capillary. Near the venous end of the capillary, the CHP has dwindled to about 18 mm Hg due to loss of fluid. Because the BCOP remains steady at 25 mm Hg, water is drawn into the capillary, that is, reabsorption occurs. Another way of expressing this is to say that at the venous end of the capillary, there is an NFP of –7 mm Hg.

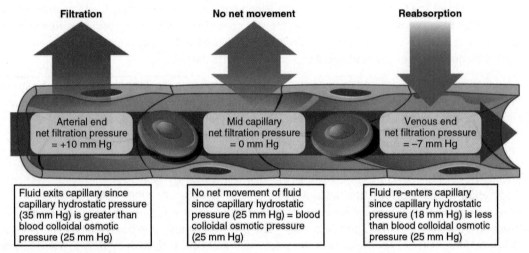

FIGURE 20.16   **Capillary Exchange**   Net filtration occurs near the arterial end of the capillary since capillary hydrostatic pressure (CHP) is greater than blood colloidal osmotic pressure (BCOP). There is no net movement of fluid near the midpoint since CHP = BCOP. Net reabsorption occurs near the venous end since BCOP is greater than CHP.

The Role of Lymphatic Capillaries

Since overall CHP is higher than BCOP, it is inevitable that more net fluid will exit the capillary through filtration at the arterial end than enters through reabsorption at the venous end. Considering all capillaries over the course of a day, this can be quite a substantial amount of fluid: Approximately 24 liters per day are filtered, whereas 20.4 liters are reabsorbed. This excess fluid is picked up by capillaries of the lymphatic system. These extremely thin-walled vessels have copious numbers of valves that ensure unidirectional flow through ever-larger lymphatic vessels that eventually drain into the subclavian veins in the neck. An important function of the lymphatic system is to return the fluid (lymph) to the blood. Lymph may be thought of as recycled blood plasma. (Seek additional content for more detail on the lymphatic system.)

⊛ INTERACTIVE LINK

Watch this video (http://openstax.org/l/capillaryfunct) to explore capillaries and how they function in the body. Capillaries are never more than 100 micrometers away. What is the main component of interstitial fluid?

20.4 Homeostatic Regulation of the Vascular System

LEARNING OBJECTIVES

By the end of this section, you will be able to:
- Discuss the mechanisms involved in the neural regulation of vascular homeostasis
- Describe the contribution of a variety of hormones to the renal regulation of blood pressure
- Identify the effects of exercise on vascular homeostasis
- Discuss how hypertension, hemorrhage, and circulatory shock affect vascular health

In order to maintain homeostasis in the cardiovascular system and provide adequate blood to the tissues, blood flow must be redirected continually to the tissues as they become more active. In a very real sense, the cardiovascular system engages in resource allocation, because there is not enough blood flow to distribute blood equally to all tissues simultaneously. For example, when an individual is exercising, more blood will be directed to skeletal muscles, the heart, and the lungs. Following a meal, more blood is directed to the digestive system. Only the brain receives a more or less constant supply of blood whether you are active, resting, thinking, or engaged in any other activity.

Table 20.3 provides the distribution of systemic blood at rest and during exercise. Although most of the data appears logical, the values for the distribution of blood to the integument may seem surprising. During exercise, the body distributes more blood to the body surface where it can dissipate the excess heat generated by increased activity into the environment.

Systemic Blood Flow During Rest, Mild Exercise, and Maximal Exercise in a Healthy Young Individual

Organ	Resting (mL/min)	Mild exercise (mL/min)	Maximal exercise (mL/min)
Skeletal muscle	1200	4500	12,500
Heart	250	350	750
Brain	750	750	750
Integument	500	1500	1900
Kidney	1100	900	600
Gastrointestinal	1400	1100	600
Others (i.e., liver, spleen)	600	400	400
Total	5800	9500	17,500

TABLE 20.3

Three homeostatic mechanisms ensure adequate blood flow, blood pressure, distribution, and ultimately perfusion: neural, endocrine, and autoregulatory mechanisms. They are summarized in Figure 20.17.

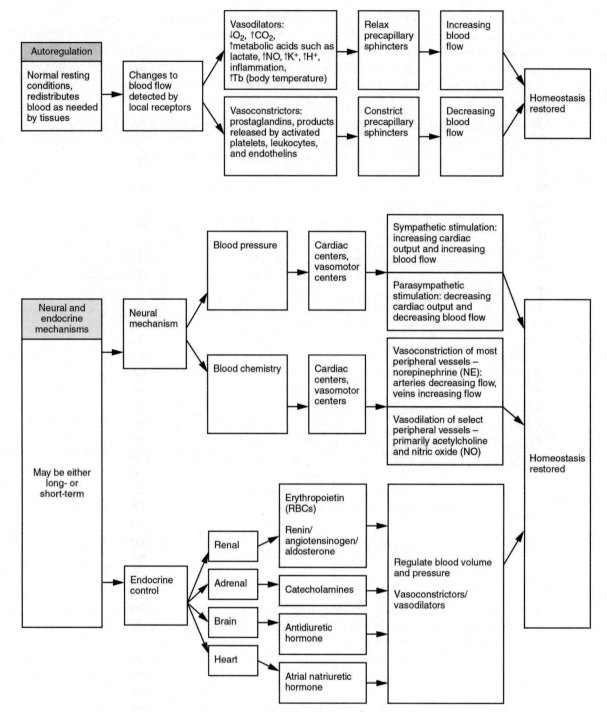

FIGURE 20.17   Summary of Factors Maintaining Vascular Homeostasis   Adequate blood flow, blood pressure, distribution, and perfusion involve autoregulatory, neural, and endocrine mechanisms.

Neural Regulation

The nervous system plays a critical role in the regulation of vascular homeostasis. The primary regulatory sites include the cardiovascular centers in the brain that control both cardiac and vascular functions. In addition, more generalized neural responses from the limbic system and the autonomic nervous system are factors.

The Cardiovascular Centers in the Brain

Neurological regulation of blood pressure and flow depends on the cardiovascular centers located in the medulla oblongata. This cluster of neurons responds to changes in blood pressure as well as blood concentrations of oxygen, carbon dioxide, and hydrogen ions. The cardiovascular center contains three distinct paired components:

- The cardioaccelerator centers stimulate cardiac function by regulating heart rate and stroke volume via sympathetic stimulation from the cardiac accelerator nerve.
- The cardioinhibitor centers slow cardiac function by decreasing heart rate and stroke volume via parasympathetic stimulation from the vagus nerve.
- The vasomotor centers control vessel tone or contraction of the smooth muscle in the tunica media. Changes in diameter affect peripheral resistance, pressure, and flow, which affect cardiac output. The majority of these neurons act via the release of the neurotransmitter norepinephrine from sympathetic neurons.

Although each center functions independently, they are not anatomically distinct.

There is also a small population of neurons that control vasodilation in the vessels of the brain and skeletal muscles by relaxing the smooth muscle fibers in the vessel tunics. Many of these are cholinergic neurons, that is, they release acetylcholine, which in turn stimulates the vessels' endothelial cells to release nitric oxide (NO), which causes vasodilation. Others release norepinephrine that binds to β_2 receptors. A few neurons release NO directly as a neurotransmitter.

Recall that mild stimulation of the skeletal muscles maintains muscle tone. A similar phenomenon occurs with vascular tone in vessels. As noted earlier, arterioles are normally partially constricted: With maximal stimulation, their radius may be reduced to one-half of the resting state. Full dilation of most arterioles requires that this sympathetic stimulation be suppressed. When it is, an arteriole can expand by as much as 150 percent. Such a significant increase can dramatically affect resistance, pressure, and flow.

Baroreceptor Reflexes

Baroreceptors are specialized stretch receptors located within thin areas of blood vessels and heart chambers that respond to the degree of stretch caused by the presence of blood. They send impulses to the cardiovascular center to regulate blood pressure. Vascular baroreceptors are found primarily in sinuses (small cavities) within the aorta and carotid arteries: The **aortic sinuses** are found in the walls of the ascending aorta just superior to the aortic valve, whereas the **carotid sinuses** are in the base of the internal carotid arteries. There are also low-pressure baroreceptors located in the walls of the venae cavae and right atrium.

When blood pressure increases, the baroreceptors are stretched more tightly and initiate action potentials at a higher rate. At lower blood pressures, the degree of stretch is lower and the rate of firing is slower. When the cardiovascular center in the medulla oblongata receives this input, it triggers a reflex that maintains homeostasis (Figure 20.18):

- When blood pressure rises too high, the baroreceptors fire at a higher rate and trigger parasympathetic stimulation of the heart. As a result, cardiac output falls. Sympathetic stimulation of the peripheral arterioles will also decrease, resulting in vasodilation. Combined, these activities cause blood pressure to fall.
- When blood pressure drops too low, the rate of baroreceptor firing decreases. This will trigger an increase in sympathetic stimulation of the heart, causing cardiac output to increase. It will also trigger sympathetic stimulation of the peripheral vessels, resulting in vasoconstriction. Combined, these activities cause blood pressure to rise.

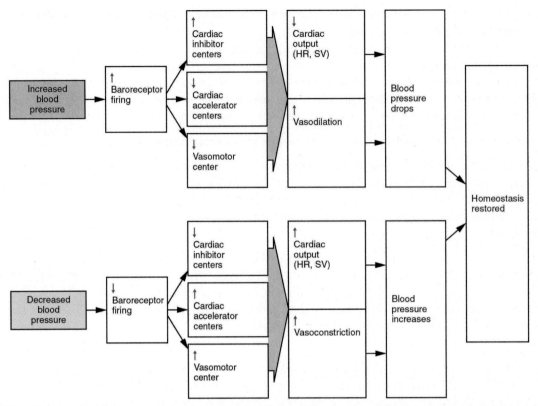

FIGURE 20.18   Baroreceptor Reflexes for Maintaining Vascular Homeostasis   Increased blood pressure results in increased rates of baroreceptor firing, whereas decreased blood pressure results in slower rates of fire, both initiating the homeostatic mechanism to restore blood pressure.

The baroreceptors in the venae cavae and right atrium monitor blood pressure as the blood returns to the heart from the systemic circulation. Normally, blood flow into the aorta is the same as blood flow back into the right atrium. If blood is returning to the right atrium more rapidly than it is being ejected from the left ventricle, the atrial receptors will stimulate the cardiovascular centers to increase sympathetic firing and increase cardiac output until homeostasis is achieved. The opposite is also true. This mechanism is referred to as the **atrial reflex**.

Chemoreceptor Reflexes

In addition to the baroreceptors are chemoreceptors that monitor levels of oxygen, carbon dioxide, and hydrogen ions (pH), and thereby contribute to vascular homeostasis. Chemoreceptors monitoring the blood are located in close proximity to the baroreceptors in the aortic and carotid sinuses. They signal the cardiovascular center as well as the respiratory centers in the medulla oblongata.

Since tissues consume oxygen and produce carbon dioxide and acids as waste products, when the body is more active, oxygen levels fall and carbon dioxide levels rise as cells undergo cellular respiration to meet the energy needs of activities. This causes more hydrogen ions to be produced, causing the blood pH to drop. When the body is resting, oxygen levels are higher, carbon dioxide levels are lower, more hydrogen is bound, and pH rises. (Seek additional content for more detail about pH.)

The chemoreceptors respond to increasing carbon dioxide and hydrogen ion levels (falling pH) by stimulating the cardioaccelerator and vasomotor centers, increasing cardiac output and constricting peripheral vessels. The cardioinhibitor centers are suppressed. With falling carbon dioxide and hydrogen ion levels (increasing pH), the cardioinhibitor centers are stimulated, and the cardioaccelerator and vasomotor centers are suppressed, decreasing cardiac output and causing peripheral vasodilation. In order to maintain adequate supplies of oxygen to the cells and remove waste products such as carbon dioxide, it is essential that the respiratory system respond to changing metabolic demands. In turn, the cardiovascular system will transport these gases to the lungs for exchange, again in accordance with metabolic demands. This interrelationship of cardiovascular and respiratory control cannot be overemphasized.

Other neural mechanisms can also have a significant impact on cardiovascular function. These include the limbic system that links physiological responses to psychological stimuli, as well as generalized sympathetic and parasympathetic stimulation.

Endocrine Regulation

Endocrine control over the cardiovascular system involves the catecholamines, epinephrine and norepinephrine, as well as several hormones that interact with the kidneys in the regulation of blood volume.

Epinephrine and Norepinephrine

The catecholamines epinephrine and norepinephrine are released by the adrenal medulla, and enhance and extend the body's sympathetic or "fight-or-flight" response (see Figure 20.17). They increase heart rate and force of contraction, while temporarily constricting blood vessels to organs not essential for flight-or-fight responses and redirecting blood flow to the liver, muscles, and heart.

Antidiuretic Hormone

Antidiuretic hormone (ADH), also known as vasopressin, is secreted by the cells in the hypothalamus and transported via the hypothalamic-hypophyseal tracts to the posterior pituitary where it is stored until released upon nervous stimulation. The primary trigger prompting the hypothalamus to release ADH is increasing osmolarity of tissue fluid, usually in response to significant loss of blood volume. ADH signals its target cells in the kidneys to reabsorb more water, thus preventing the loss of additional fluid in the urine. This will increase overall fluid levels and help restore blood volume and pressure. In addition, ADH constricts peripheral vessels.

Renin-Angiotensin-Aldosterone Mechanism

The renin-angiotensin-aldosterone mechanism has a major effect upon the cardiovascular system (Figure 20.19). Renin is an enzyme, although because of its importance in the renin-angiotensin-aldosterone pathway, some sources identify it as a hormone. Specialized cells in the kidneys , called juxtaglomerular (JG) cells, respond to decreased blood pressure by secreting renin into the blood. Renin converts the plasma protein angiotensinogen, which is produced by the liver, into its active form—angiotensin I. Angiotensin I circulates in the blood and is then converted into angiotensin II in the lungs. This reaction is catalyzed by the enzyme angiotensin-converting enzyme (ACE).

Angiotensin II is a powerful vasoconstrictor, greatly increasing blood pressure. It also stimulates the release of ADH and aldosterone, a hormone produced by the adrenal cortex. Aldosterone increases the reabsorption of sodium into the blood by the kidneys. Since water follows sodium, this increases the reabsorption of water. This in turn increases blood volume, raising blood pressure. Angiotensin II also stimulates the thirst center in the hypothalamus, so an individual will likely consume more fluids, again increasing blood volume and pressure.

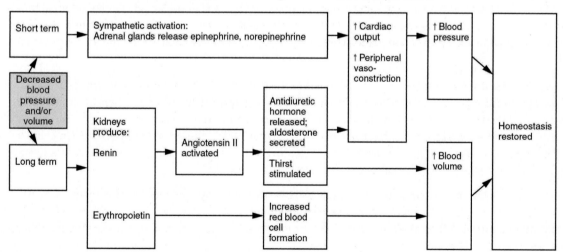

FIGURE 20.19   Hormones Involved in Renal Control of Blood Pressure   In the renin-angiotensin-aldosterone mechanism, increasing angiotensin II will stimulate the production of antidiuretic hormone and aldosterone. In addition to renin, the kidneys produce erythropoietin, which stimulates the production of red blood cells, further increasing blood volume.

Erythropoietin

Erythropoietin (EPO) is released by the kidneys when blood flow and/or oxygen levels decrease. EPO stimulates the production of erythrocytes within the bone marrow. Erythrocytes are the major formed element of the blood and may contribute 40 percent or more to blood volume, a significant factor of viscosity, resistance, pressure, and flow. In addition, EPO is a vasoconstrictor. Overproduction of EPO or excessive intake of synthetic EPO, often to enhance athletic performance, will increase viscosity, resistance, and pressure, and decrease flow in addition to its contribution as a vasoconstrictor.

Atrial Natriuretic Hormone

Secreted by cells in the atria of the heart, atrial natriuretic hormone (ANH) (also known as atrial natriuretic peptide) is secreted when blood volume is high enough to cause extreme stretching of the cardiac cells. Cells in the ventricle produce a hormone with similar effects, called B-type natriuretic hormone. Natriuretic hormones are antagonists to angiotensin II. They promote loss of sodium and water from the kidneys, and suppress renin, aldosterone, and ADH production and release. All of these actions promote loss of fluid from the body, so blood volume and blood pressure drop.

Autoregulation of Perfusion

As the name would suggest, autoregulation mechanisms require neither specialized nervous stimulation nor endocrine control. Rather, these are local, self-regulatory mechanisms that allow each region of tissue to adjust its blood flow—and thus its perfusion. These local mechanisms include chemical signals and myogenic controls.

Chemical Signals Involved in Autoregulation

Chemical signals work at the level of the precapillary sphincters to trigger either constriction or relaxation. As you know, opening a precapillary sphincter allows blood to flow into that particular capillary, whereas constricting a precapillary sphincter temporarily shuts off blood flow to that region. The factors involved in regulating the precapillary sphincters include the following:

- Opening of the sphincter is triggered in response to decreased oxygen concentrations; increased carbon dioxide concentrations; increasing levels of lactic acid or other byproducts of cellular metabolism; increasing concentrations of potassium ions or hydrogen ions (falling pH); inflammatory chemicals such as histamines; and increased body temperature. These conditions in turn stimulate the release of NO, a powerful vasodilator, from endothelial cells (see Figure 20.17).
- Contraction of the precapillary sphincter is triggered by the opposite levels of the regulators, which prompt the release of endothelins, powerful vasoconstricting peptides secreted by endothelial cells. Platelet secretions and certain prostaglandins may also trigger constriction.

Again, these factors alter tissue perfusion via their effects on the precapillary sphincter mechanism, which regulates blood flow to capillaries. Since the amount of blood is limited, not all capillaries can fill at once, so blood flow is allocated based upon the needs and metabolic state of the tissues as reflected in these parameters. Bear in mind, however, that dilation and constriction of the arterioles feeding the capillary beds is the primary control mechanism.

The Myogenic Response

The **myogenic response** is a reaction to the stretching of the smooth muscle in the walls of arterioles as changes in blood flow occur through the vessel. This may be viewed as a largely protective function against dramatic fluctuations in blood pressure and blood flow to maintain homeostasis. If perfusion of an organ is too low (ischemia), the tissue will experience low levels of oxygen (hypoxia). In contrast, excessive perfusion could damage the organ's smaller and more fragile vessels. The myogenic response is a localized process that serves to stabilize blood flow in the capillary network that follows that arteriole.

When blood flow is low, the vessel's smooth muscle will be only minimally stretched. In response, it relaxes, allowing the vessel to dilate and thereby increase the movement of blood into the tissue. When blood flow is too high, the smooth muscle will contract in response to the increased stretch, prompting vasoconstriction that reduces blood flow.

Figure 20.20 summarizes the effects of nervous, endocrine, and local controls on arterioles.

Access for free at openstax.org

Control	Factor	Vasoconstriction	Vasodilation
Neural	Sympathetic stimulation	Arterioles within integument, abdominal viscera, and mucosa membrane; skeletal muscle (at high levels); varied in veins and venules	Arterioles within heart; skeletal muscles at low to moderate levels
	Parasympathetic	No known innervation for most	Arterioles in external genitalia, no known innervation for most other arterioles or veins
Endocrine	Epinephrine	Similar to sympathetic stimulation for extended flight-or-fight responses; at high levels, binds to specialized alpha (α) receptors	Similar to sympathetic stimulation for extended fight-or-flight responses; at low to moderate levels, binds to specialized beta (β) receptors
	Norepinephrine	Similar to epinephrine	Similar to epinephrine
	Angiotensin II	Powerful generalized vasoconstrictor; also stimulates release of aldosterone and ADH	n/a
	ANH (peptide)	n/a	Powerful generalized vasodilator; also promotes loss of fluid volume from kidneys, hence reducing blood volume, pressure, and flow
	ADH	Moderately strong generalized vasoconstrictor; also causes body to retain more fluid via kidneys, increasing blood volume and pressure	n/a
Other factors	Decreasing levels of oxygen	n/a	Vasodilation, also opens precapillary sphincters
	Decreasing pH	n/a	Vasodilation, also opens precapillary sphincters
	Increasing levels of carbon dioxide	n/a	Vasodilation, also opens precapillary sphincters
	Increasing levels of potassium ion	n/a	Vasodilation, also opens precapillary sphincters
	Increasing levels of prostaglandins	Vasoconstriction, closes precapillary sphincters for many	Vasodilation, opens precapillary sphincters for many
	Increasing levels of adenosine	n/a	Vasodilation
	Increasing levels of NO	n/a	Vasodilation, also opens precapillary sphincters
	Increasing levels of lactic acid and other metabolites	n/a	Vasodilation, also opens precapillary sphincters
	Increasing levels of endothelins	Vasoconstriction	n/a
	Increasing levels of platelet secretions	Vasoconstriction	n/a
	Increasing hyperthermia	n/a	Vasodilation
	Stretching of vascular wall (myogenic)	Vasoconstriction	n/a
	Increasing levels of histamines from basophils and mast cells	n/a	Vasodilation

FIGURE 20.20   **Summary of Mechanisms Regulating Arteriole Smooth Muscle and Veins**

Effect of Exercise on Vascular Homeostasis

The heart is a muscle and, like any muscle, it responds dramatically to exercise. For a healthy young adult, cardiac output (heart rate × stroke volume) increases in the nonathlete from approximately 5.0 liters (5.25 quarts) per minute to a maximum of about 20 liters (21 quarts) per minute. Accompanying this will be an increase in blood pressure from about 120/80 to 185/75. However, well-trained aerobic athletes can increase these values substantially. For these individuals, cardiac output soars from approximately 5.3 liters (5.57 quarts) per minute resting to more than 30 liters (31.5 quarts) per minute during maximal exercise. Along with this increase in cardiac output, blood pressure increases from 120/80 at rest to 200/90 at maximum values.

In addition to improved cardiac function, exercise increases the size and mass of the heart. The average weight of the heart for the nonathlete is about 300 g, whereas in an athlete it will increase to 500 g. This increase in size generally makes the heart stronger and more efficient at pumping blood, increasing both stroke volume and cardiac output.

Tissue perfusion also increases as the body transitions from a resting state to light exercise and eventually to heavy exercise (see Figure 20.20). These changes result in selective vasodilation in the skeletal muscles, heart, lungs, liver, and integument. Simultaneously, vasoconstriction occurs in the vessels leading to the kidneys and most of the digestive and reproductive organs. The flow of blood to the brain remains largely unchanged whether at rest or exercising, since the vessels in the brain largely do not respond to regulatory stimuli, in most cases, because they lack the appropriate receptors.

As vasodilation occurs in selected vessels, resistance drops and more blood rushes into the organs they supply. This blood eventually returns to the venous system. Venous return is further enhanced by both the skeletal muscle and respiratory pumps. As blood returns to the heart more quickly, preload rises and the Frank-Starling principle tells us that contraction of the cardiac muscle in the atria and ventricles will be more forceful. Eventually, even the best-trained athletes will fatigue and must undergo a period of rest following exercise. Cardiac output and distribution of blood then return to normal.

Regular exercise promotes cardiovascular health in a variety of ways. Because an athlete's heart is larger than a nonathlete's, stroke volume increases, so the athletic heart can deliver the same amount of blood as the nonathletic heart but with a lower heart rate. This increased efficiency allows the athlete to exercise for longer periods of time before muscles fatigue and places less stress on the heart. Exercise also lowers overall cholesterol levels by removing from the circulation a complex form of cholesterol, triglycerides, and proteins known as low-density lipoproteins (LDLs), which are widely associated with increased risk of cardiovascular disease. Although there is no way to remove deposits of plaque from the walls of arteries other than specialized surgery, exercise does promote the health of vessels by decreasing the rate of plaque formation and reducing blood pressure, so the heart does not have to generate as much force to overcome resistance.

Generally as little as 30 minutes of noncontinuous exercise over the course of each day has beneficial effects and has been shown to lower the rate of heart attack by nearly 50 percent. While it is always advisable to follow a healthy diet, stop smoking, and lose weight, studies have clearly shown that fit, overweight people may actually be healthier overall than sedentary slender people. Thus, the benefits of moderate exercise are undeniable.

Clinical Considerations in Vascular Homeostasis

Any disorder that affects blood volume, vascular tone, or any other aspect of vascular functioning is likely to affect vascular homeostasis as well. That includes hypertension, hemorrhage, and shock.

Hypertension and Hypotension

New guidelines in 2017 from the American College of Cardiology and American Heart Association list normal blood pressure (BP) as less than 120/80 mm Hg and elevated BP as systolic P between 120–129 and diastolic P less than 80 mm Hg. Chronically elevated blood pressure is known clinically as **hypertension**. The new guidelines list hypertension that should be treated as 130/80 mm Hg. Tens of millions of Americans currently suffer from hypertension. Unfortunately, hypertension is typically a silent disorder; therefore, hypertensive patients may fail to recognize the seriousness of their condition and fail to follow their treatment plan. The result is often a heart attack or stroke. Hypertension may also lead to an aneurysm (ballooning of a blood vessel caused by a weakening of the wall), peripheral arterial disease (obstruction of vessels in peripheral regions of the body), chronic kidney disease, or heart failure.

⊘ INTERACTIVE LINK

Listen to this CDC podcast (http://openstax.org/l/CDCpodcast) to learn about hypertension, often described as a "silent killer." What steps can you take to reduce your risk of a heart attack or stroke?

Hemorrhage

Minor blood loss is managed by hemostasis and repair. Hemorrhage is a loss of blood that cannot be controlled by hemostatic mechanisms. Initially, the body responds to hemorrhage by initiating mechanisms aimed at increasing blood pressure and maintaining blood flow. Ultimately, however, blood volume will need to be restored, either through physiological processes or through medical intervention.

In response to blood loss, stimuli from the baroreceptors trigger the cardiovascular centers to stimulate sympathetic responses to increase cardiac output and vasoconstriction. This typically prompts the heart rate to increase to about 180–200 contractions per minute, restoring cardiac output to normal levels. Vasoconstriction of the arterioles increases vascular resistance, whereas constriction of the veins increases venous return to the heart. Both of these steps will help increase blood pressure. Sympathetic stimulation also triggers the release of epinephrine and norepinephrine, which enhance both cardiac output and vasoconstriction. If blood loss were less than 20 percent of total blood volume, these responses together would usually return blood pressure to normal and redirect the remaining blood to the tissues.

Additional endocrine involvement is necessary, however, to restore the lost blood volume. The angiotensin-renin-aldosterone mechanism stimulates the thirst center in the hypothalamus, which increases fluid consumption to help restore the lost blood. More importantly, it increases renal reabsorption of sodium and water, reducing water loss in urine output. The kidneys also increase the production of EPO, stimulating the formation of erythrocytes that not only deliver oxygen to the tissues but also increase overall blood volume. Figure 20.21 summarizes the responses to loss of blood volume.

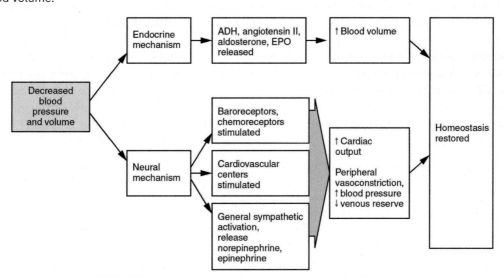

FIGURE 20.21   Homeostatic Responses to Loss of Blood Volume

Circulatory Shock

The loss of too much blood may lead to **circulatory shock**, a life-threatening condition in which the circulatory system is unable to maintain blood flow to adequately supply sufficient oxygen and other nutrients to the tissues to maintain cellular metabolism. It should not be confused with emotional or psychological shock. Typically, the patient in circulatory shock will demonstrate an increased heart rate but decreased blood pressure, but there are cases in which blood pressure will remain normal. Urine output will fall dramatically, and the patient may appear confused or lose consciousness. Urine output less than 1 mL/kg body weight/hour is cause for concern. Unfortunately, shock is an example of a positive-feedback loop that, if uncorrected, may lead to the death of the patient.

There are several recognized forms of shock:

- **Hypovolemic shock** in adults is typically caused by hemorrhage, although in children it may be caused by fluid losses related to severe vomiting or diarrhea. Other causes for hypovolemic shock include extensive burns, exposure to some toxins, and excessive urine loss related to diabetes insipidus or ketoacidosis. Typically, patients present with a rapid, almost tachycardic heart rate; a weak pulse often described as "thready;" cool, clammy skin, particularly in the extremities, due to restricted peripheral blood flow; rapid, shallow breathing; hypothermia; thirst; and dry mouth. Treatments generally involve providing intravenous fluids to restore the patient to normal function and various drugs such as dopamine, epinephrine, and norepinephrine to raise blood pressure.
- **Cardiogenic shock** results from the inability of the heart to maintain cardiac output. Most often, it results from a myocardial infarction (heart attack), but it may also be caused by arrhythmias, valve disorders, cardiomyopathies, cardiac failure, or simply insufficient flow of blood through the cardiac vessels. Treatment involves repairing the damage to the heart or its vessels to resolve the underlying cause, rather than treating

cardiogenic shock directly.

- **Vascular shock** occurs when arterioles lose their normal muscular tone and dilate dramatically. It may arise from a variety of causes, and treatments almost always involve fluid replacement and medications, called inotropic or pressor agents, which restore tone to the muscles of the vessels. In addition, eliminating or at least alleviating the underlying cause of the condition is required. This might include antibiotics and antihistamines, or select steroids, which may aid in the repair of nerve damage. A common cause is **sepsis** (or septicemia), also called "blood poisoning," which is a widespread bacterial infection that results in an organismal-level inflammatory response known as **septic shock. Neurogenic shock** is a form of vascular shock that occurs with cranial or spinal injuries that damage the cardiovascular centers in the medulla oblongata or the nervous fibers originating from this region. **Anaphylactic shock** is a severe allergic response that causes the widespread release of histamines, triggering vasodilation throughout the body.
- **Obstructive shock**, as the name would suggest, occurs when a significant portion of the vascular system is blocked. It is not always recognized as a distinct condition and may be grouped with cardiogenic shock, including pulmonary embolism and cardiac tamponade. Treatments depend upon the underlying cause and, in addition to administering fluids intravenously, often include the administration of anticoagulants, removal of fluid from the pericardial cavity, or air from the thoracic cavity, and surgery as required. The most common cause is a pulmonary embolism, a clot that lodges in the pulmonary vessels and interrupts blood flow. Other causes include stenosis of the aortic valve; cardiac tamponade, in which excess fluid in the pericardial cavity interferes with the ability of the heart to fully relax and fill with blood (resulting in decreased preload); and a pneumothorax, in which an excessive amount of air is present in the thoracic cavity, outside of the lungs, which interferes with venous return, pulmonary function, and delivery of oxygen to the tissues.

20.5 Circulatory Pathways

LEARNING OBJECTIVES

By the end of this section, you will be able to:
- Identify the vessels through which blood travels within the pulmonary circuit, beginning from the right ventricle of the heart and ending at the left atrium
- Create a flow chart showing the major systemic arteries through which blood travels from the aorta and its major branches, to the most significant arteries feeding into the right and left upper and lower limbs
- Create a flow chart showing the major systemic veins through which blood travels from the feet to the right atrium of the heart

Virtually every cell, tissue, organ, and system in the body is impacted by the circulatory system. This includes the generalized and more specialized functions of transport of materials, capillary exchange, maintaining health by transporting white blood cells and various immunoglobulins (antibodies), hemostasis, regulation of body temperature, and helping to maintain acid-base balance. In addition to these shared functions, many systems enjoy a unique relationship with the circulatory system. Figure 20.22 summarizes these relationships.

System	Role of Circulatory System
Digestive 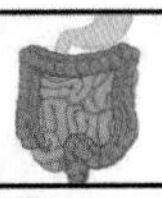	Absorbs nutrients and water; delivers nutrients (except most lipids) to liver for processing by hepatic portal vein; provides nutrients essential for hematopoiesis and building hemoglobin
Endocrine 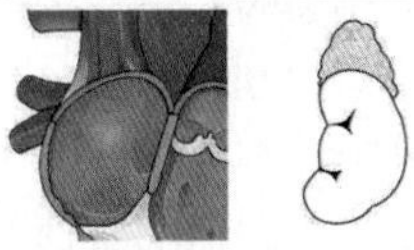	Delivers hormones: atrial natriuretic hormone (peptide) secreted by the heart atrial cells to help regulate blood volumes and pressures; epinephrine, ANH, angiotensin II, ADH, and thyroxine to help regulate blood pressure; estrogen to promote vascular health in women and men
Integumentary 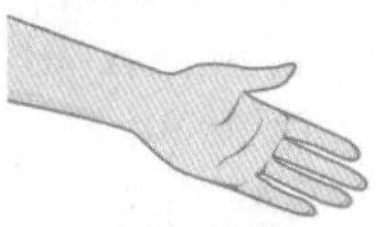	Carries clotting factors, platelets, and white blood cells for hemostasis, fighting infection, and repairing damage; regulates temperature by controlling blood flow to the surface, where heat can be dissipated; provides some coloration of integument; acts as a blood reservoir
Lymphatic 	Transports various white blood cells, including those produced by lymphatic tissue, and immunoglobulins (antibodies) throughout the body to maintain health; carries excess tissue fluid not able to be reabsorbed by the vascular capillaries back to the lymphatic system for processing
Muscular 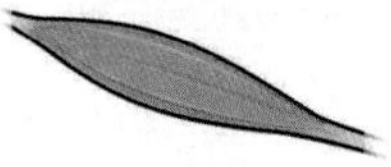	Provides nutrients and oxygen for contraction; removes lactic acid and distributes heat generated by contraction; muscular pumps aid in venous return; exercise contributes to cardiovascular health and helps to prevent atherosclerosis
Nervous 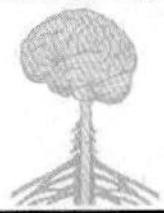	Produces cerebrospinal fluid (CSF) within choroid plexuses; contributes to blood–brain barrier; cardiac and vasomotor centers regulate cardiac output and blood flow through vessels via autonomic system
Reproductive 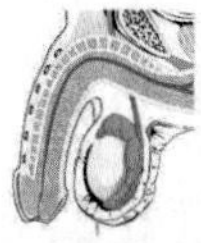	Aids in erection of genitalia in both sexes during sexual arousal; transports gonadotropic hormones that regulate reproductive functions
Respiratory 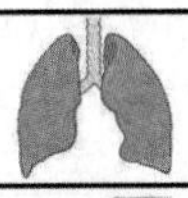	Provides blood for critical exchange of gases to carry oxygen needed for metabolic reactions and carbon dioxide generated as byproducts of these processes
Skeletal 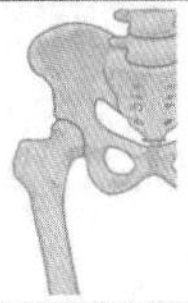	Provides calcium, phosphate, and other minerals critical for bone matrix; transports hormones regulating buildup and absorption of matrix including growth hormone (somatotropin), thyroid hormone, calcitonins, and parathyroid hormone; erythropoietin stimulates myeloid cell hematopoiesis; some level of protection for select vessels by bony structures
Urinary 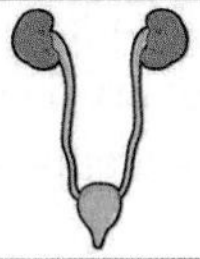	Delivers 20% of resting circulation to kidneys for filtering, reabsorption of useful products, and secretion of excesses; regulates blood volume and pressure by regulating fluid loss in the form of urine and by releasing the enzyme renin that is essential in the renin-angiotensin-aldosterone mechanism

FIGURE 20.22   Interaction of the Circulatory System with Other Body Systems

As you learn about the vessels of the systemic and pulmonary circuits, notice that many arteries and veins share the same names, parallel one another throughout the body, and are very similar on the right and left sides of the body. These pairs of vessels will be traced through only one side of the body. Where differences occur in branching patterns or when vessels are singular, this will be indicated. For example, you will find a pair of femoral arteries and a pair of femoral veins, with one vessel on each side of the body. In contrast, some vessels closer to the midline of the body, such as the aorta, are unique. Moreover, some superficial veins, such as the great saphenous vein in the femoral region, have no arterial counterpart. Another phenomenon that can make the study of vessels challenging is that names of vessels can change with location. Like a street that changes name as it passes through an intersection, an artery or vein can change names as it passes an anatomical landmark. For example, the left subclavian artery becomes the axillary artery as it passes through the body wall and into the axillary region, and then becomes the brachial artery as it flows from the axillary region into the upper arm (or brachium). You will also find examples of anastomoses where two blood vessels that previously branched reconnect. Anastomoses are especially common in veins, where they help maintain blood flow even when one vessel is blocked or narrowed, although there are some important ones in the arteries supplying the brain.

As you read about circular pathways, notice that there is an occasional, very large artery referred to as a **trunk**, a term indicating that the vessel gives rise to several smaller arteries. For example, the celiac trunk gives rise to the left gastric, common hepatic, and splenic arteries.

As you study this section, imagine you are on a "Voyage of Discovery" similar to Lewis and Clark's expedition in 1804–1806, which followed rivers and streams through unfamiliar territory, seeking a water route from the Atlantic to the Pacific Ocean. You might envision being inside a miniature boat, exploring the various branches of the circulatory system. This simple approach has proven effective for many students in mastering these major circulatory patterns. Another approach that works well for many students is to create simple line drawings similar to the ones provided, labeling each of the major vessels. It is beyond the scope of this text to name every vessel in the body. However, we will attempt to discuss the major pathways for blood and acquaint you with the major named arteries and veins in the body. Also, please keep in mind that individual variations in circulation patterns are not uncommon.

⊘ INTERACTIVE LINK

Visit this site (http://openstax.org/l/arts1) for a brief summary of the arteries.

Pulmonary Circulation

Recall that blood returning from the systemic circuit enters the right atrium (Figure 20.23) via the superior and inferior venae cavae and the coronary sinus, which drains the blood supply of the heart muscle. These vessels will be described more fully later in this section. This blood is relatively low in oxygen and relatively high in carbon dioxide, since much of the oxygen has been extracted for use by the tissues and the waste gas carbon dioxide was picked up to be transported to the lungs for elimination. From the right atrium, blood moves into the right ventricle, which pumps it to the lungs for gas exchange. This system of vessels is referred to as the **pulmonary circuit**.

The single vessel exiting the right ventricle is the **pulmonary trunk**. At the base of the pulmonary trunk is the pulmonary semilunar valve, which prevents backflow of blood into the right ventricle during ventricular diastole. As the pulmonary trunk reaches the superior surface of the heart, it curves posteriorly and rapidly bifurcates (divides) into two branches, a left and a right **pulmonary artery**. To prevent confusion between these vessels, it is important to refer to the vessel exiting the heart as the pulmonary trunk, rather than also calling it a pulmonary artery. The pulmonary arteries in turn branch many times within the lung, forming a series of smaller arteries and arterioles that eventually lead to the pulmonary capillaries. The pulmonary capillaries surround lung structures known as alveoli that are the sites of oxygen and carbon dioxide exchange.

Once gas exchange is completed, oxygenated blood flows from the pulmonary capillaries into a series of pulmonary venules that eventually lead to a series of larger **pulmonary veins**. Four pulmonary veins, two on the left and two on the right, return blood to the left atrium. At this point, the pulmonary circuit is complete. Table 20.4 defines the major arteries and veins of the pulmonary circuit discussed in the text.

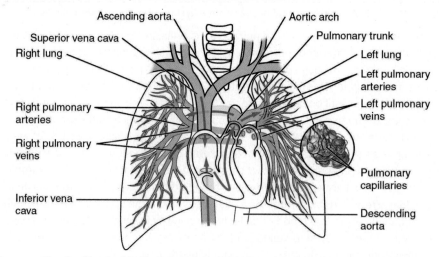

FIGURE 20.23 Pulmonary Circuit   Blood exiting from the right ventricle flows into the pulmonary trunk, which bifurcates into the two

pulmonary arteries. These vessels branch to supply blood to the pulmonary capillaries, where gas exchange occurs within the lung alveoli. Blood returns via the pulmonary veins to the left atrium.

Pulmonary Arteries and Veins

Vessel	Description
Pulmonary trunk	Single large vessel exiting the right ventricle that divides to form the right and left pulmonary arteries
Pulmonary arteries	Left and right vessels that form from the pulmonary trunk and lead to smaller arterioles and eventually to the pulmonary capillaries
Pulmonary veins	Two sets of paired vessels—one pair on each side—that are formed from the small venules, leading away from the pulmonary capillaries to flow into the left atrium

TABLE 20.4

Overview of Systemic Arteries

Blood relatively high in oxygen concentration is returned from the pulmonary circuit to the left atrium via the four pulmonary veins. From the left atrium, blood moves into the left ventricle, which pumps blood into the aorta. The aorta and its branches—the systemic arteries—send blood to virtually every organ of the body (Figure 20.24).

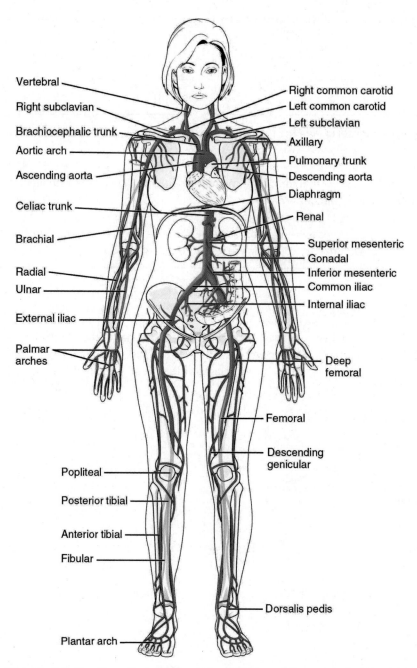

FIGURE 20.24 Systemic Arteries The major systemic arteries shown here deliver oxygenated blood throughout the body.

The Aorta

The **aorta** is the largest artery in the body (Figure 20.25). It arises from the left ventricle and eventually descends to the abdominal region, where it bifurcates at the level of the fourth lumbar vertebra into the two common iliac arteries. The aorta consists of the ascending aorta, the aortic arch, and the descending aorta, which passes through the diaphragm and a landmark that divides into the superior thoracic and inferior abdominal components. Arteries originating from the aorta ultimately distribute blood to virtually all tissues of the body. At the base of the aorta is the aortic semilunar valve that prevents backflow of blood into the left ventricle while the heart is relaxing. After exiting the heart, the **ascending aorta** moves in a superior direction for approximately 5 cm and ends at the sternal angle. Following this ascent, it reverses direction, forming a graceful arc to the left, called the **aortic arch**. The aortic arch descends toward the inferior portions of the body and ends at the level of the intervertebral disk between the fourth and fifth thoracic vertebrae. Beyond this point, the **descending aorta** continues close to the bodies of the vertebrae and passes through an opening in the diaphragm known as the **aortic hiatus**. Superior to the diaphragm, the aorta is called the **thoracic aorta**, and inferior to the diaphragm, it is called the **abdominal aorta**. The abdominal aorta terminates when it bifurcates into the two common iliac arteries at the level of the fourth lumbar vertebra. See Figure 20.25 for an illustration of the ascending aorta, the aortic arch, and the initial segment of the descending aorta plus major branches; Table 20.5 summarizes the structures of the aorta.

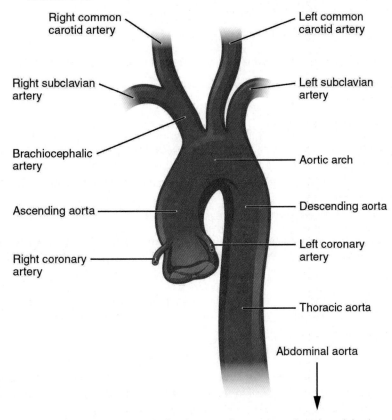

FIGURE 20.25   Aorta   The aorta has distinct regions, including the ascending aorta, aortic arch, and the descending aorta, which includes the thoracic and abdominal regions.

Components of the Aorta

Vessel	Description
Aorta	Largest artery in the body, originating from the left ventricle and descending to the abdominal region, where it bifurcates into the common iliac arteries at the level of the fourth lumbar vertebra; arteries originating from the aorta distribute blood to virtually all tissues of the body
Ascending aorta	Initial portion of the aorta, rising superiorly from the left ventricle for a distance of approximately 5 cm
Aortic arch	Graceful arc to the left that connects the ascending aorta to the descending aorta; ends at the intervertebral disk between the fourth and fifth thoracic vertebrae
Descending aorta	Portion of the aorta that continues inferiorly past the end of the aortic arch; subdivided into the thoracic aorta and the abdominal aorta

TABLE 20.5

Vessel	Description
Thoracic aorta	Portion of the descending aorta superior to the aortic hiatus
Abdominal aorta	Portion of the aorta inferior to the aortic hiatus and superior to the common iliac arteries

TABLE 20.5

Coronary Circulation

The first vessels that branch from the ascending aorta are the paired coronary arteries (see Figure 20.25), which arise from two of the three sinuses in the ascending aorta just superior to the aortic semilunar valve. These sinuses contain the aortic baroreceptors and chemoreceptors critical to maintain cardiac function. The left coronary artery arises from the left posterior aortic sinus. The right coronary artery arises from the anterior aortic sinus. Normally, the right posterior aortic sinus does not give rise to a vessel.

The coronary arteries encircle the heart, forming a ring-like structure that divides into the next level of branches that supplies blood to the heart tissues. (Seek additional content for more detail on cardiac circulation.)

Aortic Arch Branches

There are three major branches of the aortic arch: the brachiocephalic artery, the left common carotid artery, and the left subclavian (literally "under the clavicle") artery. As you would expect based upon proximity to the heart, each of these vessels is classified as an elastic artery.

The brachiocephalic artery is located only on the right side of the body; there is no corresponding artery on the left. The brachiocephalic artery branches into the right subclavian artery and the right common carotid artery. The left subclavian and left common carotid arteries arise independently from the aortic arch but otherwise follow a similar pattern and distribution to the corresponding arteries on the right side (see Figure 20.23).

Each **subclavian artery** supplies blood to the arms, chest, shoulders, back, and central nervous system. It then gives rise to three major branches: the internal thoracic artery, the vertebral artery, and the thyrocervical artery. The **internal thoracic artery**, or mammary artery, supplies blood to the thymus, the pericardium of the heart, and the anterior chest wall. The **vertebral artery** passes through the vertebral foramen in the cervical vertebrae and then through the foramen magnum into the cranial cavity to supply blood to the brain and spinal cord. The paired vertebral arteries join together to form the large basilar artery at the base of the medulla oblongata. This is an example of an anastomosis. The subclavian artery also gives rise to the **thyrocervical artery** that provides blood to the thyroid, the cervical region of the neck, and the upper back and shoulder.

The **common carotid artery** divides into internal and external carotid arteries. The right common carotid artery arises from the brachiocephalic artery and the left common carotid artery arises directly from the aortic arch. The **external carotid artery** supplies blood to numerous structures within the face, lower jaw, neck, esophagus, and larynx. These branches include the lingual, facial, occipital, maxillary, and superficial temporal arteries. The **internal carotid artery** initially forms an expansion known as the carotid sinus, containing the carotid baroreceptors and chemoreceptors. Like their counterparts in the aortic sinuses, the information provided by these receptors is critical to maintaining cardiovascular homeostasis (see Figure 20.23).

The internal carotid arteries along with the vertebral arteries are the two primary suppliers of blood to the human brain. Given the central role and vital importance of the brain to life, it is critical that blood supply to this organ remains uninterrupted. Recall that blood flow to the brain is remarkably constant, with approximately 20 percent of blood flow directed to this organ at any given time. When blood flow is interrupted, even for just a few seconds, a **transient ischemic attack (TIA)**, or mini-stroke, may occur, resulting in loss of consciousness or temporary loss of neurological function. In some cases, the damage may be permanent. Loss of blood flow for longer periods, typically between 3 and 4 minutes, will likely produce irreversible brain damage or a stroke, also called a **cerebrovascular accident (CVA)**. The locations of the arteries in the brain not only provide blood flow to the brain tissue but also prevent interruption in the flow of blood. Both the carotid and vertebral arteries branch once they enter the cranial cavity, and some of these branches form a structure known as the **arterial circle** (or **circle of Willis**), an anastomosis that is remarkably like a traffic circle that sends off branches (in this case, arterial branches to the brain). As a rule, branches to the anterior portion of the cerebrum are normally fed by the internal carotid arteries; the remainder of the brain receives blood flow from branches associated with the vertebral arteries.

The internal carotid artery continues through the carotid canal of the temporal bone and enters the base of the brain through the carotid foramen where it gives rise to several branches (Figure 20.26 and Figure 20.27). One of these branches is the **anterior cerebral artery** that supplies blood to the frontal lobe of the cerebrum. Another branch, the **middle cerebral artery**, supplies blood to the temporal and parietal lobes, which are the most common sites of CVAs. The **ophthalmic artery**, the third major branch, provides blood to the eyes.

The right and left anterior cerebral arteries join together to form an anastomosis called the **anterior communicating artery**. The initial segments of the anterior cerebral arteries and the anterior communicating artery form the anterior portion of the arterial circle. The posterior portion of the arterial circle is formed by a left and a right **posterior communicating artery** that branches from the **posterior cerebral artery**, which arises from the basilar artery. It provides blood to the posterior portion of the cerebrum and brain stem. The **basilar artery** is an anastomosis that begins at the junction of the two vertebral arteries and sends branches to the cerebellum and brain stem. It flows into the posterior cerebral arteries. Table 20.6 summarizes the aortic arch branches, including the major branches supplying the brain.

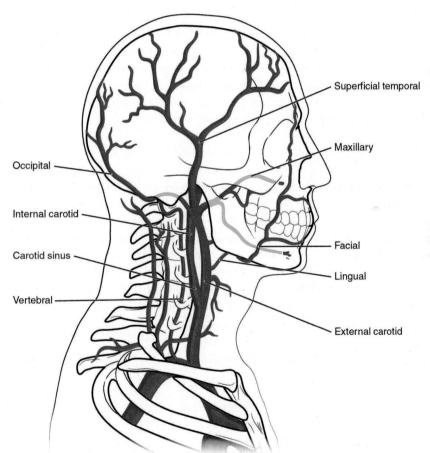

FIGURE 20.26   Arteries Supplying the Head and Neck   The common carotid artery gives rise to the external and internal carotid arteries. The external carotid artery remains superficial and gives rise to many arteries of the head. The internal carotid artery first forms the carotid sinus and then reaches the brain via the carotid canal and carotid foramen, emerging into the cranium via the foramen lacerum. The vertebral artery branches from the subclavian artery and passes through the transverse foramen in the cervical vertebrae, entering the base of the skull at the vertebral foramen. The subclavian artery continues toward the arm as the axillary artery.

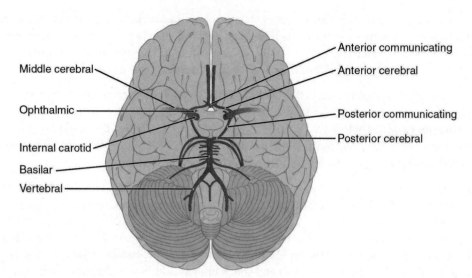

FIGURE 20.27 Arteries Serving the Brain This inferior view shows the network of arteries serving the brain. The structure is referred to as the arterial circle or circle of Willis.

Aortic Arch Branches and Brain Circulation

Vessel	Description
Brachiocephalic artery	Single vessel located on the right side of the body; the first vessel branching from the aortic arch; gives rise to the right subclavian artery and the right common carotid artery; supplies blood to the head, neck, upper limb, and wall of the thoracic region
Subclavian artery	The right subclavian artery arises from the brachiocephalic artery while the left subclavian artery arises from the aortic arch; gives rise to the internal thoracic, vertebral, and thyrocervical arteries; supplies blood to the arms, chest, shoulders, back, and central nervous system
Internal thoracic artery	Also called the mammary artery; arises from the subclavian artery; supplies blood to the thymus, pericardium of the heart, and anterior chest wall
Vertebral artery	Arises from the subclavian artery and passes through the vertebral foramen through the foramen magnum to the brain; joins with the internal carotid artery to form the arterial circle; supplies blood to the brain and spinal cord
Thyrocervical artery	Arises from the subclavian artery; supplies blood to the thyroid, the cervical region, the upper back, and shoulder
Common carotid artery	The right common carotid artery arises from the brachiocephalic artery and the left common carotid artery arises from the aortic arch; each gives rise to the external and internal carotid arteries; supplies the respective sides of the head and neck
External carotid artery	Arises from the common carotid artery; supplies blood to numerous structures within the face, lower jaw, neck, esophagus, and larynx

TABLE 20.6

Vessel	Description
Internal carotid artery	Arises from the common carotid artery and begins with the carotid sinus; goes through the carotid canal of the temporal bone to the base of the brain; combines with the branches of the vertebral artery, forming the arterial circle; supplies blood to the brain
Arterial circle or circle of Willis	An anastomosis located at the base of the brain that ensures continual blood supply; formed from the branches of the internal carotid and vertebral arteries; supplies blood to the brain
Anterior cerebral artery	Arises from the internal carotid artery; supplies blood to the frontal lobe of the cerebrum
Middle cerebral artery	Another branch of the internal carotid artery; supplies blood to the temporal and parietal lobes of the cerebrum
Ophthalmic artery	Branch of the internal carotid artery; supplies blood to the eyes
Anterior communicating artery	An anastomosis of the right and left internal carotid arteries; supplies blood to the brain
Posterior communicating artery	Branches of the posterior cerebral artery that form part of the posterior portion of the arterial circle; supplies blood to the brain
Posterior cerebral artery	Branch of the basilar artery that forms a portion of the posterior segment of the arterial circle of Willis; supplies blood to the posterior portion of the cerebrum and brain stem
Basilar artery	Formed from the fusion of the two vertebral arteries; sends branches to the cerebellum, brain stem, and the posterior cerebral arteries; the main blood supply to the brain stem

TABLE 20.6

Thoracic Aorta and Major Branches

The thoracic aorta begins at the level of vertebra T5 and continues through to the diaphragm at the level of T12, initially traveling within the mediastinum to the left of the vertebral column. As it passes through the thoracic region, the thoracic aorta gives rise to several branches, which are collectively referred to as visceral branches and parietal branches (Figure 20.28). Those branches that supply blood primarily to visceral organs are known as the **visceral branches** and include the bronchial arteries, pericardial arteries, esophageal arteries, and the mediastinal arteries, each named after the tissues it supplies. Each **bronchial artery** (typically two on the left and one on the right) supplies systemic blood to the lungs and visceral pleura, in addition to the blood pumped to the lungs for oxygenation via the pulmonary circuit. The bronchial arteries follow the same path as the respiratory branches, beginning with the bronchi and ending with the bronchioles. There is considerable, but not total, intermingling of the systemic and pulmonary blood at anastomoses in the smaller branches of the lungs. This may sound incongruous—that is, the mixing of systemic arterial blood high in oxygen with the pulmonary arterial blood lower in oxygen—but the systemic vessels also deliver nutrients to the lung tissue just as they do elsewhere in the body. The mixed blood drains into typical pulmonary veins, whereas the bronchial artery branches remain separate and drain into bronchial veins described later. Each **pericardial artery** supplies blood to the pericardium, the **esophageal artery** provides blood to the esophagus, and the **mediastinal artery** provides blood to the mediastinum. The remaining thoracic aorta branches are collectively referred to as **parietal branches** or somatic branches, and include the intercostal and superior phrenic arteries. Each **intercostal artery** provides blood to the muscles of the thoracic cavity and vertebral column. The **superior phrenic artery** provides blood to the superior surface of the diaphragm. Table 20.7 lists the arteries of the thoracic region.

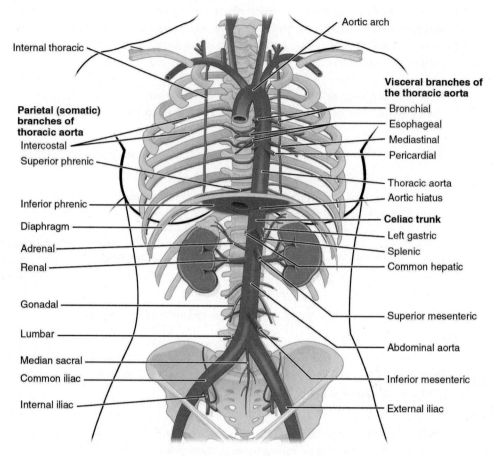

FIGURE 20.28   Arteries of the Thoracic and Abdominal Regions   The thoracic aorta gives rise to the arteries of the visceral and parietal branches.

Arteries of the Thoracic Region

Vessel	Description
Visceral branches	A group of arterial branches of the thoracic aorta; supplies blood to the viscera (i.e., organs) of the thorax
Bronchial artery	Systemic branch from the aorta that provides oxygenated blood to the lungs; this blood supply is in addition to the pulmonary circuit that brings blood for oxygenation
Pericardial artery	Branch of the thoracic aorta; supplies blood to the pericardium
Esophageal artery	Branch of the thoracic aorta; supplies blood to the esophagus
Mediastinal artery	Branch of the thoracic aorta; supplies blood to the mediastinum

TABLE 20.7

Vessel	Description
Parietal branches	Also called somatic branches, a group of arterial branches of the thoracic aorta; include those that supply blood to the thoracic wall, vertebral column, and the superior surface of the diaphragm
Intercostal artery	Branch of the thoracic aorta; supplies blood to the muscles of the thoracic cavity and vertebral column
Superior phrenic artery	Branch of the thoracic aorta; supplies blood to the superior surface of the diaphragm

TABLE 20.7

Abdominal Aorta and Major Branches

After crossing through the diaphragm at the aortic hiatus, the thoracic aorta is called the abdominal aorta (see Figure 20.28). This vessel remains to the left of the vertebral column and is embedded in adipose tissue behind the peritoneal cavity. It formally ends at approximately the level of vertebra L4, where it bifurcates to form the common iliac arteries. Before this division, the abdominal aorta gives rise to several important branches. A single **celiac trunk** (artery) emerges and divides into the **left gastric artery** to supply blood to the stomach and esophagus, the **splenic artery** to supply blood to the spleen, and the **common hepatic artery**, which in turn gives rise to the **hepatic artery proper** to supply blood to the liver, the **right gastric artery** to supply blood to the stomach, the **cystic artery** to supply blood to the gall bladder, and several branches, one to supply blood to the duodenum and another to supply blood to the pancreas. Two additional single vessels arise from the abdominal aorta. These are the superior and inferior mesenteric arteries. The **superior mesenteric artery** arises approximately 2.5 cm after the celiac trunk and branches into several major vessels that supply blood to the small intestine (duodenum, jejunum, and ileum), the pancreas, and a majority of the large intestine. The **inferior mesenteric artery** supplies blood to the distal segment of the large intestine, including the rectum. It arises approximately 5 cm superior to the common iliac arteries.

In addition to these single branches, the abdominal aorta gives rise to several significant paired arteries along the way. These include the inferior phrenic arteries, the adrenal arteries, the renal arteries, the gonadal arteries, and the lumbar arteries. Each **inferior phrenic artery** is a counterpart of a superior phrenic artery and supplies blood to the inferior surface of the diaphragm. The **adrenal artery** supplies blood to the adrenal (suprarenal) glands and arises near the superior mesenteric artery. Each **renal artery** branches approximately 2.5 cm inferior to the superior mesenteric arteries and supplies a kidney. The right renal artery is longer than the left since the aorta lies to the left of the vertebral column and the vessel must travel a greater distance to reach its target. Renal arteries branch repeatedly to supply blood to the kidneys. Each **gonadal artery** supplies blood to the gonads, or reproductive organs, and is also described as either an ovarian artery or a testicular artery (internal spermatic), depending upon the sex of the individual. An **ovarian artery** supplies blood to an ovary, uterine (Fallopian) tube, and the uterus, and is located within the suspensory ligament of the uterus. It is considerably shorter than a **testicular artery**, which ultimately travels outside the body cavity to the testes, forming one component of the spermatic cord. The gonadal arteries arise inferior to the renal arteries and are generally retroperitoneal. The ovarian artery continues to the uterus where it forms an anastomosis with the uterine artery that supplies blood to the uterus. Both the uterine arteries and vaginal arteries, which distribute blood to the vagina, are branches of the internal iliac artery. The four paired **lumbar arteries** are the counterparts of the intercostal arteries and supply blood to the lumbar region, the abdominal wall, and the spinal cord. In some instances, a fifth pair of lumbar arteries emerges from the median sacral artery.

The aorta divides at approximately the level of vertebra L4 into a left and a right **common iliac artery** but continues as a small vessel, the **median sacral artery**, into the sacrum. The common iliac arteries provide blood to the pelvic region and ultimately to the lower limbs. They split into external and internal iliac arteries approximately at the level of the lumbar-sacral articulation. Each **internal iliac artery** sends branches to the urinary bladder, the walls of the pelvis, the external genitalia, and the medial portion of the femoral region. In females, they also provide blood to the uterus and vagina. The much larger **external iliac artery** supplies blood to each of the lower limbs. Figure 20.29 shows the distribution of the major branches of the aorta into the thoracic and abdominal regions. Figure 20.30 shows the distribution of the major branches of the common iliac arteries. Table 20.8 summarizes the major branches of the abdominal aorta.

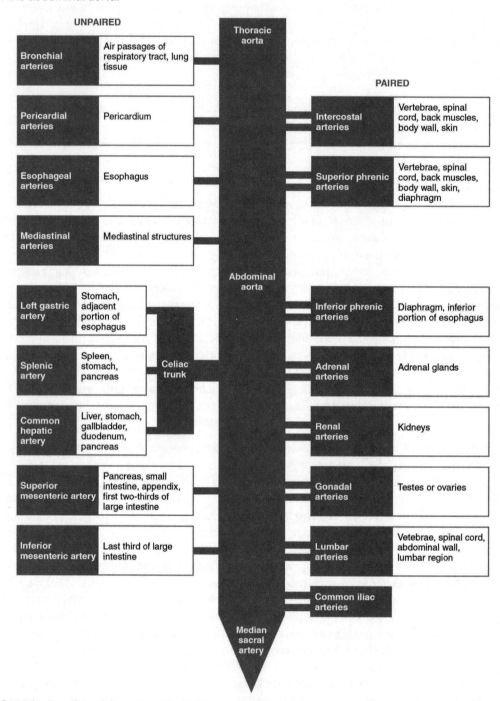

FIGURE 20.29 Major Branches of the Aorta   The flow chart summarizes the distribution of the major branches of the aorta into the thoracic and abdominal regions.

Access for free at openstax.org

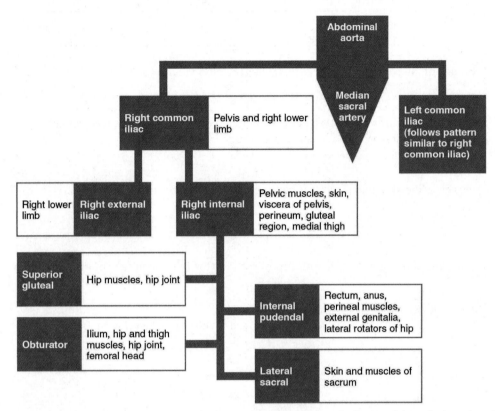

FIGURE 20.30 Major Branches of the Iliac Arteries The flow chart summarizes the distribution of the major branches of the common iliac arteries into the pelvis and lower limbs. The left side follows a similar pattern to the right.

Vessels of the Abdominal Aorta

Vessel	Description
Celiac trunk	Also called the celiac artery; a major branch of the abdominal aorta; gives rise to the left gastric artery, the splenic artery, and the common hepatic artery that forms the hepatic artery to the liver, the right gastric artery to the stomach, and the cystic artery to the gall bladder
Left gastric artery	Branch of the celiac trunk; supplies blood to the stomach
Splenic artery	Branch of the celiac trunk; supplies blood to the spleen
Common hepatic artery	Branch of the celiac trunk that forms the hepatic artery, the right gastric artery, and the cystic artery
Hepatic artery proper	Branch of the common hepatic artery; supplies systemic blood to the liver
Right gastric artery	Branch of the common hepatic artery; supplies blood to the stomach

TABLE 20.8

Vessel	Description
Cystic artery	Branch of the common hepatic artery; supplies blood to the gall bladder
Superior mesenteric artery	Branch of the abdominal aorta; supplies blood to the small intestine (duodenum, jejunum, and ileum), the pancreas, and a majority of the large intestine
Inferior mesenteric artery	Branch of the abdominal aorta; supplies blood to the distal segment of the large intestine and rectum
Inferior phrenic arteries	Branches of the abdominal aorta; supply blood to the inferior surface of the diaphragm
Adrenal artery	Branch of the abdominal aorta; supplies blood to the adrenal (suprarenal) glands
Renal artery	Branch of the abdominal aorta; supplies each kidney
Gonadal artery	Branch of the abdominal aorta; supplies blood to the gonads or reproductive organs; also described as ovarian arteries or testicular arteries, depending upon the sex of the individual
Ovarian artery	Branch of the abdominal aorta; supplies blood to ovary, uterine (Fallopian) tube, and uterus
Testicular artery	Branch of the abdominal aorta; ultimately travels outside the body cavity to the testes and forms one component of the spermatic cord
Lumbar arteries	Branches of the abdominal aorta; supply blood to the lumbar region, the abdominal wall, and spinal cord
Common iliac artery	Branch of the aorta that leads to the internal and external iliac arteries
Median sacral artery	Continuation of the aorta into the sacrum
Internal iliac artery	Branch from the common iliac arteries; supplies blood to the urinary bladder, walls of the pelvis, external genitalia, and the medial portion of the femoral region; in females, also provides blood to the uterus and vagina
External iliac artery	Branch of the common iliac artery that leaves the body cavity and becomes a femoral artery; supplies blood to the lower limbs

TABLE 20.8

Access for free at openstax.org

Arteries Serving the Upper Limbs

As the subclavian artery exits the thorax into the axillary region, it is renamed the **axillary artery**. Although it does branch and supply blood to the region near the head of the humerus (via the humeral circumflex arteries), the majority of the vessel continues into the upper arm, or brachium, and becomes the brachial artery (Figure 20.31). The **brachial artery** supplies blood to much of the brachial region and divides at the elbow into several smaller branches, including the deep brachial arteries, which provide blood to the posterior surface of the arm, and the ulnar collateral arteries, which supply blood to the region of the elbow. As the brachial artery approaches the coronoid fossa, it bifurcates into the radial and ulnar arteries, which continue into the forearm, or antebrachium. The **radial artery** and **ulnar artery** parallel their namesake bones, giving off smaller branches until they reach the wrist, or carpal region. At this level, they fuse to form the superficial and deep **palmar arches** that supply blood to the hand, as well as the **digital arteries** that supply blood to the digits. Figure 20.32 shows the distribution of systemic arteries from the heart into the upper limb. Table 20.9 summarizes the arteries serving the upper limbs.

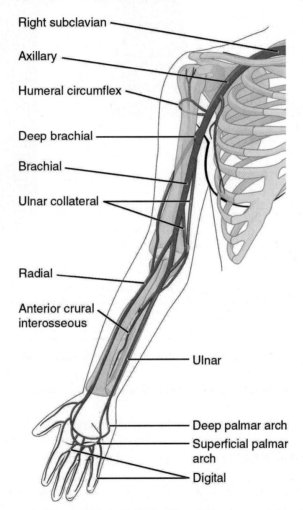

FIGURE 20.31   Major Arteries Serving the Thorax and Upper Limb   The arteries that supply blood to the arms and hands are extensions of the subclavian arteries.

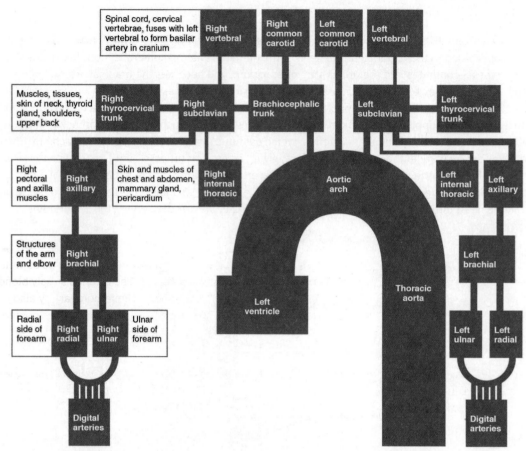

FIGURE 20.32   Major Arteries of the Upper Limb   The flow chart summarizes the distribution of the major arteries from the heart into the upper limb.

Arteries Serving the Upper Limbs

Vessel	Description
Axillary artery	Continuation of the subclavian artery as it penetrates the body wall and enters the axillary region; supplies blood to the region near the head of the humerus (humeral circumflex arteries); the majority of the vessel continues into the brachium and becomes the brachial artery
Brachial artery	Continuation of the axillary artery in the brachium; supplies blood to much of the brachial region; gives off several smaller branches that provide blood to the posterior surface of the arm in the region of the elbow; bifurcates into the radial and ulnar arteries at the coronoid fossa
Radial artery	Formed at the bifurcation of the brachial artery; parallels the radius; gives off smaller branches until it reaches the carpal region where it fuses with the ulnar artery to form the superficial and deep palmar arches; supplies blood to the lower arm and carpal region
Ulnar artery	Formed at the bifurcation of the brachial artery; parallels the ulna; gives off smaller branches until it reaches the carpal region where it fuses with the radial artery to form the superficial and deep palmar arches; supplies blood to the lower arm and carpal region

TABLE 20.9

Vessel	Description
Palmar arches (superficial and deep)	Formed from anastomosis of the radial and ulnar arteries; supply blood to the hand and digital arteries
Digital arteries	Formed from the superficial and deep palmar arches; supply blood to the digits

TABLE 20.9

Arteries Serving the Lower Limbs

The external iliac artery exits the body cavity and enters the femoral region of the lower leg (Figure 20.33). As it passes through the body wall, it is renamed the **femoral artery**. It gives off several smaller branches as well as the lateral **deep femoral artery** that in turn gives rise to a **lateral circumflex artery**. These arteries supply blood to the deep muscles of the thigh as well as ventral and lateral regions of the integument. The femoral artery also gives rise to the **genicular artery**, which provides blood to the region of the knee. As the femoral artery passes posterior to the knee near the popliteal fossa, it is called the popliteal artery. The **popliteal artery** branches into the anterior and posterior tibial arteries.

The **anterior tibial artery** is located between the tibia and fibula, and supplies blood to the muscles and integument of the anterior tibial region. Upon reaching the tarsal region, it becomes the **dorsalis pedis artery**, which branches repeatedly and provides blood to the tarsal and dorsal regions of the foot. The **posterior tibial artery** provides blood to the muscles and integument on the posterior surface of the tibial region. The fibular or peroneal artery branches from the posterior tibial artery. It bifurcates and becomes the **medial plantar artery** and **lateral plantar artery**, providing blood to the plantar surfaces. There is an anastomosis with the dorsalis pedis artery, and the medial and lateral plantar arteries form two arches called the **dorsal arch** (also called the arcuate arch) and the **plantar arch**, which provide blood to the remainder of the foot and toes. Figure 20.34 shows the distribution of the major systemic arteries in the lower limb. Table 20.10 summarizes the major systemic arteries discussed in the text.

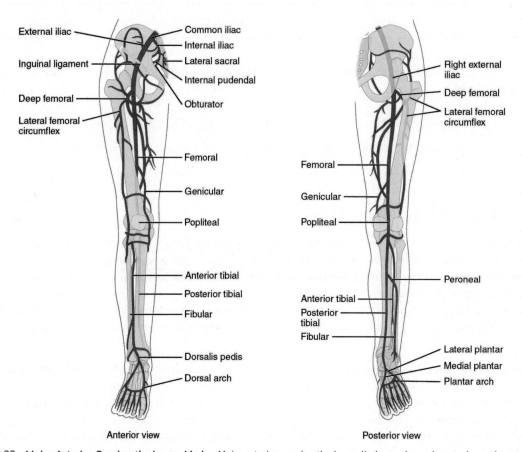

FIGURE 20.33 Major Arteries Serving the Lower Limb   Major arteries serving the lower limb are shown in anterior and posterior views.

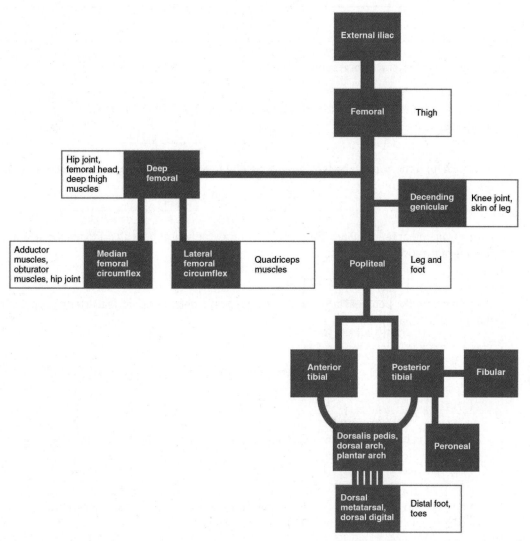

FIGURE 20.34 Systemic Arteries of the Lower Limb   The flow chart summarizes the distribution of the systemic arteries from the external iliac artery into the lower limb.

Arteries Serving the Lower Limbs

Vessel	Description
Femoral artery	Continuation of the external iliac artery after it passes through the body cavity; divides into several smaller branches, the lateral deep femoral artery, and the genicular artery; becomes the popliteal artery as it passes posterior to the knee
Deep femoral artery	Branch of the femoral artery; gives rise to the lateral circumflex arteries
Lateral circumflex artery	Branch of the deep femoral artery; supplies blood to the deep muscles of the thigh and the ventral and lateral regions of the integument

TABLE 20.10

Vessel	Description
Genicular artery	Branch of the femoral artery; supplies blood to the region of the knee
Popliteal artery	Continuation of the femoral artery posterior to the knee; branches into the anterior and posterior tibial arteries
Anterior tibial artery	Branches from the popliteal artery; supplies blood to the anterior tibial region; becomes the dorsalis pedis artery
Dorsalis pedis artery	Forms from the anterior tibial artery; branches repeatedly to supply blood to the tarsal and dorsal regions of the foot
Posterior tibial artery	Branches from the popliteal artery and gives rise to the fibular or peroneal artery; supplies blood to the posterior tibial region
Medial plantar artery	Arises from the bifurcation of the posterior tibial arteries; supplies blood to the medial plantar surfaces of the foot
Lateral plantar artery	Arises from the bifurcation of the posterior tibial arteries; supplies blood to the lateral plantar surfaces of the foot
Dorsal or arcuate arch	Formed from the anastomosis of the dorsalis pedis artery and the medial and plantar arteries; branches supply the distal portions of the foot and digits
Plantar arch	Formed from the anastomosis of the dorsalis pedis artery and the medial and plantar arteries; branches supply the distal portions of the foot and digits

TABLE 20.10

Overview of Systemic Veins

Systemic veins return blood to the right atrium. Since the blood has already passed through the systemic capillaries, it will be relatively low in oxygen concentration. In many cases, there will be veins draining organs and regions of the body with the same name as the arteries that supplied these regions and the two often parallel one another. This is often described as a "complementary" pattern. However, there is a great deal more variability in the venous circulation than normally occurs in the arteries. For the sake of brevity and clarity, this text will discuss only the most commonly encountered patterns. However, keep this variation in mind when you move from the classroom to clinical practice.

In both the neck and limb regions, there are often both superficial and deeper levels of veins. The deeper veins generally correspond to the complementary arteries. The superficial veins do not normally have direct arterial counterparts, but in addition to returning blood, they also make contributions to the maintenance of body temperature. When the ambient temperature is warm, more blood is diverted to the superficial veins where heat can be more easily dissipated to the environment. In colder weather, there is more constriction of the superficial veins and blood is diverted deeper where the body can retain more of the heat.

Access for free at openstax.org

The "Voyage of Discovery" analogy and stick drawings mentioned earlier remain valid techniques for the study of systemic veins, but veins present a more difficult challenge because there are numerous anastomoses and multiple branches. It is like following a river with many tributaries and channels, several of which interconnect. Tracing blood flow through arteries follows the current in the direction of blood flow, so that we move from the heart through the large arteries and into the smaller arteries to the capillaries. From the capillaries, we move into the smallest veins and follow the direction of blood flow into larger veins and back to the heart. Figure 20.35 outlines the path of the major systemic veins.

INTERACTIVE LINK

Visit this site (http://openstax.org/l/veinsum) for a brief online summary of the veins.

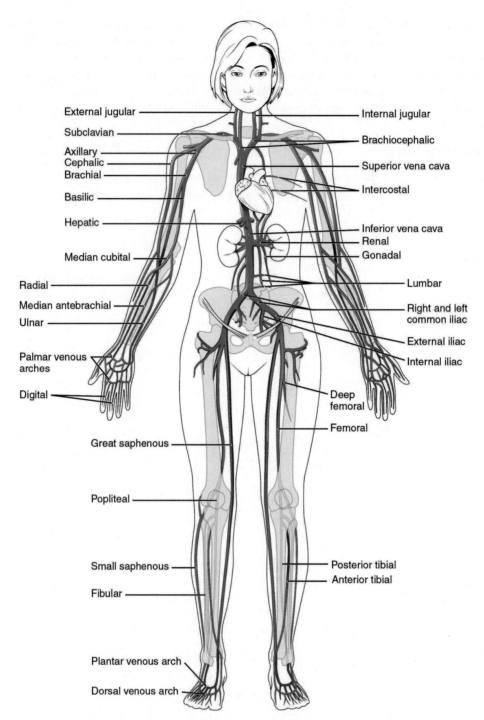

FIGURE 20.35 Major Systemic Veins of the Body   The major systemic veins of the body are shown here in an anterior view.

The right atrium receives all of the systemic venous return. Most of the blood flows into either the superior vena cava or inferior vena cava. If you draw an imaginary line at the level of the diaphragm, systemic venous circulation from above that line will generally flow into the superior vena cava; this includes blood from the head, neck, chest, shoulders, and upper limbs. The exception to this is that most venous blood flow from the coronary veins flows directly into the coronary sinus and from there directly into the right atrium. Beneath the diaphragm, systemic venous flow enters the inferior vena cava, that is, blood from the abdominal and pelvic regions and the lower limbs.

The Superior Vena Cava

The **superior vena cava** drains most of the body superior to the diaphragm ([Figure 20.36]). On both the left and right sides, the **subclavian vein** forms when the axillary vein passes through the body wall from the axillary region. It fuses with the external and internal jugular veins from the head and neck to form the **brachiocephalic vein**. Each

vertebral vein also flows into the brachiocephalic vein close to this fusion. These veins arise from the base of the brain and the cervical region of the spinal cord, and flow largely through the intervertebral foramina in the cervical vertebrae. They are the counterparts of the vertebral arteries. Each **internal thoracic vein**, also known as an internal mammary vein, drains the anterior surface of the chest wall and flows into the brachiocephalic vein.

The remainder of the blood supply from the thorax drains into the azygos vein. Each **intercostal vein** drains muscles of the thoracic wall, each **esophageal vein** delivers blood from the inferior portions of the esophagus, each **bronchial vein** drains the systemic circulation from the lungs, and several smaller veins drain the mediastinal region. Bronchial veins carry approximately 13 percent of the blood that flows into the bronchial arteries; the remainder intermingles with the pulmonary circulation and returns to the heart via the pulmonary veins. These veins flow into the **azygos vein**, and with the smaller **hemiazygos vein** (hemi- = "half") on the left of the vertebral column, drain blood from the thoracic region. The hemiazygos vein does not drain directly into the superior vena cava but enters the brachiocephalic vein via the superior intercostal vein.

The azygos vein passes through the diaphragm from the thoracic cavity on the right side of the vertebral column and begins in the lumbar region of the thoracic cavity. It flows into the superior vena cava at approximately the level of T2, making a significant contribution to the flow of blood. It combines with the two large left and right brachiocephalic veins to form the superior vena cava.

Table 20.11 summarizes the veins of the thoracic region that flow into the superior vena cava.

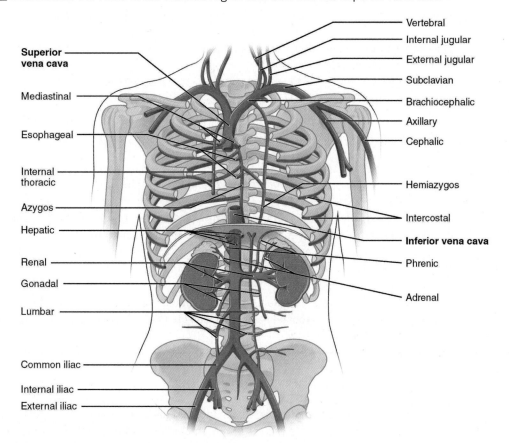

FIGURE 20.36   Veins of the Thoracic and Abdominal Regions   Veins of the thoracic and abdominal regions drain blood from the area above the diaphragm, returning it to the right atrium via the superior vena cava.

Veins of the Thoracic Region

Vessel	Description
Superior vena cava	Large systemic vein; drains blood from most areas superior to the diaphragm; empties into the right atrium
Subclavian vein	Located deep in the thoracic cavity; formed by the axillary vein as it enters the thoracic cavity from the axillary region; drains the axillary and smaller local veins near the scapular region and leads to the brachiocephalic vein
Brachiocephalic veins	Pair of veins that form from a fusion of the external and internal jugular veins and the subclavian vein; subclavian, external and internal jugulars, vertebral, and internal thoracic veins flow into it; drain the upper thoracic region and lead to the superior vena cava
Vertebral vein	Arises from the base of the brain and the cervical region of the spinal cord; passes through the intervertebral foramina in the cervical vertebrae; drains smaller veins from the cranium, spinal cord, and vertebrae, and leads to the brachiocephalic vein; counterpart of the vertebral artery
Internal thoracic veins	Also called internal mammary veins; drain the anterior surface of the chest wall and lead to the brachiocephalic vein
Intercostal vein	Drains the muscles of the thoracic wall and leads to the azygos vein
Esophageal vein	Drains the inferior portions of the esophagus and leads to the azygos vein
Bronchial vein	Drains the systemic circulation from the lungs and leads to the azygos vein
Azygos vein	Originates in the lumbar region and passes through the diaphragm into the thoracic cavity on the right side of the vertebral column; drains blood from the intercostal veins, esophageal veins, bronchial veins, and other veins draining the mediastinal region, and leads to the superior vena cava
Hemiazygos vein	Smaller vein complementary to the azygos vein; drains the esophageal veins from the esophagus and the left intercostal veins, and leads to the brachiocephalic vein via the superior intercostal vein

TABLE 20.11

Veins of the Head and Neck

Blood from the brain and the superficial facial vein flow into each **internal jugular vein** (Figure 20.37). Blood from the more superficial portions of the head, scalp, and cranial regions, including the **temporal vein** and **maxillary vein,** flow into each **external jugular vein**. Although the external and internal jugular veins are separate vessels, there are anastomoses between them close to the thoracic region. Blood from the external jugular vein empties into the subclavian vein. Table 20.12 summarizes the major veins of the head and neck.

Major Veins of the Head and Neck

Vessel	Description
Internal jugular vein	Parallel to the common carotid artery, which is more or less its counterpart, and passes through the jugular foramen and canal; primarily drains blood from the brain, receives the superficial facial vein, and empties into the subclavian vein
Temporal vein	Drains blood from the temporal region and flows into the external jugular vein
Maxillary vein	Drains blood from the maxillary region and flows into the external jugular vein
External jugular vein	Drains blood from the more superficial portions of the head, scalp, and cranial regions, and leads to the subclavian vein

TABLE 20.12

Venous Drainage of the Brain

Circulation to the brain is both critical and complex (see Figure 20.37). Many smaller veins of the brain stem and the superficial veins of the cerebrum lead to larger vessels referred to as intracranial sinuses. These include the superior and inferior sagittal sinuses, straight sinus, cavernous sinuses, left and right sinuses, the petrosal sinuses, and the occipital sinuses. Ultimately, sinuses will lead back to either the inferior jugular vein or vertebral vein.

Most of the veins on the superior surface of the cerebrum flow into the largest of the sinuses, the **superior sagittal sinus**. It is located midsagittally between the meningeal and periosteal layers of the dura mater within the falx cerebri and, at first glance in images or models, can be mistaken for the subarachnoid space. Most reabsorption of cerebrospinal fluid occurs via the chorionic villi (arachnoid granulations) into the superior sagittal sinus. Blood from most of the smaller vessels originating from the inferior cerebral veins flows into the **great cerebral vein** and into the **straight sinus**. Other cerebral veins and those from the eye socket flow into the **cavernous sinus**, which flows into the **petrosal sinus** and then into the internal jugular vein. The **occipital sinus**, sagittal sinus, and straight sinuses all flow into the left and right transverse sinuses near the lambdoid suture. The **transverse sinuses** in turn flow into the **sigmoid sinuses** that pass through the jugular foramen and into the internal jugular vein. The internal jugular vein flows parallel to the common carotid artery and is more or less its counterpart. It empties into the brachiocephalic vein. The veins draining the cervical vertebrae and the posterior surface of the skull, including some blood from the occipital sinus, flow into the vertebral veins. These parallel the vertebral arteries and travel through the transverse foramina of the cervical vertebrae. The vertebral veins also flow into the brachiocephalic veins. Table 20.13 summarizes the major veins of the brain.

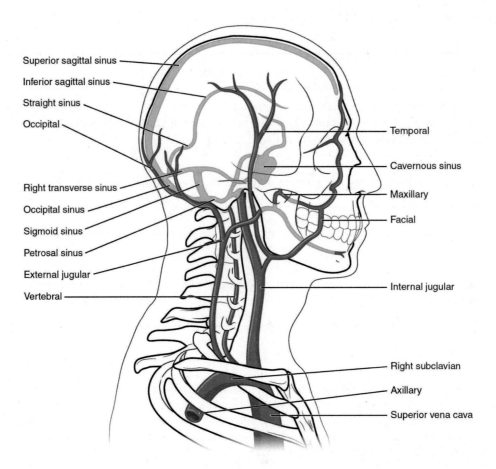

FIGURE 20.37   Veins of the Head and Neck   This left lateral view shows the veins of the head and neck, including the intercranial sinuses.

Major Veins of the Brain

Vessel	Description
Superior sagittal sinus	Enlarged vein located midsagittally between the meningeal and periosteal layers of the dura mater within the falx cerebri; receives most of the blood drained from the superior surface of the cerebrum and leads to the inferior jugular vein and the vertebral vein
Great cerebral vein	Receives most of the smaller vessels from the inferior cerebral veins and leads to the straight sinus
Straight sinus	Enlarged vein that drains blood from the brain; receives most of the blood from the great cerebral vein and leads to the left or right transverse sinus
Cavernous sinus	Enlarged vein that receives blood from most of the other cerebral veins and the eye socket, and leads to the petrosal sinus
Petrosal sinus	Enlarged vein that receives blood from the cavernous sinus and leads into the internal jugular veins

TABLE 20.13

Vessel	Description
Occipital sinus	Enlarged vein that drains the occipital region near the falx cerebelli and leads to the left and right transverse sinuses, and also the vertebral veins
Transverse sinuses	Pair of enlarged veins near the lambdoid suture that drains the occipital, sagittal, and straight sinuses, and leads to the sigmoid sinuses
Sigmoid sinuses	Enlarged vein that receives blood from the transverse sinuses and leads through the jugular foramen to the internal jugular vein

TABLE 20.13

Veins Draining the Upper Limbs

The **digital veins** in the fingers come together in the hand to form the **palmar venous arches** (Figure 20.38). From here, the veins come together to form the radial vein, the ulnar vein, and the median antebrachial vein. The **radial vein** and the **ulnar vein** parallel the bones of the forearm and join together at the antebrachium to form the **brachial vein**, a deep vein that flows into the axillary vein in the brachium.

The **median antebrachial vein** parallels the ulnar vein, is more medial in location, and joins the **basilic vein** in the forearm. As the basilic vein reaches the antecubital region, it gives off a branch called the **median cubital vein** that crosses at an angle to join the cephalic vein. The median cubital vein is the most common site for drawing venous blood in humans. The basilic vein continues through the arm medially and superficially to the axillary vein.

The **cephalic vein** begins in the antebrachium and drains blood from the superficial surface of the arm into the axillary vein. It is extremely superficial and easily seen along the surface of the biceps brachii muscle in individuals with good muscle tone and in those without excessive subcutaneous adipose tissue in the arms.

The **subscapular vein** drains blood from the subscapular region and joins the cephalic vein to form the **axillary vein**. As it passes through the body wall and enters the thorax, the axillary vein becomes the subclavian vein.

Many of the larger veins of the thoracic and abdominal region and upper limb are further represented in the flow chart in Figure 20.39. Table 20.14 summarizes the veins of the upper limbs.

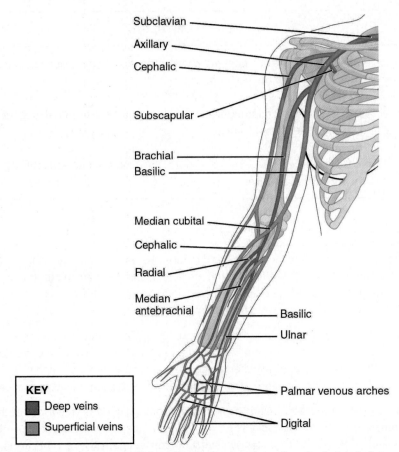

Subclavian

Axillary

Cephalic

Subscapular

Brachial

Basilic

Median cubital

Cephalic

Radial

Median
antebrachial

Basilic

Ulnar

Palmar venous arches

Digital

KEY
■ Deep veins
■ Superficial veins

FIGURE 20.38   Veins of the Upper Limb   This anterior view shows the veins that drain the upper limb.

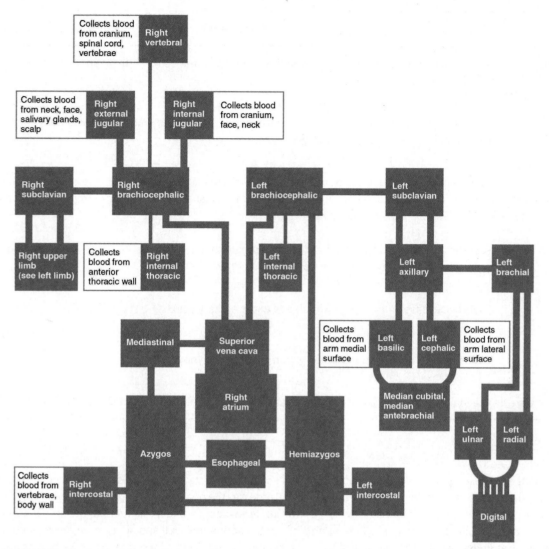

FIGURE 20.39   Veins Flowing into the Superior Vena Cava   The flow chart summarizes the distribution of the veins flowing into the superior vena cava.

Veins of the Upper Limbs

Vessel	Description
Digital veins	Drain the digits and lead to the palmar arches of the hand and dorsal venous arch of the foot
Palmar venous arches	Drain the hand and digits, and lead to the radial vein, ulnar veins, and the median antebrachial vein
Radial vein	Vein that parallels the radius and radial artery; arises from the palmar venous arches and leads to the brachial vein
Ulnar vein	Vein that parallels the ulna and ulnar artery; arises from the palmar venous arches and leads to the brachial vein

TABLE 20.14

Vessel	Description
Brachial vein	Deeper vein of the arm that forms from the radial and ulnar veins in the lower arm; leads to the axillary vein
Median antebrachial vein	Vein that parallels the ulnar vein but is more medial in location; intertwines with the palmar venous arches; leads to the basilic vein
Basilic vein	Superficial vein of the arm that arises from the median antebrachial vein, intersects with the median cubital vein, parallels the ulnar vein, and continues into the upper arm; along with the brachial vein, it leads to the axillary vein
Median cubital vein	Superficial vessel located in the antecubital region that links the cephalic vein to the basilic vein in the form of a v; a frequent site from which to draw blood
Cephalic vein	Superficial vessel in the upper arm; leads to the axillary vein
Subscapular vein	Drains blood from the subscapular region and leads to the axillary vein
Axillary vein	The major vein in the axillary region; drains the upper limb and becomes the subclavian vein

TABLE 20.14

The Inferior Vena Cava

Other than the small amount of blood drained by the azygos and hemiazygos veins, most of the blood inferior to the diaphragm drains into the inferior vena cava before it is returned to the heart (see Figure 20.36). Lying just beneath the parietal peritoneum in the abdominal cavity, the **inferior vena cava** parallels the abdominal aorta, where it can receive blood from abdominal veins. The lumbar portions of the abdominal wall and spinal cord are drained by a series of **lumbar veins**, usually four on each side. The ascending lumbar veins drain into either the azygos vein on the right or the hemiazygos vein on the left, and return to the superior vena cava. The remaining lumbar veins drain directly into the inferior vena cava.

Blood supply from the kidneys flows into each **renal vein**, normally the largest veins entering the inferior vena cava. A number of other, smaller veins empty into the left renal vein. Each **adrenal vein** drains the adrenal or suprarenal glands located immediately superior to the kidneys. The right adrenal vein enters the inferior vena cava directly, whereas the left adrenal vein enters the left renal vein.

From the male reproductive organs, each **testicular vein** flows from the scrotum, forming a portion of the spermatic cord. Each **ovarian vein** drains an ovary in females. Each of these veins is generically called a **gonadal vein**. The right gonadal vein empties directly into the inferior vena cava, and the left gonadal vein empties into the left renal vein.

Each side of the diaphragm drains into a **phrenic vein**; the right phrenic vein empties directly into the inferior vena cava, whereas the left phrenic vein empties into the left renal vein. Blood supply from the liver drains into each **hepatic vein** and directly into the inferior vena cava. Since the inferior vena cava lies primarily to the right of the vertebral column and aorta, the left renal vein is longer, as are the left phrenic, adrenal, and gonadal veins. The longer length of the left renal vein makes the left kidney the primary target of surgeons removing this organ for donation. Figure 20.40 provides a flow chart of the veins flowing into the inferior vena cava. Table 20.15 summarizes the major veins of the abdominal region.

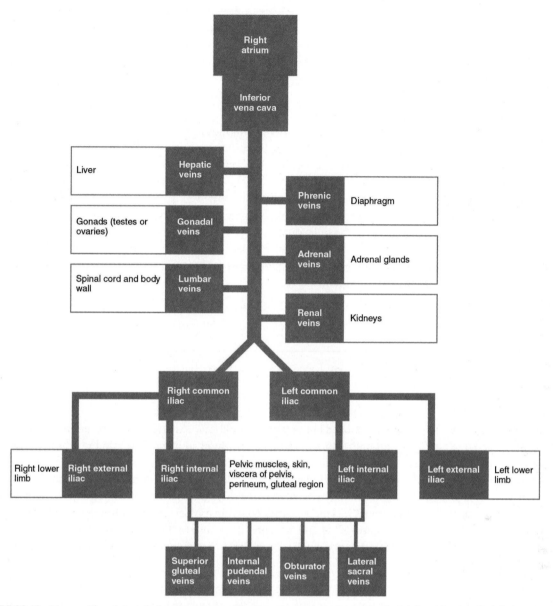

FIGURE 20.40   Venous Flow into Inferior Vena Cava   The flow chart summarizes veins that deliver blood to the inferior vena cava.

Major Veins of the Abdominal Region

Vessel	Description
Inferior vena cava	Large systemic vein that drains blood from areas largely inferior to the diaphragm; empties into the right atrium
Lumbar veins	Series of veins that drain the lumbar portion of the abdominal wall and spinal cord; the ascending lumbar veins drain into the azygos vein on the right or the hemiazygos vein on the left; the remaining lumbar veins drain directly into the inferior vena cava
Renal vein	Largest vein entering the inferior vena cava; drains the kidneys and flows into the inferior vena cava

TABLE 20.15

Vessel	Description
Adrenal vein	Drains the adrenal or suprarenal; the right adrenal vein enters the inferior vena cava directly and the left adrenal vein enters the left renal vein
Testicular vein	Drains the testes and forms part of the spermatic cord; the right testicular vein empties directly into the inferior vena cava and the left testicular vein empties into the left renal vein
Ovarian vein	Drains the ovary; the right ovarian vein empties directly into the inferior vena cava and the left ovarian vein empties into the left renal vein
Gonadal vein	Generic term for a vein draining a reproductive organ; may be either an ovarian vein or a testicular vein, depending on the sex of the individual
Phrenic vein	Drains the diaphragm; the right phrenic vein flows into the inferior vena cava and the left phrenic vein empties into the left renal vein
Hepatic vein	Drains systemic blood from the liver and flows into the inferior vena cava

TABLE 20.15

Veins Draining the Lower Limbs

The superior surface of the foot drains into the digital veins, and the inferior surface drains into the **plantar veins**, which flow into a complex series of anastomoses in the feet and ankles, including the **dorsal venous arch** and the **plantar venous arch** (Figure 20.41). From the dorsal venous arch, blood supply drains into the anterior and posterior tibial veins. The **anterior tibial vein** drains the area near the tibialis anterior muscle and combines with the posterior tibial vein and the fibular vein to form the popliteal vein. The **posterior tibial vein** drains the posterior surface of the tibia and joins the popliteal vein. The **fibular vein** drains the muscles and integument in proximity to the fibula and also joins the popliteal vein. The **small saphenous vein** located on the lateral surface of the leg drains blood from the superficial regions of the lower leg and foot, and flows into to the **popliteal vein**. As the popliteal vein passes behind the knee in the popliteal region, it becomes the femoral vein. It is palpable in patients without excessive adipose tissue.

Close to the body wall, the great saphenous vein, the deep femoral vein, and the femoral circumflex vein drain into the femoral vein. The **great saphenous vein** is a prominent surface vessel located on the medial surface of the leg and thigh that collects blood from the superficial portions of these areas. The **deep femoral vein**, as the name suggests, drains blood from the deeper portions of the thigh. The **femoral circumflex vein** forms a loop around the femur just inferior to the trochanters and drains blood from the areas in proximity to the head and neck of the femur.

As the **femoral vein** penetrates the body wall from the femoral portion of the upper limb, it becomes the **external iliac vein**, a large vein that drains blood from the leg to the common iliac vein. The pelvic organs and integument drain into the **internal iliac vein**, which forms from several smaller veins in the region, including the umbilical veins that run on either side of the bladder. The external and internal iliac veins combine near the inferior portion of the sacroiliac joint to form the common iliac vein. In addition to blood supply from the external and internal iliac veins, the **middle sacral vein** drains the sacral region into the **common iliac vein**. Similar to the common iliac arteries, the common iliac veins come together at the level of L5 to form the inferior vena cava.

Figure 20.42 is a flow chart of veins flowing into the lower limb. Table 20.16 summarizes the major veins of the lower limbs.

Access for free at openstax.org

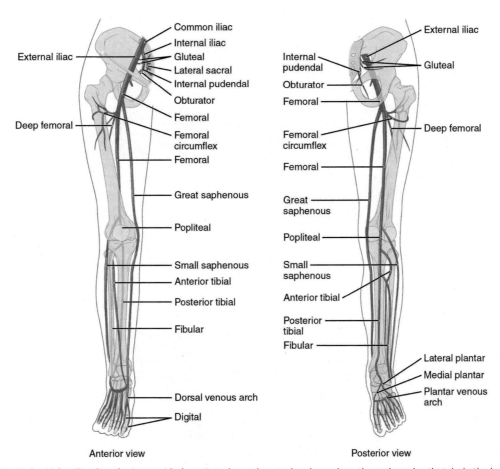

Anterior view   Posterior view

FIGURE 20.41   Major Veins Serving the Lower Limbs   Anterior and posterior views show the major veins that drain the lower limb into the inferior vena cava.

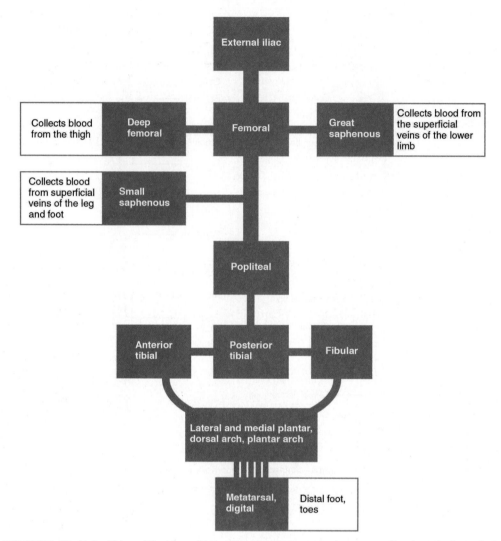

FIGURE 20.42 **Major Veins of the Lower Limb**   The flow chart summarizes venous flow from the lower limb.

Veins of the Lower Limbs

Vessel	Description
Plantar veins	Drain the foot and flow into the plantar venous arch
Dorsal venous arch	Drains blood from digital veins and vessels on the superior surface of the foot
Plantar venous arch	Formed from the plantar veins; flows into the anterior and posterior tibial veins through anastomoses
Anterior tibial vein	Formed from the dorsal venous arch; drains the area near the tibialis anterior muscle and flows into the popliteal vein

TABLE 20.16

Vessel	Description
Posterior tibial vein	Formed from the dorsal venous arch; drains the area near the posterior surface of the tibia and flows into the popliteal vein
Fibular vein	Drains the muscles and integument near the fibula and flows into the popliteal vein
Small saphenous vein	Located on the lateral surface of the leg; drains blood from the superficial regions of the lower leg and foot, and flows into the popliteal vein
Popliteal vein	Drains the region behind the knee and forms from the fusion of the fibular, anterior, and posterior tibial veins; flows into the femoral vein
Great saphenous vein	Prominent surface vessel located on the medial surface of the leg and thigh; drains the superficial portions of these areas and flows into the femoral vein
Deep femoral vein	Drains blood from the deeper portions of the thigh and flows into the femoral vein
Femoral circumflex vein	Forms a loop around the femur just inferior to the trochanters; drains blood from the areas around the head and neck of the femur; flows into the femoral vein
Femoral vein	Drains the upper leg; receives blood from the great saphenous vein, the deep femoral vein, and the femoral circumflex vein; becomes the external iliac vein when it crosses the body wall
External iliac vein	Formed when the femoral vein passes into the body cavity; drains the legs and flows into the common iliac vein
Internal iliac vein	Drains the pelvic organs and integument; formed from several smaller veins in the region; flows into the common iliac vein
Middle sacral vein	Drains the sacral region and flows into the left common iliac vein
Common iliac vein	Flows into the inferior vena cava at the level of L5; the left common iliac vein drains the sacral region; formed from the union of the external and internal iliac veins near the inferior portion of the sacroiliac joint

TABLE 20.16

Hepatic Portal System

The liver is a complex biochemical processing plant. It packages nutrients absorbed by the digestive system; produces plasma proteins, clotting factors, and bile; and disposes of worn-out cell components and waste products. Instead of entering the circulation directly, absorbed nutrients and certain wastes (for example, materials produced by the spleen) travel to the liver for processing. They do so via the **hepatic portal system** (Figure 20.43). Portal systems begin and end in capillaries. In this case, the initial capillaries from the stomach, small intestine, large intestine, and spleen lead to the hepatic portal vein and end in specialized capillaries within the liver, the hepatic sinusoids. You saw the only other portal system with the hypothalamic-hypophyseal portal vessel in the endocrine chapter.

The hepatic portal system consists of the hepatic portal vein and the veins that drain into it. The hepatic portal vein itself is relatively short, beginning at the level of L2 with the confluence of the superior mesenteric and splenic veins. It also receives branches from the inferior mesenteric vein, plus the splenic veins and all their tributaries. The superior mesenteric vein receives blood from the small intestine, two-thirds of the large intestine, and the stomach. The inferior mesenteric vein drains the distal third of the large intestine, including the descending colon, the sigmoid colon, and the rectum. The splenic vein is formed from branches from the spleen, pancreas, and portions of the stomach, and the inferior mesenteric vein. After its formation, the hepatic portal vein also receives branches from the gastric veins of the stomach and cystic veins from the gall bladder. The hepatic portal vein delivers materials from these digestive and circulatory organs directly to the liver for processing.

Because of the hepatic portal system, the liver receives its blood supply from two different sources: from normal systemic circulation via the hepatic artery and from the hepatic portal vein. The liver processes the blood from the portal system to remove certain wastes and excess nutrients, which are stored for later use. This processed blood, as well as the systemic blood that came from the hepatic artery, exits the liver via the right, left, and middle hepatic veins, and flows into the inferior vena cava. Overall systemic blood composition remains relatively stable, since the liver is able to metabolize the absorbed digestive components.

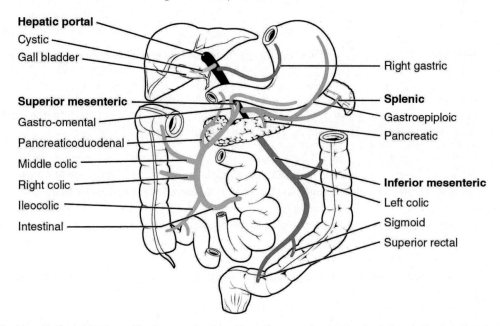

FIGURE 20.43 Hepatic Portal System   The liver receives blood from the normal systemic circulation via the hepatic artery. It also receives and processes blood from other organs, delivered via the veins of the hepatic portal system. All blood exits the liver via the hepatic vein, which delivers the blood to the inferior vena cava. (Different colors are used to help distinguish among the different vessels in the system.)

20.6 Development of Blood Vessels and Fetal Circulation

LEARNING OBJECTIVES

By the end of this section, you will be able to:

- Describe the development of blood vessels
- Describe the fetal circulation

In a developing embryo,the heart has developed enough by day 21 post-fertilization to begin beating. Circulation patterns are clearly established by the fourth week of embryonic life. It is critical to the survival of the developing human that the circulatory system forms early to supply the growing tissue with nutrients and gases, and to remove waste products. Blood cells and vessel production in structures outside the embryo proper called the yolk sac, chorion, and connecting stalk begin about 15 to 16 days following fertilization. Development of these circulatory elements within the embryo itself begins approximately 2 days later. You will learn more about the formation and function of these early structures when you study the chapter on development. During those first few weeks, blood vessels begin to form from the embryonic mesoderm. The precursor cells are known as **hemangioblasts**. These in turn differentiate into **angioblasts**, which give rise to the blood vessels and pluripotent stem cells, which differentiate into the formed elements of blood. (Seek additional content for more detail on fetal development and circulation.) Together, these cells form masses known as **blood islands** scattered throughout the embryonic disc. Spaces appear on the blood islands that develop into vessel lumens. The endothelial lining of the vessels arise from the angioblasts within these islands. Surrounding mesenchymal cells give rise to the smooth muscle and connective tissue layers of the vessels. While the vessels are developing, the pluripotent stem cells begin to form the blood.

Vascular tubes also develop on the blood islands, and they eventually connect to one another as well as to the developing, tubular heart. Thus, the developmental pattern, rather than beginning from the formation of one central vessel and spreading outward, occurs in many regions simultaneously with vessels later joining together. This **angiogenesis**—the creation of new blood vessels from existing ones—continues as needed throughout life as we grow and develop.

Blood vessel development often follows the same pattern as nerve development and travels to the same target tissues and organs. This occurs because the many factors directing growth of nerves also stimulate blood vessels to follow a similar pattern. Whether a given vessel develops into an artery or a vein is dependent upon local concentrations of signaling proteins.

As the embryo grows within the mother's uterus, its requirements for nutrients and gas exchange also grow. The placenta—a circulatory organ unique to pregnancy—develops jointly from the embryo and uterine wall structures to fill this need. Emerging from the placenta is the **umbilical vein**, which carries oxygen-rich blood from the pregnant person to the fetal inferior vena cava via the ductus venosus to the heart that pumps it into fetal circulation. Two **umbilical arteries** carry oxygen-depleted fetal blood, including wastes and carbon dioxide, to the placenta. Remnants of the umbilical arteries remain in the adult. (Seek additional content for more information on the role of the placenta in fetal circulation.)

There are three major shunts—alternate paths for blood flow—found in the circulatory system of the fetus. Two of these shunts divert blood from the pulmonary to the systemic circuit, whereas the third connects the umbilical vein to the inferior vena cava. The first two shunts are critical during fetal life, when the lungs are compressed, filled with amniotic fluid, and nonfunctional, and gas exchange is provided by the placenta. These shunts close shortly after birth, however, when the newborn begins to breathe. The third shunt persists a bit longer but becomes nonfunctional once the umbilical cord is severed. The three shunts are as follows (Figure 20.44):

- The **foramen ovale** is an opening in the interatrial septum that allows blood to flow from the right atrium to the left atrium. A valve associated with this opening prevents backflow of blood during the fetal period. As the newborn begins to breathe and blood pressure in the atria increases, this shunt closes. The fossa ovalis remains in the interatrial septum after birth, marking the location of the former foramen ovale.
- The **ductus arteriosus** is a short, muscular vessel that connects the pulmonary trunk to the aorta. Most of the blood pumped from the right ventricle into the pulmonary trunk is thereby diverted into the aorta. Only enough blood reaches the fetal lungs to maintain the developing lung tissue. When the newborn takes the first breath, pressure within the lungs drops dramatically, and both the lungs and the pulmonary vessels expand. As the amount of oxygen increases, the smooth muscles in the wall of the ductus arteriosus constrict, sealing off the passage. Eventually, the muscular and endothelial components of the ductus arteriosus degenerate, leaving only the connective tissue component of the ligamentum arteriosum.
- The **ductus venosus** is a temporary blood vessel that branches from the umbilical vein, allowing much of the freshly oxygenated blood from the placenta—the organ of gas exchange between the pregnant person and fetus—to bypass the fetal liver and go directly to the fetal heart. The ductus venosus closes slowly during the first weeks of infancy and degenerates to become the ligamentum venosum.

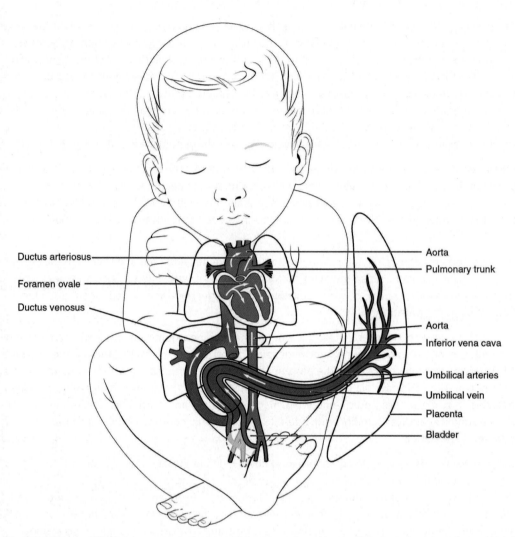

FIGURE 20.44 Fetal Shunts   The foramen ovale in the interatrial septum allows blood to flow from the right atrium to the left atrium. The ductus arteriosus is a temporary vessel, connecting the aorta to the pulmonary trunk. The ductus venosus links the umbilical vein to the inferior vena cava largely through the liver.

Key Terms

abdominal aorta   portion of the aorta inferior to the aortic hiatus and superior to the common iliac arteries

adrenal artery   branch of the abdominal aorta; supplies blood to the adrenal (suprarenal) glands

adrenal vein   drains the adrenal or suprarenal glands that are immediately superior to the kidneys; the right adrenal vein enters the inferior vena cava directly and the left adrenal vein enters the left renal vein

anaphylactic shock   type of shock that follows a severe allergic reaction and results from massive vasodilation

angioblasts   stem cells that give rise to blood vessels

angiogenesis   development of new blood vessels from existing vessels

anterior cerebral artery   arises from the internal carotid artery; supplies the frontal lobe of the cerebrum

anterior communicating artery   anastomosis of the right and left internal carotid arteries; supplies blood to the brain

anterior tibial artery   branches from the popliteal artery; supplies blood to the anterior tibial region; becomes the dorsalis pedis artery

anterior tibial vein   forms from the dorsal venous arch; drains the area near the tibialis anterior muscle and leads to the popliteal vein

aorta   largest artery in the body, originating from the left ventricle and descending to the abdominal region where it bifurcates into the common iliac arteries at the level of the fourth lumbar vertebra; arteries originating from the aorta distribute blood to virtually all tissues of the body

aortic arch   arc that connects the ascending aorta to the descending aorta; ends at the intervertebral disk between the fourth and fifth thoracic vertebrae

aortic hiatus   opening in the diaphragm that allows passage of the thoracic aorta into the abdominal region where it becomes the abdominal aorta

aortic sinuses   small pockets in the ascending aorta near the aortic valve that are the locations of the baroreceptors (stretch receptors) and chemoreceptors that trigger a reflex that aids in the regulation of vascular homeostasis

arterial circle   (also, circle of Willis) anastomosis located at the base of the brain that ensures continual blood supply; formed from branches of the internal carotid and vertebral arteries; supplies blood to the brain

arteriole   (also, resistance vessel) very small artery that leads to a capillary

arteriovenous anastomosis   short vessel connecting an arteriole directly to a venule and bypassing the capillary beds

artery   blood vessel that conducts blood away from the heart; may be a conducting or distributing vessel

ascending aorta   initial portion of the aorta, rising from the left ventricle for a distance of approximately 5 cm

atrial reflex   mechanism for maintaining vascular homeostasis involving atrial baroreceptors: if blood is returning to the right atrium more rapidly than it is being ejected from the left ventricle, the atrial receptors will stimulate the cardiovascular centers to increase sympathetic firing and increase cardiac output until the situation is reversed; the opposite is also true

axillary artery   continuation of the subclavian artery as it penetrates the body wall and enters the axillary region; supplies blood to the region near the head of the humerus (humeral circumflex arteries); the majority of the vessel continues into the brachium and becomes the brachial artery

axillary vein   major vein in the axillary region; drains the upper limb and becomes the subclavian vein

azygos vein   originates in the lumbar region and passes through the diaphragm into the thoracic cavity on the right side of the vertebral column; drains blood from the intercostal veins, esophageal veins, bronchial veins, and other veins draining the mediastinal region; leads to the superior vena cava

basilar artery   formed from the fusion of the two vertebral arteries; sends branches to the cerebellum, brain stem, and the posterior cerebral arteries; the main blood supply to the brain stem

basilic vein   superficial vein of the arm that arises from the palmar venous arches, intersects with the median cubital vein, parallels the ulnar vein, and continues into the upper arm; along with the brachial vein, it leads to the axillary vein

blood colloidal osmotic pressure (BCOP)   pressure exerted by colloids suspended in blood within a vessel; a primary determinant is the presence of plasma proteins

blood flow   movement of blood through a vessel, tissue, or organ that is usually expressed in terms of volume per unit of time

blood hydrostatic pressure   force blood exerts against the walls of a blood vessel or heart chamber

blood islands   masses of developing blood vessels and formed elements from mesodermal cells scattered throughout the embryonic disc

blood pressure   force exerted by the blood against

the wall of a vessel or heart chamber; can be described with the more generic term hydrostatic pressure

brachial artery   continuation of the axillary artery in the brachium; supplies blood to much of the brachial region; gives off several smaller branches that provide blood to the posterior surface of the arm in the region of the elbow; bifurcates into the radial and ulnar arteries at the coronoid fossa

brachial vein   deeper vein of the arm that forms from the radial and ulnar veins in the lower arm; leads to the axillary vein

brachiocephalic artery   single vessel located on the right side of the body; the first vessel branching from the aortic arch; gives rise to the right subclavian artery and the right common carotid artery; supplies blood to the head, neck, upper limb, and wall of the thoracic region

brachiocephalic vein   one of a pair of veins that form from a fusion of the external and internal jugular veins and the subclavian vein; subclavian, external and internal jugulars, vertebral, and internal thoracic veins lead to it; drains the upper thoracic region and flows into the superior vena cava

bronchial artery   systemic branch from the aorta that provides oxygenated blood to the lungs in addition to the pulmonary circuit

bronchial vein   drains the systemic circulation from the lungs and leads to the azygos vein

capacitance   ability of a vein to distend and store blood

capacitance vessels   veins

capillary   smallest of blood vessels where physical exchange occurs between the blood and tissue cells surrounded by interstitial fluid

capillary bed   network of 10–100 capillaries connecting arterioles to venules

capillary hydrostatic pressure (CHP)   force blood exerts against a capillary

cardiogenic shock   type of shock that results from the inability of the heart to maintain cardiac output

carotid sinuses   small pockets near the base of the internal carotid arteries that are the locations of the baroreceptors and chemoreceptors that trigger a reflex that aids in the regulation of vascular homeostasis

cavernous sinus   enlarged vein that receives blood from most of the other cerebral veins and the eye socket, and leads to the petrosal sinus

celiac trunk   (also, celiac artery) major branch of the abdominal aorta; gives rise to the left gastric artery, the splenic artery, and the common hepatic artery that forms the hepatic artery to the liver, the right

gastric artery to the stomach, and the cystic artery to the gall bladder

cephalic vein   superficial vessel in the upper arm; leads to the axillary vein

cerebrovascular accident (CVA)   blockage of blood flow to the brain; also called a stroke

circle of Willis   (also, arterial circle) anastomosis located at the base of the brain that ensures continual blood supply; formed from branches of the internal carotid and vertebral arteries; supplies blood to the brain

circulatory shock   also simply called shock; a life-threatening medical condition in which the circulatory system is unable to supply enough blood flow to provide adequate oxygen and other nutrients to the tissues to maintain cellular metabolism

common carotid artery   right common carotid artery arises from the brachiocephalic artery, and the left common carotid arises from the aortic arch; gives rise to the external and internal carotid arteries; supplies the respective sides of the head and neck

common hepatic artery   branch of the celiac trunk that forms the hepatic artery, the right gastric artery, and the cystic artery

common iliac artery   branch of the aorta that leads to the internal and external iliac arteries

common iliac vein   one of a pair of veins that flows into the inferior vena cava at the level of L5; the left common iliac vein drains the sacral region; divides into external and internal iliac veins near the inferior portion of the sacroiliac joint

compliance   degree to which a blood vessel can stretch as opposed to being rigid

continuous capillary   most common type of capillary, found in virtually all tissues except epithelia and cartilage; contains very small gaps in the endothelial lining that permit exchange

cystic artery   branch of the common hepatic artery; supplies blood to the gall bladder

deep femoral artery   branch of the femoral artery; gives rise to the lateral circumflex arteries

deep femoral vein   drains blood from the deeper portions of the thigh and leads to the femoral vein

descending aorta   portion of the aorta that continues downward past the end of the aortic arch; subdivided into the thoracic aorta and the abdominal aorta

diastolic pressure   lower number recorded when measuring arterial blood pressure; represents the minimal value corresponding to the pressure that remains during ventricular relaxation

digital arteries   formed from the superficial and deep palmar arches; supply blood to the digits

digital veins   drain the digits and feed into the palmar arches of the hand and dorsal venous arch of the foot

dorsal arch   (also, arcuate arch) formed from the anastomosis of the dorsalis pedis artery and medial and plantar arteries; branches supply the distal portions of the foot and digits

dorsal venous arch   drains blood from digital veins and vessels on the superior surface of the foot

dorsalis pedis artery   forms from the anterior tibial artery; branches repeatedly to supply blood to the tarsal and dorsal regions of the foot

ductus arteriosus   shunt in the fetal pulmonary trunk that diverts oxygenated blood back to the aorta

ductus venosus   shunt that causes oxygenated blood to bypass the fetal liver on its way to the inferior vena cava

elastic artery   (also, conducting artery) artery with abundant elastic fibers located closer to the heart, which maintains the pressure gradient and conducts blood to smaller branches

esophageal artery   branch of the thoracic aorta; supplies blood to the esophagus

esophageal vein   drains the inferior portions of the esophagus and leads to the azygos vein

external carotid artery   arises from the common carotid artery; supplies blood to numerous structures within the face, lower jaw, neck, esophagus, and larynx

external elastic membrane   membrane composed of elastic fibers that separates the tunica media from the tunica externa; seen in larger arteries

external iliac artery   branch of the common iliac artery that leaves the body cavity and becomes a femoral artery; supplies blood to the lower limbs

external iliac vein   formed when the femoral vein passes into the body cavity; drains the legs and leads to the common iliac vein

external jugular vein   one of a pair of major veins located in the superficial neck region that drains blood from the more superficial portions of the head, scalp, and cranial regions, and leads to the subclavian vein

femoral artery   continuation of the external iliac artery after it passes through the body cavity; divides into several smaller branches, the lateral deep femoral artery, and the genicular artery; becomes the popliteal artery as it passes posterior to the knee

femoral circumflex vein   forms a loop around the femur just inferior to the trochanters; drains blood from the areas around the head and neck of the femur; leads to the femoral vein

femoral vein   drains the upper leg; receives blood from the great saphenous vein, the deep femoral vein, and the femoral circumflex vein; becomes the external iliac vein when it crosses the body wall

fenestrated capillary   type of capillary with pores or fenestrations in the endothelium that allow for rapid passage of certain small materials

fibular vein   drains the muscles and integument near the fibula and leads to the popliteal vein

filtration   in the cardiovascular system, the movement of material from a capillary into the interstitial fluid, moving from an area of higher pressure to lower pressure

foramen ovale   shunt that directly connects the right and left atria and helps to divert oxygenated blood from the fetal pulmonary circuit

genicular artery   branch of the femoral artery; supplies blood to the region of the knee

gonadal artery   branch of the abdominal aorta; supplies blood to the gonads or reproductive organs; also described as ovarian arteries or testicular arteries, depending upon the sex of the individual

gonadal vein   generic term for a vein draining a reproductive organ; may be either an ovarian vein or a testicular vein, depending on the sex of the individual

great cerebral vein   receives most of the smaller vessels from the inferior cerebral veins and leads to the straight sinus

great saphenous vein   prominent surface vessel located on the medial surface of the leg and thigh; drains the superficial portions of these areas and leads to the femoral vein

hemangioblasts   embryonic stem cells that appear in the mesoderm and give rise to both angioblasts and pluripotent stem cells

hemiazygos vein   smaller vein complementary to the azygos vein; drains the esophageal veins from the esophagus and the left intercostal veins, and leads to the brachiocephalic vein via the superior intercostal vein

hepatic artery proper   branch of the common hepatic artery; supplies systemic blood to the liver

hepatic portal system   specialized circulatory pathway that carries blood from digestive organs to the liver for processing before being sent to the systemic circulation

hepatic vein   drains systemic blood from the liver and flows into the inferior vena cava

hypertension   chronic and persistent blood pressure measurements of 140/90 mm Hg or above

hypervolemia   abnormally high levels of fluid and

blood within the body

hypovolemia   abnormally low levels of fluid and blood within the body

hypovolemic shock   type of circulatory shock caused by excessive loss of blood volume due to hemorrhage or possibly dehydration

hypoxia   lack of oxygen supply to the tissues

inferior mesenteric artery   branch of the abdominal aorta; supplies blood to the distal segment of the large intestine and rectum

inferior phrenic artery   branch of the abdominal aorta; supplies blood to the inferior surface of the diaphragm

inferior vena cava   large systemic vein that drains blood from areas largely inferior to the diaphragm; empties into the right atrium

intercostal artery   branch of the thoracic aorta; supplies blood to the muscles of the thoracic cavity and vertebral column

intercostal vein   drains the muscles of the thoracic wall and leads to the azygos vein

internal carotid artery   arises from the common carotid artery and begins with the carotid sinus; goes through the carotid canal of the temporal bone to the base of the brain; combines with branches of the vertebral artery forming the arterial circle; supplies blood to the brain

internal elastic membrane   membrane composed of elastic fibers that separates the tunica intima from the tunica media; seen in larger arteries

internal iliac artery   branch from the common iliac arteries; supplies blood to the urinary bladder, walls of the pelvis, external genitalia, and the medial portion of the femoral region; in females, also provide blood to the uterus and vagina

internal iliac vein   drains the pelvic organs and integument; formed from several smaller veins in the region; leads to the common iliac vein

internal jugular vein   one of a pair of major veins located in the neck region that passes through the jugular foramen and canal, flows parallel to the common carotid artery that is more or less its counterpart; primarily drains blood from the brain, receives the superficial facial vein, and empties into the subclavian vein

internal thoracic artery   (also, mammary artery) arises from the subclavian artery; supplies blood to the thymus, pericardium of the heart, and the anterior chest wall

internal thoracic vein   (also, internal mammary vein) drains the anterior surface of the chest wall and leads to the brachiocephalic vein

interstitial fluid colloidal osmotic pressure (IFCOP)   pressure exerted by the colloids within the interstitial fluid

interstitial fluid hydrostatic pressure (IFHP)   force exerted by the fluid in the tissue spaces

ischemia   insufficient blood flow to the tissues

Korotkoff sounds   noises created by turbulent blood flow through the vessels

lateral circumflex artery   branch of the deep femoral artery; supplies blood to the deep muscles of the thigh and the ventral and lateral regions of the integument

lateral plantar artery   arises from the bifurcation of the posterior tibial arteries; supplies blood to the lateral plantar surfaces of the foot

left gastric artery   branch of the celiac trunk; supplies blood to the stomach

lumbar arteries   branches of the abdominal aorta; supply blood to the lumbar region, the abdominal wall, and spinal cord

lumbar veins   drain the lumbar portion of the abdominal wall and spinal cord; the superior lumbar veins drain into the azygos vein on the right or the hemiazygos vein on the left; blood from these vessels is returned to the superior vena cava rather than the inferior vena cava

lumen   interior of a tubular structure such as a blood vessel or a portion of the alimentary canal through which blood, chyme, or other substances travel

maxillary vein   drains blood from the maxillary region and leads to the external jugular vein

mean arterial pressure (MAP)   average driving force of blood to the tissues; approximated by taking diastolic pressure and adding 1/3 of pulse pressure

medial plantar artery   arises from the bifurcation of the posterior tibial arteries; supplies blood to the medial plantar surfaces of the foot

median antebrachial vein   vein that parallels the ulnar vein but is more medial in location; intertwines with the palmar venous arches

median cubital vein   superficial vessel located in the antecubital region that links the cephalic vein to the basilic vein in the form of a v; a frequent site for a blood draw

median sacral artery   continuation of the aorta into the sacrum

mediastinal artery   branch of the thoracic aorta; supplies blood to the mediastinum

metarteriole   short vessel arising from a terminal arteriole that branches to supply a capillary bed

microcirculation   blood flow through the capillaries

middle cerebral artery   another branch of the internal carotid artery; supplies blood to the temporal and parietal lobes of the cerebrum

middle sacral vein drains the sacral region and leads to the left common iliac vein

muscular artery (also, distributing artery) artery with abundant smooth muscle in the tunica media that branches to distribute blood to the arteriole network

myogenic response constriction or dilation in the walls of arterioles in response to pressures related to blood flow; reduces high blood flow or increases low blood flow to help maintain consistent flow to the capillary network

nervi vasorum small nerve fibers found in arteries and veins that trigger contraction of the smooth muscle in their walls

net filtration pressure (NFP) force driving fluid out of the capillary and into the tissue spaces; equal to the difference of the capillary hydrostatic pressure and the blood colloidal osmotic pressure

neurogenic shock type of shock that occurs with cranial or high spinal injuries that damage the cardiovascular centers in the medulla oblongata or the nervous fibers originating from this region

obstructive shock type of shock that occurs when a significant portion of the vascular system is blocked

occipital sinus enlarged vein that drains the occipital region near the falx cerebelli and flows into the left and right transverse sinuses, and also into the vertebral veins

ophthalmic artery branch of the internal carotid artery; supplies blood to the eyes

ovarian artery branch of the abdominal aorta; supplies blood to the ovary, uterine (Fallopian) tube, and uterus

ovarian vein drains the ovary; the right ovarian vein leads to the inferior vena cava and the left ovarian vein leads to the left renal vein

palmar arches superficial and deep arches formed from anastomoses of the radial and ulnar arteries; supply blood to the hand and digital arteries

palmar venous arches drain the hand and digits, and feed into the radial and ulnar veins

parietal branches (also, somatic branches) group of arterial branches of the thoracic aorta; includes those that supply blood to the thoracic cavity, vertebral column, and the superior surface of the diaphragm

perfusion distribution of blood into the capillaries so the tissues can be supplied

pericardial artery branch of the thoracic aorta; supplies blood to the pericardium

petrosal sinus enlarged vein that receives blood from the cavernous sinus and flows into the internal jugular vein

phrenic vein drains the diaphragm; the right phrenic vein flows into the inferior vena cava and the left phrenic vein leads to the left renal vein

plantar arch formed from the anastomosis of the dorsalis pedis artery and medial and plantar arteries; branches supply the distal portions of the foot and digits

plantar veins drain the foot and lead to the plantar venous arch

plantar venous arch formed from the plantar veins; leads to the anterior and posterior tibial veins through anastomoses

popliteal artery continuation of the femoral artery posterior to the knee; branches into the anterior and posterior tibial arteries

popliteal vein continuation of the femoral vein behind the knee; drains the region behind the knee and forms from the fusion of the fibular and anterior and posterior tibial veins

posterior cerebral artery branch of the basilar artery that forms a portion of the posterior segment of the arterial circle; supplies blood to the posterior portion of the cerebrum and brain stem

posterior communicating artery branch of the posterior cerebral artery that forms part of the posterior portion of the arterial circle; supplies blood to the brain

posterior tibial artery branch from the popliteal artery that gives rise to the fibular or peroneal artery; supplies blood to the posterior tibial region

posterior tibial vein forms from the dorsal venous arch; drains the area near the posterior surface of the tibia and leads to the popliteal vein

precapillary sphincters circular rings of smooth muscle that surround the entrance to a capillary and regulate blood flow into that capillary

pulmonary artery one of two branches, left and right, that divides off from the pulmonary trunk and leads to smaller arterioles and eventually to the pulmonary capillaries

pulmonary circuit system of blood vessels that provide gas exchange via a network of arteries, veins, and capillaries that run from the heart, through the body, and back to the lungs

pulmonary trunk single large vessel exiting the right ventricle that divides to form the right and left pulmonary arteries

pulmonary veins two sets of paired vessels, one pair on each side, that are formed from the small venules leading away from the pulmonary capillaries that flow into the left atrium

pulse alternating expansion and recoil of an artery as blood moves through the vessel; an indicator of heart rate

pulse pressure difference between the systolic and diastolic pressures

radial artery formed at the bifurcation of the brachial artery; parallels the radius; gives off smaller branches until it reaches the carpal region where it fuses with the ulnar artery to form the superficial and deep palmar arches; supplies blood to the lower arm and carpal region

radial vein parallels the radius and radial artery; arises from the palmar venous arches and leads to the brachial vein

reabsorption in the cardiovascular system, the movement of material from the interstitial fluid into the capillaries

renal artery branch of the abdominal aorta; supplies each kidney

renal vein largest vein entering the inferior vena cava; drains the kidneys and leads to the inferior vena cava

resistance any condition or parameter that slows or counteracts the flow of blood

respiratory pump increase in the volume of the thorax during inhalation that decreases air pressure, enabling venous blood to flow into the thoracic region, then exhalation increases pressure, moving blood into the atria

right gastric artery branch of the common hepatic artery; supplies blood to the stomach

sepsis (also, septicemia) organismal-level inflammatory response to a massive infection

septic shock (also, blood poisoning) type of shock that follows a massive infection resulting in organism-wide inflammation

sigmoid sinuses enlarged veins that receive blood from the transverse sinuses; flow through the jugular foramen and into the internal jugular vein

sinusoid capillary rarest type of capillary, which has extremely large intercellular gaps in the basement membrane in addition to clefts and fenestrations; found in areas such as the bone marrow and liver where passage of large molecules occurs

skeletal muscle pump effect on increasing blood pressure within veins by compression of the vessel caused by the contraction of nearby skeletal muscle

small saphenous vein located on the lateral surface of the leg; drains blood from the superficial regions of the lower leg and foot, and leads to the popliteal vein

sphygmomanometer blood pressure cuff attached to a device that measures blood pressure

splenic artery branch of the celiac trunk; supplies blood to the spleen

straight sinus enlarged vein that drains blood from the brain; receives most of the blood from the great cerebral vein and flows into the left or right transverse sinus

subclavian artery right subclavian arises from the brachiocephalic artery, whereas the left subclavian artery arises from the aortic arch; gives rise to the internal thoracic, vertebral, and thyrocervical arteries; supplies blood to the arms, chest, shoulders, back, and central nervous system

subclavian vein located deep in the thoracic cavity; becomes the axillary vein as it enters the axillary region; drains the axillary and smaller local veins near the scapular region; leads to the brachiocephalic vein

subscapular vein drains blood from the subscapular region and leads to the axillary vein

superior mesenteric artery branch of the abdominal aorta; supplies blood to the small intestine (duodenum, jejunum, and ileum), the pancreas, and a majority of the large intestine

superior phrenic artery branch of the thoracic aorta; supplies blood to the superior surface of the diaphragm

superior sagittal sinus enlarged vein located midsagittally between the meningeal and periosteal layers of the dura mater within the falx cerebri; receives most of the blood drained from the superior surface of the cerebrum and leads to the inferior jugular vein and the vertebral vein

superior vena cava large systemic vein; drains blood from most areas superior to the diaphragm; empties into the right atrium

systolic pressure larger number recorded when measuring arterial blood pressure; represents the maximum value following ventricular contraction

temporal vein drains blood from the temporal region and leads to the external jugular vein

testicular artery branch of the abdominal aorta; will ultimately travel outside the body cavity to the testes and form one component of the spermatic cord

testicular vein drains the testes and forms part of the spermatic cord; the right testicular vein empties directly into the inferior vena cava and the left testicular vein empties into the left renal vein

thoracic aorta portion of the descending aorta superior to the aortic hiatus

thoroughfare channel continuation of the metarteriole that enables blood to bypass a capillary bed and flow directly into a venule, creating a vascular shunt

thyrocervical artery arises from the subclavian artery; supplies blood to the thyroid, the cervical region, the upper back, and shoulder

transient ischemic attack (TIA)   temporary loss of neurological function caused by a brief interruption in blood flow; also known as a mini-stroke

transverse sinuses   pair of enlarged veins near the lambdoid suture that drain the occipital, sagittal, and straight sinuses, and leads to the sigmoid sinuses

trunk   large vessel that gives rise to smaller vessels

tunica externa   (also, tunica adventitia) outermost layer or tunic of a vessel (except capillaries)

tunica intima   (also, tunica interna) innermost lining or tunic of a vessel

tunica media   middle layer or tunic of a vessel (except capillaries)

ulnar artery   formed at the bifurcation of the brachial artery; parallels the ulna; gives off smaller branches until it reaches the carpal region where it fuses with the radial artery to form the superficial and deep palmar arches; supplies blood to the lower arm and carpal region

ulnar vein   parallels the ulna and ulnar artery; arises from the palmar venous arches and leads to the brachial vein

umbilical arteries   pair of vessels that runs within the umbilical cord and carries fetal blood low in oxygen and high in waste to the placenta for exchange with maternal blood

umbilical vein   single vessel that originates in the placenta and runs within the umbilical cord, carrying oxygen- and nutrient-rich blood to the fetal heart

vasa vasorum   small blood vessels located within the walls or tunics of larger vessels that supply nourishment to and remove wastes from the cells of the vessels

vascular shock   type of shock that occurs when arterioles lose their normal muscular tone and dilate dramatically

vascular shunt   continuation of the metarteriole and thoroughfare channel that allows blood to bypass the capillary beds to flow directly from the arterial to the venous circulation

vascular tone   contractile state of smooth muscle in a blood vessel

vascular tubes   rudimentary blood vessels in a developing fetus

vasoconstriction   constriction of the smooth muscle of a blood vessel, resulting in a decreased vascular diameter

vasodilation   relaxation of the smooth muscle in the wall of a blood vessel, resulting in an increased vascular diameter

vasomotion   irregular, pulsating flow of blood through capillaries and related structures

vein   blood vessel that conducts blood toward the heart

venous reserve   volume of blood contained within systemic veins in the integument, bone marrow, and liver that can be returned to the heart for circulation, if needed

venule   small vessel leading from the capillaries to veins

vertebral artery   arises from the subclavian artery and passes through the vertebral foramen through the foramen magnum to the brain; joins with the internal carotid artery to form the arterial circle; supplies blood to the brain and spinal cord

vertebral vein   arises from the base of the brain and the cervical region of the spinal cord; passes through the intervertebral foramina in the cervical vertebrae; drains smaller veins from the cranium, spinal cord, and vertebrae, and leads to the brachiocephalic vein; counterpart of the vertebral artery

visceral branches   branches of the descending aorta that supply blood to the viscera

Chapter Review

20.1 Structure and Function of Blood Vessels

Blood pumped by the heart flows through a series of vessels known as arteries, arterioles, capillaries, venules, and veins before returning to the heart. Arteries transport blood away from the heart and branch into smaller vessels, forming arterioles. Arterioles distribute blood to capillary beds, the sites of exchange with the body tissues. Capillaries lead back to small vessels known as venules that flow into the larger veins and eventually back to the heart.

The arterial system is a relatively high-pressure system, so arteries have thick walls that appear round in cross section. The venous system is a lower-pressure system, containing veins that have larger lumens and thinner walls. They often appear flattened. Arteries, arterioles, venules, and veins are composed of three tunics known as the tunica intima, tunica media, and tunica externa. Capillaries have only a tunica intima layer. The tunica intima is a thin layer composed of a simple squamous epithelium known as endothelium and a small amount of connective tissue. The tunica media is a thicker area composed of variable amounts of smooth muscle and connective tissue. It is the thickest layer in all but the largest arteries. The tunica externa is primarily a layer of connective tissue, although in veins, it also contains some smooth muscle. Blood flow through vessels can be dramatically influenced by vasoconstriction and vasodilation in their walls.

20.2 Blood Flow, Blood Pressure, and Resistance

Blood flow is the movement of blood through a vessel, tissue, or organ. The slowing or blocking of blood flow is called resistance. Blood pressure is the force that blood exerts upon the walls of the blood vessels or chambers of the heart. The components of blood pressure include systolic pressure, which results from ventricular contraction, and diastolic pressure, which results from ventricular relaxation. Pulse pressure is the difference between systolic and diastolic measures, and mean arterial pressure is the "average" pressure of blood in the arterial system, driving blood into the tissues. Pulse, the expansion and recoiling of an artery, reflects the heartbeat. The variables affecting blood flow and blood pressure in the systemic circulation are cardiac output, compliance, blood volume, blood viscosity, and the length and diameter of the blood vessels. In the arterial system, vasodilation and vasoconstriction of the arterioles is a significant factor in systemic blood pressure: Slight vasodilation greatly decreases resistance and increases flow, whereas slight vasoconstriction greatly increases resistance and decreases flow. In the arterial system, as resistance increases, blood pressure increases and flow decreases. In the venous system, constriction increases blood pressure as it does in arteries; the increasing pressure helps to return blood to the heart. In addition, constriction causes the vessel lumen to become more rounded, decreasing resistance and increasing blood flow. Venoconstriction, while less important than arterial vasoconstriction, works with the skeletal muscle pump, the respiratory pump, and their valves to promote venous return to the heart.

20.3 Capillary Exchange

Small molecules can cross into and out of capillaries via simple or facilitated diffusion. Some large molecules can cross in vesicles or through clefts, fenestrations, or gaps between cells in capillary walls. However, the bulk flow of capillary and tissue fluid occurs via filtration and reabsorption. Filtration, the movement of fluid out of the capillaries, is driven by the CHP. Reabsorption, the influx of tissue fluid into the capillaries, is driven by the BCOP. Filtration predominates in the arterial end of the capillary; in the middle section, the opposing pressures are virtually

identical so there is no net exchange, whereas reabsorption predominates at the venule end of the capillary. The hydrostatic and colloid osmotic pressures in the interstitial fluid are negligible in healthy circumstances.

20.4 Homeostatic Regulation of the Vascular System

Neural, endocrine, and autoregulatory mechanisms affect blood flow, blood pressure, and eventually perfusion of blood to body tissues. Neural mechanisms include the cardiovascular centers in the medulla oblongata, baroreceptors in the aorta and carotid arteries and right atrium, and associated chemoreceptors that monitor blood levels of oxygen, carbon dioxide, and hydrogen ions. Endocrine controls include epinephrine and norepinephrine, as well as ADH, the renin-angiotensin-aldosterone mechanism, ANH, and EPO. Autoregulation is the local control of vasodilation and constriction by chemical signals and the myogenic response. Exercise greatly improves cardiovascular function and reduces the risk of cardiovascular diseases, including hypertension, a leading cause of heart attacks and strokes. Significant hemorrhage can lead to a form of circulatory shock known as hypovolemic shock. Sepsis, obstruction, and widespread inflammation can also cause circulatory shock.

20.5 Circulatory Pathways

The right ventricle pumps oxygen-depleted blood into the pulmonary trunk and right and left pulmonary arteries, which carry it to the right and left lungs for gas exchange. Oxygen-rich blood is transported by pulmonary veins to the left atrium. The left ventricle pumps this blood into the aorta. The main regions of the aorta are the ascending aorta, aortic arch, and descending aorta, which is further divided into the thoracic and abdominal aorta. The coronary arteries branch from the ascending aorta. After oxygenating tissues in the capillaries, systemic blood is returned to the right atrium from the venous system via the superior vena cava, which drains most of the veins superior to the diaphragm, the inferior vena cava, which drains most of the veins inferior to the diaphragm, and the coronary veins via the coronary sinus. The hepatic portal system carries blood to the liver for processing before it enters circulation. Review the figures provided in this section for circulation of blood through the blood vessels.

20.6 Development of Blood Vessels and Fetal Circulation

Blood vessels begin to form from the embryonic mesoderm. The precursor hemangioblasts differentiate into angioblasts, which give rise to the blood vessels and pluripotent stem cells that differentiate into the formed elements of the blood. Together, these cells form blood islands scattered throughout the embryo. Extensions known as vascular tubes eventually connect the vascular network. As the embryo grows within the mother's womb, the placenta develops to supply blood rich in oxygen and nutrients via the umbilical vein and to remove wastes in oxygen-depleted blood via the umbilical arteries. Three major shunts found in the fetus are the foramen ovale and ductus arteriosus, which divert blood from the pulmonary to the systemic circuit, and the ductus venosus, which carries freshly oxygenated blood high in nutrients to the fetal heart.

Interactive Link Questions

1. Watch this video (http://openstax.org/l/capillaryfunct) to explore capillaries and how they function in the body. Capillaries are never more than 100 micrometers away. What is the main component of interstitial fluid?

2. Listen to this CDC podcast (http://openstax.org/l/CDCpodcast) to learn about hypertension, often described as a "silent killer." What steps can you take to reduce your risk of a heart attack or stroke?

Review Questions

3. The endothelium is found in the _____.
   a. tunica intima
   b. tunica media
   c. tunica externa
   d. lumen

4. Nervi vasorum control _____.
   a. vasoconstriction
   b. vasodilation
   c. capillary permeability
   d. both vasoconstriction and vasodilation

5. Closer to the heart, arteries would be expected to have a higher percentage of _____.
   a. endothelium
   b. smooth muscle fibers
   c. elastic fibers
   d. collagenous fibers

6. Which of the following best describes veins?
   a. thick walled, small lumens, low pressure, lack valves
   b. thin walled, large lumens, low pressure, have valves
   c. thin walled, small lumens, high pressure, have valves
   d. thick walled, large lumens, high pressure, lack valves

7. An especially leaky type of capillary found in the liver and certain other tissues is called a _____.
   a. capillary bed
   b. fenestrated capillary
   c. sinusoid capillary
   d. metarteriole

8. In a blood pressure measurement of 110/70, the number 70 is the _____.
   a. systolic pressure
   b. diastolic pressure
   c. pulse pressure
   d. mean arterial pressure

9. A healthy elastic artery _____.
   a. is compliant
   b. reduces blood flow
   c. is a resistance artery
   d. has a thin wall and irregular lumen

10. Which of the following statements is *true*?
    a. The longer the vessel, the lower the resistance and the greater the flow.
    b. As blood volume decreases, blood pressure and blood flow also decrease.
    c. Increased viscosity increases blood flow.
    d. All of the above are true.

11. Slight vasodilation in an arteriole prompts a _____.
    a. slight increase in resistance
    b. huge increase in resistance
    c. slight decrease in resistance
    d. huge decrease in resistance

12. Venoconstriction increases which of the following?
    a. blood pressure within the vein
    b. blood flow within the vein
    c. return of blood to the heart
    d. all of the above

13. Hydrostatic pressure is _____.
    a. greater than colloid osmotic pressure at the venous end of the capillary bed
    b. the pressure exerted by fluid in an enclosed space
    c. about zero at the midpoint of a capillary bed
    d. all of the above

14. Net filtration pressure is calculated by _____.
    a. adding the capillary hydrostatic pressure to the interstitial fluid hydrostatic pressure
    b. subtracting the fluid drained by the lymphatic vessels from the total fluid in the interstitial fluid
    c. adding the blood colloid osmotic pressure to the capillary hydrostatic pressure
    d. subtracting the blood colloid osmotic pressure from the capillary hydrostatic pressure

15. Which of the following statements is true?
    a. In one day, more fluid exits the capillary through filtration than enters through reabsorption.
    b. In one day, approximately 35 mm of blood are filtered and 7 mm are reabsorbed.
    c. In one day, the capillaries of the lymphatic system absorb about 20.4 liters of fluid.
    d. None of the above are true.

16. Clusters of neurons in the medulla oblongata that regulate blood pressure are known collectively as _____.
    a. baroreceptors
    b. angioreceptors
    c. the cardiomotor mechanism
    d. the cardiovascular center

17. In the renin-angiotensin-aldosterone mechanism, _____.
    a. decreased blood pressure prompts the release of renin from the liver
    b. aldosterone prompts increased urine output
    c. aldosterone prompts the kidneys to reabsorb sodium
    d. all of the above

18. In the myogenic response, _____.
    a. muscle contraction promotes venous return to the heart
    b. ventricular contraction strength is decreased
    c. vascular smooth muscle responds to stretch
    d. endothelins dilate muscular arteries

19. A form of circulatory shock common in young children with severe diarrhea or vomiting is _____.
    a. hypovolemic shock
    b. anaphylactic shock
    c. obstructive shock
    d. hemorrhagic shock

20. The coronary arteries branch off of the _____.
    a. aortic valve
    b. ascending aorta
    c. aortic arch
    d. thoracic aorta

21. Which of the following statements is true?
    a. The left and right common carotid arteries both branch off of the brachiocephalic trunk.
    b. The brachial artery is the distal branch of the axillary artery.
    c. The radial and ulnar arteries join to form the palmar arch.
    d. All of the above are true.

22. Arteries serving the stomach, pancreas, and liver all branch from the _____.
    a. superior mesenteric artery
    b. inferior mesenteric artery
    c. celiac trunk
    d. splenic artery

23. The right and left brachiocephalic veins _____.
    a. drain blood from the right and left internal jugular veins
    b. drain blood from the right and left subclavian veins
    c. drain into the superior vena cava
    d. all of the above are true

24. The hepatic portal system delivers blood from the digestive organs to the _____.
    a. liver
    b. hypothalamus
    c. spleen
    d. left atrium

25. Blood islands are _____.
    a. clusters of blood-filtering cells in the placenta
    b. masses of pluripotent stem cells scattered throughout the fetal bone marrow
    c. vascular tubes that give rise to the embryonic tubular heart
    d. masses of developing blood vessels and formed elements scattered throughout the embryonic disc

26. Which of the following statements is true?
    a. Two umbilical veins carry oxygen-depleted blood from the fetal circulation to the placenta.
    b. One umbilical vein carries oxygen-rich blood from the placenta to the fetal heart.
    c. Two umbilical arteries carry oxygen-depleted blood to the fetal lungs.
    d. None of the above are true.

27. The ductus venosus is a shunt that allows _____.
    a. fetal blood to flow from the right atrium to the left atrium
    b. fetal blood to flow from the right ventricle to the left ventricle
    c. most freshly oxygenated blood to flow into the fetal heart
    d. most oxygen-depleted fetal blood to flow directly into the fetal pulmonary trunk

Critical Thinking Questions

28. Arterioles are often referred to as resistance vessels. Why?

29. Cocaine use causes vasoconstriction. Is this likely to increase or decrease blood pressure, and why?

30. A blood vessel with a few smooth muscle fibers and connective tissue, and only a very thin tunica externa conducts blood toward the heart. What type of vessel is this?

31. You measure a patient's blood pressure at 130/85. Calculate the patient's pulse pressure and mean arterial pressure. Determine whether each pressure is low, normal, or high.

32. An obese patient comes to the clinic complaining of swollen feet and ankles, fatigue, shortness of breath, and often feeling "spaced out." She is a cashier in a grocery store, a job that requires her to stand all day. Outside of work, she engages in no physical activity. She confesses that, because of her weight, she finds even walking uncomfortable. Explain how the skeletal muscle pump might play a role in this patient's signs and symptoms.

33. A patient arrives at the emergency department with dangerously low blood pressure. The patient's blood colloid osmotic pressure is normal. How would you expect this situation to affect the patient's net filtration pressure?

34. True or false? The plasma proteins suspended in blood cross the capillary cell membrane and enter the tissue fluid via facilitated diffusion. Explain your thinking.

35. A patient arrives in the emergency department with a blood pressure of 70/45 confused and complaining of thirst. Why?

36. Nitric oxide is broken down very quickly after its release. Why?

37. Identify the ventricle of the heart that pumps oxygen-depleted blood and the arteries of the body that carry oxygen-depleted blood.

38. What organs do the gonadal veins drain?

39. What arteries play the leading roles in supplying blood to the brain?

40. All tissues, including malignant tumors, need a blood supply. Explain why drugs called angiogenesis inhibitors would be used in cancer treatment.

41. Explain the location and importance of the ductus arteriosus in fetal circulation.

CHAPTER 21
The Lymphatic and Immune System

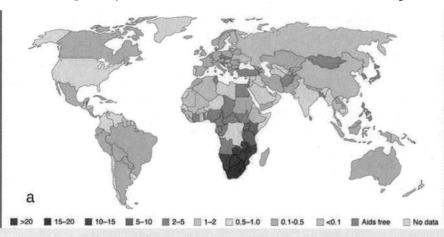

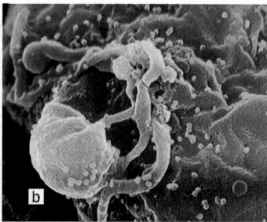

■ >20 ■ 15–20 ■ 10–15 ■ 5–10 ■ 2–5 □ 1–2 □ 0.5–1.0 ■ 0.1-0.5 □ <0.1 ■ Aids free □ No data

Figure 21.1 The Worldwide AIDS Epidemic (a) As of 2008, more than 15 percent of adults were infected with HIV in certain African countries. This grim picture had changed little by 2012. (b) In this scanning electron micrograph, HIV virions (green particles) are budding off the surface of a macrophage (pink structure). (credit b: C. Goldsmith)

CHAPTER OBJECTIVES
After studying this chapter, you will be able to:

- Identify the components and anatomy of the lymphatic system
- Discuss the role of the innate immune response against pathogens
- Describe the power of the adaptive immune response to cure disease
- Explain immunological deficiencies and over-reactions of the immune system
- Discuss the role of the immune response in transplantation and cancer
- Describe the interaction of the immune and lymphatic systems with other body systems

INTRODUCTION In June 1981, the Centers for Disease Control and Prevention (CDC), in Atlanta, Georgia, published a report of an unusual cluster of five patients in Los Angeles, California. All five were diagnosed with a rare pneumonia caused by a fungus called *Pneumocystis jirovecii* (formerly known as *Pneumocystis carinii*).

Why was this unusual? Although commonly found in the lungs of healthy individuals, this fungus is an opportunistic pathogen that causes disease in individuals with suppressed or underdeveloped immune systems. The very young, whose immune systems have yet to mature, and the elderly, whose immune systems have declined with age, are particularly susceptible. The five patients from LA, though, were between 29 and 36 years of age and should have been in the prime of their lives, immunologically speaking. What could be going on?

A few days later, a cluster of eight cases was reported in New York City, also involving young patients, this time exhibiting a rare form of skin cancer known as Kaposi's sarcoma. This cancer of the cells that line the blood and lymphatic vessels was previously observed as a relatively innocuous disease of the elderly. The disease that doctors saw in 1981 was frighteningly more severe, with multiple, fast-growing lesions that spread to all parts of the body, including the trunk and face. Could the immune systems of these young patients have been compromised in some way? Indeed, when they were tested, they exhibited extremely low numbers of a specific type of white blood cell in their bloodstreams, indicating that they had somehow lost a major part of the immune system.

Acquired immune deficiency syndrome, or AIDS, turned out to be a new disease caused by the previously unknown human immunodeficiency virus (HIV). Although nearly 100 percent fatal in those with active HIV infections in the early years, the development of anti-HIV drugs has transformed HIV infection into a chronic, manageable disease and not the certain death sentence it once was. One positive outcome resulting from the emergence of HIV disease was that the public's attention became focused as never before on the importance of having a functional and healthy immune system.

21.1 Anatomy of the Lymphatic and Immune Systems

LEARNING OBJECTIVES

By the end of this section, you will be able to:

- Describe the structure and function of the lymphatic tissue (lymph fluid, vessels, ducts, and organs)
- Describe the structure and function of the primary and secondary lymphatic organs
- Discuss the cells of the immune system, how they function, and their relationship with the lymphatic system

The **immune system** is the complex collection of cells and organs that destroys or neutralizes pathogens that would otherwise cause disease or death. The lymphatic system, for most people, is associated with the immune system to such a degree that the two systems are virtually indistinguishable. The **lymphatic system** is the system of vessels, cells, and organs that carries excess fluids to the bloodstream and filters pathogens from the blood. The swelling of lymph nodes during an infection and the transport of lymphocytes via the lymphatic vessels are but two examples of the many connections between these critical organ systems.

Functions of the Lymphatic System

A major function of the lymphatic system is to drain body fluids and return them to the bloodstream. Blood pressure causes leakage of fluid from the capillaries, resulting in the accumulation of fluid in the interstitial space—that is, spaces between individual cells in the tissues. In humans, 20 liters of plasma is released into the interstitial space of the tissues each day due to capillary filtration. Once this filtrate is out of the bloodstream and in the tissue spaces, it is referred to as interstitial fluid. Of this, 17 liters is reabsorbed directly by the blood vessels. But what happens to the remaining three liters? This is where the lymphatic system comes into play. It drains the excess fluid and empties it back into the bloodstream via a series of vessels, trunks, and ducts. **Lymph** is the term used to describe interstitial fluid once it has entered the lymphatic system. When the lymphatic system is damaged in some way, such as by being blocked by cancer cells or destroyed by injury, protein-rich interstitial fluid accumulates (sometimes "backs up" from the lymph vessels) in the tissue spaces. This inappropriate accumulation of fluid referred to as lymphedema may lead to serious medical consequences.

As the vertebrate immune system evolved, the network of lymphatic vessels became convenient avenues for transporting the cells of the immune system. Additionally, the transport of dietary lipids and fat-soluble vitamins absorbed in the gut uses this system.

Cells of the immune system not only use lymphatic vessels to make their way from interstitial spaces back into the circulation, but they also use lymph nodes as major staging areas for the development of critical immune responses. A **lymph node** is one of the small, bean-shaped organs located throughout the lymphatic system.

⊘ INTERACTIVE LINK

Visit this website (http://openstax.org/l/lymphsystem) for an overview of the lymphatic system. What are the three main components of the lymphatic system?

Structure of the Lymphatic System

The lymphatic vessels begin as a blind ending, or closed at one end, capillaries, which feed into larger and larger lymphatic vessels, and eventually empty into the bloodstream by a series of ducts. Along the way, the lymph travels through the lymph nodes, which are commonly found near the groin, armpits, neck, chest, and abdomen. Humans have about 500–600 lymph nodes throughout the body (Figure 21.2).

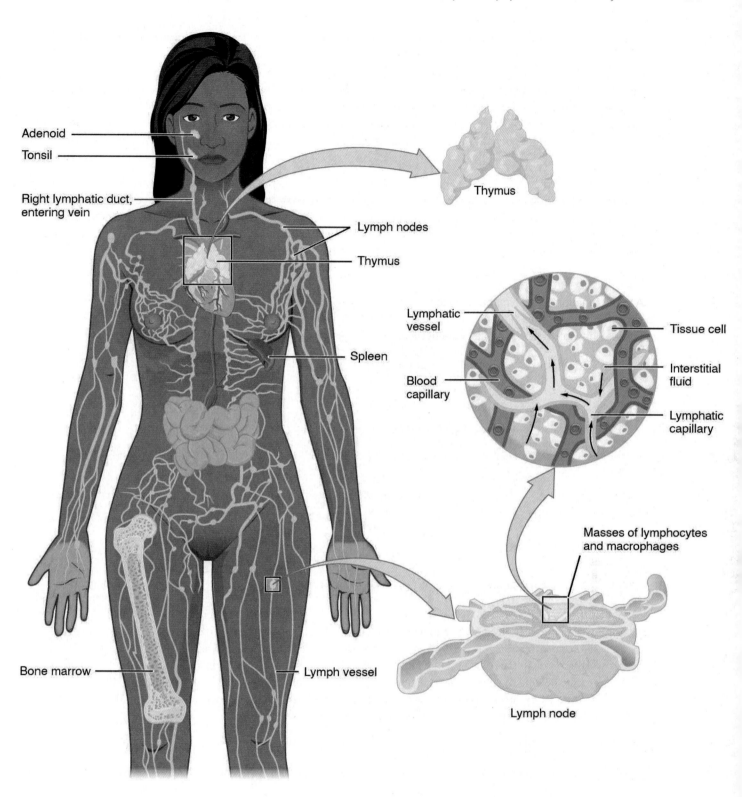

Adenoid

Tonsil

Right lymphatic duct, entering vein

Thymus

Lymph nodes

Thymus

Spleen

Lymphatic vessel

Tissue cell

Blood capillary

Interstitial fluid

Lymphatic capillary

Masses of lymphocytes and macrophages

Bone marrow

Lymph vessel

Lymph node

FIGURE 21.2 Anatomy of the Lymphatic System   Lymphatic vessels in the arms and legs convey lymph to the larger lymphatic vessels in the torso.

A major distinction between the lymphatic and cardiovascular systems in humans is that lymph is not actively pumped by the heart, but is forced through the vessels by the movements of the body, the contraction of skeletal muscles during body movements, and breathing. One-way valves (semi-lunar valves) in lymphatic vessels keep the lymph moving toward the heart. Lymph flows from the lymphatic capillaries, through lymphatic vessels, and then is dumped into the circulatory system via the lymphatic ducts located at the junction of the jugular and subclavian veins in the neck.

Lymphatic Capillaries

Lymphatic capillaries, also called the terminal lymphatics, are vessels where interstitial fluid enters the lymphatic system to become lymph fluid. Located in almost every tissue in the body, these vessels are interlaced among the arterioles and venules of the circulatory system in the soft connective tissues of the body (Figure 21.3). Exceptions are the central nervous system, bone marrow, bones, teeth, and the cornea of the eye, which do not contain lymph vessels.

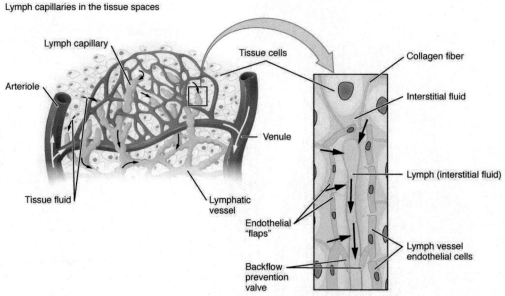

FIGURE 21.3 Lymphatic Capillaries   Lymphatic capillaries are interlaced with the arterioles and venules of the cardiovascular system. Collagen fibers anchor a lymphatic capillary in the tissue (inset). Interstitial fluid slips through spaces between the overlapping endothelial cells that compose the lymphatic capillary.

Lymphatic capillaries are formed by a one cell-thick layer of endothelial cells and represent the open end of the system, allowing interstitial fluid to flow into them via overlapping cells (see Figure 21.3). When interstitial pressure is low, the endothelial flaps close to prevent "backflow." As interstitial pressure increases, the spaces between the cells open up, allowing the fluid to enter. Entry of fluid into lymphatic capillaries is also enabled by the collagen filaments that anchor the capillaries to surrounding structures. As interstitial pressure increases, the filaments pull on the endothelial cell flaps, opening up them even further to allow easy entry of fluid.

In the small intestine, lymphatic capillaries called lacteals are critical for the transport of dietary lipids and lipid-soluble vitamins to the bloodstream. In the small intestine, dietary triglycerides combine with other lipids and proteins, and enter the lacteals to form a milky fluid called **chyle**. The chyle then travels through the lymphatic system, eventually entering the bloodstream.

Larger Lymphatic Vessels, Trunks, and Ducts

The lymphatic capillaries empty into larger lymphatic vessels, which are similar to veins in terms of their three-tunic structure and the presence of valves. These one-way valves are located fairly close to one another, and each one causes a bulge in the lymphatic vessel, giving the vessels a beaded appearance (see Figure 21.3).

The superficial and deep lymphatics eventually merge to form larger lymphatic vessels known as **lymphatic trunks**. On the right side of the body, the right sides of the head, thorax, and right upper limb drain lymph fluid into the right subclavian vein via the right lymphatic duct (Figure 21.4). On the left side of the body, the remaining portions of the body drain into the larger thoracic duct, which drains into the left subclavian vein. The thoracic duct itself begins just beneath the diaphragm in the **cisterna chyli**, a sac-like chamber that receives lymph from the lower abdomen, pelvis, and lower limbs by way of the left and right lumbar trunks and the intestinal trunk.

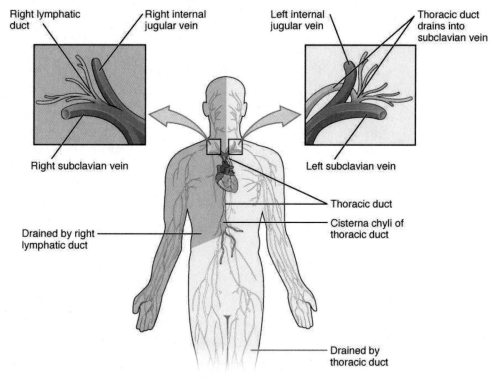

FIGURE 21.4   Major Trunks and Ducts of the Lymphatic System   The thoracic duct drains a much larger portion of the body than does the right lymphatic duct.

The overall drainage system of the body is asymmetrical (see Figure 21.4). The **right lymphatic duct** receives lymph from only the upper right side of the body. The lymph from the rest of the body enters the bloodstream through the **thoracic duct** via all the remaining lymphatic trunks. In general, lymphatic vessels of the subcutaneous tissues of the skin, that is, the superficial lymphatics, follow the same routes as veins, whereas the deep lymphatic vessels of the viscera generally follow the paths of arteries.

The Organization of Immune Function

The immune system is a collection of barriers, cells, and soluble proteins that interact and communicate with each other in extraordinarily complex ways. The modern model of immune function is organized into three phases based on the timing of their effects. The three temporal phases consist of the following:

- **Barrier defenses** such as the skin and mucous membranes, which act instantaneously to prevent pathogenic invasion into the body tissues
- The rapid but nonspecific **innate immune response**, which consists of a variety of specialized cells and soluble factors
- The slower but more specific and effective **adaptive immune response**, which involves many cell types and soluble factors, but is primarily controlled by white blood cells (leukocytes) known as **lymphocytes**, which help control immune responses

The cells of the blood, including all those involved in the immune response, arise in the bone marrow via various differentiation pathways from hematopoietic stem cells (Figure 21.5). In contrast with embryonic stem cells, hematopoietic stem cells are present throughout adulthood and allow for the continuous differentiation of blood cells to replace those lost to age or function. These cells can be divided into three classes based on function:

- Phagocytic cells, which ingest pathogens to destroy them
- Lymphocytes, which specifically coordinate the activities of adaptive immunity
- Cells containing cytoplasmic granules, which help mediate immune responses against parasites and

intracellular pathogens such as viruses

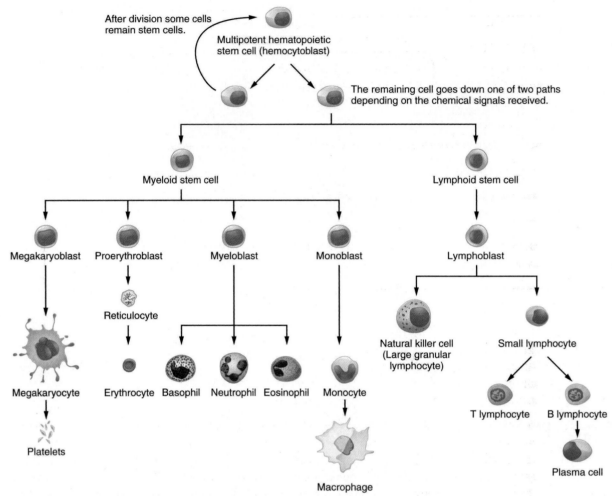

FIGURE 21.5   Hematopoietic System of the Bone Marrow   All the cells of the immune response as well as of the blood arise by differentiation from hematopoietic stem cells. Platelets are cell fragments involved in the clotting of blood.

Lymphocytes: B Cells, T Cells, Plasma Cells, and Natural Killer Cells

As stated above, lymphocytes are the primary cells of adaptive immune responses (Table 21.1). The two basic types of lymphocytes, B cells and T cells, are identical morphologically with a large central nucleus surrounded by a thin layer of cytoplasm. They are distinguished from each other by their surface protein markers as well as by the molecules they secrete. While B cells mature in red bone marrow and T cells mature in the thymus, they both initially develop from bone marrow. T cells migrate from bone marrow to the thymus gland where they further mature. B cells and T cells are found in many parts of the body, circulating in the bloodstream and lymph, and residing in secondary lymphoid organs, including the spleen and lymph nodes, which will be described later in this section. The human body contains approximately 10^{12} lymphocytes.

B Cells

B cells are immune cells that function primarily by producing antibodies. An **antibody** is any of the group of proteins that binds specifically to pathogen-associated molecules known as antigens. An **antigen** is a chemical structure on the surface of a pathogen that binds to T or B lymphocyte antigen receptors. Once activated by binding to antigen, B cells differentiate into cells that secrete a soluble form of their surface antibodies. These activated B cells are known as plasma cells.

T Cells

The **T cell**, on the other hand, does not secrete antibody but performs a variety of functions in the adaptive immune response. Different T cell types have the ability to either secrete soluble factors that communicate with other cells of the adaptive immune response or destroy cells infected with intracellular pathogens. The roles of T and B lymphocytes in the adaptive immune response will be discussed further in this chapter.

Plasma Cells

Another type of lymphocyte of importance is the plasma cell. A **plasma cell** is a B cell that has differentiated in response to antigen binding, and has thereby gained the ability to secrete soluble antibodies. These cells differ in morphology from standard B and T cells in that they contain a large amount of cytoplasm packed with the protein-synthesizing machinery known as rough endoplasmic reticulum.

Natural Killer Cells

A fourth important lymphocyte is the natural killer cell, a participant in the innate immune response. A **natural killer cell (NK)** is a circulating blood cell that contains cytotoxic (cell-killing) granules in its extensive cytoplasm. It shares this mechanism with the cytotoxic T cells of the adaptive immune response. NK cells are among the body's first lines of defense against viruses and certain types of cancer.

Lymphocytes

Type of lymphocyte	Primary function
B lymphocyte	Generates diverse antibodies
T lymphocyte	Secretes chemical messengers
Plasma cell	Secretes antibodies
NK cell	Destroys virally infected cells

TABLE 21.1

⊘ INTERACTIVE LINK

Visit this website (http://openstax.org/l/immunecells) to learn about the many different cell types in the immune system and their very specialized jobs. What is the role of the dendritic cell in an HIV infection?

Primary Lymphoid Organs and Lymphocyte Development

Understanding the differentiation and development of B and T cells is critical to the understanding of the adaptive immune response. It is through this process that the body (ideally) learns to destroy only pathogens and leaves the body's own cells relatively intact. The **primary lymphoid organs** are the bone marrow and thymus gland. The lymphoid organs are where lymphocytes mature, proliferate, and are selected, which enables them to attack pathogens without harming the cells of the body.

Bone Marrow

In the embryo, blood cells are made in the yolk sac. As development proceeds, this function is taken over by the spleen, lymph nodes, and liver. Later, the bone marrow takes over most hematopoietic functions, although the final stages of the differentiation of some cells may take place in other organs. The red **bone marrow** is a loose collection of cells where hematopoiesis occurs, and the yellow bone marrow is a site of energy storage, which consists largely of fat cells (Figure 21.6). The B cell undergoes nearly all of its development in the red bone marrow, whereas the immature T cell, called a **thymocyte**, leaves the bone marrow and matures largely in the thymus gland.

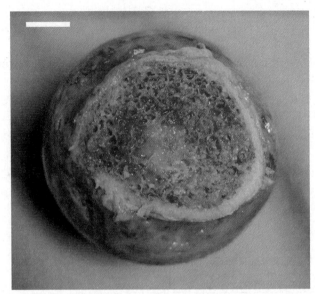

FIGURE 21.6   Bone Marrow   Red bone marrow fills the head of the femur, and a spot of yellow bone marrow is visible in the center. The white reference bar is 1 cm.

Thymus

The **thymus** gland is a bilobed organ found in the space between the sternum and the aorta of the heart (Figure 21.7). Connective tissue holds the lobes closely together but also separates them and forms a capsule.

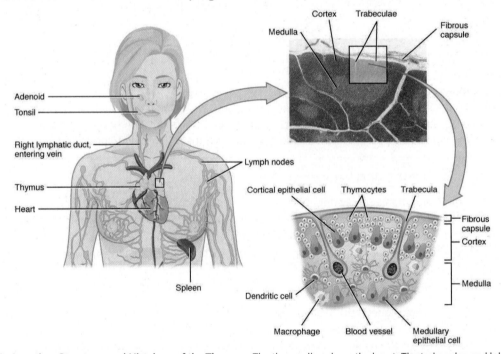

FIGURE 21.7   Location, Structure, and Histology of the Thymus   The thymus lies above the heart. The trabeculae and lobules, including the darkly staining cortex and the lighter staining medulla of each lobule, are clearly visible in the light micrograph of the thymus of a newborn. LM × 100. (Micrograph provided by the Regents of the University of Michigan Medical School © 2012)

🔗 INTERACTIVE LINK

View the University of Michigan WebScope (http://openstax.org/l/thymusMG) to explore the tissue sample in greater detail.

The connective tissue capsule further divides the thymus into lobules via extensions called trabeculae. The outer region of the organ is known as the cortex and contains large numbers of thymocytes with some epithelial cells, macrophages, and dendritic cells (two types of phagocytic cells that are derived from monocytes). The cortex is densely packed so it stains more intensely than the rest of the thymus (see Figure 21.7). The medulla, where thymocytes migrate before leaving the thymus, contains a less dense collection of thymocytes, epithelial cells, and dendritic cells.

Aging and the...

Immune System

By the year 2050, 25 percent of the population of the United States will be 60 years of age or older. The CDC estimates that 80 percent of those 60 years and older have one or more chronic disease associated with deficiencies of the immune systems. This loss of immune function with age is called immunosenescence. To treat this growing population, medical professionals must better understand the aging process. One major cause of age-related immune deficiencies is thymic involution, the shrinking of the thymus gland that begins at birth, at a rate of about three percent tissue loss per year, and continues until 35–45 years of age, when the rate declines to about one percent loss per year for the rest of one's life. At that pace, the total loss of thymic epithelial tissue and thymocytes would occur at about 120 years of age. Thus, this age is a theoretical limit to a healthy human lifespan.

Thymic involution has been observed in all vertebrate species that have a thymus gland. Animal studies have shown that transplanted thymic grafts between inbred strains of mice involuted according to the age of the donor and not of the recipient, implying the process is genetically programmed. There is evidence that the thymic microenvironment, so vital to the development of naïve T cells, loses thymic epithelial cells according to the decreasing expression of the FOXN1 gene with age.

It is also known that thymic involution can be altered by hormone levels. Sex hormones such as estrogen and testosterone enhance involution, and the hormonal changes in pregnant people cause a temporary thymic involution that reverses itself, when the size of the thymus and its hormone levels return to normal, usually after lactation ceases. What does all this tell us? Can we reverse immunosenescence, or at least slow it down? The potential is there for using thymic transplants from younger donors to keep thymic output of naïve T cells high. Gene therapies that target gene expression are also seen as future possibilities. The more we learn through immunosenescence research, the more opportunities there will be to develop therapies, even though these therapies will likely take decades to develop. The ultimate goal is for everyone to live and be healthy longer, but there may be limits to immortality imposed by our genes and hormones.

Secondary Lymphoid Organs and their Roles in Active Immune Responses

Lymphocytes develop and mature in the primary lymphoid organs, but they mount immune responses from the **secondary lymphoid organs**. A **naïve lymphocyte** is one that has left the primary organ and entered a secondary lymphoid organ. Naïve lymphocytes are fully functional immunologically, but have yet to encounter an antigen to respond to. In addition to circulating in the blood and lymph, lymphocytes concentrate in secondary lymphoid organs, which include the lymph nodes, spleen, and lymphoid nodules. All of these tissues have many features in common, including the following:

- The presence of lymphoid follicles, the sites of the formation of lymphocytes, with specific B cell-rich and T cell-rich areas
- An internal structure of reticular fibers with associated fixed macrophages
- **Germinal centers**, which are the sites of rapidly dividing and differentiating B lymphocytes
- Specialized post-capillary vessels known as **high endothelial venules**; the cells lining these venules are thicker and more columnar than normal endothelial cells, which allow cells from the blood to directly enter these tissues

Lymph Nodes

Lymph nodes function to remove debris and pathogens from the lymph, and are thus sometimes referred to as the "filters of the lymph" (Figure 21.8). Any bacteria that infect the interstitial fluid are taken up by the lymphatic capillaries and transported to a regional lymph node. Dendritic cells and macrophages within this organ internalize and kill many of the pathogens that pass through, thereby removing them from the body. The lymph node is also the site of adaptive immune responses mediated by T cells, B cells, and accessory cells of the adaptive immune system. Like the thymus, the bean-shaped lymph nodes are surrounded by a tough capsule of connective tissue and are separated into compartments by trabeculae, the extensions of the capsule. In addition to the structure provided by the capsule and trabeculae, the structural support of the lymph node is provided by a series of reticular fibers laid down by fibroblasts.

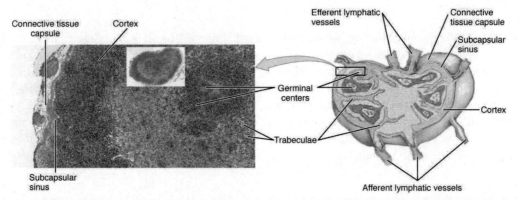

FIGURE 21.8   Structure and Histology of a Lymph Node   Lymph nodes are masses of lymphatic tissue located along the larger lymph vessels. The micrograph of the lymph nodes shows a germinal center, which consists of rapidly dividing B cells surrounded by a layer of T cells and other accessory cells. LM × 128. (Micrograph provided by the Regents of the University of Michigan Medical School © 2012)

INTERACTIVE LINK

View the University of Michigan WebScope (http://openstax.org/l/lymphnodeMG) to explore the tissue sample in greater detail.

The major routes into the lymph node are via **afferent lymphatic vessels** (see Figure 21.8). Cells and lymph fluid that leave the lymph node may do so by another set of vessels known as the **efferent lymphatic vessels**. Lymph enters the lymph node via the subcapsular sinus, which is occupied by dendritic cells, macrophages, and reticular fibers. Within the cortex of the lymph node are lymphoid follicles, which consist of germinal centers of rapidly dividing B cells surrounded by a layer of T cells and other accessory cells. As the lymph continues to flow through the node, it enters the medulla, which consists of medullary cords of B cells and plasma cells, and the medullary sinuses where the lymph collects before leaving the node via the efferent lymphatic vessels.

Spleen

In addition to the lymph nodes, the **spleen** is a major secondary lymphoid organ (Figure 21.9). It is about 12 cm (5 in) long and is attached to the lateral border of the stomach via the gastrosplenic ligament. The spleen is a fragile organ without a strong capsule, and is dark red due to its extensive vascularization. The spleen is sometimes called the "filter of the blood" because of its extensive vascularization and the presence of macrophages and dendritic cells that remove microbes and other materials from the blood, including dying red blood cells. The spleen also functions as the location of immune responses to blood-borne pathogens.

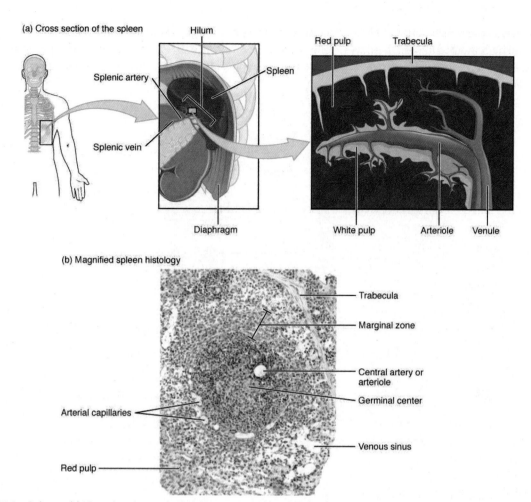

(a) Cross section of the spleen

Hilum

Splenic artery

Spleen

Splenic vein

Diaphragm

Red pulp

Trabecula

White pulp

Arteriole

Venule

(b) Magnified spleen histology

Trabecula

Marginal zone

Central artery or arteriole

Germinal center

Arterial capillaries

Venous sinus

Red pulp

FIGURE 21.9   Spleen   (a) The spleen is attached to the stomach. (b) A micrograph of spleen tissue shows the germinal center. The marginal zone is the region between the red pulp and white pulp, which sequesters particulate antigens from the circulation and presents these antigens to lymphocytes in the white pulp. EM × 660. (Micrograph provided by the Regents of the University of Michigan Medical School © 2012)

The spleen is also divided by trabeculae of connective tissue, and within each splenic nodule is an area of red pulp, consisting of mostly red blood cells, and white pulp, which resembles the lymphoid follicles of the lymph nodes. Upon entering the spleen, the splenic artery splits into several arterioles (surrounded by white pulp) and eventually into sinusoids. Blood from the capillaries subsequently collects in the venous sinuses and leaves via the splenic vein. The red pulp consists of reticular fibers with fixed macrophages attached, free macrophages, and all of the other cells typical of the blood, including some lymphocytes. The white pulp surrounds a central arteriole and consists of germinal centers of dividing B cells surrounded by T cells and accessory cells, including macrophages and dendritic cells. Thus, the red pulp primarily functions as a filtration system of the blood, using cells of the relatively nonspecific immune response, and white pulp is where adaptive T and B cell responses are mounted.

Lymphoid Nodules

The other lymphoid tissues, the **lymphoid nodules**, have a simpler architecture than the spleen and lymph nodes in that they consist of a dense cluster of lymphocytes without a surrounding fibrous capsule. These nodules are located in the respiratory and digestive tracts, areas routinely exposed to environmental pathogens.

Tonsils are lymphoid nodules located along the inner surface of the pharynx and are important in developing immunity to oral pathogens (Figure 21.10). The tonsil located at the back of the throat, the pharyngeal tonsil, is sometimes referred to as the adenoid when swollen. Such swelling is an indication of an active immune response to infection. Histologically, tonsils do not contain a complete capsule, and the epithelial layer invaginates deeply into the interior of the tonsil to form tonsillar crypts. These structures, which accumulate all sorts of materials taken into the body through eating and breathing, actually "encourage" pathogens to penetrate deep into the tonsillar tissues where they are acted upon by numerous lymphoid follicles and eliminated. This seems to be the major function of tonsils—to help children's bodies recognize, destroy, and develop immunity to common environmental pathogens so that they will be protected in their later lives. Tonsils are often removed in those children who have recurring throat infections, especially those involving the palatine tonsils on either side of the throat, whose swelling may interfere with their breathing and/or swallowing.

(a) Locations of the tonsils

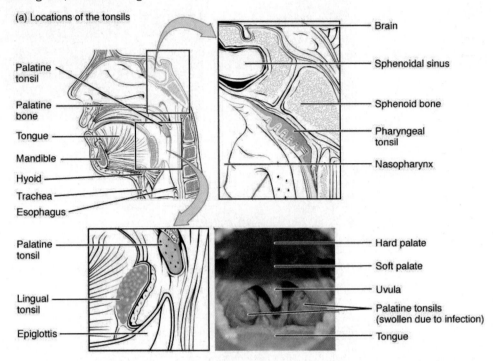

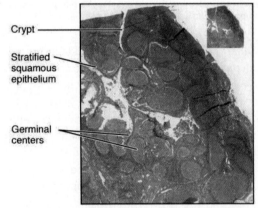

(b) Histology of palatine tonsil

FIGURE 21.10   Locations and Histology of the Tonsils   (a) The pharyngeal tonsil is located on the roof of the posterior superior wall of the nasopharynx. The palatine tonsils lay on each side of the pharynx. (b) A micrograph shows the palatine tonsil tissue. LM × 40. (Micrograph provided by the Regents of the University of Michigan Medical School © 2012)

🔗 INTERACTIVE LINK

View the University of Michigan WebScope (http://openstax.org/l/tonsilMG) to explore the tissue sample in greater detail.

Mucosa-associated lymphoid tissue (MALT) consists of an aggregate of lymphoid follicles directly associated with the mucous membrane epithelia. MALT makes up dome-shaped structures found underlying the mucosa of the gastrointestinal tract, breast tissue, lungs, and eyes. Peyer's patches, a type of MALT in the small intestine, are especially important for immune responses against ingested substances (Figure 21.11). Peyer's patches contain specialized endothelial cells called M (or microfold) cells that sample material from the intestinal lumen and transport it to nearby follicles so that adaptive immune responses to potential pathogens can be mounted. A similar process occurs involving MALT in the mucosa and submucosa of the appendix. A blockage of the lumen triggers these cells to elicit an inflammatory response that can lead to appendicitis.

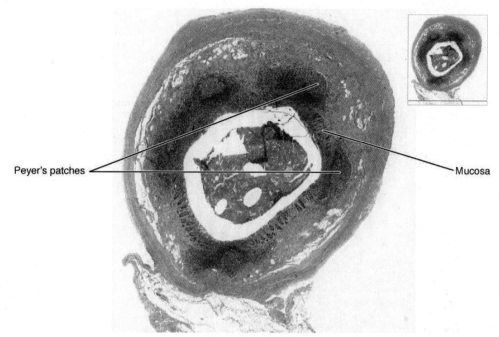

FIGURE 21.11   **Mucosa-associated Lymphoid Tissue (MALT) Nodule**   LM × 40. (Micrograph provided by the Regents of the University of Michigan Medical School © 2012)

Bronchus-associated lymphoid tissue (BALT) consists of lymphoid follicular structures with an overlying epithelial layer found along the bifurcations of the bronchi, and between bronchi and arteries. They also have the typically less-organized structure of other lymphoid nodules. These tissues, in addition to the tonsils, are effective against inhaled pathogens.

21.2 Barrier Defenses and the Innate Immune Response

LEARNING OBJECTIVES

By the end of this section, you will be able to:

- Describe the barrier defenses of the body
- Show how the innate immune response is important and how it helps guide and prepare the body for adaptive immune responses
- Describe various soluble factors that are part of the innate immune response
- Explain the steps of inflammation and how they lead to destruction of a pathogen
- Discuss early induced immune responses and their level of effectiveness

The immune system can be divided into two overlapping mechanisms to destroy pathogens: the innate immune response, which is relatively rapid but nonspecific and thus not always effective, and the adaptive immune response, which is slower in its development during an initial infection with a pathogen, but is highly specific and effective at attacking a wide variety of pathogens (Figure 21.12).

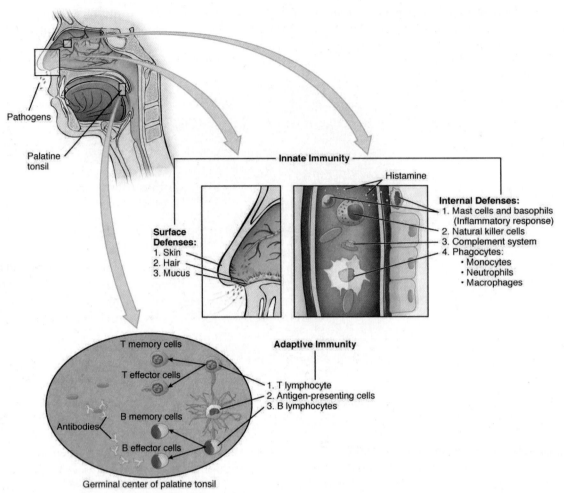

FIGURE 21.12   Cooperation between Innate and Adaptive Immune Responses   The innate immune system enhances adaptive immune responses so they can be more effective.

Any discussion of the innate immune response usually begins with the physical barriers that prevent pathogens from entering the body, destroy them after they enter, or flush them out before they can establish themselves in the hospitable environment of the body's soft tissues. Barrier defenses are part of the body's most basic defense mechanisms. The barrier defenses are not a response to infections, but they are continuously working to protect against a broad range of pathogens.

The different modes of barrier defenses are associated with the external surfaces of the body, where pathogens may try to enter (Table 21.2). The primary barrier to the entrance of microorganisms into the body is the skin. Not only is the skin covered with a layer of dead, keratinized epithelium that is too dry for bacteria in which to grow, but as these cells are continuously sloughed off from the skin, they carry bacteria and other pathogens with them. Additionally, sweat and other skin secretions may lower pH, contain toxic lipids, and physically wash microbes away.

Barrier Defenses

Site	Specific defense	Protective aspect
Skin	Epidermal surface	Keratinized cells of surface, Langerhans cells
Skin (sweat/secretions)	Sweat glands, sebaceous glands	Low pH, washing action

TABLE 21.2

Site	Specific defense	Protective aspect
Oral cavity	Salivary glands	Lysozyme
Stomach	Gastrointestinal tract	Low pH
Mucosal surfaces	Mucosal epithelium	Nonkeratinized epithelial cells
Normal flora (nonpathogenic bacteria)	Mucosal tissues	Prevent pathogens from growing on mucosal surfaces

TABLE 21.2

Another barrier is the saliva in the mouth, which is rich in lysozyme—an enzyme that destroys bacteria by digesting their cell walls. The acidic environment of the stomach, which is fatal to many pathogens, is also a barrier. Additionally, the mucus layer of the gastrointestinal tract, respiratory tract, reproductive tract, eyes, ears, and nose traps both microbes and debris, and facilitates their removal. In the case of the upper respiratory tract, ciliated epithelial cells move potentially contaminated mucus upwards to the mouth, where it is then swallowed into the digestive tract, ending up in the harsh acidic environment of the stomach. Considering how often you breathe compared to how often you eat or perform other activities that expose you to pathogens, it is not surprising that multiple barrier mechanisms have evolved to work in concert to protect this vital area.

Cells of the Innate Immune Response

A phagocyte is a cell that is able to surround and engulf a particle or cell, a process called **phagocytosis**. The phagocytes of the immune system engulf other particles or cells, either to clean an area of debris, old cells, or to kill pathogenic organisms such as bacteria. The phagocytes are the body's fast acting, first line of immunological defense against organisms that have breached barrier defenses and have entered the vulnerable tissues of the body.

Phagocytes: Macrophages and Neutrophils

Many of the cells of the immune system have a phagocytic ability, at least at some point during their life cycles. Phagocytosis is an important and effective mechanism of destroying pathogens during innate immune responses. The phagocyte takes the organism inside itself as a phagosome, which subsequently fuses with a lysosome and its digestive enzymes, effectively killing many pathogens. On the other hand, some bacteria including *Mycobacteria tuberculosis*, the cause of tuberculosis, may be resistant to these enzymes and are therefore much more difficult to clear from the body. Macrophages, neutrophils, and dendritic cells are the major phagocytes of the immune system.

A **macrophage** is an irregularly shaped phagocyte that is amoeboid in nature and is the most versatile of the phagocytes in the body. Macrophages move through tissues and squeeze through capillary walls using pseudopodia. They not only participate in innate immune responses but have also evolved to cooperate with lymphocytes as part of the adaptive immune response. Macrophages exist in many tissues of the body, either freely roaming through connective tissues or fixed to reticular fibers within specific tissues such as lymph nodes. When pathogens breach the body's barrier defenses, macrophages are the first line of defense (Table 21.3). They are called different names, depending on the tissue: Kupffer cells in the liver, histiocytes in connective tissue, and alveolar macrophages in the lungs.

A **neutrophil** is a phagocytic cell that is attracted via chemotaxis from the bloodstream to infected tissues. These spherical cells are granulocytes. A granulocyte contains cytoplasmic granules, which in turn contain a variety of vasoactive mediators such as histamine. In contrast, macrophages are agranulocytes. An agranulocyte has few or no cytoplasmic granules. Whereas macrophages act like sentries, always on guard against infection, neutrophils can be thought of as military reinforcements that are called into a battle to hasten the destruction of the enemy. Although, usually thought of as the primary pathogen-killing cell of the inflammatory process of the innate immune response, new research has suggested that neutrophils play a role in the adaptive immune response as well, just as macrophages do.

A **monocyte** is a circulating precursor cell that differentiates into either a macrophage or dendritic cell, which can be rapidly attracted to areas of infection by signal molecules of inflammation.

Phagocytic Cells of the Innate Immune System

Cell	Cell type	Primary location	Function in the innate immune response
Macrophage	Agranulocyte	Body cavities/organs	Phagocytosis
Neutrophil	Granulocyte	Blood	Phagocytosis
Monocyte	Agranulocyte	Blood	Precursor of macrophage/dendritic cell

TABLE 21.3

Natural Killer Cells

NK cells are a type of lymphocyte that have the ability to induce apoptosis, that is, programmed cell death, in cells infected with intracellular pathogens such as obligate intracellular bacteria and viruses. NK cells recognize these cells by mechanisms that are still not well understood, but that presumably involve their surface receptors. NK cells can induce apoptosis, in which a cascade of events inside the cell causes its own death by either of two mechanisms:

1) NK cells are able to respond to chemical signals and express the fas ligand. The **fas ligand** is a surface molecule that binds to the fas molecule on the surface of the infected cell, sending it apoptotic signals, thus killing the cell and the pathogen within it; or

2) The granules of the NK cells release perforins and granzymes. A **perforin** is a protein that forms pores in the membranes of infected cells. A **granzyme** is a protein-digesting enzyme that enters the cell via the perforin pores and triggers apoptosis intracellularly.

Both mechanisms are especially effective against virally infected cells. If apoptosis is induced before the virus has the ability to synthesize and assemble all its components, no infectious virus will be released from the cell, thus preventing further infection.

Recognition of Pathogens

Cells of the innate immune response, the phagocytic cells, and the cytotoxic NK cells recognize patterns of pathogen-specific molecules, such as bacterial cell wall components or bacterial flagellar proteins, using pattern recognition receptors. A **pattern recognition receptor (PRR)** is a membrane-bound receptor that recognizes characteristic features of a pathogen and molecules released by stressed or damaged cells.

These receptors, which are thought to have evolved prior to the adaptive immune response, are present on the cell surface whether they are needed or not. Their variety, however, is limited by two factors. First, the fact that each receptor type must be encoded by a specific gene requires the cell to allocate most or all of its DNA to make receptors able to recognize all pathogens. Secondly, the variety of receptors is limited by the finite surface area of the cell membrane. Thus, the innate immune system must "get by" using only a limited number of receptors that are active against as wide a variety of pathogens as possible. This strategy is in stark contrast to the approach used by the adaptive immune system, which uses large numbers of different receptors, each highly specific to a particular pathogen.

Should the cells of the innate immune system come into contact with a species of pathogen they recognize, the cell will bind to the pathogen and initiate phagocytosis (or cellular apoptosis in the case of an intracellular pathogen) in an effort to destroy the offending microbe. Receptors vary somewhat according to cell type, but they usually include receptors for bacterial components and for complement, discussed below.

Soluble Mediators of the Innate Immune Response

The previous discussions have alluded to chemical signals that can induce cells to change various physiological characteristics, such as the expression of a particular receptor. These soluble factors are secreted during innate or early induced responses, and later during adaptive immune responses.

Cytokines and Chemokines

A **cytokine** is signaling molecule that allows cells to communicate with each other over short distances. Cytokines are secreted into the intercellular space, and the action of the cytokine induces the receiving cell to change its physiology. A **chemokine** is a soluble chemical mediator similar to cytokines except that its function is to attract cells (chemotaxis) from longer distances.

⊘ INTERACTIVE LINK

Visit this website (http://openstax.org/l/chemotaxis) to learn about phagocyte chemotaxis. Phagocyte chemotaxis is the movement of phagocytes according to the secretion of chemical messengers in the form of interleukins and other chemokines. By what means does a phagocyte destroy a bacterium that it has ingested?

Early induced Proteins

Early induced proteins are those that are not constitutively present in the body, but are made as they are needed early during the innate immune response. **Interferons** are an example of early induced proteins. Cells infected with viruses secrete interferons that travel to adjacent cells and induce them to make antiviral proteins. Thus, even though the initial cell is sacrificed, the surrounding cells are protected. Other early induced proteins specific for bacterial cell wall components are mannose-binding protein and C-reactive protein, made in the liver, which bind specifically to polysaccharide components of the bacterial cell wall. Phagocytes such as macrophages have receptors for these proteins, and they are thus able to recognize them as they are bound to the bacteria. This brings the phagocyte and bacterium into close proximity and enhances the phagocytosis of the bacterium by the process known as opsonization. **Opsonization** is the tagging of a pathogen for phagocytosis by the binding of an antibody or an antimicrobial protein.

Complement System

The **complement** system is a series of proteins constitutively found in the blood plasma. As such, these proteins are not considered part of the **early induced immune response**, even though they share features with some of the antibacterial proteins of this class. Made in the liver, they have a variety of functions in the innate immune response, using what is known as the "alternate pathway" of complement activation. Additionally, complement functions in the adaptive immune response as well, in what is called the classical pathway. The complement system consists of several proteins that enzymatically alter and fragment later proteins in a series, which is why it is termed cascade. Once activated, the series of reactions is irreversible, and releases fragments that have the following actions:

- Bind to the cell membrane of the pathogen that activates it, labeling it for phagocytosis (opsonization)
- Diffuse away from the pathogen and act as chemotactic agents to attract phagocytic cells to the site of inflammation
- Form damaging pores in the plasma membrane of the pathogen

Figure 21.13 shows the classical pathway, which requires antibodies of the adaptive immune response. The alternate pathway does not require an antibody to become activated.

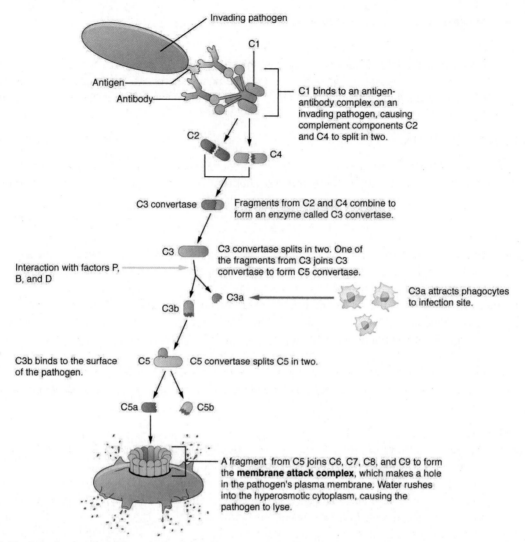

FIGURE 21.13   Complement Cascade and Function   The classical pathway, used during adaptive immune responses, occurs when C1 reacts with antibodies that have bound an antigen.

The splitting of the C3 protein is the common step to both pathways. In the alternate pathway, C3 is activated spontaneously and, after reacting with the molecules factor P, factor B, and factor D, splits apart. The larger fragment, C3b, binds to the surface of the pathogen and C3a, the smaller fragment, diffuses outward from the site of activation and attracts phagocytes to the site of infection. Surface-bound C3b then activates the rest of the cascade, with the last five proteins, C5–C9, forming the membrane-attack complex (MAC). The MAC can kill certain pathogens by disrupting their osmotic balance. The MAC is especially effective against a broad range of bacteria. The classical pathway is similar, except the early stages of activation require the presence of antibody bound to antigen, and thus is dependent on the adaptive immune response. The earlier fragments of the cascade also have important functions. Phagocytic cells such as macrophages and neutrophils are attracted to an infection site by chemotactic attraction to smaller complement fragments. Additionally, once they arrive, their receptors for surface-bound C3b opsonize the pathogen for phagocytosis and destruction.

Inflammatory Response

The hallmark of the innate immune response is **inflammation**. Inflammation is something everyone has experienced. Stub a toe, cut a finger, or do any activity that causes tissue damage and inflammation will result, with its four characteristics: heat, redness, pain, and swelling ("loss of function" is sometimes mentioned as a fifth characteristic). It is important to note that inflammation does not have to be initiated by an infection, but can also be caused by tissue injuries. The release of damaged cellular contents into the site of injury is enough to stimulate the response, even in the absence of breaks in physical barriers that would allow pathogens to enter (by hitting your thumb with a hammer, for example). The inflammatory reaction brings in phagocytic cells to the damaged area to clear cellular debris and to set the stage for wound repair (Figure 21.14).

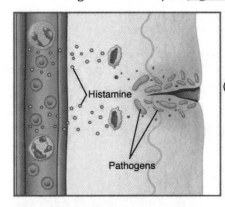

① Mast cells detect injury to nearby cells and release histamine, initiating inflammatory response.

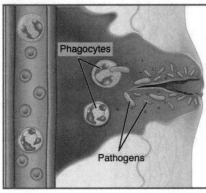

② Histamine increases blood flow to the wound sites, bringing in phagocytes and other immune cells that neutralize pathogens. The blood influx causes the wound to swell, redden, and become warm and painful.

FIGURE 21.14

This reaction also brings in the cells of the innate immune system, allowing them to get rid of the sources of a possible infection. Inflammation is part of a very basic form of immune response. The process not only brings fluid and cells into the site to destroy the pathogen and remove it and debris from the site, but also helps to isolate the site, limiting the spread of the pathogen. **Acute inflammation** is a short-term inflammatory response to an insult to the body. If the cause of the inflammation is not resolved, however, it can lead to chronic inflammation, which is associated with major tissue destruction and fibrosis. **Chronic inflammation** is ongoing inflammation. It can be caused by foreign bodies, persistent pathogens, and autoimmune diseases such as rheumatoid arthritis.

There are four important parts to the inflammatory response:

- *Tissue Injury.* The released contents of injured cells stimulate the release of **mast cell** granules and their potent inflammatory mediators such as histamine, leukotrienes, and prostaglandins. **Histamine** increases the diameter of local blood vessels (vasodilation), causing an increase in blood flow. Histamine also increases the permeability of local capillaries, causing plasma to leak out and form interstitial fluid. This causes the swelling associated with inflammation.

  Additionally, injured cells, phagocytes, and basophils are sources of inflammatory mediators, including prostaglandins and leukotrienes. Leukotrienes attract neutrophils from the blood by chemotaxis and increase vascular permeability. Prostaglandins cause vasodilation by relaxing vascular smooth muscle and are a major cause of the pain associated with inflammation. Nonsteroidal anti-inflammatory drugs such as aspirin and ibuprofen relieve pain by inhibiting prostaglandin production.

- *Vasodilation.* Many inflammatory mediators such as histamine are vasodilators that increase the diameters of local capillaries. This causes increased blood flow and is responsible for the heat and redness of inflamed tissue. It allows greater access of the blood to the site of inflammation.

- *Increased Vascular Permeability.* At the same time, inflammatory mediators increase the permeability of the local vasculature, causing leakage of fluid into the interstitial space, resulting in the swelling, or edema, associated with inflammation.

- *Recruitment of Phagocytes.* Leukotrienes are particularly good at attracting neutrophils from the blood to the site of infection by chemotaxis. Following an early neutrophil infiltrate stimulated by macrophage cytokines, more macrophages are recruited to clean up the debris left over at the site. When local infections are severe, neutrophils are attracted to the sites of infections in large numbers, and as they phagocytose the pathogens and subsequently die, their accumulated cellular remains are visible as pus at the infection site.

Overall, inflammation is valuable for many reasons. Not only are the pathogens killed and debris removed, but the increase in vascular permeability encourages the entry of clotting factors, the first step towards wound repair. Inflammation also facilitates the transport of antigen to lymph nodes by dendritic cells for the development of the adaptive immune response.

21.3 The Adaptive Immune Response: T lymphocytes and Their Functional Types

LEARNING OBJECTIVES

By the end of this section, you will be able to:

- Explain the advantages of the adaptive immune response over the innate immune response
- List the various characteristics of an antigen
- Describe the types of T cell antigen receptors
- Outline the steps of T cell development
- Describe the major T cell types and their functions

Innate immune responses (and early induced responses) are in many cases ineffective at completely controlling pathogen growth. However, they slow pathogen growth and allow time for the adaptive immune response to strengthen and either control or eliminate the pathogen. The innate immune system also sends signals to the cells of the adaptive immune system, guiding them in how to attack the pathogen. Thus, these are the two important arms of the immune response.

The Benefits of the Adaptive Immune Response

The specificity of the adaptive immune response—its ability to specifically recognize and make a response against a wide variety of pathogens—is its great strength. Antigens, the small chemical groups often associated with pathogens, are recognized by receptors on the surface of B and T lymphocytes. The adaptive immune response to these antigens is so versatile that it can respond to nearly any pathogen. This increase in specificity comes because the adaptive immune response has a unique way to develop as many as 10^{11}, or 100 trillion, different receptors to recognize nearly every conceivable pathogen. How could so many different types of antibodies be encoded? And what about the many specificities of T cells? There is not nearly enough DNA in a cell to have a separate gene for each specificity. The mechanism was finally worked out in the 1970s and 1980s using the new tools of molecular genetics.

Primary Disease and Immunological Memory

The immune system's first exposure to a pathogen is called a **primary adaptive response**. Symptoms of a first infection, called primary disease, are always relatively severe because it takes time for an initial adaptive immune response to a pathogen to become effective.

Upon re-exposure to the same pathogen, a secondary adaptive immune response is generated, which is stronger and faster than the primary response. The **secondary adaptive response** often eliminates a pathogen before it can cause significant tissue damage or any symptoms. Without symptoms, there is no disease, and the individual is not even aware of the infection. This secondary response is the basis of **immunological memory**, which protects us from getting diseases repeatedly from the same pathogen. By this mechanism, an individual's exposure to pathogens early in life spares the person from these diseases later in life.

Self Recognition

A third important feature of the adaptive immune response is its ability to distinguish between self-antigens, those that are normally present in the body, and foreign antigens, those that might be on a potential pathogen. As T and B cells mature, there are mechanisms in place that prevent them from recognizing self-antigen, preventing a damaging immune response against the body. These mechanisms are not 100 percent effective, however, and their breakdown leads to autoimmune diseases, which will be discussed later in this chapter.

T Cell-Mediated Immune Responses

The primary cells that control the adaptive immune response are the lymphocytes, the T and B cells. T cells are particularly important, as they not only control a multitude of immune responses directly, but also control B cell immune responses in many cases as well. Thus, many of the decisions about how to attack a pathogen are made at the T cell level, and knowledge of their functional types is crucial to understanding the functioning and regulation of adaptive immune responses as a whole.

T lymphocytes recognize antigens based on a two-chain protein receptor. The most common and important of these are the alpha-beta T cell receptors (Figure 21.15).

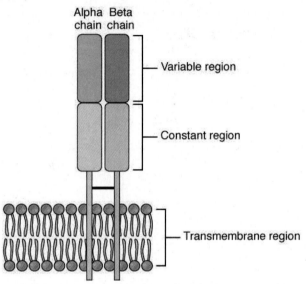

FIGURE 21.15   Alpha-beta T Cell Receptor   Notice the constant and variable regions of each chain, anchored by the transmembrane region.

There are two chains in the T cell receptor, and each chain consists of two domains. The **variable region domain** is furthest away from the T cell membrane and is so named because its amino acid sequence varies between receptors. In contrast, the **constant region domain** has less variation. The differences in the amino acid sequences of the variable domains are the molecular basis of the diversity of antigens the receptor can recognize. Thus, the antigen-binding site of the receptor consists of the terminal ends of both receptor chains, and the amino acid sequences of those two areas combine to determine its antigenic specificity. Each T cell produces only one type of receptor and thus is specific for a single particular antigen.

Antigens

Antigens on pathogens are usually large and complex, and consist of many antigenic determinants. An **antigenic determinant** (epitope) is one of the small regions within an antigen to which a receptor can bind, and antigenic determinants are limited by the size of the receptor itself. They usually consist of six or fewer amino acid residues in a protein, or one or two sugar moieties in a carbohydrate antigen. Antigenic determinants on a carbohydrate antigen are usually less diverse than on a protein antigen. Carbohydrate antigens are found on bacterial cell walls and on red blood cells (the ABO blood group antigens). Protein antigens are complex because of the variety of three-dimensional shapes that proteins can assume, and are especially important for the immune responses to viruses and worm parasites. It is the interaction of the shape of the antigen and the complementary shape of the amino acids of the antigen-binding site that accounts for the chemical basis of specificity (Figure 21.16).

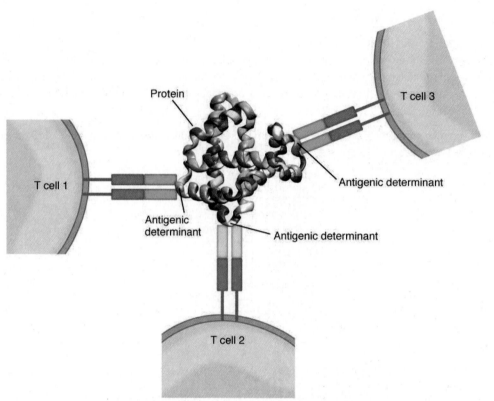

FIGURE 21.16 Antigenic Determinants   A typical protein antigen has multiple antigenic determinants, shown by the ability of T cells with three different specificities to bind to different parts of the same antigen.

Antigen Processing and Presentation

Although Figure 21.16 shows T cell receptors interacting with antigenic determinants directly, the mechanism that T cells use to recognize antigens is, in reality, much more complex. T cells do not recognize free-floating or cell-bound antigens as they appear on the surface of the pathogen. They only recognize antigen on the surface of specialized cells called antigen-presenting cells. Antigens are internalized by these cells. **Antigen processing** is a mechanism that enzymatically cleaves the antigen into smaller pieces. The antigen fragments are then brought to the cell's surface and associated with a specialized type of antigen-presenting protein known as a **major histocompatibility complex (MHC)** molecule. The MHC is the cluster of genes that encode these antigen-presenting molecules. The association of the antigen fragments with an MHC molecule on the surface of a cell is known as **antigen presentation** and results in the recognition of antigen by a T cell. This association of antigen and MHC occurs inside the cell, and it is the complex of the two that is brought to the surface. The peptide-binding cleft is a small indentation at the end of the MHC molecule that is furthest away from the cell membrane; it is here that the processed fragment of antigen sits. MHC molecules are capable of presenting a variety of antigens, depending on the amino acid sequence, in their peptide-binding clefts. It is the combination of the MHC molecule and the fragment of the original peptide or carbohydrate that is actually physically recognized by the T cell receptor (Figure 21.17).

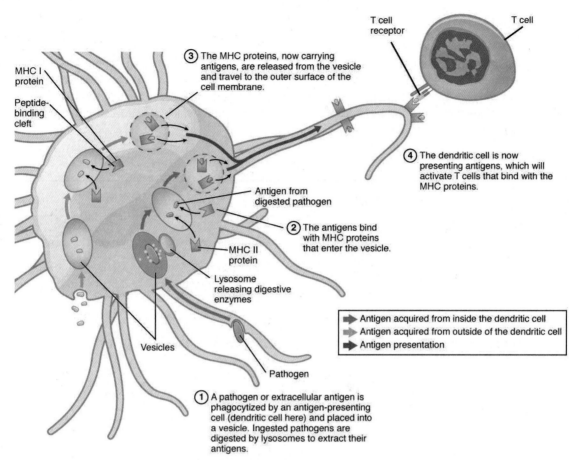

(3) The MHC proteins, now carrying antigens, are released from the vesicle and travel to the outer surface of the cell membrane.

T cell receptor

T cell

MHC I protein

Peptide-binding cleft

(4) The dendritic cell is now presenting antigens, which will activate T cells that bind with the MHC proteins.

Antigen from digested pathogen

(2) The antigens bind with MHC proteins that enter the vesicle.

MHC II protein

Lysosome releasing digestive enzymes

➡ Antigen acquired from inside the dendritic cell
➡ Antigen acquired from outside of the dendritic cell
➡ Antigen presentation

Vesicles

Pathogen

(1) A pathogen or extracellular antigen is phagocytized by an antigen-presenting cell (dendritic cell here) and placed into a vesicle. Ingested pathogens are digested by lysosomes to extract their antigens.

FIGURE 21.17 Antigen Processing and Presentation

Two distinct types of MHC molecules, **MHC class I** and **MHC class II**, play roles in antigen presentation. Although produced from different genes, they both have similar functions. They bring processed antigen to the surface of the cell via a transport vesicle and present the antigen to the T cell and its receptor. Antigens from different classes of pathogens, however, use different MHC classes and take different routes through the cell to get to the surface for presentation. The basic mechanism, though, is the same. Antigens are processed by digestion, are brought into the endomembrane system of the cell, and then are expressed on the surface of the antigen-presenting cell for antigen recognition by a T cell. Intracellular antigens are typical of viruses, which replicate inside the cell, and certain other intracellular parasites and bacteria. These antigens are processed in the cytosol by an enzyme complex known as the proteasome and are then brought into the endoplasmic reticulum by the transporter associated with antigen processing (TAP) system, where they interact with class I MHC molecules and are eventually transported to the cell surface by a transport vesicle.

Extracellular antigens, characteristic of many bacteria, parasites, and fungi that do not replicate inside the cell's cytoplasm, are brought into the endomembrane system of the cell by receptor-mediated endocytosis. The resulting vesicle fuses with vesicles from the Golgi complex, which contain pre-formed MHC class II molecules. After fusion of these two vesicles and the association of antigen and MHC, the new vesicle makes its way to the cell surface.

Professional Antigen-presenting Cells

Many cell types express class I molecules for the presentation of intracellular antigens. These MHC molecules may then stimulate a cytotoxic T cell immune response, eventually destroying the cell and the pathogen within. This is especially important when it comes to the most common class of intracellular pathogens, the virus. Viruses infect nearly every tissue of the body, so all these tissues must necessarily be able to express class I MHC or no T cell response can be made.

On the other hand, class II MHC molecules are expressed only on the cells of the immune system, specifically cells that affect other arms of the immune response. Thus, these cells are called "professional" antigen-presenting cells to distinguish them from those that bear class I MHC. The three types of professional antigen presenters are macrophages, dendritic cells, and B cells (Table 21.4).

Macrophages stimulate T cells to release cytokines that enhance phagocytosis. Dendritic cells also kill pathogens by phagocytosis (see Figure 21.17), but their major function is to bring antigens to regional draining lymph nodes. The lymph nodes are the locations in which most T cell responses against pathogens of the interstitial tissues are mounted. Macrophages are found in the skin and in the lining of mucosal surfaces, such as the nasopharynx, stomach, lungs, and intestines. B cells may also present antigens to T cells, which are necessary for certain types of antibody responses, to be covered later in this chapter.

Classes of Antigen-presenting Cells

MHC	Cell type	Phagocytic?	Function
Class I	Many	No	Stimulates cytotoxic T cell immune response
Class II	Macrophage	Yes	Stimulates phagocytosis and presentation at primary infection site
Class II	Dendritic	Yes, in tissues	Brings antigens to regional lymph nodes
Class II	B cell	Yes, internalizes surface Ig and antigen	Stimulates antibody secretion by B cells

TABLE 21.4

T Cell Development and Differentiation

The process of eliminating T cells that might attack the cells of one's own body is referred to as **T cell tolerance**. While thymocytes are in the cortex of the thymus, they are referred to as "double negatives," meaning that they do not bear the CD4 or CD8 molecules that you can use to follow their pathways of differentiation (Figure 21.18). In the cortex of the thymus, they are exposed to cortical epithelial cells. In a process known as **positive selection**, double-negative thymocytes bind to the MHC molecules they observe on the thymic epithelia, and the MHC molecules of "self" are selected. This mechanism kills many thymocytes during T cell differentiation. In fact, only two percent of the thymocytes that enter the thymus leave it as mature, functional T cells.

Access for free at openstax.org

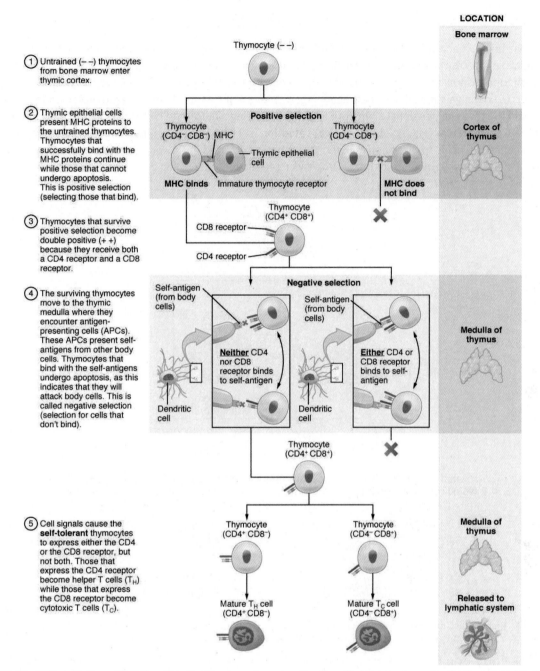

FIGURE 21.18 Differentiation of T Cells within the Thymus   Immature T-cells, called thymocytes, enter the thymus and go through a series of developmental stages that ensures both function and tolerance before they leave and become functional components of the adaptive immune response.

Later, the cells become double positives that express both CD4 and CD8 markers and move from the cortex to the junction between the cortex and medulla. It is here that negative selection takes place. In **negative selection**, self-antigens are brought into the thymus from other parts of the body by professional antigen-presenting cells. The T cells that bind to these self-antigens are selected for negatively and are killed by apoptosis. In summary, the only T cells left are those that can bind to MHC molecules of the body with foreign antigens presented on their binding clefts, preventing an attack on one's own body tissues, at least under normal circumstances. Tolerance can be broken, however, by the development of an autoimmune response, to be discussed later in this chapter.

The cells that leave the thymus become single positives, expressing either CD4 or CD8, but not both (see Figure 21.18). The CD4$^+$ T cells will bind to class II MHC and the CD8$^+$ cells will bind to class I MHC. The discussion that follows explains the functions of these molecules and how they can be used to differentiate between the different T cell functional types.

Mechanisms of T Cell-mediated Immune Responses

Mature T cells become activated by recognizing processed foreign antigen in association with a self-MHC molecule and begin dividing rapidly by mitosis. This proliferation of T cells is called **clonal expansion** and is necessary to make the immune response strong enough to effectively control a pathogen. How does the body select only those T cells that are needed against a specific pathogen? Again, the specificity of a T cell is based on the amino acid sequence and the three-dimensional shape of the antigen-binding site formed by the variable regions of the two chains of the T cell receptor (Figure 21.19). **Clonal selection** is the process of antigen binding only to those T cells that have receptors specific to that antigen. Each T cell that is activated has a specific receptor "hard-wired" into its DNA, and all of its progeny will have identical DNA and T cell receptors, forming clones of the original T cell.

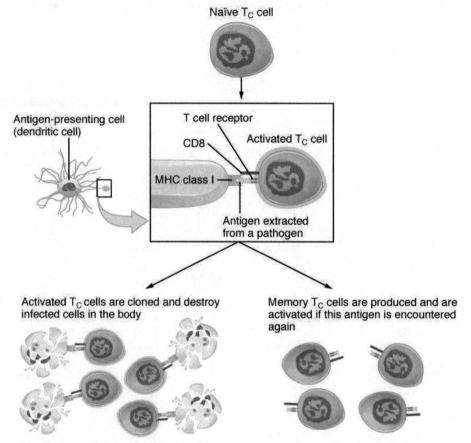

FIGURE 21.19   Clonal Selection and Expansion of T Lymphocytes   Stem cells differentiate into T cells with specific receptors, called clones. The clones with receptors specific for antigens on the pathogen are selected for and expanded.

Clonal Selection and Expansion

The clonal selection theory was proposed by Frank Burnet in the 1950s. However, the term clonal selection is not a complete description of the theory, as clonal expansion goes hand in glove with the selection process. The main tenet of the theory is that a typical individual has a multitude (10^{11}) of different types of T cell clones based on their receptors. In this use, a **clone** is a group of lymphocytes that share the same **antigen receptor**. Each clone is necessarily present in the body in low numbers. Otherwise, the body would not have room for lymphocytes with so many specificities.

Only those clones of lymphocytes whose receptors are activated by the antigen are stimulated to proliferate. Keep in mind that most antigens have multiple antigenic determinants, so a T cell response to a typical antigen involves a polyclonal response. A **polyclonal response** is the stimulation of multiple T cell clones. Once activated, the selected clones increase in number and make many copies of each cell type, each clone with its unique receptor. By the time this process is complete, the body will have large numbers of specific lymphocytes available to fight the infection (see Figure 21.19).

Access for free at openstax.org

The Cellular Basis of Immunological Memory

As already discussed, one of the major features of an adaptive immune response is the development of immunological memory.

During a primary adaptive immune response, both **memory T cells** and **effector T cells** are generated. Memory T cells are long-lived and can even persist for a lifetime. Memory cells are primed to act rapidly. Thus, any subsequent exposure to the pathogen will elicit a very rapid T cell response. This rapid, secondary adaptive response generates large numbers of effector T cells so fast that the pathogen is often overwhelmed before it can cause any symptoms of disease. This is what is meant by immunity to a disease. The same pattern of primary and secondary immune responses occurs in B cells and the antibody response, as will be discussed later in the chapter.

T Cell Types and their Functions

In the discussion of T cell development, you saw that mature T cells express either the CD4 marker or the CD8 marker, but not both. These markers are cell adhesion molecules that keep the T cell in close contact with the antigen-presenting cell by directly binding to the MHC molecule (to a different part of the molecule than does the antigen). Thus, T cells and antigen-presenting cells are held together in two ways: by CD4 or CD8 attaching to MHC and by the T cell receptor binding to antigen (Figure 21.20).

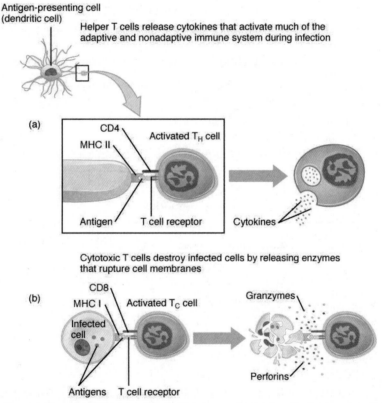

FIGURE 21.20   Pathogen Presentation   (a) CD4 is associated with helper and regulatory T cells. An extracellular pathogen is processed and presented in the binding cleft of a class II MHC molecule, and this interaction is strengthened by the CD4 molecule. (b) CD8 is associated with cytotoxic T cells. An intracellular pathogen is presented by a class I MHC molecule, and CD8 interacts with it.

Although the correlation is not 100 percent, CD4-bearing T cells are associated with helper functions and CD8-bearing T cells are associated with cytotoxicity. These functional distinctions based on CD4 and CD8 markers are useful in defining the function of each type.

Helper T Cells and their Cytokines

Helper T cells (Th), bearing the CD4 molecule, function by secreting cytokines that act to enhance other immune responses. There are two classes of Th cells, and they act on different components of the immune response. These cells are not distinguished by their surface molecules but by the characteristic set of cytokines they secrete (Table 21.5).

Th1 cells are a type of helper T cell that secretes cytokines that regulate the immunological activity and development of a variety of cells, including macrophages and other types of T cells.

Th2 cells, on the other hand, are cytokine-secreting cells that act on B cells to drive their differentiation into plasma cells that make antibody. In fact, T cell help is required for antibody responses to most protein antigens, and these are called T cell-dependent antigens.

Cytotoxic T cells

Cytotoxic T cells (Tc) are T cells that kill target cells by inducing apoptosis using the same mechanism as NK cells. They either express Fas ligand, which binds to the fas molecule on the target cell, or act by using perforins and granzymes contained in their cytoplasmic granules. As was discussed earlier with NK cells, killing a virally infected cell before the virus can complete its replication cycle results in the production of no infectious particles. As more Tc cells are developed during an immune response, they overwhelm the ability of the virus to cause disease. In addition, each Tc cell can kill more than one target cell, making them especially effective. Tc cells are so important in the antiviral immune response that some speculate that this was the main reason the adaptive immune response evolved in the first place.

Regulatory T Cells

Regulatory T cells (Treg), or suppressor T cells, are the most recently discovered of the types listed here, so less is understood about them. In addition to CD4, they bear the molecules CD25 and FOXP3. Exactly how they function is still under investigation, but it is known that they suppress other T cell immune responses. This is an important feature of the immune response, because if clonal expansion during immune responses were allowed to continue uncontrolled, these responses could lead to autoimmune diseases and other medical issues.

Not only do T cells directly destroy pathogens, but they regulate nearly all other types of the adaptive immune response as well, as evidenced by the functions of the T cell types, their surface markers, the cells they work on, and the types of pathogens they work against (see Table 21.5).

Functions of T Cell Types and Their Cytokines

T cell	Main target	Function	Pathogen	Surface marker	MHC	Cytokines or mediators
Tc	Infected cells	Cytotoxicity	Intracellular	CD8	Class I	Perforins, granzymes, and fas ligand
Th1	Macrophage	Helper inducer	Extracellular	CD4	Class II	Interferon-γ and TGF-β
Th2	B cell	Helper inducer	Extracellular	CD4	Class II	IL-4, IL-6, IL-10, and others
Treg	Th cell	Suppressor	None	CD4, CD25	?	TGF-β and IL-10

TABLE 21.5

21.4 The Adaptive Immune Response: B-lymphocytes and Antibodies

LEARNING OBJECTIVES

By the end of this section, you will be able to:

- Explain how B cells mature and how B cell tolerance develops
- Discuss how B cells are activated and differentiate into plasma cells
- Describe the structure of the antibody classes and their functions

Antibodies were the first component of the adaptive immune response to be characterized by scientists working on the immune system. It was already known that individuals who survived a bacterial infection were immune to re-infection with the same pathogen. Early microbiologists took serum from an immune patient and mixed it with a fresh culture of the same type of bacteria, then observed the bacteria under a microscope. The bacteria became clumped in a process called agglutination. When a different bacterial species was used, the agglutination did not happen. Thus, there was something in the serum of immune individuals that could specifically bind to and agglutinate bacteria.

Scientists now know the cause of the agglutination is an antibody molecule, also called an **immunoglobulin**. What is an antibody? An antibody protein is essentially a secreted form of a B cell receptor. (In fact, surface immunoglobulin is another name for the B cell receptor.) Not surprisingly, the same genes encode both the secreted antibodies and the surface immunoglobulins. One minor difference in the way these proteins are synthesized distinguishes a naïve B cell with antibody on its surface from an antibody-secreting plasma cell with no antibodies on its surface. The antibodies of the plasma cell have the exact same antigen-binding site and specificity as their B cell precursors.

There are five different classes of antibody found in humans: IgM, IgD, IgG, IgA, and IgE. Each of these has specific functions in the immune response, so by learning about them, researchers can learn about the great variety of antibody functions critical to many adaptive immune responses.

B cells do not recognize antigen in the complex fashion of T cells. B cells can recognize native, unprocessed antigen and do not require the participation of MHC molecules and antigen-presenting cells.

B Cell Differentiation and Activation

B cells differentiate in the bone marrow. During the process of maturation, up to 100 trillion different clones of B cells are generated, which is similar to the diversity of antigen receptors seen in T cells.

B cell differentiation and the development of tolerance are not quite as well understood as it is in T cells. **Central tolerance** is the destruction or inactivation of B cells that recognize self-antigens in the bone marrow, and its role is critical and well established. In the process of **clonal deletion**, immature B cells that bind strongly to self-antigens expressed on tissues are signaled to induce their own destruction by apoptosis, removing them from the population. In the process of **clonal anergy**, however, B cells exposed to soluble antigen in the bone marrow are not physically deleted, but become unable to function.

Another mechanism called peripheral tolerance is a direct result of T cell tolerance. In **peripheral tolerance**, functional, mature B cells leave the bone marrow but have yet to be exposed to self-antigen. Most protein antigens require signals from helper T cells (Th2) to proceed to make antibody. When a B cell binds to a self-antigen but receives no signals from a nearby Th2 cell to produce antibody, the cell is signaled to undergo apoptosis and is destroyed. This is yet another example of the control that T cells have over the adaptive immune response.

After B cells are activated by their binding to antigen, they differentiate into plasma cells. Plasma cells often leave the secondary lymphoid organs, where the response is generated, and migrate back to the bone marrow, where the whole differentiation process started. After secreting antibodies for a specific period, they die, as most of their energy is devoted to making antibodies and not to maintaining themselves. Thus, plasma cells are said to be terminally differentiated.

The final B cell of interest is the memory B cell, which results from the clonal expansion of an activated B cell. Memory B cells function in a way similar to memory T cells. They lead to a stronger and faster secondary response when compared to the primary response, as illustrated below.

Antibody Structure

Antibodies are glycoproteins consisting of two types of polypeptide chains with attached carbohydrates. The **heavy chain** and the **light chain** are the two polypeptides that form the antibody. The main differences between the classes of antibodies are in the differences between their heavy chains, but as you shall see, the light chains have an important role, forming part of the antigen-binding site on the antibody molecules.

Four-chain Models of Antibody Structures

All antibody molecules have two identical heavy chains and two identical light chains. (Some antibodies contain multiple units of this four-chain structure.) The **Fc region** of the antibody is formed by the two heavy chains coming together, usually linked by disulfide bonds (Figure 21.21). The Fc portion of the antibody is important in that many effector cells of the immune system have Fc receptors. Cells having these receptors can then bind to antibody-coated pathogens, greatly increasing the specificity of the effector cells. At the other end of the molecule are two identical antigen-binding sites.

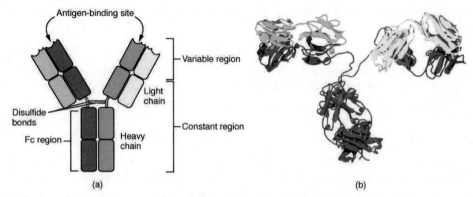

FIGURE 21.21   Antibody and IgG2 Structures   The typical four chain structure of a generic antibody (a) and the corresponding three-dimensional structure of the antibody IgG2 (b). (credit b: modification of work by Tim Vickers)

Five Classes of Antibodies and their Functions

In general, antibodies have two basic functions. They can act as the B cell antigen receptor or they can be secreted, circulate, and bind to a pathogen, often labeling it for identification by other forms of the immune response. Of the five antibody classes, notice that only two can function as the antigen receptor for naïve B cells: IgM and **IgD** (Figure 21.22). Mature B cells that leave the bone marrow express both IgM and IgD, but both antibodies have the same antigen specificity. Only IgM is secreted, however, and no other nonreceptor function for IgD has been discovered.

The Five Immunoglobulin (Ig) Classes					
	IgM pentamer	IgG monomer	Secretory IgA dimer	IgE monomer	IgD monomer
		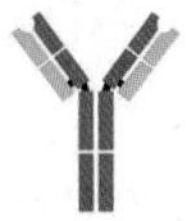	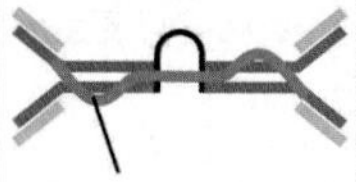 Secretory component	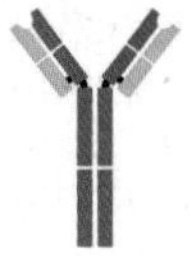	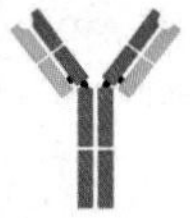
Heavy chains	μ	γ	α	ε	δ
Number of antigen binding sites	10	2	4	2	2
Molecular weight (Daltons)	900,000	150,000	385,000	200,000	180,000
Percentage of total antibody in serum	6%	80%	13%	0.002%	1%
Crosses placenta	no	yes	no	no	no
Fixes complement	yes	yes	no	no	no
Fc binds to		phagocytes		mast cells and basophils	
Function	Main antibody of primary responses, best at fixing complement; the monomer form of IgM serves as the B cell receptor	Main blood antibody of secondary responses, neutralizes toxins, opsonization	Secreted into mucus, tears, saliva, colostrum	Antibody of allergy and antiparasitic activity	B cell receptor

FIGURE 21.22   Five Classes of Antibodies

IgM consists of five four-chain structures (20 total chains with 10 identical antigen-binding sites) and is thus the largest of the antibody molecules. IgM is usually the first antibody made during a primary response. Its 10 antigen-binding sites and large shape allow it to bind well to many bacterial surfaces. It is excellent at binding complement proteins and activating the complement cascade, consistent with its role in promoting chemotaxis, opsonization, and cell lysis. Thus, it is a very effective antibody against bacteria at early stages of a primary antibody response. As the primary response proceeds, the antibody produced in a B cell can change to IgG, IgA, or IgE by the process known as class switching. **Class switching** is the change of one antibody class to another. While the class of antibody changes, the specificity and the antigen-binding sites do not. Thus, the antibodies made are still specific to the pathogen that stimulated the initial IgM response.

IgG is a major antibody of late primary responses and the main antibody of secondary responses in the blood. This is because class switching occurs during primary responses. IgG is a monomeric antibody that clears pathogens from the blood and can activate complement proteins (although not as well as IgM), taking advantage of its antibacterial activities. Furthermore, this class of antibody is the one that crosses the placenta to protect the developing fetus from disease exits the blood to the interstitial fluid to fight extracellular pathogens.

IgA exists in two forms, a four-chain monomer in the blood and an eight-chain structure, or dimer, in exocrine gland secretions of the mucous membranes, including mucus, saliva, and tears. Thus, dimeric IgA is the only antibody to leave the interior of the body to protect body surfaces. IgA is also of importance to newborns, because this antibody is present in mother's breast milk (colostrum), which serves to protect the infant from disease.

IgE is usually associated with allergies and anaphylaxis. It is present in the lowest concentration in the blood, because its Fc region binds strongly to an IgE-specific Fc receptor on the surfaces of mast cells. IgE makes mast cell degranulation very specific, such that if a person is allergic to peanuts, there will be peanut-specific IgE bound to their mast cells. In this person, eating peanuts will cause the mast cells to degranulate, sometimes causing severe allergic reactions, including anaphylaxis, a severe, systemic allergic response that can cause death.

Clonal Selection of B Cells

Clonal selection and expansion work much the same way in B cells as in T cells. Only B cells with appropriate antigen specificity are selected for and expanded (Figure 21.23). Eventually, the plasma cells secrete antibodies with antigenic specificity identical to those that were on the surfaces of the selected B cells. Notice in the figure that both plasma cells and memory B cells are generated simultaneously.

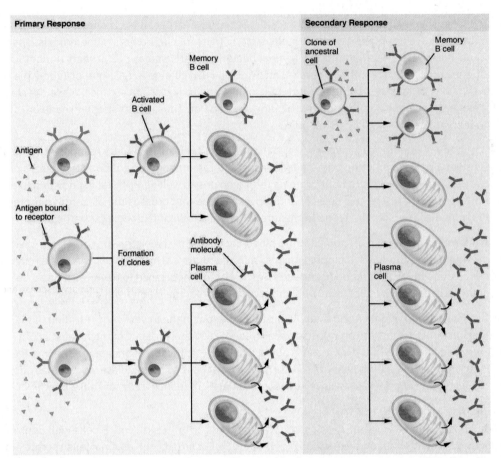

FIGURE 21.23 **Clonal Selection of B Cells** During a primary B cell immune response, both antibody-secreting plasma cells and memory B cells are produced. These memory cells lead to the differentiation of more plasma cells and memory B cells during secondary responses.

Primary versus Secondary B Cell Responses

Primary and secondary responses as they relate to T cells were discussed earlier. This section will look at these responses with B cells and antibody production. Because antibodies are easily obtained from blood samples, they are easy to follow and graph (Figure 21.24). As you will see from the figure, the primary response to an antigen (representing a pathogen) is delayed by several days. This is the time it takes for the B cell clones to expand and differentiate into plasma cells. The level of antibody produced is low, but it is sufficient for immune protection. The second time a person encounters the same antigen, there is no time delay, and the amount of antibody made is much higher. Thus, the secondary antibody response overwhelms the pathogens quickly and, in most situations, no symptoms are felt. When a different antigen is used, another primary response is made with its low antibody levels and time delay.

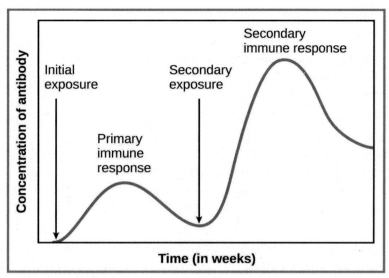

FIGURE 21.24 Primary and Secondary Antibody Responses   Antigen A is given once to generate a primary response and later to generate a secondary response. When a different antigen is given for the first time, a new primary response is made.

Active versus Passive Immunity

Immunity to pathogens, and the ability to control pathogen growth so that damage to the tissues of the body is limited, can be acquired by (1) the active development of an immune response in the infected individual or (2) the passive transfer of immune components from an immune individual to a nonimmune one. Both active and passive immunity have examples in the natural world and as part of medicine.

Active immunity is the resistance to pathogens acquired during an adaptive immune response within an individual (Table 21.6). Naturally acquired active immunity, the response to a pathogen, is the focus of this chapter. Artificially acquired active immunity involves the use of vaccines. A vaccine is a killed or weakened pathogen or its components that, when administered to a healthy individual, leads to the development of immunological memory (a weakened primary immune response) without causing much in the way of symptoms. Thus, with the use of vaccines, one can avoid the damage from disease that results from the first exposure to the pathogen, yet reap the benefits of protection from immunological memory. The advent of vaccines was one of the major medical advances of the twentieth century and led to the eradication of smallpox and the control of many infectious diseases, including polio, measles, and whooping cough.

Active versus Passive Immunity

	Natural	Artificial
Active	Adaptive immune response	Vaccine response
Passive	Trans-placental antibodies/breastfeeding	Immune globulin injections

TABLE 21.6

Passive immunity arises from the transfer of antibodies to an individual without requiring them to mount their own active immune response. Naturally acquired passive immunity is seen during fetal development. IgG is transferred from the maternal circulation to the fetus via the placenta, protecting the fetus from infection and protecting the newborn for the first few months of its life. As already stated, a newborn benefits from the IgA antibodies it obtains from milk during breastfeeding. The fetus and newborn thus benefit from the immunological memory based on the pathogens to which the pregnant person has been exposed. In medicine, artificially acquired passive immunity usually involves injections of immunoglobulins, taken from animals previously exposed to a specific pathogen. This treatment is a fast-acting method of temporarily protecting an individual who was possibly exposed to a pathogen. The downside to both types of passive immunity is the lack of the development of immunological memory. Once the antibodies are transferred, they are effective for only a limited time before they degrade.

INTERACTIVE LINK

Immunity can be acquired in an active or passive way, and it can be natural or artificial. Watch this video (http://openstax.org/l/immunity) to see an animated discussion of passive and active immunity. What is an example of natural immunity acquired passively?

T cell-dependent versus T cell-independent Antigens

As discussed previously, Th2 cells secrete cytokines that drive the production of antibodies in a B cell, responding to complex antigens such as those made by proteins. On the other hand, some antigens are T cell independent. A **T cell-independent antigen** usually is in the form of repeated carbohydrate moieties found on the cell walls of bacteria. Each antibody on the B cell surface has two binding sites, and the repeated nature of T cell-independent antigen leads to crosslinking of the surface antibodies on the B cell. The crosslinking is enough to activate it in the absence of T cell cytokines.

A **T cell-dependent antigen**, on the other hand, usually is not repeated to the same degree on the pathogen and thus does not crosslink surface antibody with the same efficiency. To elicit a response to such antigens, the B and T cells must come close together (Figure 21.25). The B cell must receive two signals to become activated. Its surface immunoglobulin must recognize native antigen. Some of this antigen is internalized, processed, and presented to the Th2 cells on a class II MHC molecule. The T cell then binds using its antigen receptor and is activated to secrete cytokines that diffuse to the B cell, finally activating it completely. Thus, the B cell receives signals from both its surface antibody and the T cell via its cytokines, and acts as a professional antigen-presenting cell in the process.

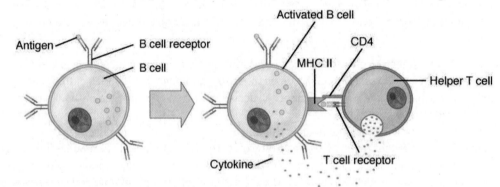

FIGURE 21.25   T and B Cell Binding   To elicit a response to a T cell-dependent antigen, the B and T cells must come close together. To become fully activated, the B cell must receive two signals from the native antigen and the T cell's cytokines.

21.5 The Immune Response against Pathogens

LEARNING OBJECTIVES

By the end of this section, you will be able to:

- Explain the development of immunological competence
- Describe the mucosal immune response
- Discuss immune responses against bacterial, viral, fungal, and animal pathogens
- Describe different ways pathogens evade immune responses

Now that you understand the development of mature, naïve B cells and T cells, and some of their major functions, how do all of these various cells, proteins, and cytokines come together to actually resolve an infection? Ideally, the immune response will rid the body of a pathogen entirely. The adaptive immune response, with its rapid clonal expansion, is well suited to this purpose. Think of a primary infection as a race between the pathogen and the immune system. The pathogen bypasses barrier defenses and starts multiplying in the host's body. During the first 4 to 5 days, the innate immune response will partially control, but not stop, pathogen growth. As the adaptive immune response gears up, however, it will begin to clear the pathogen from the body, while at the same time becoming stronger and stronger. When following antibody responses in patients with a particular disease such as a virus, this clearance is referred to as seroconversion (sero- = "serum"). **Seroconversion** is the reciprocal relationship between virus levels in the blood and antibody levels. As the antibody levels rise, the virus levels decline, and this is a sign that the immune response is being at least partially effective (partially, because in many diseases, seroconversion does not necessarily mean a patient is getting well).

An excellent example of this is seroconversion during HIV disease (Figure 21.26). Notice that antibodies are made early in this disease, and the increase in anti-HIV antibodies correlates with a decrease in detectable virus in the blood. Although these antibodies are an important marker for diagnosing the disease, they are not sufficient to completely clear the virus. Several years later, the vast majority of these individuals, if untreated, will lose their entire adaptive immune response, including the ability to make antibodies, during the final stages of AIDS.

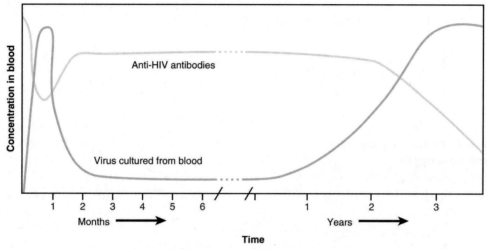

FIGURE 21.26   HIV Disease Progression   Seroconversion, the rise of anti-HIV antibody levels and the concomitant decline in measurable virus levels, happens during the first several months of HIV disease. Unfortunately, this antibody response is ineffective at controlling the disease, as seen by the progression of the disease towards AIDS, in which all adaptive immune responses are compromised.

Everyday Connection

Disinfectants: Fighting the Good Fight?

"Wash your hands!" Parents have been telling their children this for generations. Dirty hands can spread disease. But is it possible to get rid of enough pathogens that children will never get sick? Are children who avoid exposure to pathogens better off? The answers to both these questions appears to be no.

Antibacterial wipes, soaps, gels, and even toys with antibacterial substances embedded in their plastic are ubiquitous in our society. Still, these products do not rid the skin and gastrointestinal tract of bacteria, and it would be harmful to our health if they did. We need these nonpathogenic bacteria on and within our bodies to keep the pathogenic ones from growing. The urge to keep children perfectly clean is thus probably misguided. Children will get sick anyway, and the later benefits of immunological memory far outweigh the minor discomforts of most childhood diseases. In fact, getting diseases such as chickenpox or measles later in life is much harder on the adult and are associated with symptoms significantly worse than those seen in the childhood illnesses. Of course, vaccinations help children avoid some illnesses, but there are so many pathogens, we will never be immune to them all.

Could over-cleanliness be the reason that allergies are increasing in more developed countries? Some scientists think so. Allergies are based on an IgE antibody response. Many scientists think the system evolved to help the body rid itself of worm parasites. The hygiene theory is the idea that the immune system is geared to respond to antigens, and if pathogens are not present, it will respond instead to inappropriate antigens such as allergens and self-antigens. This is one explanation for the rising incidence of allergies in developed countries, where the response to nonpathogens like pollen, shrimp, and cat dander cause allergic responses while not serving any protective function.

The Mucosal Immune Response

Mucosal tissues are major barriers to the entry of pathogens into the body. The IgA (and sometimes IgM) antibodies in mucus and other secretions can bind to the pathogen, and in the cases of many viruses and bacteria, neutralize them. **Neutralization** is the process of coating a pathogen with antibodies, making it physically impossible for the pathogen to bind to receptors. Neutralization, which occurs in the blood, lymph, and other body fluids and secretions, protects the body constantly. Neutralizing antibodies are the basis for the disease protection offered by vaccines. Vaccinations for diseases that commonly enter the body via mucous membranes, such as influenza, are usually formulated to enhance IgA production.

Immune responses in some mucosal tissues such as the Peyer's patches (see Figure 21.11) in the small intestine take up particulate antigens by specialized cells known as microfold or M cells (Figure 21.27). These cells allow the body to sample potential pathogens from the intestinal lumen. Dendritic cells then take the antigen to the regional lymph nodes, where an immune response is mounted.

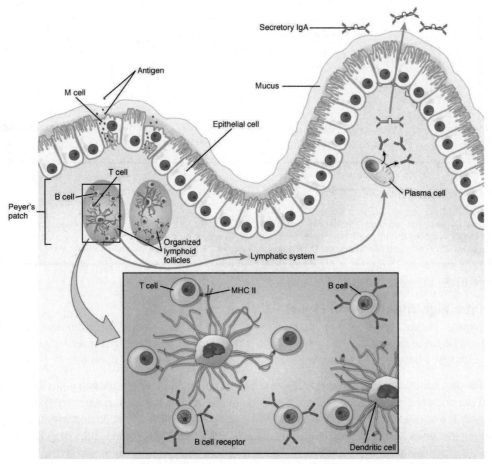

FIGURE 21.27 IgA Immunity   The nasal-associated lymphoid tissue and Peyer's patches of the small intestine generate IgA immunity. Both use M cells to transport antigen inside the body so that immune responses can be mounted.

Defenses against Bacteria and Fungi

The body fights bacterial pathogens with a wide variety of immunological mechanisms, essentially trying to find one that is effective. Bacteria such as *Mycobacterium leprae*, the cause of leprosy, are resistant to lysosomal enzymes and can persist in macrophage organelles or escape into the cytosol. In such situations, infected macrophages receiving cytokine signals from Th1 cells turn on special metabolic pathways. **Macrophage oxidative metabolism** is hostile to intracellular bacteria, often relying on the production of nitric oxide to kill the bacteria inside the macrophage.

Fungal infections, such as those from *Aspergillus*, *Candida*, and *Pneumocystis*, are largely opportunistic infections that take advantage of suppressed immune responses. Most of the same immune mechanisms effective against bacteria have similar effects on fungi, both of which have characteristic cell wall structures that protect their cells.

Defenses against Parasites

Worm parasites such as helminths are seen as the primary reason why the mucosal immune response, IgE-mediated allergy and asthma, and eosinophils evolved. These parasites were at one time very common in human society. When infecting a human, often via contaminated food, some worms take up residence in the gastrointestinal tract. Eosinophils are attracted to the site by T cell cytokines, which release their granule contents upon their arrival. Mast cell degranulation also occurs, and the fluid leakage caused by the increase in local vascular permeability is thought to have a flushing action on the parasite, expelling its larvae from the body. Furthermore, if IgE labels the parasite, the eosinophils can bind to it by its Fc receptor.

Defenses against Viruses

The primary mechanisms against viruses are NK cells, interferons, and cytotoxic T cells. Antibodies are effective against viruses mostly during protection, where an immune individual can neutralize them based on a previous exposure. Antibodies have no effect on viruses or other intracellular pathogens once they enter the cell, since antibodies are not able to penetrate the plasma membrane of the cell. Many cells respond to viral infections by downregulating their expression of MHC class I molecules. This is to the advantage of the virus, because without class I expression, cytotoxic T cells have no activity. NK cells, however, can recognize virally infected class I-negative cells and destroy them. Thus, NK and cytotoxic T cells have complementary activities against virally infected cells.

Interferons have activity in slowing viral replication and are used in the treatment of certain viral diseases, such as hepatitis B and C, but their ability to eliminate the virus completely is limited. The cytotoxic T cell response, though, is key, as it eventually overwhelms the virus and kills infected cells before the virus can complete its replicative cycle. Clonal expansion and the ability of cytotoxic T cells to kill more than one target cell make these cells especially effective against viruses. In fact, without cytotoxic T cells, it is likely that humans would all die at some point from a viral infection (if no vaccine were available).

Evasion of the Immune System by Pathogens

It is important to keep in mind that although the immune system has evolved to be able to control many pathogens, pathogens themselves have evolved ways to evade the immune response. An example already mentioned is in *Mycobacterium tuberculosis*, which has evolved a complex cell wall that is resistant to the digestive enzymes of the macrophages that ingest them, and thus persists in the host, causing the chronic disease tuberculosis. This section briefly summarizes other ways in which pathogens can "outwit" immune responses. But keep in mind, although it seems as if pathogens have a will of their own, they do not. All of these evasive "strategies" arose strictly by evolution, driven by selection.

Bacteria sometimes evade immune responses because they exist in multiple strains, such as different groups of *Staphylococcus aureus*. *S. aureus* is commonly found in minor skin infections, such as boils, and some healthy people harbor it in their nose. One small group of strains of this bacterium, however, called methicillin-resistant *Staphylococcus aureus*, has become resistant to multiple antibiotics and is essentially untreatable. Different bacterial strains differ in the antigens on their surfaces. The immune response against one strain (antigen) does not affect the other; thus, the species survives.

Another method of immune evasion is mutation. Because viruses' surface molecules mutate continuously, viruses like influenza change enough each year that the flu vaccine for one year may not protect against the flu common to the next. New vaccine formulations must be derived for each flu season.

Genetic recombination—the combining of gene segments from two different pathogens—is an efficient form of immune evasion. For example, the influenza virus contains gene segments that can recombine when two different viruses infect the same cell. Recombination between human and pig influenza viruses led to the 2010 H1N1 swine flu outbreak.

Pathogens can produce immunosuppressive molecules that impair immune function, and there are several different types. Viruses are especially good at evading the immune response in this way, and many types of viruses have been shown to suppress the host immune response in ways much more subtle than the wholesale destruction caused by HIV.

21.6 Diseases Associated with Depressed or Overactive Immune Responses

LEARNING OBJECTIVES

By the end of this section, you will be able to:

- Discuss inherited and acquired immunodeficiencies
- Explain the four types of hypersensitivity and how they differ
- Give an example of how autoimmune disease breaks tolerance

This section is about how the immune system goes wrong. When it goes haywire, and becomes too weak or too strong, it leads to a state of disease. The factors that maintain immunological homeostasis are complex and incompletely understood.

Immunodeficiencies

As you have seen, the immune system is quite complex. It has many pathways using many cell types and signals. Because it is so complex, there are many ways for it to go wrong. Inherited immunodeficiencies arise from gene mutations that affect specific components of the immune response. There are also acquired immunodeficiencies with potentially devastating effects on the immune system, such as HIV.

Inherited Immunodeficiencies

A list of all inherited immunodeficiencies is well beyond the scope of this book. The list is almost as long as the list of cells, proteins, and signaling molecules of the immune system itself. Some deficiencies, such as those for complement, cause only a higher susceptibility to some Gram-negative bacteria. Others are more severe in their consequences. Certainly, the most serious of the inherited immunodeficiencies is **severe combined immunodeficiency disease (SCID)**. This disease is complex because it is caused by many different genetic defects. What groups them together is the fact that both the B cell and T cell arms of the adaptive immune response are affected.

Children with this disease usually die of opportunistic infections within their first year of life unless they receive a bone marrow transplant. Such a procedure had not yet been perfected for David Vetter, the "boy in the bubble," who was treated for SCID by having to live almost his entire life in a sterile plastic cocoon for the 12 years before his death from infection in 1984. One of the features that make bone marrow transplants work as well as they do is the proliferative capability of hematopoietic stem cells of the bone marrow. Only a small amount of bone marrow from a healthy donor is given intravenously to the recipient. It finds its own way to the bone where it populates it, eventually reconstituting the patient's immune system, which is usually destroyed beforehand by treatment with radiation or chemotherapeutic drugs.

New treatments for SCID using gene therapy, inserting nondefective genes into cells taken from the patient and giving them back, have the advantage of not needing the tissue match required for standard transplants. Although not a standard treatment, this approach holds promise, especially for those in whom standard bone marrow transplantation has failed.

Human Immunodeficiency Virus/AIDS

Although many viruses cause suppression of the immune system, only one wipes it out completely, and that is the previously mentioned HIV. It is worth discussing the biology of this virus, which can lead to the well-known AIDS, so that its full effects on the immune system can be understood. The virus is transmitted through semen, vaginal fluids, and blood, and can be caught by risky sexual behaviors and the sharing of needles by intravenous drug users. There are sometimes, but not always, flu-like symptoms in the first 1 to 2 weeks after infection. This is later followed by seroconversion. The anti-HIV antibodies formed during seroconversion are the basis for most initial HIV screening done in the United States. Because seroconversion takes different lengths of time in different individuals, multiple AIDS tests are given months apart to confirm or eliminate the possibility of infection.

After seroconversion, the amount of virus circulating in the blood drops and stays at a low level for several years. During this time, the levels of $CD4^+$ cells, especially helper T cells, decline steadily, until at some point, the immune response is so weak that opportunistic disease and eventually death result. HIV uses CD4 as the receptor to get inside cells, but it also needs a co-receptor, such as CCR5 or CXCR4. These co-receptors, which usually bind to chemokines, present another target for anti-HIV drug development. Although other antigen-presenting cells are infected with HIV, given that CD4$^+$ helper T cells play an important role in T cell immune responses and antibody responses, it should be no surprise that both types of immune responses are eventually seriously compromised.

Treatment for the disease consists of drugs that target virally encoded proteins that are necessary for viral replication but are absent from normal human cells. By targeting the virus itself and sparing the cells, this approach has been successful in significantly prolonging the lives of HIV-positive individuals. On the other hand, an HIV vaccine has been 30 years in development and is still years away. Because the virus mutates rapidly to evade the immune system, scientists have been looking for parts of the virus that do not change and thus would be good targets for a vaccine candidate.

Hypersensitivities

The word "hypersensitivity" simply means sensitive beyond normal levels of activation. Allergies and inflammatory responses to nonpathogenic environmental substances have been observed since the dawn of history. Hypersensitivity is a medical term describing symptoms that are now known to be caused by unrelated mechanisms of immunity. Still, it is useful for this discussion to use the four types of hypersensitivities as a guide to understand these mechanisms (Figure 21.28).

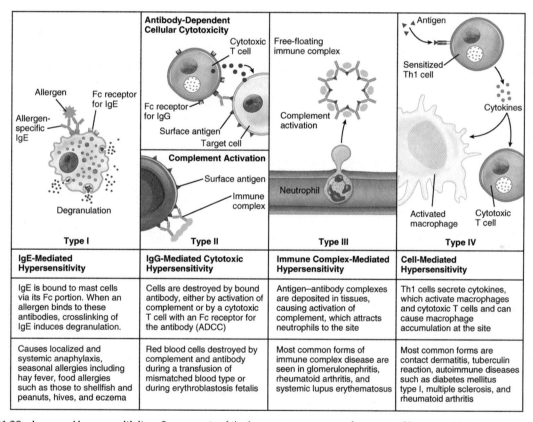

Type I	Type II	Type III	Type IV
IgE-Mediated Hypersensitivity	**IgG-Mediated Cytotoxic Hypersensitivity**	**Immune Complex-Mediated Hypersensitivity**	**Cell-Mediated Hypersensitivity**
IgE is bound to mast cells via its Fc portion. When an allergen binds to these antibodies, crosslinking of IgE induces degranulation.	Cells are destroyed by bound antibody, either by activation of complement or by a cytotoxic T cell with an Fc receptor for the antibody (ADCC)	Antigen–antibody complexes are deposited in tissues, causing activation of complement, which attracts neutrophils to the site	Th1 cells secrete cytokines, which activate macrophages and cytotoxic T cells and can cause macrophage accumulation at the site
Causes localized and systemic anaphylaxis, seasonal allergies including hay fever, food allergies such as those to shellfish and peanuts, hives, and eczema	Red blood cells destroyed by complement and antibody during a transfusion of mismatched blood type or during erythroblastosis fetalis	Most common forms of immune complex disease are seen in glomerulonephritis, rheumatoid arthritis, and systemic lupus erythematosus	Most common forms are contact dermatitis, tuberculin reaction, autoimmune diseases such as diabetes mellitus type I, multiple sclerosis, and rheumatoid arthritis

FIGURE 21.28 Immune Hypersensitivity Components of the immune system cause four types of hypersensitivity. Notice that types I–III are B cell mediated, whereas type IV hypersensitivity is exclusively a T cell phenomenon.

Immediate (Type I) Hypersensitivity

Antigens that cause allergic responses are often referred to as allergens. The specificity of the **immediate hypersensitivity** response is predicated on the binding of allergen-specific IgE to the mast cell surface. The process of producing allergen-specific IgE is called sensitization, and is a necessary prerequisite for the symptoms of immediate hypersensitivity to occur. Allergies and allergic asthma are mediated by mast cell degranulation that is caused by the crosslinking of the antigen-specific IgE molecules on the mast cell surface. The mediators released have various vasoactive effects already discussed, but the major symptoms of inhaled allergens are the nasal edema and runny nose caused by the increased vascular permeability and increased blood flow of nasal blood vessels. As these mediators are released with mast cell degranulation, **type I hypersensitivity** reactions are usually rapid and occur within just a few minutes, hence the term immediate hypersensitivity.

Most allergens are in themselves nonpathogenic and therefore innocuous. Some individuals develop mild allergies, which are usually treated with antihistamines. Others develop severe allergies that may cause anaphylactic shock, which can potentially be fatal within 20 to 30 minutes if untreated. This drop in blood pressure (shock) with accompanying contractions of bronchial smooth muscle is caused by systemic mast cell degranulation when an allergen is eaten (for example, shellfish and peanuts), injected (by a bee sting or being administered penicillin), or inhaled (asthma). Because epinephrine raises blood pressure and relaxes bronchial smooth muscle, it is routinely used to counteract the effects of anaphylaxis and can be lifesaving. Patients with known severe allergies are encouraged to keep automatic epinephrine injectors with them at all times, especially when away from easy access to hospitals.

Allergists use skin testing to identify allergens in type I hypersensitivity. In skin testing, allergen extracts are injected into the epidermis, and a positive result of a soft, pale swelling at the site surrounded by a red zone (called the wheal and flare response), caused by the release of histamine and the granule mediators, usually occurs within 30 minutes. The soft center is due to fluid leaking from the blood vessels and the redness is caused by the increased blood flow to the area that results from the dilation of local blood vessels at the site.

Type II and Type III Hypersensitivities

Type II hypersensitivity, which involves IgG-mediated lysis of cells by complement proteins, occurs during mismatched blood transfusions and blood compatibility diseases such as erythroblastosis fetalis (see section on transplantation). **Type III hypersensitivity** occurs with diseases such as systemic lupus erythematosus, where soluble antigens, mostly DNA and other material from the nucleus, and antibodies accumulate in the blood to the point that the antigen and antibody precipitate along blood vessel linings. These immune complexes often lodge in the kidneys, joints, and other organs where they can activate complement proteins and cause inflammation.

Delayed (Type IV) Hypersensitivity

Delayed hypersensitivity, or type IV hypersensitivity, is basically a standard cellular immune response. In delayed hypersensitivity, the first exposure to an antigen is called **sensitization**, such that on re-exposure, a secondary cellular response results, secreting cytokines that recruit macrophages and other phagocytes to the site. These sensitized T cells, of the Th1 class, will also activate cytotoxic T cells. The time it takes for this reaction to occur accounts for the 24- to 72-hour delay in development.

The classical test for delayed hypersensitivity is the tuberculin test for tuberculosis, where bacterial proteins from *M. tuberculosis* are injected into the skin. A couple of days later, a positive test is indicated by a raised red area that is hard to the touch, called an induration, which is a consequence of the cellular infiltrate, an accumulation of activated macrophages. A positive tuberculin test means that the patient has been exposed to the bacteria and exhibits a cellular immune response to it.

Another type of delayed hypersensitivity is contact sensitivity, where substances such as the metal nickel cause a red and swollen area upon contact with the skin. The individual must have been previously sensitized to the metal. A much more severe case of contact sensitivity is poison ivy, but many of the harshest symptoms of the reaction are associated with the toxicity of its oils and are not T cell mediated.

Autoimmune Responses

The worst cases of the immune system over-reacting are autoimmune diseases. Somehow, tolerance breaks down and the immune systems in individuals with these diseases begin to attack their own bodies, causing significant damage. The trigger for these diseases is, more often than not, unknown, and the treatments are usually based on resolving the symptoms using immunosuppressive and anti-inflammatory drugs such as steroids. These diseases can be localized and crippling, as in rheumatoid arthritis, or diffuse in the body with multiple symptoms that differ in different individuals, as is the case with systemic lupus erythematosus (Figure 21.29).

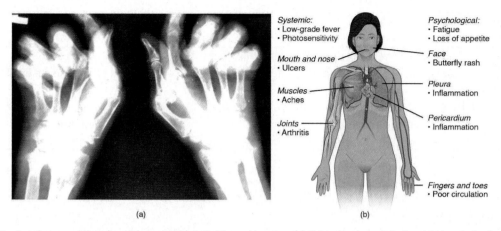

FIGURE 21.29 Autoimmune Disorders: Rheumatoid Arthritis and Lupus   (a) Extensive damage to the right hand of a rheumatoid arthritis sufferer is shown in the x-ray. (b) The diagram shows a variety of possible symptoms of systemic lupus erythematosus.

Environmental triggers seem to play large roles in autoimmune responses. One explanation for the breakdown of tolerance is that, after certain bacterial infections, an immune response to a component of the bacterium cross-reacts with a self-antigen. This mechanism is seen in rheumatic fever, a result of infection with *Streptococcus* bacteria, which causes strep throat. The antibodies to this pathogen's M protein cross-react with an antigenic component of heart myosin, a major contractile protein of the heart that is critical to its normal function. The antibody binds to these molecules and activates complement proteins, causing damage to the heart, especially to the heart valves. On the other hand, some theories propose that having multiple common infectious diseases actually prevents autoimmune responses. The fact that autoimmune diseases are rare in countries that have a high incidence of infectious diseases supports this idea, another example of the hygiene hypothesis discussed earlier in this chapter.

There are genetic factors in autoimmune diseases as well. Some diseases are associated with the MHC genes that an individual expresses. The reason for this association is likely because if one's MHC molecules are not able to present a certain self-antigen, then that particular autoimmune disease cannot occur. Overall, there are more than 80 different autoimmune diseases, which are a significant health problem in the elderly. Table 21.7 lists several of the most common autoimmune diseases, the antigens that are targeted, and the segment of the adaptive immune response that causes the damage.

Autoimmune Diseases

Disease	Autoantigen	Symptoms
Celiac disease	Tissue transglutaminase	Damage to small intestine
Diabetes mellitus type I	Beta cells of pancreas	Low insulin production; inability to regulate serum glucose
Graves' disease	Thyroid-stimulating hormone receptor (antibody blocks receptor)	Hyperthyroidism
Hashimoto's thyroiditis	Thyroid-stimulating hormone receptor (antibody mimics hormone and stimulates receptor)	Hypothyroidism
Lupus erythematosus	Nuclear DNA and proteins	Damage of many body systems

TABLE 21.7

Disease	Autoantigen	Symptoms
Myasthenia gravis	Acetylcholine receptor in neuromuscular junctions	Debilitating muscle weakness
Rheumatoid arthritis	Joint capsule antigens	Chronic inflammation of joints

TABLE 21.7

21.7 Transplantation and Cancer Immunology

LEARNING OBJECTIVES

By the end of this section, you will be able to:

- Explain why blood typing is important and what happens when mismatched blood is used in a transfusion
- Describe how tissue typing is done during organ transplantation and the role of transplant anti-rejection drugs
- Show how the immune response is able to control some cancers and how this immune response might be enhanced by cancer vaccines

The immune responses to transplanted organs and to cancer cells are both important medical issues. With the use of tissue typing and anti-rejection drugs, transplantation of organs and the control of the anti-transplant immune response have made huge strides in the past 50 years. Today, these procedures are commonplace. **Tissue typing** is the determination of MHC molecules in the tissue to be transplanted to better match the donor to the recipient. The immune response to cancer, on the other hand, has been more difficult to understand and control. Although it is clear that the immune system can recognize some cancers and control them, others seem to be resistant to immune mechanisms.

The Rh Factor

Red blood cells can be typed based on their surface antigens. ABO blood type, in which individuals are type A, B, AB, or O according to their genetics, is one example. A separate antigen system seen on red blood cells is the Rh antigen. When someone is "A positive" for example, the positive refers to the presence of the Rh antigen, whereas someone who is "A negative" would lack this molecule.

An interesting consequence of Rh factor expression is seen in **erythroblastosis fetalis**, a hemolytic disease of the newborn (Figure 21.30). This disease occurs when people negative for Rh antigen have multiple Rh-positive children. During the birth of a first Rh-positive child, the birth parent makes a primary anti-Rh antibody response to the fetal blood cells that enter the pregnant person's bloodstream. If the same parent has a second Rh-positive child, IgG antibodies against Rh-positive blood mounted during this secondary response cross the placenta and attack the fetal blood, causing anemia. This is a consequence of the fact that the fetus is not genetically identical to the birth parent, and thus the parent is capable of mounting an immune response against it. This disease is treated with antibodies specific for Rh factor. These are given to the pregnant person during the first and subsequent births, destroying any fetal blood that might enter their system and preventing the immune response.

Access for free at openstax.org

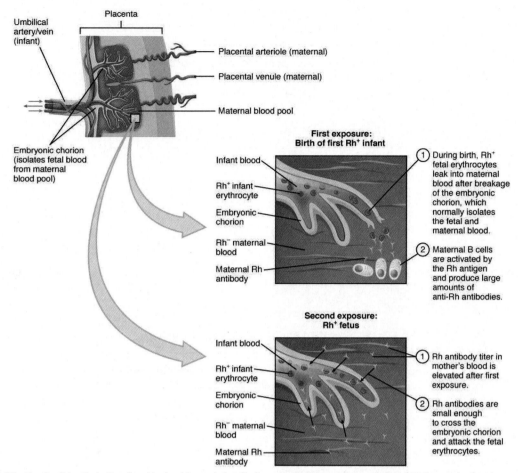

FIGURE 21.30 Erythroblastosis Fetalis   Erythroblastosis fetalis (hemolytic disease of the newborn) is the result of an immune response in an Rh-negative person who has multiple children with an Rh-positive person. During the first birth, fetal blood enters the pregnant person's circulatory system, and anti-Rh antibodies are made. During the gestation of the second child, these antibodies cross the placenta and attack the blood of the fetus. The treatment for this disease is to give the carrier anti-Rh antibodies (RhoGAM) during the first pregnancy to destroy Rh-positive fetal red blood cells from entering their system and causing the anti-Rh antibody response in the first place.

Tissue Transplantation

Tissue transplantation is more complicated than blood transfusions because of two characteristics of MHC molecules. These molecules are the major cause of transplant rejection (hence the name "histocompatibility"). **MHC polygeny** refers to the multiple MHC proteins on cells, and **MHC polymorphism** refers to the multiple alleles for each individual MHC locus. Thus, there are many alleles in the human population that can be expressed (Table 21.8 and Table 21.9). When a donor organ expresses MHC molecules that are different from the recipient, the latter will often mount a cytotoxic T cell response to the organ and reject it. Histologically, if a biopsy of a transplanted organ exhibits massive infiltration of T lymphocytes within the first weeks after transplant, it is a sign that the transplant is likely to fail. The response is a classical, and very specific, primary T cell immune response. As far as medicine is concerned, the immune response in this scenario does the patient no good at all and causes significant harm.

Partial Table of Alleles of the Human MHC (Class I)

Gene	# of alleles	# of possible MHC I protein components
A	2132	1527
B	2798	2110
C	1672	1200
E	11	3
F	22	4
G	50	16

TABLE 21.8

Partial Table of Alleles of the Human MHC (Class II)

Gene	# of alleles	# of possible MHC II protein components
DRA	7	2
DRB	1297	958
DQA1	49	31
DQB1	179	128
DPA1	36	18
DPB1	158	136
DMA	7	4
DMB	13	7
DOA	12	3
DOB	13	5

TABLE 21.9

Immunosuppressive drugs such as cyclosporine A have made transplants more successful, but matching the MHC molecules is still key. In humans, there are six MHC molecules that show the most polymorphisms, three class I molecules (A, B, and C) and three class II molecules called DP, DQ, and DR. A successful transplant usually requires a match between at least 3–4 of these molecules, with more matches associated with greater success. Family members, since they share a similar genetic background, are much more likely to share MHC molecules than unrelated individuals do. In fact, due to the extensive polymorphisms in these MHC molecules, unrelated donors are found only through a worldwide database. The system is not foolproof however, as there are not enough individuals in the system to provide the organs necessary to treat all patients needing them.

One disease of transplantation occurs with bone marrow transplants, which are used to treat various diseases, including SCID and leukemia. Because the bone marrow cells being transplanted contain lymphocytes capable of mounting an immune response, and because the recipient's immune response has been destroyed before receiving the transplant, the donor cells may attack the recipient tissues, causing **graft-versus-host disease**. Symptoms of this disease, which usually include a rash and damage to the liver and mucosa, are variable, and attempts have been made to moderate the disease by first removing mature T cells from the donor bone marrow before transplanting it.

Immune Responses Against Cancer

It is clear that with some cancers, for example Kaposi's sarcoma, a healthy immune system does a good job at controlling them (Figure 21.31). This disease, which is caused by the human herpesvirus, is almost never observed in individuals with strong immune systems, such as the young and immunocompetent. Other examples of cancers caused by viruses include liver cancer caused by the hepatitis B virus and cervical cancer caused by the human papilloma virus. As these last two viruses have vaccines available for them, getting vaccinated can help prevent these two types of cancer by stimulating the immune response.

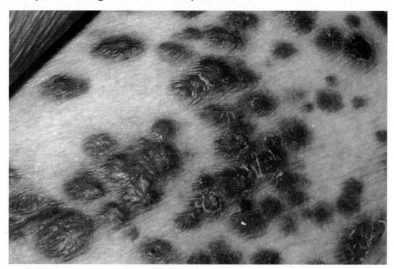

FIGURE 21.31   Karposi's Sarcoma Lesions   (credit: National Cancer Institute)

On the other hand, as cancer cells are often able to divide and mutate rapidly, they may escape the immune response, just as certain pathogens such as HIV do. There are three stages in the immune response to many cancers: elimination, equilibrium, and escape. Elimination occurs when the immune response first develops toward tumor-specific antigens specific to the cancer and actively kills most cancer cells, followed by a period of controlled equilibrium during which the remaining cancer cells are held in check. Unfortunately, many cancers mutate, so they no longer express any specific antigens for the immune system to respond to, and a subpopulation of cancer cells escapes the immune response, continuing the disease process.

This fact has led to extensive research in trying to develop ways to enhance the early immune response to completely eliminate the early cancer and thus prevent a later escape. One method that has shown some success is the use of cancer vaccines, which differ from viral and bacterial vaccines in that they are directed against the cells of one's own body. Treated cancer cells are injected into cancer patients to enhance their anti-cancer immune response and thereby prolong survival. The immune system has the capability to detect these cancer cells and proliferate faster than the cancer cells do, overwhelming the cancer in a similar way as they do for viruses. Cancer vaccines have been developed for malignant melanoma, a highly fatal skin cancer, and renal (kidney) cell carcinoma. These vaccines are still in the development stages, but some positive and encouraging results have been obtained clinically.

It is tempting to focus on the complexity of the immune system and the problems it causes as a negative. The upside to immunity, however, is so much greater: The benefit of staying alive far outweighs the negatives caused when the system does sometimes go awry. Working on "autopilot," the immune system helps to maintain your health and kill pathogens. The only time you really miss the immune response is when it is not being effective and illness results, or, as in the extreme case of HIV disease, the immune system is gone completely.

Everyday Connection

How Stress Affects the Immune Response: The Connections between the Immune, Nervous, and Endocrine Systems of the Body

The immune system cannot exist in isolation. After all, it has to protect the entire body from infection. Therefore, the immune system is required to interact with other organ systems, sometimes in complex ways. Thirty years of research focusing on the connections between the immune system, the central nervous system, and the endocrine system have led to a new science with the unwieldy name of called **psychoneuroimmunology**. The physical connections between these systems have been known for centuries: All primary and secondary organs are connected to sympathetic nerves. What is more complex, though, is the interaction of neurotransmitters, hormones, cytokines, and other soluble signaling molecules, and the mechanism of "crosstalk" between the systems. For example, white blood cells, including lymphocytes and phagocytes, have receptors for various neurotransmitters released by associated neurons. Additionally, hormones such as cortisol (naturally produced by the adrenal cortex) and prednisone (synthetic) are well known for their abilities to suppress T cell immune mechanisms, hence, their prominent use in medicine as long-term, anti-inflammatory drugs.

One well-established interaction of the immune, nervous, and endocrine systems is the effect of stress on immune health. In the human vertebrate evolutionary past, stress was associated with the fight-or-flight response, largely mediated by the central nervous system and the adrenal medulla. This stress was necessary for survival. The physical action of fighting or running, whichever the animal decides, usually resolves the problem in one way or another. On the other hand, there are no physical actions to resolve most modern day stresses, including short-term stressors like taking examinations and long-term stressors such as being unemployed or losing a spouse. The effect of stress can be felt by nearly every organ system, and the immune system is no exception (Table 21.10).

Effects of Stress on Body Systems

System	Stress-related illness
Integumentary system	Acne, rashes, irritation
Nervous system	Headaches, depression, anxiety, irritability, loss of appetite, lack of motivation, reduced mental performance
Muscular and skeletal systems	Muscle and joint pain, neck and shoulder pain
Circulatory system	Increased heart rate, hypertension, increased probability of heart attacks
Digestive system	Indigestion, heartburn, stomach pain, nausea, diarrhea, constipation, weight gain or loss
Immune system	Depressed ability to fight infections
Male reproductive system	Lowered sperm production, impotence, reduced sexual desire
Female reproductive system	Irregular menstrual cycle, reduced sexual desire

TABLE 21.10

At one time, it was assumed that all types of stress reduced all aspects of the immune response, but the last few decades of research have painted a different picture. First, most short-term stress does not impair the immune system in healthy individuals enough to lead to a greater incidence of diseases. However, older individuals and those with suppressed immune responses due to disease or immunosuppressive drugs may respond even to short-term stressors by getting sicker more often. It has been found that short-term stress diverts the body's resources towards enhancing innate immune responses, which have the ability to act fast and would seem to help the body prepare better for possible infections associated with the trauma that may result from a fight-or-flight exchange. The diverting of resources away from the adaptive immune response, however, causes its own share of problems in fighting disease.

Chronic stress, unlike short-term stress, may inhibit immune responses even in otherwise healthy adults. The suppression of both innate and adaptive immune responses is clearly associated with increases in some diseases, as seen when individuals lose a spouse or have other long-term stresses, such as taking care of a spouse with a fatal disease or dementia. The new science of psychoneuroimmunology, while still in its relative infancy, has great potential to make exciting advances in our understanding of how the nervous, endocrine, and immune systems have evolved together and communicate with each other.

Key Terms

active immunity   immunity developed from an individual's own immune system

acute inflammation   inflammation occurring for a limited time period; rapidly developing

adaptive immune response   relatively slow but very specific and effective immune response controlled by lymphocytes

afferent lymphatic vessels   lead into a lymph node

antibody   antigen-specific protein secreted by plasma cells; immunoglobulin

antigen   molecule recognized by the receptors of B and T lymphocytes

antigen presentation   binding of processed antigen to the protein-binding cleft of a major histocompatibility complex molecule

antigen processing   internalization and digestion of antigen in an antigen-presenting cell

antigen receptor   two-chain receptor by which lymphocytes recognize antigen

antigenic determinant   (also, epitope) one of the chemical groups recognized by a single type of lymphocyte antigen receptor

B cells   lymphocytes that act by differentiating into an antibody-secreting plasma cell

barrier defenses   antipathogen defenses deriving from a barrier that physically prevents pathogens from entering the body to establish an infection

bone marrow   tissue found inside bones; the site of all blood cell differentiation and maturation of B lymphocytes

bronchus-associated lymphoid tissue (BALT)   lymphoid nodule associated with the respiratory tract

central tolerance   B cell tolerance induced in immature B cells of the bone marrow

chemokine   soluble, long-range, cell-to-cell communication molecule

chronic inflammation   inflammation occurring for long periods of time

chyle   lipid-rich lymph inside the lymphatic capillaries of the small intestine

cisterna chyli   bag-like vessel that forms the beginning of the thoracic duct

class switching   ability of B cells to change the class of antibody they produce without altering the specificity for antigen

clonal anergy   process whereby B cells that react to soluble antigens in bone marrow are made nonfunctional

clonal deletion   removal of self-reactive B cells by inducing apoptosis

clonal expansion   growth of a clone of selected lymphocytes

clonal selection   stimulating growth of lymphocytes that have specific receptors

clone   group of lymphocytes sharing the same antigen receptor

complement   enzymatic cascade of constitutive blood proteins that have antipathogen effects, including the direct killing of bacteria

constant region domain   part of a lymphocyte antigen receptor that does not vary much between different receptor types

cytokine   soluble, short-range, cell-to-cell communication molecule

cytotoxic T cells (Tc)   T lymphocytes with the ability to induce apoptosis in target cells

delayed hypersensitivity   (type IV) T cell-mediated immune response against pathogens infiltrating interstitial tissues, causing cellular infiltrate

early induced immune response   includes antimicrobial proteins stimulated during the first several days of an infection

effector T cells   immune cells with a direct, adverse effect on a pathogen

efferent lymphatic vessels   lead out of a lymph node

erythroblastosis fetalis   disease of Rh factor-positive newborns in Rh-negative mothers with multiple Rh-positive children; resulting from the action of maternal antibodies against fetal blood

fas ligand   molecule expressed on cytotoxic T cells and NK cells that binds to the fas molecule on a target cell and induces it do undergo apoptosis

Fc region   in an antibody molecule, the site where the two termini of the heavy chains come together; many cells have receptors for this portion of the antibody, adding functionality to these molecules

germinal centers   clusters of rapidly proliferating B cells found in secondary lymphoid tissues

graft-versus-host disease   in bone marrow transplants; occurs when the transplanted cells mount an immune response against the recipient

granzyme   apoptosis-inducing substance contained in granules of NK cells and cytotoxic T cells

heavy chain   larger protein chain of an antibody

helper T cells (Th)   T cells that secrete cytokines to enhance other immune responses, involved in activation of both B and T cell lymphocytes

high endothelial venules   vessels containing unique endothelial cells specialized to allow migration of lymphocytes from the blood to the lymph node

histamine   vasoactive mediator in granules of mast cells and is the primary cause of allergies and anaphylactic shock

IgA antibody whose dimer is secreted by exocrine glands, is especially effective against digestive and respiratory pathogens, and can pass immunity to an infant through breastfeeding

IgD class of antibody whose only known function is as a receptor on naive B cells; important in B cell activation

IgE antibody that binds to mast cells and causes antigen-specific degranulation during an allergic response

IgG main blood antibody of late primary and early secondary responses; passed from carrier to unborn child via placenta

IgM antibody whose monomer is a surface receptor of naive B cells; the pentamer is the first antibody made blood plasma during primary responses

immediate hypersensitivity (type I) IgE-mediated mast cell degranulation caused by crosslinking of surface IgE by antigen

immune system series of barriers, cells, and soluble mediators that combine to response to infections of the body with pathogenic organisms

immunoglobulin protein antibody; occurs as one of five main classes

immunological memory ability of the adaptive immune response to mount a stronger and faster immune response upon re-exposure to a pathogen

inflammation basic innate immune response characterized by heat, redness, pain, and swelling

innate immune response rapid but relatively nonspecific immune response

interferons early induced proteins made in virally infected cells that cause nearby cells to make antiviral proteins

light chain small protein chain of an antibody

lymph fluid contained within the lymphatic system

lymph node one of the bean-shaped organs found associated with the lymphatic vessels

lymphatic capillaries smallest of the lymphatic vessels and the origin of lymph flow

lymphatic system network of lymphatic vessels, lymph nodes, and ducts that carries lymph from the tissues and back to the bloodstream.

lymphatic trunks large lymphatics that collect lymph from smaller lymphatic vessels and empties into the blood via lymphatic ducts

lymphocytes white blood cells characterized by a large nucleus and small rim of cytoplasm

lymphoid nodules unencapsulated patches of lymphoid tissue found throughout the body

macrophage ameboid phagocyte found in several tissues throughout the body

macrophage oxidative metabolism metabolism turned on in macrophages by T cell signals that help destroy intracellular bacteria

major histocompatibility complex (MHC) gene cluster whose proteins present antigens to T cells

mast cell cell found in the skin and the lining of body cells that contains cytoplasmic granules with vasoactive mediators such as histamine

memory T cells long-lived immune cell reserved for future exposure to a pathogen

MHC class I found on most cells of the body, it binds to the CD8 molecule on T cells

MHC class II found on macrophages, dendritic cells, and B cells, it binds to CD4 molecules on T cells

MHC polygeny multiple MHC genes and their proteins found in body cells

MHC polymorphism multiple alleles for each individual MHC locus

monocyte precursor to macrophages and dendritic cells seen in the blood

mucosa-associated lymphoid tissue (MALT) lymphoid nodule associated with the mucosa

naïve lymphocyte mature B or T cell that has not yet encountered antigen for the first time

natural killer cell (NK) cytotoxic lymphocyte of innate immune response

negative selection selection against thymocytes in the thymus that react with self-antigen

neutralization inactivation of a virus by the binding of specific antibody

neutrophil phagocytic white blood cell recruited from the bloodstream to the site of infection via the bloodstream

opsonization enhancement of phagocytosis by the binding of antibody or antimicrobial protein

passive immunity transfer of immunity to a pathogen to an individual that lacks immunity to this pathogen usually by the injection of antibodies

pattern recognition receptor (PRR) leukocyte receptor that binds to specific cell wall components of different bacterial species

perforin molecule in NK cell and cytotoxic T cell granules that form pores in the membrane of a target cell

peripheral tolerance mature B cell made tolerant by lack of T cell help

phagocytosis movement of material from the outside to the inside of the cells via vesicles made from invaginations of the plasma membrane

plasma cell differentiated B cell that is actively secreting antibody

polyclonal response response by multiple clones to a complex antigen with many determinants

positive selection selection of thymocytes within the

thymus that interact with self, but not non-self, MHC molecules

primary adaptive response   immune system's response to the first exposure to a pathogen

primary lymphoid organ   site where lymphocytes mature and proliferate; red bone marrow and thymus gland

psychoneuroimmunology   study of the connections between the immune, nervous, and endocrine systems

regulatory T cells (Treg)   (also, suppressor T cells) class of CD4 T cells that regulates other T cell responses

right lymphatic duct   drains lymph fluid from the upper right side of body into the right subclavian vein

secondary adaptive response   immune response observed upon re-exposure to a pathogen, which is stronger and faster than a primary response

secondary lymphoid organs   sites where lymphocytes mount adaptive immune responses; examples include lymph nodes and spleen

sensitization   first exposure to an antigen

seroconversion   clearance of pathogen in the serum and the simultaneous rise of serum antibody

severe combined immunodeficiency disease (SCID)   genetic mutation that affects both T cell and B cell arms of the immune response

spleen   secondary lymphoid organ that filters pathogens from the blood (white pulp) and removes degenerating or damaged blood cells (red pulp)

T cell   lymphocyte that acts by secreting molecules that regulate the immune system or by causing the destruction of foreign cells, viruses, and cancer cells

T cell tolerance   process during T cell differentiation where most T cells that recognize antigens from

one's own body are destroyed

T cell-dependent antigen   antigen that binds to B cells, which requires signals from T cells to make antibody

T cell-independent antigen   binds to B cells, which do not require signals from T cells to make antibody

Th1 cells   cells that secrete cytokines that enhance the activity of macrophages and other cells

Th2 cells   cells that secrete cytokines that induce B cells to differentiate into antibody-secreting plasma cells

thoracic duct   large duct that drains lymph from the lower limbs, left thorax, left upper limb, and the left side of the head

thymocyte   immature T cell found in the thymus

thymus   primary lymphoid organ; where T lymphocytes proliferate and mature

tissue typing   typing of MHC molecules between a recipient and donor for use in a potential transplantation procedure

tonsils   lymphoid nodules associated with the nasopharynx

type I hypersensitivity   immediate response mediated by mast cell degranulation caused by the crosslinking of the antigen-specific IgE molecules on the mast cell surface

type II hypersensitivity   cell damage caused by the binding of antibody and the activation of complement, usually against red blood cells

type III hypersensitivity   damage to tissues caused by the deposition of antibody-antigen (immune) complexes followed by the activation of complement

variable region domain   part of a lymphocyte antigen receptor that varies considerably between different receptor types

Chapter Review

21.1 Anatomy of the Lymphatic and Immune Systems

The lymphatic system is a series of vessels, ducts, and trunks that remove interstitial fluid from the tissues and return it the blood. The lymphatics are also used to transport dietary lipids and cells of the immune system. Cells of the immune system all come from the hematopoietic system of the bone marrow. Primary lymphoid organs, the bone marrow and thymus gland, are the locations where lymphocytes of the adaptive immune system proliferate and mature. Secondary lymphoid organs are site in which mature lymphocytes congregate to mount immune responses. Many immune system cells use the lymphatic and circulatory systems for transport throughout the body to search

for and then protect against pathogens.

21.2 Barrier Defenses and the Innate Immune Response

Innate immune responses are critical to the early control of infections. Whereas barrier defenses are the body's first line of physical defense against pathogens, innate immune responses are the first line of physiological defense. Innate responses occur rapidly, but with less specificity and effectiveness than the adaptive immune response. Innate responses can be caused by a variety of cells, mediators, and antibacterial proteins such as complement. Within the first few days of an infection, another series of antibacterial proteins are induced, each with activities against certain bacteria, including opsonization of certain species. Additionally, interferons are induced that protect cells from viruses in their vicinity. Finally, the innate immune response does not stop when the adaptive immune response is developed. In fact, both can cooperate and one can influence the other in their responses against pathogens.

21.3 The Adaptive Immune Response: T lymphocytes and Their Functional Types

T cells recognize antigens with their antigen receptor, a complex of two protein chains on their surface. They do not recognize self-antigens, however, but only processed antigen presented on their surfaces in a binding groove of a major histocompatibility complex molecule. T cells develop in the thymus, where they learn to use self-MHC molecules to recognize only foreign antigens, thus making them tolerant to self-antigens. There are several functional types of T lymphocytes, the major ones being helper, regulatory, and cytotoxic T cells.

21.4 The Adaptive Immune Response: B-lymphocytes and Antibodies

B cells, which develop within the bone marrow, are responsible for making five different classes of antibodies, each with its own functions. B cells have their own mechanisms for tolerance, but in peripheral tolerance, the B cells that leave the bone marrow remain inactive due to T cell tolerance. Some B cells do not need T cell cytokines to make antibody, and they bypass this need by the crosslinking of their surface immunoglobulin by repeated carbohydrate residues found in the cell walls of many bacterial species. Others require T cells to become activated.

21.5 The Immune Response against Pathogens

Early childhood is a time when the body develops much of its immunological memory that protects it from diseases in adulthood. The components of the immune response that have the maximum effectiveness against a pathogen are often associated with the class of pathogen involved. Bacteria and fungi are especially susceptible to damage by complement

proteins, whereas viruses are taken care of by interferons and cytotoxic T cells. Worms are attacked by eosinophils. Pathogens have shown the ability, however, to evade the body's immune responses, some leading to chronic infections or even death. The immune system and pathogens are in a slow, evolutionary race to see who stays on top. Modern medicine, hopefully, will keep the results skewed in humans' favor.

21.6 Diseases Associated with Depressed or Overactive Immune Responses

The immune response can be under-reactive or over-reactive. Suppressed immunity can result from inherited genetic defects or by acquiring viruses. Over-reactive immune responses include the hypersensitivities: B cell- and T cell-mediated immune responses designed to control pathogens, but that lead to symptoms or medical complications. The worst cases of over-reactive immune responses are autoimmune diseases, where an individual's immune system attacks their own body because of the breakdown of immunological tolerance. These diseases are more common in the aged, so treating them will be a challenge in the future as the aged population in the world increases.

21.7 Transplantation and Cancer Immunology

Blood transfusion and organ transplantation both require an understanding of the immune response to prevent medical complications. Blood needs to be typed so that natural antibodies against mismatched blood will not destroy it, causing more harm than good to the recipient. Transplanted organs must be matched by their MHC molecules and, with the use of immunosuppressive drugs, can be successful even if an exact tissue match cannot be made. Another aspect to the immune response is its ability to control and eradicate cancer. Although this has been shown to occur with some rare cancers and those caused by known viruses, the normal immune response to most cancers is not sufficient to control cancer growth. Thus, cancer vaccines designed to enhance these immune responses show promise for certain types of cancer.

Interactive Link Questions

1. Visit this website (http://openstax.org/l/lymphsystem) for an overview of the lymphatic system. What are the three main components of the lymphatic system?

2. Visit this website (http://openstax.org/l/immunecells) to learn about the many different cell types in the immune system and their very specialized jobs. What is the role of the dendritic cell in infection by HIV?

3. Visit this website (http://openstax.org/l/
    chemotaxis) to learn about phagocyte chemotaxis.
    Phagocyte chemotaxis is the movement of
    phagocytes according to the secretion of chemical
    messengers in the form of interleukins and other
    chemokines. By what means does a phagocyte
    destroy a bacterium that it has ingested?

4. Immunity can be acquired in an active or passive
    way, and it can be natural or artificial. Watch this
    video (http://openstax.org/l/immunity) to see an
    animated discussion of passive and active
    immunity. What is an example of natural immunity
    acquired passively?

Review Questions

5. Which of the following cells is phagocytic?
    a. plasma cell
    b. macrophage
    c. B cell
    d. NK cell

6. Which structure allows lymph from the lower right
    limb to enter the bloodstream?
    a. thoracic duct
    b. right lymphatic duct
    c. right lymphatic trunk
    d. left lymphatic trunk

7. Which of the following cells is important in the
    innate immune response?
    a. B cells
    b. T cells
    c. macrophages
    d. plasma cells

8. Which of the following cells would be most active in
    early, antiviral immune responses the first time one
    is exposed to pathogen?
    a. macrophage
    b. T cell
    c. neutrophil
    d. natural killer cell

9. Which of the lymphoid nodules is most likely to see
    food antigens first?
    a. tonsils
    b. Peyer's patches
    c. bronchus-associated lymphoid tissue
    d. mucosa-associated lymphoid tissue

10. Which of the following signs is *not* characteristic of
    inflammation?
    a. redness
    b. pain
    c. cold
    d. swelling

11. Which of the following is *not* important in the
    antiviral innate immune response?
    a. interferons
    b. natural killer cells
    c. complement
    d. microphages

12. Enhanced phagocytosis of a cell by the binding of
    a specific protein is called _____.
    a. endocytosis
    b. opsonization
    c. anaphylaxis
    d. complement activation

13. Which of the following leads to the redness of
    inflammation?
    a. increased vascular permeability
    b. anaphylactic shock
    c. increased blood flow
    d. complement activation

14. T cells that secrete cytokines that help antibody
    responses are called _____.
    a. Th1
    b. Th2
    c. regulatory T cells
    d. thymocytes

15. The taking in of antigen and digesting it for later
    presentation is called _____.
    a. antigen presentation
    b. antigen processing
    c. endocytosis
    d. exocytosis

16. Why is clonal expansion so important?
    a. to select for specific cells
    b. to secrete cytokines
    c. to kill target cells
    d. to increase the numbers of specific cells

17. The elimination of self-reactive thymocytes is
    called _____.
    a. positive selection.
    b. negative selection.
    c. tolerance.
    d. clonal selection.

18. Which type of T cell is most effective against viruses?
    a. Th1
    b. Th2
    c. cytotoxic T cells
    d. regulatory T cells

19. Removing functionality from a B cell without killing it is called _____.
    a. clonal selection
    b. clonal expansion
    c. clonal deletion
    d. clonal anergy

20. Which class of antibody crosses the placenta in pregnant people?
    a. IgM
    b. IgA
    c. IgE
    d. IgG

21. Which class of antibody has no known function other than as an antigen receptor?
    a. IgM
    b. IgA
    c. IgE
    d. IgD

22. When does class switching occur?
    a. primary response
    b. secondary response
    c. tolerance
    d. memory response

23. Which class of antibody is found in mucus?
    a. IgM
    b. IgA
    c. IgE
    d. IgD

24. Which enzymes in macrophages are important for clearing intracellular bacteria?
    a. metabolic
    b. mitochondrial
    c. nuclear
    d. lysosomal

25. What type of chronic lung disease is caused by a *Mycobacterium*?
    a. asthma
    b. emphysema
    c. tuberculosis
    d. leprosy

26. Which type of immune response is most *directly* effective against bacteria?
    a. natural killer cells
    b. complement
    c. cytotoxic T cells
    d. helper T cells

27. What is the reason that you have to be immunized with a new influenza vaccine each year?
    a. the vaccine is only protective for a year
    b. mutation
    c. macrophage oxidative metabolism
    d. memory response

28. Which type of immune response works in concert with cytotoxic T cells against virally infected cells?
    a. natural killer cells
    b. complement
    c. antibodies
    d. memory

29. Which type of hypersensitivity involves soluble antigen-antibody complexes?
    a. type I
    b. type II
    c. type III
    d. type IV

30. What causes the delay in delayed hypersensitivity?
    a. inflammation
    b. cytokine release
    c. recruitment of immune cells
    d. histamine release

31. Which of the following is a critical feature of immediate hypersensitivity?
    a. inflammation
    b. cytotoxic T cells
    c. recruitment of immune cells
    d. histamine release

32. Which of the following is an autoimmune disease of the heart?
    a. rheumatoid arthritis
    b. lupus
    c. rheumatic fever
    d. Hashimoto's thyroiditis

33. What drug is used to counteract the effects of anaphylactic shock?
    a. epinephrine
    b. antihistamines
    c. antibiotics
    d. aspirin

34. Which of the following terms means "many genes"?
   a. polymorphism
   b. polygeny
   c. polypeptide
   d. multiple alleles

35. Why do we have natural antibodies?
   a. We don't know why.
   b. immunity to environmental bacteria
   c. immunity to transplants
   d. from clonal selection

36. Which type of cancer is associated with HIV disease?
   a. Kaposi's sarcoma
   b. melanoma
   c. lymphoma
   d. renal cell carcinoma

37. How does cyclosporine A work?
   a. suppresses antibodies
   b. suppresses T cells
   c. suppresses macrophages
   d. suppresses neutrophils

38. What disease is associated with bone marrow transplants?
   a. diabetes mellitus type I
   b. melanoma
   c. headache
   d. graft-versus-host disease

Critical Thinking Questions

39. Describe the flow of lymph from its origins in interstitial fluid to its emptying into the venous bloodstream.

40. Describe the process of inflammation in an area that has been traumatized, but not infected.

41. Describe two early induced responses and what pathogens they affect.

42. Describe the processing and presentation of an intracellular antigen.

43. Describe clonal selection and expansion.

44. Describe how secondary B cell responses are developed.

45. Describe the role of IgM in immunity.

46. Describe how seroconversion works in HIV disease.

47. Describe tuberculosis and the innocent bystander effect.

48. Describe anaphylactic shock in someone sensitive to peanuts?

49. Describe rheumatic fever and how tolerance is broken.

50. Describe how stress affects immune responses.

CHAPTER 22

The Respiratory System

Figure 22.1 Mountain Climbers The thin air at high elevations can strain the human respiratory system. (credit: "bortescristian"/flickr.com)

CHAPTER OBJECTIVES
After studying this chapter, you will be able to:
- List the structures of the respiratory system
- List the major functions of the respiratory system
- Outline the forces that allow for air movement into and out of the lungs
- Outline the process of gas exchange
- Summarize the process of oxygen and carbon dioxide transport within the respiratory system
- Create a flow chart illustrating how respiration is controlled
- Discuss how the respiratory system responds to exercise
- Describe the development of the respiratory system in the embryo

INTRODUCTION Hold your breath. Really! See how long you can hold your breath as you continue reading…How long can you do it? Chances are you are feeling uncomfortable already. A typical human cannot survive without breathing for more than 3 minutes, and even if you wanted to hold your breath longer, your autonomic nervous system would take control. This is because every cell in the body needs to run the oxidative stages of cellular respiration, the process by which energy is produced in the form of adenosine triphosphate (ATP). For oxidative phosphorylation to occur, oxygen is used as a reactant and carbon dioxide is released as a waste product. You may be surprised to learn that although oxygen is a critical need for cells, it is actually the accumulation of carbon dioxide that primarily drives your need to breathe. Carbon dioxide is exhaled and oxygen is inhaled through the respiratory system, which includes muscles to move air into and out of the lungs, passageways through which air moves, and microscopic gas exchange surfaces covered by capillaries. The circulatory system transports gases from the lungs to tissues throughout the body and vice versa. A variety of diseases can affect the respiratory system, such as asthma, emphysema, chronic obstruction pulmonary disorder (COPD), and lung cancer. All of these conditions affect the gas exchange process and result in labored breathing and other difficulties.

22.1 Organs and Structures of the Respiratory System

LEARNING OBJECTIVES

By the end of this section, you will be able to:

- List the structures that make up the respiratory system
- Describe how the respiratory system processes oxygen and CO_2
- Compare and contrast the functions of upper respiratory tract with the lower respiratory tract

The major organs of the respiratory system function primarily to provide oxygen to body tissues for cellular respiration, remove the waste product carbon dioxide, and help to maintain acid-base balance. Portions of the respiratory system are also used for non-vital functions, such as sensing odors, speech production, and for straining, such as during childbirth or coughing (Figure 22.2).

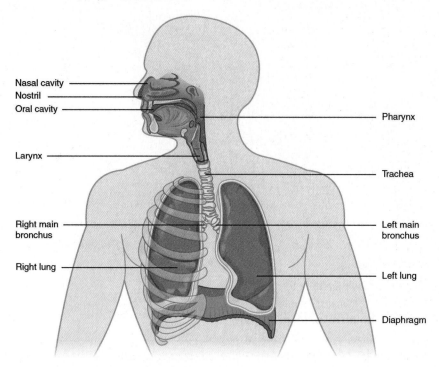

FIGURE 22.2 Major Respiratory Structures The major respiratory structures span the nasal cavity to the diaphragm.

Functionally, the respiratory system can be divided into a conducting zone and a respiratory zone. The **conducting zone** of the respiratory system includes the organs and structures not directly involved in gas exchange. The gas exchange occurs in the **respiratory zone**.

Conducting Zone

The major functions of the conducting zone are to provide a route for incoming and outgoing air, remove debris and pathogens from the incoming air, and warm and humidify the incoming air. Several structures within the conducting zone perform other functions as well. The epithelium of the nasal passages, for example, is essential to sensing odors, and the bronchial epithelium that lines the lungs can metabolize some airborne carcinogens.

The Nose and its Adjacent Structures

The major entrance and exit for the respiratory system is through the nose. When discussing the nose, it is helpful to divide it into two major sections: the external nose, and the nasal cavity or internal nose.

The **external nose** consists of the surface and skeletal structures that result in the outward appearance of the nose and contribute to its numerous functions (Figure 22.3). The **root** is the region of the nose located between the eyebrows. The **bridge** is the part of the nose that connects the root to the rest of the nose. The **dorsum nasi** is the length of the nose. The **apex** is the tip of the nose. On either side of the apex, the nostrils are formed by the alae (singular = ala). An **ala** is a cartilaginous structure that forms the lateral side of each **naris** (plural = nares), or nostril opening. The **philtrum** is the concave surface that connects the apex of the nose to the upper lip.

Access for free at openstax.org

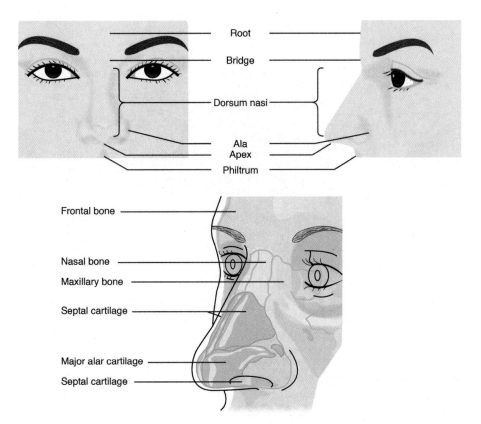

FIGURE 22.3 Nose   This illustration shows features of the external nose (top) and skeletal features of the nose (bottom).

Underneath the thin skin of the nose are its skeletal features (see Figure 22.3, lower illustration). While the root and bridge of the nose consist of bone, the protruding portion of the nose is composed of cartilage. As a result, when looking at a skull, the nose is missing. The **nasal bone** is one of a pair of bones that lies under the root and bridge of the nose. The nasal bone articulates superiorly with the frontal bone and laterally with the maxillary bones. Septal cartilage is flexible hyaline cartilage connected to the nasal bone, forming the dorsum nasi. The **alar cartilage** consists of the apex of the nose; it surrounds the naris.

The nares open into the nasal cavity, which is separated into left and right sections by the nasal septum (Figure 22.4). The **nasal septum** is formed anteriorly by a portion of the septal cartilage (the flexible portion you can touch with your fingers) and posteriorly by the perpendicular plate of the ethmoid bone (a cranial bone located just posterior to the nasal bones) and the thin vomer bones (whose name refers to its plough shape). Each lateral wall of the nasal cavity has three bony projections, called the superior, middle, and inferior nasal conchae. The inferior conchae are separate bones, whereas the superior and middle conchae are portions of the ethmoid bone. Conchae serve to increase the surface area of the nasal cavity and to disrupt the flow of air as it enters the nose, causing air to bounce along the epithelium, where it is cleaned and warmed. The conchae and **meatuses** also conserve water and prevent dehydration of the nasal epithelium by trapping water during exhalation. The floor of the nasal cavity is composed of the palate. The hard palate at the anterior region of the nasal cavity is composed of bone. The soft palate at the posterior portion of the nasal cavity consists of muscle tissue. Air exits the nasal cavities via the internal nares and moves into the pharynx.

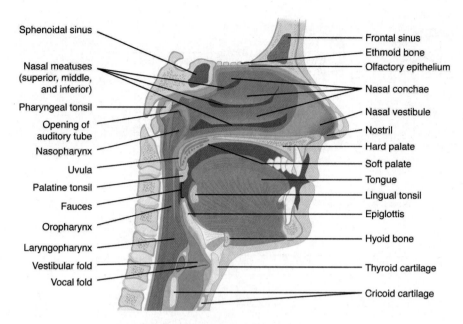

FIGURE 22.4   Upper Airway

Several bones that help form the walls of the nasal cavity have air-containing spaces called the paranasal sinuses, which serve to warm and humidify incoming air. Sinuses are lined with a mucosa. Each **paranasal sinus** is named for its associated bone: frontal sinus, maxillary sinus, sphenoidal sinus, and ethmoidal sinus. The sinuses produce mucus and lighten the weight of the skull.

The nares and anterior portion of the nasal cavities are lined with mucous membranes, containing sebaceous glands and hair follicles that serve to prevent the passage of large debris, such as dirt, through the nasal cavity. An olfactory epithelium used to detect odors is found deeper in the nasal cavity.

The conchae, meatuses, and paranasal sinuses are lined by **respiratory epithelium** composed of pseudostratified ciliated columnar epithelium (Figure 22.5). The epithelium contains goblet cells, one of the specialized, columnar epithelial cells that produce mucus to trap debris. The cilia of the respiratory epithelium help remove the mucus and debris from the nasal cavity with a constant beating motion, sweeping materials towards the throat to be swallowed. Interestingly, cold air slows the movement of the cilia, resulting in accumulation of mucus that may in turn lead to a runny nose during cold weather. This moist epithelium functions to warm and humidify incoming air. Capillaries located just beneath the nasal epithelium warm the air by convection. Serous and mucus-producing cells also secrete the lysozyme enzyme and proteins called defensins, which have antibacterial properties. Immune cells that patrol the connective tissue deep to the respiratory epithelium provide additional protection.

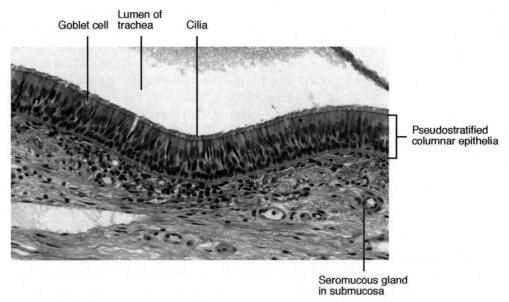

FIGURE 22.5   **Pseudostratified Ciliated Columnar Epithelium**   Respiratory epithelium is pseudostratified ciliated columnar epithelium. Seromucous glands provide lubricating mucus. LM × 680. (Micrograph provided by the Regents of University of Michigan Medical School © 2012)

⌲ INTERACTIVE LINK

View the University of Michigan WebScope (http://openstax.org/l/pseudoMG) to explore the tissue sample in greater detail.

Pharynx

The **pharynx** is a tube formed by skeletal muscle and lined by mucous membrane that is continuous with that of the nasal cavities (see Figure 22.4). The pharynx is divided into three major regions: the nasopharynx, the oropharynx, and the laryngopharynx (Figure 22.6).

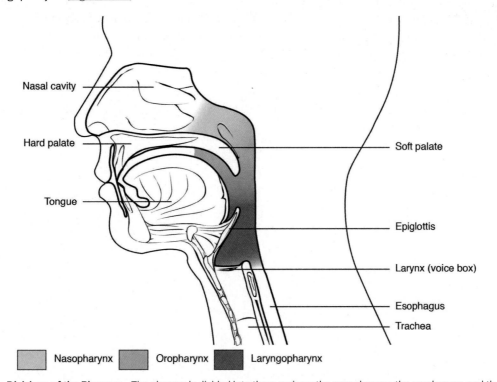

FIGURE 22.6   **Divisions of the Pharynx**   The pharynx is divided into three regions: the nasopharynx, the oropharynx, and the laryngopharynx.

The **nasopharynx** is flanked by the conchae of the nasal cavity, and it serves only as an airway. At the top of the nasopharynx are the pharyngeal tonsils. A **pharyngeal tonsil**, also called an adenoid, is an aggregate of lymphoid reticular tissue similar to a lymph node that lies at the superior portion of the nasopharynx. The function of the pharyngeal tonsil is not well understood, but it contains a rich supply of lymphocytes and is covered with ciliated epithelium that traps and destroys invading pathogens that enter during inhalation. The pharyngeal tonsils are large in children, but interestingly, tend to regress with age and may even disappear. The uvula is a small bulbous, teardrop-shaped structure located at the apex of the soft palate. Both the uvula and soft palate move like a pendulum during swallowing, swinging upward to close off the nasopharynx to prevent ingested materials from entering the nasal cavity. In addition, auditory (Eustachian) tubes that connect to each middle ear cavity open into the nasopharynx. This connection is why colds often lead to ear infections.

The **oropharynx** is a passageway for both air and food. The oropharynx is bordered superiorly by the nasopharynx and anteriorly by the oral cavity. The **fauces** is the opening at the connection between the oral cavity and the oropharynx. As the nasopharynx becomes the oropharynx, the epithelium changes from pseudostratified ciliated columnar epithelium to stratified squamous epithelium. The oropharynx contains two distinct sets of tonsils, the palatine and lingual tonsils. A **palatine tonsil** is one of a pair of structures located laterally in the oropharynx in the area of the fauces. The **lingual tonsil** is located at the base of the tongue. Similar to the pharyngeal tonsil, the palatine and lingual tonsils are composed of lymphoid tissue, and trap and destroy pathogens entering the body through the oral or nasal cavities.

The **laryngopharynx** is inferior to the oropharynx and posterior to the larynx. It continues the route for ingested material and air until its inferior end, where the digestive and respiratory systems diverge. The stratified squamous epithelium of the oropharynx is continuous with the laryngopharynx. Anteriorly, the laryngopharynx opens into the larynx, whereas posteriorly, it enters the esophagus.

Larynx

The **larynx** is a cartilaginous structure inferior to the laryngopharynx that connects the pharynx to the trachea and helps regulate the volume of air that enters and leaves the lungs (Figure 22.7). The structure of the larynx is formed by several pieces of cartilage. Three large cartilage pieces—the thyroid cartilage (anterior), epiglottis (superior), and cricoid cartilage (inferior)—form the major structure of the larynx. The **thyroid cartilage** is the largest piece of cartilage that makes up the larynx. The thyroid cartilage consists of the **laryngeal prominence**, or "Adam's apple," which tends to be more prominent in males. The thick **cricoid cartilage** forms a ring, with a wide posterior region and a thinner anterior region. Three smaller, paired cartilages—the arytenoids, corniculates, and cuneiforms—attach to the epiglottis and the vocal cords and muscle that help move the vocal cords to produce speech.

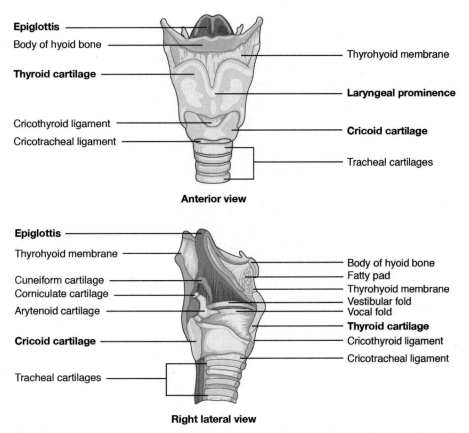

FIGURE 22.7   Larynx   The larynx extends from the laryngopharynx and the hyoid bone to the trachea.

The **epiglottis**, attached to the thyroid cartilage, is a very flexible piece of elastic cartilage that covers the opening of the trachea (see Figure 22.4). When in the "closed" position, the unattached end of the epiglottis rests on the glottis. The **glottis** is composed of the vestibular folds, the true vocal cords, and the space between these folds (Figure 22.8). A **vestibular fold**, or false vocal cord, is one of a pair of folded sections of mucous membrane. A **true vocal cord** is one of the white, membranous folds attached by muscle to the thyroid and arytenoid cartilages of the larynx on their outer edges. The inner edges of the true vocal cords are free, allowing oscillation to produce sound. The size of the membranous folds of the true vocal cords differs between individuals, producing voices with different pitch ranges. Folds in males tend to be larger than those in females, which create a deeper voice. The act of swallowing causes the pharynx and larynx to lift upward, allowing the pharynx to expand and the epiglottis of the larynx to swing downward, closing the opening to the trachea. These movements produce a larger area for food to pass through, while preventing food and beverages from entering the trachea.

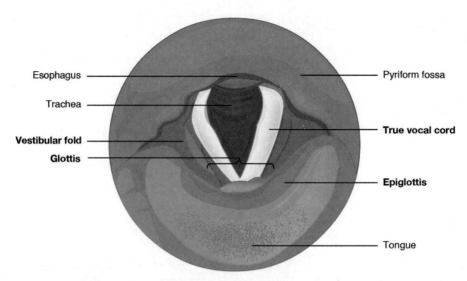

FIGURE 22.8   Vocal Cords   The true vocal cords and vestibular folds of the larynx are viewed inferiorly from the laryngopharynx.

Continuous with the laryngopharynx, the superior portion of the larynx is lined with stratified squamous epithelium, transitioning into pseudostratified ciliated columnar epithelium that contains goblet cells. Similar to the nasal cavity and nasopharynx, this specialized epithelium produces mucus to trap debris and pathogens as they enter the trachea. The cilia beat the mucus upward towards the laryngopharynx, where it can be swallowed down the esophagus.

Trachea

The trachea (windpipe) extends from the larynx toward the lungs (Figure 22.9**a**). The **trachea** is formed by 16 to 20 stacked, C-shaped pieces of hyaline cartilage that are connected by dense connective tissue. The **trachealis muscle** and elastic connective tissue together form the **fibroelastic membrane**, a flexible membrane that closes the posterior surface of the trachea, connecting the C-shaped cartilages. The fibroelastic membrane allows the trachea to stretch and expand slightly during inhalation and exhalation, whereas the rings of cartilage provide structural support and prevent the trachea from collapsing. In addition, the trachealis muscle can be contracted to force air through the trachea during exhalation. The trachea is lined with pseudostratified ciliated columnar epithelium, which is continuous with the larynx. The esophagus borders the trachea posteriorly.

Access for free at openstax.org

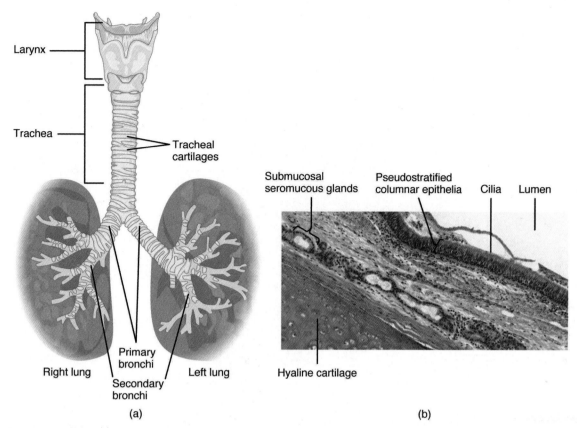

FIGURE 22.9 Trachea (a) The tracheal tube is formed by stacked, C-shaped pieces of hyaline cartilage. (b) The layer visible in this cross-section of tracheal wall tissue between the hyaline cartilage and the lumen of the trachea is the mucosa, which is composed of pseudostratified ciliated columnar epithelium that contains goblet cells. LM × 1220. (Micrograph provided by the Regents of University of Michigan Medical School © 2012)

Bronchial Tree

The trachea branches into the right and left primary **bronchi** at the carina. These bronchi are also lined by pseudostratified ciliated columnar epithelium containing mucus-producing goblet cells (Figure 22.9**b**). The carina is a raised structure that contains specialized nervous tissue that induces violent coughing if a foreign body, such as food, is present. Rings of cartilage, similar to those of the trachea, support the structure of the bronchi and prevent their collapse. The primary bronchi enter the lungs at the hilum, a concave region where blood vessels, lymphatic vessels, and nerves also enter the lungs. The bronchi continue to branch into a bronchial tree. A **bronchial tree** (or respiratory tree) is the collective term used for these multiple-branched bronchi. The main function of the bronchi, like other conducting zone structures, is to provide a passageway for air to move into and out of each lung. In addition, the mucous membrane traps debris and pathogens.

A **bronchiole** branches from the tertiary bronchi. Bronchioles, which are about 1 mm in diameter, further branch until they become the tiny terminal bronchioles, which lead to the structures of gas exchange. There are more than 1000 terminal bronchioles in each lung. The muscular walls of the bronchioles do not contain cartilage like those of the bronchi. This muscular wall can change the size of the tubing to increase or decrease airflow through the tube.

Respiratory Zone

In contrast to the conducting zone, the respiratory zone includes structures that are directly involved in gas exchange. The respiratory zone begins where the terminal bronchioles join a **respiratory bronchiole**, the smallest type of bronchiole (Figure 22.10), which then leads to an alveolar duct, opening into a cluster of alveoli.

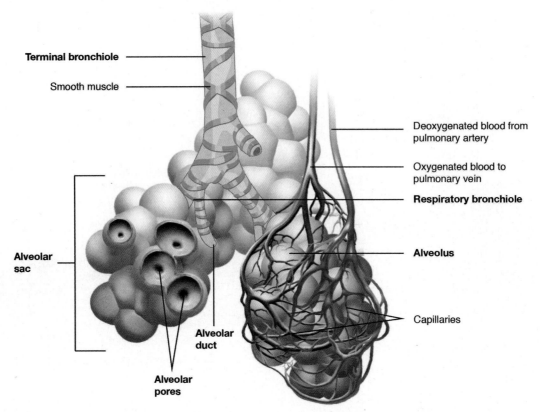

FIGURE 22.10   Respiratory Zone   Bronchioles lead to alveolar sacs in the respiratory zone, where gas exchange occurs.

Alveoli

An **alveolar duct** is a tube composed of smooth muscle and connective tissue, which opens into a cluster of alveoli. An **alveolus** is one of the many small, grape-like sacs that are attached to the alveolar ducts.

An **alveolar sac** is a cluster of many individual alveoli that are responsible for gas exchange. An alveolus is approximately 200 μm in diameter with elastic walls that allow the alveolus to stretch during air intake, which greatly increases the surface area available for gas exchange. Alveoli are connected to their neighbors by **alveolar pores**, which help maintain equal air pressure throughout the alveoli and lung (Figure 22.11).

Access for free at openstax.org

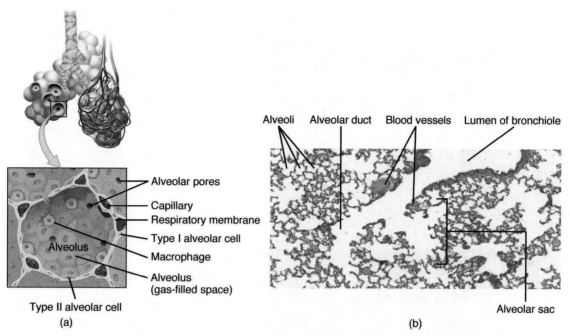

FIGURE 22.11   Structures of the Respiratory Zone   (a) The alveolus is responsible for gas exchange. (b) A micrograph shows the alveolar structures within lung tissue. LM × 178. (Micrograph provided by the Regents of University of Michigan Medical School © 2012)

The alveolar wall consists of three major cell types: type I alveolar cells, type II alveolar cells, and alveolar macrophages. A **type I alveolar cell** is a squamous epithelial cell of the alveoli, which constitute up to 97 percent of the alveolar surface area. These cells are about 25 nm thick and are highly permeable to gases. A **type II alveolar cell** is interspersed among the type I cells and secretes **pulmonary surfactant**, a substance composed of phospholipids and proteins that reduces the surface tension of the alveoli. Roaming around the alveolar wall is the **alveolar macrophage**, a phagocytic cell of the immune system that removes debris and pathogens that have reached the alveoli.

The simple squamous epithelium formed by type I alveolar cells is attached to a thin, elastic basement membrane. This epithelium is extremely thin and borders the endothelial membrane of capillaries. Taken together, the alveoli and capillary membranes form a **respiratory membrane** that is approximately 0.5 μm (micrometers) thick. The respiratory membrane allows gases to cross by simple diffusion, allowing oxygen to be picked up by the blood for transport and CO_2 to be released into the air of the alveoli.

Diseases of the...

Respiratory System: Asthma   Asthma is common condition that affects the lungs in both adults and children. Approximately 8.2 percent of adults (18.7 million) and 9.4 percent of children (7 million) in the United States suffer from asthma. In addition, asthma is the most frequent cause of hospitalization in children.

Asthma is a chronic disease characterized by inflammation and edema of the airway, and bronchospasms (that is, constriction of the bronchioles), which can inhibit air from entering the lungs. In addition, excessive mucus secretion can occur, which further contributes to airway occlusion (Figure 22.12). Cells of the immune system, such as eosinophils and mononuclear cells, may also be involved in infiltrating the walls of the bronchi and bronchioles.

Bronchospasms occur periodically and lead to an "asthma attack." An attack may be triggered by environmental factors such as dust, pollen, pet hair, or dander, changes in the weather, mold, tobacco smoke, and respiratory infections, or by exercise and stress.

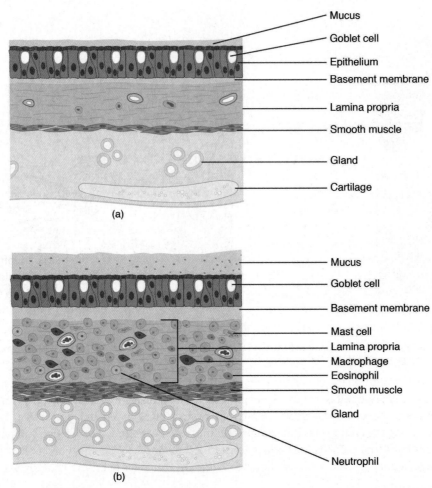

FIGURE 22.12 Normal and Bronchial Asthma Tissues   (a) Normal lung tissue does not have the characteristics of lung tissue during (b) an asthma attack, which include thickened mucosa, increased mucus-producing goblet cells, and eosinophil infiltrates.

Symptoms of an asthma attack involve coughing, shortness of breath, wheezing, and tightness of the chest. Symptoms of a severe asthma attack that requires immediate medical attention would include difficulty breathing that results in blue (cyanotic) lips or face, confusion, drowsiness, a rapid pulse, sweating, and severe anxiety. The severity of the condition, frequency of attacks, and identified triggers influence the type of medication that an individual may require. Longer-term treatments are used for those with more severe asthma. Short-term, fast-acting drugs that are used to treat an asthma attack are typically administered via an inhaler. For young children or individuals who have difficulty using an inhaler, asthma medications can be administered via a nebulizer.

In many cases, the underlying cause of the condition is unknown. However, recent research has demonstrated that certain viruses, such as human rhinovirus C (HRVC), and the bacteria *Mycoplasma pneumoniae* and *Chlamydia pneumoniae* that are contracted in infancy or early childhood, may contribute to the development of many cases of asthma.

INTERACTIVE LINK

Visit this site (http://openstax.org/l/asthma) to learn more about what happens during an asthma attack. What are the three changes that occur inside the airways during an asthma attack?

22.2 The Lungs

LEARNING OBJECTIVES

By the end of this section, you will be able to:
- Describe the overall function of the lung
- Summarize the blood flow pattern associated with the lungs
- Outline the anatomy of the blood supply to the lungs
- Describe the pleura of the lungs and their function

A major organ of the respiratory system, each **lung** houses structures of both the conducting and respiratory zones. The main function of the lungs is to perform the exchange of oxygen and carbon dioxide with air from the atmosphere. To this end, the lungs exchange respiratory gases across a very large epithelial surface area—about 70 square meters—that is highly permeable to gases.

Gross Anatomy of the Lungs

The lungs are pyramid-shaped, paired organs that are connected to the trachea by the right and left bronchi; on the inferior surface, the lungs are bordered by the diaphragm. The diaphragm is a dome-shaped muscle located at the base of the lungs and thoracic cavity. The lungs are enclosed by the pleurae, which are attached to the mediastinum. The right lung is shorter and wider than the left lung, and the left lung occupies a smaller volume than the right. The **cardiac notch** is an indentation on the surface of the left lung, and it allows space for the heart (Figure 22.13). The apex of the lung is the superior region, whereas the base is the opposite region near the diaphragm. The costal surface of the lung borders the ribs. The mediastinal surface faces the midline.

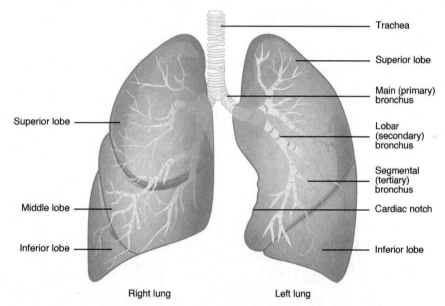

Right lung   **Left lung**

FIGURE 22.13   Gross Anatomy of the Lungs

Each lung is composed of smaller units called lobes. Fissures separate these lobes from each other. The right lung consists of three lobes: the superior, middle, and inferior lobes. The left lung consists of two lobes: the superior and inferior lobes. A bronchopulmonary segment is a division of a lobe, and each lobe houses multiple bronchopulmonary segments. Each segment receives air from its own tertiary bronchus and is supplied with blood by its own artery. Some diseases of the lungs typically affect one or more bronchopulmonary segments, and in some cases, the diseased segments can be surgically removed with little influence on neighboring segments. A pulmonary lobule is a subdivision formed as the bronchi branch into bronchioles. Each lobule receives its own large bronchiole that has multiple branches. An interlobular septum is a wall, composed of connective tissue, which separates lobules from one another.

Blood Supply and Nervous Innervation of the Lungs

The blood supply of the lungs plays an important role in gas exchange and serves as a transport system for gases throughout the body. In addition, innervation by the both the parasympathetic and sympathetic nervous systems provides an important level of control through dilation and constriction of the airway.

Blood Supply

The major function of the lungs is to perform gas exchange, which requires blood from the pulmonary circulation. This blood supply contains deoxygenated blood and travels to the lungs where erythrocytes, also known as red blood cells, pick up oxygen to be transported to tissues throughout the body. The **pulmonary artery** is an artery that arises from the pulmonary trunk and carries deoxygenated, arterial blood to the alveoli. The pulmonary artery branches multiple times as it follows the bronchi, and each branch becomes progressively smaller in diameter. One arteriole and an accompanying venule supply and drain one pulmonary lobule. As they near the alveoli, the pulmonary arteries become the pulmonary capillary network. The pulmonary capillary network consists of tiny vessels with very thin walls that lack smooth muscle fibers. The capillaries branch and follow the bronchioles and structure of the alveoli. It is at this point that the capillary wall meets the alveolar wall, creating the respiratory membrane. Once the blood is oxygenated, it drains from the alveoli by way of multiple pulmonary veins, which exit the lungs through the **hilum**.

Nervous Innervation

Dilation and constriction of the airway are achieved through nervous control by the parasympathetic and sympathetic nervous systems. The parasympathetic system causes **bronchoconstriction**, whereas the sympathetic nervous system stimulates **bronchodilation**. Reflexes such as coughing, and the ability of the lungs to regulate oxygen and carbon dioxide levels, also result from this autonomic nervous system control. Sensory nerve fibers arise from the vagus nerve, and from the second to fifth thoracic ganglia. The **pulmonary plexus** is a region on the lung root formed by the entrance of the nerves at the hilum. The nerves then follow the bronchi in the lungs and branch to innervate muscle fibers, glands, and blood vessels.

Pleura of the Lungs

Each lung is enclosed within a cavity that is surrounded by the pleura. The pleura (plural = pleurae) is a serous membrane that surrounds the lung. The right and left pleurae, which enclose the right and left lungs, respectively, are separated by the mediastinum. The pleurae consist of two layers. The **visceral pleura** is the layer that is superficial to the lungs, and extends into and lines the lung fissures (Figure 22.14). In contrast, the **parietal pleura** is the outer layer that connects to the thoracic wall, the mediastinum, and the diaphragm. The visceral and parietal pleurae connect to each other at the hilum. The **pleural cavity** is the space between the visceral and parietal layers.

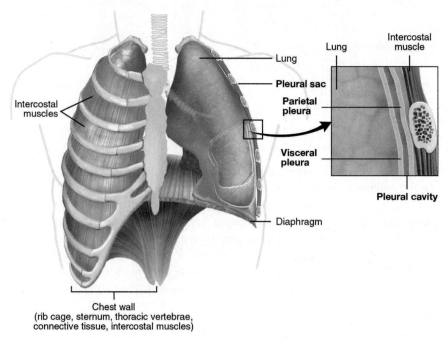

FIGURE 22.14   Parietal and Visceral Pleurae of the Lungs

Access for free at openstax.org

The pleurae perform two major functions: They produce pleural fluid and create cavities that separate the major organs. **Pleural fluid** is secreted by mesothelial cells from both pleural layers and acts to lubricate their surfaces. This lubrication reduces friction between the two layers to prevent trauma during breathing, and creates surface tension that helps maintain the position of the lungs against the thoracic wall. This adhesive characteristic of the pleural fluid causes the lungs to enlarge when the thoracic wall expands during ventilation, allowing the lungs to fill with air. The pleurae also create a division between major organs that prevents interference due to the movement of the organs, while preventing the spread of infection.

Everyday Connection

The Effects of Second-Hand Tobacco Smoke

The burning of a tobacco cigarette creates multiple chemical compounds that are released through mainstream smoke, which is inhaled by the smoker, and through sidestream smoke, which is the smoke that is given off by the burning cigarette. Second-hand smoke, which is a combination of sidestream smoke and the mainstream smoke that is exhaled by the smoker, has been demonstrated by numerous scientific studies to cause disease. At least 40 chemicals in sidestream smoke have been identified that negatively impact human health, leading to the development of cancer or other conditions, such as immune system dysfunction, liver toxicity, cardiac arrhythmias, pulmonary edema, and neurological dysfunction. Furthermore, second-hand smoke has been found to harbor at least 250 compounds that are known to be toxic, carcinogenic, or both. Some major classes of carcinogens in second-hand smoke are polyaromatic hydrocarbons (PAHs), N-nitrosamines, aromatic amines, formaldehyde, and acetaldehyde.

Tobacco and second-hand smoke are considered to be carcinogenic. Exposure to second-hand smoke can cause lung cancer in individuals who are not tobacco users themselves. It is estimated that the risk of developing lung cancer is increased by up to 30 percent in nonsmokers who live with an individual who smokes in the house, as compared to nonsmokers who are not regularly exposed to second-hand smoke. Children are especially affected by second-hand smoke. Children who live with an individual who smokes inside the home have a larger number of lower respiratory infections, which are associated with hospitalizations, and higher risk of sudden infant death syndrome (SIDS). Second-hand smoke in the home has also been linked to a greater number of ear infections in children, as well as worsening symptoms of asthma.

22.3 The Process of Breathing

LEARNING OBJECTIVES

By the end of this section, you will be able to:

- Describe the mechanisms that drive breathing
- Discuss how pressure, volume, and resistance are related
- List the steps involved in pulmonary ventilation
- Discuss the physical factors related to breathing
- Discuss the meaning of respiratory volume and capacities
- Define respiratory rate
- Outline the mechanisms behind the control of breathing
- Describe the respiratory centers of the medulla oblongata
- Describe the respiratory centers of the pons
- Discuss factors that can influence the respiratory rate

Pulmonary ventilation is the act of breathing, which can be described as the movement of air into and out of the lungs. The major mechanisms that drive pulmonary ventilation are atmospheric pressure (P_{atm}); the air pressure within the alveoli, called intra-alveolar pressure (P_{alv}); and the pressure within the pleural cavity, called intrapleural pressure (P_{ip}).

Mechanisms of Breathing

The intra-alveolar and intrapleural pressures are dependent on certain physical features of the lung. However, the ability to breathe—to have air enter the lungs during inspiration and air leave the lungs during expiration—is dependent on the air pressure of the atmosphere and the air pressure within the lungs.

Pressure Relationships

Inspiration (or inhalation) and expiration (or exhalation) are dependent on the differences in pressure between the atmosphere and the lungs. In a gas, pressure is a force created by the movement of gas molecules that are confined. For example, a certain number of gas molecules in a two-liter container has more room than the same number of gas molecules in a one-liter container (Figure 22.15). In this case, the force exerted by the movement of the gas molecules against the walls of the two-liter container is lower than the force exerted by the gas molecules in the one-liter container. Therefore, the pressure is lower in the two-liter container and higher in the one-liter container. At a constant temperature, changing the volume occupied by the gas changes the pressure, as does changing the number of gas molecules. **Boyle's law** describes the relationship between volume and pressure in a gas at a constant temperature. Boyle discovered that the pressure of a gas is inversely proportional to its volume: If volume increases, pressure decreases. Likewise, if volume decreases, pressure increases. Pressure and volume are inversely related ($P = k/V$). Therefore, the pressure in the one-liter container (one-half the volume of the two-liter container) would be twice the pressure in the two-liter container. Boyle's law is expressed by the following formula:

$$P_1 V_1 = P_2 V_2$$

In this formula, P_1 represents the initial pressure and V_1 represents the initial volume, whereas the final pressure and volume are represented by P_2 and V_2, respectively. If the two- and one-liter containers were connected by a tube and the volume of one of the containers were changed, then the gases would move from higher pressure (lower volume) to lower pressure (higher volume).

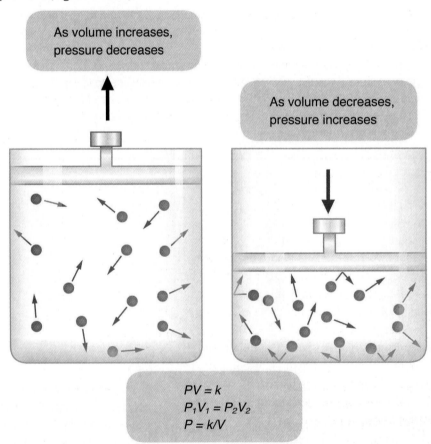

As volume increases, pressure decreases

As volume decreases, pressure increases

$$PV = k$$
$$P_1V_1 = P_2V_2$$
$$P = k/V$$

FIGURE 22.15 **Boyle's Law** In a gas, pressure increases as volume decreases.

Pulmonary ventilation is dependent on three types of pressure: atmospheric, intra-alveolar, and intrapleural. **Atmospheric pressure** is the amount of force that is exerted by gases in the air surrounding any given surface, such as the body. Atmospheric pressure can be expressed in terms of the unit atmosphere, abbreviated atm, or in millimeters of mercury (mm Hg). One atm is equal to 760 mm Hg, which is the atmospheric pressure at sea level. Typically, for respiration, other pressure values are discussed in relation to atmospheric pressure. Therefore, negative pressure is pressure lower than the atmospheric pressure, whereas positive pressure is pressure that it is greater than the atmospheric pressure. A pressure that is equal to the atmospheric pressure is expressed as zero.

Intra-alveolar pressure (intrapulmonary pressure) is the pressure of the air within the alveoli, which changes during the different phases of breathing (Figure 22.16). Because the alveoli are connected to the atmosphere via the tubing of the airways (similar to the two- and one-liter containers in the example above), the intrapulmonary pressure of the alveoli always equalizes with the atmospheric pressure.

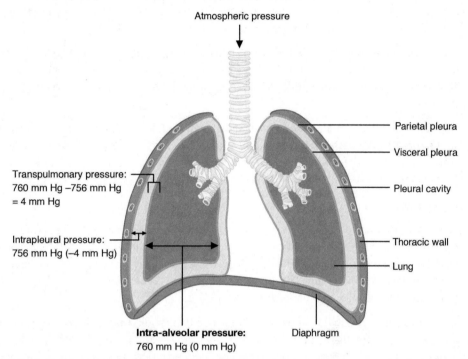

FIGURE 22.16   Intrapulmonary and Intrapleural Pressure Relationships   Intra-alveolar pressure changes during the different phases of the cycle. It equalizes at 760 mm Hg but does not remain at 760 mm Hg.

Intrapleural pressure is the pressure of the air within the pleural cavity, between the visceral and parietal pleurae. Similar to intra-alveolar pressure, intrapleural pressure also changes during the different phases of breathing. However, due to certain characteristics of the lungs, the intrapleural pressure is always lower than, or negative to, the intra-alveolar pressure (and therefore also to atmospheric pressure). Although it fluctuates during inspiration and expiration, intrapleural pressure remains approximately −4 mm Hg throughout the breathing cycle.

Competing forces within the thorax cause the formation of the negative intrapleural pressure. One of these forces relates to the elasticity of the lungs themselves—elastic tissue pulls the lungs inward, away from the thoracic wall. Surface tension of alveolar fluid, which is mostly water, also creates an inward pull of the lung tissue. This inward tension from the lungs is countered by opposing forces from the pleural fluid and thoracic wall. Surface tension within the pleural cavity pulls the lungs outward. Too much or too little pleural fluid would hinder the creation of the negative intrapleural pressure; therefore, the level must be closely monitored by the mesothelial cells and drained by the lymphatic system. Since the parietal pleura is attached to the thoracic wall, the natural elasticity of the chest wall opposes the inward pull of the lungs. Ultimately, the outward pull is slightly greater than the inward pull, creating the −4 mm Hg intrapleural pressure relative to the intra-alveolar pressure. **Transpulmonary pressure** is the difference between the intrapleural and intra-alveolar pressures, and it determines the size of the lungs. A higher transpulmonary pressure corresponds to a larger lung.

Physical Factors Affecting Ventilation

In addition to the differences in pressures, breathing is also dependent upon the contraction and relaxation of muscle fibers of both the diaphragm and thorax. The lungs themselves are passive during breathing, meaning they are not involved in creating the movement that helps inspiration and expiration. This is because of the adhesive nature of the pleural fluid, which allows the lungs to be pulled outward when the thoracic wall moves during inspiration. The recoil of the thoracic wall during expiration causes compression of the lungs. Contraction and relaxation of the diaphragm and intercostals muscles (found between the ribs) cause most of the pressure changes that result in inspiration and expiration. These muscle movements and subsequent pressure changes cause air to either rush in or be forced out of the lungs.

Other characteristics of the lungs influence the effort that must be expended to ventilate. Resistance is a force that slows motion, in this case, the flow of gases. The size of the airway is the primary factor affecting resistance. A small tubular diameter forces air through a smaller space, causing more collisions of air molecules with the walls of the airways. The following formula helps to describe the relationship between airway resistance and pressure changes:

$$F = \Delta P / R$$

As noted earlier, there is surface tension within the alveoli caused by water present in the lining of the alveoli. This surface tension tends to inhibit expansion of the alveoli. However, pulmonary surfactant secreted by type II alveolar cells mixes with that water and helps reduce this surface tension. Without pulmonary surfactant, the alveoli would collapse during expiration.

Thoracic wall compliance is the ability of the thoracic wall to stretch while under pressure. This can also affect the effort expended in the process of breathing. In order for inspiration to occur, the thoracic cavity must expand. The expansion of the thoracic cavity directly influences the capacity of the lungs to expand. If the tissues of the thoracic wall are not very compliant, it will be difficult to expand the thorax to increase the size of the lungs.

Pulmonary Ventilation

The difference in pressures drives pulmonary ventilation because air flows down a pressure gradient, that is, air flows from an area of higher pressure to an area of lower pressure. Air flows into the lungs largely due to a difference in pressure; atmospheric pressure is greater than intra-alveolar pressure, and intra-alveolar pressure is greater than intrapleural pressure. Air flows out of the lungs during expiration based on the same principle; pressure within the lungs becomes greater than the atmospheric pressure.

Pulmonary ventilation comprises two major steps: inspiration and expiration. **Inspiration** is the process that causes air to enter the lungs, and **expiration** is the process that causes air to leave the lungs (Figure 22.17). A **respiratory cycle** is one sequence of inspiration and expiration. In general, two muscle groups are used during normal inspiration: the diaphragm and the external intercostal muscles. Additional muscles can be used if a bigger breath is required. When the diaphragm contracts, it moves inferiorly toward the abdominal cavity, creating a larger thoracic cavity and more space for the lungs. Contraction of the external intercostal muscles moves the ribs upward and outward, causing the rib cage to expand, which increases the volume of the thoracic cavity. Due to the adhesive force of the pleural fluid, the expansion of the thoracic cavity forces the lungs to stretch and expand as well. This increase in volume leads to a decrease in intra-alveolar pressure, creating a pressure lower than atmospheric pressure. As a result, a pressure gradient is created that drives air into the lungs.

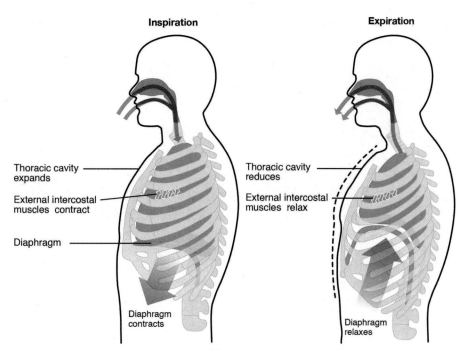

FIGURE 22.17 Inspiration and Expiration Inspiration and expiration occur due to the expansion and contraction of the thoracic cavity, respectively.

The process of normal expiration is passive, meaning that energy is not required to push air out of the lungs. Instead, the elasticity of the lung tissue causes the lung to recoil, as the diaphragm and intercostal muscles relax following inspiration. In turn, the thoracic cavity and lungs decrease in volume, causing an increase in intrapulmonary pressure. The intrapulmonary pressure rises above atmospheric pressure, creating a pressure gradient that causes air to leave the lungs.

There are different types, or modes, of breathing that require a slightly different process to allow inspiration and expiration. **Quiet breathing**, also known as eupnea, is a mode of breathing that occurs at rest and does not require the cognitive thought of the individual. During quiet breathing, the diaphragm and external intercostals must contract.

A deep breath, called diaphragmatic breathing, requires the diaphragm to contract. As the diaphragm relaxes, air passively leaves the lungs. A shallow breath, called costal breathing, requires contraction of the intercostal muscles. As the intercostal muscles relax, air passively leaves the lungs.

In contrast, **forced breathing**, also known as hyperpnea, is a mode of breathing that can occur during exercise or actions that require the active manipulation of breathing, such as singing. During forced breathing, inspiration and expiration both occur due to muscle contractions. In addition to the contraction of the diaphragm and intercostal muscles, other accessory muscles must also contract. During forced inspiration, muscles of the neck, including the scalenes, contract and lift the thoracic wall, increasing lung volume. During forced expiration, accessory muscles of the abdomen, including the obliques, contract, forcing abdominal organs upward against the diaphragm. This helps to push the diaphragm further into the thorax, pushing more air out. In addition, accessory muscles (primarily the internal intercostals) help to compress the rib cage, which also reduces the volume of the thoracic cavity.

Respiratory Volumes and Capacities

Respiratory volume is the term used for various volumes of air moved by or associated with the lungs at a given point in the respiratory cycle. There are four major types of respiratory volumes: tidal, residual, inspiratory reserve, and expiratory reserve (Figure 22.18). **Tidal volume (TV)** is the amount of air that normally enters the lungs during quiet breathing, which is about 500 milliliters. **Expiratory reserve volume (ERV)** is the amount of air you can forcefully exhale past a normal tidal expiration, up to 1200 milliliters for males. **Inspiratory reserve volume (IRV)** is produced by a deep inhalation, past a tidal inspiration. This is the extra volume that can be brought into the lungs during a forced inspiration. **Residual volume (RV)** is the air left in the lungs if you exhale as much air as possible. The residual volume makes breathing easier by preventing the alveoli from collapsing. Respiratory volume is dependent on a variety of factors, and measuring the different types of respiratory volumes can provide important clues about a person's respiratory health (Figure 22.19).

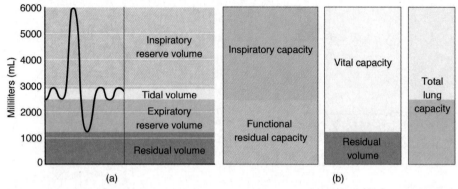

FIGURE 22.18   Respiratory Volumes and Capacities   These two graphs show (a) respiratory volumes and (b) the combination of volumes that results in respiratory capacity.

Pulmonary function test	Instrument	Measures	Function
Spirometry	Spirometer	Forced vital capacity (FVC)	Volume of air that is exhaled after maximum inhalation
		Forced expiratory volume (FEV)	Volume of air exhaled during one forced breath
		Forced expiratory flow, 25–75 percent	Air flow in the middle of exhalation
		Peak expiratory flow (PEF)	Rate of exhalation
		Maximum voluntary ventilation (MVV)	Volume of air that can be inspired and expired in 1 minute
		Slow vital capacity (SVC)	Volume of air that can be slowly exhaled after inhaling past the tidal volume
		Total lung capacity (TLC)	Volume of air in the lungs after maximum inhalation
		Functional residual capacity (FRC)	Volume of air left in the lungs after normal expiration
		Residual volume (RV)	Volume of air in the lungs after maximum exhalation
		Total lung capacity (TLC)	Maximum volume of air that the lungs can hold
		Expiratory reserve volume (ERV)	The volume of air that can be exhaled beyond normal exhalation
Gas diffusion	Blood gas analyzer	Arterial blood gases	Concentration of oxygen and carbon dioxide in the blood

FIGURE 22.19   Pulmonary Function Testing

Respiratory capacity is the combination of two or more selected volumes, which further describes the amount of air in the lungs during a given time. For example, **total lung capacity (TLC)** is the sum of all of the lung volumes (TV, ERV, IRV, and RV), which represents the total amount of air a person can hold in the lungs after a forceful inhalation. TLC is about 6000 mL air for males, and about 4200 mL for females. **Vital capacity (VC)** is the amount of air a person can move into or out of their lungs, and is the sum of all of the volumes except residual volume (TV, ERV, and IRV), which is between 4000 and 5000 milliliters. **Inspiratory capacity (IC)** is the maximum amount of air that can be inhaled past a normal tidal expiration, is the sum of the tidal volume and inspiratory reserve volume. On the other hand, the **functional residual capacity (FRC)** is the amount of air that remains in the lung after a normal tidal expiration; it is the sum of expiratory reserve volume and residual volume (see Figure 22.18).

⊚ INTERACTIVE LINK

Watch this video (http://openstax.org/l/spirometers) to learn more about lung volumes and spirometers. Explain how spirometry test results can be used to diagnose respiratory diseases or determine the effectiveness of disease treatment.

Access for free at openstax.org

In addition to the air that creates respiratory volumes, the respiratory system also contains **anatomical dead space**, which is air that is present in the airway that never reaches the alveoli and therefore never participates in gas exchange. **Alveolar dead space** involves air found within alveoli that are unable to function, such as those affected by disease or abnormal blood flow. **Total dead space** is the anatomical dead space and alveolar dead space together, and represents all of the air in the respiratory system that is not being used in the gas exchange process.

Respiratory Rate and Control of Ventilation

Breathing usually occurs without thought, although at times you can consciously control it, such as when you swim under water, sing a song, or blow bubbles. The **respiratory rate** is the total number of breaths, or respiratory cycles, that occur each minute. Respiratory rate can be an important indicator of disease, as the rate may increase or decrease during an illness or in a disease condition. The respiratory rate is controlled by the respiratory center located within the medulla oblongata in the brain, which responds primarily to changes in carbon dioxide, oxygen, and pH levels in the blood.

The normal respiratory rate of a child decreases from birth to adolescence. A child under 1 year of age has a normal respiratory rate between 30 and 60 breaths per minute, but by the time a child is about 10 years old, the normal rate is closer to 18 to 30. By adolescence, the normal respiratory rate is similar to that of adults, 12 to 18 breaths per minute.

Ventilation Control Centers

The control of ventilation is a complex interplay of multiple regions in the brain that signal the muscles used in pulmonary ventilation to contract (Table 22.1). The result is typically a rhythmic, consistent ventilation rate that provides the body with sufficient amounts of oxygen, while adequately removing carbon dioxide.

Summary of Ventilation Regulation

System component	Function
Medullary respiratory center	Sets the basic rhythm of breathing
Ventral respiratory group (VRG)	Generates the breathing rhythm and integrates data coming into the medulla
Dorsal respiratory group (DRG)	Integrates input from the stretch receptors and the chemoreceptors in the periphery
Pontine respiratory group (PRG)	Influences and modifies the medulla oblongata's functions
Aortic body	Monitors blood PCO_2, PO_2, and pH
Carotid body	Monitors blood PCO_2, PO_2, and pH
Hypothalamus	Monitors emotional state and body temperature
Cortical areas of the brain	Control voluntary breathing
Proprioceptors	Send impulses regarding joint and muscle movements
Pulmonary irritant reflexes	Protect the respiratory zones of the system from foreign material
Inflation reflex	Protects the lungs from over-inflating

TABLE 22.1

Neurons that innervate the muscles of the respiratory system are responsible for controlling and regulating pulmonary ventilation. The major brain centers involved in pulmonary ventilation are the medulla oblongata and the pontine respiratory group (Figure 22.20).

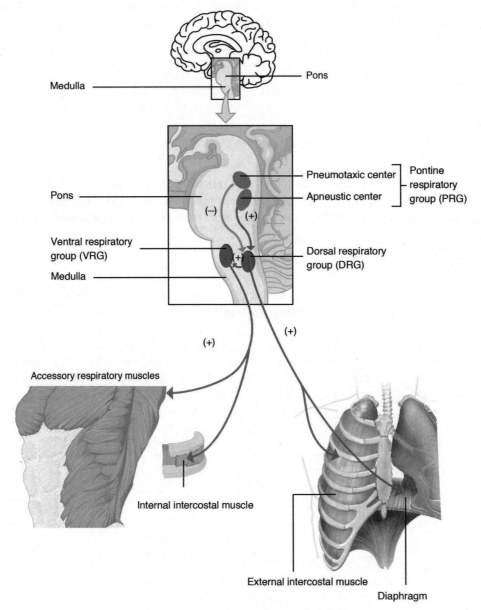

FIGURE 22.20   **Respiratory Centers of the Brain**

The medulla oblongata contains the **dorsal respiratory group (DRG)** and the **ventral respiratory group (VRG)**. The DRG is involved in maintaining a constant breathing rhythm by stimulating the diaphragm and intercostal muscles to contract, resulting in inspiration. When activity in the DRG ceases, it no longer stimulates the diaphragm and intercostals to contract, allowing them to relax, resulting in expiration. The VRG is involved in forced breathing, as the neurons in the VRG stimulate the accessory muscles involved in forced breathing to contract, resulting in forced inspiration. The VRG also stimulates the accessory muscles involved in forced expiration to contract.

The second respiratory center of the brain is located within the pons, called the pontine respiratory group, and consists of the apneustic and pneumotaxic centers. The **apneustic center** is a double cluster of neuronal cell bodies that stimulate neurons in the DRG, controlling the depth of inspiration, particularly for deep breathing. The **pneumotaxic center** is a network of neurons that inhibits the activity of neurons in the DRG, allowing relaxation after inspiration, and thus controlling the overall rate.

Factors That Affect the Rate and Depth of Respiration

The respiratory rate and the depth of inspiration are regulated by the medulla oblongata and pons; however, these regions of the brain do so in response to systemic stimuli. It is a dose-response, negative-feedback relationship in which the greater the stimulus, the greater the response. Thus, increasing stimuli results in forced breathing. Multiple systemic factors are involved in stimulating the brain to produce pulmonary ventilation.

The major factor that stimulates the medulla oblongata and pons to produce respiration is surprisingly not oxygen concentration, but rather the concentration of carbon dioxide in the blood. As you recall, carbon dioxide is a waste product of cellular respiration and can be toxic. Concentrations of chemicals are sensed by chemoreceptors. A **central chemoreceptor** is one of the specialized receptors that are located in the brain and brainstem, whereas a **peripheral chemoreceptor** is one of the specialized receptors located in the carotid arteries and aortic arch. Concentration changes in certain substances, such as carbon dioxide or hydrogen ions, stimulate these receptors, which in turn signal the respiration centers of the brain. In the case of carbon dioxide, as the concentration of CO_2 in the blood increases, it readily diffuses across the blood-brain barrier, where it collects in the extracellular fluid. As will be explained in more detail later, increased carbon dioxide levels lead to increased levels of hydrogen ions, decreasing pH. The increase in hydrogen ions in the brain triggers the central chemoreceptors to stimulate the respiratory centers to initiate contraction of the diaphragm and intercostal muscles. As a result, the rate and depth of respiration increase, allowing more carbon dioxide to be expelled, which brings more air into and out of the lungs promoting a reduction in the blood levels of carbon dioxide, and therefore hydrogen ions, in the blood. In contrast, low levels of carbon dioxide in the blood cause low levels of hydrogen ions in the brain, leading to a decrease in the rate and depth of pulmonary ventilation, producing shallow, slow breathing.

Another factor involved in influencing the respiratory activity of the brain is systemic arterial concentrations of hydrogen ions. Increasing carbon dioxide levels can lead to increased H^+ levels, as mentioned above, as well as other metabolic activities, such as lactic acid accumulation after strenuous exercise. Peripheral chemoreceptors of the aortic arch and carotid arteries sense arterial levels of hydrogen ions. When peripheral chemoreceptors sense decreasing, or more acidic, pH levels, they stimulate an increase in ventilation to remove carbon dioxide from the blood at a quicker rate. Removal of carbon dioxide from the blood helps to reduce hydrogen ions, thus increasing systemic pH.

Blood levels of oxygen are also important in influencing respiratory rate. The peripheral chemoreceptors are responsible for sensing large changes in blood oxygen levels. If blood oxygen levels become quite low—about 60 mm Hg or less—then peripheral chemoreceptors stimulate an increase in respiratory activity. The chemoreceptors are only able to sense dissolved oxygen molecules, not the oxygen that is bound to hemoglobin. As you recall, the majority of oxygen is bound by hemoglobin; when dissolved levels of oxygen drop, hemoglobin releases oxygen. Therefore, a large drop in oxygen levels is required to stimulate the chemoreceptors of the aortic arch and carotid arteries.

The hypothalamus and other brain regions associated with the limbic system also play roles in influencing the regulation of breathing by interacting with the respiratory centers. The hypothalamus and other regions associated with the limbic system are involved in regulating respiration in response to emotions, pain, and temperature. For example, an increase in body temperature causes an increase in respiratory rate. Feeling excited or the fight-or-flight response will also result in an increase in respiratory rate.

Disorders of the...

Respiratory System: Sleep Apnea

Sleep apnea is a chronic disorder that can occur in children or adults, and is characterized by the cessation of breathing during sleep. These episodes may last for several seconds or several minutes, and may differ in the frequency with which they are experienced. Sleep apnea leads to poor sleep, which is reflected in the symptoms of fatigue, evening napping, irritability, memory problems, and morning headaches. In addition, many individuals with sleep apnea experience a dry throat in the morning after waking from sleep, which may be due to excessive snoring.

There are two types of sleep apnea: obstructive sleep apnea and central sleep apnea. Obstructive sleep apnea is caused by an obstruction of the airway during sleep, which can occur at different points in the airway, depending on the underlying cause of the obstruction. For example, the tongue and throat muscles of some individuals with obstructive sleep apnea may relax excessively, causing the muscles to push into the airway. Another example is obesity, which is a known risk factor for sleep apnea, as excess adipose tissue in the neck region can push the soft tissues towards the lumen of the airway, causing the trachea to narrow.

In central sleep apnea, the respiratory centers of the brain do not respond properly to rising carbon dioxide levels and therefore do not stimulate the contraction of the diaphragm and intercostal muscles regularly. As a result, inspiration does not occur and breathing stops for a short period. In some cases, the cause of central sleep apnea is unknown. However, some medical conditions, such as stroke and congestive heart failure, may cause damage to the pons or medulla oblongata. In addition, some pharmacologic agents, such as morphine, can affect the respiratory centers, causing a decrease in the respiratory rate. The symptoms of central sleep apnea are similar to those of obstructive sleep apnea.

A diagnosis of sleep apnea is usually done during a sleep study, where the patient is monitored in a sleep laboratory for several nights. The patient's blood oxygen levels, heart rate, respiratory rate, and blood pressure are monitored, as are brain activity and the volume of air that is inhaled and exhaled. Treatment of sleep apnea commonly includes the use of a device called a continuous positive airway pressure (CPAP) machine during sleep. The CPAP machine has a mask that covers the nose, or the nose and mouth, and forces air into the airway at regular intervals. This pressurized air can help to gently force the airway to remain open, allowing more normal ventilation to occur. Other treatments include lifestyle changes to decrease weight, eliminate alcohol and other sleep apnea–promoting drugs, and changes in sleep position. In addition to these treatments, patients with central sleep apnea may need supplemental oxygen during sleep.

22.4 Gas Exchange

LEARNING OBJECTIVES

By the end of this section, you will be able to:

- Compare the composition of atmospheric air and alveolar air
- Describe the mechanisms that drive gas exchange
- Discuss the importance of sufficient ventilation and perfusion, and how the body adapts when they are insufficient
- Discuss the process of external respiration
- Describe the process of internal respiration

The purpose of the respiratory system is to perform gas exchange. Pulmonary ventilation provides air to the alveoli for this gas exchange process. At the respiratory membrane, where the alveolar and capillary walls meet, gases move across the membranes, with oxygen entering the bloodstream and carbon dioxide exiting. It is through this mechanism that blood is oxygenated and carbon dioxide, the waste product of cellular respiration, is removed from the body.

Gas Exchange

In order to understand the mechanisms of gas exchange in the lung, it is important to understand the underlying principles of gases and their behavior. In addition to Boyle's law, several other gas laws help to describe the behavior of gases.

Gas Laws and Air Composition

Gas molecules exert force on the surfaces with which they are in contact; this force is called pressure. In natural systems, gases are normally present as a mixture of different types of molecules. For example, the atmosphere consists of oxygen, nitrogen, carbon dioxide, and other gaseous molecules, and this gaseous mixture exerts a certain pressure referred to as atmospheric pressure (Table 22.2). **Partial pressure** (P_x) is the pressure of a single type of gas in a mixture of gases. For example, in the atmosphere, oxygen exerts a partial pressure, and nitrogen exerts another partial pressure, independent of the partial pressure of oxygen (Figure 22.21). **Total pressure** is the sum of all the partial pressures of a gaseous mixture. **Dalton's law** describes the behavior of nonreactive gases in a gaseous mixture and states that a specific gas type in a mixture exerts its own pressure; thus, the total pressure exerted by a mixture of gases is the sum of the partial pressures of the gases in the mixture.

Partial Pressures of Atmospheric Gases

Gas	Percent of total composition	Partial pressure (mm Hg)
Nitrogen (N_2)	78.6	597.4
Oxygen (O_2)	20.9	158.8
Water (H_2O)	0.4	3.0
Carbon dioxide (CO_2)	0.04	0.3
Others	0.06	0.5
Total composition/total atmospheric pressure	100%	760.0

TABLE 22.2

FIGURE 22.21 Partial and Total Pressures of a Gas   Partial pressure is the force exerted by a gas. The sum of the partial pressures of all the gases in a mixture equals the total pressure.

Partial pressure is extremely important in predicting the movement of gases. Recall that gases tend to equalize their pressure in two regions that are connected. A gas will move from an area where its partial pressure is higher to an area where its partial pressure is lower. In addition, the greater the partial pressure difference between the two areas, the more rapid is the movement of gases.

Solubility of Gases in Liquids

Henry's law describes the behavior of gases when they come into contact with a liquid, such as blood. Henry's law states that the concentration of gas in a liquid is directly proportional to the solubility and partial pressure of that gas. The greater the partial pressure of the gas, the greater the number of gas molecules that will dissolve in the liquid. The concentration of the gas in a liquid is also dependent on the solubility of the gas in the liquid. For example, although nitrogen is present in the atmosphere, very little nitrogen dissolves into the blood, because the solubility of nitrogen in blood is very low. The exception to this occurs in scuba divers; the composition of the compressed air that divers breathe causes nitrogen to have a higher partial pressure than normal, causing it to dissolve in the blood in greater amounts than normal. Too much nitrogen in the bloodstream results in a serious condition that can be fatal if not corrected. Gas molecules establish an equilibrium between those molecules dissolved in liquid and those in air.

The composition of air in the atmosphere and in the alveoli differs. In both cases, the relative concentration of gases is nitrogen > oxygen > water vapor > carbon dioxide. The amount of water vapor present in alveolar air is greater than that in atmospheric air (Table 22.3). Recall that the respiratory system works to humidify incoming air, thereby causing the air present in the alveoli to have a greater amount of water vapor than atmospheric air. In addition, alveolar air contains a greater amount of carbon dioxide and less oxygen than atmospheric air. This is no surprise, as gas exchange removes oxygen from and adds carbon dioxide to alveolar air. Both deep and forced breathing cause the alveolar air composition to be changed more rapidly than during quiet breathing. As a result, the partial pressures of oxygen and carbon dioxide change, affecting the diffusion process that moves these materials across the membrane. This will cause oxygen to enter and carbon dioxide to leave the blood more quickly.

Composition and Partial Pressures of Alveolar Air

Gas	Percent of total composition	Partial pressure (mm Hg)
Nitrogen (N_2)	74.9	569
Oxygen (O_2)	13.7	104
Water (H_2O)	6.2	40
Carbon dioxide (CO_2)	5.2	47
Total composition/total alveolar pressure	100%	760.0

TABLE 22.3

Ventilation and Perfusion

Two important aspects of gas exchange in the lung are ventilation and perfusion. **Ventilation** is the movement of air into and out of the lungs, and perfusion is the flow of blood in the pulmonary capillaries. For gas exchange to be efficient, the volumes involved in ventilation and perfusion should be compatible. However, factors such as regional gravity effects on blood, blocked alveolar ducts, or disease can cause ventilation and perfusion to be imbalanced.

The partial pressure of oxygen in alveolar air is about 104 mm Hg, whereas the partial pressure of oxygenated blood in pulmonary veins is about 100 mm Hg. When ventilation is sufficient, oxygen enters the alveoli at a high rate, and the partial pressure of oxygen in the alveoli remains high. In contrast, when ventilation is insufficient, the partial pressure of oxygen in the alveoli drops. Without the large difference in partial pressure between the alveoli and the blood, oxygen does not diffuse efficiently across the respiratory membrane. The body has mechanisms that counteract this problem. In cases when ventilation is not sufficient for an alveolus, the body redirects blood flow to alveoli that are receiving sufficient ventilation. This is achieved by constricting the pulmonary arterioles that serves the dysfunctional alveolus, which redirects blood to other alveoli that have sufficient ventilation. At the same time, the pulmonary arterioles that serve alveoli receiving sufficient ventilation vasodilate, which brings in greater blood flow. Factors such as carbon dioxide, oxygen, and pH levels can all serve as stimuli for adjusting blood flow in the capillary networks associated with the alveoli.

Ventilation is regulated by the diameter of the airways, whereas perfusion is regulated by the diameter of the blood vessels. The diameter of the bronchioles is sensitive to the partial pressure of carbon dioxide in the alveoli. A greater partial pressure of carbon dioxide in the alveoli causes the bronchioles to increase their diameter as will a decreased level of oxygen in the blood supply, allowing carbon dioxide to be exhaled from the body at a greater rate. As mentioned above, a greater partial pressure of oxygen in the alveoli causes the pulmonary arterioles to dilate, increasing blood flow.

Gas Exchange

Gas exchange occurs at two sites in the body: in the lungs, where oxygen is picked up and carbon dioxide is released at the respiratory membrane, and at the tissues, where oxygen is released and carbon dioxide is picked up. External respiration is the exchange of gases with the external environment, and occurs in the alveoli of the lungs. Internal respiration is the exchange of gases with the internal environment, and occurs in the tissues. The actual exchange of gases occurs due to simple diffusion. Energy is not required to move oxygen or carbon dioxide across membranes. Instead, these gases follow pressure gradients that allow them to diffuse. The anatomy of the lung maximizes the diffusion of gases: The respiratory membrane is highly permeable to gases; the respiratory and blood capillary membranes are very thin; and there is a large surface area throughout the lungs.

External Respiration

The pulmonary artery carries deoxygenated blood into the lungs from the heart, where it branches and eventually becomes the capillary network composed of pulmonary capillaries. These pulmonary capillaries create the respiratory membrane with the alveoli (Figure 22.22). As the blood is pumped through this capillary network, gas exchange occurs. Although a small amount of the oxygen is able to dissolve directly into plasma from the alveoli, most of the oxygen is picked up by erythrocytes (red blood cells) and binds to a protein called hemoglobin, a process described later in this chapter. Oxygenated hemoglobin is red, causing the overall appearance of bright red oxygenated blood, which returns to the heart through the pulmonary veins. Carbon dioxide is released in the opposite direction of oxygen, from the blood to the alveoli. Some of the carbon dioxide is returned on hemoglobin, but can also be dissolved in plasma or is present as a converted form, also explained in greater detail later in this chapter.

External respiration occurs as a function of partial pressure differences in oxygen and carbon dioxide between the alveoli and the blood in the pulmonary capillaries.

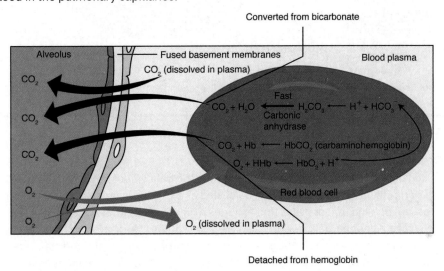

FIGURE 22.22   External Respiration   In external respiration, oxygen diffuses across the respiratory membrane from the alveolus to the capillary, whereas carbon dioxide diffuses out of the capillary into the alveolus.

Although the solubility of oxygen in blood is not high, there is a drastic difference in the partial pressure of oxygen in the alveoli versus in the blood of the pulmonary capillaries. This difference is about 64 mm Hg: The partial pressure of oxygen in the alveoli is about 104 mm Hg, whereas its partial pressure in the blood of the capillary is about 40 mm Hg. This large difference in partial pressure creates a very strong pressure gradient that causes oxygen to rapidly cross the respiratory membrane from the alveoli into the blood.

The partial pressure of carbon dioxide is also different between the alveolar air and the blood of the capillary. However, the partial pressure difference is less than that of oxygen, about 5 mm Hg. The partial pressure of carbon dioxide in the blood of the capillary is about 45 mm Hg, whereas its partial pressure in the alveoli is about 40 mm Hg. However, the solubility of carbon dioxide is much greater than that of oxygen—by a factor of about 20—in both blood and alveolar fluids. As a result, the relative concentrations of oxygen and carbon dioxide that diffuse across the respiratory membrane are similar.

Internal Respiration

Internal respiration is gas exchange that occurs at the level of body tissues (Figure 22.23). Similar to external respiration, internal respiration also occurs as simple diffusion due to a partial pressure gradient. However, the partial pressure gradients are opposite of those present at the respiratory membrane. The partial pressure of oxygen in tissues is low, about 40 mm Hg, because oxygen is continuously used for cellular respiration. In contrast, the partial pressure of oxygen in the blood is about 100 mm Hg. This creates a pressure gradient that causes oxygen to dissociate from hemoglobin, diffuse out of the blood, cross the interstitial space, and enter the tissue. Hemoglobin that has little oxygen bound to it loses much of its brightness, so that blood returning to the heart is more burgundy in color.

Considering that cellular respiration continuously produces carbon dioxide, the partial pressure of carbon dioxide is lower in the blood than it is in the tissue, causing carbon dioxide to diffuse out of the tissue, cross the interstitial fluid, and enter the blood. It is then carried back to the lungs either bound to hemoglobin, dissolved in plasma, or in a converted form. By the time blood returns to the heart, the partial pressure of oxygen has returned to about 40 mm Hg, and the partial pressure of carbon dioxide has returned to about 45 mm Hg. The blood is then pumped back to the lungs to be oxygenated once again during external respiration.

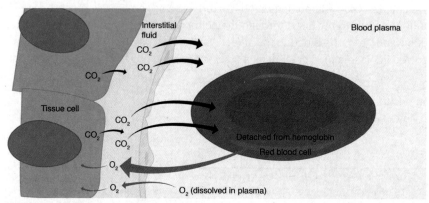

FIGURE 22.23   Internal Respiration   Oxygen diffuses out of the capillary and into cells, whereas carbon dioxide diffuses out of cells and into the capillary.

Everyday Connection

Hyperbaric Chamber Treatment

A type of device used in some areas of medicine that exploits the behavior of gases is hyperbaric chamber treatment. A hyperbaric chamber is a unit that can be sealed and expose a patient to either 100 percent oxygen with increased pressure or a mixture of gases that includes a higher concentration of oxygen than normal atmospheric air, also at a higher partial pressure than the atmosphere. There are two major types of chambers: monoplace and multiplace. Monoplace chambers are typically for one patient, and the staff tending to the patient observes the patient from outside of the chamber (Figure 22.24). Some facilities have special monoplace hyperbaric chambers that allow multiple patients to be treated at once, usually in a sitting or reclining position, to help ease feelings of isolation or claustrophobia. Multiplace chambers are large enough for multiple patients to be treated at one time, and the staff attending these patients is present inside the chamber. In a multiplace chamber, patients are often treated with air via a mask or hood, and the chamber is pressurized.

FIGURE 22.24 Hyperbaric Chamber   (credit: "komunews"/flickr.com)

Hyperbaric chamber treatment is based on the behavior of gases. As you recall, gases move from a region of higher partial pressure to a region of lower partial pressure. In a hyperbaric chamber, the atmospheric pressure is increased, causing a greater amount of oxygen than normal to diffuse into the bloodstream of the patient. Hyperbaric chamber therapy is used to treat a variety of medical problems, such as wound and graft healing, anaerobic bacterial infections, and carbon monoxide poisoning. Exposure to and poisoning by carbon monoxide is difficult to reverse, because hemoglobin's affinity for carbon monoxide is much stronger than its affinity for oxygen, causing carbon monoxide to replace oxygen in the blood. Hyperbaric chamber therapy can treat carbon monoxide poisoning, because the increased atmospheric pressure causes more oxygen to diffuse into the bloodstream. At this increased pressure and increased concentration of oxygen, carbon monoxide is displaced from hemoglobin. Another example is the treatment of anaerobic bacterial infections, which are created by bacteria that cannot or prefer not to live in the presence of oxygen. An increase in blood and tissue levels of oxygen helps to kill the anaerobic bacteria that are responsible for the infection, as oxygen is toxic to anaerobic bacteria. For wounds and grafts, the chamber stimulates the healing process by increasing energy production needed for repair. Increasing oxygen transport allows cells to ramp up cellular respiration and thus ATP production, the energy needed to build new structures.

22.5 Transport of Gases

LEARNING OBJECTIVES

By the end of this section, you will be able to:
- Describe the principles of oxygen transport
- Describe the structure of hemoglobin
- Compare and contrast fetal and adult hemoglobin
- Describe the principles of carbon dioxide transport

The other major activity in the lungs is the process of respiration, the process of gas exchange. The function of respiration is to provide oxygen for use by body cells during cellular respiration and to eliminate carbon dioxide, a waste product of cellular respiration, from the body. In order for the exchange of oxygen and carbon dioxide to occur, both gases must be transported between the external and internal respiration sites. Although carbon dioxide is more soluble than oxygen in blood, both gases require a specialized transport system for the majority of the gas molecules to be moved between the lungs and other tissues.

Oxygen Transport in the Blood

Even though oxygen is transported via the blood, you may recall that oxygen is not very soluble in liquids. A small amount of oxygen does dissolve in the blood and is transported in the bloodstream, but it is only about 1.5% of the total amount. The majority of oxygen molecules are carried from the lungs to the body's tissues by a specialized transport system, which relies on the erythrocyte—the red blood cell. Erythrocytes contain a metalloprotein, hemoglobin, which serves to bind oxygen molecules to the erythrocyte (Figure 22.25). Heme is the portion of hemoglobin that contains iron, and it is heme that binds oxygen. Each hemoglobin molecule contains four iron-containing heme molecules, and because of this, one hemoglobin molecule is capable of carrying up to four molecules of oxygen. As oxygen diffuses across the respiratory membrane from the alveolus to the capillary, it also diffuses into the red blood cell and is bound by hemoglobin. The following reversible chemical reaction describes the production of the final product, **oxyhemoglobin** (HbO_2), which is formed when oxygen binds to hemoglobin. Oxyhemoglobin is a bright red-colored molecule that contributes to the bright red color of oxygenated blood.

$$Hb + O_2 \leftrightarrow HbO_2$$

In this formula, Hb represents reduced hemoglobin, that is, hemoglobin that does not have oxygen bound to it. There are multiple factors involved in how readily heme binds to and dissociates from oxygen, which will be discussed in the subsequent sections.

FIGURE 22.25   Erythrocyte and Hemoglobin   Hemoglobin consists of four subunits, each of which contains one molecule of iron.

Function of Hemoglobin

Hemoglobin is composed of subunits, a protein structure that is referred to as a quaternary structure. Each of the four subunits that make up hemoglobin is arranged in a ring-like fashion, with an iron atom covalently bound to the heme in the center of each subunit. Binding of the first oxygen molecule causes a conformational change in hemoglobin that allows the second molecule of oxygen to bind more readily. As each molecule of oxygen is bound, it further facilitates the binding of the next molecule, until all four heme sites are occupied by oxygen. The opposite occurs as well: After the first oxygen molecule dissociates and is "dropped off" at the tissues, the next oxygen molecule dissociates more readily. When all four heme sites are occupied, the hemoglobin is said to be saturated. When one to three heme sites are occupied, the hemoglobin is said to be partially saturated. Therefore, when considering the blood as a whole, the percent of the available heme units that are bound to oxygen at a given time is called hemoglobin saturation. Hemoglobin saturation of 100 percent means that every heme unit in all of the erythrocytes of the body is bound to oxygen. In a healthy individual with normal hemoglobin levels, hemoglobin saturation generally ranges from 95 percent to 99 percent.

Oxygen Dissociation from Hemoglobin

Partial pressure is an important aspect of the binding of oxygen to and disassociation from heme. An **oxygen–hemoglobin dissociation curve** is a graph that describes the relationship of partial pressure to the binding of oxygen to heme and its subsequent dissociation from heme (Figure 22.26). Remember that gases travel from an area of higher partial pressure to an area of lower partial pressure. In addition, the affinity of an oxygen molecule for heme increases as more oxygen molecules are bound. Therefore, in the oxygen–hemoglobin saturation curve, as the

Access for free at openstax.org

partial pressure of oxygen increases, a proportionately greater number of oxygen molecules are bound by heme. Not surprisingly, the oxygen–hemoglobin saturation/dissociation curve also shows that the lower the partial pressure of oxygen, the fewer oxygen molecules are bound to heme. As a result, the partial pressure of oxygen plays a major role in determining the degree of binding of oxygen to heme at the site of the respiratory membrane, as well as the degree of dissociation of oxygen from heme at the site of body tissues.

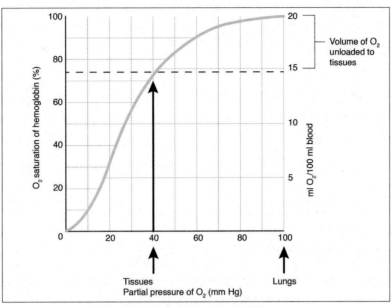

(a) Partial pressure of oxygen and hemoglobin saturation

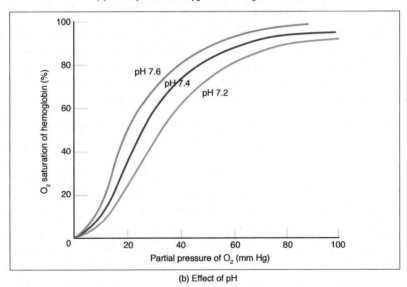

(b) Effect of pH

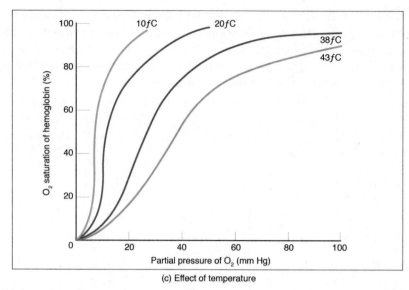

(c) Effect of temperature

FIGURE 22.26   Oxygen-Hemoglobin Dissociation and Effects of pH and Temperature   These three graphs show (a) the relationship between the partial pressure of oxygen and hemoglobin saturation, (b) the effect of pH on the oxygen–hemoglobin dissociation curve, and (c) the effect of temperature on the oxygen–hemoglobin dissociation curve.

The mechanisms behind the oxygen–hemoglobin saturation/dissociation curve also serve as automatic control mechanisms that regulate how much oxygen is delivered to different tissues throughout the body. This is important because some tissues have a higher metabolic rate than others. Highly active tissues, such as muscle, rapidly use oxygen to produce ATP, lowering the partial pressure of oxygen in the tissue to about 20 mm Hg. The partial pressure of oxygen inside capillaries is about 100 mm Hg, so the difference between the two becomes quite high, about 80 mm Hg. As a result, a greater number of oxygen molecules dissociate from hemoglobin and enter the tissues. The reverse is true of tissues, such as adipose (body fat), which have lower metabolic rates. Because less oxygen is used by these cells, the partial pressure of oxygen within such tissues remains relatively high, resulting in fewer oxygen molecules dissociating from hemoglobin and entering the tissue interstitial fluid. Although venous blood is said to be deoxygenated, some oxygen is still bound to hemoglobin in its red blood cells. This provides an oxygen reserve that can be used when tissues suddenly demand more oxygen.

Factors other than partial pressure also affect the oxygen–hemoglobin saturation/dissociation curve. For example, a higher temperature promotes hemoglobin and oxygen to dissociate faster, whereas a lower temperature inhibits dissociation (see Figure 22.26, **middle**). However, the human body tightly regulates temperature, so this factor may not affect gas exchange throughout the body. The exception to this is in highly active tissues, which may release a larger amount of energy than is given off as heat. As a result, oxygen readily dissociates from hemoglobin, which is a mechanism that helps to provide active tissues with more oxygen.

Certain hormones, such as androgens, epinephrine, thyroid hormones, and growth hormone, can affect the oxygen–hemoglobin saturation/disassociation curve by stimulating the production of a compound called 2,3-bisphosphoglycerate (BPG) by erythrocytes. BPG is a byproduct of glycolysis. Because erythrocytes do not contain mitochondria, glycolysis is the sole method by which these cells produce ATP. BPG promotes the disassociation of oxygen from hemoglobin. Therefore, the greater the concentration of BPG, the more readily oxygen dissociates from hemoglobin, despite its partial pressure.

The pH of the blood is another factor that influences the oxygen–hemoglobin saturation/dissociation curve (see Figure 22.26). The **Bohr effect** is a phenomenon that arises from the relationship between pH and oxygen's affinity for hemoglobin: A lower, more acidic pH promotes oxygen dissociation from hemoglobin. In contrast, a higher, or more basic, pH inhibits oxygen dissociation from hemoglobin. The greater the amount of carbon dioxide in the blood, the more molecules that must be converted, which in turn generates hydrogen ions and thus lowers blood pH. Furthermore, blood pH may become more acidic when certain byproducts of cell metabolism, such as lactic acid, carbonic acid, and carbon dioxide, are released into the bloodstream.

Hemoglobin of the Fetus

The fetus has its own circulation with its own erythrocytes; however, it is dependent on the pregnant person for

Access for free at openstax.org

oxygen. Blood is supplied to the fetus by way of the umbilical cord, which is connected to the placenta and separated from maternal blood by the chorion. The mechanism of gas exchange at the chorion is similar to gas exchange at the respiratory membrane. However, the partial pressure of oxygen is lower in the maternal blood in the placenta, at about 35 to 50 mm Hg, than it is in maternal arterial blood. The difference in partial pressures between maternal and fetal blood is not large, as the partial pressure of oxygen in fetal blood at the placenta is about 20 mm Hg. Therefore, there is not as much diffusion of oxygen into the fetal blood supply. The fetus' hemoglobin overcomes this problem by having a greater affinity for oxygen than maternal hemoglobin (Figure 22.27). Both fetal and adult hemoglobin have four subunits, but two of the subunits of fetal hemoglobin have a different structure that causes fetal hemoglobin to have a greater affinity for oxygen than does adult hemoglobin.

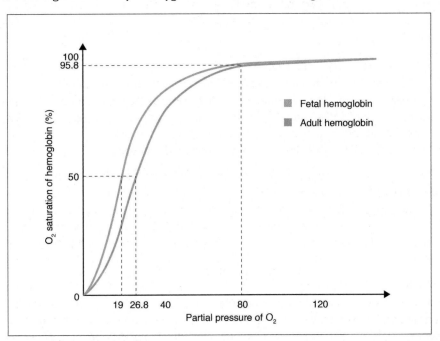

FIGURE 22.27 Oxygen-Hemoglobin Dissociation Curves in Fetus and Adult Fetal hemoglobin has a greater affinity for oxygen than does adult hemoglobin.

Carbon Dioxide Transport in the Blood

Carbon dioxide is transported by three major mechanisms. The first mechanism of carbon dioxide transport is by blood plasma, as some carbon dioxide molecules dissolve in the blood. The second mechanism is transport in the form of bicarbonate (HCO_3^-), which also dissolves in plasma. The third mechanism of carbon dioxide transport is similar to the transport of oxygen by erythrocytes (Figure 22.28).

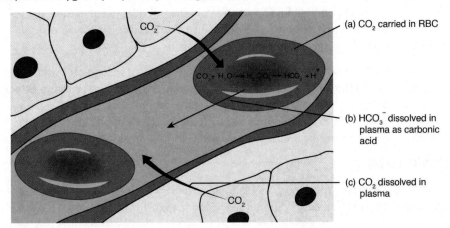

FIGURE 22.28 Carbon Dioxide Transport Carbon dioxide is transported by three different methods: (a) in erythrocytes; (b) after forming carbonic acid (H_2CO_3), which is dissolved in plasma; (c) and in plasma.

Dissolved Carbon Dioxide

Although carbon dioxide is not considered to be highly soluble in blood, a small fraction—about 7 to 10 percent—of the carbon dioxide that diffuses into the blood from the tissues dissolves in plasma. The dissolved carbon dioxide then travels in the bloodstream and when the blood reaches the pulmonary capillaries, the dissolved carbon dioxide diffuses across the respiratory membrane into the alveoli, where it is then exhaled during pulmonary ventilation.

Bicarbonate Buffer

A large fraction—about 70 percent—of the carbon dioxide molecules that diffuse into the blood is transported to the lungs as bicarbonate. Most bicarbonate is produced in erythrocytes after carbon dioxide diffuses into the capillaries, and subsequently into red blood cells. **Carbonic anhydrase (CA)** causes carbon dioxide and water to form carbonic acid (H_2CO_3), which dissociates into two ions: bicarbonate (HCO_3^-) and hydrogen (H^+). The following formula depicts this reaction:

$$CO_2 + H_2O \overset{CA}{\leftrightarrow} H_2CO_3 \leftrightarrow H^+ + HCO_3{}_-$$

Bicarbonate tends to build up in the erythrocytes, so that there is a greater concentration of bicarbonate in the erythrocytes than in the surrounding blood plasma. As a result, some of the bicarbonate will leave the erythrocytes and move down its concentration gradient into the plasma in exchange for chloride (Cl^-) ions. This phenomenon is referred to as the **chloride shift** and occurs because by exchanging one negative ion for another negative ion, neither the electrical charge of the erythrocytes nor that of the blood is altered.

At the pulmonary capillaries, the chemical reaction that produced bicarbonate (shown above) is reversed, and carbon dioxide and water are the products. Much of the bicarbonate in the plasma re-enters the erythrocytes in exchange for chloride ions. Hydrogen ions and bicarbonate ions join to form carbonic acid, which is converted into carbon dioxide and water by carbonic anhydrase. Carbon dioxide diffuses out of the erythrocytes and into the plasma, where it can further diffuse across the respiratory membrane into the alveoli to be exhaled during pulmonary ventilation.

Carbaminohemoglobin

About 20 percent of carbon dioxide is bound by hemoglobin and is transported to the lungs. Carbon dioxide does not bind to iron as oxygen does; instead, carbon dioxide binds amino acid moieties on the globin portions of hemoglobin to form **carbaminohemoglobin**, which forms when hemoglobin and carbon dioxide bind. When hemoglobin is not transporting oxygen, it tends to have a bluish-purple tone to it, creating the darker maroon color typical of deoxygenated blood. The following formula depicts this reversible reaction:

$$CO_2 + Hb \leftrightarrow HbCO_2$$

Similar to the transport of oxygen by heme, the binding and dissociation of carbon dioxide to and from hemoglobin is dependent on the partial pressure of carbon dioxide. Because carbon dioxide is released from the lungs, blood that leaves the lungs and reaches body tissues has a lower partial pressure of carbon dioxide than is found in the tissues. As a result, carbon dioxide leaves the tissues because of its higher partial pressure, enters the blood, and then moves into red blood cells, binding to hemoglobin. In contrast, in the pulmonary capillaries, the partial pressure of carbon dioxide is high compared to within the alveoli. As a result, carbon dioxide dissociates readily from hemoglobin and diffuses across the respiratory membrane into the air.

In addition to the partial pressure of carbon dioxide, the oxygen saturation of hemoglobin and the partial pressure of oxygen in the blood also influence the affinity of hemoglobin for carbon dioxide. The **Haldane effect** is a phenomenon that arises from the relationship between the partial pressure of oxygen and the affinity of hemoglobin for carbon dioxide. Hemoglobin that is saturated with oxygen does not readily bind carbon dioxide. However, when oxygen is not bound to heme and the partial pressure of oxygen is low, hemoglobin readily binds to carbon dioxide.

⊚ INTERACTIVE LINK

Watch this video (http://openstax.org/l/oxyblood) to see the transport of oxygen from the lungs to the tissues. Why is oxygenated blood bright red, whereas deoxygenated blood tends to be more of a purple color?

22.6 Modifications in Respiratory Functions

LEARNING OBJECTIVES

By the end of this section, you will be able to:

- Define the terms hyperpnea and hyperventilation
- Describe the effect of exercise on the respiratory system
- Describe the effect of high altitude on the respiratory system
- Discuss the process of acclimatization

At rest, the respiratory system performs its functions at a constant, rhythmic pace, as regulated by the respiratory centers of the brain. At this pace, ventilation provides sufficient oxygen to all the tissues of the body. However, there are times that the respiratory system must alter the pace of its functions in order to accommodate the oxygen demands of the body.

Hyperpnea

Hyperpnea is an increased depth and rate of ventilation to meet an increase in oxygen demand as might be seen in exercise or disease, particularly diseases that target the respiratory or digestive tracts. This does not significantly alter blood oxygen or carbon dioxide levels, but merely increases the depth and rate of ventilation to meet the demand of the cells. In contrast, **hyperventilation** is an increased ventilation rate that is independent of the cellular oxygen needs and leads to abnormally low blood carbon dioxide levels and high (alkaline) blood pH.

Interestingly, exercise does not cause hyperpnea as one might think. Muscles that perform work during exercise do increase their demand for oxygen, stimulating an increase in ventilation. However, hyperpnea during exercise appears to occur before a drop in oxygen levels within the muscles can occur. Therefore, hyperpnea must be driven by other mechanisms, either instead of or in addition to a drop in oxygen levels. The exact mechanisms behind exercise hyperpnea are not well understood, and some hypotheses are somewhat controversial. However, in addition to low oxygen, high carbon dioxide, and low pH levels, there appears to be a complex interplay of factors related to the nervous system and the respiratory centers of the brain.

First, a conscious decision to partake in exercise, or another form of physical exertion, results in a psychological stimulus that may trigger the respiratory centers of the brain to increase ventilation. In addition, the respiratory centers of the brain may be stimulated through the activation of motor neurons that innervate muscle groups that are involved in the physical activity. Finally, physical exertion stimulates proprioceptors, which are receptors located within the muscles, joints, and tendons, which sense movement and stretching; proprioceptors thus create a stimulus that may also trigger the respiratory centers of the brain. These neural factors are consistent with the sudden increase in ventilation that is observed immediately as exercise begins. Because the respiratory centers are stimulated by psychological, motor neuron, and proprioceptor inputs throughout exercise, the fact that there is also a sudden decrease in ventilation immediately after the exercise ends when these neural stimuli cease, further supports the idea that they are involved in triggering the changes of ventilation.

High Altitude Effects

An increase in altitude results in a decrease in atmospheric pressure. Although the proportion of oxygen relative to gases in the atmosphere remains at 21 percent, its partial pressure decreases (Table 22.4). As a result, it is more difficult for a body to achieve the same level of oxygen saturation at high altitude than at low altitude, due to lower atmospheric pressure. In fact, hemoglobin saturation is lower at high altitudes compared to hemoglobin saturation at sea level. For example, hemoglobin saturation is about 67 percent at 19,000 feet above sea level, whereas it reaches about 98 percent at sea level.

Partial Pressure of Oxygen at Different Altitudes

Example location	Altitude (feet above sea level)	Atmospheric pressure (mm Hg)	Partial pressure of oxygen (mm Hg)
New York City, New York	0	760	159
Boulder, Colorado	5000	632	133
Aspen, Colorado	8000	565	118
Pike's Peak, Colorado	14,000	447	94
Denali (Mt. McKinley), Alaska	20,000	350	73
Mt. Everest, Tibet	29,000	260	54

TABLE 22.4

As you recall, partial pressure is extremely important in determining how much gas can cross the respiratory membrane and enter the blood of the pulmonary capillaries. A lower partial pressure of oxygen means that there is a smaller difference in partial pressures between the alveoli and the blood, so less oxygen crosses the respiratory membrane. As a result, fewer oxygen molecules are bound by hemoglobin. Despite this, the tissues of the body still receive a sufficient amount of oxygen during rest at high altitudes. This is due to two major mechanisms. First, the number of oxygen molecules that enter the tissue from the blood is nearly equal between sea level and high altitudes. At sea level, hemoglobin saturation is higher, but only a quarter of the oxygen molecules are actually released into the tissue. At high altitudes, a greater proportion of molecules of oxygen are released into the tissues. Secondly, at high altitudes, a greater amount of BPG is produced by erythrocytes, which enhances the dissociation of oxygen from hemoglobin. Physical exertion, such as skiing or hiking, can lead to altitude sickness due to the low amount of oxygen reserves in the blood at high altitudes. At sea level, there is a large amount of oxygen reserve in venous blood (even though venous blood is thought of as "deoxygenated") from which the muscles can draw during physical exertion. Because the oxygen saturation is much lower at higher altitudes, this venous reserve is small, resulting in pathological symptoms of low blood oxygen levels. You may have heard that it is important to drink more water when traveling at higher altitudes than you are accustomed to. This is because your body will increase micturition (urination) at high altitudes to counteract the effects of lower oxygen levels. By removing fluids, blood plasma levels drop but not the total number of erythrocytes. In this way, the overall concentration of erythrocytes in the blood increases, which helps tissues obtain the oxygen they need.

Acute mountain sickness (AMS), or altitude sickness, is a condition that results from acute exposure to high altitudes due to a low partial pressure of oxygen at high altitudes. AMS typically can occur at 2400 meters (8000 feet) above sea level. AMS is a result of low blood oxygen levels, as the body has acute difficulty adjusting to the low partial pressure of oxygen. In serious cases, AMS can cause pulmonary or cerebral edema. Symptoms of AMS include nausea, vomiting, fatigue, lightheadedness, drowsiness, feeling disoriented, increased pulse, and nosebleeds. The only treatment for AMS is descending to a lower altitude; however, pharmacologic treatments and supplemental oxygen can improve symptoms. AMS can be prevented by slowly ascending to the desired altitude, allowing the body to acclimate, as well as maintaining proper hydration.

Acclimatization

Especially in situations where the ascent occurs too quickly, traveling to areas of high altitude can cause AMS. **Acclimatization** is the process of adjustment that the respiratory system makes due to chronic exposure to a high altitude. Over a period of time, the body adjusts to accommodate the lower partial pressure of oxygen. The low partial pressure of oxygen at high altitudes results in a lower oxygen saturation level of hemoglobin in the blood. In turn, the tissue levels of oxygen are also lower. As a result, the kidneys are stimulated to produce the hormone erythropoietin (EPO), which stimulates the production of erythrocytes, resulting in a greater number of circulating erythrocytes in an individual at a high altitude over a long period. With more red blood cells, there is more hemoglobin to help transport the available oxygen. Even though there is low saturation of each hemoglobin molecule, there will be more hemoglobin present, and therefore more oxygen in the blood. Over time, this allows the person to partake in physical exertion without developing AMS.

22.7 Embryonic Development of the Respiratory System

LEARNING OBJECTIVES

By the end of this section, you will be able to:
- Create a timeline of the phases of respiratory development in the fetus
- Propose reasons for fetal breathing movements
- Explain how the lungs become inflated after birth

Development of the respiratory system begins early in the fetus. It is a complex process that includes many structures, most of which arise from the endoderm. Towards the end of development, the fetus can be observed making breathing movements. Until birth, however, the pregnant person provides all of the oxygen to the fetus as well as removes all of the fetal carbon dioxide via the placenta.

Time Line

The development of the respiratory system begins at about week 4 of gestation. By week 28, enough alveoli have matured that a baby born prematurely at this time can usually breathe on its own. The respiratory system, however, is not fully developed until early childhood, when a full complement of mature alveoli is present.

Weeks 4–7

Respiratory development in the embryo begins around week 4. Ectodermal tissue from the anterior head region invaginates posteriorly to form olfactory pits, which fuse with endodermal tissue of the developing pharynx. An **olfactory pit** is one of a pair of structures that will enlarge to become the nasal cavity. At about this same time, the lung bud forms. The **lung bud** is a dome-shaped structure composed of tissue that bulges from the foregut. The **foregut** is endoderm just inferior to the pharyngeal pouches. The **laryngotracheal bud** is a structure that forms from the longitudinal extension of the lung bud as development progresses. The portion of this structure nearest the pharynx becomes the trachea, whereas the distal end becomes more bulbous, forming bronchial buds. A **bronchial bud** is one of a pair of structures that will eventually become the bronchi and all other lower respiratory structures (Figure 22.29).

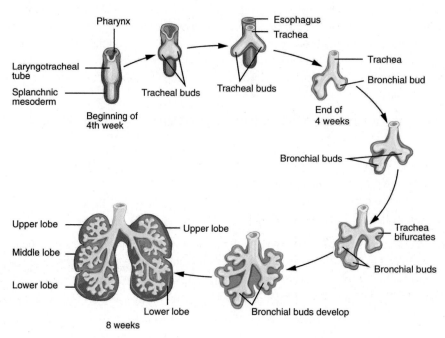

FIGURE 22.29   Development of the Lower Respiratory System

Weeks 7–16

Bronchial buds continue to branch as development progresses until all of the segmental bronchi have been formed. Beginning around week 13, the lumens of the bronchi begin to expand in diameter. By week 16, respiratory bronchioles form. The fetus now has all major lung structures involved in the airway.

Weeks 16–24

Once the respiratory bronchioles form, further development includes extensive vascularization, or the development of the blood vessels, as well as the formation of alveolar ducts and alveolar precursors. At about week 19, the respiratory bronchioles have formed. In addition, cells lining the respiratory structures begin to differentiate to form type I and type II pneumocytes. Once type II cells have differentiated, they begin to secrete small amounts of pulmonary surfactant. Around week 20, fetal breathing movements may begin.

Weeks 24–Term

Major growth and maturation of the respiratory system occurs from week 24 until term. More alveolar precursors develop, and larger amounts of pulmonary surfactant are produced. Surfactant levels are not generally adequate to create effective lung compliance until about the eighth month of pregnancy. The respiratory system continues to expand, and the surfaces that will form the respiratory membrane develop further. At this point, pulmonary capillaries have formed and continue to expand, creating a large surface area for gas exchange. The major milestone of respiratory development occurs at around week 28, when sufficient alveolar precursors have matured so that a baby born prematurely at this time can usually breathe on its own. However, alveoli continue to develop and mature into childhood. A full complement of functional alveoli does not appear until around 8 years of age.

Fetal "Breathing"

Although the function of fetal breathing movements is not entirely clear, they can be observed starting at 20–21 weeks of development. Fetal breathing movements involve muscle contractions that cause the inhalation of amniotic fluid and exhalation of the same fluid, with pulmonary surfactant and mucus. Fetal breathing movements are not continuous and may include periods of frequent movements and periods of no movements. Maternal factors can influence the frequency of breathing movements. For example, high blood glucose levels, called hyperglycemia, can boost the number of breathing movements. Conversely, low blood glucose levels, called hypoglycemia, can reduce the number of fetal breathing movements. Tobacco use is also known to lower fetal breathing rates. Fetal breathing may help tone the muscles in preparation for breathing movements once the fetus is born. It may also help the alveoli to form and mature. Fetal breathing movements are considered a sign of robust health.

Birth

Prior to birth, the lungs are filled with amniotic fluid, mucus, and surfactant. As the fetus is squeezed through the birth canal, the fetal thoracic cavity is compressed, expelling much of this fluid. Some fluid remains, however, but is rapidly absorbed by the body shortly after birth. The first inhalation occurs within 10 seconds after birth and not only serves as the first inspiration, but also acts to inflate the lungs. Pulmonary surfactant is critical for inflation to occur, as it reduces the surface tension of the alveoli. Preterm birth around 26 weeks frequently results in severe respiratory distress, although with current medical advancements, some babies may survive. Prior to 26 weeks, sufficient pulmonary surfactant is not produced, and the surfaces for gas exchange have not formed adequately; therefore, survival is low.

Disorders of the...

Respiratory System: Respiratory Distress Syndrome

Respiratory distress syndrome (RDS) primarily occurs in infants born prematurely. Up to 50 percent of infants born between 26 and 28 weeks and fewer than 30 percent of infants born between 30 and 31 weeks develop RDS. RDS results from insufficient production of pulmonary surfactant, thereby preventing the lungs from properly inflating at birth. A small amount of pulmonary surfactant is produced beginning at around 20 weeks; however, this is not sufficient for inflation of the lungs. As a result, dyspnea occurs and gas exchange cannot be performed properly. Blood oxygen levels are low, whereas blood carbon dioxide levels and pH are high.

The primary cause of RDS is premature birth, which may be due to a variety of known or unknown causes. Other risk factors include gestational diabetes, cesarean delivery, second-born twins, and family history of RDS. The presence of RDS can lead to other serious disorders, such as septicemia (infection of the blood) or pulmonary hemorrhage. Therefore, it is important that RDS is immediately recognized and treated to prevent death and reduce the risk of developing other disorders.

Medical advances have resulted in an improved ability to treat RDS and support the infant until proper lung development can occur. At the time of delivery, treatment may include resuscitation and intubation if the infant does not breathe on their own. These infants would need to be placed on a ventilator to mechanically assist with the breathing process. If spontaneous breathing occurs, application of nasal continuous positive airway pressure (CPAP) may be required. In addition, pulmonary surfactant is typically administered. Death due to RDS has been reduced by 50 percent due to the introduction of pulmonary surfactant therapy. Other therapies may include corticosteroids, supplemental oxygen, and assisted ventilation. Supportive therapies, such as temperature regulation, nutritional support, and antibiotics, may be administered to the premature infant as well.

Key Terms

acclimatization   process of adjustment that the respiratory system makes due to chronic exposure to high altitudes

acute mountain sickness (AMS)   condition that occurs a result of acute exposure to high altitude due to a low partial pressure of oxygen

ala   (plural = alae) small, flaring structure of a nostril that forms the lateral side of the nares

alar cartilage   cartilage that supports the apex of the nose and helps shape the nares; it is connected to the septal cartilage and connective tissue of the alae

alveolar dead space   air space within alveoli that are unable to participate in gas exchange

alveolar duct   small tube that leads from the terminal bronchiole to the respiratory bronchiole and is the point of attachment for alveoli

alveolar macrophage   immune system cell of the alveolus that removes debris and pathogens

alveolar pore   opening that allows airflow between neighboring alveoli

alveolar sac   cluster of alveoli

alveolus   small, grape-like sac that performs gas exchange in the lungs

anatomical dead space   air space present in the airway that never reaches the alveoli and therefore never participates in gas exchange

apex   tip of the external nose

apneustic center   network of neurons within the pons that stimulate the neurons in the dorsal respiratory group; controls the depth of inspiration

atmospheric pressure   amount of force that is exerted by gases in the air surrounding any given surface

Bohr effect   relationship between blood pH and oxygen dissociation from hemoglobin

Boyle's law   relationship between volume and pressure as described by the formula: $P_1V_1 = P_2V_2$

bridge   portion of the external nose that lies in the area of the nasal bones

bronchial bud   structure in the developing embryo that forms when the laryngotracheal bud extends and branches to form two bulbous structures

bronchial tree   collective name for the multiple branches of the bronchi and bronchioles of the respiratory system

bronchiole   branch of bronchi that are 1 mm or less in diameter and terminate at alveolar sacs

bronchoconstriction   decrease in the size of the bronchiole due to relaxation of the muscular wall

bronchodilation   increase in the size of the bronchiole due to contraction of the muscular wall

bronchus   tube connected to the trachea that branches into many subsidiaries and provides a passageway for air to enter and leave the lungs

carbaminohemoglobin   bound form of hemoglobin and carbon dioxide

carbonic anhydrase (CA)   enzyme that catalyzes the reaction that causes carbon dioxide and water to form carbonic acid

cardiac notch   indentation on the surface of the left lung that allows space for the heart

central chemoreceptor   one of the specialized receptors that are located in the brain that sense changes in hydrogen ion, oxygen, or carbon dioxide concentrations in the brain

chloride shift   facilitated diffusion that exchanges bicarbonate (HCO_3^-) with chloride (Cl^-) ions

conducting zone   region of the respiratory system that includes the organs and structures that provide passageways for air and are not directly involved in gas exchange

cricoid cartilage   portion of the larynx composed of a ring of cartilage with a wide posterior region and a thinner anterior region; attached to the esophagus

Dalton's law   statement of the principle that a specific gas type in a mixture exerts its own pressure, as if that specific gas type was not part of a mixture of gases

dorsal respiratory group (DRG)   region of the medulla oblongata that stimulates the contraction of the diaphragm and intercostal muscles to induce inspiration

dorsum nasi   intermediate portion of the external nose that connects the bridge to the apex and is supported by the nasal bone

epiglottis   leaf-shaped piece of elastic cartilage that is a portion of the larynx that swings to close the trachea during swallowing

expiration   (also, exhalation) process that causes the air to leave the lungs

expiratory reserve volume (ERV)   amount of air that can be forcefully exhaled after a normal tidal exhalation

external nose   region of the nose that is easily visible to others

external respiration   gas exchange that occurs in the alveoli

fauces   portion of the posterior oral cavity that connects the oral cavity to the oropharynx

fibroelastic membrane   specialized membrane that connects the ends of the C-shape cartilage in the trachea; contains smooth muscle fibers

forced breathing   (also, hyperpnea) mode of

breathing that occurs during exercise or by active thought that requires muscle contraction for both inspiration and expiration

foregut   endoderm of the embryo towards the head region

functional residual capacity (FRC)   sum of ERV and RV, which is the amount of air that remains in the lungs after a tidal expiration

glottis   opening between the vocal folds through which air passes when producing speech

Haldane effect   relationship between the partial pressure of oxygen and the affinity of hemoglobin for carbon dioxide

Henry's law   statement of the principle that the concentration of gas in a liquid is directly proportional to the solubility and partial pressure of that gas

hilum   concave structure on the mediastinal surface of the lungs where blood vessels, lymphatic vessels, nerves, and a bronchus enter the lung

hyperpnea   increased rate and depth of ventilation due to an increase in oxygen demand that does not significantly alter blood oxygen or carbon dioxide levels

hyperventilation   increased ventilation rate that leads to abnormally low blood carbon dioxide levels and high (alkaline) blood pH

inspiration   (also, inhalation) process that causes air to enter the lungs

inspiratory capacity (IC)   sum of the TV and IRV, which is the amount of air that can maximally be inhaled past a tidal expiration

inspiratory reserve volume (IRV)   amount of air that enters the lungs due to deep inhalation past the tidal volume

internal respiration   gas exchange that occurs at the level of body tissues

intra-alveolar pressure   (intrapulmonary pressure) pressure of the air within the alveoli

intrapleural pressure   pressure of the air within the pleural cavity

laryngeal prominence   region where the two lamine of the thyroid cartilage join, forming a protrusion known as "Adam's apple"

laryngopharynx   portion of the pharynx bordered by the oropharynx superiorly and esophagus and trachea inferiorly; serves as a route for both air and food

laryngotracheal   bud forms from the lung bud, has a tracheal end and bulbous bronchial buds at the distal end

larynx   cartilaginous structure that produces the voice, prevents food and beverages from entering the trachea, and regulates the volume of air that enters and leaves the lungs

lingual tonsil   lymphoid tissue located at the base of the tongue

lung   organ of the respiratory system that performs gas exchange

lung bud   median dome that forms from the endoderm of the foregut

meatus   one of three recesses (superior, middle, and inferior) in the nasal cavity attached to the conchae that increase the surface area of the nasal cavity

naris   (plural = nares) opening of the nostrils

nasal bone   bone of the skull that lies under the root and bridge of the nose and is connected to the frontal and maxillary bones

nasal septum   wall composed of bone and cartilage that separates the left and right nasal cavities

nasopharynx   portion of the pharynx flanked by the conchae and oropharynx that serves as an airway

olfactory pit   invaginated ectodermal tissue in the anterior portion of the head region of an embryo that will form the nasal cavity

oropharynx   portion of the pharynx flanked by the nasopharynx, oral cavity, and laryngopharynx that is a passageway for both air and food

oxygen–hemoglobin dissociation curve   graph that describes the relationship of partial pressure to the binding and disassociation of oxygen to and from heme

oxyhemoglobin   ($Hb-O_2$) bound form of hemoglobin and oxygen

palatine tonsil   one of the paired structures composed of lymphoid tissue located anterior to the uvula at the roof of isthmus of the fauces

paranasal sinus   one of the cavities within the skull that is connected to the conchae that serve to warm and humidify incoming air, produce mucus, and lighten the weight of the skull; consists of frontal, maxillary, sphenoidal, and ethmoidal sinuses

parietal pleura   outermost layer of the pleura that connects to the thoracic wall, mediastinum, and diaphragm

partial pressure   force exerted by each gas in a mixture of gases

peripheral chemoreceptor   one of the specialized receptors located in the aortic arch and carotid arteries that sense changes in pH, carbon dioxide, or oxygen blood levels

pharyngeal tonsil   structure composed of lymphoid tissue located in the nasopharynx

pharynx   region of the conducting zone that forms a tube of skeletal muscle lined with respiratory epithelium; located between the nasal conchae and the esophagus and trachea

philtrum   concave surface of the face that connects the apex of the nose to the top lip

pleural cavity   space between the visceral and parietal pleurae

pleural fluid   substance that acts as a lubricant for the visceral and parietal layers of the pleura during the movement of breathing

pneumotaxic center   network of neurons within the pons that inhibit the activity of the neurons in the dorsal respiratory group; controls rate of breathing

pulmonary artery   artery that arises from the pulmonary trunk and carries deoxygenated, arterial blood to the alveoli

pulmonary plexus   network of autonomic nervous system fibers found near the hilum of the lung

pulmonary surfactant   substance composed of phospholipids and proteins that reduces the surface tension of the alveoli; made by type II alveolar cells

pulmonary ventilation   exchange of gases between the lungs and the atmosphere; breathing

quiet breathing   (also, eupnea) mode of breathing that occurs at rest and does not require the cognitive thought of the individual

residual volume (RV)   amount of air that remains in the lungs after maximum exhalation

respiratory bronchiole   specific type of bronchiole that leads to alveolar sacs

respiratory cycle   one sequence of inspiration and expiration

respiratory epithelium   ciliated lining of much of the conducting zone that is specialized to remove debris and pathogens, and produce mucus

respiratory membrane   alveolar and capillary wall together, which form an air-blood barrier that facilitates the simple diffusion of gases

respiratory rate   total number of breaths taken each minute

respiratory volume   varying amounts of air within the lung at a given time

respiratory zone   includes structures of the respiratory system that are directly involved in gas exchange

root   region of the external nose between the eyebrows

thoracic wall compliance   ability of the thoracic wall to stretch while under pressure

thyroid cartilage   largest piece of cartilage that makes up the larynx and consists of two lamine

tidal volume (TV)   amount of air that normally enters the lungs during quiet breathing

total dead space   sum of the anatomical dead space and alveolar dead space

total lung capacity (TLC)   total amount of air that can be held in the lungs; sum of TV, ERV, IRV, and RV

total pressure   sum of all the partial pressures of a gaseous mixture

trachea   tube composed of cartilaginous rings and supporting tissue that connects the lung bronchi and the larynx; provides a route for air to enter and exit the lung

trachealis muscle   smooth muscle located in the fibroelastic membrane of the trachea

transpulmonary pressure   pressure difference between the intrapleural and intra-alveolar pressures

true vocal cord   one of the pair of folded, white membranes that have a free inner edge that oscillates as air passes through to produce sound

type I alveolar cell   squamous epithelial cells that are the major cell type in the alveolar wall; highly permeable to gases

type II alveolar cell   cuboidal epithelial cells that are the minor cell type in the alveolar wall; secrete pulmonary surfactant

ventilation   movement of air into and out of the lungs; consists of inspiration and expiration

ventral respiratory group (VRG)   region of the medulla oblongata that stimulates the contraction of the accessory muscles involved in respiration to induce forced inspiration and expiration

vestibular fold   part of the folded region of the glottis composed of mucous membrane; supports the epiglottis during swallowing

visceral pleura   innermost layer of the pleura that is superficial to the lungs and extends into the lung fissures

vital capacity (VC)   sum of TV, ERV, and IRV, which is all the volumes that participate in gas exchange

Chapter Review

22.1 Organs and Structures of the Respiratory System

The respiratory system is responsible for obtaining oxygen and getting rid of carbon dioxide, and aiding in speech production and in sensing odors. From a functional perspective, the respiratory system can be

divided into two major areas: the conducting zone and the respiratory zone. The conducting zone consists of all of the structures that provide passageways for air to travel into and out of the lungs: the nasal cavity, pharynx, trachea, bronchi, and most bronchioles. The nasal passages contain the conchae and meatuses that expand the surface area of the cavity, which helps to warm and humidify incoming air, while removing debris and pathogens. The pharynx is composed of three major sections: the nasopharynx, which is continuous with the nasal cavity; the oropharynx, which borders the nasopharynx and the oral cavity; and the laryngopharynx, which borders the oropharynx, trachea, and esophagus. The respiratory zone includes the structures of the lung that are directly involved in gas exchange: the terminal bronchioles and alveoli.

The lining of the conducting zone is composed mostly of pseudostratified ciliated columnar epithelium with goblet cells. The mucus traps pathogens and debris, whereas beating cilia move the mucus superiorly toward the throat, where it is swallowed. As the bronchioles become smaller and smaller, and nearer the alveoli, the epithelium thins and is simple squamous epithelium in the alveoli. The endothelium of the surrounding capillaries, together with the alveolar epithelium, forms the respiratory membrane. This is a blood-air barrier through which gas exchange occurs by simple diffusion.

22.2 The Lungs

The lungs are the major organs of the respiratory system and are responsible for performing gas exchange. The lungs are paired and separated into lobes; The left lung consists of two lobes, whereas the right lung consists of three lobes. Blood circulation is very important, as blood is required to transport oxygen from the lungs to other tissues throughout the body. The function of the pulmonary circulation is to aid in gas exchange. The pulmonary artery provides deoxygenated blood to the capillaries that form respiratory membranes with the alveoli, and the pulmonary veins return newly oxygenated blood to the heart for further transport throughout the body. The lungs are innervated by the parasympathetic and sympathetic nervous systems, which coordinate the bronchodilation and bronchoconstriction of the airways. The lungs are enclosed by the pleura, a membrane that is composed of visceral and parietal pleural layers. The space between these two layers is called the pleural cavity. The mesothelial cells of the pleural membrane create pleural fluid, which serves as both a lubricant (to reduce friction during breathing) and as an adhesive to adhere the lungs to the thoracic wall (to facilitate movement of the lungs during ventilation).

22.3 The Process of Breathing

Pulmonary ventilation is the process of breathing, which is driven by pressure differences between the lungs and the atmosphere. Atmospheric pressure is the force exerted by gases present in the atmosphere. The force exerted by gases within the alveoli is called intra-alveolar (intrapulmonary) pressure, whereas the force exerted by gases in the pleural cavity is called intrapleural pressure. Typically, intrapleural pressure is lower, or negative to, intra-alveolar pressure. The difference in pressure between intrapleural and intra-alveolar pressures is called transpulmonary pressure. In addition, intra-alveolar pressure will equalize with the atmospheric pressure. Pressure is determined by the volume of the space occupied by a gas and is influenced by resistance. Air flows when a pressure gradient is created, from a space of higher pressure to a space of lower pressure. Boyle's law describes the relationship between volume and pressure. A gas is at lower pressure in a larger volume because the gas molecules have more space to in which to move. The same quantity of gas in a smaller volume results in gas molecules crowding together, producing increased pressure.

Resistance is created by inelastic surfaces, as well as the diameter of the airways. Resistance reduces the flow of gases. The surface tension of the alveoli also influences pressure, as it opposes the expansion of the alveoli. However, pulmonary surfactant helps to reduce the surface tension so that the alveoli do not collapse during expiration. The ability of the lungs to stretch, called lung compliance, also plays a role in gas flow. The more the lungs can stretch, the greater the potential volume of the lungs. The greater the volume of the lungs, the lower the air pressure within the lungs.

Pulmonary ventilation consists of the process of inspiration (or inhalation), where air enters the lungs, and expiration (or exhalation), where air leaves the lungs. During inspiration, the diaphragm and external intercostal muscles contract, causing the rib cage to expand and move outward, and expanding the thoracic cavity and lung volume. This creates a lower pressure within the lung than that of the atmosphere, causing air to be drawn into the lungs. During expiration, the diaphragm and intercostals relax, causing the thorax and lungs to recoil. The air pressure within the lungs increases to above the pressure of the atmosphere, causing air to be forced out of the lungs. However, during forced exhalation, the internal intercostals and abdominal muscles may be involved in forcing air out of the lungs.

Respiratory volume describes the amount of air in a given space within the lungs, or which can be moved by the lung, and is dependent on a variety of factors. Tidal volume refers to the amount of air that enters the lungs during quiet breathing, whereas inspiratory reserve volume is the amount of air that enters the lungs when a person inhales past the tidal volume. Expiratory reserve volume is the extra amount of air that can leave with forceful expiration, following tidal expiration. Residual volume is the amount of air that is left in the lungs after expelling the expiratory reserve volume. Respiratory capacity is the combination of two or more volumes. Anatomical dead space refers to the air within the respiratory structures that never participates in gas exchange, because it does not reach functional alveoli. Respiratory rate is the number of breaths taken per minute, which may change during certain diseases or conditions.

Both respiratory rate and depth are controlled by the respiratory centers of the brain, which are stimulated by factors such as chemical and pH changes in the blood. These changes are sensed by central chemoreceptors, which are located in the brain, and peripheral chemoreceptors, which are located in the aortic arch and carotid arteries. A rise in carbon dioxide or a decline in oxygen levels in the blood stimulates an increase in respiratory rate and depth.

22.4 Gas Exchange

The behavior of gases can be explained by the principles of Dalton's law and Henry's law, both of which describe aspects of gas exchange. Dalton's law states that each specific gas in a mixture of gases exerts force (its partial pressure) independently of the other gases in the mixture. Henry's law states that the amount of a specific gas that dissolves in a liquid is a function of its partial pressure. The greater the partial pressure of a gas, the more of that gas will dissolve in a liquid, as the gas moves toward equilibrium. Gas molecules move down a pressure gradient; in other words, gas moves from a region of high pressure to a region of low pressure. The partial pressure of oxygen is high in the alveoli and low in the blood of the pulmonary capillaries. As a result, oxygen diffuses across the respiratory membrane from the alveoli into the blood. In contrast, the partial pressure of carbon dioxide is high in the pulmonary capillaries and low in the alveoli. Therefore, carbon dioxide diffuses across the respiratory membrane from the blood into the alveoli. The amount of oxygen and carbon dioxide that diffuses across the respiratory membrane is similar.

Ventilation is the process that moves air into and out of the alveoli, and perfusion affects the flow of blood in the capillaries. Both are important in gas exchange, as ventilation must be sufficient to create a high partial pressure of oxygen in the alveoli. If ventilation is insufficient and the partial pressure of oxygen drops in the alveolar air, the capillary is constricted and blood flow is redirected to alveoli with sufficient ventilation. External respiration refers to gas exchange that occurs in the alveoli, whereas internal respiration refers to gas exchange that occurs in the tissue. Both are driven by partial pressure differences.

22.5 Transport of Gases

Oxygen is primarily transported through the blood by erythrocytes. These cells contain a metalloprotein called hemoglobin, which is composed of four subunits with a ring-like structure. Each subunit contains one atom of iron bound to a molecule of heme. Heme binds oxygen so that each hemoglobin molecule can bind up to four oxygen molecules. When all of the heme units in the blood are bound to oxygen, hemoglobin is considered to be saturated. Hemoglobin is partially saturated when only some heme units are bound to oxygen. An oxygen–hemoglobin saturation/dissociation curve is a common way to depict the relationship of how easily oxygen binds to or dissociates from hemoglobin as a function of the partial pressure of oxygen. As the partial pressure of oxygen increases, the more readily hemoglobin binds to oxygen. At the same time, once one molecule of oxygen is bound by hemoglobin, additional oxygen molecules more readily bind to hemoglobin. Other factors such as temperature, pH, the partial pressure of carbon dioxide, and the concentration of 2,3-bisphosphoglycerate can enhance or inhibit the binding of hemoglobin and oxygen as well. Fetal hemoglobin has a different structure than adult hemoglobin, which results in fetal hemoglobin having a greater affinity for oxygen than adult hemoglobin.

Carbon dioxide is transported in blood by three different mechanisms: as dissolved carbon dioxide, as bicarbonate, or as carbaminohemoglobin. A small portion of carbon dioxide remains. The largest amount of transported carbon dioxide is as bicarbonate, formed in erythrocytes. For this conversion, carbon dioxide is combined with water with the aid of an enzyme called carbonic anhydrase. This combination forms carbonic acid, which spontaneously dissociates into bicarbonate and hydrogen ions. As bicarbonate builds up in erythrocytes, it is moved across the membrane into the plasma in exchange for chloride ions by a mechanism called the chloride shift. At the pulmonary capillaries, bicarbonate re-enters erythrocytes in exchange for chloride ions, and the reaction with carbonic anhydrase is reversed, recreating carbon dioxide and water. Carbon dioxide then diffuses out of the erythrocyte and across the respiratory membrane into the air. An intermediate amount of carbon dioxide binds directly to hemoglobin to form carbaminohemoglobin. The partial pressures of carbon dioxide and oxygen, as well as the oxygen saturation of hemoglobin, influence how readily hemoglobin binds carbon dioxide. The less saturated hemoglobin is and the lower the partial pressure of oxygen in the blood is, the more readily hemoglobin binds to carbon dioxide. This is an example of the Haldane effect.

22.6 Modifications in Respiratory Functions

Normally, the respiratory centers of the brain maintain a consistent, rhythmic breathing cycle. However, in certain cases, the respiratory system must adjust to situational changes in order to supply the body with sufficient oxygen. For example, exercise results in increased ventilation, and chronic exposure to a high altitude results in a greater number of circulating erythrocytes. Hyperpnea, an increase in the rate and depth of ventilation, appears to be a function of three neural mechanisms that include a psychological stimulus, motor neuron activation of skeletal muscles, and the activation of proprioceptors in the muscles, joints, and tendons. As a result, hyperpnea related to exercise is initiated when exercise begins, as opposed to when tissue oxygen demand actually increases.

In contrast, acute exposure to a high altitude, particularly during times of physical exertion, does result in low blood and tissue levels of oxygen. This change is caused by a low partial pressure of oxygen in the air, because the atmospheric pressure at high altitudes is lower than the atmospheric pressure at sea level. This can lead to a condition called acute mountain sickness (AMS) with symptoms that include headaches, disorientation, fatigue, nausea, and lightheadedness. Over a long period of time, a person's body will adjust to the high altitude, a process called acclimatization. During acclimatization, the low tissue

levels of oxygen will cause the kidneys to produce greater amounts of the hormone erythropoietin, which stimulates the production of erythrocytes. Increased levels of circulating erythrocytes provide an increased amount of hemoglobin that helps supply an individual with more oxygen, preventing the symptoms of AMS.

22.7 Embryonic Development of the Respiratory System

The development of the respiratory system in the fetus begins at about 4 weeks and continues into childhood. Ectodermal tissue in the anterior portion of the head region invaginates posteriorly, forming olfactory pits, which ultimately fuse with endodermal tissue of the early pharynx. At about this same time, a protrusion of endodermal tissue extends anteriorly from the foregut, producing a lung bud, which continues to elongate until it forms the laryngotracheal bud. The proximal portion of this structure will mature into the trachea, whereas the bulbous end will branch to form two bronchial buds. These buds then branch repeatedly, so that at about week 16, all major airway structures are present. Development progresses after week 16 as respiratory bronchioles and alveolar ducts form, and extensive vascularization occurs. Alveolar type I cells also begin to take shape. Type II pulmonary cells develop and begin to produce small amounts of surfactant. As the fetus grows, the respiratory system continues to expand as more alveoli develop and more surfactant is produced. Beginning at about week 36 and lasting into childhood, alveolar precursors mature to become fully functional alveoli. At birth, compression of the thoracic cavity forces much of the fluid in the lungs to be expelled. The first inhalation inflates the lungs. Fetal breathing movements begin around week 20 or 21, and occur when contractions of the respiratory muscles cause the fetus to inhale and exhale amniotic fluid. These movements continue until birth and may help to tone the muscles in preparation for breathing after birth and are a sign of good health.

Interactive Link Questions

1. Visit this site (http://openstax.org/l/asthma) to learn more about what happens during an asthma attack. What are the three changes that occur inside the airways during an asthma attack?

2. Watch this video (http://openstax.org/l/spirometers) to learn more about lung volumes and spirometers. Explain how spirometry test results can be used to diagnose respiratory diseases or determine the effectiveness of disease treatment.

3. Watch this video (http://openstax.org/l/oxyblood) to see the transport of oxygen from the lungs to the tissues. Why is oxygenated blood bright red, whereas deoxygenated blood tends to be more of a purple color?

Review Questions

4. Which of the following anatomical structures is *not* part of the conducting zone?
   a. pharynx
   b. nasal cavity
   c. alveoli
   d. bronchi

5. What is the function of the conchae in the nasal cavity?
   a. increase surface area
   b. exchange gases
   c. maintain surface tension
   d. maintain air pressure

6. The fauces connects which of the following structures to the oropharynx?
   a. nasopharynx
   b. laryngopharynx
   c. nasal cavity
   d. oral cavity

7. Which of the following are structural features of the trachea?
   a. C-shaped cartilage
   b. smooth muscle fibers
   c. cilia
   d. all of the above

8. Which of the following structures is *not* part of the bronchial tree?
   a. alveoli
   b. bronchi
   c. terminal bronchioles
   d. respiratory bronchioles

9. What is the role of alveolar macrophages?
   a. to secrete pulmonary surfactant
   b. to secrete antimicrobial proteins
   c. to remove pathogens and debris
   d. to facilitate gas exchange

10. Which of the following structures separates the lung into lobes?
   a. mediastinum
   b. fissure
   c. root
   d. pleura

11. A section of the lung that receives its own tertiary bronchus is called the _____.
   a. bronchopulmonary segment
   b. pulmonary lobule
   c. interpulmonary segment
   d. respiratory segment

12. The _____ circulation picks up oxygen for cellular use and drops off carbon dioxide for removal from the body.
   a. pulmonary
   b. interlobular
   c. respiratory
   d. bronchial

13. The pleura that surrounds the lungs consists of two layers, the _____.
   a. visceral and parietal pleurae.
   b. mediastinum and parietal pleurae.
   c. visceral and mediastinum pleurae.
   d. none of the above

14. Which of the following processes does atmospheric pressure play a role in?
   a. pulmonary ventilation
   b. production of pulmonary surfactant
   c. resistance
   d. surface tension

15. A decrease in volume leads to a(n) _____ pressure.
   a. decrease in
   b. equalization of
   c. increase in
   d. zero

16. The pressure difference between the intra-alveolar and intrapleural pressures is called _____.
   a. atmospheric pressure
   b. pulmonary pressure
   c. negative pressure
   d. transpulmonary pressure

17. Gas flow decreases as _____ increases.
   a. resistance
   b. pressure
   c. airway diameter
   d. friction

18. Contraction of the external intercostal muscles causes which of the following to occur?
   a. The diaphragm moves downward.
   b. The rib cage is compressed.
   c. The thoracic cavity volume decreases.
   d. The ribs and sternum move upward.

19. Which of the following prevents the alveoli from collapsing?
    a. residual volume
    b. tidal volume
    c. expiratory reserve volume
    d. inspiratory reserve volume

20. Gas moves from an area of _____ partial pressure to an area of _____ partial pressure.
    a. low; high
    b. low; low
    c. high; high
    d. high; low

21. When ventilation is not sufficient, which of the following occurs?
    a. The capillary constricts.
    b. The capillary dilates.
    c. The partial pressure of oxygen in the affected alveolus increases.
    d. The bronchioles dilate.

22. Gas exchange that occurs at the level of the tissues is called _____.
    a. external respiration
    b. interpulmonary respiration
    c. internal respiration
    d. pulmonary ventilation

23. The partial pressure of carbon dioxide is 45 mm Hg in the blood and 40 mm Hg in the alveoli. What happens to the carbon dioxide?
    a. It diffuses into the blood.
    b. It diffuses into the alveoli.
    c. The gradient is too small for carbon dioxide to diffuse.
    d. It decomposes into carbon and oxygen.

24. Oxyhemoglobin forms by a chemical reaction between which of the following?
    a. hemoglobin and carbon dioxide
    b. carbonic anhydrase and carbon dioxide
    c. hemoglobin and oxygen
    d. carbonic anhydrase and oxygen

25. Which of the following factors play a role in the oxygen–hemoglobin saturation/dissociation curve?
    a. temperature
    b. pH
    c. BPG
    d. all of the above

26. Which of the following occurs during the chloride shift?
    a. Chloride is removed from the erythrocyte.
    b. Chloride is exchanged for bicarbonate.
    c. Bicarbonate is removed from the erythrocyte.
    d. Bicarbonate is removed from the blood.

27. A low partial pressure of oxygen promotes hemoglobin binding to carbon dioxide. This is an example of the _____.
    a. Haldane effect
    b. Bohr effect
    c. Dalton's law
    d. Henry's law

28. Increased ventilation that results in an increase in blood pH is called _____.
    a. hyperventilation
    b. hyperpnea
    c. acclimatization
    d. apnea

29. Exercise can trigger symptoms of AMS due to which of the following?
    a. low partial pressure of oxygen
    b. low atmospheric pressure
    c. abnormal neural signals
    d. small venous reserve of oxygen

30. Which of the following stimulates the production of erythrocytes?
    a. AMS
    b. high blood levels of carbon dioxide
    c. low atmospheric pressure
    d. erythropoietin

31. The olfactory pits form from which of the following?
    a. mesoderm
    b. cartilage
    c. ectoderm
    d. endoderm

32. A full complement of mature alveoli are present by _____.
    a. early childhood, around 8 years of age
    b. birth
    c. 37 weeks
    d. 16 weeks

33. If a baby is born prematurely before type II cells produce sufficient pulmonary surfactant, which of the following might you expect?
  a. difficulty expressing fluid
  b. difficulty inflating the lungs
  c. difficulty with pulmonary capillary flow
  d. no difficulty as type I cells can provide enough surfactant for normal breathing

34. When do fetal breathing movements begin?
  a. around week 20
  b. around week 37
  c. around week 16
  d. after birth

35. What happens to the fluid that remains in the lungs after birth?
  a. It reduces the surface tension of the alveoli.
  b. It is expelled shortly after birth.
  c. It is absorbed shortly after birth.
  d. It lubricates the pleurae.

Critical Thinking Questions

36. Describe the three regions of the pharynx and their functions.

37. If a person sustains an injury to the epiglottis, what would be the physiological result?

38. Compare and contrast the conducting and respiratory zones.

39. Compare and contrast the right and left lungs.

40. Why are the pleurae not damaged during normal breathing?

41. Describe what is meant by the term "lung compliance."

42. Outline the steps involved in quiet breathing.

43. What is respiratory rate and how is it controlled?

44. Compare and contrast Dalton's law and Henry's law.

45. A smoker develops damage to several alveoli that then can no longer function. How does this affect gas exchange?

46. Compare and contrast adult hemoglobin and fetal hemoglobin.

47. Describe the relationship between the partial pressure of oxygen and the binding of oxygen to hemoglobin.

48. Describe three ways in which carbon dioxide can be transported.

49. Describe the neural factors involved in increasing ventilation during exercise.

50. What is the major mechanism that results in acclimatization?

51. During what timeframe does a fetus have enough mature structures to breathe on its own if born prematurely? Describe the other structures that develop during this phase.

52. Describe fetal breathing movements and their purpose.

CHAPTER 23
The Digestive System

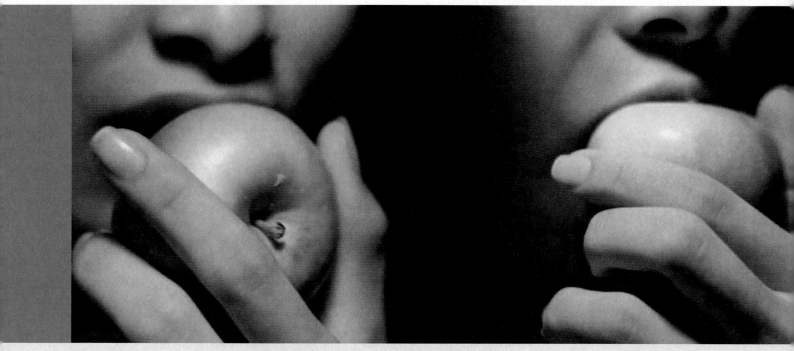

Figure 23.1 Eating Apples Eating may be one of the simple pleasures in life, but digesting even one apple requires the coordinated work of many organs. (credit: "Aimanness Photography"/Flickr)

CHAPTER OBJECTIVES

After studying this chapter, you will be able to:

- List and describe the functional anatomy of the organs and accessory organs of the digestive system
- Discuss the processes and control of ingestion, propulsion, mechanical digestion, chemical digestion, absorption, and defecation
- Discuss the roles of the liver, pancreas, and gallbladder in digestion
- Compare and contrast the digestion of the three macronutrients

INTRODUCTION The digestive system is continually at work, yet people seldom appreciate the complex tasks it performs in a choreographed biologic symphony. Consider what happens when you eat an apple. Of course, you enjoy the apple's taste as you chew it, but in the hours that follow, unless something goes amiss and you get a stomachache, you don't notice that your digestive system is working. You may be taking a walk or studying or sleeping, having forgotten all about the apple, but your stomach and intestines are busy digesting it and absorbing its vitamins and other nutrients. By the time any waste material is excreted, the body has appropriated all it can use from the apple. In short, whether you pay attention or not, the organs of the digestive system perform their specific functions, allowing you to use the food you eat to keep you going. This chapter examines the structure and functions of these organs, and explores the mechanics and chemistry of the digestive processes.

23.1 Overview of the Digestive System

LEARNING OBJECTIVES

By the end of this section, you will be able to:

- Identify the organs of the alimentary canal from proximal to distal, and briefly state their function
- Identify the accessory digestive organs and briefly state their function
- Describe the four fundamental tissue layers of the alimentary canal
- Contrast the contributions of the enteric and autonomic nervous systems to digestive system functioning
- Explain how the peritoneum anchors the digestive organs

The function of the digestive system is to break down the foods you eat, release their nutrients, and absorb those nutrients into the body. Although the small intestine is the workhorse of the system, where the majority of digestion occurs, and where most of the released nutrients are absorbed into the blood or lymph, each of the digestive system organs makes a vital contribution to this process (Figure 23.2).

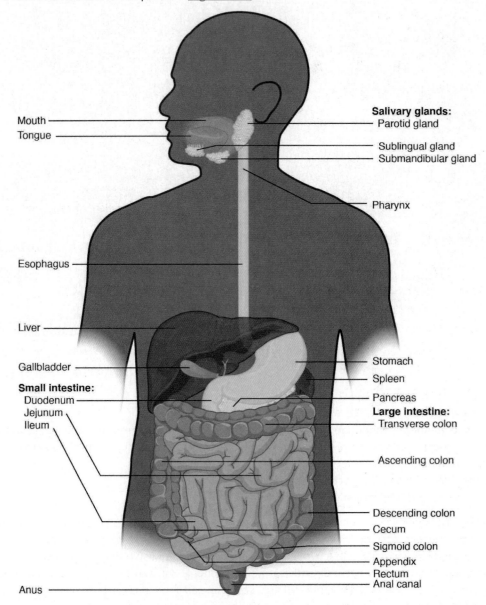

FIGURE 23.2   Components of the Digestive System   All digestive organs play integral roles in the life-sustaining process of digestion.

As is the case with all body systems, the digestive system does not work in isolation; it functions cooperatively with the other systems of the body. Consider for example, the interrelationship between the digestive and cardiovascular systems. Arteries supply the digestive organs with oxygen and processed nutrients, and veins drain the digestive tract. These intestinal veins, constituting the hepatic portal system, are unique; they do not return blood directly to the heart. Rather, this blood is diverted to the liver where its nutrients are off-loaded for processing before blood completes its circuit back to the heart. At the same time, the digestive system provides nutrients to the heart muscle and vascular tissue to support their functioning. The interrelationship of the digestive and endocrine systems is also critical. Hormones secreted by several endocrine glands, as well as endocrine cells of the pancreas, the stomach, and the small intestine, contribute to the control of digestion and nutrient metabolism. In turn, the digestive system provides the nutrients to fuel endocrine function. Table 23.1 gives a quick glimpse at how these other systems contribute to the functioning of the digestive system.

Contribution of Other Body Systems to the Digestive System

Body system	Benefits received by the digestive system
Cardiovascular	Blood supplies digestive organs with oxygen and processed nutrients
Endocrine	Endocrine hormones help regulate secretion in digestive glands and accessory organs
Integumentary	Skin helps protect digestive organs and synthesizes vitamin D for calcium absorption
Lymphatic	Mucosa-associated lymphoid tissue and other lymphatic tissue defend against entry of pathogens; lacteals absorb lipids; and lymphatic vessels transport lipids to bloodstream
Muscular	Skeletal muscles support and protect abdominal organs
Nervous	Sensory and motor neurons help regulate secretions and muscle contractions in the digestive tract
Respiratory	Respiratory organs provide oxygen and remove carbon dioxide
Skeletal	Bones help protect and support digestive organs
Urinary	Kidneys convert vitamin D into its active form, allowing calcium absorption in the small intestine

TABLE 23.1

Digestive System Organs

The easiest way to understand the digestive system is to divide its organs into two main categories. The first group is the organs that make up the alimentary canal. Accessory digestive organs comprise the second group and are critical for orchestrating the breakdown of food and the assimilation of its nutrients into the body. Accessory digestive organs, despite their name, are critical to the function of the digestive system.

Alimentary Canal Organs

Also called the gastrointestinal (GI) tract or gut, the **alimentary canal** (aliment- = "to nourish") is a one-way tube about 7.62 meters (25 feet) in length during life and closer to 10.67 meters (35 feet) in length when measured after death, once smooth muscle tone is lost. The main function of the organs of the alimentary canal is to nourish the body. This tube begins at the mouth and terminates at the anus. Between those two points, the canal is modified as the pharynx, esophagus, stomach, and small and large intestines to fit the functional needs of the body. Both the mouth and anus are open to the external environment; thus, food and wastes within the alimentary canal are technically considered to be outside the body. Only through the process of absorption do the nutrients in food enter into and nourish the body's "inner space."

Accessory Structures

Each **accessory digestive organ** aids in the breakdown of food (Figure 23.3). Within the mouth, the teeth and tongue begin mechanical digestion, whereas the salivary glands begin chemical digestion. Once food products enter the small intestine, the gallbladder, liver, and pancreas release secretions—such as bile and enzymes—essential for digestion to continue. Together, these are called accessory organs because they sprout from the lining cells of the developing gut (mucosa) and augment its function; indeed, you could not live without their vital contributions, and many significant diseases result from their malfunction. Even after development is complete, they maintain a connection to the gut by way of ducts.

Histology of the Alimentary Canal

Throughout its length, the alimentary tract is composed of the same four tissue layers; the details of their structural arrangements vary to fit their specific functions. Starting from the lumen and moving outwards, these layers are the mucosa, submucosa, muscularis, and serosa, which is continuous with the mesentery (see Figure 23.3).

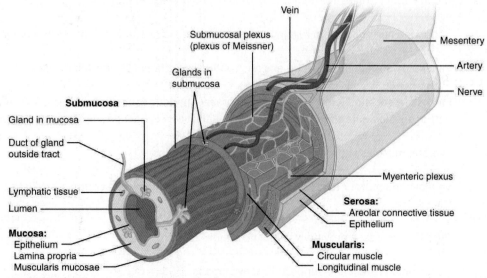

FIGURE 23.3   Layers of the Alimentary Canal   The wall of the alimentary canal has four basic tissue layers: the mucosa, submucosa, muscularis, and serosa.

The **mucosa** is referred to as a mucous membrane, because mucus production is a characteristic feature of gut epithelium. The membrane consists of epithelium, which is in direct contact with ingested food, and the lamina propria, a layer of connective tissue analogous to the dermis. In addition, the mucosa has a thin, smooth muscle layer, called the muscularis mucosae (not to be confused with the muscularis layer, described below).

Epithelium—In the mouth, pharynx, esophagus, and anal canal, the epithelium is primarily a non-keratinized, stratified squamous epithelium. In the stomach and intestines, it is a simple columnar epithelium. Notice that the epithelium is in direct contact with the lumen, the space inside the alimentary canal. Interspersed among its epithelial cells are goblet cells, which secrete mucus and fluid into the lumen, and enteroendocrine cells, which secrete hormones into the interstitial spaces between cells. Epithelial cells have a very brief lifespan, averaging from only a couple of days (in the mouth) to about a week (in the gut). This process of rapid renewal helps preserve the health of the alimentary canal, despite the wear and tear resulting from continued contact with foodstuffs.

Lamina propria—In addition to loose connective tissue, the lamina propria contains numerous blood and lymphatic vessels that transport nutrients absorbed through the alimentary canal to other parts of the body. The lamina propria also serves an immune function by housing clusters of lymphocytes, making up the mucosa-associated lymphoid tissue (MALT). These lymphocyte clusters are particularly substantial in the distal ileum where they are known as Peyer's patches. When you consider that the alimentary canal is exposed to foodborne bacteria and other foreign matter, it is not hard to appreciate why the immune system has evolved a means of defending against the pathogens encountered within it.

Muscularis mucosae—This thin layer of smooth muscle is in a constant state of tension, pulling the mucosa of the stomach and small intestine into undulating folds. These folds dramatically increase the surface area available for digestion and absorption.

As its name implies, the **submucosa** lies immediately beneath the mucosa. A broad layer of dense connective tissue, it connects the overlying mucosa to the underlying muscularis. It includes blood and lymphatic vessels (which transport absorbed nutrients), and a scattering of submucosal glands that release digestive secretions. Additionally, it serves as a conduit for a dense branching network of nerves, the submucosal plexus, which functions as described below.

The third layer of the alimentary canal is the **muscularis** (also called the muscularis externa). The muscularis in the small intestine is made up of a double layer of smooth muscle: an inner circular layer and an outer longitudinal layer. The contractions of these layers promote mechanical digestion, expose more of the food to digestive chemicals, and move the food along the canal. In the most proximal and distal regions of the alimentary canal, including the mouth, pharynx, anterior part of the esophagus, and external anal sphincter, the muscularis is made up of skeletal muscle, which gives you voluntary control over swallowing and defecation. The basic two-layer structure found in the small intestine is modified in the organs proximal and distal to it. The stomach is equipped for its churning function by the addition of a third layer, the oblique muscle. While the colon has two layers like the small intestine, its longitudinal layer is segregated into three narrow parallel bands, the tenia coli, which make it look like a series of pouches rather than a simple tube.

The **serosa** is the portion of the alimentary canal superficial to the muscularis. Present only in the region of the alimentary canal within the abdominal cavity, it consists of a layer of visceral peritoneum overlying a layer of loose connective tissue. Instead of serosa, the mouth, pharynx, and esophagus have a dense sheath of collagen fibers called the adventitia. These tissues serve to hold the alimentary canal in place near the ventral surface of the vertebral column.

Nerve Supply

As soon as food enters the mouth, it is detected by receptors that send impulses along the sensory neurons of cranial nerves. Without these nerves, not only would your food be without taste, but you would also be unable to feel either the food or the structures of your mouth, and you would be unable to avoid biting yourself as you chew, an action enabled by the motor branches of cranial nerves.

Intrinsic innervation of much of the alimentary canal is provided by the enteric nervous system, which runs from the esophagus to the anus, and contains approximately 100 million motor, sensory, and interneurons (unique to this system compared to all other parts of the peripheral nervous system). These enteric neurons are grouped into two plexuses. The **myenteric plexus** (plexus of Auerbach) lies in the muscularis layer of the alimentary canal and is responsible for **motility**, especially the rhythm and force of the contractions of the muscularis. The **submucosal plexus** (plexus of Meissner) lies in the submucosal layer and is responsible for regulating digestive secretions and reacting to the presence of food (see Figure 23.3).

Extrinsic innervations of the alimentary canal are provided by the autonomic nervous system, which includes both sympathetic and parasympathetic nerves. In general, sympathetic activation (the fight-or-flight response) restricts the activity of enteric neurons, thereby decreasing GI secretion and motility. In contrast, parasympathetic activation (the rest-and-digest response) increases GI secretion and motility by stimulating neurons of the enteric nervous system.

Blood Supply

The blood vessels serving the digestive system have two functions. They transport the protein and carbohydrate nutrients absorbed by mucosal cells after food is digested in the lumen. Lipids are absorbed via lacteals, tiny structures of the lymphatic system. The blood vessels' second function is to supply the organs of the alimentary canal with the nutrients and oxygen needed to drive their cellular processes.

Specifically, the more anterior parts of the alimentary canal are supplied with blood by arteries branching off the aortic arch and thoracic aorta. Below this point, the alimentary canal is supplied with blood by arteries branching from the abdominal aorta. The celiac trunk services the liver, stomach, and duodenum, whereas the superior and inferior mesenteric arteries supply blood to the remaining small and large intestines.

The veins that collect nutrient-rich blood from the small intestine (where most absorption occurs) empty into the hepatic portal system. This venous network takes the blood into the liver where the nutrients are either processed or stored for later use. Only then does the blood drained from the alimentary canal viscera circulate back to the heart. To appreciate just how demanding the digestive process is on the cardiovascular system, consider that while you are "resting and digesting," about one-fourth of the blood pumped with each heartbeat enters arteries serving the intestines.

The Peritoneum

The digestive organs within the abdominal cavity are held in place by the peritoneum, a broad serous membranous sac made up of squamous epithelial tissue surrounded by connective tissue. It is composed of two different regions: the parietal peritoneum, which lines the abdominal wall, and the visceral peritoneum, which envelopes the abdominal organs (Figure 23.4). The peritoneal cavity is the space bounded by the visceral and parietal peritoneal surfaces. A few milliliters of watery fluid act as a lubricant to minimize friction between the serosal surfaces of the peritoneum.

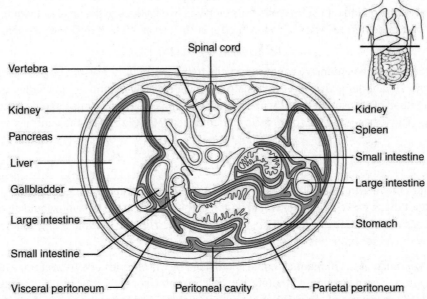

FIGURE 23.4   The Peritoneum   A cross-section of the abdomen shows the relationship between abdominal organs and the peritoneum (darker lines).

Disorders of the...

Digestive System: Peritonitis

Inflammation of the peritoneum is called peritonitis. Chemical peritonitis can develop any time the wall of the alimentary canal is breached, allowing the contents of the lumen entry into the peritoneal cavity. For example, when an ulcer perforates the stomach wall, gastric juices spill into the peritoneal cavity. Hemorrhagic peritonitis occurs after a ruptured tubal pregnancy or traumatic injury to the liver or spleen fills the peritoneal cavity with blood. Even more severe peritonitis is associated with bacterial infections seen with appendicitis, colonic diverticulitis, and pelvic inflammatory disease (infection of uterine tubes, usually by sexually transmitted bacteria). Peritonitis is life threatening and often results in emergency surgery to correct the underlying problem and intensive antibiotic therapy. When your great grandparents and even your parents were young, the mortality from peritonitis was high. Aggressive surgery, improvements in anesthesia safety, the advance of critical care expertise, and antibiotics have greatly improved the mortality rate from this condition. Even so, the mortality rate still ranges from 30 to 40 percent.

The visceral peritoneum includes multiple large folds that envelope various abdominal organs, holding them to the dorsal surface of the body wall. Within these folds are blood vessels, lymphatic vessels, and nerves that innervate the organs with which they are in contact, supplying their adjacent organs. The five major peritoneal folds are described in Table 23.2. Note that during fetal development, certain digestive structures, including the first portion of the small intestine (called the duodenum), the pancreas, and portions of the large intestine (the ascending and descending colon, and the rectum) remain completely or partially posterior to the peritoneum. Thus, the location of these organs is described as **retroperitoneal**.

The Five Major Peritoneal Folds

Fold	Description
Greater omentum	Apron-like structure that lies superficial to the small intestine and transverse colon; a site of fat deposition in people who are overweight
Falciform ligament	Anchors the liver to the anterior abdominal wall and inferior border of the diaphragm
Lesser omentum	Suspends the stomach from the inferior border of the liver; provides a pathway for structures connecting to the liver
Mesentery	Vertical band of tissue anterior to the lumbar vertebrae and anchoring all of the small intestine except the initial portion (the duodenum)
Mesocolon	Attaches two portions of the large intestine (the transverse and sigmoid colon) to the posterior abdominal wall

TABLE 23.2

⊘ INTERACTIVE LINK

By clicking on this link (http://openstax.org/l/fooddigestion) you can watch a short video of what happens to the food you eat, as it passes from your mouth to your intestine. Along the way, note how the food changes consistency and form. How does this change in consistency facilitate your gaining nutrients from food?

23.2 Digestive System Processes and Regulation

LEARNING OBJECTIVES

By the end of this section, you will be able to:

- Discuss six fundamental activities of the digestive system, giving an example of each
- Compare and contrast the neural and hormonal controls involved in digestion

The digestive system uses mechanical and chemical activities to break food down into absorbable substances during its journey through the digestive system. Table 23.3 provides an overview of the basic functions of the digestive organs.

⊘ INTERACTIVE LINK

Visit this site (http://openstax.org/l/fooddigestion2) for an overview of digestion of food in different regions of the digestive tract. Note the route of non-fat nutrients from the small intestine to their release as nutrients to the body.

Functions of the Digestive Organs

Organ	Major functions	Other functions
Mouth	• Ingests food • Chews and mixes food • Begins chemical breakdown of carbohydrates • Moves food into the pharynx • Begins breakdown of lipids via lingual lipase	• Moistens and dissolves food, allowing you to taste it • Cleans and lubricates the teeth and oral cavity • Has some antimicrobial activity
Pharynx	• Propels food from the oral cavity to the esophagus	• Lubricates food and passageways
Esophagus	• Propels food to the stomach	• Lubricates food and passageways
Stomach	• Mixes and churns food with gastric juices to form chyme • Begins chemical breakdown of proteins • Releases food into the duodenum as chyme • Absorbs some fat-soluble substances (for example, alcohol, aspirin) • Possesses antimicrobial functions	• Stimulates protein-digesting enzymes • Secretes intrinsic factor required for vitamin B_{12} absorption in small intestine
Small intestine	• Mixes chyme with digestive juices • Propels food at a rate slow enough for digestion and absorption • Absorbs breakdown products of carbohydrates, proteins, lipids, and nucleic acids, along with vitamins, minerals, and water • Performs physical digestion via segmentation	• Provides optimal medium for enzymatic activity
Accessory organs	• Liver: produces bile salts, which emulsify lipids, aiding their digestion and absorption • Gallbladder: stores, concentrates, and releases bile • Pancreas: produces digestive enzymes and bicarbonate	• Bicarbonate-rich pancreatic juices help neutralize acidic chyme and provide optimal environment for enzymatic activity
Large intestine	• Further breaks down food residues • Absorbs most residual water, electrolytes, and vitamins produced by enteric bacteria • Propels feces toward rectum • Eliminates feces	• Food residue is concentrated and temporarily stored prior to defecation • Mucus eases passage of feces through colon

TABLE 23.3

Digestive Processes

The processes of digestion include six activities: ingestion, propulsion, mechanical or physical digestion, chemical digestion, absorption, and defecation.

The first of these processes, **ingestion**, refers to the entry of food into the alimentary canal through the mouth. There, the food is chewed and mixed with saliva, which contains enzymes that begin breaking down the carbohydrates in the food plus some lipid digestion via lingual lipase. Chewing increases the surface area of the food and allows an appropriately sized bolus to be produced.

Food leaves the mouth when the tongue and pharyngeal muscles propel it into the esophagus. This act of swallowing, the last voluntary act until defecation, is an example of **propulsion**, which refers to the movement of food through the digestive tract. It includes both the voluntary process of swallowing and the involuntary process of peristalsis. **Peristalsis** consists of sequential, alternating waves of contraction and relaxation of alimentary wall smooth muscles, which act to propel food along (Figure 23.5). These waves also play a role in mixing food with digestive juices. Peristalsis is so powerful that foods and liquids you swallow enter your stomach even if you are standing on your head.

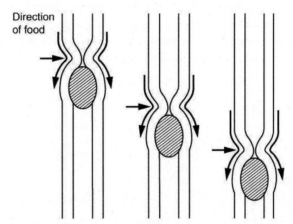

FIGURE 23.5   Peristalsis   Peristalsis moves food through the digestive tract with alternating waves of muscle contraction and relaxation.

Digestion includes both mechanical and chemical processes. **Mechanical digestion** is a purely physical process that does not change the chemical nature of the food. Instead, it makes the food smaller to increase both surface area and mobility. It includes **mastication**, or chewing, as well as tongue movements that help break food into smaller bits and mix food with saliva. Although there may be a tendency to think that mechanical digestion is limited to the first steps of the digestive process, it occurs after the food leaves the mouth, as well. The mechanical churning of food in the stomach serves to further break it apart and expose more of its surface area to digestive juices, creating an acidic "soup" called **chyme**. **Segmentation**, which occurs mainly in the small intestine, consists of localized contractions of circular muscle of the muscularis layer of the alimentary canal. These contractions isolate small sections of the intestine, moving their contents back and forth while continuously subdividing, breaking up, and mixing the contents. By moving food back and forth in the intestinal lumen, segmentation mixes food with digestive juices and facilitates absorption.

In **chemical digestion**, starting in the mouth, digestive secretions break down complex food molecules into their chemical building blocks (for example, proteins into separate amino acids). These secretions vary in composition, but typically contain water, various enzymes, acids, and salts. The process is completed in the small intestine.

Food that has been broken down is of no value to the body unless it enters the bloodstream and its nutrients are put to work. This occurs through the process of **absorption**, which takes place primarily within the small intestine. There, most nutrients are absorbed from the lumen of the alimentary canal into the bloodstream through the epithelial cells that make up the mucosa. Lipids are absorbed into lacteals and are transported via the lymphatic vessels to the bloodstream (the subclavian veins near the heart). The details of these processes will be discussed later.

In **defecation**, the final step in digestion, undigested materials are removed from the body as feces.

Aging and the...

Digestive System: From Appetite Suppression to Constipation

Age-related changes in the digestive system begin in the mouth and can affect virtually every aspect of the digestive system. Taste buds become less sensitive, so food isn't as appetizing as it once was. A slice of pizza is a challenge, not a treat, when you have lost teeth, your gums are diseased, and your salivary glands aren't producing enough saliva. Swallowing can be difficult, and ingested food moves slowly through the alimentary canal because of reduced strength and tone of muscular tissue. Neurosensory feedback is also dampened, slowing the transmission of messages that stimulate the release of enzymes and hormones.

Pathologies that affect the digestive organs—such as hiatal hernia, gastritis, and peptic ulcer disease—can occur at greater frequencies as you age. Problems in the small intestine may include duodenal ulcers, maldigestion, and malabsorption. Problems in the large intestine include hemorrhoids, diverticular disease, and constipation. Conditions that affect the function of accessory organs—and their abilities to deliver pancreatic enzymes and bile to the small intestine—include jaundice, acute pancreatitis, cirrhosis, and gallstones.

In some cases, a single organ is in charge of a digestive process. For example, ingestion occurs only in the mouth and defecation only in the anus. However, most digestive processes involve the interaction of several organs and occur gradually as food moves through the alimentary canal (Figure 23.6).

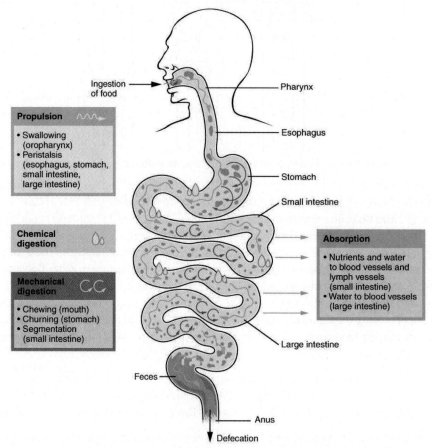

FIGURE 23.6   Digestive Processes   The digestive processes are ingestion, propulsion, mechanical digestion, chemical digestion, absorption, and defecation.

Some chemical digestion occurs in the mouth. Some absorption can occur in the mouth and stomach, for example, alcohol and aspirin.

Regulatory Mechanisms

Neural and endocrine regulatory mechanisms work to maintain the optimal conditions in the lumen needed for digestion and absorption. These regulatory mechanisms, which stimulate digestive activity through mechanical and chemical activity, are controlled both extrinsically and intrinsically.

Neural Controls

The walls of the alimentary canal contain a variety of sensors that help regulate digestive functions. These include mechanoreceptors, chemoreceptors, and osmoreceptors, which are capable of detecting mechanical, chemical, and osmotic stimuli, respectively. For example, these receptors can sense when the presence of food has caused the stomach to expand, whether food particles have been sufficiently broken down, how much liquid is present, and the type of nutrients in the food (lipids, carbohydrates, and/or proteins). Stimulation of these receptors provokes an appropriate reflex that furthers the process of digestion. This may entail sending a message that activates the glands that secrete digestive juices into the lumen, or it may mean the stimulation of muscles within the alimentary canal, thereby activating peristalsis and segmentation that move food along the intestinal tract.

The walls of the entire alimentary canal are embedded with nerve plexuses that interact with the central nervous system and other nerve plexuses—either within the same digestive organ or in different ones. These interactions prompt several types of reflexes. Extrinsic nerve plexuses orchestrate long reflexes, which involve the central and autonomic nervous systems and work in response to stimuli from outside the digestive system. Short reflexes, on the other hand, are orchestrated by intrinsic nerve plexuses within the alimentary canal wall. These two plexuses and their connections were introduced earlier as the enteric nervous system. Short reflexes regulate activities in one area of the digestive tract and may coordinate local peristaltic movements and stimulate digestive secretions. For example, the sight, smell, and taste of food initiate long reflexes that begin with a sensory neuron delivering a signal to the medulla oblongata. The response to the signal is to stimulate cells in the stomach to begin secreting digestive juices in preparation for incoming food. In contrast, food that distends the stomach initiates short reflexes that cause cells in the stomach wall to increase their secretion of digestive juices.

Hormonal Controls

A variety of hormones are involved in the digestive process. The main digestive hormone of the stomach is gastrin, which is secreted in response to the presence of food. Gastrin stimulates the secretion of gastric acid by the parietal cells of the stomach mucosa. Other GI hormones are produced and act upon the gut and its accessory organs. Hormones produced by the duodenum include secretin, which stimulates a watery secretion of bicarbonate by the pancreas; cholecystokinin (CCK), which stimulates the secretion of pancreatic enzymes and bile from the liver and release of bile from the gallbladder; and gastric inhibitory peptide, which inhibits gastric secretion and slows gastric emptying and motility. These GI hormones are secreted by specialized epithelial cells, called endocrinocytes, located in the mucosal epithelium of the stomach and small intestine. These hormones then enter the bloodstream, through which they can reach their target organs.

23.3 The Mouth, Pharynx, and Esophagus

LEARNING OBJECTIVES

By the end of this section, you will be able to:

- Describe the structures of the mouth, including its three accessory digestive organs
- Group the 32 adult teeth according to name, location, and function
- Describe the process of swallowing, including the roles of the tongue, upper esophageal sphincter, and epiglottis
- Trace the pathway food follows from ingestion into the mouth through release into the stomach

In this section, you will examine the anatomy and functions of the three main organs of the upper alimentary canal—the mouth, pharynx, and esophagus—as well as three associated accessory organs—the tongue, salivary glands, and teeth.

The Mouth

The cheeks, tongue, and palate frame the mouth, which is also called the **oral cavity** (or buccal cavity). The structures of the mouth are illustrated in Figure 23.7.

At the entrance to the mouth are the lips, or **labia** (singular = labium). Their outer covering is skin, which transitions to a mucous membrane in the mouth proper. Lips are very vascular with a thin layer of keratin; hence, the reason they are "red." They have a huge representation on the cerebral cortex, which probably explains the human fascination with kissing! The lips cover the orbicularis oris muscle, which regulates what comes in and goes out of the mouth. The **labial frenulum** is a midline fold of mucous membrane that attaches the inner surface of each lip to the gum. The cheeks make up the oral cavity's sidewalls. While their outer covering is skin, their inner covering is mucous membrane. This membrane is made up of non-keratinized, stratified squamous epithelium. Between the skin and mucous membranes are connective tissue and buccinator muscles. The next time you eat some food, notice how the buccinator muscles in your cheeks and the orbicularis oris muscle in your lips contract, helping you keep the food from falling out of your mouth. Additionally, notice how these muscles work when you are speaking.

The pocket-like part of the mouth that is framed on the inside by the gums and teeth, and on the outside by the cheeks and lips is called the **oral vestibule**. Moving farther into the mouth, the opening between the oral cavity and throat (oropharynx) is called the **fauces** (like the kitchen "faucet"). The main open area of the mouth, or oral cavity proper, runs from the gums and teeth to the fauces.

When you are chewing, you do not find it difficult to breathe simultaneously. The next time you have food in your mouth, notice how the arched shape of the roof of your mouth allows you to handle both digestion and respiration at the same time. This arch is called the palate. The anterior region of the palate serves as a wall (or septum) between the oral and nasal cavities as well as a rigid shelf against which the tongue can push food. It is created by the maxillary and palatine bones of the skull and, given its bony structure, is known as the hard palate. If you run your tongue along the roof of your mouth, you'll notice that the hard palate ends in the posterior oral cavity, and the tissue becomes fleshier. This part of the palate, known as the **soft palate**, is composed mainly of skeletal muscle. You can therefore manipulate, subconsciously, the soft palate—for instance, to yawn, swallow, or sing (see Figure 23.7).

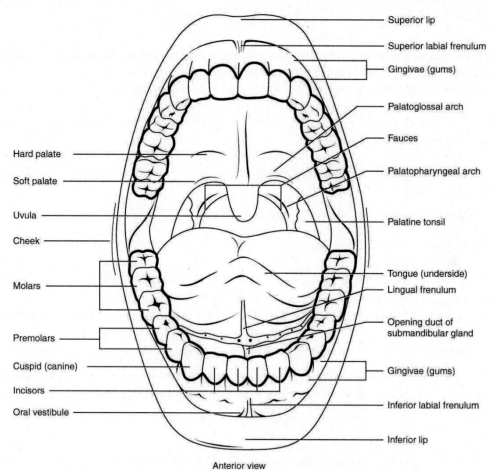

FIGURE 23.7   Mouth   The mouth includes the lips, tongue, palate, gums, and teeth.

A fleshy bead of tissue called the uvula drops down from the center of the posterior edge of the soft palate. Although some have suggested that the uvula is a vestigial organ, it serves an important purpose. When you swallow, the soft palate and uvula move upward, helping to keep foods and liquid from entering the nasal cavity. Unfortunately, it can also contribute to the sound produced by snoring. Two muscular folds extend downward from the soft palate, on either side of the uvula. Toward the front, the **palatoglossal arch** lies next to the base of the tongue; behind it, the **palatopharyngeal arch** forms the superior and lateral margins of the fauces. Between these two arches are the palatine tonsils, clusters of lymphoid tissue that protect the pharynx. The lingual tonsils are located at the base of the tongue.

The Tongue

Perhaps you have heard it said that the **tongue** is the strongest muscle in the body. Those who stake this claim cite its strength proportionate to its size. Although it is difficult to quantify the relative strength of different muscles, it remains indisputable that the tongue is a workhorse, facilitating ingestion, mechanical digestion, chemical digestion (lingual lipase), sensation (of taste, texture, and temperature of food), swallowing, and vocalization.

The tongue is attached to the mandible, the styloid processes of the temporal bones, and the hyoid bone. The hyoid is unique in that it only distantly/indirectly articulates with other bones. The tongue is positioned over the floor of the oral cavity. A medial septum extends the entire length of the tongue, dividing it into symmetrical halves.

Beneath its mucous membrane covering, each half of the tongue is composed of the same number and type of intrinsic and extrinsic skeletal muscles. The intrinsic muscles (those within the tongue) are the longitudinalis inferior, longitudinalis superior, transversus linguae, and verticalis linguae muscles. These allow you to change the size and shape of your tongue, as well as to stick it out, if you wish. Having such a flexible tongue facilitates both swallowing and speech.

As you learned in your study of the muscular system, the extrinsic muscles of the tongue are the palatoglossus, hyoglossus, styloglossus, and genioglossus muscles. These muscles originate outside the tongue and insert into connective tissues within the tongue. The mylohyoid is responsible for raising the tongue, the hyoglossus pulls it down and back, the styloglossus pulls it up and back, and the genioglossus pulls it forward. Working in concert, these muscles perform three important digestive functions in the mouth: (1) position food for optimal chewing, (2) gather food into a **bolus** (rounded mass), and (3) position food so it can be swallowed.

The top and sides of the tongue are studded with papillae, extensions of lamina propria of the mucosa, which are covered in stratified squamous epithelium (Figure 23.8). Fungiform papillae, which are mushroom shaped, cover a large area of the tongue; they tend to be larger toward the rear of the tongue and smaller on the tip and sides. In contrast, filiform papillae are long and thin. Fungiform papillae contain taste buds, and filiform papillae have touch receptors that help the tongue move food around in the mouth. The filiform papillae create an abrasive surface that performs mechanically, much like a cat's rough tongue that is used for grooming. Lingual glands in the lamina propria of the tongue secrete mucus and a watery serous fluid that contains the enzyme **lingual lipase**, which plays a minor role in breaking down triglycerides but does not begin working until it is activated in the stomach. A fold of mucous membrane on the underside of the tongue, the **lingual frenulum**, tethers the tongue to the floor of the mouth. People with the congenital anomaly ankyloglossia, also known by the non-medical term "tongue tie," have a lingual frenulum that is too short or otherwise malformed. Severe ankyloglossia can impair speech and must be corrected with surgery.

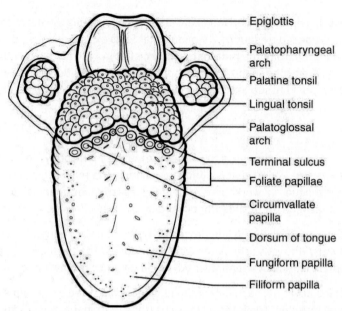

FIGURE 23.8 Tongue This superior view of the tongue shows the locations and types of lingual papillae.

The Salivary Glands

Many small **salivary glands** are housed within the mucous membranes of the mouth and tongue. These minor exocrine glands are constantly secreting saliva, either directly into the oral cavity or indirectly through ducts, even while you sleep. In fact, an average of 1 to 1.5 liters of saliva is secreted each day. Usually just enough saliva is present to moisten the mouth and teeth. Secretion increases when you eat, because saliva is essential to moisten food and initiate the chemical breakdown of carbohydrates. Small amounts of saliva are also secreted by the labial glands in the lips. In addition, the buccal glands in the cheeks, palatal glands in the palate, and lingual glands in the tongue help ensure that all areas of the mouth are supplied with adequate saliva.

The Major Salivary Glands

Outside the oral mucosa are three pairs of major salivary glands, which secrete the majority of saliva into ducts that open into the mouth:

- The **submandibular glands**, which are in the floor of the mouth, secrete saliva into the mouth through the submandibular ducts.
- The **sublingual glands**, which lie below the tongue, use the lesser sublingual ducts to secrete saliva into the oral cavity.
- The **parotid glands** lie between the skin and the masseter muscle, near the ears. They secrete saliva into the mouth through the parotid duct, which is located near the second upper molar tooth (<u>Figure 23.9</u>).

Saliva

Saliva is essentially (98 to 99.5 percent) water. The remaining 4.5 percent is a complex mixture of ions, glycoproteins, enzymes, growth factors, and waste products. Perhaps the most important ingredient in saliva from the perspective of digestion is the enzyme **salivary amylase**, which initiates the breakdown of carbohydrates. Food does not spend enough time in the mouth to allow all the carbohydrates to break down, but salivary amylase continues acting until it is inactivated by stomach acids. Bicarbonate and phosphate ions function as chemical buffers, maintaining saliva at a pH between 6.35 and 6.85. Salivary mucus helps lubricate food, facilitating movement in the mouth, bolus formation, and swallowing. Saliva contains immunoglobulin A, which prevents microbes from penetrating the epithelium, and lysozyme, which makes saliva antimicrobial. Saliva also contains epidermal growth factor, which might have given rise to the adage "a mother's kiss can heal a wound."

Each of the major salivary glands secretes a unique formulation of saliva according to its cellular makeup. For example, the parotid glands secrete a watery solution that contains salivary amylase. The submandibular glands have cells similar to those of the parotid glands, as well as mucus-secreting cells. Therefore, saliva secreted by the submandibular glands also contains amylase but in a liquid thickened with mucus. The sublingual glands contain mostly mucous cells, and they secrete the thickest saliva with the least amount of salivary amylase.

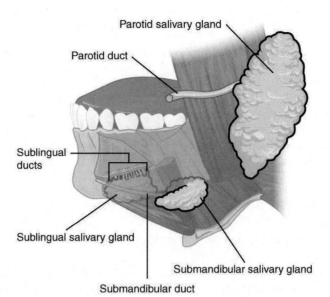

FIGURE 23.9 **Salivary glands** The major salivary glands are located outside the oral mucosa and deliver saliva into the mouth through ducts.

 HOMEOSTATIC IMBALANCES

The Parotid Glands: Mumps

Infections of the nasal passages and pharynx can attack any salivary gland. The parotid glands are the usual site of infection with the virus that causes mumps (paramyxovirus). Mumps manifests by enlargement and inflammation of the parotid glands, causing a characteristic swelling between the ears and the jaw. Symptoms include fever and throat pain, which can be severe when swallowing acidic substances such as orange juice.

In about one-third of males who are past puberty, mumps also causes testicular inflammation, typically affecting only one testis and rarely resulting in sterility. With the increasing use and effectiveness of mumps vaccines, the incidence of mumps has decreased dramatically. According to the U.S. Centers for Disease Control and Prevention (CDC), the number of mumps cases dropped from more than 150,000 in 1968 to fewer than 1700 in 1993 to only 11 reported cases in 2011.

Regulation of Salivation

The autonomic nervous system regulates **salivation** (the secretion of saliva). In the absence of food, parasympathetic stimulation keeps saliva flowing at just the right level for comfort as you speak, swallow, sleep, and generally go about life. Over-salivation can occur, for example, if you are stimulated by the smell of food, but that food is not available for you to eat. Drooling is an extreme instance of the overproduction of saliva. During times of stress, such as before speaking in public, sympathetic stimulation takes over, reducing salivation and producing the symptom of dry mouth often associated with anxiety. When you are dehydrated, salivation is reduced, causing the mouth to feel dry and prompting you to take action to quench your thirst.

Salivation can be stimulated by the sight, smell, and taste of food. It can even be stimulated by thinking about food. You might notice whether reading about food and salivation right now has had any effect on your production of saliva.

How does the salivation process work while you are eating? Food contains chemicals that stimulate taste receptors on the tongue, which send impulses to the superior and inferior salivatory nuclei in the brain stem. These two nuclei then send back parasympathetic impulses through fibers in the glossopharyngeal and facial nerves, which stimulate salivation. Even after you swallow food, salivation is increased to cleanse the mouth and to water down and neutralize any irritating chemical remnants, such as that hot sauce in your burrito. Most saliva is swallowed along with food and is reabsorbed, so that fluid is not lost.

The Teeth

The teeth, or **dentes** (singular = dens), are organs similar to bones that you use to tear, grind, and otherwise mechanically break down food.

Types of Teeth

During the course of your lifetime, you have two sets of teeth (one set of teeth is a **dentition**). Your 20 **deciduous teeth**, or baby teeth, first begin to appear at about 6 months of age. Between approximately age 6 and 12, these teeth are replaced by 32 **permanent teeth**. Moving from the center of the mouth toward the side, these are as follows (Figure 23.10):

- The eight **incisors**, four top and four bottom, are the sharp front teeth you use for biting into food.
- The four **cuspids** (or canines) flank the incisors and have a pointed edge (cusp) to tear up food. These fang-like teeth are superb for piercing tough or fleshy foods.
- Posterior to the cuspids are the eight **premolars** (or bicuspids), which have an overall flatter shape with two rounded cusps useful for mashing foods.
- The most posterior and largest are the 12 **molars**, which have several pointed cusps used to crush food so it is ready for swallowing. The third members of each set of three molars, top and bottom, are commonly referred to as the wisdom teeth, because their eruption is commonly delayed until early adulthood. It is not uncommon for wisdom teeth to fail to erupt; that is, they remain impacted. In these cases, the teeth are typically removed by orthodontic surgery.

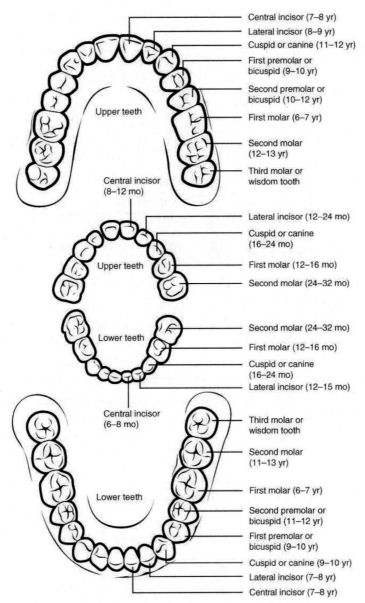

FIGURE 23.10   Permanent and Deciduous Teeth   This figure of two human dentitions shows the arrangement of teeth in the maxilla and mandible, and the relationship between the deciduous and permanent teeth.

Anatomy of a Tooth

The teeth are secured in the alveolar processes (sockets) of the maxilla and the mandible. **Gingivae** (commonly called the gums) are soft tissues that line the alveolar processes and surround the necks of the teeth. Teeth are also held in their sockets by a connective tissue called the periodontal ligament.

The two main parts of a tooth are the **crown**, which is the portion projecting above the gum line, and the **root**, which is embedded within the maxilla and mandible. Both parts contain an inner **pulp cavity**, containing loose connective tissue through which run nerves and blood vessels. The region of the pulp cavity that runs through the root of the tooth is called the root canal. Surrounding the pulp cavity is **dentin**, a bone-like tissue. In the root of each tooth, the dentin is covered by an even harder bone-like layer called **cementum**. In the crown of each tooth, the dentin is covered by an outer layer of **enamel**, the hardest substance in the body (Figure 23.11).

Although enamel protects the underlying dentin and pulp cavity, it is still nonetheless susceptible to mechanical and chemical erosion, or what is known as tooth decay. The most common form, dental caries (cavities) develops when colonies of bacteria feeding on sugars in the mouth release acids that cause soft tissue inflammation and degradation of the calcium crystals of the enamel. The digestive functions of the mouth are summarized in Table 23.4.

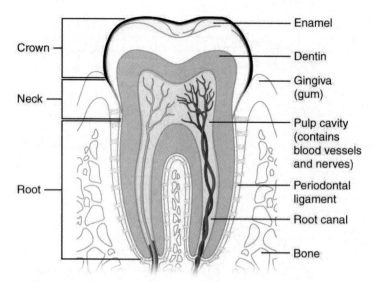

FIGURE 23.11   The Structure of the Tooth   This longitudinal section through a molar in its alveolar socket shows the relationships between enamel, dentin, and pulp.

Digestive Functions of the Mouth

Structure	Action	Outcome
Lips and cheeks	Confine food between teeth	• Food is chewed evenly during mastication
Salivary glands	Secrete saliva	• Moisten and lubricate the lining of the mouth and pharynx • Moisten, soften, and dissolve food • Clean the mouth and teeth • Salivary amylase breaks down starch
Tongue's extrinsic muscles	Move tongue sideways, and in and out	• Manipulate food for chewing • Shape food into a bolus • Manipulate food for swallowing
Tongue's intrinsic muscles	Change tongue shape	• Manipulate food for swallowing
Taste buds	Sense food in mouth and sense taste	• Nerve impulses from taste buds are conducted to salivary nuclei in the brain stem and then to salivary glands, stimulating saliva secretion
Lingual glands	Secrete lingual lipase	• Activated in the stomach • Break down triglycerides into fatty acids and diglycerides
Teeth	Shred and crush food	• Break down solid food into smaller particles for deglutition

TABLE 23.4

The Pharynx

The **pharynx** (throat) is involved in both digestion and respiration. It receives food and air from the mouth, and air from the nasal cavities. When food enters the pharynx, involuntary muscle contractions close off the air passageways.

A short tube of skeletal muscle lined with a mucous membrane, the pharynx runs from the posterior oral and nasal cavities to the opening of the esophagus and larynx. It has three subdivisions. The most superior, the nasopharynx, is involved only in breathing and speech. The other two subdivisions, the **oropharynx** and the **laryngopharynx**, are used for both breathing and digestion. The oropharynx begins inferior to the nasopharynx and is continuous below with the laryngopharynx (Figure 23.12). The inferior border of the laryngopharynx connects to the esophagus, whereas the anterior portion connects to the larynx, allowing air to flow into the bronchial tree.

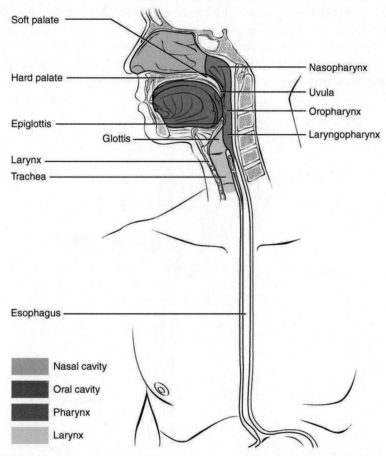

FIGURE 23.12   Pharynx   The pharynx runs from the nostrils to the esophagus and the larynx.

Histologically, the wall of the oropharynx is similar to that of the oral cavity. The mucosa includes a stratified squamous epithelium that is endowed with mucus-producing glands. During swallowing, the elevator skeletal muscles of the pharynx contract, raising and expanding the pharynx to receive the bolus of food. Once received, these muscles relax and the constrictor muscles of the pharynx contract, forcing the bolus into the esophagus and initiating peristalsis.

Usually during swallowing, the soft palate and uvula rise reflexively to close off the entrance to the nasopharynx. At the same time, the larynx is pulled superiorly and the cartilaginous epiglottis, its most superior structure, folds inferiorly, covering the glottis (the opening to the larynx); this process effectively blocks access to the trachea and bronchi. When the food "goes down the wrong way," it goes into the trachea. When food enters the trachea, the reaction is to cough, which usually forces the food up and out of the trachea, and back into the pharynx.

The Esophagus

The **esophagus** is a muscular tube that connects the pharynx to the stomach. It is approximately 25.4 cm (10 in) in length, located posterior to the trachea, and remains in a collapsed form when not engaged in swallowing. As you can see in Figure 23.13, the esophagus runs a mainly straight route through the mediastinum of the thorax. To enter the abdomen, the esophagus penetrates the diaphragm through an opening called the esophageal hiatus.

Passage of Food through the Esophagus

The **upper esophageal sphincter**, which is continuous with the inferior pharyngeal constrictor, controls the movement of food from the pharynx into the esophagus. The upper two-thirds of the esophagus consists of both smooth and skeletal muscle fibers, with the latter fading out in the bottom third of the esophagus. Rhythmic waves of peristalsis, which begin in the upper esophagus, propel the bolus of food toward the stomach. Meanwhile, secretions from the esophageal mucosa lubricate the esophagus and food. Food passes from the esophagus into the stomach at the **lower esophageal sphincter** (also called the gastroesophageal or cardiac sphincter). Recall that sphincters are muscles that surround tubes and serve as valves, closing the tube when the sphincters contract and opening it when they relax. The lower esophageal sphincter relaxes to let food pass into the stomach, and then contracts to prevent stomach acids from backing up into the esophagus. Surrounding this sphincter is the muscular diaphragm, which helps close off the sphincter when no food is being swallowed. When the lower esophageal sphincter does not completely close, the stomach's contents can reflux (that is, back up into the esophagus), causing heartburn or gastroesophageal reflux disease (GERD).

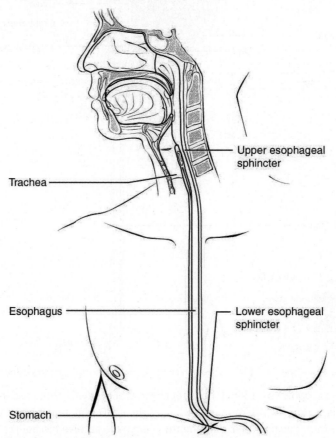

FIGURE 23.13   Esophagus   The upper esophageal sphincter controls the movement of food from the pharynx to the esophagus. The lower esophageal sphincter controls the movement of food from the esophagus to the stomach.

Histology of the Esophagus

The mucosa of the esophagus is made up of an epithelial lining that contains non-keratinized, stratified squamous epithelium, with a layer of basal and parabasal cells. This epithelium protects against erosion from food particles. The mucosa's lamina propria contains mucus-secreting glands. The muscularis layer changes according to location: In the upper third of the esophagus, the muscularis is skeletal muscle. In the middle third, it is both skeletal and smooth muscle. In the lower third, it is smooth muscle. As mentioned previously, the most superficial layer of the esophagus is called the adventitia, not the serosa. In contrast to the stomach and intestines, the loose connective tissue of the adventitia is not covered by a fold of visceral peritoneum. The digestive functions of the esophagus are identified in Table 23.5.

Digestive Functions of the Esophagus

Action	Outcome
Upper esophageal sphincter relaxation	Allows the bolus to move from the laryngopharynx to the esophagus
Peristalsis	Propels the bolus through the esophagus
Lower esophageal sphincter relaxation	Allows the bolus to move from the esophagus into the stomach and prevents chyme from entering the esophagus
Mucus secretion	Lubricates the esophagus, allowing easy passage of the bolus

TABLE 23.5

Deglutition

Deglutition is another word for swallowing—the movement of food from the mouth to the stomach. The entire process takes about 4 to 8 seconds for solid or semisolid food, and about 1 second for very soft food and liquids. Although this sounds quick and effortless, deglutition is, in fact, a complex process that involves both the skeletal muscle of the tongue and the muscles of the pharynx and esophagus. It is aided by the presence of mucus and saliva. There are three stages in deglutition: the voluntary phase, the pharyngeal phase, and the esophageal phase (Figure 23.14). The autonomic nervous system controls the latter two phases.

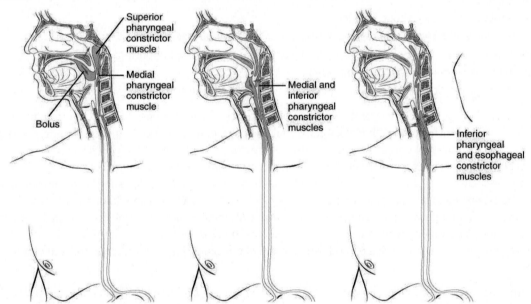

FIGURE 23.14   Deglutition   Deglutition includes the voluntary phase and two involuntary phases: the pharyngeal phase and the esophageal phase.

The Voluntary Phase

The **voluntary phase** of deglutition (also known as the oral or buccal phase) is so called because you can control when you swallow food. In this phase, chewing has been completed and swallowing is set in motion. The tongue moves upward and backward against the palate, pushing the bolus to the back of the oral cavity and into the oropharynx. Other muscles keep the mouth closed and prevent food from falling out. At this point, the two involuntary phases of swallowing begin.

The Pharyngeal Phase

In the pharyngeal phase, stimulation of receptors in the oropharynx sends impulses to the deglutition center (a collection of neurons that controls swallowing) in the medulla oblongata. Impulses are then sent back to the uvula and soft palate, causing them to move upward and close off the nasopharynx. The laryngeal muscles also constrict to prevent aspiration of food into the trachea. At this point, deglutition apnea takes place, which means that breathing ceases for a very brief time. Contractions of the pharyngeal constrictor muscles move the bolus through the oropharynx and laryngopharynx. Relaxation of the upper esophageal sphincter then allows food to enter the esophagus.

The Esophageal Phase

The entry of food into the esophagus marks the beginning of the esophageal phase of deglutition and the initiation of peristalsis. As in the previous phase, the complex neuromuscular actions are controlled by the medulla oblongata. Peristalsis propels the bolus through the esophagus and toward the stomach. The circular muscle layer of the muscularis contracts, pinching the esophageal wall and forcing the bolus forward. At the same time, the longitudinal muscle layer of the muscularis also contracts, shortening this area and pushing out its walls to receive the bolus. In this way, a series of contractions keeps moving food toward the stomach. When the bolus nears the stomach, distention of the esophagus initiates a short reflex relaxation of the lower esophageal sphincter that allows the bolus to pass into the stomach. During the esophageal phase, esophageal glands secrete mucus that lubricates the bolus and minimizes friction.

🔗 INTERACTIVE LINK

Watch this animation (http://openstax.org/l/swallowing) to see how swallowing is a complex process that involves the nervous system to coordinate the actions of upper respiratory and digestive activities. During which stage of swallowing is there a risk of food entering respiratory pathways and how is this risk blocked?

23.4 The Stomach

LEARNING OBJECTIVES

By the end of this section, you will be able to:

- Label on a diagram the four main regions of the stomach, its curvatures, and its sphincter
- Identify the four main types of secreting cells in gastric glands, and their important products
- Explain why the stomach does not digest itself
- Describe the mechanical and chemical digestion of food entering the stomach

Although a minimal amount of carbohydrate digestion occurs in the mouth, chemical digestion really gets underway in the stomach. An expansion of the alimentary canal that lies immediately inferior to the esophagus, the stomach links the esophagus to the first part of the small intestine (the duodenum) and is relatively fixed in place at its esophageal and duodenal ends. In between, however, it can be a highly active structure, contracting and continually changing position and size. These contractions provide mechanical assistance to digestion. The empty stomach is only about the size of your fist, but can stretch to hold as much as 4 liters of food and fluid, or more than 75 times its empty volume, and then return to its resting size when empty. Although you might think that the size of a person's stomach is related to how much food that individual consumes, body weight does not correlate with stomach size. Rather, when you eat greater quantities of food—such as at holiday dinner—you stretch the stomach more than when you eat less.

Popular culture tends to refer to the stomach as the location where all digestion takes place. Of course, this is not true. An important function of the stomach is to serve as a temporary holding chamber. You can ingest a meal far more quickly than it can be digested and absorbed by the small intestine. Thus, the stomach holds food and parses only small amounts into the small intestine at a time. Foods are not processed in the order they are eaten; rather, they are mixed together with digestive juices in the stomach until they are converted into chyme, which is released into the small intestine.

As you will see in the sections that follow, the stomach plays several important roles in chemical digestion, including the continued digestion of carbohydrates and the initial digestion of proteins and triglycerides. Little if any nutrient absorption occurs in the stomach, with the exception of the negligible amount of nutrients in alcohol.

Structure

There are four main regions in the **stomach**: the cardia, fundus, body, and pylorus (Figure 23.15). The **cardia** (or cardiac region) is the point where the esophagus connects to the stomach and through which food passes into the stomach. Located inferior to the diaphragm, above and to the left of the cardia, is the dome-shaped **fundus**. Below the fundus is the **body**, the main part of the stomach. The funnel-shaped **pylorus** connects the stomach to the duodenum. The wider end of the funnel, the **pyloric antrum**, connects to the body of the stomach. The narrower end is called the **pyloric canal**, which connects to the duodenum. The smooth muscle **pyloric sphincter** is located at this latter point of connection and controls stomach emptying. In the absence of food, the stomach deflates inward, and its mucosa and submucosa fall into a large fold called a **ruga**.

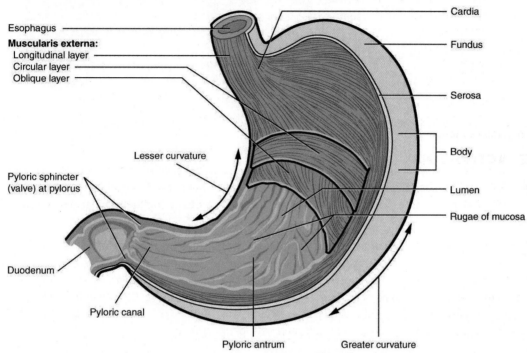

FIGURE 23.15   Stomach   The stomach has four major regions: the cardia, fundus, body, and pylorus. The addition of an inner oblique smooth muscle layer gives the muscularis the ability to vigorously churn and mix food.

The convex lateral surface of the stomach is called the greater curvature; the concave medial border is the lesser curvature. The stomach is held in place by the lesser omentum, which extends from the liver to the lesser curvature, and the greater omentum, which runs from the greater curvature to the posterior abdominal wall.

Histology

The wall of the stomach is made of the same four layers as most of the rest of the alimentary canal, but with adaptations to the mucosa and muscularis for the unique functions of this organ. In addition to the typical circular and longitudinal smooth muscle layers, the muscularis has an inner oblique smooth muscle layer (Figure 23.16). As a result, in addition to moving food through the canal, the stomach can vigorously churn food, mechanically breaking it down into smaller particles.

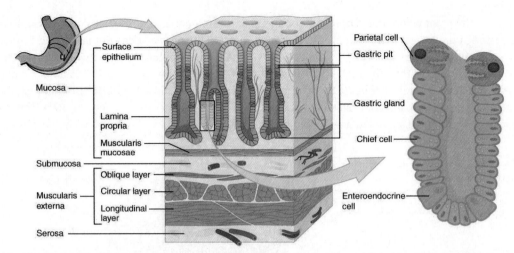

FIGURE 23.16   Histology of the Stomach   The stomach wall is adapted for the functions of the stomach. In the epithelium, gastric pits lead to gastric glands that secrete gastric juice. The gastric glands (one gland is shown enlarged on the right) contain different types of cells that secrete a variety of enzymes, including hydrochloride acid, which activates the protein-digesting enzyme pepsin.

The stomach mucosa's epithelial lining consists only of surface mucus cells, which secrete a protective coat of alkaline mucus. A vast number of **gastric pits** dot the surface of the epithelium, giving it the appearance of a well-used pincushion, and mark the entry to each **gastric gland**, which secretes a complex digestive fluid referred to as gastric juice.

Although the walls of the gastric pits are made up primarily of mucus cells, the gastric glands are made up of different types of cells. The glands of the cardia and pylorus are composed primarily of mucus-secreting cells. Cells that make up the pyloric antrum secrete mucus and a number of hormones, including the majority of the stimulatory hormone, **gastrin**. The much larger glands of the fundus and body of the stomach, the site of most chemical digestion, produce most of the gastric secretions. These glands are made up of a variety of secretory cells. These include parietal cells, chief cells, mucous neck cells, and enteroendocrine cells.

Parietal cells—Located primarily in the middle region of the gastric glands are **parietal cells**, which are among the most highly differentiated of the body's epithelial cells. These relatively large cells produce both **hydrochloric acid (HCl)** and **intrinsic factor**. HCl is responsible for the high acidity (pH 1.5 to 3.5) of the stomach contents and is needed to activate the protein-digesting enzyme, pepsin. The acidity also kills much of the bacteria you ingest with food and helps to denature proteins, making them more available for enzymatic digestion. Intrinsic factor is a glycoprotein necessary for the absorption of vitamin B_{12} in the small intestine.

Chief cells—Located primarily in the basal regions of gastric glands are **chief cells**, which secrete **pepsinogen**, the inactive proenzyme form of pepsin. HCl is necessary for the conversion of pepsinogen to pepsin.

Mucous neck cells—Gastric glands in the upper part of the stomach contain **mucous neck cells** that secrete thin, acidic mucus that is much different from the mucus secreted by the goblet cells of the surface epithelium. The role of this mucus is not currently known.

Enteroendocrine cells—Finally, **enteroendocrine cells** found in the gastric glands secrete various hormones into the interstitial fluid of the lamina propria. These include gastrin, which is released mainly by enteroendocrine **G cells**.

Table 23.6 describes the digestive functions of important hormones secreted by the stomach.

🔗 INTERACTIVE LINK

Watch this animation (http://openstax.org/l/stomach1) that depicts the structure of the stomach and how this structure functions in the initiation of protein digestion. This view of the stomach shows the characteristic rugae. What is the function of these rugae?

Access for free at openstax.org

Hormones Secreted by the Stomach

Hormone	Production site	Production stimulus	Target organ	Action
Gastrin	Stomach mucosa, mainly G cells of the pyloric antrum	Presence of peptides and amino acids in stomach	Stomach	Increases secretion by gastric glands; promotes gastric emptying
Gastrin	Stomach mucosa, mainly G cells of the pyloric antrum	Presence of peptides and amino acids in stomach	Small intestine	Promotes intestinal muscle contraction
Gastrin	Stomach mucosa, mainly G cells of the pyloric antrum	Presence of peptides and amino acids in stomach	Ileocecal valve	Relaxes valve
Gastrin	Stomach mucosa, mainly G cells of the pyloric antrum	Presence of peptides and amino acids in stomach	Large intestine	Triggers mass movements
Ghrelin	Stomach mucosa, mainly fundus	Fasting state (levels increase just prior to meals)	Hypothalamus	Regulates food intake, primarily by stimulating hunger and satiety
Histamine	Stomach mucosa	Presence of food in the stomach	Stomach	Stimulates parietal cells to release HCl
Serotonin	Stomach mucosa	Presence of food in the stomach	Stomach	Contracts stomach muscle
Somatostatin	Mucosa of stomach, especially pyloric antrum; also duodenum	Presence of food in the stomach; sympathetic axon stimulation	Stomach	Restricts all gastric secretions, gastric motility, and emptying
Somatostatin	Mucosa of stomach, especially pyloric antrum; also duodenum	Presence of food in the stomach; sympathetic axon stimulation	Pancreas	Restricts pancreatic secretions
Somatostatin	Mucosa of stomach, especially pyloric antrum; also duodenum	Presence of food in the stomach; sympathetic axon stimulation	Small intestine	Reduces intestinal absorption by reducing blood flow

TABLE 23.6

Gastric Secretion

The secretion of gastric juice is controlled by both nerves and hormones. Stimuli in the brain, stomach, and small intestine activate or inhibit gastric juice production. This is why the three phases of gastric secretion are called the cephalic, gastric, and intestinal phases (Figure 23.17). However, once gastric secretion begins, all three phases can occur simultaneously.

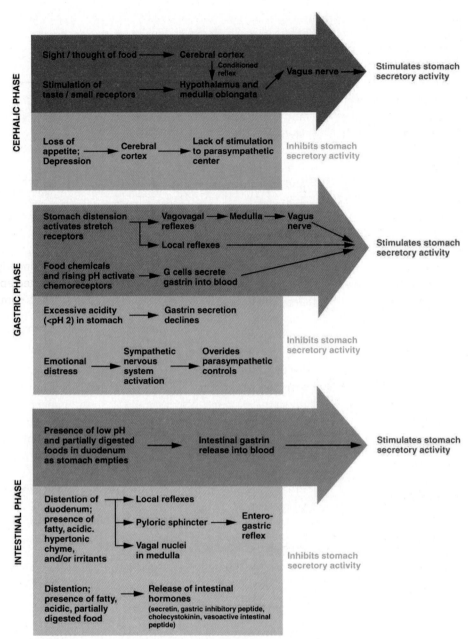

FIGURE 23.17 The Three Phases of Gastric Secretion   Gastric secretion occurs in three phases: cephalic, gastric, and intestinal. During each phase, the secretion of gastric juice can be stimulated or inhibited.

The **cephalic phase** (reflex phase) of gastric secretion, which is relatively brief, takes place before food enters the stomach. The smell, taste, sight, or thought of food triggers this phase. For example, when you bring a piece of sushi to your lips, impulses from receptors in your taste buds or the nose are relayed to your brain, which returns signals that increase gastric secretion to prepare your stomach for digestion. This enhanced secretion is a conditioned reflex, meaning it occurs only if you like or want a particular food. Depression and loss of appetite can suppress the cephalic reflex.

The **gastric phase** of secretion lasts 3 to 4 hours, and is set in motion by local neural and hormonal mechanisms triggered by the entry of food into the stomach. For example, when your sushi reaches the stomach, it creates distention that activates the stretch receptors. This stimulates parasympathetic neurons to release acetylcholine, which then provokes increased secretion of gastric juice. Partially digested proteins, caffeine, and rising pH stimulate the release of gastrin from enteroendocrine G cells, which in turn induces parietal cells to increase their production of HCl, which is needed to create an acidic environment for the conversion of pepsinogen to pepsin, and protein digestion. Additionally, the release of gastrin activates vigorous smooth muscle contractions. However, it should be noted that the stomach does have a natural means of avoiding excessive acid secretion and potential

Access for free at openstax.org

heartburn. Whenever pH levels drop too low, cells in the stomach react by suspending HCl secretion and increasing mucous secretions.

The **intestinal phase** of gastric secretion has both excitatory and inhibitory elements. The duodenum has a major role in regulating the stomach and its emptying. When partially digested food fills the duodenum, intestinal mucosal cells release a hormone called intestinal (enteric) gastrin, which further excites gastric juice secretion. This stimulatory activity is brief, however, because when the intestine distends with chyme, the enterogastric reflex inhibits secretion. One of the effects of this reflex is to close the pyloric sphincter, which blocks additional chyme from entering the duodenum.

The Mucosal Barrier

The mucosa of the stomach is exposed to the highly corrosive acidity of gastric juice. Gastric enzymes that can digest protein can also digest the stomach itself. The stomach is protected from self-digestion by the **mucosal barrier**. This barrier has several components. First, the stomach wall is covered by a thick coating of bicarbonate-rich mucus. This mucus forms a physical barrier, and its bicarbonate ions neutralize acid. Second, the epithelial cells of the stomach's mucosa meet at tight junctions, which block gastric juice from penetrating the underlying tissue layers. Finally, stem cells located where gastric glands join the gastric pits quickly replace damaged epithelial mucosal cells, when the epithelial cells are shed. In fact, the surface epithelium of the stomach is completely replaced every 3 to 6 days.

 HOMEOSTATIC IMBALANCES

Ulcers: When the Mucosal Barrier Breaks Down

As effective as the mucosal barrier is, it is not a "fail-safe" mechanism. Sometimes, gastric juice eats away at the superficial lining of the stomach mucosa, creating erosions, which mostly heal on their own. Deeper and larger erosions are called ulcers.

Why does the mucosal barrier break down? A number of factors can interfere with its ability to protect the stomach lining. The majority of all ulcers are caused by either excessive intake of non-steroidal anti-inflammatory drugs (NSAIDs), including aspirin, or *Helicobacter pylori* infection.

Antacids help relieve symptoms of ulcers such as "burning" pain and indigestion. When ulcers are caused by NSAID use, switching to other classes of pain relievers allows healing. When caused by *H. pylori* infection, antibiotics are effective.

A potential complication of ulcers is perforation: Perforated ulcers create a hole in the stomach wall, resulting in peritonitis (inflammation of the peritoneum). These ulcers must be repaired surgically.

Digestive Functions of the Stomach

The stomach participates in virtually all the digestive activities with the exception of ingestion and defecation. Although almost all absorption takes place in the small intestine, the stomach does absorb some drugs, such as alcohol and aspirin.

Mechanical Digestion

Within a few moments after food enters your stomach, mixing waves begin to occur at intervals of approximately 20 seconds. A **mixing wave** is a unique type of peristalsis that mixes and softens the food with gastric juices to create chyme. The initial mixing waves are relatively gentle, but these are followed by more intense waves, starting at the body of the stomach and increasing in force as they reach the pylorus. It is fair to say that long before your sushi exits through the pyloric sphincter, it bears little resemblance to the sushi you ate.

The pylorus, which holds around 30 mL (1 fluid ounce) of chyme, acts as a filter, permitting only liquids and small food particles to pass through the mostly, but not fully, closed pyloric sphincter. In a process called **gastric emptying**, rhythmic mixing waves force about 3 mL of chyme at a time through the pyloric sphincter and into the duodenum. Release of a greater amount of chyme at one time would overwhelm the capacity of the small intestine to handle it. The rest of the chyme is pushed back into the body of the stomach, where it continues mixing. This process is repeated when the next mixing waves force more chyme into the duodenum.

Gastric emptying is regulated by both the stomach and the duodenum. The presence of chyme in the duodenum activates receptors that inhibit gastric secretion. This prevents additional chyme from being released by the stomach before the duodenum is ready to process it.

Chemical Digestion

The fundus plays an important role, because it stores both undigested food and gases that are released during the process of chemical digestion. Food may sit in the fundus of the stomach for a while before being mixed with the chyme. While the food is in the fundus, the digestive activities of salivary amylase continue until the food begins mixing with the acidic chyme. Ultimately, mixing waves incorporate this food with the chyme, the acidity of which inactivates salivary amylase and activates lingual lipase. Lingual lipase then begins breaking down triglycerides into free fatty acids, and mono- and diglycerides.

The breakdown of protein begins in the stomach through the actions of HCl and the enzyme pepsin.

Its numerous digestive functions notwithstanding, there is only one stomach function necessary to life: the production of intrinsic factor. The intestinal absorption of vitamin B_{12}, which is necessary for both the production of mature red blood cells and normal neurological functioning, cannot occur without intrinsic factor. People who undergo total gastrectomy (stomach removal)—for life-threatening stomach cancer, for example—can survive with minimal digestive dysfunction if they receive vitamin B_{12} injections.

The contents of the stomach are completely emptied into the duodenum within 2 to 4 hours after you eat a meal. Different types of food take different amounts of time to process. Foods heavy in carbohydrates empty fastest, followed by high-protein foods. Meals with a high triglyceride content remain in the stomach the longest. Since enzymes in the small intestine digest fats slowly, food can stay in the stomach for 6 hours or longer when the duodenum is processing fatty chyme. However, note that this is still a fraction of the 24 to 72 hours that full digestion typically takes from start to finish.

23.5 The Small and Large Intestines

LEARNING OBJECTIVES

By the end of this section, you will be able to:

- Compare and contrast the location and gross anatomy of the small and large intestines
- Identify three main adaptations of the small intestine wall that increase its absorptive capacity
- Describe the mechanical and chemical digestion of chyme upon its release into the small intestine
- List three features unique to the wall of the large intestine and identify their contributions to its function
- Identify the beneficial roles of the bacterial flora in digestive system functioning
- Trace the pathway of food waste from its point of entry into the large intestine through its exit from the body as feces

The word intestine is derived from a Latin root meaning "internal," and indeed, the two organs together nearly fill the interior of the abdominal cavity. In addition, called the small and large bowel, or colloquially the "guts," they constitute the greatest mass and length of the alimentary canal and, with the exception of ingestion, perform all digestive system functions.

The Small Intestine

Chyme released from the stomach enters the **small intestine**, which is the primary digestive organ in the body. Not only is this where most digestion occurs, it is also where practically all absorption occurs. The longest part of the alimentary canal, the small intestine is about 3.05 meters (10 feet) long in a living person (but about twice as long in a cadaver due to the loss of muscle tone). Since this makes it about five times longer than the large intestine, you might wonder why it is called "small." In fact, its name derives from its relatively smaller diameter of only about 2.54 cm (1 in), compared with 7.62 cm (3 in) for the large intestine. As we'll see shortly, in addition to its length, the folds and projections of the lining of the small intestine work to give it an enormous surface area, which is approximately 200 m^2, more than 100 times the surface area of your skin. This large surface area is necessary for complex processes of digestion and absorption that occur within it.

Structure

The coiled tube of the small intestine is subdivided into three regions. From proximal (at the stomach) to distal, these are the duodenum, jejunum, and ileum (Figure 23.18).

The shortest region is the 25.4-cm (10-in) **duodenum**, which begins at the pyloric sphincter. Just past the pyloric sphincter, it bends posteriorly behind the peritoneum, becoming retroperitoneal, and then makes a C-shaped curve around the head of the pancreas before ascending anteriorly again to return to the peritoneal cavity and join the jejunum. The duodenum can therefore be subdivided into four segments: the superior, descending, horizontal, and ascending duodenum.

Of particular interest is the **hepatopancreatic ampulla** (ampulla of Vater). Located in the duodenal wall, the ampulla marks the transition from the anterior portion of the alimentary canal to the mid-region, and is where the bile duct (through which bile passes from the liver) and the **main pancreatic duct** (through which pancreatic juice passes from the pancreas) join. This ampulla opens into the duodenum at a tiny volcano-shaped structure called the **major duodenal papilla**. The **hepatopancreatic sphincter** (sphincter of Oddi) regulates the flow of both bile and pancreatic juice from the ampulla into the duodenum.

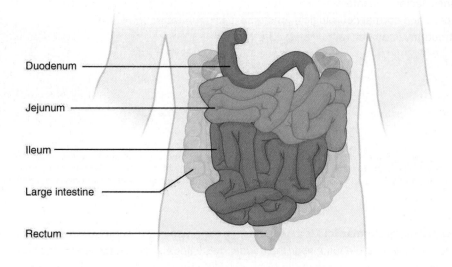

FIGURE 23.18   Small Intestine   The three regions of the small intestine are the duodenum, jejunum, and ileum.

The **jejunum** is about 0.9 meters (3 feet) long (in life) and runs from the duodenum to the ileum. Jejunum means "empty" in Latin and supposedly was so named by the ancient Greeks who noticed it was always empty at death. No clear demarcation exists between the jejunum and the final segment of the small intestine, the ileum.

The **ileum** is the longest part of the small intestine, measuring about 1.8 meters (6 feet) in length. It is thicker, more vascular, and has more developed mucosal folds than the jejunum. The ileum joins the cecum, the first portion of the large intestine, at the **ileocecal sphincter** (or valve). The jejunum and ileum are tethered to the posterior abdominal wall by the mesentery. The large intestine frames these three parts of the small intestine.

Parasympathetic nerve fibers from the vagus nerve and sympathetic nerve fibers from the thoracic splanchnic nerve provide extrinsic innervation to the small intestine. The superior mesenteric artery is its main arterial supply. Veins run parallel to the arteries and drain into the superior mesenteric vein. Nutrient-rich blood from the small intestine is then carried to the liver via the hepatic portal vein.

Histology

The wall of the small intestine is composed of the same four layers typically present in the alimentary system. However, three features of the mucosa and submucosa are unique. These features, which increase the absorptive surface area of the small intestine more than 600-fold, include circular folds, villi, and microvilli (Figure 23.19). These adaptations are most abundant in the proximal two-thirds of the small intestine, where the majority of absorption occurs.

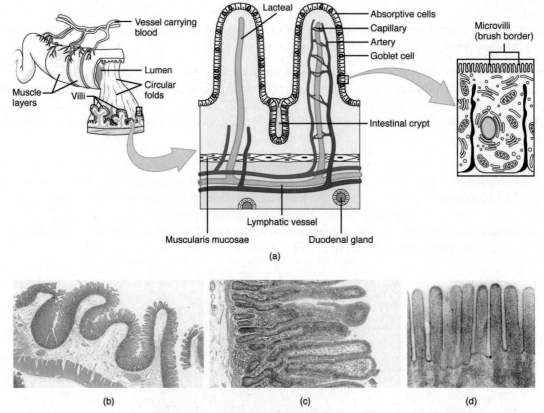

FIGURE 23.19   Histology of the Small Intestine   (a) The absorptive surface of the small intestine is vastly enlarged by the presence of circular folds, villi, and microvilli. (b) Micrograph of the circular folds. (c) Micrograph of the villi. (d) Electron micrograph of the microvilli. From left to right, LM x 56, LM x 508, EM x 196,000. (credit b-d: Micrograph provided by the Regents of University of Michigan Medical School © 2012)

Circular folds

Also called a plica circulare, a **circular fold** is a deep ridge in the mucosa and submucosa. Beginning near the proximal part of the duodenum and ending near the middle of the ileum, these folds facilitate absorption. Their shape causes the chyme to spiral, rather than move in a straight line, through the small intestine. Spiraling slows the movement of chyme and provides the time needed for nutrients to be fully absorbed.

Villi

Within the circular folds are small (0.5–1 mm long) hairlike vascularized projections called **villi** (singular = villus) that give the mucosa a furry texture. There are about 20 to 40 villi per square millimeter, increasing the surface area of the epithelium tremendously. The mucosal epithelium, primarily composed of absorptive cells, covers the villi. In addition to muscle and connective tissue to support its structure, each villus contains a capillary bed composed of one arteriole and one venule, as well as a lymphatic capillary called a **lacteal**. The breakdown products of carbohydrates and proteins (sugars and amino acids) can enter the bloodstream directly, but lipid breakdown products are absorbed by the lacteals and transported to the bloodstream via the lymphatic system.

Microvilli

As their name suggests, **microvilli** (singular = microvillus) are much smaller (1 μm) than villi. They are cylindrical apical surface extensions of the plasma membrane of the mucosa's epithelial cells, and are supported by microfilaments within those cells. Although their small size makes it difficult to see each microvillus, their combined microscopic appearance suggests a mass of bristles, which is termed the **brush border**. Fixed to the surface of the microvilli membranes are enzymes that finish digesting carbohydrates and proteins. There are an estimated 200 million microvilli per square millimeter of small intestine, greatly expanding the surface area of the plasma membrane and thus greatly enhancing absorption.

Intestinal Glands

In addition to the three specialized absorptive features just discussed, the mucosa between the villi is dotted with deep crevices that each lead into a tubular **intestinal gland** (crypt of Lieberkühn), which is formed by cells that line the crevices (see Figure 23.19). These produce **intestinal juice**, a slightly alkaline (pH 7.4 to 7.8) mixture of water and mucus. Each day, about 0.95 to 1.9 liters (1 to 2 quarts) are secreted in response to the distention of the small intestine or the irritating effects of chyme on the intestinal mucosa.

The submucosa of the duodenum is the only site of the complex mucus-secreting **duodenal glands** (Brunner's glands), which produce a bicarbonate-rich alkaline mucus that buffers the acidic chyme as it enters from the stomach.

The roles of the cells in the small intestinal mucosa are detailed in Table 23.7.

Cells of the Small Intestinal Mucosa

Cell type	Location in the mucosa	Function
Absorptive	Epithelium/intestinal glands	Digestion and absorption of nutrients in chyme
Goblet	Epithelium/intestinal glands	Secretion of mucus
Paneth	Intestinal glands	Secretion of the bactericidal enzyme lysozyme; phagocytosis
G cells	Intestinal glands of duodenum	Secretion of the hormone intestinal gastrin
I cells	Intestinal glands of duodenum	Secretion of the hormone cholecystokinin, which stimulates release of pancreatic juices and bile
K cells	Intestinal glands	Secretion of the hormone glucose-dependent insulinotropic peptide, which stimulates the release of insulin
M cells	Intestinal glands of duodenum and jejunum	Secretion of the hormone motilin, which accelerates gastric emptying, stimulates intestinal peristalsis, and stimulates the production of pepsin
S cells	Intestinal glands	Secretion of the hormone secretin

TABLE 23.7

Intestinal MALT

The lamina propria of the small intestine mucosa is studded with quite a bit of MALT. In addition to solitary lymphatic nodules, aggregations of intestinal MALT, which are typically referred to as Peyer's patches, are concentrated in the distal ileum, and serve to keep bacteria from entering the bloodstream. Peyer's patches are most prominent in young people and become less distinct as you age, which coincides with the general activity of our immune system.

⊙ INTERACTIVE LINK

Watch this animation (http://openstax.org/l/sintestine) that depicts the structure of the small intestine, and, in particular, the villi. Epithelial cells continue the digestion and absorption of nutrients and transport these nutrients to the lymphatic and circulatory systems. In the small intestine, the products of food digestion are absorbed by different structures in the villi. Which structure absorbs and transports fats?

Mechanical Digestion in the Small Intestine

The movement of intestinal smooth muscles includes both segmentation and a form of peristalsis called migrating motility complexes. The kind of peristaltic mixing waves seen in the stomach are not observed here.

If you could see into the small intestine when it was going through segmentation, it would look as if the contents were being shoved incrementally back and forth, as the rings of smooth muscle repeatedly contract and then relax. Segmentation in the small intestine does not force chyme through the tract. Instead, it combines the chyme with digestive juices and pushes food particles against the mucosa to be absorbed. The duodenum is where the most rapid segmentation occurs, at a rate of about 12 times per minute. In the ileum, segmentations are only about eight times per minute (<u>Figure 23.20</u>).

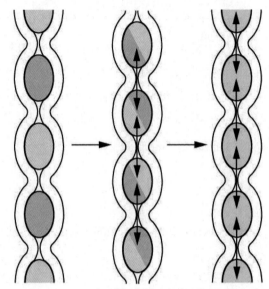

FIGURE 23.20   Segmentation   Segmentation separates chyme and then pushes it back together, mixing it and providing time for digestion and absorption.

When most of the chyme has been absorbed, the small intestinal wall becomes less distended. At this point, the localized segmentation process is replaced by transport movements. The duodenal mucosa secretes the hormone **motilin**, which initiates peristalsis in the form of a **migrating motility complex**. These complexes, which begin in the duodenum, force chyme through a short section of the small intestine and then stop. The next contraction begins a little bit farther down than the first, forces chyme a bit farther through the small intestine, then stops. These complexes move slowly down the small intestine, forcing chyme on the way, taking around 90 to 120 minutes to finally reach the end of the ileum. At this point, the process is repeated, starting in the duodenum.

The ileocecal valve, a sphincter, is usually in a constricted state, but when motility in the ileum increases, this sphincter relaxes, allowing food residue to enter the first portion of the large intestine, the cecum. Relaxation of the ileocecal sphincter is controlled by both nerves and hormones. First, digestive activity in the stomach provokes the **gastroileal reflex**, which increases the force of ileal segmentation. Second, the stomach releases the hormone gastrin, which enhances ileal motility, thus relaxing the ileocecal sphincter. After chyme passes through, backward pressure helps close the sphincter, preventing backflow into the ileum. Because of this reflex, your lunch is completely emptied from your stomach and small intestine by the time you eat your dinner. It takes about 3 to 5 hours for all chyme to leave the small intestine.

Chemical Digestion in the Small Intestine

The digestion of proteins and carbohydrates, which partially occurs in the stomach, is completed in the small intestine with the aid of intestinal and pancreatic juices. Lipids arrive in the intestine largely undigested, so much of the focus here is on lipid digestion, which is facilitated by bile and the enzyme pancreatic lipase.

Moreover, intestinal juice combines with pancreatic juice to provide a liquid medium that facilitates absorption. The intestine is also where most water is absorbed, via osmosis. The small intestine's absorptive cells also synthesize digestive enzymes and then place them in the plasma membranes of the microvilli. This distinguishes the small intestine from the stomach; that is, enzymatic digestion occurs not only in the lumen, but also on the luminal

Access for free at openstax.org

surfaces of the mucosal cells.

For optimal chemical digestion, chyme must be delivered from the stomach slowly and in small amounts. This is because chyme from the stomach is typically hypertonic, and if large quantities were forced all at once into the small intestine, the resulting osmotic water loss from the blood into the intestinal lumen would result in potentially life-threatening low blood volume. In addition, continued digestion requires an upward adjustment of the low pH of stomach chyme, along with rigorous mixing of the chyme with bile and pancreatic juices. Both processes take time, so the pumping action of the pylorus must be carefully controlled to prevent the duodenum from being overwhelmed with chyme.

Disorders of the...

Small Intestine: Lactose Intolerance

Lactose intolerance is a condition characterized by indigestion caused by dairy products. It occurs when the absorptive cells of the small intestine do not produce enough lactase, the enzyme that digests the milk sugar lactose. In most mammals, lactose intolerance increases with age. In contrast, some human populations are able to maintain the ability to produce lactase as adults.

In people with lactose intolerance, the lactose in chyme is not digested. Bacteria in the large intestine ferment the undigested lactose, a process that produces gas. In addition to gas, symptoms include abdominal cramps, bloating, and diarrhea. Symptom severity ranges from mild discomfort to severe pain; however, symptoms resolve once the lactose is eliminated in feces.

The hydrogen breath test is used to help diagnose lactose intolerance. Lactose-tolerant people have very little hydrogen in their breath. Those with lactose intolerance exhale hydrogen, which is one of the gases produced by the bacterial fermentation of lactose in the colon. After the hydrogen is absorbed from the intestine, it is transported through blood vessels into the lungs. There are a number of lactose-free dairy products available in grocery stores. In addition, dietary supplements are available. Taken with food, they provide lactase to help digest lactose.

The Large Intestine

The **large intestine** is the terminal part of the alimentary canal. The primary function of this organ is to finish absorption of nutrients and water, synthesize certain vitamins, form feces, and eliminate feces from the body.

Structure

The large intestine runs from the appendix to the anus. It frames the small intestine on three sides. Despite its being about one-half as long as the small intestine, it is called large because it is more than twice the diameter of the small intestine, about 3 inches.

Subdivisions

The large intestine is subdivided into four main regions: the cecum, the colon, the rectum, and the anus. The ileocecal valve, located at the opening between the ileum and the large intestine, controls the flow of chyme from the small intestine to the large intestine.

Cecum

The first part of the large intestine is the **cecum**, a sac-like structure that is suspended inferior to the ileocecal valve. It is about 6 cm (2.4 in) long, receives the contents of the ileum, and continues the absorption of water and salts. The **appendix** (or vermiform appendix) is a winding tube that attaches to the cecum. Although the 7.6-cm (3-in) long appendix contains lymphoid tissue, suggesting an immunologic function, this organ is generally considered vestigial. However, at least one recent report postulates a survival advantage conferred by the appendix: In diarrheal illness, the appendix may serve as a bacterial reservoir to repopulate the enteric bacteria for those surviving the initial phases of the illness. Moreover, its twisted anatomy provides a haven for the accumulation and multiplication of enteric bacteria. The **mesoappendix**, the mesentery of the appendix, tethers it to the mesentery of the ileum.

Colon

The cecum blends seamlessly with the **colon**. Upon entering the colon, the food residue first travels up the **ascending colon** on the right side of the abdomen. At the inferior surface of the liver, the colon bends to form the **right colic flexure** (hepatic flexure) and becomes the **transverse colon**. The region defined as hindgut begins with the last third of the transverse colon and continues on. Food residue passing through the transverse colon travels across to the left side of the abdomen, where the colon angles sharply immediately inferior to the spleen, at the **left colic flexure** (splenic flexure). From there, food residue passes through the **descending colon**, which runs down the left side of the posterior abdominal wall. After entering the pelvis inferiorly, it becomes the s-shaped **sigmoid colon**, which extends medially to the midline (Figure 23.21). The ascending and descending colon, and the rectum (discussed next) are located in the retroperitoneum. The transverse and sigmoid colon are tethered to the posterior abdominal wall by the mesocolon.

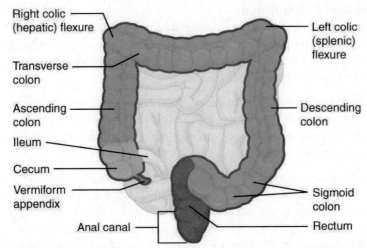

FIGURE 23.21 Large Intestine   The large intestine includes the cecum, colon, and rectum.

HOMEOSTATIC IMBALANCES

Colorectal Cancer

Each year, approximately 140,000 Americans are diagnosed with colorectal cancer, and another 49,000 die from it, making it one of the most deadly malignancies. People with a family history of colorectal cancer are at increased risk. Smoking, excessive alcohol consumption, and a diet high in animal fat and protein also increase the risk. Despite popular opinion to the contrary, studies support the conclusion that dietary fiber and calcium do not reduce the risk of colorectal cancer.

Colorectal cancer may be signaled by constipation or diarrhea, cramping, abdominal pain, and rectal bleeding. Bleeding from the rectum may be either obvious or occult (hidden in feces). Since most colon cancers arise from benign mucosal growths called polyps, cancer prevention is focused on identifying these polyps. The colonoscopy is both diagnostic and therapeutic. Colonoscopy not only allows identification of precancerous polyps, the procedure also enables them to be removed before they become malignant. Screening for fecal occult blood tests and colonoscopy is recommended for those over 50 years of age.

Rectum

Food residue leaving the sigmoid colon enters the **rectum** in the pelvis, near the third sacral vertebra. The final 20.3 cm (8 in) of the alimentary canal, the rectum extends anterior to the sacrum and coccyx. Even though rectum is Latin for "straight," this structure follows the curved contour of the sacrum and has three lateral bends that create a trio of internal transverse folds called the **rectal valves**. These valves help separate the feces from gas to prevent the simultaneous passage of feces and gas.

Anal Canal

Finally, food residue reaches the last part of the large intestine, the **anal canal**, which is located in the perineum, completely outside of the abdominopelvic cavity. This 3.8–5 cm (1.5–2 in) long structure opens to the exterior of the body at the anus. The anal canal includes two sphincters. The **internal anal sphincter** is made of smooth muscle, and its contractions are involuntary. The **external anal sphincter** is made of skeletal muscle, which is under voluntary control. Except when defecating, both usually remain closed.

Histology

There are several notable differences between the walls of the large and small intestines (Figure 23.22). For example, few enzyme-secreting cells are found in the wall of the large intestine, and there are no circular folds or villi. Other than in the anal canal, the mucosa of the colon is simple columnar epithelium made mostly of enterocytes (absorptive cells) and goblet cells. In addition, the wall of the large intestine has far more intestinal glands, which contain a vast population of enterocytes and goblet cells. These goblet cells secrete mucus that eases the movement of feces and protects the intestine from the effects of the acids and gases produced by enteric bacteria. The enterocytes absorb water and salts as well as vitamins produced by your intestinal bacteria.

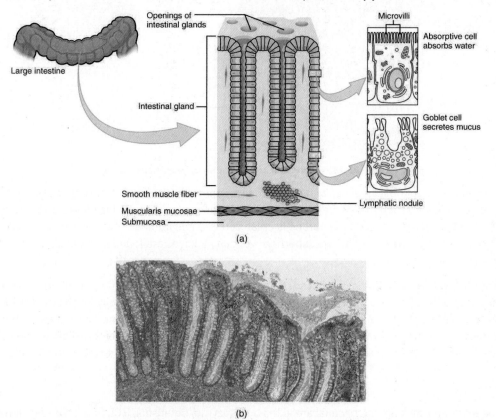

FIGURE 23.22   Histology of the large Intestine   (a) The histologies of the large intestine and small intestine (not shown) are adapted for the digestive functions of each organ. (b) This micrograph shows the colon's simple columnar epithelium and goblet cells. LM x 464. (credit b: Micrograph provided by the Regents of University of Michigan Medical School © 2012)

Anatomy

Three features are unique to the large intestine: teniae coli, haustra, and epiploic appendages (Figure 23.23). The **teniae coli** are three bands of smooth muscle that make up the longitudinal muscle layer of the muscularis of the large intestine, except at its terminal end. Tonic contractions of the teniae coli bunch up the colon into a succession of pouches called **haustra** (singular = haustrum), which are responsible for the wrinkled appearance of the colon. Attached to the teniae coli are small, fat-filled sacs of visceral peritoneum called **epiploic appendages**. The purpose of these is unknown. Although the rectum and anal canal have neither teniae coli nor haustra, they do have well-developed layers of muscularis that create the strong contractions needed for defecation.

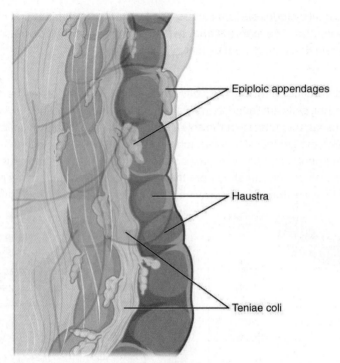

FIGURE 23.23   Teniae Coli, Haustra, and Epiploic Appendages

The stratified squamous epithelial mucosa of the anal canal connects to the skin on the outside of the anus. This mucosa varies considerably from that of the rest of the colon to accommodate the high level of abrasion as feces pass through. The anal canal's mucous membrane is organized into longitudinal folds, each called an **anal column**, which house a grid of arteries and veins. Two superficial venous plexuses are found in the anal canal: one within the anal columns and one at the anus.

Depressions between the anal columns, each called an **anal sinus**, secrete mucus that facilitates defecation. The **pectinate line** (or dentate line) is a horizontal, jagged band that runs circumferentially just below the level of the anal sinuses, and represents the junction between the hindgut and external skin. The mucosa above this line is fairly insensitive, whereas the area below is very sensitive. The resulting difference in pain threshold is due to the fact that the upper region is innervated by visceral sensory fibers, and the lower region is innervated by somatic sensory fibers.

Bacterial Flora

Most bacteria that enter the alimentary canal are killed by lysozyme, defensins, HCl, or protein-digesting enzymes. However, trillions of bacteria live within the large intestine and are referred to as the **bacterial flora**. Most of the more than 700 species of these bacteria are nonpathogenic commensal organisms that cause no harm as long as they stay in the gut lumen. In fact, many facilitate chemical digestion and absorption, and some synthesize certain vitamins, mainly biotin, pantothenic acid, and vitamin K. Some are linked to increased immune response. A refined system prevents these bacteria from crossing the mucosal barrier. First, peptidoglycan, a component of bacterial cell walls, activates the release of chemicals by the mucosa's epithelial cells, which draft immune cells, especially dendritic cells, into the mucosa. Dendritic cells open the tight junctions between epithelial cells and extend probes into the lumen to evaluate the microbial antigens. The dendritic cells with antigens then travel to neighboring lymphoid follicles in the mucosa where T cells inspect for antigens. This process triggers an IgA-mediated response, if warranted, in the lumen that blocks the commensal organisms from infiltrating the mucosa and setting off a far greater, widespread systematic reaction.

Digestive Functions of the Large Intestine

The residue of chyme that enters the large intestine contains few nutrients except water, which is reabsorbed as the residue lingers in the large intestine, typically for 12 to 24 hours. Thus, it may not surprise you that the large intestine can be completely removed without significantly affecting digestive functioning. For example, in severe cases of inflammatory bowel disease, the large intestine can be removed by a procedure known as a colectomy.

Often, a new fecal pouch can be crafted from the small intestine and sutured to the anus, but if not, an ileostomy can be created by bringing the distal ileum through the abdominal wall, allowing the watery chyme to be collected in a bag-like adhesive appliance.

Mechanical Digestion

In the large intestine, mechanical digestion begins when chyme moves from the ileum into the cecum, an activity regulated by the ileocecal sphincter. Right after you eat, peristalsis in the ileum forces chyme into the cecum. When the cecum is distended with chyme, contractions of the ileocecal sphincter strengthen. Once chyme enters the cecum, colon movements begin.

Mechanical digestion in the large intestine includes a combination of three types of movements. The presence of food residues in the colon stimulates a slow-moving **haustral contraction**. This type of movement involves sluggish segmentation, primarily in the transverse and descending colons. When a haustrum is distended with chyme, its muscle contracts, pushing the residue into the next haustrum. These contractions occur about every 30 minutes, and each last about 1 minute. These movements also mix the food residue, which helps the large intestine absorb water. The second type of movement is peristalsis, which, in the large intestine, is slower than in the more proximal portions of the alimentary canal. The third type is a **mass movement**. These strong waves start midway through the transverse colon and quickly force the contents toward the rectum. Mass movements usually occur three or four times per day, either while you eat or immediately afterward. Distension in the stomach and the breakdown products of digestion in the small intestine provoke the **gastrocolic reflex**, which increases motility, including mass movements, in the colon. Fiber in the diet both softens the stool and increases the power of colonic contractions, optimizing the activities of the colon.

Chemical Digestion

Although the glands of the large intestine secrete mucus, they do not secrete digestive enzymes. Therefore, chemical digestion in the large intestine occurs exclusively because of bacteria in the lumen of the colon. Through the process of **saccharolytic fermentation**, bacteria break down some of the remaining carbohydrates. This results in the discharge of hydrogen, carbon dioxide, and methane gases that create **flatus** (gas) in the colon; flatulence is excessive flatus. Each day, up to 1500 mL of flatus is produced in the colon. More is produced when you eat foods such as beans, which are rich in otherwise indigestible sugars and complex carbohydrates like soluble dietary fiber.

Absorption, Feces Formation, and Defecation

The small intestine absorbs about 90 percent of the water you ingest (either as liquid or within solid food). The large intestine absorbs most of the remaining water, a process that converts the liquid chyme residue into semisolid **feces** ("stool"). Feces is composed of undigested food residues, unabsorbed digested substances, millions of bacteria, old epithelial cells from the GI mucosa, inorganic salts, and enough water to let it pass smoothly out of the body. Of every 500 mL (17 ounces) of food residue that enters the cecum each day, about 150 mL (5 ounces) become feces.

Feces are eliminated through contractions of the rectal muscles. You help this process by a voluntary procedure called **Valsalva's maneuver**, in which you increase intra-abdominal pressure by contracting your diaphragm and abdominal wall muscles, and closing your glottis.

The process of defecation begins when mass movements force feces from the colon into the rectum, stretching the rectal wall and provoking the defecation reflex, which eliminates feces from the rectum. This parasympathetic reflex is mediated by the spinal cord. It contracts the sigmoid colon and rectum, relaxes the internal anal sphincter, and initially contracts the external anal sphincter. The presence of feces in the anal canal sends a signal to the brain, which gives you the choice of voluntarily opening the external anal sphincter (defecating) or keeping it temporarily closed. If you decide to delay defecation, it takes a few seconds for the reflex contractions to stop and the rectal walls to relax. The next mass movement will trigger additional defecation reflexes until you defecate.

If defecation is delayed for an extended time, additional water is absorbed, making the feces firmer and potentially leading to constipation. On the other hand, if the waste matter moves too quickly through the intestines, not enough water is absorbed, and diarrhea can result. This can be caused by the ingestion of foodborne pathogens. In general, diet, health, and stress determine the frequency of bowel movements. The number of bowel movements varies greatly between individuals, ranging from two or three per day to three or four per week.

⌾ INTERACTIVE LINK

By watching this animation (http://openstax.org/l/foodgroups) you will see that for the various food groups—proteins, fats, and carbohydrates—digestion begins in different parts of the digestion system, though all end in the same place. Of the three major food classes (carbohydrates, fats, and proteins), which is digested in the mouth, the stomach, and the small intestine?

23.6 Accessory Organs in Digestion: The Liver, Pancreas, and Gallbladder

LEARNING OBJECTIVES

By the end of this section, you will be able to:

- State the main digestive roles of the liver, pancreas, and gallbladder
- Identify three main features of liver histology that are critical to its function
- Discuss the composition and function of bile
- Identify the major types of enzymes and buffers present in pancreatic juice

Chemical digestion in the small intestine relies on the activities of three accessory digestive organs: the liver, pancreas, and gallbladder (Figure 23.24). The digestive role of the liver is to produce bile and export it to the duodenum. The gallbladder primarily stores, concentrates, and releases bile. The pancreas produces pancreatic juice, which contains digestive enzymes and bicarbonate ions, and delivers it to the duodenum.

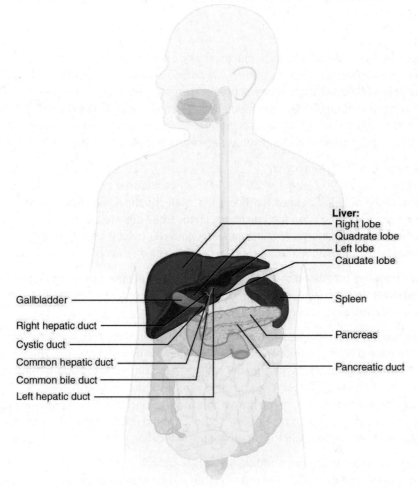

FIGURE 23.24   **Accessory Organs**   The liver, pancreas, and gallbladder are considered accessory digestive organs, but their roles in the digestive system are vital.

The Liver

The **liver** is the largest gland in the body, weighing about three pounds in an adult. It is also one of the most important organs. In addition to being an accessory digestive organ, it plays a number of roles in metabolism and regulation. The liver lies inferior to the diaphragm in the right upper quadrant of the abdominal cavity and receives protection from the surrounding ribs.

The liver is divided into two primary lobes: a large right lobe and a much smaller left lobe. In the right lobe, some anatomists also identify an inferior quadrate lobe and a posterior caudate lobe, which are defined by internal features. The liver is connected to the abdominal wall and diaphragm by five peritoneal folds referred to as ligaments. These are the falciform ligament, the coronary ligament, two lateral ligaments, and the ligamentum teres hepatis. The falciform ligament and ligamentum teres hepatis are actually remnants of the umbilical vein, and separate the right and left lobes anteriorly. The lesser omentum tethers the liver to the lesser curvature of the stomach.

The **porta hepatis** ("gate to the liver") is where the **hepatic artery** and **hepatic portal vein** enter the liver. These two vessels, along with the common hepatic duct, run behind the lateral border of the lesser omentum on the way to their destinations. As shown in Figure 23.25, the hepatic artery delivers oxygenated blood from the heart to the liver. The hepatic portal vein delivers partially deoxygenated blood containing nutrients absorbed from the small intestine and actually supplies more oxygen to the liver than do the much smaller hepatic arteries. In addition to nutrients, drugs and toxins are also absorbed. After processing the bloodborne nutrients and toxins, the liver releases nutrients needed by other cells back into the blood, which drains into the central vein and then through the hepatic vein to the inferior vena cava. With this hepatic portal circulation, all blood from the alimentary canal passes through the liver. This largely explains why the liver is the most common site for the metastasis of cancers that originate in the alimentary canal.

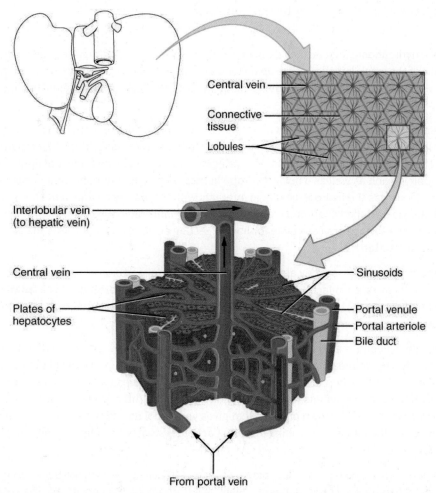

FIGURE 23.25 Microscopic Anatomy of the Liver The liver receives oxygenated blood from the hepatic artery and nutrient-rich deoxygenated blood from the hepatic portal vein.

Histology

The liver has three main components: hepatocytes, bile canaliculi, and hepatic sinusoids. A **hepatocyte** is the liver's main cell type, accounting for around 80 percent of the liver's volume. These cells play a role in a wide variety of secretory, metabolic, and endocrine functions. Plates of hepatocytes called hepatic laminae radiate outward from the portal vein in each **hepatic lobule**.

Between adjacent hepatocytes, grooves in the cell membranes provide room for each **bile canaliculus** (plural = canaliculi). These small ducts accumulate the bile produced by hepatocytes. From here, bile flows first into bile ductules and then into bile ducts. The bile ducts unite to form the larger right and left hepatic ducts, which themselves merge and exit the liver as the **common hepatic duct**. This duct then joins with the cystic duct from the gallbladder, forming the **common bile duct** through which bile flows into the small intestine.

A **hepatic sinusoid** is an open, porous blood space formed by fenestrated capillaries from nutrient-rich hepatic portal veins and oxygen-rich hepatic arteries. Hepatocytes are tightly packed around the fenestrated endothelium of these spaces, giving them easy access to the blood. From their central position, hepatocytes process the nutrients, toxins, and waste materials carried by the blood. Materials such as bilirubin are processed and excreted into the bile canaliculi. Other materials including proteins, lipids, and carbohydrates are processed and secreted into the sinusoids or just stored in the cells until called upon. The hepatic sinusoids combine and send blood to a **central vein**. Blood then flows through a **hepatic vein** into the inferior vena cava. This means that blood and bile flow in opposite directions. The hepatic sinusoids also contain star-shaped **reticuloendothelial cells** (Kupffer cells), phagocytes that remove dead red and white blood cells, bacteria, and other foreign material that enter the sinusoids. The **portal triad** is a distinctive arrangement around the perimeter of hepatic lobules, consisting of three basic structures: a bile duct, a hepatic artery branch, and a hepatic portal vein branch.

Bile

Recall that lipids are hydrophobic, that is, they do not dissolve in water. Thus, before they can be digested in the watery environment of the small intestine, large lipid globules must be broken down into smaller lipid globules, a process called emulsification. **Bile** is a mixture secreted by the liver to accomplish the emulsification of lipids in the small intestine.

Hepatocytes secrete about one liter of bile each day. A yellow-brown or yellow-green alkaline solution (pH 7.6 to 8.6), bile is a mixture of water, bile salts, bile pigments, phospholipids (such as lecithin), electrolytes, cholesterol, and triglycerides. The components most critical to emulsification are bile salts and phospholipids, which have a nonpolar (hydrophobic) region as well as a polar (hydrophilic) region. The hydrophobic region interacts with the large lipid molecules, whereas the hydrophilic region interacts with the watery chyme in the intestine. This results in the large lipid globules being pulled apart into many tiny lipid fragments of about 1 μm in diameter. This change dramatically increases the surface area available for lipid-digesting enzyme activity. This is the same way dish soap works on fats mixed with water.

Bile salts act as emulsifying agents, so they are also important for the absorption of digested lipids. While most constituents of bile are eliminated in feces, bile salts are reclaimed by the **enterohepatic circulation**. Once bile salts reach the ileum, they are absorbed and returned to the liver in the hepatic portal blood. The hepatocytes then excrete the bile salts into newly formed bile. Thus, this precious resource is recycled.

Bilirubin, the main bile pigment, is a waste product produced when the spleen removes old or damaged red blood cells from the circulation. These breakdown products, including proteins, iron, and toxic bilirubin, are transported to the liver via the splenic vein of the hepatic portal system. In the liver, proteins and iron are recycled, whereas bilirubin is excreted in the bile. It accounts for the green color of bile. Bilirubin is eventually transformed by intestinal bacteria into stercobilin, a brown pigment that gives your stool its characteristic color! In some disease states, bile does not enter the intestine, resulting in white ('acholic') stool with a high fat content, since virtually no fats are broken down or absorbed.

Hepatocytes work non-stop, but bile production increases when fatty chyme enters the duodenum and stimulates the secretion of the gut hormone secretin. Between meals, bile is produced but conserved. The valve-like hepatopancreatic ampulla closes, allowing bile to divert to the gallbladder, where it is concentrated and stored until the next meal.

⊘ INTERACTIVE LINK

Watch this video (http://openstax.org/l/liver) to see the structure of the liver and how this structure supports the functions of the liver, including the processing of nutrients, toxins, and wastes. At rest, about 1500 mL of blood per minute flow through the liver. What percentage of this blood flow comes from the hepatic portal system?

The Pancreas

The soft, oblong, glandular **pancreas** lies transversely in the retroperitoneum behind the stomach. Its head is nestled into the "c-shaped" curvature of the duodenum with the body extending to the left about 15.2 cm (6 in) and ending as a tapering tail in the hilum of the spleen. It is a curious mix of exocrine (secreting digestive enzymes) and endocrine (releasing hormones into the blood) functions (Figure 23.26).

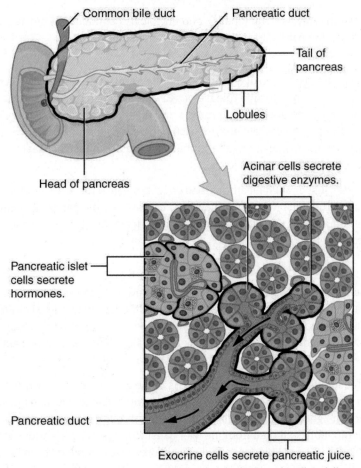

FIGURE 23.26 Exocrine and Endocrine Pancreas The pancreas has a head, a body, and a tail. It delivers pancreatic juice to the duodenum through the pancreatic duct.

The exocrine part of the pancreas arises as little grape-like cell clusters, each called an **acinus** (plural = acini), located at the terminal ends of pancreatic ducts. These acinar cells secrete enzyme-rich **pancreatic juice** into tiny merging ducts that form two dominant ducts. The larger duct fuses with the common bile duct (carrying bile from the liver and gallbladder) just before entering the duodenum via a common opening (the hepatopancreatic ampulla). The smooth muscle sphincter of the hepatopancreatic ampulla controls the release of pancreatic juice and bile into the small intestine. The second and smaller pancreatic duct, the **accessory duct** (duct of Santorini), runs from the pancreas directly into the duodenum, approximately 1 inch above the hepatopancreatic ampulla. When present, it is a persistent remnant of pancreatic development.

Scattered through the sea of exocrine acini are small islands of endocrine cells, the islets of Langerhans. These vital cells produce the hormones pancreatic polypeptide, insulin, glucagon, and somatostatin.

Pancreatic Juice

The pancreas produces over a liter of pancreatic juice each day. Unlike bile, it is clear and composed mostly of water along with some salts, sodium bicarbonate, and several digestive enzymes. Sodium bicarbonate is responsible for the slight alkalinity of pancreatic juice (pH 7.1 to 8.2), which serves to buffer the acidic gastric juice in chyme, inactivate pepsin from the stomach, and create an optimal environment for the activity of pH-sensitive digestive enzymes in the small intestine. Pancreatic enzymes are active in the digestion of sugars, proteins, and fats.

The pancreas produces protein-digesting enzymes in their inactive forms. These enzymes are activated in the duodenum. If produced in an active form, they would digest the pancreas (which is exactly what occurs in the disease, pancreatitis). The intestinal brush border enzyme **enteropeptidase** stimulates the activation of trypsin from trypsinogen of the pancreas, which in turn changes the pancreatic enzymes procarboxypeptidase and chymotrypsinogen into their active forms, carboxypeptidase and chymotrypsin.

The enzymes that digest starch (amylase), fat (lipase), and nucleic acids (nuclease) are secreted in their active forms, since they do not attack the pancreas as do the protein-digesting enzymes.

Pancreatic Secretion

Regulation of pancreatic secretion is the job of hormones and the parasympathetic nervous system. The entry of acidic chyme into the duodenum stimulates the release of secretin, which in turn causes the duct cells to release bicarbonate-rich pancreatic juice. The presence of proteins and fats in the duodenum stimulates the secretion of CCK, which then stimulates the acini to secrete enzyme-rich pancreatic juice and enhances the activity of secretin. Parasympathetic regulation occurs mainly during the cephalic and gastric phases of gastric secretion, when vagal stimulation prompts the secretion of pancreatic juice.

Usually, the pancreas secretes just enough bicarbonate to counterbalance the amount of HCl produced in the stomach. Hydrogen ions enter the blood when bicarbonate is secreted by the pancreas. Thus, the acidic blood draining from the pancreas neutralizes the alkaline blood draining from the stomach, maintaining the pH of the venous blood that flows to the liver.

The Gallbladder

The **gallbladder** is 8–10 cm (~3–4 in) long and is nested in a shallow area on the posterior aspect of the right lobe of the liver. This muscular sac stores, concentrates, and, when stimulated, propels the bile into the duodenum via the common bile duct. It is divided into three regions. The fundus is the widest portion and tapers medially into the body, which in turn narrows to become the neck. The neck angles slightly superiorly as it approaches the hepatic duct. The cystic duct is 1–2 cm (less than 1 in) long and turns inferiorly as it bridges the neck and hepatic duct.

The simple columnar epithelium of the gallbladder mucosa is organized in rugae, similar to those of the stomach. There is no submucosa in the gallbladder wall. The wall's middle, muscular coat is made of smooth muscle fibers. When these fibers contract, the gallbladder's contents are ejected through the **cystic duct** and into the bile duct (Figure 23.27). Visceral peritoneum reflected from the liver capsule holds the gallbladder against the liver and forms the outer coat of the gallbladder. The gallbladder's mucosa absorbs water and ions from bile, concentrating it by up to 10-fold.

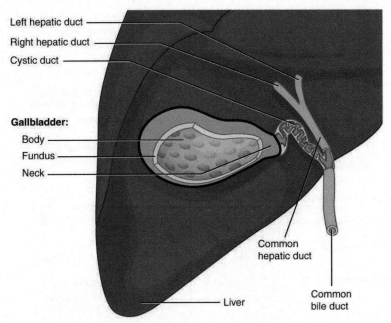

FIGURE 23.27   Gallbladder   The gallbladder stores and concentrates bile, and releases it into the two-way cystic duct when it is needed by the small intestine.

23.7 Chemical Digestion and Absorption: A Closer Look

LEARNING OBJECTIVES

By the end of this section, you will be able to:

- Identify the locations and primary secretions involved in the chemical digestion of carbohydrates, proteins, lipids, and nucleic acids
- Compare and contrast absorption of the hydrophilic and hydrophobic nutrients

As you have learned, the process of mechanical digestion is relatively simple. It involves the physical breakdown of food but does not alter its chemical makeup. Chemical digestion, on the other hand, is a complex process that reduces food into its chemical building blocks, which are then absorbed to nourish the cells of the body (Figure 23.28). In this section, you will look more closely at the processes of chemical digestion and absorption.

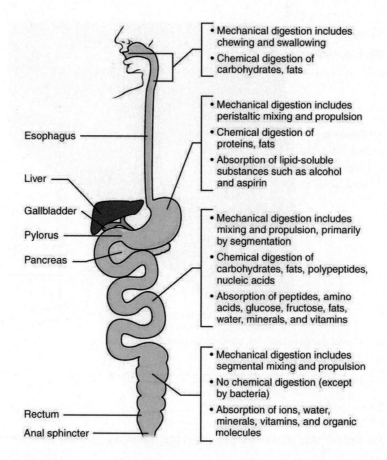

Mechanical digestion includes chewing and swallowing
Chemical digestion of carbohydrates, fats

Mechanical digestion includes peristaltic mixing and propulsion
Chemical digestion of proteins, fats
Absorption of lipid-soluble substances such as alcohol and aspirin

Mechanical digestion includes mixing and propulsion, primarily by segmentation
Chemical digestion of carbohydrates, fats, polypeptides, nucleic acids
Absorption of peptides, amino acids, glucose, fructose, fats, water, minerals, and vitamins

Mechanical digestion includes segmental mixing and propulsion
No chemical digestion (except by bacteria)
Absorption of ions, water, minerals, vitamins, and organic molecules

Esophagus
Liver
Gallbladder
Pylorus
Pancreas
Rectum
Anal sphincter

FIGURE 23.28   Digestion and Absorption   Digestion begins in the mouth and continues as food travels through the small intestine. Most absorption occurs in the small intestine.

Chemical Digestion

Large food molecules (for example, proteins, lipids, nucleic acids, and starches) must be broken down into subunits that are small enough to be absorbed by the lining of the alimentary canal. This is accomplished by enzymes through hydrolysis. The many enzymes involved in chemical digestion are summarized in Table 23.8.

The Digestive Enzymes

Enzyme Category	Enzyme Name	Source	Substrate	Product
Salivary Enzymes	Lingual lipase	Lingual glands	Triglycerides	Free fatty acids, and mono- and diglycerides
Salivary Enzymes	Salivary amylase	Salivary glands	Polysaccharides	Disaccharides and trisaccharides
Gastric enzymes	Gastric lipase	Chief cells	Triglycerides	Fatty acids and monoacylglycerides
Gastric enzymes	Pepsin*	Chief cells	Proteins	Peptides

TABLE 23.8 *These enzymes have been activated by other substances.

Enzyme Category	Enzyme Name	Source	Substrate	Product
Brush border enzymes	α-Dextrinase	Small intestine	α-Dextrins	Glucose
Brush border enzymes	Enteropeptidase	Small intestine	Trypsinogen	Trypsin
Brush border enzymes	Lactase	Small intestine	Lactose	Glucose and galactose
Brush border enzymes	Maltase	Small intestine	Maltose	Glucose
Brush border enzymes	Nucleosidases and phosphatases	Small intestine	Nucleotides	Phosphates, nitrogenous bases, and pentoses
Brush border enzymes	Peptidases	Small intestine	• Aminopeptidase: amino acids at the amino end of peptides • Dipeptidase: dipeptides	• Aminopeptidase: amino acids and peptides • Dipeptidase: amino acids
Brush border enzymes	Sucrase	Small intestine	Sucrose	Glucose and fructose
Pancreatic enzymes	Carboxy-peptidase*	Pancreatic acinar cells	Amino acids at the carboxyl end of peptides	Amino acids and peptides
Pancreatic enzymes	Chymotrypsin*	Pancreatic acinar cells	Proteins	Peptides
Pancreatic enzymes	Elastase*	Pancreatic acinar cells	Proteins	Peptides
Pancreatic enzymes	Nucleases	Pancreatic acinar cells	• Ribonuclease: ribonucleic acids • Deoxyribonuclease: deoxyribonucleic acids	Nucleotides

TABLE 23.8 *These enzymes have been activated by other substances.

Enzyme Category	Enzyme Name	Source	Substrate	Product
Pancreatic enzymes	Pancreatic amylase	Pancreatic acinar cells	Polysaccharides (starches)	α-Dextrins, disaccharides (maltose), trisaccharides (maltotriose)
Pancreatic enzymes	Pancreatic lipase	Pancreatic acinar cells	Triglycerides that have been emulsified by bile salts	Fatty acids and monoacylglycerides
Pancreatic enzymes	Trypsin*	Pancreatic acinar cells	Proteins	Peptides

TABLE 23.8 *These enzymes have been activated by other substances.

Carbohydrate Digestion

The average American diet is about 50 percent carbohydrates, which may be classified according to the number of monomers they contain of simple sugars (monosaccharides and disaccharides) and/or complex sugars (polysaccharides). Glucose, galactose, and fructose are the three monosaccharides that are commonly consumed and are readily absorbed. Your digestive system is also able to break down the disaccharide sucrose (regular table sugar: glucose + fructose), lactose (milk sugar: glucose + galactose), and maltose (grain sugar: glucose + glucose), and the polysaccharides glycogen and starch (chains of monosaccharides). Your bodies do not produce enzymes that can break down most fibrous polysaccharides, such as cellulose. While indigestible polysaccharides do not provide any nutritional value, they do provide dietary fiber, which helps propel food through the alimentary canal.

The chemical digestion of starches begins in the mouth and has been reviewed above.

In the small intestine, **pancreatic amylase** does the 'heavy lifting' for starch and carbohydrate digestion (Figure 23.29). After amylases break down starch into smaller fragments, the brush border enzyme **α-dextrinase** starts working on **α-dextrin**, breaking off one glucose unit at a time. Three brush border enzymes hydrolyze sucrose, lactose, and maltose into monosaccharides. **Sucrase** splits sucrose into one molecule of fructose and one molecule of glucose; **maltase** breaks down maltose and maltotriose into two and three glucose molecules, respectively; and **lactase** breaks down lactose into one molecule of glucose and one molecule of galactose. Insufficient lactase can lead to lactose intolerance.

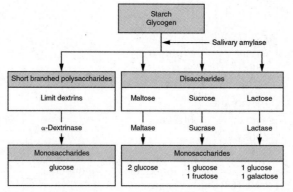

FIGURE 23.29   **Carbohydrate Digestion Flow Chart**   Carbohydrates are broken down into their monomers in a series of steps.

Protein Digestion

Proteins are polymers composed of amino acids linked by peptide bonds to form long chains. Digestion reduces them to their constituent amino acids. You usually consume about 15 to 20 percent of your total calorie intake as protein.

Access for free at openstax.org

The digestion of protein starts in the stomach, where HCl and pepsin break proteins into smaller polypeptides, which then travel to the small intestine (Figure 23.30). Chemical digestion in the small intestine is continued by pancreatic enzymes, including chymotrypsin and trypsin, each of which act on specific bonds in amino acid sequences. At the same time, the cells of the brush border secrete enzymes such as **aminopeptidase** and **dipeptidase**, which further break down peptide chains. This results in molecules small enough to enter the bloodstream (Figure 23.31).

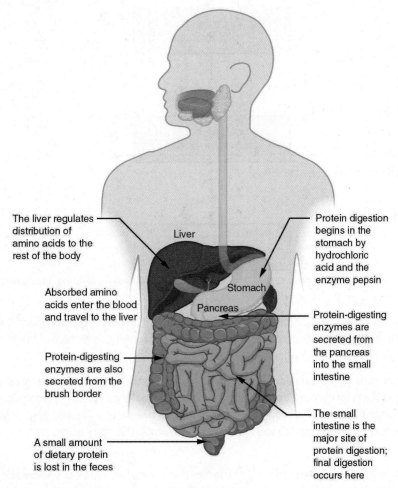

The liver regulates distribution of amino acids to the rest of the body

Liver

Absorbed amino acids enter the blood and travel to the liver

Pancreas

Stomach

Protein digestion begins in the stomach by hydrochloric acid and the enzyme pepsin

Protein-digesting enzymes are secreted from the pancreas into the small intestine

Protein-digesting enzymes are also secreted from the brush border

A small amount of dietary protein is lost in the feces

The small intestine is the major site of protein digestion; final digestion occurs here

FIGURE 23.30   Digestion of Protein   The digestion of protein begins in the stomach and is completed in the small intestine.

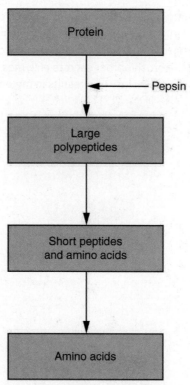

FIGURE 23.31 Digestion of Protein Flow Chart   Proteins are successively broken down into their amino acid components.

Lipid Digestion

A healthy diet limits lipid intake to 35 percent of total calorie intake. The most common dietary lipids are triglycerides, which are made up of a glycerol molecule bound to three fatty acid chains. Small amounts of dietary cholesterol and phospholipids are also consumed.

The three lipases responsible for lipid digestion are lingual lipase, gastric lipase, and **pancreatic lipase**. However, because the pancreas is the only consequential source of lipase, virtually all lipid digestion occurs in the small intestine. Pancreatic lipase breaks down each triglyceride into two free fatty acids and a monoglyceride. The fatty acids include both short-chain (less than 10 to 12 carbons) and long-chain fatty acids.

Nucleic Acid Digestion

The nucleic acids DNA and RNA are found in most of the foods you eat. Two types of **pancreatic nuclease** are responsible for their digestion: **deoxyribonuclease**, which digests DNA, and **ribonuclease**, which digests RNA. The nucleotides produced by this digestion are further broken down by two intestinal brush border enzymes (**nucleosidase** and **phosphatase**) into pentoses, phosphates, and nitrogenous bases, which can be absorbed through the alimentary canal wall. The large food molecules that must be broken down into subunits are summarized Table 23.9

Absorbable Food Substances

Source	Substance
Carbohydrates	Monosaccharides: glucose, galactose, and fructose
Proteins	Single amino acids, dipeptides, and tripeptides

TABLE 23.9

Access for free at openstax.org

Source	Substance
Triglycerides	Monoacylglycerides, glycerol, and free fatty acids
Nucleic acids	Pentose sugars, phosphates, and nitrogenous bases

TABLE 23.9

Absorption

The mechanical and digestive processes have one goal: to convert food into molecules small enough to be absorbed by the epithelial cells of the intestinal villi. The absorptive capacity of the alimentary canal is almost endless. Each day, the alimentary canal processes up to 10 liters of food, liquids, and GI secretions, yet less than one liter enters the large intestine. Almost all ingested food, 80 percent of electrolytes, and 90 percent of water are absorbed in the small intestine. Although the entire small intestine is involved in the absorption of water and lipids, most absorption of carbohydrates and proteins occurs in the jejunum. Notably, bile salts and vitamin B_{12} are absorbed in the terminal ileum. By the time chyme passes from the ileum into the large intestine, it is essentially indigestible food residue (mainly plant fibers like cellulose), some water, and millions of bacteria (Figure 23.32).

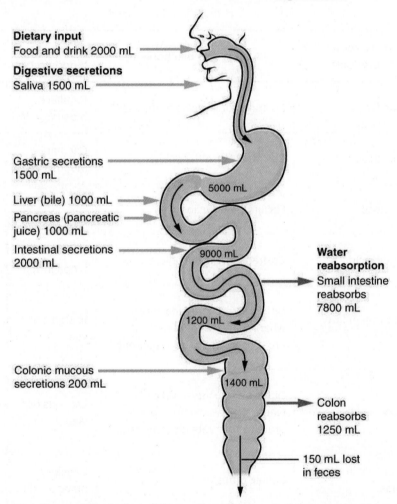

Dietary input
Food and drink 2000 mL

Digestive secretions
Saliva 1500 mL

Gastric secretions
1500 mL

5000 mL

Liver (bile) 1000 mL

Pancreas (pancreatic
juice) 1000 mL

Intestinal secretions
2000 mL

9000 mL

Water
reabsorption
Small intestine
reabsorbs
7800 mL

1200 mL

Colonic mucous
secretions 200 mL

1400 mL

Colon
reabsorbs
1250 mL

150 mL lost
in feces

FIGURE 23.32 Digestive Secretions and Absorption of Water   Absorption is a complex process, in which nutrients from digested food are harvested.

Absorption can occur through five mechanisms: (1) active transport, (2) passive diffusion, (3) facilitated diffusion, (4) co-transport (or secondary active transport), and (5) endocytosis. As you will recall from Chapter 3, active transport refers to the movement of a substance across a cell membrane going from an area of lower concentration to an area of higher concentration (up the concentration gradient). In this type of transport, proteins within the cell membrane act as "pumps," using cellular energy (ATP) to move the substance. Passive diffusion refers to the movement of substances from an area of higher concentration to an area of lower concentration, while facilitated diffusion refers to the movement of substances from an area of higher to an area of lower concentration using a carrier protein in the cell membrane. Co-transport uses the movement of one molecule through the membrane from higher to lower concentration to power the movement of another from lower to higher. Finally, endocytosis is a transportation process in which the cell membrane engulfs material. It requires energy, generally in the form of ATP.

Because the cell's plasma membrane is made up of hydrophobic phospholipids, water-soluble nutrients must use transport molecules embedded in the membrane to enter cells. Moreover, substances cannot pass between the epithelial cells of the intestinal mucosa because these cells are bound together by tight junctions. Thus, substances can only enter blood capillaries by passing through the apical surfaces of epithelial cells and into the interstitial fluid. Water-soluble nutrients enter the capillary blood in the villi and travel to the liver via the hepatic portal vein.

In contrast to the water-soluble nutrients, lipid-soluble nutrients can diffuse through the plasma membrane. Once inside the cell, they are packaged for transport via the base of the cell and then enter the lacteals of the villi to be transported by lymphatic vessels to the systemic circulation via the thoracic duct. The absorption of most nutrients through the mucosa of the intestinal villi requires active transport fueled by ATP. The routes of absorption for each food category are summarized in Table 23.10.

Absorption in the Alimentary Canal

Food	Breakdown products	Absorption mechanism	Entry to bloodstream	Destination
Carbohydrates	Glucose	Co-transport with sodium ions	Capillary blood in villi	Liver via hepatic portal vein
Carbohydrates	Galactose	Co-transport with sodium ions	Capillary blood in villi	Liver via hepatic portal vein
Carbohydrates	Fructose	Facilitated diffusion	Capillary blood in villi	Liver via hepatic portal vein
Protein	Amino acids	Co-transport with sodium ions	Capillary blood in villi	Liver via hepatic portal vein
Lipids	Long-chain fatty acids	Diffusion into intestinal cells, where they are combined with proteins to create chylomicrons	Lacteals of villi	Systemic circulation via lymph entering thoracic duct
Lipids	Monoacylglycerides	Diffusion into intestinal cells, where they are combined with proteins to create chylomicrons	Lacteals of villi	Systemic circulation via lymph entering thoracic duct
Lipids	Short-chain fatty acids	Simple diffusion	Capillary blood in villi	Liver via hepatic portal vein

TABLE 23.10

Food	Breakdown products	Absorption mechanism	Entry to bloodstream	Destination
Lipids	Glycerol	Simple diffusion	Capillary blood in villi	Liver via hepatic portal vein
Nucleic Acids	Nucleic acid digestion products	Active transport via membrane carriers	Capillary blood in villi	Liver via hepatic portal vein

TABLE 23.10

Carbohydrate Absorption

All carbohydrates are absorbed in the form of monosaccharides. The small intestine is highly efficient at this, absorbing monosaccharides at an estimated rate of 120 grams per hour. All normally digested dietary carbohydrates are absorbed; indigestible fibers are eliminated in the feces. The monosaccharides glucose and galactose are transported into the epithelial cells by common protein carriers via secondary active transport (that is, co-transport with sodium ions). The monosaccharides leave these cells via facilitated diffusion and enter the capillaries through intercellular clefts. The monosaccharide fructose (which is in fruit) is absorbed and transported by facilitated diffusion alone. The monosaccharides combine with the transport proteins immediately after the disaccharides are broken down.

Protein Absorption

Active transport mechanisms, primarily in the duodenum and jejunum, absorb most proteins as their breakdown products, amino acids. Almost all (95 to 98 percent) protein is digested and absorbed in the small intestine. The type of carrier that transports an amino acid varies. Most carriers are linked to the active transport of sodium. Short chains of two amino acids (dipeptides) or three amino acids (tripeptides) are also transported actively. However, after they enter the absorptive epithelial cells, they are broken down into their amino acids before leaving the cell and entering the capillary blood via diffusion.

Lipid Absorption

About 95 percent of lipids are absorbed in the small intestine. Bile salts not only speed up lipid digestion, they are also essential to the absorption of the end products of lipid digestion. Short-chain fatty acids are relatively water soluble and can enter the absorptive cells (enterocytes) directly. The small size of short-chain fatty acids enables them to be absorbed by enterocytes via simple diffusion, and then take the same path as monosaccharides and amino acids into the blood capillary of a villus.

The large and hydrophobic long-chain fatty acids and monoacylglycerides are not so easily suspended in the watery intestinal chyme. However, bile salts and lecithin resolve this issue by enclosing them in a **micelle**, which is a tiny sphere with polar (hydrophilic) ends facing the watery environment and hydrophobic tails turned to the interior, creating a receptive environment for the long-chain fatty acids. The core also includes cholesterol and fat-soluble vitamins. Without micelles, lipids would sit on the surface of chyme and never come in contact with the absorptive surfaces of the epithelial cells. Micelles can easily squeeze between microvilli and get very near the luminal cell surface. At this point, lipid substances exit the micelle and are absorbed via simple diffusion.

The free fatty acids and monoacylglycerides that enter the epithelial cells are reincorporated into triglycerides. The triglycerides are mixed with phospholipids and cholesterol, and surrounded with a protein coat. This new complex, called a **chylomicron**, is a water-soluble lipoprotein. After being processed by the Golgi apparatus, chylomicrons are released from the cell (Figure 23.33). Too big to pass through the basement membranes of blood capillaries, chylomicrons instead enter the large pores of lacteals. The lacteals come together to form the lymphatic vessels. The chylomicrons are transported in the lymphatic vessels and empty through the thoracic duct into the subclavian vein of the circulatory system. Once in the bloodstream, the enzyme **lipoprotein lipase** breaks down the triglycerides of the chylomicrons into free fatty acids and glycerol. These breakdown products then pass through capillary walls to be used for energy by cells or stored in adipose tissue as fat. Liver cells combine the remaining chylomicron remnants with proteins, forming lipoproteins that transport cholesterol in the blood.

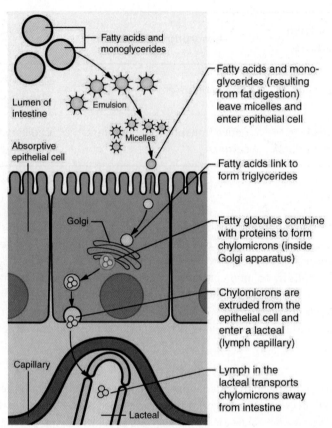

Lumen of intestine

Emulsion

Absorptive epithelial cell

Micelles

Fatty acids and monoglycerides

Fatty acids and mono-glycerides (resulting from fat digestion) leave micelles and enter epithelial cell

Fatty acids link to form triglycerides

Golgi

Fatty globules combine with proteins to form chylomicrons (inside Golgi apparatus)

Chylomicrons are extruded from the epithelial cell and enter a lacteal (lymph capillary)

Capillary

Lymph in the lacteal transports chylomicrons away from intestine

Lacteal

FIGURE 23.33   Lipid Absorption   Unlike amino acids and simple sugars, lipids are transformed as they are absorbed through epithelial cells.

Nucleic Acid Absorption

The products of nucleic acid digestion—pentose sugars, nitrogenous bases, and phosphate ions—are transported by carriers across the villus epithelium via active transport. These products then enter the bloodstream.

Mineral Absorption

The electrolytes absorbed by the small intestine are from both GI secretions and ingested foods. Since electrolytes dissociate into ions in water, most are absorbed via active transport throughout the entire small intestine. During absorption, co-transport mechanisms result in the accumulation of sodium ions inside the cells, whereas anti-port mechanisms reduce the potassium ion concentration inside the cells. To restore the sodium-potassium gradient across the cell membrane, a sodium-potassium pump requiring ATP pumps sodium out and potassium in.

In general, all minerals that enter the intestine are absorbed, whether you need them or not. Iron and calcium are exceptions; they are absorbed in the duodenum in amounts that meet the body's current requirements, as follows:

Iron—The ionic iron needed for the production of hemoglobin is absorbed into mucosal cells via active transport. Once inside mucosal cells, ionic iron binds to the protein ferritin, creating iron-ferritin complexes that store iron until needed. When the body has enough iron, most of the stored iron is lost when worn-out epithelial cells slough off. When the body needs iron because, for example, it is lost during acute or chronic bleeding, there is increased uptake of iron from the intestine and accelerated release of iron into the bloodstream. Since females experience significant iron loss during menstruation, they have around four times as many iron transport proteins in their intestinal epithelial cells as do males.

Calcium—Blood levels of ionic calcium determine the absorption of dietary calcium. When blood levels of ionic calcium drop, parathyroid hormone (PTH) secreted by the parathyroid glands stimulates the release of calcium ions from bone matrices and increases the reabsorption of calcium by the kidneys. PTH also upregulates the activation of vitamin D in the kidney, which then facilitates intestinal calcium ion absorption.

Vitamin Absorption

The small intestine absorbs the vitamins that occur naturally in food and supplements. Fat-soluble vitamins (A, D, E, and K) are absorbed along with dietary lipids in micelles via simple diffusion. This is why you are advised to eat some fatty foods when you take fat-soluble vitamin supplements. Most water-soluble vitamins (including most B vitamins and vitamin C) also are absorbed by simple diffusion. An exception is vitamin B_{12}, which is a very large molecule. Intrinsic factor secreted in the stomach binds to vitamin B_{12}, preventing its digestion and creating a complex that binds to mucosal receptors in the terminal ileum, where it is taken up by endocytosis.

Water Absorption

Each day, about nine liters of fluid enter the small intestine. About 2.3 liters are ingested in foods and beverages, and the rest is from GI secretions. About 90 percent of this water is absorbed in the small intestine. Water absorption is driven by the concentration gradient of the water: The concentration of water is higher in chyme than it is in epithelial cells. Thus, water moves down its concentration gradient from the chyme into cells. As noted earlier, much of the remaining water is then absorbed in the colon.

Key Terms

absorption   passage of digested products from the intestinal lumen through mucosal cells and into the bloodstream or lacteals

accessory digestive organ   includes teeth, tongue, salivary glands, gallbladder, liver, and pancreas

accessory duct   (also, duct of Santorini) duct that runs from the pancreas into the duodenum

acinus   cluster of glandular epithelial cells in the pancreas that secretes pancreatic juice in the pancreas

alimentary canal   continuous muscular digestive tube that extends from the mouth to the anus

aminopeptidase   brush border enzyme that acts on proteins

anal canal   final segment of the large intestine

anal column   long fold of mucosa in the anal canal

anal sinus   recess between anal columns

appendix   (vermiform appendix) coiled tube attached to the cecum

ascending colon   first region of the colon

bacterial flora   bacteria in the large intestine

bile   alkaline solution produced by the liver and important for the emulsification of lipids

bile canaliculus   small duct between hepatocytes that collects bile

bilirubin   main bile pigment, which is responsible for the brown color of feces

body   mid-portion of the stomach

bolus   mass of chewed food

brush border   fuzzy appearance of the small intestinal mucosa created by microvilli

cardia   (also, cardiac region) part of the stomach surrounding the cardiac orifice (esophageal hiatus)

cecum   pouch forming the beginning of the large intestine

cementum   bone-like tissue covering the root of a tooth

central vein   vein that receives blood from hepatic sinusoids

cephalic phase   (also, reflex phase) initial phase of gastric secretion that occurs before food enters the stomach

chemical digestion   enzymatic breakdown of food

chief cell   gastric gland cell that secretes pepsinogen

chylomicron   large lipid-transport compound made up of triglycerides, phospholipids, cholesterol, and proteins

chyme   soupy liquid created when food is mixed with digestive juices

circular fold   (also, plica circulare) deep fold in the mucosa and submucosa of the small intestine

colon   part of the large intestine between the cecum and the rectum

common bile duct   structure formed by the union of the common hepatic duct and the gallbladder's cystic duct

common hepatic duct   duct formed by the merger of the two hepatic ducts

crown   portion of tooth visible superior to the gum line

cuspid   (also, canine) pointed tooth used for tearing and shredding food

cystic duct   duct through which bile drains and enters the gallbladder

deciduous tooth   one of 20 "baby teeth"

defecation   elimination of undigested substances from the body in the form of feces

deglutition   three-stage process of swallowing

dens   tooth

dentin   bone-like tissue immediately deep to the enamel of the crown or cementum of the root of a tooth

dentition   set of teeth

deoxyribonuclease   pancreatic enzyme that digests DNA

descending colon   part of the colon between the transverse colon and the sigmoid colon

dipeptidase   brush border enzyme that acts on proteins

duodenal gland   (also, Brunner's gland) mucous-secreting gland in the duodenal submucosa

duodenum   first part of the small intestine, which starts at the pyloric sphincter and ends at the jejunum

enamel   covering of the dentin of the crown of a tooth

enteroendocrine cell   gastric gland cell that releases hormones

enterohepatic circulation   recycling mechanism that conserves bile salts

enteropeptidase   intestinal brush-border enzyme that activates trypsinogen to trypsin

epiploic appendage   small sac of fat-filled visceral peritoneum attached to teniae coli

esophagus   muscular tube that runs from the pharynx to the stomach

external anal sphincter   voluntary skeletal muscle sphincter in the anal canal

fauces   opening between the oral cavity and the oropharynx

feces   semisolid waste product of digestion

flatus   gas in the intestine

fundus   dome-shaped region of the stomach above and to the left of the cardia

G cell   gastrin-secreting enteroendocrine cell

gallbladder   accessory digestive organ that stores and

concentrates bile

gastric emptying   process by which mixing waves gradually cause the release of chyme into the duodenum

gastric gland   gland in the stomach mucosal epithelium that produces gastric juice

gastric phase   phase of gastric secretion that begins when food enters the stomach

gastric pit   narrow channel formed by the epithelial lining of the stomach mucosa

gastrin   peptide hormone that stimulates secretion of hydrochloric acid and gut motility

gastrocolic reflex   propulsive movement in the colon activated by the presence of food in the stomach

gastroileal reflex   long reflex that increases the strength of segmentation in the ileum

gingiva   gum

haustral contraction   slow segmentation in the large intestine

haustrum   small pouch in the colon created by tonic contractions of teniae coli

hepatic artery   artery that supplies oxygenated blood to the liver

hepatic lobule   hexagonal-shaped structure composed of hepatocytes that radiate outward from a central vein

hepatic portal vein   vein that supplies deoxygenated nutrient-rich blood to the liver

hepatic sinusoid   blood capillaries between rows of hepatocytes that receive blood from the hepatic portal vein and the branches of the hepatic artery

hepatic vein   vein that drains into the inferior vena cava

hepatocytes   major functional cells of the liver

hepatopancreatic ampulla   (also, ampulla of Vater) bulb-like point in the wall of the duodenum where the bile duct and main pancreatic duct unite

hepatopancreatic sphincter   (also, sphincter of Oddi) sphincter regulating the flow of bile and pancreatic juice into the duodenum

hydrochloric acid (HCl)   digestive acid secreted by parietal cells in the stomach

ileocecal sphincter   sphincter located where the small intestine joins with the large intestine

ileum   end of the small intestine between the jejunum and the large intestine

incisor   midline, chisel-shaped tooth used for cutting into food

ingestion   taking food into the GI tract through the mouth

internal anal sphincter   involuntary smooth muscle sphincter in the anal canal

intestinal gland   (also, crypt of Lieberkühn) gland in the small intestinal mucosa that secretes intestinal juice

intestinal juice   mixture of water and mucus that helps absorb nutrients from chyme

intestinal phase   phase of gastric secretion that begins when chyme enters the intestine

intrinsic factor   glycoprotein required for vitamin B_{12} absorption in the small intestine

jejunum   middle part of the small intestine between the duodenum and the ileum

labial frenulum   midline mucous membrane fold that attaches the inner surface of the lips to the gums

labium   lip

lactase   brush border enzyme that breaks down lactose into glucose and galactose

lacteal   lymphatic capillary in the villi

large intestine   terminal portion of the alimentary canal

laryngopharynx   part of the pharynx that functions in respiration and digestion

left colic flexure   (also, splenic flexure) point where the transverse colon curves below the inferior end of the spleen

lingual frenulum   mucous membrane fold that attaches the bottom of the tongue to the floor of the mouth

lingual lipase   digestive enzyme from glands in the tongue that acts on triglycerides

lipoprotein lipase   enzyme that breaks down triglycerides in chylomicrons into fatty acids and monoglycerides

liver   largest gland in the body whose main digestive function is the production of bile

lower esophageal sphincter   smooth muscle sphincter that regulates food movement from the esophagus to the stomach

main pancreatic duct   (also, duct of Wirsung) duct through which pancreatic juice drains from the pancreas

major duodenal papilla   point at which the hepatopancreatic ampulla opens into the duodenum

maltase   brush border enzyme that breaks down maltose and maltotriose into two and three molecules of glucose, respectively

mass movement   long, slow, peristaltic wave in the large intestine

mastication   chewing

mechanical digestion   chewing, mixing, and segmentation that prepares food for chemical digestion

mesoappendix   mesentery of the appendix

micelle   tiny lipid-transport compound composed of bile salts and phospholipids with a fatty acid and monoacylglyceride core

microvillus small projection of the plasma membrane of the absorptive cells of the small intestinal mucosa

migrating motility complex form of peristalsis in the small intestine

mixing wave unique type of peristalsis that occurs in the stomach

molar tooth used for crushing and grinding food

motilin hormone that initiates migrating motility complexes

motility movement of food through the GI tract

mucosa innermost lining of the alimentary canal

mucosal barrier protective barrier that prevents gastric juice from destroying the stomach itself

mucous neck cell gastric gland cell that secretes a uniquely acidic mucus

muscularis muscle (skeletal or smooth) layer of the alimentary canal wall

myenteric plexus (plexus of Auerbach) major nerve supply to alimentary canal wall; controls motility

nucleosidase brush border enzyme that digests nucleotides

oral cavity (also, buccal cavity) mouth

oral vestibule part of the mouth bounded externally by the cheeks and lips, and internally by the gums and teeth

oropharynx part of the pharynx continuous with the oral cavity that functions in respiration and digestion

palatoglossal arch muscular fold that extends from the lateral side of the soft palate to the base of the tongue

palatopharyngeal arch muscular fold that extends from the lateral side of the soft palate to the side of the pharynx

pancreas accessory digestive organ that secretes pancreatic juice

pancreatic amylase enzyme secreted by the pancreas that completes the chemical digestion of carbohydrates in the small intestine

pancreatic juice secretion of the pancreas containing digestive enzymes and bicarbonate

pancreatic lipase enzyme secreted by the pancreas that participates in lipid digestion

pancreatic nuclease enzyme secreted by the pancreas that participates in nucleic acid digestion

parietal cell gastric gland cell that secretes hydrochloric acid and intrinsic factor

parotid gland one of a pair of major salivary glands located inferior and anterior to the ears

pectinate line horizontal line that runs like a ring, perpendicular to the inferior margins of the anal sinuses

pepsinogen inactive form of pepsin

peristalsis muscular contractions and relaxations that propel food through the GI tract

permanent tooth one of 32 adult teeth

pharynx throat

phosphatase brush border enzyme that digests nucleotides

porta hepatis "gateway to the liver" where the hepatic artery and hepatic portal vein enter the liver

portal triad bile duct, hepatic artery branch, and hepatic portal vein branch

premolar (also, bicuspid) transitional tooth used for mastication, crushing, and grinding food

propulsion voluntary process of swallowing and the involuntary process of peristalsis that moves food through the digestive tract

pulp cavity deepest portion of a tooth, containing nerve endings and blood vessels

pyloric antrum wider, more superior part of the pylorus

pyloric canal narrow, more inferior part of the pylorus

pyloric sphincter sphincter that controls stomach emptying

pylorus lower, funnel-shaped part of the stomach that is continuous with the duodenum

rectal valve one of three transverse folds in the rectum where feces is separated from flatus

rectum part of the large intestine between the sigmoid colon and anal canal

reticuloendothelial cell (also, Kupffer cell) phagocyte in hepatic sinusoids that filters out material from venous blood from the alimentary canal

retroperitoneal located posterior to the peritoneum

ribonuclease pancreatic enzyme that digests RNA

right colic flexure (also, hepatic flexure) point, at the inferior surface of the liver, where the ascending colon turns abruptly to the left

root portion of a tooth embedded in the alveolar processes beneath the gum line

ruga fold of alimentary canal mucosa and submucosa in the empty stomach and other organs

saccharolytic fermentation anaerobic decomposition of carbohydrates

saliva aqueous solution of proteins and ions secreted into the mouth by the salivary glands

salivary amylase digestive enzyme in saliva that acts on starch

salivary gland an exocrine gland that secretes a digestive fluid called saliva

salivation secretion of saliva

segmentation alternating contractions and relaxations of non-adjacent segments of the intestine that move food forward and backward, breaking it apart and mixing it with digestive juices

serosa   outermost layer of the alimentary canal wall present in regions within the abdominal cavity

sigmoid colon   end portion of the colon, which terminates at the rectum

small intestine   section of the alimentary canal where most digestion and absorption occurs

soft palate   posterior region of the bottom portion of the nasal cavity that consists of skeletal muscle

stomach   alimentary canal organ that contributes to chemical and mechanical digestion of food from the esophagus before releasing it, as chyme, to the small intestine

sublingual gland   one of a pair of major salivary glands located beneath the tongue

submandibular gland   one of a pair of major salivary glands located in the floor of the mouth

submucosa   layer of dense connective tissue in the alimentary canal wall that binds the overlying mucosa to the underlying muscularis

submucosal plexus   (plexus of Meissner) nerve supply that regulates activity of glands and smooth muscle

sucrase   brush border enzyme that breaks down sucrose into glucose and fructose

tenia coli   one of three smooth muscle bands that make up the longitudinal muscle layer of the muscularis in all of the large intestine except the terminal end

tongue   accessory digestive organ of the mouth, the bulk of which is composed of skeletal muscle

transverse colon   part of the colon between the ascending colon and the descending colon

upper esophageal sphincter   skeletal muscle sphincter that regulates food movement from the pharynx to the esophagus

Valsalva's maneuver   voluntary contraction of the diaphragm and abdominal wall muscles and closing of the glottis, which increases intra-abdominal pressure and facilitates defecation

villus   projection of the mucosa of the small intestine

voluntary phase   initial phase of deglutition, in which the bolus moves from the mouth to the oropharynx

α-dextrin   breakdown product of starch

α-dextrinase   brush border enzyme that acts on α-dextrins

Chapter Review

23.1 Overview of the Digestive System

The digestive system includes the organs of the alimentary canal and accessory structures. The alimentary canal forms a continuous tube that is open to the outside environment at both ends. The organs of the alimentary canal are the mouth, pharynx, esophagus, stomach, small intestine, and large intestine. The accessory digestive structures include the teeth, tongue, salivary glands, liver, pancreas, and gallbladder. The wall of the alimentary canal is composed of four basic tissue layers: mucosa, submucosa, muscularis, and serosa. The enteric nervous system provides intrinsic innervation, and the autonomic nervous system provides extrinsic innervation.

23.2 Digestive System Processes and Regulation

The digestive system ingests and digests food, absorbs released nutrients, and excretes food components that are indigestible. The six activities involved in this process are ingestion, motility, mechanical digestion, chemical digestion, absorption, and defecation. These processes are regulated by neural and hormonal mechanisms.

23.3 The Mouth, Pharynx, and Esophagus

In the mouth, the tongue and the teeth begin mechanical digestion, and saliva begins chemical digestion. The pharynx, which plays roles in breathing and vocalization as well as digestion, runs from the nasal and oral cavities superiorly to the esophagus inferiorly (for digestion) and to the larynx anteriorly (for respiration). During deglutition (swallowing), the soft palate rises to close off the nasopharynx, the larynx elevates, and the epiglottis folds over the glottis. The esophagus includes an upper esophageal sphincter made of skeletal muscle, which regulates the movement of food from the pharynx to the esophagus. It also has a lower esophageal sphincter, made of smooth muscle, which controls the passage of food from the esophagus to the stomach. Cells in the esophageal wall secrete mucus that eases the passage of the food bolus.

23.4 The Stomach

The stomach participates in all digestive activities except ingestion and defecation. It vigorously churns food. It secretes gastric juices that break down food and absorbs certain drugs, including aspirin and some alcohol. The stomach begins the digestion of protein and continues the digestion of carbohydrates and fats. It stores food as an acidic liquid called chyme, and releases it gradually into the small intestine through the pyloric sphincter.

23.5 The Small and Large Intestines

The three main regions of the small intestine are the duodenum, the jejunum, and the ileum. The small intestine is where digestion is completed and virtually all absorption occurs. These two activities are facilitated by structural adaptations that increase the mucosal surface area by 600-fold, including circular folds, villi, and microvilli. There are around 200 million microvilli per square millimeter of small intestine, which contain brush border enzymes that complete the digestion of carbohydrates and proteins. Combined with pancreatic juice, intestinal juice provides the liquid medium needed to further digest and absorb substances from chyme. The small intestine is also the site of unique mechanical digestive movements. Segmentation moves the chyme back and forth, increasing mixing and opportunities for absorption. Migrating motility complexes propel the residual chyme toward the large intestine.

The main regions of the large intestine are the cecum, the colon, and the rectum. The large intestine absorbs water and forms feces, and is responsible for defecation. Bacterial flora break down additional carbohydrate residue, and synthesize certain vitamins. The mucosa of the large intestinal wall is generously endowed with goblet cells, which secrete mucus that eases the passage of feces. The entry of feces into the rectum activates the defecation reflex.

23.6 Accessory Organs in Digestion: The Liver, Pancreas, and Gallbladder

Chemical digestion in the small intestine cannot occur without the help of the liver and pancreas. The liver produces bile and delivers it to the common hepatic

duct. Bile contains bile salts and phospholipids, which emulsify large lipid globules into tiny lipid droplets, a necessary step in lipid digestion and absorption. The gallbladder stores and concentrates bile, releasing it when it is needed by the small intestine.

The pancreas produces the enzyme- and bicarbonate-rich pancreatic juice and delivers it to the small intestine through ducts. Pancreatic juice buffers the acidic gastric juice in chyme, inactivates pepsin from the stomach, and enables the optimal functioning of digestive enzymes in the small intestine.

23.7 Chemical Digestion and Absorption: A Closer Look

The small intestine is the site of most chemical digestion and almost all absorption. Chemical digestion breaks large food molecules down into their chemical building blocks, which can then be absorbed through the intestinal wall and into the general circulation. Intestinal brush border enzymes and pancreatic enzymes are responsible for the majority of chemical digestion. The breakdown of fat also requires bile.

Most nutrients are absorbed by transport mechanisms at the apical surface of enterocytes. Exceptions include lipids, fat-soluble vitamins, and most water-soluble vitamins. With the help of bile salts and lecithin, the dietary fats are emulsified to form micelles, which can carry the fat particles to the surface of the enterocytes. There, the micelles release their fats to diffuse across the cell membrane. The fats are then reassembled into triglycerides and mixed with other lipids and proteins into chylomicrons that can pass into lacteals. Other absorbed monomers travel from blood capillaries in the villus to the hepatic portal vein and then to the liver.

Interactive Link Questions

1. By clicking on this link (http://openstax.org/l/fooddigestion), you can watch a short video of what happens to the food you eat as it passes from your mouth to your intestine. Along the way, note how the food changes consistency and form. How does this change in consistency facilitate your gaining nutrients from food?

2. Visit this site (http://openstax.org/l/fooddigestion2) for an overview of digestion of food in different regions of the digestive tract. Note the route of non-fat nutrients from the small intestine to their release as nutrients to the body.

3. Watch this animation (http://openstax.org/l/swallowing) to see how swallowing is a complex process that involves the nervous system to coordinate the actions of upper respiratory and digestive activities. During which stage of swallowing is there a risk of food entering respiratory pathways and how is this risk blocked?

4. Watch this animation (http://openstax.org/l/stomach1) that depicts the structure of the stomach and how this structure functions in the initiation of protein digestion. This view of the stomach shows the characteristic rugae. What is the function of these rugae?

5. Watch this animation (http://openstax.org/l/sintestine) that depicts the structure of the small intestine, and, in particular, the villi. Epithelial cells continue the digestion and absorption of nutrients and transport these nutrients to the lymphatic and circulatory systems. In the small intestine, the products of food digestion are absorbed by different structures in the villi. Which structure absorbs and transports fats?

6. By watching this animation (http://openstax.org/l/foodgroups), you will see that for the various food groups—proteins, fats, and carbohydrates—digestion begins in different parts of the digestion system, though all end in the same place. Of the three major food classes (carbohydrates, fats, and proteins), which is digested in the mouth, the stomach, and the small intestine?

7. Watch this video (http://openstax.org/l/liver) to see the structure of the liver and how this structure supports the functions of the liver, including the processing of nutrients, toxins, and wastes. At rest, about 1500 mL of blood per minute flow through the liver. What percentage of this blood flow comes from the hepatic portal system?

Review Questions

8. Which of these organs is not considered an accessory digestive structure?
   a. mouth
   b. salivary glands
   c. pancreas
   d. liver

9. Which of the following organs is supported by a layer of adventitia rather than serosa?
   a. esophagus
   b. stomach
   c. small intestine
   d. large intestine

10. Which of the following membranes covers the stomach?
    a. falciform ligament
    b. mesocolon
    c. parietal peritoneum
    d. visceral peritoneum

11. Which of these processes occurs in the mouth?
    a. ingestion
    b. mechanical digestion
    c. chemical digestion
    d. all of the above

12. Which of these processes occurs throughout most of the alimentary canal?
    a. ingestion
    b. propulsion
    c. segmentation
    d. absorption

13. Which of the following stimuli activates sensors in the walls of digestive organs?
    a. breakdown products of digestion
    b. distension
    c. pH of chyme
    d. all of the above

14. Which of these statements about reflexes in the GI tract is false?
    a. Short reflexes are provoked by nerves near the GI tract.
    b. Short reflexes are mediated by the enteric nervous system.
    c. Food that distends the stomach initiates long reflexes.
    d. Long reflexes can be provoked by stimuli originating outside the GI tract.

15. Which of these ingredients in saliva is responsible for activating salivary amylase?
    a. mucus
    b. phosphate ions
    c. chloride ions
    d. urea

16. Which of these statements about the pharynx is true?
    a. It extends from the nasal and oral cavities superiorly to the esophagus anteriorly.
    b. The oropharynx is continuous superiorly with the nasopharynx.
    c. The nasopharynx is involved in digestion.
    d. The laryngopharynx is composed partially of cartilage.

17. Which structure is located where the esophagus penetrates the diaphragm?
    a. esophageal hiatus
    b. cardiac orifice
    c. upper esophageal sphincter
    d. lower esophageal sphincter

18. Which phase of deglutition involves contraction of the longitudinal muscle layer of the muscularis?
    a. voluntary phase
    b. buccal phase
    c. pharyngeal phase
    d. esophageal phase

19. Which of these cells secrete hormones?
    a. parietal cells
    b. mucous neck cells
    c. enteroendocrine cells
    d. chief cells

20. Where does the majority of chemical digestion in the stomach occur?
    a. fundus and body
    b. cardia and fundus
    c. body and pylorus
    d. body

21. During gastric emptying, chyme is released into the duodenum through the _____.
    a. esophageal hiatus
    b. pyloric antrum
    c. pyloric canal
    d. pyloric sphincter

22. Parietal cells secrete _____.
    a. gastrin
    b. hydrochloric acid
    c. pepsin
    d. pepsinogen

23. In which part of the alimentary canal does most digestion occur?
    a. stomach
    b. proximal small intestine
    c. distal small intestine
    d. ascending colon

24. Which of these is most associated with villi?
    a. haustra
    b. lacteals
    c. bacterial flora
    d. intestinal glands

25. What is the role of the small intestine's MALT?
    a. secreting mucus
    b. buffering acidic chyme
    c. activating pepsin
    d. preventing bacteria from entering the bloodstream

26. Which part of the large intestine attaches to the appendix?
    a. cecum
    b. ascending colon
    c. transverse colon
    d. descending colon

27. Which of these statements about bile is true?
    a. About 500 mL is secreted daily.
    b. Its main function is the denaturation of proteins.
    c. It is synthesized in the gallbladder.
    d. Bile salts are recycled.

28. Pancreatic juice _____.
    a. deactivates bile.
    b. is secreted by pancreatic islet cells.
    c. buffers chyme.
    d. is released into the cystic duct.

29. Where does the chemical digestion of starch begin?
    a. mouth
    b. esophagus
    c. stomach
    d. small intestine

30. Which of these is involved in the chemical digestion of protein?
    a. pancreatic amylase
    b. trypsin
    c. sucrase
    d. pancreatic nuclease

31. Where are most fat-digesting enzymes produced?
    a. small intestine
    b. gallbladder
    c. liver
    d. pancreas

32. Which of these nutrients is absorbed mainly in the duodenum?
    a. glucose
    b. iron
    c. sodium
    d. water

Critical Thinking Questions

33. Explain how the enteric nervous system supports the digestive system. What might occur that could result in the autonomic nervous system having a negative impact on digestion?

34. What layer of the alimentary canal tissue is capable of helping to protect the body against disease, and through what mechanism?

35. Offer a theory to explain why segmentation occurs and peristalsis slows in the small intestine.

36. It has been several hours since you last ate. Walking past a bakery, you catch a whiff of freshly baked bread. What type of reflex is triggered, and what is the result?

37. The composition of saliva varies from gland to gland. Discuss how saliva produced by the parotid gland differs in action from saliva produced by the sublingual gland.

38. During a hockey game, the puck hits a player in the mouth, knocking out all eight of their most anterior teeth. Which teeth did the player lose and how does this loss affect food ingestion?

39. What prevents swallowed food from entering the airways?

40. Explain the mechanism responsible for gastroesophageal reflux.

41. Describe the three processes involved in the esophageal phase of deglutition.

42. Explain how the stomach is protected from self-digestion and why this is necessary.

43. Describe unique anatomical features that enable the stomach to perform digestive functions.

44. Explain how nutrients absorbed in the small intestine pass into the general circulation.

45. Why is it important that chyme from the stomach is delivered to the small intestine slowly and in small amounts?

46. Describe three of the differences between the walls of the large and small intestines.

47. Why does the pancreas secrete some enzymes in their inactive forms, and where are these enzymes activated?

48. Describe the location of hepatocytes in the liver and how this arrangement enhances their function.

49. Explain the role of bile salts and lecithin in the emulsification of lipids (fats).

50. How is vitamin B_{12} absorbed?

CHAPTER 24
Metabolism and Nutrition

Figure 24.1 **Metabolism** Metabolism is the sum of all energy-requiring and energy-consuming processes of the body. Many factors contribute to overall metabolism, including lean muscle mass, the amount and quality of food consumed, and the physical demands placed on the human body. (credit: "tableatny"/flickr.com)

CHAPTER OBJECTIVES

After studying this chapter, you will be able to:

- Describe the processes involved in anabolic and catabolic reactions
- List and describe the steps necessary for carbohydrate, lipid, and protein metabolism
- Explain the processes that regulate glucose levels during the absorptive and postabsorptive states
- Explain how metabolism is essential to maintaining body temperature (thermoregulation)
- Summarize the importance of vitamins and minerals in the diet

INTRODUCTION Eating is essential to life. Many of us look to eating as not only a necessity, but also a pleasure. You may have been told since childhood to start the day with a good breakfast to give you the energy to get through most of the day. You most likely have heard about the importance of a balanced diet, with plenty of fruits and vegetables. But what does this all mean to your body and the physiological processes it carries out each day? You need to absorb a range of nutrients so that your cells have the building blocks for metabolic processes that release the energy for the cells to carry out their daily jobs, to manufacture new proteins, cells, and body parts, and to recycle materials in the cell.

This chapter will take you through some of the chemical reactions essential to life, the sum of which is referred to as metabolism. The focus of these discussions will be anabolic reactions and catabolic reactions. You will examine the various chemical reactions that are important to sustain life, including why you must have oxygen, how mitochondria transfer energy, and the importance of certain "metabolic" hormones and vitamins.

Metabolism varies, depending on age, sex, activity level, fuel consumption, and lean body mass. Your own metabolic rate fluctuates throughout life. By modifying your diet and exercise regimen, you can increase both lean body mass and metabolic rate. Factors affecting metabolism also play important roles in controlling muscle mass. Aging is known to decrease the metabolic rate by as much as 5 percent per year. Additionally, because males tend have more lean muscle mass then females, their basal metabolic rate (metabolic rate at rest) is higher; therefore, males tend to burn more calories than females do. Lastly, an individual's inherent metabolic rate is a function of the proteins and enzymes derived from their genetic background. Thus, your genes play a big role in your metabolism. Nonetheless, each person's body engages in the same overall metabolic processes.

24.1 Overview of Metabolic Reactions

LEARNING OBJECTIVES

By the end of this section, you will be able to:

- Describe the process by which polymers are broken down into monomers
- Describe the process by which monomers are combined into polymers
- Discuss the role of ATP in metabolism
- Explain oxidation-reduction reactions
- Describe the hormones that regulate anabolic and catabolic reactions

Metabolic processes are constantly taking place in the body. **Metabolism** is the sum of all of the chemical reactions that are involved in catabolism and anabolism. The reactions governing the breakdown of food to obtain energy are called catabolic reactions. Conversely, anabolic reactions use the energy produced by catabolic reactions to synthesize larger molecules from smaller ones, such as when the body forms proteins by stringing together amino acids. Both sets of reactions are critical to maintaining life.

Because catabolic reactions produce energy and anabolic reactions use energy, ideally, energy usage would balance the energy produced. If the net energy change is positive (catabolic reactions release more energy than the anabolic reactions use), then the body stores the excess energy by building fat molecules for long-term storage. On the other hand, if the net energy change is negative (catabolic reactions release less energy than anabolic reactions use), the body uses stored energy to compensate for the deficiency of energy released by catabolism.

Catabolic Reactions

Catabolic reactions break down large organic molecules into smaller molecules, releasing the energy contained in the chemical bonds. These energy releases (conversions) are not 100 percent efficient. The amount of energy released is less than the total amount contained in the molecule. Approximately 40 percent of energy yielded from catabolic reactions is directly transferred to the high-energy molecule adenosine triphosphate (ATP). ATP, the energy currency of cells, can be used immediately to power molecular machines that support cell, tissue, and organ function. This includes building new tissue and repairing damaged tissue. ATP can also be stored to fulfill future energy demands. The remaining 60 percent of the energy released from catabolic reactions is given off as heat, which tissues and body fluids absorb.

Structurally, ATP molecules consist of an adenine, a ribose, and three phosphate groups (Figure 24.2). The chemical bond between the second and third phosphate groups, termed a high-energy bond, represents the greatest source of energy in a cell. It is the first bond that catabolic enzymes break when cells require energy to do work. The products of this reaction are a molecule of adenosine diphosphate (ADP) and a lone phosphate group (P_i). ATP, ADP, and P_i are constantly being cycled through reactions that build ATP and store energy, and reactions that break down ATP and release energy.

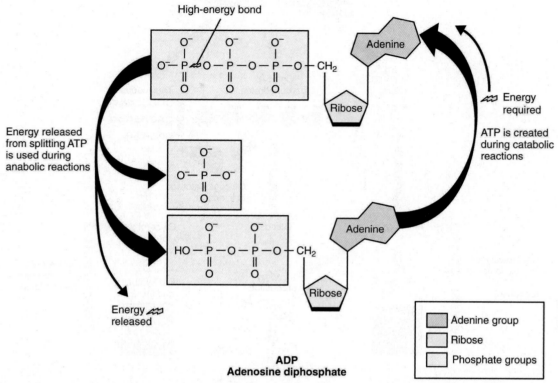

FIGURE 24.2 Structure of ATP Molecule Adenosine triphosphate (ATP) is the energy molecule of the cell. During catabolic reactions, ATP is created and energy is stored until needed during anabolic reactions.

The energy from ATP drives all bodily functions, such as contracting muscles, maintaining the electrical potential of nerve cells, and absorbing food in the gastrointestinal tract. The metabolic reactions that produce ATP come from various sources (Figure 24.3).

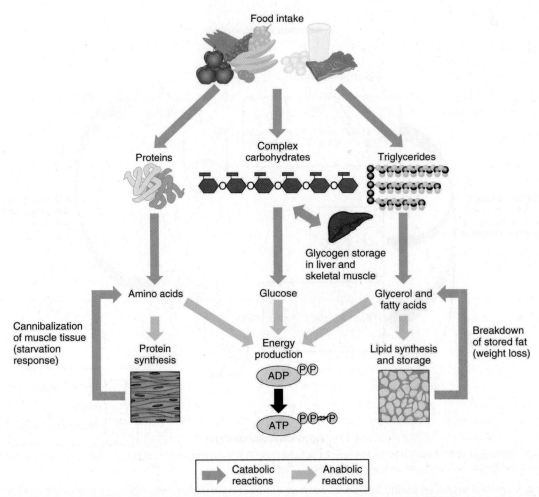

FIGURE 24.3 Sources of ATP During catabolic reactions, proteins are broken down into amino acids, lipids are broken down into fatty acids, and polysaccharides are broken down into monosaccharides. These building blocks are then used for the synthesis of molecules in anabolic reactions.

Of the four major macromolecular groups (carbohydrates, lipids, proteins, and nucleic acids) that are processed by digestion, carbohydrates are considered the most common source of energy to fuel the body. They take the form of either complex carbohydrates, polysaccharides like starch and glycogen, or simple sugars (monosaccharides) like glucose and fructose. Sugar catabolism breaks polysaccharides down into their individual monosaccharides. Among the monosaccharides, glucose is the most common fuel for ATP production in cells, and as such, there are a number of endocrine control mechanisms to regulate glucose concentration in the bloodstream. Excess glucose is either stored as an energy reserve in the liver and skeletal muscles as the complex polymer glycogen, or it is converted into fat (triglyceride) in adipose cells (adipocytes).

Among the lipids (fats), triglycerides are most often used for energy via a metabolic process called β-oxidation. About one-half of excess fat is stored in adipocytes that accumulate in the subcutaneous tissue under the skin, whereas the rest is stored in adipocytes in other tissues and organs.

Proteins, which are polymers, can be broken down into their monomers, individual amino acids. Amino acids can be used as building blocks of new proteins or broken down further for the production of ATP. When one is chronically starving, this use of amino acids for energy production can lead to a wasting away of the body, as more and more proteins are broken down.

Nucleic acids are present in most of the foods you eat. During digestion, nucleic acids including DNA and various RNAs are broken down into their constituent nucleotides. These nucleotides are readily absorbed and transported throughout the body to be used by individual cells during nucleic acid metabolism.

Anabolic Reactions

In contrast to catabolic reactions, **anabolic reactions** involve the joining of smaller molecules into larger ones. Anabolic reactions combine monosaccharides to form polysaccharides, fatty acids to form triglycerides, amino acids to form proteins, and nucleotides to form nucleic acids. These processes require energy in the form of ATP molecules generated by catabolic reactions. Anabolic reactions, also called **biosynthesis reactions**, create new molecules that form new cells and tissues, and revitalize organs.

Hormonal Regulation of Metabolism

Catabolic and anabolic hormones in the body help regulate metabolic processes. **Catabolic hormones** stimulate the breakdown of molecules and the production of energy. These include cortisol, glucagon, adrenaline/epinephrine, and cytokines. All of these hormones are mobilized at specific times to meet the needs of the body. **Anabolic hormones** are required for the synthesis of molecules and include growth hormone, insulin-like growth factor, insulin, testosterone, and estrogen. Table 24.1 summarizes the function of each of the catabolic hormones and Table 24.2 summarizes the functions of the anabolic hormones.

Catabolic Hormones

Hormone	Function
Cortisol	Released from the adrenal gland in response to stress; its main role is to increase blood glucose levels by gluconeogenesis (breaking down fats and proteins)
Glucagon	Released from alpha cells in the pancreas either when starving or when the body needs to generate additional energy; it stimulates the breakdown of glycogen in the liver to increase blood glucose levels; its effect is the opposite of insulin; glucagon and insulin are a part of a negative-feedback system that stabilizes blood glucose levels
Adrenaline/epinephrine	Released in response to the activation of the sympathetic nervous system; increases heart rate and heart contractility, constricts blood vessels, is a bronchodilator that opens (dilates) the bronchi of the lungs to increase air volume in the lungs, and stimulates gluconeogenesis

TABLE 24.1

Anabolic Hormones

Hormone	Function
Growth hormone (GH)	Synthesized and released from the pituitary gland; stimulates the growth of cells, tissues, and bones
Insulin-like growth factor (IGF)	Stimulates the growth of muscle and bone while also inhibiting cell death (apoptosis)
Insulin	Produced by the beta cells of the pancreas; plays an essential role in carbohydrate and fat metabolism, controls blood glucose levels, and promotes the uptake of glucose into body cells; causes cells in muscle, adipose tissue, and liver to take up glucose from the blood and store it in the liver and muscle as glycogen; its effect is the opposite of glucagon; glucagon and insulin are a part of a negative-feedback system that stabilizes blood glucose levels

TABLE 24.2

Hormone	Function
Testosterone	Produced by the testes in males and the ovaries in females; stimulates an increase in muscle mass and strength as well as the growth and strengthening of bone
Estrogen	Produced primarily by the ovaries, it is also produced by the liver and adrenal glands; its anabolic functions include increasing metabolism and fat deposition

TABLE 24.2

Disorders of the...

Metabolic Processes: Cushing Syndrome and Addison's Disease

As might be expected for a fundamental physiological process like metabolism, errors or malfunctions in metabolic processing lead to a pathophysiology or—if uncorrected—a disease state. Metabolic diseases are most commonly the result of malfunctioning proteins or enzymes that are critical to one or more metabolic pathways. Protein or enzyme malfunction can be the consequence of a genetic alteration or mutation. However, normally functioning proteins and enzymes can also have deleterious effects if their availability is not appropriately matched with metabolic need. For example, excessive production of the hormone cortisol (see Table 24.1) gives rise to Cushing syndrome. Clinically, Cushing syndrome is characterized by rapid weight gain, especially in the trunk and face region, depression, and anxiety. It is worth mentioning that tumors of the pituitary that produce adrenocorticotropic hormone (ACTH), which subsequently stimulates the adrenal cortex to release excessive cortisol, produce similar effects. This indirect mechanism of cortisol overproduction is referred to as Cushing disease.

Patients with Cushing syndrome can exhibit high blood glucose levels and are at an increased risk of becoming obese. They also show slow growth, accumulation of fat between the shoulders, weak muscles, bone pain (because cortisol causes proteins to be broken down to make glucose via gluconeogenesis), and fatigue. Other symptoms include excessive sweating (hyperhidrosis), capillary dilation, and thinning of the skin, which can lead to easy bruising. The treatments for Cushing syndrome are all focused on reducing excessive cortisol levels. Depending on the cause of the excess, treatment may be as simple as discontinuing the use of cortisol ointments. In cases of tumors, surgery is often used to remove the offending tumor. Where surgery is inappropriate, radiation therapy can be used to reduce the size of a tumor or ablate portions of the adrenal cortex. Finally, medications are available that can help to regulate the amounts of cortisol.

Insufficient cortisol production is equally problematic. Adrenal insufficiency, or Addison's disease, is characterized by the reduced production of cortisol from the adrenal gland. It can result from malfunction of the adrenal glands—they do not produce enough cortisol—or it can be a consequence of decreased ACTH availability from the pituitary. Patients with Addison's disease may have low blood pressure, paleness, extreme weakness, fatigue, slow or sluggish movements, lightheadedness, and salt cravings due to the loss of sodium and high blood potassium levels (hyperkalemia). Victims also may suffer from loss of appetite, chronic diarrhea, vomiting, mouth lesions, and patchy skin color. Diagnosis typically involves blood tests and imaging tests of the adrenal and pituitary glands. Treatment involves cortisol replacement therapy, which usually must be continued for life.

Oxidation-Reduction Reactions

The chemical reactions underlying metabolism involve the transfer of electrons from one compound to another by processes catalyzed by enzymes. The electrons in these reactions commonly come from hydrogen atoms, which consist of an electron and a proton. A molecule gives up a hydrogen atom, in the form of a hydrogen ion (H^+) and an electron, breaking the molecule into smaller parts. The loss of an electron, or **oxidation**, releases a small amount of energy; both the electron and the energy are then passed to another molecule in the process of **reduction**, or the gaining of an electron. These two reactions always happen together in an **oxidation-reduction reaction** (also called a redox reaction)—when an electron is passed between molecules, the donor is oxidized and the recipient is reduced. Oxidation-reduction reactions often happen in a series, so that a molecule that is reduced is subsequently oxidized, passing on not only the electron it just received but also the energy it received. As the series of reactions progresses, energy accumulates that is used to combine P_i and ADP to form ATP, the high-energy molecule that the body uses for fuel.

Oxidation-reduction reactions are catalyzed by enzymes that trigger the removal of hydrogen atoms. Coenzymes work with enzymes and accept hydrogen atoms. The two most common coenzymes of oxidation-reduction reactions are **nicotinamide adenine dinucleotide (NAD)** and **flavin adenine dinucleotide (FAD)**. Their respective reduced coenzymes are **NADH** and **FADH$_2$**, which are energy-containing molecules used to transfer energy during the creation of ATP.

24.2 Carbohydrate Metabolism

LEARNING OBJECTIVES

By the end of this section, you will be able to:

- Explain the processes of glycolysis
- Describe the pathway of a pyruvate molecule through the Krebs cycle
- Explain the transport of electrons through the electron transport chain
- Describe the process of ATP production through oxidative phosphorylation
- Summarize the process of gluconeogenesis

Carbohydrates are organic molecules composed of carbon, hydrogen, and oxygen atoms. The family of carbohydrates includes both simple and complex sugars. Glucose and fructose are examples of simple sugars, and starch, glycogen, and cellulose are all examples of complex sugars. The complex sugars are also called **polysaccharides** and are made of multiple **monosaccharide** molecules. Polysaccharides serve as energy storage (e.g., starch and glycogen) and as structural components (e.g., chitin in insects and cellulose in plants).

During digestion, carbohydrates are broken down into simple, soluble sugars that can be transported across the intestinal wall into the circulatory system to be transported throughout the body. Carbohydrate digestion begins in the mouth with the action of **salivary amylase** on starches and ends with monosaccharides being absorbed across the epithelium of the small intestine. Once the absorbed monosaccharides are transported to the tissues, the process of **cellular respiration** begins (Figure 24.4). This section will focus first on glycolysis, a process where the monosaccharide glucose is oxidized, releasing the energy stored in its bonds to produce ATP.

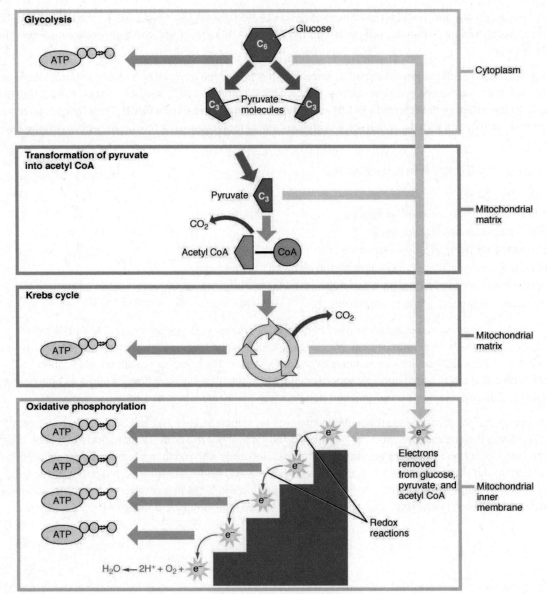

FIGURE 24.4   Cellular Respiration   Cellular respiration oxidizes glucose molecules through glycolysis, the Krebs cycle, and oxidative phosphorylation to produce ATP.

Glycolysis

Glucose is the body's most readily available source of energy. After digestive processes break polysaccharides down into monosaccharides, including glucose, the monosaccharides are transported across the wall of the small intestine and into the circulatory system, which transports them to the liver. In the liver, hepatocytes either pass the glucose on through the circulatory system or store excess glucose as glycogen. Cells in the body take up the circulating glucose in response to insulin and, through a series of reactions called **glycolysis**, transfer some of the energy in glucose to ADP to form ATP (Figure 24.5). The last step in glycolysis produces the product **pyruvate**.

Glycolysis begins with the phosphorylation of glucose by hexokinase to form glucose-6-phosphate. This step uses one ATP, which is the donor of the phosphate group. Under the action of phosphofructokinase, glucose-6-phosphate is converted into fructose-6-phosphate. At this point, a second ATP donates its phosphate group, forming fructose-1,6-bisphosphate. This six-carbon sugar is split to form two phosphorylated three-carbon molecules, glyceraldehyde-3-phosphate and dihydroxyacetone phosphate, which are both converted into glyceraldehyde-3-phosphate. The glyceraldehyde-3-phosphate is further phosphorylated with groups donated by dihydrogen phosphate present in the cell to form the three-carbon molecule 1,3-bisphosphoglycerate. The energy of this reaction comes from the oxidation of (removal of electrons from) glyceraldehyde-3-phosphate. In a series of reactions leading to pyruvate, the two phosphate groups are then transferred to two ADPs to form two ATPs. Thus, glycolysis uses two ATPs but generates four ATPs, yielding a net gain of two ATPs and two molecules of pyruvate. In the presence of oxygen, pyruvate continues on to the Krebs cycle (also called the **citric acid cycle** or **tricarboxylic acid cycle (TCA)**, where additional energy is extracted and passed on.

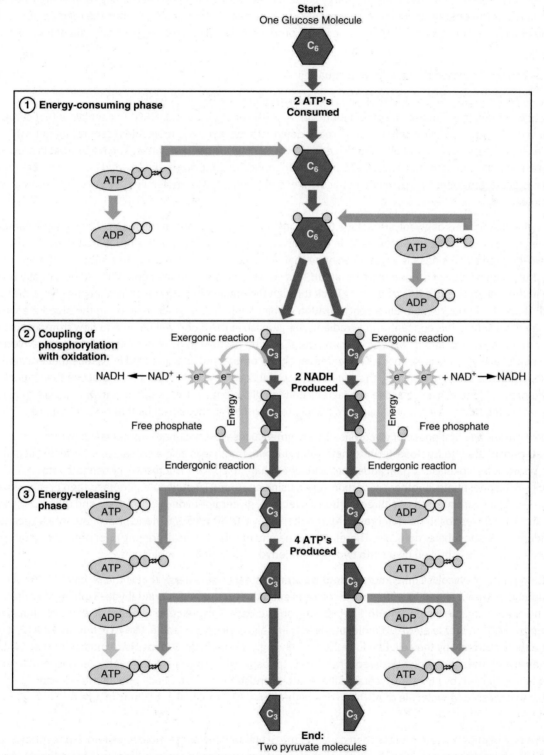

FIGURE 24.5   Glycolysis Overview   During the energy-consuming phase of glycolysis, two ATPs are consumed, transferring two phosphates to the glucose molecule. The glucose molecule then splits into two three-carbon compounds, each containing a phosphate. During the second phase, an additional phosphate is added to each of the three-carbon compounds. The energy for this endergonic reaction is provided by the removal (oxidation) of two electrons from each three-carbon compound. During the energy-releasing phase, the phosphates are removed from both three-carbon compounds and used to produce four ATP molecules.

⟨∅⟩ INTERACTIVE LINK

Watch this video (http://openstax.org/l/glycolysis1) to learn about glycolysis.

Glycolysis can be divided into two phases: energy consuming (also called chemical priming) and energy yielding. The first phase is the **energy-consuming phase**, so it requires two ATP molecules to start the reaction for each molecule of glucose. However, the end of the reaction produces four ATPs, resulting in a net gain of two ATP energy molecules.

Glycolysis can be expressed as the following equation:

$$\text{Glucose} + 2\text{ATP} + 2\text{NAD}^+ + 4\text{ADP} + 2\text{P}_i \;\rightarrow\; 2\,\text{Pyruvate} + 4\text{ATP} + 2\text{NADH} + 2\text{H}^+$$

This equation states that glucose, in combination with ATP (the energy source), NAD$^+$ (a coenzyme that serves as an electron acceptor), and inorganic phosphate, breaks down into two pyruvate molecules, generating four ATP molecules—for a net yield of two ATP—and two energy-containing NADH coenzymes. The NADH that is produced in this process will be used later to produce ATP in the mitochondria. Importantly, by the end of this process, one glucose molecule generates two pyruvate molecules, two high-energy ATP molecules, and two electron-carrying NADH molecules.

The following discussions of glycolysis include the enzymes responsible for the reactions. When glucose enters a cell, the enzyme hexokinase (or glucokinase, in the liver) rapidly adds a phosphate to convert it into **glucose-6-phosphate**. A kinase is a type of enzyme that adds a phosphate molecule to a substrate (in this case, glucose, but it can be true of other molecules also). This conversion step requires one ATP and essentially traps the glucose in the cell, preventing it from passing back through the plasma membrane, thus allowing glycolysis to proceed. It also functions to maintain a concentration gradient with higher glucose levels in the blood than in the tissues. By establishing this concentration gradient, the glucose in the blood will be able to flow from an area of high concentration (the blood) into an area of low concentration (the tissues) to be either used or stored. **Hexokinase** is found in nearly every tissue in the body. **Glucokinase**, on the other hand, is expressed in tissues that are active when blood glucose levels are high, such as the liver. Hexokinase has a higher affinity for glucose than glucokinase and therefore is able to convert glucose at a faster rate than glucokinase. This is important when levels of glucose are very low in the body, as it allows glucose to travel preferentially to those tissues that require it more.

In the next step of the first phase of glycolysis, the enzyme glucose-6-phosphate isomerase converts glucose-6-phosphate into fructose-6-phosphate. Like glucose, fructose is also a six carbon-containing sugar. The enzyme phosphofructokinase-1 then adds one more phosphate to convert fructose-6-phosphate into fructose-1-6-bisphosphate, another six-carbon sugar, using another ATP molecule. Aldolase then breaks down this fructose-1-6-bisphosphate into two three-carbon molecules, glyceraldehyde-3-phosphate and dihydroxyacetone phosphate. The triosephosphate isomerase enzyme then converts dihydroxyacetone phosphate into a second glyceraldehyde-3-phosphate molecule. Therefore, by the end of this chemical-priming or energy-consuming phase, one glucose molecule is broken down into two glyceraldehyde-3-phosphate molecules.

The second phase of glycolysis, the **energy-yielding phase**, creates the energy that is the product of glycolysis. Glyceraldehyde-3-phosphate dehydrogenase converts each three-carbon glyceraldehyde-3-phosphate produced during the energy-consuming phase into 1,3-bisphosphoglycerate. This reaction releases an electron that is then picked up by NAD$^+$ to create an NADH molecule. NADH is a high-energy molecule, like ATP, but unlike ATP, it is not used as energy currency by the cell. Because there are two glyceraldehyde-3-phosphate molecules, two NADH molecules are synthesized during this step. Each 1,3-bisphosphoglycerate is subsequently dephosphorylated (i.e., a phosphate is removed) by phosphoglycerate kinase into 3-phosphoglycerate. Each phosphate released in this reaction can convert one molecule of ADP into one high-energy ATP molecule, resulting in a gain of two ATP molecules.

The enzyme phosphoglycerate mutase then converts the 3-phosphoglycerate molecules into 2-phosphoglycerate. The enolase enzyme then acts upon the 2-phosphoglycerate molecules to convert them into phosphoenolpyruvate molecules. The last step of glycolysis involves the dephosphorylation of the two phosphoenolpyruvate molecules by pyruvate kinase to create two pyruvate molecules and two ATP molecules.

In summary, one glucose molecule breaks down into two pyruvate molecules, and creates two net ATP molecules and two NADH molecules by glycolysis. Therefore, glycolysis generates energy for the cell and creates pyruvate molecules that can be processed further through the aerobic Krebs cycle (also called the citric acid cycle or tricarboxylic acid cycle); converted into lactic acid or alcohol (in yeast) by fermentation; or used later for the synthesis of glucose through gluconeogenesis.

Anaerobic Respiration

When oxygen is limited or absent, pyruvate enters an anaerobic pathway called fermentation. In these reactions, pyruvate can be converted into lactic acid. In addition to generating an additional ATP, this pathway serves to keep the pyruvate concentration low so glycolysis continues, and it oxidizes NADH into the NAD$^+$ needed by glycolysis. In this reaction, lactic acid replaces oxygen as the final electron acceptor. Anaerobic respiration occurs in most cells of the body when oxygen is limited or mitochondria are absent or nonfunctional. For example, because erythrocytes (red blood cells) lack mitochondria, they must produce their ATP from anaerobic respiration. This is an effective pathway of ATP production for short periods of time, ranging from seconds to a few minutes. The lactic acid produced diffuses into the plasma and is carried to the liver, where it is converted back into pyruvate or glucose via the Cori cycle. Similarly, when a person exercises, muscles use ATP faster than oxygen can be delivered to them. They depend on glycolysis and lactic acid production for rapid ATP production.

Aerobic Respiration

In the presence of oxygen, pyruvate can enter the Krebs cycle where additional energy is extracted as electrons are transferred from the pyruvate to the receptors NAD$^+$, GDP, and FAD, with carbon dioxide being a "waste product" (Figure 24.6). The NADH and FADH$_2$ pass electrons on to the electron transport chain, which uses the transferred energy to produce ATP. As the terminal step in the electron transport chain, oxygen is the **terminal electron acceptor** and creates water inside the mitochondria.

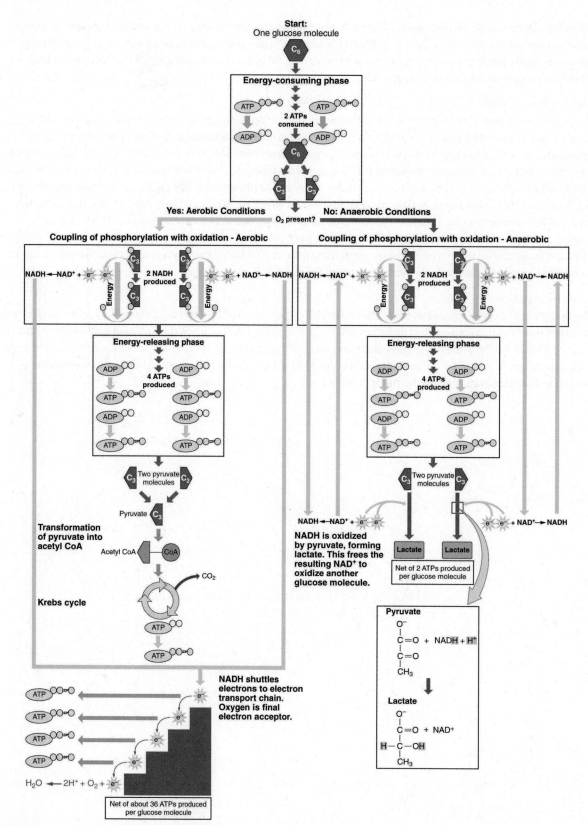

FIGURE 24.6 Aerobic versus Anaerobic Respiration   The process of anaerobic respiration converts glucose into two lactate molecules in the absence of oxygen or within erythrocytes that lack mitochondria. During aerobic respiration, glucose is oxidized into two pyruvate molecules.

Krebs Cycle/Citric Acid Cycle/Tricarboxylic Acid Cycle

The pyruvate molecules generated during glycolysis are transported across the mitochondrial membrane into the

Access for free at openstax.org

inner mitochondrial matrix, where they are metabolized by enzymes in a pathway called the **Krebs cycle** (Figure 24.7). The Krebs cycle is also commonly called the citric acid cycle or the tricarboxylic acid (TCA) cycle. During the Krebs cycle, high-energy molecules, including ATP, NADH, and $FADH_2$, are created. NADH and $FADH_2$ then pass electrons through the electron transport chain in the mitochondria to generate more ATP molecules.

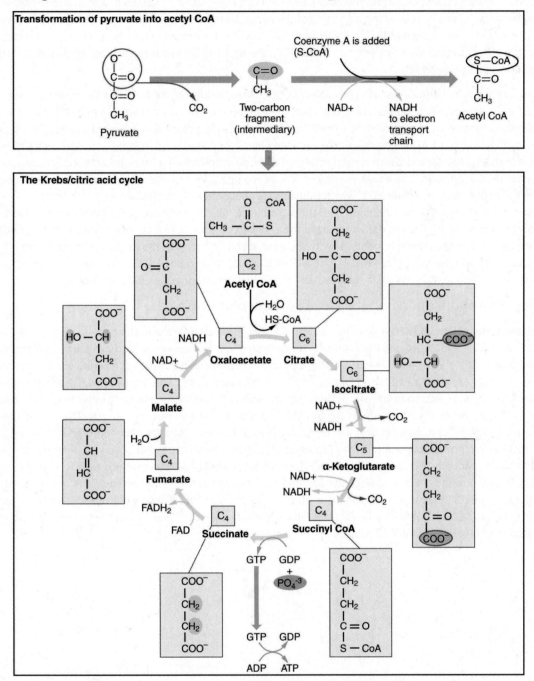

FIGURE 24.7   Krebs Cycle   During the Krebs cycle, each pyruvate that is generated by glycolysis is converted into a two-carbon acetyl CoA molecule. The acetyl CoA is systematically processed through the cycle and produces high-energy NADH, $FADH_2$, and ATP molecules.

⊘ INTERACTIVE LINK

Watch this animation (http://openstax.org/l/krebscycle) to observe the Krebs cycle.

The three-carbon pyruvate molecule generated during glycolysis moves from the cytoplasm into the mitochondrial matrix, where it is converted by the enzyme pyruvate dehydrogenase into a two-carbon **acetyl coenzyme A (acetyl CoA)** molecule. This reaction is an oxidative decarboxylation reaction. It converts the three-carbon pyruvate into a two-carbon acetyl CoA molecule, releasing carbon dioxide and transferring two electrons that combine with NAD^+ to form NADH. Acetyl CoA enters the Krebs cycle by combining with a four-carbon molecule, oxaloacetate, to form the six-carbon molecule citrate, or citric acid, at the same time releasing the coenzyme A molecule.

The six-carbon citrate molecule is systematically converted to a five-carbon molecule and then a four-carbon molecule, ending with oxaloacetate, the beginning of the cycle. Along the way, each citrate molecule will produce one ATP, one $FADH_2$, and three NADH. The $FADH_2$ and NADH will enter the oxidative phosphorylation system located in the inner mitochondrial membrane. In addition, the Krebs cycle supplies the starting materials to process and break down proteins and fats.

To start the Krebs cycle, citrate synthase combines acetyl CoA and oxaloacetate to form a six-carbon citrate molecule; CoA is subsequently released and can combine with another pyruvate molecule to begin the cycle again. The aconitase enzyme converts citrate into isocitrate. In two successive steps of oxidative decarboxylation, two molecules of CO_2 and two NADH molecules are produced when isocitrate dehydrogenase converts isocitrate into the five-carbon α-ketoglutarate, which is then catalyzed and converted into the four-carbon succinyl CoA by α-ketoglutarate dehydrogenase. The enzyme succinyl CoA dehydrogenase then converts succinyl CoA into succinate and forms the high-energy molecule GTP, which transfers its energy to ADP to produce ATP. Succinate dehydrogenase then converts succinate into fumarate, forming a molecule of $FADH_2$. Fumarase then converts fumarate into malate, which malate dehydrogenase then converts back into oxaloacetate while reducing NAD^+ to NADH. Oxaloacetate is then ready to combine with the next acetyl CoA to start the Krebs cycle again (see Figure 24.7). For each turn of the cycle, three NADH, one ATP (through GTP), and one $FADH_2$ are created. Each carbon of pyruvate is converted into CO_2, which is released as a byproduct of oxidative (aerobic) respiration.

Oxidative Phosphorylation and the Electron Transport Chain

The **electron transport chain (ETC)** uses the NADH and $FADH_2$ produced by the Krebs cycle to generate ATP. Electrons from NADH and $FADH_2$ are transferred through protein complexes embedded in the inner mitochondrial membrane by a series of enzymatic reactions. The electron transport chain consists of a series of four enzyme complexes (Complex I – Complex IV) and two coenzymes (ubiquinone and Cytochrome c), which act as electron carriers and proton pumps used to transfer H^+ ions into the space between the inner and outer mitochondrial membranes (Figure 24.8). The ETC couples the transfer of electrons between a donor (like NADH) and an electron acceptor (like O_2) with the transfer of protons (H^+ ions) across the inner mitochondrial membrane, enabling the process of **oxidative phosphorylation**. In the presence of oxygen, energy is passed, stepwise, through the electron carriers to collect gradually the energy needed to attach a phosphate to ADP and produce ATP. The role of molecular oxygen, O_2, is as the terminal electron acceptor for the ETC. This means that once the electrons have passed through the entire ETC, they must be passed to another, separate molecule. These electrons, O_2, and H^+ ions from the matrix combine to form new water molecules. This is the basis for your need to breathe in oxygen. Without oxygen, electron flow through the ETC ceases.

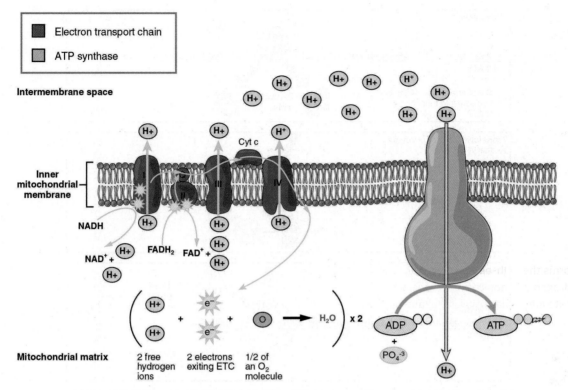

FIGURE 24.8 Electron Transport Chain   The electron transport chain is a series of electron carriers and ion pumps that are used to pump H⁺ ions out of the inner mitochondrial matrix.

🔗 INTERACTIVE LINK

Watch this video (http://openstax.org/l/ETchain) to learn about the electron transport chain.

The electrons released from NADH and FADH₂ are passed along the chain by each of the carriers, which are reduced when they receive the electron and oxidized when passing it on to the next carrier. Each of these reactions releases a small amount of energy, which is used to pump H⁺ ions across the inner membrane. The accumulation of these protons in the space between the membranes creates a proton gradient with respect to the mitochondrial matrix.

Also embedded in the inner mitochondrial membrane is an amazing protein pore complex called **ATP synthase**. Effectively, it is a turbine that is powered by the flow of H⁺ ions across the inner membrane down a gradient and into the mitochondrial matrix. As the H⁺ ions traverse the complex, the shaft of the complex rotates. This rotation enables other portions of ATP synthase to encourage ADP and P$_i$ to create ATP. In accounting for the total number of ATP produced per glucose molecule through aerobic respiration, it is important to remember the following points:

- A net of two ATP are produced through glycolysis (four produced and two consumed during the energy-consuming stage). However, these two ATP are used for transporting the NADH produced during glycolysis from the cytoplasm into the mitochondria. Therefore, the net production of ATP during glycolysis is zero.
- In all phases after glycolysis, the number of ATP, NADH, and FADH₂ produced must be multiplied by two to reflect how each glucose molecule produces two pyruvate molecules.
- In the ETC, about three ATP are produced for every oxidized NADH. However, only about two ATP are produced for every oxidized FADH₂. The electrons from FADH₂ produce less ATP, because they start at a lower point in the ETC (Complex II) compared to the electrons from NADH (Complex I) (see Figure 24.8).

Therefore, for every glucose molecule that enters aerobic respiration, a net total of 36 ATPs are produced (Figure 24.9).

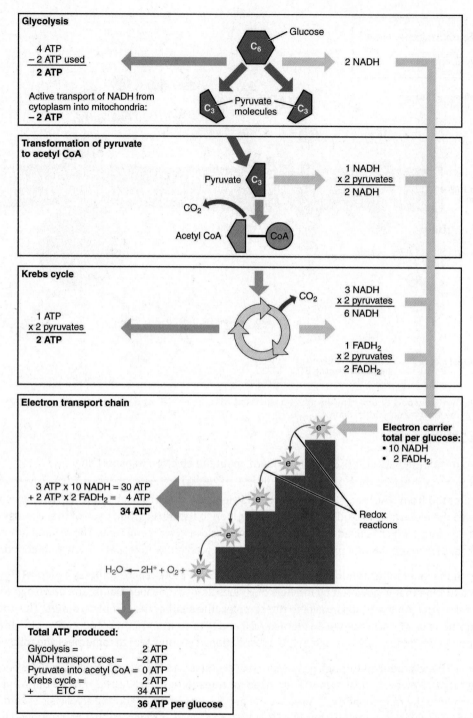

FIGURE 24.9 Carbohydrate Metabolism   Carbohydrate metabolism involves glycolysis, the Krebs cycle, and the electron transport chain.

Gluconeogenesis

Gluconeogenesis is the synthesis of new glucose molecules from pyruvate, lactate, glycerol, or the amino acids alanine or glutamine. This process takes place primarily in the liver during periods of low glucose, that is, under conditions of fasting, starvation, and low carbohydrate diets. So, the question can be raised as to why the body would create something it has just spent a fair amount of effort to break down? Certain key organs, including the brain, can use only glucose as an energy source; therefore, it is essential that the body maintain a minimum blood glucose concentration. When the blood glucose concentration falls below that certain point, new glucose is synthesized by the liver to raise the blood concentration to normal.

Gluconeogenesis is not simply the reverse of glycolysis. There are some important differences (Figure 24.10). Pyruvate is a common starting material for gluconeogenesis. First, the pyruvate is converted into oxaloacetate. Oxaloacetate then serves as a substrate for the enzyme phosphoenolpyruvate carboxykinase (PEPCK), which transforms oxaloacetate into phosphoenolpyruvate (PEP). From this step, gluconeogenesis is nearly the reverse of glycolysis. PEP is converted back into 2-phosphoglycerate, which is converted into 3-phosphoglycerate. Then, 3-phosphoglycerate is converted into 1,3 bisphosphoglycerate and then into glyceraldehyde-3-phosphate. Two molecules of glyceraldehyde-3-phosphate then combine to form fructose-1-6-bisphosphate, which is converted into fructose 6-phosphate and then into glucose-6-phosphate. Finally, a series of reactions generates glucose itself. In gluconeogenesis (as compared to glycolysis), the enzyme hexokinase is replaced by glucose-6-phosphatase, and the enzyme phosphofructokinase-1 is replaced by fructose-1,6-bisphosphatase. This helps the cell to regulate glycolysis and gluconeogenesis independently of each other.

As will be discussed as part of lipolysis, fats can be broken down into glycerol, which can be phosphorylated to form dihydroxyacetone phosphate or DHAP. DHAP can either enter the glycolytic pathway or be used by the liver as a substrate for gluconeogenesis.

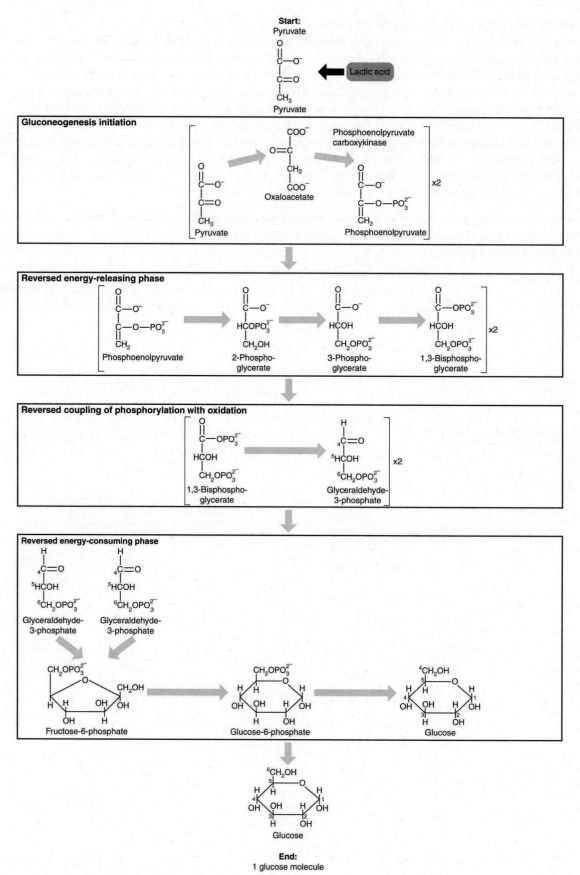

FIGURE 24.10   Gluconeogenesis   Gluconeogenesis is the synthesis of glucose from pyruvate, lactate, glycerol, alanine, or glutamate.

> ### Aging and the...
>
> **Body's Metabolic Rate**
> The human body's metabolic rate decreases nearly 2 percent per decade after age 30. Changes in body composition, including reduced lean muscle mass, are mostly responsible for this decrease. The most dramatic loss of muscle mass, and consequential decline in metabolic rate, occurs between 50 and 70 years of age. Loss of muscle mass is the equivalent of reduced strength, which tends to inhibit seniors from engaging in sufficient physical activity. This results in a positive-feedback system where the reduced physical activity leads to even more muscle loss, further reducing metabolism.
>
> There are several things that can be done to help prevent general declines in metabolism and to fight back against the cyclic nature of these declines. These include eating breakfast, eating small meals frequently, consuming plenty of lean protein, drinking water to remain hydrated, exercising (including strength training), and getting enough sleep. These measures can help keep energy levels from dropping and curb the urge for increased calorie consumption from excessive snacking. While these strategies are not guaranteed to maintain metabolism, they do help prevent muscle loss and may increase energy levels. Some experts also suggest avoiding sugar, which can lead to excess fat storage. Spicy foods and green tea might also be beneficial. Because stress activates cortisol release, and cortisol slows metabolism, avoiding stress, or at least practicing relaxation techniques, can also help.

24.3 Lipid Metabolism

LEARNING OBJECTIVES

By the end of this section, you will be able to:

- Explain how energy can be derived from fat
- Explain the purpose and process of ketogenesis
- Describe the process of ketone body oxidation
- Explain the purpose and the process of lipogenesis

Fats (or triglycerides) within the body are ingested as food or synthesized by adipocytes or hepatocytes from carbohydrate precursors (Figure 24.11). Lipid metabolism entails the oxidation of fatty acids to either generate energy or synthesize new lipids from smaller constituent molecules. Lipid metabolism is associated with carbohydrate metabolism, as products of glucose (such as acetyl CoA) can be converted into lipids.

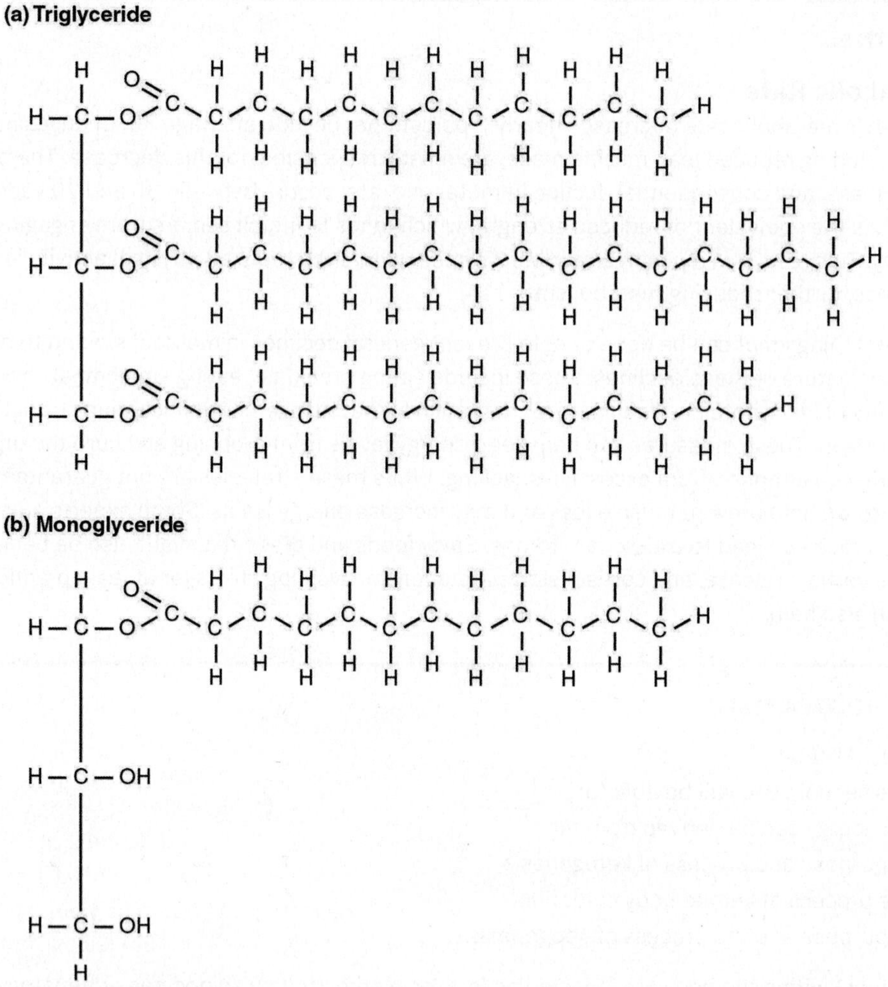

(a) Triglyceride

(b) Monoglyceride

FIGURE 24.11   Triglyceride Broken Down into a Monoglyceride   A triglyceride molecule (a) breaks down into a monoglyceride (b).

Lipid metabolism begins in the intestine where ingested **triglycerides** are broken down into smaller chain fatty acids and subsequently into **monoglyceride molecules** (see Figure 24.11b) by **pancreatic lipases**, enzymes that break down fats after they are emulsified by **bile salts**. When food reaches the small intestine in the form of chyme, a digestive hormone called **cholecystokinin (CCK)** is released by intestinal cells in the intestinal mucosa. CCK stimulates the release of pancreatic lipase from the pancreas and stimulates the contraction of the gallbladder to release stored bile salts into the intestine. CCK also travels to the brain, where it can act as a hunger suppressant.

Together, the pancreatic lipases and bile salts break down triglycerides into free fatty acids. These fatty acids can be transported across the intestinal membrane. However, once they cross the membrane, they are recombined to again form triglyceride molecules. Within the intestinal cells, these triglycerides are packaged along with cholesterol molecules in phospholipid vesicles called **chylomicrons** (Figure 24.12). The chylomicrons enable fats and cholesterol to move within the aqueous environment of your lymphatic and circulatory systems. Chylomicrons leave the enterocytes by exocytosis and enter the lymphatic system via lacteals in the villi of the intestine. From the lymphatic system, the chylomicrons are transported to the circulatory system. Once in the circulation, they can either go to the liver or be stored in fat cells (adipocytes) that comprise adipose (fat) tissue found throughout the body.

Access for free at openstax.org

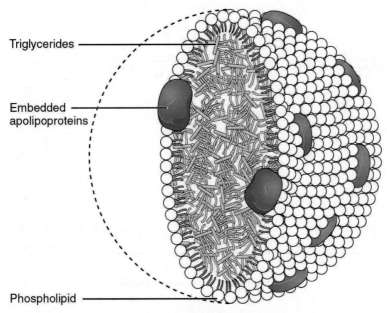

Triglycerides

Embedded
apolipoproteins

Phospholipid

FIGURE 24.12 Chylomicrons   Chylomicrons contain triglycerides, cholesterol molecules, and other apolipoproteins (protein molecules). They function to carry these water-insoluble molecules from the intestine, through the lymphatic system, and into the bloodstream, which carries the lipids to adipose tissue for storage.

Lipolysis

To obtain energy from fat, triglycerides must first be broken down by hydrolysis into their two principal components, fatty acids and glycerol. This process, called **lipolysis**, takes place in the cytoplasm. The resulting fatty acids are oxidized by β-oxidation into acetyl CoA, which is used by the Krebs cycle. The glycerol that is released from triglycerides after lipolysis directly enters the glycolysis pathway as DHAP. Because one triglyceride molecule yields three fatty acid molecules with as much as 16 or more carbons in each one, fat molecules yield more energy than carbohydrates and are an important source of energy for the human body. Triglycerides yield more than twice the energy per unit mass when compared to carbohydrates and proteins. Therefore, when glucose levels are low, triglycerides can be converted into acetyl CoA molecules and used to generate ATP through aerobic respiration.

The breakdown of fatty acids, called **fatty acid oxidation** or **beta (β)-oxidation**, begins in the cytoplasm, where fatty acids are converted into fatty acyl CoA molecules. This fatty acyl CoA combines with carnitine to create a fatty acyl carnitine molecule, which helps to transport the fatty acid across the mitochondrial membrane. Once inside the mitochondrial matrix, the fatty acyl carnitine molecule is converted back into fatty acyl CoA and then into acetyl CoA (Figure 24.13). The newly formed acetyl CoA enters the Krebs cycle and is used to produce ATP in the same way as acetyl CoA derived from pyruvate.

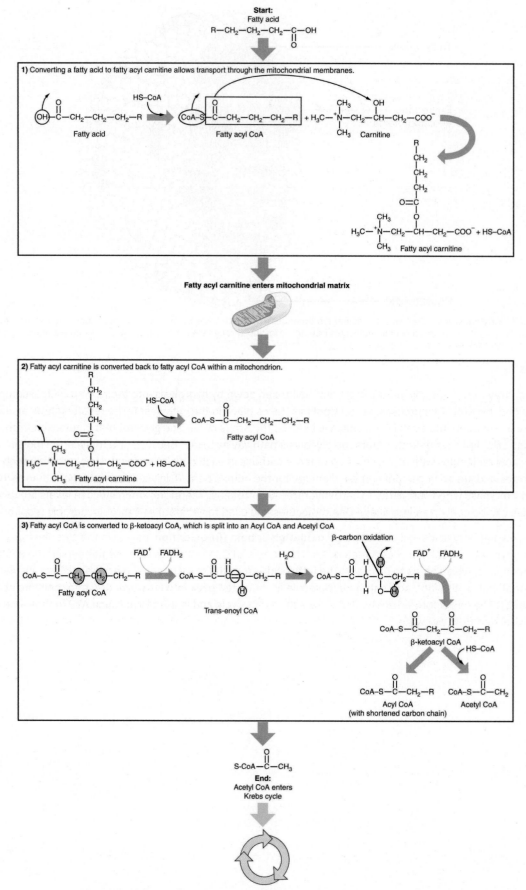

FIGURE 24.13 Breakdown of Fatty Acids   During fatty acid oxidation, triglycerides can be broken down into acetyl CoA molecules and

used for energy when glucose levels are low.

Ketogenesis

If excessive acetyl CoA is created from the oxidation of fatty acids and the Krebs cycle is overloaded and cannot handle it, the acetyl CoA is diverted to create **ketone bodies**. These ketone bodies can serve as a fuel source if glucose levels are too low in the body. Ketones serve as fuel in times of prolonged starvation or when patients suffer from uncontrolled diabetes and cannot utilize most of the circulating glucose. In both cases, fat stores are liberated to generate energy through the Krebs cycle and will generate ketone bodies when too much acetyl CoA accumulates.

In this ketone synthesis reaction, excess acetyl CoA is converted into **hydroxymethylglutaryl CoA (HMG CoA)**. HMG CoA is a precursor of cholesterol and is an intermediate that is subsequently converted into β-hydroxybutyrate, the primary ketone body in the blood (Figure 24.14).

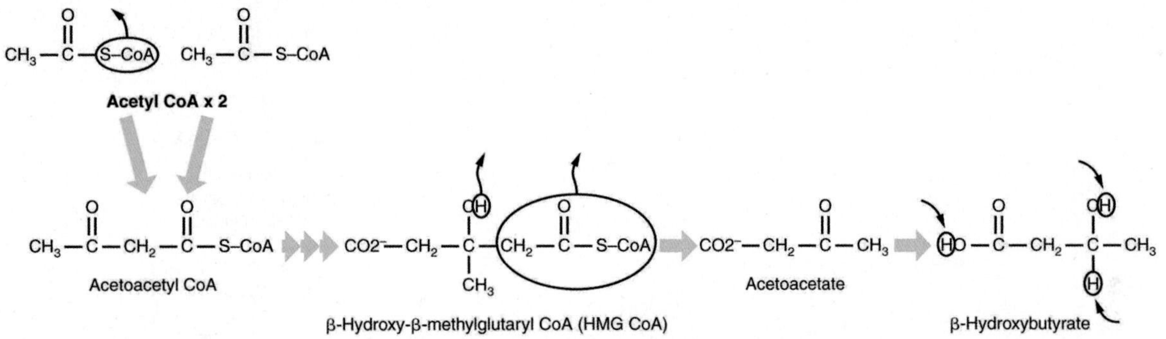

FIGURE 24.14 Ketogenesis Excess acetyl CoA is diverted from the Krebs cycle to the ketogenesis pathway. This reaction occurs in the mitochondria of liver cells. The result is the production of β-hydroxybutyrate, the primary ketone body found in the blood.

Ketone Body Oxidation

Organs that have classically been thought to be dependent solely on glucose, such as the brain, can actually use ketones as an alternative energy source. This keeps the brain functioning when glucose is limited. When ketones are produced faster than they can be used, they can be broken down into CO_2 and acetone. The acetone is removed by exhalation. One symptom of ketogenesis is that the patient's breath smells sweet like alcohol. This effect provides one way of telling if a person with diabetes is properly controlling the disease. The carbon dioxide produced can acidify the blood, leading to diabetic ketoacidosis, a dangerous condition in people with diabetes.

Ketones oxidize to produce energy for the brain. **beta (β)-hydroxybutyrate** is oxidized to acetoacetate and NADH is released. An HS-CoA molecule is added to acetoacetate, forming acetoacetyl CoA. The carbon within the acetoacetyl CoA that is not bonded to the CoA then detaches, splitting the molecule in two. This carbon then attaches to another free HS-CoA, resulting in two acetyl CoA molecules. These two acetyl CoA molecules are then processed through the Krebs cycle to generate energy (Figure 24.15).

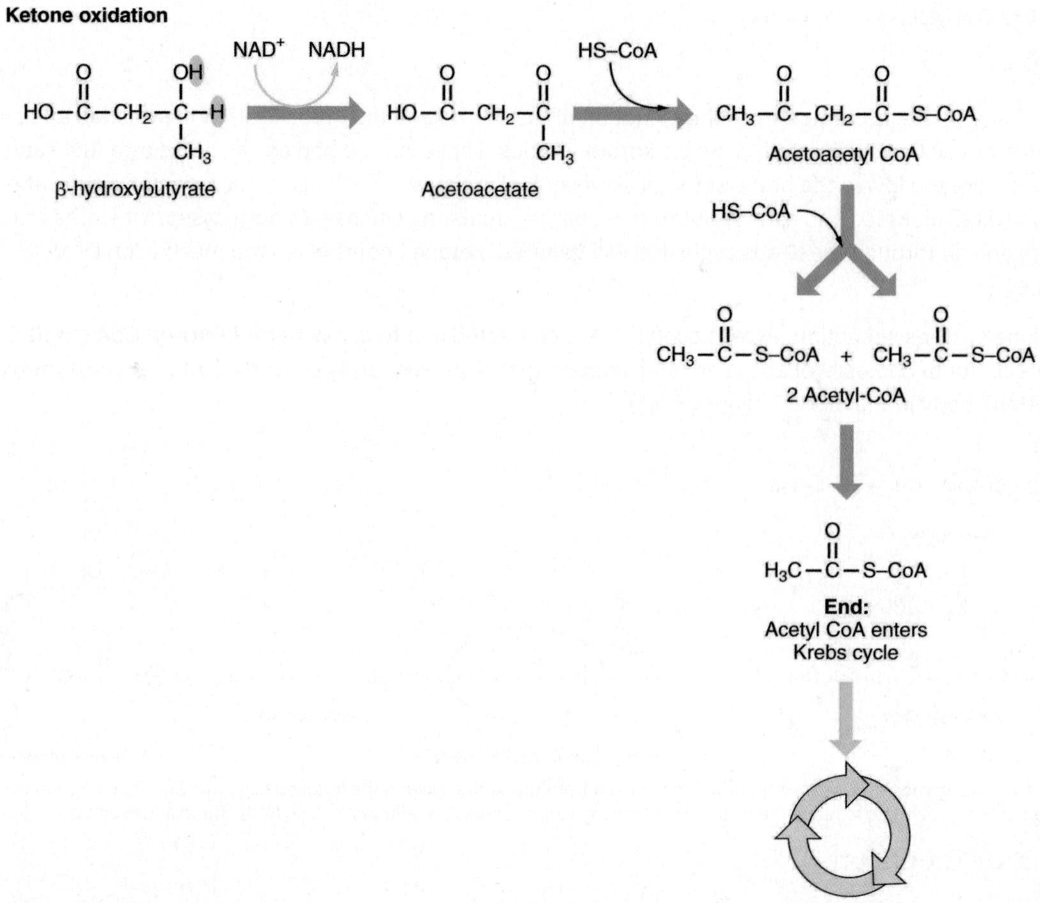

Ketone oxidation

FIGURE 24.15 **Ketone Oxidation**   When glucose is limited, ketone bodies can be oxidized to produce acetyl CoA to be used in the Krebs cycle to generate energy.

Lipogenesis

When glucose levels are plentiful, the excess acetyl CoA generated by glycolysis can be converted into fatty acids, triglycerides, cholesterol, steroids, and bile salts. This process, called **lipogenesis**, creates lipids (fat) from the acetyl CoA and takes place in the cytoplasm of adipocytes (fat cells) and hepatocytes (liver cells). When you eat more glucose or carbohydrates than your body needs, your system uses acetyl CoA to turn the excess into fat. Although there are several metabolic sources of acetyl CoA, it is most commonly derived from glycolysis. Acetyl CoA availability is significant, because it initiates lipogenesis. Lipogenesis begins with acetyl CoA and advances by the subsequent addition of two carbon atoms from another acetyl CoA; this process is repeated until fatty acids are the appropriate length. Because this is a bond-creating anabolic process, ATP is consumed. However, the creation of triglycerides and lipids is an efficient way of storing the energy available in carbohydrates. Triglycerides and lipids, high-energy molecules, are stored in adipose tissue until they are needed.

Although lipogenesis occurs in the cytoplasm, the necessary acetyl CoA is created in the mitochondria and cannot be transported across the mitochondrial membrane. To solve this problem, pyruvate is converted into both oxaloacetate and acetyl CoA. Two different enzymes are required for these conversions. Oxaloacetate forms via the action of pyruvate carboxylase, whereas the action of pyruvate dehydrogenase creates acetyl CoA. Oxaloacetate and acetyl CoA combine to form citrate, which can cross the mitochondrial membrane and enter the cytoplasm. In the cytoplasm, citrate is converted back into oxaloacetate and acetyl CoA. Oxaloacetate is converted into malate and then into pyruvate. Pyruvate crosses back across the mitochondrial membrane to wait for the next cycle of lipogenesis. The acetyl CoA is converted into malonyl CoA that is used to synthesize fatty acids. Figure 24.16 summarizes the pathways of lipid metabolism.

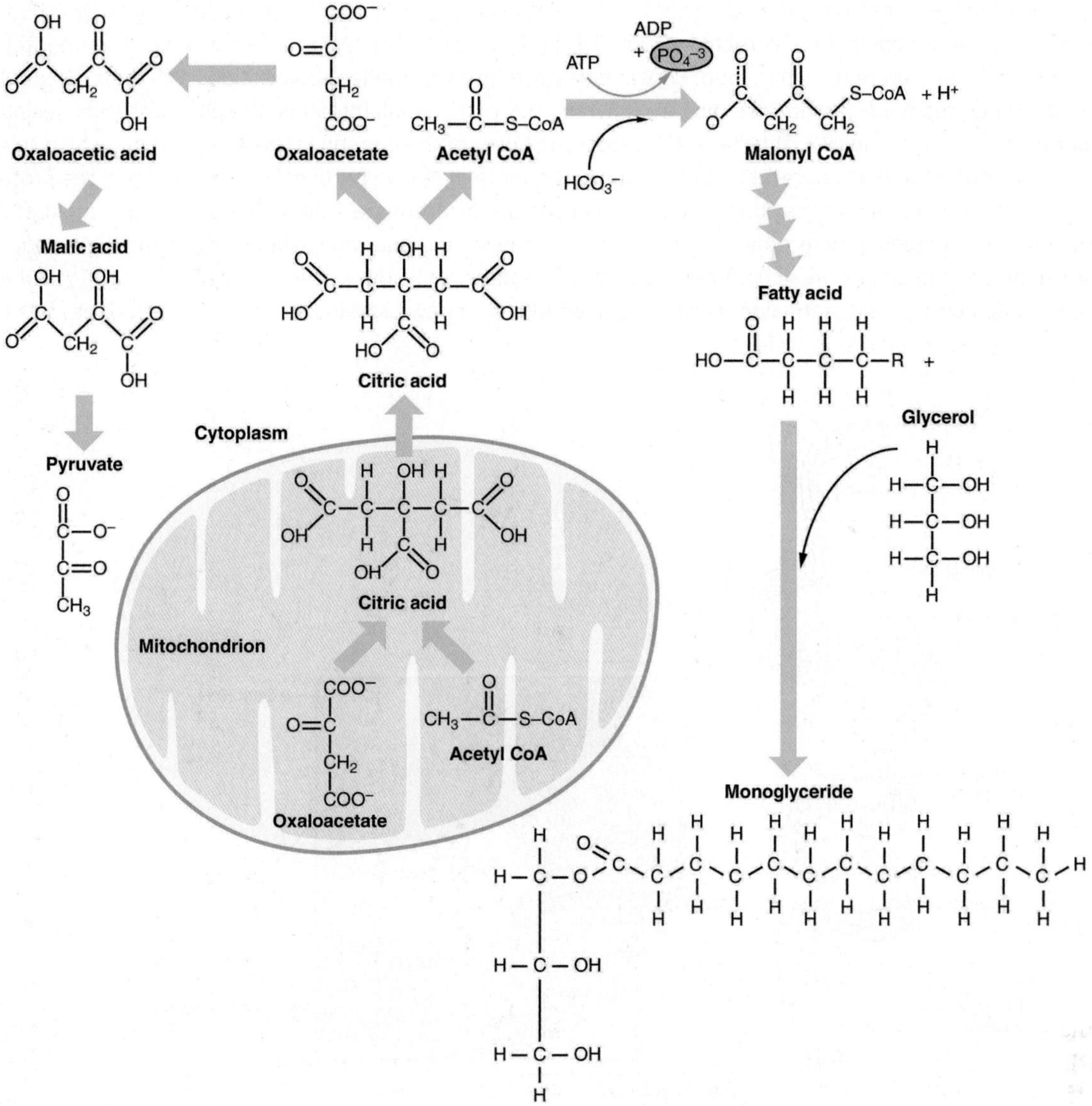

FIGURE 24.16 **Lipid Metabolism** Lipids may follow one of several pathways during metabolism. Glycerol and fatty acids follow different pathways.

24.4 Protein Metabolism

LEARNING OBJECTIVES

By the end of this section, you will be able to:

- Describe how the body digests proteins
- Explain how the urea cycle prevents toxic concentrations of nitrogen
- Differentiate between glucogenic and ketogenic amino acids
- Explain how protein can be used for energy

Much of the body is made of protein, and these proteins take on a myriad of forms. They represent cell signaling receptors, signaling molecules, structural members, enzymes, intracellular trafficking components, extracellular matrix scaffolds, ion pumps, ion channels, oxygen and CO_2 transporters (hemoglobin). That is not even the complete list! There is protein in bones (collagen), muscles, and tendons; the hemoglobin that transports oxygen; and enzymes that catalyze all biochemical reactions. Protein is also used for growth and repair. Amid all these necessary functions, proteins also hold the potential to serve as a metabolic fuel source. Proteins are not stored for later use, so excess proteins must be converted into glucose or triglycerides, and used to supply energy or build energy reserves. Although the body can synthesize proteins from amino acids, food is an important source of those amino acids, especially because humans cannot synthesize all of the 20 amino acids used to build proteins.

The digestion of proteins begins in the stomach. When protein-rich foods enter the stomach, they are greeted by a mixture of the enzyme **pepsin** and hydrochloric acid (HCl; 0.5 percent). The latter produces an environmental pH of 1.5–3.5 that denatures proteins within food. Pepsin cuts proteins into smaller polypeptides and their constituent amino acids. When the food-gastric juice mixture (chyme) enters the small intestine, the pancreas releases **sodium bicarbonate** to neutralize the HCl. This helps to protect the lining of the intestine. The small intestine also releases digestive hormones, including **secretin** and CCK, which stimulate digestive processes to break down the proteins further. Secretin also stimulates the pancreas to release sodium bicarbonate. The pancreas releases most of the digestive enzymes, including the proteases trypsin, chymotrypsin, and **elastase**, which aid protein digestion. Together, all of these enzymes break complex proteins into smaller individual amino acids (Figure 24.17), which are then transported across the intestinal mucosa to be used to create new proteins, or to be converted into fats or acetyl CoA and used in the Krebs cycle.

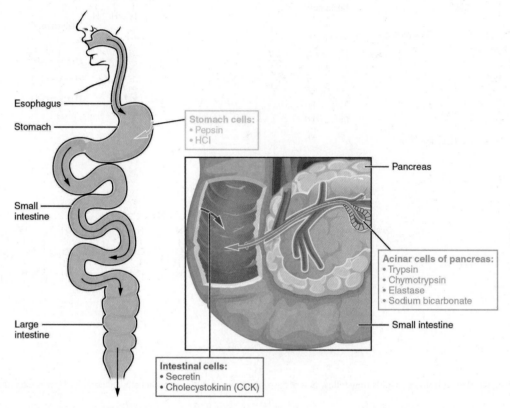

FIGURE 24.17   Digestive Enzymes and Hormones   Enzymes in the stomach and small intestine break down proteins into amino acids. HCl in the stomach aids in proteolysis, and hormones secreted by intestinal cells direct the digestive processes.

In order to avoid breaking down the proteins that make up the pancreas and small intestine, pancreatic enzymes are released as **inactive proenzymes** that are only activated in the small intestine. In the pancreas, vesicles store **trypsin** and **chymotrypsin** as **trypsinogen** and **chymotrypsinogen**. Once released into the small intestine, an enzyme found in the wall of the small intestine, called **enterokinase**, binds to trypsinogen and converts it into its active form, trypsin. Trypsin then binds to chymotrypsinogen to convert it into the active chymotrypsin. Trypsin and chymotrypsin break down large proteins into smaller peptides, a process called **proteolysis**. These smaller peptides are catabolized into their constituent amino acids, which are transported across the apical surface of the intestinal mucosa in a process that is mediated by sodium-amino acid transporters. These transporters bind sodium and then bind the amino acid to transport it across the membrane. At the basal surface of the mucosal cells, the sodium and amino acid are released. The sodium can be reused in the transporter, whereas the amino acids are transferred into the bloodstream to be transported to the liver and cells throughout the body for protein synthesis.

Freely available amino acids are used to create proteins. If amino acids exist in excess, the body has no capacity or mechanism for their storage; thus, they are converted into glucose or ketones, or they are decomposed. Amino acid decomposition results in hydrocarbons and nitrogenous waste. However, high concentrations of nitrogenous byproducts are toxic. The urea cycle processes nitrogen and facilitates its excretion from the body.

Access for free at openstax.org

Urea Cycle

The **urea cycle** is a set of biochemical reactions that produces urea from ammonium ions in order to prevent a toxic level of ammonium in the body. It occurs primarily in the liver and, to a lesser extent, in the kidney. Prior to the urea cycle, ammonium ions are produced from the breakdown of amino acids. In these reactions, an amine group, or ammonium ion, from the amino acid is exchanged with a keto group on another molecule. This **transamination** event creates a molecule that is necessary for the Krebs cycle and an ammonium ion that enters into the urea cycle to be eliminated.

In the urea cycle, ammonium is combined with CO_2, resulting in urea and water. The urea is eliminated through the kidneys in the urine (Figure 24.18).

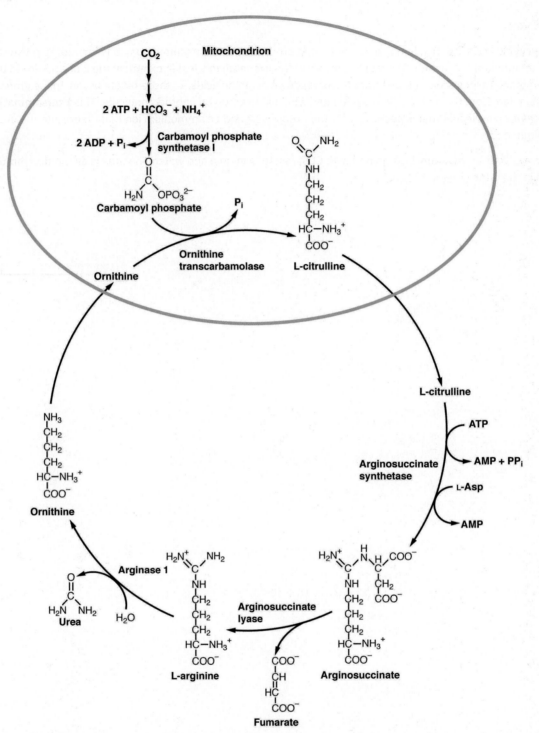

FIGURE 24.18 Urea Cycle Nitrogen is transaminated, creating ammonia and intermediates of the Krebs cycle. Ammonia is processed in the urea cycle to produce urea that is eliminated through the kidneys.

Amino acids can also be used as a source of energy, especially in times of starvation. Because the processing of amino acids results in the creation of metabolic intermediates, including pyruvate, acetyl CoA, acetoacyl CoA, oxaloacetate, and α-ketoglutarate, amino acids can serve as a source of energy production through the Krebs cycle (Figure 24.19). Figure 24.20 summarizes the pathways of catabolism and anabolism for carbohydrates, lipids, and proteins.

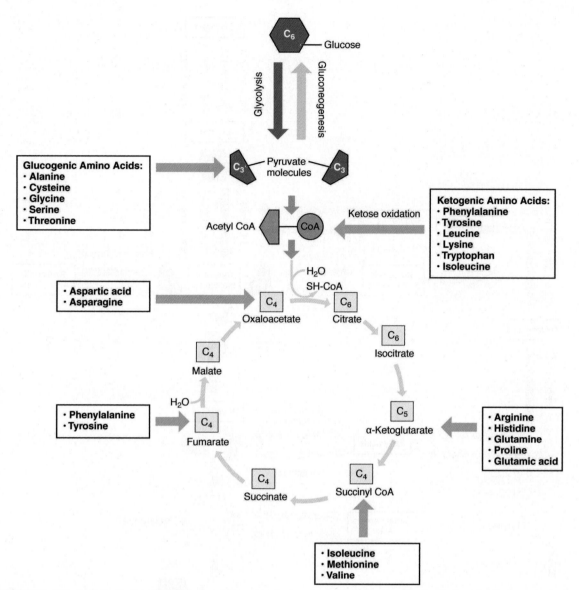

FIGURE 24.19 Energy from Amino Acids   Amino acids can be broken down into precursors for glycolysis or the Krebs cycle. Amino acids (in bold) can enter the cycle through more than one pathway.

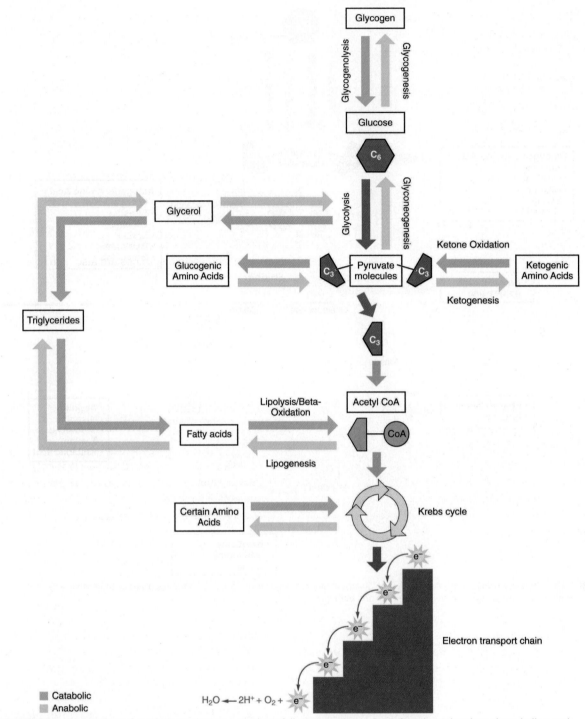

FIGURE 24.20 Catabolic and Anabolic Pathways Nutrients follow a complex pathway from ingestion through anabolism and catabolism to energy production.

Disorders of the...

Metabolism: Pyruvate Dehydrogenase Complex Deficiency and Phenylketonuria

Pyruvate dehydrogenase complex deficiency (PDCD) and phenylketonuria (PKU) are genetic disorders. Pyruvate dehydrogenase is the enzyme that converts pyruvate into acetyl CoA, the molecule necessary to begin the Krebs cycle to produce ATP. With low levels of the pyruvate dehydrogenase complex (PDC), the rate of cycling through the Krebs cycle is dramatically reduced. This results in a decrease in the total amount of energy that is produced by the cells of the body. PDC deficiency results in a neurodegenerative disease that ranges in severity, depending on the levels of the PDC enzyme. It may cause developmental defects, muscle spasms, and death. Treatments can include diet modification, vitamin supplementation, and gene therapy; however, damage to the central nervous system usually cannot be reversed.

PKU affects about 1 in every 15,000 births in the United States. People afflicted with PKU lack sufficient activity of the enzyme phenylalanine hydroxylase and are therefore unable to break down phenylalanine into tyrosine adequately. Because of this, levels of phenylalanine rise to toxic levels in the body, which results in damage to the central nervous system and brain. Symptoms include delayed neurological development, hyperactivity, intellectual disability, seizures, rash, tremors, and uncontrolled movements of the arms and legs. Pregnant people with PKU are at a high risk for exposing the fetus to too much phenylalanine, which can cross the placenta and affect fetal development. Babies exposed to excess phenylalanine in utero may present with heart defects, physical and/or intellectual disability, and microcephaly. Every infant in the United States and Canada is tested at birth to determine whether PKU is present. The earlier a modified diet is begun, the less severe the symptoms will be. The person must closely follow a strict diet that is low in phenylalanine to avoid symptoms and damage. Phenylalanine is found in high concentrations in artificial sweeteners, including aspartame. Therefore, these sweeteners must be avoided. Some animal products and certain starches are also high in phenylalanine, and intake of these foods should be carefully monitored.

24.5 Metabolic States of the Body

LEARNING OBJECTIVES

By the end of this section, you will be able to:

- Describe what defines each of the three metabolic states
- Describe the processes that occur during the absorptive state of metabolism
- Describe the processes that occur during the postabsorptive state of metabolism
- Explain how the body processes glucose when the body is starved of fuel

You eat periodically throughout the day; however, your organs, especially the brain, need a continuous supply of glucose. How does the body meet this constant demand for energy? Your body processes the food you eat both to use immediately and, importantly, to store as energy for later demands. If there were no method in place to store excess energy, you would need to eat constantly in order to meet energy demands. Distinct mechanisms are in place to facilitate energy storage, and to make stored energy available during times of fasting and starvation.

The Absorptive State

The **absorptive state**, or the fed state, occurs after a meal when your body is digesting the food and absorbing the nutrients (anabolism exceeds catabolism). Digestion begins the moment you put food into your mouth, as the food is broken down into its constituent parts to be absorbed through the intestine. The digestion of carbohydrates begins in the mouth, whereas the digestion of proteins and fats begins in the stomach and small intestine. The constituent parts of these carbohydrates, fats, and proteins are transported across the intestinal wall and enter the bloodstream (sugars and amino acids) or the lymphatic system (fats). From the intestines, these systems transport them to the liver, adipose tissue, or muscle cells that will process and use, or store, the energy.

Depending on the amounts and types of nutrients ingested, the absorptive state can linger for up to 4 hours. The ingestion of food and the rise of glucose concentrations in the bloodstream stimulate pancreatic beta cells to release **insulin** into the bloodstream, where it initiates the absorption of blood glucose by liver hepatocytes, and by adipose and muscle cells. Once inside these cells, glucose is immediately converted into glucose-6-phosphate. By doing this, a concentration gradient is established where glucose levels are higher in the blood than in the cells. This allows for glucose to continue moving from the blood to the cells where it is needed. Insulin also stimulates the storage of glucose as glycogen in the liver and muscle cells where it can be used for later energy needs of the body. Insulin also promotes the synthesis of protein in muscle. As you will see, muscle protein can be catabolized and used as fuel in times of starvation.

If energy is exerted shortly after eating, the dietary fats and sugars that were just ingested will be processed and used immediately for energy. If not, the excess glucose is stored as glycogen in the liver and muscle cells, or as fat in adipose tissue; excess dietary fat is also stored as triglycerides in adipose tissues.

Figure 24.21 summarizes the metabolic processes occurring in the body during the absorptive state.

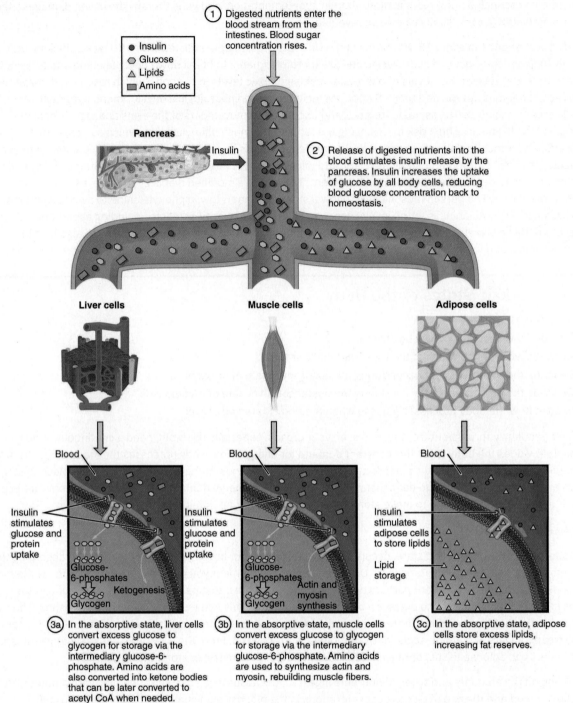

FIGURE 24.21 Absorptive State   During the absorptive state, the body digests food and absorbs the nutrients.

The Postabsorptive State

The **postabsorptive state**, or the fasting state, occurs when the food has been digested, absorbed, and stored. You commonly fast overnight, but skipping meals during the day puts your body in the postabsorptive state as well. During this state, the body must rely initially on stored **glycogen**. Glucose levels in the blood begin to drop as it is absorbed and used by the cells. In response to the decrease in glucose, insulin levels also drop. Glycogen and triglyceride storage slows. However, due to the demands of the tissues and organs, blood glucose levels must be maintained in the normal range of 80–120 mg/dL. In response to a drop in blood glucose concentration, the hormone glucagon is released from the alpha cells of the pancreas. Glucagon acts upon the liver cells, where it inhibits the synthesis of glycogen and stimulates the breakdown of stored glycogen back into glucose. This glucose is released from the liver to be used by the peripheral tissues and the brain. As a result, blood glucose levels begin to rise. Gluconeogenesis will also begin in the liver to replace the glucose that has been used by the peripheral tissues.

After ingestion of food, fats and proteins are processed as described previously; however, the glucose processing changes a bit. The peripheral tissues preferentially absorb glucose. The liver, which normally absorbs and processes glucose, will not do so after a prolonged fast. The gluconeogenesis that has been ongoing in the liver will continue after fasting to replace the glycogen stores that were depleted in the liver. After these stores have been replenished, excess glucose that is absorbed by the liver will be converted into triglycerides and fatty acids for long-term storage. Figure 24.22 summarizes the metabolic processes occurring in the body during the postabsorptive state.

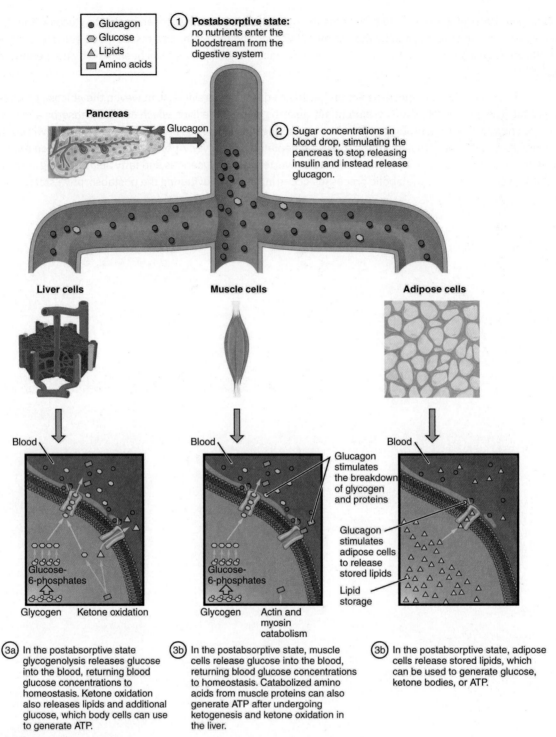

FIGURE 24.22 Postabsorptive State   During the postabsorptive state, the body must rely on stored glycogen for energy.

Starvation

When the body is deprived of nourishment for an extended period of time, it goes into "survival mode." The first priority for survival is to provide enough glucose or fuel for the brain. The second priority is the conservation of amino acids for proteins. Therefore, the body uses ketones to satisfy the energy needs of the brain and other glucose-dependent organs, and to maintain proteins in the cells (see Figure 24.2). Because glucose levels are very low during starvation, glycolysis will shut off in cells that can use alternative fuels. For example, muscles will switch from using glucose to fatty acids as fuel. As previously explained, fatty acids can be converted into acetyl CoA and processed through the Krebs cycle to make ATP. Pyruvate, lactate, and alanine from muscle cells are not converted into acetyl CoA and used in the Krebs cycle, but are exported to the liver to be used in the synthesis of glucose. As starvation continues, and more glucose is needed, glycerol from fatty acids can be liberated and used as a source for gluconeogenesis.

After several days of starvation, ketone bodies become the major source of fuel for the heart and other organs. As starvation continues, fatty acids and triglyceride stores are used to create ketones for the body. This prevents the continued breakdown of proteins that serve as carbon sources for gluconeogenesis. Once these stores are fully depleted, proteins from muscles are released and broken down for glucose synthesis. Overall survival is dependent on the amount of fat and protein stored in the body.

24.6 Energy and Heat Balance

LEARNING OBJECTIVES

By the end of this section, you will be able to:

- Describe how the body regulates temperature
- Explain the significance of the metabolic rate

The body tightly regulates the body temperature through a process called **thermoregulation**, in which the body can maintain its temperature within certain boundaries, even when the surrounding temperature is very different. The core temperature of the body remains steady at around 36.5–37.5 °C (or 97.7–99.5 °F). In the process of ATP production by cells throughout the body, approximately 60 percent of the energy produced is in the form of heat used to maintain body temperature. Thermoregulation is an example of negative feedback.

The hypothalamus in the brain is the master switch that works as a thermostat to regulate the body's core temperature (Figure 24.23). If the temperature is too high, the hypothalamus can initiate several processes to lower it. These include increasing the circulation of the blood to the surface of the body to allow for the dissipation of heat through the skin and initiation of sweating to allow evaporation of water on the skin to cool its surface. Conversely, if the temperature falls below the set core temperature, the hypothalamus can initiate shivering to generate heat. The body uses more energy and generates more heat. In addition, thyroid hormone will stimulate more energy use and heat production by cells throughout the body. An environment is said to be **thermoneutral** when the body does not expend or release energy to maintain its core temperature. For a naked human, this is an ambient air temperature of around 84 °F. If the temperature is higher, for example, when wearing clothes, the body compensates with cooling mechanisms. The body loses heat through the mechanisms of heat exchange.

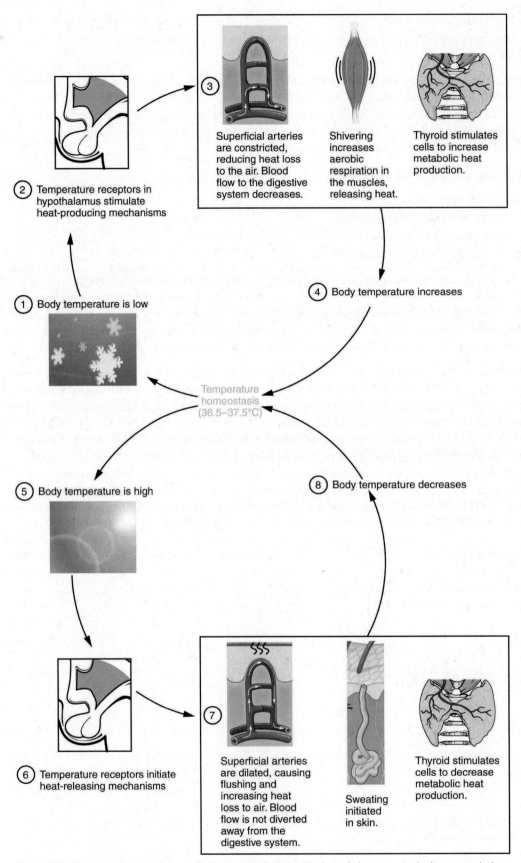

FIGURE 24.23 Hypothalamus Controls Thermoregulation   The hypothalamus controls thermoregulation.

Mechanisms of Heat Exchange

When the environment is not thermoneutral, the body uses four mechanisms of heat exchange to maintain homeostasis: conduction, convection, radiation, and evaporation. Each of these mechanisms relies on the property of heat to flow from a higher concentration to a lower concentration; therefore, each of the mechanisms of heat exchange varies in rate according to the temperature and conditions of the environment.

Conduction is the transfer of heat by two objects that are in direct contact with one another. It occurs when the skin comes in contact with a cold or warm object. For example, when holding a glass of ice water, the heat from your skin will warm the glass and in turn melt the ice. Alternatively, on a cold day, you might warm up by wrapping your cold hands around a hot mug of coffee. Only about 3 percent of the body's heat is lost through conduction.

Convection is the transfer of heat to the air surrounding the skin. The warmed air rises away from the body and is replaced by cooler air that is subsequently heated. Convection can also occur in water. When the water temperature is lower than the body's temperature, the body loses heat by warming the water closest to the skin, which moves away to be replaced by cooler water. The convection currents created by the temperature changes continue to draw heat away from the body more quickly than the body can replace it, resulting in hyperthermia. About 15 percent of the body's heat is lost through convection.

Radiation is the transfer of heat via infrared waves. This occurs between any two objects when their temperatures differ. A radiator can warm a room via radiant heat. On a sunny day, the radiation from the sun warms the skin. The same principle works from the body to the environment. About 60 percent of the heat lost by the body is lost through radiation.

Evaporation is the transfer of heat by the evaporation of water. Because it takes a great deal of energy for a water molecule to change from a liquid to a gas, evaporating water (in the form of sweat) takes with it a great deal of energy from the skin. However, the rate at which evaporation occurs depends on relative humidity—more sweat evaporates in lower humidity environments. Sweating is the primary means of cooling the body during exercise, whereas at rest, about 20 percent of the heat lost by the body occurs through evaporation.

Metabolic Rate

The **metabolic rate** is the amount of energy consumed minus the amount of energy expended by the body. The **basal metabolic rate (BMR)** describes the amount of daily energy expended by humans at rest, in a neutrally temperate environment, while in the postabsorptive state. It measures how much energy the body needs for normal, basic, daily activity. About 70 percent of all daily energy expenditure comes from the basic functions of the organs in the body. Another 20 percent comes from physical activity, and the remaining 10 percent is necessary for body thermoregulation or temperature control. This rate will be higher if a person is more active or has more lean body mass. As you age, the BMR generally decreases as the percentage of less lean muscle mass decreases.

24.7 Nutrition and Diet

LEARNING OBJECTIVES

By the end of this section, you will be able to:

- Explain how different foods can affect metabolism
- Describe a healthy diet, as recommended by the U.S. Department of Agriculture (USDA)
- List reasons why vitamins and minerals are critical to a healthy diet

The carbohydrates, lipids, and proteins in the foods you eat are used for energy to power molecular, cellular, and organ system activities. Importantly, the energy is stored primarily as fats. The quantity and quality of food that is ingested, digested, and absorbed affects the amount of fat that is stored as excess calories. Diet—both what you eat and how much you eat—has a dramatic impact on your health. Eating too much or too little food can lead to serious medical issues, including cardiovascular disease, cancer, anorexia, and diabetes, among others. Combine an unhealthy diet with unhealthy environmental conditions, such as smoking, and the potential medical complications increase significantly.

Food and Metabolism

The amount of energy that is needed or ingested per day is measured in calories. The nutritional **Calorie** (C) is the amount of heat it takes to raise 1 kg (1000 g) of water by 1 °C. This is different from the calorie (c) used in the physical sciences, which is the amount of heat it takes to raise 1 g of water by 1 °C. When we refer to "calorie," we are referring to the nutritional Calorie.

On average, a person needs 1500 to 2000 calories per day to sustain (or carry out) daily activities. The total number of calories needed by one person is dependent on their body mass, age, height, gender, activity level, and the amount of exercise per day. If exercise is regular part of one's day, more calories are required. As a rule, people underestimate the number of calories ingested and overestimate the amount they burn through exercise. This can lead to ingestion of too many calories per day. The accumulation of an extra 3500 calories adds one pound of weight. If an excess of 200 calories per day is ingested, one extra pound of body weight will be gained every 18 days. At that rate, an extra 20 pounds can be gained over the course of a year. Of course, this increase in calories could be offset by increased exercise. Running or jogging one mile burns almost 100 calories.

The type of food ingested also affects the body's metabolic rate. Processing of carbohydrates requires less energy than processing of proteins. In fact, the breakdown of carbohydrates requires the least amount of energy, whereas the processing of proteins demands the most energy. In general, the amount of calories ingested and the amount of calories burned determines the overall weight. To lose weight, the number of calories burned per day must exceed the number ingested. Calories are in almost everything you ingest, so when considering calorie intake, beverages must also be considered.

To help provide guidelines regarding the types and quantities of food that should be eaten every day, the USDA has updated their food guidelines from MyPyramid to MyPlate. They have put the recommended elements of a healthy meal into the context of a place setting of food. MyPlate categorizes food into the standard six food groups: fruits, vegetables, grains, protein foods, dairy, and oils. The accompanying website gives clear recommendations regarding quantity and type of each food that you should consume each day, as well as identifying which foods belong in each category. The accompanying graphic (Figure 24.24) gives a clear visual with general recommendations for a healthy and balanced meal. The guidelines recommend to "Make half your plate fruits and vegetables." The other half is grains and protein, with a slightly higher quantity of grains than protein. Dairy products are represented by a drink, but the quantity can be applied to other dairy products as well.

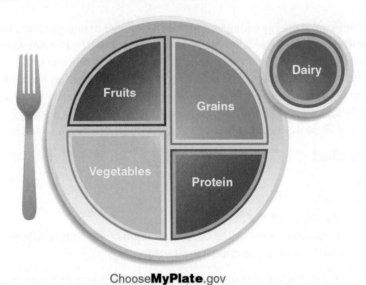

Choose**MyPlate**.gov

FIGURE 24.24 MyPlate   The U.S. Department of Agriculture developed food guidelines called MyPlate to help demonstrate how to maintain a healthy lifestyle.

ChooseMyPlate.gov provides extensive online resources for planning a healthy diet and lifestyle, including offering weight management tips and recommendations for physical activity. It also includes the SuperTracker, a web-based application to help you analyze your own diet and physical activity.

Everyday Connection

Metabolism and Obesity

Obesity in the United States is epidemic. The rate of obesity has been steadily rising since the 1980s. In the 1990s, most states reported that less than 10 percent of their populations was obese, and the state with the highest rate reported that only 15 percent of their population was considered obese. By 2010, the U.S. Centers for Disease Control and Prevention reported that nearly 36 percent of adults over 20 years old were obese and an additional 33 percent were overweight, leaving only about 30 percent of the population at a healthy weight. These studies find the highest levels of obesity are concentrated in the southern states. They also find the level of childhood obesity is rising.

Obesity is defined by the **body mass index (BMI)**, which is a measure of a person's weight in kilograms divided by height in meters squared. The normal, or healthy, BMI range is between 18 and 24.9 kg/m^2. Overweight is defined as a BMI of 25 to 29.9 kg/m^2, and obesity is considered to be a BMI greater than 30 kg/m^2. Obesity can arise from a number of factors, including overeating, poor diet, sedentary lifestyle, limited sleep, genetic factors, and even diseases or drugs. Severe obesity (morbid obesity) or long-term obesity can result in serious medical conditions, including coronary heart disease; type 2 diabetes; endometrial, breast, or colon cancer; hypertension (high blood pressure); dyslipidemia (high cholesterol or elevated triglycerides); stroke; liver disease; gall bladder disease; sleep apnea or respiratory diseases; osteoarthritis; and infertility. Research has shown that losing weight can help reduce or reverse the complications associated with these conditions.

Vitamins

Vitamins are organic compounds found in foods and are a necessary part of the biochemical reactions in the body. They are involved in a number of processes, including mineral and bone metabolism, and cell and tissue growth, and they act as cofactors for energy metabolism. The B vitamins play the largest role of any vitamins in metabolism (Table 24.3 and Table 24.4).

You get most of your vitamins through your diet, although some can be formed from the precursors absorbed during digestion. For example, the body synthesizes vitamin A from the β-carotene in orange vegetables like carrots and sweet potatoes. Vitamins are either fat-soluble or water-soluble. Fat-soluble vitamins A, D, E, and K, are absorbed through the intestinal tract with lipids in chylomicrons. Vitamin D is also synthesized in the skin through exposure to sunlight. Because they are carried in lipids, fat-soluble vitamins can accumulate in the lipids stored in the body. If excess vitamins are retained in the lipid stores in the body, hypervitaminosis can result.

Water-soluble vitamins, including the eight B vitamins and vitamin C, are absorbed with water in the gastrointestinal tract. These vitamins move easily through bodily fluids, which are water based, so they are not stored in the body. Excess water-soluble vitamins are excreted in the urine. Therefore, hypervitaminosis of water-soluble vitamins rarely occurs, except with an excess of vitamin supplements.

Fat-soluble Vitamins

Vitamin and alternative name	Sources	Recommended daily allowance	Function	Problems associated with deficiency
A retinal or β-carotene	Yellow and orange fruits and vegetables, dark green leafy vegetables, eggs, milk, liver	700–900 µg	Eye and bone development, immune function	Night blindness, epithelial changes, immune system deficiency
D cholecalciferol	Dairy products, egg yolks; also synthesized in the skin from exposure to sunlight	5–15 µg	Aids in calcium absorption, promoting bone growth	Rickets, bone pain, muscle weakness, increased risk of death from cardiovascular disease, cognitive impairment, asthma in children, cancer
E tocopherols	Seeds, nuts, vegetable oils, avocados, wheat germ	15 mg	Antioxidant	Anemia
K phylloquinone	Dark green leafy vegetables, broccoli, Brussels sprouts, cabbage	90–120 µg	Blood clotting, bone health	Hemorrhagic disease of newborn in infants; uncommon in adults

TABLE 24.3

Water-soluble Vitamins

Vitamin and alternative name	Sources	Recommended daily allowance	Function	Problems associated with deficiency
B_1 thiamine	Whole grains, enriched bread and cereals, milk, meat	1.1–1.2 mg	Carbohydrate metabolism	Beriberi, Wernicke-Korsakoff syndrome
B_2 riboflavin	Brewer's yeast, almonds, milk, organ meats, legumes, enriched breads and cereals, broccoli, asparagus	1.1–1.3 mg	Synthesis of FAD for metabolism, production of red blood cells	Fatigue, slowed growth, digestive problems, light sensitivity, epithelial problems like cracks in the corners of the mouth

TABLE 24.4

Vitamin and alternative name	Sources	Recommended daily allowance	Function	Problems associated with deficiency
B_3 niacin	Meat, fish, poultry, enriched breads and cereals, peanuts	14–16 mg	Synthesis of NAD, nerve function, cholesterol production	Cracked, scaly skin; dementia; diarrhea; also known as pellagra
B_5 pantothenic acid	Meat, poultry, potatoes, oats, enriched breads and cereals, tomatoes	5 mg	Synthesis of coenzyme A in fatty acid metabolism	Rare: symptoms may include fatigue, insomnia, depression, irritability
B_6 pyridoxine	Potatoes, bananas, beans, seeds, nuts, meat, poultry, fish, eggs, dark green leafy vegetables, soy, organ meats	1.3–1.5 mg	Sodium and potassium balance, red blood cell synthesis, protein metabolism	Confusion, irritability, depression, mouth and tongue sores
B_7 biotin	Liver, fruits, meats	30 µg	Cell growth, metabolism of fatty acids, production of blood cells	Rare in developed countries; symptoms include dermatitis, hair loss, loss of muscular coordination
B_9 folic acid	Liver, legumes, dark green leafy vegetables, enriched breads and cereals, citrus fruits	400 µg	DNA/protein synthesis	Poor growth, gingivitis, appetite loss, shortness of breath, gastrointestinal problems, mental deficits
B_{12} cyanocobalamin	Fish, meat, poultry, dairy products, eggs	2.4 µg	Fatty acid oxidation, nerve cell function, red blood cell production	Pernicious anemia, leading to nerve cell damage
C ascorbic acid	Citrus fruits, red berries, peppers, tomatoes, broccoli, dark green leafy vegetables	75–90 mg	Necessary to produce collagen for formation of connective tissue and teeth, and for wound healing	Dry hair, gingivitis, bleeding gums, dry and scaly skin, slow wound healing, easy bruising, compromised immunity; can lead to scurvy

TABLE 24.4

Minerals

Minerals in food are inorganic compounds that work with other nutrients to ensure the body functions properly. Minerals cannot be made in the body; they come from the diet. The amount of minerals in the body is small—only 4 percent of the total body mass—and most of that consists of the minerals that the body requires in moderate quantities: potassium, sodium, calcium, phosphorus, magnesium, and chloride.

The most common minerals in the body are calcium and phosphorous, both of which are stored in the skeleton and necessary for the hardening of bones. Most minerals are ionized, and their ionic forms are used in physiological processes throughout the body. Sodium and chloride ions are electrolytes in the blood and extracellular tissues, and iron ions are critical to the formation of hemoglobin. There are additional trace minerals that are still important to the body's functions, but their required quantities are much lower.

Like vitamins, minerals can be consumed in toxic quantities (although it is rare). A healthy diet includes most of the minerals your body requires, so supplements and processed foods can add potentially toxic levels of minerals. Table 24.5 and Table 24.6 provide a summary of minerals and their function in the body.

Major Minerals

Mineral	Sources	Recommended daily allowance	Function	Problems associated with deficiency
Potassium	Meats, some fish, fruits, vegetables, legumes, dairy products	4700 mg	Nerve and muscle function; acts as an electrolyte	Hypokalemia: weakness, fatigue, muscle cramping, gastrointestinal problems, cardiac problems
Sodium	Table salt, milk, beets, celery, processed foods	2300 mg	Blood pressure, blood volume, muscle and nerve function	Rare
Calcium	Dairy products, dark green leafy vegetables, blackstrap molasses, nuts, brewer's yeast, some fish	1000 mg	Bone structure and health; nerve and muscle functions, especially cardiac function	Slow growth, weak and brittle bones
Phosphorous	Meat, milk	700 mg	Bone formation, metabolism, ATP production	Rare
Magnesium	Whole grains, nuts, leafy green vegetables	310–420 mg	Enzyme activation, production of energy, regulation of other nutrients	Agitation, anxiety, sleep problems, nausea and vomiting, abnormal heart rhythms, low blood pressure, muscular problems
Chloride	Most foods, salt, vegetables, especially seaweed, tomatoes, lettuce, celery, olives	2300 mg	Balance of body fluids, digestion	Loss of appetite, muscle cramps

TABLE 24.5

Trace Minerals

Mineral	Sources	Recommended daily allowance	Function	Problems associated with deficiency
Iron	Meat, poultry, fish, shellfish, legumes, nuts, seeds, whole grains, dark leafy green vegetables	8–18 mg	Transport of oxygen in blood, production of ATP	Anemia, weakness, fatigue
Zinc	Meat, fish, poultry, cheese, shellfish	8–11 mg	Immunity, reproduction, growth, blood clotting, insulin and thyroid function	Loss of appetite, poor growth, weight loss, skin problems, hair loss, vision problems, lack of taste or smell
Copper	Seafood, organ meats, nuts, legumes, chocolate, enriched breads and cereals, some fruits and vegetables	900 μg	Red blood cell production, nerve and immune system function, collagen formation, acts as an antioxidant	Anemia, low body temperature, bone fractures, low white blood cell concentration, irregular heartbeat, thyroid problems
Iodine	Fish, shellfish, garlic, lima beans, sesame seeds, soybeans, dark leafy green vegetables	150 μg	Thyroid function	Hypothyroidism: fatigue, weight gain, dry skin, temperature sensitivity
Sulfur	Eggs, meat, poultry, fish, legumes	None	Component of amino acids	Protein deficiency
Fluoride	Fluoridated water	3–4 mg	Maintenance of bone and tooth structure	Increased cavities, weak bones and teeth
Manganese	Nuts, seeds, whole grains, legumes	1.8–2.3 mg	Formation of connective tissue and bones, blood clotting, sex hormone development, metabolism, brain and nerve function	Infertility, bone malformation, weakness, seizures
Cobalt	Fish, nuts, leafy green vegetables, whole grains	None	Component of B_{12}	None

TABLE 24.6

Mineral	Sources	Recommended daily allowance	Function	Problems associated with deficiency
Selenium	Brewer's yeast, wheat germ, liver, butter, fish, shellfish, whole grains	55 μg	Antioxidant, thyroid function, immune system function	Muscle pain
Chromium	Whole grains, lean meats, cheese, black pepper, thyme, brewer's yeast	25–35 μg	Insulin function	High blood sugar, triglyceride, and cholesterol levels
Molybdenum	Legumes, whole grains, nuts	45 μg	Cofactor for enzymes	Rare

TABLE 24.6

Key Terms

absorptive state   also called the fed state; the metabolic state occurring during the first few hours after ingesting food in which the body is digesting food and absorbing the nutrients

acetyl coenzyme A (acetyl CoA)   starting molecule of the Krebs cycle

anabolic hormones   hormones that stimulate the synthesis of new, larger molecules

anabolic reactions   reactions that build smaller molecules into larger molecules

ATP synthase   protein pore complex that creates ATP

basal metabolic rate (BMR)   amount of energy expended by the body at rest

beta (β)-hydroxybutyrate   primary ketone body produced in the body

beta (β)-oxidation   fatty acid oxidation

bile salts   salts that are released from the liver in response to lipid ingestion and surround the insoluble triglycerides to aid in their conversion to monoglycerides and free fatty acids

biosynthesis reactions   reactions that create new molecules, also called anabolic reactions

body mass index (BMI)   relative amount of body weight compared to the overall height; a BMI ranging from 18–24.9 is considered normal weight, 25–29.9 is considered overweight, and greater than 30 is considered obese

calorie   amount of heat it takes to raise 1 kg (1000 g) of water by 1 °C

catabolic hormones   hormones that stimulate the breakdown of larger molecules

catabolic reactions   reactions that break down larger molecules into their constituent parts

cellular respiration   production of ATP from glucose oxidation via glycolysis, the Krebs cycle, and oxidative phosphorylation

cholecystokinin (CCK)   hormone that stimulates the release of pancreatic lipase and the contraction of the gallbladder to release bile salts

chylomicrons   vesicles containing cholesterol and triglycerides that transport lipids out of the intestinal cells and into the lymphatic and circulatory systems

chymotrypsin   pancreatic enzyme that digests protein

chymotrypsinogen   proenzyme that is activated by trypsin into chymotrypsin

citric acid cycle   also called the Krebs cycle or the tricarboxylic acid cycle; converts pyruvate into CO_2 and high-energy $FADH_2$, NADH, and ATP molecules

conduction   transfer of heat through physical contact

convection   transfer of heat between the skin and air or water

elastase   pancreatic enzyme that digests protein

electron transport chain (ETC)   ATP production pathway in which electrons are passed through a series of oxidation-reduction reactions that forms water and produces a proton gradient

energy-consuming phase   first phase of glycolysis, in which two molecules of ATP are necessary to start the reaction

energy-yielding phase   second phase of glycolysis, during which energy is produced

enterokinase   enzyme located in the wall of the small intestine that activates trypsin

evaporation   transfer of heat that occurs when water changes from a liquid to a gas

$FADH_2$ high-energy molecule needed for glycolysis

fatty acid oxidation   breakdown of fatty acids into smaller chain fatty acids and acetyl CoA

flavin adenine dinucleotide (FAD)   coenzyme used to produce $FADH_2$

glucokinase   cellular enzyme, found in the liver, which converts glucose into glucose-6-phosphate upon uptake into the cell

gluconeogenesis   process of glucose synthesis from pyruvate or other molecules

glucose-6-phosphate   phosphorylated glucose produced in the first step of glycolysis

glycogen   form that glucose assumes when it is stored

glycolysis   series of metabolic reactions that breaks down glucose into pyruvate and produces ATP

hexokinase   cellular enzyme, found in most tissues, that converts glucose into glucose-6-phosphate upon uptake into the cell

hydroxymethylglutaryl CoA (HMG CoA)   molecule created in the first step of the creation of ketone bodies from acetyl CoA

inactive proenzymes   forms in which proteases are stored and released to prevent the inappropriate digestion of the native proteins of the stomach, pancreas, and small intestine

insulin   hormone secreted by the pancreas that stimulates the uptake of glucose into the cells

ketone bodies   alternative source of energy when glucose is limited, created when too much acetyl CoA is created during fatty acid oxidation

Krebs cycle   also called the citric acid cycle or the tricarboxylic acid cycle, converts pyruvate into CO_2 and high-energy $FADH_2$, NADH, and ATP molecules

lipogenesis   synthesis of lipids that occurs in the liver or adipose tissues

lipolysis   breakdown of triglycerides into glycerol and fatty acids

metabolic rate   amount of energy consumed minus

the amount of energy expended by the body

metabolism   sum of all catabolic and anabolic reactions that take place in the body

minerals   inorganic compounds required by the body to ensure proper function of the body

monoglyceride molecules   lipid consisting of a single fatty acid chain attached to a glycerol backbone

monosaccharide   smallest, monomeric sugar molecule

NADH   high-energy molecule needed for glycolysis

nicotinamide adenine dinucleotide (NAD)   coenzyme used to produce NADH

oxidation   loss of an electron

oxidation-reduction reaction   (also, redox reaction) pair of reactions in which an electron is passed from one molecule to another, oxidizing one and reducing the other

oxidative phosphorylation   process that converts high-energy NADH and $FADH_2$ into ATP

pancreatic lipases   enzymes released from the pancreas that digest lipids in the diet

pepsin   enzyme that begins to break down proteins in the stomach

polysaccharides   complex carbohydrates made up of many monosaccharides

postabsorptive state   also called the fasting state; the metabolic state occurring after digestion when food is no longer the body's source of energy and it must rely on stored glycogen

proteolysis   process of breaking proteins into smaller peptides

pyruvate   three-carbon end product of glycolysis and starting material that is converted into acetyl CoA that enters the Krebs cycle

radiation   transfer of heat via infrared waves

reduction   gaining of an electron

salivary amylase   digestive enzyme that is found in the saliva and begins the digestion of carbohydrates in the mouth

secretin   hormone released in the small intestine to aid in digestion

sodium bicarbonate   anion released into the small intestine to neutralize the pH of the food from the stomach

terminal electron acceptor   oxygen, the recipient of the free hydrogen at the end of the electron transport chain

thermoneutral   external temperature at which the body does not expend any energy for thermoregulation, about 84 °F

thermoregulation   process of regulating the temperature of the body

transamination   transfer of an amine group from one molecule to another as a way to turn nitrogen waste into ammonia so that it can enter the urea cycle

tricarboxylic acid cycle (TCA)   also called the Krebs cycle or the citric acid cycle; converts pyruvate into CO_2 and high-energy $FADH_2$, NADH, and ATP molecules

triglycerides   lipids, or fats, consisting of three fatty acid chains attached to a glycerol backbone

trypsin   pancreatic enzyme that activates chymotrypsin and digests protein

trypsinogen   proenzyme form of trypsin

urea cycle   process that converts potentially toxic nitrogen waste into urea that can be eliminated through the kidneys

vitamins   organic compounds required by the body to perform biochemical reactions like metabolism and bone, cell, and tissue growth

Chapter Review

24.1 Overview of Metabolic Reactions

Metabolism is the sum of all catabolic (break down) and anabolic (synthesis) reactions in the body. The metabolic rate measures the amount of energy used to maintain life. An organism must ingest a sufficient amount of food to maintain its metabolic rate if the organism is to stay alive for very long.

Catabolic reactions break down larger molecules, such as carbohydrates, lipids, and proteins from ingested food, into their constituent smaller parts. They also include the breakdown of ATP, which releases the energy needed for metabolic processes in all cells throughout the body.

Anabolic reactions, or biosynthetic reactions, synthesize larger molecules from smaller constituent parts, using ATP as the energy source for these reactions. Anabolic reactions build bone, muscle mass, and new proteins, fats, and nucleic acids. Oxidation-reduction reactions transfer electrons across molecules by oxidizing one molecule and reducing another, and collecting the released energy to convert P_i and ADP into ATP. Errors in metabolism alter the processing of carbohydrates, lipids, proteins, and nucleic acids, and can result in a number of disease states.

24.2 Carbohydrate Metabolism

Metabolic enzymes catalyze catabolic reactions that break down carbohydrates contained in food. The energy released is used to power the cells and systems that make up your body. Excess or unutilized energy is stored as fat or glycogen for later use. Carbohydrate metabolism begins in the mouth, where the enzyme salivary amylase begins to break down complex sugars into monosaccharides. These can then be transported across the intestinal membrane into the bloodstream and then to body tissues. In the cells, glucose, a six-carbon sugar, is processed through a sequence of reactions into smaller sugars, and the energy stored inside the molecule is released. The first step of carbohydrate catabolism is glycolysis, which produces pyruvate, NADH, and ATP. Under anaerobic conditions, the pyruvate can be converted into lactate to keep glycolysis working. Under aerobic conditions, pyruvate enters the Krebs cycle, also called the citric acid cycle or tricarboxylic acid cycle. In addition to ATP, the Krebs cycle produces high-energy $FADH_2$ and NADH molecules, which provide electrons to the oxidative phosphorylation process that generates more high-energy ATP molecules. For each molecule of glucose that is processed in glycolysis, a net of 36 ATPs can be created by aerobic respiration.

Under anaerobic conditions, ATP production is limited to those generated by glycolysis. While a total of four ATPs are produced by glycolysis, two are needed to begin glycolysis, so there is a net yield of two ATP molecules.

In conditions of low glucose, such as fasting, starvation, or low carbohydrate diets, glucose can be synthesized from lactate, pyruvate, glycerol, alanine, or glutamate. This process, called gluconeogenesis, is almost the reverse of glycolysis and serves to create glucose molecules for glucose-dependent organs, such as the brain, when glucose levels fall below normal.

24.3 Lipid Metabolism

Lipids are available to the body from three sources. They can be ingested in the diet, stored in the adipose tissue of the body, or synthesized in the liver. Fats ingested in the diet are digested in the small intestine. The triglycerides are broken down into monoglycerides and free fatty acids, then imported across the intestinal mucosa. Once across, the triglycerides are resynthesized and transported to the liver or adipose tissue. Fatty acids are oxidized through fatty acid or β-oxidation into two-carbon acetyl CoA molecules, which can then enter the Krebs cycle to generate ATP. If excess acetyl CoA is created and overloads the capacity of the Krebs cycle, the acetyl CoA can be used to synthesize ketone bodies. When glucose is limited, ketone bodies can be oxidized and used for fuel. Excess acetyl CoA generated from excess glucose or carbohydrate ingestion can be used for fatty acid synthesis or lipogenesis. Acetyl CoA is used to create lipids, triglycerides, steroid hormones, cholesterol, and bile salts. Lipolysis is the breakdown of triglycerides into glycerol and fatty acids, making them easier for the body to process.

24.4 Protein Metabolism

Digestion of proteins begins in the stomach, where HCl and pepsin begin the process of breaking down proteins into their constituent amino acids. As the chyme enters the small intestine, it mixes with bicarbonate and digestive enzymes. The bicarbonate neutralizes the acidic HCl, and the digestive enzymes break down the proteins into smaller peptides and amino acids. Digestive hormones secretin and CCK are released from the small intestine to aid in digestive processes, and digestive proenzymes are released from the pancreas (trypsinogen and chymotrypsinogen). Enterokinase, an enzyme located in the wall of the small intestine, activates trypsin, which in turn activates chymotrypsin. These enzymes liberate the individual amino acids that are then transported via sodium-amino acid transporters across the intestinal wall into the cell. The amino acids are then transported into the bloodstream for dispersal to the liver and cells throughout the body to be used to create new proteins. When in excess, the amino acids are processed and stored as glucose or ketones. The nitrogen waste that is liberated in this process is converted to urea in the urea acid cycle and eliminated in the urine. In times of starvation, amino acids can be used as an energy source and processed through the Krebs cycle.

24.5 Metabolic States of the Body

There are three main metabolic states of the body: absorptive (fed), postabsorptive (fasting), and starvation. During any given day, your metabolism switches between absorptive and postabsorptive states. Starvation states happen very rarely in generally well-nourished individuals. When the body is fed, glucose, fats, and proteins are absorbed across the intestinal membrane and enter the bloodstream and lymphatic system to be used immediately for fuel. Any excess is stored for later fasting stages. As blood glucose levels rise, the pancreas releases insulin to stimulate the uptake of glucose by hepatocytes in the liver, muscle cells/fibers, and adipocytes (fat cells), and to promote its conversion to glycogen. As the postabsorptive state begins, glucose levels drop, and there is a corresponding drop in insulin levels. Falling glucose levels trigger the pancreas to release glucagon to turn off glycogen synthesis in the liver and stimulate its breakdown into glucose. The glucose is released into the bloodstream to serve as a fuel source for cells throughout the body. If glycogen stores are depleted during fasting, alternative sources, including fatty acids and proteins, can be metabolized and used as fuel. When the body once again enters the absorptive state after fasting, fats and proteins are digested and used to replenish fat and protein stores, whereas glucose is processed and used first to replenish the glycogen stores in the peripheral tissues, then in the liver. If the fast is not broken and starvation begins to set in, during the initial days, glucose produced from gluconeogenesis is still used by the brain and organs. After a few days, however, ketone bodies are created from fats and serve as the preferential fuel source for the heart and other organs, so that the brain can still use glucose. Once these stores are depleted, proteins will be catabolized first from the organs with fast turnover, such as the intestinal lining. Muscle will be spared to prevent the wasting of muscle tissue; however, these proteins will be used if alternative stores are not available.

24.6 Energy and Heat Balance

Some of the energy from the food that is ingested is used to maintain the core temperature of the body. Most of the energy derived from the food is released as heat. The core temperature is kept around 36.5–37.5 °C (97.7–99.5 °F). This is tightly regulated by the hypothalamus in the brain, which senses changes in the core temperature and operates like a thermostat to increase sweating or shivering, or inducing other

mechanisms to return the temperature to its normal range. The body can also gain or lose heat through mechanisms of heat exchange. Conduction transfers heat from one object to another through physical contact. Convection transfers heat to air or water. Radiation transfers heat via infrared radiation. Evaporation transfers heat as water changes state from a liquid to a gas.

24.7 Nutrition and Diet

Nutrition and diet affect your metabolism. More energy is required to break down fats and proteins than carbohydrates; however, all excess calories that are ingested will be stored as fat in the body. On average, a person requires 1500 to 2000 calories for normal daily activity, although routine exercise will increase that amount. If you ingest more than that, the remainder is stored for later use. Conversely, if you ingest less than that, the energy stores in your body will be depleted. Both the quantity and quality of the food you eat affect your metabolism and can affect your overall health. Eating too much or too little can result in serious medical conditions, including cardiovascular disease, cancer, and diabetes.

Vitamins and minerals are essential parts of the diet. They are needed for the proper function of metabolic pathways in the body. Vitamins are not stored in the body, so they must be obtained from the diet or synthesized from precursors available in the diet. Minerals are also obtained from the diet, but they are also stored, primarily in skeletal tissues.

Review Questions

1. A monosaccharide is formed from a polysaccharide in what kind of reaction?
   a. oxidation–reduction reaction
   b. anabolic reaction
   c. catabolic reaction
   d. biosynthetic reaction

2. If anabolic reactions exceed catabolic reactions, the result will be _____.
   a. weight loss
   b. weight gain
   c. metabolic rate change
   d. development of disease

3. When NAD becomes NADH, the coenzyme has been _____.
   a. reduced
   b. oxidized
   c. metabolized
   d. hydrolyzed

4. Anabolic reactions use energy by _____.
   a. turning ADP into ATP
   b. removing a phosphate group from ATP
   c. producing heat
   d. breaking down molecules into smaller parts

5. Glycolysis results in the production of two _____ molecules from a single molecule of glucose. In the absence of _____, the end product of glycolysis is _____.
   a. acetyl CoA, pyruvate, lactate
   b. ATP, carbon, pyruvate
   c. pyruvate, oxygen, lactate
   d. pyruvate, carbon, acetyl CoA

6. The Krebs cycle converts _____ through a cycle of reactions. In the process, ATP, _____, and _____ are produced.
   a. acetyl CoA; FAD, NAD
   b. acetyl CoA; FADH$_2$; NADH
   c. pyruvate; NAD; FADH$_2$
   d. pyruvate; oxygen; oxaloacetate

7. Which pathway produces the most ATP molecules?
   a. lactic acid fermentation
   b. the Krebs cycle
   c. the electron transport chain
   d. glycolysis

8. Aerobic cellular respiration results in the production of these two products.
   a. NADH and FADH$_2$
   b. ATP and pyruvate
   c. ATP and glucose
   d. ATP and H$_2$O

9. When NAD$^+$ becomes NADH, the coenzyme has been _____.
   a. reduced
   b. oxidized
   c. metabolized
   d. hydrolyzed

10. Lipids in the diet can be _____.
    a. broken down into energy for the body
    b. stored as triglycerides for later use
    c. converted into acetyl CoA
    d. all of the above

11. The gallbladder provides _____ that aid(s) in transport of lipids across the intestinal membrane.
    a. lipases
    b. cholesterol
    c. proteins
    d. bile salts

12. Triglycerides are transported by chylomicrons because _____.
    a. they cannot move easily in the blood stream because they are fat based, while the blood is water based
    b. they are too small to move by themselves
    c. the chylomicrons contain enzymes they need for anabolism
    d. they cannot fit across the intestinal membrane

13. Which molecule produces the most ATP?
    a. carbohydrates
    b. FADH$_2$
    c. triglycerides
    d. NADH

14. Which molecules can enter the Krebs cycle?
    a. chylomicrons
    b. acetyl CoA
    c. monoglycerides
    d. ketone bodies

15. Acetyl CoA can be converted to all of the following except _____.
    a. ketone bodies
    b. fatty acids
    c. polysaccharides
    d. triglycerides

16. Digestion of proteins begins in the _____ where _____ and _____ mix with food to break down protein into _____.
    a. stomach; amylase; HCl; amino acids
    b. mouth; pepsin; HCl; fatty acids
    c. stomach; lipase; HCl; amino acids
    d. stomach; pepsin; HCl; amino acids

17. Amino acids are needed to _____.
    a. build new proteins
    b. serve as fat stores
    c. supply energy for the cell
    d. create red blood cells

18. If an amino acid is not used to create new proteins, it can be _____.
    a. converted to acetyl CoA
    b. converted to glucose or ketones
    c. converted to nitrogen
    d. stored to be used later

19. During the absorptive state, glucose levels are _____, insulin levels are _____, and glucagon levels _____.
    a. high; low; stay the same
    b. low; low; stay the same
    c. high; high; are high
    d. high; high; are low

20. Starvation sets in after 3 to 4 days without food. Which hormones change in response to low glucose levels?
    a. glucagon and insulin
    b. ketones and glucagon
    c. insulin, glucose, and glucagon
    d. insulin and ketones

21. The postabsorptive state relies on stores of
    _____ in the _____.
    a. insulin; pancreas
    b. glucagon; pancreas
    c. glycogen; liver
    d. glucose; liver

22. The body's temperature is controlled by the
    _____. This temperature is always kept
    between _____.
    a. pituitary; 36.5–37.5 °C
    b. hypothalamus; 97.7–99.5 °F
    c. hypothalamus; 36.5–37.5 °F
    d. pituitary; 97.7–99.5 °F

23. Fever increases the body temperature and can
    induce chills to help cool the temperature back
    down. What other mechanisms are in place to
    regulate the body temperature?
    a. shivering
    b. sweating
    c. erection of the hairs on the arms and legs
    d. all of the above

24. The heat you feel on your chair when you stand up
    was transferred from your skin via _____.
    a. conduction
    b. convection
    c. radiation
    d. evaporation

25. A crowded room warms up through the
    mechanism of _____.
    a. conduction
    b. convection
    c. radiation
    d. evaporation

26. A deficiency in vitamin A can result in _____.
    a. improper bone development
    b. scurvy
    c. improper eye development or sight
    d. all of the above

27. Rickets results in improper bone development in
    children that arises from the malabsorption of
    calcium and a deficiency in _____.
    a. vitamin D
    b. vitamin C
    c. vitamin B_{12}
    d. niacin

28. Consuming which type of food will help the most
    with weight loss?
    a. fats
    b. vegetables
    c. lean meats
    d. fruits

29. Which of the following is stored in the body?
    a. thiamine
    b. phosphorous
    c. folic acid
    d. vitamin C

Critical Thinking Questions

30. Describe how metabolism can be altered.
31. Describe how Addison's disease can be treated.
32. Explain how glucose is metabolized to yield ATP.
33. Insulin is released when food is ingested and
    stimulates the uptake of glucose into the cell.
    Discuss the mechanism cells employ to create a
    concentration gradient to ensure continual uptake
    of glucose from the bloodstream.
34. Discuss how carbohydrates can be stored as fat.
35. If a person with diabetes that has breath smells
    like alcohol, what could this mean?
36. Amino acids are not stored in the body. Describe
    how excess amino acids are processed in the cell.
37. Release of trypsin and chymotrypsin in their active
    form can result in the digestion of the pancreas or
    small intestine itself. What mechanism does the
    body employ to prevent its self-destruction?

38. In type II diabetes, insulin is produced but is
    nonfunctional. These patients are described as
    "starving in a sea of plenty," because their blood
    glucose levels are high, but none of the glucose is
    transported into the cells. Describe how this leads
    to malnutrition.
39. Ketone bodies are used as an alternative source of
    fuel during starvation. Describe how ketones are
    synthesized.
40. How does vasoconstriction help increase the core
    temperature of the body?
41. How can the ingestion of food increase the body
    temperature?
42. Weight loss and weight gain are complex
    processes. What are some of the main factors that
    influence weight gain in people?

Access for free at openstax.org

43. Some low-fat or non-fat foods contain a large amount of sugar to replace the fat content of the food. Discuss how this leads to increased fat in the body (and weight gain) even though the item is non-fat.

CHAPTER 25
The Urinary System

Figure 25.1 **Sewage Treatment Plant** (credit: "thekirbster"/flickr.com)

CHAPTER OBJECTIVES

After studying this chapter, you will be able to:

- Describe the composition of urine
- Label structures of the urinary system
- Characterize the roles of each of the parts of the urinary system
- Illustrate the macroscopic and microscopic structures of the kidney
- Trace the flow of blood through the kidney
- Outline how blood is filtered in the kidney nephron
- Provide symptoms of kidney failure
- List some of the solutes filtered, secreted, and reabsorbed in different parts of the nephron
- Describe the role of a portal system in the kidney
- Explain how urine osmolarity is hormonally regulated
- Describe the regulation of major ions by the kidney
- Summarize the role of the kidneys in maintaining acid–base balance

INTRODUCTION The urinary system has roles you may be well aware of: cleansing the blood and ridding the body of wastes probably come to mind. However, there are additional, equally important functions played by the system. Take for example, regulation of pH, a function shared with the lungs and the buffers in the blood. Additionally, the regulation of blood pressure is a role shared with the heart and blood vessels. What about regulating the concentration of solutes in the blood? Did you know that the kidney is important in determining the concentration of red blood cells? Eighty-five percent of the erythropoietin (EPO) produced to stimulate red blood cell production is produced in the kidneys. The kidneys also perform the final synthesis step of vitamin D production, converting calcidiol to calcitriol, the active form of vitamin D.

If the kidneys fail, these functions are compromised or lost altogether, with devastating effects on homeostasis. The affected individual might experience weakness, lethargy, shortness of breath, anemia, widespread edema (swelling), metabolic acidosis, rising potassium levels, heart arrhythmias, and more. Each of these functions is vital to your well-being and survival. The urinary system, controlled by the nervous system, also stores urine until a convenient time for disposal and then provides the anatomical structures to transport this waste liquid to the outside of the body. Failure of nervous control or the anatomical structures leading to a loss of control of urination results in a condition called incontinence.

This chapter will help you to understand the anatomy of the urinary system and how it enables the physiologic functions critical to homeostasis. It is best to think of the kidney as a regulator of plasma makeup rather than simply a urine producer. As you read each section, ask yourself this question: "What happens if this does not work?" This question will help you to understand how the urinary system maintains homeostasis and affects all the other systems of the body and the quality of one's life.

⊘ INTERACTIVE LINK

Watch this video (http://openstax.org/l/urineintro) from the Howard Hughes Medical Institute for an introduction to the urinary system.

25.1 Physical Characteristics of Urine

LEARNING OBJECTIVES

By the end of this section, you will be able to:
- Compare and contrast blood plasma, glomerular filtrate, and urine characteristics
- Describe the characteristics of a normal urine sample, including normal range of pH, osmolarity, and volume

The urinary system's ability to filter the blood resides in about 2 to 3 million tufts of specialized capillaries—the glomeruli—distributed more or less equally between the two kidneys. Because the glomeruli filter the blood based mostly on particle size, large elements like blood cells, platelets, antibodies, and albumen are excluded. The glomerulus is the first part of the nephron, which then continues as a highly specialized tubular structure responsible for creating the final urine composition. All other solutes, such as ions, amino acids, vitamins, and wastes, are filtered to create a filtrate composition very similar to plasma. The glomeruli create about 200 liters (189 quarts) of this filtrate every day, yet you excrete less than two liters of waste you call urine.

Characteristics of the urine change, depending on influences such as water intake, exercise, environmental temperature, nutrient intake, and other factors (Table 25.1). Some of the characteristics such as color and odor are rough descriptors of your state of hydration. For example, if you exercise or work outside, and sweat a great deal, your urine will turn darker and produce a slight odor, even if you drink plenty of water. Athletes are often advised to consume water until their urine is clear. This is good advice; however, it takes time for the kidneys to process body fluids and store it in the bladder. Another way of looking at this is that the quality of the urine produced is an average over the time it takes to make that urine. Producing clear urine may take only a few minutes if you are drinking a lot of water or several hours if you are working outside and not drinking much.

Normal Urine Characteristics

Characteristic	Normal values
Color	Pale yellow to deep amber
Odor	Odorless
Volume	750–2000 mL/24 hour
pH	4.5–8.0
Specific gravity	1.003–1.032

TABLE 25.1

Characteristic	Normal values
Osmolarity	40–1350 mOsmol/kg
Urobilinogen	0.2–1.0 mg/100 mL
White blood cells	0–2 HPF (per high-power field of microscope)
Leukocyte esterase	None
Protein	None or trace
Bilirubin	<0.3 mg/100 mL
Ketones	None
Nitrites	None
Blood	None
Glucose	None

TABLE 25.1

Urinalysis (urine analysis) often provides clues to renal disease. Normally, only traces of protein are found in urine, and when higher amounts are found, damage to the glomeruli is the likely basis. Unusually large quantities of urine may point to diseases like diabetes mellitus or hypothalamic tumors that cause diabetes insipidus. The color of urine is determined mostly by the breakdown products of red blood cell destruction (Figure 25.2). The "heme" of hemoglobin is converted by the liver into water-soluble forms that can be excreted into the bile and indirectly into the urine. This yellow pigment is **urochrome**. Urine color may also be affected by certain foods like beets, berries, and fava beans. A kidney stone or a cancer of the urinary system may produce sufficient bleeding to manifest as pink or even bright red urine. Diseases of the liver or obstructions of bile drainage from the liver impart a dark "tea" or "cola" hue to the urine. Dehydration produces darker, concentrated urine that may also possess the slight odor of ammonia. Most of the ammonia produced from protein breakdown is converted into urea by the liver, so ammonia is rarely detected in fresh urine. The strong ammonia odor you may detect in bathrooms or alleys is due to the breakdown of urea into ammonia by bacteria in the environment. About one in five people detect a distinctive odor in their urine after consuming asparagus; other foods such as onions, garlic, and fish can impart their own aromas! These food-caused odors are harmless.

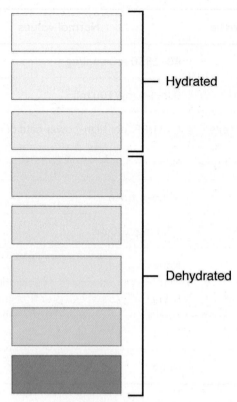

FIGURE 25.2   Urine Color

Urine volume varies considerably. The normal range is one to two liters per day (Table 25.2). The kidneys must produce a minimum urine volume of about 500 mL/day to rid the body of wastes. Output below this level may be caused by severe dehydration or renal disease and is termed **oliguria**. The virtual absence of urine production is termed **anuria**. Excessive urine production is **polyuria**, which may be due to diabetes mellitus or diabetes insipidus. In diabetes mellitus, blood glucose levels exceed the number of available sodium-glucose transporters in the kidney, and glucose appears in the urine. The osmotic nature of glucose attracts water, leading to its loss in the urine. In the case of diabetes insipidus, insufficient pituitary antidiuretic hormone (ADH) release or insufficient numbers of ADH receptors in the collecting ducts means that too few water channels are inserted into the cell membranes that line the collecting ducts of the kidney. Insufficient numbers of water channels (aquaporins) reduce water absorption, resulting in high volumes of very dilute urine.

Urine Volumes

Volume condition	Volume	Causes
Normal	1–2 L/day	
Polyuria	>2.5 L/day	Diabetes mellitus; diabetes insipidus; excess caffeine or alcohol; kidney disease; certain drugs, such as diuretics; sickle cell anemia; excessive water intake

TABLE 25.2

Volume condition	Volume	Causes
Oliguria	300–500 mL/day	Dehydration; blood loss; diarrhea; cardiogenic shock; kidney disease; enlarged prostate
Anuria	<50 mL/day	Kidney failure; obstruction, such as kidney stone or tumor; enlarged prostate

TABLE 25.2

The pH (hydrogen ion concentration) of the urine can vary more than 1000-fold, from a normal low of 4.5 to a maximum of 8.0. Diet can influence pH; meats lower the pH, whereas citrus fruits, vegetables, and dairy products raise the pH. Chronically high or low pH can lead to disorders, such as the development of kidney stones or osteomalacia.

Specific gravity is a measure of the quantity of solutes per unit volume of a solution and is traditionally easier to measure than osmolarity. Urine will always have a specific gravity greater than pure water (water = 1.0) due to the presence of solutes. Laboratories can now measure urine osmolarity directly, which is a more accurate indicator of urinary solutes than **specific gravity**. Remember that osmolarity is the number of osmoles or milliosmoles per liter of fluid (mOsmol/L). Urine osmolarity ranges from a low of 50–100 mOsmol/L to as high as 1200 mOsmol/L H_2O.

Cells are not normally found in the urine. The presence of leukocytes may indicate a urinary tract infection. **Leukocyte esterase** is released by leukocytes; if detected in the urine, it can be taken as indirect evidence of a urinary tract infection (UTI).

Protein does not normally leave the glomerular capillaries, so only trace amounts of protein should be found in the urine, approximately 10 mg/100 mL in a random sample. If excessive protein is detected in the urine, it usually means that the glomerulus is damaged and is allowing protein to "leak" into the filtrate.

Ketones are byproducts of fat metabolism. Finding ketones in the urine suggests that the body is using fat as an energy source in preference to glucose. In diabetes mellitus when there is not enough insulin (type I diabetes mellitus) or because of insulin resistance (type II diabetes mellitus), there is plenty of glucose, but without the action of insulin, the cells cannot take it up, so it remains in the bloodstream. Instead, the cells are forced to use fat as their energy source, and fat consumed at such a level produces excessive ketones as byproducts. These excess ketones will appear in the urine. Ketones may also appear if there is a severe deficiency of proteins or carbohydrates in the diet.

Nitrates (NO_3^-) occur normally in the urine. Gram-negative bacteria metabolize nitrate into nitrite (NO_2^-), and its presence in the urine is indirect evidence of infection.

There should be no blood found in the urine. It may sometimes appear in urine samples as a result of menstrual contamination, but this is not an abnormal condition. Now that you understand what the normal characteristics of urine are, the next section will introduce you to how you store and dispose of this waste product and how you make it.

25.2 Gross Anatomy of Urine Transport

LEARNING OBJECTIVES

By the end of this section, you will be able to:
- Identify the ureters, urinary bladder, and urethra, as well as their location, structure, histology, and function
- Compare and contrast male and female urethras
- Describe the micturition reflex
- Describe voluntary and involuntary neural control of micturition

Rather than start with urine formation, this section will start with urine excretion. Urine is a fluid of variable composition that requires specialized structures to remove it from the body safely and efficiently. Blood is filtered, and the filtrate is transformed into urine at a relatively constant rate throughout the day. This processed liquid is stored until a convenient time for excretion. All structures involved in the transport and storage of the urine are large enough to be visible to the naked eye. This transport and storage system not only stores the waste, but it protects the tissues from damage due to the wide range of pH and osmolarity of the urine, prevents infection by foreign organisms, and for the male, provides reproductive functions.

Urethra

The **urethra** transports urine from the bladder to the outside of the body for disposal. The urethra is the only urologic organ that shows any significant anatomic difference between males and females; all other urine transport structures are identical (Figure 25.3).

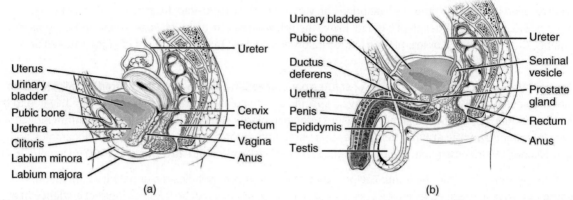

FIGURE 25.3   Female and Male Urethras   The urethra transports urine from the bladder to the outside of the body. This image shows (a) a female urethra and (b) a male urethra.

The urethra in both males and females begins inferior and central to the two ureteral openings forming the three points of a triangular-shaped area at the base of the bladder called the **trigone** (Greek tri- = "triangle" and the root of the word "trigonometry"). The urethra tracks posterior and inferior to the pubic symphysis (see Figure 25.3**a**). In both males and females, the proximal urethra is lined by transitional epithelium, whereas the terminal portion is a nonkeratinized, stratified squamous epithelium. In the male, pseudostratified columnar epithelium lines the urethra between these two cell types. Voiding is regulated by an involuntary autonomic nervous system-controlled **internal urinary sphincter**, consisting of smooth muscle and voluntary skeletal muscle that forms the **external urinary sphincter** below it.

Female Urethra

The external urethral orifice is embedded in the anterior vaginal wall inferior to the clitoris, superior to the vaginal opening (introitus), and medial to the labia minora. Its short length, about 4 cm, is less of a barrier to fecal bacteria than the longer male urethra and the best explanation for the greater incidence of UTI in females. Voluntary control of the external urethral sphincter is a function of the pudendal nerve. It arises in the sacral region of the spinal cord, traveling via the S2–S4 nerves of the sacral plexus.

Male Urethra

The male urethra passes through the prostate gland immediately inferior to the bladder before passing below the pubic symphysis (see Figure 25.3**b**). The length of the male urethra varies between people but averages 20 cm in length. It is divided into four regions: the preprostatic urethra, the prostatic urethra, the membranous urethra, and the spongy or penile urethra. The preprostatic urethra is very short and incorporated into the bladder wall. The prostatic urethra passes through the prostate gland. During sexual intercourse, it receives sperm via the ejaculatory ducts and secretions from the seminal vesicles. Paired Cowper's glands (bulbourethral glands) produce and secrete mucus into the urethra to buffer urethral pH during sexual stimulation. The mucus neutralizes the usually acidic environment and lubricates the urethra, decreasing the resistance to ejaculation. The membranous urethra passes through the deep muscles of the perineum, where it is invested by the overlying urethral sphincters. The spongy urethra exits at the tip (external urethral orifice) of the penis after passing through the corpus spongiosum. Mucous glands are found along much of the length of the urethra and protect the urethra from extremes of urine pH. Innervation is the same in both males and females.

Access for free at openstax.org

Bladder

The urinary bladder collects urine from both ureters (Figure 25.4). The bladder lies anterior to the uterus in females, posterior to the pubic bone and anterior to the rectum. During late pregnancy, its capacity is reduced due to compression by the enlarging uterus, resulting in increased frequency of urination. In males, the anatomy is similar, minus the uterus, and with the addition of the prostate inferior to the bladder. The bladder is a **retroperitoneal** organ whose "dome" distends superiorly when the bladder is filling with urine.

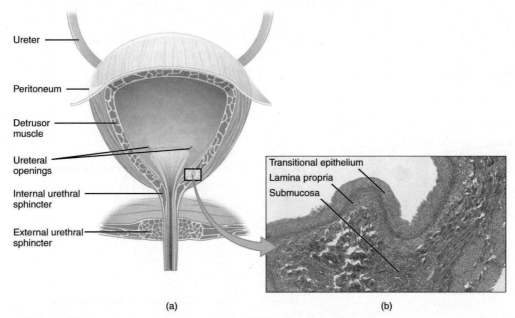

FIGURE 25.4 Bladder   (a) Anterior cross section of the bladder. (b) The detrusor muscle of the bladder (source: monkey tissue) LM × 448. (Micrograph provided by the Regents of the University of Michigan Medical School © 2012)

🔗 INTERACTIVE LINK

View the University of Michigan WebScope (http://openstax.org/l/bladderMG) to explore the tissue sample in greater detail.

The bladder is a highly distensible organ comprised of irregular crisscrossing bands of smooth muscle collectively called the **detrusor muscle**. The interior surface is made of transitional cellular epithelium that is structurally suited for the large volume fluctuations of the bladder. When empty, it resembles columnar epithelia, but when stretched, it "transitions" (hence the name) to a squamous appearance (see Figure 25.4). Volumes in adults can range from nearly zero to 500–600 mL.

The detrusor muscle contracts with significant force in the young. The bladder's strength diminishes with age, but voluntary contractions of abdominal skeletal muscles can increase intra-abdominal pressure to promote more forceful bladder emptying. Such voluntary contraction is also used in forceful defecation and childbirth.

Micturition Reflex

Micturition is a less-often used, but proper term for urination or voiding. It results from an interplay of involuntary and voluntary actions by the internal and external urethral sphincters. When bladder volume reaches about 150 mL, an urge to void is sensed but is easily overridden. Voluntary control of urination relies on consciously preventing relaxation of the external urethral sphincter to maintain urinary continence. As the bladder fills, subsequent urges become harder to ignore. Ultimately, voluntary constraint fails with resulting **incontinence**, which will occur as bladder volume approaches 300 to 400 mL.

Normal micturition is a result of stretch receptors in the bladder wall that transmit nerve impulses to the sacral region of the spinal cord to generate a spinal reflex. The resulting parasympathetic neural outflow causes contraction of the detrusor muscle and relaxation of the involuntary internal urethral sphincter. At the same time, the spinal cord inhibits somatic motor neurons, resulting in the relaxation of the skeletal muscle of the external urethral sphincter. The micturition reflex is active in infants but with maturity, children learn to override the reflex by asserting external sphincter control, thereby delaying voiding (potty training). This reflex may be preserved even in the face of spinal cord injury that results in paraplegia or quadriplegia. However, relaxation of the external sphincter may not be possible in all cases, and therefore, periodic catheterization may be necessary for bladder emptying.

Nerves involved in the control of urination include the hypogastric, pelvic, and pudendal (Figure 25.5). Voluntary micturition requires an intact spinal cord and functional pudendal nerve arising from the **sacral micturition center**. Since the external urinary sphincter is voluntary skeletal muscle, actions by cholinergic neurons maintain contraction (and thereby continence) during filling of the bladder. At the same time, sympathetic nervous activity via the hypogastric nerves suppresses contraction of the detrusor muscle. With further bladder stretch, afferent signals traveling over sacral pelvic nerves activate parasympathetic neurons. This activates efferent neurons to release acetylcholine at the neuromuscular junctions, producing detrusor contraction and bladder emptying.

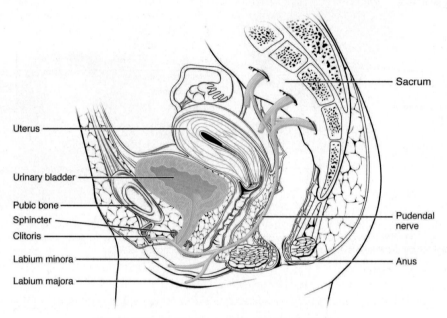

FIGURE 25.5 • **Nerves Innervating the Urinary System**

Ureters

The kidneys and ureters are completely retroperitoneal, and the bladder has a peritoneal covering only over the dome. As urine is formed, it drains into the calyces of the kidney, which merge to form the funnel-shaped renal pelvis in the hilum of each kidney. The renal pelvis narrows to become the ureter of each kidney. As urine passes through the ureter, it does not passively drain into the bladder but rather is propelled by waves of peristalsis. As the ureters enter the pelvis, they sweep laterally, hugging the pelvic walls. As they approach the bladder, they turn medially and pierce the bladder wall obliquely. This is important because it creates a one-way valve (a **physiological sphincter** rather than an **anatomical sphincter**) that allows urine into the bladder but prevents reflux of urine from the bladder back into the ureter. Children born lacking this oblique course of the ureter through the bladder wall are susceptible to "vesicoureteral reflux," which dramatically increases their risk of serious UTI. Pregnancy also increases the likelihood of reflux and UTI.

The ureters are approximately 30 cm long. The inner mucosa is lined with transitional epithelium (Figure 25.6) and scattered goblet cells that secrete protective mucus. The muscular layer of the ureter consists of longitudinal and circular smooth muscles that create the peristaltic contractions to move the urine into the bladder without the aid of gravity. Finally, a loose adventitial layer composed of collagen and fat anchors the ureters between the parietal peritoneum and the posterior abdominal wall.

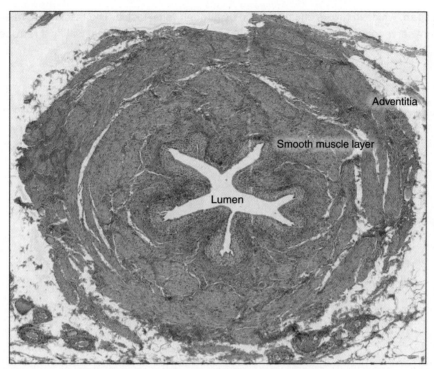

FIGURE 25.6   Ureter   Peristaltic contractions help to move urine through the lumen with contributions from fluid pressure and gravity. LM × 128. (Micrograph provided by the Regents of the University of Michigan Medical School © 2012)

25.3 Gross Anatomy of the Kidney

LEARNING OBJECTIVES

By the end of this section, you will be able to:

- Describe the external structure of the kidney, including its location, support structures, and covering
- Identify the major internal divisions and structures of the kidney
- Identify the major blood vessels associated with the kidney and trace the path of blood through the kidney
- Compare and contrast the cortical and juxtamedullary nephrons
- Name structures found in the cortex and medulla
- Describe the physiological characteristics of the cortex and medulla

The kidneys lie on either side of the spine in the retroperitoneal space between the parietal peritoneum and the posterior abdominal wall, well protected by muscle, fat, and ribs. They are roughly the size of your fist, and the male kidney is typically a bit larger than the female kidney. The kidneys are well vascularized, receiving about 25 percent of the cardiac output at rest.

🔗 INTERACTIVE LINK

There have never been sufficient kidney donations to provide a kidney to each person needing one. Watch this video (http://openstax.org/l/TED) to learn about the TED (Technology, Entertainment, Design) Conference held in March 2011. In this video, Dr. Anthony Atala discusses a cutting-edge technique in which a new kidney is "printed." The successful utilization of this technology is still several years in the future, but imagine a time when you can print a replacement organ or tissue on demand.

External Anatomy

The left kidney is located at about the T12 to L3 vertebrae, whereas the right is lower due to slight displacement by the liver. Upper portions of the kidneys are somewhat protected by the eleventh and twelfth ribs (Figure 25.7). Each kidney weighs about 125–175 g in males and 115–155 g in females. They are about 11–14 cm in length, 6 cm wide, and 4 cm thick, and are directly covered by a fibrous capsule composed of dense, irregular connective tissue that helps to hold their shape and protect them. This capsule is covered by a shock-absorbing layer of adipose tissue called the **renal fat pad**, which in turn is encompassed by a tough renal fascia. The fascia and, to a lesser extent, the overlying peritoneum serve to firmly anchor the kidneys to the posterior abdominal wall in a retroperitoneal position.

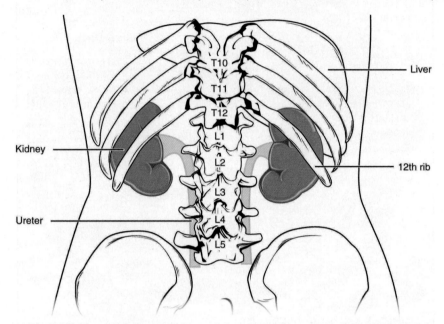

FIGURE 25.7   Kidneys   The kidneys are slightly protected by the ribs and are surrounded by fat for protection (not shown).

On the superior aspect of each kidney is the adrenal gland. The adrenal cortex directly influences renal function through the production of the hormone aldosterone to stimulate sodium reabsorption.

Internal Anatomy

A frontal section through the kidney reveals an outer region called the **renal cortex** and an inner region called the **medulla** (Figure 25.8). The **renal columns** are connective tissue extensions that radiate downward from the cortex through the medulla to separate the most characteristic features of the medulla, the **renal pyramids** and **renal papillae**. The papillae are bundles of collecting ducts that transport urine made by nephrons to the **calyces** of the kidney for excretion. The renal columns also serve to divide the kidney into 6–8 lobes and provide a supportive framework for vessels that enter and exit the cortex. The pyramids and renal columns taken together constitute the kidney lobes.

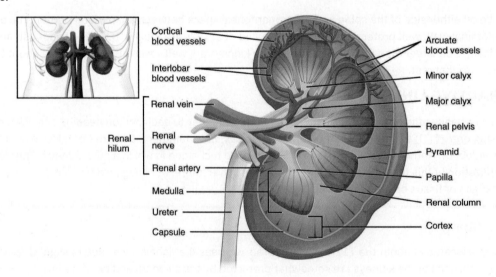

FIGURE 25.8   Left Kidney

Renal Hilum

The **renal hilum** is the entry and exit site for structures servicing the kidneys: vessels, nerves, lymphatics, and ureters. The medial-facing hila are tucked into the sweeping convex outline of the cortex. Emerging from the hilum is the renal pelvis, which is formed from the major and minor calyxes in the kidney. The smooth muscle in the renal pelvis funnels urine via peristalsis into the ureter. The renal arteries form directly from the descending aorta, whereas the renal veins return cleansed blood directly to the inferior vena cava. The artery, vein, and renal pelvis are arranged in an anterior-to-posterior order.

Nephrons and Vessels

The renal artery first divides into segmental arteries, followed by further branching to form interlobar arteries that pass through the renal columns to reach the cortex (Figure 25.9). The interlobar arteries, in turn, branch into arcuate arteries, cortical radiate arteries, and then into afferent arterioles. The afferent arterioles service about 1.3 million nephrons in each kidney.

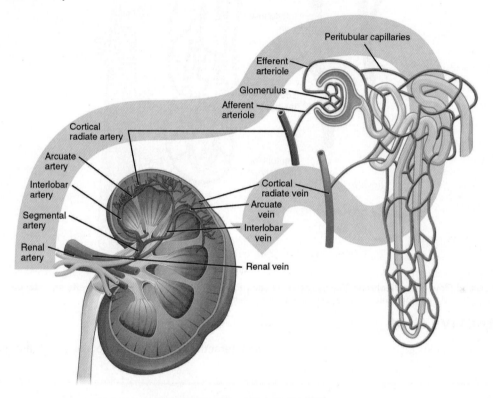

FIGURE 25.9   Blood Flow in the Kidney

Nephrons are the "functional units" of the kidney; they cleanse the blood and balance the constituents of the circulation. The afferent arterioles form a tuft of high-pressure capillaries about 200 μm in diameter, the **glomerulus**. The rest of the nephron consists of a continuous sophisticated tubule whose proximal end surrounds the glomerulus in an intimate embrace—this is **Bowman's capsule**. The glomerulus and Bowman's capsule together form the **renal corpuscle**. As mentioned earlier, these glomerular capillaries filter the blood based on particle size. After passing through the renal corpuscle, the capillaries form a second arteriole, the **efferent arteriole** (Figure 25.10). These will next form a capillary network around the more distal portions of the nephron tubule, the **peritubular capillaries** and **vasa recta**, before returning to the venous system. As the glomerular filtrate progresses through the nephron, these capillary networks recover most of the solutes and water, and return them to the circulation. Since a capillary bed (the glomerulus) drains into a vessel that in turn forms a second capillary bed, the definition of a portal system is met. This is the only portal system in which an arteriole is found between the first and second capillary beds. (Portal systems also link the hypothalamus to the anterior pituitary, and the blood vessels of the digestive viscera to the liver.)

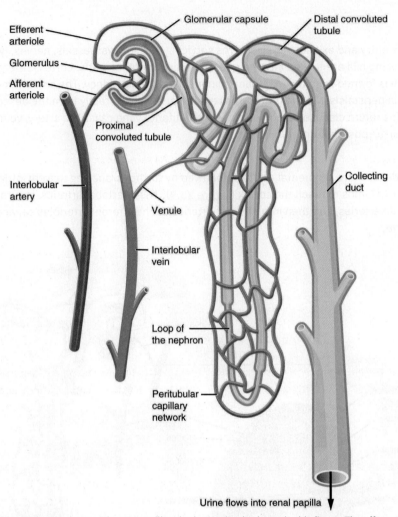

FIGURE 25.10   Blood Flow in the Nephron   The two capillary beds are clearly shown in this figure. The efferent arteriole is the connecting vessel between the glomerulus and the peritubular capillaries and vasa recta.

🔗 INTERACTIVE LINK

Visit this link (http://openstax.org/l/bloodflow5) to view an interactive tutorial of the flow of blood through the kidney.

Cortex

In a dissected kidney, it is easy to identify the cortex; it appears lighter in color compared to the rest of the kidney. All of the renal corpuscles as well as both the **proximal convoluted tubules (PCTs)** and **distal convoluted tubules** are found here. Some nephrons have a short **loop of Henle** that does not dip beyond the cortex. These nephrons are called **cortical nephrons**. About 15 percent of nephrons have long loops of Henle that extend deep into the medulla and are called **juxtamedullary nephrons**.

25.4 Microscopic Anatomy of the Kidney

LEARNING OBJECTIVES

By the end of this section, you will be able to:
- Distinguish the histological differences between the renal cortex and medulla
- Describe the structure of the filtration membrane
- Identify the major structures and subdivisions of the renal corpuscles, renal tubules, and renal capillaries
- Discuss the function of the peritubular capillaries and vasa recta
- Identify the location of the juxtaglomerular apparatus and describe the cells that line it
- Describe the histology of the proximal convoluted tubule, loop of Henle, distal convoluted tubule, and collecting ducts

The renal structures that conduct the essential work of the kidney cannot be seen by the naked eye. Only a light or electron microscope can reveal these structures. Even then, serial sections and computer reconstruction are necessary to give us a comprehensive view of the functional anatomy of the nephron and its associated blood vessels.

Nephrons: The Functional Unit

Nephrons take a simple filtrate of the blood and modify it into urine. Many changes take place in the different parts of the nephron before urine is created for disposal. The term **forming urine** will be used hereafter to describe the filtrate as it is modified into true urine. The principle task of the nephron population is to balance the plasma to homeostatic set points and excrete potential toxins in the urine. They do this by accomplishing three principle functions—filtration, reabsorption, and secretion. They also have additional secondary functions that exert control in three areas: blood pressure (via production of **renin**), red blood cell production (via the hormone EPO), and calcium absorption (via conversion of calcidiol into calcitriol, the active form of vitamin D).

Renal Corpuscle

As discussed earlier, the renal corpuscle consists of a tuft of capillaries called the glomerulus that is largely surrounded by Bowman's (glomerular) capsule. The glomerulus is a high-pressure capillary bed between afferent and efferent arterioles. Bowman's capsule surrounds the glomerulus to form a lumen, and captures and directs this filtrate to the PCT. The outermost part of Bowman's capsule, the parietal layer, is a simple squamous epithelium. It transitions onto the glomerular capillaries in an intimate embrace to form the visceral layer of the capsule. Here, the cells are not squamous, but uniquely shaped cells (**podocytes**) extending finger-like arms (**pedicels**) to cover the glomerular capillaries (Figure 25.11). These projections interdigitate to form **filtration slits**, leaving small gaps between the digits to form a sieve. As blood passes through the glomerulus, 10 to 20 percent of the plasma filters between these sieve-like fingers to be captured by Bowman's capsule and funneled to the PCT. Where the fenestrae (windows) in the glomerular capillaries match the spaces between the podocyte "fingers," the only thing separating the capillary lumen and the lumen of Bowman's capsule is their shared basement membrane (Figure 25.12). These three features comprise what is known as the filtration membrane. This membrane permits very rapid movement of filtrate from capillary to capsule though pores that are only 70 nm in diameter.

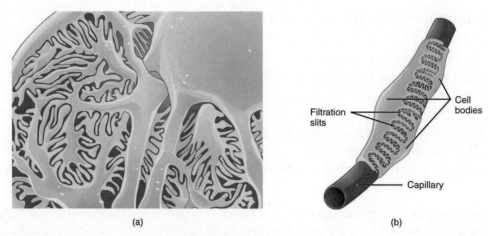

FIGURE 25.11 **Podocytes**   Podocytes interdigitate with structures called pedicels and filter substances in a way similar to fenestrations. In (a), the large cell body can be seen at the top right corner, with branches extending from the cell body. The smallest finger-like extensions are the pedicels. Pedicels on one podocyte always interdigitate with the pedicels of another podocyte. (b) This capillary has three podocytes wrapped around it.

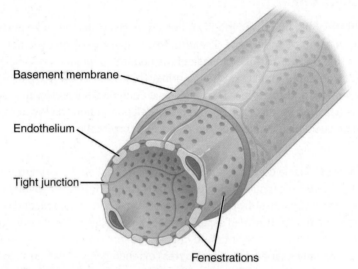

FIGURE 25.12 **Fenestrated Capillary**   Fenestrations allow many substances to diffuse from the blood based primarily on size.

The **fenestrations** prevent filtration of blood cells or large proteins, but allow most other constituents through. These substances cross readily if they are less than 4 nm in size and most pass freely up to 8 nm in size. An additional factor affecting the ability of substances to cross this barrier is their electric charge. The proteins associated with these pores are negatively charged, so they tend to repel negatively charged substances and allow positively charged substances to pass more readily. The basement membrane prevents filtration of medium-to-large proteins such as globulins. There are also **mesangial** cells in the filtration membrane that can contract to help regulate the rate of filtration of the glomerulus. Overall, filtration is regulated by fenestrations in capillary endothelial cells, podocytes with filtration slits, membrane charge, and the basement membrane between capillary cells. The result is the creation of a filtrate that does not contain cells or large proteins, and has a slight predominance of positively charged substances.

Lying just outside Bowman's capsule and the glomerulus is the **juxtaglomerular apparatus (JGA)** (Figure 25.13). At the juncture where the afferent and efferent arterioles enter and leave Bowman's capsule, the initial part of the distal convoluted tubule (DCT) comes into direct contact with the arterioles. The wall of the DCT at that point forms a part of the JGA known as the **macula densa**. This cluster of cuboidal epithelial cells monitors the fluid composition of fluid flowing through the DCT. In response to the concentration of Na^+ in the fluid flowing past them, these cells release paracrine signals. They also have a single, nonmotile cilium that responds to the rate of fluid movement in the tubule. The paracrine signals released in response to changes in flow rate and Na^+ concentration are adenosine triphosphate (ATP) and adenosine.

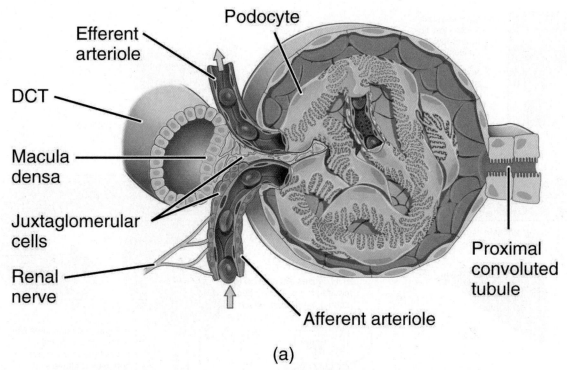

Efferent arteriole

Podocyte

DCT

Macula densa

Juxtaglomerular cells

Renal nerve

Afferent arteriole

Proximal convoluted tubule

(a)

FIGURE 25.13 Juxtaglomerular Apparatus and Glomerulus   (a) The JGA allows specialized cells to monitor the composition of the fluid in the DCT and adjust the glomerular filtration rate. (b) This micrograph shows the glomerulus and surrounding structures. LM × 1540. (Micrograph provided by the Regents of University of Michigan Medical School © 2012)

A second cell type in this apparatus is the **juxtaglomerular cell**. This is a modified, smooth muscle cell lining the afferent arteriole that can contract or relax in response to ATP or adenosine released by the macula densa. Such contraction and relaxation regulate blood flow to the glomerulus. If the osmolarity of the filtrate is too high (hyperosmotic), the juxtaglomerular cells will contract, decreasing the glomerular filtration rate (GFR) so less plasma is filtered, leading to less urine formation and greater retention of fluid. This will ultimately decrease blood osmolarity toward the physiologic norm. If the osmolarity of the filtrate is too low, the juxtaglomerular cells will relax, increasing the GFR and enhancing the loss of water to the urine, causing blood osmolarity to rise. In other words, when blood osmolarity goes up, filtration and urine formation decrease and water is retained. When blood osmolarity goes down, filtration and urine formation increase and water is lost by way of the urine. The net result of these opposing actions is to keep the rate of filtration relatively constant. A second function of the macula densa cells is to regulate renin release from the juxtaglomerular cells of the afferent arteriole (Figure 25.14). Active renin is a protein comprised of 304 amino acids that cleaves several amino acids from **angiotensinogen** to produce **angiotensin I**. Angiotensin I is not biologically active until converted to angiotensin II by **angiotensin-converting enzyme (ACE)** from the lungs. **Angiotensin II** is a systemic vasoconstrictor that helps to regulate blood pressure by increasing it. Angiotensin II also stimulates the release of the steroid hormone aldosterone from the adrenal cortex. Aldosterone stimulates Na^+ reabsorption by the kidney, which also results in water retention and increased blood pressure.

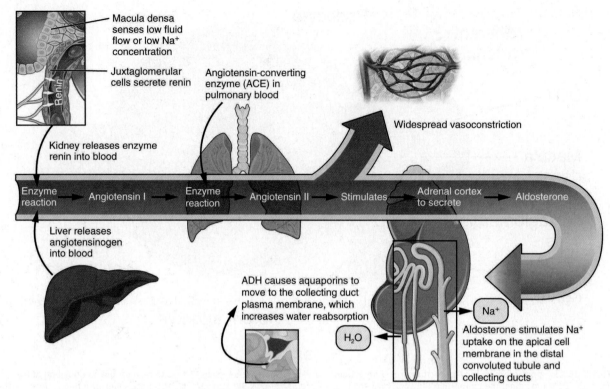

FIGURE 25.14   Conversion of Angiotensin I to Angiotensin II   The enzyme renin converts the pro-enzyme angiotensin I; the lung-derived enzyme ACE converts angiotensin I into active angiotensin II.

Proximal Convoluted Tubule (PCT)

Filtered fluid collected by Bowman's capsule enters into the PCT. It is called convoluted due to its tortuous path. Simple cuboidal cells form this tubule with prominent microvilli on the luminal surface, forming a **brush border**. These microvilli create a large surface area to maximize the absorption and secretion of solutes (Na^+, Cl^-, glucose, etc.), the most essential function of this portion of the nephron. These cells actively transport ions across their membranes, so they possess a high concentration of mitochondria in order to produce sufficient ATP.

Loop of Henle

The descending and ascending portions of the loop of Henle (sometimes referred to as the nephron loop) are, of course, just continuations of the same tubule. They run adjacent and parallel to each other after having made a hairpin turn at the deepest point of their descent. The descending loop of Henle consists of an initial short, thick portion and long, thin portion, whereas the ascending loop consists of an initial short, thin portion followed by a long, thick portion. The descending thick portion consists of simple cuboidal epithelium similar to that of the PCT. The descending and ascending thin portions consists of simple squamous epithelium. As you will see later, these are important differences, since different portions of the loop have different permeabilities for solutes and water. The ascending thick portion consists of simple cuboidal epithelium similar to the DCT.

Distal Convoluted Tubule (DCT)

The DCT, like the PCT, is very tortuous and formed by simple cuboidal epithelium, but it is shorter than the PCT. These cells are not as active as those in the PCT; thus, there are fewer microvilli on the apical surface. However, these cells must also pump ions against their concentration gradient, so you will find of large numbers of mitochondria, although fewer than in the PCT.

Collecting Ducts

The collecting ducts are continuous with the nephron but not technically part of it. In fact, each duct collects filtrate from several nephrons for final modification. Collecting ducts merge as they descend deeper in the medulla to form about 30 terminal ducts, which empty at a papilla. They are lined with simple squamous epithelium with receptors for ADH. When stimulated by ADH, these cells will insert **aquaporin** channel proteins into their membranes, which as their name suggests, allow water to pass from the duct lumen through the cells and into the interstitial spaces to be recovered by the vasa recta. This process allows for the recovery of large amounts of water from the filtrate back into the blood. In the absence of ADH, these channels are not inserted, resulting in the excretion of water in the form of dilute urine. Most, if not all, cells of the body contain aquaporin molecules, whose channels are so small that only water can pass. At least 10 types of aquaporins are known in humans, and six of those are found in the kidney. The function of all aquaporins is to allow the movement of water across the lipid-rich, hydrophobic cell membrane (Figure 25.15).

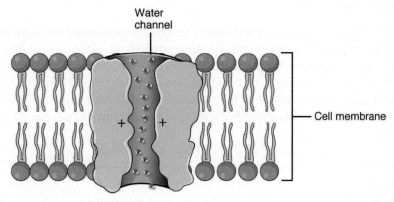

FIGURE 25.15 Aquaporin Water Channel   Positive charges inside the channel prevent the leakage of electrolytes across the cell membrane, while allowing water to move due to osmosis.

25.5 Physiology of Urine Formation

LEARNING OBJECTIVES

By the end of this section, you will be able to:

- Describe the hydrostatic and colloid osmotic forces that favor and oppose filtration
- Describe glomerular filtration rate (GFR), state the average value of GFR, and explain how clearance rate can be used to measure GFR
- Predict specific factors that will increase or decrease GFR
- State the percent of the filtrate that is normally reabsorbed and explain why the process of reabsorption is so important
- Calculate daily urine production
- List common symptoms of kidney failure

Having reviewed the anatomy and microanatomy of the urinary system, now is the time to focus on the physiology. You will discover that different parts of the nephron utilize specific processes to produce urine: filtration, reabsorption, and secretion. You will learn how each of these processes works and where they occur along the nephron and collecting ducts. The physiologic goal is to modify the composition of the plasma and, in doing so, produce the waste product urine.

Failure of the renal anatomy and/or physiology can lead suddenly or gradually to renal failure. In this event, a number of symptoms, signs, or laboratory findings point to the diagnosis (Table 25.3).

Symptoms of Kidney Failure

Weakness
Lethargy
Shortness of breath
Widespread edema
Anemia
Metabolic acidosis
Metabolic alkalosis
Heart arrhythmias
Uremia (high urea level in the blood)
Loss of appetite

TABLE 25.3

Fatigue
Excessive urination
Oliguria (too little urine output)

TABLE 25.3

Glomerular Filtration Rate (GFR)

The volume of filtrate formed by both kidneys per minute is termed the **glomerular filtration rate (GFR)**. The heart pumps about 5 L blood per min under resting conditions. Approximately 20 percent or one liter enters the kidneys to be filtered. On average, this liter results in the production of about 125 mL/min filtrate produced in males (range of 90 to 140 mL/min) and 105 mL/min filtrate produced in females (range of 80 to 125 mL/min). This amount equates to a volume of about 180 L/day in males and 150 L/day in females. Ninety-nine percent of this filtrate is returned to the circulation by reabsorption so that only about 1–2 liters of urine are produced per day (Table 25.4).

Calculating Urine Formation per Day

	Flow per minute (mL)	Calculation
Renal blood flow	1050	Cardiac output is about 5000 mL/minute, of which 21 percent flows through the kidney. 5000*0.21 = 1050 mL blood/min
Renal plasma flow	578	Renal plasma flow equals the blood flow per minute times the hematocrit. If a person has a hematocrit of 45, then the renal plasma flow is 55 percent. 1050*0.55 = 578 mL plasma/min
Glomerular filtration rate	110	The GFR is the amount of plasma entering Bowman's capsule per minute. It is the renal plasma flow times the fraction that enters the renal capsule (19 percent). 578*0.19 = 110 mL filtrate/min
Urine	1296 ml/day	The filtrate not recovered by the kidney is the urine that will be eliminated. It is the GFR times the fraction of the filtrate that is not reabsorbed (0.8 percent). 110*.008 = 0.9 mL urine /min Multiply urine/min times 60 minutes times 24 hours to get daily urine production. 0.9*60*24 = 1296 mL/day urine

TABLE 25.4

GFR is influenced by the hydrostatic pressure and colloid osmotic pressure on either side of the capillary membrane of the glomerulus. Recall that filtration occurs as pressure forces fluid and solutes through a semipermeable barrier with the solute movement constrained by particle size. Hydrostatic pressure is the pressure produced by a fluid against a surface. If you have a fluid on both sides of a barrier, both fluids exert a pressure in opposing directions. Net fluid movement will be in the direction of the lower pressure. Osmosis is the movement of solvent (water) across a membrane that is impermeable to a solute in the solution. This creates a pressure, osmotic pressure, which will exist until the solute concentration is the same on both sides of a semipermeable membrane. As long as the concentration differs, water will move. Glomerular filtration occurs when glomerular hydrostatic pressure exceeds the luminal hydrostatic pressure of Bowman's capsule. There is also an opposing force, the osmotic pressure, which is typically higher in the glomerular capillary.

To understand why this is so, look more closely at the microenvironment on either side of the filtration membrane. You will find osmotic pressure exerted by the solutes inside the lumen of the capillary as well as inside of Bowman's capsule. Since the filtration membrane limits the size of particles crossing the membrane, the osmotic pressure inside the glomerular capillary is higher than the osmotic pressure in Bowman's capsule. Recall that cells and the medium-to-large proteins cannot pass between the podocyte processes or through the fenestrations of the capillary endothelial cells. This means that red and white blood cells, platelets, albumins, and other proteins too large to pass through the filter remain in the capillary, creating an average colloid osmotic pressure of 30 mm Hg within the capillary. The absence of proteins in Bowman's space (the lumen within Bowman's capsule) results in an osmotic pressure near zero. Thus, the only pressure moving fluid across the capillary wall into the lumen of Bowman's space is hydrostatic pressure. Hydrostatic (fluid) pressure is sufficient to push water through the membrane despite the osmotic pressure working against it. The sum of all of the influences, both osmotic and hydrostatic, results in a **net filtration pressure (NFP)** of about 10 mm Hg (Figure 25.16).

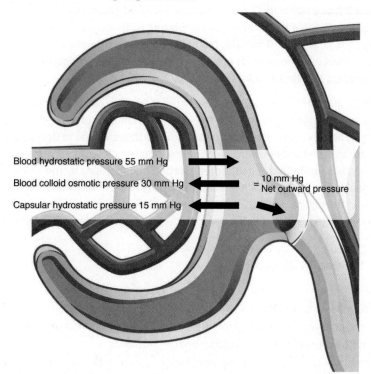

Blood hydrostatic pressure 55 mm Hg

Blood colloid osmotic pressure 30 mm Hg

Capsular hydrostatic pressure 15 mm Hg

= 10 mm Hg Net outward pressure

FIGURE 25.16   Net Filtration Pressure   The NFP is the sum of osmotic and hydrostatic pressures.

A proper concentration of solutes in the blood is important in maintaining osmotic pressure both in the glomerulus and systemically. There are disorders in which too much protein passes through the filtration slits into the kidney filtrate. This excess protein in the filtrate leads to a deficiency of circulating plasma proteins. In turn, the presence of protein in the urine increases its osmolarity; this holds more water in the filtrate and results in an increase in urine volume. Because there is less circulating protein, principally albumin, the osmotic pressure of the blood falls. Less osmotic pressure pulling water into the capillaries tips the balance towards hydrostatic pressure, which tends to push it out of the capillaries. The net effect is that water is lost from the circulation to interstitial tissues and cells. This "plumps up" the tissues and cells, a condition termed **systemic edema**.

Net Filtration Pressure (NFP)

NFP determines filtration rates through the kidney. It is determined as follows:

NFP = Glomerular blood hydrostatic pressure (GBHP) − [capsular hydrostatic pressure (CHP) + blood colloid osmotic pressure (BCOP)] = 10 mm Hg

That is:

NFP = GBHP − [CHP + BCOP] = 10 mm Hg

Or:

NFP = 55 − [15 + 30] = 10 mm Hg

As you can see, there is a low net pressure across the filtration membrane. Intuitively, you should realize that minor changes in osmolarity of the blood or changes in capillary blood pressure result in major changes in the amount of filtrate formed at any given point in time. The kidney is able to cope with a wide range of blood pressures. In large part, this is due to the autoregulatory nature of smooth muscle. When you stretch it, it contracts. Thus, when blood pressure goes up, smooth muscle in the afferent capillaries contracts to limit any increase in blood flow and filtration rate. When blood pressure drops, the same capillaries relax to maintain blood flow and filtration rate. The net result is a relatively steady flow of blood into the glomerulus and a relatively steady filtration rate in spite of significant systemic blood pressure changes. Mean arterial blood pressure is calculated by adding 1/3 of the difference between the systolic and diastolic pressures to the diastolic pressure. Therefore, if the blood pressure is 110/80, the difference between systolic and diastolic pressure is 30. One third of this is 10, and when you add this to the diastolic pressure of 80, you arrive at a calculated mean arterial pressure of 90 mm Hg. Therefore, if you use mean arterial pressure for the GBHP in the formula for calculating NFP, you can determine that as long as mean arterial pressure is above approximately 60 mm Hg, the pressure will be adequate to maintain glomerular filtration. Blood pressures below this level will impair renal function and cause systemic disorders that are severe enough to threaten survival. This condition is called shock.

Determination of the GFR is one of the tools used to assess the kidney's excretory function. This is more than just an academic exercise. Since many drugs are excreted in the urine, a decline in renal function can lead to toxic accumulations. Additionally, administration of appropriate drug dosages for those drugs primarily excreted by the kidney requires an accurate assessment of GFR. GFR can be estimated closely by intravenous administration of **inulin**. Inulin is a plant polysaccharide that is neither reabsorbed nor secreted by the kidney. Its appearance in the urine is directly proportional to the rate at which it is filtered by the renal corpuscle. However, since measuring inulin clearance is cumbersome in the clinical setting, most often, the GFR is estimated by measuring naturally occurring creatinine, a protein-derived molecule produced by muscle metabolism that is not reabsorbed and only slightly secreted by the nephron.

25.6 Tubular Reabsorption

LEARNING OBJECTIVES

By the end of this section, you will be able to:

- List specific transport mechanisms occurring in different parts of the nephron, including active transport, osmosis, facilitated diffusion, and passive electrochemical gradients
- List the different membrane proteins of the nephron, including channels, transporters, and ATPase pumps
- Compare and contrast passive and active tubular reabsorption
- Explain why the differential permeability or impermeability of specific sections of the nephron tubules is necessary for urine formation
- Describe how and where water, organic compounds, and ions are reabsorbed in the nephron
- Explain the role of the loop of Henle, the vasa recta, and the countercurrent multiplication mechanisms in the concentration of urine
- List the locations in the nephron where tubular secretion occurs

With up to 180 liters per day passing through the nephrons of the kidney, it is quite obvious that most of that fluid and its contents must be reabsorbed. That recovery occurs in the PCT, loop of Henle, DCT, and the collecting ducts (Table 25.5 and Figure 25.17). Various portions of the nephron differ in their capacity to reabsorb water and specific solutes. While much of the reabsorption and secretion occur passively based on concentration gradients, the amount of water that is reabsorbed or lost is tightly regulated. This control is exerted directly by ADH and aldosterone, and indirectly by renin. Most water is recovered in the PCT, loop of Henle, and DCT. About 10 percent (about 18 L) reaches the collecting ducts. The collecting ducts, under the influence of ADH, can recover almost all of the water passing through them, in cases of dehydration, or almost none of the water, in cases of over-hydration.

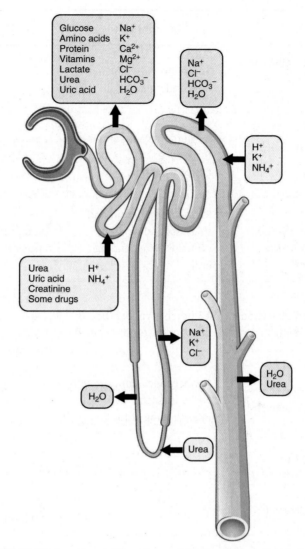

FIGURE 25.17   Locations of Secretion and Reabsorption in the Nephron

Substances Secreted or Reabsorbed in the Nephron and Their Locations

Substance	PCT	Loop of Henle	DCT	Collecting ducts
Glucose	Almost 100 percent reabsorbed; secondary active transport with Na^+			
Oligopeptides, proteins, amino acids	Almost 100 percent reabsorbed; symport with Na^+			
Vitamins	Reabsorbed			
Lactate	Reabsorbed			
Creatinine	Secreted			

TABLE 25.5

Substance	PCT	Loop of Henle	DCT	Collecting ducts
Urea	50 percent reabsorbed by diffusion; also secreted	Secretion, diffusion in descending limb		Reabsorption in medullary collecting ducts; diffusion
Sodium	65 percent actively reabsorbed	25 percent reabsorbed in thick ascending limb; active transport	5 percent reabsorbed; active	5 percent reabsorbed, stimulated by aldosterone; active
Chloride	Reabsorbed, symport with Na^+, diffusion	Reabsorbed in thin and thick ascending limb; diffusion in ascending limb	Reabsorbed; diffusion	Reabsorbed; symport
Water	67 percent reabsorbed osmotically with solutes	15 percent reabsorbed in descending limb; osmosis	8 percent reabsorbed if ADH; osmosis	Variable amounts reabsorbed, controlled by ADH, osmosis
HCO_3^-	80–90 percent symport reabsorption with Na^+	Reabsorbed, symport with Na^+ and antiport with Cl^-; in ascending limb		Reabsorbed antiport with Cl^-
H^+	Secreted; diffusion		Secreted; active	Secreted; active
NH_4^+	Secreted; diffusion		Secreted; diffusion	Secreted; diffusion
Some drugs	Secreted		Secreted; active	Secreted; active
Potassium	65 percent reabsorbed; diffusion	20 percent reabsorbed in thick ascending limb; symport	Secreted; active	Secretion controlled by aldosterone; active
Calcium	Reabsorbed; diffusion	Reabsorbed in thick ascending limb; diffusion		Reabsorbed if parathyroid hormone present; active
Magnesium	Reabsorbed; diffusion	Reabsorbed in thick ascending limb; diffusion	Reabsorbed	
Phosphate	85 percent reabsorbed, inhibited by parathyroid hormone, diffusion		Reabsorbed; diffusion	

TABLE 25.5

Mechanisms of Recovery

Mechanisms by which substances move across membranes for reabsorption or secretion include active transport, diffusion, facilitated diffusion, secondary active transport, and osmosis. These were discussed in an earlier chapter, and you may wish to review them.

Active transport utilizes energy, usually the energy found in a phosphate bond of ATP, to move a substance across a membrane from a low to a high concentration. It is very specific and must have an appropriately shaped receptor for the substance to be transported. An example would be the active transport of Na^+ out of a cell and K^+ into a cell by the Na^+/K^+ pump. Both ions are moved in opposite directions from a lower to a higher concentration.

Simple diffusion moves a substance from a higher to a lower concentration down its concentration gradient. It requires no energy and only needs to be soluble.

Facilitated diffusion is similar to diffusion in that it moves a substance down its concentration gradient. The difference is that it requires specific membrane receptors or channel proteins for movement. The movement of glucose and, in certain situations, Na^+ ions, is an example of facilitated diffusion. In some cases of mediated transport, two different substances share the same channel protein port; these mechanisms are described by the terms symport and antiport.

Symport mechanisms move two or more substances in the same direction at the same time, whereas antiport mechanisms move two or more substances in opposite directions across the cell membrane. Both mechanisms may utilize concentration gradients maintained by ATP pumps. As described previously, when active transport powers the transport of another substance in this way, it is called "secondary active transport." Glucose reabsorption in the kidneys is by secondary active transport. Na^+/K^+ ATPases on the basal membrane of a tubular cell constantly pump Na^+ out of the cell, maintaining a strong electrochemical gradient for Na^+ to move into the cell from the tubular lumen. On the luminal (apical) surface, a Na^+/glucose symport protein assists both Na+ and glucose movement into the cell. The cotransporter moves glucose into the cell against its concentration gradient as Na^+ moves down the electrochemical gradient created by the basal membranes Na^+/K^+ ATPases. The glucose molecule then diffuses across the basal membrane by facilitated diffusion into the interstitial space and from there into peritubular capillaries.

Most of the Ca^{++}, Na^+, glucose, and amino acids must be reabsorbed by the nephron to maintain homeostatic plasma concentrations. Other substances, such as urea, K^+, ammonia (NH_3), creatinine, and some drugs are secreted into the filtrate as waste products. Acid–base balance is maintained through actions of the lungs and kidneys: The lungs rid the body of H^+, whereas the kidneys secrete or reabsorb H^+ and HCO_3^- (Table 25.6). In the case of urea, about 50 percent is passively reabsorbed by the PCT. More is recovered by in the collecting ducts as needed. ADH induces the insertion of urea transporters and aquaporin channel proteins.

Substances Filtered and Reabsorbed by the Kidney per 24 Hours

Substance	Amount filtered (grams)	Amount reabsorbed (grams)	Amount in urine (grams)
Water	180 L	179 L	1 L
Proteins	10–20	10–20	0
Chlorine	630	625	5
Sodium	540	537	3
Bicarbonate	300	299.7	0.3
Glucose	180	180	0

TABLE 25.6

Substance	Amount filtered (grams)	Amount reabsorbed (grams)	Amount in urine (grams)
Urea	53	28	25
Potassium	28	24	4
Uric acid	8.5	7.7	0.8
Creatinine	1.4	0	1.4

TABLE 25.6

Reabsorption and Secretion in the PCT

The renal corpuscle filters the blood to create a filtrate that differs from blood mainly in the absence of cells and large proteins. From this point to the ends of the collecting ducts, the filtrate or forming urine is undergoing modification through secretion and reabsorption before true urine is produced. The first point at which the forming urine is modified is in the PCT. Here, some substances are reabsorbed, whereas others are secreted. Note the use of the term "reabsorbed." All of these substances were "absorbed" in the digestive tract—99 percent of the water and most of the solutes filtered by the nephron must be reabsorbed. Water and substances that are reabsorbed are returned to the circulation by the peritubular and vasa recta capillaries. It is important to understand the difference between the glomerulus and the peritubular and vasa recta capillaries. The glomerulus has a relatively high pressure inside its capillaries and can sustain this by dilating the afferent arteriole while constricting the efferent arteriole. This assures adequate filtration pressure even as the systemic blood pressure varies. Movement of water into the peritubular capillaries and vasa recta will be influenced primarily by osmolarity and concentration gradients. Sodium is actively pumped out of the PCT into the interstitial spaces between cells and diffuses down its concentration gradient into the peritubular capillary. As it does so, water will follow passively to maintain an isotonic fluid environment inside the capillary. This is called obligatory water reabsorption, because water is "obliged" to follow the Na$^+$ (Figure 25.18).

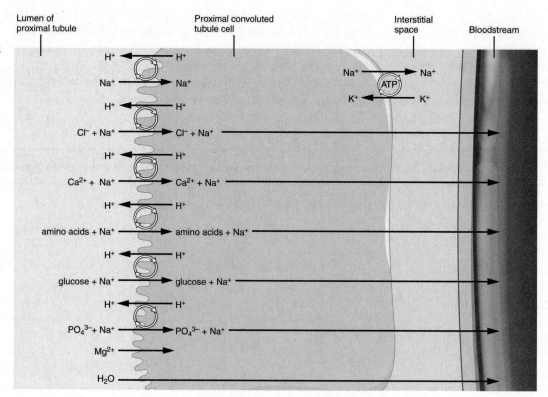

FIGURE 25.18   Substances Reabsorbed and Secreted by the PCT

Access for free at openstax.org

More substances move across the membranes of the PCT than any other portion of the nephron. Many of these substances (amino acids and glucose) use symport mechanisms for transport along with Na$^+$. Antiport, active transport, diffusion, and facilitated diffusion are additional mechanisms by which substances are moved from one side of a membrane to the other. Recall that cells have two surfaces: apical and basal. The apical surface is the one facing the lumen or open space of a cavity or tube, in this case, the inside of the PCT. The basal surface of the cell faces the connective tissue base to which the cell attaches (basement membrane) or the cell membrane closer to the basement membrane if there is a stratified layer of cells. In the PCT, there is a single layer of simple cuboidal endothelial cells against the basement membrane. The numbers and particular types of pumps and channels vary between the apical and basilar surfaces. A few of the substances that are transported with Na$^+$ (symport mechanism) on the apical membrane include Cl$^-$, Ca^{++}, amino acids, glucose, and PO_4^{3-}. Sodium is actively exchanged for K$^+$ using ATP on the basal membrane. Most of the substances transported by a symport mechanism on the apical membrane are transported by facilitated diffusion on the basal membrane. At least three ions, K$^+$, Ca^{++}, and Mg^{++}, diffuse laterally between adjacent cell membranes (transcellular).

About 67 percent of the water, Na$^+$, and K$^+$ entering the nephron is reabsorbed in the PCT and returned to the circulation. Almost 100 percent of glucose, amino acids, and other organic substances such as vitamins are normally recovered here. Some glucose may appear in the urine if circulating glucose levels are high enough that all the glucose transporters in the PCT are saturated, so that their capacity to move glucose is exceeded (transport maximum, or T$_m$). In males, the maximum amount of glucose that can be recovered is about 375 mg/min, whereas in females, it is about 300 mg/min. This recovery rate translates to an arterial concentration of about 200 mg/dL. Though an exceptionally high sugar intake might cause sugar to appear briefly in the urine, the appearance of **glycosuria** usually points to type I or II diabetes mellitus. The transport of glucose from the lumen of the PCT to the interstitial space is similar to the way it is absorbed by the small intestine. Both glucose and Na$^+$ bind simultaneously to the same symport proteins on the apical surface of the cell to be transported in the same direction, toward the interstitial space. Sodium moves down its electrochemical and concentration gradient into the cell and takes glucose with it. Na$^+$ is then actively pumped out of the cell at the basal surface of the cell into the interstitial space. Glucose leaves the cell to enter the interstitial space by facilitated diffusion. The energy to move glucose comes from the Na$^+$/K$^+$ ATPase that pumps Na$^+$ out of the cell on the basal surface. Fifty percent of Cl$^-$ and variable quantities of Ca^{++}, Mg^{++}, and HPO_4^{2-} are also recovered in the PCT.

Recovery of bicarbonate (HCO$_3^-$) is vital to the maintenance of acid–base balance, since it is a very powerful and fast-acting buffer. An important enzyme is used to catalyze this mechanism: carbonic anhydrase (CA). This same enzyme and reaction is used in red blood cells in the transportation of CO$_2$, in the stomach to produce hydrochloric acid, and in the pancreas to produce HCO$_3^-$ to buffer acidic chyme from the stomach. In the kidney, most of the CA is located within the cell, but a small amount is bound to the brush border of the membrane on the apical surface of the cell. In the lumen of the PCT, HCO$_3^-$ combines with hydrogen ions to form carbonic acid (H$_2$CO$_3$). This is enzymatically catalyzed into CO$_2$ and water, which diffuse across the apical membrane into the cell. Water can move osmotically across the lipid bilayer membrane due to the presence of aquaporin water channels. Inside the cell, the reverse reaction occurs to produce bicarbonate ions (HCO$_3^-$). These bicarbonate ions are cotransported with Na$^+$ across the basal membrane to the interstitial space around the PCT (Figure 25.19). At the same time this is occurring, a Na$^+$/H$^+$ antiporter excretes H$^+$ into the lumen, while it recovers Na$^+$. Note how the hydrogen ion is recycled so that bicarbonate can be recovered. Also, note that a Na$^+$ gradient is created by the Na$^+$/K$^+$ pump.

$$HCO_3^- + H^+ \leftrightarrow H_2CO_3 \leftrightarrow CO_2 + H_2O$$

The significant recovery of solutes from the PCT lumen to the interstitial space creates an osmotic gradient that promotes water recovery. As noted before, water moves through channels created by the aquaporin proteins. These proteins are found in all cells in varying amounts and help regulate water movement across membranes and through cells by creating a passageway across the hydrophobic lipid bilayer membrane. Changing the number of aquaporin proteins in membranes of the collecting ducts also helps to regulate the osmolarity of the blood. The movement of many positively charged ions also creates an electrochemical gradient. This charge promotes the movement of negative ions toward the interstitial spaces and the movement of positive ions toward the lumen.

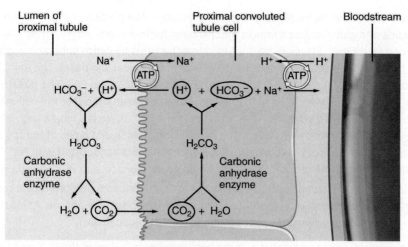

FIGURE 25.19   Reabsorption of Bicarbonate from the PCT

Reabsorption and Secretion in the Loop of Henle

The loop of Henle consists of two sections: thick and thin descending and thin and thick ascending sections. The loops of cortical nephrons do not extend into the renal medulla very far, if at all. Juxtamedullary nephrons have loops that extend variable distances, some very deep into the medulla. The descending and ascending portions of the loop are highly specialized to enable recovery of much of the Na^+ and water that were filtered by the glomerulus. As the forming urine moves through the loop, the osmolarity will change from isosmotic with blood (about 278–300 mOsmol/kg) to both a very hypertonic solution of about 1200 mOsmol/kg and a very hypotonic solution of about 100 mOsmol/kg. These changes are accomplished by osmosis in the descending limb and active transport in the ascending limb. Solutes and water recovered from these loops are returned to the circulation by way of the vasa recta.

Descending Loop

The majority of the descending loop is comprised of simple squamous epithelial cells; to simplify the function of the loop, this discussion focuses on these cells. These membranes have permanent aquaporin channel proteins that allow unrestricted movement of water from the descending loop into the surrounding interstitium as osmolarity increases from about 300 mOsmol/kg to about 1200 mOsmol/kg in the filtrate. This increase results in reabsorption of up to 15 percent of the water entering the nephron. Modest amounts of urea, Na^+, and other ions are also recovered here.

Most of the solutes that were filtered in the glomerulus have now been recovered along with a majority of water, about 82 percent. As the forming urine enters the ascending loop, major adjustments will be made to the concentration of solutes to create what you perceive as urine.

Ascending Loop

The ascending loop is made of very short thin and longer thick portions. Once again, to simplify the function, this section only considers the thick portion. The thick portion is lined with simple cuboidal epithelium without a brush border. It is completely impermeable to water due to the absence of aquaporin proteins, but ions, mainly Na^+ and CL^-, are actively reabsorbed by a cotransport system. This has two significant effects: Removal of NaCl while retaining water leads to a hypoosomotic filtrate by the time it reaches the DCT; pumping NaCl into the interstitial space contributes to the hyperosmotic environment in the kidney medulla.

The Na^+/K^+ ATPase pumps in the basal membrane create an electrochemical gradient, allowing reabsorption of Cl^- by Na^+/Cl^- symporters in the apical membrane. At the same time that Na^+ is actively pumped from the basal side of the cell into the interstitial fluid, Cl^- follows the Na^+ from the lumen into the interstitial fluid by a paracellular route between cells through **leaky tight junctions**. These are found between cells of the ascending loop, where they allow certain solutes to move according to their concentration gradient. Most of the K^+ that enters the cell via symporters returns to the lumen (down its concentration gradient) through leaky channels in the apical membrane. Note the environment now created in the interstitial space: With the "back door exiting" K^+, there is one Na^+ and two Cl^- ions left in the interstitium surrounding the ascending loop. Therefore, in comparison to the lumen of the loop, the interstitial space is now a negatively charged environment. This negative charge attracts cations (Na^+, K^+, Ca^{++}, and Mg^{++}) from the lumen via a paracellular route to the interstitial space and vasa recta.

Countercurrent Multiplier System

The structure of the loop of Henle and associated vasa recta create a **countercurrent multiplier system** (Figure 25.20). The countercurrent term comes from the fact that the descending and ascending loops are next to each other and their fluid flows in opposite directions (countercurrent). The multiplier term is due to the action of solute pumps that increase (multiply) the concentrations of urea and Na^+ deep in the medulla.

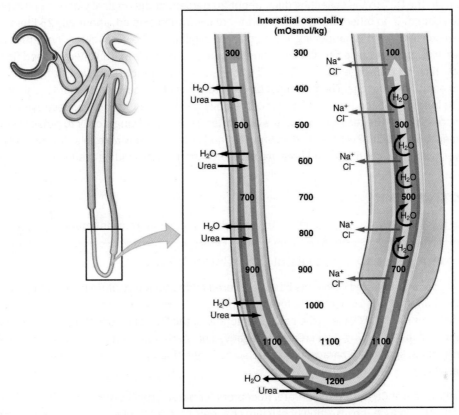

FIGURE 25.20   Countercurrent Multiplier System

As discussed above, the ascending loop actively reabsorbs NaCl out of the forming urine into the interstitial spaces. In addition, collecting ducts have urea pumps that actively pump urea into the interstitial spaces. This results in the recovery of NaCl to the circulation via the vasa recta and creates a high osmolar environment in the depths of the medulla.

Ammonia (NH_3) is a toxic byproduct of protein metabolism. It is formed as amino acids are deaminated by liver hepatocytes. That means that the amine group, NH_2, is removed from amino acids as they are broken down. Most of the resulting ammonia is converted into urea by liver hepatocytes. Urea is not only less toxic but is utilized to aid in the recovery of water by the loop of Henle and collecting ducts. At the same time that water is freely diffusing out of the descending loop through aquaporin channels into the interstitial spaces of the medulla, urea freely diffuses into the lumen of the descending loop as it descends deeper into the medulla, much of it to be reabsorbed from the forming urine when it reaches the collecting duct. Thus, the movement of Na^+ and urea into the interstitial spaces by these mechanisms creates the hyperosmotic environment of the medulla. The net result of this countercurrent multiplier system is to recover both water and Na^+ in the circulation.

The amino acid glutamine can be deaminated by the kidney. As NH_2 from the amino acid is converted into NH_3 and pumped into the lumen of the PCT, Na^+ and HCO_3^- are excreted into the interstitial fluid of the renal pyramid via a symport mechanism. When this process occurs in the cells of the PCT, the added benefit is a net loss of a hydrogen ion (complexed to ammonia to form the weak acid NH_4^+) in the urine and a gain of a bicarbonate ion (HCO_3^-) in the blood. Ammonia and bicarbonate are exchanged in a one-to-one ratio. This exchange is yet another means by which the body can buffer and excrete acid. The presence of aquaporin channels in the descending loop allows prodigious quantities of water to leave the loop and enter the hyperosmolar interstitium of the pyramid, where it is returned to the circulation by the vasa recta. As the loop turns to become the ascending loop, there is an absence of aquaporin channels, so water cannot leave the loop. However, in the basal membrane of cells of the thick ascending loop, ATPase pumps actively remove Na^+ from the cell. A $Na^+/K^+/2Cl^-$ symporter in the apical membrane passively allows these ions to enter the cell cytoplasm from the lumen of the loop down a concentration gradient created by the pump. This mechanism works to dilute the fluid of the ascending loop ultimately to approximately 50–100 mOsmol/L.

At the transition from the DCT to the collecting duct, about 20 percent of the original water is still present and about 10 percent of the sodium. If no other mechanism for water reabsorption existed, about 20–25 liters of urine would be produced. Now consider what is happening in the adjacent capillaries, the vasa recta. They are recovering both solutes and water at a rate that preserves the countercurrent multiplier system. In general, blood flows slowly in capillaries to allow time for exchange of nutrients and wastes. In the vasa recta particularly, this rate of flow is important for two additional reasons. The flow must be slow to allow blood cells to lose and regain water without either crenating or bursting. Second, a rapid flow would remove too much Na^+ and urea, destroying the osmolar gradient that is necessary for the recovery of solutes and water. Thus, by flowing slowly to preserve the countercurrent mechanism, as the vasa recta descend, Na^+ and urea are freely able to enter the capillary, while water freely leaves; as they ascend, Na^+ and urea are secreted into the surrounding medulla, while water reenters and is removed.

⌾ INTERACTIVE LINK

Watch this video (http://openstax.org/l/multiplier) to learn about the countercurrent multiplier system.

Reabsorption and Secretion in the Distal Convoluted Tubule

Approximately 80 percent of filtered water has been recovered by the time the dilute forming urine enters the DCT. The DCT will recover another 10–15 percent before the forming urine enters the collecting ducts. Aldosterone increases the amount of Na^+/K^+ ATPase in the basal membrane of the DCT and collecting duct. The movement of Na^+ out of the lumen of the collecting duct creates a negative charge that promotes the movement of Cl^- out of the lumen into the interstitial space by a paracellular route across tight junctions. Peritubular capillaries receive the solutes and water, returning them to the circulation.

Cells of the DCT also recover Ca^{++} from the filtrate. Receptors for parathyroid hormone (PTH) are found in DCT cells and when bound to PTH, induce the insertion of calcium channels on their luminal surface. The channels enhance Ca^{++} recovery from the forming urine. In addition, as Na^+ is pumped out of the cell, the resulting electrochemical gradient attracts Ca^{++} into the cell. Finally, calcitriol (1,25 dihydroxyvitamin D, the active form of vitamin D) is very important for calcium recovery. It induces the production of calcium-binding proteins that transport Ca^{++} into the cell. These binding proteins are also important for the movement of calcium inside the cell and aid in exocytosis of calcium across the basolateral membrane. Any Ca^{++} not reabsorbed at this point is lost in the urine.

Collecting Ducts and Recovery of Water

Solutes move across the membranes of the collecting ducts, which contain two distinct cell types, principal cells and intercalated cells. A **principal cell** possesses channels for the recovery or loss of sodium and potassium. An **intercalated cell** secretes or absorbs acid or bicarbonate. As in other portions of the nephron, there is an array of micromachines (pumps and channels) on display in the membranes of these cells.

Regulation of urine volume and osmolarity are major functions of the collecting ducts. By varying the amount of water that is recovered, the collecting ducts play a major role in maintaining the body's normal osmolarity. If the blood becomes hyperosmotic, the collecting ducts recover more water to dilute the blood; if the blood becomes hyposmotic, the collecting ducts recover less of the water, leading to concentration of the blood. Another way of saying this is: If plasma osmolarity rises, more water is recovered and urine volume decreases; if plasma osmolarity decreases, less water is recovered and urine volume increases. This function is regulated by the posterior pituitary hormone ADH (vasopressin). With mild dehydration, plasma osmolarity rises slightly. This increase is detected by osmoreceptors in the hypothalamus, which stimulates the release of ADH from the posterior pituitary. If plasma osmolarity decreases slightly, the opposite occurs.

When stimulated by ADH, aquaporin channels are inserted into the apical membrane of principal cells, which line the collecting ducts. As the ducts descend through the medulla, the osmolarity surrounding them increases (due to the countercurrent mechanisms described above). If aquaporin water channels are present, water will be osmotically pulled from the collecting duct into the surrounding interstitial space and into the peritubular capillaries. Therefore, the final urine will be more concentrated. If less ADH is secreted, fewer aquaporin channels are inserted and less water is recovered, resulting in dilute urine. By altering the number of aquaporin channels, the volume of water recovered or lost is altered. This, in turn, regulates the blood osmolarity, blood pressure, and osmolarity of the urine.

As Na^+ is pumped from the forming urine, water is passively recaptured for the circulation; this preservation of vascular volume is critically important for the maintenance of a normal blood pressure. Aldosterone is secreted by the adrenal cortex in response to angiotensin II stimulation. As an extremely potent vasoconstrictor, angiotensin II functions immediately to increase blood pressure. By also stimulating aldosterone production, it provides a longer-lasting mechanism to support blood pressure by maintaining vascular volume (water recovery).

In addition to receptors for ADH, principal cells have receptors for the steroid hormone aldosterone. While ADH is primarily involved in the regulation of water recovery, aldosterone regulates Na^+ recovery. Aldosterone stimulates principal cells to manufacture luminal Na^+ and K^+ channels as well as Na^+/K^+ ATPase pumps on the basal membrane of the cells. When aldosterone output increases, more Na^+ is recovered from the forming urine and water follows the Na^+ passively. As the pump recovers Na^+ for the body, it is also pumping K^+ into the forming urine, since the pump moves K^+ in the opposite direction. When aldosterone decreases, more Na^+ remains in the forming urine and more K^+ is recovered in the circulation. Symport channels move Na^+ and Cl^- together. Still other channels in the principal cells secrete K^+ into the collecting duct in direct proportion to the recovery of Na^+.

Intercalated cells play significant roles in regulating blood pH. Intercalated cells reabsorb K^+ and HCO_3^- while secreting H^+. This function lowers the acidity of the plasma while increasing the acidity of the urine.

25.7 Regulation of Renal Blood Flow

LEARNING OBJECTIVES

By the end of this section, you will be able to:

- Describe the myogenic and tubuloglomerular feedback mechanisms and explain how they affect urine volume and composition
- Describe the function of the juxtaglomerular apparatus

It is vital that the flow of blood through the kidney be at a suitable rate to allow for filtration. This rate determines how much solute is retained or discarded, how much water is retained or discarded, and ultimately, the osmolarity of blood and the blood pressure of the body.

Sympathetic Nerves

The kidneys are innervated by the sympathetic neurons of the autonomic nervous system via the celiac plexus and splanchnic nerves. Reduction of sympathetic stimulation results in vasodilation and increased blood flow through the kidneys during resting conditions. When the frequency of action potentials increases, the arteriolar smooth muscle constricts (vasoconstriction), resulting in diminished glomerular flow, so less filtration occurs. Under conditions of stress, sympathetic nervous activity increases, resulting in the direct vasoconstriction of afferent arterioles (norepinephrine effect) as well as stimulation of the adrenal medulla. The adrenal medulla, in turn, produces a generalized vasoconstriction through the release of epinephrine. This includes vasoconstriction of the afferent arterioles, further reducing the volume of blood flowing through the kidneys. This process redirects blood to other organs with more immediate needs. If blood pressure falls, the sympathetic nerves will also stimulate the release of renin. Additional renin increases production of the powerful vasoconstrictor angiotensin II. Angiotensin II, as discussed above, will also stimulate aldosterone production to augment blood volume through retention of more Na^+ and water. Only a 10 mm Hg pressure differential across the glomerulus is required for normal GFR, so very small changes in afferent arterial pressure significantly increase or decrease GFR.

Autoregulation

The kidneys are very effective at regulating the rate of blood flow over a wide range of blood pressures. Your blood pressure will decrease when you are relaxed or sleeping. It will increase when exercising. Yet, despite these changes, the filtration rate through the kidney will change very little. This is due to two internal autoregulatory mechanisms that operate without outside influence: the myogenic mechanism and the tubuloglomerular feedback mechanism.

Arteriole Myogenic Mechanism

The **myogenic mechanism** regulating blood flow within the kidney depends upon a characteristic shared by most smooth muscle cells of the body. When you stretch a smooth muscle cell, it contracts; when you stop, it relaxes, restoring its resting length. This mechanism works in the afferent arteriole that supplies the glomerulus. When blood pressure increases, smooth muscle cells in the wall of the arteriole are stretched and respond by contracting to resist the pressure, resulting in little change in flow. When blood pressure drops, the same smooth muscle cells relax to lower resistance, allowing a continued even flow of blood.

Tubuloglomerular Feedback

The **tubuloglomerular feedback** mechanism involves the JGA and a paracrine signaling mechanism utilizing ATP, adenosine, and nitric oxide (NO). This mechanism stimulates either contraction or relaxation of afferent arteriolar smooth muscle cells (Table 25.7). Recall that the DCT is in intimate contact with the afferent and efferent arterioles of the glomerulus. Specialized macula densa cells in this segment of the tubule respond to changes in the fluid flow rate and Na^+ concentration. As GFR increases, there is less time for NaCl to be reabsorbed in the PCT, resulting in higher osmolarity in the filtrate. The increased fluid movement more strongly deflects single nonmotile cilia on macula densa cells. This increased osmolarity of the forming urine, and the greater flow rate within the DCT, activates macula densa cells to respond by releasing ATP and adenosine (a metabolite of ATP). ATP and adenosine act locally as paracrine factors to stimulate the myogenic juxtaglomerular cells of the afferent arteriole to constrict, slowing blood flow and reducing GFR. Conversely, when GFR decreases, less Na^+ is in the forming urine, and most will be reabsorbed before reaching the macula densa, which will result in decreased ATP and adenosine, allowing the afferent arteriole to dilate and increase GFR. NO has the opposite effect, relaxing the afferent arteriole at the same time ATP and adenosine are stimulating it to contract. Thus, NO fine-tunes the effects of adenosine and ATP on GFR.

Paracrine Mechanisms Controlling Glomerular Filtration Rate

Change in GFR	NaCl Absorption	Role of ATP and adenosine/Role of NO	Effect on GFR
Increased GFR	Tubular NaCl increases	ATP and adenosine increase, causing vasoconstriction	Vasoconstriction slows GFR
Decreased GFR	Tubular NaCl decreases	ATP and adenosine decrease, causing vasodilation	Vasodilation increases GFR
Increased GFR	Tubular NaCl increases	NO increases, causing vasodilation	Vasodilation increases GFR
Decreased GFR	Tubular NaCl decreases	NO decreases, causing vasoconstricton	Vasoconstriction decreases GFR

TABLE 25.7

25.8 Endocrine Regulation of Kidney Function

LEARNING OBJECTIVES

By the end of this section, you will be able to:

- Describe how each of the following functions in the extrinsic control of GFR: renin–angiotensin mechanism, natriuretic peptides, and sympathetic adrenergic activity
- Describe how each of the following works to regulate reabsorption and secretion, so as to affect urine volume and composition: renin–angiotensin system, aldosterone, antidiuretic hormone, and natriuretic peptides
- Name and define the roles of other hormones that regulate kidney control

Several hormones have specific, important roles in regulating kidney function. They act to stimulate or inhibit blood flow. Some of these are endocrine, acting from a distance, whereas others are paracrine, acting locally.

Renin–Angiotensin–Aldosterone

Renin is an enzyme that is produced by the juxtaglomerular (JG) cells of the afferent arteriole at the JGA. It enzymatically converts angiotensinogen (made by the liver, freely circulating) into angiotensin I. Its release is stimulated by prostaglandins and NO from the JGA in response to decreased extracellular fluid volume.

ACE is not a hormone but it is functionally important in regulating systemic blood pressure and kidney function. It is produced in the lungs but binds to the surfaces of endothelial cells in the afferent arterioles and glomerulus. It enzymatically converts inactive angiotensin I into active angiotensin II. ACE is important in raising blood pressure. People with high blood pressure are sometimes prescribed ACE inhibitors to lower their blood pressure.

Angiotensin II is a potent vasoconstrictor that plays an immediate role in the regulation of blood pressure. It acts systemically to cause vasoconstriction as well as constriction of both the afferent and efferent arterioles of the glomerulus. In instances of blood loss or dehydration, it reduces both GFR and renal blood flow, thereby limiting fluid loss and preserving blood volume. Its release is usually stimulated by decreases in blood pressure, and so the preservation of adequate blood pressure is its primary role.

Aldosterone, often called the "salt-retaining hormone," is released from the adrenal cortex in response to angiotensin II or directly in response to increased plasma K^+. It promotes Na^+ reabsorption by the nephron, promoting the retention of water. It is also important in regulating K^+, promoting its excretion. (This dual effect on two minerals and its origin in the adrenal cortex explains its designation as a mineralocorticoid.) As a result, renin has an immediate effect on blood pressure due to angiotensin II–stimulated vasoconstriction and a prolonged effect through Na^+ recovery due to aldosterone. At the same time that aldosterone causes increased recovery of Na^+, it also causes greater loss of K^+. Progesterone is a steroid that is structurally similar to aldosterone. It binds to the aldosterone receptor and weakly stimulates Na^+ reabsorption and increased water recovery. This process is unimportant in males due to low levels of circulating progesterone. It may cause increased retention of water during some periods of the menstrual cycle in females when progesterone levels increase.

Antidiuretic Hormone (ADH)

Diuretics are drugs that can increase water loss by interfering with the recapture of solutes and water from the forming urine. They are often prescribed to lower blood pressure. Coffee, tea, and alcoholic beverages are familiar diuretics. ADH, a 9-amino acid peptide released by the posterior pituitary, works to do the exact opposite. It promotes the recovery of water, decreases urine volume, and maintains plasma osmolarity and blood pressure. It does so by stimulating the movement of aquaporin proteins into the apical cell membrane of principal cells of the collecting ducts to form water channels, allowing the transcellular movement of water from the lumen of the collecting duct into the interstitial space in the medulla of the kidney by osmosis. From there, it enters the vasa recta capillaries to return to the circulation. Water is attracted by the high osmotic environment of the deep kidney medulla.

Endothelin

Endothelins, 21-amino acid peptides, are extremely powerful vasoconstrictors. They are produced by endothelial cells of the renal blood vessels, mesangial cells, and cells of the DCT. Hormones stimulating endothelin release include angiotensin II, bradykinin, and epinephrine. They do not typically influence blood pressure in healthy people. On the other hand, in people with diabetic kidney disease, endothelin is chronically elevated, resulting in sodium retention. They also diminish GFR by damaging the podocytes and by potently vasoconstricting both the afferent and efferent arterioles.

Natriuretic Hormones

Natriuretic hormones are peptides that stimulate the kidneys to excrete sodium—an effect opposite that of aldosterone. Natriuretic hormones act by inhibiting aldosterone release and therefore inhibiting Na^+ recovery in the collecting ducts. If Na^+ remains in the forming urine, its osmotic force will cause a concurrent loss of water. Natriuretic hormones also inhibit ADH release, which of course will result in less water recovery. Therefore, natriuretic peptides inhibit both Na^+ and water recovery. One example from this family of hormones is atrial natriuretic hormone (ANH), a 28-amino acid peptide produced by heart atria in response to over-stretching of the atrial wall. The over-stretching occurs in persons with elevated blood pressure or heart failure. It increases GFR through concurrent vasodilation of the afferent arteriole and vasoconstriction of the efferent arteriole. These events lead to an increased loss of water and sodium in the forming urine. It also decreases sodium reabsorption in the DCT. There is also B-type natriuretic peptide (BNP) of 32 amino acids produced in the ventricles of the heart. It has a 10-fold lower affinity for its receptor, so its effects are less than those of ANH. Its role may be to provide "fine tuning" for the regulation of blood pressure. BNP's longer biologic half-life makes it a good diagnostic marker of congestive heart failure (Figure 25.21).

Parathyroid Hormone

Parathyroid hormone (PTH) is an 84-amino acid peptide produced by the parathyroid glands in response to decreased circulating Ca^{++} levels. Among its targets is the PCT, where it stimulates the hydroxylation of calcidiol to calcitriol (1,25-hydroxycholecalciferol, the active form of vitamin D). It also blocks reabsorption of phosphate (PO_3^-), causing its loss in the urine. The retention of phosphate would result in the formation of calcium phosphate in the plasma, reducing circulating Ca^{++} levels. By ridding the blood of phosphate, higher circulating Ca^{++} levels are permitted.

	Stimulus	Effect on GFR	Effect on RBF
VASOCONSTRICTORS			
Sympathetic nerves (epinephrine and norepinephrine)	↓ECFV	↓	↓
Angiotensin II	↓ECFV	↓	↓
Endothelin	↑Stretch, bradykinin, angiotensin II, epinephrine ↓ECFV	↓	↓
VASODILATORS			
Prostaglandins (PGE1, PGE2, and PGI2)	↓ECFV ↑shear stress, angiotensin II	No change/↑	↑
Nitric oxide (NO)	↑shear stress, acetylcholine, histamine, bradykinin, ATP, adenosine	↑	↑
Bradykinin	Prostaglandins, ↓ACE	↑	↑
Natriuretic peptides (ANP, B-type)	↑ECFV	↑	No change
ACE = angiotensin-converting enzyme; ECFV = extracellular fluid volume; GFR = glomerular filtration rate; RBF = renal blood flow; ANP = atrial natriuretic peptide; B-type = ventricular natriuretic peptide			

FIGURE 25.21   Major Hormones That Influence GFR and RFB

Access for free at openstax.org

25.9 Regulation of Fluid Volume and Composition

LEARNING OBJECTIVES

By the end of this section, you will be able to:

- Explain the mechanism of action of diuretics
- Explain why the differential permeability or impermeability of specific sections of the nephron tubules is necessary for urine formation

The major hormones influencing total body water are ADH, aldosterone, and ANH. Circumstances that lead to fluid depletion in the body include blood loss and dehydration. Homeostasis requires that volume and osmolarity be preserved. Blood volume is important in maintaining sufficient blood pressure, and there are nonrenal mechanisms involved in its preservation, including vasoconstriction, which can act within seconds of a drop in pressure. Thirst mechanisms are also activated to promote the consumption of water lost through respiration, evaporation, or urination. Hormonal mechanisms are activated to recover volume while maintaining a normal osmotic environment. These mechanisms act principally on the kidney.

Volume-sensing Mechanisms

The body cannot directly measure blood volume, but blood pressure can be measured. Blood pressure often reflects blood volume and is measured by baroreceptors in the aorta and carotid sinuses. When blood pressure increases, baroreceptors send more frequent action potentials to the central nervous system, leading to widespread vasodilation. Included in this vasodilation are the afferent arterioles supplying the glomerulus, resulting in increased GFR, and water loss by the kidneys. If pressure decreases, fewer action potentials travel to the central nervous system, resulting in more sympathetic stimulation-producing vasoconstriction, which will result in decreased filtration and GFR, and water loss.

Decreased blood pressure is also sensed by the granular cells in the afferent arteriole of the JGA. In response, the enzyme renin is released. You saw earlier in the chapter that renin activity leads to an almost immediate rise in blood pressure as activated angiotensin II produces vasoconstriction. The rise in pressure is sustained by the aldosterone effects initiated by angiotensin II; this includes an increase in Na^+ retention and water volume. As an aside, late in the menstrual cycle, progesterone has a modest influence on water retention. Due to its structural similarity to aldosterone, progesterone binds to the aldosterone receptor in the collecting duct of the kidney, causing the same, albeit weaker, effect on Na^+ and water retention.

Cardiomyocytes of the atria also respond to greater stretch (as blood pressure rises) by secreting ANH. ANH opposes the action of aldosterone by inhibiting the recovery of Na^+ by the DCT and collecting ducts. More Na^+ is lost, and as water follows, total blood volume and pressure decline. In low-pressure states, ANH does not seem to have much effect.

ADH is also called vasopressin. Early researchers found that in cases of unusually high secretion of ADH, the hormone caused vasoconstriction (vasopressor activity, hence the name). Only later were its antidiuretic properties identified. Synthetic ADH is still used occasionally to stem life-threatening esophagus bleeding in alcoholics.

When blood volume drops 5–10 percent, causing a decrease in blood pressure, there is a rapid and significant increase in ADH release from the posterior pituitary. Immediate vasoconstriction to increase blood pressure is the result. ADH also causes activation of aquaporin channels in the collecting ducts to affect the recovery of water to help restore vascular volume.

Diuretics and Fluid Volume

A **diuretic** is a compound that increases urine volume. Three familiar drinks contain diuretic compounds: coffee, tea, and alcohol. The caffeine in coffee and tea works by promoting vasodilation in the nephron, which increases GFR. Alcohol increases GFR by inhibiting ADH release from the posterior pituitary, resulting in less water recovery by the collecting duct. In cases of high blood pressure, diuretics may be prescribed to reduce blood volume and, thereby, reduce blood pressure. The most frequently prescribed anti-hypertensive diuretic is hydrochlorothiazide. It inhibits the Na^+/Cl^- symporter in the DCT and collecting duct. The result is a loss of Na^+ with water following passively by osmosis.

Osmotic diuretics promote water loss by osmosis. An example is the indigestible sugar mannitol, which is most often administered to reduce brain swelling after head injury. However, it is not the only sugar that can produce a diuretic effect. In cases of poorly controlled diabetes mellitus, glucose levels exceed the capacity of the tubular glucose symporters, resulting in glucose in the urine. The unrecovered glucose becomes a powerful osmotic diuretic. Classically, in the days before glucose could be detected in the blood and urine, clinicians identified diabetes mellitus by the three Ps: polyuria (diuresis), polydipsia (increased thirst), and polyphagia (increased hunger).

Regulation of Extracellular Na$^+$

Sodium has a very strong osmotic effect and attracts water. It plays a larger role in the osmolarity of the plasma than any other circulating component of the blood. If there is too much Na$^+$ present, either due to poor control or excess dietary consumption, a series of metabolic problems ensue. There is an increase in total volume of water, which leads to hypertension (high blood pressure). Over a long period, this increases the risk of serious complications such as heart attacks, strokes, and aneurysms. It can also contribute to system-wide edema (swelling).

Mechanisms for regulating Na$^+$ concentration include the renin–angiotensin–aldosterone system and ADH (see Figure 25.14). Aldosterone stimulates the uptake of Na$^+$ on the apical cell membrane of cells in the DCT and collecting ducts, whereas ADH helps to regulate Na$^+$ concentration indirectly by regulating the reabsorption of water.

Regulation of Extracellular K$^+$

Potassium is present in a 30-fold greater concentration inside the cell than outside the cell. A generalization can be made that K$^+$ and Na$^+$ concentrations will move in opposite directions. When more Na$^+$ is reabsorbed, more K$^+$ is secreted; when less Na$^+$ is reabsorbed (leading to excretion by the kidney), more K$^+$ is retained. When aldosterone causes a recovery of Na$^+$ in the nephron, a negative electrical gradient is created that promotes the secretion of K$^+$ and Cl$^-$ into the lumen.

Regulation of Cl$^-$

Chloride is important in acid–base balance in the extracellular space and has other functions, such as in the stomach, where it combines with hydrogen ions in the stomach lumen to form hydrochloric acid, aiding digestion. Its close association with Na$^+$ in the extracellular environment makes it the dominant anion of this compartment, and its regulation closely mirrors that of Na$^+$.

Regulation of Ca^{++} and Phosphate

The parathyroid glands monitor and respond to circulating levels of Ca^{++} in the blood. When levels drop too low, PTH is released to stimulate the DCT to reabsorb Ca^{++} from the forming urine. When levels are adequate or high, less PTH is released and more Ca^{++} remains in the forming urine to be lost. Phosphate levels move in the opposite direction. When Ca^{++} levels are low, PTH inhibits reabsorption of HPO_4^{2-} so that its blood level drops, allowing Ca^{++} levels to rise. PTH also stimulates the renal conversion of calcidiol into calcitriol, the active form of vitamin D. Calcitriol then stimulates the intestines to absorb more Ca^{++} from the diet.

Regulation of H$^+$, Bicarbonate, and pH

The acid–base homeostasis of the body is a function of chemical buffers and physiologic buffering provided by the lungs and kidneys. Buffers, especially proteins, HCO_3^-, and ammonia have a very large capacity to absorb or release H$^+$ as needed to resist a change in pH. They can act within fractions of a second. The lungs can rid the body of excess acid very rapidly (seconds to minutes) through the conversion of HCO_3^- into CO_2, which is then exhaled. It is rapid but has limited capacity in the face of a significant acid challenge. The kidneys can rid the body of both acid and base. The renal capacity is large but slow (minutes to hours). The cells of the PCT actively secrete H$^+$ into the forming urine as Na$^+$ is reabsorbed. The body rids itself of excess H$^+$ and raises blood pH. In the collecting ducts, the apical surfaces of intercalated cells have proton pumps that actively secrete H$^+$ into the luminal, forming urine to remove it from the body.

As hydrogen ions are pumped into the forming urine, it is buffered by bicarbonate (HCO_3^-), $H_2PO_4^-$ (dihydrogen phosphate ion), or ammonia (forming NH_4^+, ammonium ion). Urine pH typically varies in a normal range from 4.5 to

8.0.

Regulation of Nitrogen Wastes

Nitrogen wastes are produced by the breakdown of proteins during normal metabolism. Proteins are broken down into amino acids, which in turn are deaminated by having their nitrogen groups removed. Deamination converts the amino (NH_2) groups into ammonia (NH_3), ammonium ion (NH_4^+), urea, or uric acid (Figure 25.22). Ammonia is extremely toxic, so most of it is very rapidly converted into urea in the liver. Human urinary wastes typically contain primarily urea with small amounts of ammonium and very little uric acid.

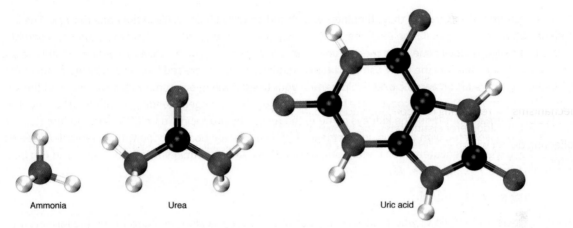

Ammonia   Urea   Uric acid

FIGURE 25.22   **Nitrogen Wastes**

Elimination of Drugs and Hormones

Water-soluble drugs may be excreted in the urine and are influenced by one or all of the following processes: glomerular filtration, tubular secretion, or tubular reabsorption. Drugs that are structurally small can be filtered by the glomerulus with the filtrate. Large drug molecules such as heparin or those that are bound to plasma proteins cannot be filtered and are not readily eliminated. Some drugs can be eliminated by carrier proteins that enable secretion of the drug into the tubule lumen. There are specific carriers that eliminate basic (such as dopamine or histamine) or acidic drugs (such as penicillin or indomethacin). As is the case with other substances, drugs may be both filtered and reabsorbed passively along a concentration gradient.

25.10 The Urinary System and Homeostasis

LEARNING OBJECTIVES

By the end of this section, you will be able to:
- Describe the role of the kidneys in vitamin D activation
- Describe the role of the kidneys in regulating erythropoiesis
- Provide specific examples to demonstrate how the urinary system responds to maintain homeostasis in the body
- Explain how the urinary system relates to other body systems in maintaining homeostasis
- Predict factors or situations affecting the urinary system that could disrupt homeostasis
- Predict the types of problems that would occur in the body if the urinary system could not maintain homeostasis

All systems of the body are interrelated. A change in one system may affect all other systems in the body, with mild to devastating effects. A failure of urinary continence can be embarrassing and inconvenient, but is not life threatening. The loss of other urinary functions may prove fatal. A failure to synthesize vitamin D is one such example.

Vitamin D Synthesis

In order for vitamin D to become active, it must undergo a hydroxylation reaction in the kidney, that is, an –OH group must be added to calcidiol to make calcitriol (1,25-dihydroxycholecalciferol). Activated vitamin D is important for absorption of Ca^{++} in the digestive tract, its reabsorption in the kidney, and the maintenance of normal serum concentrations of Ca^{++} and phosphate. Calcium is vitally important in bone health, muscle contraction, hormone secretion, and neurotransmitter release. Inadequate Ca^{++} leads to disorders like osteoporosis and **osteomalacia** in adults and rickets in children. Deficits may also result in problems with cell proliferation, neuromuscular function, blood clotting, and the inflammatory response. Recent research has confirmed that vitamin D receptors are present in most, if not all, cells of the body, reflecting the systemic importance of vitamin D. Many scientists have suggested it be referred to as a hormone rather than a vitamin.

Erythropoiesis

EPO is a 193-amino acid protein that stimulates the formation of red blood cells in the bone marrow. The kidney produces 85 percent of circulating EPO; the liver, the remainder. If you move to a higher altitude, the partial pressure of oxygen is lower, meaning there is less pressure to push oxygen across the alveolar membrane and into the red blood cell. One way the body compensates is to manufacture more red blood cells by increasing EPO production. If you start an aerobic exercise program, your tissues will need more oxygen to cope, and the kidney will respond with more EPO. If erythrocytes are lost due to severe or prolonged bleeding, or under produced due to disease or severe malnutrition, the kidneys come to the rescue by producing more EPO. Renal failure (loss of EPO production) is associated with anemia, which makes it difficult for the body to cope with increased oxygen demands or to supply oxygen adequately even under normal conditions. Anemia diminishes performance and can be life threatening.

Blood Pressure Regulation

Due to osmosis, water follows where Na^+ leads. Much of the water the kidneys recover from the forming urine follows the reabsorption of Na^+. ADH stimulation of aquaporin channels allows for regulation of water recovery in the collecting ducts. Normally, all of the glucose is recovered, but loss of glucose control (diabetes mellitus) may result in an osmotic dieresis severe enough to produce severe dehydration and death. A loss of renal function means a loss of effective vascular volume control, leading to hypotension (low blood pressure) or hypertension (high blood pressure), which can lead to stroke, heart attack, and aneurysm formation.

The kidneys cooperate with the lungs, liver, and adrenal cortex through the renin–angiotensin–aldosterone system (see Figure 25.14). The liver synthesizes and secretes the inactive precursor angiotensinogen. When the blood pressure is low, the kidney synthesizes and releases renin. Renin converts angiotensinogen into angiotensin I, and ACE produced in the lung converts angiotensin I into biologically active angiotensin II (Figure 25.23). The immediate and short-term effect of angiotensin II is to raise blood pressure by causing widespread vasoconstriction. angiotensin II also stimulates the adrenal cortex to release the steroid hormone aldosterone, which results in renal reabsorption of Na^+ and its associated osmotic recovery of water. The reabsorption of Na^+ helps to raise and maintain blood pressure over a longer term.

Access for free at openstax.org

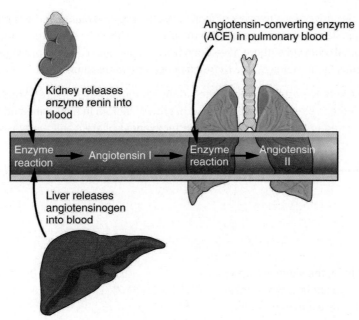

FIGURE 25.23   The Enzyme Renin Converts the Pro-enzyme Angiotensin

Regulation of Osmolarity

Blood pressure and osmolarity are regulated in a similar fashion. Severe hypo-osmolarity can cause problems like lysis (rupture) of blood cells or widespread edema, which is due to a solute imbalance. Inadequate solute concentration (such as protein) in the plasma results in water moving toward an area of greater solute concentration, in this case, the interstitial space and cell cytoplasm. If the kidney glomeruli are damaged by an autoimmune illness, large quantities of protein may be lost in the urine. The resultant drop in serum osmolarity leads to widespread edema that, if severe, may lead to damaging or fatal brain swelling. Severe hypertonic conditions may arise with severe dehydration from lack of water intake, severe vomiting, or uncontrolled diarrhea. When the kidney is unable to recover sufficient water from the forming urine, the consequences may be severe (lethargy, confusion, muscle cramps, and finally, death) .

Recovery of Electrolytes

Sodium, calcium, and potassium must be closely regulated. The role of Na^+ and Ca^{++} homeostasis has been discussed at length. Failure of K^+ regulation can have serious consequences on nerve conduction, skeletal muscle function, and most significantly, on cardiac muscle contraction and rhythm.

pH Regulation

Recall that enzymes lose their three-dimensional conformation and, therefore, their function if the pH is too acidic or basic. This loss of conformation may be a consequence of the breaking of hydrogen bonds. Move the pH away from the optimum for a specific enzyme and you may severely hamper its function throughout the body, including hormone binding, central nervous system signaling, or myocardial contraction. Proper kidney function is essential for pH homeostasis.

Everyday Connection

Stem Cells and Repair of Kidney Damage

Stem cells are unspecialized cells that can reproduce themselves via cell division, sometimes after years of inactivity. Under certain conditions, they may differentiate into tissue-specific or organ-specific cells with special functions. In some cases, stem cells may continually divide to produce a mature cell and to replace themselves. Stem cell therapy has an enormous potential to improve the quality of life or save the lives of people suffering from debilitating or life-threatening diseases. There have been several studies in animals, but since stem cell therapy is still in its infancy, there have been limited experiments in humans.

Acute kidney injury can be caused by a number of factors, including transplants and other surgeries. It affects 7–10 percent of all hospitalized patients, resulting in the deaths of 35–40 percent of inpatients. In limited studies using mesenchymal stem cells, there have been fewer instances of kidney damage after surgery, the length of hospital stays has been reduced, and there have been fewer readmissions after release.

How do these stem cells work to protect or repair the kidney? Scientists are unsure at this point, but some evidence has shown that these stem cells release several growth factors in endocrine and paracrine ways. As further studies are conducted to assess the safety and effectiveness of stem cell therapy, we will move closer to a day when kidney injury is rare, and curative treatments are routine.

Key Terms

anatomical sphincter smooth or skeletal muscle surrounding the lumen of a vessel or hollow organ that can restrict flow when contracted

angiotensin I protein produced by the enzymatic action of renin on angiotensinogen; inactive precursor of angiotensin II

angiotensin II protein produced by the enzymatic action of ACE on inactive angiotensin I; actively causes vasoconstriction and stimulates aldosterone release by the adrenal cortex

angiotensin-converting enzyme (ACE) enzyme produced by the lungs that catalyzes the reaction of inactive angiotensin I into active angiotensin II

angiotensinogen inactive protein in the circulation produced by the liver; precursor of angiotensin I; must be modified by the enzymes renin and ACE to be activated

anuria absence of urine produced; production of 50 mL or less per day

aquaporin protein-forming water channels through the lipid bilayer of the cell; allows water to cross; activation in the collecting ducts is under the control of ADH

Bowman's capsule cup-shaped sack lined by a simple squamous epithelium (parietal surface) and specialized cells called podocytes (visceral surface) that participate in the filtration process; receives the filtrate which then passes on to the PCTs

brush border formed by microvilli on the surface of certain cuboidal cells; in the kidney it is found in the PCT; increases surface area for absorption in the kidney

calyces cup-like structures receiving urine from the collecting ducts where it passes on to the renal pelvis and ureter

cortical nephrons nephrons with loops of Henle that do not extend into the renal medulla

countercurrent multiplier system involves the descending and ascending loops of Henle directing forming urine in opposing directions to create a concentration gradient when combined with variable permeability and sodium pumping

detrusor muscle smooth muscle in the bladder wall; fibers run in all directions to reduce the size of the organ when emptying it of urine

distal convoluted tubules portions of the nephron distal to the loop of Henle that receive hyposmotic filtrate from the loop of Henle and empty into collecting ducts

diuretic compound that increases urine output, leading to decreased water conservation

efferent arteriole arteriole carrying blood from the glomerulus to the capillary beds around the convoluted tubules and loop of Henle; portion of the portal system

endothelins group of vasoconstrictive, 21-amino acid peptides; produced by endothelial cells of the renal blood vessels, mesangial cells, and cells of the DCT

external urinary sphincter skeletal muscle; must be relaxed consciously to void urine

fenestrations small windows through a cell, allowing rapid filtration based on size; formed in such a way as to allow substances to cross through a cell without mixing with cell contents

filtration slits formed by pedicels of podocytes; substances filter between the pedicels based on size

forming urine filtrate undergoing modifications through secretion and reabsorption before true urine is produced

glomerular filtration rate (GFR) rate of renal filtration

glomerulus tuft of capillaries surrounded by Bowman's capsule; filters the blood based on size

glycosuria presence of glucose in the urine; caused by high blood glucose levels that exceed the ability of the kidneys to reabsorb the glucose; usually the result of untreated or poorly controlled diabetes mellitus

incontinence loss of ability to control micturition

intercalated cell specialized cell of the collecting ducts that secrete or absorb acid or bicarbonate; important in acid–base balance

internal urinary sphincter smooth muscle at the juncture of the bladder and urethra; relaxes as the bladder fills to allow urine into the urethra

inulin plant polysaccharide injected to determine GFR; is neither secreted nor absorbed by the kidney, so its appearance in the urine is directly proportional to its filtration rate

juxtaglomerular apparatus (JGA) located at the juncture of the DCT and the afferent and efferent arterioles of the glomerulus; plays a role in the regulation of renal blood flow and GFR

juxtaglomerular cell modified smooth muscle cells of the afferent arteriole; secretes renin in response to a drop in blood pressure

juxtamedullary nephrons nephrons adjacent to the border of the cortex and medulla with loops of Henle that extend into the renal medulla

leaky tight junctions tight junctions in which the sealing strands of proteins between the membranes of adjacent cells are fewer in number and incomplete; allows limited intercellular movement of solvent and solutes

leukocyte esterase   enzyme produced by leukocytes that can be detected in the urine and that serves as an indirect indicator of urinary tract infection

loop of Henle   descending and ascending portions between the proximal and distal convoluted tubules; those of cortical nephrons do not extend into the medulla, whereas those of juxtamedullary nephrons do extend into the medulla

macula densa   cells found in the part of the DCT forming the JGA; sense Na$^+$ concentration in the forming urine

medulla   inner region of kidney containing the renal pyramids

mesangial   contractile cells found in the glomerulus; can contract or relax to regulate filtration rate

micturition   also called urination or voiding

myogenic mechanism   mechanism by which smooth muscle responds to stretch by contracting; an increase in blood pressure causes vasoconstriction and a decrease in blood pressure causes vasodilation so that blood flow downstream remains steady

nephrons   functional units of the kidney that carry out all filtration and modification to produce urine; consist of renal corpuscles, proximal and distal convoluted tubules, and descending and ascending loops of Henle; drain into collecting ducts

net filtration pressure (NFP)   pressure of fluid across the glomerulus; calculated by taking the hydrostatic pressure of the capillary and subtracting the colloid osmotic pressure of the blood and the hydrostatic pressure of Bowman's capsule

oliguria   below normal urine production of 400–500 mL/day

osteomalacia   softening of bones due to a lack of mineralization with calcium and phosphate; most often due to lack of vitamin D; in children, osteomalacia is termed rickets; not to be confused with osteoporosis

pedicels   finger-like projections of podocytes surrounding glomerular capillaries; interdigitate to form a filtration membrane

peritubular capillaries   second capillary bed of the renal portal system; surround the proximal and distal convoluted tubules; associated with the vasa recta

physiological sphincter   sphincter consisting of circular smooth muscle indistinguishable from adjacent muscle but possessing differential innervations, permitting its function as a sphincter; structurally weak

podocytes   cells forming finger-like processes; form the visceral layer of Bowman's capsule; pedicels of the podocytes interdigitate to form a filtration membrane

polyuria   urine production in excess of 2.5 L/day; may be caused by diabetes insipidus, diabetes mellitus, or excessive use of diuretics

principal cell   found in collecting ducts and possess channels for the recovery or loss of sodium and potassium; under the control of aldosterone; also have aquaporin channels under ADH control to regulate recovery of water

proximal convoluted tubules (PCTs)   tortuous tubules receiving filtrate from Bowman's capsule; most active part of the nephron in reabsorption and secretion

renal columns   extensions of the renal cortex into the renal medulla; separates the renal pyramids; contains blood vessels and connective tissues

renal corpuscle   consists of the glomerulus and Bowman's capsule

renal cortex   outer part of kidney containing all of the nephrons; some nephrons have loops of Henle extending into the medulla

renal fat pad   adipose tissue between the renal fascia and the renal capsule that provides protective cushioning to the kidney

renal hilum   recessed medial area of the kidney through which the renal artery, renal vein, ureters, lymphatics, and nerves pass

renal papillae   medullary area of the renal pyramids where collecting ducts empty urine into the minor calyces

renal pyramids   six to eight cone-shaped tissues in the medulla of the kidney containing collecting ducts and the loops of Henle of juxtamedullary nephrons

renin   enzyme produced by juxtaglomerular cells in response to decreased blood pressure or sympathetic nervous activity; catalyzes the conversion of angiotensinogen into angiotensin I

retroperitoneal   behind the peritoneum; in the case of the kidney and ureters, between the parietal peritoneum and the abdominal wall

sacral micturition center   group of neurons in the sacral region of the spinal cord that controls urination; acts reflexively unless its action is modified by higher brain centers to allow voluntary urination

specific gravity   weight of a liquid compared to pure water, which has a specific gravity of 1.0; any solute added to water will increase its specific gravity

systemic edema   increased fluid retention in the interstitial spaces and cells of the body; can be seen as swelling over large areas of the body, particularly the lower extremities

trigone   area at the base of the bladder marked by the two ureters in the posterior–lateral aspect and the urethral orifice in the anterior aspect oriented like points on a triangle

tubuloglomerular feedback   feedback mechanism involving the JGA; macula densa cells monitor Na⁺ concentration in the terminal portion of the ascending loop of Henle and act to cause vasoconstriction or vasodilation of afferent and efferent arterioles to alter GFR

urethra   transports urine from the bladder to the outside environment

urinalysis   analysis of urine to diagnose disease

urochrome   heme-derived pigment that imparts the typical yellow color of urine

vasa recta   branches of the efferent arterioles that parallel the course of the loops of Henle and are continuous with the peritubular capillaries; with the glomerulus, form a portal system

Chapter Review

25.1 Physical Characteristics of Urine

The kidney glomerulus filters blood mainly based on particle size to produce a filtrate lacking cells or large proteins. Most of the ions and molecules in the filtrate are needed by the body and must be reabsorbed farther down the nephron tubules, resulting in the formation of urine. Urine characteristics change depending on water intake, exercise, environmental temperature, and nutrient intake. Urinalysis analyzes characteristics of the urine and is used to diagnose diseases. A minimum of 400 to 500 mL urine must be produced daily to rid the body of wastes. Excessive quantities of urine may indicate diabetes insipidus or diabetes mellitus. The pH range of urine is 4.5 to 8.0, and is affected by diet. Osmolarity ranges from 50 to 1200 milliosmoles, and is a reflection of the amount of water being recovered or lost by renal nephrons.

25.2 Gross Anatomy of Urine Transport

The urethra is the only urinary structure that differs significantly between males and females. This is due to the dual role of the male urethra in transporting both urine and semen. The urethra arises from the trigone area at the base of the bladder. Urination is controlled by an involuntary internal sphincter of smooth muscle and a voluntary external sphincter of skeletal muscle. The shorter female urethra contributes to the higher incidence of bladder infections in females. The male urethra receives secretions from the prostate gland, Cowper's gland, and seminal vesicles as well as sperm. The bladder is largely retroperitoneal and can hold up to 500–600 mL urine. Micturition is the process of voiding the urine and involves both involuntary and voluntary actions. Voluntary control of micturition requires a mature and intact sacral micturition center. It also requires an intact spinal cord. Loss of control of micturition is called incontinence and results in voiding when the bladder contains about 250 mL urine. The ureters are retroperitoneal and lead from the renal pelvis of the kidney to the trigone area at the base of the bladder. A thick muscular wall consisting of longitudinal and circular smooth muscle helps move urine toward the bladder by way of peristaltic contractions.

25.3 Gross Anatomy of the Kidney

As noted previously, the structure of the kidney is divided into two principle regions—the peripheral rim of cortex and the central medulla. The two kidneys receive about 25 percent of cardiac output. They are protected in the retroperitoneal space by the renal fat pad and overlying ribs and muscle. Ureters, blood vessels, lymph vessels, and nerves enter and leave at the renal hilum. The renal arteries arise directly from the aorta, and the renal veins drain directly into the inferior vena cava. Kidney function is derived from the actions of about 1.3 million nephrons per kidney; these are the "functional units." A capillary bed, the glomerulus, filters blood and the filtrate is captured by Bowman's capsule. A portal system is formed when the blood flows through a second capillary bed surrounding the proximal and distal convoluted tubules and the loop of Henle. Most water and solutes are recovered by this second capillary bed. This filtrate is processed and finally gathered by collecting ducts that drain into the minor calyces, which merge to form major calyces; the filtrate then proceeds to the renal pelvis and finally the ureters.

25.4 Microscopic Anatomy of the Kidney

The functional unit of the kidney, the nephron, consists of the renal corpuscle, PCT, loop of Henle, and DCT. Cortical nephrons have short loops of Henle, whereas juxtamedullary nephrons have long loops of Henle extending into the medulla. About 15 percent of nephrons are juxtamedullary. The glomerulus is a capillary bed that filters blood principally based on particle size. The filtrate is captured by Bowman's capsule and directed to the PCT. A filtration membrane is formed by the fused basement membranes of the podocytes and the capillary endothelial cells that they embrace. Contractile mesangial cells further perform a role in regulating the rate at which the blood is filtered. Specialized cells in the JGA produce paracrine signals to regulate blood flow and filtration rates of the glomerulus. Other JGA cells produce the enzyme renin, which plays a central role in blood pressure regulation. The filtrate enters the PCT where absorption and secretion of several substances occur. The descending and ascending limbs of the loop of Henle consist of thick and thin segments. Absorption and secretion continue in the DCT but to a lesser extent than in the PCT. Each collecting duct collects forming urine from several nephrons and responds to the posterior pituitary hormone ADH by inserting aquaporin water channels into the cell membrane to fine tune water recovery.

25.5 Physiology of Urine Formation

The entire volume of the blood is filtered through the kidneys about 300 times per day, and 99 percent of the water filtered is recovered. The GFR is influenced by hydrostatic pressure and colloid osmotic pressure. Under normal circumstances, hydrostatic pressure is significantly greater and filtration occurs. The hydrostatic pressure of the glomerulus depends on systemic blood pressure, autoregulatory mechanisms, sympathetic nervous activity, and paracrine hormones. The kidney can function normally under a wide range of blood pressures due to the autoregulatory nature of smooth muscle.

25.6 Tubular Reabsorption

The kidney regulates water recovery and blood pressure by producing the enzyme renin. It is renin that starts a series of reactions, leading to the production of the vasoconstrictor angiotensin II and the salt-retaining steroid aldosterone. Water recovery is also powerfully and directly influenced by the hormone ADH. Even so, it only influences the last 10 percent of water available for recovery after filtration at the glomerulus, because 90 percent of water is recovered before reaching the collecting ducts. Depending on the body's fluid status at any given time, the collecting ducts can recover none or almost all of the water reaching them.

Mechanisms of solute recovery include active transport, simple diffusion, and facilitated diffusion. Most filtered substances are reabsorbed. Urea, NH_3, creatinine, and some drugs are filtered or secreted as wastes. H^+ and HCO_3^- are secreted or reabsorbed as needed to maintain acid–base balance. Movement of water from the glomerulus is primarily due to pressure,

whereas that of peritubular capillaries and vasa recta is due to osmolarity and concentration gradients. The PCT is the most metabolically active part of the nephron and uses a wide array of protein micromachines to maintain homeostasis—symporters, antiporters, and ATPase active transporters—in conjunction with diffusion, both simple and facilitated. Almost 100 percent of glucose, amino acids, and vitamins are recovered in the PCT. Bicarbonate (HCO_3^-) is recovered using the same enzyme, carbonic anhydrase (CA), found in erythrocytes. The recovery of solutes creates an osmotic gradient to promote the recovery of water. The descending loop of the juxtaglomerular nephrons reaches an osmolarity of up to 1200 mOsmol/kg, promoting the recovery of water. The ascending loop is impervious to water but actively recovers Na^+, reducing filtrate osmolarity to 50–100 mOsmol/kg. The descending and ascending loop and vasa recta form a countercurrent multiplier system to increase Na^+ concentration in the kidney medulla. The collecting ducts actively pump urea into the medulla, further contributing to the high osmotic environment. The vasa recta recover the solute and water in the medulla, returning them to the circulation. Nearly 90 percent of water is recovered before the forming urine reaches the DCT, which will recover another 10 percent. Calcium recovery in the DCT is influenced by PTH and active vitamin D. In the collecting ducts, ADH stimulates aquaporin channel insertion to increase water recovery and thereby regulate osmolarity of the blood. Aldosterone stimulates Na^+ recovery by the collecting duct.

25.7 Regulation of Renal Blood Flow

The kidneys are innervated by sympathetic nerves of the autonomic nervous system. Sympathetic nervous activity decreases blood flow to the kidney, making more blood available to other areas of the body during times of stress. The arteriolar myogenic mechanism maintains a steady blood flow by causing arteriolar smooth muscle to contract when blood pressure increases and causing it to relax when blood pressure decreases. Tubuloglomerular feedback involves paracrine signaling at the JGA to cause vasoconstriction or vasodilation to maintain a steady rate of blood flow.

25.8 Endocrine Regulation of Kidney Function

Endocrine hormones act from a distance and paracrine hormones act locally. The renal enzyme renin converts angiotensinogen into angiotensin I. The lung enzyme, ACE, converts angiotensin I into active angiotensin II.

Angiotensin II is an active vasoconstrictor that increases blood pressure. Angiotensin II also stimulates aldosterone release from the adrenal cortex, causing the collecting duct to retain Na⁺, which promotes water retention and a longer-term rise in blood pressure. ADH promotes water recovery by the collecting ducts by stimulating the insertion of aquaporin water channels into cell membranes. Endothelins are elevated in cases of diabetic kidney disease, increasing Na⁺ retention and decreasing GFR. Natriuretic hormones, released primarily from the atria of the heart in response to stretching of the atrial walls, stimulate Na⁺ excretion and thereby decrease blood pressure. PTH stimulates the final step in the formation of active vitamin D3 and reduces phosphate reabsorption, resulting in higher circulating Ca^{++} levels.

25.9 Regulation of Fluid Volume and Composition

The major hormones regulating body fluids are ADH, aldosterone and ANH. Progesterone is similar in structure to aldosterone and can bind to and weakly stimulate aldosterone receptors, providing a similar but diminished response. Blood pressure is a reflection of blood volume and is monitored by baroreceptors in the aortic arch and carotid sinuses. When blood pressure increases, more action potentials are sent to the central nervous system, resulting in greater vasodilation, greater GFR, and more water lost in the urine. ANH is released by the cardiomyocytes when blood pressure increases, causing Na⁺ and water loss. ADH at high levels causes vasoconstriction in addition to its action on the collecting ducts to recover more water. Diuretics increase urine volume. Mechanisms for controlling Na⁺ concentration in the blood include the renin–angiotensin–aldosterone system and ADH. When Na⁺ is retained, K⁺ is excreted; when Na⁺ is lost, K⁺ is retained. When circulating Ca^{++} decreases, PTH stimulates the reabsorption of Ca^{++} and inhibits reabsorption of HPO_4^{2-}. pH is regulated through buffers, expiration of CO_2, and excretion of acid or base by the kidneys. The breakdown of amino acids produces ammonia. Most ammonia is converted into less-toxic urea in the liver and excreted in the urine. Regulation of drugs is by glomerular filtration, tubular secretion, and tubular reabsorption.

25.10 The Urinary System and Homeostasis

The effects of failure of parts of the urinary system may range from inconvenient (incontinence) to fatal (loss of filtration and many others). The kidneys catalyze the final reaction in the synthesis of active vitamin D that in turn helps regulate Ca^{++}. The kidney hormone EPO stimulates erythrocyte development and promotes adequate O_2 transport. The kidneys help regulate blood pressure through Na⁺ and water retention and loss. The kidneys work with the adrenal cortex, lungs, and liver in the renin–angiotensin–aldosterone system to regulate blood pressure. They regulate osmolarity of the blood by regulating both solutes and water. Three electrolytes are more closely regulated than others: Na⁺, Ca^{++}, and K⁺. The kidneys share pH regulation with the lungs and plasma buffers, so that proteins can preserve their three-dimensional conformation and thus their function.

Review Questions

1. Diabetes insipidus or diabetes mellitus would most likely be indicated by _____.
a. anuria
b. polyuria
c. oliguria
d. none of the above

2. The color of urine is determined mainly by _____.
a. diet
b. filtration rate
c. byproducts of red blood cell breakdown
d. filtration efficiency

3. Production of less than 50 mL/day of urine is called _____.
a. normal
b. polyuria
c. oliguria
d. anuria

4. Peristaltic contractions occur in the _____.
a. urethra
b. bladder
c. ureters
d. urethra, bladder, and ureters

5. Somatic motor neurons must be _____ to relax the external urethral sphincter to allow urination.
a. stimulated
b. inhibited

6. Which part of the urinary system is *not* completely retroperitoneal?
a. kidneys
b. ureters
c. bladder
d. nephrons

7. The renal pyramids are separated from each other by extensions of the renal cortex called _____.
a. renal medulla
b. minor calyces
c. medullary cortices
d. renal columns

8. The primary structure found within the medulla is the _____.
a. loop of Henle
b. minor calyces
c. portal system
d. ureter

9. The right kidney is slightly lower because _____.
a. it is displaced by the liver
b. it is displace by the heart
c. it is slightly smaller
d. it needs protection of the lower ribs

10. Blood filtrate is captured in the lumen of the _____.
a. glomerulus
b. Bowman's capsule
c. calyces
d. renal papillae

11. What are the names of the capillaries following the efferent arteriole?
a. arcuate and medullary
b. interlobar and interlobular
c. peritubular and vasa recta
d. peritubular and medullary

12. The functional unit of the kidney is called _____.
a. the renal hilus
b. the renal corpuscle
c. the nephron
d. Bowman's capsule

13. _____ pressure must be greater on the capillary side of the filtration membrane to achieve filtration.
a. Osmotic
b. Hydrostatic

14. Production of urine to modify plasma makeup is the result of _____.
a. filtration
b. absorption
c. secretion
d. filtration, absorption, and secretion

15. Systemic blood pressure must stay above 60 so that the proper amount of filtration occurs.
a. true
b. false

16. Aquaporin channels are only found in the collecting duct.
a. true
b. false

17. Most absorption and secretion occurs in this part of the nephron.
a. proximal convoluted tubule
b. descending loop of Henle
c. ascending loop of Henle
d. distal convoluted tubule
e. collecting ducts

18. The fine tuning of water recovery or disposal occurs in _____.
a. the proximal convoluted tubule
b. the collecting ducts
c. the ascending loop of Henle
d. the distal convoluted tubule

19. Vasodilation of blood vessels to the kidneys is due to _____.
a. more frequent action potentials
b. less frequent action potentials

20. When blood pressure increases, blood vessels supplying the kidney will _____ to mount a steady rate of filtration.
a. contract
b. relax

21. Which of these three paracrine chemicals cause vasodilation?
a. ATP
b. adenosine
c. nitric oxide

22. What hormone directly opposes the actions of natriuretic hormones?
a. renin
b. nitric oxide
c. dopamine
d. aldosterone

23. Which of these is a vasoconstrictor?
    a. nitric oxide
    b. natriuretic hormone
    c. bradykinin
    d. angiotensin II

24. What signal causes the heart to secrete atrial natriuretic hormone?
    a. increased blood pressure
    b. decreased blood pressure
    c. increased Na$^+$ levels
    d. decreased Na$^+$ levels

25. Which of these beverages does *not* have a diuretic effect?
    a. tea
    b. coffee
    c. alcohol
    d. milk

26. Progesterone can bind to receptors for which hormone that, when released, activates water retention?
    a. aldosterone
    b. ADH
    c. PTH
    d. ANH

27. Renin is released in response to _____.
    a. increased blood pressure
    b. decreased blood pressure
    c. ACE
    d. diuretics

28. Which step in vitamin D production does the kidney perform?
    a. converts cholecalciferol into calcidiol
    b. converts calcidiol into calcitriol
    c. stores vitamin D
    d. none of these

29. Which hormone does the kidney produce that stimulates red blood cell production?
    a. thrombopoietin
    b. vitamin D
    c. EPO
    d. renin

30. If there were no aquaporin channels in the collecting duct, _____.
    a. you would develop systemic edema
    b. you would retain excess Na$^+$
    c. you would lose vitamins and electrolytes
    d. you would suffer severe dehydration

Critical Thinking Questions

31. What is suggested by the presence of white blood cells found in the urine?

32. Both diabetes mellitus and diabetes insipidus produce large urine volumes, but how would other characteristics of the urine differ between the two diseases?

33. Why are people with female reproductive systems more likely to contract bladder infections than people with male reproductive systems?

34. Describe how forceful urination is accomplished.

35. What anatomical structures provide protection to the kidney?

36. How does the renal portal system differ from the hypothalamo–hypophyseal and digestive portal systems?

37. Name the structures found in the renal hilum.

38. Which structures make up the renal corpuscle?

39. What are the major structures comprising the filtration membrane?

40. Give the formula for net filtration pressure.

41. Name at least five symptoms of kidney failure.

42. Which vessels and what part of the nephron are involved in countercurrent multiplication?

43. Give the approximate osmolarity of fluid in the proximal convoluted tubule, deepest part of the loop of Henle, distal convoluted tubule, and the collecting ducts.

44. Explain what happens to Na$^+$ concentration in the nephron when GFR increases.

45. If you want the kidney to excrete more Na$^+$ in the urine, what do you want the blood flow to do?

46. What organs produce which hormones or enzymes in the renin–angiotensin system?

47. PTH affects absorption and reabsorption of what?

48. Why is ADH also called vasopressin?

49. How can glucose be a diuretic?

50. How does lack of protein in the blood cause edema?

51. Which three electrolytes are most closely regulated by the kidney?

CHAPTER 26
Fluid, Electrolyte, and Acid-Base Balance

Figure 26.1   Venus Williams Perspiring on the Tennis Court The body has critically important mechanisms for balancing the intake and output of bodily fluids. An athlete must continuously replace the water and electrolytes lost in sweat. (credit: "Edwin Martinez1"/Wikimedia Commons)

CHAPTER OBJECTIVES
After studying this chapter, you will be able to:

- Identify the body's main fluid compartments
- Define plasma osmolality and identify two ways in which plasma osmolality is maintained
- Identify the six ions most important to the function of the body
- Define buffer and discuss the role of buffers in the body
- Explain why bicarbonate must be conserved rather than reabsorbed in the kidney
- Identify the normal range of blood pH and name the conditions where one has a blood pH that is either too high or too low

INTRODUCTION Homeostasis, or the maintenance of constant conditions in the body, is a fundamental property of all living things. In the human body, the substances that participate in chemical reactions must remain within narrows ranges of concentration. Too much or too little of a single substance can disrupt your bodily functions. Because metabolism relies on reactions that are all interconnected, any disruption might affect multiple organs or even organ systems. Water is the most ubiquitous substance in the chemical reactions of life. The interactions of various aqueous solutions—solutions in which water is the solvent—are continuously monitored and adjusted by a large suite of interconnected feedback systems in your body. Understanding the ways in which the body maintains these critical balances is key to understanding good health.

26.1 Body Fluids and Fluid Compartments

LEARNING OBJECTIVES
By the end of this section, you will be able to:

- Explain the importance of water in the body
- Contrast the composition of the intracellular fluid with that of the extracellular fluid
- Explain the importance of protein channels in the movement of solutes
- Identify the causes and symptoms of edema

The chemical reactions of life take place in aqueous solutions. The dissolved substances in a solution are called solutes. In the human body, solutes vary in different parts of the body, but may include proteins—including those that transport lipids, carbohydrates, and, very importantly, electrolytes. Often in medicine, a mineral dissociated from a salt that carries an electrical charge (an ion) is called an electrolyte. For instance, sodium ions (Na^+) and chloride ions (Cl^-) are often referred to as electrolytes.

In the body, water moves through semi-permeable membranes of cells and from one compartment of the body to another by a process called osmosis. Osmosis is basically the diffusion of water from regions of higher concentration of water to regions of lower concentration of water, along an osmotic gradient across a semi-permeable membrane. As a result, water will move into and out of cells and tissues, depending on the relative concentrations of the water and solutes found there. An appropriate balance of solutes inside and outside of cells must be maintained to ensure normal function.

Body Water Content

Human beings are mostly water, ranging from about 75 percent of body mass in infants to about 50–60 percent in adults, to as low as 45 percent in old age. The percent of body water changes with development, because the proportions of the body given over to each organ and to muscles, fat, bone, and other tissues change from infancy to adulthood (Figure 26.2). Your brain and kidneys have the highest proportions of water, which composes 80–85 percent of their masses. In contrast, teeth have the lowest proportion of water, at 8–10 percent.

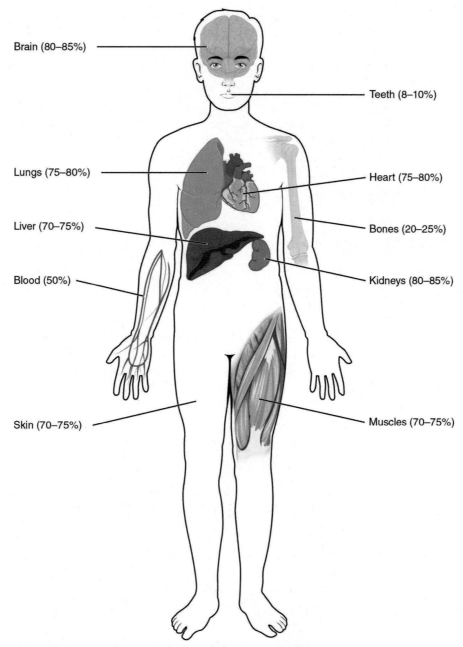

FIGURE 26.2 Water Content of the Body's Organs and Tissues   Water content varies in different body organs and tissues, from as little as 8 percent in the teeth to as much as 85 percent in the brain.

Fluid Compartments

Body fluids can be discussed in terms of their specific **fluid compartment**, a location that is largely separate from another compartment by some form of a physical barrier. The **intracellular fluid (ICF)** compartment is the system that includes all fluid enclosed in cells by their plasma membranes. **Extracellular fluid (ECF)** surrounds all cells in the body. Extracellular fluid has two primary constituents: the fluid component of the blood (called plasma) and the **interstitial fluid (IF)** that surrounds all cells not in the blood (Figure 26.3).

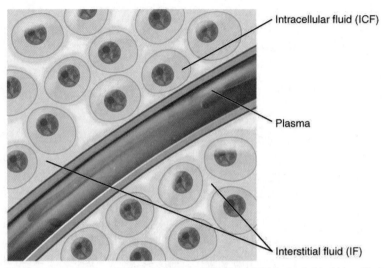

FIGURE 26.3   Fluid Compartments in the Human Body   The intracellular fluid (ICF) is the fluid within cells. The interstitial fluid (IF) is part of the extracellular fluid (ECF) between the cells. Blood plasma is the second part of the ECF. Materials travel between cells and the plasma in capillaries through the IF.

Intracellular Fluid

The ICF lies within cells and is the principal component of the cytosol/cytoplasm. The ICF makes up about 60 percent of the total water in the human body, and in an average-size adult male, the ICF accounts for about 25 liters (seven gallons) of fluid (Figure 26.4). This fluid volume tends to be very stable, because the amount of water in living cells is closely regulated. If the amount of water inside a cell falls to a value that is too low, the cytosol becomes too concentrated with solutes to carry on normal cellular activities; if too much water enters a cell, the cell may burst and be destroyed.

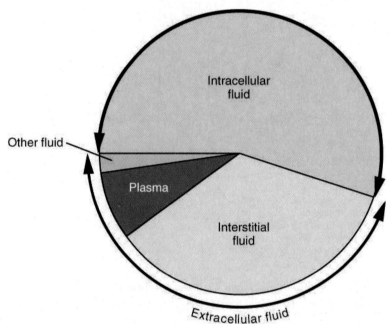

FIGURE 26.4   A Pie Graph Showing the Proportion of Total Body Fluid in Each of the Body's Fluid Compartments   Most of the water in the body is intracellular fluid. The second largest volume is the interstitial fluid, which surrounds cells that are not blood cells.

Extracellular Fluid

The ECF accounts for the other one-third of the body's water content. Approximately 20 percent of the ECF is found in plasma. Plasma travels through the body in blood vessels and transports a range of materials, including blood cells, proteins (including clotting factors and antibodies), electrolytes, nutrients, gases, and wastes. Gases, nutrients, and waste materials travel between capillaries and cells through the IF. Cells are separated from the IF by a selectively permeable cell membrane that helps regulate the passage of materials between the IF and the interior of the cell.

The body has other water-based ECF. These include the cerebrospinal fluid that bathes the brain and spinal cord, lymph, the synovial fluid in joints, the pleural fluid in the pleural cavities, the pericardial fluid in the cardiac sac, the peritoneal fluid in the peritoneal cavity, and the aqueous humor of the eye. Because these fluids are outside of cells, these fluids are also considered components of the ECF compartment.

Composition of Body Fluids

The compositions of the two components of the ECF—plasma and IF—are more similar to each other than either is to the ICF (Figure 26.5). Blood plasma has high concentrations of sodium, chloride, bicarbonate, and protein. The IF has high concentrations of sodium, chloride, and bicarbonate, but a relatively lower concentration of protein. In contrast, the ICF has elevated amounts of potassium, phosphate, magnesium, and protein. Overall, the ICF contains high concentrations of potassium and phosphate (HPO_4^{2-}), whereas both plasma and the ECF contain high concentrations of sodium and chloride.

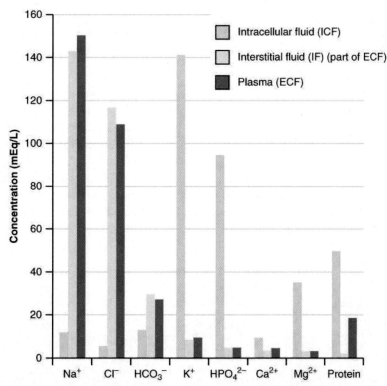

FIGURE 26.5   **The Concentrations of Different Elements in Key Bodily Fluids**   The graph shows the composition of the ICF, IF, and plasma. The compositions of plasma and IF are similar to one another but are quite different from the composition of the ICF.

⊘ INTERACTIVE LINK

Watch this video (http://openstax.org/l/bodyfluids) to learn more about body fluids, fluid compartments, and electrolytes. When blood volume decreases due to sweating, from what source is water taken in by the blood?

Most body fluids are neutral in charge. Thus, cations, or positively charged ions, and anions, or negatively charged ions, are balanced in fluids. As seen in the previous graph, sodium (Na^+) ions and chloride (Cl^-) ions are concentrated in the ECF of the body, whereas potassium (K^+) ions are concentrated inside cells. Although sodium and potassium can "leak" through "pores" into and out of cells, respectively, the high levels of potassium and low levels of sodium in the ICF are maintained by sodium-potassium pumps in the cell membranes. These pumps use the energy supplied by ATP to pump sodium out of the cell and potassium into the cell (Figure 26.6).

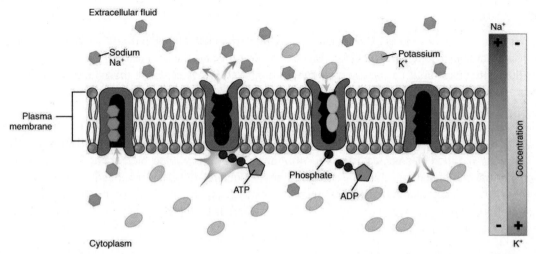

FIGURE 26.6   The Sodium-Potassium Pump   The sodium-potassium pump is powered by ATP to transfer sodium out of the cytoplasm and into the ECF. The pump also transfers potassium out of the ECF and into the cytoplasm. (credit: modification of work by Mariana Ruiz Villarreal)

Fluid Movement between Compartments

Hydrostatic pressure, the force exerted by a fluid against a wall, causes movement of fluid between compartments. The hydrostatic pressure of blood is the pressure exerted by blood against the walls of the blood vessels by the pumping action of the heart. In capillaries, hydrostatic pressure (also known as capillary blood pressure) is higher than the opposing "colloid osmotic pressure" in blood—a "constant" pressure primarily produced by circulating albumin—at the arteriolar end of the capillary (Figure 26.7). This pressure forces plasma and nutrients out of the capillaries and into surrounding tissues. Fluid and the cellular wastes in the tissues enter the capillaries at the venule end, where the hydrostatic pressure is less than the osmotic pressure in the vessel. Filtration pressure squeezes fluid from the plasma in the blood to the IF surrounding the tissue cells. The surplus fluid in the interstitial space that is not returned directly back to the capillaries is drained from tissues by the lymphatic system, and then re-enters the vascular system at the subclavian veins.

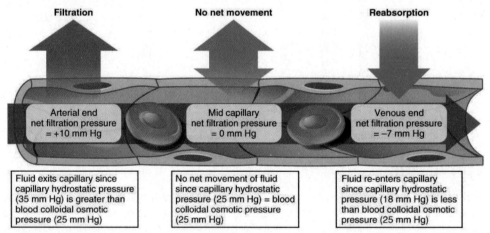

FIGURE 26.7   Capillary Exchange   Net filtration occurs near the arterial end of the capillary since capillary hydrostatic pressure (CHP) is greater than blood colloidal osmotic pressure (BCOP). There is no net movement of fluid near the midpoint of the capillary since CHP = BCOP. Net reabsorption occurs near the venous end of the capillary since BCOP is greater than CHP.

🔗 INTERACTIVE LINK

Watch this video (http://openstax.org/l/dynamicfluid) to see an explanation of the dynamics of fluid in the body's compartments. What happens in the tissue when capillary blood pressure is less than osmotic pressure?

Hydrostatic pressure is especially important in governing the movement of water in the nephrons of the kidneys to ensure proper filtering of the blood to form urine. As hydrostatic pressure in the kidneys increases, the amount of water leaving the capillaries also increases, and more urine filtrate is formed. If hydrostatic pressure in the kidneys drops too low, as can happen in dehydration, the functions of the kidneys will be impaired, and less nitrogenous wastes will be removed from the bloodstream. Extreme dehydration can result in kidney failure.

Fluid also moves between compartments along an osmotic gradient. Recall that an osmotic gradient is produced by the difference in concentration of all solutes on either side of a semi-permeable membrane. The magnitude of the osmotic gradient is proportional to the difference in the concentration of solutes on one side of the cell membrane to that on the other side. Water will move by osmosis from the side where its concentration is high (and the concentration of solute is low) to the side of the membrane where its concentration is low (and the concentration of solute is high). In the body, water moves by osmosis from plasma to the IF (and the reverse) and from the IF to the ICF (and the reverse). In the body, water moves constantly into and out of fluid compartments as conditions change in different parts of the body.

For example, if you are sweating, you will lose water through your skin. Sweating depletes your tissues of water and increases the solute concentration in those tissues. As this happens, water diffuses from your blood into sweat glands and surrounding skin tissues that have become dehydrated because of the osmotic gradient. Additionally, as water leaves the blood, it is replaced by the water in other tissues throughout your body that are not dehydrated. If this continues, dehydration spreads throughout the body. When a dehydrated person drinks water and rehydrates, the water is redistributed by the same gradient, but in the opposite direction, replenishing water in all of the tissues.

Solute Movement between Compartments

The movement of some solutes between compartments is active, which consumes energy and is an active transport process, whereas the movement of other solutes is passive, which does not require energy. Active transport allows cells to move a specific substance against its concentration gradient through a membrane protein, requiring energy in the form of ATP. For example, the sodium-potassium pump employs active transport to pump sodium out of cells and potassium into cells, with both substances moving against their concentration gradients.

Passive transport of a molecule or ion depends on its ability to pass through the membrane, as well as the existence of a concentration gradient that allows the molecules to diffuse from an area of higher concentration to an area of lower concentration. Some molecules, like gases, lipids, and water itself (which also utilizes water channels in the membrane called aquaporins), slip fairly easily through the cell membrane; others, including polar molecules like glucose, amino acids, and ions do not. Some of these molecules enter and leave cells using facilitated transport, whereby the molecules move down a concentration gradient through specific protein channels in the membrane. This process does not require energy. For example, glucose is transferred into cells by glucose transporters that use facilitated transport (Figure 26.8).

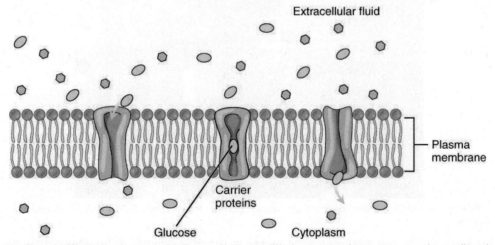

FIGURE 26.8   Facilitated Diffusion   Glucose molecules use facilitated diffusion to move down a concentration gradient through the carrier protein channels in the membrane. (credit: modification of work by Mariana Ruiz Villarreal)

Disorders of the...

Fluid Balance: Edema

Edema is the accumulation of excess water in the tissues. It is most common in the soft tissues of the extremities. The physiological causes of edema include water leakage from blood capillaries. Edema is almost always caused by an underlying medical condition, by the use of certain therapeutic drugs, by pregnancy, by localized injury, or by an allergic reaction. In the limbs, the symptoms of edema include swelling of the subcutaneous tissues, an increase in the normal size of the limb, and stretched, tight skin. One quick way to check for subcutaneous edema localized in a limb is to press a finger into the suspected area. Edema is likely if the depression persists for several seconds after the finger is removed (which is called "pitting").

Pulmonary edema is excess fluid in the air sacs of the lungs, a common symptom of heart and/or kidney failure. People with pulmonary edema likely will experience difficulty breathing, and they may experience chest pain. Pulmonary edema can be life threatening, because it compromises gas exchange in the lungs, and anyone having symptoms should immediately seek medical care.

In pulmonary edema resulting from heart failure, excessive leakage of water occurs because fluids get "backed up" in the pulmonary capillaries of the lungs, when the left ventricle of the heart is unable to pump sufficient blood into the systemic circulation. Because the left side of the heart is unable to pump out its normal volume of blood, the blood in the pulmonary circulation gets "backed up," starting with the left atrium, then into the pulmonary veins, and then into pulmonary capillaries. The resulting increased hydrostatic pressure within pulmonary capillaries, as blood is still coming in from the pulmonary arteries, causes fluid to be pushed out of them and into lung tissues.

Other causes of edema include damage to blood vessels and/or lymphatic vessels, or a decrease in osmotic pressure in chronic and severe liver disease, where the liver is unable to manufacture plasma proteins (Figure 26.9). A decrease in the normal levels of plasma proteins results in a decrease of colloid osmotic pressure (which counterbalances the hydrostatic pressure) in the capillaries. This process causes loss of water from the blood to the surrounding tissues, resulting in edema.

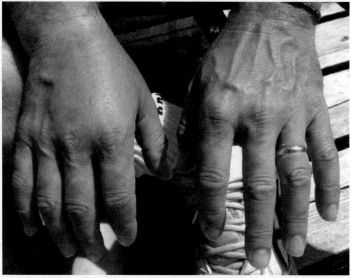

FIGURE 26.9   Edema   An allergic reaction can cause capillaries in the hand to leak excess fluid that accumulates in the tissues. (credit: Jane Whitney)

Mild, transient edema of the feet and legs may be caused by sitting or standing in the same position for long periods of time, as in the work of a toll collector or a supermarket cashier. This is because deep veins in the lower limbs rely on skeletal muscle contractions to push on the veins and thus "pump" blood back to the heart. Otherwise, the venous blood pools in the lower limbs and can leak into surrounding tissues.

Medications that can result in edema include vasodilators, calcium channel blockers used to treat hypertension, non-steroidal anti-inflammatory drugs, estrogen therapies, and some diabetes medications. Underlying medical conditions that can contribute to edema include congestive heart failure, kidney damage and kidney disease, disorders that affect the veins of the legs, and cirrhosis and other liver disorders.

Therapy for edema usually focuses on elimination of the cause. Activities that can reduce the effects of the condition include appropriate exercises to keep the blood and lymph flowing through the affected areas. Other therapies include elevation of the affected part to assist drainage, massage and compression of the areas to move the fluid out of the tissues, and decreased salt intake to decrease sodium and water retention.

26.2 Water Balance

LEARNING OBJECTIVES

By the end of this section, you will be able to:

- Explain how water levels in the body influence the thirst cycle
- Identify the main route by which water leaves the body
- Describe the role of ADH and its effect on body water levels
- Define dehydration and identify common causes of dehydration

On a typical day, the average adult will take in about 2500 mL (almost 3 quarts) of aqueous fluids. Although most of the intake comes through the digestive tract, about 230 mL (8 ounces) per day is generated metabolically, in the last steps of aerobic respiration. Additionally, each day about the same volume (2500 mL) of water leaves the body by different routes; most of this lost water is removed as urine. The kidneys also can adjust blood volume though mechanisms that draw water out of the filtrate and urine. The kidneys can regulate water levels in the body; they conserve water if you are dehydrated, and they can make urine more dilute to expel excess water if necessary. Water is lost through the skin through evaporation from the skin surface without overt sweating and from air expelled from the lungs. This type of water loss is called insensible water loss because a person is usually unaware of it.

Regulation of Water Intake

Osmolality is the ratio of solutes in a solution to a volume of solvent in a solution. **Plasma osmolality** is thus the ratio of solutes to water in blood plasma. A person's plasma osmolality value reflects the state of hydration. A healthy body maintains plasma osmolality within a narrow range, by employing several mechanisms that regulate both water intake and output.

Drinking water is considered voluntary. So how is water intake regulated by the body? Consider someone who is experiencing **dehydration**, a net loss of water that results in insufficient water in blood and other tissues. The water that leaves the body, as exhaled air, sweat, or urine, is ultimately extracted from blood plasma. As the blood becomes more concentrated, the thirst response—a sequence of physiological processes—is triggered (Figure 26.10). Osmoreceptors are sensory receptors in the thirst center in the hypothalamus that monitor the concentration of solutes (osmolality) of the blood. If blood osmolality increases above its ideal value, the hypothalamus transmits signals that result in a conscious awareness of thirst. The person should (and normally does) respond by drinking water. The hypothalamus of a dehydrated person also releases antidiuretic hormone (ADH) through the posterior pituitary gland. ADH signals the kidneys to recover water from urine, effectively diluting the blood plasma. To conserve water, the hypothalamus of a dehydrated person also sends signals via the sympathetic nervous system to the salivary glands in the mouth. The signals result in a decrease in watery, serous output (and an increase in stickier, thicker mucus output). These changes in secretions result in a "dry mouth" and the sensation of thirst.

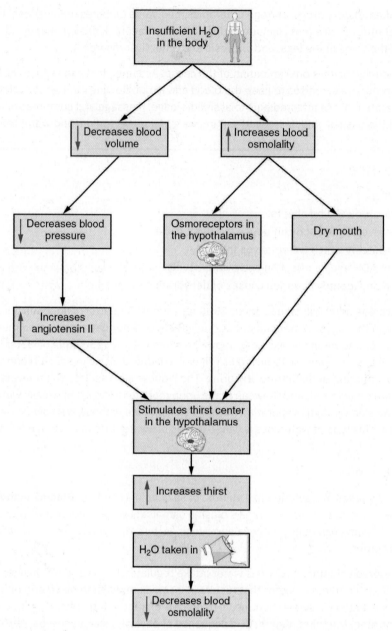

FIGURE 26.10   A Flowchart Showing the Thirst Response   The thirst response begins when osmoreceptors detect a decrease in water levels in the blood.

Decreased blood volume resulting from water loss has two additional effects. First, baroreceptors, blood-pressure receptors in the arch of the aorta and the carotid arteries in the neck, detect a decrease in blood pressure that results from decreased blood volume. The heart is ultimately signaled to increase its rate and/or strength of contractions to compensate for the lowered blood pressure.

Second, the kidneys have a renin-angiotensin hormonal system that increases the production of the active form of the hormone angiotensin II, which helps stimulate thirst, but also stimulates the release of the hormone aldosterone from the adrenal glands. Aldosterone increases the reabsorption of sodium in the distal tubules of the nephrons in the kidneys, and water follows this reabsorbed sodium back into the blood.

If adequate fluids are not consumed, dehydration results and a person's body contains too little water to function correctly. A person who repeatedly vomits or who has diarrhea may become dehydrated, and infants, because their body mass is so low, can become dangerously dehydrated very quickly. Endurance athletes such as distance runners often become dehydrated during long races. Dehydration can be a medical emergency, and a dehydrated person may lose consciousness, become comatose, or die, if their body is not rehydrated quickly.

Regulation of Water Output

Water loss from the body occurs predominantly through the renal system. A person produces an average of 1.5 liters (1.6 quarts) of urine per day. Although the volume of urine varies in response to hydration levels, there is a minimum volume of urine production required for proper bodily functions. The kidney excretes 100 to 1200 milliosmoles of solutes per day to rid the body of a variety of excess salts and other water-soluble chemical wastes, most notably creatinine, urea, and uric acid. Failure to produce the minimum volume of urine means that metabolic wastes cannot be effectively removed from the body, a situation that can impair organ function. The minimum level of urine production necessary to maintain normal function is about 0.47 liters (0.5 quarts) per day.

The kidneys also must make adjustments in the event of ingestion of too much fluid. **Diuresis**, which is the production of urine in excess of normal levels, begins about 30 minutes after drinking a large quantity of fluid. Diuresis reaches a peak after about 1 hour, and normal urine production is reestablished after about 3 hours.

Role of ADH

Antidiuretic hormone (ADH), also known as vasopressin, controls the amount of water reabsorbed from the collecting ducts and tubules in the kidney. This hormone is produced in the hypothalamus and is delivered to the posterior pituitary for storage and release (Figure 26.11). When the osmoreceptors in the hypothalamus detect an increase in the concentration of blood plasma, the hypothalamus signals the release of ADH from the posterior pituitary into the blood.

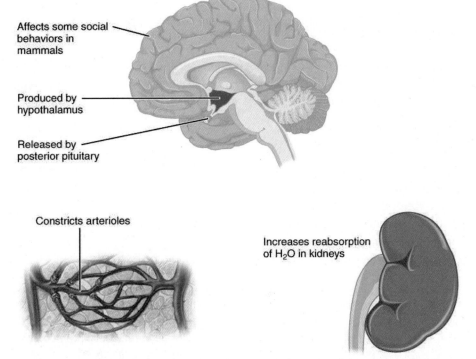

Affects some social behaviors in mammals

Produced by hypothalamus

Released by posterior pituitary

Constricts arterioles

Increases reabsorption of H_2O in kidneys

FIGURE 26.11   **Antidiuretic Hormone (ADH)**   ADH is produced in the hypothalamus and released by the posterior pituitary gland. It causes the kidneys to retain water, constricts arterioles in the peripheral circulation, and affects some social behaviors in mammals.

ADH has two major effects. It constricts the arterioles in the peripheral circulation, which reduces the flow of blood to the extremities and thereby increases the blood supply to the core of the body. ADH also causes the epithelial cells that line the renal collecting tubules to move water channel proteins, called aquaporins, from the interior of the cells to the apical surface, where these proteins are inserted into the cell membrane (Figure 26.12). The result is an increase in the water permeability of these cells and, thus, a large increase in water passage from the urine through the walls of the collecting tubules, leading to more reabsorption of water into the bloodstream. When the blood plasma becomes less concentrated and the level of ADH decreases, aquaporins are removed from collecting tubule cell membranes, and the passage of water out of urine and into the blood decreases.

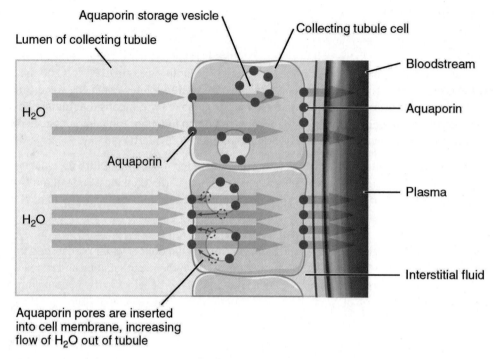

FIGURE 26.12   Aquaporins   The binding of ADH to receptors on the cells of the collecting tubule results in aquaporins being inserted into the plasma membrane, shown in the lower cell. This dramatically increases the flow of water out of the tubule and into the bloodstream.

A diuretic is a compound that increases urine output and therefore decreases water conservation by the body. Diuretics are used to treat hypertension, congestive heart failure, and fluid retention associated with menstruation. Alcohol acts as a diuretic by inhibiting the release of ADH. Additionally, caffeine, when consumed in high concentrations, acts as a diuretic.

26.3 Electrolyte Balance

LEARNING OBJECTIVES

By the end of this section, you will be able to:

- List the role of the six most important electrolytes in the body
- Name the disorders associated with abnormally high and low levels of the six electrolytes
- Identify the predominant extracellular anion
- Describe the role of aldosterone on the level of water in the body

The body contains a large variety of ions, or electrolytes, which perform a variety of functions. Some ions assist in the transmission of electrical impulses along cell membranes in neurons and muscles. Other ions help to stabilize protein structures in enzymes. Still others aid in releasing hormones from endocrine glands. All of the ions in plasma contribute to the osmotic balance that controls the movement of water between cells and their environment.

Electrolytes in living systems include sodium, potassium, chloride, bicarbonate, calcium, phosphate, magnesium, copper, zinc, iron, manganese, molybdenum, copper, and chromium. In terms of body functioning, six electrolytes are most important: sodium, potassium, chloride, bicarbonate, calcium, and phosphate.

Roles of Electrolytes

These six ions aid in nerve excitability, endocrine secretion, membrane permeability, buffering body fluids, and controlling the movement of fluids between compartments. These ions enter the body through the digestive tract. More than 90 percent of the calcium and phosphate that enters the body is incorporated into bones and teeth, with bone serving as a mineral reserve for these ions. In the event that calcium and phosphate are needed for other functions, bone tissue can be broken down to supply the blood and other tissues with these minerals. Phosphate is a normal constituent of nucleic acids; hence, blood levels of phosphate will increase whenever nucleic acids are broken down.

Access for free at openstax.org

Excretion of ions occurs mainly through the kidneys, with lesser amounts lost in sweat and in feces. Excessive sweating may cause a significant loss, especially of sodium and chloride. Severe vomiting or diarrhea will cause a loss of chloride and bicarbonate ions. Adjustments in respiratory and renal functions allow the body to regulate the levels of these ions in the ECF.

Table 26.1 lists the reference values for blood plasma, cerebrospinal fluid (CSF), and urine for the six ions addressed in this section. In a clinical setting, sodium, potassium, and chloride are typically analyzed in a routine urine sample. In contrast, calcium and phosphate analysis requires a collection of urine across a 24-hour period, because the output of these ions can vary considerably over the course of a day. Urine values reflect the rates of excretion of these ions. Bicarbonate is the one ion that is not normally excreted in urine; instead, it is conserved by the kidneys for use in the body's buffering systems.

Electrolyte and Ion Reference Values

Name	Chemical symbol	Plasma	CSF	Urine
Sodium	Na^+	136.00–146.00 (mM)	138.00–150.00 (mM)	40.00–220.00 (mM)
Potassium	K^+	3.50–5.00 (mM)	0.35–3.5 (mM)	25.00–125.00 (mM)
Chloride	Cl^-	98.00–107.00 (mM)	118.00–132.00 (mM)	110.00–250.00 (mM)
Bicarbonate	HCO_3^-	22.00–29.00 (mM)	------	------
Calcium	Ca^{++}	2.15–2.55 (mmol/day)	------	Up to 7.49 (mmol/day)
Phosphate	HPO_4^{2-}	0.81–1.45 (mmol/day)	------	12.90–42.00 (mmol/day)

TABLE 26.1

Sodium

Sodium is the major cation of the extracellular fluid. It is responsible for one-half of the osmotic pressure gradient that exists between the interior of cells and their surrounding environment. People eating a typical Western diet, which is very high in NaCl, routinely take in 130 to 160 mmol/day of sodium, but humans require only 1 to 2 mmol/day. This excess sodium appears to be a major factor in hypertension (high blood pressure) in some people. Excretion of sodium is accomplished primarily by the kidneys. Sodium is freely filtered through the glomerular capillaries of the kidneys, and although much of the filtered sodium is reabsorbed in the proximal convoluted tubule, some remains in the filtrate and urine, and is normally excreted.

Hyponatremia is a lower-than-normal concentration of sodium, usually associated with excess water accumulation in the body, which dilutes the sodium. An absolute loss of sodium may be due to a decreased intake of the ion coupled with its continual excretion in the urine. An abnormal loss of sodium from the body can result from several conditions, including excessive sweating, vomiting, or diarrhea; the use of diuretics; excessive production of urine, which can occur in diabetes; and acidosis, either metabolic acidosis or diabetic ketoacidosis.

A relative decrease in blood sodium can occur because of an imbalance of sodium in one of the body's other fluid compartments, like IF, or from a dilution of sodium due to water retention related to edema or congestive heart failure. At the cellular level, hyponatremia results in increased entry of water into cells by osmosis, because the concentration of solutes within the cell exceeds the concentration of solutes in the now-diluted ECF. The excess water causes swelling of the cells; the swelling of red blood cells—decreasing their oxygen-carrying efficiency and making them potentially too large to fit through capillaries—along with the swelling of neurons in the brain can result in brain damage or even death.

Hypernatremia is an abnormal increase of blood sodium. It can result from water loss from the blood, resulting in the hemoconcentration of all blood constituents. Hormonal imbalances involving ADH and aldosterone may also result in higher-than-normal sodium values.

Potassium

Potassium is the major intracellular cation. It helps establish the resting membrane potential in neurons and muscle fibers after membrane depolarization and action potentials. In contrast to sodium, potassium has very little effect on osmotic pressure. The low levels of potassium in blood and CSF are due to the sodium-potassium pumps in cell membranes, which maintain the normal potassium concentration gradients between the ICF and ECF. The recommendation for daily intake/consumption of potassium is 4700 mg. Potassium is excreted, both actively and passively, through the renal tubules, especially the distal convoluted tubule and collecting ducts. Potassium participates in the exchange with sodium in the renal tubules under the influence of aldosterone, which also relies on basolateral sodium-potassium pumps.

Hypokalemia is an abnormally low potassium blood level. Similar to the situation with hyponatremia, hypokalemia can occur because of either an absolute reduction of potassium in the body or a relative reduction of potassium in the blood due to the redistribution of potassium. An absolute loss of potassium can arise from decreased intake, frequently related to starvation. It can also come about from vomiting, diarrhea, or alkalosis.

Some insulin-dependent diabetic patients experience a relative reduction of potassium in the blood from the redistribution of potassium. When insulin is administered and glucose is taken up by cells, potassium passes through the cell membrane along with glucose, decreasing the amount of potassium in the blood and IF, which can cause hyperpolarization of the cell membranes of neurons, reducing their responses to stimuli.

Hyperkalemia, an elevated potassium blood level, also can impair the function of skeletal muscles, the nervous system, and the heart. Hyperkalemia can result from increased dietary intake of potassium. In such a situation, potassium from the blood ends up in the ECF in abnormally high concentrations. This can result in a partial depolarization (excitation) of the plasma membrane of skeletal muscle fibers, neurons, and cardiac cells of the heart, and can also lead to an inability of cells to repolarize. For the heart, this means that it won't relax after a contraction, and will effectively "seize" and stop pumping blood, which is fatal within minutes. Because of such effects on the nervous system, a person with hyperkalemia may also exhibit mental confusion, numbness, and weakened respiratory muscles.

Chloride

Chloride is the predominant extracellular anion. Chloride is a major contributor to the osmotic pressure gradient between the ICF and ECF, and plays an important role in maintaining proper hydration. Chloride functions to balance cations in the ECF, maintaining the electrical neutrality of this fluid. The paths of secretion and reabsorption of chloride ions in the renal system follow the paths of sodium ions.

Hypochloremia, or lower-than-normal blood chloride levels, can occur because of defective renal tubular absorption. Vomiting, diarrhea, and metabolic acidosis can also lead to hypochloremia. **Hyperchloremia**, or higher-than-normal blood chloride levels, can occur due to dehydration, excessive intake of dietary salt (NaCl) or swallowing of sea water, aspirin intoxication, congestive heart failure, and the hereditary, chronic lung disease, cystic fibrosis. In people who have cystic fibrosis, chloride levels in sweat are two to five times those of normal levels, and analysis of sweat is often used in the diagnosis of the disease.

🔗 INTERACTIVE LINK

Read this article (http://openstax.org/l/saltwater) for an explanation of the effect of seawater on humans. What effect does drinking seawater have on the body?

Bicarbonate

Bicarbonate is the second most abundant anion in the blood. Its principal function is to maintain your body's acid-base balance by being part of buffer systems. This role will be discussed in a different section.

Bicarbonate ions result from a chemical reaction that starts with carbon dioxide (CO_2) and water, two molecules that are produced at the end of aerobic metabolism. Only a small amount of CO_2 can be dissolved in body fluids. Thus, over 90 percent of the CO_2 is converted into bicarbonate ions, HCO_3^-, through the following reactions:

$$CO_2 + H_2O \leftrightarrow H_2CO_3 \leftrightarrow HCO_3^- + H^+$$

The bidirectional arrows indicate that the reactions can go in either direction, depending on the concentrations of the reactants and products. Carbon dioxide is produced in large amounts in tissues that have a high metabolic rate. Carbon dioxide is converted into bicarbonate in the cytoplasm of red blood cells through the action of an enzyme called carbonic anhydrase. Bicarbonate is transported in the blood. Once in the lungs, the reactions reverse direction, and CO_2 is regenerated from bicarbonate to be exhaled as metabolic waste.

Calcium

About two pounds of calcium in your body are bound up in bone, which provides hardness to the bone and serves as a mineral reserve for calcium and its salts for the rest of the tissues. Teeth also have a high concentration of calcium within them. A little more than one-half of blood calcium is bound to proteins, leaving the rest in its ionized form. Calcium ions, Ca^{2+}, are necessary for muscle contraction, enzyme activity, and blood coagulation. In addition, calcium helps to stabilize cell membranes and is essential for the release of neurotransmitters from neurons and of hormones from endocrine glands.

Calcium is absorbed through the intestines under the influence of activated vitamin D. A deficiency of vitamin D leads to a decrease in absorbed calcium and, eventually, a depletion of calcium stores from the skeletal system, potentially leading to rickets in children and osteomalacia in adults, contributing to osteoporosis.

Hypocalcemia, or abnormally low calcium blood levels, is seen in hypoparathyroidism, which may follow the removal of the thyroid gland, because the four nodules of the parathyroid gland are embedded in it. **Hypercalcemia**, or abnormally high calcium blood levels, is seen in primary hyperparathyroidism. Some malignancies may also result in hypercalcemia.

Phosphate

Phosphate is present in the body in three ionic forms: H_2PO_4, HPO_4^{2-}, and PO_4^{3-}. The most common form is HPO_4^{2-}. Bone and teeth bind up 85 percent of the body's phosphate as part of calcium-phosphate salts. Phosphate is found in phospholipids, such as those that make up the cell membrane, and in ATP, nucleotides, and buffers.

Hypophosphatemia, or abnormally low phosphate blood levels, occurs with heavy use of antacids, during alcohol withdrawal, and during malnourishment. In the face of phosphate depletion, the kidneys usually conserve phosphate, but during starvation, this conservation is impaired greatly. **Hyperphosphatemia**, or abnormally increased levels of phosphates in the blood, occurs if there is decreased renal function or in cases of acute lymphocytic leukemia. Additionally, because phosphate is a major constituent of the ICF, any significant destruction of cells can result in dumping of phosphate into the ECF.

Regulation of Sodium and Potassium

Sodium is reabsorbed from the renal filtrate, and potassium is excreted into the filtrate in the renal collecting tubule. The control of this exchange is governed principally by two hormones—aldosterone and angiotensin II.

Aldosterone

Recall that aldosterone increases the excretion of potassium and the reabsorption of sodium in the distal tubule. Aldosterone is released if blood levels of potassium increase, if blood levels of sodium severely decrease, or if blood pressure decreases. Its net effect is to conserve and increase water levels in the plasma by reducing the excretion of sodium, and thus water, from the kidneys. In a negative feedback loop, increased osmolality of the ECF (which follows aldosterone-stimulated sodium absorption) inhibits the release of the hormone (Figure 26.13).

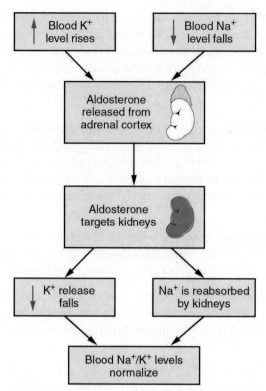

FIGURE 26.13 The Aldosterone Feedback Loop Aldosterone, which is released by the adrenal gland, facilitates reabsorption of Na⁺ and thus the reabsorption of water.

Angiotensin II

Angiotensin II causes vasoconstriction and an increase in systemic blood pressure. This action increases the glomerular filtration rate, resulting in more material filtered out of the glomerular capillaries and into Bowman's capsule. Angiotensin II also signals an increase in the release of aldosterone from the adrenal cortex.

In the distal convoluted tubules and collecting ducts of the kidneys, aldosterone stimulates the synthesis and activation of the sodium-potassium pump (Figure 26.14). Sodium passes from the filtrate, into and through the cells of the tubules and ducts, into the ECF and then into capillaries. Water follows the sodium due to osmosis. Thus, aldosterone causes an increase in blood sodium levels and blood volume. Aldosterone's effect on potassium is the reverse of that of sodium; under its influence, excess potassium is pumped into the renal filtrate for excretion from the body.

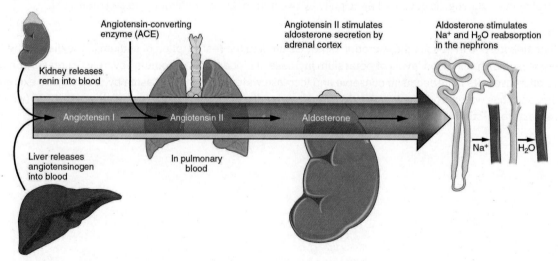

FIGURE 26.14 The Renin-Angiotensin System Angiotensin II stimulates the release of aldosterone from the adrenal cortex.

Regulation of Calcium and Phosphate

Calcium and phosphate are both regulated through the actions of three hormones: parathyroid hormone (PTH), dihydroxyvitamin D (calcitriol), and calcitonin. All three are released or synthesized in response to the blood levels of calcium.

PTH is released from the parathyroid gland in response to a decrease in the concentration of blood calcium. The hormone activates osteoclasts to break down bone matrix and release inorganic calcium-phosphate salts. PTH also increases the gastrointestinal absorption of dietary calcium by converting vitamin D into **dihydroxyvitamin D** (calcitriol), an active form of vitamin D that intestinal epithelial cells require to absorb calcium.

PTH raises blood calcium levels by inhibiting the loss of calcium through the kidneys. PTH also increases the loss of phosphate through the kidneys.

Calcitonin is released from the thyroid gland in response to elevated blood levels of calcium. The hormone increases the activity of osteoblasts, which remove calcium from the blood and incorporate calcium into the bony matrix.

26.4 Acid-Base Balance

LEARNING OBJECTIVES

By the end of this section, you will be able to:

- Identify the most powerful buffer system in the body
- Explain the way in which the respiratory system affects blood pH

Proper physiological functioning depends on a very tight balance between the concentrations of acids and bases in the blood. Acid-balance balance is measured using the pH scale, as shown in Figure 26.15. A variety of buffering systems permits blood and other bodily fluids to maintain a narrow pH range, even in the face of perturbations. A buffer is a chemical system that prevents a radical change in fluid pH by dampening the change in hydrogen ion concentrations in the case of excess acid or base. Most commonly, the substance that absorbs the ions is either a weak acid, which takes up hydroxyl ions, or a weak base, which takes up hydrogen ions.

pH	Examples of solutions
0	Battery acid, strong hydrofluoric acid
1	Hydrochloric acid secreted by stomach lining
2	Lemon juice, gastric acid, vinegar
3	Grapefruit juice, orange juice, soda
4	Tomato juice, acid rain
5	Soft drinking water, black coffee
6	Urine, saliva
7	"Pure" water
8	Sea water
9	Baking soda
10	Great Salt Lake, milk of magnesia
11	Ammonia solution
12	Soapy water
13	Bleach, oven cleaner
14	Liquid drain cleaner

FIGURE 26.15   **The pH Scale**   This chart shows where many common substances fall on the pH scale.

Buffer Systems in the Body

The buffer systems in the human body are extremely efficient, and different systems work at different rates. It takes only seconds for the chemical buffers in the blood to make adjustments to pH. The respiratory tract can adjust the blood pH upward in minutes by exhaling CO_2 from the body. The renal system can also adjust blood pH through the excretion of hydrogen ions (H^+) and the conservation of bicarbonate, but this process takes hours to days to have an effect.

The buffer systems functioning in blood plasma include plasma proteins, phosphate, and bicarbonate and carbonic acid buffers. The kidneys help control acid-base balance by excreting hydrogen ions and generating bicarbonate that helps maintain blood plasma pH within a normal range. Protein buffer systems work predominantly inside cells.

Protein Buffers in Blood Plasma and Cells

Nearly all proteins can function as buffers. Proteins are made up of amino acids, which contain positively charged amino groups and negatively charged carboxyl groups. The charged regions of these molecules can bind hydrogen and hydroxyl ions, and thus function as buffers. Buffering by proteins accounts for two-thirds of the buffering power of the blood and most of the buffering within cells.

Hemoglobin as a Buffer

Hemoglobin is the principal protein inside of red blood cells and accounts for one-third of the mass of the cell. During the conversion of CO_2 into bicarbonate, hydrogen ions liberated in the reaction are buffered by hemoglobin,

Access for free at openstax.org

which is reduced by the dissociation of oxygen. This buffering helps maintain normal pH. The process is reversed in the pulmonary capillaries to re-form CO_2, which then can diffuse into the air sacs to be exhaled into the atmosphere. This process is discussed in detail in the chapter on the respiratory system.

Phosphate Buffer

Phosphates are found in the blood in two forms: sodium dihydrogen phosphate (NaH_2PO_4), which is a weak acid, and sodium monohydrogen phosphate (Na_2HPO_4), which is a weak base. When Na_2HPO_4 comes into contact with a strong acid, such as HCl, the base picks up a second hydrogen ion to form the weak acid NaH_2PO_4 and sodium chloride, NaCl. When $NaHPO_4$ (the weak acid) comes into contact with a strong base, such as sodium hydroxide (NaOH), the weak acid reverts back to the weak base and produces water. Acids and bases are still present, but they hold onto the ions.

$HCl + Na_2HPO_4 \rightarrow NaH_2PO_4 + NaCl$
(strong acid) + (weak base) $\rightarrow$ (weak acid) + (salt)
$NaOH + NaH_2PO_4 \rightarrow Na_2HPO_4 + H_2O$
(strong base) + (weak acid) $\rightarrow$ (weak base) + (water)

Bicarbonate-Carbonic Acid Buffer

The bicarbonate-carbonic acid buffer works in a fashion similar to phosphate buffers. The bicarbonate is regulated in the blood by sodium, as are the phosphate ions. When sodium bicarbonate ($NaHCO_3$), comes into contact with a strong acid, such as HCl, carbonic acid (H_2CO_3), which is a weak acid, and NaCl are formed. When carbonic acid comes into contact with a strong base, such as NaOH, bicarbonate and water are formed.

$NaHCO_3 + HCl \rightarrow H_2CO_3 + NaCl$
(sodium bicarbonate) + (strong acid) $\rightarrow$ (weak acid) + (salt)
$H_2CO_3 + NaOH \rightarrow NaHCO_3 + H_2O$
(weak acid) + (strong base) $\rightarrow$ (sodium bicarbonate) + (water)

As with the phosphate buffer, a weak acid or weak base captures the free ions, and a significant change in pH is prevented. Bicarbonate ions and carbonic acid are present in the blood in a 20:1 ratio if the blood pH is within the normal range. With 20 times more bicarbonate than carbonic acid, this capture system is most efficient at buffering changes that would make the blood more acidic. This is useful because most of the body's metabolic wastes, such as lactic acid and ketone bodies, are acids. Carbonic acid levels in the blood are controlled by the expiration of CO_2 through the lungs. In red blood cells, carbonic anhydrase forces the dissociation of the acid, rendering the blood less acidic. Because of this acid dissociation, CO_2 is exhaled (see equations above). The level of bicarbonate in the blood is controlled through the renal system, where bicarbonate ions in the renal filtrate are conserved and passed back into the blood. However, the bicarbonate buffer is the primary buffering system of the IF surrounding the cells in tissues throughout the body.

Respiratory Regulation of Acid-Base Balance

The respiratory system contributes to the balance of acids and bases in the body by regulating the blood levels of carbonic acid (Figure 26.16). CO_2 in the blood readily reacts with water to form carbonic acid, and the levels of CO_2 and carbonic acid in the blood are in equilibrium. When the CO_2 level in the blood rises (as it does when you hold your breath), the excess CO_2 reacts with water to form additional carbonic acid, lowering blood pH. Increasing the rate and/or depth of respiration (which you might feel the "urge" to do after holding your breath) allows you to exhale more CO_2. The loss of CO_2 from the body reduces blood levels of carbonic acid and thereby adjusts the pH upward, toward normal levels. As you might have surmised, this process also works in the opposite direction. Excessive deep and rapid breathing (as in hyperventilation) rids the blood of CO_2 and reduces the level of carbonic acid, making the blood too alkaline. This brief alkalosis can be remedied by rebreathing air that has been exhaled into a paper bag. Rebreathing exhaled air will rapidly bring blood pH down toward normal.

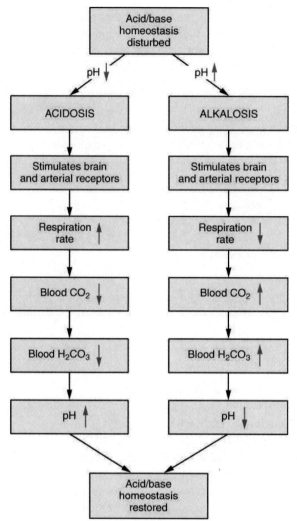

FIGURE 26.16   Respiratory Regulation of Blood pH   The respiratory system can reduce blood pH by removing CO_2 from the blood.

The chemical reactions that regulate the levels of CO_2 and carbonic acid occur in the lungs when blood travels through the lung's pulmonary capillaries. Minor adjustments in breathing are usually sufficient to adjust the pH of the blood by changing how much CO_2 is exhaled. In fact, doubling the respiratory rate for less than 1 minute, removing "extra" CO_2, would increase the blood pH by 0.2. This situation is common if you are exercising strenuously over a period of time. To keep up the necessary energy production, you would produce excess CO_2 (and lactic acid if exercising beyond your aerobic threshold). In order to balance the increased acid production, the respiration rate goes up to remove the CO_2. This helps to keep you from developing acidosis.

The body regulates the respiratory rate by the use of chemoreceptors, which primarily use CO_2 as a signal. Peripheral blood sensors are found in the walls of the aorta and carotid arteries. These sensors signal the brain to provide immediate adjustments to the respiratory rate if CO_2 levels rise or fall. Yet other sensors are found in the brain itself. Changes in the pH of CSF affect the respiratory center in the medulla oblongata, which can directly modulate breathing rate to bring the pH back into the normal range.

Hypercapnia, or abnormally elevated blood levels of CO_2, occurs in any situation that impairs respiratory functions, including pneumonia and congestive heart failure. Reduced breathing (hypoventilation) due to drugs such as morphine, barbiturates, or ethanol (or even just holding one's breath) can also result in hypercapnia. **Hypocapnia**, or abnormally low blood levels of CO_2, occurs with any cause of hyperventilation that drives off the CO_2, such as salicylate toxicity, elevated room temperatures, fever, or hysteria.

Renal Regulation of Acid-Base Balance

The renal regulation of the body's acid-base balance addresses the metabolic component of the buffering system.

Whereas the respiratory system (together with breathing centers in the brain) controls the blood levels of carbonic acid by controlling the exhalation of CO_2, the renal system controls the blood levels of bicarbonate. A decrease of blood bicarbonate can result from the inhibition of carbonic anhydrase by certain diuretics or from excessive bicarbonate loss due to diarrhea. Blood bicarbonate levels are also typically lower in people who have Addison's disease (chronic adrenal insufficiency), in which aldosterone levels are reduced, and in people who have renal damage, such as chronic nephritis. Finally, low bicarbonate blood levels can result from elevated levels of ketones (common in unmanaged diabetes mellitus), which bind bicarbonate in the filtrate and prevent its conservation.

Bicarbonate ions, HCO_3^-, found in the filtrate, are essential to the bicarbonate buffer system, yet the cells of the tubule are not permeable to bicarbonate ions. The steps involved in supplying bicarbonate ions to the system are seen in Figure 26.17 and are summarized below:

- Step 1: Sodium ions are reabsorbed from the filtrate in exchange for H^+ by an antiport mechanism in the apical membranes of cells lining the renal tubule.
- Step 2: The cells produce bicarbonate ions that can be shunted to peritubular capillaries.
- Step 3: When CO_2 is available, the reaction is driven to the formation of carbonic acid, which dissociates to form a bicarbonate ion and a hydrogen ion.
- Step 4: The bicarbonate ion passes into the peritubular capillaries and returns to the blood. The hydrogen ion is secreted into the filtrate, where it can become part of new water molecules and be reabsorbed as such, or removed in the urine.

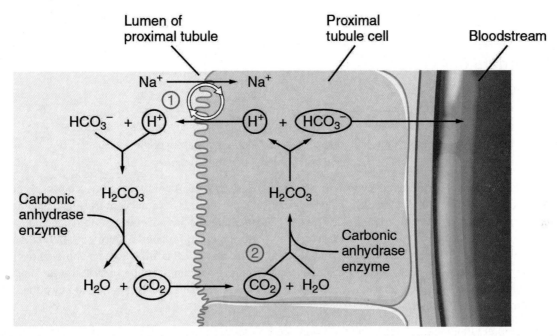

FIGURE 26.17   Conservation of Bicarbonate in the Kidney   Tubular cells are not permeable to bicarbonate; thus, bicarbonate is conserved rather than reabsorbed. Steps 1 and 2 of bicarbonate conservation are indicated.

It is also possible that salts in the filtrate, such as sulfates, phosphates, or ammonia, will capture hydrogen ions. If this occurs, the hydrogen ions will not be available to combine with bicarbonate ions and produce CO_2. In such cases, bicarbonate ions are not conserved from the filtrate to the blood, which will also contribute to a pH imbalance and acidosis.

The hydrogen ions also compete with potassium to exchange with sodium in the renal tubules. If more potassium is present than normal, potassium, rather than the hydrogen ions, will be exchanged, and increased potassium enters the filtrate. When this occurs, fewer hydrogen ions in the filtrate participate in the conversion of bicarbonate into CO_2 and less bicarbonate is conserved. If there is less potassium, more hydrogen ions enter the filtrate to be exchanged with sodium and more bicarbonate is conserved.

Chloride ions are important in neutralizing positive ion charges in the body. If chloride is lost, the body uses bicarbonate ions in place of the lost chloride ions. Thus, lost chloride results in an increased reabsorption of bicarbonate by the renal system.

Disorders of the...

Acid-Base Balance: Ketoacidosis

Diabetic acidosis, or ketoacidosis, occurs most frequently in people with poorly controlled diabetes mellitus. When certain tissues in the body cannot get adequate amounts of glucose, they depend on the breakdown of fatty acids for energy. When acetyl groups break off the fatty acid chains, the acetyl groups then non-enzymatically combine to form ketone bodies, acetoacetic acid, beta-hydroxybutyric acid, and acetone, all of which increase the acidity of the blood. In this condition, the brain isn't supplied with enough of its fuel—glucose—to produce all of the ATP it requires to function.

Ketoacidosis can be severe and, if not detected and treated properly, can lead to diabetic coma, which can be fatal. A common early symptom of ketoacidosis is deep, rapid breathing as the body attempts to drive off CO_2 and compensate for the acidosis. Another common symptom is fruity-smelling breath, due to the exhalation of acetone. Other symptoms include dry skin and mouth, a flushed face, nausea, vomiting, and stomach pain. Treatment for diabetic coma is ingestion or injection of sugar; its prevention is the proper daily administration of insulin.

A person who is diabetic and uses insulin can initiate ketoacidosis if a dose of insulin is missed. Among people with type 2 diabetes, those of Hispanic and African-American descent are more likely to go into ketoacidosis than those of other ethnic backgrounds, although the reason for this is unknown.

26.5 Disorders of Acid-Base Balance

LEARNING OBJECTIVES

By the end of this section, you will be able to:

- Identify the three blood variables considered when making a diagnosis of acidosis or alkalosis
- Identify the source of compensation for blood pH problems of a respiratory origin
- Identify the source of compensation for blood pH problems of a metabolic/renal origin

Normal arterial blood pH is restricted to a very narrow range of 7.35 to 7.45. A person who has a blood pH below 7.35 is considered to be in acidosis (actually, "physiological acidosis," because blood is not truly acidic until its pH drops below 7), and a continuous blood pH below 7.0 can be fatal. Acidosis has several symptoms, including headache and confusion, and the individual can become lethargic and easily fatigued (Figure 26.18). A person who has a blood pH above 7.45 is considered to be in alkalosis, and a pH above 7.8 is fatal. Some symptoms of alkalosis include cognitive impairment (which can progress to unconsciousness), tingling or numbness in the extremities, muscle twitching and spasm, and nausea and vomiting. Both acidosis and alkalosis can be caused by either metabolic or respiratory disorders.

As discussed earlier in this chapter, the concentration of carbonic acid in the blood is dependent on the level of CO_2 in the body and the amount of CO_2 gas exhaled through the lungs. Thus, the respiratory contribution to acid-base balance is usually discussed in terms of CO_2 (rather than of carbonic acid). Remember that a molecule of carbonic acid is lost for every molecule of CO_2 exhaled, and a molecule of carbonic acid is formed for every molecule of CO_2 retained.

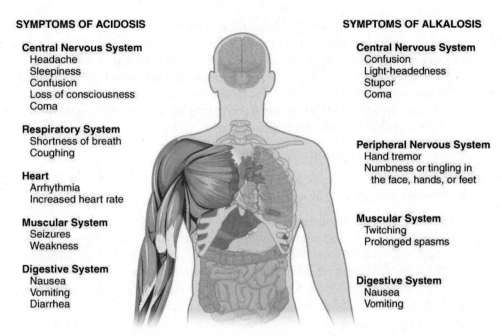

SYMPTOMS OF ACIDOSIS

Central Nervous System
Headache
Sleepiness
Confusion
Loss of consciousness
Coma

Respiratory System
Shortness of breath
Coughing

Heart
Arrhythmia
Increased heart rate

Muscular System
Seizures
Weakness

Digestive System
Nausea
Vomiting
Diarrhea

SYMPTOMS OF ALKALOSIS

Central Nervous System
Confusion
Light-headedness
Stupor
Coma

Peripheral Nervous System
Hand tremor
Numbness or tingling in
  the face, hands, or feet

Muscular System
Twitching
Prolonged spasms

Digestive System
Nausea
Vomiting

FIGURE 26.18 Symptoms of Acidosis and Alkalosis   Symptoms of acidosis affect several organ systems. Both acidosis and alkalosis can be diagnosed using a blood test.

Metabolic Acidosis: Primary Bicarbonate Deficiency

Metabolic acidosis occurs when the blood is too acidic (pH below 7.35) due to too little bicarbonate, a condition called primary bicarbonate deficiency. At the normal pH of 7.40, the ratio of bicarbonate to carbonic acid buffer is 20:1. If a person's blood pH drops below 7.35, then the person is in metabolic acidosis. The most common cause of metabolic acidosis is the presence of organic acids or excessive ketone bodies in the blood. Table 26.2 lists some other causes of metabolic acidosis.

Common Causes of Metabolic Acidosis and Blood Metabolites

Cause	Metabolite
Diarrhea	Bicarbonate
Uremia	Phosphoric, sulfuric, and lactic acids
Diabetic ketoacidosis	Increased ketone bodies
Strenuous exercise	Lactic acid
Methanol	Formic acid*
Paraldehyde	β-Hydroxybutyric acid*
Isopropanol	Propionic acid*
Ethylene glycol	Glycolic acid, and some oxalic and formic acids*
Salicylate/aspirin	Sulfasalicylic acid (SSA)*

TABLE 26.2 *Acid metabolites from ingested chemical.

The first three of the eight causes of metabolic acidosis listed are medical (or unusual physiological) conditions.

Strenuous exercise can cause temporary metabolic acidosis due to the production of lactic acid. The last five causes result from the ingestion of specific substances. The active form of aspirin is its metabolite, sulfasalicylic acid. An overdose of aspirin causes acidosis due to the acidity of this metabolite. Metabolic acidosis can also result from uremia, which is the retention of urea and uric acid. Metabolic acidosis can also arise from diabetic ketoacidosis, wherein an excess of ketone bodies are present in the blood. Other causes of metabolic acidosis are a decrease in the excretion of hydrogen ions, which inhibits the conservation of bicarbonate ions, and excessive loss of bicarbonate ions through the gastrointestinal tract due to diarrhea.

Metabolic Alkalosis: Primary Bicarbonate Excess

Metabolic alkalosis is the opposite of metabolic acidosis. It occurs when the blood is too alkaline (pH above 7.45) due to too much bicarbonate (called primary bicarbonate excess).

A transient excess of bicarbonate in the blood can follow ingestion of excessive amounts of bicarbonate, citrate, or antacids for conditions such as stomach acid reflux—known as heartburn. Cushing's disease, which is the chronic hypersecretion of adrenocorticotropic hormone (ACTH) by the anterior pituitary gland, can cause chronic metabolic alkalosis. The oversecretion of ACTH results in elevated aldosterone levels and an increased loss of potassium by urinary excretion. Other causes of metabolic alkalosis include the loss of hydrochloric acid from the stomach through vomiting, potassium depletion due to the use of diuretics for hypertension, and the excessive use of laxatives.

Respiratory Acidosis: Primary Carbonic Acid/CO$_2$ Excess

Respiratory acidosis occurs when the blood is overly acidic due to an excess of carbonic acid, resulting from too much CO$_2$ in the blood. Respiratory acidosis can result from anything that interferes with respiration, such as pneumonia, emphysema, or congestive heart failure.

Respiratory Alkalosis: Primary Carbonic Acid/CO$_2$ Deficiency

Respiratory alkalosis occurs when the blood is overly alkaline due to a deficiency in carbonic acid and CO$_2$ levels in the blood. This condition usually occurs when too much CO$_2$ is exhaled from the lungs, as occurs in hyperventilation, which is breathing that is deeper or more frequent than normal. An elevated respiratory rate leading to hyperventilation can be due to extreme emotional upset or fear, fever, infections, hypoxia, or abnormally high levels of catecholamines, such as epinephrine and norepinephrine. Surprisingly, aspirin overdose—salicylate toxicity—can result in respiratory alkalosis as the body tries to compensate for initial acidosis.

🔗 INTERACTIVE LINK

Watch this video (http://openstax.org/l/altitude) to see a demonstration of the effect altitude has on blood pH. What effect does high altitude have on blood pH, and why?

Compensation Mechanisms

Various compensatory mechanisms exist to maintain blood pH within a narrow range, including buffers, respiration, and renal mechanisms. Although compensatory mechanisms usually work very well, when one of these mechanisms is not working properly (like kidney failure or respiratory disease), they have their limits. If the pH and bicarbonate to carbonic acid ratio are changed too drastically, the body may not be able to compensate. Moreover, extreme changes in pH can denature proteins. Extensive damage to proteins in this way can result in disruption of normal metabolic processes, serious tissue damage, and ultimately death.

Respiratory Compensation
Respiratory compensation for metabolic acidosis increases the respiratory rate to drive off CO$_2$ and readjust the bicarbonate to carbonic acid ratio to the 20:1 level. This adjustment can occur within minutes. Respiratory compensation for metabolic alkalosis is not as adept as its compensation for acidosis. The normal response of the respiratory system to elevated pH is to increase the amount of CO$_2$ in the blood by decreasing the respiratory rate to conserve CO$_2$. There is a limit to the decrease in respiration, however, that the body can tolerate. Hence, the respiratory route is less efficient at compensating for metabolic alkalosis than for acidosis.

Metabolic Compensation

Metabolic and renal compensation for respiratory diseases that can create acidosis revolves around the conservation of bicarbonate ions. In cases of respiratory acidosis, the kidney increases the conservation of bicarbonate and secretion of H^+ through the exchange mechanism discussed earlier. These processes increase the concentration of bicarbonate in the blood, reestablishing the proper relative concentrations of bicarbonate and carbonic acid. In cases of respiratory alkalosis, the kidneys decrease the production of bicarbonate and reabsorb H^+ from the tubular fluid. These processes can be limited by the exchange of potassium by the renal cells, which use a K^+-H^+ exchange mechanism (antiporter).

Diagnosing Acidosis and Alkalosis

Lab tests for pH, CO_2 partial pressure (PCO_2), and HCO_3^- can identify acidosis and alkalosis, indicating whether the imbalance is respiratory or metabolic, and the extent to which compensatory mechanisms are working. The blood pH value, as shown in Table 26.3, indicates whether the blood is in acidosis, the normal range, or alkalosis. The PCO_2 and total HCO_3^- values aid in determining whether the condition is metabolic or respiratory, and whether the patient has been able to compensate for the problem. Table 26.3 lists the conditions and laboratory results that can be used to classify these conditions. Metabolic acid-base imbalances typically result from kidney disease, and the respiratory system usually responds to compensate.

Types of Acidosis and Alkalosis

	pH	PCO$_2$	Total HCO$_3^-$
Metabolic acidosis	↓	N, then ↓	↓
Respiratory acidosis	↓	↑	N, then ↑
Metabolic alkalosis	↑	N, then ↑	↑
Respiratory alkalosis	↑	↓	N, then ↓

TABLE 26.3 Reference values (arterial): pH: 7.35–7.45; pCO$_2$: male: 35–48 mm Hg, female: 32–45 mm Hg; total venous bicarbonate: 22–29 mM. N denotes normal; ↑ denotes a rising or increased value; and ↓ denotes a falling or decreased value.

Metabolic acidosis is problematic, as lower-than-normal amounts of bicarbonate are present in the blood. The PCO_2 would be normal at first, but if compensation has occurred, it would decrease as the body reestablishes the proper ratio of bicarbonate and carbonic acid/CO_2.

Respiratory acidosis is problematic, as excess CO_2 is present in the blood. Bicarbonate levels would be normal at first, but if compensation has occurred, they would increase in an attempt to reestablish the proper ratio of bicarbonate and carbonic acid/CO_2.

Alkalosis is characterized by a higher-than-normal pH. Metabolic alkalosis is problematic, as elevated pH and excess bicarbonate are present. The PCO_2 would again be normal at first, but if compensation has occurred, it would increase as the body attempts to reestablish the proper ratios of bicarbonate and carbonic acid/CO_2.

Respiratory alkalosis is problematic, as CO_2 deficiency is present in the bloodstream. The bicarbonate concentration would be normal at first. When renal compensation occurs, however, the bicarbonate concentration in blood decreases as the kidneys attempt to reestablish the proper ratios of bicarbonate and carbonic acid/CO_2 by eliminating more bicarbonate to bring the pH into the physiological range.

Key Terms

antidiuretic hormone (ADH)   also known as vasopressin, a hormone that increases the volume of water reabsorbed from the collecting tubules of the kidney

dehydration   state of containing insufficient water in blood and other tissues

dihydroxyvitamin D   active form of vitamin D required by the intestinal epithelial cells for the absorption of calcium

diuresis   excess production of urine

extracellular fluid (ECF)   fluid exterior to cells; includes the interstitial fluid, blood plasma, and fluids found in other reservoirs in the body

fluid compartment   fluid inside all cells of the body constitutes a compartment system that is largely segregated from other systems

hydrostatic pressure   pressure exerted by a fluid against a wall, caused by its own weight or pumping force

hypercalcemia   abnormally increased blood levels of calcium

hypercapnia   abnormally elevated blood levels of CO_2

hyperchloremia   higher-than-normal blood chloride levels

hyperkalemia   higher-than-normal blood potassium levels

hypernatremia   abnormal increase in blood sodium levels

hyperphosphatemia   abnormally increased blood phosphate levels

hypocalcemia   abnormally low blood levels of calcium

hypocapnia   abnormally low blood levels of CO_2

hypochloremia   lower-than-normal blood chloride levels

hypokalemia   abnormally decreased blood levels of potassium

hyponatremia   lower-than-normal levels of sodium in the blood

hypophosphatemia   abnormally low blood phosphate levels

interstitial fluid (IF)   fluid in the small spaces between cells not contained within blood vessels

intracellular fluid (ICF)   fluid in the cytosol of cells

metabolic acidosis   condition wherein a deficiency of bicarbonate causes the blood to be overly acidic

metabolic alkalosis   condition wherein an excess of bicarbonate causes the blood to be overly alkaline

plasma osmolality   ratio of solutes to a volume of solvent in the plasma; plasma osmolality reflects a person's state of hydration

respiratory acidosis   condition wherein an excess of carbonic acid or CO_2 causes the blood to be overly acidic

respiratory alkalosis   condition wherein a deficiency of carbonic acid/CO_2 levels causes the blood to be overly alkaline

Chapter Review

26.1 Body Fluids and Fluid Compartments

Your body is mostly water. Body fluids are aqueous solutions with differing concentrations of materials, called solutes. An appropriate balance of water and solute concentrations must be maintained to ensure cellular functions. If the cytosol becomes too concentrated due to water loss, cell functions deteriorate. If the cytosol becomes too dilute due to water intake by cells, cell membranes can be damaged, and the cell can burst. Hydrostatic pressure is the force exerted by a fluid against a wall and causes movement of fluid between compartments. Fluid can also move between compartments along an osmotic gradient. Active transport processes require ATP to move some solutes against their concentration gradients between compartments. Passive transport of a molecule or ion depends on its ability to pass easily through the membrane, as well as the existence of a high to low concentration gradient.

26.2 Water Balance

Homeostasis requires that water intake and output be balanced. Most water intake comes through the digestive tract via liquids and food, but roughly 10 percent of water available to the body is generated at the end of aerobic respiration during cellular metabolism. Urine produced by the kidneys accounts for the largest amount of water leaving the body. The kidneys can adjust the concentration of the urine to reflect the body's water needs, conserving water if the body is dehydrated or making urine more dilute to expel excess water when necessary. ADH is a hormone that helps the body to retain water by increasing water reabsorption by the kidneys.

26.3 Electrolyte Balance

Electrolytes serve various purposes, such as helping to conduct electrical impulses along cell membranes in neurons and muscles, stabilizing enzyme structures, and releasing hormones from endocrine glands. The ions in plasma also contribute to the osmotic balance that controls the movement of water between cells and their environment. Imbalances of these ions can result in various problems in the body, and their concentrations are tightly regulated. Aldosterone and angiotensin II control the exchange of sodium and potassium between the renal filtrate and the renal collecting tubule. Calcium and phosphate are regulated by PTH, calcitriol, and calcitonin.

26.4 Acid-Base Balance

A variety of buffering systems exist in the body that helps maintain the pH of the blood and other fluids within a narrow range—between pH 7.35 and 7.45. A buffer is a substance that prevents a radical change in fluid pH by absorbing excess hydrogen or hydroxyl ions. Most commonly, the substance that absorbs the ion is either a weak acid, which takes up a hydroxyl ion (OH^-), or a weak base, which takes up a hydrogen ion

(H^+). Several substances serve as buffers in the body, including cell and plasma proteins, hemoglobin, phosphates, bicarbonate ions, and carbonic acid. The bicarbonate buffer is the primary buffering system of the IF surrounding the cells in tissues throughout the body. The respiratory and renal systems also play major roles in acid-base homeostasis by removing CO_2 and hydrogen ions, respectively, from the body.

26.5 Disorders of Acid-Base Balance

Acidosis and alkalosis describe conditions in which a person's blood is, respectively, too acidic (pH below 7.35) and too alkaline (pH above 7.45). Each of these conditions can be caused either by metabolic problems related to bicarbonate levels or by respiratory problems related to carbonic acid and CO_2 levels. Several compensatory mechanisms allow the body to maintain a normal pH.

Interactive Link Questions

1. Watch this video (http://openstax.org/l/bodyfluids) to learn more about body fluids, fluid compartments, and electrolytes. When blood volume decreases due to sweating, from what source is water taken in by the blood?

2. Watch this video (http://openstax.org/l/dynamicfluid) to see an explanation of the dynamics of fluid in the body's compartments. What happens in tissues when capillary blood pressure is less than osmotic pressure?

3. Read this article (http://openstax.org/l/saltwater) for an explanation of the effect of seawater on humans. What effect does drinking seawater have on the body?

4. Watch this video (http://openstax.org/l/altitude) to see a demonstration of the effect altitude has on blood pH. What effect does high altitude have on blood pH, and why?

Review Questions

5. Solute contributes to the movement of water between cells and the surrounding medium by _____.
    a. osmotic pressure
    b. hydrostatic pressure
    c. Brownian movement
    d. random motion

6. A cation has a(n) _____ charge.
    a. neutral
    b. positive
    c. alternating
    d. negative

7. Interstitial fluid (IF) is _____.
    a. the fluid in the cytosol of the cells
    b. the fluid component of blood
    c. the fluid that bathes all of the body's cells except for blood cells
    d. the intracellular fluids found between membranes

8. The largest amount of water comes into the body via _____.
    a. metabolism
    b. foods
    c. liquids
    d. humidified air

9. The largest amount of water leaves the body via _____.
    a. the GI tract
    b. the skin as sweat
    c. expiration
    d. urine

10. Insensible water loss is water lost via _____.
    a. skin evaporation and in air from the lungs
    b. urine
    c. excessive sweating
    d. vomiting or diarrhea

11. How soon after drinking a large glass of water will a person start increasing their urine output?
    a. 5 minutes
    b. 30 minutes
    c. 1 hour
    d. 3 hours

12. Bone serves as a mineral reserve for which two ions?
    a. sodium and potassium
    b. calcium and phosphate
    c. chloride and bicarbonate
    d. calcium and bicarbonate

13. Electrolytes are lost mostly through _____.
    a. renal function
    b. sweating
    c. feces
    d. respiration

14. The major cation in extracellular fluid is _____.
    a. sodium
    b. potassium
    c. chloride
    d. bicarbonate

15. The major cation in intracellular fluid is _____.
    a. sodium
    b. potassium
    c. chloride
    d. bicarbonate

16. The major anion in extracellular fluid is _____.
    a. sodium
    b. potassium
    c. chloride
    d. bicarbonate

17. Most of the body's calcium is found in _____.
    a. teeth
    b. bone
    c. plasma
    d. extracellular fluids

18. Abnormally increased blood levels of sodium are termed _____.
    a. hyperkalemia
    b. hyperchloremia
    c. hypernatremia
    d. hypercalcemia

19. The ion with the lowest blood level is _____.
    a. sodium
    b. potassium
    c. chloride
    d. bicarbonate

20. Which two ions are most affected by aldosterone?
    a. sodium and potassium
    b. chloride and bicarbonate
    c. calcium and phosphate
    d. sodium and phosphate

21. Which of the following is the most important buffer inside red blood cells?
    a. plasma proteins
    b. hemoglobin
    c. phosphate buffers
    d. bicarbonate: carbonic acid buffer

22. Which explanation best describes why plasma proteins can function as buffers?
    a. Plasma proteins combine with bicarbonate to make a stronger buffer.
    b. Plasma proteins are immune to damage from acids.
    c. Proteins have both positive and negative charges on their surface.
    d. Proteins are alkaline.

23. The buffer that is adjusted to control acid-base balance is _____.
    a. plasma protein
    b. hemoglobin
    c. phosphate buffer
    d. bicarbonate: carbonic acid buffer

24. Carbonic acid levels are controlled through the _____.
    a. respiratory system
    b. renal system
    c. digestive system
    d. metabolic rate of cells

25. Bicarbonate ion concentrations in the blood are controlled through the _____.
    a. respiratory system
    b. renal system
    c. digestive system
    d. metabolic rate of cells

26. Which reaction is catalyzed by carbonic anhydrase?
    a. $HPO_4^{2-} + H^+ \leftrightarrow H_2PO_4^-$
    b. $CO_2 + H_2O \leftrightarrow H_2CO_3$
    c. $H_2PO_4^- + OH^- \leftrightarrow HPO_4^{2-} + H_2O$
    d. $H_2CO_3 \leftrightarrow HCO_3^- + H^+$

27. Which of the following is a cause of metabolic acidosis?
    a. excessive HCl loss
    b. increased aldosterone
    c. diarrhea
    d. prolonged use of diuretics

28. Which of the following is a cause of respiratory acidosis?
    a. emphysema
    b. low blood K^+
    c. increased aldosterone
    d. increased blood ketones

29. At a pH of 7.40, the carbonic acid ratio is

    _____.
    a. 35:1
    b. 4:1
    c. 20:1
    d. 3:1

30. Which of the following is characterized as metabolic alkalosis?
    a. increased pH, decreased pCO_2, decreased HCO_3^-
    b. increased pH, increased pCO_2, increased HCO_3^-
    c. decreased pH, decreased pCO_2, decreased HCO_3^-
    d. decreased pH, increased pCO_2, increased HCO_3^-

Critical Thinking Questions

31. Plasma contains more sodium than chloride. How can this be if individual ions of sodium and chloride exactly balance each other out, and plasma is electrically neutral?

32. How is fluid moved from compartment to compartment?

33. Describe the effect of ADH on renal collecting tubules.

34. Why is it important for the amount of water intake to equal the amount of water output?

35. Explain how the CO_2 generated by cells and exhaled in the lungs is carried as bicarbonate in the blood.

36. How can one have an imbalance in a substance, but not actually have elevated or deficient levels of that substance in the body?

37. Describe the conservation of bicarbonate ions in the renal system.

38. Describe the control of blood carbonic acid levels through the respiratory system.

39. Case Study: Brooks is a 64-year-old admitted to the emergency room for asthma. Their laboratory results are as follows: pH 7.31, pCO_2 higher than normal, and total HCO_3^- also higher than normal. Classify their acid-base balance as acidosis or alkalosis, and as metabolic or respiratory. Is there evidence of compensation? Propose the mechanism by which asthma contributed to the lab results seen.

40. Case Study: Kim is a 38-year-old woman admitted to the hospital for bulimia. Her laboratory results are as follows: pH 7.48, pCO_2 in the normal range, and total HCO_3^- higher than normal. Classify her acid-base balance as acidosis or alkalosis, and as metabolic or respiratory. Is there evidence of compensation? Propose the mechanism by which bulimia contributed to the lab results seen.

CHAPTER 27
The Reproductive System

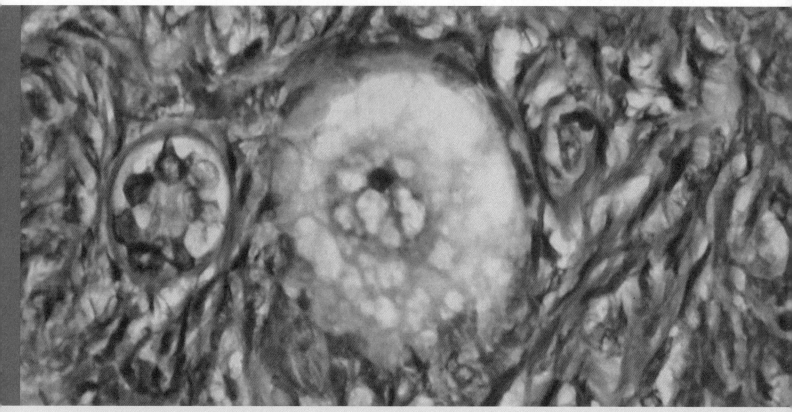

Figure 27.1 **Ovulation** Following a surge of luteinizing hormone (LH), an oocyte (immature egg cell) will be released into the uterine tube, where it will then be available to be fertilized by sperm. Ovulation marks the end of the follicular phase of the ovarian cycle and the start of the luteal phase.

CHAPTER OBJECTIVES
After studying this chapter, you will be able to:

- Describe the anatomy of the reproductive systems, including their accessory structures
- Explain the role of hypothalamic and pituitary hormones in reproductive function
- Trace the path of a sperm cell from its initial production through fertilization of an oocyte
- Explain the events in the ovary prior to ovulation
- Describe the development and maturation of the sex organs and the emergence of secondary sex characteristics during puberty

INTRODUCTION Small, uncoordinated, and slick with amniotic fluid, a newborn encounters the world outside of her the womb. We do not often consider that a child's birth is proof of the healthy functioning of reproductive systems. Moreover, endocrine systems had to secrete the appropriate regulating hormones to induce the production and release of unique male and female gametes, reproductive cells containing genetic material (one set of 23 chromosomes). Reproductive behavior or medical innovation had to facilitate the transfer of male gametes—the sperm—to the female gamete, an oocyte (egg). Finally, combination of the gametes (fertilization) had to occur, followed by implantation and development. In this chapter, you will explore the reproductive systems, whose functioning can culminate in the powerful sound of a newborn's first cry.

27.1 Anatomy and Physiology of the Testicular Reproductive System

LEARNING OBJECTIVES

By the end of this section, you will be able to:

- Describe the structure and function of the organs of the testicular reproductive system
- Describe the structure and function of the sperm cell
- Explain the events during spermatogenesis that produce haploid sperm from diploid cells
- Identify the importance of testosterone in reproductive function

People often use the words "female" and "male" to describe two different concepts: our sense of gender identity, and our biological sex as determined by our X/Y chromosomes, hormones, sex organs, and other physical characteristics. For some people, gender identity is different from biological sex or their sex assigned at birth. In this chapter and the next chapter, "female" and "male" refer to sex only, and the typical reproductive anatomy of XX and XY individuals is discussed.

Unique for its role in reproduction, a **gamete** is a specialized sex cell, which in humans carries 23 chromosomes—one half the number in body cells. In almost all sexually reproducing species, these two haploid cells differ in size; the smaller gamete is called the male gamete and the larger one is called the female gamete. At fertilization, the chromosomes in one male gamete, called a **sperm** (or spermatozoon), combine with the chromosomes in one female gamete, called an oocyte. The function of the male, or testicular, reproductive system (Figure 27.2) is to produce sperm and transfer them to the female reproductive tract. The paired testes are a crucial component in this process, as they produce both sperm and androgens, the hormones that support male reproductive physiology. In male humans, the most important androgen is testosterone. For people with a penis, several accessory organs and ducts aid the process of sperm maturation and transport the sperm and other seminal components to the penis, which may deliver sperm to the female reproductive tract. In this section, we examine each of these different structures, and discuss the process of sperm production and transport.

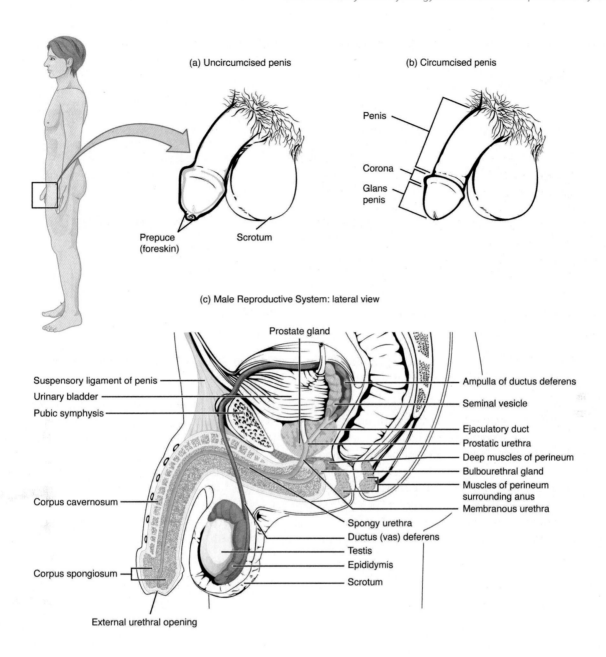

FIGURE 27.2   Testicular Reproductive System   The structures of the testicular reproductive system include the testes, the epididymides, the penis, and the ducts and glands that produce and carry semen. Sperm exit the scrotum through the ductus deferens, which is bundled in the spermatic cord. The seminal vesicles and prostate gland add fluids to the sperm to create semen.

Scrotum

The testes are located in a skin-covered, highly pigmented, muscular sack called the **scrotum** that extends from the body behind the penis (see Figure 27.2). This location is important in sperm production, which occurs within the testes, and proceeds more efficiently when the testes are kept 2 to 4°C below core body temperature.

The dartos muscle makes up the subcutaneous muscle layer of the scrotum (Figure 27.3). It continues internally to make up the scrotal septum, a wall that divides the scrotum into two compartments, each housing one testis. Descending from the internal oblique muscle of the abdominal wall are the two cremaster muscles, which cover each testis like a muscular net. By contracting simultaneously, the dartos and cremaster muscles can elevate the testes in cold weather (or water), moving the testes closer to the body and decreasing the surface area of the scrotum to retain heat. Alternatively, as the environmental temperature increases, the scrotum relaxes, moving the testes farther from the body core and increasing scrotal surface area, which promotes heat loss. Externally, the scrotum has a raised medial thickening on the surface called the raphae.

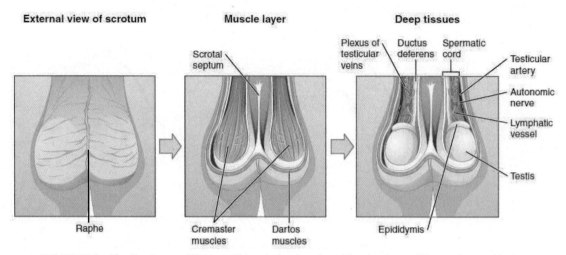

FIGURE 27.3   The Scrotum and Testes   This anterior view shows the structures of the scrotum and testes.

Testes

The **testes** (singular = testis) are the male **gonads**—that is, the male reproductive organs. They produce both sperm and androgens, such as testosterone, and are active throughout the reproductive lifespan.

Paired ovals, adult testes are each approximately 4 to 5 cm in length and are housed within the scrotum (see Figure 27.3). They are surrounded by two distinct layers of protective connective tissue (Figure 27.4). The outer tunica vaginalis is a serous membrane that has both a parietal and a thin visceral layer. Beneath the tunica vaginalis is the tunica albuginea, a tough, white, dense connective tissue layer covering the testis itself. Not only does the tunica albuginea cover the outside of the testis, it also invaginates to form septa that divide the testis into 300 to 400 structures called lobules. Within the lobules, sperm develop in structures called seminiferous tubules. During the seventh month of the developmental period of a male fetus, each testis moves through the abdominal musculature to descend into the scrotal cavity. This is called the "descent of the testis." Cryptorchidism is the clinical term used when one or both of the testes fail to descend into the scrotum prior to birth.

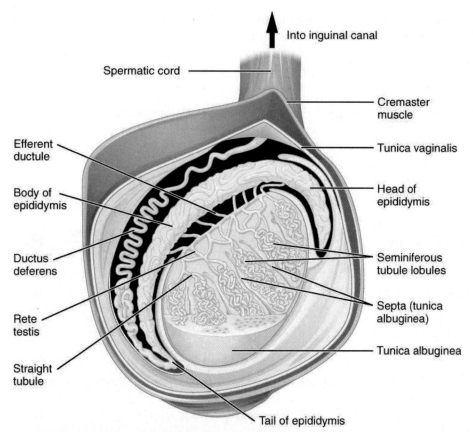

FIGURE 27.4 Anatomy of the Testis   This sagittal view shows the seminiferous tubules, the site of sperm production. Formed sperm are transferred to the epididymis, where they mature. They leave the epididymis during an ejaculation via the ductus deferens.

The tightly coiled **seminiferous tubules** form the bulk of each testis. They are composed of developing sperm cells surrounding a lumen, the hollow center of the tubule, where formed sperm are released into the duct system of the testis. Specifically, from the lumens of the seminiferous tubules, sperm move into the straight tubules (or tubuli recti), and from there into a fine meshwork of tubules called the rete testes. Sperm leave the rete testes, and the testis itself, through the 15 to 20 efferent ductules that cross the tunica albuginea.

Inside the seminiferous tubules are six different cell types. These include supporting cells called sustentacular cells, as well as five types of developing sperm cells called germ cells. Germ cell development progresses from the basement membrane—at the perimeter of the tubule—toward the lumen. Let's look more closely at these cell types.

Sertoli Cells

Surrounding all stages of the developing sperm cells are elongate, branching **Sertoli cells**. Sertoli cells are a type of supporting cell called a sustentacular cell, or sustentocyte, that are typically found in epithelial tissue. Sertoli cells secrete signaling molecules that promote sperm production and can control whether germ cells live or die. They extend physically around the germ cells from the peripheral basement membrane of the seminiferous tubules to the lumen. Tight junctions between these sustentacular cells create the **blood–testis barrier**, which keeps bloodborne substances from reaching the germ cells and, at the same time, keeps surface antigens on developing germ cells from escaping into the bloodstream and prompting an autoimmune response.

Germ Cells

The least mature cells, the **spermatogonia** (singular = spermatogonium), line the basement membrane inside the tubule. Spermatogonia are the stem cells of the testis, which means that they are still able to differentiate into a variety of different cell types throughout adulthood. Spermatogonia divide to produce primary and secondary spermatocytes, then spermatids, which finally produce formed sperm. The process that begins with spermatogonia and concludes with the production of sperm is called **spermatogenesis**.

Spermatogenesis

As just noted, spermatogenesis occurs in the seminiferous tubules that form the bulk of each testis (see Figure

27.4). The process begins at puberty, after which time sperm are produced constantly throughout a male's life. One production cycle, from spermatogonia through formed sperm, takes approximately 64 days. A new cycle starts approximately every 16 days, although this timing is not synchronous across the seminiferous tubules. Sperm counts—the total number of sperm a person produces—slowly decline after age 35, and some studies suggest that smoking can lower sperm counts irrespective of age.

The process of spermatogenesis begins with mitosis of the diploid spermatogonia (Figure 27.5). Because these cells are diploid ($2n$), they each have a complete copy of the person's genetic material, or 46 chromosomes. However, mature gametes are haploid ($1n$), containing 23 chromosomes—meaning that daughter cells of spermatogonia must undergo a second cellular division through the process of meiosis.

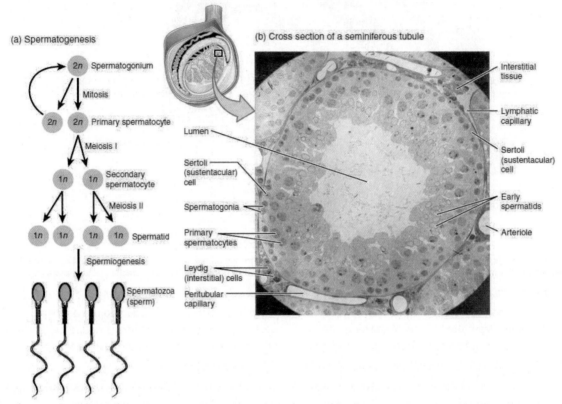

FIGURE 27.5 Spermatogenesis (a) Mitosis of a spermatogonial stem cell involves a single cell division that results in two identical, diploid daughter cells (spermatogonia to primary spermatocyte). Meiosis has two rounds of cell division: primary spermatocyte to secondary spermatocyte, and then secondary spermatocyte to spermatid. This produces four haploid daughter cells (spermatids). (b) In this electron micrograph of a cross-section of a seminiferous tubule from a rat, the lumen is the light-shaded area in the center of the image. The location of the primary spermatocytes is near the basement membrane, and the early spermatids are approaching the lumen (tissue source: rat). EM × 900. (Micrograph provided by the Regents of University of Michigan Medical School © 2012)

Two identical diploid cells result from spermatogonia mitosis. One of these cells remains a spermatogonium, and the other becomes a primary **spermatocyte**, the next stage in the process of spermatogenesis. As in mitosis, DNA is replicated in a primary spermatocyte, before it undergoes a cell division called meiosis I. During meiosis I each of the 23 pairs of chromosomes separates. This results in two cells, called secondary spermatocytes, each with only half the number of chromosomes. Now a second round of cell division (meiosis II) occurs in both of the secondary spermatocytes. During meiosis II each of the 23 replicated chromosomes divides, similar to what happens during mitosis. Thus, meiosis results in separating the chromosome pairs. This second meiotic division results in a total of four cells with only half of the number of chromosomes. Each of these new cells is a **spermatid**. Although haploid, early spermatids look very similar to cells in the earlier stages of spermatogenesis, with a round shape, central nucleus, and large amount of cytoplasm. A process called **spermiogenesis** transforms these early spermatids, reducing the cytoplasm, and beginning the formation of the parts of a true sperm. The fifth stage of germ cell formation—spermatozoa, or formed sperm—is the end result of this process, which occurs in the portion of the tubule nearest the lumen. Eventually, the sperm are released into the lumen and are moved along a series of ducts in the testis toward a structure called the epididymis for the next step of sperm maturation.

Structure of Formed Sperm

Sperm are smaller than most cells in the body; in fact, the volume of a sperm cell is 85,000 times less than that of the female gamete. Approximately 100 to 300 million sperm are produced each day, whereas females typically ovulate only one oocyte per month. As is true for most cells in the body, the structure of sperm cells speaks to their function. Sperm have a distinctive head, mid-piece, and tail region (Figure 27.6). The head of the sperm contains the extremely compact haploid nucleus with very little cytoplasm. These qualities contribute to the overall small size of the sperm (the head is only 5 μm long). A structure called the acrosome covers most of the head of the sperm cell as a "cap" that is filled with lysosomal enzymes important for preparing sperm to participate in fertilization. Tightly packed mitochondria fill the mid-piece of the sperm. ATP produced by these mitochondria will power the flagellum, which extends from the neck and the mid-piece through the tail of the sperm, enabling it to move the entire sperm cell. The central strand of the flagellum, the axial filament, is formed from one centriole inside the maturing sperm cell during the final stages of spermatogenesis.

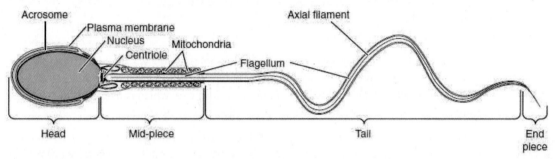

FIGURE 27.6   Structure of Sperm   Sperm cells are divided into a head, containing DNA; a mid-piece, containing mitochondria; and a tail, providing motility. The acrosome is oval and somewhat flattened.

Sperm Transport

To fertilize an egg without medical intervention, sperm must be moved from the seminiferous tubules in the testes, through the epididymis, and—later during ejaculation—along the length of the penis and out into the female reproductive tract.

Role of the Epididymis

From the lumen of the seminiferous tubules, the immotile sperm are surrounded by testicular fluid and moved to the **epididymis** (plural = epididymides), a coiled tube attached to the testis where newly formed sperm continue to mature (see Figure 27.4). Though the epididymis does not take up much room in its tightly coiled state, it would be approximately 6 m (20 feet) long if straightened. It takes an average of 12 days for sperm to move through the coils of the epididymis, with the shortest recorded transit time in humans being one day. Sperm enter the head of the epididymis and are moved along predominantly by the contraction of smooth muscles lining the epididymal tubes. As they are moved along the length of the epididymis, the sperm further mature and acquire the ability to move under their own power. Once inside the female reproductive tract, they will use this ability to move independently toward the unfertilized egg. The more mature sperm are then stored in the tail of the epididymis (the final section) until ejaculation occurs.

Duct System

During ejaculation, sperm exit the tail of the epididymis and are pushed by smooth muscle contraction to the **ductus deferens** (also called the vas deferens). The ductus deferens is a thick, muscular tube that is bundled together inside the scrotum with connective tissue, blood vessels, and nerves into a structure called the **spermatic cord** (see Figure 27.2 and Figure 27.3). Because the ductus deferens is physically accessible within the scrotum, surgical sterilization to interrupt sperm delivery can be performed by cutting and sealing a small section of the ductus (vas) deferens. This procedure is called a vasectomy, and it is an effective form of birth control. Although it may be possible to reverse a vasectomy, clinicians consider the procedure permanent, and advise people to undergo it only if they are certain they no longer wish to have children.

⊘ INTERACTIVE LINK

Interactive Link Feature

Watch this video (http://openstax.org/l/vasectomy) to learn about a vasectomy. As described in this video, a vasectomy is a procedure in which a small section of the ductus (vas) deferens is removed from the scrotum. This interrupts the path taken by sperm through the ductus deferens. If sperm do not exit through the vas, either because the person has had a vasectomy or has not ejaculated, in what region of the testis do they remain?

From each epididymis, each ductus deferens extends superiorly into the abdominal cavity through the **inguinal canal** in the abdominal wall. From here, the ductus deferens continues posteriorly to the pelvic cavity, ending posterior to the bladder where it dilates in a region called the ampulla (meaning "flask").

Sperm make up only 5 percent of the final volume of **semen**, the thick, milky fluid that is ejaculated. The bulk of semen is produced by three critical accessory glands of the male reproductive system: the seminal vesicles, the prostate, and the bulbourethral glands.

Seminal Vesicles

As sperm pass through the ampulla of the ductus deferens at ejaculation, they mix with fluid from the associated **seminal vesicle** (see Figure 27.2). The paired seminal vesicles are glands that contribute approximately 60 percent of the semen volume. Seminal vesicle fluid contains large amounts of fructose, which is used by the sperm mitochondria to generate ATP to allow movement through the female reproductive tract.

The fluid, now containing both sperm and seminal vesicle secretions, next moves into the associated **ejaculatory duct**, a short structure formed from the ampulla of the ductus deferens and the duct of the seminal vesicle. The paired ejaculatory ducts transport the seminal fluid into the next structure, the prostate gland.

Prostate Gland

As shown in Figure 27.2, the centrally located **prostate gland** sits anterior to the rectum at the base of the bladder surrounding the prostatic urethra (the portion of the urethra that runs within the prostate). About the size of a walnut, the prostate is formed of both muscular and glandular tissues. It excretes an alkaline, milky fluid to the passing seminal fluid—now called semen—that is critical to first coagulate and then decoagulate the semen following ejaculation. The temporary thickening of semen helps retain it within the female reproductive tract, providing time for sperm to utilize the fructose provided by seminal vesicle secretions. When the semen regains its fluid state, sperm can then pass farther into the female reproductive tract.

The prostate normally doubles in size during puberty. At approximately age 25, it gradually begins to enlarge again. This enlargement does not usually cause problems; however, abnormal growth of the prostate, or benign prostatic hyperplasia (BPH), can cause constriction of the urethra as it passes through the middle of the prostate gland, leading to a number of lower urinary tract symptoms, such as a frequent and intense urge to urinate, a weak stream, and a sensation that the bladder has not emptied completely. By age 60, approximately 40 percent of males have some degree of BPH. By age 80, the number of affected individuals has jumped to as many as 80 percent. Treatments for BPH attempt to relieve the pressure on the urethra so that urine can flow more normally. Mild to moderate symptoms are treated with medication, whereas severe enlargement of the prostate is treated by surgery in which a portion of the prostate tissue is removed.

Another common disorder involving the prostate is prostate cancer. According to the Centers for Disease Control and Prevention (CDC), prostate cancer is the second most common cancer in males. However, some forms of prostate cancer grow very slowly and thus may not ever require treatment. Aggressive forms of prostate cancer, in contrast, involve metastasis to vulnerable organs like the lungs and brain. There is no link between BPH and prostate cancer, but the symptoms are similar. Prostate cancer is detected by a medical history, a blood test, and a rectal exam that allows physicians to palpate the prostate and check for unusual masses. If a mass is detected, the cancer diagnosis is confirmed by biopsy of the cells.

Bulbourethral Glands

The final addition to semen is made by two **bulbourethral glands** (or Cowper's glands) that release a thick, salty fluid that lubricates the end of the urethra and the vagina, and helps to clean urine residues from the penile urethra. The fluid from these accessory glands is released after the male becomes sexually aroused, and shortly before the release of the semen. It is therefore sometimes called pre-ejaculate. It is important to note that, in addition to the lubricating proteins, it is possible for bulbourethral fluid to pick up sperm already present in the urethra, and therefore it may be able to cause pregnancy.

⊘ INTERACTIVE LINK

Interactive Link Feature

Watch this video (http://openstax.org/l/spermpath) to explore the structures of the male reproductive system and the path of sperm, which starts in the testes and ends as the sperm leave the penis through the urethra. Where are sperm deposited after they leave the ejaculatory duct?

The Penis

The **penis** is the male organ of copulation (sexual intercourse). It is flaccid for non-sexual actions, such as urination, and turgid and rod-like with sexual arousal. When erect, the stiffness of the organ allows it to penetrate into the vagina and deposit semen into the female reproductive tract.

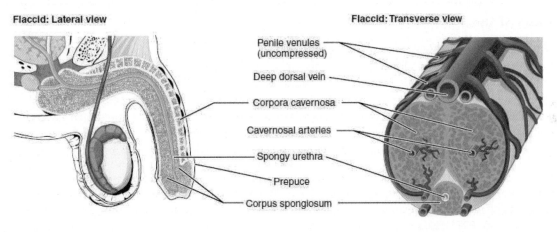

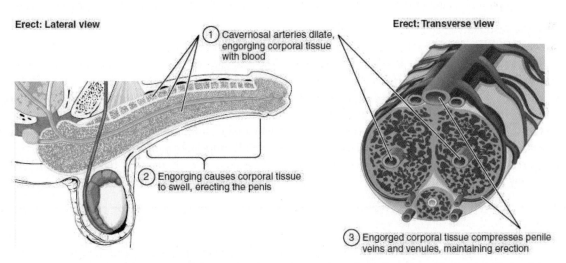

FIGURE 27.7   Cross-Sectional Anatomy of the Penis   Three columns of erectile tissue make up most of the volume of the penis.

The shaft of the penis surrounds the urethra (Figure 27.7). The shaft is composed of three column-like chambers of erectile tissue that span the length of the shaft. Each of the two larger lateral chambers is called a **corpus cavernosum** (plural = corpora cavernosa). Together, these make up the bulk of the penis. The **corpus spongiosum**, which can be felt as a raised ridge on the erect penis, is a smaller chamber that surrounds the spongy, or penile, urethra. The end of the penis, called the **glans penis**, has a high concentration of nerve endings, resulting in very sensitive skin that influences the likelihood of ejaculation (see Figure 27.2). The skin from the shaft extends down over the glans and forms a collar called the **prepuce** (or foreskin). The foreskin also contains a dense concentration of nerve endings, and both lubricate and protect the sensitive skin of the glans penis. A surgical procedure called circumcision, often performed for religious or social reasons, removes the prepuce, typically within days of birth.

Both sexual arousal and REM sleep (during which dreaming occurs) can induce an erection. Penile erections are the result of vasocongestion, or engorgement of the tissues because of more arterial blood flowing into the penis than is leaving in the veins. During sexual arousal, nitric oxide (NO) is released from nerve endings near blood vessels within the corpora cavernosa and spongiosum. Release of NO activates a signaling pathway that results in relaxation of the smooth muscles that surround the penile arteries, causing them to dilate. This dilation increases the amount of blood that can enter the penis and induces the endothelial cells in the penile arterial walls to also secrete NO and perpetuate the vasodilation. The rapid increase in blood volume fills the erectile chambers, and the increased pressure of the filled chambers compresses the thin-walled penile venules, preventing venous drainage of the penis. The result of this increased blood flow to the penis and reduced blood return from the penis is erection. Depending on the flaccid dimensions of a penis, it can increase in size slightly or greatly during erection, with the average length of an erect penis measuring approximately 15 cm.

Disorders of the...

Male Reproductive System

Erectile dysfunction (ED) is a condition in which a person has difficulty either initiating or maintaining an erection. The combined prevalence of minimal, moderate, and complete ED is approximately 40 percent in males at age 40, and reaches nearly 70 percent by 70 years of age. In addition to aging, ED is associated with diabetes, vascular disease, psychiatric disorders, prostate disorders, the use of some drugs such as certain antidepressants, and problems with the testes resulting in low testosterone concentrations. These physical and emotional conditions can lead to interruptions in the vasodilation pathway and result in an inability to achieve an erection.

Recall that the release of NO induces relaxation of the smooth muscles that surround the penile arteries, leading to the vasodilation necessary to achieve an erection. To reverse the process of vasodilation, an enzyme called phosphodiesterase (PDE) degrades a key component of the NO signaling pathway called cGMP. There are several different forms of this enzyme, and PDE type 5 is the type of PDE found in the tissues of the penis. Scientists discovered that inhibiting PDE5 increases blood flow, and allows vasodilation of the penis to occur.

PDEs and the vasodilation signaling pathway are found in the vasculature in other parts of the body. In the 1990s, clinical trials of a PDE5 inhibitor called sildenafil were initiated to treat hypertension and angina pectoris (chest pain caused by poor blood flow through the heart). The trial showed that the drug was not effective at treating heart conditions, but many men experienced erection and priapism (erection lasting longer than 4 hours). Because of this, a clinical trial was started to investigate the ability of sildenafil to promote erections in men suffering from ED. In 1998, the FDA approved the drug, marketed as Viagra®. Since approval of the drug, sildenafil and similar PDE inhibitors now generate over a billion dollars a year in sales, and are reported to be effective in treating approximately 70 to 85 percent of cases of ED. Importantly, men with health problems—especially those with cardiac disease taking nitrates—should avoid Viagra or talk to their physician to find out if they are a candidate for the use of this drug, as deaths have been reported for at-risk users.

Testosterone

Testosterone, an androgen, is a steroid hormone produced by **Leydig cells**. The alternate term for Leydig cells, interstitial cells, reflects their location between the seminiferous tubules in the testes. In male embryos, testosterone is secreted by Leydig cells by the seventh week of development, with peak concentrations reached in the second trimester. This early release of testosterone results in the anatomical differentiation of the male sexual organs. In childhood, testosterone concentrations are low. They increase during puberty, activating characteristic physical changes and initiating spermatogenesis.

Functions of Testosterone

The continued presence of testosterone is necessary to keep the male reproductive system working properly, and

Leydig cells produce approximately 6 to 7 mg of testosterone per day. Testicular steroidogenesis (the manufacture of androgens, including testosterone) results in testosterone concentrations that are 100 times higher in the testes than in the circulation. Maintaining these normal concentrations of testosterone promotes spermatogenesis, whereas low levels of testosterone can lead to infertility. In addition to intratesticular secretion, testosterone is also released into the systemic circulation and plays an important role in muscle development, bone growth, the development of secondary sex characteristics, and maintaining libido (sex drive) in both males and females. In females, the ovaries secrete small amounts of testosterone, although most is converted to estradiol. A small amount of testosterone is also secreted by the adrenal glands in both sexes.

Control of Testosterone

The regulation of testosterone concentrations throughout the body is critical for male reproductive function. The intricate interplay between the endocrine system and the reproductive system is shown in Figure 27.8.

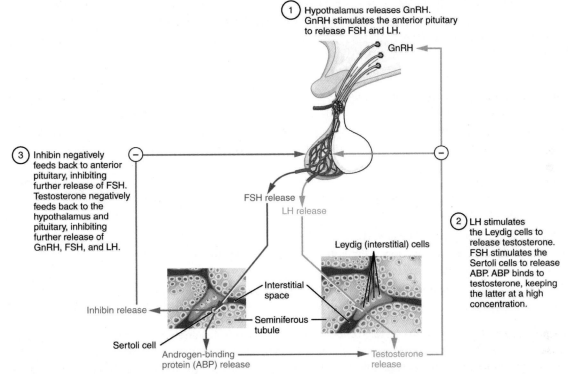

FIGURE 27.8   Regulation of Testosterone Production   The hypothalamus and pituitary gland regulate the production of testosterone and the cells that assist in spermatogenesis. GnRH activates the anterior pituitary to produce LH and FSH, which in turn stimulate Leydig cells and Sertoli cells, respectively. The system is a negative feedback loop because the end products of the pathway, testosterone and inhibin, interact with the activity of GnRH to inhibit their own production.

The regulation of Leydig cell production of testosterone begins outside of the testes. The hypothalamus and the pituitary gland in the brain integrate external and internal signals to control testosterone synthesis and secretion. The regulation begins in the hypothalamus. Pulsatile release of a hormone called **gonadotropin-releasing hormone (GnRH)** from the hypothalamus stimulates the endocrine release of hormones from the pituitary gland. Binding of GnRH to its receptors on the anterior pituitary gland stimulates release of the two gonadotropins: luteinizing hormone (LH) and follicle-stimulating hormone (FSH). These two hormones are critical for reproductive function in all humans. In the testes, FSH binds predominantly to the Sertoli cells within the seminiferous tubules to promote spermatogenesis. FSH also stimulates the Sertoli cells to produce hormones called inhibins, which function to inhibit FSH release from the pituitary, thus reducing testosterone secretion. These polypeptide hormones correlate directly with Sertoli cell function and sperm number; inhibin B can be used as a marker of spermatogenic activity. LH binds to receptors on Leydig cells in the testes and upregulates the production of testosterone.

A negative feedback loop predominantly controls the synthesis and secretion of both FSH and LH. Low blood concentrations of testosterone stimulate the hypothalamic release of GnRH. GnRH then stimulates the anterior pituitary to secrete LH into the bloodstream. In the testis, LH binds to LH receptors on Leydig cells and stimulates the release of testosterone. When concentrations of testosterone in the blood reach a critical threshold, testosterone itself will bind to androgen receptors on both the hypothalamus and the anterior pituitary, inhibiting the synthesis and secretion of GnRH and LH, respectively. When the blood concentrations of testosterone once again decline, testosterone no longer interacts with the receptors to the same degree and GnRH and LH are once again secreted, stimulating more testosterone production. This same process occurs with FSH and inhibin to control spermatogenesis.

Aging and the...

Male Reproductive System

Declines in Leydig cell activity can occur in males beginning at 40 to 50 years of age. The resulting reduction in circulating testosterone concentrations can lead to symptoms of andropause, also known as male menopause. While the reduction in sex steroids is akin to female menopause, there is no clear sign—such as a lack of a menstrual period—to denote the initiation of andropause. Instead, people with this condition report feelings of fatigue, reduced muscle mass, depression, anxiety, irritability, loss of libido, and insomnia. A reduction in spermatogenesis resulting in lowered fertility is also reported, and sexual dysfunction can also be associated with andropausal symptoms.

Whereas some researchers believe that certain aspects of andropause are difficult to tease apart from aging in general, testosterone replacement is sometimes prescribed to alleviate some symptoms. Recent studies have shown a benefit from androgen replacement therapy on the new onset of depression in elderly males; however, other studies caution against testosterone replacement for long-term treatment of andropause symptoms, showing that high doses can sharply increase the risk of both heart disease and prostate cancer.

27.2 Anatomy and Physiology of the Ovarian Reproductive System

LEARNING OBJECTIVES

By the end of this section, you will be able to:

- Describe the structure and function of the organs of the ovarian reproductive system
- List the steps of oogenesis
- Describe the hormonal changes that occur during the ovarian and menstrual cycles
- Trace the path of an oocyte from ovary to fertilization

The female, or ovarian, reproductive system functions to produce gametes and reproductive hormones, just like the male reproductive system; however, it also has the additional task of supporting the developing fetus and delivering it to the outside world. Unlike its male counterpart, the female reproductive system is located primarily inside the pelvic cavity (Figure 27.9). Recall that the ovaries are the female gonads. The gamete they produce is called an **oocyte**. We'll discuss the production of oocytes in detail shortly. First, let's look at some of the structures of the female reproductive system.

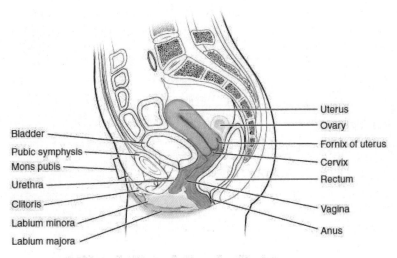

(a) Human female reproductive system: lateral view

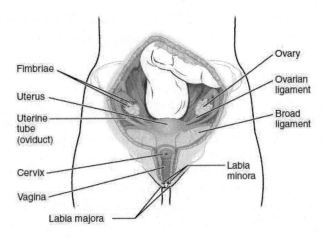

(b) Human female reproductive system: anterior view

FIGURE 27.9   Female Reproductive System   The major organs of the female reproductive system are located inside the pelvic cavity.

External Female Genitals

The external female reproductive structures are referred to collectively as the **vulva** ([Figure 27.10](#)). The **mons pubis** is a pad of fat that is located at the anterior, over the pubic bone. After puberty, it becomes covered in pubic hair. The **labia majora** (labia = "lips"; majora = "larger") are folds of hair-covered skin that begin just posterior to the mons pubis. The thinner and more pigmented **labia minora** (labia = "lips"; minora = "smaller") extend medial to the labia majora. Although they naturally vary in shape and size from person to person, the labia minora serve to protect the urethra and the entrance to the reproductive tract.

The superior, anterior portions of the labia minora come together to encircle the **clitoris** (or glans clitoris), an organ that originates from the same cells as the glans penis and has abundant nerves that make it important in sexual sensation and orgasm. The **hymen** is a thin membrane that sometimes partially covers the entrance to the vagina. An intact hymen cannot be used as an indication of "virginity"; even at birth, this is only a partial membrane, as menstrual fluid and other secretions must be able to exit the body, regardless of penile–vaginal intercourse. The vaginal opening is located between the opening of the urethra and the anus. It is flanked by outlets to the **Bartholin's glands** (or greater vestibular glands).

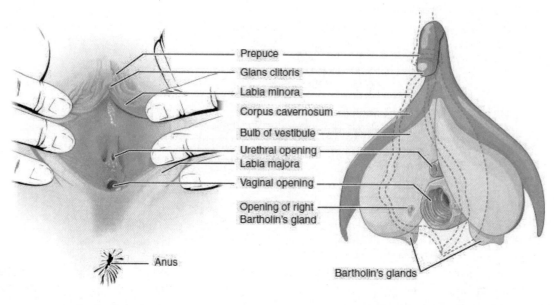

Prepuce

Glans clitoris

Labia minora

Corpus cavernosum

Bulb of vestibule

Urethral opening

Labia majora

Vaginal opening

Opening of right
Bartholin's gland

Anus

Bartholin's glands

Vulva: External anterior view   **Vulva: Internal anteriolateral view**

FIGURE 27.10   **The Vulva**   The external female genitalia are referred to collectively as the vulva.

Vagina

The **vagina**, shown at the bottom of Figure 27.9 and Figure 27.10, is a muscular canal (approximately 10 cm long) that serves as the entrance to the reproductive tract. It also serves as the exit from the uterus during menses and childbirth. The outer walls of the anterior and posterior vagina are formed into longitudinal columns, or ridges, and the superior portion of the vagina—called the fornix—meets the protruding uterine cervix. The walls of the vagina are lined with an outer, fibrous adventitia; a middle layer of smooth muscle; and an inner mucous membrane with transverse folds called **rugae**. Together, the middle and inner layers allow the expansion of the vagina to accommodate intercourse and childbirth. The thin, perforated hymen can partially surround the opening to the vaginal orifice. The hymen can be ruptured with strenuous physical exercise, penile–vaginal intercourse, and childbirth. The Bartholin's glands and the lesser vestibular glands (located near the clitoris) secrete mucus, which keeps the vestibular area moist.

The vagina is home to a normal population of microorganisms that help to protect against infection by pathogenic bacteria, yeast, or other organisms that can enter the vagina. In a healthy person, the most predominant type of vaginal bacteria is from the genus *Lactobacillus*. This family of beneficial bacterial flora secretes lactic acid, and thus protects the vagina by maintaining an acidic pH (below 4.5). Potential pathogens are less likely to survive in these acidic conditions. Lactic acid, in combination with other vaginal secretions, makes the vagina a self-cleansing organ. However, douching—or washing out the vagina with fluid—can disrupt the normal balance of healthy microorganisms, and actually increase risk for infections and irritation. Indeed, the American College of Obstetricians and Gynecologists recommend that people do not douche, and that they allow the vagina to maintain its normal healthy population of protective microbial flora.

Ovaries

The **ovaries** are the female gonads (see Figure 27.9). Paired ovals, they are each about 2 to 3 cm in length, about the size of an almond. The ovaries are located within the pelvic cavity, and are supported by the mesovarium, an extension of the peritoneum that connects the ovaries to the **broad ligament**. Extending from the mesovarium itself is the suspensory ligament that contains the ovarian blood and lymph vessels. Finally, the ovary itself is attached to the uterus via the ovarian ligament.

The ovary comprises an outer covering of cuboidal epithelium called the ovarian surface epithelium that is superficial to a dense connective tissue covering called the tunica albuginea. Beneath the tunica albuginea is the cortex, or outer portion, of the organ. The cortex is composed of a tissue framework called the ovarian stroma that forms the bulk of the adult ovary. Oocytes develop within the outer layer of this stroma, each surrounded by

Access for free at openstax.org

supporting cells. This grouping of an oocyte and its supporting cells is called a **follicle**. The growth and development of ovarian follicles will be described shortly. Beneath the cortex lies the inner ovarian medulla, the site of blood vessels, lymph vessels, and the nerves of the ovary. You will learn more about the overall anatomy of the female reproductive system at the end of this section.

The Ovarian Cycle

The **ovarian cycle** is a set of predictable changes in oocytes and ovarian follicles. During the reproductive years, it is a roughly 28-day cycle that can be correlated with, but is not the same as, the menstrual cycle (discussed shortly). The cycle includes two interrelated processes: oogenesis (the production of gametes) and folliculogenesis (the growth and development of ovarian follicles).

Oogenesis

Gametogenesis in females is called **oogenesis**. The process begins with the ovarian stem cells, or **oogonia** (Figure 27.11). Oogonia are formed during fetal development, and divide via mitosis, much like spermatogonia in the testis. Unlike spermatogonia, however, oogonia form primary oocytes in the fetal ovary prior to birth. These primary oocytes are then arrested in this stage of meiosis I, only to resume it years later, beginning at puberty and continuing until the person is near menopause (the cessation of a female's reproductive functions). The number of primary oocytes present in the ovaries declines from one to two million in an infant, to approximately 400,000 at puberty, to zero by the end of menopause.

The initiation of **ovulation**—the release of an oocyte from the ovary—marks the transition from puberty into reproductive maturity. From then on, throughout a the reproductive years, ovulation occurs approximately once every 28 days. Just prior to ovulation, a surge of luteinizing hormone triggers the resumption of meiosis in a primary oocyte. This initiates the transition from primary to secondary oocyte. However, as you can see in Figure 27.11, this cell division does not result in two identical cells. Instead, the cytoplasm is divided unequally, and one daughter cell is much larger than the other. This larger cell, the secondary oocyte, eventually leaves the ovary during ovulation. The smaller cell, called the first **polar body**, may or may not complete meiosis and produce second polar bodies; in either case, it eventually disintegrates. Therefore, even though oogenesis produces up to four cells, only one survives.

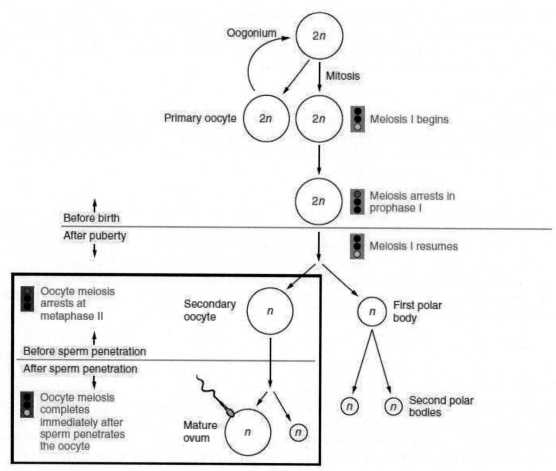

FIGURE 27.11 Oogenesis   The unequal cell division of oogenesis produces one to three polar bodies that later degrade, as well as a single haploid ovum, which is produced only if there is penetration of the secondary oocyte by a sperm cell.

How does the diploid secondary oocyte become an **ovum**—the haploid female gamete? Meiosis of a secondary oocyte is completed only if a sperm succeeds in penetrating its barriers. Meiosis II then resumes, producing one haploid ovum that, at the instant of fertilization by a (haploid) sperm, becomes the first diploid cell of the new offspring (a zygote). Thus, the ovum can be thought of as a brief, transitional, haploid stage between the diploid oocyte and diploid zygote.

The larger amount of cytoplasm contained in the female gamete is used to supply the developing zygote with nutrients during the period between fertilization and implantation into the uterus. Interestingly, sperm contribute only DNA at fertilization —not cytoplasm. Therefore, the cytoplasm and all of the cytoplasmic organelles in the developing embryo are of egg-derived origin. This includes mitochondria, which contain their own DNA. Scientific research in the 1980s determined that mitochondrial DNA was maternally inherited, meaning that you can trace your mitochondrial DNA directly to your biological mother, her mother, and so on back through your female ancestors.

> ### Everyday Connection
>
> ### Mapping Human History with Mitochondrial DNA
> When we talk about human DNA, we're usually referring to nuclear DNA; that is, the DNA coiled into chromosomal bundles in the nucleus of our cells. We inherit half of our nuclear DNA from one parent, and half from the other parent. However, mitochondrial DNA (mtDNA) comes only from the mitochondria in the cytoplasm of the fat ovum we inherit from our mother. Our mother received mtDNA from their mother, who got it from their mother, and so on. Each of our cells contains approximately 1700 mitochondria, with each mitochondrion packed with mtDNA containing approximately 37 genes.

Mutations (changes) in mtDNA occur spontaneously in a somewhat organized pattern at regular intervals in human history. By analyzing these mutational relationships, researchers have been able to determine that we can all trace our ancestry back to one female who lived in Africa about 200,000 years ago. More precisely, that human is our most recent common ancestor through matrilineal descent.

This doesn't mean that everyone's mtDNA today looks exactly like that of our common ancestor. Because of the spontaneous mutations in mtDNA that have occurred over the centuries, researchers can map different "branches" off of the "main trunk" of our mtDNA family tree. Your mtDNA might have a pattern of mutations that aligns more closely with one branch, and your neighbor's may align with another branch. Still, all branches eventually lead back to the common ancestor.

But what happened to the mtDNA of all of the other *Homo sapiens* females who were living 200,000 years ago? Researchers explain that, over the centuries, their female descendants died childless or with only male children, and thus, their maternal line—and its mtDNA—ended.

Folliculogenesis

Again, ovarian follicles are oocytes and their supporting cells. They grow and develop in a process called **folliculogenesis**, which typically leads to ovulation of one follicle approximately every 28 days, along with death to multiple other follicles. The death of ovarian follicles is called atresia, and can occur at any point during follicular development. Recall that, a female infant at birth will have one to two million oocytes within the ovarian follicles, and that this number declines throughout life until menopause, when no follicles remain. As you'll see next, follicles progress from primordial, to primary, to secondary and tertiary stages prior to ovulation—with the oocyte inside the follicle remaining as a primary oocyte until right before ovulation.

Folliculogenesis begins with follicles in a resting state. These small **primordial follicles** are present in newborn females and are the prevailing follicle type in the adult ovary (Figure 27.12). Primordial follicles have only a single flat layer of support cells, called **granulosa cells**, that surround the oocyte, and they can stay in this resting state for years—some until right before menopause.

After puberty, a few primordial follicles will respond to a recruitment signal each day, and will join a pool of immature growing follicles called **primary follicles**. Primary follicles start with a single layer of granulosa cells, but the granulosa cells then become active and transition from a flat or squamous shape to a rounded, cuboidal shape as they increase in size and proliferate. As the granulosa cells divide, the follicles—now called **secondary follicles** (see Figure 27.12)—increase in diameter, adding a new outer layer of connective tissue, blood vessels, and **theca cells**—cells that work with the granulosa cells to produce estrogens.

Within the growing secondary follicle, the primary oocyte now secretes a thin acellular membrane called the zona pellucida that will play a critical role in fertilization. A thick fluid, called follicular fluid, that has formed between the granulosa cells also begins to collect into one large pool, or **antrum**. Follicles in which the antrum has become large and fully formed are considered **tertiary follicles** (or antral follicles). Several follicles reach the tertiary stage at the same time, and most of these will undergo atresia. The one that does not die will continue to grow and develop until ovulation, when it will expel its secondary oocyte surrounded by several layers of granulosa cells from the ovary. Keep in mind that most follicles don't make it to this point. In fact, roughly 99 percent of the follicles in the ovary will undergo atresia, which can occur at any stage of folliculogenesis.

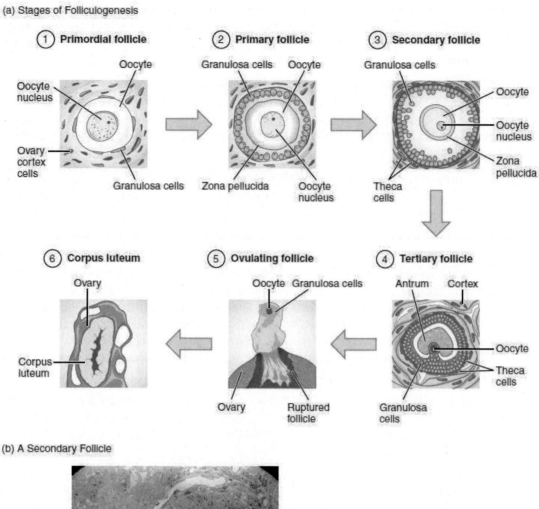

(a) Stages of Folliculogenesis

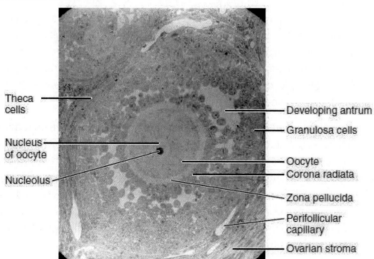

(b) A Secondary Follicle

FIGURE 27.12 Folliculogenesis   (a) The maturation of a follicle is shown in a clockwise direction proceeding from the primordial follicles. FSH stimulates the growth of a tertiary follicle, and LH stimulates the production of estrogen by granulosa and theca cells. Once the follicle is mature, it ruptures and releases the oocyte. Cells remaining in the follicle then develop into the corpus luteum. (b) In this electron micrograph of a secondary follicle, the oocyte, theca cells (thecae folliculi), and developing antrum are clearly visible. EM × 1100. (Micrograph provided by the Regents of University of Michigan Medical School © 2012)

Hormonal Control of the Ovarian Cycle

The process of development that we have just described, from primordial follicle to early tertiary follicle, takes approximately two months in humans. The final stages of development of a small cohort of tertiary follicles, ending with ovulation of a secondary oocyte, occur over a course of approximately 28 days. These changes are regulated by many of the same hormones that regulate the male reproductive system, including GnRH, LH, and FSH.

As in males, the hypothalamus produces GnRH, a hormone that signals the anterior pituitary gland to produce the gonadotropins FSH and LH (Figure 27.13). These gonadotropins leave the pituitary and travel through the bloodstream to the ovaries, where they bind to receptors on the granulosa and theca cells of the follicles. FSH stimulates the follicles to grow (hence its name of follicle-stimulating hormone), and the five or six tertiary follicles expand in diameter. The release of LH also stimulates the granulosa and theca cells of the follicles to produce the sex steroid hormone estradiol, a type of estrogen. This phase of the ovarian cycle, when the tertiary follicles are growing and secreting estrogen, is known as the follicular phase.

The more granulosa and theca cells a follicle has (that is, the larger and more developed it is), the more estrogen it will produce in response to LH stimulation. As a result of these large follicles producing large amounts of estrogen, systemic plasma estrogen concentrations increase. Following a classic negative feedback loop, the high concentrations of estrogen will stimulate the hypothalamus and pituitary to reduce the production of GnRH, LH, and FSH. Because the large tertiary follicles require FSH to grow and survive at this point, this decline in FSH caused by negative feedback leads most of them to die (atresia). Typically only one follicle, now called the dominant follicle, will survive this reduction in FSH, and this follicle will be the one that releases an oocyte. Scientists have studied many factors that lead to a particular follicle becoming dominant: size, the number of granulosa cells, and the number of FSH receptors on those granulosa cells all contribute to a follicle becoming the one surviving dominant follicle.

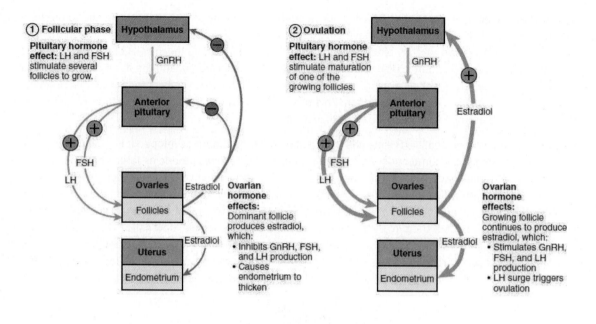

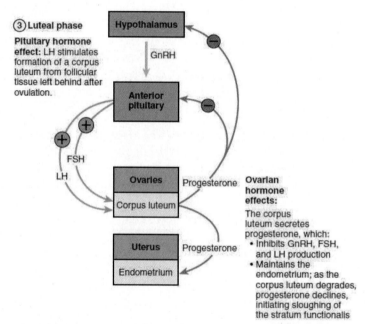

FIGURE 27.13   Hormonal Regulation of Ovulation   The hypothalamus and pituitary gland regulate the ovarian cycle and ovulation. GnRH activates the anterior pituitary to produce LH and FSH, which stimulate the production of estrogen and progesterone by the ovaries.

When only the one dominant follicle remains in the ovary, it again begins to secrete estrogen. It produces more estrogen than all of the developing follicles did together before the negative feedback occurred. It produces so much estrogen that the normal negative feedback doesn't occur. Instead, these extremely high concentrations of systemic plasma estrogen trigger a regulatory switch in the anterior pituitary that responds by secreting large amounts of LH and FSH into the bloodstream (see Figure 27.13). The positive feedback loop by which more estrogen triggers release of more LH and FSH only occurs at this point in the cycle.

It is this large burst of LH (called the LH surge) that leads to ovulation of the dominant follicle. The LH surge induces many changes in the dominant follicle, including stimulating the resumption of meiosis of the primary oocyte to a secondary oocyte. As noted earlier, the polar body that results from unequal cell division simply degrades. The LH surge also triggers proteases (enzymes that cleave proteins) to break down structural proteins in the ovary wall on the surface of the bulging dominant follicle. This degradation of the wall, combined with pressure from the large, fluid-filled antrum, results in the expulsion of the oocyte surrounded by granulosa cells into the peritoneal cavity.

This release is ovulation.

In the next section, you will follow the ovulated oocyte as it travels toward the uterus, but there is one more important event that occurs in the ovarian cycle. The surge of LH also stimulates a change in the granulosa and theca cells that remain in the follicle after the oocyte has been ovulated. This change is called luteinization (recall that the full name of LH is luteinizing hormone), and it transforms the collapsed follicle into a new endocrine structure called the **corpus luteum**, a term meaning "yellowish body" (see Figure 27.12). Instead of estrogen, the luteinized granulosa and theca cells of the corpus luteum begin to produce large amounts of the sex steroid hormone progesterone, a hormone that is critical for the establishment and maintenance of pregnancy. Progesterone triggers negative feedback at the hypothalamus and pituitary, which keeps GnRH, LH, and FSH secretions low, so no new dominant follicles develop at this time.

The post-ovulatory phase of progesterone secretion is known as the luteal phase of the ovarian cycle. If pregnancy does not occur within 10 to 12 days, the corpus luteum will stop secreting progesterone and degrade into the **corpus albicans**, a nonfunctional "whitish body" that will disintegrate in the ovary over a period of several months. During this time of reduced progesterone secretion, FSH and LH are once again stimulated, and the follicular phase begins again with a new cohort of early tertiary follicles beginning to grow and secrete estrogen.

The Uterine Tubes

The **uterine tubes** (also called fallopian tubes or oviducts) serve as the conduit of the oocyte from the ovary to the uterus (Figure 27.14). Each of the two uterine tubes is close to, but not directly connected to, the ovary and divided into sections. The **isthmus** is the narrow medial end of each uterine tube that is connected to the uterus. The wide distal **infundibulum** flares out with slender, finger-like projections called **fimbriae**. The middle region of the tube, called the **ampulla**, is where fertilization often occurs. The uterine tubes also have three layers: an outer serosa, a middle smooth muscle layer, and an inner mucosal layer. In addition to its mucus-secreting cells, the inner mucosa contains ciliated cells that beat in the direction of the uterus, producing a current that will be critical to move the oocyte.

Following ovulation, the secondary oocyte surrounded by a few granulosa cells is released into the peritoneal cavity. The nearby uterine tube, either left or right, receives the oocyte. Unlike sperm, oocytes lack flagella, and therefore cannot move on their own. So how do they travel into the uterine tube and toward the uterus? High concentrations of estrogen that occur around the time of ovulation induce contractions of the smooth muscle along the length of the uterine tube. These contractions occur every 4 to 8 seconds, and the result is a coordinated movement that sweeps the surface of the ovary and the pelvic cavity. Current flowing toward the uterus is generated by coordinated beating of the cilia that line the outside and lumen of the length of the uterine tube. These cilia beat more strongly in response to the high estrogen concentrations that occur around the time of ovulation. As a result of these mechanisms, the oocyte–granulosa cell complex is pulled into the interior of the tube. Once inside, the muscular contractions and beating cilia move the oocyte slowly toward the uterus. When fertilization does occur, sperm typically meet the egg while it is still moving through the ampulla.

⊘ INTERACTIVE LINK

Interactive Link
Watch this video (http://openstax.org/l/ovulation) to observe ovulation and its initiation in response to the release of FSH and LH from the pituitary gland. What specialized structures help guide the oocyte from the ovary into the uterine tube?

If the oocyte is successfully fertilized, the resulting zygote will begin to divide into two cells, then four, and so on, as it makes its way through the uterine tube and into the uterus. There, it will implant and continue to grow. If the egg is not fertilized, it will simply degrade—either in the uterine tube or in the uterus, where it may be shed with the next menstrual period.

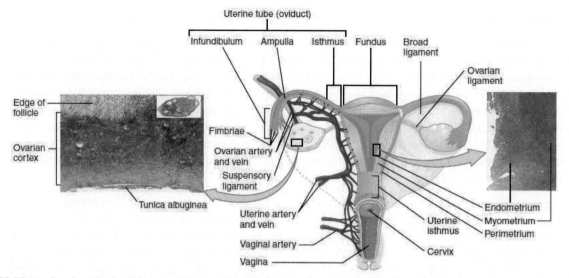

FIGURE 27.14   Ovaries, Uterine Tubes, and Uterus   This anterior view shows the relationship of the ovaries, uterine tubes (oviducts), and uterus. Sperm enter through the vagina, and fertilization of an ovulated oocyte usually occurs in the distal uterine tube. From left to right, LM × 400, LM × 20. (Micrographs provided by the Regents of University of Michigan Medical School © 2012)

The open-ended structure of the uterine tubes can have significant health consequences if bacteria or other contagions enter through the vagina and move through the uterus, into the tubes, and then into the pelvic cavity. If this is left unchecked, a bacterial infection (sepsis) could quickly become life-threatening. The spread of an infection in this manner is of special concern when unskilled practitioners perform abortions in non-sterile conditions. Sepsis is also associated with sexually transmitted bacterial infections, especially gonorrhea and chlamydia. These increase a person's risk for pelvic inflammatory disease (PID), infection of the uterine tubes or other reproductive organs. Even when resolved, PID can leave scar tissue in the tubes, leading to infertility.

⊘ INTERACTIVE LINK

Interactive Link
Watch this series of videos (http://openstax.org/l/oocyte) to look at the movement of the oocyte through the ovary. The cilia in the uterine tube promote movement of the oocyte. What would likely occur if the cilia were paralyzed at the time of ovulation?

The Uterus and Cervix

The **uterus** is the muscular organ that nourishes and supports the growing embryo (see Figure 27.14). Its average size is approximately 5 cm wide by 7 cm long (approximately 2 in by 3 in) when a female is not pregnant. It has three sections. The portion of the uterus superior to the opening of the uterine tubes is called the **fundus**. The middle section of the uterus is called the **body of uterus** (or corpus). The **cervix** is the narrow inferior portion of the uterus that projects into the vagina. The cervix produces mucus secretions that become thin and stringy under the influence of high systemic plasma estrogen concentrations, and these secretions can facilitate sperm movement through the reproductive tract.

Several ligaments maintain the position of the uterus within the abdominopelvic cavity. The broad ligament is a fold of peritoneum that serves as a primary support for the uterus, extending laterally from both sides of the uterus and attaching it to the pelvic wall. The round ligament attaches to the uterus near the uterine tubes, and extends to the labia majora. Finally, the uterosacral ligament stabilizes the uterus posteriorly by its connection from the cervix to the pelvic wall.

The wall of the uterus is made up of three layers. The most superficial layer is the serous membrane, or **perimetrium**, which consists of epithelial tissue that covers the exterior portion of the uterus. The middle layer, or **myometrium**, is a thick layer of smooth muscle responsible for uterine contractions. Most of the uterus is myometrial tissue, and the muscle fibers run horizontally, vertically, and diagonally, allowing the powerful contractions that occur during labor and the less powerful contractions (or cramps) that help to expel menstrual blood during a woman's period. Anteriorly directed myometrial contractions also occur near the time of ovulation,

Access for free at openstax.org

and are thought to possibly facilitate the transport of sperm through the female reproductive tract.

The innermost layer of the uterus is called the **endometrium**. The endometrium contains a connective tissue lining, the lamina propria, which is covered by epithelial tissue that lines the lumen. Structurally, the endometrium consists of two layers: the stratum basalis and the stratum functionalis (the basal and functional layers). The stratum basalis layer is part of the lamina propria and is adjacent to the myometrium; this layer does not shed during menses. In contrast, the thicker stratum functionalis layer contains the glandular portion of the lamina propria and the endothelial tissue that lines the uterine lumen. It is the stratum functionalis that grows and thickens in response to increased levels of estrogen and progesterone. In the luteal phase of the menstrual cycle, special branches off of the uterine artery called spiral arteries supply the thickened stratum functionalis. This inner functional layer provides the proper site of implantation for the fertilized egg, and—should fertilization not occur—it is only the stratum functionalis layer of the endometrium that sheds during menstruation.

Recall that during the follicular phase of the ovarian cycle, the tertiary follicles are growing and secreting estrogen. At the same time, the stratum functionalis of the endometrium is thickening to prepare for a potential implantation. The post-ovulatory increase in progesterone, which characterizes the luteal phase, is key for maintaining a thick stratum functionalis. As long as a functional corpus luteum is present in the ovary, the endometrial lining is prepared for implantation. Indeed, if an embryo implants, signals are sent to the corpus luteum to continue secreting progesterone to maintain the endometrium, and thus maintain the pregnancy. If an embryo does not implant, no signal is sent to the corpus luteum and it degrades, ceasing progesterone production and ending the luteal phase. Without progesterone, the endometrium thins and, under the influence of prostaglandins, the spiral arteries of the endometrium constrict and rupture, preventing oxygenated blood from reaching the endometrial tissue. As a result, endometrial tissue dies and blood, pieces of the endometrial tissue, and white blood cells are shed through the vagina during menstruation, or the **menses**. The first menses after puberty, called **menarche**, can occur either before or after the first ovulation.

The Menstrual Cycle

Now that we have discussed the maturation of the cohort of tertiary follicles in the ovary, the build-up and then shedding of the endometrial lining in the uterus, and the function of the uterine tubes and vagina, we can put everything together to talk about the three phases of the **menstrual cycle**—the series of changes in which the uterine lining is shed, rebuilds, and prepares for implantation.

The timing of the menstrual cycle starts with the first day of menses, referred to as day one of a period. Cycle length is determined by counting the days between the onset of bleeding in two subsequent cycles. Because the average length of a menstrual cycle is 28 days, this is the time period used to identify the timing of events in the cycle. However, the length of the menstrual cycle varies, and even in the same person from one cycle to the next, typically from 21 to 32 days.

Just as the hormones produced by the granulosa and theca cells of the ovary "drive" the follicular and luteal phases of the ovarian cycle, they also control the three distinct phases of the menstrual cycle. These are the menses phase, the proliferative phase, and the secretory phase.

Menses Phase

The **menses phase** of the menstrual cycle is the phase during which the lining is shed; that is, the days that the person menstruates. Although it averages approximately five days, the menses phase can last from 2 to 7 days, or longer. As shown in Figure 27.15, the menses phase occurs during the early days of the follicular phase of the ovarian cycle, when progesterone, FSH, and LH levels are low. Recall that progesterone concentrations decline as a result of the degradation of the corpus luteum, marking the end of the luteal phase. This decline in progesterone triggers the shedding of the stratum functionalis of the endometrium.

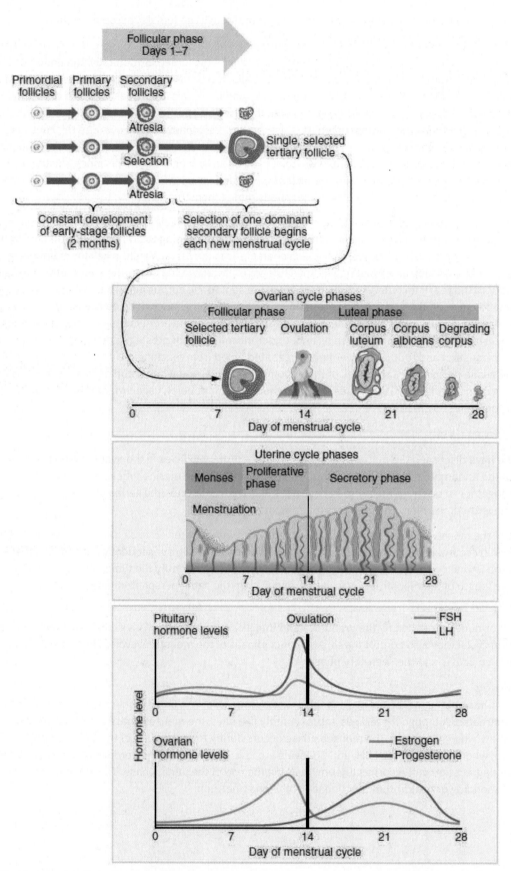

FIGURE 27.15 Hormone Levels in Ovarian and Menstrual Cycles   The correlation of the hormone levels and their effects on the female reproductive system is shown in this timeline of the ovarian and menstrual cycles. The menstrual cycle begins at day one with the start of menses. Ovulation occurs around day 14 of a 28-day cycle, triggered by the LH surge.

Proliferative Phase

Once menstrual flow ceases, the endometrium begins to proliferate again, marking the beginning of the **proliferative phase** of the menstrual cycle (see Figure 27.15). It occurs when the granulosa and theca cells of the tertiary follicles begin to produce increased amounts of estrogen. These rising estrogen concentrations stimulate the endometrial lining to rebuild.

Recall that the high estrogen concentrations will eventually lead to a decrease in FSH as a result of negative feedback, resulting in atresia of all but one of the developing tertiary follicles. The switch to positive feedback—which occurs with the elevated estrogen production from the dominant follicle—then stimulates the LH surge that will trigger ovulation. In a typical 28-day menstrual cycle, ovulation occurs on day 14. Ovulation marks the end of the proliferative phase as well as the end of the follicular phase.

Secretory Phase

In addition to prompting the LH surge, high estrogen levels increase the uterine tube contractions that facilitate the pick-up and transfer of the ovulated oocyte. High estrogen levels also slightly decrease the acidity of the vagina, making it more hospitable to sperm. In the ovary, the luteinization of the granulosa cells of the collapsed follicle forms the progesterone-producing corpus luteum, marking the beginning of the luteal phase of the ovarian cycle. In the uterus, progesterone from the corpus luteum begins the **secretory phase** of the menstrual cycle, in which the endometrial lining prepares for implantation (see Figure 27.15). Over the next 10 to 12 days, the endometrial glands secrete a fluid rich in glycogen. If fertilization has occurred, this fluid will nourish the ball of cells now developing from the zygote. At the same time, the spiral arteries develop to provide blood to the thickened stratum functionalis.

If no pregnancy occurs within approximately 10 to 12 days, the corpus luteum will degrade into the corpus albicans. Levels of both estrogen and progesterone will fall, and the endometrium will grow thinner. Prostaglandins will be secreted that cause constriction of the spiral arteries, reducing oxygen supply. The endometrial tissue will die, resulting in menses—or the first day of the next cycle.

Disorders of the...

Female Reproductive System

Research over many years has confirmed that cervical cancer is most often caused by a sexually transmitted infection with human papillomavirus (HPV). There are over 100 related viruses in the HPV family, and the characteristics of each strain determine the outcome of the infection. In all cases, the virus enters body cells and uses its own genetic material to take over the host cell's metabolic machinery and produce more virus particles.

HPV infections are common in all people. Indeed, a recent study determined that 42.5 percent of females had HPV at the time of testing. These people ranged in age from 14 to 59 years and differed in race, ethnicity, and number of sexual partners. Of note, the prevalence of HPV infection was 53.8 percent among females aged 20 to 24 years, the age group with the highest infection rate.

HPV strains are classified as high or low risk according to their potential to cause cancer. Though most HPV infections do not cause disease, the disruption of normal cellular functions in the low-risk forms of HPV can cause the human host to develop genital warts. Often, the body is able to clear an HPV infection by normal immune responses within 2 years. However, the more serious, high-risk infection by certain types of HPV can result in cancer of the cervix (Figure 27.16). Infection with either of the cancer-causing variants HPV 16 or HPV 18 has been linked to more than 70 percent of all cervical cancer diagnoses. Although even these high-risk HPV strains can be cleared from the body over time, infections persist in some individuals. If this happens, the HPV infection can influence the cells of the cervix to develop precancerous changes.

Risk factors for cervical cancer include having unprotected sex; having multiple sexual partners; a first sexual experience at a younger age, when the cells of the cervix are not fully mature; failure to receive the HPV vaccine; a compromised immune system; and smoking. The risk of developing cervical cancer is doubled with cigarette smoking.

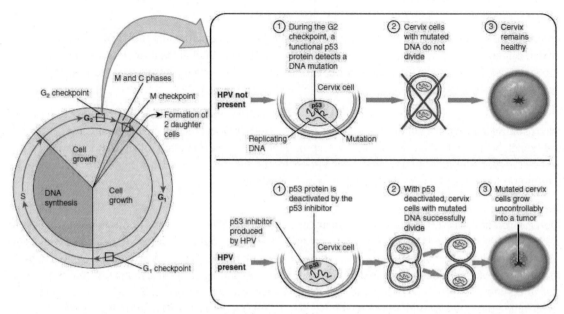

FIGURE 27.16   Development of Cervical Cancer   In most cases, cells infected with the HPV virus heal on their own. In some cases, however, the virus continues to spread and becomes an invasive cancer.

When the high-risk types of HPV enter a cell, two viral proteins are used to neutralize proteins that the host cells use as checkpoints in the cell cycle. The best studied of these proteins is p53. In a normal cell, p53 detects DNA damage in the cell's genome and either halts the progression of the cell cycle—allowing time for DNA repair to occur—or initiates apoptosis. Both of these processes prevent the accumulation of mutations in a cell's genome. High-risk HPV can neutralize p53, keeping the cell in a state in which fast growth is possible and impairing apoptosis, allowing mutations to accumulate in the cellular DNA.

The prevalence of cervical cancer in the United States is very low because of regular screening exams called pap smears. Pap smears sample cells of the cervix, allowing the detection of abnormal cells. If pre-cancerous cells are detected, there are several highly effective techniques that are currently in use to remove them before they pose a danger. However, people in lower-income countries often do not have access to regular pap smears. As a result, these females in lower-income countries account for as many as 80 percent of the cases of cervical cancer worldwide.

In 2006, the first vaccine against the high-risk types of HPV was approved. There are now two HPV vaccines available: Gardasil® and Cervarix®. Whereas these vaccines were initially only targeted for females, because HPV is sexually transmitted, all people require vaccination for this approach to achieve its maximum efficacy. A recent study suggests that the HPV vaccine has cut the rates of HPV infection by the four targeted strains at least in half. Unfortunately, the high cost of manufacturing the vaccine is currently limiting access to many people worldwide.

The Breasts

Whereas the breasts are located far from the other female reproductive organs, they are considered accessory organs of the female reproductive system. The function of the breasts is to supply milk to an infant in a process called lactation. The external features of the breast include a nipple surrounded by a pigmented **areola** (Figure 27.17), whose coloration may deepen during pregnancy. The areola is typically circular and can vary in size from 25 to 100 mm in diameter. The areolar region is characterized by small, raised areolar glands that secrete lubricating fluid during lactation to protect the nipple from chafing. When a baby nurses, or draws milk from the breast, the entire areolar region is taken into the mouth.

Breast milk is produced by the **mammary glands**, which are modified sweat glands. The milk itself exits the breast through the nipple via 15 to 20 **lactiferous ducts** that open on the surface of the nipple. These lactiferous ducts each extend to a **lactiferous sinus** that connects to a glandular lobe within the breast itself that contains groups of milk-secreting cells in clusters called **alveoli** (see Figure 27.17). The clusters can change in size depending on the amount of milk in the alveolar lumen. Once milk is made in the alveoli, stimulated myoepithelial cells that surround the alveoli contract to push the milk to the lactiferous sinuses. From here, the baby can draw milk through the lactiferous ducts by suckling. The lobes themselves are surrounded by fat tissue, which determines the size of the breast; breast size differs between individuals and does not affect the amount of milk produced. Supporting the breasts are multiple bands of connective tissue called **suspensory ligaments** that connect the breast tissue to the dermis of the overlying skin.

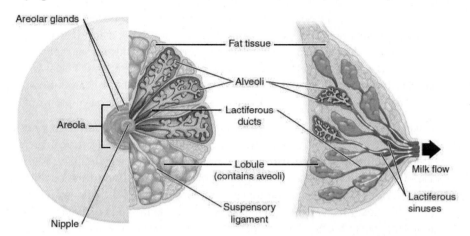

FIGURE 27.17 Anatomy of the Breast During lactation, milk moves from the alveoli through the lactiferous ducts to the nipple.

During the normal hormonal fluctuations in the menstrual cycle, breast tissue responds to changing levels of estrogen and progesterone, which can lead to swelling and breast tenderness in some individuals, especially during the secretory phase. If pregnancy occurs, the increase in hormones leads to further development of the mammary tissue and enlargement of the breasts.

Hormonal Birth Control

Birth control pills take advantage of the negative feedback system that regulates the ovarian and menstrual cycles to stop ovulation and prevent pregnancy. Typically they work by providing a constant level of both estrogen and progesterone, which negatively feeds back onto the hypothalamus and pituitary, thus preventing the release of FSH and LH. Without FSH, the follicles do not mature, and without the LH surge, ovulation does not occur. Although the estrogen in birth control pills does stimulate some thickening of the endometrial wall, it is reduced compared with a normal cycle and is less likely to support implantation.

Some birth control pills contain 21 active pills containing hormones, and 7 inactive pills (placebos). The decline in hormones during the week that the person takes the placebo pills triggers menses, although it is typically lighter than a normal menstrual flow because of the reduced endometrial thickening. Newer types of birth control pills have been developed that deliver low-dose estrogens and progesterone for the entire cycle (these are meant to be taken 365 days a year), and menses never occurs. While some people prefer to have the proof of a lack of pregnancy that a monthly period provides, menstruation every 28 days is not required for health reasons, and there are no reported adverse effects of not having a menstrual period in an otherwise healthy individual.

Because birth control pills function by providing constant estrogen and progesterone levels and disrupting negative feedback, skipping even just one or two pills at certain points of the cycle (or even being several hours late taking the pill) can lead to an increase in FSH and LH and result in ovulation. It is important, therefore, to follow the directions on the birth control pill package to successfully prevent pregnancy.

Aging and the...

Female Reproductive System

Female fertility (the ability to conceive) peaks when people are in their twenties, and is slowly reduced until 35 years of age. After that time, fertility declines more rapidly, until it ends completely at the end of menopause. Menopause is the cessation of the menstrual cycle that occurs as a result of the loss of ovarian follicles and the hormones that they produce. Menopause is considered complete if an individual has not menstruated in a full year. After that point, they are considered postmenopausal. The average age for this change is consistent worldwide at between 50 and 52 years of age, but it can normally occur at any time in a person's forties or fifties. Poor health, including smoking, can lead to earlier loss of fertility and earlier menopause.

As the age of menopause approaches, depletion of the number of viable follicles in the ovaries due to atresia affects the hormonal regulation of the menstrual cycle. During the years leading up to menopause, there is a decrease in the levels of the hormone inhibin, which normally participates in a negative feedback loop to the pituitary to control the production of FSH. The menopausal decrease in inhibin leads to an increase in FSH. The presence of FSH stimulates more follicles to grow and secrete estrogen. Because small, secondary follicles also respond to increases in FSH levels, larger numbers of follicles are stimulated to grow; however, most undergo atresia and die. Eventually, this process leads to the depletion of all follicles in the ovaries, and the production of estrogen falls off dramatically. It is primarily the lack of estrogens that leads to the symptoms of menopause.

The earliest changes occur during the menopausal transition, often referred to as peri-menopause, when a mestrual cycle becomes irregular but does not stop entirely. Although the levels of estrogen are still nearly the same as before the transition, the level of progesterone produced by the corpus luteum is reduced. This decline in progesterone can lead to abnormal growth, or hyperplasia, of the endometrium. This condition is a concern because it increases the risk of developing endometrial cancer. Two harmless conditions that can develop during the transition are uterine fibroids, which are benign masses of cells, and irregular bleeding. As estrogen levels change, other symptoms that occur are hot flashes and night sweats, trouble sleeping, vaginal dryness, mood swings, difficulty focusing, and thinning of hair on the head along with the growth of more hair on the face. Depending on the individual, these symptoms can be entirely absent, moderate, or severe.

After menopause, lower amounts of estrogens can lead to other changes. Cardiovascular disease becomes as prevalent in females as in males, possibly because estrogens reduce the amount of cholesterol in the blood vessels. When estrogen is lacking, many people find that they suddenly have problems with high cholesterol and the cardiovascular issues that accompany it. Osteoporosis is another problem because bone density decreases rapidly in the first years after menopause. The reduction in bone density leads to a higher incidence of fractures.

Hormone therapy (HT), which employs medication (synthetic estrogens and progestins) to increase estrogen and progestin levels, can alleviate some of the symptoms of menopause. In 2002, the Women's Health Initiative began a study to observe for the long-term outcomes of hormone replacement therapy over 8.5 years. However, the study was prematurely terminated after 5.2 years because of evidence of a higher than normal risk of breast cancer in patients taking estrogen-only HT. The potential positive effects on cardiovascular disease were also not realized in the estrogen-only patients. The results of other hormone replacement studies over the last 50 years, including a 2012 study that followed over 1,000 menopausal women for 10 years, have shown cardiovascular benefits from estrogen and no increased risk for cancer. Some researchers believe that the age group tested in the 2002 trial may have been too old to benefit from the therapy, thus skewing the results. In the meantime, intense debate and study of the benefits and risks of replacement therapy is ongoing. Current guidelines approve HT for the reduction of hot flashes or flushes, but this treatment is generally only considered when people first start showing signs of menopausal changes, is used in the lowest dose possible for the shortest time possible (5 years or less), and it is suggested that people on HT have regular pelvic and breast exams.

27.3 Development of the Male and Female Reproductive Systems

LEARNING OBJECTIVES

By the end of this section, you will be able to:

- Explain how bipotential tissues are directed to develop into male or female sex organs
- Name the rudimentary duct systems in the embryo that are precursors to male or female internal sex organs
- Describe the hormonal changes that bring about puberty, and the secondary sex characteristics

The development of the reproductive systems begins soon after fertilization of the egg, with primordial gonads beginning to develop approximately one month after conception. Reproductive development continues in utero, but there is little change in the reproductive system between infancy and puberty.

Development of the Sexual Organs in the Embryo and Fetus

Mammalian sex determination is generally determined by X and Y chromosomes. Individuals homozygous for X (XX) are female in sex and heterozygous individuals (XY) are male. The presence of a Y chromosome triggers the development of a certain set of male characteristics and its absence results in female characteristics. Nondisjunction during meiosis can produce other combinations such as XXY, XYY, and XO which are called chromosomal intersex.

Without much chemical prompting, all fertilized eggs would develop into females. To become a male, an individual must be exposed to the cascade of factors initiated by a single gene on the male Y chromosome. This is called the SRY (*Sex*-determining *Region* of the *Y* chromosome). Because females do not have a Y chromosome, they do not have the *SRY* gene. Without a functional *SRY* gene, an individual will be female.

In both male and female embryos, the same group of cells has the potential to develop into either the male or female gonads; this tissue is considered bipotential. The *SRY* gene actively recruits other genes that begin to develop the testes, and suppresses genes that are important in female development. As part of this *SRY*-prompted cascade, germ cells in the bipotential gonads differentiate into spermatogonia. Without *SRY*, different genes are expressed, oogonia form, and primordial follicles develop in the primitive ovary.

Soon after the formation of the testis, the Leydig cells begin to secrete testosterone. Testosterone can influence tissues that are bipotential to become male reproductive structures. For example, with exposure to testosterone, cells that could become either the glans penis or the glans clitoris form the glans penis. Without testosterone, these same cells differentiate into the clitoris.

Not all tissues in the reproductive tract are bipotential. The internal reproductive structures (for example the uterus, uterine tubes, and part of the vagina in females; and the epididymis, ductus deferens, and seminal vesicles in males) form from one of two rudimentary duct systems in the embryo. For typical reproductive function in the adult, one set of these ducts must develop properly, and the other must degrade. In males, secretions from sustentacular cells trigger a degradation of the female duct, called the **Müllerian duct**. At the same time, testosterone secretion stimulates growth of the male tract, the **Wolffian duct**. Without such sustentacular cell secretion, the Müllerian duct will develop; without testosterone, the Wolffian duct will degrade. Thus, the developing offspring will be female. For more information and a figure of differentiation of the gonads, seek additional content on fetal development.

🔗 INTERACTIVE LINK

Interactive Link Feature
The different genitalia of fetuses develop from the same tissues in the embryo. View this [animation](http://openstax.org/l/fetus) to see a comparison of the development of structures of the ovarian and testicular reproductive systems in a growing fetus. Where are the testes located for most of gestational time?

Further Sexual Development Occurs at Puberty

Puberty is the stage of development at which individuals become sexually mature. Though the outcomes of puberty for different sexes are very different, the hormonal control of the process is very similar. In addition, though the timing of these events varies between individuals, the sequence of changes that occur is predictable for male and female adolescents. As shown in Figure 27.18, a concerted release of hormones from the hypothalamus (GnRH), the anterior pituitary (LH and FSH), and the gonads (either testosterone or estrogen) is responsible for the maturation of the reproductive systems and the development of **secondary sex characteristics**, which are physical changes that serve auxiliary roles in reproduction.

The first changes begin around the age of eight or nine when the production of LH becomes detectable. The release of LH occurs primarily at night during sleep and precedes the physical changes of puberty by several years. In pre-pubertal children, the sensitivity of the negative feedback system in the hypothalamus and pituitary is very high. This means that very low concentrations of androgens or estrogens will negatively feed back onto the hypothalamus and pituitary, keeping the production of GnRH, LH, and FSH low.

As an individual approaches puberty, two changes in sensitivity occur. The first is a decrease of sensitivity in the hypothalamus and pituitary to negative feedback, meaning that it takes increasingly larger concentrations of sex steroid hormones to stop the production of LH and FSH. The second change in sensitivity is an increase in sensitivity of the gonads to the FSH and LH signals, meaning the gonads of adults are more responsive to gonadotropins than are the gonads of children. As a result of these two changes, the levels of LH and FSH slowly increase and lead to the enlargement and maturation of the gonads, which in turn leads to secretion of higher levels of sex hormones and the initiation of spermatogenesis and folliculogenesis.

In addition to age, multiple factors can affect the age of onset of puberty, including genetics, environment, and psychological stress. One of the more important influences may be nutrition; historical data demonstrate the effect of better and more consistent nutrition on the age of menarche in the United States, which decreased from an average age of approximately 17 years of age in 1860 to the current age of approximately 12.75 years in 1960, as it remains today. Some studies indicate a link between puberty onset and the amount of stored fat in an individual. This effect is more pronounced in females, but has been documented in both sexes. Body fat, corresponding with secretion of the hormone leptin by adipose cells, appears to have a strong role in determining menarche. This may reflect to some extent the high metabolic costs of gestation and lactation. In females who are extremely lean and highly active, such as gymnasts, there is often a delay in the onset of puberty.

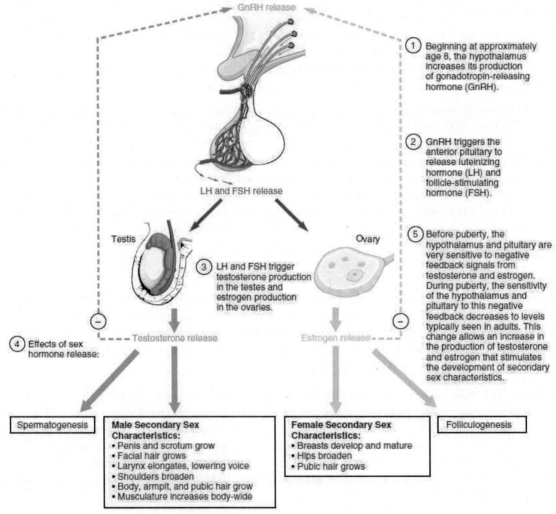

FIGURE 27.18 Hormones of Puberty   During puberty, the release of LH and FSH from the anterior pituitary stimulates the gonads to produce sex hormones in both male and female adolescents.

Signs of Puberty

Different sex steroid hormone concentrations between the sexes also contribute to the development and function of secondary sexual characteristics. Examples of secondary sexual characteristics are listed in Table 27.1.

Access for free at openstax.org

Development of the Secondary Sexual Characteristics

Male	Female
Increased larynx size and deepening of the voice	Deposition of fat, predominantly in breasts and hips
Increased muscular development	Breast development
Growth of facial, axillary, and pubic hair, and increased growth of body hair	Broadening of the pelvis and growth of axillary and pubic hair

TABLE 27.1

As a female reaches puberty, typically the first change that is visible is the development of the breast tissue. This is followed by the growth of axillary and pubic hair. A growth spurt normally starts at approximately age 9 to 11, and may last two years or more. During this time, height can increase 3 inches a year. The next step in puberty is menarche, the start of menstruation.

In males, the growth of the testes is typically the first physical sign of the beginning of puberty, which is followed by growth and pigmentation of the scrotum and growth of the penis. The next step is the growth of hair, including armpit, pubic, chest, and facial hair. Testosterone stimulates the growth of the larynx and thickening and lengthening of the vocal folds, which causes the voice to drop in pitch. The first fertile ejaculations typically appear at approximately 15 years of age, but this age can vary widely across individuals. Unlike the early growth spurt observed in females, the male growth spurt occurs toward the end of puberty, at approximately age 11 to 13, and height can increase as much as 4 inches a year. In some males, pubertal development can continue through the early 20s.

Key Terms

alveoli   (of the breast) milk-secreting cells in the mammary gland

ampulla   (of the uterine tube) middle portion of the uterine tube in which fertilization often occurs

antrum   fluid-filled chamber that characterizes a mature tertiary (antral) follicle

areola   highly pigmented, circular area surrounding the raised nipple and containing areolar glands that secrete fluid important for lubrication during suckling

Bartholin's glands   (also, greater vestibular glands) glands that produce a thick mucus that maintains moisture in the vulva area; also referred to as the greater vestibular glands

blood–testis barrier   tight junctions between Sertoli cells that prevent bloodborne pathogens from gaining access to later stages of spermatogenesis and prevent the potential for an autoimmune reaction to haploid sperm

body of uterus   middle section of the uterus

broad ligament   wide ligament that supports the uterus by attaching laterally to both sides of the uterus and pelvic wall

bulbourethral glands   (also, Cowper's glands) glands that secrete a lubricating mucus that cleans and lubricates the urethra prior to and during ejaculation

cervix   elongate inferior end of the uterus where it connects to the vagina

clitoris   (also, glans clitoris) nerve-rich area of the vulva that contributes to sexual sensation during intercourse

corpus albicans   nonfunctional structure remaining in the ovarian stroma following structural and functional regression of the corpus luteum

corpus cavernosum   either of two columns of erectile tissue in the penis that fill with blood during an erection

corpus luteum   transformed follicle after ovulation that secretes progesterone

corpus spongiosum   (plural = corpora cavernosa) column of erectile tissue in the penis that fills with blood during an erection and surrounds the penile urethra on the ventral portion of the penis

ductus deferens   (also, vas deferens) duct that transports sperm from the epididymis through the spermatic cord and into the ejaculatory duct; also referred as the vas deferens

ejaculatory duct   duct that connects the ampulla of the ductus deferens with the duct of the seminal vesicle at the prostatic urethra

endometrium   inner lining of the uterus, part of which builds up during the secretory phase of the menstrual cycle and then sheds with menses

epididymis   (plural = epididymides) coiled tubular structure in which sperm start to mature and are stored until ejaculation

fimbriae   fingerlike projections on the distal uterine tubes

follicle   ovarian structure of one oocyte and surrounding granulosa (and later theca) cells

folliculogenesis   development of ovarian follicles from primordial to tertiary under the stimulation of gonadotropins

fundus   (of the uterus) domed portion of the uterus that is superior to the uterine tubes

gamete   haploid reproductive cell that contributes genetic material to form an offspring

glans penis   bulbous end of the penis that contains a large number of nerve endings

gonadotropin-releasing hormone (GnRH)   hormone released by the hypothalamus that regulates the production of follicle-stimulating hormone and luteinizing hormone from the pituitary gland

gonads   reproductive organs (testes and ovaries) that produce gametes and reproductive hormones

granulosa cells   supportive cells in the ovarian follicle that produce estrogen

hymen   membrane that covers part of the opening of the vagina

infundibulum   (of the uterine tube) wide, distal portion of the uterine tube terminating in fimbriae

inguinal canal   opening in abdominal wall that connects the testes to the abdominal cavity

isthmus   narrow, medial portion of the uterine tube that joins the uterus

labia majora   hair-covered folds of skin located behind the mons pubis

labia minora   thin, pigmented, hairless flaps of skin located medial and deep to the labia majora

lactiferous ducts   ducts that connect the mammary glands to the nipple and allow for the transport of milk

lactiferous sinus   area of milk collection between alveoli and lactiferous duct

Leydig cells   cells between the seminiferous tubules of the testes that produce testosterone; a type of interstitial cell

mammary glands   glands inside the breast that secrete milk

menarche   first menstruation in a pubertal female

menses   shedding of the inner portion of the endometrium out though the vagina; also referred to as menstruation

menses phase   phase of the menstrual cycle in which

the endometrial lining is shed

menstrual cycle   approximately 28-day cycle of changes in the uterus consisting of a menses phase, a proliferative phase, and a secretory phase

mons pubis   mound of fatty tissue located at the front of the vulva

Müllerian duct   duct system present in the embryo that will eventually form the internal female reproductive structures

myometrium   smooth muscle layer of uterus that allows for uterine contractions during labor and expulsion of menstrual blood

oocyte   cell that results from the division of the oogonium and undergoes meiosis I at the LH surge and meiosis II at fertilization to become a haploid ovum

oogenesis   process by which oogonia divide by mitosis to primary oocytes, which undergo meiosis to produce the secondary oocyte and, upon fertilization, the ovum

oogonia   ovarian stem cells that undergo mitosis during female fetal development to form primary oocytes

ovarian cycle   approximately 28-day cycle of changes in the ovary consisting of a follicular phase and a luteal phase

ovaries   female gonads that produce oocytes and sex steroid hormones (notably estrogen and progesterone)

ovulation   release of a secondary oocyte and associated granulosa cells from an ovary

ovum   haploid female gamete resulting from completion of meiosis II at fertilization

penis   male organ of copulation

perimetrium   outer epithelial layer of uterine wall

polar body   smaller cell produced during the process of meiosis in oogenesis

prepuce   (also, foreskin) flap of skin that forms a collar around, and thus protects and lubricates, the glans penis; also referred as the foreskin

primary follicles   ovarian follicles with a primary oocyte and one layer of cuboidal granulosa cells

primordial follicles   least developed ovarian follicles that consist of a single oocyte and a single layer of flat (squamous) granulosa cells

proliferative phase   phase of the menstrual cycle in which the endometrium proliferates

prostate gland   doughnut-shaped gland at the base of the bladder surrounding the urethra and contributing fluid to semen during ejaculation

puberty   life stage during which a male or female adolescent becomes anatomically and physiologically capable of reproduction

rugae   (of the vagina) folds of skin in the vagina that allow it to stretch during intercourse and childbirth

scrotum   external pouch of skin and muscle that houses the testes

secondary follicles   ovarian follicles with a primary oocyte and multiple layers of granulosa cells

secondary sex characteristics   physical characteristics that are influenced by sex steroid hormones and have supporting roles in reproductive function

secretory phase   phase of the menstrual cycle in which the endometrium secretes a nutrient-rich fluid in preparation for implantation of an embryo

semen   ejaculatory fluid composed of sperm and secretions from the seminal vesicles, prostate, and bulbourethral glands

seminal vesicle   gland that produces seminal fluid, which contributes to semen

seminiferous tubules   tube structures within the testes where spermatogenesis occurs

Sertoli cells   cells that support germ cells through the process of spermatogenesis; a type of sustentacular cell

sperm   (also, spermatozoon) male gamete

spermatic cord   bundle of nerves and blood vessels that supplies the testes; contains ductus deferens

spermatid   immature sperm cells produced by meiosis II of secondary spermatocytes

spermatocyte   cell that results from the division of spermatogonium and undergoes meiosis I and meiosis II to form spermatids

spermatogenesis   formation of new sperm, occurs in the seminiferous tubules of the testes

spermatogonia   (singular = spermatogonium) diploid precursor cells that become sperm

spermiogenesis   transformation of spermatids to spermatozoa during spermatogenesis

suspensory ligaments   bands of connective tissue that suspend the breast onto the chest wall by attachment to the overlying dermis

tertiary follicles   (also, antral follicles) ovarian follicles with a primary or secondary oocyte, multiple layers of granulosa cells, and a fully formed antrum

testes   (singular = testis) male gonads

theca cells   estrogen-producing cells in a maturing ovarian follicle

uterine tubes   (also, fallopian tubes or oviducts) ducts that facilitate transport of an ovulated oocyte to the uterus

uterus   muscular hollow organ in which a fertilized egg develops into a fetus

vagina   tunnel-like organ that provides access to the

uterus for the insertion of semen and from the uterus for the birth of a baby

vulva   external female genitalia

Wolffian duct   duct system present in the embryo that will eventually form the internal male reproductive structures

Chapter Review

27.1 Anatomy and Physiology of the Testicular Reproductive System

Gametes are the reproductive cells that combine to form offspring. Organs called gonads produce the gametes, along with the hormones that regulate human reproduction. The male gametes are called sperm. Spermatogenesis, the production of sperm, occurs within the seminiferous tubules that make up most of the testis. The scrotum is the muscular sac that holds the testes outside of the body cavity.

Spermatogenesis begins with mitotic division of spermatogonia (stem cells) to produce primary spermatocytes that undergo the two divisions of meiosis to become secondary spermatocytes, then the haploid spermatids. During spermiogenesis, spermatids are transformed into spermatozoa (formed sperm). Upon release from the seminiferous tubules, sperm are moved to the epididymis where they continue to mature. During ejaculation, sperm exit the epididymis through the ductus deferens, a duct in the spermatic cord that leaves the scrotum. The ampulla of the ductus deferens meets the seminal vesicle, a gland that contributes fructose and proteins, at the ejaculatory duct. The fluid continues through the prostatic urethra, where secretions from the prostate are added to form semen. These secretions help the sperm to travel through the urethra and into the female reproductive tract. Secretions from the bulbourethral glands protect sperm and cleanse and lubricate the penile (spongy) urethra.

The penis is the male organ of copulation. Columns of erectile tissue called the corpora cavernosa and corpus spongiosum fill with blood when sexual arousal activates vasodilatation in the blood vessels of the penis. Testosterone regulates and maintains the sex organs and sex drive, and induces the physical changes of puberty. Interplay between the testes and the endocrine system precisely control the production of testosterone with a negative feedback loop.

27.2 Anatomy and Physiology of the Ovarian Reproductive System

The external female genitalia are collectively called the vulva. The vagina is the pathway into and out of the uterus. The penis is inserted into the vagina to deliver sperm, and the baby exits the uterus through the vagina during childbirth.

The ovaries produce oocytes, the female gametes, in a process called oogenesis. As with spermatogenesis, meiosis produces the haploid gamete (in this case, an ovum); however, it is completed only in an oocyte that has been penetrated by a sperm. In the ovary, an oocyte surrounded by supporting cells is called a follicle. In folliculogenesis, primordial follicles develop into primary, secondary, and tertiary follicles. Early tertiary follicles with their fluid-filled antrum will be stimulated by an increase in FSH, a gonadotropin produced by the anterior pituitary, to grow in the 28-day ovarian cycle. Supporting granulosa and theca cells in the growing follicles produce estrogens, until the level of estrogen in the bloodstream is high enough that it triggers negative feedback at the hypothalamus and pituitary. This results in a reduction of FSH and LH, and most tertiary follicles in the ovary undergo atresia (they die). One follicle, usually the one with the most FSH receptors, survives this period and is now called the dominant follicle. The dominant follicle produces more estrogen, triggering positive feedback and the LH surge that will induce ovulation. Following ovulation, the granulosa cells of the empty follicle luteinize and transform into the progesterone-producing corpus luteum. The ovulated oocyte with its surrounding granulosa cells is picked up by the infundibulum of the uterine tube, and beating cilia help to transport it through the tube toward the uterus. Fertilization occurs within the uterine tube, and the final stage of meiosis is completed.

The uterus has three regions: the fundus, the body, and the cervix. It has three layers: the outer perimetrium, the muscular myometrium, and the inner endometrium. The endometrium responds to estrogen released by the follicles during the menstrual cycle and grows thicker with an increase in blood vessels in preparation for pregnancy. If the egg is not fertilized, no signal is sent to extend the life of the corpus luteum, and it degrades, stopping progesterone production. This decline in progesterone results in the sloughing of the inner portion of the endometrium in a process called menses, or menstruation.

The breasts are accessory organs that may be utilized after the birth of a child to produce milk in a process called lactation. Birth control pills provide constant levels of estrogen and progesterone to negatively feed back on the hypothalamus and pituitary, and suppress the release of FSH and LH, which inhibits ovulation and prevents pregnancy.

27.3 Development of the Male and Female Reproductive Systems

The reproductive systems of males and females begin to develop soon after conception. A gene on the Y chromosome called *SRY* is critical in stimulating a cascade of events that simultaneously stimulate testis development and repress the development of female structures. Testosterone produced by Leydig cells in the embryonic testis stimulates the development of male sexual organs. If testosterone is not present, female sexual organs will develop.

Whereas the gonads and some other reproductive tissues are considered bipotential, the tissue that forms the internal reproductive structures stems from

ducts that will develop into only male (Wolffian) or female (Müllerian) structures. To be able to reproduce as an adult, one of these systems must develop properly and the other must degrade.

Further development of the reproductive systems occurs at puberty. The initiation of the changes that occur in puberty is the result of a decrease in sensitivity to negative feedback in the hypothalamus and pituitary gland, and an increase in sensitivity of the gonads to FSH and LH stimulation. These changes lead to increases in either estrogen or testosterone. The increase in sex steroid hormones leads to maturation of the gonads and other reproductive organs. The initiation of spermatogenesis begins, as well as ovulation and menstruation. Increases in sex steroid hormones also lead to the development of secondary sex characteristics.

Interactive Link Questions

1. Watch this video (http://openstax.org/l/vasectomy) to learn about vasectomy. As described in this video, a vasectomy is a procedure in which a small section of the ductus (vas) deferens is removed from the scrotum. This interrupts the path taken by sperm through the ductus deferens. If sperm do not exit through the vas, either because the person has had a vasectomy or has not ejaculated, in what region of the testis do they remain?

2. Watch this video (http://openstax.org/l/spermpath) to explore the structures of the male reproductive system and the path of sperm that starts in the testes and ends as the sperm leave the penis through the urethra. Where are sperm deposited after they leave the ejaculatory duct?

3. Watch this video (http://openstax.org/l/ovulation) to observe ovulation and its initiation in response to the release of FSH and LH from the pituitary gland. What specialized structures help guide the oocyte from the ovary into the uterine tube?

4. Watch this series of videos (http://openstax.org/l/oocyte) to look at the movement of the oocyte through the ovary. The cilia in the uterine tube promote movement of the oocyte. What would likely occur if the cilia were paralyzed at the time of ovulation?

5. The different genitalia of fetuses develop from the same tissues in the embryo. View this animation (http://openstax.org/l/fetus) that compares the development of structures of the female and male reproductive systems in a growing fetus. Where are the testes located for most of gestational time?

Review Questions

6. What are male gametes called?
   a. ova
   b. sperm
   c. testes
   d. testosterone

7. Leydig cells _____.
   a. secrete testosterone
   b. activate the sperm flagellum
   c. support spermatogenesis
   d. secrete seminal fluid

8. Which hypothalamic hormone contributes to the regulation of the male reproductive system?
   a. luteinizing hormone
   b. gonadotropin-releasing hormone
   c. follicle-stimulating hormone
   d. androgens

9. What is the function of the epididymis?
   a. sperm maturation and storage
   b. produces the bulk of seminal fluid
   c. provides nitric oxide needed for erections
   d. spermatogenesis

10. Spermatogenesis takes place in the _____.
   a. prostate gland
   b. glans penis
   c. seminiferous tubules
   d. ejaculatory duct

11. What are the female gonads called?
   a. oocytes
   b. ova
   c. oviducts
   d. ovaries

12. When do the oogonia undergo mitosis?
   a. before birth
   b. at puberty
   c. at the beginning of each menstrual cycle
   d. during fertilization

13. From what structure does the corpus luteum originate?
   a. uterine corpus
   b. dominant follicle
   c. fallopian tube
   d. corpus albicans

14. Where does fertilization of the egg by the sperm typically occur?
   a. vagina
   b. uterus
   c. uterine tube
   d. ovary

15. Why do estrogen levels fall after menopause?
   a. The ovaries degrade.
   b. There are no follicles left to produce estrogen.
   c. The pituitary secretes a menopause-specific hormone.
   d. The cells of the endometrium degenerate.

16. The vulva includes the _____.
   a. lactiferous duct, rugae, and hymen
   b. lactiferous duct, endometrium, and bulbourethral glands
   c. mons pubis, endometrium, and hymen
   d. mons pubis, labia majora, and Bartholin's glands

17. What controls whether an embryo will develop testes or ovaries?
   a. pituitary gland
   b. hypothalamus
   c. Y chromosome
   d. presence or absence of estrogen

18. Without *SRY* expression, an embryo will develop _____.
   a. male reproductive structures
   b. female reproductive structures
   c. no reproductive structures
   d. male reproductive structures 50 percent of the time and female reproductive structures 50 percent of the time

19. The timing of puberty can be influenced by which of the following?
   a. genes
   b. stress
   c. amount of body fat
   d. all of the above

Critical Thinking Questions

20. Briefly explain why mature gametes carry only one set of chromosomes.

21. What special features are evident in sperm cells but not in somatic cells, and how do these specializations function?

22. What do each of the three male accessory glands contribute to the semen?

23. Describe how penile erection occurs.

24. While anabolic steroids (synthetic testosterone) bulk up muscles, they can also affect testosterone production in the testis. Using what you know about negative feedback, describe what would happen to testosterone production in the testis if a male takes large amounts of synthetic testosterone.

25. Follow the path of ejaculated sperm from the vagina to the oocyte. Include all structures of the female reproductive tract that the sperm must travel through to reach the egg.

26. Identify some differences between meiosis in males and females.

27. Explain the hormonal regulation of the phases of the menstrual cycle.

28. Endometriosis is a disease characterized by the presence of endometrial-like tissue found outside the uterus—in the uterine tubes, on the ovaries, or even in the pelvic cavity. Offer a hypothesis as to why endometriosis increases a woman's risk of infertility.

29. Identify the changes in sensitivity that occur in the hypothalamus, pituitary, and gonads as a person approaches puberty. Explain how these changes lead to the increases of sex steroid hormone secretions that drive many pubertal changes.

30. Explain how the internal female and male reproductive structures develop from two different duct systems.

31. Explain what would occur during fetal development to an XY individual with a mutation causing a nonfunctional *SRY* gene.

CHAPTER 28
Development and Inheritance

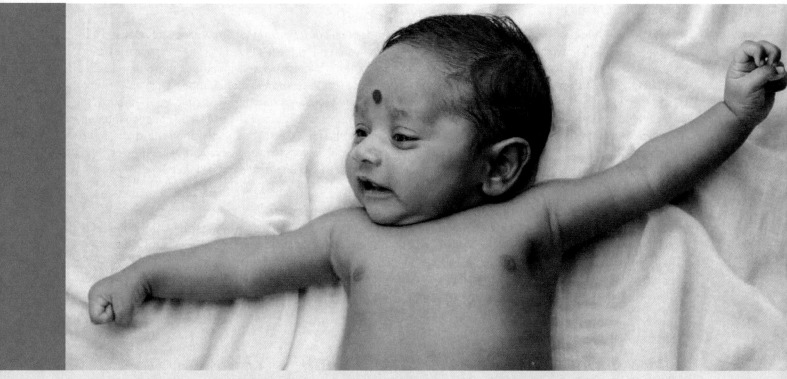

Figure 28.1 Newborn A single fertilized egg develops over the span of nine months into an infant consisting of trillions of cells and capable of surviving outside the womb. (credit: "Seattleye"/flickr.com)

CHAPTER OBJECTIVES
After studying this chapter, you will be able to:
- List and explain the steps involved in fertilization
- Describe the major events in embryonic development
- Describe the major events in fetal development
- Discuss the adaptations of the body to pregnancy
- Describe the physiologic adjustments that the newborn must make in the first hours of extrauterine life
- Summarize the physiology of lactation
- Classify and describe the different patterns of inheritance

INTRODUCTION In approximately nine months, a single cell—a fertilized egg—develops into a fully formed infant consisting of trillions of cells with myriad specialized functions. The dramatic changes of fertilization, embryonic development, and fetal development are followed by remarkable adaptations of the newborn to life outside the womb. An offspring's normal development depends upon the appropriate synthesis of structural and functional proteins. This, in turn, is governed by the genetic material inherited from the egg and sperm, as well as environmental factors.

28.1 Fertilization

LEARNING OBJECTIVES
By the end of this section, you will be able to:
- Describe the obstacles that sperm must overcome to reach an oocyte
- Explain capacitation and its importance in fertilization
- Summarize the events that occur as a sperm fertilizes an oocyte

Fertilization occurs when a sperm and an oocyte (egg) combine and their nuclei fuse. Because each of these reproductive cells is a haploid cell containing half of the genetic material needed to form a human being, their combination forms a diploid cell. This new single cell, called a **zygote**, contains all of the genetic material needed to form a human—half from each biological parent.

Transit of Sperm

Fertilization is a numbers game. During ejaculation, hundreds of millions of sperm (spermatozoa) are released into the vagina. Almost immediately, millions of these sperm are overcome by the acidity of the vagina (approximately pH 3.8), and millions more may be blocked from entering the uterus by thick cervical mucus. Of those that do enter, thousands are destroyed by phagocytic uterine leukocytes. Thus, the race into the uterine tubes, which is the most typical site for sperm to encounter the oocyte, is reduced to a few thousand contenders. Their journey—thought to be facilitated by uterine contractions—usually takes from 30 minutes to 2 hours. If the sperm do not encounter an oocyte immediately, they can survive in the uterine tubes for another 3–5 days. Thus, fertilization can still occur if intercourse takes place a few days before ovulation. In comparison, an oocyte can survive independently for only approximately 24 hours following ovulation. Intercourse more than a day after ovulation will therefore usually not result in fertilization.

During the journey, fluids in the female reproductive tract prepare the sperm for fertilization through a process called **capacitation**, or priming. The fluids improve the motility of the spermatozoa. They also deplete cholesterol molecules embedded in the membrane of the head of the sperm, thinning the membrane in such a way that will help facilitate the release of the lysosomal (digestive) enzymes needed for the sperm to penetrate the oocyte's exterior once contact is made. Sperm must undergo the process of capacitation in order to have the "capacity" to fertilize an oocyte. If they reach the oocyte before capacitation is complete, they will be unable to penetrate the oocyte's thick outer layer of cells.

Contact Between Sperm and Oocyte

Upon ovulation, the oocyte released by the ovary is swept into—and along—the uterine tube. Fertilization must occur in the distal uterine tube because an unfertilized oocyte cannot survive the 72-hour journey to the uterus. As you will recall from your study of the oogenesis, this oocyte (specifically a secondary oocyte) is surrounded by two protective layers. The **corona radiata** is an outer layer of follicular (granulosa) cells that form around a developing oocyte in the ovary and remain with it upon ovulation. The underlying **zona pellucida** (pellucid = "transparent") is a transparent, but thick, glycoprotein membrane that surrounds the cell's plasma membrane.

As it is swept along the distal uterine tube, the oocyte encounters the surviving capacitated sperm, which stream toward it in response to chemical attractants released by the cells of the corona radiata. To reach the oocyte itself, the sperm must penetrate the two protective layers. The sperm first burrow through the cells of the corona radiata. Then, upon contact with the zona pellucida, the sperm bind to receptors in the zona pellucida. This initiates a process called the **acrosomal reaction** in which the enzyme-filled "cap" of the sperm, called the **acrosome**, releases its stored digestive enzymes. These enzymes clear a path through the zona pellucida that allows sperm to reach the oocyte. Finally, a single sperm makes contact with sperm-binding receptors on the oocyte's plasma membrane (Figure 28.2). The plasma membrane of that sperm then fuses with the oocyte's plasma membrane, and the head and mid-piece of the "winning" sperm enter the oocyte interior.

How do sperm penetrate the corona radiata? Some sperm undergo a spontaneous acrosomal reaction, which is an acrosomal reaction not triggered by contact with the zona pellucida. The digestive enzymes released by this reaction digest the extracellular matrix of the corona radiata. As you can see, the first sperm to reach the oocyte is never the one to fertilize it. Rather, hundreds of sperm cells must undergo the acrosomal reaction, each helping to degrade the corona radiata and zona pellucida until a path is created to allow one sperm to contact and fuse with the plasma membrane of the oocyte. If you consider the loss of millions of sperm between entry into the vagina and degradation of the zona pellucida, you can understand why a low sperm count can cause male infertility.

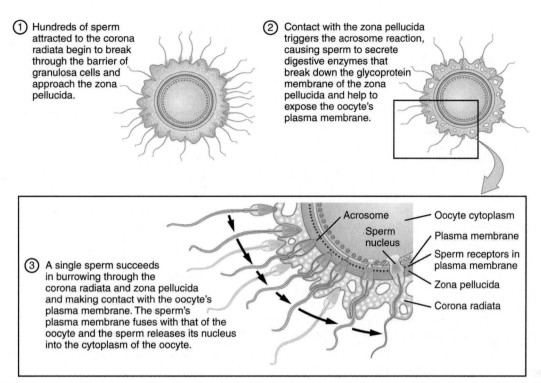

① Hundreds of sperm attracted to the corona radiata begin to break through the barrier of granulosa cells and approach the zona pellucida.

② Contact with the zona pellucida triggers the acrosome reaction, causing sperm to secrete digestive enzymes that break down the glycoprotein membrane of the zona pellucida and help to expose the oocyte's plasma membrane.

③ A single sperm succeeds in burrowing through the corona radiata and zona pellucida and making contact with the oocyte's plasma membrane. The sperm's plasma membrane fuses with that of the oocyte and the sperm releases its nucleus into the cytoplasm of the oocyte.

Acrosome
Sperm nucleus
Oocyte cytoplasm
Plasma membrane
Sperm receptors in plasma membrane
Zona pellucida
Corona radiata

FIGURE 28.2   Sperm and the Process of Fertilization   Before fertilization, hundreds of capacitated sperm must break through the surrounding corona radiata and zona pellucida so that one can contact and fuse with the oocyte plasma membrane.

When the first sperm fuses with the oocyte, the oocyte deploys two mechanisms to prevent **polyspermy**, which is penetration by more than one sperm. This is critical because if more than one sperm were to fertilize the oocyte, the resulting zygote would be a triploid organism with three sets of chromosomes. This is incompatible with life.

The first mechanism is the fast block, which involves a near instantaneous change in sodium ion permeability upon binding of the first sperm, depolarizing the oocyte plasma membrane and preventing the fusion of additional sperm cells. The fast block sets in almost immediately and lasts for about a minute, during which time an influx of calcium ions following sperm penetration triggers the second mechanism, the slow block. In this process, referred to as the **cortical reaction**, cortical granules sitting immediately below the oocyte plasma membrane fuse with the membrane and release zonal inhibiting proteins and mucopolysaccharides into the space between the plasma membrane and the zona pellucida. Zonal inhibiting proteins cause the release of any other attached sperm and destroy the oocyte's sperm receptors, thus preventing any more sperm from binding. The mucopolysaccharides then coat the nascent zygote in an impenetrable barrier that, together with hardened zona pellucida, is called a **fertilization membrane**.

The Zygote

Recall that at the point of fertilization, the oocyte has not yet completed meiosis; all secondary oocytes remain arrested in metaphase of meiosis II until fertilization. Only upon fertilization does the oocyte complete meiosis. The unneeded complement of genetic material that results is stored in a second polar body that is eventually ejected. At this moment, the oocyte has become an ovum, the female haploid gamete. The two haploid nuclei derived from the sperm and oocyte and contained within the egg are referred to as pronuclei. They decondense, expand, and replicate their DNA in preparation for mitosis. The pronuclei then migrate toward each other, their nuclear envelopes disintegrate, and the male- and female-derived genetic material intermingles. This step completes the process of fertilization and results in a single-celled diploid zygote with all the genetic instructions it needs to develop into a human.

Most of the time, a person releases a single egg during an ovulation cycle. However, in approximately 1 percent of ovulation cycles, two eggs are released and both are fertilized. Two zygotes form, implant, and develop, resulting in the birth of dizygotic (or fraternal) twins. Because dizygotic twins develop from two eggs fertilized by two sperm, they are no more identical than siblings born at different times.

Much less commonly, a zygote can divide into two separate offspring during early development. This results in the birth of monozygotic (or identical) twins. Although the zygote can split as early as the two-cell stage, splitting occurs most commonly during the early blastocyst stage, with roughly 70–100 cells present. These two scenarios are distinct from each other, in that the twin embryos that separated at the two-cell stage will have individual placentas, whereas twin embryos that form from separation at the blastocyst stage will share a placenta and a chorionic cavity.

Everyday Connection

In Vitro Fertilization

IVF, which stands for in vitro fertilization, is an assisted reproductive technology. In vitro, which in Latin translates to "in glass," refers to a procedure that takes place outside of the body. There are many different indications for IVF. The procedure is used frequently in supporting LGBTQ people, people using surrogates/gestational carriers, and also people who have difficulties reproducing. For example, a person may produce healthy eggs, but the eggs cannot reach the uterus because the uterine tubes are blocked or otherwise compromised. A person may have a low sperm count, low sperm motility, sperm with an unusually high percentage of morphological abnormalities, or sperm that are incapable of penetrating the zona pellucida of an egg.

A typical IVF procedure begins with egg collection. A normal ovulation cycle produces only one oocyte, but the number can be boosted significantly (to 10–20 oocytes) by administering a short course of gonadotropins. The course begins with follicle-stimulating hormone (FSH) analogs, which support the development of multiple follicles, and ends with a luteinizing hormone (LH) analog that triggers ovulation. Right before the ova would be released from the ovary, they are harvested using ultrasound-guided oocyte retrieval. In this procedure, ultrasound allows a physician to visualize mature follicles. The ova are aspirated (sucked out) using a syringe.

In parallel, sperm are obtained from the male partner or from a sperm bank. The sperm are prepared by washing to remove seminal fluid because seminal fluid contains a peptide, FPP (or, fertilization promoting peptide), that—in high concentrations—prevents capacitation of the sperm. The sperm sample is also concentrated, to increase the sperm count per milliliter.

Next, the eggs and sperm are mixed in a petri dish. The ideal ratio is 75,000 sperm to one egg. If there are severe problems with the sperm—for example, the count is exceedingly low, or the sperm are completely nonmotile, or incapable of binding to or penetrating the zona pellucida—a sperm can be injected into an egg. This is called intracytoplasmic sperm injection (ICSI).

The embryos are then incubated until they either reach the eight-cell stage or the blastocyst stage. In the United States, fertilized eggs are typically cultured to the blastocyst stage because this results in a higher pregnancy rate. Finally, the embryos are transferred to a woman's uterus using a plastic catheter (tube). Figure 28.3 illustrates the steps involved in IVF.

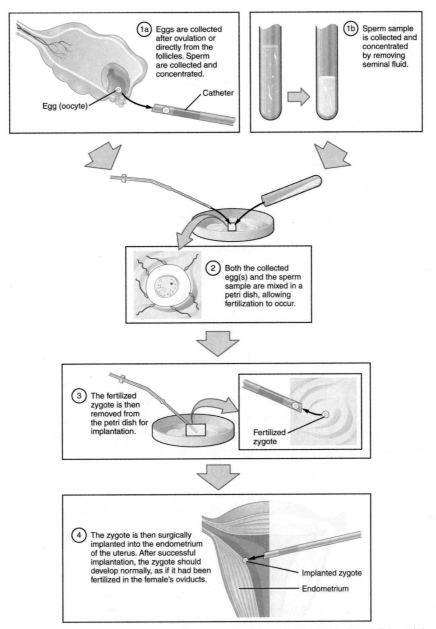

FIGURE 28.3 IVF In vitro fertilization involves egg collection from the ovaries, fertilization in a petri dish, and the transfer of embryos into the uterus.

IVF is a relatively new and still evolving technology, and until recently it was necessary to transfer multiple embryos to achieve a good chance of a pregnancy. Today, however, transferred embryos are much more likely to implant successfully, so countries that regulate the IVF industry cap the number of embryos that can be transferred per cycle at two. This reduces the risk of multiple-birth pregnancies.

The rate of success for IVF is correlated with the age of the gestational carrier (which may be the child's mother or a surrogate). More than 40 percent of females under 35 succeed in giving birth following IVF, but the rate drops to a little over 10 percent in females over 40.

🔗 INTERACTIVE LINK

Go to this site (http://openstax.org/l/fertilization) to view resources covering various aspects of fertilization, including movies and animations showing sperm structure and motility, ovulation, and fertilization.

28.2 Embryonic Development

LEARNING OBJECTIVES

By the end of this section, you will be able to:

- Distinguish the stages of embryonic development that occur before implantation
- Describe the process of implantation
- List and describe four embryonic membranes
- Explain gastrulation
- Describe how the placenta is formed and identify its functions
- Explain how an embryo transforms from a flat disc of cells into a three-dimensional shape resembling a human
- Summarize the process of organogenesis

Throughout this chapter, we will express embryonic and fetal ages in terms of weeks from fertilization, commonly called conception. The period of time required for full development of a fetus in utero is referred to as **gestation** (gestare = "to carry" or "to bear"). It can be subdivided into distinct gestational periods. The first 2 weeks of prenatal development are referred to as the pre-embryonic stage. A developing human is referred to as an **embryo** during weeks 3–8, and a **fetus** from the ninth week of gestation until birth. In this section, we'll cover the pre-embryonic and embryonic stages of development, which are characterized by cell division, migration, and differentiation. By the end of the embryonic period, all of the organ systems are structured in rudimentary form, although the organs themselves are either nonfunctional or only semi-functional.

Pre-implantation Embryonic Development

Following fertilization, the zygote and its associated membranes, together referred to as the **conceptus**, continue to be projected toward the uterus by peristalsis and beating cilia of the epithelial cells of the Fallopian tube. During its journey to the uterus, the zygote undergoes five or six rapid mitotic cell divisions. Although each **cleavage** results in more cells, it does not increase the total volume of the conceptus (Figure 28.4). Each daughter cell produced by cleavage is called a **blastomere** (blastos = "germ," in the sense of a seed or sprout).

Approximately 3 days after fertilization, a 16-cell conceptus reaches the uterus. The cells that had been loosely grouped are now compacted and look more like a solid mass. The name given to this structure is the **morula** (morula = "little mulberry"). Once inside the uterus, the conceptus floats freely for several more days. It continues to divide, creating a ball of approximately 100 cells, and consuming nutritive endometrial secretions called uterine milk while the uterine lining thickens. The ball of now tightly bound cells starts to secrete fluid and organize themselves around a fluid-filled cavity, the **blastocoel**. At this developmental stage, the conceptus is referred to as a **blastocyst**. Within this structure, a group of cells forms into an **inner cell mass**, which is fated to become the embryo. The cells that form the outer shell are called **trophoblasts** (trophe = "to feed" or "to nourish"). These cells will develop into the chorionic sac and the fetal portion of the **placenta** (the organ of nutrient, waste, and gas exchange between a pregnant person and the developing offspring).

The inner mass of embryonic cells is totipotent during this stage, meaning that each cell has the potential to differentiate into any cell type in the human body. Totipotency lasts for only a few days before the cells' fates are set as being the precursors to a specific lineage of cells.

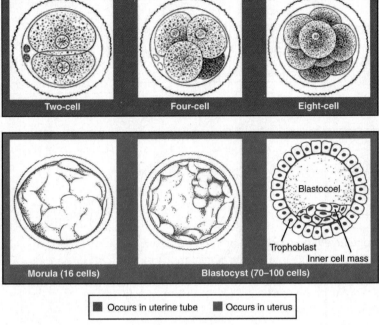

Two-cell

Four-cell

Eight-cell

Morula (16 cells)

Blastocyst (70–100 cells)

Blastocoel

Trophoblast

Inner cell mass

■ Occurs in uterine tube   ■ Occurs in uterus

FIGURE 28.4   Pre-Embryonic Cleavages   Pre-embryonic cleavages make use of the abundant cytoplasm of the conceptus as the cells rapidly divide without changing the total volume.

As the blastocyst forms, the trophoblast excretes enzymes that begin to degrade the zona pellucida. In a process called "hatching," the conceptus breaks free of the zona pellucida in preparation for implantation.

⊘ **INTERACTIVE LINK**

View this time-lapse movie (http://openstax.org/l/conceptus) of a conceptus starting at day 3. What is the first structure you see? At what point in the movie does the blastocoel first appear? What event occurs at the end of the movie?

Implantation

At the end of the first week, the blastocyst comes in contact with the uterine wall and adheres to it, embedding itself in the uterine lining via the trophoblast cells. Thus begins the process of **implantation**, which signals the end of the pre-embryonic stage of development (Figure 28.5). Implantation can be accompanied by minor bleeding. The blastocyst typically implants in the fundus of the uterus or on the posterior wall. However, if the endometrium is not fully developed and ready to receive the blastocyst, the blastocyst will detach and find a better spot. A significant percentage (50–75 percent) of blastocysts fail to implant; when this occurs, the blastocyst is shed with the endometrium during menses. The high rate of implantation failure is one reason why pregnancy typically requires several ovulation cycles to achieve.

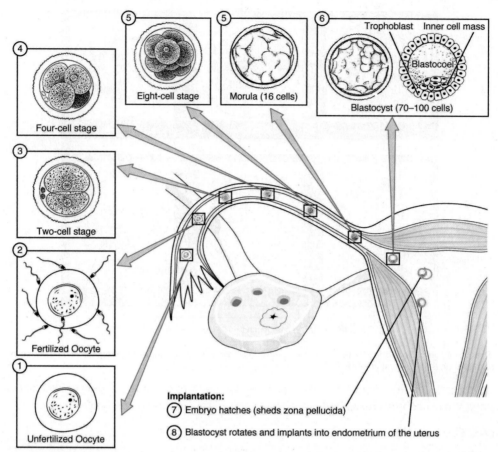

④ Four-cell stage

③ Two-cell stage

② Fertilized Oocyte

① Unfertilized Oocyte

⑤ Eight-cell stage

⑤ Morula (16 cells)

⑥ Trophoblast   Inner cell mass

Blastocoel

Blastocyst (70–100 cells)

Implantation:
⑦ Embryo hatches (sheds zona pellucida)

⑧ Blastocyst rotates and implants into endometrium of the uterus

FIGURE 28.5 Pre-Embryonic Development Ovulation, fertilization, pre-embryonic development, and implantation occur at specific locations within the female reproductive system in a time span of approximately 1 week.

When implantation succeeds and the blastocyst adheres to the endometrium, the superficial cells of the trophoblast fuse with each other, forming the **syncytiotrophoblast**, a multinucleated body that digests endometrial cells to firmly secure the blastocyst to the uterine wall. In response, the uterine mucosa rebuilds itself and envelops the blastocyst (Figure 28.6). The trophoblast secretes **human chorionic gonadotropin (hCG)**, a hormone that directs the corpus luteum to survive, enlarge, and continue producing progesterone and estrogen to suppress menses. These functions of hCG are necessary for creating an environment suitable for the developing embryo. As a result of this increased production, hCG accumulates in the maternal bloodstream and is excreted in the urine. Implantation is complete by the middle of the second week. Just a few days after implantation, the trophoblast has secreted enough hCG for an at-home urine pregnancy test to give a positive result.

Access for free at openstax.org

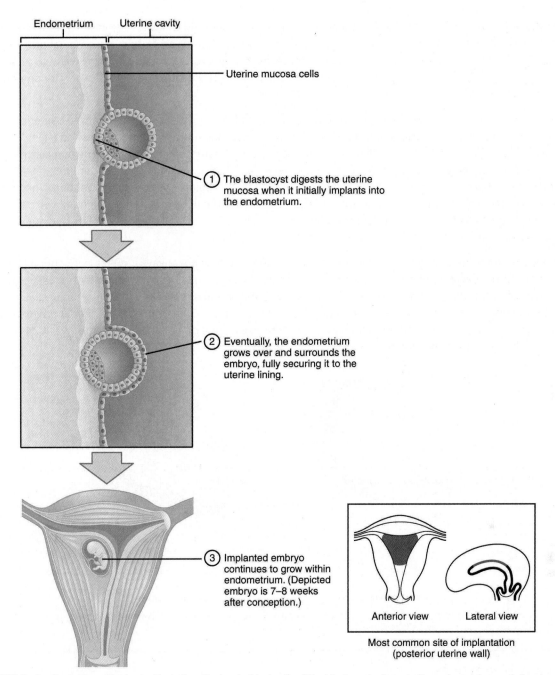

FIGURE 28.6 Implantation During implantation, the trophoblast cells of the blastocyst adhere to the endometrium and digest endometrial cells until it is attached securely.

Most of the time an embryo implants within the body of the uterus in a location that can support growth and development. However, in one to two percent of cases, the embryo implants either outside the uterus (an **ectopic pregnancy**) or in a region of uterus that can create complications for the pregnancy. If the embryo implants in the inferior portion of the uterus, the placenta can potentially grow over the opening of the cervix, a condition call **placenta previa**.

Disorders of the...

Development of the Embryo

In the vast majority of ectopic pregnancies, the embryo does not complete its journey to the uterus and implants in the uterine tube, referred to as a tubal pregnancy. However, there are also ovarian ectopic pregnancies (in which the egg never left the ovary) and abdominal ectopic pregnancies (in which an egg was "lost" to the abdominal cavity during the transfer from ovary to uterine tube, or in which an embryo from a tubal pregnancy re-implanted in the abdomen). Once in the abdominal cavity, an embryo can implant into any well-vascularized structure—the rectouterine cavity (Douglas' pouch), the mesentery of the intestines, and the greater omentum are some common sites.

Tubal pregnancies can be caused by scar tissue within the tube following a sexually transmitted bacterial infection. The scar tissue impedes the progress of the embryo into the uterus—in some cases "snagging" the embryo and, in other cases, blocking the tube completely. Approximately one half of tubal pregnancies resolve spontaneously. Implantation in a uterine tube causes bleeding, which appears to stimulate smooth muscle contractions and expulsion of the embryo. In the remaining cases, medical or surgical intervention is necessary. If an ectopic pregnancy is detected early, the embryo's development can be arrested by the administration of the cytotoxic drug methotrexate, which inhibits the metabolism of folic acid. If diagnosis is late and the uterine tube is already ruptured, surgical repair is essential.

Even if the embryo has successfully found its way to the uterus, it does not always implant in an optimal location (the fundus or the posterior wall of the uterus). Placenta previa can result if an embryo implants close to the internal os of the uterus (the internal opening of the cervix). As the fetus grows, the placenta can partially or completely cover the opening of the cervix (Figure 28.7). Although it occurs in only 0.5 percent of pregnancies, placenta previa is the leading cause of antepartum hemorrhage (profuse vaginal bleeding after week 24 of pregnancy but prior to childbirth).

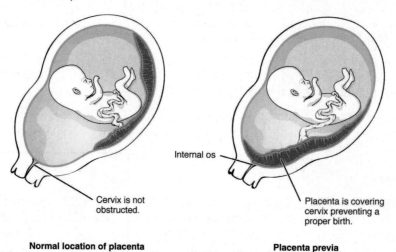

Internal os

Cervix is not obstructed.

Placenta is covering cervix preventing a proper birth.

Normal location of placenta   **Placenta previa**

FIGURE 28.7   **Placenta Previa**   An embryo that implants too close to the opening of the cervix can lead to placenta previa, a condition in which the placenta partially or completely covers the cervix.

Embryonic Membranes

During the second week of development, with the embryo implanted in the uterus, cells within the blastocyst start to organize into layers. Some grow to form the extra-embryonic membranes needed to support and protect the growing embryo: the amnion, the yolk sac, the allantois, and the chorion.

At the beginning of the second week, the cells of the inner cell mass form into a two-layered disc of embryonic cells, and a space—the **amniotic cavity**—opens up between it and the trophoblast (Figure 28.8). Cells from the upper layer of the disc (the **epiblast**) extend around the amniotic cavity, creating a membranous sac that forms into the **amnion** by the end of the second week. The amnion fills with amniotic fluid and eventually grows to surround the embryo. Early in development, amniotic fluid consists almost entirely of a filtrate of maternal plasma, but as the kidneys of the fetus begin to function at approximately the eighth week, they add urine to the volume of amniotic fluid. Floating within the amniotic fluid, the embryo—and later, the fetus—is protected from trauma and rapid temperature changes. It can move freely within the fluid and can prepare for swallowing and breathing out of the uterus.

Access for free at openstax.org

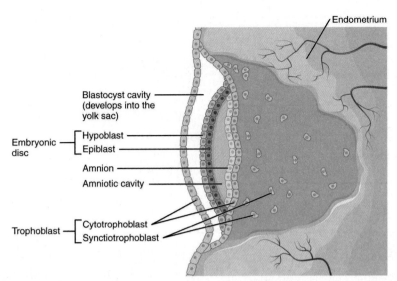

FIGURE 28.8 Development of the Embryonic Disc   Formation of the embryonic disc leaves spaces on either side that develop into the amniotic cavity and the yolk sac.

On the ventral side of the embryonic disc, opposite the amnion, cells in the lower layer of the embryonic disk (the **hypoblast**) extend into the blastocyst cavity and form a **yolk sac**. The yolk sac supplies some nutrients absorbed from the trophoblast and also provides primitive blood circulation to the developing embryo for the second and third week of development. When the placenta takes over nourishing the embryo at approximately week 4, the yolk sac has been greatly reduced in size and its main function is to serve as the source of blood cells and germ cells (cells that will give rise to gametes). During week 3, a finger-like outpocketing of the yolk sac develops into the **allantois**, a primitive excretory duct of the embryo that will become part of the urinary bladder. Together, the stalks of the yolk sac and allantois establish the outer structure of the umbilical cord.

The last of the extra-embryonic membranes is the **chorion**, which is the one membrane that surrounds all others. The development of the chorion will be discussed in more detail shortly, as it relates to the growth and development of the placenta.

Embryogenesis

As the third week of development begins, the two-layered disc of cells becomes a three-layered disc through the process of **gastrulation**, during which the cells transition from totipotency to multipotency. The embryo, which takes the shape of an oval-shaped disc, forms an indentation called the **primitive streak** along the dorsal surface of the epiblast. A node at the caudal or "tail" end of the primitive streak emits growth factors that direct cells to multiply and migrate. Cells migrate toward and through the primitive streak and then move laterally to create two new layers of cells. The first layer is the **endoderm**, a sheet of cells that displaces the hypoblast and lies adjacent to the yolk sac. The second layer of cells fills in as the middle layer, or **mesoderm**. The cells of the epiblast that remain (not having migrated through the primitive streak) become the **ectoderm** (Figure 28.9).

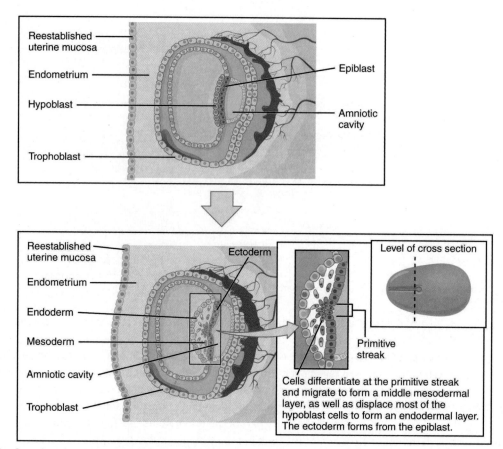

FIGURE 28.9   **Germ Layers**   Formation of the three primary germ layers occurs during the first 2 weeks of development. The embryo at this stage is only a few millimeters in length.

Each of these germ layers will develop into specific structures in the embryo. Whereas the ectoderm and endoderm form tightly connected epithelial sheets, the mesodermal cells are less organized and exist as a loosely connected cell community. The ectoderm gives rise to cell lineages that differentiate to become the central and peripheral nervous systems, sensory organs, epidermis, hair, and nails. Mesodermal cells ultimately become the skeleton, muscles, connective tissue, heart, blood vessels, and kidneys. The endoderm goes on to form the epithelial lining of the gastrointestinal tract, liver, and pancreas, as well as the lungs (Figure 28.10).

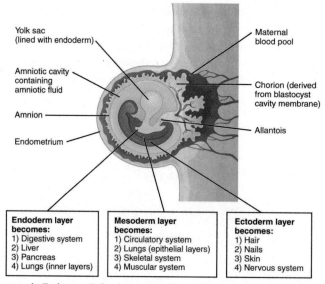

FIGURE 28.10   **Fates of Germ Layers in Embryo**   Following gastrulation of the embryo in the third week, embryonic cells of the ectoderm, mesoderm, and endoderm begin to migrate and differentiate into the cell lineages that will give rise to mature organs and organ systems in the infant.

Access for free at openstax.org

Development of the Placenta

During the first several weeks of development, the cells of the endometrium—referred to as decidual cells—nourish the nascent embryo. During prenatal weeks 4–12, the developing placenta gradually takes over the role of feeding the embryo, and the decidual cells are no longer needed. The mature placenta is composed of tissues derived from the embryo, as well as maternal tissues of the endometrium. The placenta connects to the conceptus via the **umbilical cord**, which carries deoxygenated blood and wastes from the fetus through two umbilical arteries; nutrients and oxygen are carried from the pregnant person to the fetus through the single umbilical vein. The umbilical cord is surrounded by the amnion, and the spaces within the cord around the blood vessels are filled with Wharton's jelly, a mucous connective tissue.

The maternal portion of the placenta develops from the deepest layer of the endometrium, the decidua basalis. To form the embryonic portion of the placenta, the syncytiotrophoblast and the underlying cells of the trophoblast (cytotrophoblast cells) begin to proliferate along with a layer of extraembryonic mesoderm cells. These form the **chorionic membrane**, which envelops the entire conceptus as the chorion. The chorionic membrane forms finger-like structures called **chorionic villi** that burrow into the endometrium like tree roots, making up the fetal portion of the placenta. The cytotrophoblast cells perforate the chorionic villi, burrow farther into the endometrium, and remodel maternal blood vessels to augment maternal blood flow surrounding the villi. Meanwhile, fetal mesenchymal cells derived from the mesoderm fill the villi and differentiate into blood vessels, including the three umbilical blood vessels that connect the embryo to the developing placenta (Figure 28.11).

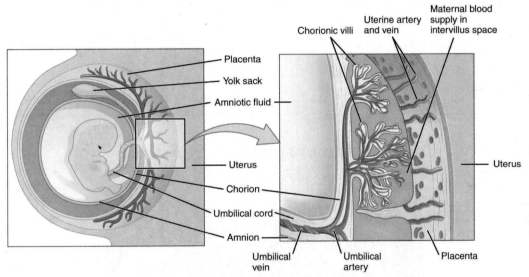

FIGURE 28.11   Cross-Section of the Placenta   In the placenta, maternal and fetal blood components are conducted through the surface of the chorionic villi, but maternal and fetal bloodstreams never mix directly.

The placenta develops throughout the embryonic period and during the first several weeks of the fetal period; **placentation** is complete by weeks 14–16. As a fully developed organ, the placenta provides nutrition and excretion, respiration, and endocrine function (Table 28.1 and Figure 28.12). It receives blood from the fetus through the umbilical arteries. Capillaries in the chorionic villi filter fetal wastes out of the blood and return clean, oxygenated blood to the fetus through the umbilical vein. Nutrients and oxygen are transferred from maternal blood surrounding the villi through the capillaries and into the fetal bloodstream. Some substances move across the placenta by simple diffusion. Oxygen, carbon dioxide, and any other lipid-soluble substances take this route. Other substances move across by facilitated diffusion. This includes water-soluble glucose. The fetus has a high demand for amino acids and iron, and those substances are moved across the placenta by active transport.

Maternal and fetal blood does not commingle because blood cells cannot move across the placenta. This separation prevents the pregnant person's cytotoxic T cells from reaching and subsequently destroying the fetus, which bears "non-self" antigens. Further, it ensures the fetal red blood cells do not enter the pregnant person's circulation and trigger antibody development (if they carry "non-self" antigens)—at least until the final stages of pregnancy or birth. This is the reason that, even in the absence of preventive treatment, an Rh^- person doesn't develop antibodies that could cause hemolytic disease in their first Rh^+ fetus.

Although blood cells are not exchanged, the chorionic villi provide ample surface area for the two-way exchange of substances between maternal and fetal blood. The rate of exchange increases throughout gestation as the villi become thinner and increasingly branched. The placenta is permeable to lipid-soluble fetotoxic substances: alcohol, nicotine, barbiturates, antibiotics, certain pathogens, and many other substances that can be dangerous or fatal to the developing embryo or fetus. For these reasons, pregnant people should avoid fetotoxic substances. Alcohol consumption by pregnant people, for example, can result in a range of abnormalities referred to as fetal alcohol spectrum disorders (FASD). These include organ and facial malformations, as well as cognitive and behavioral disorders.

Functions of the Placenta

Nutrition and digestion	Respiration	Endocrine function
• Mediates diffusion of maternal glucose, amino acids, fatty acids, vitamins, and minerals • Stores nutrients during early pregnancy to accommodate increased fetal demand later in pregnancy • Excretes and filters fetal nitrogenous wastes into maternal blood	• Mediates maternal-to-fetal oxygen transport and fetal-to-maternal carbon dioxide transport	• Secretes several hormones, including hCG, estrogens, and progesterone, to maintain the pregnancy and stimulate maternal and fetal development • Mediates the transmission of maternal hormones into fetal blood and vice versa

TABLE 28.1

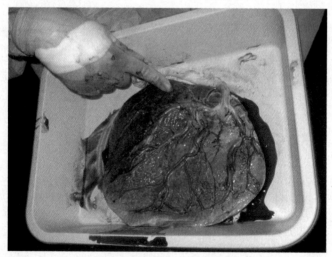

FIGURE 28.12 Placenta   This post-expulsion placenta and umbilical cord (white) are viewed from the fetal side.

Organogenesis

Following gastrulation, rudiments of the central nervous system develop from the ectoderm in the process of **neurulation** (Figure 28.13). Specialized neuroectodermal tissues along the length of the embryo thicken into the **neural plate**. During the fourth week, tissues on either side of the plate fold upward into a **neural fold**. The two folds converge to form the **neural tube**. The tube lies atop a rod-shaped, mesoderm-derived **notochord**, which eventually becomes the nucleus pulposus of intervertebral discs. Block-like structures called **somites** form on either side of the tube, eventually differentiating into the axial skeleton, skeletal muscle, and dermis. During the fourth and fifth weeks, the anterior neural tube dilates and subdivides to form vesicles that will become the brain structures.

Folate, one of the B vitamins, is important to the healthy development of the neural tube. A deficiency of maternal folate in the first weeks of pregnancy can result in neural tube defects, including spina bifida—a birth defect in which spinal tissue protrudes through the newborn's vertebral column, which has failed to completely close. A more severe neural tube defect is anencephaly, a partial or complete absence of brain tissue.

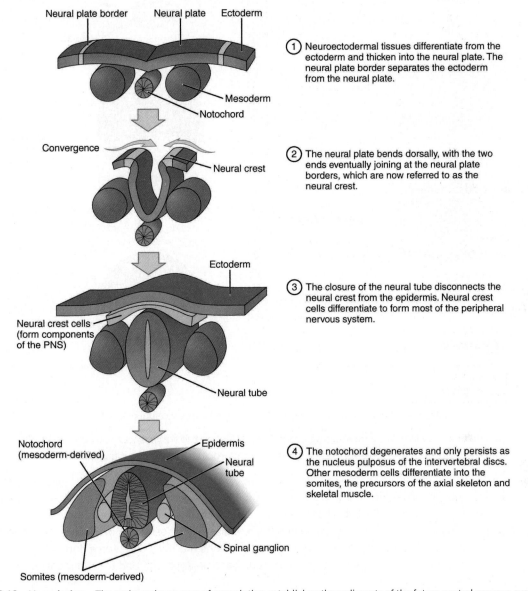

FIGURE 28.13   Neurulation   The embryonic process of neurulation establishes the rudiments of the future central nervous system and skeleton.

The embryo, which begins as a flat sheet of cells, begins to acquire a cylindrical shape through the process of **embryonic folding** (Figure 28.14). The embryo folds laterally and again at either end, forming a C-shape with distinct head and tail ends. The embryo envelops a portion of the yolk sac, which protrudes with the umbilical cord from what will become the abdomen. The folding essentially creates a tube, called the primitive gut, that is lined by the endoderm. The amniotic sac, which was sitting on top of the flat embryo, envelops the embryo as it folds.

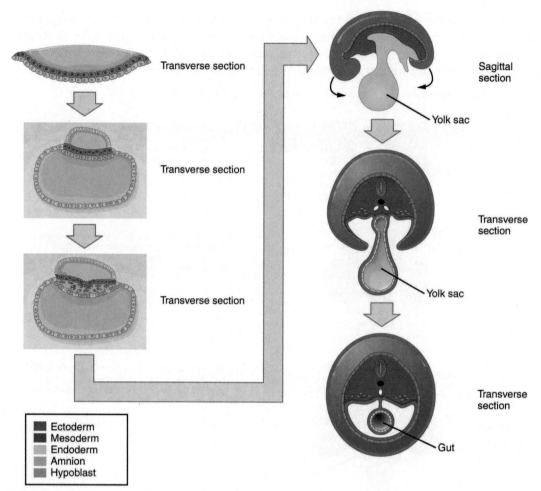

FIGURE 28.14 Embryonic Folding   Embryonic folding converts a flat sheet of cells into a hollow, tube-like structure.

Within the first 8 weeks of gestation, a developing embryo establishes the rudimentary structures of all of its organs and tissues from the ectoderm, mesoderm, and endoderm. This process is called **organogenesis**.

Like the central nervous system, the heart also begins its development in the embryo as a tube-like structure, connected via capillaries to the chorionic villi. Cells of the primitive tube-shaped heart are capable of electrical conduction and contraction. The heart begins beating in the beginning of the fourth week, although it does not actually pump embryonic blood until a week later, when the oversized liver has begun producing red blood cells. (This is a temporary responsibility of the embryonic liver that the bone marrow will assume during fetal development.) During weeks 4–5, the eye pits form, limb buds become apparent, and the rudiments of the pulmonary system are formed.

During the sixth week, uncontrolled fetal limb movements begin to occur. The gastrointestinal system develops too rapidly for the embryonic abdomen to accommodate it, and the intestines temporarily loop into the umbilical cord. Paddle-shaped hands and feet develop fingers and toes by the process of apoptosis (programmed cell death), which causes the tissues between the fingers to disintegrate. By week 7, the facial structure is more complex and includes nostrils, outer ears, and lenses (Figure 28.15). By the eighth week, the head is nearly as large as the rest of the embryo's body, and all major brain structures are in place. The external genitalia are apparent, but at this point, male and female embryos are indistinguishable. Bone begins to replace cartilage in the embryonic skeleton through the process of ossification. By the end of the embryonic period, the embryo is approximately 3 cm (1.2 in) from crown to rump and weighs approximately 8 g (0.25 oz).

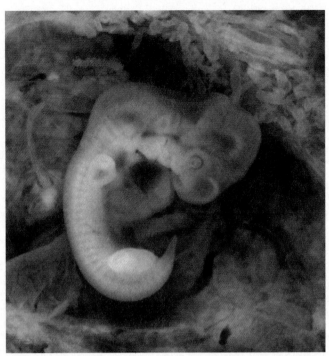

FIGURE 28.15 **Embryo at 7 Weeks**   An embryo at the end of 7 weeks of development is only 10 mm in length, but its developing eyes, limb buds, and tail are already visible. (This embryo was derived from an ectopic pregnancy.) (credit: Ed Uthman)

⊚ INTERACTIVE LINK

Watch this video (http://openstax.org/l/embryogenesis) to view the process of embryogenesis from fertilization through pregnancy to birth. Can you identify when neurulation occurs in the embryo?

28.3 Fetal Development

LEARNING OBJECTIVES

By the end of this section, you will be able to:

- Differentiate between the embryonic period and the fetal period
- Briefly describe the process of sexual differentiation
- Describe the fetal circulatory system and explain the role of the shunts
- Trace the development of a fetus from the end of the embryonic period to birth

As you will recall, a developing human is called a fetus from the ninth week of gestation until birth. This 30-week period of development is marked by continued cell growth and differentiation, which fully develop the structures and functions of the immature organ systems formed during the embryonic period. The completion of fetal development results in a newborn who, although still immature in many ways, is capable of survival outside the womb.

Sexual Differentiation

Sexual differentiation does not begin until the fetal period, during weeks 9–12. Embryonic males and females, though genetically distinguishable, are morphologically identical (Figure 28.16). Bipotential gonads, or gonads that can develop into male or female sexual organs, are connected to a central cavity called the cloaca via Müllerian ducts and Wolffian ducts. (The cloaca is an extension of the primitive gut.) Several events lead to sexual differentiation during this period.

During male fetal development, the bipotential gonads become the testes and associated epididymis. The Müllerian ducts degenerate. The Wolffian ducts become the vas deferens, and the cloaca becomes the urethra and rectum.

During female fetal development, the bipotential gonads develop into ovaries. The Wolffian ducts degenerate. The Müllerian ducts become the uterine tubes and uterus, and the cloaca divides and develops into a vagina, a urethra, and a rectum.

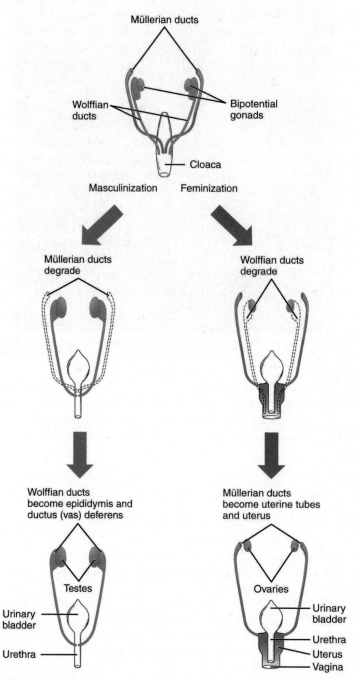

FIGURE 28.16   Sexual Differentiation   Differentiation of the male and female reproductive systems does not occur until the fetal period of development.

The Fetal Circulatory System

During prenatal development, the fetal circulatory system is integrated with the placenta via the umbilical cord so that the fetus receives both oxygen and nutrients from the placenta. However, after childbirth, the umbilical cord is severed, and the newborn's circulatory system must be reconfigured. When the heart first forms in the embryo, it exists as two parallel tubes derived from mesoderm and lined with endothelium, which then fuse together. As the embryo develops into a fetus, the tube-shaped heart folds and further differentiates into the four chambers present in a mature heart. Unlike a mature cardiovascular system, however, the fetal cardiovascular system also includes circulatory shortcuts, or shunts. A **shunt** is an anatomical (or sometimes surgical) diversion that allows blood flow to bypass immature organs such as the lungs and liver until childbirth.

The placenta provides the fetus with necessary oxygen and nutrients via the umbilical vein. (Remember that veins carry blood toward the heart. In this case, the blood flowing to the fetal heart is oxygenated because it comes from the placenta. The respiratory system is immature and cannot yet oxygenate blood on its own.) From the umbilical vein, the oxygenated blood flows toward the inferior vena cava, all but bypassing the immature liver, via the **ductus venosus** shunt (Figure 28.17). The liver receives just a trickle of blood, which is all that it needs in its immature, semifunctional state. Blood flows from the inferior vena cava to the right atrium, mixing with fetal venous blood along the way.

Although the fetal liver is semifunctional, the fetal lungs are nonfunctional. The fetal circulation therefore bypasses the lungs by shifting some of the blood through the **foramen ovale**, a shunt that directly connects the right and left atria and avoids the pulmonary trunk altogether. Most of the rest of the blood is pumped to the right ventricle, and from there, into the pulmonary trunk, which splits into pulmonary arteries. However, a shunt within the pulmonary artery, the **ductus arteriosus**, diverts a portion of this blood into the aorta. This ensures that only a small volume of oxygenated blood passes through the immature pulmonary circuit, which has only minor metabolic requirements. Blood vessels of uninflated lungs have high resistance to flow, a condition that encourages blood to flow to the aorta, which presents much lower resistance. The oxygenated blood moves through the foramen ovale into the left atrium, where it mixes with the now deoxygenated blood returning from the pulmonary circuit. This blood then moves into the left ventricle, where it is pumped into the aorta. Some of this blood moves through the coronary arteries into the myocardium, and some moves through the carotid arteries to the brain.

The descending aorta carries partially oxygenated and partially deoxygenated blood into the lower regions of the body. It eventually passes into the umbilical arteries through branches of the internal iliac arteries. The deoxygenated blood collects waste as it circulates through the fetal body and returns to the umbilical cord. Thus, the two umbilical arteries carry blood low in oxygen and high in carbon dioxide and fetal wastes. This blood is filtered through the placenta, where wastes diffuse into the maternal circulation. Oxygen and nutrients from the pregnant person diffuse into the placenta and from there into the fetal blood, and the process repeats.

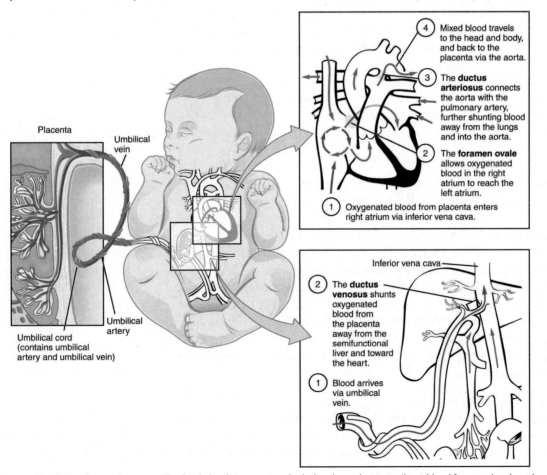

FIGURE 28.17 Fetal Circulatory System The fetal circulatory system includes three shunts to divert blood from undeveloped and

partially functioning organs, as well as blood supply to and from the placenta.

Other Organ Systems

During weeks 9–12 of fetal development, the brain continues to expand, the body elongates, and ossification continues. Fetal movements are frequent during this period, but are jerky and not well-controlled. The bone marrow begins to take over the process of erythrocyte production—a task that the liver performed during the embryonic period. The liver now secretes bile. The fetus circulates amniotic fluid by swallowing it and producing urine. The eyes are well-developed by this stage, but the eyelids are fused shut. The fingers and toes begin to develop nails. By the end of week 12, the fetus measures approximately 9 cm (3.5 in) from crown to rump.

Weeks 13–16 are marked by sensory organ development. The eyes move closer together; blinking motions begin, although the eyes remain sealed shut. The lips exhibit sucking motions. The ears move upward and lie flatter against the head. The scalp begins to grow hair. The excretory system is also developing: the kidneys are well-formed, and **meconium**, or fetal feces, begins to accumulate in the intestines. Meconium consists of ingested amniotic fluid, cellular debris, mucus, and bile.

During approximately weeks 16–20, as the fetus grows and limb movements become more powerful, the pregnant person may begin to feel **quickening**, or fetal movements. However, space restrictions limit these movements and typically force the growing fetus into the "fetal position," with the arms crossed and the legs bent at the knees. Sebaceous glands coat the skin with a waxy, protective substance called **vernix caseosa** that protects and moisturizes the skin and may provide lubrication during childbirth. A silky hair called **lanugo** also covers the skin during weeks 17–20, but it is shed as the fetus continues to grow. Extremely premature infants sometimes exhibit residual lanugo.

Developmental weeks 21–30 are characterized by rapid weight gain, which is important for maintaining a stable body temperature after birth. The bone marrow completely takes over erythrocyte synthesis, and the axons of the spinal cord begin to be myelinated, or coated in the electrically insulating glial cell sheaths that are necessary for efficient nervous system functioning. (The process of myelination is not completed until adolescence.) During this period, the fetus grows eyelashes. The eyelids are no longer fused and can be opened and closed. The lungs begin producing surfactant, a substance that reduces surface tension in the lungs and assists proper lung expansion after birth. Inadequate surfactant production in premature newborns may result in respiratory distress syndrome, and as a result, the newborn may require surfactant replacement therapy, supplemental oxygen, or maintenance in a continuous positive airway pressure (CPAP) chamber during their first days or weeks of life. In male fetuses, the testes descend into the scrotum near the end of this period. The fetus at 30 weeks measures 28 cm (11 in) from crown to rump and exhibits the approximate body proportions of a full-term newborn, but still is much leaner.

🔗 INTERACTIVE LINK

Visit this site (http://openstax.org/l/pregstages) for a summary of the stages of pregnancy, as experienced by the pregnant person, and view the stages of development of the fetus throughout gestation. At what point in fetal development can a regular heartbeat be detected?

The fetus continues to lay down subcutaneous fat from week 31 until birth. The added fat fills out the hypodermis, and the skin transitions from red and wrinkled to soft and pink. Lanugo is shed, and the nails grow to the tips of the fingers and toes. Immediately before birth, the average crown-to-rump length is 35.5–40.5 cm (14–16 in), and the fetus weighs approximately 2.5–4 kg (5.5–8.8 lbs). Once born, the newborn is no longer confined to the fetal position, so subsequent measurements are made from head-to-toe instead of from crown-to-rump. At birth, the average length is approximately 51 cm (20 in).

Disorders of the...

Developing Fetus

Throughout the second half of gestation, the fetal intestines accumulate a tarry, greenish black meconium. The newborn's first stools consist almost entirely of meconium; they later transition to seedy yellow stools or slightly formed tan stools as meconium is cleared and replaced with digested breast milk or formula, respectively.

Unlike these later stools, meconium is sterile; it is devoid of bacteria because the fetus is in a sterile environment and has not consumed any breast milk or formula. Typically, an infant does not pass meconium until after birth. However, in 5–20 percent of births, the fetus has a bowel movement in utero, which can cause major complications in the newborn.

The passage of meconium in the uterus signals fetal distress, particularly fetal hypoxia (i.e., oxygen deprivation). This may be caused by maternal drug abuse (especially tobacco or cocaine), maternal hypertension, depletion of amniotic fluid, long labor or difficult birth, or a defect in the placenta that prevents it from delivering adequate oxygen to the fetus. Meconium passage is typically a complication of full-term or post-term newborns because it is rarely passed before 34 weeks of gestation, when the gastrointestinal system has matured and is appropriately controlled by nervous system stimuli. Fetal distress can stimulate the vagus nerve to trigger gastrointestinal peristalsis and relaxation of the anal sphincter. Notably, fetal hypoxic stress also induces a gasping reflex, increasing the likelihood that meconium will be inhaled into the fetal lungs.

Although meconium is a sterile substance, it interferes with the antibiotic properties of the amniotic fluid and makes the newborn and pregnant person more vulnerable to bacterial infections at birth and during the perinatal period. Specifically, inflammation of the fetal membranes, inflammation of the uterine lining, or neonatal sepsis (infection in the newborn) may occur. Meconium also irritates delicate fetal skin and can cause a rash.

The first sign that a fetus has passed meconium usually does not come until childbirth, when the amniotic sac ruptures. Normal amniotic fluid is clear and watery, but amniotic fluid in which meconium has been passed is stained greenish or yellowish.

Aspiration of meconium with the first breath can result in labored breathing, a barrel-shaped chest, or a low Apgar score. An obstetrician can identify meconium aspiration by listening to the lungs with a stethoscope for a coarse rattling sound. Blood gas tests and chest X-rays of the infant can confirm meconium aspiration. Inhaled meconium after birth could obstruct a newborn's airways leading to alveolar collapse, interfere with surfactant function by stripping it from the lungs, or cause pulmonary inflammation or hypertension. Any of these complications will make the newborn much more vulnerable to pulmonary infection, including pneumonia.

28.4 Changes During Pregnancy, Labor, and Birth

LEARNING OBJECTIVES

By the end of this section, you will be able to:
- Explain how estrogen, progesterone, and hCG are involved in maintaining pregnancy
- List the contributors to weight gain during pregnancy
- Describe the major changes to the maternal digestive, circulatory, and integumentary systems during pregnancy
- Summarize the events leading to labor
- Identify and describe each of the three stages of childbirth

A full-term pregnancy lasts approximately 270 days (approximately 38.5 weeks) from conception to birth. Because it is easier to remember the first day of the last menstrual period (LMP) than to estimate the date of conception, obstetricians set the due date as 284 days (approximately 40.5 weeks) from the LMP. This assumes that conception occurred on day 14 of the menstrual cycle, which is usually a good approximation. The 40 weeks of an average pregnancy are usually discussed in terms of three **trimesters**, each approximately 13 weeks. During the second and third trimesters, the pre-pregnancy uterus—about the size of a fist—grows dramatically to contain the fetus, causing a number of anatomical changes in the pregnant person (Figure 28.18).

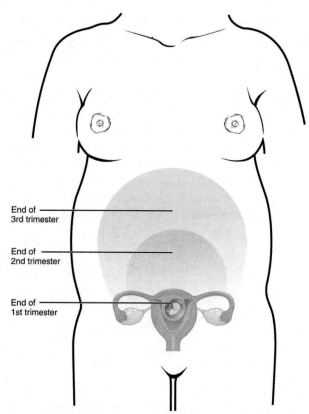

End of
3rd trimester

End of
2nd trimester

End of
1st trimester

FIGURE 28.18   Size of Uterus throughout Pregnancy   The uterus grows throughout pregnancy to accommodate the fetus.

Effects of Hormones

Virtually all of the effects of pregnancy can be attributed in some way to the influence of hormones—particularly estrogens, progesterone, and hCG. During weeks 7–12 from the LMP, the pregnancy hormones are primarily generated by the corpus luteum. Progesterone secreted by the corpus luteum stimulates the production of decidual cells of the endometrium that nourish the blastocyst before placentation. As the placenta develops and the corpus luteum degenerates during weeks 12–17, the placenta gradually takes over as the endocrine organ of pregnancy.

The placenta converts weak androgens secreted by the maternal and fetal adrenal glands to estrogens, which are necessary for pregnancy to progress. Estrogen levels climb throughout the pregnancy, increasing 30-fold by childbirth. Estrogens have the following actions:

- They suppress FSH and LH production, effectively preventing ovulation. (This function is the biological basis of hormonal birth control pills.)
- They induce the growth of fetal tissues and are necessary for the maturation of the fetal lungs and liver.
- They promote fetal viability by regulating progesterone production and triggering fetal synthesis of cortisol, which helps with the maturation of the lungs, liver, and endocrine organs such as the thyroid gland and adrenal gland.
- They stimulate maternal tissue growth, leading to uterine enlargement and mammary duct expansion and branching.

Relaxin, another hormone secreted by the corpus luteum and then by the placenta, helps prepare the body for childbirth. It increases the elasticity of the symphysis pubis joint and pelvic ligaments, making room for the growing fetus and allowing expansion of the pelvic outlet for childbirth. Relaxin also helps dilate the cervix during labor.

The placenta takes over the synthesis and secretion of progesterone throughout pregnancy as the corpus luteum degenerates. Like estrogen, progesterone suppresses FSH and LH. It also inhibits uterine contractions, protecting the fetus from preterm birth. This hormone decreases in late gestation, allowing uterine contractions to intensify and eventually progress to true labor. The placenta also produces hCG. In addition to promoting survival of the corpus luteum, hCG stimulates the male fetal gonads to secrete testosterone, which is essential for the development of the male reproductive system.

The anterior pituitary enlarges and ramps up its hormone production during pregnancy, raising the levels of thyrotropin, prolactin, and adrenocorticotropic hormone (ACTH). Thyrotropin, in conjunction with placental hormones, increases the production of thyroid hormone, which raises the maternal metabolic rate. This can markedly augment a pregnant person's appetite and cause hot flashes. Prolactin stimulates enlargement of the mammary glands in preparation for milk production. ACTH stimulates maternal cortisol secretion, which contributes to fetal protein synthesis. In addition to the pituitary hormones, increased parathyroid levels mobilize calcium from maternal bones for fetal use.

Weight Gain

The second and third trimesters of pregnancy are associated with dramatic changes in maternal anatomy and physiology. The most obvious anatomical sign of pregnancy is the dramatic enlargement of the abdominal region, coupled with weight gain. This weight results from the growing fetus as well as the enlarged uterus, amniotic fluid, and placenta. Additional breast tissue and dramatically increased blood volume also contribute to weight gain (Table 28.2). Surprisingly, fat storage accounts for only approximately 2.3 kg (5 lbs) in a normal pregnancy and serves as a reserve for the increased metabolic demand of breastfeeding.

During the first trimester, a pregnant person does not need to consume additional calories to maintain a healthy pregnancy. However, a weight gain of approximately 0.45 kg (1 lb) per month is common. During the second and third trimesters, the appetite increases, but it is only necessary to consume an additional 300 calories per day to support the growing fetus. Most pregnant people gain approximately 0.45 kg (1 lb) per week.

Contributors to Weight Gain During Pregnancy

Component	Weight (kg)	Weight (lb)
Fetus	3.2–3.6	7–8
Placenta and fetal membranes	0.9–1.8	2–4
Amniotic fluid	0.9–1.4	2–3
Breast tissue	0.9–1.4	2–3
Blood	1.4	4
Fat	0.9–4.1	3–9
Uterus	0.9–2.3	2–5
Total	10–16.3	22–36

TABLE 28.2

Changes in Organ Systems During Pregnancy

As the body adapts to pregnancy, characteristic physiologic changes occur. These changes can sometimes prompt symptoms often referred to collectively as the common discomforts of pregnancy.

Digestive and Urinary System Changes

Nausea and vomiting, sometimes triggered by an increased sensitivity to odors, are common during the first few weeks to months of pregnancy. This phenomenon is often referred to as "morning sickness," although the nausea may persist all day. The source of pregnancy nausea is thought to be the increased circulation of pregnancy-related hormones, specifically circulating estrogen, progesterone, and hCG. Decreased intestinal peristalsis may also contribute to nausea. By about week 12 of pregnancy, nausea typically subsides.

A common gastrointestinal complaint during the later stages of pregnancy is gastric reflux, or heartburn, which results from the upward, constrictive pressure of the growing uterus on the stomach. The same decreased peristalsis that may contribute to nausea in early pregnancy is also thought to be responsible for pregnancy-related constipation as pregnancy progresses.

The downward pressure of the uterus also compresses the urinary bladder, leading to frequent urination. The problem is exacerbated by increased urine production. In addition, the maternal urinary system processes both maternal and fetal wastes, further increasing the total volume of urine.

Circulatory System Changes

Blood volume increases substantially during pregnancy, so that by childbirth, it exceeds its preconception volume by 30 percent, or approximately 1–2 liters. The greater blood volume helps to manage the demands of fetal nourishment and fetal waste removal. In conjunction with increased blood volume, the pulse and blood pressure also rise moderately during pregnancy. As the fetus grows, the uterus compresses underlying pelvic blood vessels, hampering venous return from the legs and pelvic region. As a result, many pregnant people develop varicose veins or hemorrhoids.

Respiratory System Changes

During the second half of pregnancy, the respiratory minute volume (volume of gas inhaled or exhaled by the lungs per minute) increases by 50 percent to compensate for the oxygen demands of the fetus and the increased maternal metabolic rate. The growing uterus exerts upward pressure on the diaphragm, decreasing the volume of each inspiration and potentially causing shortness of breath, or dyspnea. During the last several weeks of pregnancy, the pelvis becomes more elastic, and the fetus descends lower in a process called **lightening**. This typically ameliorates dyspnea.

The respiratory mucosa swell in response to increased blood flow during pregnancy, leading to nasal congestion and nose bleeds, particularly when the weather is cold and dry. Humidifier use and increased fluid intake are often recommended to counteract congestion.

Integumentary System Changes

The dermis stretches extensively to accommodate the growing uterus, breast tissue, and fat deposits on the thighs and hips. Torn connective tissue beneath the dermis can cause striae (stretch marks) on the abdomen, which appear as red or purple marks during pregnancy that fade to a silvery white color in the months after childbirth.

An increase in melanocyte-stimulating hormone, in conjunction with estrogens, darkens the areolae and creates a line of pigment from the umbilicus to the pubis called the linea nigra (Figure 28.19). Melanin production during pregnancy may also darken or discolor skin on the face to create a chloasma, or "mask of pregnancy."

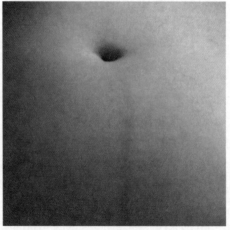

FIGURE 28.19   Linea Nigra   The linea nigra, a dark medial line running from the umbilicus to the pubis, forms during pregnancy and persists for a few weeks following childbirth. The linea nigra shown here corresponds to a pregnancy that is 22 weeks along.

Physiology of Labor

Childbirth, or **parturition**, typically occurs within a week of the due date, unless the pregnancy involves more than one fetus, which usually causes labor to begin early. As a pregnancy progresses into its final weeks, several physiological changes occur in response to hormones that trigger labor.

First, recall that progesterone inhibits uterine contractions throughout the first several months of pregnancy. As the pregnancy enters its seventh month, progesterone levels plateau and then drop. Estrogen levels, however, continue to rise in the maternal circulation (Figure 28.20). The increasing ratio of estrogen to progesterone makes the myometrium (the uterine smooth muscle) more sensitive to stimuli that promote contractions (because progesterone no longer inhibits them). Moreover, in the eighth month of pregnancy, fetal cortisol rises, which boosts estrogen secretion by the placenta and further overpowers the uterine-calming effects of progesterone. Some people may feel the result of the decreasing levels of progesterone in late pregnancy as weak and irregular peristaltic **Braxton Hicks contractions**, also called false labor. These contractions can often be relieved with rest or hydration.

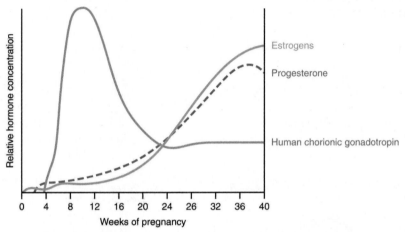

FIGURE 28.20   Hormones Initiating Labor   A positive feedback loop of hormones works to initiate labor.

A common sign that labor will be short is the so-called "bloody show." During pregnancy, a plug of mucus accumulates in the cervical canal, blocking the entrance to the uterus. Approximately 1–2 days prior to the onset of true labor, this plug loosens and is expelled, along with a small amount of blood.

Meanwhile, the posterior pituitary has been boosting its secretion of oxytocin, a hormone that stimulates the contractions of labor. At the same time, the myometrium increases its sensitivity to oxytocin by expressing more receptors for this hormone. As labor nears, oxytocin begins to stimulate stronger, more painful uterine contractions, which—in a positive feedback loop—stimulate the secretion of prostaglandins from fetal membranes. Like oxytocin, prostaglandins also enhance uterine contractile strength. The fetal pituitary also secretes oxytocin, which increases prostaglandins even further. Given the importance of oxytocin and prostaglandins to the initiation and maintenance of labor, it is not surprising that, when a pregnancy is not progressing to labor and needs to be induced, a pharmaceutical version of these compounds (called pitocin) is administered by intravenous drip.

Finally, stretching of the myometrium and cervix by a full-term fetus in the vertex (head-down) position is regarded as a stimulant to uterine contractions. The sum of these changes initiates the regular contractions known as **true labor**, which become more powerful and more frequent with time. The pain of labor is attributed to myometrial hypoxia during uterine contractions.

Stages of Childbirth

The process of childbirth can be divided into three stages: cervical dilation, expulsion of the newborn, and afterbirth (Figure 28.21).

Cervical Dilation

For vaginal birth to occur, the cervix must dilate fully to 10 cm in diameter—wide enough to deliver the newborn's head. The **dilation** stage is the longest stage of labor and typically takes 6–12 hours. However, it varies widely and may take minutes, hours, or days, depending in part on whether the person has given birth before; in each subsequent labor, this stage tends to be shorter.

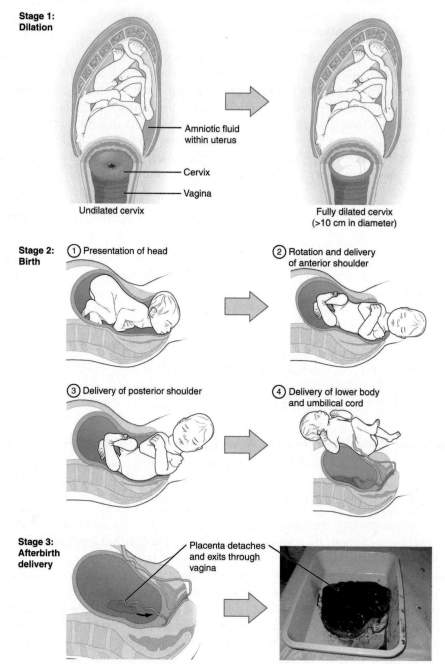

Stage 1: Dilation

Amniotic fluid within uterus

Cervix

Vagina

Undilated cervix

Fully dilated cervix (>10 cm in diameter)

Stage 2: Birth

① Presentation of head

② Rotation and delivery of anterior shoulder

③ Delivery of posterior shoulder

④ Delivery of lower body and umbilical cord

Stage 3: Afterbirth delivery

Placenta detaches and exits through vagina

FIGURE 28.21   Stages of Childbirth   The stages of childbirth include Stage 1, early cervical dilation; Stage 2, full dilation and expulsion of the newborn; and Stage 3, delivery of the placenta and associated fetal membranes. (The position of the newborn's shoulder is described relative to the person giving birth.)

True labor progresses in a positive feedback loop in which uterine contractions stretch the cervix, causing it to dilate and efface, or become thinner. Cervical stretching induces reflexive uterine contractions that dilate and efface the cervix further. In addition, cervical dilation boosts oxytocin secretion from the pituitary, which in turn triggers more powerful uterine contractions. When labor begins, uterine contractions may occur only every 3–30 minutes and last only 20–40 seconds; however, by the end of this stage, contractions may occur as frequently as every 1.5–2 minutes and last for a full minute.

Each contraction sharply reduces oxygenated blood flow to the fetus. For this reason, it is critical that a period of relaxation occur after each contraction. Fetal distress, measured as a sustained decrease or increase in the fetal

Access for free at openstax.org

heart rate, can result from severe contractions that are too powerful or lengthy for oxygenated blood to be restored to the fetus. Such a situation can be cause for an emergency birth with vacuum, forceps, or surgically by Caesarian section.

The amniotic membranes rupture before the onset of labor in about 12 percent of people; they typically rupture at the end of the dilation stage in response to excessive pressure from the fetal head entering the birth canal.

Expulsion Stage

The **expulsion** stage begins when the fetal head enters the birth canal and ends with birth of the newborn. It typically takes up to 2 hours, but it can last longer or be completed in minutes, depending in part on the orientation of the fetus. The vertex presentation known as the occiput anterior vertex is the most common presentation and is associated with the greatest ease of vaginal birth. The fetus faces the maternal spinal cord and the smallest part of the head (the posterior aspect called the occiput) exits the birth canal first.

In fewer than 5 percent of births, the infant is oriented in the breech presentation, or buttocks down. In a complete breech, both legs are crossed and oriented downward. In a frank breech presentation, the legs are oriented upward. Before the 1960s, it was common for breech presentations to be delivered vaginally. Today, most breech births are accomplished by Caesarian section.

Vaginal birth is associated with significant stretching of the vaginal canal, the cervix, and the perineum. Until recent decades, it was routine procedure for an obstetrician to numb the perineum and perform an **episiotomy**, an incision in the posterior vaginal wall and perineum. The perineum is now more commonly allowed to tear on its own during birth. Both an episiotomy and a perineal tear need to be sutured shortly after birth to ensure optimal healing. Although suturing the jagged edges of a perineal tear may be more difficult than suturing an episiotomy, tears heal more quickly, are less painful, and are associated with less damage to the muscles around the vagina and rectum.

Upon birth of the newborn's head, an obstetrician will aspirate mucus from the mouth and nose before the newborn's first breath. Once the head is birthed, the rest of the body usually follows quickly. The umbilical cord is then double-clamped, and a cut is made between the clamps. This completes the second stage of childbirth.

Afterbirth

The delivery of the placenta and associated membranes, commonly referred to as the **afterbirth**, marks the final stage of childbirth. After expulsion of the newborn, the myometrium continues to contract. This movement shears the placenta from the back of the uterine wall. It is then easily delivered through the vagina. Continued uterine contractions then reduce blood loss from the site of the placenta. Delivery of the placenta marks the beginning of the postpartum period—the period of approximately 6 weeks immediately following childbirth during which the body gradually returns to a non-pregnant state. If the placenta does not birth spontaneously within approximately 30 minutes, it is considered retained, and the obstetrician may attempt manual removal. If this is not successful, surgery may be required.

It is important that the obstetrician examines the expelled placenta and fetal membranes to ensure that they are intact. If fragments of the placenta remain in the uterus, they can cause postpartum hemorrhage. Uterine contractions continue for several hours after birth to return the uterus to its pre-pregnancy size in a process called **involution**, which also allows the abdominal organs to return to their pre-pregnancy locations. Breastfeeding facilitates this process.

Although postpartum uterine contractions limit blood loss from the detachment of the placenta, the person who has recently given birth does experience a postpartum vaginal discharge called **lochia**. This is made up of uterine lining cells, erythrocytes, leukocytes, and other debris. Thick, dark, lochia rubra (red lochia) typically continues for 2–3 days, and is replaced by lochia serosa, a thinner, pinkish form that continues until about the tenth postpartum day. After this period, a scant, creamy, or watery discharge called lochia alba (white lochia) may continue for another 1–2 weeks.

28.5 Adjustments of the Infant at Birth and Postnatal Stages

LEARNING OBJECTIVES

By the end of this section, you will be able to:

- Discuss the importance of an infant's first breath
- Explain the closing of the cardiac shunts
- Describe thermoregulation in the newborn
- Summarize the importance of intestinal flora in the newborn

From a fetal perspective, the process of birth is a crisis. In the womb, the fetus was snuggled in a soft, warm, dark, and quiet world. The placenta provided nutrition and oxygen continuously. Suddenly, the contractions of labor and vaginal childbirth forcibly squeeze the fetus through the birth canal, limiting oxygenated blood flow during contractions and shifting the skull bones to accommodate the small space. After birth, the newborn's system must make drastic adjustments to a world that is colder, brighter, and louder, and where they will experience hunger and thirst. The neonatal period (neo- = "new"; -natal = "birth") spans the first to the thirtieth day of life outside of the uterus.

Respiratory Adjustments

Although the fetus "practices" breathing by inhaling amniotic fluid in utero, there is no air in the uterus and thus no true opportunity to breathe. (There is also no need to breathe because the placenta supplies the fetus with all the oxygenated blood it needs.) During gestation, the partially collapsed lungs are filled with amniotic fluid and exhibit very little metabolic activity. Several factors stimulate newborns to take their first breath at birth. First, labor contractions temporarily constrict umbilical blood vessels, reducing oxygenated blood flow to the fetus and elevating carbon dioxide levels in the blood. High carbon dioxide levels cause acidosis and stimulate the respiratory center in the brain, triggering the newborn to take a breath.

The first breath typically is taken within 10 seconds of birth, after mucus is aspirated from the infant's mouth and nose. The first breaths inflate the lungs to nearly full capacity and dramatically decrease lung pressure and resistance to blood flow, causing a major circulatory reconfiguration. Pulmonary alveoli open, and alveolar capillaries fill with blood. Amniotic fluid in the lungs drains or is absorbed, and the lungs immediately take over the task of the placenta, exchanging carbon dioxide for oxygen by the process of respiration.

Circulatory Adjustments

The process of clamping and cutting the umbilical cord collapses the umbilical blood vessels. In the absence of medical assistance, this occlusion would occur naturally within 20 minutes of birth because the Wharton's jelly within the umbilical cord would swell in response to the lower temperature outside of the mother's body, and the blood vessels would constrict. Natural occlusion has occurred when the umbilical cord is no longer pulsating. For the most part, the collapsed vessels atrophy and become fibrotic remnants, existing in the mature circulatory system as ligaments of the abdominal wall and liver. The ductus venosus degenerates to become the ligamentum venosum beneath the liver. Only the proximal sections of the two umbilical arteries remain functional, taking on the role of supplying blood to the upper part of the bladder (Figure 28.22).

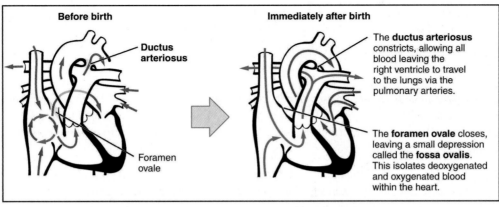

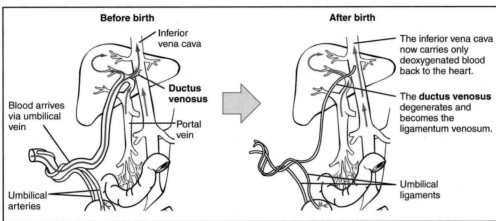

FIGURE 28.22 Neonatal Circulatory System A newborn's circulatory system reconfigures immediately after birth. The three fetal shunts have been closed permanently, facilitating blood flow to the liver and lungs.

The newborn's first breath is vital to initiate the transition from the fetal to the neonatal circulatory pattern. Inflation of the lungs decreases blood pressure throughout the pulmonary system, as well as in the right atrium and ventricle. In response to this pressure change, the flow of blood temporarily reverses direction through the foramen ovale, moving from the left to the right atrium, and blocking the shunt with two flaps of tissue. Within 1 year, the tissue flaps usually fuse over the shunt, turning the foramen ovale into the fossa ovalis. The ductus arteriosus constricts as a result of increased oxygen concentration, and becomes the ligamentum arteriosum. Closing of the ductus arteriosus ensures that all blood pumped to the pulmonary circuit will be oxygenated by the newly functional neonatal lungs.

Thermoregulatory Adjustments

The fetus floats in warm amniotic fluid that is maintained at a temperature of approximately 98.6°F with very little fluctuation. Birth exposes newborns to a cooler environment in which they have to regulate their own body temperature. Newborns have a higher ratio of surface area to volume than adults. This means that their body has less volume throughout which to produce heat, and more surface area from which to lose heat. As a result, newborns produce heat more slowly and lose it more quickly. Newborns also have immature musculature that limits their ability to generate heat by shivering. Moreover, their nervous systems are underdeveloped, so they cannot quickly constrict superficial blood vessels in response to cold. They also have little subcutaneous fat for insulation. All these factors make it harder for newborns to maintain their body temperature.

Newborns, however, do have a special method for generating heat: **nonshivering thermogenesis**, which involves the breakdown of **brown adipose tissue**, or brown fat, which is distributed over the back, chest, and shoulders. Brown fat differs from the more familiar white fat in two ways:

- It is highly vascularized. This allows for faster delivery of oxygen, which leads to faster cellular respiration.
- It is packed with a special type of mitochondria that are able to engage in cellular respiration reactions that produce less ATP and more heat than standard cellular respiration reactions.

The breakdown of brown fat occurs automatically upon exposure to cold, so it is an important heat regulator in newborns. During fetal development, the placenta secretes inhibitors that prevent metabolism of brown adipose fat and promote its accumulation in preparation for birth.

Gastrointestinal and Urinary Adjustments

In adults, the gastrointestinal tract harbors bacterial flora—trillions of bacteria that aid in digestion, produce vitamins, and protect from the invasion or replication of pathogens. In stark contrast, the fetal intestine is sterile. The first consumption of breast milk or formula floods the neonatal gastrointestinal tract with beneficial bacteria that begin to establish the bacterial flora.

The fetal kidneys filter blood and produce urine, but the neonatal kidneys are still immature and inefficient at concentrating urine. Therefore, newborns produce very dilute urine, making it particularly important for infants to obtain sufficient fluids from breast milk or formula.

 HOMEOSTATIC IMBALANCES

Homeostasis in the Newborn: Apgar Score

In the minutes following birth, a newborn must undergo dramatic systemic changes to be able to survive outside the womb. An obstetrician, midwife, or nurse can estimate how well a newborn is doing by obtaining an Apgar score. The Apgar score was introduced in 1952 by the anesthesiologist Dr. Virginia Apgar as a method to assess the effects on the newborn of anesthesia given to the person giving birth. Healthcare providers now use it to assess the general wellbeing of the newborn, whether or not analgesics or anesthetics were used.

Five criteria—skin color, heart rate, reflex, muscle tone, and respiration—are assessed, and each criterion is assigned a score of 0, 1, or 2. Scores are taken at 1 minute after birth and again at 5 minutes after birth. Each time that scores are taken, the five scores are added together. High scores (out of a possible 10) indicate the baby has made the transition from the womb well, whereas lower scores indicate that the baby may be in distress.

The technique for determining an Apgar score is quick and easy, painless for the newborn, and does not require any instruments except for a stethoscope. A convenient way to remember the five scoring criteria is to apply the mnemonic APGAR, for "appearance" (skin color), "pulse" (heart rate), "grimace" (reflex), "activity" (muscle tone), and "respiration."

Of the five Apgar criteria, heart rate and respiration are the most critical. Poor scores for either of these measurements may indicate the need for immediate medical attention to resuscitate or stabilize the newborn. In general, any score lower than 7 at the 5-minute mark indicates that medical assistance may be needed. A total score below 5 indicates an emergency situation. Normally, a newborn will get an intermediate score of 1 for some of the Apgar criteria and will progress to a 2 by the 5-minute assessment. Scores of 8 or above are normal.

28.6 Lactation

LEARNING OBJECTIVES

By the end of this section, you will be able to:
- Describe the structure of the lactating breast
- Summarize the process of lactation
- Explain how the composition of breast milk changes during the first days of lactation and in the course of a single feeding

Lactation is the process by which milk is synthesized and secreted from the mammary glands of the postpartum female breast in response to an infant sucking at the nipple. Breast milk provides ideal nutrition and passive immunity for the infant, encourages mild uterine contractions to return the uterus to its pre-pregnancy size (i.e., involution), and induces a substantial metabolic increase in the postpartum person, consuming the fat reserves stored during pregnancy.

Structure of the Lactating Breast

Mammary glands are modified sweat glands. The non-pregnant and non-lactating female breast is composed primarily of adipose and collagenous tissue, with mammary glands making up a very minor proportion of breast volume. The mammary gland is composed of milk-transporting lactiferous ducts, which expand and branch extensively during pregnancy in response to estrogen, growth hormone, cortisol, and prolactin. Moreover, in response to progesterone, clusters of breast alveoli bud from the ducts and expand outward toward the chest wall. Breast alveoli are balloon-like structures lined with milk-secreting cuboidal cells, or lactocytes, that are surrounded by a net of contractile myoepithelial cells. Milk is secreted from the lactocytes, fills the alveoli, and is squeezed into the ducts. Clusters of alveoli that drain to a common duct are called lobules; the lactating female has 12–20 lobules organized radially around the nipple. Milk drains from lactiferous ducts into lactiferous sinuses that meet at 4 to 18 perforations in the nipple, called nipple pores. The small bumps of the areola (the darkened skin around the nipple) are called Montgomery glands. They secrete oil to cleanse the nipple opening and prevent chapping and cracking of the nipple during breastfeeding.

The Process of Lactation

The pituitary hormone **prolactin** is instrumental in the establishment and maintenance of breast milk supply. It also is important for the mobilization of maternal micronutrients for breast milk.

Near the fifth week of pregnancy, the level of circulating prolactin begins to increase, eventually rising to approximately 10–20 times the pre-pregnancy concentration. We noted earlier that, during pregnancy, prolactin and other hormones prepare the breasts anatomically for the secretion of milk. The level of prolactin plateaus in late pregnancy, at a level high enough to initiate milk production. However, estrogen, progesterone, and other placental hormones inhibit prolactin-mediated milk synthesis during pregnancy. It is not until the placenta is expelled that this inhibition is lifted and milk production commences.

After childbirth, the baseline prolactin level drops sharply, but it is restored for a 1-hour spike during each feeding to stimulate the production of milk for the next feeding. With each prolactin spike, estrogen and progesterone also increase slightly.

When the infant suckles, sensory nerve fibers in the areola trigger a neuroendocrine reflex that results in milk secretion from lactocytes into the alveoli. The posterior pituitary releases oxytocin, which stimulates myoepithelial cells to squeeze milk from the alveoli so it can drain into the lactiferous ducts, collect in the lactiferous sinuses, and discharge through the nipple pores. It takes less than 1 minute from the time when an infant begins suckling (the latent period) until milk is secreted (the let-down). Figure 28.23 summarizes the positive feedback loop of the **let-down reflex**.

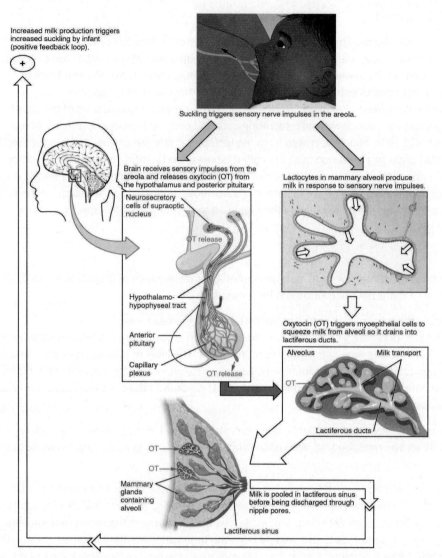

Increased milk production triggers increased suckling by infant (positive feedback loop).

+

Suckling triggers sensory nerve impulses in the areola.

Brain receives sensory impulses from the areola and releases oxytocin (OT) from the hypothalamus and posterior pituitary.

Neurosecretory cells of supraoptic nucleus

OT release

Hypothalamo-hypophyseal tract

Anterior pituitary

Capillary plexus

OT release

Lactocytes in mammary alveoli produce milk in response to sensory nerve impulses.

Oxytocin (OT) triggers myoepithelial cells to squeeze milk from alveoli so it drains into lactiferous ducts.

Alveolus

Milk transport

OT

Lactiferous ducts

OT

OT

Mammary glands containing alveoli

Milk is pooled in lactiferous sinus before being discharged through nipple pores.

Lactiferous sinus

FIGURE 28.23   Let-Down Reflex   A positive feedback loop ensures continued milk production as long as the infant continues to breastfeed.

The prolactin-mediated synthesis of milk changes with time. Frequent milk removal by breastfeeding (or pumping) will maintain high circulating prolactin levels for several months. However, even with continued breastfeeding, baseline prolactin will decrease over time to its pre-pregnancy level. In addition to prolactin and oxytocin, growth hormone, cortisol, parathyroid hormone, and insulin contribute to lactation, in part by facilitating the transport of maternal amino acids, fatty acids, glucose, and calcium to breast milk.

Changes in the Composition of Breast Milk

In the final weeks of pregnancy, the alveoli swell with **colostrum**, a thick, yellowish substance that is high in protein but contains less fat and glucose than mature breast milk (Table 28.3). Before childbirth, some people experience leakage of colostrum from the nipples. In contrast, mature breast milk does not leak during pregnancy and is not secreted until several days after childbirth.

Access for free at openstax.org

Compositions of Human Colostrum, Mature Breast Milk, and Cow's Milk (g/L)

	Human colostrum	Human breast milk	Cow's milk*
Total protein	23	11	31
Immunoglobulins	19	0.1	1
Fat	30	45	38
Lactose	57	71	47
Calcium	0.5	0.3	1.4
Phosphorus	0.16	0.14	0.90
Sodium	0.50	0.15	0.41

TABLE 28.3 *Cow's milk should never be given to an infant. Its composition is not suitable and its proteins are difficult for the infant to digest.

Colostrum is secreted during the first 48–72 hours postpartum. Only a small volume of colostrum is produced—approximately 3 ounces in a 24-hour period—but it is sufficient for the newborn in the first few days of life. Colostrum is rich with immunoglobulins, which confer gastrointestinal, and also likely systemic, immunity as the newborn adjusts to a nonsterile environment.

After about the third postpartum day, the breast secretes transitional milk that represents an intermediate between mature milk and colostrum. This is followed by mature milk from approximately postpartum day 10 (see Table 28.3). As you can see in the accompanying table, cow's milk is not a substitute for breast milk. It contains less lactose, less fat, and more protein and minerals. Moreover, the proteins in cow's milk are difficult for an infant's immature digestive system to metabolize and absorb.

The first few weeks of breastfeeding may involve leakage, soreness, and periods of milk engorgement as the relationship between milk supply and infant demand becomes established. Once this period is complete, the lactating person will produce approximately 1.5 liters of milk per day for a single infant, and more if the person has twins or triplets. As the infant goes through growth spurts, the milk supply constantly adjusts to accommodate changes in demand. A person can continue to lactate for years, but once breastfeeding is stopped for approximately 1 week, any remaining milk will be reabsorbed; in most cases, no more will be produced, even if suckling or pumping is resumed.

Mature milk changes from the beginning to the end of a feeding. The early milk, called **foremilk**, is watery, translucent, and rich in lactose and protein. Its purpose is to quench the infant's thirst. **Hindmilk** is delivered toward the end of a feeding. It is opaque, creamy, and rich in fat, and serves to satisfy the infant's appetite.

During the first days of a newborn's life, it is important for meconium to be cleared from the intestines and for bilirubin to be kept low in the circulation. Recall that bilirubin, a product of erythrocyte breakdown, is processed by the liver and secreted in bile. It enters the gastrointestinal tract and exits the body in the stool. Breast milk has laxative properties that help expel meconium from the intestines and clear bilirubin through the excretion of bile. A high concentration of bilirubin in the blood causes jaundice. Some degree of jaundice is normal in newborns, but a high level of bilirubin—which is neurotoxic—can cause brain damage. Newborns, who do not yet have a fully functional blood–brain barrier, are highly vulnerable to the bilirubin circulating in the blood. Indeed, hyperbilirubinemia, a high level of circulating bilirubin, is the most common condition requiring medical attention in newborns. Newborns with hyperbilirubinemia are treated with phototherapy because UV light helps to break down the bilirubin quickly.

28.7 Patterns of Inheritance

LEARNING OBJECTIVES

By the end of this section, you will be able to:

- Differentiate between genotype and phenotype
- Describe how alleles determine a person's traits
- Summarize Mendel's experiments and relate them to human genetics
- Explain the inheritance of autosomal dominant and recessive and sex-linked genetic disorders

We have discussed the events that lead to the development of a newborn. But what makes each newborn unique? The answer lies, of course, in the DNA in the sperm and oocyte that combined to produce that first diploid cell, the human zygote.

From Genotype to Phenotype

Each human body cell has a full complement of DNA stored in 23 pairs of chromosomes. Figure 28.24 shows the pairs in a systematic arrangement called a **karyotype**. Among these is one pair of chromosomes, called the **sex chromosomes**, that determines the sex of the individual (XX in females, XY in males). The remaining 22 chromosome pairs are called **autosomal chromosomes**. Each of these chromosomes carries hundreds or even thousands of genes, each of which codes for the assembly of a particular protein—that is, genes are "expressed" as proteins. An individual's complete genetic makeup is referred to as their **genotype**. The characteristics that the genes express, whether they are physical, behavioral, or biochemical, are a person's **phenotype**.

In genetics and reproduction, "parent" is often used to describe the individual organisms that contribute genetic material to offspring, usually in the form of gamete cells and their chromosomes. The concept of a genetic parent is distinct from social and legal concepts of parenthood, and may differ from those whom people consider their parents.

You inherit one chromosome in each pair—a full complement of 23—from each parent. This occurs when the sperm and oocyte combine at the moment of your conception. Homologous chromosomes—those that make up a complementary pair—have genes for the same characteristics in the same location on the chromosome. Because one copy of a gene, an **allele**, is inherited from each parent, the alleles in these complementary pairs may vary. Take for example an allele that encodes for dimples. A child may inherit the allele encoding for dimples on the chromosome from the one parent and the allele that encodes for smooth skin (no dimples) on the chromosome from the other parent.

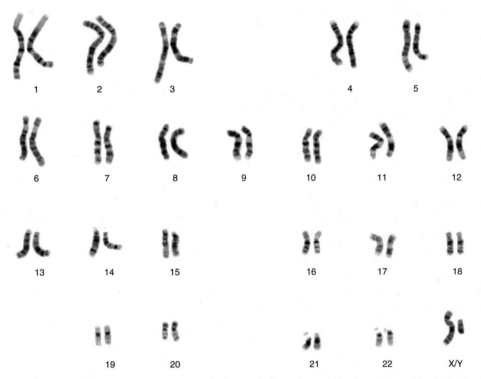

FIGURE 28.24 Chromosomal Complement of a Male   Each pair of chromosomes contains hundreds to thousands of genes. The banding patterns are nearly identical for the two chromosomes within each pair, indicating the same organization of genes. As is visible in this karyotype, the only exception to this is the XY sex chromosome pair in males. (credit: National Human Genome Research Institute)

Although a person can have two identical alleles for a single gene (a **homozygous** state), it is also possible for a person to have two different alleles (a **heterozygous** state). The two alleles can interact in several different ways. The expression of an allele can be dominant, for which the activity of this gene will mask the expression of a nondominant, or recessive, allele. Sometimes dominance is complete; at other times, it is incomplete. In some cases, both alleles are expressed at the same time in a form of expression known as codominance.

In the simplest scenario, a single pair of genes will determine a single heritable characteristic. However, it is quite common for multiple genes to interact to confer a feature. For instance, eight or more genes—each with their own alleles—determine eye color in humans. Moreover, although any one person can only have two alleles corresponding to a given gene, more than two alleles commonly exist in a population. This phenomenon is called multiple alleles. For example, there are three different alleles that encode ABO blood type; these are designated I^A, I^B, and i.

Over 100 years of theoretical and experimental genetics studies, and the more recent sequencing and annotation of the human genome, have helped scientists to develop a better understanding of how an individual's genotype is expressed as their phenotype. This body of knowledge can help scientists and medical professionals to predict, or at least estimate, some of the features that an offspring will inherit by examining the genotypes or phenotypes of the parents. One important application of this knowledge is to identify an individual's risk for certain heritable genetic disorders. However, most diseases have a multigenic pattern of inheritance and can also be affected by the environment, so examining the genotypes or phenotypes of a person's parents will provide only limited information about the risk of inheriting a disease. Only for a handful of single-gene disorders can genetic testing allow clinicians to calculate the probability with which a child born to the two parents tested may inherit a specific disease.

Mendel's Theory of Inheritance

Our contemporary understanding of genetics rests on the work of a nineteenth-century monk. Working in the mid-1800s, long before anyone knew about genes or chromosomes, Gregor Mendel discovered that garden peas transmit their physical characteristics to subsequent generations in a discrete and predictable fashion. When he mated, or crossed, two pure-breeding pea plants that differed by a certain characteristic, the first-generation offspring all looked like one of the parents. For instance, when he crossed tall and dwarf pure-breeding pea plants, all of the offspring were tall. Mendel called tallness **dominant** because it was expressed in offspring when it was present in a purebred parent. He called dwarfism **recessive** because it was masked in the offspring if one of the purebred parents possessed the dominant characteristic. Note that tallness and dwarfism are variations on the characteristic of height. Mendel called such a variation a **trait**. We now know that these traits are the expression of different alleles of the gene encoding height.

Mendel performed thousands of crosses in pea plants with differing traits for a variety of characteristics. And he repeatedly came up with the same results—among the traits he studied, one was always dominant, and the other was always recessive. (Remember, however, that this dominant–recessive relationship between alleles is not always the case; some alleles are codominant, and sometimes dominance is incomplete.)

Using his understanding of dominant and recessive traits, Mendel tested whether a recessive trait could be lost altogether in a pea lineage or whether it would resurface in a later generation. By crossing the second-generation offspring of purebred parents with each other, he showed that the latter was true: recessive traits reappeared in third-generation plants in a ratio of 3:1 (three offspring having the dominant trait and one having the recessive trait). Mendel then proposed that characteristics such as height were determined by heritable "factors" that were transmitted, one from each parent, and inherited in pairs by offspring.

In the language of genetics, Mendel's theory applied to humans says that if an individual receives two dominant alleles, one from each parent, the individual's phenotype will express the dominant trait. If an individual receives two recessive alleles, then the recessive trait will be expressed in the phenotype. Individuals who have two identical alleles for a given gene, whether dominant or recessive, are said to be homozygous for that gene (homo- = "same"). Conversely, an individual who has one dominant allele and one recessive allele is said to be heterozygous for that gene (hetero- = "different" or "other"). In this case, the dominant trait will be expressed, and the individual will be phenotypically identical to an individual who possesses two dominant alleles for the trait.

It is common practice in genetics to use capital and lowercase letters to represent dominant and recessive alleles. Using Mendel's pea plants as an example, if a tall pea plant is homozygous, it will possess two tall alleles (*TT*). A dwarf pea plant must be homozygous because its dwarfism can only be expressed when two recessive alleles are present (*tt*). A heterozygous pea plant (*Tt*) would be tall and phenotypically indistinguishable from a tall homozygous pea plant because of the dominant tall allele. Mendel deduced that a 3:1 ratio of dominant to recessive would be produced by the random segregation of heritable factors (genes) when crossing two heterozygous pea plants. In other words, for any given gene, parents are equally likely to pass down either one of their alleles to their offspring in a haploid gamete, and the result will be expressed in a dominant–recessive pattern if both parents are heterozygous for the trait.

Because of the random segregation of gametes, the laws of chance and probability come into play when predicting the likelihood of a given phenotype. Consider a cross between an individual with two dominant alleles for a trait (*AA*) and an individual with two recessive alleles for the same trait (*aa*). All of the parental gametes from the dominant individual would be *A*, and all of the parental gametes from the recessive individual would be *a* (Figure 28.25). All of the offspring of that second generation, inheriting one allele from each parent, would have the genotype *Aa*, and the probability of expressing the phenotype of the dominant allele would be 4 out of 4, or 100 percent.

This seems simple enough, but the inheritance pattern gets interesting when the second-generation *Aa* individuals are crossed. In this generation, 50 percent of each parent's gametes are *A* and the other 50 percent are *a*. By Mendel's principle of random segregation, the possible combinations of gametes that the offspring can receive are *AA*, *Aa*, *aA* (which is the same as *Aa*), and *aa*. Because segregation and fertilization are random, each offspring has a 25 percent chance of receiving any of these combinations. Therefore, if an *Aa* × *Aa* cross were performed 1000 times, approximately 250 (25 percent) of the offspring would be *AA*; 500 (50 percent) would be *Aa* (that is, *Aa* plus *aA*); and 250 (25 percent) would be *aa*. The genotypic ratio for this inheritance pattern is 1:2:1. However, we have already established that *AA* and *Aa* (and *aA*) individuals all express the dominant trait (i.e., share the same phenotype), and can therefore be combined into one group. The result is Mendel's third-generation phenotype ratio of 3:1.

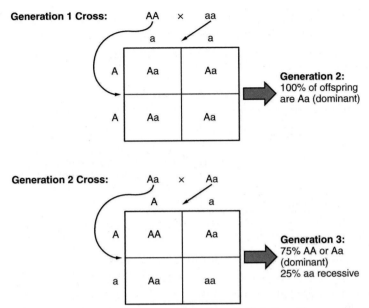

FIGURE 28.25   Random Segregation   In the formation of gametes, it is equally likely that either one of a pair alleles from one parent will be passed on to the offspring. This figure follows the possible combinations of alleles through two generations following a first-generation cross of homozygous dominant and homozygous recessive parents. The recessive phenotype, which is masked in the second generation, has a 1 in 4, or 25 percent, chance of reappearing in the third generation.

Mendel's observation of pea plants also included many crosses that involved multiple traits, which prompted him to formulate the principle of independent assortment. The law states that the members of one pair of genes (alleles) from a parent will sort independently from other pairs of genes during the formation of gametes. Applied to pea plants, that means that the alleles associated with the different traits of the plant, such as color, height, or seed type, will sort independently of one another. This holds true except when two alleles happen to be located close to one other on the same chromosome. Independent assortment provides for a great degree of diversity in offspring.

Mendelian genetics represent the fundamentals of inheritance, but there are two important qualifiers to consider when applying Mendel's findings to inheritance studies in humans. First, as we've already noted, not all genes are inherited in a dominant–recessive pattern. Although all diploid individuals have two alleles for every gene, allele pairs may interact to create several types of inheritance patterns, including incomplete dominance and codominance.

Secondly, Mendel performed his studies using thousands of pea plants. He was able to identify a 3:1 phenotypic ratio in second-generation offspring because his large sample size overcame the influence of variability resulting from chance. In contrast, no human couple has ever had thousands of children. If we know that parents are both heterozygous for a recessive genetic disorder, we would predict that one in every four of their children would be affected by the disease. In real life, however, the influence of chance could change that ratio significantly. For example, if parents are both heterozygous for cystic fibrosis, a recessive genetic disorder that is expressed only when the individual has two defective alleles, we would expect one in four of their children to have cystic fibrosis. However, it is entirely possible for them to have seven children, none of whom is affected, or for them to have two children, both of whom are affected. For each individual child, the presence or absence of a single gene disorder depends on which alleles that child inherits from their parents.

Autosomal Dominant Inheritance

In the case of cystic fibrosis, the disorder is recessive to the normal phenotype. However, a genetic abnormality may be dominant to the normal phenotype. When the dominant allele is located on one of the 22 pairs of autosomes (non-sex chromosomes), we refer to its inheritance pattern as **autosomal dominant**. An example of an autosomal dominant disorder is neurofibromatosis type I, a disease that induces tumor formation within the nervous system that leads to skin and skeletal deformities. Consider a couple in which one parent is heterozygous for this disorder (and who therefore has neurofibromatosis), *Nn*, and one parent is homozygous for the normal gene, *nn*. The heterozygous parent would have a 50 percent chance of passing the dominant allele for this disorder to their offspring, and the homozygous parent would always pass the normal allele. Therefore, four possible offspring genotypes are equally likely to occur: *Nn, Nn, nn,* and *nn.* That is, every child of this couple would have a 50 percent chance of inheriting neurofibromatosis. This inheritance pattern is shown in Figure 28.26, in a form called a **Punnett square**, named after its creator, the British geneticist Reginald Punnett.

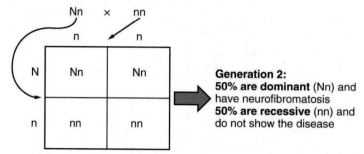

FIGURE 28.26   Autosomal Dominant Inheritance   Inheritance pattern of an autosomal dominant disorder, such as neurofibromatosis, is shown in a Punnett square.

Other genetic diseases that are inherited in this pattern are achondroplastic dwarfism, Marfan syndrome, and Huntington's disease. Because autosomal dominant disorders are expressed by the presence of just one gene, an individual with the disorder will know that they have at least one faulty gene. The expression of the disease may manifest later in life, after the childbearing years, which is the case in Huntington's disease (discussed in more detail later in this section).

Autosomal Recessive Inheritance

When a genetic disorder is inherited in an **autosomal recessive** pattern, the disorder corresponds to the recessive phenotype. Heterozygous individuals will not display symptoms of this disorder, because their unaffected gene will compensate. Such an individual is called a **carrier**. Carriers for an autosomal recessive disorder may never know their genotype unless they have a child with the disorder.

An example of an autosomal recessive disorder is cystic fibrosis (CF), which we introduced earlier. CF is characterized by the chronic accumulation of a thick, tenacious mucus in the lungs and digestive tract. Decades ago, children with CF rarely lived to adulthood. With advances in medical technology, the average lifespan in developed countries has increased into middle adulthood. CF is a relatively common disorder that occurs in approximately 30,000 people in the United States. A child born to two CF carriers would have a 25 percent chance of inheriting the disease. This is the same 3:1 dominant:recessive ratio that Mendel observed in his pea plants would apply here. The pattern is shown in Figure 28.27, using a diagram that tracks the likely incidence of an autosomal recessive disorder on the basis of parental genotypes.

On the other hand, a child born to a CF carrier and someone with two unaffected alleles would have a 0 percent probability of inheriting CF, but would have a 50 percent chance of being a carrier. Other examples of autosome recessive genetic illnesses include the blood disorder sickle-cell anemia, the fatal neurological disorder Tay–Sachs disease, and the metabolic disorder phenylketonuria.

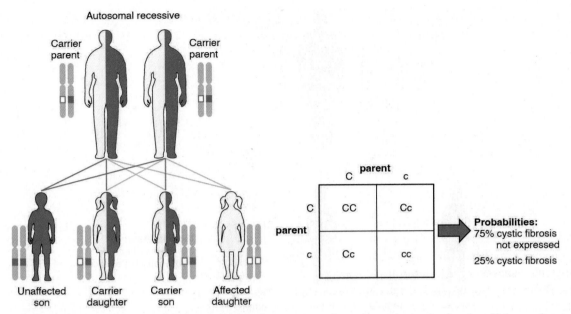

FIGURE 28.27   Autosomal Recessive Inheritance   The inheritance pattern of an autosomal recessive disorder with two carrier parents reflects a 3:1 probability of expression among offspring. (credit: U.S. National Library of Medicine)

X-linked Dominant or Recessive Inheritance

An **X-linked** transmission pattern involves genes located on the X chromosome of the 23rd pair (Figure 28.28). Recall that a male has one X and one Y chromosome. When a male transmits a Y chromosome, the child is male, and when a male parent transmits an X chromosome, the child is female. A female can transmit only an X chromosome, as both her sex chromosomes are X chromosomes.

When an abnormal allele for a gene that occurs on the X chromosome is dominant over the normal allele, the pattern is described as **X-linked dominant**. This is the case with vitamin D–resistant rickets: an affected male would pass the disease gene to all of the female offspring, but none of the male offspring, because the male transmits only the Y chromosome to male offspring (see Figure 28.28**a**). If it is the female parent who is affected, all of the offspring—male or female—would have a 50 percent chance of inheriting the disorder because the female parent can only pass an X chromosome on to children (see Figure 28.28**b**). For an affected female, the inheritance pattern would be identical to that of an autosomal dominant inheritance pattern in which one parent is heterozygous and the other is homozygous for the normal gene.

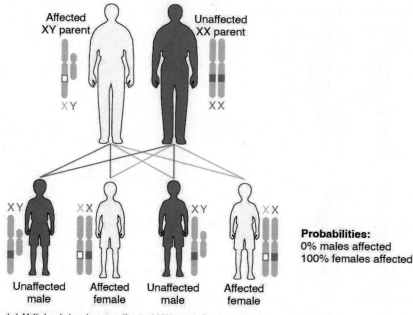

Affected XY parent

Unaffected XX parent

XY

XX

XY   XX   XY   XX

Unaffected
male

Affected
female

Unaffected
male

Affected
female

Probabilities:
0% males affected
100% females affected

(a) X-linked dominant, affected XY parent

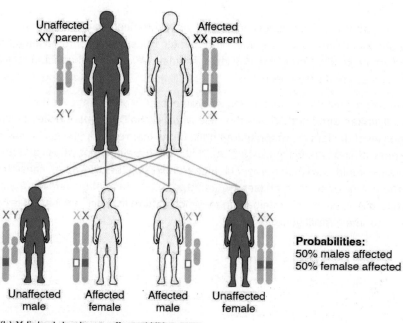

Unaffected XY parent

Affected XX parent

XY

XX

XY   XX   XY   XX

Unaffected
male

Affected
female

Affected
male

Unaffected
female

Probabilities:
50% males affected
50% femalse affected

(b) X-linked dominant, affected XX parent

FIGURE 28.28   X-Linked Patterns of Inheritance   A chart of X-linked dominant inheritance patterns differs depending on which parent is affected with the disease. (credit: U.S. National Library of Medicine)

X-linked recessive inheritance is much more common because females can be carriers of the disease yet still have a normal phenotype. Diseases transmitted by X-linked recessive inheritance include color blindness, the blood-clotting disorder hemophilia, and some forms of muscular dystrophy. For an example of X-linked recessive inheritance, consider parents in which the female is an unaffected carrier and the male is normal. None of the female offspring would have the disease because they receive a normal gene from their male parent. However, they have a 50 percent chance of receiving the disease gene from their female parent and becoming a carrier. In contrast, 50 percent of the male offspring would be affected (Figure 28.29).

With X-linked recessive diseases, males either have the disease or are genotypically normal—they cannot be carriers. Females, however, can be genotypically normal, a carrier who is phenotypically normal, or affected with the disease. A female can inherit the gene for an X-linked recessive illness when the female parent is a carrier or affected, or the male parent is affected. Female offspring will be affected by the disease only if they inherit an X-linked recessive gene from both parents. As you can imagine, X-linked recessive disorders affect many more males than females. For example, color blindness affects at least 1 in 20 males, but only about 1 in 400 females.

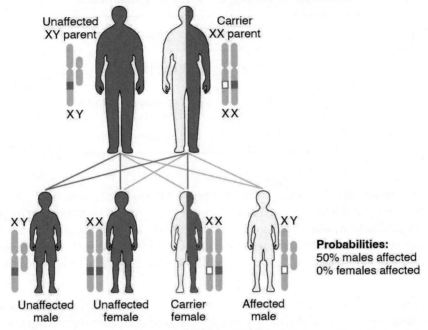

FIGURE 28.29   X-Linked Recessive Inheritance   Given two parents in which the male is normal and the female is a carrier of an X-linked recessive disorder, a male offspring would have a 50 percent probability of being affected with the disorder, whereas female offspring would either be carriers or entirely unaffected. (credit: U.S. National Library of Medicine)

Other Inheritance Patterns: Incomplete Dominance, Codominance, and Lethal Alleles

Not all genetic disorders are inherited in a dominant–recessive pattern. In **incomplete dominance**, the offspring express a heterozygous phenotype that is intermediate between one parent's homozygous dominant trait and the other parent's homozygous recessive trait. An example of this can be seen in snapdragons when red-flowered plants and white-flowered plants are crossed to produce pink-flowered plants. In humans, incomplete dominance occurs with one of the genes for hair texture. When one parent passes a curly hair allele (the incompletely dominant allele) and the other parent passes a straight-hair allele, the effect on the offspring will be intermediate, resulting in hair that is wavy.

Codominance is characterized by the equal, distinct, and simultaneous expression of both parents' different alleles. This pattern differs from the intermediate, blended features seen in incomplete dominance. A classic example of codominance in humans is ABO blood type. People are blood type A if they have an allele for an enzyme that facilitates the production of surface antigen A on their erythrocytes. This allele is designated I^A. In the same manner, people are blood type B if they express an enzyme for the production of surface antigen B. People who have alleles for both enzymes (I^A and I^B) produce both surface antigens A and B. As a result, they are blood type AB. Because the effect of both alleles (or enzymes) is observed, we say that the I^A and I^B alleles are codominant. There is also a third allele that determines blood type. This allele (*i*) produces a nonfunctional enzyme. People who have two *i* alleles do not produce either A or B surface antigens: they have type O blood. If a person has I^A and *i* alleles, the person will have blood type A. Notice that it does not make any difference whether a person has two I^A alleles or one I^A and one *i* allele. In both cases, the person is blood type A. Because I^A masks *i*, we say that I^A is dominant to *i*. Table 28.4 summarizes the expression of blood type.

Expression of Blood Types

Blood type	Genotype	Pattern of inheritance
A	$I^A I^A$ or $I^A i$	I^A is dominant to i
B	$I^B I^B$ or $I^B i$	I^B is dominant to i
AB	$I^A I^B$	I^A is co-dominant to I^B
O	ii	Two recessive alleles

TABLE 28.4

Certain combinations of alleles can be lethal, meaning they prevent the individual from developing in utero, or cause a shortened life span. In **recessive lethal** inheritance patterns, a child who is born to two heterozygous (carrier) parents and who inherited the faulty allele from both would not survive. An example of this is Tay–Sachs, a fatal disorder of the nervous system. In this disorder, parents with one copy of the allele for the disorder are carriers. If they both transmit their abnormal allele, their offspring will develop the disease and will die in childhood, usually before age 5.

Dominant lethal inheritance patterns are much more rare because neither heterozygotes nor homozygotes survive. Of course, dominant lethal alleles that arise naturally through mutation and cause miscarriages or stillbirths are never transmitted to subsequent generations. However, some dominant lethal alleles, such as the allele for Huntington's disease, cause a shortened life span but may not be identified until after the person reaches reproductive age and has children. Huntington's disease causes irreversible nerve cell degeneration and death in 100 percent of affected individuals, but it may not be expressed until the individual reaches middle age. In this way, dominant lethal alleles can be maintained in the human population. Individuals with a family history of Huntington's disease are typically offered genetic counseling, which can help them decide whether or not they wish to be tested for the faulty gene.

Mutations

A **mutation** is a change in the sequence of DNA nucleotides that may or may not affect a person's phenotype. Mutations can arise spontaneously from errors during DNA replication, or they can result from environmental insults such as radiation, certain viruses, or exposure to tobacco smoke or other toxic chemicals. Because genes encode for the assembly of proteins, a mutation in the nucleotide sequence of a gene can change amino acid sequence and, consequently, a protein's structure and function. Spontaneous mutations occurring during meiosis are thought to account for many spontaneous abortions (miscarriages).

Chromosomal Disorders

Sometimes a genetic disease is not caused by a mutation in a gene, but by the presence of an incorrect number of chromosomes. For example, Down syndrome is caused by having three copies of chromosome 21. This is known as trisomy 21. The most common cause of trisomy 21 is chromosomal nondisjunction during meiosis. The frequency of nondisjunction events appears to increase with age, so the frequency of bearing a child with Down syndrome increases in females over 36. The age of the male parent matters less because nondisjunction is much less likely to occur in a sperm than in an egg.

Whereas Down syndrome is caused by having three copies of a chromosome, Turner syndrome is caused by having just one copy of the X chromosome. This is known as monosomy. The affected child is always female. Women with Turner syndrome are sterile because their sexual organs do not mature.

CAREER CONNECTION

Genetic Counselor

Given the intricate orchestration of gene expression, cell migration, and cell differentiation during prenatal development, it is amazing that the vast majority of newborns are healthy and free of major birth defects. When a person over 35 is pregnant or intends to become pregnant, or their partner is over 55, or if there is a family history of a genetic disorder, they may want to speak to a genetic counselor to discuss the likelihood that their child may be affected by a genetic or chromosomal disorder. A genetic counselor can interpret a couple's family history and estimate the risks to their future offspring.

For many genetic diseases, a DNA test can determine whether a person is a carrier. For instance, carrier status for Fragile X, an X-linked disorder associated with intellectual disabilites, or for cystic fibrosis can be determined with a simple blood draw to obtain DNA for testing. A genetic counselor can educate a couple about the implications of such a test and help them decide whether to undergo testing. For chromosomal disorders, the available testing options include a blood test, amniocentesis (in which amniotic fluid is tested), and chorionic villus sampling (in which tissue from the placenta is tested). Each of these has advantages and drawbacks. A genetic counselor can also help a couple cope with the news that either one or both partners is a carrier of a genetic illness, or that their unborn child has been diagnosed with a chromosomal disorder or other birth defect.

To become a genetic counselor, one needs to complete a 4-year undergraduate program and then obtain a Master of Science in Genetic Counseling from an accredited university. Board certification is attained after passing examinations by the American Board of Genetic Counseling. Genetic counselors are essential professionals in many branches of medicine, but there is a particular demand for preconception and prenatal genetic counselors.

INTERACTIVE LINK

Visit the National Society of Genetic Counselors website (http://openstax.org/l/gencounselor1) for more information about genetic counselors.

INTERACTIVE LINK

Visit the American Board of Genetic Counselors, Inc., website (http://openstax.org/l/gencounselor2) for more information about genetic counselors.

Key Terms

acrosomal reaction   release of digestive enzymes by sperm that enables them to burrow through the corona radiata and penetrate the zona pellucida of an oocyte prior to fertilization

acrosome   cap-like vesicle located at the anterior-most region of a sperm that is rich with lysosomal enzymes capable of digesting the protective layers surrounding the oocyte

afterbirth   third stage of childbirth in which the placenta and associated fetal membranes are expelled

allantois   finger-like outpocketing of yolk sac forms the primitive excretory duct of the embryo; precursor to the urinary bladder

allele   alternative forms of a gene that occupy a specific locus on a specific gene

amnion   transparent membranous sac that encloses the developing fetus and fills with amniotic fluid

amniotic cavity   cavity that opens up between the inner cell mass and the trophoblast; develops into amnion

autosomal chromosome   in humans, the 22 pairs of chromosomes that are not the sex chromosomes (XX or XY)

autosomal dominant   pattern of dominant inheritance that corresponds to a gene on one of the 22 autosomal chromosomes

autosomal recessive   pattern of recessive inheritance that corresponds to a gene on one of the 22 autosomal chromosomes

blastocoel   fluid-filled cavity of the blastocyst

blastocyst   term for the conceptus at the developmental stage that consists of about 100 cells shaped into an inner cell mass that is fated to become the embryo and an outer trophoblast that is fated to become the associated fetal membranes and placenta

blastomere   daughter cell of a cleavage

Braxton Hicks contractions   weak and irregular peristaltic contractions that can occur in the second and third trimesters; they do not indicate that childbirth is imminent

brown adipose tissue   highly vascularized fat tissue that is packed with mitochondria; these properties confer the ability to oxidize fatty acids to generate heat

capacitation   process that occurs in the female reproductive tract in which sperm are prepared for fertilization; leads to increased motility and changes in their outer membrane that improve their ability to release enzymes capable of digesting an oocyte's outer layers

carrier   heterozygous individual who does not display symptoms of a recessive genetic disorder but can transmit the disorder to their offspring

chorion   membrane that develops from the syncytiotrophoblast, cytotrophoblast, and mesoderm; surrounds the embryo and forms the fetal portion of the placenta through the chorionic villi

chorionic membrane   precursor to the chorion; forms from extra-embryonic mesoderm cells

chorionic villi   projections of the chorionic membrane that burrow into the endometrium and develop into the placenta

cleavage   form of mitotic cell division in which the cell divides but the total volume remains unchanged; this process serves to produce smaller and smaller cells

codominance   pattern of inheritance that corresponds to the equal, distinct, and simultaneous expression of two different alleles

colostrum   thick, yellowish substance secreted from a mother's breasts in the first postpartum days; rich in immunoglobulins

conceptus   pre-implantation stage of a fertilized egg and its associated membranes

corona radiata   in an oocyte, a layer of granulosa cells that surrounds the oocyte and that must be penetrated by sperm before fertilization can occur

cortical reaction   following fertilization, the release of cortical granules from the oocyte's plasma membrane into the zona pellucida creating a fertilization membrane that prevents any further attachment or penetration of sperm; part of the slow block to polyspermy

dilation   first stage of childbirth, involving an increase in cervical diameter

dominant   describes a trait that is expressed both in homozygous and heterozygous form

dominant lethal   inheritance pattern in which individuals with one or two copies of a lethal allele do not survive in utero or have a shortened life span

ductus arteriosus   shunt in the pulmonary trunk that diverts oxygenated blood back to the aorta

ductus venosus   shunt that causes oxygenated blood to bypass the fetal liver on its way to the inferior vena cava

ectoderm   primary germ layer that develops into the central and peripheral nervous systems, sensory organs, epidermis, hair, and nails

ectopic pregnancy   implantation of an embryo outside of the uterus

embryo   developing human during weeks 3–8

Access for free at openstax.org

embryonic folding   process by which an embryo develops from a flat disc of cells to a three-dimensional shape resembling a cylinder

endoderm   primary germ layer that goes on to form the gastrointestinal tract, liver, pancreas, and lungs

epiblast   upper layer of cells of the embryonic disc that forms from the inner cell mass; gives rise to all three germ layers

episiotomy   incision made in the posterior vaginal wall and perineum that facilitates vaginal birth

expulsion   second stage of childbirth, during which the mother bears down with contractions; this stage ends in birth

fertilization   unification of genetic material from male and female haploid gametes

fertilization membrane   impenetrable barrier that coats a nascent zygote; part of the slow block to polyspermy

fetus   developing human during the time from the end of the embryonic period (week 9) to birth

foramen ovale   shunt that directly connects the right and left atria and helps divert oxygenated blood from the fetal pulmonary circuit

foremilk   watery, translucent breast milk that is secreted first during a feeding and is rich in lactose and protein; quenches the infant's thirst

gastrulation   process of cell migration and differentiation into three primary germ layers following cleavage and implantation

genotype   complete genetic makeup of an individual

gestation   in human development, the period required for embryonic and fetal development in utero; pregnancy

heterozygous   having two different alleles for a given gene

hindmilk   opaque, creamy breast milk delivered toward the end of a feeding; rich in fat; satisfies the infant's appetite

homozygous   having two identical alleles for a given gene

human chorionic gonadotropin (hCG)   hormone that directs the corpus luteum to survive, enlarge, and continue producing progesterone and estrogen to suppress menses and secure an environment suitable for the developing embryo

hypoblast   lower layer of cells of the embryonic disc that extend into the blastocoel to form the yolk sac

implantation   process by which a blastocyst embeds itself in the uterine endometrium

incomplete dominance   pattern of inheritance in which a heterozygous genotype expresses a phenotype intermediate between dominant and recessive phenotypes

inner cell mass   cluster of cells within the blastocyst that is fated to become the embryo

involution   postpartum shrinkage of the uterus back to its pre-pregnancy volume

karyotype   systematic arrangement of images of chromosomes into homologous pairs

lactation   process by which milk is synthesized and secreted from the mammary glands of the postpartum female breast in response to sucking at the nipple

lanugo   silk-like hairs that coat the fetus; shed later in fetal development

let-down reflex   release of milk from the alveoli triggered by infant suckling

lightening   descent of the fetus lower into the pelvis in late pregnancy; also called "dropping"

lochia   postpartum vaginal discharge that begins as blood and ends as a whitish discharge; the end of lochia signals that the site of placental attachment has healed

meconium   fetal wastes consisting of ingested amniotic fluid, cellular debris, mucus, and bile

mesoderm   primary germ layer that becomes the skeleton, muscles, connective tissue, heart, blood vessels, and kidneys

morula   tightly packed sphere of blastomeres that has reached the uterus but has not yet implanted itself

mutation   change in the nucleotide sequence of DNA

neural fold   elevated edge of the neural groove

neural plate   thickened layer of neuroepithelium that runs longitudinally along the dorsal surface of an embryo and gives rise to nervous system tissue

neural tube   precursor to structures of the central nervous system, formed by the invagination and separation of neuroepithelium

neurulation   embryonic process that establishes the central nervous system

nonshivering thermogenesis   process of breaking down brown adipose tissue to produce heat in the absence of a shivering response

notochord   rod-shaped, mesoderm-derived structure that provides support for growing fetus

organogenesis   development of the rudimentary structures of all of an embryo's organs from the germ layers

parturition   childbirth

phenotype   physical or biochemical manifestation of the genotype; expression of the alleles

placenta   organ that forms during pregnancy to nourish the developing fetus; also regulates waste and gas exchange between mother and fetus

placenta previa   low placement of fetus within uterus causes placenta to partially or completely cover the opening of the cervix as it grows

placentation   formation of the placenta; complete by weeks 14–16 of pregnancy

polyspermy   penetration of an oocyte by more than one sperm

primitive streak   indentation along the dorsal surface of the epiblast through which cells migrate to form the endoderm and mesoderm during gastrulation

prolactin   pituitary hormone that establishes and maintains the supply of breast milk; also important for the mobilization of maternal micronutrients for breast milk

Punnett square   grid used to display all possible combinations of alleles transmitted by parents to offspring and predict the mathematical probability of offspring inheriting a given genotype

quickening   fetal movements that are strong enough to be felt by the mother

recessive   describes a trait that is only expressed in homozygous form and is masked in heterozygous form

recessive lethal   inheritance pattern in which individuals with two copies of a lethal allele do not survive in utero or have a shortened life span

sex chromosomes   pair of chromosomes involved in sex determination; in males, the XY chromosomes; in females, the XX chromosomes

shunt   circulatory shortcut that diverts the flow of blood from one region to another

somite   one of the paired, repeating blocks of tissue located on either side of the notochord in the early embryo

syncytiotrophoblast   superficial cells of the trophoblast that fuse to form a multinucleated body that digests endometrial cells to firmly secure the

blastocyst to the uterine wall

trait   variation of an expressed characteristic

trimester   division of the duration of a pregnancy into three 3-month terms

trophoblast   fluid-filled shell of squamous cells destined to become the chorionic villi, placenta, and associated fetal membranes

true labor   regular contractions that immediately precede childbirth; they do not abate with hydration or rest, and they become more frequent and powerful with time

umbilical cord   connection between the developing conceptus and the placenta; carries deoxygenated blood and wastes from the fetus and returns nutrients and oxygen from the mother

vernix caseosa   waxy, cheese-like substance that protects the delicate fetal skin until birth

X-linked   pattern of inheritance in which an allele is carried on the X chromosome of the 23rd pair

X-linked dominant   pattern of dominant inheritance that corresponds to a gene on the X chromosome of the 23rd pair

X-linked recessive   pattern of recessive inheritance that corresponds to a gene on the X chromosome of the 23rd pair

yolk sac   membrane associated with primitive circulation to the developing embryo; source of the first blood cells and germ cells and contributes to the umbilical cord structure

zona pellucida   thick, gel-like glycoprotein membrane that coats the oocyte and must be penetrated by sperm before fertilization can occur

zygote   fertilized egg; a diploid cell resulting from the fertilization of haploid gametes from the male and female lines

Chapter Review

28.1 Fertilization

Hundreds of millions of sperm deposited in the vagina travel toward the oocyte, but only a few hundred actually reach it. The number of sperm that reach the oocyte is greatly reduced because of conditions within the female reproductive tract. Many sperm are overcome by the acidity of the vagina, others are blocked by mucus in the cervix, whereas others are attacked by phagocytic leukocytes in the uterus. Those sperm that do survive undergo a change in response to those conditions. They go through the process of capacitation, which improves their motility and alters the membrane surrounding the acrosome, the cap-like structure in the head of a sperm that contains the digestive enzymes needed for it to attach to and penetrate the oocyte.

The oocyte that is released by ovulation is protected by a thick outer layer of granulosa cells known as the corona radiata and by the zona pellucida, a thick glycoprotein membrane that lies just outside the oocyte's plasma membrane. When capacitated sperm make contact with the oocyte, they release the digestive enzymes in the acrosome (the acrosomal reaction) and are thus able to attach to the oocyte and burrow through to the oocyte's zona pellucida. One of the sperm will then break through to the oocyte's plasma membrane and release its haploid nucleus into the oocyte. The oocyte's membrane structure changes in response (cortical reaction), preventing any further penetration by another sperm and forming a fertilization membrane. Fertilization is complete upon unification of the haploid nuclei of the two gametes, producing a diploid zygote.

28.2 Embryonic Development

As the zygote travels toward the uterus, it undergoes numerous cleavages in which the number of cells doubles (blastomeres). Upon reaching the uterus, the conceptus has become a tightly packed sphere of cells called the morula, which then forms into a blastocyst consisting of an inner cell mass within a fluid-filled cavity surrounded by trophoblasts. The blastocyst implants in the uterine wall, the trophoblasts fuse to form a syncytiotrophoblast, and the conceptus is enveloped by the endometrium. Four embryonic membranes form to support the growing embryo: the amnion, the yolk sac, the allantois, and the chorion. The chorionic villi of the chorion extend into the endometrium to form the fetal portion of the placenta. The placenta supplies the growing embryo with oxygen and nutrients; it also removes carbon dioxide and other metabolic wastes.

Following implantation, embryonic cells undergo gastrulation, in which they differentiate and separate into an embryonic disc and establish three primary germ layers (the endoderm, mesoderm, and ectoderm). Through the process of embryonic folding, the fetus begins to take shape. Neurulation starts the process of the development of structures of the central nervous system and organogenesis establishes the basic plan for all organ systems.

28.3 Fetal Development

The fetal period lasts from the ninth week of development until birth. During this period, male and female gonads differentiate. The fetal circulatory system becomes much more specialized and efficient than its embryonic counterpart. It includes three shunts—the ductus venosus, the foramen ovale, and the ductus arteriosus—that enable it to bypass the semifunctional liver and pulmonary circuit until after childbirth. The brain continues to grow and its structures differentiate. Facial features develop, the body elongates, and the skeleton ossifies. In the womb, the developing fetus moves, blinks, practices sucking, and circulates amniotic fluid. The fetus grows from an embryo measuring approximately 3.3 cm (1.3 in) and weighing 7 g (0.25 oz) to an infant measuring approximately 51 cm (20 in) and weighing an average of approximately 3.4 kg (7.5 lbs). Embryonic organ structures that were primitive and nonfunctional develop to the point that the newborn can survive in the outside world.

28.4 Changes During Pregnancy, Labor, and Birth

Hormones (especially estrogens, progesterone, and hCG) secreted by the corpus luteum and later by the placenta are responsible for most of the changes experienced during pregnancy. Estrogen maintains the pregnancy, promotes fetal viability, and stimulates tissue growth in the mother and developing fetus. Progesterone prevents new ovarian follicles from developing and suppresses uterine contractility.

Pregnancy weight gain primarily occurs in the breasts and abdominal region. Nausea, heartburn, and frequent urination are common during pregnancy. Maternal blood volume increases by 30 percent during pregnancy and respiratory minute volume increases by 50 percent. The skin may develop stretch marks and melanin production may increase.

Toward the late stages of pregnancy, a drop in progesterone and stretching forces from the fetus lead to increasing uterine irritability and prompt labor. Contractions serve to dilate the cervix and expel the newborn. Delivery of the placenta and associated fetal membranes follows.

28.5 Adjustments of the Infant at Birth and Postnatal Stages

The first breath a newborn takes at birth inflates the lungs and dramatically alters the circulatory system, closing the three shunts that directed oxygenated blood away from the lungs and liver during fetal life. Clamping and cutting the umbilical cord collapses the three umbilical blood vessels. The proximal umbilical arteries remain a part of the circulatory system, whereas the distal umbilical arteries and the umbilical vein become fibrotic. The newborn keeps warm by breaking down brown adipose tissue in the process of nonshivering thermogenesis. The first consumption of breast milk or formula floods the newborn's sterile gastrointestinal tract with beneficial bacteria that eventually establish themselves as the bacterial flora, which aid in digestion.

28.6 Lactation

The lactating mother supplies all the hydration and nutrients that a growing infant needs for the first 4–6 months of life. During pregnancy, the body prepares for lactation by stimulating the growth and development of branching lactiferous ducts and alveoli lined with milk-secreting lactocytes, and by creating colostrum. These functions are attributable to the actions of several hormones, including prolactin. Following childbirth, suckling triggers oxytocin release, which stimulates myoepithelial cells to squeeze milk from alveoli. Breast milk then drains toward the nipple pores to be consumed by the infant. Colostrum, the milk produced in the first postpartum days, provides immunoglobulins that increase the newborn's immune defenses. Colostrum, transitional milk, and mature breast milk are ideally suited to each stage of the newborn's development, and breastfeeding helps the newborn's digestive system expel meconium and clear bilirubin. Mature milk changes from the beginning to the end of a feeding. Foremilk quenches the infant's thirst, whereas hindmilk satisfies the infant's appetite.

28.7 Patterns of Inheritance

There are two aspects to a person's genetic makeup. Their genotype refers to the genetic makeup of the chromosomes found in all their cells and the alleles that are passed down from their parents. Their phenotype is the expression of that genotype, based on the interaction of the paired alleles, as well as how environmental conditions affect that expression.

Working with pea plants, Mendel discovered that the factors that account for different traits in parents are discretely transmitted to offspring in pairs, one from each parent. He articulated the principles of random segregation and independent assortment to account for the inheritance patterns he observed. Mendel's factors are genes, with differing variants being referred to as alleles and those alleles being dominant or recessive in expression. Each parent passes one allele for every gene on to offspring, and offspring are equally likely to inherit any combination of allele pairs. When Mendel crossed heterozygous individuals, he repeatedly found a 3:1 dominant–recessive ratio. He correctly postulated that the expression of the recessive trait was masked in heterozygotes but would resurface in their offspring in a predictable manner.

Human genetics focuses on identifying different alleles and understanding how they express themselves. Medical researchers are especially interested in the identification of inheritance patterns for genetic disorders, which provides the means to estimate the risk that a given couple's offspring will inherit a genetic disease or disorder. Patterns of inheritance in humans include autosomal dominance and recessiveness, X-linked dominance and recessiveness, incomplete dominance, codominance, and lethality. A change in the nucleotide sequence of DNA, which may or may not manifest in a phenotype, is called a mutation.

Interactive Link Questions

1. View this time-lapse movie (http://openstax.org/l/conceptus) of a conceptus starting at day 3. What is the first structure you see? At what point in the movie does the blastocoel first appear? What event occurs at the end of the movie?

2. Visit this site (http://openstax.org/l/pregstages) for a summary of the stages of pregnancy, as experienced by the pregnant person, and view the stages of development of the fetus throughout gestation. At what point in fetal development can a regular heartbeat be detected?

Review Questions

3. Sperm and ova are similar in terms of _____.
   a. size
   b. quantity produced per year
   c. chromosome number
   d. flagellar motility

4. Although the male ejaculate contains hundreds of millions of sperm, _____.
   a. most do not reach the oocyte
   b. most are destroyed by the alkaline environment of the uterus
   c. it takes millions to penetrate the outer layers of the oocyte
   d. most are destroyed by capacitation

5. As sperm first reach the oocyte, they will contact the _____.
   a. acrosome
   b. corona radiata
   c. sperm-binding receptors
   d. zona pellucida

6. Fusion of pronuclei occurs during _____.
   a. spermatogenesis
   b. ovulation
   c. fertilization
   d. capacitation

7. Sperm must first complete _____ to enable the fertilization of an oocyte.
   a. capacitation
   b. the acrosomal reaction
   c. the cortical reaction
   d. the fast block

8. Cleavage produces daughter cells called _____.
   a. trophoblasts
   b. blastocysts
   c. morulae
   d. blastomeres

9. The conceptus, upon reaching the uterus, first _____.
   a. implants
   b. divides
   c. disintegrates
   d. hatches

10. The inner cell mass of the blastocyst is destined to become the _____.
   a. embryo
   b. trophoblast
   c. chorionic villi
   d. placenta

11. Which primary germ layer gave rise to the cells that eventually became the central nervous system?
   a. endoderm
   b. ectoderm
   c. acrosome
   d. mesoderm

12. What would happen if the trophoblast did not secrete hCG upon implantation of the blastocyst?
   a. The cells would not continue to divide.
   b. The corpus luteum would continue to produce progesterone and estrogen.
   c. Menses would flush the blastocyst out of the uterus.
   d. The uterine mucosa would not envelop the blastocyst.

13. During what process does the amnion envelop the embryo?
   a. embryonic folding
   b. gastrulation
   c. implantation
   d. organogenesis

14. The placenta is formed from _____.
   a. the embryo's mesenchymal cells
   b. the mother's endometrium only
   c. the mother's endometrium and the embryo's chorionic membrane
   d. the mother's endometrium and the embryo's umbilical cord

15. The foramen ovale causes the fetal circulatory system to bypass the _____.
   a. liver
   b. lungs
   c. kidneys
   d. gonads

16. What happens to the urine excreted by the fetus when the kidneys begin to function?
   a. The umbilical cord carries it to the placenta for removal.
   b. The endometrium absorbs it.
   c. It adds to the amniotic fluid.
   d. It is turned into meconium.

17. During weeks 9–12 of fetal development, _____.
   a. bone marrow begins to assume erythrocyte production
   b. meconium begins to accumulate in the intestines
   c. surfactant production begins in the fetal lungs
   d. the spinal cord begins to be myelinated

18. Progesterone secreted by the placenta suppresses _____ to prevent maturation of ovarian follicles.
   a. LH and estrogen
   b. hCG and FSH
   c. FSH and LH
   d. estrogen and hCG

19. Which of the following is a possible culprit of "morning sickness"?
   a. increased minute respiration
   b. decreased intestinal peristalsis
   c. decreased aldosterone secretion
   d. increased blood volume

20. How does the decrease in progesterone at the last weeks of pregnancy help to bring on labor?
   a. stimulating FSH production
   b. decreasing the levels of estrogens
   c. dilating the cervix
   d. decreasing the inhibition of uterine contractility

21. Which of these fetal presentations is the easiest for vaginal birth?
    a. complete breech
    b. vertex occiput anterior
    c. frank breech
    d. vertex occiput posterior

22. Which of these shunts exists between the right and left atria?
    a. foramen ovale
    b. ductus venosus
    c. ductus arteriosis
    d. foramen venosus

23. Why is brown fat important?
    a. It is the newborn's primary source of insulation.
    b. It can be broken down to generate heat for thermoregulation.
    c. It can be broken down for energy between feedings.
    d. It can be converted to white fat.

24. Constriction of umbilical blood vessels during vaginal birth _____.
    a. causes respiratory alkalosis
    b. inhibits the respiratory center in the brain
    c. elevates carbon dioxide levels in the blood
    d. both a and b

25. Alveoli are connected to the lactiferous sinuses by _____.
    a. lactocytes
    b. lactiferous ducts
    c. nipple pores
    d. lobules

26. How is colostrum most important to a newborn?
    a. It helps boost the newborn's immune system.
    b. It provides much needed fat.
    c. It satisfies the newborn's thirst.
    d. It satisfies the infant's appetite.

27. Mature breast milk _____.
    a. has more sodium than cow's milk
    b. has more calcium than cow's milk
    c. has more protein than cow's milk
    d. has more fat than cow's milk

28. Marfan syndrome is inherited in an autosomal dominant pattern. Which of the following is true?
    a. Female offspring are more likely to be carriers of the disease.
    b. Male offspring are more likely to inherit the disease.
    c. Male and female offspring have the same likelihood of inheriting the disease.
    d. Female offspring are more likely to inherit the disease.

29. In addition to codominance, the ABO blood group antigens are also an example of _____.
    a. incomplete dominance
    b. X-linked recessive inheritance
    c. multiple alleles
    d. recessive lethal inheritance

30. Zoe has cystic fibrosis. Which of the following is the most likely explanation?
    a. Zoe probably inherited one faulty allele from her father, who is a carrier, and one normal allele from her mother.
    b. Zoe probably inherited one faulty allele from her mother, who must also have cystic fibrosis, and one normal allele from her father.
    c. Zoe must have inherited faulty alleles from both parents, both of whom must also have cystic fibrosis.
    d. Zoe must have inherited faulty alleles from both parents, both of whom are carriers.

Critical Thinking Questions

31. Darcy and Raul are having difficulty conceiving a child. Darcy ovulates every 28 days, and Raul's sperm count is normal. If we could observe Raul's sperm about an hour after ejaculation, however, we'd see that they appear to be moving only sluggishly. When Raul's sperm eventually encounter Darcy's oocyte, they appear to be incapable of generating an adequate acrosomal reaction. Which process has probably gone wrong?

32. On Saturday night, a female has unprotected sex with a male. On Tuesday morning, she experiences the twinge of mid-cycle pain that she typically feels when she is ovulating. This makes her extremely anxious that she might soon learn she is pregnant. Is the concern valid? Why or why not?

33. Approximately 3 weeks after her last menstrual period, a sexually active woman experiences a brief episode of abdominopelvic cramping and minor bleeding. What might be the explanation?

34. The Food and Nutrition Board of the Institute of Medicine recommends that all people who might become pregnant consume at least 400 µg/day of folate from supplements or fortified foods. Why?

35. What is the physiological benefit of incorporating shunts into the fetal circulatory system?

36. Why would a premature infant require supplemental oxygen?

37. Devin is 35 weeks pregnant with their first child when they begin experiencing diffuse, mild contractions for several hours. Examination reveals, however, that the plug of mucus blocking their cervix is intact and the cervix has not yet begun to dilate. Devin is advised to return home. Why?

38. Janine is 41 weeks pregnant with her first child when she arrives at the birthing unit reporting that she believes she has been in labor "for days" but that "it's just not going anywhere." During the clinical exam, she experiences a few mild contractions, each lasting about 15–20 seconds; however, her cervix is found to be only 2 cm dilated, and the amniotic sac is intact. Janine is admitted to the birthing unit and an IV infusion of pitocin is started. Why?

39. Describe how the newborn's first breath alters the circulatory pattern.

40. Newborns are at much higher risk for dehydration than adults. Why?

41. Describe the transit of breast milk from lactocytes to nipple pores.

42. A person who stopped breastfeeding suddenly is experiencing breast engorgement and leakage, just like they did in the first few weeks of breastfeeding. Why?

43. Explain why it was essential that Mendel perform his crosses using a large sample size?

44. How can a female carrier of an X-linked recessive disorder have a female child who is affected?

REFERENCES

3.2 The Cytoplasm and Cellular Organelles

Kolata, G. Severe diet doesn't prolong life, at least in monkeys. *New York Times* [Internet]. 2012 Aug. 29 [cited 2013 Jan 21]; Available from:

http://www.nytimes.com/2012/08/30/science/low-calorie-diet-doesnt-prolong-life-study-of-monkeys-finds.html?_r=2&ref=caloricrestriction& (http://www.nytimes.com/2012/08/30/science/low-calorie-diet-doesnt-prolong-life-study-of-monkeys-finds.html?_r=2&ref=caloricrestriction&)

4.5 Nervous Tissue Mediates Perception and Response

Stern, P. Focus issue: getting excited about glia. Science [Internet]. 2010 [cited 2012 Dec 4]; 3(147):330-773. Available from:

http://stke.sciencemag.org/cgi/content/abstract/sigtrans;3/147/eg11 (http://stke.sciencemag.org/cgi/content/abstract/sigtrans;3/147/eg11)

Ming GL, Song H. Adult neurogenesis in the mammalian central nervous system. Annu. Rev. Neurosci. 2005 [cited 2012 Dec 4]; 28:223–250.

4.6 Tissue Injury and Aging

Emerson, RW. Old age. Atlantic. 1862 [cited 2012 Dec 4]; 9(51):134–140.

5.3 Functions of the Integumentary System

American Academy of Dermatology (US). Tattoos and body piercings [Internet]. Schaumburg, IL; c2013 [cited 2012 Nov 1]. Available from: http://www.aad.org/media-resources/stats-and-facts/prevention-and-care/tattoos-and-body-piercings/ (http://www.aad.org/media-resources/stats-and-facts/prevention-and-care/tattoos-and-body-piercings/).

5.4 Diseases, Disorders, and Injuries of the Integumentary System

American Cancer Society (US). Skin cancer: basal and squamous cell [Internet]. c2013 [cited 2012 Nov 1]. Available from: http://www.cancer.org/acs/groups/cid/documents/webcontent/003139-pdf.pdf (http://www.cancer.org/acs/groups/cid/documents/webcontent/003139-pdf.pdf).

Lucile Packard Children's Hospital at Stanford (US). Classification and treatment of burns [Internet]. Palo Alto (CA). c2012 [cited 2012 Nov 1]. Available from: https://www.stanfordchildrens.org/en/topic/default?id=classification-of-burns-90-P09575 (https://www.stanfordchildrens.org/en/topic/default?id=classification-of-burns-90-P09575).

Mayo Clinic (US). Basal cell carcinoma [Internet]. Scottsdale (AZ); c2012 [cited 2012 Nov 1]. Available from: http://www.mayoclinic.com/health/basal-cell-carcinoma/ds00925/dsection=treatments-and-drugs (http://www.mayoclinic.com/health/basal-cell-carcinoma/ds00925/dsection=treatments-and-drugs).

Beck, J. FYI: how much can a human body sweat before it runs out? Popular Science [Internet]. New York (NY); c2012 [cited 2012 Nov 1]. Available from: http://www.popsci.com/science/article/2011-01/fyi-how-much-can-human-body-sweat-it-runs-out (http://www.popsci.com/science/article/2011-01/fyi-how-much-can-human-body-sweat-it-runs-out).

Skin Cancer Foundation (US). Skin cancer facts [Internet]. New York (NY); c2013 [cited 2012 Nov 1]. Available from: http://www.skincancer.org/skin-cancer-information/skin-cancer-facts#top (http://www.skincancer.org/skin-cancer-information/skin-cancer-facts#top).

7.2 The Skull

Centers for Disease Control and Prevention (US). Injury prevention and control: traumatic brain injury [Internet]. Atlanta, GA; [cited 2013 Mar 18]. Available from: http://www.cdc.gov/traumaticbraininjury/statistics.html (https://www.cdc.gov/TraumaticBrainInjury/data/index.html).

12.1 Basic Structure and Function of the Nervous System

Kramer, PD. Listening to prozac. 1st ed. New York (NY): Penguin Books; 1993.

18.6 Blood Typing

Garratty G, Glynn SA, McEntire R; Retrovirus Epidemiology Donor Study. ABO and Rh(D) phenotype frequencies of different racial/ethnic groups in the United States. Transfusion. Available from: https://pubmed.ncbi.nlm.nih.gov/15104651/ (https://pubmed.ncbi.nlm.nih.gov/15104651/)https://pubmed.ncbi.nlm.nih.gov/15104651/

19.4 Cardiac Physiology

Spreeuw, J., & Owadally, I. (2013). Investigating the Broken-Heart Effect: A Model for Short-Term Dependence between the Remaining Lifetimes of Joint Lives. Annals of Actuarial Science. Available from: https://www.cambridge.org/core/journals/annals-of-actuarial-science/article/abs/investigating-the-brokenheart-effect-a-model-for-shortterm-dependence-between-the-remaining-lifetimes-of-joint-lives/CE4BCF96E671F09B44259F0ED7E8216A (https://www.cambridge.org/core/journals/annals-of-actuarial-science/article/abs/investigating-the-brokenheart-effect-a-model-for-shortterm-dependence-between-the-remaining-lifetimes-of-joint-lives/CE4BCF96E671F09B44259F0ED7E8216A)

20.4 Homeostatic Regulation of the Vascular System

Centers for Disease Control and Prevention (US). Getting blood pressure under control: high blood pressure is out of control for too many Americans [Internet]. Atlanta (GA); [cited 2013 Apr 26]. Available from: https://www.cdc.gov/bloodpressure/facts.htm (https://www.cdc.gov/bloodpressure/facts.htm)

21.7 Transplantation and Cancer Immunology

Robinson J, Mistry K, McWilliam H, Lopez R, Parham P, Marsh SG. Nucleic acid research. IMGT/HLA Database [Internet]. 2011 [cited 2013 Apr 1]; 39:D1171–1176. Available from: http://europepmc.org/abstract/MED/21071412 (http://europepmc.org/abstract/MED/21071412)

Robinson J, Malik A, Parham P, Bodmer JG, Marsh SG. Tissue antigens. IMGT/HLA Database [Internet]. 2000 [cited 2013 Apr 1]; 55(3):280–287. Available from: https://pubmed.ncbi.nlm.nih.gov/10777106/ (https://pubmed.ncbi.nlm.nih.gov/10777106/)

22.1 Organs and Structures of the Respiratory System

Bizzintino J, Lee WM, Laing IA, Vang F, Pappas T, Zhang G, Martin AC, Khoo SK, Cox DW, Geelhoed GC, et al. Association between human rhinovirus C and severity of acute asthma in children. Eur Respir J [Internet]. 2010 [cited 2013 Mar 22]; 37(5):1037–1042. Available from: https://erj.ersjournals.com/content/37/5/1037 (https://erj.ersjournals.com/content/

37/5/1037)

Kumar V, Ramzi S, Robbins SL. Robbins Basic Pathology. 7th ed. Philadelphia (PA): Elsevier Ltd; 2005.

Martin RJ, Kraft M, Chu HW, Berns, EA, Cassell GH. A link between chronic asthma and chronic infection. J Allergy Clin Immunol [Internet]. 2001 [cited 2013 Mar 22]; 107(4):595-601. Available from: http://www.jacionline.org/article/S0091-6749(01)31561-0/fulltext (http://www.jacionline.org/article/S0091-6749(01)31561-0/fulltext)

23.3 The Mouth, Pharynx, and Esophagus

van Loon FPL, Holmes SJ, Sirotkin B, Williams W, Cochi S, Hadler S, Lindegren ML. Morbidity and Mortality Weekly Report: Mumps surveillance -- United States, 1988–1993 [Internet]. Atlanta, GA: Center for Disease Control; [cited 2013 Apr 3]. Available from: http://www.cdc.gov/mmwr/preview/mmwrhtml/00038546.htm (http://www.cdc.gov/mmwr/preview/mmwrhtml/00038546.htm).

23.5 The Small and Large Intestines

American Cancer Society (US). Cancer facts and figures: colorectal cancer: 2011–2013 [Internet]. c2013 [cited 2013 Apr 3]. Available from: http://www.cancer.org/Research/CancerFactsFigures/ColorectalCancerFactsFigures/colorectal-cancer-facts-figures-2011-2013-page (http://www.cancer.org/Research/CancerFactsFigures/ColorectalCancerFactsFigures/colorectal-cancer-facts-figures-2011-2013-page).

The Nutrition Source. Fiber and colon cancer: following the scientific trail [Internet]. Boston (MA): Harvard School of Public Health; c2012 [cited 2013 Apr 3]. Available from: https://www.hsph.harvard.edu/nutritionsource/carbohydrates/fiber/ (https://www.hsph.harvard.edu/nutritionsource/carbohydrates/fiber/).

Centers for Disease Control and Prevention (US). Morbidity and mortality weekly report: notifiable diseases and mortality tables [Internet]. Atlanta (GA); [cited 2013 Apr 3]. Available from: http://www.cdc.gov/mmwr/preview/mmwrhtml/mm6101md.htm?s_cid=mm6101md_w (http://www.cdc.gov/mmwr/preview/mmwrhtml/mm6101md.htm?s_cid=mm6101md_w).

25.10 The Urinary System and Homeostasis

Bagul A, Frost JH, Drage M. Stem cells and their role in renal ischaemia reperfusion injury. Am J Nephrol [Internet]. 2013 [cited 2013 Apr 15]; 37(1):16–29. Available from: http://www.karger.com/Article/FullText/345731 (http://www.karger.com/Article/FullText/345731)

INDEX

Symbols

α-dextrin   1040

α-dextrinase   1040

A

abdominal aorta   846

abdominopelvic cavity   27

abducens nerve   522

abduct   400

Abduction   330

abductor   403

abductor digiti minimi   430

abductor pollicis brevis   430

abductor pollicis longus   428

ABO blood group   740

absolute refractory period   474

absorption   1003

absorptive state   1087

accessory digestive organ   997

accessory duct   1035

Acclimatization   982

accommodation   640

accommodation–convergence reflex   640

acetabular labrum   337

acetabulum   287

acetyl coenzyme A (acetyl CoA) 1069

acetylcholine (ACh)   364, 597

acid   58

acinus   1035

Acne   182

acromegaly   678

acromial end of the clavicle   276

acromial process   277

acromioclavicular joint   277

acromion   277

acrosomal reaction   1224

acrosome   1224

actin   361

action potential   364, 466

activation energy   54

activation gate   474

Active immunity   925

active transport   85

Acute inflammation   911

Acute mountain sickness (AMS) 982

adaptive immune response   897

adduction   330

adductor   403

adductor brevis   435

adductor longus   435

adductor magnus   435

adductor pollicis   430

adductor tubercle   292

adenosine triphosphate (ATP) 15, 65

adenylyl cyclase   669

Adipocytes   142

Adipose tissue   142

adrenal artery   853

adrenal cortex   688

adrenal glands   688

adrenal medulla   594, 688

adrenal vein   872

adrenergic   597

adrenocorticotropic hormone (ACTH)   679

Aerobic respiration   370

afferent branch   599

afferent lymphatic vessels   902

afterbirth   1249

Afterload   797

agglutination   739

agonist   396, 612

agranular leukocytes   730

ala   948

alar cartilage   949

alar plate   509

alarm reaction   689

Albinism   171

Albumin   714

Aldosterone   689

alimentary canal   997

Alkaloids   544

allantois   1233

allele   1256

alpha (α)-adrenergic receptor 597

alpha cell   694

Alveolar dead space   967

alveolar duct   956

alveolar macrophage   957

alveolar pores   956

Alveolar process of the mandible 242

alveolar process of the maxilla 240

alveolar sac   956

alveoli   1210

alveolus   956

amacrine cells   554

amino acid   68

aminopeptidase   1041

amnion   1232

amniotic cavity   1232

amphiarthrosis   315

amphipathic   82

ampulla   550, 1205

amygdala   502

Anabolic hormones   1061

anabolic reactions   1061

anabolism   14, 14

anagen   174

anal canal   1028

anal column   1030

anal sinus   1030

anal triangle   420

Anaphase   110

Anaphylactic shock   842

anastomosis   768

anatomical dead space   967

anatomical neck   278

anatomical position   23

anatomical sphincter   1116

anatomy   8

anchoring junction   132

anconeus   426

anemia   725

angioblasts   879

angiogenesis   379, 879

angiotensin I   1123

Angiotensin II   1123

angiotensin-converting enzyme 689

angiotensin-converting enzyme (ACE)   1123

angiotensinogen   1123

angle of the mandible   242

angle of the rib   260

anion   47

ankle joint   295

annular ligament   336

anosmia   545

antagonist   396, 612

Anterior   24

anterior (ventral) sacral foramen   255

anterior arch   253

anterior border of the tibia   294

anterior cardiac veins   770

anterior cerebral artery   849

anterior columns   510

anterior communicating artery   849

anterior compartment of the arm   426

anterior compartment of the forearm   428

anterior compartment of the leg   438

anterior compartment of the thigh   436

anterior corticospinal tract   576

anterior cranial fossa   232

anterior cruciate ligament   340

anterior horn   509

anterior inferior iliac spine   286

anterior interventricular artery   768

anterior interventricular sulcus   757

anterior longitudinal ligament   257

anterior median fissure   509

anterior sacroiliac ligament   287

anterior scalene   414

anterior spinal artery   512

anterior superior iliac spine   286

anterior talofibular ligament   343

anterior tibial artery   859

anterior tibial vein   874

anterograde amnesia   632

antibodies   714

antibody   898

anticholinergic drugs   613

anticoagulant   738

anticodon   105

antidiuretic hormone (ADH)   676, 1165

antigen   898

antigen presentation   914

Antigen processing   914

antigen receptor   918

antigenic determinant   913

Antithrombin   738

antrum   1201

anulus fibrosus   256

anuria   1112

aorta   846

aortic arch   846

aortic hiatus   846

aortic sinuses   835

aortic valve   765

apex   948

aphasia   633

apical   130

apical ectodermal ridge   297

apneustic center   968

Apocrine secretion   139

apocrine sweat gland   176

aponeurosis   360

Apoptosis   151

appendicular   403

appendicular skeleton   229

appendix   1027

aquaporin   1124

aqueous humor   554

arachnoid granulations   514

arachnoid mater   513

arachnoid trabeculae   513

arcuate line of the ilium   286

areola   1210

Areolar tissue   143

arm   278

arrector pili   174

arterial circle   849

arteriole   814

arteriovenous anastomosis   816

artery   813

articular capsule   321

articular cartilage   198, 321

articular disc   322

Articular tubercle   234

articulation   198, 314

artificial pacemaker   783

ascending aorta   846

ascending colon   1028

ascending pathway   559

Ascending tracts   510

association area   567

Astrocyte   150, 461

ataxia   651

atlanto-occipital joint   333

atlantoaxial joint   333

atlas   253

Atmospheric pressure   962

atom   41

atomic number   42

ATP synthase   1071

ATPase   369

atrial natriuretic peptide (ANP)   697

atrial reflex   793, 836

atrioventricular (AV) node   775

atrioventricular bundle   775

atrioventricular bundle branches   775

atrioventricular septum   760

atrioventricular valves   760

atrium   754

atrophy   152, 378

audition   546

auricle   546, 757

auricular surface of the ilium   286

autocrine   664

autolysis   94

autonomic nervous system (ANS)   456

autonomic tone   606, 790

Autophagy   94

autorhythmicity   383, 772

autosomal chromosomes   1256

autosomal dominant   1259

autosomal recessive   1260

axial   403

axial skeleton   228

axillary artery   857

axillary nerve   525

axillary vein   869

axis   253

axon   453

axon hillock   459

axon segment   459

axon terminal 459
axoplasm 459
azygos vein 865

B

B cells 898
B lymphocytes 731
Babinski sign 647
Bachmann's bundle 774
bacterial flora 1030
Bainbridge reflex 793
ball-and-socket joint 325
baroreceptor 600
baroreceptor reflex 792
Barrier defenses 897
Bartholin's glands 1197
basal cell 165
Basal cell carcinoma 180
basal forebrain 500
basal lamina 130
basal metabolic rate (BMR) 1093
basal nuclei 500
basal plate 509
base 59
base of the metatarsal bone 296
basement membrane 130
basilar artery 512, 849
basilar membrane 547
basilic vein 869
Basophils 730
bedsore 185
belly 398
beta (β)-adrenergic receptor 597
beta (β)-hydroxybutyrate 1079
beta (β)-oxidation 1077
beta cell 694
Betz cells 574
bi 403
biaxial joint 316
biceps brachii 426
biceps femoris 437
bicipital groove 278
bicuspid valve 765
Bile 1034
bile canaliculus 1034
bile salts 1076
bilirubin 723, 1034
biliverdin 723
binocular depth cues 567
biogenic amine 480

biosynthesis reactions 1061
bipennate 399
Bipolar 460
bipolar cells 554
blastocoel 1228
blastocyst 1228
blastomere 1228
blood 711
blood colloidal osmotic pressure
(BCOP) 831
Blood flow 821
Blood hydrostatic pressure 831
blood islands 879
blood pressure 821
blood-brain barrier (BBB) 462
blood–testis barrier 1189
body 1017
body mass index (BMI) 1095
body of the rib 260
body of uterus 1206
Bohr effect 978
bolus 1007
bond 47
Bone 191
bone marrow 899
bone marrow biopsy 718
bone marrow transplant 719
Bowman's capsule 1119
Boyle's law 962
brachial artery 857
brachial plexus 525
brachial vein 869
brachialis 426
brachiocephalic vein 864
brachioradialis 426
brain 452
brain case 229
brain stem 495
Braxton Hicks contractions 1247
brevis 403
bridge 948
broad ligament 1198
Broca's area 501, 573
Brodmann's areas 501
bronchi 955
bronchial artery 851
bronchial bud 983
bronchial tree 955
bronchial vein 865

bronchiole 955
bronchoconstriction 960
bronchodilation 960
Bronchus-associated lymphoid
tissue (BALT) 905
brown adipose tissue 1251
bruise 724
brush border 1024, 1124
buccinator 404
buffer 60
buffy coat 712
bulbourethral glands 1192
bulbus cordis 800
bundle of His 775
bursa 322

C

calcaneal tendon 439
calcaneofibular ligament 343
calcaneus 295
calcitonin 684
callus 185
calmodulin 384
Calorie 1093
calvaria 232
calyces 1118
canaliculi 201
capacitance 819
capacitance vessels 819
capacitation 1224
capillary 814
capillary bed 816
capillary hydrostatic pressure
(CHP) 831
capitate 280
capitulum 279
capsaicin 551
carbaminohemoglobin 722, 980
carbohydrate 62
Carbonic anhydrase (CA) 980
cardia 1016
cardiac accelerator nerves 609
cardiac cycle 784
Cardiac muscle 148, 359
cardiac notch 752, 959
Cardiac output (CO) 788
cardiac plexus 790
cardiac reflexes 792
cardiac reserve 789
cardiac skeleton 760

cardiogenic area   800
cardiogenic cords   800
Cardiogenic shock   841
cardiomyocyte   768
cardiovascular center   609
Carotid canal   234, 246, 512
carotid sinuses   835
carpal bone   278
carpal tunnel   282
carpometacarpal joint   282
carrier   1260
cartilage   191
cartilaginous joint   314
Catabolic hormones   1061
Catabolic reactions   1058
catabolism   14, 14
catagen   174
catalyst   54
cation   47
cauda equina   509
caudal   25
caudate   502
caval opening   418
cavernous sinus   867
cecum   1027
celiac ganglion   593
celiac trunk   853
cell   10
cell cycle   107
cell junction   130
cell membrane   82
cellular respiration   1063
cementum   1011
central canal   203, 515
central chemoreceptor   969
central nervous system (CNS)   452
central neuron   591
central sulcus   500
Central tolerance   921
central vein   1034
centriole   97
centromere   108
centrosome   110
cephalic flexure   496
cephalic phase   1020
cephalic vein   869
cerebellum   508
cerebral aqueduct   515

cerebral cortex   466, 500
cerebral hemisphere   500
cerebral peduncles   574
cerebrocerebellum   650
cerebrospinal fluid (CSF)   462
cerebrovascular accident (CVA)   848
cerebrum   500
cervical curve   250
cervical enlargement   576
cervical plexus   525
cervical vertebrae   252
cervix   1206
channel protein   83
check reflex   651
checkpoint   110
chemical digestion   1003
Chemical energy   51
chemical synapse   478
chemokine   909
chemoreceptor   541
chief cells   1018
chief sensory nucleus   561
chloride shift   980
cholecystokinin (CCK)   1076
cholinergic   597
cholinergic system   479
chondrocytes   145
chordae tendineae   763
chorion   1233
chorionic membrane   1235
chorionic villi   1235
choroid   554
choroid plexus   463, 516
chromaffin   690
chromaffin cells   595
chromatin   100
chromosome   100
Chronic inflammation   911
chyle   896
chylomicron   1045
chylomicrons   1076
chyme   1003
chymotrypsin   1082
chymotrypsinogen   1082
Cilia   97
ciliary body   554
ciliary ganglion   595
circadian rhythm   564

circle of Willis   512, 849
Circular   399
circular fold   1024
circulatory shock   841
Circumduction   330
circumflex artery   768
cisterna chyli   897
citric acid cycle   1065
clasp-knife response   648
Class switching   923
clavicle   275
clavicular notch   259
cleavage   1228
cleavage furrow   110
clitoris   1197
clonal anergy   921
clonal deletion   921
clonal expansion   918
Clonal selection   918
clone   918
closed reduction   212
Clotting   152
clotting factors   735
coagulation   734
coccyx   228
cochlea   546
cochlear duct   546
Codominance   1263
codon   104
Collagen fiber   142
Collateral ganglia   593
colloid   56, 681
colon   1028
Colony-stimulating factors (CSFs)   718
colostrum   1254
common bile duct   1034
common carotid arteries   512
common carotid artery   848
common hepatic artery   853
common hepatic duct   1034
common iliac artery   853
common iliac vein   874
common pathway   737
compact bone   197
complement   909
Compliance   825
compound   41, 47
compressor urethrae   420

Computed tomography (CT)   29
concentration   54
concentration gradient   85
concentric contraction   372
conceptus   1228
conducting zone   948
Conduction   1093
Conduction aphasia   633
conductive hearing   638
condylar process of the
mandible   242
condyle   242
condyloid joint   325
cone photoreceptor   555
conjugate gaze   639
Connective tissue   126
connective tissue membrane
129
Connective tissue proper   141
constant region domain   913
continuous capillary   815
continuous conduction   475
Contractility   358
contraction phase   375
contralateral   559
control center   20
Convection   1093
convergence   640
convergent   399
coordination exam   626
coracobrachialis   425
coracoclavicular ligament   277
coracohumeral ligament   335
coracoid process   277
corn   185
cornea   554
corneal reflex   578
corona radiata   1224
coronal suture   239
Coronary arteries   768
coronary sinus   763
coronary sulcus   757
Coronary veins   770
coronoid fossa   279
coronoid process of the
mandible   242
coronoid process of the ulna   279
corpus albicans   1205
corpus callosum   500

corpus cavernosum   1193
corpus luteum   1205
corpus spongiosum   1193
corrugator supercilii   404
cortex   173
cortical nephrons   1120
cortical reaction   1225
cortico-ponto-cerebellar
pathway   650
corticobulbar tract   574
corticospinal tract   574
cortisol   689
costal cartilage   260
costal facet   254
costal groove   260
costoclavicular ligament   276
countercurrent multiplier system
1135
covalent bond   49
coxal bone   285
cranial   24
cranial cavity   27, 232
cranial nerve   519
cranial nerve exam   626
cranial nerve ganglion   519
craniosacral system   595
cranium   229
Creatine phosphate   369
cribriform plate   237
cricoid cartilage   952
crista galli   237
crown   1011
cuboid   295
cupula   550
cuspids   1010
cutaneous membrane   130
cuticle   173
cyclic adenosine monophosphate
(cAMP)   669
cyclin   111
cyclin-dependent kinase (CDK)
111
cystic artery   853
cystic duct   1036
cytoarchitecture   630
cytokine   909
Cytokines   718
Cytokinesis   108
cytoplasm   91

cytoskeleton   97
Cytosol   91
Cytotoxic T cells (Tc)   920

D
Dalton's law   970
deciduous teeth   1010
decomposition reaction   53
decussates   559
Deep   25
deep anterior compartment   428
deep femoral artery   859
deep femoral vein   874
deep posterior compartment of
the forearm   428
deep tendon reflex   647
deep transverse perineal   420
defecation   1003
defensins   730
deglutition   408, 1015
dehydration   1163
Delayed hypersensitivity   932
delta cell   694
deltoid   425
deltoid ligament   343
deltoid tuberosity   278
Denaturation   70
dendrite   453
dens   253
dense body   384
dense connective tissue   141
dentes   1010
dentin   1011
dentition   1010
deoxyhemoglobin   722
deoxyribonuclease   1042
Deoxyribonucleic acid (DNA)   72
depolarization   472
depolarize   364
Depression   331
dermal papilla   165
dermis   167
descending aorta   846
descending colon   1028
descending tracts   510
desmosome   166, 382
detrusor muscle   1115
Development   16
diabetes mellitus   696
diacylglycerol (DAG)   670

diapedesis 728

diaphragm 417

diaphysis 197

diarthrosis 315

diastole 784

diastolic pressure 821

diencephalon 495

differentiation 16

Diffusion 85

digastric 410

digital arteries 857

digital veins 869

dihydroxyvitamin D 1171

dilation 1247

dipeptidase 1041

diploë 198

diploid 107

diplopia 640

direct pathway 503

disaccharide 63

disinhibition 503

Distal 25

distal convoluted tubules 1120

distal radioulnar joint 280

distal tibiofibular joint 295

disulfide bond 70

Diuresis 1165

diuretic 1141

DNA polymerase 102

DNA replication 101

dominant 1257

Dominant lethal 1264

dorsal 24

dorsal (posterior) cavity 26

dorsal (posterior) nerve root 509

dorsal (posterior) root ganglion 518

dorsal arch 859

dorsal column system 559

dorsal group 439

dorsal interossei 430

dorsal longitudinal fasciculus 608

dorsal nucleus of the vagus nerve 595

dorsal respiratory group (DRG) 968

dorsal stream 569

dorsal venous arch 874

dorsalis pedis artery 859

Dorsiflexion 331

dorsum nasi 948

downregulation 671

ductus arteriosus 879, 1241

ductus deferens 1191

ductus venosus 879, 1241

duodenal glands 1025

duodenum 1023

dura mater 513

dural sinuses 513

E

ear ossicles 228

early induced immune response 909

eccentric contraction 372

eccrine sweat gland 176

ectoderm 127, 1233

ectopic pregnancy 1231

Eczema 182

edema 628

Edinger–Westphal nucleus 595

effector 20

effector protein 480

effector T cells 919

efferent arteriole 1119

efferent branch 599

efferent lymphatic vessels 902

ejaculatory duct 1192

ejection fraction 789

elastase 1082

elastic artery 813

Elastic cartilage 145

Elastic fiber 142

elasticity 358

Elastin fibers 168

elbow joint 279, 336

electrical gradient 88

electrical synapse 478

electrocardiogram (ECG) 778

electrochemical exclusion 469

electron 41

electron shell 45

electron transport chain (ETC) 1070

eleidin 167

element 40

elevation 331

embolus 627, 739

embryo 1228

embryonic folding 1237

emigration 728

enamel 1011

encapsulated ending 541

end diastolic volume (EDV) 785

end systolic volume (ESV) 785

endocardial tubes 800

endocardium 759

endochondral ossification 207

endocrine gland 137, 663

endocrine system 662

Endocytosis 88

endoderm 127, 1233

endogenous 597

endogenous chemical 610

endometrium 1207

endomysium 360

endoneurium 520

endoplasmic reticulum (ER) 92

endosteum 197

Endothelins 1139

endothelium 133, 759

energy-consuming phase 1066

energy-yielding phase 1066

enteric nervous system 518

enteric nervous system (ENS) 456

enteric plexus 520

enteroendocrine cells 1018

enterohepatic circulation 1034

enterokinase 1082

enteropeptidase 1036

enzyme 54

Eosinophils 730

ependymal cell 462

epiblast 1232

epicardial coronary arteries 768

epicardium 756

epicranial aponeurosis 404

epidermis 164

epididymis 1191

epiglottis 953

epimysium 359

epinephrine 597, 690

epineurium 520

epiphyseal line 210

epiphyseal plate 197

epiphysis 197

epiploic appendages 1029
episiotomy 1249
episodic memory 632
epithalamus 505
epithelial membrane 129
Epithelial tissue 126
eponychium 175
equilibrium 550
erector spinae group 413
erythroblastosis fetalis 934
erythrocyte 719
erythropoietin (EPO) 698, 717
esophageal artery 851
esophageal plexus 520
esophageal vein 865
esophagus 1013
estrogens 692
ethmoid air cell 246
ethmoid bone 237
Evaporation 1093
eversion 331
exchange reaction 53
excitability 357
excitable membrane 468
excitation-contraction coupling 362
excitatory postsynaptic potential (EPSP) 477
executive functions 571
exocrine gland 137
exocrine system 663
exocytosis 89
exogenous 597
exogenous chemical 610
exon 104
expiration 964
Expiratory reserve volume (ERV) 965
expressive aphasia 633
expulsion 1249
extensibility 358
extension 329
extensor 403
extensor carpi radialis brevis 428
extensor carpi ulnaris 428
extensor digiti minimi 428
extensor digitorum 428
extensor digitorum brevis 439
extensor digitorum longus 438

extensor hallucis longus 438
extensor indicis 429
extensor pollicis brevis 428
extensor pollicis longus 429
extensor radialis longus 428
extensor retinaculum 429
External acoustic meatus 234
external anal sphincter 1029
external callus 214
external carotid artery 848
external ear 546
external elastic membrane 813
external iliac artery 854
external iliac vein 874
external intercostal 419
external jugular vein 866
external nose 948
external oblique 416
external occipital protuberance 236
External respiration 973
external root sheath 174
external urinary sphincter 1114
exteroceptor 541
Extracellular fluid (ECF) 83, 1157
extraocular muscles 522, 553
extrapyramidal system 576
extrinsic eye muscles 405
extrinsic ligament 321
extrinsic muscles of the hand 428
extrinsic muscles of the tongue 642
extrinsic pathway 737

F
facet 254
facial bones 229
facial nerve 522
Facilitated diffusion 86
FADH2 1063
false ribs 260
fas ligand 908
fascicle 360, 397
fascicles 520
fasciculation 648
fasciculus cuneatus 559
fasciculus gracilis 559
fast glycolytic (FG) 377

Fast oxidative (FO) 377
fatty acid oxidation 1077
fauces 641, 952, 1006
Fc region 921
feces 1031
femoral artery 859
femoral circumflex vein 874
femoral nerve 525
femoral triangle 435
femoral vein 874
femoropatellar joint 339
femur 290
fenestrated capillary 815
fenestrations 1122
ferritin 723
Fertilization 1223
fertilization membrane 1225
fetus 1228
fibrillation 648
fibrin 734
Fibrinogen 714
Fibrinolysis 737
fibroblast 142
Fibrocartilage 145
fibrocyte 142
fibroelastic membrane 954
fibrosis 386
fibrous joint 314
fibrous tunic 554
fibula 290
fibular collateral ligament 340
fibular nerve 525
fibular notch 294
fibular vein 874
fibularis brevis 439
fibularis longus 439
fibularis tertius 438
fight-or-flight response 590
filling time 796
filtration 831
filtration slits 1121
fimbriae 1205
first messenger 669
first-degree burn 184
fixator 396
flaccid paralysis 648
flaccidity 647
flagellum 97
flat bone 196

flatus   1031

flavin adenine dinucleotide (FAD)
1063

Flexion   329, 396

flexor   403

flexor carpi radialis   428

flexor carpi ulnaris   428

flexor digiti minimi brevis   430

flexor digitorum longus   439

flexor digitorum profundus   428

flexor digitorum superficialis   428

flexor hallucis longus   439

flexor pollicis brevis   430

flexor pollicis longus   428

flexor retinaculum   282, 429

floating ribs   260

flocculonodular lobe   650

fluid compartment   1157

fluid connective tissue   141

follicle   1199

follicle-stimulating hormone
(FSH)   679

folliculogenesis   1201

fontanelle   260

fontanelles   317

foot   290

Foramen lacerum   246

foramen magnum   236, 512

foramen ovale   760, 879, 1241

Foramen ovale of the middle
cranial fossa   246

Foramen rotundum   246

Foramen spinosum   246

forced breathing   965

forearm   278

forebrain   495

foregut   983

foremilk   1255

formed elements   712

forming urine   1121

fossa   277

fossa ovalis   760

fourth ventricle   515

fourth-degree burn   184

fovea   554

fovea capitis   290

fracture   212

fracture hematoma   214

Frank-Starling mechanism   796

free nerve ending   540

frontal bone   235

frontal eye fields   501, 573

frontal lobe   500

frontal plane   25

frontal sinus   246

frontalis   404

functional group   61

functional residual capacity
(FRC)   966

fundus   1017, 1206

fusiform   398

G

G cells   1018

G protein   480, 669

G protein–coupled receptor   597

G0 phase   108

G1 phase   108

G2 phase   108

gait   650

gait exam   626

gallbladder   1036

gamete   1186

ganglion   453

ganglionic neuron   593

gap junction   132

gastric emptying   1021

gastric gland   1018

gastric phase   1020

gastric pits   1018

gastric plexuses   520

gastrin   1018

gastrocnemius   439

gastrocolic reflex   1031

gastroileal reflex   1026

gastrulation   1233

gated   469

gene   103

Gene expression   103

general adaptation syndrome
(GAS)   689

general sense   542

generator potential   476

genicular artery   859

genioglossus   409

geniohyoid   410

genome   102

genotype   1256

Germinal centers   901

gestation   1228

gigantism   678

Gingivae   1011

glabella   235

glans penis   1193

glassy membrane   174

glenohumeral joint   276, 335

glenohumeral ligament   335

glenoid cavity   276

glenoid labrum   335

glial cell   452

globin   722

globulins   714

globus pallidus   502

glomerular filtration rate (GFR)
1126

glomerulus   1119

glossopharyngeal nerve   522

glottis   953

glucagon   694

glucocorticoids   689

Glucokinase   1066

Gluconeogenesis   1072

glucose-6-phosphate   1066

gluteal group   432

gluteal tuberosity   291

gluteus maximus   432

gluteus medius   432

gluteus minimus   432

glycocalyx   84

glycogen   1088

Glycolysis   370, 1064

glycoprotein   84

glycosuria   1133

gnosis   634

goblet cell   134

goiter   684

Golgi apparatus   93

gomphosis   318

gonadal artery   853

gonadal vein   872

gonadotropin-releasing hormone
(GnRH)   1195

gonadotropins   679

gonads   1188

gracilis   435

graded muscle response   376

graded potential   466

graft-versus-host disease   937

Granular leukocytes 729
granulosa cells 1201
granzyme 908
graphesthesia 634
gray matter 453
gray rami communicantes 593
great cardiac vein 770
great cerebral vein 867
great saphenous vein 874
greater pelvis 288
greater sciatic foramen 288
greater sciatic notch 286
greater splanchnic nerve 593
greater trochanter 291
greater tubercle 278
greater wings of the sphenoid bone 236
Gross anatomy 8
ground substance 140
Growth 16
growth hormone (GH) 677
gustation 542
gustatory receptor cells 542
gyrus 500

H

Hair 172
hair bulb 172
hair cells 548
hair follicle 172
hair matrix 172
hair papilla 172
hair root 172
hair shaft 172
Haldane effect 980
hallux 296
hamate 280
hamstring group 437
hand 278
hard palate 240
haustra 1029
haustral contraction 1031
head of the femur 290
head of the fibula 295
head of the humerus 278
head of the metatarsal bone 296
head of the radius 280
head of the rib 260
head of the ulna 280
heart block 783

heart bulge 799
heart rate (HR) 788
heart sounds 786
heavy chain 921
helicase 102
Helper T cells (Th) 919
hemangioblasts 879
hematocrit 712
hematopoiesis 194
hematopoietic stem cell 716
heme 722
hemiazygos vein 865
hemisection 646
hemocytoblast 716
Hemoglobin 721
hemolysis 739
hemolytic disease of the newborn (HDN) 741
hemophilia 738
hemopoiesis 716
hemopoietic growth factors 716
hemorrhage 733
hemorrhagic stroke 628
hemosiderin 723
hemostasis 733
Henry's law 971
heparin 738
hepatic artery 1033
hepatic artery proper 853
hepatic lobule 1034
hepatic portal system 877
hepatic portal vein 1033
hepatic sinusoid 1034
hepatic vein 872, 1034
hepatocyte 1034
hepatopancreatic ampulla 1023
hepatopancreatic sphincter 1023
heterozygous 1257
Hexokinase 1066
high endothelial venules 901
hilum 960
hindbrain 495
Hindmilk 1255
hinge joint 325
hip bone 285
hip joint 290
hippocampus 502
histamine 151, 911

histology 126
histone 100
hole 198
holocrine secretion 139
Homeostasis 8
homologous 107
homozygous 1257
hook of the hamate bone 280
horizontal plate 241
hormone 662
hormone receptor 668
human chorionic gonadotropin (hCG) 1230
humeroradial joint 336
humeroulnar joint 336
humerus 278
Hyaline cartilage 145
hydrochloric acid (HCl) 1018
hydrogen bond 50
hydrophilic 82
hydrophobic 82
Hydrostatic pressure 1160
hydroxymethylglutaryl CoA (HMG CoA) 1079
hymen 1197
hyoglossus 409
hyoid bone 228
hypercalcemia 219, 1169
Hypercapnia 1174
Hyperchloremia 1168
Hyperextension 330
hyperflexia 648
hyperflexion 330
hyperglycemia 697
Hyperkalemia 1168
Hypernatremia 1167
hyperparathyroidism 687
Hyperphosphatemia 1169
hyperplasia 386
Hyperpnea 981
hypertension 840
hyperthyroidism 684
hypertonia 377
hypertonic 87
hypertrophic cardiomyopathy 754
hypertrophy 378
hyperventilation 981
Hypervolemia 826

hypoblast 1233
Hypocalcemia 219, 1169
Hypocapnia 1174
Hypochloremia 1168
hypodermis 168
hypoglossal canal 246
hypoglossal nerve 522
Hypokalemia 1168
Hyponatremia 1167
hyponychium 175
hypoparathyroidism 687
Hypophosphatemia 1169
hypophyseal (pituitary) fossa 236
hypophyseal portal system 677
hypothalamus 505, 674
hypothenar 430
hypothenar eminence 430
hypothyroidism 684
hypotonia 377
hypotonic 87
hypotonicity 647
hypovolemia 628, 826
Hypovolemic shock 841
hypoxemia 722
hypoxia 822

I

IgA 923
IgD 922
IgE 923
IgG 923
IgM 922
ileocecal sphincter 1023
ileum 1023
iliac crest 286
iliac fossa 286
iliacus 432
iliococcygeus 419
iliocostalis cervicis 413
iliocostalis group 413
iliocostalis lumborum 413
iliocostalis thoracis 413
iliofemoral ligament 337
iliopsoas group 432
iliotibial tract 435
ilium 286
immediate hypersensitivity 931
immune system 894
immunoglobulin 921

immunoglobulins 714
immunological memory 912
implantation 1229
inactivation gate 474
inactive proenzymes 1082
incisors 1010
incomplete dominance 1263
incontinence 1115
incus 546
indirect pathway 503
Inferior 25
inferior angle of the scapula 276
inferior articular process 251
inferior cerebellar peduncle (ICP) 649
inferior colliculus 507, 562
inferior extensor retinaculum 438
inferior gemellus 435
inferior mesenteric artery 853
inferior mesenteric ganglion 593
inferior nasal concha 231
inferior oblique 553
inferior olive 508, 650
inferior phrenic artery 853
inferior pubic ramus 287
inferior rectus 553
Inferior rotation 332
inferior vena cava 755, 872
Inflammation 151, 910
infraglenoid tubercle 276
infrahyoid muscles 410
infraorbital foramen 230
infraspinatus 425
infraspinous fossa 277
infratemporal fossa 231
infundibulum 674, 1205
ingestion 1003
inguinal canal 1192
inhibin 692
inhibitory postsynaptic potential (IPSP) 477
initial segment 459
innate immune response 897
inner cell mass 1228
inner ear 546
inner segment 555
inner synaptic layer 554
innermost intercostal 419

inorganic compound 55
inositol triphosphate (IP3) 670
insertion 396
Inspiration 964
Inspiratory capacity (IC) 966
Inspiratory reserve volume (IRV) 965
insulin 695, 1087
insulin-like growth factors (IGFs) 678
integral protein 83
integration 455
integumentary system 163
interatrial band 774
interatrial septum 760
interaural intensity difference 561
interaural time difference 561
intercalated cell 1136
intercalated disc 382, 772
intercondylar eminence 294
intercondylar fossa 292
intercostal artery 851
intercostal muscles 418
intercostal nerves 526
intercostal vein 865
Interferons 909
Interleukins 718
intermediate 430
intermediate cuneiform 296
intermediate filament 98
Internal acoustic meatus 234
internal anal sphincter 1029
internal callus 214
internal capsule 574
internal carotid arteries 512
internal carotid artery 848
internal elastic membrane 813
internal iliac artery 853
internal iliac vein 874
internal intercostal 419
internal jugular vein 866
internal oblique 416
Internal respiration 973
internal root sheath 174
internal thoracic artery 848
internal thoracic vein 865
internal urinary sphincter 1114
internodal pathways 774

internuclear ophthalmoplegia 640
interoceptor   541
interosseous border of the fibula 295
interosseous border of the radius 280
interosseous border of the tibia 294
interosseous border of the ulna 279
interosseous membrane   318
interosseous membrane of the forearm   280
interosseous membrane of the leg   294
interphalangeal joint   283
Interphase   108
interstitial fluid (IF)   1157
Interstitial fluid (IF)   83
interstitial fluid colloidal osmotic pressure (IFCOP)   831
interstitial fluid hydrostatic pressure (IFHP)   831
intertrochanteric crest   291
intertrochanteric line   291
intertubercular groove (sulcus) 278
interventricular foramina   515
interventricular septum   760
intervertebral disc   248, 256
intervertebral foramen   251
intestinal gland   1024
intestinal juice   1025
intestinal phase   1021
intorsion   639
Intra-alveolar pressure   963
intracapsular ligament   321
intracellular fluid (ICF)   1157
Intracellular fluid (ICF)   83
intramembranous ossification 206
intramural ganglia   595
Intrapleural pressure   963
intrinsic factor   1018
intrinsic ligament   321
intrinsic muscles of the hand 429
intrinsic muscles of the tongue

intrinsic pathway   737
intron   104
inulin   1128
Inversion   331
involution   1249
ion   47
ionic bond   48
ionotropic receptor   469
ipsilateral   559
iris   554
irregular bone   196
ischemia   822
ischemic stroke   628
ischial ramus   286
ischial spine   286
ischial tuberosity   286
ischiococcygeus   419
ischiofemoral ligament   337
ischiopubic ramus   287
ischium   286
isometric contraction   372
isotonic   87
isotonic contractions   372
isotope   43
isovolumic contraction   785
isovolumic ventricular relaxation phase   785
isthmus   1205

J

jaundice   724
jaw-jerk reflex   638
jejunum   1023
joint   314
joint cavity   314
joint interzone   345
jugular (suprasternal) notch   259
jugular foramen   246
jugular veins   513
juxtaglomerular apparatus (JGA) 1122
juxtaglomerular cell   1123
juxtamedullary nephrons   1120

K

karyotype   1256
keloid   185
Keratin   164
keratinocyte   164

keratohyalin   167
ketone bodies   1079
kinesthesia   501, 542
kinetic energy   51
kinetochore   110
knee joint   294
Korotkoff sounds   824
Krebs cycle   1069
kyphosis   250

L

labia   1005
labia majora   1197
labia minora   1197
labial frenulum   1006
lacrimal bone   242
lacrimal duct   552
lacrimal fossa   242
lacrimal gland   552
lactase   1040
Lactation   1252
lacteal   1024
lactic acid   370
lactiferous ducts   1210
lactiferous sinus   1210
lacuna   201
lacunae   145
lambdoid suture   239
lamina   251
lamina propria   130
Langerhans cell   166
lanugo   1242
large intestine   1027
laryngeal prominence   952
laryngopharynx   952, 1013
laryngotracheal bud   983
larynx   952
latch-bridges   385
latent period   375
Lateral   25
lateral (external) rotation   330
lateral apertures   516
lateral border of the scapula   276
lateral circumflex artery   859
lateral columns   510
lateral compartment of the leg 439
lateral condyle of the femur   291
lateral condyle of the tibia   294
lateral corticospinal tract   575

lateral cuneiform   296

lateral epicondyle of the femur   292

lateral epicondyle of the humerus   278

Lateral excursion   331

Lateral flexion   329

lateral geniculate nucleus   564

lateral horn   509

lateral malleolus   295

lateral meniscus   340

lateral plantar artery   859

lateral pterygoid   408

lateral pterygoid plate   236

lateral rectus   553

lateral sacral crest   255

lateral sulcus   500

lateral supracondylar ridge   278

lateral tibiofemoral joint   339

lateral ventricles   515

lateralis   403

latissimus dorsi   423

leakage channel   470

leaky tight junctions   1134

left atrioventricular valve   765

left colic flexure   1028

left gastric artery   853

leg   290

lens   554

leptin   698

lesser pelvis   288

lesser sciatic foramen   288

lesser sciatic notch   286

lesser splanchnic nerve   593

lesser trochanter   291

lesser tubercle   278

lesser wings of the sphenoid bone   236

let-down reflex   1253

Leukemia   732

leukocyte   727

Leukocyte esterase   1113

leukocytosis   732

Leukopenia   732

levator ani   419

levator palpebrae superioris   553

Leydig cells   1194

ligament   316

ligament of the head of the

femur   290, 338

ligamentum flavum   257

ligand   84

ligand-gated cation channel   597

ligand-gated channel   469

light chain   921

lightening   1246

limb bud   297

limbic cortex   500

limbic lobe   608

limbic system   500

linea alba   416

linea aspera   291

lingual frenulum   1007

lingual lipase   1007

lingual tonsil   952

Lingula   243

lipid   65

lipogenesis   1080

lipolysis   1077

lipoprotein lipase   1045

liver   1032

Localization of function   626

lochia   1249

long bone   195

long reflex   602

longissimus capitis   413

longissimus cervicis   413

longissimus group   413

longissimus thoracis   413

longitudinal fissure   500

longus   403

loop of Henle   1120

loose connective tissue   141

lordosis   250

lower esophageal sphincter   1014

lower motor neuron   467

lumbar arteries   853

lumbar curve   250

lumbar enlargement   576

lumbar plexus   525

lumbar puncture   514

lumbar veins   872

Lumbar vertebrae   255

lumbrical   430

lumen   810

lunate   280

lung   959

lung bud   983

lunula   175

Luteinizing hormone (LH)   679

Lymph   894

lymph node   894

Lymphatic capillaries   896

lymphatic system   894

lymphatic trunks   896

Lymphocytes   731, 897

lymphoid nodules   903

Lymphoid stem cells   717

Lymphoma   732

lysosome   94

lysozyme   730

M

macromolecule   62

macrophage   723, 907

Macrophage oxidative metabolism   928

macula   550

macula densa   1122

Magnetic resonance imaging (MRI)   30

main pancreatic duct   1023

major duodenal papilla   1023

major histocompatibility complex (MHC)   914

malleus   546

maltase   1040

mammary glands   1210

mandible   230, 242

Mandibular foramen   242

Mandibular fossa   234

mandibular notch   242

manubrium   259

marginal arteries   769

mass movement   1031

mass number   42

masseter   407

mast cell   911

mastication   407, 1003

mastoid process   233

matrix   140

matter   40

maxillary bone   240

maxillary sinus   246

maxillary vein   866

maximus   403

Mean arterial pressure (MAP)

822

meatuses   949

Mechanical digestion   1003

mechanically gated channel   469

mechanoreceptor   541

meconium   1242

Medial   25

medial (internal) rotation   330

medial border of the scapula   276

medial compartment of the thigh   435

medial condyle of the femur   292

medial condyle of the tibia   294

medial cuneiform   296

medial epicondyle of the femur   292

medial epicondyle of the humerus   278

Medial excursion   331

medial forebrain bundle   608

medial geniculate nucleus   562

medial lemniscus   560

medial longitudinal fasciculus (MLF)   639

medial malleolus   294

medial meniscus   340

medial plantar artery   859

medial pterygoid   408

medial pterygoid plate   236

medial rectus   553

medial tibiofemoral joint   339

medialis   403

median antebrachial vein   869

median aperture   516

median cubital vein   869

median nerve   525

median sacral artery   853

median sacral crest   255

mediastinal artery   851

medius   403

medulla   173, 1118

medullary cavity   197

megakaryocyte   732

Meissner corpuscle   177

Melanin   166

melanocyte   166

melanoma   181

melanosome   169

melatonin   691

membrane potential   471

memory cell   731

memory T cells   919

menarche   1207

meninges   513

meniscus   322

menses   1207

menses phase   1207

menstrual cycle   1207

Mental foramen   242

Mental protuberance   242

mental status exam   626

Merkel cell   166

Merocrine secretion   138

mesangial   1122

mesencephalic nuclei   561

mesencephalon   495

mesenchymal cell   142

mesenchyme   141

mesenteric plexus   595

mesoappendix   1027

mesoderm   127, 799, 1233

mesothelium   133, 756

messenger RNA (mRNA)   103

Metabolic acidosis   1177

Metabolic alkalosis   1178

metabolic rate   1093

Metabolism   14, 1058

metabotropic receptor   480

metacarpal bone   278

metacarpophalangeal joint   282

Metaphase   110

metaphase plate   110

metarteriole   816

metastasis   180

metatarsal bone   290

metatarsophalangeal joint   296

metencephalon   495

MHC class I   915

MHC class II   915

MHC polygeny   935

MHC polymorphism   935

micelle   1045

microcirculation   814

microfilament   97

Microglia   462

microscopic anatomy   8

microtubule   97

microvilli   1024

Micturition   1115

midbrain   495

midcarpal joint   281

middle cardiac vein   770

middle cerebellar peduncle (MCP)   649

middle cerebral artery   849

middle cranial fossa   232

middle ear   546

middle nasal concha   231

middle sacral vein   874

middle scalene   414

migrating motility complex   1026

mineralocorticoids   689

Minerals   1097

minimus   403

mitochondrion   95

Mitosis   108

mitotic phase   109

mitotic spindle   110

mitral valve   765

mixing wave   1021

modeling   211

moderator band   763

molars   1010

molecule   47

monocyte   907

Monocytes   731

monoglyceride molecules   1076

monosaccharide   62, 1063

mons pubis   1197

morula   1228

motilin   1026

motility   999

motor end-plate   364

motor exam   626

motor unit   373

mucosa   998

Mucosa-associated lymphoid tissue (MALT)   904

mucosal barrier   1021

mucous connective tissue   141

mucous gland   140

mucous membrane   129

mucous neck cells   1018

Müllerian duct   1213

multiaxial joint   316

multifidus   413

multimodal integration area   567

multipennate 399
Multipolar 460
multipotent 113
murmur 787
muscarinic receptor 479, 597
muscle tension 372
Muscle tissue 126
muscle tone 377
muscular artery 814
muscularis 998
mutation 96, 1264
mydriasis 612
myelencephalon 495
myelin 150, 453
myelin sheath 463
Myeloid stem cells 717
myenteric plexus 999
mylohyoid 410
Mylohyoid line 242
myoblast 386
myocardial conducting cells 772
myocardial contractile cells 772
myocardium 758
myocyte 148
myofibril 364
myogenic mechanism 1138
myogenic response 838
myogram 375
myometrium 1206
myosin 361
myotube 386

N
NADH 1063
nail bed 175
nail body 175
nail cuticle 175
nail fold 175
nail root 175
naïve lymphocyte 901
naris 948
nasal bone 242, 949
nasal cavity 231
nasal conchae 244
nasal septum 231, 244, 949
nasolacrimal canal 242
nasopharynx 952
Natural killer (NK) cells 731
natural killer cell (NK) 899
navicular 296

neck of the femur 291
neck of the radius 280
neck of the rib 260
Necrosis 151
Negative feedback 20
negative inotropic factors 797
negative selection 917
Neonatal hypothyroidism 684
Nephrons 1119
nerve 454
nerve plexus 525
nervi vasorum 813
Nervous tissue 126
net filtration pressure (NFP) 831, 1127
neural crest 494
neural fold 494, 1236
neural groove 494
neural plate 494, 1236
neural tube 494, 1236
neural tunic 554
neuraxis 496
Neurogenic shock 842
neuroglia 149
neurological exam 626
neuromuscular junction (NMJ) 362
neuron 149, 453
neuropeptide 480
neurotransmitter 364, 466
neurulation 1236
Neutralization 927
neutron 41
neutrophil 907
neutrophils 730
nicotinamide adenine dinucleotide (NAD) 1063
nicotinic receptor 479, 597
nociceptor 541
node of Ranvier 459
nonshivering thermogenesis 1251
nonspecific channel 469
norepinephrine 597, 690
normal range 20
notochord 260, 1236
nuchal ligament 257
nuclear envelope 99
nuclear pore 99

nucleolus 100
nucleosidase 1042
nucleosome 100
nucleotide 72
nucleus 91, 453
nucleus ambiguus 595
nucleus cuneatus 559
nucleus gracilis 559
nucleus pulposus 256
nutrient 17
nutrient foramen 205

O
oblique 403
Obstructive shock 842
obturator externus 435
obturator foramen 287
obturator internus 435
occipital bone 236
occipital condyle 236
occipital lobe 500
occipital sinus 867
occipital sinuses 513
occipitalis 404
occipitofrontalis 404
oculomotor nerve 522
odorant molecules 544
olecranon fossa 279
olecranon process 279
olfaction 505, 544
olfactory bulb 544
olfactory epithelium 544
olfactory nerve 522
olfactory pit 983
olfactory sensory neuron 544
Oligodendrocyte 150, 462
oligopotent 113
oliguria 1112
omohyoid 411
oocyte 1196
oogenesis 1199
oogonia 1199
Open reduction 212
ophthalmic artery 849
opponens digiti minimi 430
opponens pollicis 430
Opposition 332
opsins 555
Opsonization 909
optic canal 243, 245

optic chiasm   563
optic disc   554
optic nerve   522, 554
optic tract   564
oral cavity   1005
oral vestibule   1006
orbicularis oculi   404
orbicularis oris   404
orbit   230
organ   11
organ system   11
organelle   91
organelles   11
organic compound   55
organism   13
organogenesis   1238
organs of Corti   547
origin   396
oropharynx   952, 1013
orthopedist   193
orthostatic reflex   512
Osmoreceptors   541, 676
Osmosis   86
osseous tissue   191
ossicles   546
ossification   206
ossification center   206
osteoblast   201
osteoclast   201
osteocyte   201
osteogenic cell   201
osteoid   206
osteomalacia   1144
osteon   203
Osteoporosis   217
otolithic membrane   550
outer segment   555
outer synaptic layer   554
oval window   546
ovarian artery   853
ovarian cycle   1199
ovarian vein   872
ovaries   1198
ovulation   1199
ovum   1200
oxidation   1062
oxidation-reduction reaction   1062
oxidative phosphorylation   1070

oxygen debt   371
oxygen–hemoglobin dissociation curve   976
oxyhemoglobin   722, 976
oxytocin   676

P

P wave   779
pacemaker   774
pacesetter cell   385
Pacinian corpuscle   177
packed cell volume (PCV)   713
palatine bone   241
palatine process   240
palatine tonsil   952
palatoglossal arch   1007
palatoglossus   409
palatopharyngeal arch   1007
palmar arches   857
palmar interossei   430
palmar venous arches   869
palmaris longus   428
palpebral conjunctiva   552
pancreas   693, 1035
pancreatic amylase   1040
pancreatic islets   693
pancreatic juice   1035
pancreatic lipase   1042
pancreatic lipases   1076
pancreatic nuclease   1042
papillae   542
papillary layer   168
papillary muscle   763
paracrine   664
Parallel   398
paramedian pontine reticular formation (PPRF)   639
paranasal sinus   950
paranasal sinuses   246
parasympathetic division   590
parasympathomimetic drugs   613
parathyroid glands   685
parathyroid hormone (PTH)   685
paravertebral ganglia   520, 593
parenchyma   142
paresis   648
parietal bone   233
parietal branches   851
parietal cells   1018

parietal lobe   500
parietal pleura   960
parieto-occipital sulcus   501
parotid glands   1008
Partial pressure   970
parturition   1247
Passive immunity   925
Passive transport   84
patella   290
patellar ligament   340, 436
patellar surface   292
pattern recognition receptor (PRR)   908
pectinate line   1030
pectinate muscles   763
pectineal line   287
pectineus   435
pectoral girdle   275, 421
pectoralis major   423
pectoralis minor   421
pedicels   1121
pedicle   251
pelvic brim   288
pelvic diaphragm   419
pelvic girdle   285, 432
pelvic inlet   288
pelvic outlet   288
pelvis   285
penis   1193
Pennate   399
pepsin   1082
pepsinogen   1018
peptide bond   69
perforating canal   203
perforin   908
perfusion   814
pericardial artery   851
pericardial cavity   752
pericardial sac   756
pericardium   28, 756
perichondrium   207
pericyte   387
perimetrium   1206
perimysium   360
perineum   420
perineurium   520
periodic table of the elements   42
periodontal ligament   318
periosteum   197

peripheral chemoreceptor   969
peripheral nervous system (PNS)
452
Peripheral proteins   84
peripheral tolerance   921
Peristalsis   1003
peritoneum   28
peritubular capillaries   1119
permanent teeth   1010
peroxisome   95
perpendicular plate of the
ethmoid bone   231
petrosal sinus   867
petrous ridge   233
pH   59
Phagocytosis   89, 907
phalanx bone of the foot   290
phalanx bone of the hand   278
pharyngeal tonsil   952
pharynx   951, 1013
phenotype   1256
philtrum   948
phosphatase   1042
phosphodiesterase (PDE)   670
phospholipid   67
Phosphorylation   74
phosphorylation cascade   669
photoisomerization   557
photon   556
photoreceptor   541
phrenic nerve   525
phrenic vein   872
physiological sphincter   1116
physiology   8
pia mater   513
pineal gland   691
pinealocyte   691
pinocytosis   89
piriformis   435
pisiform   280
pituitary dwarfism   678
pituitary gland   674
pivot joint   324
placenta   1228
placenta previa   1231
placentation   1235
plane   25
plane joint   325
plantar aponeurosis   439

plantar arch   859
plantar flexion   331
plantar group   439
plantar reflex   647
plantar veins   874
plantar venous arch   874
plantaris   439
plasma   712
plasma cell   899
Plasma osmolality   1163
plasmin   737
platelet plug   734
platelets   712
pleura   28
pleural cavity   960
Pleural fluid   961
plexus   520
pluripotent   113
pluripotent stem cell   716
pneumotaxic center   968
podocytes   1121
polar body   1199
polar molecule   49
pollex   283
polyclonal response   918
polycythemia   727
polymorphonuclear   730
polypeptide   105
polyribosome   107
Polysaccharides   62, 1063
polyspermy   1225
polyuria   1112
popliteal artery   859
popliteal fossa   437
popliteal vein   874
popliteus   439
porta hepatis   1033
portal triad   1034
positive chemotaxis   728
Positive feedback   22
positive inotropic factors   797
positive selection   916
Positron emission tomography
(PET)   31
postabsorptive state   1088
postcentral gyrus   501
Posterior   24
posterior (dorsal) sacral foramen
255

posterior arch   253
posterior cardiac vein   770
posterior cerebral artery   849
posterior columns   510
posterior communicating artery
849
posterior compartment of the leg
439
posterior compartment of the
thigh   437
posterior cranial fossa   232
posterior cruciate ligament   340
posterior horn   509
posterior inferior iliac spine   286
posterior interventricular artery
769
posterior interventricular sulcus
757
posterior longitudinal ligament
257
posterior median sulcus   509
posterior sacroiliac ligament   287
posterior scalene   414
posterior superior iliac spine   286
posterior talofibular ligament
343
posterior tibial artery   859
posterior tibial vein   874
posterolateral sulcus   509
postganglionic fiber   594
postsynaptic potential (PSP)   477
Potential energy   51
power stroke   368
PP cell   694
praxis   633
precapillary sphincters   816
precentral gyrus   501
precentral gyrus of the frontal
cortex   467
prefrontal lobe   501
preganglionic fiber   594
preload   785
premolars   1010
premotor area   501
premotor cortex   573
prepotential depolarization   776
prepuce   1194
Pressure   19
prevertebral ganglia   520, 593

primary adaptive response   912
primary curve   250
primary follicles   1201
primary lymphoid organs   899
primary ossification center   209
primary sensory cortex   567
primary union   152
primary vesicles   495
prime mover   396
primitive atrium   800
primitive heart tube   800
primitive streak   1233
primitive ventricle   800
primordial follicles   1201
principal cell   1136
procedural memory   632
process   453
product   52
progesterone   692
projection   198
prolactin   1253
prolactin (PRL)   679
proliferative phase   1209
proliferative zone   210
promoter   104
pronated position   330
Pronation   331
pronator drift   647
pronator quadratus   426
pronator teres   426
Prone   24
propagation   466
Prophase   110
proprioception   501, 542
proprioceptor   541
propulsion   1003
prosencephalon   495
prostaglandin   68
prostate gland   1192
protein   68
protein kinase   669
proteolysis   1082
proteome   103
proton   41
Protraction   331
Proximal   25
proximal convoluted tubules (PCTs)   1120
proximal radioulnar joint   279,

325
proximal tibiofibular joint   295
Pseudostratified columnar epithelium   134
psoas major   432
psychoneuroimmunology   938
pterion   239
Puberty   1213
pubic arch   287
pubic body   287
pubic symphysis   286
pubic tubercle   287
pubis   286
pubococcygeus   419
pubofemoral ligament   337
pulmonary arteries   755
pulmonary artery   844, 960
pulmonary capillaries   755
pulmonary circuit   754, 844
pulmonary plexus   960
pulmonary surfactant   957
pulmonary trunk   755, 844
pulmonary valve   765
pulmonary veins   755, 844
Pulmonary ventilation   961
pulp cavity   1011
pulse   823
pulse pressure   822
Punnett square   1260
pupil   554
purine   72
Purkinje fibers   776
putamen   502
pyloric antrum   1017
pyloric canal   1017
pyloric sphincter   1017
pylorus   1017
pyramidal decussation   574
pyramidine   72
pyramids   574
pyruvate   1064
pyruvic acid   370

Q

QRS complex   779
quadratus femoris   435
quadratus lumborum   416
quadriceps femoris group   436
quadriceps tendon   436
quickening   1242

Quiet breathing   965

R

radial artery   857
radial collateral ligament   336
radial fossa   279
radial nerve   525
radial notch of the ulna   279
radial tuberosity   280
radial vein   869
Radiation   1093
radioactive isotope   44
radiocarpal joint   280
radius   278
ramus of the mandible   242
reabsorption   831
reactant   52
Reactive oxygen species (ROS)   96
receptive aphasia   633
receptor   84
receptor cell   541
receptor potential   476
Receptor-mediated endocytosis   89
recessive   1258
recessive lethal   1264
recruitment   374
rectal valves   1028
rectum   1028
rectus   403
rectus abdominis   416
rectus femoris   436
rectus sheaths   416
red blood cells (RBCs)   712
Red marrow   194
red nucleus   576, 650
reduction   1062
referred pain   601
reflex arc   599
refractory period   474
Regional anatomy   8
Regulatory T cells (Treg)   920
relative refractory period   474
relaxation phase   375
remodeling   211
renal artery   853
renal columns   1118
renal corpuscle   1119
renal cortex   1118

renal fat pad   1118
renal hilum   1119
renal papillae   1118
renal pyramids   1118
renal vein   872
renin   1121
repolarization   472
reposition   332
Reproduction   16
reserve zone   209
Residual volume (RV)   965
resistance   475, 821
Respiratory acidosis   1178
Respiratory alkalosis   1178
respiratory bronchiole   955
respiratory cycle   964
respiratory epithelium   950
respiratory membrane   957
respiratory pump   830
respiratory rate   967
Respiratory volume   965
respiratory zone   948
response   455
Responsiveness   15
rest and digest   590
resting membrane potential   472
Reticular fiber   142
reticular formation   507
reticular lamina   130
reticular layer   168
Reticular tissue   143
reticulocyte   721
reticuloendothelial cells   1034
reticulospinal tract   576
retina   554
retinacula   429
retinal   556
retinal ganglion cell (RGC)   554
retraction   331
retrograde amnesia   632
retroperitoneal   1000, 1115
Rh blood group   740
rhodopsin   555
rhombencephalon   495
rhomboid major   421
rhomboid minor   421
ribonuclease   1042
Ribonucleic acid (RNA)   72
Ribosomal RNA (rRNA)   105

ribosome   93
ribs   228
rickets   180
right atrioventricular valve   764
right colic flexure   1028
right gastric artery   853
right lymphatic duct   897
Rinne test   638
RNA polymerase   104
rod photoreceptor   555
Romberg test   646
root   948, 1011
Rotation   330
rotator cuff   335, 425
round window   546
rubrospinal tract   576, 650
ruga   1017
rugae   1198

S

S phase   108
saccade   639
saccharolytic fermentation   1031
saccule   550
sacral canal   255
sacral foramina   255
sacral hiatus   255
sacral micturition center   1116
sacral plexus   525
sacral promontory   255
sacrococcygeal curve   250
sacroiliac joint   286
sacrospinous ligament   287
sacrotuberous ligament   287
sacrum   228
saddle joint   325
sagittal plane   25
sagittal suture   239
Saliva   1008
salivary amylase   1008, 1063
salivary glands   1008
salivation   1009
saltatory conduction   475
saphenous nerve   525
sarcolemma   361
sarcomere   361
sarcopenia   378
sarcoplasm   361
sarcoplasmic reticulum (SR)   361
sartorius   436

satellite cell   386, 463
scala tympani   546
scala vestibuli   546
scalene muscles   414
scaphoid   280
scapula   275
scar   185
Schwann cell   150, 463
sciatic nerve   525
sciatica   525
sclera   554
sclerotome   260
scoliosis   250
scrotum   1187
sebaceous gland   176
sebum   176
second messenger   669
second-degree burn   184
secondary adaptive response   912
secondary curve   250
secondary follicles   1201
secondary lymphoid organs   901
secondary ossification center   209
secondary sex characteristics   1213
secondary union   152
secondary vesicles   495
secretin   1082
secretory phase   1209
section   25
segmental muscle group   414
Segmentation   1003
selective permeability   84
sella turcica   236
semen   1192
semicircular canals   550
semilunar valves   760
semimembranosus   437
seminal vesicle   1192
seminiferous tubules   1189
semispinalis capitis   413
semispinalis cervicis   413
semispinalis thoracis   413
semitendinosus   437
sensation   455
sensitization   932
sensor   20

sensorineural hearing 638
sensory exam 626
sensory homunculus 565
sensory modality 542
sepsis 842
septal cartilage 244
septic shock 842
septum 760
septum primum 760
Seroconversion 926
serosa 999
serous gland 140
serous membrane 27, 130
serratus anterior 421
Sertoli cells 1189
serum 737
sesamoid bone 196
set point 20
severe combined
immunodeficiency disease
(SCID) 930
sex chromosomes 1256
shaft of the femur 291
shaft of the fibula 295
shaft of the humerus 278
shaft of the radius 280
shaft of the tibia 294
shaft of the ulna 279
short bone 195
short reflex 602
short-term memory 632
shunt 1240
sickle cell disease 726
sigmoid colon 1028
sigmoid sinuses 513, 867
simple columnar epithelium 134
simple cuboidal epithelium 133
simple squamous epithelium
133
sinoatrial (SA) node 774
sinus rhythm 774
sinus venosus 800
sinusoid capillary 815
sister chromatid 108
size exclusion 469
Skeletal muscle 148, 358
skeletal muscle pump 829
skeletal system 191
skeleton 228

skull 228
Slow oxidative (SO) 377
small cardiac vein 770
small intestine 1022
small saphenous vein 874
Smooth muscle 148, 359
Snellen chart 636
sodium bicarbonate 1082
sodium-potassium pump 88
soft palate 1006
soleal line 294
soleus 439
solitary nucleus 561
solution 55
soma 453
somatic cell 107
somatic nervous system (SNS)
456
somatic reflex 599
somatosensation 501, 542
somite 260
somites 386, 1236
spasticity 648
Spatial summation 477
special sense 542
specific gravity 1113
sperm 1186
spermatic cord 1191
spermatid 1190
spermatocyte 1190
spermatogenesis 1189
spermatogonia 1189
spermiogenesis 1190
sphenoid bone 236
sphenoid sinus 246
sphincter urethrovaginalis 420
sphygmomanometer 824
spinal accessory nerve 522
spinal cavity 27
spinal cord 452
spinal nerve 519
spinal trigeminal nucleus 561
spinalis capitis 413
spinalis cervicis 413
spinalis group 413
spinalis thoracis 413
spine of the scapula 277
spinocerebellar tract 646
spinocerebellum 650

spinothalamic tract 559
spinous process 251
spiral ganglia 546
spleen 902
splenic artery 853
splenius 412
splenius capitis 412
splenius cervicis 412
spliceosome 104
splicing 104
spongy bone 203
spontaneous depolarization 776
Squamous cell carcinoma 181
squamous suture 239
stage of exhaustion 689
stage of resistance 689
stapes 546
stem cell 112
stereocilia 548
stereognosis 634
sternal angle 259
sternal end of the clavicle 276
sternoclavicular joint 276
sternocleidomastoid 411
sternohyoid 411
sternothyroid 411
sternum 228
steroid 67
stimulus 455
stomach 1016
straight sinus 513, 867
stratified columnar epithelium
135
Stratified cuboidal epithelium
135
Stratified squamous epithelium
135
stratum basale 165
stratum corneum 167
stratum granulosum 167
stratum lucidum 167
stratum spinosum 166
stress-relaxation response 386
stretch mark 185
stretch reflex 578
striation 148
striatum 502
stroke 628
stroke volume (SV) 788

styloglossus   409
stylohyoid   410
Styloid process   234
styloid process of the radius   280
styloid process of the ulna   280
Stylomastoid foramen   234
subacromial bursa   335
subarachnoid space   514
subclavian artery   848
subclavian vein   864
subclavius   421
subcortical nuclei   502
subcutaneous bursa   322
sublingual glands   1008
submandibular glands   1008
submodalities   542
submucosa   998
submucosal plexus   999
submuscular bursa   322
subpubic angle   287
subscapular bursa   335
subscapular fossa   277
subscapular vein   869
subscapularis   425
substantia nigra pars compacta
504
substantia nigra pars reticulata
503
substrate   71
subtalar joint   343
subtendinous bursa   322
subthalamus   505
Sucrase   1040
sudoriferous glands   175
sulcus   500, 757
summate   477
Superficial   25
superficial anterior compartment
of the forearm   428
superficial posterior compartment
of the forearm   428
superficial reflex   647
Superior   24
superior angle of the scapula
276
superior articular process   251
superior articular process of the
sacrum   255
superior border of the scapula

276
superior cerebellar peduncle
(SCP)   649
superior cervical ganglion   593
superior colliculus   507, 562
superior extensor retinaculum
438
superior gemellus   435
superior mesenteric artery   853
superior mesenteric ganglion
593
superior nasal concha   231
superior nuchal line   236
superior oblique   553
Superior orbital fissure   245
superior phrenic artery   851
superior pubic ramus   287
superior rectus   553
superior rotation   331
superior sagittal sinus   513, 867
superior vena cava   755, 864
supinated position   330
Supination   331
supinator   426
supine   24
supplemental motor area   573
Supportive connective tissue
141
suprachiasmatic nucleus   564
supraglenoid tubercle   276
Suprahyoid muscles   410
supraorbital foramen   230
supraorbital margin   230
suprascapular notch   276
supraspinatus   425
supraspinous fossa   277
supraspinous ligament   257
surgical neck   278
suspension   56
suspensory ligaments   1211
sustentaculum tali   295
suture   239, 317
sympathetic chain ganglia   520,
591
sympathetic division   590
sympatholytic drug   611
sympathomimetic drug   611
symphysis   320
synapses   459

synaptic cleft   364, 478
synaptic end bulb   459
synarthrosis   314
synchondrosis   319
syncytiotrophoblast   1230
syndesmosis   318
synergist   396
synostosis   317
synovial fluid   321
synovial joint   314
synovial membrane   129, 321
synthesis reaction   52
systemic anatomy   8
systemic circuit   754
systemic edema   1127
systemic nerve   525
systole   784
systolic pressure   821

T

T cell   898
T cell tolerance   916
T cell-dependent antigen   926
T cell-independent antigen   926
T lymphocytes   731
T wave   779
T-tubules   364
talocrural joint   342
talus   295
target effector   592
target heart rate   790
tarsal bone   290
taste buds   542
tectorial membrane   548
tectospinal tract   576
tectum   507
tegmentum   507
telencephalon   495
telogen   174
Telophase   110
temporal bone   233
temporal fossa   231
temporal lobe   500
temporal process of the zygomatic
bone   231
Temporal summation   477
temporal vein   866
temporalis   407
temporomandibular joint (TMJ)
333

tendinous intersections   416
tendon   321
tendon sheath   322
teniae coli   1029
tensor fascia latae   434
teres major   425
teres minor   425
terminal electron acceptor   1067
terminal ganglia   520, 595
tertiary follicles   1201
testes   1188
testicular artery   853
testicular vein   872
testosterone   692
tetanus   376
Th1 cells   920
Th2 cells   920
thalamus   466, 505
Thalassemia   727
theca cells   1201
thenar   430
thenar eminence   430
thermoneutral   1091
thermoreceptor   466, 541
thermoregulation   1091
thick filament   361
thigh   290
thin filament   361
third ventricle   515
third-degree burn   184
thoracic aorta   846
thoracic cage   228
thoracic cavity   27
thoracic curve   250
thoracic duct   897
thoracic vertebrae   254
Thoracic wall compliance   964
thoracolumbar system   591
thoroughfare channel   816
threshold   466
thrombin   737
thrombocytes   732
thrombocytopenia   732
Thrombocytosis   732
Thrombopoietin   718
thrombosis   738
thrombus   738
thymocyte   899
thymosins   699

thymus   699, 900
thyrocervical artery   848
thyrohyoid   411
thyroid cartilage   952
thyroid gland   680
thyroid-stimulating hormone
(TSH)   678
thyroxine   682
tibia   290
tibial collateral ligament   340
tibial nerve   525
tibial tuberosity   294
tibialis anterior   438
tibialis posterior   439
Tidal volume (TV)   965
tight junction   132
tissue   11, 126
tissue factor   737
tissue membrane   128
Tissue typing   934
tongue   1007
Tonsils   903
topographical   558
Total dead space   967
total lung capacity (TLC)   966
Total pressure   970
totipotent   113, 127
totipotent stem cell   716
trabeculae   203
trabeculae carneae   763
trachea   954
trachealis muscle   954
tract   454
trait   1258
transamination   1083
transcription   104
transcription factor   114
transduction   540
Transfer RNA (tRNA)   105
transferrin   723
transient ischemic attack (TIA)
628, 848
transitional epithelium   135
Translation   105
Transpulmonary pressure   963
transverse colon   1028
transverse foramen   252
transverse plane   25
transverse process   251

transverse sinuses   513, 867
transversospinales   413
transversus abdominis   416
trapezium   280
trapezius   421
trapezoid   280
treppe   376
tri   403
triad   364
tricarboxylic acid cycle (TCA)
1065
triceps brachii   426
tricuspid valve   764
trigeminal ganglion   519
trigeminal nerve   522
triglyceride   65
triglycerides   1076
trigone   1114
triiodothyronine   682
trimesters   1243
triplet   103
triquetrum   280
trochlea   279, 553
trochlear nerve   522
trochlear notch   279
trophoblasts   1228
tropomyosin   361
troponin   361
true labor   1247
true ribs   260
true vocal cord   953
truncus arteriosus   800
trunk   844
trypsin   1082
trypsinogen   1082
tubercle of the rib   260
tubuloglomerular feedback   1138
tunica externa   813
tunica intima   812
tunica media   813
twitch   375
tympanic membrane   546
type I alveolar cell   957
type I hypersensitivity   931
type II alveolar cell   957
Type II hypersensitivity   932
Type III hypersensitivity   932

U

ulna   278

ulnar artery 857
ulnar collateral ligament 336
ulnar nerve 525
ulnar notch of the radius 280
ulnar tuberosity 279
ulnar vein 869
Ultrasonography 31
Umami 542
umbilical arteries 879
umbilical cord 1235
umbilical vein 879
uniaxial joint 316
unipennate 399
Unipolar 460
unipotent 113
universal donor 742
universal recipient 742
upper esophageal sphincter 1014
upper motor neuron 467
upregulation 671
urea cycle 1083
urethra 1114
Urinalysis 1111
urochrome 1111
urogenital triangle 420
uterine tubes 1205
uterus 1206
utricle 550

V

vagina 1198
vagus nerve 522
valence shell 46
Valsalva's maneuver 1031
valve 760
variable region domain 913
varicosity 385, 598
vasa recta 1119
vasa vasorum 811
Vascular shock 842
vascular shunt 816
vascular spasm 734
vascular tone 826
Vascular tubes 879
vascular tunic 554
vasoconstriction 813
vasodilation 151, 813

vasomotion 816
vasomotor nerves 609
vastus intermedius 436
vastus lateralis 436
vastus medialis 436
vein 817
venous reserve 820
Ventilation 972
ventral 24
ventral (anterior) cavity 26
ventral (anterior) nerve root 509
ventral posterior nucleus 561
ventral respiratory group (VRG) 968
ventral stream 569
ventricle 462, 754
ventricles 515
ventricular ejection phase 785
venule 816
vermis 650
vernix caseosa 1242
vertebra 228
vertebral (spinal) canal 251
vertebral arch 251
vertebral arteries 512
vertebral artery 848
vertebral column 228
vertebral foramen 251
vertebral vein 865
vesicle 88
vestibular fold 953
vestibular ganglion 550
vestibular nuclei 562
vestibule 546
vestibulo-ocular reflex (VOR) 563, 640
vestibulocerebellum 650
vestibulocochlear nerve 522
vestibulospinal tract 576
villi 1024
visceral branches 851
visceral muscle 386
visceral pleura 960
visceral reflex 599
visceral sense 542
Vision 552
visual acuity 554

Vital capacity (VC) 966
vitamin D 180
Vitamins 1095
vitiligo 171
vitreous humor 554
voltage-gated channel 470
voltage-gated sodium channels 364
voluntary phase 1015
vomer bone 231
vulva 1197

W

wave summation 376
Weber test 638
Wernicke's area 633
white blood cells (WBCs) 712
white matter 453
white rami communicantes 593
Wolffian duct 1213
working memory 571
wound contraction 152

X

X-linked 1261
X-linked dominant 1261
X-linked recessive 1262
X-ray 28
xiphoid process 259

Y

Yellow marrow 194
yolk sac 1233

Z

zona fasciculata 688
zona glomerulosa 688
zona pellucida 1224
zona reticularis 688
zone of calcified matrix 210
zone of maturation and hypertrophy 210
zonule fibers 554
zygapophysial joints 333
zygomatic arch 231
zygomatic bone 242
zygomatic process of the temporal bone 231
zygote 1224

Access for free at openstax.org